COMPREHENSIVE
MEDICINAL CHEMISTRY

IN 6 VOLUMES

COMPREHENSIVE MEDICINAL CHEMISTRY

The Rational Design, Mechanistic Study & Therapeutic Application of Chemical Compounds

Chairman of the Editorial Board
CORWIN HANSCH
Pomona College, Claremont, CA, USA

Joint Executive Editors
PETER G. SAMMES
Brunel University of West London, Uxbridge, UK

JOHN B. TAYLOR
Rhône-Poulenc Ltd, Dagenham, UK

Volume 3
MEMBRANES & RECEPTORS

Volume Editor
JOHN C. EMMETT
formerly Smith Kline & French Ltd, Welwyn, UK

PERGAMON PRESS

Member of Maxwell Macmillan Pergamon Publishing Corporation
OXFORD • NEW YORK • BEIJING • FRANKFURT
SÃO PAULO • SYDNEY • TOKYO • TORONTO

U.K.	Pergamon Press plc, Headington Hill Hall, Oxford OX3 0BW, England
U.S.A.	Pergamon Press, Inc., Maxwell House, Fairview Park, Elmsford, New York 10523, U.S.A.
PEOPLE'S REPUBLIC OF CHINA	Pergamon Press, Room 4037, Qianmen Hotel, Beijing, People's Republic of China
FEDERAL REPUBLIC OF GERMANY	Pergamon Press GmbH, Hammerweg 6, D-6242 Kronberg, Federal Republic of Germany
BRAZIL	Pergamon Editora Ltda, Rua Eça de Queiros, 346, CEP 04011, Paraiso, São Paulo, Brazil
AUSTRALIA	Pergamon Press Australia Pty Ltd., P.O. Box 544, Potts Point, N.S.W. 2011, Australia
JAPAN	Pergamon Press, 5th Floor, Matsuoka Central Building, 1-7-1 Nishishinjuku, Shinjuku-ku, Tokyo 160, Japan
CANADA	Pergamon Press Canada Ltd., Suite No. 241, 253 College Street, Toronto, Ontario, Canada M5T 1R5

First edition 1990

Library of Congress Cataloging in Publication Data
Comprehensive medicinal chemistry: the rational design, mechanistic study & therapeutic application of chemical compounds/ chairman of the editorial board, Corwin Hansch; joint executive editors, Peter G. Sammes, John B. Taylor. — 1st ed.
p. cm.
Includes index.
1. Pharmaceutical chemistry. I. Hansch, Corwin. II. Sammes, P. G. (Peter George) III. Taylor, J. B. (John Bodenham), 1939– .
[DNLM: 1. Chemistry, Pharmaceutical. QV 744 C737]
RS402.C65
615'.19—dc20
DNLM/DLC   89–16329

British Library Cataloguing in Publication Data
Hansch, Corwin
Comprehensive medicinal chemistry
1. Pharmaceutics
I. Title
615'.19

ISBN 0–08–037059–4 (Vol. 3)
ISBN 0–08–032530–0 (set)

Printed in Great Britain by
BPCC Hazell Books Ltd, Aylesbury, Bucks, England

Contents

Preface

Medicinal chemistry is a subject which has seen enormous growth in the past decade. Traditionally accepted as a branch of organic chemistry, and the near exclusive province of the organic chemist, the subject has reached an enormous level of complexity today. The science now employs the most sophisticated developments in technology and instrumentation, including powerful molecular graphics systems with 'drug design' software, all aspects of high resolution spectroscopy, and the use of robots. Moreover, the medicinal chemist (very much a new breed of organic chemist) works in very close collaboration and mutual understanding with a number of other specialists, notably the molecular biologist, the genetic engineer, and the biopharmacist, as well as traditional partners in biology.

Current books on medicinal chemistry inevitably reflect traditional attitudes and approaches to the field and cover unevenly, if at all, much of modern thinking in the field. In addition, such works are largely based on a classical organic structure and therapeutic grouping of biologically active molecules. The aim of *Comprehensive Medicinal Chemistry* is to present the subject, the modern role of which is the understanding of structure–activity relationships and drug design from the mechanistic viewpoint, as a field in its own right, integrating with its central chemistry all the necessary ancillary disciplines.

To ensure that a broad coverage is obtained at an authoritative level, more than 250 authors and editors from 15 countries have been enlisted. The contributions have been organized into five major themes. Thus Volume 1 covers general principles, Volume 2 deals with enzymes and other molecular targets, Volume 3 describes membranes and receptors, Volume 4 covers quantitative drug design, and Volume 5 discusses biopharmaceutics. As well as a cumulative subject index, Volume 6 contains a unique drug compendium containing information on over 5500 compounds currently on the market. All six volumes are being published simultaneously, to provide a work that covers all major topics of interest.

Because of the mechanistic approach adopted, Volumes 1–5 do not discuss those drugs whose modes of action are unknown, although they will be included in the compendium in Volume 6. The mechanisms of action of such agents remain a future challenge for the medicinal chemist.

We should like to acknowledge the way in which the staff at the publisher, particularly Dr Colin Drayton (who initially proposed the project), Dr Helen McPherson and their editorial team, have supported the editors and authors in their endeavour to produce a work of reference that is both complete and up-to-date.

Comprehensive Medicinal Chemistry is a milestone in the literature of the subject in terms of coverage, clarity and a sustained high level of presentation. We are confident it will appeal to academic and industrial researchers in chemistry, biology, medicine and pharmacy, as well as teachers of the subject at all levels.

CORWIN HANSCH
Claremont, USA

PETER G. SAMMES
Uxbridge, UK

JOHN B. TAYLOR
Dagenham, UK

Contributors to Volume 3

Dr M. Bryszewska
Department of Biochemistry, Health Sciences Centre, McMaster University, 1200 Main Street West, Hamilton, Ontario L8N 3Z5, Canada

Dr M. A. Buck
Section of Receptor Biochemistry and Molecular Biology, National Institute of Neurological and Communicative Disorders and Stroke, National Institutes of Health, Park Building, Room 405, Bethesda, MD 20892, USA

Dr T. Buhl
Pharmakologisches Institut für Naturwissenschaftler, Fachbereich Biochemie, Pharmazie und Lebensmittelchemie, Johann Wolfgang Goethe-Universität, Theodor-Stern-Kai 7, Gebaude 75A, D-6000 Frankfurt/Main, FRG

Dr K. Bunce
Pharmacology Division, Glaxo Group Research Ltd, Ware, Herts SG12 0DJ, UK

Dr J. Burmester
Department of Biochemistry, College of Agriculture and Life Sciences, University of Wisconsin-Madison, Madison, WI 53706, USA

Dr M. P. Caulfield
Parathyroid Hormone Laboratory, Merck Sharp & Dohme Laboratories, W26-207 West Point, PA 19486, USA

Dr A. T. Chiu
E. I. du Pont de Nemours & Co., Medical Products Department, Division of Cardiovascular Science, Experimental Station, Building 400/4257, Wilmington, DE 19898, USA

Dr R. A. Coleman
Pharmacology Division, Glaxo Group Research Ltd, Ware, Herts SG12 0DJ, UK

Dr D. G. Cooper
Smith Kline & French Research Ltd, The Frythe, Welwyn, Herts AL6 9AR, UK

Dr R. Daines
Pulmonary and Cardiovascular Medicinal Chemistry, Smith Kline & French Laboratories, P.O. Box 1539, King of Prussia, PA 19406, USA

Dr H. Darwish
Department of Biochemistry, College of Agriculture and Life Sciences, University of Wisconsin-Madison, Madison, WI 53706, USA

Professor H. F. DeLuca
Department of Biochemistry, College of Agriculture and Life Sciences, University of Wisconsin-Madison, Madison, WI 53706, USA

Dr G. J. Durant
Department of Medical Chemistry & Pharmacognosy, College of Pharmacy, University of Toledo, Toledo, OH 43606, USA

Dr A. S. Dutta
Chemistry Department II, Pharmaceuticals Division, ICI plc, Alderley Park, Macclesfield, Cheshire SK10 4TG, UK

Professor R. M. Epand
Department of Biochemistry, Health Sciences Centre, McMaster University, 1200 Main Street West, Hamilton, Ontario L8N 3Z5, Canada

Dr J. R. Fozard
Sandoz Ltd, Preclinical Research, CH-4002 Basel, Switzerland

Dr C. M. Fraser
Section of Receptor Biochemistry and Molecular Biology, National Institute of Neurological and

Communicative Disorders and Stroke, National Institutes of Health, Park Building, Room 405, Bethesda, MD 20892, USA

Professor R. I. Fryer
Department of Chemistry, Rutgers, The State University of New Jersey, 73 Warren Street, Newark, NJ 07102, USA

Professor C. R. Ganellin, FRS
Department of Chemistry, University College London, 20 Gordon Street, London WC1H 0AJ, UK

Dr J. Gleason
Pulmonary and Cardiovascular Medicinal Chemistry, Smith Kline & French Laboratories, P.O. Box 1539, King of Prussia, PA 19406, USA

Dr M. F. Hibert
Merrell Dow Research Institute, Strasbourg Research Centre, 16 Rue d'Ankara, F-67084 Strasbourg Cedex, France

Professor A. S. Horn
Department of Pharmaceutical Chemistry and Pharmacognosy, University of Groningen, 2 Antonius Deusinglaan, 9713 AW Groningen, The Netherlands

Professor V. J. Hruby
Department of Chemistry, Faculty of Science, University of Arizona, Tucson, AZ 85721, USA

Dr P. P. A. Humphrey
Pharmacology Division, Glaxo Group Research Ltd, Ware, Herts SG12 0DJ, UK

Dr J. C. Hunter
Parke-Davis Research Unit, Addenbrookes Hospital Site, Hills Road, Cambridge CB2 2QB, UK

Dr F. Ince
Research & Development Laboratories, Fisons plc, Pharmaceutical Division, Bakewell Road, Loughborough, Leics LE11 0RH, UK

Dr K. A. Jacobson
Department of Health and Human Services, National Institute of Arthritis, Diabetes and Digestive and Kidney Diseases, National Institutes of Health, Building 8A, Room B1A-17, Bethesda, MD 20892, USA

Dr M. N. Khan
Polypeptide Hormone Laboratory, Department of Medicine, McGill University and Royal Victoria Hospital, Montreal, Quebec H3A 1A1, Canada

Mr I. Kennedy
Pharmacology Division, Glaxo Group Research Ltd, Ware, Herts SG12 0DJ, UK

Dr W. Kingsbury
Pulmonary and Cardiovascular Medicinal Chemistry, Smith Kline & French Laboratories, P.O. Box 1539, King of Prussia, PA 19406, USA

Dr J. Krisinger
Department of Biochemistry, College of Agriculture and Life Sciences, University of Wisconsin-Madison, Madison, WI 53706, USA

Professor P. Krogsgaard-Larsen
Department of Chemistry BC, The Royal Danish School of Pharmacy, 2 Universitetsparken, DK-2100, Copenhagen, Denmark

Professor G. Lambrecht
Pharmakologisches Institut für Naturwissenschaftler, Fachbereich Biochemie, Pharmazie und Lebensmittelchemie, Johann Wolfgang Goethe-Universität, Theodor-Stern-Kai 7, Gebaude 75A, D-6000 Frankfurt/Main, FRG

Dr A. G. Lee
Department of Biochemistry, Medical and Biological Sciences Building, University of Southampton, Bassett Crescent East, Southampton SO9 3TU, UK

Dr P. D. Leeson
Merck Sharp & Dohme Research Laboratories, Neuroscience Research Centre, Terlings Park, Eastwick Road, Harlow, Essex CM20 2QR, UK

Dr P. Lumley
Pharmacology Division, Glaxo Group Research Ltd, Ware, Herts SG12 0DJ, UK

Mr B. G. Main
Chemistry Department II, Pharmaceuticals Division, ICI plc, Alderley Park, Macclesfield, Cheshire SK10 4TG, UK

Dr J. Martinez
Centre CNRS-INSERM de Pharmacologie-Endocrinologie, Rue de la Cardonille, F-34094 Montpellier, France

Dr A. K. Mir
Sandoz Ltd, Preclinical Research, CH-4002 Basel, Switzerland

Professor G. J. Moore
Department of Medical Biochemistry, University of Calgary, 3300 Hospital Drive NW, Calgary, Alberta T2N 4N1, Canada

Dr J.-P. Mornon
Université Paris VI, URA 09, 4 Place Jussieu, Tour 16, F-75230 Paris, France

Professor E. Mutschler
Pharmakologisches Institut für Naturwissenschaftler, Fachbereich Biochemie, Pharmazie und Lebensmittelchemie, Johann Wolfgang Goethe-Universität, Theodor-Stern-Kai 7, Gebaude 75A, D-6000 Frankfurt/Main, FRG

Dr J. A. Nicholas
The Upjohn Company, Cancer and Viral Diseases Research, Kalamazoo, MI 49001, USA

Dr T. Ojasoo
Roussel-Uclaf, 35 Boulevard des Invalides, F-75007 Paris, France

Dr B. V. L. Potter
Department of Chemistry, University of Leicester, University Road, Leicester LE1 7RH, UK

Dr J.-P. Raynaud
Roussel-Uclaf, 35 Boulevard des Invalides, F-75007 Paris, France

Dr D. C. Rees
Parke-Davis Research Unit, Addenbrookes Hospital Site, Hills Road, Cambridge CB2 2QB, UK

Dr M. A. Sills
Res 106, Ciba-Geigy, Summit, NJ 07901, USA

Dr D. D. Smith
Department of Chemistry, Faculty of Science, University of Arizona, Tucson, AZ 85721, USA

Dr C. B. Srikant
Fraser Laboratories for Diabetes Research, Room M3-15, Royal Victoria Hospital, 687 Pine Avenue West, Montreal, Quebec H3A 1A1, Canada

Dr M. J. M. C. Thoolen
E. I. du Pont de Nemours & Co., Medical Products Department, Division of Cardiovascular Science, Experimental Station, Building 400/4257, Wilmington, DE 19898, USA

Dr P. B. M. W. M. Timmermans
E. I. du Pont de Nemours & Co., Medical Products Department, Division of Cardiovascular Science, Experimental Station, Building 400/4257, Wilmington, DE 19898, USA

Dr D. J. Triggle
Office of the Dean, School of Pharmacy, State University of New York at Buffalo, C126 Cooke-Hochstetter Complex, Buffalo, NY 14260, USA

Dr A. H. Underwood
Compound and Technology Acquisitions, Smith Kline & French Research Ltd, The Frythe, Welwyn, Herts AL6 9AR, UK

Dr J. C. Venter
Section of Receptor Biochemistry and Molecular Biology, National Institute of Neurological and Communicative Disorders and Stroke, National Institutes of Health, Park Building, Room 405, Bethesda, MD 20892, USA

Dr M. C. Venuti
Genentech Inc., 460 Point San Bruno Blvd, South San Francisco, CA 94080, USA

Dr G. P. Vlasuk
Cardiovascular Pharmacology, Merck Sharp & Dohme Research Laboratories, West Point, PA 19486, USA

Dr J. Wess
Pharmakologisches Institut für Naturwissenschaftler, Fachbereich Biochemie, Pharmazie und Lebensmittelchemie, Johann Wolfgang Goethe-Universität, Theodor-Stern-Kai 7, Gebaude 75A, D-6000 Frankfurt/Main, FRG

Dr W. Wierenga
The Upjohn Company, Cancer and Viral Diseases Research, Kalamazoo, MI 49001, USA

Dr M. Williams
Abbot Laboratories, 1 Abbott Park Road, Abbot Park, IL 60064, USA

Dr R. J. Winquist
Boehringer Ingelheim Pharmaceuticals Inc., 90 East Ridge, PO Box 368, Ridgefield, CT 06877, USA

Dr R. C. Young
Smith Kline & French Research Ltd, The Frythe, Welwyn, Herts AL6 9AR, UK

Contents of All Volumes

Volume 2 Enzymes and Other Molecular Targets

Volume 3 Membranes and Receptors

Volume 4 Quantitative Drug Design

Volume 5 Biopharmaceutics

11.1

Structure and Function of Cell Membranes

ANTHONY G. LEE

University of Southampton, UK

11.1.1 MEMBRANES AND CELLS

11.1.1.1 Introduction[1-4]

Logically, a cell can have an independent existence only if it has a surrounding boundary or membrane with which to define the point where the cell ends and the environment begins. All communication between the cell and its environment must then proceed *via* this cell membrane, since the outer plasma membrane is the face that the cell presents to the outside world; many of the most interesting properties of the membrane reflect its role in controlling the passage of information to and from the cell. Of course, in the majority of cells, the outer plasma membrane is not the only membrane present; visualization of eukaryotic cells in the electron microscope has shown that a number of membranous structures are also present within the cell. Some of these membranes surround organelles, such as the nucleus and mitochondria, whereas others form interconnecting networks within the cell, such as the endoplasmic reticulum and the Golgi apparatus. The most commonly found structures are listed in Table 1 and illustrated in Figure 1.

The numbers of these various organelles, and the relative amounts of the various membrane systems, vary between cells and reflect the function of the cell. The mammalian red blood cell has only the outer plasma membrane. In most mammalian cells, and particularly in secretory cells, the endoplasmic reticulum, consisting of a system of flattened tubes or sacs, is very extensive and fills most of the cytoplasm. The endoplasmic reticulum is frequently covered by ribosomes engaged in the synthesis of membrane and secretory proteins. Other areas of the endoplasmic reticulum appear smooth under the electron microscope and are free of ribosomes. Smooth endoplasmic reticulum contains enzymes involved in lipid synthesis and is particularly extensive in cells specializing in lipid metabolism such as the hepatocyte, the main cell type of the liver. The smooth endoplasmic reticulum also contains enzymes involved in detoxification, both of drugs and of harmful products of metabolism. Cytochrome P450 in this region of the membrane adds hydroxyl groups to a variety of hydrophobic molecules, using NADPH and a reductase, also in the membrane. Other enzymes in the endoplasmic reticulum then add sulfate or glucuronic acid to these hydroxyl groups to generate water soluble derivatives that can be excreted. The amount of smooth endoplasmic reticulum in liver cells increases markedly if large quantities of a drug, such as phenobarbitol, are present in the

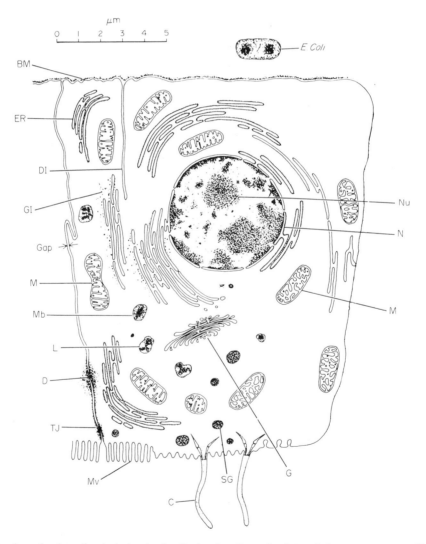

Figure 1 A schematic view of a typical animal cell, showing the major intracellular compartments; BM, basement membrane; ER, endoplasmic reticulum; DI, deep indentation of plasma membrane; GI, glycogen granules; Gap, space between adjacent cells; M, mitochondria; Mb, microbody; L, lysosome; D, desmosome; SG, secretion granule; TJ, tight junction; Mv, microvilli; C, cilium; G, Golgi apparatus; N, nucleus (reproduced from D. E. Metzler, 'Biochemistry', 1977, by permission of Academic Press)

Table 1 Cell Organelles and Membranes

Membrane or organelle	Function
Plasma membrane	Diffusion barrier, active transport of ions, nutrients, *etc.* Transduction of extracellular messages, electrically excitable membrane
Rough endoplasmic reticulum	Covered with ribosomes, involved in synthesis of proteins
Smooth endoplasmic reticulum	Free of ribosomes, involved in detoxification, synthesis of phospholipids and steroids
Golgi apparatus	'Packaging' of proteins to be used elsewhere
Lysosomes	Vesicles containing enzymes used in autodigestion and breakdown of materials engulfed during phagocytosis and endocytosis
Mitochondria	Organelles responsible for energy production (ATP)
Nuclear envelope	Surrounding the nucleus, consists of an inner and an outer membrane, fused in places to form pores through which RNA can pass between the nucleus and the cytoplasm
Peroxisomes	(Or microbodies) contain enzymes involved in oxidation of amino acids, *etc.*
Phagosomes	Vesicles containing particulate material from outside the cell, formed by sealing off portions of the plasma membrane
Pinocytotic vesicles	Small vesicles containing soluble material, formed by sealing off portions of the plasma membrane
Microsomes	Name given to fragments of membranes produced when cells are homogenized, principally derived from endoplasmic reticulum and Golgi apparatus

circulation; the smooth endoplasmic reticulum can double in size after a few days. On removal of the drug, the smooth endoplasmic reticulum returns to its normal size in about five days.

Enzymes involved in cholesterol biosynthesis and in the conversion of cholesterol into steroid hormones are also found in the smooth endoplasmic reticulum, so that the smooth endoplasmic reticulum is also extensive in cells involved in hormone production, such as those of the testis. A specialized form of the smooth endoplasmic reticulum is found in muscle cells, and is called the sarcoplasmic reticulum. The major protein found in the sarcoplasmic reticulum is the $(Ca^{2+}-Mg^{2+})$-ATPase, a Ca^{2+} pump involved in removing Ca^{2+} from the cytosol of the muscle cell, thus allowing relaxation of myofibrils following muscle contraction.

In many cells, a stack of disc-shaped flattened cisternae, referred to as the Golgi apparatus, is found close to the nucleus. Large numbers of small (*ca.* 50 nm diameter) vesicles are always found close to the Golgi apparatus. Some of these vesicles are 'coated' by a polyhedral lattice and are thus referred to as coated vesicles. These coated vesicles appear to bud off from the Golgi cisternae. In cells specialized for the production of large amounts of secretory products, numerous large (*ca.* 1000 nm diameter) secretory vesicles are also seen close to the Golgi apparatus, together with the smaller coated vesicles. The Golgi apparatus is involved in a variety of biochemical processes, but its principal function is in the post-translational modification of the carbohydrate structure of glycoproteins. Secretory proteins are delivered from the endoplasmic reticulum to the Golgi apparatus in coated vesicles. Glycosidases and glycosyltransferases in the Golgi apparatus then modify the core oligosaccharides previously synthesized in the endoplasmic reticulum and the mature proteins are then transported in vesicles to the plasma membrane.

Surrounding the nucleus in a mammalian cell is the nuclear envelope, which separates the nucleoplasm from the cytoplasm. The nuclear envelope consists of two membranes, fused together at numerous points to give pores 65–75 nm in diameter, spanning the envelope. The pores allow the passage of mRNA molecules, regulator proteins, and small molecules and ions (of molecular weight less than *ca.* 1000) between nucleus and cytoplasm. The nuclear envelope is formed from the endoplasmic reticulum following cell division.

Mitochondria are oval-shaped structures, typically *ca.* 3 μm in length. They are bounded by two membranes, the inner membrane being extensively invaginated. It is in the inner membrane that mitochondrial electron transport occurs. Mitochondria are found in greatest number in cells which are energetically very active, such as muscle cells.

Lysosomes are vesicles bounded by a single membrane which contain a wide variety of degradative enzymes used in the digestion of material brought into the cell by phagocytosis or absorptive endocytosis. Breakdown of cellular components also occurs in lysosomes. Peroxisomes are also vesicles bounded by a single membrane, and contain enzymes to oxidize amino acids, xanthine and possibly fatty acids. They also contain catalase to break down hydrogen peroxide produced by oxidative reactions. In macrophages, which are designed to locate, sequester and kill invading pathogenic microorganisms, phagosomes are very common.

The diversity of membrane types found in a normal mammalian cell considerably complicates the study of cell membranes. A further complicating factor is that plasma membranes are generally not homogeneous but, rather, contain distinct regions specialized for particular functions. Such specialized membrane structures commonly appear in the region where two or more cells come into proximity, as at the gap junctions found between epithelial cells. A particularly important example is the specialized region of the plasma membrane which occurs where nerve cells contact other cells (nerve, muscle, *etc.*): the synapse.

Despite these complexities, it is reasonable to expect all cell membranes to exhibit a number of common basic features, since they have so many of their functions in common. This is particularly apparent for the outer plasma membrane. The most obvious function of the plasma membrane is to define the boundaries of the cell: it has to keep the inside of the cell inside and the outside of the cell outside. This is no easy task. The membrane has to be flexible to allow for the changes of shape that will occur with movement, either of the body or of the cell itself. The membrane needs to show selectivity to allow nutrients to enter the cell and waste products to be eliminated and, particularly for excitable cells, it must provide a high degree of electrical insulation and be able to regulate the movement of inorganic ions. Finally, as the outermost part of the cell, the plasma membrane is responsible for the flow of information between the cell and its environment. Before any message can be acted upon, it must first be recognized by the membrane. This, of course, is made possible by the presence in the membrane of specific receptors for external stimuli.

The basic barrier properties of the cell membrane are provided by the lipid component of the membrane; this provides both the flexibility of the structure and its impermeability to hydrophilic polar molecules. The membrane also contains a variety of proteins responsible for the transport of small molecules, either actively against a concentration gradient or passively down a concentration gradient. Transport of large particles such as proteins into the cell occurs by a different mechanism; following binding of the macromolecule, usually to a specific receptor protein in the membrane, the bound species aggregate into small patches which then pinch off to form a vesicle in the cytoplasm. The vesicles so formed (endocytotic vesicles) usually fuse with lysosomes following which their contents are digested.

Signalling between cells is often mediated by small, water soluble species such as hormones or neurotransmitters. These signals are recognized by specific receptor proteins in the outer cell membrane. Many messengers exert their effects without entering the cell; following binding of the small molecule, an ion gate in the membrane can open, allowing movement of ions into the cell, with consequent changes in cell function, or a membrane-bound enzyme can be activated again modifying cell metabolism. Other messengers do enter the cell, as in the absorptive endocytosis of hormone–receptor complexes.

The outer cell membrane obviously has a crucial role to play in cell adhesion. Many of the proteins in the outer membrane have attached to them extensive carbohydrate structures, extending out from the membrane into the external medium. A common component of these carbohydrates is sialic acid, which serves to give the cell a large negative charge. Glycoproteins and glycolipids in the outer membranes are also very immunogenic and are used by the immune system to distinguish between self and non-self.

One of the major roles of intracellular membranes is in compartmentalization, in separating specific regions of space within the cell in which particular sequences of biochemical reactions can occur. Thus lysosomes serve to compartmentalize proteolytic enzymes which would otherwise damage the cell, and also maintain an environment more acid than the rest of the cell to optimize the function of the acid hydrolases that they contain. Membranes can also provide a surface on which a complex sequence of enzyme-catalyzed reactions can occur. An obvious example is in the mitochondrion. The very considerable membrane area which is available for such purposes is illustrated in Table 2, which lists the sizes and numbers of the major organelles of a liver cell. To put these figures into perspective, it means that the cells in a human liver would contain about 30 000 m^2 of endoplasmic reticulum, equivalent to the area of 100 tennis courts.

11.1.1.2 Preparation of Membrane Fractions

For detailed biochemical or pharmacological studies, particularly for studies at the molecular level, it is necessary to prepare purified membrane fractions. This is still a major problem. Ideally, a membrane fractionation scheme would start with a single type of cell, because given membrane fragments will differ between cell types; this, however, is rarely possible. Red blood cells can readily be obtained pure and have the additional advantage of containing only a single membrane, the plasma membrane; consequently they have been used in many membrane studies. Relatively few studies have been reported with cultured mammalian cells because of the problem of producing sufficiently large amounts of material. Generally, the heterogeneity of cell type in a particular organ is ignored so that, for example, many studies have been performed on liver plasma membrane preparations ignoring the fact that liver is made up of roughly equal numbers of parenchymal and reticuloendothelial cells.

Most membrane fractionation schemes start with disruption of the cell, usually by a method based on mild shear forces, such as homogenization in a Potter–Elvejhem homogenizer. Tissue is cut into small pieces in buffer and is forced between a rotating Teflon pestle and the walls of a close-fitting glass tube by raising and lowering the glass tube. Typically the radial clearance between the pestle and the tube wall is chosen to be between 0.05 and 0.5 mm. The composition of the buffer is important, and is often a sucrose solution that is slightly hypotonic (*e.g.* 0.25 M) at pH 7.4. The cell homogenate is then fractionated by centrifugation. Typically, a low speed centrifugation will be used to pellet the mitochondria and nucleus, followed by higher speed centrifugations to pellet the broken inner membranes (referred to as the microsomal fraction) and the plasma membrane. Density gradient centrifugation will then be used for further purification. Further purification is sometimes possible using affinity chromatography, but such methods have been relatively little used.

Following purification, it is necessary to characterize the isolated membrane fractions. Electron microscopy is very useful in looking for contamination of fractions with whole cells or organelles like mitochondria; it can also be used to characterize morphologically distinct membranes such as the rough endoplasmic reticulum. Final characterization, however, most commonly makes use of enzyme and chemical markers. A plasma membrane fraction, for example, can be characterized by the presence of (Na^+-K^+)-ATPase, the mitochondrial inner membrane by cytochrome oxidase, and nuclear membranes by DNA.

Problems of membrane purification are particularly acute for a very heterogeneous tissue such as brain. By homogenization and differential centrifugation of brain, it is possible to prepare first a crude nuclear pellet by low speed centrifugation, then a crude mitochondrial pellet by moderate speed centrifugation of the nuclear supernatant, then a crude microsomal pellet by high speed centrifugation of the mitochondrial supernatant, and finally a high speed supernatant containing the soluble components of the cell. The crude mitochondrial pellet contains a component unique to brain, known as the synaptosome. During homogenization of brain, the shearing forces cause the postsynaptic cell to break just beyond the synaptic cleft and the presynaptic cell to break just beyond the terminal bouton of the axonal process. The torn surfaces then reseal to form a particle which represents 'pinched-off' nerve endings. A number of procedures for the preparation of these synaptosomes have been published.[6, 7] The initial step is generally to homogenize the brain tissue in nine volumes of 0.32 M sucrose using a Potter–Elvejhem homogenizer with 0.25 mm clearance. The resulting homogenate is spun at $1000 \times g$ for 10 min to remove the nuclear pellet, and then at $20000 \times g$ to obtain the crude mitochondrial pellet. The synaptosomal fraction is then isolated by resuspending the mitochondrial pellet in 0.32 M sucrose and layering it on to a discontinuous gradient of 0.8 and 1.2 M sucrose. On spinning at $53000 \times g$ for 2 h, mitochondria form a pellet at the bottom of the gradient, myelin floats at the top of the 0.8 M sucrose layer, and the synaptosomes form a diffuse layer at the 0.8–1.2 M sucrose interface. Separation is also possible on Ficoll gradients. Such preparations contain synaptosomes from a wide variety of cell types and are also contaminated to varying degrees with other membrane fragments.

Synaptosomes frequently have adhering fragments of postsynaptic membrane and also contain presynaptic mitochondria, synaptic vesicles and axoplasm as well as the outer postsynaptic membrane. Further fractionation is possible following disruption of the synaptosomes by osmotic shock, gentle homogenization or detergent treatment, followed by gradient centrifugation.

11.1.2 MEMBRANE COMPOSITION

11.1.2.1 Introduction: The Fluid Mosaic Model[4, 8–10]

Analysis of membranes shows the presence of three components; lipid, protein and carbohydrate. The carbohydrate component is always found bound either to the lipid component as glycolipid or bound to protein as glycoprotein. The exact proportion of lipid and protein in the membrane varies according to the membrane (Figure 2). Since the role of the lipid bilayer in the membrane is essentially passive, with the protein component being responsible for the specific functions of the membrane, the amount of protein in the membrane reflects the level of activity expected of the membrane. Plasma membranes generally contain about 50% dry weight of protein. Myelin is unusual in containing relatively little protein, reflecting its exceptionally low enzymatic activity: the

Table 2 Organelles of a Single Rat Liver Cell[5]

	Volume (μm^3)		Membrane surface area (μm^2)
Total cytoplasm of cell	5100	Smooth endoplasmic reticulum	17 000
Mitochondria (total)	995	Rough endoplasmic reticulum	30 400
Lysosomes (total)	10	Mitochondrial outer membrane	7470
		Mitochondrial inner membrane	39 600

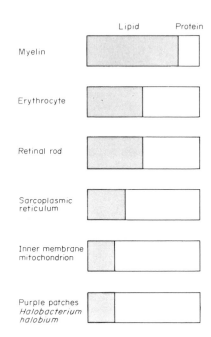

Figure 2 Relative weights of lipid and protein components of representative biological membranes (reproduced from J. B. Finean, R. Coleman and R. H. Mitchell, 'Membranes and their Cellular Functions', 1978, by permission of Blackwell Scientific Publications)

main role of myelin is as an electrical insulator around nerve cells. Internal membranes such as sarcoplasmic reticulum and mitochondrial membranes show very high enzymatic activities and so contain relatively large amounts of protein.

In all biological membranes these components are assembled in a very similar fashion. All membranes have the following features in common: (i) membranes are very thin, being between 6 and 10 nm across; this implies that they can be only a few molecules thick; (ii) the lipid component of the membrane provides the basic structural matrix of the membrane, and is the permeability barrier; (iii) the protein component of the membrane is largely responsible for the specific functions of the membrane; and (iv) the lipid and protein components of the membrane are held together by non-covalent interactions.

These ideas are all summarized in the fluid mosaic model for the membrane (Figure 3).[25] In this model, protein molecules are pictured as 'floating' in a 'sea' of lipid molecules, the latter being organized as a bilayer. The concept that the membrane is a fluid structure has, of course, considerable influence on ideas about organization in the plane of the membrane. Diffusion of lipid molecules in the plane of the membrane is described by a diffusion coefficient D of about 10^{-8} cm^2 s^{-1}. For two-dimensional diffusion, as in the plane of the membrane, the distance x moved from the origin in a time t is related to the diffusion coefficient by

$$x = (4Dt)^{1/2} \tag{1}$$

Thus in 1 s a lipid will, on average, move to a position *ca.* 0.3 μm from its starting point.

Many membrane proteins are also relatively free to diffuse in the plane of the membrane. Protein diffusion coefficients have been measured using the technique of fluorescence recovery after photobleaching (FRAP). Proteins (or lipids) on a cell surface are labelled with a fluorescent dye. The

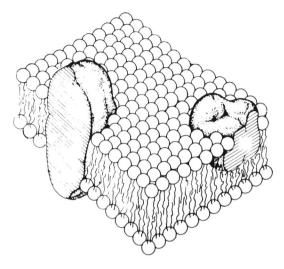

Figure 3 The fluid mosaic model of the membrane (reproduced from ref. 25 by permission of the American Association for the Advancement of Science)

dye on a small spot of the surface is bleached irreversibly by focusing a light beam from a laser on to that spot. If the labelled protein molecules are free to diffuse on the surface of the cell, then, with time, the fluorescence of the bleached area will increase as neighbouring, unbleached molecules diffuse in. The rate of recovery of fluorescence gives the diffusion coefficient. Typically, it is found that some protein molecules are relatively free to diffuse in the surface whereas others are completely immobile. It is believed that immobilization occurs through interactions with other membrane proteins and with the intracellular network that makes up the fibrous cytoskeleton. Even those proteins that are relatively free to diffuse have diffusion coefficients (typically $1-5 \times 10^{-10} \, \mathrm{cm^2 \, s^{-1}}$) considerably less than those measured for lipids in the same membrane. This cannot be attributed simply to the greater size of the protein molecules, since theoretical calculations have shown that the rate of diffusion in the membrane will be almost independent of size. Rather, it must again reflect interactions between protein molecules.

Restriction of protein diffusion in the membrane is important for the formation of specialized regions in a cell membrane. Obvious examples are the synapses, where the acetylcholine receptor is concentrated in the region of the postsynaptic membrane, and tight junctions in epithelia which serve to maintain a distinctive protein composition for the apical and basolateral surfaces.

11.1.2.2 Lipid Structure

The lipids are an unusual class of biological molecule. Most components of the cell are water soluble, because the cell is largely made up of water. The lipids, however, are insoluble in water but highly soluble in organic solvents such as chloroform or methanol. Lipids such as triglycerides are used as an energy store by the cell, but the lipids of importance for membrane structure are the phospholipids, glycolipids and cholesterol.

Despite their chemical diversity, membrane lipids all have one feature in common, and that is that they are amphipathic, with distinct hydrophobic and hydrophilic regions; it is this property that enables them to provide the basic structural framework of the membrane (see Section 11.1.2.4). The most abundant of the membrane lipids of mammalian cells are the phospholipids. Phospholipids are based either on glycerol (the glycerophospholipids) or on sphingosine (the sphingolipids); the former are the most common. The structure of a glycerophospholipid consists of three parts; a glycerol backbone, a phosphorylated alcohol making the lipid headgroup, and two fatty acyl chains (Figure 4). The fatty acyl chains provide the hydrophobic portion of the molecule and the phosphate ester the hydrophilic portion. Corresponding phospholipids with one fatty acyl chain (the lysophospholipids) are intermediates in phospholipid metabolism and are not normal components of biological membranes.

By varying the fatty acid and alcohol groups, a wide variety of chemically distinct structures can be generated. The fatty acids found in the lipids of animal cells are generally unbranched, with an even number of carbon atoms between 14 and 24. In a typical lipid molecule, one fatty acyl chain will

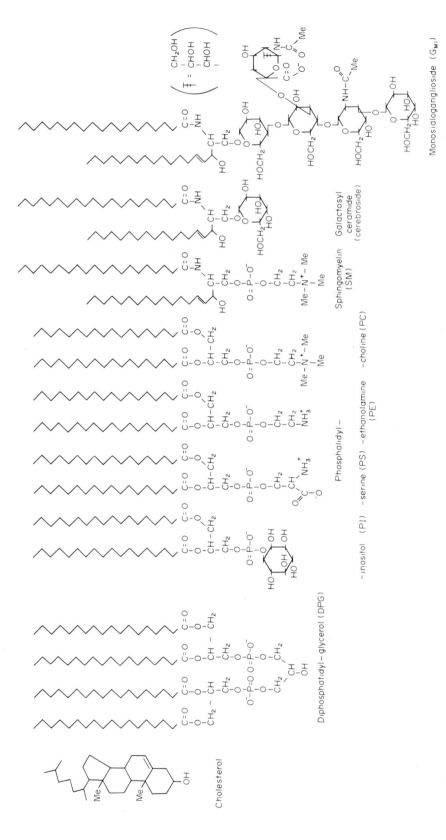

Figure 4   The structures of membrane lipids (reproduced from J. B. Finean, R. Coleman and R. H. Mitchell, 'Membranes and their Cellular Functions', 1978, by permission of Blackwell Scientific Publications)

be saturated and one unsaturated; the unsaturated chain contains one or more C=C double bond in a *cis* configuration. The chemical structures and trivial names of the most common of the fatty acids are given in Table 3.

Esterification of two fatty acyl chains to a molecule of glycerophosphate gives phosphatidic acid which in turn can link to the bases choline, ethanolamine, serine or inositol to give, respectively, phosphatidylcholine, phosphatidylethanolamine, phosphatidylserine or phosphatidylinositol (Table 4). All the phospholipids carry a phosphate group which will bear a single negative charge at physiological pH. In addition, choline and ethanolamine contain amino groups which will be positively charged at pH 7 so that phosphatidylcholine and phosphatidylethanolamine will be zwitterions with no net charge. Serine, however, has one negative and one positive charge at pH 7, so that phosphatidylserine will carry a single net negative charge. The inositol group is uncharged so that phosphatidylinositol will also carry a single net negative charge; the charge on the phosphoinositides will depend on the number of phosphate groups on the inositol ring (Table 4). Phosphatidylglycerol is a major phospholipid component of bacteria, but is found in only trace amounts in animal tissue. Phosphatidylglycerol is, however, the biosynthetic precursor of cardiolipin (also called diphosphatidylglycerol), a phospholipid unusual in having four fatty acyl chains and two negative charges, found (in animal tissues) only in the inner mitochondrial membrane.

Plasmalogens are very closely related in structure to the phospholipids described above, differing only in that one of the fatty acyl chains is linked to the glycerol backbone of the molecule by an ether linkage rather than through the ester linkages shown in Figure 4. The sphingolipids are also similar in structure to the phospholipids, differing in that the backbone of the molecule is not glycerol but a sphingosine, a long chain amino alcohol; sphingomyelin has an additional fatty acid amide attached to the amino group of sphingosine as well as a choline in a phosphodiester linkage to the C-1 position (Figure 4). The ceramides are a related class of sphingolipids with a free hydroxyl group at the C-1 position. Esterification of sugars through this hydroxyl group gives rise to the cerebrosides (containing only a single galactosyl residue) or to the gangliosides (containing complex oligosaccharides). The structure of a ganglioside is shown in Figure 4, and some of the more commonly occurring of the sugar headgroups are shown in Table 5. Since the gangliosides contain sialic acid, they are negatively charged: gangliosides appear to be important in cell function as receptors for hormones and toxins. The fatty acid moieties of the sphingolipids are rather unusual, and tend to be longer than those typically found in phosphatidylcholines [*i.e.* lignoceric acid (24:0) and nervonic acid (24:1)]; α-hydroxy fatty acids are also found in these lipids.

The last of the lipids shown in Figure 4 is cholesterol. This is the major sterol found in mammalian cells, where it is located almost entirely in the plasma membrane. Although its structure is entirely different to that of the other lipids, it is still amphipathic, with a hydrophobic steroid ring and a hydrophilic hydroxyl group.

11.1.2.3 Lipid Composition

The relative proportions of the lipids described above vary considerably, both between the different membranes of one cell, and between the same membranes in different cells. Table 6 gives some data for membranes of rat liver cells. One noticeable difference between the various membranes is the relatively high levels of cholesterol and sphingomyelin in the plasma membrane and their virtual absence in mitochondria. In contrast, cardiolipin is found solely in mitochondria (the small amount observed in the endoplasmic reticulum is almost certainly due to contamination of the

Table 3 Fatty Acids Commonly Found in Phospholipids

Structure	Notation[a]	Name
$Me(CH_2)_{14}CO_2H$	16:0	Palmitic acid
$Me(CH_2)_{16}CO_2H$	18:0	Stearic acid
$Me(CH_2)_5CH=CH(CH_2)_7CO_2H$	16:1	Palmitoleic acid
$Me(CH_2)_7CH=CH(CH_2)_7CO_2H$	18:1	Oleic acid
$Me(CH_2)_4(CH=CHCH_2)_2(CH_2)_6CO_2H$	18:2	Linoleic acid
$Me(CH_2)(CH=CHCH_2)_3(CH_2)_6CO_2H$	18:3	Linolenic acid
$Me(CH_2)_4(CH=CHCH_2)_4(CH_2)_2CO_2H$	20:4	Arachidonic acid

[a] Unsaturated fatty acids have *cis* double bonds. The shorthand notation gives the number of carbon atoms in the chain followed by the number of double bonds.

Table 4 Phospholipid Headgroups

Structure of base	Name of lipid	Abbreviation
—O—H	Phosphatidic acid	PA
—O—$CH_2CH_2\overset{+}{N}Me_3$	Phosphatidylcholine	PC
—O—$CH_2CH_2\overset{+}{N}H_3$	Phosphatidylethanolamine	PE
$-O-CH_2-\underset{\overset{\mid}{+NH_3}}{CH}-CO_2^-$	Phosphatidylserine	PS
—O—$CH_2CH(OH)CH_2OH$	Phosphatidylglycerol	PG
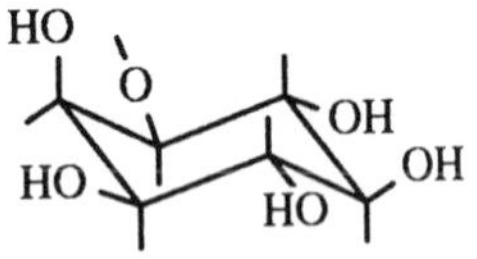 *(inositol ring structure)*	Phosphatidylinositol	PI or PtdIns
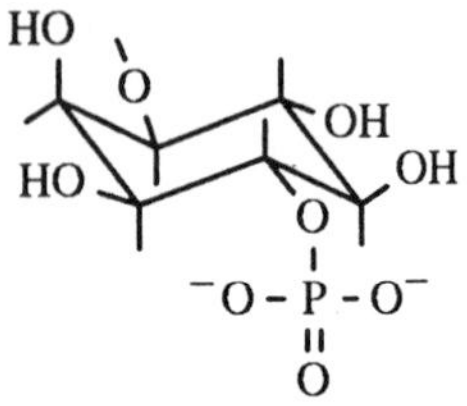 *(inositol 4-phosphate ring structure)*	Phosphatidylinositol 4-phosphate	PtdIns4P
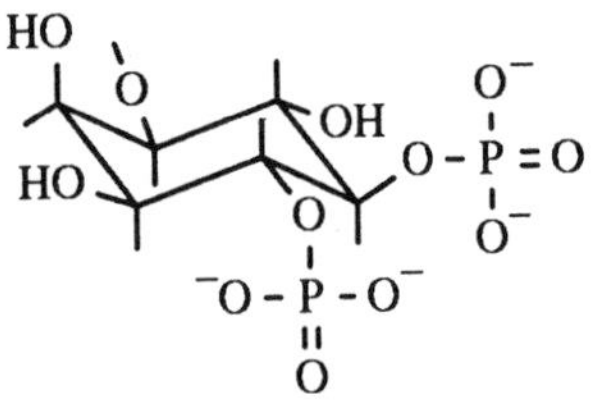 *(inositol 4,5-bisphosphate ring structure)*	Phosphatidylinositol 4,5-bisphosphate	PtdIns4,5P$_2$

Table 5 Structures of Some Commonly Occurring Ganglioside Headgroups

Sugar residue[a]	Designation
-Glc-Gal-NANA	G_{M3}

-Glc-Gal-GlcNAc
        |
     NANA
	G_{M2}

-Glc-Gal-GlcNAc-Gal
        |
     NANA
	G_{M1}

-Glc-Gal-GlcNAc-Glc
        | |
    NANA NANA
	G_{D1}

-Glc-Gal-GlcNAc-Gal
        | |
    NANA NANA
     |
   NANA
	G_{T1}

[a] Abbreviations: NANA, sialic acid; Glc, glucose; Gal, galactose; GlcNAc, *N*-acetyl-D-glucosamine

Table 6 Lipid Composition of Subcellular Organelles of Rat Liver[8]

Phospholipid[a]	Endoplasmic reticulum		Mitochondrial membranes		Lysosomal membrane	Nuclear membrane	Golgi membrane	Plasma membrane
	Rough	*Smooth*	*Inner*	*Outer*				
Lysophosphatidylcholine	2.9	2.9	0.6	—	2.9	—	5.9	1.8
Sphingomyelin	2.4	6.3	2.0	2.2	16.0	6.3	12.3	23.1
Phosphatidylcholine	59.6	54.4	40.5	49.4	41.9	52.1	45.3	43.1
Phosphatidylinositol	10.1	8.0	1.7	9.2	5.9	4.1	8.7	6.5
Phosphatidylserine	3.5	3.9	1.0	1.0	—	5.6	4.2	3.7
Phosphatidylethanolamine	20.0	22.0	38.8	34.9	20.5	25.1	17.0	20.5
Cardiolipin	1.2	2.4	17.0	4.2	—	—	—	—
Moles cholesterol/moles phospholipid	0.07	0.24	0.06	0.12	0.49	—	0.15	0.76

[a] Expressed as percentage of phospholipid phosphorus.

preparation with mitochondria). In all the membranes, however, the predominant lipids are zwitterionic, with negatively charged lipids generally constituting about 10% of the total.

The lipid composition of the same membrane taken from different animals also varies considerably. Figure 5, for example, shows that although the sum of the phosphatidylcholine and sphingomyelin contents of red blood cells of rat, pig, ox and sheep are all 40–45%, the relative amounts of phosphatidylcholine and sphingomyelin in these membranes differ considerably. The lipid distribution also differs between the two sides of most, if not all, biological membranes. Figure 6 illustrates the relative distribution of phospholipids in the human red blood cell membrane.[9] In this cell, sphingomyelin is concentrated on the outer surface and phosphatidylethanolamine on the inner surface. Results with subcellular membranes are less clear cut, but it appears, for example, that in sarcoplasmic reticulum, phosphatidylethanolamine is located preferentially on the outer (cytoplasmic) surface with phosphatidylcholine and phosphatidylserine located preferentially on the inner (luminal) surface.[10]

Even more variable than the phospholipid headgroup composition is the fatty acyl chain distribution between membranes. Table 7 illustrates the widely different fatty acyl chain compositions of the various classes of phospholipid found in the human red blood cell. It is noticeable, however, that the proportion of saturated to unsaturated fatty acids is close to one. Table 8 shows the fatty acyl chain distribution found in the phosphatidylcholine and phosphatidylethanolamine fractions of rabbit skeletal muscle sarcoplasmic reticulum, demonstrating that the saturated fatty acyl chains are found predominantly at the 1 position of the phospholipids with the unsaturated fatty acyl chains predominantly at position 2. This distribution is typical of all animal cell membranes. As for the lipid headgroups, there is no evidence that the particular fatty acyl chain content of a membrane is in any way specially suited for its function; the fatty acyl chain compositions of sarcoplasmic reticulum from rabbit, rat, chicken, human and lobster are all distinctly different.[12, 13]

The phospholipid composition of animal cell membranes is not constant; significant changes occur in development and ageing, in disease, with diet and during drug treatment. An example of developmental change is shown in Figure 7 which illustrates the changes in the relative contents of phosphatidylethanolamine and phosphatidylcholine in rabbit muscle sarcoplasmic reticulum, with development.[14] The effects of diet on the phospholipid fatty acyl chain composition of rabbit skeletal muscle sarcoplasmic reticulum have also been studied.[15] Enriching the diet in saturated fatty acids has little effect, the total content of saturated fatty acids remaining close to 50%. Addition of highly unsaturated fatty acids to the diet, however, causes marked changes in the unsaturated fatty acid content of the membrane but with little change in the ratio of saturated to unsaturated chains. These changes in composition produce no detectable change in the function of the membrane.[15] Again, these results are fairly typical of all animal membranes, where dietary effects are relatively small and where it has proved difficult, despite much effort, to relate any observed changes in membrane phospholipid composition to any changes in function of the membrane (see, for example, the data presented in ref. 16). Larger changes in phospholipid composition can be achieved with cultured cells.[17] Supplementing the growth medium of such cells with a saturated fatty acid such as palmitic acid leads to growth inhibition if the saturated fatty acyl chain composition of the cell membranes exceeds about 50%. Marked changes in unsaturated fatty acid composition can also be achieved for such cells, but in this case effects on membrane function are relatively small.[17] Particularly large

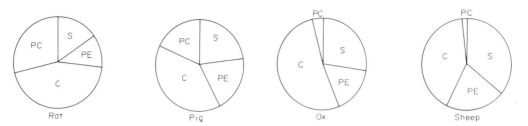

Figure 5 The relative phospholipid compositions of red blood cell membranes from rat, pig, ox and sheep. Abbreviations: PC, phosphatidylcholine; PE, phosphatidylethanolamine; S, sphingomyelin; C, cholesterol (reproduced from P. J. Quinn, 'The Molecular Biology of Cell Membranes', 1976, by permission of Macmillan)

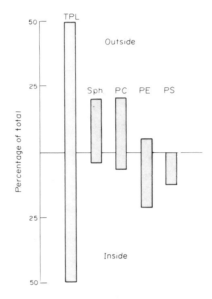

Figure 6 The distribution of phospholipids in the two sides of the human red blood cell membrane. Abbreviations: TPL, total phospholipid; Sph, sphingomyelin; others as given in Table 4 (reproduced from ref. 9 by permission of Elsevier Science Publishers B.V.)

Table 7 Fatty Acid Composition of Phospholipids from Human Erythrocytes[11]

Fatty acid[a]	Phosphatidylcholine	Phosphatidylethanolamine	Phosphatidylserine	Sphingomyelin
16:0	34	29	14	28
18:0	13	9	36	7
18:1	22	22	15	6
18:2	18	6	7	2
20:4	6	18	21	8
24:0	—	—	—	20
24:1	—	—	—	14

[a] Expressed as % of total fatty acid: some minor fatty acid components are not included in the table.

changes in phospholipid composition are possible in bacteria using mutants of phospholipid synthesis. Many of these changes in phospholipid composition were found to be compatible with cell growth, while others were not.[18] The least variable parameter is the total phospholipid content, which could not be lowered by more than 40% without inhibiting cell growth. A two- or three-fold change in the ratio of anionic to zwitterionic phospholipids was generally found to be compatible with growth, but with larger changes causing growth inhibition; the level of cardiolipin in the membrane could be varied very considerably without any obvious adverse effect. Temperature has been shown to have a very considerable effect[3] on the lipid composition of bacterial membranes, particularly on the fatty acyl chain component; in a wide range of organisms it has been shown that

Table 8 Fatty Acid Content of Phospholipids of Rabbit Muscle Sarcoplasmic Reticulum[12]

| | *Composition* (mol %) | | | | | |
| Fatty acid | *Phosphatidylcholine* | | | *Phosphatidylethanolamine* | | |
	Total	*Pos. 1*	*Pos. 2*	*Total*	*Pos. 1*	*Pos. 2*
14:0	0.2	0.4	0.6	—	—	—
16:0	40.0	74.0	5.5	26.0	49.0	5.0
18:0	4.0	8.0	0.3	14.0	26.0	2.0
18:1	17.0	8.0	26.0	14.0	5.0	21.0
18:2	25.0	8.0	41.0	6.0	2.0	11.0
20:4	8.0	—	15.0	16.0	—	27.0
22:3	1.0	—	2.0	5.0	—	9.0
22:5	2.0	—	3.0	6.0	—	11.0

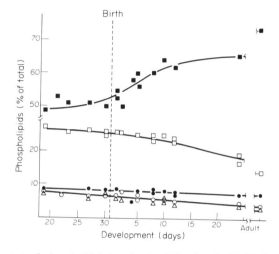

Figure 7 The change in content of phosphatidylethanolamine (□), phosphatidylcholine (■), phosphatidylserine (○), sphingomyelin (△) and phosphatidylinositol (●) of rabbit muscle sarcoplasmic reticulum with development (reproduced from ref. 14 by permission of the *European Journal of Biochemistry*)

with decreasing temperature, the average fatty acyl chain length decreases and the degree of unsaturation increases.[19, 20] Similar changes are observed in higher organisms such as fish exposed to temperature changes.[21]

Changes in the phospholipid compositions of many animal cell membranes have been reported in a wide variety of disease states, but these are commonly small and of uncertain validity. Thus many reports have appeared of changes in the phospholipid composition of sarcoplasmic reticulum and other cell membranes in muscular dystrophy, but many, if not all, of these reports can be attributed to contamination of membrane samples.[22, 23] Further, it is now known that the major forms of muscular dystrophy follow from the absence or mutation of a particular structural protein found in muscle, dystrophin.[72] Clear cases of defects in lipid metabolism are, however, well known. Thus defects in sphingolipid metabolism in nervous tissue leads to accumulation of a variety of lipids, including sphingomyelin (Niemann–Pick disease), gangliosides (Tay–Sachs disease), and cerebrosides (Gaucher's disease).[24]

11.1.2.4 The Lipid Bilayer[26, 27, 30]

The common feature of all the lipid molecules described above is that they are amphipathic. In the phospholipids, the headgroup is polar whereas the fatty acyl chains are non-polar and hydrophobic. Even cholesterol has this same dichotomy of structure, with a polar —OH group, the rest of the molecule being non-polar (Figure 4). It is the difference in properties between the two ends of the molecule which is the basis of the role of lipids in membrane formation. On dispersing in water, the polar end of the lipid will mix with the water while the non-polar end will not. These seemingly incompatible requirements can both be met if the lipid adopts a structure made up of two layers of lipid, the lipid bilayer shown in Figure 8. In this structure, the polar headgroups of the phospholipid molecules are in contact with water on the outside of the bilayer whilst the non-polar fatty acyl chains are sequestered within the interior of the bilayer. These bilayer sheets provide the basic structural element of the membrane. It should be appreciated that the formation of the lipid bilayer is a self-assembly process and that no work has to be done to get the lipids to adopt this arrangement: the driving force for bilayer formation is the hydrophobic effect.

The properties of phospholipid bilayers have been studied extensively. Lipid bilayers can be made simply by vigorously shaking dry phospholipids with water. The bilayers close on themselves to give sealed spherical vesicles (Figure 9). Simple hand shaking of phospholipids with water gives multi-lamellar vesicles (called liposomes) arranged with one bilayer membrane inside the next, like an onion. More vigorous shaking of phospholipids using ultrasound, either with a sonicating probe or in a sonicating bath, gives single shelled vesicles, as shown in Figure 9. Single shelled vesicles can also be made by mixing lipid with detergent, followed by removal of detergent on a column of Sephadex.

Phospholipid vesicles have been used to measure the permeability properties of the lipid bilayer. If phospholipid vesicles are prepared in a solution of the compound of interest, then some of that compound will be trapped in the aqueous interior of the vesicle. The rate at which the molecules leak out of the vesicles depends on the permeability of the bilayer to the compound. Measurements of leak rate have shown that phospholipid bilayers have very low permeabilities for ions and most polar molecules. Permeabilities are generally well correlated with solubilities in non-polar solvents, with molecules that are highly soluble in such solvents having high permeabilities. This is readily understood in terms of the structure of the bilayer; the centre of the bilayer is hydrophobic, and in passing from the interior space of the vesicle to the exterior, a molecule must first pass through this region. The more soluble the molecule in the bilayer centre, the less of a barrier is the bilayer to movement.

For studies of electrical properties, a more useful model membrane is the bimolecular lipid membrane (BLM) shown in Figure 10. A lipid membrane is formed across a small hole (0.5 mm diameter) in a partition, usually in the presence of a solvent such as decane. With electrodes inserted into the two aqueous compartments, the electrical resistance of the membrane can be measured. This is found to be very high, again showing that the permeability of the membrane to ions is low. The most exciting uses of the BLM, however, are in the study of ion channels incorporated into the lipid bilayer.

These studies all demonstrate a pattern of high permeability to non-polar molecules and low permeability to polar molecules, matching the basic permeability properties of biological membranes. Absolute values of permeability coefficients have been found to vary with phospholipid structure. These effects are generally attributed to differences in the fluidity of the lipid bilayer. But before discussing the meaning of lipid fluidity we should consider the phase properties of phospholipids.

Phospholipids can exist in one of two bilayer phases depending on temperature. At low temperatures phospholipids adopt a rigid, gel phase in which the fatty acyl chains are packed tightly in a fully extended, all-*trans* array. At higher temperatures they transform into a fluid, liquid crystalline phase in which the fatty acyl chains are highly disordered with relatively free rotation

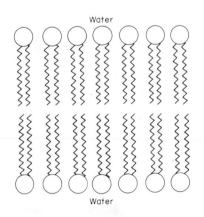

Figure 8   The lipid bilayer: circles represent phospholipid headgroups, and zigzag lines the fatty acyl chains

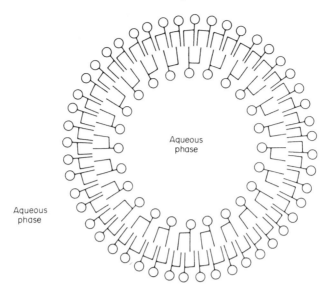

Figure 9 Sealed phospholipid vesicles (reproduced from ref. 4, from the 'Studies in Biology' series, by permission of Edward Arnold and courtesy of R. P. Gould)

Bimolecular lipid membrane (BLM)

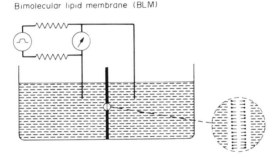

Figure 10 A bimolecular lipid membrane formed across a small hole in a partition between two compartments (reproduced from J. B. Finean, R. Coleman, and R. H. Mitchell, 'Membranes and their Cellular Function', 1978, by permission of Blackwell Scientific Publications)

about C—C bonds (see Figure 11). In a bilayer of a single species of phospholipid, the transition between the gel and liquid crystalline phases is a sharp, first-order transition, like the melting of a solid to a liquid. The temperature of the transition depends on both the headgroup of the phospholipid and on the fatty acyl chains (Table 9). The data in Table 9 show that transition temperatures increase with increasing chain length. It can also be seen that the introduction of one *cis* double bond into a saturated fatty acyl chain results in a very marked decrease in transition temperature, the introduction of a second double bond resulting in a further but smaller decrease and the introduction of still further double bonds resulting in a small increase in transition temperature. These effects can be understood in terms of the difficulty of packing unsaturated chains into a close-packed gel phase. Phase transition temperatures for phosphatidylethanolamines and phosphatidylserines are higher than those for the corresponding phosphatidylcholines by about 20 °C. It is also clear from the data in Table 9 that phospholipids containing one saturated and one unsaturated fatty acyl chain have a phase transition temperature between the phase transition temperatures for the corresponding phospholipids with two identical fatty acyl chains.

Comparison of the data in Table 9 with the membrane phospholipid compositions discussed in Section 11.1.2.3 allows us to draw an important conclusion: phospholipids in biological membranes will be in the liquid crystalline phase at physiological temperatures. This appears to be a requirement for cell survival; it has been shown, for example in bacteria, that cells stop growing when more than about half of their lipid is in the gel phase. This requirement is not hard to understand, at least in general terms. In the rigid gel phase the membrane will loose its flexibility and become 'brittle'; as

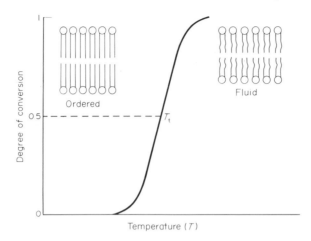

Figure 11   The phase transition of a phospholipid measured using a probe technique such as fluorescence depolarization

Table 9   Temperatures of the Gel to Liquid Crystalline Phase Transitions
for Phospholipids (in Excess Water)[27]

Fatty acyl chains[a]	Headgroup	Transition temperature (°C)
12:0/12:0	PC	−1
14:0/14:0	PC	24
16:0/16:0	PC	42
16:1/16:1	PC	−36
18:0/18:0	PC	55
18:1/18:1	PC	−20
16:0/18:0	PC	47
18:0/18:1	PC	5
18:0/18:2	PC	−16
18:0/18:3	PC	−13
16:0/16:0	PE	63
16:0/16:0	PS	55

[a] All unsaturated chains are *cis* Δ^9.

described in Section 11.1.5.2, interactions with membrane proteins are also considerably modified in the gel phase.

The most detailed information about the thermodynamics of the phase transitions of phospholipids and of mixtures of phospholipids has been obtained using calorimetric methods. The motivation for many of these studies has been to establish the mixing properties of phospholipids and to establish phase diagrams for phospholipid mixtures. These studies show that, perhaps not surprisingly, the mixing of different phospholipids is non-ideal, so that the distribution of phospholipids in the plane of the bilayer will be non-random, with like phospholipids having a higher probability of being nearest neighbours.[27]

Phase transition properties have also been studied using a variety of spectroscopic probe techniques. One much used technique is fluorescence depolarization of diphenylhexatriene (DPH).[28] Diphenylhexatriene is hydrophobic and will partition into the fatty acyl chain region of phospholipid bilayers. The fluorescence of DPH is polarized, and the degree of polarization depends on the freedom of motion of the DPH molecule in its environment; the greater the extent of the motion and the faster the motion (largely rotation about the long axis of the molecule) the less polarized will be the fluorescence. Motion of the DPH molecule is much more restricted in the rigid gel phase than in the fluid, liquid crystalline phase, so that a marked decrease in fluorescence polarization would be expected on transformation of the lipid into the liquid crystalline phase (Figure 11).

Because, as far as we know, phospholipids in all biological membranes are in the liquid crystalline phase, the properties of this phase have been studied particularly extensively. One potentially important property is the 'fluidity' of the bilayer. Figure 12 illustrates the types of motion that we might expect in a lipid bilayer in the liquid crystalline phase. There will be considerable rotation

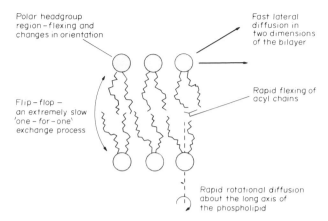

Figure 12 Modes of mobility in a phospholipid bilayer (reproduced from M. D. Houslay and K. K. Stanley, 'Dynamics of Biological Membranes', ed. M. D. Houslay, 1982, by permission of John Wiley & Sons Ltd.)

about C—C bonds of the fatty acyl chains and in the headgroup region, and fast lateral diffusion of the phospholipids in the plane of the bilayer. Flip-flop motion in which a phospholipid moves from one side of the bilayer to the other will, however, be slow since it involves moving the polar lipid headgroup through the hydrophobic core of the membrane; it is the slowness of this motion that allows an asymmetric distribution of phospholipids between the two halves of biological membranes (Section 11.1.2.3).

Although the concept of fluidity is familiar in normal bulk fluids, it is more complex in a two-dimensional bilayer system. The chemical nature of the phospholipid molecule, with fatty acyl chains 'anchored' to a relatively immobile backbone, results in a gradient of motion within the membrane, with both the rate and amplitude of motion increasing along the fatty acyl chain from the carboxyl to the methyl terminal end.[27] A proper description of the membrane requires that the rate and amplitude factors be separated. The amplitude of motion is described in terms of an order parameter which describes the time-averaged disposition in space of each group of atoms in the acyl chain. The rate of motion can be described in terms of a correlation time, a measure of the rate of motion of a group of atoms between its various possible positions in space. Formally, fluidity (and its inverse, viscosity) corresponds solely to rate of motion, but in the biological literature the word is used very informally to include both factors.

The commonest technique used to characterize membrane fluidity is fluorescence depolarization of DPH. The technique is sometimes used to determine membrane 'viscosity' by equating membrane viscosity to the viscosity of an oil in which DPH has the same polarization as in the membrane; the viscosity of the membrane can be likened to that of a light machine oil. It is clear, however, that this is a very crude measure, ignoring as it does the flexibility gradient that must exist in the membrane (see Figure 12) and failing to separate static and dynamic terms. Nevertheless, it has the great advantage of simplicity and changes in 'viscosity' at least indicate that some sort of change has occurred.

A technique capable of giving more detailed information is electron spin resonance (ESR), employing nitroxide stable free radicals. The nitroxide group can be introduced into various positions of a fatty acyl chain to probe mobility at various depths in a bilayer (Figure 13). The shape of the ESR spectrum of a spin labelled fatty acid depends markedly on the motional characteristics of the fatty acid, particularly marked being an increase in the maximum peak separation in the spectra with decreasing fluidity (Figure 14). The spectra depicted in Figure 14 clearly show the expected gradient of motion within the bilayer.

Unsaturation affects the profile of motion within the bilayer. Seelig and Waespe-Sarcevic[29] have described the hydrocarbon interior of a bilayer as a series of strata running parallel to the bilayer surface. Segments of the fatty acyl chains that are located in the same stratum are characterized by similar mobilities. Unsaturation complicates this picture. Since the C=C unit is relatively rigid, the area around the double bond will be more ordered than areas nearer the methyl end of the hydrocarbon chain. With polyunsaturated chains, such ordering effects will become more marked, but, in general, these effects of double bonds on fluidity, particularly after the first, are rather small. Large changes in bilayer fluidity are, however, caused by addition of cholesterol to a bilayer in the liquid crystalline phase, an effect largely to be understood in terms of the rigid sterol ring system of the cholesterol molecule: cholesterol induces a state with fluidity between those of the normal liquid

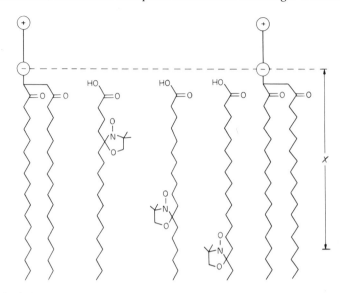

Figure 13 Location of spin label nitroxides, probing to different depths x, in phospholipid bilayers (reproduced from *Arch. Biochem. Biophys.*, 1976, **172**, 1, by permission of Academic Press)

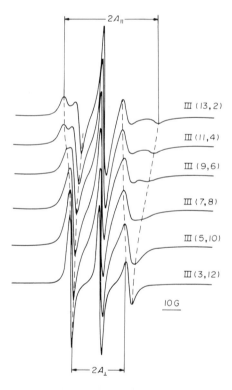

Figure 14 ESR spectra of different positional isomers of a phosphatidylcholine spin label (m, n) where m and n give the position on the fatty acyl chain with respect to the terminal methyl group and the carboxyl group, respectively (reproduced from D. Marsh and A. Watts, 'Progress in Lipid–Protein Interactions', 1985, vol. 1, by permission of Elsevier Science Publishers B.V.)

crystalline and gel states.[27] Since cholesterol is found in the outer plasma membrane, it has been suggested that one of the biological roles of cholesterol could be to reduce the permeability of the outer membrane to small molecules by increasing membrane viscosity.

Finally, it should be mentioned that the bilayer (lamellar) phase typical of biological membranes is not the only phase that can be adopted by phospholipids. The phase adopted by a lipid depends on the 'shape' of the lipid, the shape being defined by the relative areas occupied by the lipid headgroup and the fatty acyl chains. A cylindrical structure (in which the lipid headgroup and the two fatty acyl chains occupy roughly equal areas) gives a bilayer phase and other shapes a variety of non-bilayer phases. Unsaturated phosphatidylethanolamines, in particular, readily form hexagonal phases, and there has been much speculation about the possible biological importance of such phases.[30] However, it is known that the presence of membrane proteins and phosphatidylcholines tend to force phosphatidylethanolamine into a bilayer phase, and it has yet to be established that any phases other than the bilayer phase occur in biological membranes under physiological conditions.

In conclusion, these studies show that the lipid bilayer can provide the basic permeability barrier for the membrane, and that the lipids found in biological membranes are such that the membrane will be in the fluid, liquid crystalline phase. They provide few clues, however, as to why the lipid composition of the membrane should be as complex as it is; this point will be returned to in Section 11.1.5.

11.1.2.5 Membrane Proteins[31–35]

Whilst lipids provide the basic permeability barrier for the membrane, it is the protein component which confers on the membrane most of its distinctive functions. As described above (see Figure 2) the relative proportions of lipid and protein vary between membranes, but in a typical plasma membrane the molar ratio of lipid to protein is about 100:1, with about half the surface area of the membrane being occupied by lipid and half by protein; the picture of the membrane illustrated in Figure 3 therefore considerably over-estimates the separation between protein molecules in the membrane.

Membrane proteins fall into one of two broad classes. Loosely attached to the surface of the membrane are the extrinsic (or peripheral) proteins. These proteins are probably attached to the membrane by charge–charge interactions with other proteins in the membrane (or possibly with charged phospholipids in the membrane such as phosphatidylserine): they can be removed by washing with buffers of high ionic strength and are soluble and free of phospholipid. The second class of membrane protein are the intrinsic (or integral) proteins illustrated in Figure 3. These are firmly embedded in the membrane and need much harsher procedures to remove them from the membrane.

It is often difficult to establish whether a particular protein is an extrinsic membrane protein or whether it is a truly cytosolic protein that has become attached to the membrane during purification of the membrane; indeed, many extrinsic membrane proteins may be in equilibrium between bound and free forms. A typical extrinsic membrane protein is cytochrome *c* which binds to the mitochondrial inner membrane.

Intrinsic membrane proteins are now generally thought to span the lipid bilayer, although it is possible that some may penetrate only part way into the hydrophobic core of the membrane (Figure 3). The region of the intrinsic membrane protein in contact with the phospholipid fatty acyl chains must be hydrophobic, in contrast to the regions of the protein exposed to water which will be predominantly polar. To remove an intrinsic membrane protein from the membrane without denaturing it, the hydrophobic surfaces must be protected. One way to do this is to use detergents. These substances are rather like lipids in that they are amphipathic, but they have more polar groups and so are more water soluble. A typical detergent is the bile acid sodium cholate (**1**). The bile acids are planar, with all the —OH groups and the —CO$_2^-$ group on one face of the molecule; one face is thus polar whilst the other is non-polar. Cholate can then bind to a membrane, with the hydrophobic surface of the detergent interacting with the hydrophobic surfaces of the protein or lipid bilayer, but with the polar surface of the detergent exposed to water and making the whole complex soluble.

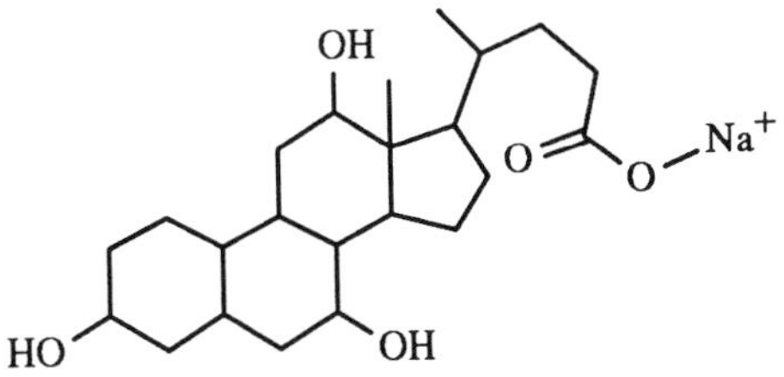

(**1**)

As well as the bile acids cholate and deoxycholate, a variety of other detergents are commonly used to solubilize membrane proteins. The most powerful of these is sodium dodecyl sulfate (SDS) which, however, usually denatures the protein; as described below, it is mostly used in molecular weight determinations. Cholate and deoxycholate have the advantage of being easily removed by column chromatography or dialysis. The non-polar detergent Triton X-100 is much used as a mild detergent but has the disadvantage of being rather difficult to remove. Triton X-100 is a commercial preparation of very heterogeneous chain length; analogous detergents of defined structure are also available such as $C_{12}E_8$ (a polyoxyethylene with an alkyl chain length of C-12 and a headgroup with eight polyoxyethylene groups). A newer detergent which has been very successful is octylglucoside. Unfortunately, the choice of the best detergent for a particular problem is, at present, very much a matter of trial and error.[31]

The procedures used for purification of a membrane protein, once solubilized, are similar to those used for cytosolic proteins. Selective denaturation using heat or pH, ammonium sulfate precipitation, density gradient centrifugation, gel filtration and ion-exchange or affinity chromatography have all been used. Inevitably, these procedures have been most successful for proteins which make up a significant fraction of their respective membranes: examples include rhodopsin from retinal rods, $(Ca^{2+}-Mg^{2+})$-ATPase from sarcoplasmic reticulum, (Na^+-K^+)-ATPase from kidney outer medulla, and the acetylcholine receptor from electroplax. Most membrane proteins unfortunately occur at low percentages of total membrane protein and are very difficult to purify in significant quantity.

Membrane proteins are generally characterized using SDS polyacrylamide gel electrophoresis (SDS-PAGE). In this technique, the membrane is first dissolved in a reducing medium containing the detergent SDS, so as to unfold the constituent polypeptides and coat them with the negatively charged SDS. The polypeptides are then separated by electrophoresis in polyacrylamide gels in the presence of an excess of SDS.[32] The rate of migration of a polypeptide in the gel is a fairly reliable guide to its molecular weight, except for glycosylated polypeptides which run abnormally. The polypeptides are detected in the gels by staining with Commassie Blue or colloidal silver or gold. Polypeptides can also be detected using antibody methods.

11.1.2.6 Structures of Membrane Proteins

The functional asymmetry of the membrane follows from an asymmetric distribution of proteins between the two surfaces of the membrane. Intrinsic membrane proteins are arranged so that all copies face the same way and extrinsic membrane proteins are found only on one side of the membrane. This asymmetry has been established for many membrane proteins using labelling reagents which cannot cross the membrane (and which thus allow the 'inside' and 'outside' faces of the membrane to be distinguished) and using proteolytic digestion.[32]

Establishing the three-dimensional structure of an intrinsic membrane protein is still very much a challenge. One of the most convincing demonstrations that intrinsic membrane proteins really are embedded in the membrane comes from freeze-fracture electron microscopy. In this technique, the sample is rapidly frozen and then fractured with a sharp knife; this cleaves the membrane along a plane in the middle of the bilayer (Figure 15) so exposing the hydrophobic core of the bilayer. The sample is then shadowed with metal to give a replica (like a death-mask) of the membrane which can be viewed in the electron microscope. Typically what is seen is a smooth surface studded with a large number of particles, the intrinsic membrane proteins.

In membranes in which one intrinsic protein makes up a large fraction of the total protein, negative stain electron microscopy often shows up the presence of ordered protein arrays. The most studied system is the purple membrane fragment from *Halobacterium halobium*, in which the protein is very largely bacteriorhodopsin, a protein responsible for pumping protons and with considerable similarity to rhodopsin. The bacteriorhodopsin molecule contains seven α-helices spanning the membrane, with the helical axes being approximately perpendicular to the plane of the membrane (Figure 16). The individual bacteriorhodopsin molecules are arranged as trimers in the membrane. A number of other membrane proteins have also been demonstrated to be present in ordered arrays. Thus, as shown in Figure 17, the $(Ca^{2+}-Mg^{2+})$-ATPase is present in the sarcoplasmic reticulum, at least under some conditions, as extended, ladder-like arrays of dimers.

To obtain a full three-dimensional structure of a membrane protein by X-ray diffraction methods, it is necessary to prepare crystals of the membrane protein, and this is still a formidable task. To date, only one membrane protein has been crystallized in a form suitable for X-ray analysis, the photosynthetic reaction centre from the bacterium *R. viridis*.[71] Although a full analysis is not yet available, it is clear that the membrane-penetrant part of the complex consists of a series of α-helices organized perpendicular to the membrane surface, as shown for bacteriorhodopsin. It seems very

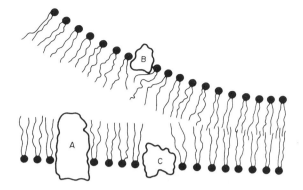

Figure 15 Cleavage of a membrane in freeze-fracture electron microscopy to expose intrinsic membrane proteins (A): extrinsic proteins are also shown (B, C) (reproduced from R. Harrison and G. G. Lunt, 'Biological Membranes', 1980, by permission of Blackie)

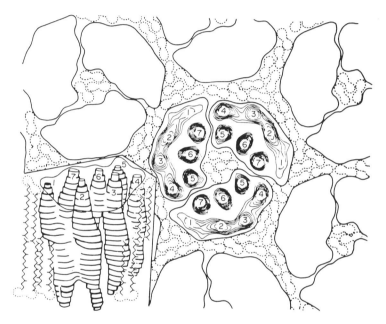

Figure 16 The arrangement of the seven α-helices of bacteriorhodopsin, and the trimeric arrangement of bacteriorhodopsin in the purple membrane, based on the studies of Henderson and Unwin (reproduced from ref. 10 by permission of Elsevier Science Publishers B.V.)

likely that this arrangement will be a feature common to all intrinsic membrane proteins. An α-helical structure is favoured within the hydrophobic core of the membrane because this structure is maximally hydrogen bonded. Transfer of a hydrogen bonded C=O and N—H pair in a protein backbone from water into a non-polar environment has been estimated to have a favourable free energy ΔG_{trans} of -1.4 kcal mol^{-1} (-5.9 kJ mol^{-1}) compared to an unfavourable change of 4.1 kcal mol^{-1} (17.1 kJ mol^{-1}) for a non-hydrogen bonded pair.[46]

Because of the lack of directly determined structures, most of our thinking about membrane protein structures has been based on predictions from amino acid sequence data. Classical methods of amino acid sequencing are generally difficult for membrane proteins, particularly for the hydrophobic regions. However, methods involving the sequencing of a DNA copy of the mRNA coding for the membrane protein have proved very fruitful, and sequences for many important membrane proteins are now available. Deriving possible structural models from such sequences usually starts with a search for very apolar segments long enough to span a lipid bilayer (typically *ca.* 25 amino acids long). A quantitative measure of the relative hydrophobicities of amino acid side chains can be made by considering the free energies of transfer of the side chain from water to a non-polar solvent such as ethanol or dioxane. These energies can be calculated in terms of the solvent-accessible surface area of the side chain and the polarity of the atoms comprising the side chain. The

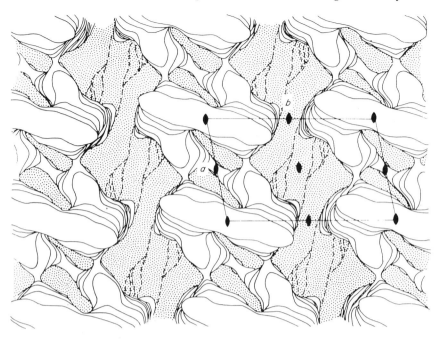

Figure 17 Surface contours of the $(Ca^{2+}-Mg^{2+})$-ATPase viewed normal to the plane of the membrane, as seen in electron micrographs in the presence of vanadate. The stippled areas indicate the surface of the lipid bilayer. The ATPase is seen to be present as rows of dimers under these conditions (reproduced with permission from *J. Mol. Biol.*, 1986, **187**, 417)

free energy of transfer of a particular residue from a random coil structure in water to an α-helical structure in a lipid bilayer can then be calculated in terms of the accessible surface area, the unsatisfied hydrogen bonds, and the free energy required to neutralize any charged groups (Table 10).[33-35] As expected, transfer of charged or highly polar amino acids to the interior of the membrane is highly unfavourable. Searching the amino acid sequence of the $(Ca^{2+}-Mg^{2+})$-ATPase in this way, for example, has located 10 hydrophobic sequences that could span the membrane (Figure 18).[36] These hydrophobic sequences thought to span the membrane are often flanked by charged amino acids, with lysine and arginine on the cytoplasmic side and any of the charged amino acids on the non-cytoplasmic side. However, not all hydrophobic α-helical segments need necessarily be membrane spanning, and the presence of charged amino acids in an otherwise hydrophobic sequence need not mean that this sequence is not buried within the membrane since charged amino acids could interact with other suitably charged residues on adjacent α-helical segments within the membrane or could, for example, be part of a water-lined pore within the membrane. Structural predictions therefore need to be treated with care. Predicted structures can sometimes be tested by raising antibodies to specific sequences thought to be located on the cytoplasmic or non-cytoplasmic side of the membrane; such studies with the acetylcholine receptor showed that the predicted structure was wrong.[37] Structural predictions can also be made for the cytoplasmic regions of membrane proteins, based on methods developed for cytosolic proteins, searching for common features such as nucleotide binding folds.

Based on the prediction methods described above, it has been suggested that a number of membrane proteins span the bilayer only once.[35] Examples include glycophorin in the human red cell membrane (Figure 19), brush border hydrolases, the μ_m chain of IgM, the major histocompatibility antigen (HLA), and a number of viral proteins. More common, however, are proteins that appear to span the membrane two or more times; examples include bacteriorhodopsin (Figure 16) and rhodopsin, which appear to have very similar structures, the $(Ca^{2+}-Mg^{2+})$-ATPase (Figure 18) and a number of related ATPases including the (Na^+-K^+)-ATPase, the anion transporter from red blood cells, the acetylcholine receptor and cytochrome P450.[34-37]

For a number of membrane proteins, the membrane-penetrant sequences are likely simply to act as 'tails', attaching the protein to the membrane, with little or no effect on the function of the protein; such proteins will show full activity when released from the membrane in soluble form by proteolytic cleavage; examples are the brush border hydrolases and the three proteins involved in fatty acid desaturation on microsomal membranes: cytochrome b_5, cytochrome b_5 reductase and fatty acid desaturase. For proteins whose functions include movement of ions or small molecules across the

Table 10 Estimated Free Energies of Transfer of Amino Acid Side Chains from a Random Coil Conformation in Water to an α-Helical Conformation in a Hydrophobic Phase[35]

Amino acid	ΔG_{trans}(kcal mol^{-1})
Phe	−3.39
Met	−2.70
Ile	−2.51
Leu	−2.41
Val	−2.00
Trp	−2.00
Cys	−1.51
Ala	−1.00
Gly	0.0
Thr	0.91
Tyr	1.12
Ser	1.51
Glu	2.41
Asn	2.92
Pro	3.32
His	3.42
Lys	4.21
Glu	5.92
Asp	7.41
Arg	11.30

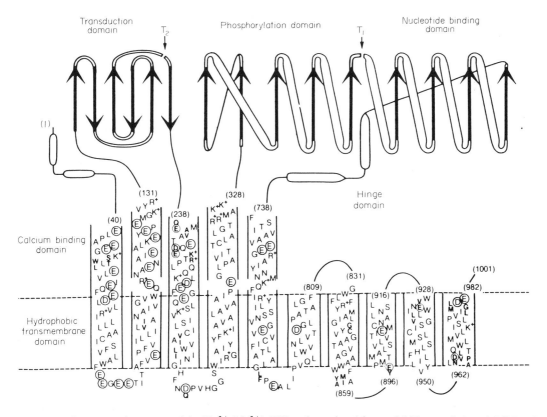

Figure 18 The suggested structure of the (Ca^{2+}–Mg^{2+})-ATPase (reproduced from ref. 36 by permission of Cell Press)

membrane, such as the transport ATPases and the acetylcholine receptor, it is likely that the membrane penetrant regions of the protein are a vital part of its structure; possible effects of the lipid bilayer on the structures and functions of such proteins are discussed in Section 11.1.5.2.

An increasing number of proteins have now been found in both prokaryotic and eukaryotic cell membranes with covalently attached lipid.[70] For some proteins this consists of fatty acids covalently

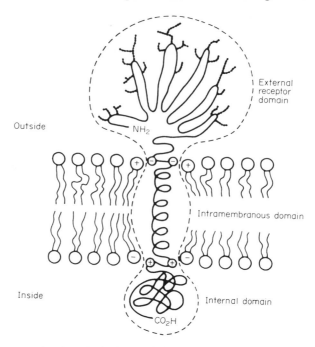

Figure 19 A suggested structure for glycophorin from red blood cell membranes (reproduced from 'Protides of the Biological Fluids', ed. H. Peeters, 1974)

linked to the protein by amide, thioester or *O*-acyl bonds. Other membrane proteins contain a covalently linked glycosylated phosphatidylinositol whose function is thought to be to anchor the protein to the membrane; examples include alkaline phosphatase and acetylcholinesterase.

11.1.3 MEMBRANE BIOSYNTHESIS

Having looked at the structures of the phospholipid and protein components of biological membranes, it is now time to turn to a very brief consideration of their modes of synthesis within the cell. These topics are described in detail in standard textbooks of biochemistry and cell biology:[1, 2] here we will only mention those aspects of biosynthesis that help us to understand the diversity of phospholipid structure found in the cell and help us to understand how protein function can be controlled.

11.1.3.1 Synthesis of Phospholipids

In trying to understand the role of phospholipids in membrane structure, it should not be forgotten that phospholipids are very much a part of the general metabolic machinery of the cell. The fatty acids, the glycerol group and the headgroups (choline, ethanolamine, serine, *etc.*) all have multiple roles in the cell, so that phospholipids in the membrane act as a store of material to be used for other purposes by the cell. The fatty acids are components of phospholipids in membranes but are also components of triacylglycerols used as energy stores and act as intermediates for the formation of eicosanoids (prostaglandins, thromboxanes and leukotrienes). Phosphatidylinositols are very much involved in cell signalling.

Fatty acids are obtained both from the diet and synthesized in the liver by the cytosolic enzymes of the acetyl-CoA carboxylase and fatty acid synthase complexes (giving mainly palmitic acid). Fatty acyl chain elongation and desaturation then occurs, mainly on the endoplasmic reticulum, liver cells having a particularly high activity (Figure 20). As shown, the first double bond is generally introduced into saturated fatty acyl chains in the Δ^9 position. Desaturation is an oxidative process requiring molecular oxygen, reduced nucleotide, and an electron transfer system consisting of a cytochrome and related reductase enzyme. Animal systems cannot introduce double bonds beyond the Δ^9 position, and the second and subsequent double bonds are always inserted between an existing double bond and the carboxyl end of the chain. Plants can, however, introduce double

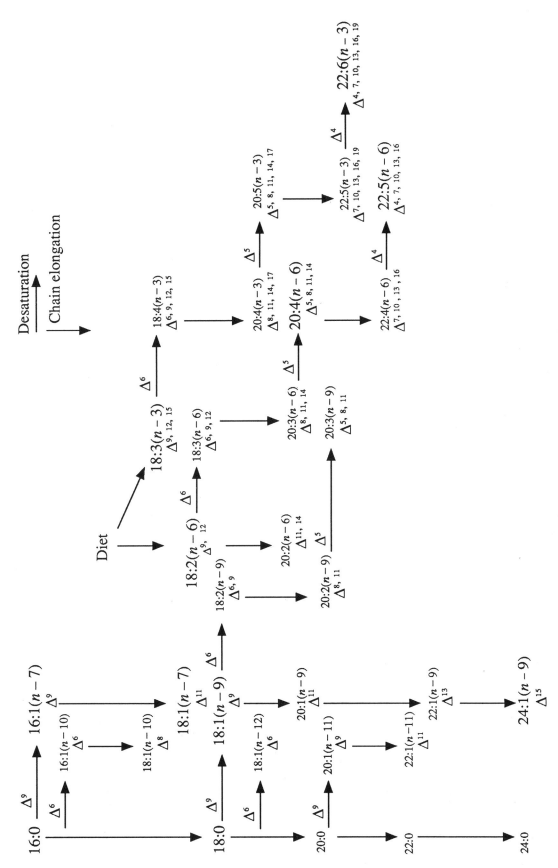

Figure 20 Major pathways of fatty acid biosynthesis by desaturation and chain elongation in animal tissues (reproduced from 'Biochemistry of Lipids and Membranes', ed. D. E. Vance and J. E. Vance, 1982, by permission of Benjamin/Cummings)

bonds beyond the Δ^9 position, and thus the essential fatty acids linoleic acid and linolenic acid (with double bonds at the Δ^{12} and Δ^{15} positions) have to be obtained from plant material in the diet. Chains can also be elongated by two carbons, maintaining the methylene interruption between double bonds; chain elongation occurs both on the endoplasmic reticulum and in mitochondria.

The major pathways for phospholipid synthesis are outlined in Figure 21. Phosphatidic acid (phosphatidate) is synthesized from fatty acyl coenzyme A and glycerophosphate. Phosphatidic acid can be converted into triacylglycerol to be used as an energy store, or for incorporation into lipoproteins to allow fatty acids to be transported from the small intestine and the liver to other organs. Alternatively, the phosphatidic acid can be channelled into the production of phospholipids. Phospholipids are synthesized on the cytoplasmic side of the endoplasmic reticulum; following synthesis they must be translocated to the inner layer of the membrane and transferred to other organelles and the plasma membrane. The mechanisms of this transfer are still unclear, although the involvement of specific phospholipid exchange proteins seems likely.

The rate of turnover of phospholipids in cells is relatively rapid. A variety of phospholipases are present in cells which can hydrolyze specific bonds, as shown in Figure 22. Mammalian cells contain high concentrations of phospholipases A_1 and A_2 in lysosomes where most phospholipid degradation occurs. Phospholipases C and D are found in bacteria and snake venoms.

The other major lipid component of membranes, cholesterol, is obtained from the diet and synthesized in the liver. It also is an important metabolic intermediate, being a precursor for bile acids, corticoids, sex hormones and vitamin D-derived hormones.

11.1.3.2 Synthesis of Membrane Proteins

There are two major questions about the assembly of proteins into biological membranes. Firstly, how do proteins become inserted into the membrane? Secondly, how are membrane proteins targeted to their final destinations in the cell? Many of our ideas about insertion of proteins into membranes have come from studies of secreted proteins. Proteins are synthesized on ribosomes, some of which occur free in the cytosol and some of which are bound to the region of the endoplasmic reticulum known as the rough endoplasmic reticulum. The synthesis of secreted proteins is initiated on free ribosomes (Figure 23). The mRNA for secreted proteins contains a sequence of codons after the initiator codon (AUG) that codes for a unique sequence at the amino terminal end of the nascent polypeptide, the signal sequence. Signal sequences are 15–25 amino acids in length and contain hydrophobic sequences, probably in an α-helical configuration. This sequence directs the ribosome to the endoplasmic reticulum, where it binds to a specific receptor. The receptor forms a hydrophilic channel across the membrane, and the nascent polypeptide chain is pushed through this channel as translation proceeds. The signal sequence is removed by a signal peptidase located on the luminal side of the endoplasmic reticulum; this occurs before translation is complete, a process referred to as cotranslational cleavage. Translation then proceeds to completion. Glycosylation also occurs in the endoplasmic reticulum as a cotranslational event.

Membrane proteins that contain a single *trans*-membranous region can be thought of as partially secreted proteins, and could be synthesized like secreted proteins, except that after completion of translation they are not released from the membrane. It is more difficult to understand how membrane proteins with two or more *trans*-membranous regions could be synthesized. It has been suggested that such proteins could contain a hairpin structure composed of two α-helices which coinsert into the membrane. A number of membrane proteins have no cleaved signal sequence at all; it has been suggested that such proteins might contain an amino terminus resembling a normal signal sequence but which is retained in the final, mature protein. As an example, the $(Ca^{2+}-Mg^{2+})$-ATPase of sarcoplasmic reticulum is made without a cleaved signal sequence.[72] In the $(Ca^{2+}-Mg^{2+})$-ATPase , the initiator methionine is acetylated and the first transmembrane loop is thought to be close to the amino terminus (Figure 18) so that possibly this could act as an integration sequence, attaching the nascent polypeptide to the endoplasmic reticulum. A different pathway is followed by the acetylcholine receptor. This is composed of four subunits with a stoichiometry of $\alpha_2\beta\gamma\delta$. Each subunit is translated from a separate mRNA, and all four polypeptides contain signal sequences that are cotranslationally cleaved on insertion into the membrane. In some way, as yet unclear, the individual subunits come together in the membrane to give the active $\alpha_2\beta\gamma\delta$ complex.[48]

Following their synthesis in the endoplasmic reticulum, membrane proteins have to be transported to their final locations. Proteins are exported from the endoplasmic reticulum as coated or uncoated vesicles; coated vesicles are surrounded by a polyhedral lattice of the protein clathrin.

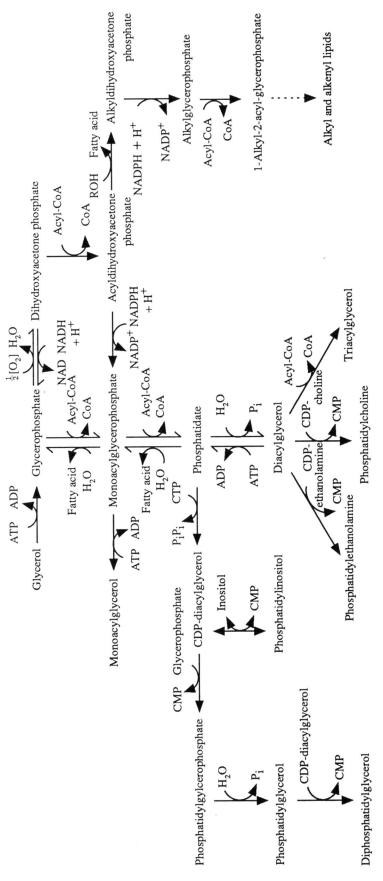

Figure 21 Pathways for glycerolipid synthesis and phosphatidic acid metabolism (reproduced from 'New Comprehensive Biochemistry', vol. 4, 'Phospholipids', ed. J. N. Hawthorne and G. B. Ansell, 1982, by permission of Elsevier Science Publishers B.V.)

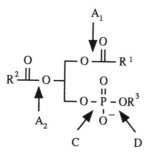

Figure 22   Sites of hydrolysis of phospholipids by phospholipases

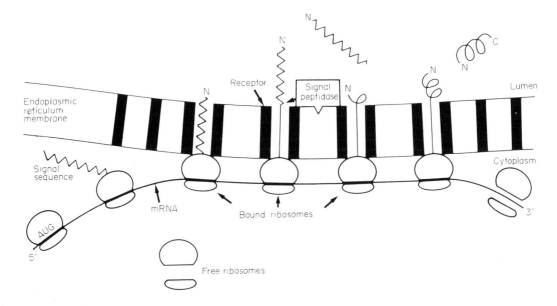

Figure 23   The signal hypothesis for the synthesis of secreted proteins (reproduced from 'Biochemistry of Lipids and Membranes', ed. D. E. Vance and J. E. Vance, 1985, by permission of Benjamin/Cummings)

These vesicles fuse with the Golgi apparatus and also carry membrane proteins from the Golgi apparatus to the plasma membrane and other membranes. In the Golgi apparatus, carbohydrate groups of glycoproteins are often extensively remodelled. During these transport processes, membrane asymmetry is preserved. The luminal side of the endoplasmic reticulum corresponds to the luminal side of the coated vesicle and of the Golgi membrane. Consequently, when a coated vesicle fuses with the plasma membrane the luminal side of the vesicle becomes the extracellular surface of the plasma membrane. Thus glycoproteins synthesized with their carbohydrate groups on the luminal side of the endoplasmic reticulum are finally inserted into the plasma membrane with their carbohydrate groups on the extracellular side.

It is not yet clear how proteins synthesized in the rough endoplasmic reticulum are sorted into those destined for endoplasmic reticulum, lysosome, Golgi and plasma membranes. It appears that enzymes to be incorporated into lysosomes receive an *N*-linked oligosaccharide in the endoplasmic reticulum and that one or more of the mannose residues of this oligosaccharide become phosphorylated in the Golgi apparatus; this phosphorylation apparently serves as the signal causing entry into lysosomes. Sorting into other organelles and membranes could involve more than one type of Golgi vesicle, and there is currently evidence for at least three distinct classes of vesicle (*cis*, medial and *trans* Golgi) each with its own distinct enzymatic activities. The synthesis of the proteins of the mitochondrial inner and outer membranes is particularly complex, because components are encoded on both nuclear and mitochondrial DNA, with those polypeptides synthesized from nuclear DNA being imported into the mitochondria post-translationally.

11.1.4 SIGNALLING AND TRANSPORT

Membranes are involved in many processes in the cell, including biosynthesis and metabolism (particularly of hydrophobic molecules) and in oxidative phosphorylation (in mitochondria). These functions are covered well in many standard works, including the four volumes of the series 'The Enzymes of Biological Membranes' edited by Martonosi[46] and will not be discussed here. Rather we will consider just those functions that are involved in some way in signalling between cells and in membrane transport.

11.1.4.1 Membrane Transport

Membranes act as semipermeable barriers, controlling movement into and out of cells and organelles. The lipid bilayer portion of the membrane is essentially impermeable to water-soluble species such as glucose, ATP, amino acids, nucleosides and ions such as H^+, Na^+, K^+, Ca^{2+}, Mg^{2+} and Cl^-. The movement of any of these species across a membrane must then be facilitated by specific transport processes. The passage of small molecules and ions across membranes is mediated by membrane proteins, collectively called permeases, each permease being specific for a limited range of molecules or ions. Large particles and proteins enter a cell across the plasma membrane by endocytosis and phagocytosis, in which small regions of the plasma membrane surround the particle or protein and are then internalized by the cell.

Transport of a small molecule into a cell can be passive or active. In passive diffusion, the transported species moves down its electrochemical or concentration gradient, and no metabolic energy is expended. For small non-polar molecules such as ethanol which have an appreciable solubility in the lipid bilayer component of the membrane, movement across the membrane can be by simple passive diffusion; the rate of diffusion across the membrane will in this case depend on the partition coefficient of the species in the membrane. Polar species cannot cross membranes in this way, but passive diffusion will still be possible if the membrane contains a permease specific for that species (a process referred to as facilitated transport). In contrast, active transport uses metabolic energy to move ions or molecules against an electrochemical gradient and so, for example, can be used to generate ion gradients across a membrane; the gradient of K^+ and Na^+ established across neuronal membranes by the $(Na^+–K^+)$-ATPase is an obvious example.

11.1.4.1.1 Facilitated transport

Many substances are transported more rapidly across biological membranes than would have been expected from their membrane partition coefficients. Transport of glucose at a concentration of 1 mmol L^{-1} into red blood cells is about 10^4 times faster at 25 °C than would have been expected for simple passive diffusion. Transport is independent of metabolic energy and only occurs as long as the concentration gradient of glucose persists. The rate of transport increases with increasing glucose concentration but reaches a maximum at high concentrations. It is specific for glucose, the L-isomer for example not entering cells at an appreciable rate. All these mark the process as one of facilitated transport.[38, 39] A specific glucose transporter exists in the red blood cell membrane, which has been purified and shown to be a protein of MW 45 000, accounting for about 2% of the total membrane protein. Although the mechanism of transport is unknown, it is likely to involve binding of glucose to a site on the exterior of the transporter followed by a conformation change in the protein in which the binding site becomes exposed to the inside of the cell (see Figure 24). In the simplest case, transport by such a mechanism can be described by an equation analogous to the Michaelis–Menten equation in enzyme kinetics, namely

$$v = v_{max}/(1 + c/K_m) \tag{1}$$

where v_{max} is the maximum rate, v is the rate at a glucose concentration of c and K_m is the concentration of glucose at which the rate of transport is half maximal; for the red blood cell, K_m is 1.5 mmol L^{-1}.

Transport of one species into a cell is frequently coupled to movement of another out of the cell. An important example found in the red blood cell membrane is the anion transporter (also known as Band 3 from its position in SDS gels). This allows a rapid exchange of Cl^- for HCO_3^- across the membrane, a process important in the movement in the blood of CO_2 from the tissues to the lungs.

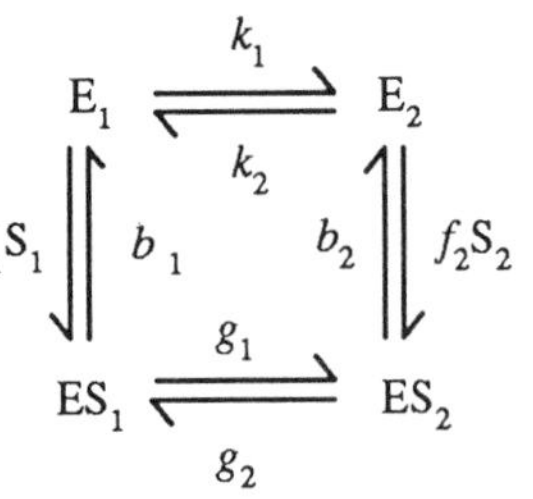

$$E_1 \underset{k_2}{\overset{k_1}{\rightleftharpoons}} E_2$$

$$f_1S_1 \Bigg\updownarrow b_1 \qquad b_2 \Bigg\updownarrow f_2S_2$$

$$ES_1 \underset{g_2}{\overset{g_1}{\rightleftharpoons}} ES_2$$

Figure 24 A kinetic scheme for the mechanism of facilitated transport of glucose. Glucose binds to the transporter protein with the glucose binding site exposed to the outside medium (E_1). A conformation change in the transporter then leads to exposure of the binding site on the inside (ES_2), and glucose can then dissociate to give E_2 which can revert to E_1. The rate constants for substrate binding/dissociation are f_1, b_1 and f_2, b_2 and for the transitions between E_1 and E_2 and ES_1 and ES_2 are k_1k_2 and g_1 and g_2 respectively (reproduced from 'The Enzymes of Biological Membranes', vol. 3, ed. A. N. Martonosi, 1985, by permission of Plenum Press Publishing Corp.)

The mechanism is thought to be analogous to that shown in Figure 24, with Cl^- binding to E_1 on the outside of the cell and HCO_3^- binding to E_2 on the inside. Again, no metabolic energy is involved.

Another important transporter of this type is the adenine nucleotide transporter of mitochondria.[40] Because ATP is synthesized inside the mitochondria from ADP generated in the cytoplasm, an efficient exchange of ATP and ADP across the mitochondrial inner membrane must be ensured. The adenine transporter carries out a passive 1:1 exchange of ADP and ATP. In nonrespiring mitochondria, the transporter shows no preference for the direction of transport of ADP and ATP. In respiring mitochondria, however, transport of ADP in and ATP out is much favoured over transport of ADP out and ATP in. This results from the differences in charge of ADP and ATP; at neutral pH, ATP^{4-} bears one more negative charge than ADP^{3-} and this favours the movement of ATP out of the mitochondria which is at a negative potential with respect to the outside. Studies of this transporter have made much use of specific inhibitors such as atractyloside (a glucoside isolated from the Mediterranean thistle *Atractylis gummifera*), which binds to the cytoplasmic face of the transporter, and bongkrekic acid (from the bacterium *Pseudomonas cocvenenans*), which binds to the matrix side.

11.1.4.1.2 *Active transport*

If an ion or small molecule is going to be moved into or out of a cell or organelle against its electrochemical gradient, then a source of energy is required to drive the transport. In the ATPases, this is achieved by coupling ion movement to the hydrolysis of ATP. In other transport proteins it is achieved by linking the transport of one component up its electrochemical gradient to the transport of a second component down its electrochemical gradient.

Three important classes of ATPase are the (Ca^{2+}–Mg^{2+})-ATPases, involved in transporting Ca^{2+} out of cells or from the cytosol of muscle cells into the interior of the sarcoplasmic reticulum, the (Na^+–K^+)-ATPases, responsible for transport of Na^+ out of a cell and K^+ in, and the (H^+–K^+)-ATPases, responsible for acid secretion in the gastric mucosa. All three types of ATPase have marked similarities. The mechanism of the (Ca^{2+}–Mg^{2+})-ATPase is shown in Figure 25. The ATPase is postulated to exist in one of two conformational states E1 or E2. In E1, the two Ca^{2+} ion binding sites per ATPase molecule are outward facing and of high affinity whereas in E2 they are inward facing and of low affinity. Binding of Ca^{2+} and MgATP to the ATPase results in phosphorylation of the ATPase on an aspartate residue. Following loss of MgADP, the phosphorylated form of the ATPase, Ca_2E1P, undergoes a change in conformation to Ca_2E2P; this is the transport step. Since the Ca^{2+} binding sites of E2 are of low affinity and inward facing, Ca^{2+} will be lost from Ca_2E2P to the inside of the sarcoplasmic reticulum, followed by dephosphorylation of the ATPase and recycling to E1. The nature of the changes on the ATPase involved in the E1–E2 change have yet to be defined, but relatively small spatial changes in the Ca^{2+} binding region seem likely, coupled to changes in the relative positions of the ATP-binding and phosphorylation domains (see Figure 18). A detailed kinetic analysis has shown that the two slowest steps in the reaction sequence are the transport step Ca_2E1P–$E2P$ and dephosphorylation; the significance of this for an understanding of how the ATPase interacts with its surrounding lipids in the membrane will become clear in Section 11.1.5.2.

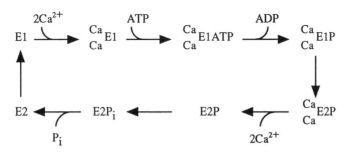

Figure 25 A kinetic scheme for the $(Ca^{2+}-Mg^{2+})$-ATPase (reproduced from *Biochem. J.*, 1986, **237**, 197, by permission of The Biochemical Society)

An essentially similar scheme has been developed to explain the mechanism of the (Na^+-K^+)-ATPase, in which the ATPase has two high affinity binding sites for K^+ on the outer surface and three high affinity binding sites for Na^+ on the inner surface, accounting for its stoichiometry of two K^+ and three Na^+ transported per ATP molecule hydrolyzed. A major difference between the $(Ca^{2+}-Mg^{2+})$-ATPase and the (Na^+-K^+)-ATPase is that whereas the former can be purified in active form as a single polypeptide, the latter is purified as a dimer of two different subunits. The larger of the two subunits is similar to the $(Ca^{2+}-Mg^{2+})$-ATPase, having a molecular weight of about 120 000 and being phosphorylated by ATP. The second subunit of the (Na^+-K^+)-ATPase is a glycoprotein of molecular weight 50 000 whose function is still unclear.

The site of acid secretion into the stomach is the parietal cell. Here, a (H^+-K^+)-ATPase couples ATP hydrolysis to the electroneutral exchange of H^+ for K^+. The mechanism and structure of the ATPase seem to be similar to the $(Ca^{2+}-Mg^{2+})$-ATPase.[41]

In mammalian cells, only the transport of Ca^{2+}, Na^+, K^+ and H^+ are known to be linked directly to the hydrolysis of ATP. Transport of molecules such as glucose and amino acids against a concentration gradient is possible, however, driven by the energy stored in a transmembrane gradient of H^+ or Na^+. In this form of active transport, the movement of the transported molecule up its concentration gradient is linked to the movement of the cotransported ion (H^+ or Na^+) down its concentration gradient. As shown in Figure 26, the transported molecule and the cotransported ion can move in the same direction (symport) or in opposite directions (antiport). Movement by facilitated diffusion, as described in Section 11.1.4.1.1 is referred to as uniport. An example of symport is the transport of glucose from the intestinal lumen across the apical surface of brush border cells, linked to the movement of Na^+ into the cell; Na^+ is pumped out of the cell, maintaining a gradient of Na^+ across the cell membrane, by a (Na^+-K^+)-ATPase located in the basolateral surface of the cell. A similar amino acid–Na^+ symport system uses the Na^+ gradient to take up amino acids from the lumen into the cell.

An important antiport system is that used in cardiac muscle cells to export Ca^{2+} ions linked to the entry of Na^+ ions. Again, the Na^+ gradient used to drive this reaction is established by a (Na^+-K^+)-ATPase. The plasma membranes of many cells contain a H^+–Na^+ antiport system used to regulate cytoplasmic pH.

11.1.4.1.3 *Phagocytosis and endocytosis*

Macromolecules and large particles are taken up by cells by pathways very different to those described above. Large particles such as bacteria or broken cell fragments are taken up by the process of phagocytosis. The first step in phagocytosis is the binding of a particle to the surface of the cell, followed by expansion of the plasma membrane along the surface of the particle to engulf it. The resulting phagocytic vesicles are typically 1 to 2 μm in diameter, and eventually fuse with lysosomes in the cell; breakdown of the particle then occurs by hydrolysis. Phagocytosis is particularly active in the macrophages.

In endocytosis, only a small region of the cell membrane invaginates to give a vesicle, typically of diameter 0.1 μm (Figure 27). Non-specific uptake of small droplets of extracellular fluid is referred to as pinocytosis. The specific uptake of a particular macromolecule is referred to as receptor-mediated endocytosis. Receptor-mediated endocytosis occurs in many types of animal cell and accounts for the uptake of low density lipoproteins (LDL) to supply cholesterol to the cell, and transferrin to

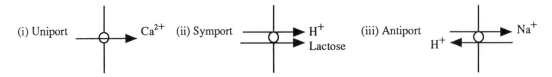

Figure 26   The processes of uniport, symport and antiport (reproduced from D. G. Nicholls, 'Bioenergetics', 1982, by permission of Academic Press)

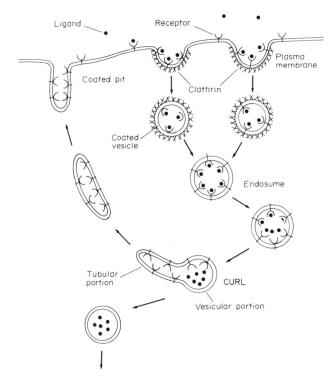

Figure 27   The process of endocytosis (reproduced from *J. Phys. Chem.*, 1986, **90**, 226 by permission of the American Chemical Society)

supply iron. In macrophages, uptake systems occur for glucose- and mannose-terminal glycoproteins and in hepatocytes for galactose-terminal glycoproteins, ensuring the removal of abnormal glycoproteins from the circulation. The initial step of receptor-mediated endocytosis is binding of the macromolecule or particle (ligand) to a specific receptor in the plasma membrane. Endocytosis of the ligand–receptor complex then occurs at specialized regions of the membrane, the coated pits. Here coated vesicles are formed, consisting of membrane vesicles surrounded by a coat of the protein clathrin. The receptors for LDL appear to be normally located in coated pits. The asialoglycoprotein receptor that binds galactose-terminal glycoproteins, however, only enters a coated pit after it has bound its ligand.

Once inside the cell, the coated vesicles lose their clathrin coat to become endosomes. The ligand then dissociates from the receptor so that the receptor can be recycled to the plasma membrane (Figure 27); this occurs after fusion of the endosomes with an uncoupling vesicle called CURL (compartment of uncoupling of receptor and ligand). The inside of the CURL is maintained at low pH, and although receptors such as the LDL and asialoglycoprotein receptors bind their ligands very tightly at neutral pH, binding is weak at pH 5, so that ligand–receptor complexes dissociate in the CURL. The membrane proteins and phospholipids that were internalized by endocytosis are then returned to the plasma membrane. This is essential since the rate of endocytic internalization can be very high: cultured fibroblasts for example internalize half their cell surface per hour, even in the absence of any specific ligand. Following dissociation of the ligand from the receptor in the CURL, fusion with lysosomes leads to final breakdown of the ligand.

The sequences of a number of the receptors have now been deduced from cloned cDNA, including those of the LDL and transferrin receptors.[42, 43]

11.1.4.2 Receptors and Ion Channels

The plasma membrane plays an essential role in cell signalling. Some hormones are lipophilic and can diffuse through the plasma membrane to their targets within the cell (*e.g.* steroids and thyroxine), but many hormones, neurotransmitters and pheromones bind to specific receptors in the outer plasma membrane. Binding of a ligand to its appropriate receptor leads to a transitory increase in the concentration of a component within the cell (the second messenger), often cAMP or Ca^{2+}. Changes in the concentration of the second messenger causes changes in the activities of one or more enzymes within the cell. Properties of these receptors will be covered in great detail in later chapters in this volume, so only a few general points will be made here.

The system of receptors linked to adenyl cyclase in the adipose cell is illustrated in Figure 28.[2] The scheme pictures epinephrine, glucagon, ACTH or vasopressin all binding to their respective receptors. Acting as communicator between the receptors and the adenyl cyclase is the G protein (so-called because it binds guanosine phosphates). The G protein is composed of three subunits, α, β and γ. The α subunit binds GTP and GDP. When GTP is bound to the G_α subunit, it dissociates from $G_\beta G_\gamma$, and can bind to the adenyl cyclase, activating it. GTP bound to G_α is, however, hydrolyzed spontaneously to GDP, and G_α with bound GDP dissociates from the adenyl cyclase and binds to the $G_\beta G_\gamma$ subunit. At rest, GDP is bound to G_α which is consequently present as the $G_\alpha G_\beta G_\gamma$ complex and the adenyl cyclase is not active. Binding of a hormone (or agonist) to its receptor results in a change in the conformation of the receptor such that it can bind to the $G_\alpha G_\beta G_\gamma$ complex, causing dissociation of the bound GDP. GTP then binds, G_α dissociates from $G_\beta G_\gamma$ and G_α then binds to the adenylate cyclase with activation of cAMP synthesis. The GTP bound to G_α is then rapidly hydrolyzed to GDP, leading to the reassociation of G_α with $G_\beta G_\gamma$ and the inactivation of the adenylate cyclase. In the adipose cell, prostaglandin PGE_1 and adenosine inhibit adenylate cyclase (Figure 28). Receptors for these compounds are believed to interact with an inhibitory G protein, called G_i. In G_i the β and γ subunits are the same as in the stimulatory G protein, but the α subunit is different; dissociation of the inhibitory $G_{i\alpha}$ subunit by binding of GTP leads to inhibition of the adenylate cyclase.

The scheme as illustrated in Figure 28 implies movement of the various proteins within the plane of the membrane. The alternative of a permanent receptor–adenylate cyclase complex seems unlikely because of the large number of hormones, and, therefore, receptors, affecting the cyclase. Evidence against static complexes and in favour of the 'mobile-receptor' hypothesis has come from experiments involving cell fusion. Freund erythroleukaemia cells containing a functional adenylate cyclase but no β-receptors were fused with turkey erythrocytes in which the adenylate cyclase had been inactivated but in which the β-receptors were normal. After fusion of the two types of cell with Sendai virus, β-agonist-sensitive cyclase activity was detected, demonstrating that the β-receptors and adenylate cyclase must have been free to diffuse within the plane of the membrane.[44, 45] The extent to which diffusion over large distances plays a role in the normal function of the system is, however, unclear. Thus measurements of the rate of lateral diffusion of the β-receptor have shown it to be very slow, suggesting that diffusion is limited by interprotein interactions or by anchoring to

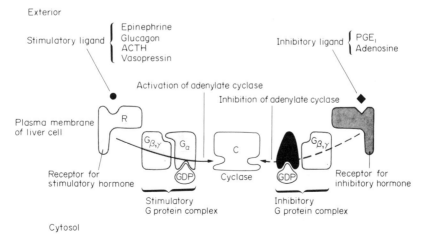

Figure 28 Hormone receptors linked to adenyl cyclase, showing the role of the G protein (reproduced from J. Darnell, H. Lodish and D. Baltimore, 'Molecular Cell Biology', 1986, by permission of Scientific American Books Inc.)

cytoskeletal structures.[47] Although the scheme shown in Figure 28 shows the G_α subunit remaining bound to the membrane after dissociation from $G_\beta G_\gamma$, recent evidence suggests that it could be released from the membrane into the intracellular medium.[50]

G proteins now seem to play a role in a number of cell signalling systems. Thus G_t or transducin has been suggested to be important in the photoreceptor, linking the bleaching of rhodopsin to the activation of a cGMP phosphodiesterase. It has also been suggested that a G protein could link the binding of growth factors to receptors on the surface of cells to the activation of the phosphatidyl-inositol 4,5-bisphosphate ($PtdIns4,5P_2$) phosphodiesterase which cleaves $PtdIns4,5P_2$ to generate the two second messengers diacylglycerol and $Ins1,4,5P_3$. Finally, recent reports suggest that G proteins could act as regulators of ion channel function in neural tissue.[49]

Binding of insulin to its receptor on the cell surface results in clustering of insulin receptors followed by internalization.[50] This is important in the regulation of the number of insulin receptors and in some of the cellular responses to insulin. Internalization of receptors also occurs on addition of bivalent anti-insulin receptor antibody. Binding of epidermal growth factor and nerve growth factor to their respective receptors also leads to clustering and internalization, but the link between these effects and the observed effects on cell growth are unclear. Insulin has been shown to increase the rate of glucose transport across the plasma membrane by recruiting new glucose permeases into the plasma membrane. In unstimulated cells, vesicles containing large numbers of glucose permease molecules are found just under the plasma membrane and, following binding of insulin to its receptor, these vesicles are induced to fuse with the plasma membrane, thus increasing the number of active permease molecules.

The insulin receptor contains two types of subunit α and β, derived from a common precursor and linked to give a β-α-α-β structure by disulfide bonds. The insulin binding site is on the α subunit, and the cytosolic domain of the receptor possesses tyrosine-specific protein kinase activity and may itself be reversibly phosphorylated on both tyrosine and serine residues. The link between binding of insulin to its receptor and the observed effects of insulin are still very much debated.[50]

A particularly important group of receptors are those found in the postsynaptic membrane for neurotransmitters. Neurotransmitters are stored in the presynaptic cell in the region of the synapse in synaptic vesicles. In the cholinergic synapse, for example, arrival of an action potential at a presynaptic terminal leads to an influx of Ca^{2+} ions through voltage-dependent Ca^{2+} channels. The resulting increase in Ca^{2+} level causes synaptic vesicles to fuse with the presynaptic membrane releasing acetylcholine into the synaptic cleft. The mechanism of this exocytosis is unclear, but could involve a phosphoprotein found in synaptic vesicles, synapsin I; synapsin I is a substrate for cAMP-dependent and calmodulin-dependent protein kinases. The membrane components of the synaptic vesicles are recovered after fusion by endocytosis.

The released acetylcholine binds to a receptor in the postsynaptic membrane. The acetylcholine receptor is a ligand-mediated cation channel, which, on binding acetylcholine, opens a channel across the membrane for Na^+ and K^+.[48] The receptor has been purified from the electroplax of electric fish (where it is present at particularly high concentration) and has been found to be made up of four subunits in a stoichiometry of $\alpha_2\beta\gamma\delta$. The α subunit contains the acetylcholine binding site. In electron microscope pictures, the receptor appears as a doughnut-like structure, with a diameter of 9 nm and a central 'hole' of diameter 2 nm: it protrudes about 7 nm from the membrane surface into the extracellular space and about 3 nm into the cytoplasm (Figure 29). mRNAs encoding all four subunits have now been cloned, and the strong homology between the sequences of the subunits suggests that they have evolved from a common progenitor. It is now clear that the two acetylcholine binding sites per oligomer are located in the large amino-terminal hydrophilic domains of the two α-subunits. What is much less clear is the relationship between the acetylcholine binding domains and the ion channel. It is now popular to assume that the ion channel is located down the centre of the structure, with the walls of the channel being made up of polar amino acid residues from each of the subunits. Such an interpretation is consistent with labelling experiments with chlorpromazine which show that, at low concentrations where it appears to bind to a single site in the channel, it labels all subunits.[48]

An important property of the acetylcholine receptor is desensitization, in which prolonged exposure to acetylcholine results in a reversible decline of the conductance response to cholinergic agonists. Desensitization has been attributed to conformation changes on the receptor giving one or more desensitized closed states with increased agonist affinity. It has been suggested that the rate of desensitization is modulated by phosphorylation of the receptor; phosphorylation by cAMP-dependent protein kinase increases the rate of desensitization.[48] Since other ligand-regulated ion channels such as the GABA, glycine and glutamate receptors also show desensitization, these slow conformational changes may be of general importance in the short term regulation of synaptic function.

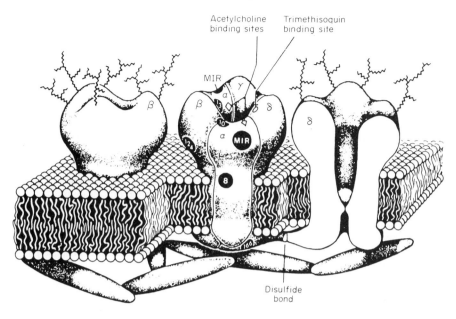

Figure 29 A structural model for the acetylcholine receptor (reproduced from 'The Enzymes of Biological Membranes', vol. 3, ed. A. N. Martonosi, 1985, by permission of Plenum Press Publishing Corp.)

Many neurotransmitter receptors are not linked directly to ion channels, but produce second messengers that modify the state of separate ion channel proteins. For example, the binding of agonists to norepinephrine β-receptors on nerve cells activates an adenylate cyclase, as described above for hormonal signalling. Some serotonin and dopamine receptors are also linked to adenylate cyclase. Increased levels of cAMP are thought to activate cAMP-dependent protein kinases, possibly leading to phosphorylation of K^+ channels. GABA receptors are linked to Cl^- channels, opening of which causes hyperpolarization of the membrane; GABA therefore produces an inhibitory postsynaptic response.

The remaining class of membrane proteins to be considered here are the voltage-dependent ion channels. Electrophysiological studies have defined many of the properties of the voltage-sensitive sodium and potassium channels found in axonal membranes. Molecular studies of the sodium channel have made much use of specific toxins, including tetrodotoxin (from puffer fish) and saxitoxin (from red marine dinoflagellates) which specifically bind to the channel and block movement of Na^+ ions, and of the alkaloid veratridine (from the seeds of *Schoenocaulon officinalis*, a Mexican plant of the lily family) which binds to the channel and causes it to remain permanently in the open, activated state. Such toxins have been used to prepare affinity columns for the purification of the channel. The major component of the sodium channel from rat brain has been shown to be a single polypeptide of molecular weight about 250 000. The polypeptide has been sequenced from cloned cDNA, and shown to contain a four-fold internal homology.[51] Possible mechanisms for the action of sodium channels are described, for example, by Hille.[52]

Finally, an important group of ion channels is that for Ca^{2+}. The study of the function and regulation of calcium channels is particularly active at the present time, and current ideas about these channels are presented elsewhere in this volume (see Chapter 14.1).

11.1.5 LIPID–PROTEIN INTERACTIONS

11.1.5.1 Introduction

It should be clear from the discussion above that the composition of biological membranes is complex. Nevertheless, it seems likely that all biological membranes are constructed according to the same few basic rules: the task is to determine these rules. One set of questions concerns the lipid component of the membrane. The basic framework of the membrane is provided by the lipid bilayer, and this choice has a number of advantages for the cell. Firstly, the components of the lipids (fatty acids, glycerol, choline, ethanolamine, *etc.*) are all present as parts of the general metabolism of the cell. Secondly, the central hydrophobic core of the bilayer ensures that the membrane will act as a permeability barrier for polar molecules such as the amino acids, sugars and nucleic acids involved in metabolism in the cell. And thirdly, protein molecules containing hydrophobic α-helices of the correct length can be firmly anchored in the bilayer. As described in Section 11.1.2.4, the structural requirements to form a stable lipid bilayer are rather easily met, leaving unanswered the question 'Why is the lipid composition of the membrane so complex?'. Although 'why' questions of this type are notoriously dangerous in biology, many attempts have been made to provide an answer, mostly along the lines that the lipid composition of the membrane needs to be finely balanced to produce a fully functional membrane and that each species of lipid is present in the membrane for some distinct purpose. Since, as we have seen, a typical membrane may contain several hundred chemically distinct species of lipid, the task of describing membrane function at the molecular level would then be extremely difficult. However, it can be argued equally well that the complexity of the lipid composition shows, not that the lipid composition is important, but that, within limits that need to be defined, it is unimportant, and that many chemically distinct lipid species can be used to produce a membrane which is functionally competent; the lipid composition of the membrane will then just reflect the current availability of fatty acids, headgroups, *etc.*, in the cell. To distinguish between these two possibilities we must develop techniques to study the dependence of membrane function on lipid composition, to see whether it is exquisitely sensitive or relatively insensitive; the necessary experiments are described below.

In establishing the rules that govern membrane function, it is, of course, necessary to consider the protein component of the membrane as well as the lipid component. In particular, proteins are present in the membrane at very high effective concentrations, with typically half the surface area of the membrane being occupied by protein molecules. This makes the study of protein–protein interactions in the membrane very important. As described in Section 11.1.2.6, a number of membrane proteins are found in the membrane in oligomeric form, the $(Ca^{2+}-Mg^{2+})$-ATPase, for example, occurring under some conditions as long rows of dimers (Figure 17). Much less is known about interactions between different classes of protein in the membrane. In general, it would seem likely that such interactions would be avoided; this could be achieved by anchoring membrane proteins to cytoskeletal elements, or through charge repulsion between like-charged proteins. It has been estimated from the rate of diffusion of the rhodopsin molecule in the retinal rod membrane, that, in the absence of unfavourable interactions between rhodopsin molecules, the rate of collision between rhodopsins will be 10^5–10^6 s^{-1}. It is unclear whether this gives a true picture of the state of affairs in a more typical membrane and, indeed, we still know very little about these higher-order interactions.

Because of the sheer complexity of most biological membranes, answers about the basic properties of the membrane have come from studies of highly simplified systems. As described in Section 11.1.2.4, the properties of the lipid bilayer portion of the membrane have been defined from studies of simple lipid bilayers. Studies of simplified membrane protein systems are considerably more restricted because relatively few membrane proteins have been purified in amounts sufficient for detailed biochemical study. Here we will concentrate on one of the best understood of these proteins, the $(Ca^{2+}-Mg^{2+})$-ATPase that can be purified from skeletal muscle sarcoplasmic reticulum. Although it is not yet clear to what extent conclusions drawn from study of this particular protein can be extended to other membrane proteins, there seems no obvious reason why it should be atypical.

11.1.5.2 Reconstitution of the $(Ca^{2+}-Mg^{2+})$-ATPase[13, 27, 53-56]

The $(Ca^{2+}-Mg^{2+})$-ATPase has been purified from sarcoplasmic reticulum as a lipid–protein complex by solution of the membrane in a detergent such as cholate, followed by sucrose gradient centrifugation. A minimum number of 30 phospholipid molecules is required to maintain the activity of the protein; this number can be compared to the number of phospholipid molecules required to form a complete (annular) shell around the ATPase in the membrane, also 30. In the lipid–protein complex, the protein is pure $(Ca^{2+}-Mg^{2+})$-ATPase, but the phospholipid is a complex mixture representative of that present in the original membrane. The technique for reconstituting the ATPase into a phospholipid bilayer of defined composition is shown in Figure 30. The lipid–protein complex is dissolved in cholate, and a large excess of the lipid of choice is added. It is known that cholate forms expandable micelles in which the planar cyclopentenophenanthrene rings are apposed and the hydroxyl groups are exposed to the aqueous environment. As illustrated in Figure 30 this may allow the ATPase to dissolve with its lipid annulus intact. Equilibration then occurs between the lipid bound to $(Ca^{2+}-Mg^{2+})$-ATPase and that in the detergent. Because the added lipid is in

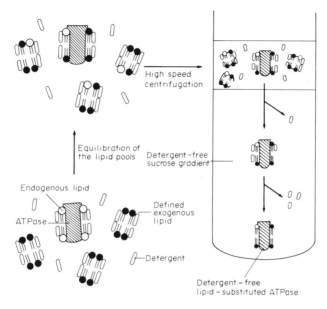

Figure 30 The process of lipid substitution for the $(Ca^{2+}-Mg^{2+})$-ATPase

large excess, most of the lipid molecules around the ATPase will now be from the added lipid. Lipid-substituted ATPase and excess lipid can be separated by centrifugation on a sucrose gradient. An important point in the procedure is that on centrifugation, detergent only enters part way into the gradient, producing a detergent front in the centrifuge tube (Fugure 30). The bulk of the detergent remains at the top of the gradient with the lipid, and relatively little breaks through with the ATPase, which reforms into membrane fragments at the bottom of the gradient. Any residual detergent associated with the ATPase can be removed by dialysis. This procedure can be used to replace essentially all the lipid around the ATPase with the chosen lipid.

A more convenient procedure is that of cholate dilution. As described, incubation of the ATPase with excess exogenous lipid in cholate leads to equilibration of the lipid pools. Therefore, if an aliquot of the detergent solution is simply diluted into buffer so that the concentration of cholate drops below its CMC, lipid bilayers will reform spontaneously, with most of the lipid around the ATPase being the added lipid, and the measured activity of the ATPase will be that for the ATPase in a bilayer of the chosen lipid.

Both the procedures described above give membrane fragments which will not, of course, accumulate Ca^{2+}, but which can be used to study ATPase activity uncoupled from Ca^{2+} accumulation. To measure accumulation of Ca^{2+}, it is necessary to reconstitute the purified ATPase into sealed vesicles. Such vesicles are readily formed by dissolving the ATPase and excess lipid in detergent, and then removing the detergent by passage down a column of Sephadex G-50.

By reconstituting the ATPase into bilayers of defined phospholipid composition, it is possible to see whether the activity of the ATPase is sensitive to the chemical structure and physical state of the surrounding phospholipid. The data in Tables 11 and 12 show that indeed it is, with the optimal phospholipid being dioleoylphosphatidylcholine. Phosphatidylcholines with longer or shorter fatty acyl chains or methyl-branched chains support lower activities (Table 11). Changing the phospholipid headgroup also leads to lower ATPase activities (Table 12). Activity is also dependent on the phase of the phospholipid. If the ATPase is reconstituted into bilayers of a phospholipid with saturated fatty acyl chains, then the phase of the phospholipid can be changed from liquid crystalline to gel by lowering the temperature. As shown in Table 11, the activity of the ATPase decreases markedly when the phospholipid transforms into the gel phase. It cannot, however, be assumed that this decrease in activity follows directly from an effect of lipid fluidity on the activity of the ATPase. It is known that molecules that are miscible with phospholipids in the liquid crystalline phase become immiscible when the phospholipid is in the gel phase. Thus it is possible that the loss of ATPase activity in the gel phase follows from separation of lipid and protein molecules within the bilayer, with consequent changes in protein–protein interaction.

The idea that the exact fluidity of the bilayer in the liquid crystalline phase is important for protein activity has been tested using the reconstituted system. The ATPase has been reconstituted into a

Table 11 Effects of Phosphatidylcholines on ATPase Activity and Relative Phosphatidylcholine Binding Constants for the $(Ca^{2+}-Mg^{2+})$-ATPase[54]

Fatty acyl chains	ATPase activity $(IU\,mg^{-1})^a$	Relative binding constant[b]
Native	18.4	—
Dimyristoleoyl (C14:1)	3.7	0.8
Dipalmitoleoyl (C16:1)	19.1	1.1
Dioleoyl (C18:1)	24.1	1.0[c]
Dieicosenoyl (C20:1)	18.2	—
Dierucoyl (C22:1)	11.5	1.3
Dinervonyl (C24:1)	3.3	1.0
Diphytanoyl	12.2	0.8
1-Myristoyl-2-oleoyl	21.0	—
1-Oleoyl-2-myristoyl	20.4	—
Dipalmitoyl at 45 °C	—	0.8
Dipalmitoyl at 10 °C	0	0.04

[a] Activities measured at 2.1 mmol L^{-1} ATP, 5 mmol L^{-1} Mg^{2+}, pH 7.2, 37 °C. [b] Binding constants measured relative to that for dioleoylphosphatidylcholine. [c] By definition.

Table 12 Effects of Phospholipid Headgroup on Activity of the $(Ca^{2+}-Mg^{2+})$-ATPase[54]

Lipid headgroup[a]	Relative ATPase activity[b]
Phosphatidylcholine	1
Phosphatidylethanolamine	0.5
Phosphatidylserine	0.3

[a] Lipid fatty acyl chains were oleic acid. [b] Activities were measured under the conditions given in Table 11.

series of phospholipid bilayers of different composition, and the ATPase activity has been measured. The fluidity of these bilayers has also been determined in terms of an ESR order parameter (see Section 11.1.2.4). It is clear from Figure 31 that there is no correlation between activity and order parameter, showing that any effects that changing fluidity in the liquid crystalline phase may have on ATPase activity are very much smaller than effects that can be attributed directly to changing phospholipid structure. This is not surprising. The fluidity of the bulk phospholipid phase is unlikely to have an effect on ATPase activity since the environment actually sensed by the membrane protein is not that of bulk phospholipid but is that of annular phospholipid; ESR experiments have shown that the mobility of phospholipid fatty acyl chains in the annulus is inhibited by the presence of the relatively immobile protein surface and mobility will thus be relatively constant and independent of the chemical structure of the phospholipid.

The effects of phospholipid structure on ATPase activity can be understood in terms of the kinetic model for ATPase activity presented in Figure 25. Since there is no single rate-controlling step in the reaction sequence, effects of phospholipids on activity can be complex. Based on simulations, it has been suggested that the steps of the reaction sequence of the ATPase sensitive to phospholipid structure are the transport step, $Ca_2E1P-Ca_2E2P$, the E2–E1 conformation change, dephosphorylation of E2P and the binding of MgATP to Ca_2E1P. The E1/E2 equilibrium constant has been shown to be close to 1, so that small differences in the interactions of phospholipids with E1 and E2 will produce large changes in the equilibrium constant; since the equilibrium constant is the ratio of the rate of the E2–E1 transition to that of the E1–E2 transition, any change in equilibrium constant will mean a change in rate constants. Since the overall reaction cycle shown in Figure 25 corresponds to the hydrolysis of ATP (for which the equilibrium constant is fixed), any change in the E1/E2 equilibrium constant must be exactly balanced by changes in the equilibrium constants of other steps in the reaction sequence, with consequent changes in the rates of those steps.

With no single rate-controlling step, it is not possible to interpret any observed breaks in Arrhenius plots of activity as a function of temperature in a simple way; in terms, for example, of a change in phase for the phospholipids: Arrhenius plots of the activities of very many membrane proteins show such breaks, and most have been attributed, without direct proof, to changes in the fluidity of the lipid phase.

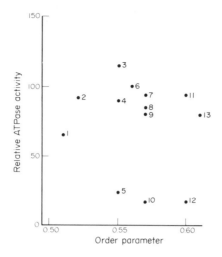

Figure 31 Relative ATPase activities for the $(Ca^{2+}-Mg^{2+})$-ATPase reconstituted with various phospholipids, as a function of the ESR order parameter for those phospholipids, at $37\,°C$ (reproduced from ref. 56, where full details are given, by permission of The American Society of Biological Chemists Inc.)

Before these results with the reconstituted $(Ca^{2+}-Mg^{2+})$-ATPase can be extrapolated to the situation in the native sarcoplasmic reticulum, it is necessary to ask whether the ATPase shows any selectivity in its interaction with phospholipids. If the ATPase were to show a higher binding constant for some phospholipids than for others, then the composition of the annular shell of lipids around the ATPase in the membrane would be different to the bulk composition of the membrane; if phospholipids supporting a low ATPase activity, for example, were excluded from the annular shell, then their presence in the membrane could be supported without any deleterious effect on ATPase activity. The problem of measuring phospholipid binding constants reduces to that of determining which phospholipids are adjacent to the ATPase when the ATPase is reconstituted into a mixture of phospholipids. This can be done using ESR techniques, but a more convenient procedure is based on fluorescence quenching. The ATPase contains a large number of tryptophan residues in hydrophobic regions of the ATPase (see Figure 18), and the fluorescence of these tryptophans can be quenched by contact with, for example, bromine atoms. If the ATPase is reconstituted into a mixture of lipids containing a brominated phospholipid (one in which some –CH groups in the fatty acyl chains have been replaced by –CBr groups) then tryptophan fluorescence is quenched, and the extent of quenching is proportional to the number of brominated phospholipids in contact with the ATPase. Thus in mixtures of brominated phospholipid with a phospholipid that binds strongly to the ATPase, fluorescence will be less quenched than in mixtures of brominated phospholipid with a phospholipid that binds weakly to the ATPase. Such experiments are readily quantified to give relative phospholipid binding constants for the ATPase.

The data in Table 11 show that the relative binding constants of a variety of phospholipids differing in headgroup and fatty acyl chain are all very similar. The phase of the phospholipid, liquid crystalline or gel, does, however, have a significant effect on binding, with gel phase lipid binding less well by a factor of *ca.* 25. This effect presumably follows from poor packing of rigid fatty acyl chains with the molecularly rough surface of the ATPase. These studies also agree with the results of ESR studies which show that the time for a phospholipid molecule to move between the annulus and the bulk lipid phase is *ca.* 10^{-7} s at $37\,°C$, a factor of only *ca.* 2 less than the time for two phospholipids to exchange positions in the bulk phase. The lipid–protein interaction is therefore very 'non-sticky', consistent with a relatively non-specific lipid–protein interaction. This is consistent with our ideas of the structures of membrane proteins. If the membrane penetrant part of the ATPase is composed of α-helices, then the protein surface presented to the phospholipid bilayer would be a molecularly rough hydrophobic surface bounded by regions composed of charged or polar groups. Interactions of phospholipids with such a surface would be expected to be relatively non-specific. Charge interactions could, however, be significant. Thus it has been shown that cholesterol is excluded from the annulus and, although this can probably be attributed in part to the rigid sterol ring, the polar —OH group is also important, since cholesterol hemisuccinate has been shown to bind more strongly at the annulus than cholesterol. The importance of the polar group has also been shown by measuring the binding of a series of long chain alkyl derivatives to the $(Ca^{2+}-Mg^{2+})$-ATPase. Oleyl alcohol and methyl oleate were found to bind very weakly at the lipid–protein interface, whereas oleic acid and particularly oleyl amine bound more strongly. Since the activity of the ATPase depends strongly on the chemical structures of the surrounding molecules, with dioleoylphosphatidylcholine giving the highest activity, binding of other hydrophobic molecules at the annulus, displacing phospholipid, would be expected to result in inhibition: this is indeed what is observed.

We can now relate these studies of model systems to the situation in the native sarcoplasmic reticulum. Since the ATPase shows relatively little selectivity in binding phospholipids, the phospholipid composition of the annulus around the ATPase will be essentially the same as the bulk phospholipid composition of the membrane. As a consequence, activity will depend on the bulk composition of the membrane and thus very major changes in the phospholipid composition of the membrane will be required to bring about significant changes in ATPase activity; the presence or absence of some minor phospholipid component will have no effect on activity. The ATPase is relatively undemanding with regard to phospholipid structure. The phospholipids need to be in the liquid crystalline phase at physiological temperatures. This can be guaranteed if the phospholipids contain one saturated and one unsaturated chain, as they do (see Tables 8 and 9). The fatty acyl chain lengths of the phospholipids need to be between C-16 and C-22 to give a bilayer of the appropriate thickness to support high activity (Table 11). As shown in Table 8 the fatty acids found in the native membrane meet this requirement. Finally, phosphatidylcholines support higher activities than do other phospholipids (Table 12), and phosphatidylcholines are the predominant class of phospholipid in the sarcoplasmic reticulum. The catholicity of the ATPase means that no tight control on the phospholipid composition of the membrane is necessary. The phospholipid composition of the membrane will be held relatively constant, of course, by the pattern of lipid biosynthesis described in Section 11.1.3.1, by the specificity of the phospholipases and by any specificity in the processes of absorption of lipids and fatty acids from the diet. It seems that this is all that is required, at least as far as the $(Ca^{2+}-Mg^{2+})$-ATPase is concerned. The complexity of the phospholipid composition of the sarcoplasmic reticulum does not then prove the fastidiousness of the ATPase, but rather the opposite: that the cell is free to construct its membrane using whichever fatty acyl chains and lipid headgroups are currently most available. A variety of fatty acyl chains will be provided by the diet. Further, for a reaction pathway such as that shown in Figure 20 leading, for example, to arachidonic acid (necessary for the synthesis of prostaglandins), intermediate fatty acid species must be present in the cell, and it would be more difficult to exclude these from the membrane than to allow their inclusion. Finally, to understand the phospholipid composition of the membrane, it is necessary to remember that the membrane is a part of the general metabolic system of the cell, and thus acts as a store of components (fatty acyl chains, choline, ethanolamine, phosphate, *etc.*) to be used by the cell, and as a source of second messengers for signalling in the cell. As Brenner has it, 'anything that is produced by evolution is bound to be a bit of a mess' (quoted in ref. 57).

To the extent that data are available for other membrane proteins, the conclusions drawn above for the $(Ca^{2+}-Mg^{2+})$-ATPase seem to be generally applicable. The effects of lipids on the human erythrocyte sugar transporter have been shown to be very similar to effects on the ATPase.[58] Rat liver microsomal stearoyl-CoA desaturase has been reconstituted into bilayers of egg yolk phosphatidylcholine (unsaturated, average fatty acyl chain length C-17) and dimyristoylphosphatidylcholine (DMPC). At temperatures above 24 °C when DMPC is in the liquid crystalline phase, the enzyme is active in both systems with the activity in egg yolk phosphatidylcholine being *ca.* 2–3 times that in the short chain lipid DMPC. At lower temperatures, when DMPC is in the gel phase, there is no activity.[59] Similar results have been obtained with rhodopsin.[60] The retinal rod outer segment disc membrane (ROS) is particularly rich in unsaturated fatty acids, and it has been suggested that this is important for the function of rhodopsin. However, when rhodopsin was reconstituted into bilayers of egg yolk phosphatidylcholine, the kinetics of the metarhodopsin I–metarhodopsin II change were identical to those in the native membrane; it was only when rhodopsin was reconstituted into a short chain phospholipid such as DMPC that a significant reduction in rate was observed. It has also been suggested that the polyunsaturated fatty acids in ROS were required to give a highly fluid membrane in which the rate of lateral diffusion of rhodopsin would be fast. However, the rate of diffusion of the related protein bacteriorhodopsin in bilayers of DMPC in the liquid crystalline phase has been found to be faster than for rhodopsin in ROS.[61] From studies of the acetylcholine receptor reconstituted into bilayers of defined composition, Fung and McNamee[62] have concluded that membrane fluidity is an important parameter, but, in fact, their experimental data are entirely consistent with the proposals made above.

The exact viscosity of the lipid component of the membrane could be more important for functions dependent on diffusion of proteins within the membrane. Thus in the mobile receptor hypothesis, the rate of collision between the receptor protein and its target protein in the membrane could be lipid dependent. However, the rate of diffusion of the β-receptor in the membrane, for example, has been determined to be very slow, presumably limited by interprotein interaction or by anchoring to cytoskeletal structures; lipid viscosity is then unlikely to have much influence.[47] Again, antibody-induced patching of some surface proteins also causes a corresponding change in the submembranous actin cytoskeleton, suggesting interactions between the membrane protein and the cytoskeleton which are likely to affect the rate of patching more than the membrane viscosity.

11.1.6 INTERACTIONS OF DRUGS WITH MEMBRANES

In the light of the discussion of membrane function given above, we can make a few predictions about likely drug targets within the membrane. Figure 32 illustrates potential drug-binding sites in the membrane. Drugs, particularly hydrophilic drugs, could bind at distinct binding sites on hydrophilic domains of membrane proteins; drugs binding at neurotransmitter binding sites and enzyme active sites would fall into this category. Hydrophobic drugs will be able to bind both to the protein and to the lipid component of the membrane. Binding to the lipid component could affect protein function in one or two ways. Firstly, drug binding could affect the fluidity of the lipid phase, this having an effect on protein function. This is a popular idea and has generated much data, but now seems almost certainly to be wrong. Effects of drugs on membrane fluidity are generally very small, and protein function, as described above, seems generally to be relatively insensitive to membrane fluidity. Secondly, if the drug is charged then binding of the drug will affect the charge on the membrane, and this could affect the function of the membrane. For example, the antihistamines are positively charged and binding to the lipid component of the membrane will introduce positive charge onto the surface of the membrane. This positive charge will repel the positively charged histamine molecule away from the surface, and so reduce its concentration in the vicinity of the histamine receptor in the membrane. The equations necessary to calculate these charge effects are given in refs. 63 and 64.

A number of binding sites for hydrophobic drugs are also possible on membrane proteins. As well as binding at sites exposed on hydrophilic domains (site E, Figure 32), binding may also be possible at fortuitous sites 'within' the protein (site D, Figure 32). Binding of hydrophobic drugs at the lipid–protein interface (annular sites B in Figure 32) certainly need to be considered. As described in Section 11.1.5.2, charge is important in determining relative strengths of binding at these sites on the $(Ca^{2+}-Mg^{2+})$-ATPase, with the strength of binding increasing in the order uncharged < negatively charged < positively charged. As expected from the nature of the lipid–protein interface, the strength of binding also increases with increasing hydrophobicity, until the point where the aqueous solubility of the drug becomes limiting.[65-68] Since the activity of membrane proteins depends on the chemical structure of the molecules surrounding them, with dioleoylphosphatidylcholine being the optimal lipid for a number of proteins, displacement of phospholipids from the lipid–protein interface by drug molecules would be expected to lead to a decrease in activity. Finally, if the protein is present in the membrane in oligomeric form, then binding is possible at protein–protein interfaces in the oligomer (site C, Figure 32). Evidence for such binding has been presented for the $(Ca^{2+}-Mg^{2+})$-ATPase[66] and for bacteriorhodopsin:[69] for the $(Ca^{2+}-Mg^{2+})$-ATPase, it has been suggested that such binding can have large effects on activity, depending on the nature of the phospholipids present in the system.

It is clear that we need to know much more about the basic principles governing the functioning of membrane proteins before we can be said to possess a really satisfactory view of the molecular pharmacology of the membrane.

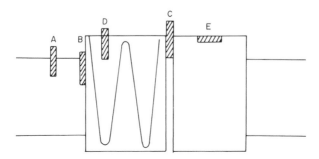

Figure 32 Possible drug binding sites on a membrane: A, in the lipid phase; B, at the lipid–protein interface; C, between protein subunits; D, between 'loops' in the protein structure; and E, at hydrophilic binding sites on the protein

ACKNOWLEDGEMENT

The author thanks the Science and Engineering Research Council for financial support.

11.1.7 REFERENCES

1. B. Albers, D. Bray, J. Lewis, M. Raff, K. Roberts and J. D. Watson, 'Molecular Biology of the Cell', Garland Publishers, New York, 1989.
2. J. Darnell, H. Lodish and D. Baltimore, 'Molecular Cell Biology', Scientific American Books, New York, 1986.
3. M. D. Houslay and K. K. Stanley, 'Dynamics of Biological Membranes', Wiley, Chichester, 1982.
4. A. P. M. Lockwood and A. G. Lee, 'The Membranes of Animal Cells', 3rd edn., part of the 'Studies in Biology' series, Edward Arnold, London, 1984.
5. J. Wiener, A. V. Loud, D. V. Kimberg and D. Spiro, *J. Cell. Biol.*, 1968, **37**, 47.
6. C. W. Cotman, *Methods Enzymol.*, 1974, **31A**, 445.
7. V. P. Whittaker, in 'Handbook of Neurochemistry', ed. A. Lajtha, Plenum Press, 1969, vol. 2.
8. D. R. Volker, in 'Biochemistry of Lipids and Membranes', ed. D. E. Vance and J. E. Vance, Benjamin/Cummings, Menlo Park, CA, 1985, p. 475.
9. A. J. Verkleij, R. F. A. Zwaal, B. Roelofsen, P. Comfurius, D. Kastelijn and L. L. M. Van Deenen, *Biochim. Biophys. Acta*, 1973, **323**, 178.
10. J. A. F. Op Den Kamp, in 'New Comprehensive Biochemistry', vol. 1, 'Membrane Structure', ed. J. B. Finean and R. H. Michell, Elsevier, Amsterdam, 1981, p. 83.
11. J. G. Hill, A. Kuksis and J. M. R. Beveridge, *J. Am. Oil Chem. Soc.*, 1965, **42**, 137.
12. L. Marai and A. Kuksis, *Can. J. Biochem.*, 1973, **51**, 1248.
13. A. G. Lee, J. M. East and R. J. Froud, *Prog. Lipid. Res.*, 1986, **25**, 41.
14. M. G. Sarzala, M. Pilarska, E. Zubrzycha and M. Michalak, *Eur. J. Biochem.*, 1975, **57**, 24.
15. G. W. Gould, J. M. McWhirter, J. M. East and A. G. Lee, *Biochem. J.*, 1987, **245**, 751.
16. C. D. Stubbs and A. D. Smith, *Biochim. Biophys. Acta*, 1984, **779**, 89.
17. A. A. Spector and M. A. Yorek, *J. Lipid Res.*, 1985, **26**, 1015.
18. C. R. H. Raetz, *Microbiol. Rev.*, 1978, **42**, 614.
19. D. de Mendoza and J. E. Cronan, *Trends Biochem. Sci.*, 1983, **8**, 49.
20. R. N. McElhaney, *Biomembranes*, 1984, **12**, 249.
21. M. V. Bell, R. J. Henderson and J. R. Sargent, *Comp. Biochem. Physiol.*, 1986, **83B**, 711.
22. R. E. Mrak, 'Muscle Membranes in Diseases of Muscle', CRC Press, Boca Raton, FL, 1985.
23. D. A. Butterfield, in 'Membrane Fluidity in Biology', ed. R. C. Aloia and J. M. Boggs, Academic Press, New York, 1985, vol. 3, p. 161.
24. G. Guroff, 'Molecular Neurobiology', Dekker, New York, 1980.
25. S. G. Singer and G. L. Nicolson, *Science (Washington, D.C.)*, 1972, **175**, 720.
26. F. Szoka and D. Papahadjopoulos, *Annu. Rev. Bioeng.*, 1980, **9**, 467.
27. A. G. Lee, in 'Membrane Fluidity in Biology', ed. R. C. Aloia, Academic Press, New York, 1983, vol. 2, p. 43.
28. A. G. Lee, *Tech. Life Sci., Sect. Biochem.*, 1984, **B422**, 1.
29. J. Seelig and N. Waespe-Sarcevic, *Biochemistry*, 1978, **17**, 3310.
30. P. R. Cullis and M. J. Hope, in 'Biochemistry of Lipids and Membranes', ed. D. E. Vance and J. E. Vance, Benjamin/Cummings, Menlo Park, CA, 1985, p. 25.
31. E. Racker, 'Reconstitutions of Transporters, Receptors, and Pathological States', Academic Press, New York, 1985.
32. A. H. Maddy, 'Biochemical Analysis of Membranes', Chapman and Hall, London, 1976.
33. H. R. Guy, *Biophys. J.*, 1984, **45**, 249.
34. P. Argos and J. K. MohanaRao, *Methods Enzymol.*, 1986, **130**, 185.
35. R. A. F. Reithmeier, in 'Biochemistry of Lipids and Membranes', ed. D. E. Vance and J. E. Vance, Benjamin/Cummings, Menlo Park, CA, 1985, p. 503.
36. C. J. Brandl, N. M. Green, B. Korczak and D. H. MacLennan, *Cell*, 1986, **44**, 597.
37. J. Lindstrom, *Trends Neurol. Sci.*, 1986, **9**, 401.
38. W. D. Stein, in 'The Enzymes of Biological Membranes', ed. A. N. Martonosi, Plenum Press, New York, 1985, vol. 3, p. 1.
39. J. E. Pessin and M. P. Czech, in 'The Enzymes of Biological Membranes', ed. A. N. Martonosi, Plenum Press, New York, 1985, vol. 3, p. 497.
40. M. Klingenberg, in 'The Enzymes of Biological Membranes', ed. A. N. Martonosi, Plenum Press, New York, 1985, vol. 4, p. 511.
41. L. D. Faller, A. Smolka and G. Sachs, in 'The Enzymes of Biological Membranes', ed. A. N. Martonosi, Plenum Press, New York, 1985, vol. 3, p. 431.
42. T. Yamamoto, C. G. Davis, M. S. Brown, W. J. Schneider, M. L. Casey, J. L. Goldstein and D. W. Russell, *Cell*, 1984, **39**, 27.
43. C. Schneider, M. J. Owen, D. Banville and J. G. Williams, *Nature (London)*, 1984, **311**, 675.
44. A. G. Gilman, *Cell*, 1984, **36**, 577.
45. R. J. Lefkowitz, J. M. Stadel and M. Caron, *Annu. Rev. Biochem.*, 1983, **52**, 159.
46. A. N. Martonosi, 'The Enzymes of Biological Membranes', 2nd edn., Plenum Press, New York, 1985, four volumes.
47. D. Axelrod, *J. Membr. Biol.*, 1983, **75**, 1.
48. J. P. Changeux and F. Revah, *Trends Neurol. Sci.*, 1987, **10**, 245.
49. K. Dunlap, G. G. Holz and S. G. Rane, *Trends Neurol. Sci.*, 1987, **10**, 240.
50. M. D. Houslay, in 'Molecular Mechanisms of Transmembrane Signalling', ed. P. Cohen and M. D. Houslay, Elsevier, Amsterdam, 1985, p. 279.
51. M. Noda, S. Shimizu, T. Tanabe, T. Takai, T. Kayano, T. Ikeda, H. Takahashi, H. Nakayama, Y. Kanaoka, N. Miknamino, K. Kangawa, H. Matsuo, M. A. Raftery, T. Hirose, S. Inayama, H. Hayashida, T. Miyata and S. Numa, *Nature (London)*, 1984, **312**, 121.

52. B. Hille, 'Ionic Channels of Excitable Membranes', Sinauer, Sunderland, USA, 1984.
53. G. B. Warren, P. A. Toon, N. J. M. Birdsall, A. G. Lee and J. C. Metcalfe, *Proc. Natl. Acad. Sci. USA*, 1974, **71**, 622.
54. A. G. Lee, in 'Advances in Membrane Fluidity', ed. R. C. Aloia, C. C. Curtain and L. M. Gordon, Liss, New York, 1988, vol. 2, p. 111.
55. A. G. Lee, *J. Bioenerg. Biomembr.*, 1987, **19**, 581.
56. J. M. East, O. T. Jones, A. C. Simmonds and A. G. Lee, *J. Biol. Chem.*, 1984, **259**, 8070.
57. R. Lewin, *Science (Washington, D.C.)*, 1984, **224**, 1327.
58. R. E. Tefft, A. Carruthers and D. L. Melchior, *Biochemistry*, 1986, **25**, 3709.
59. H. G. Enoch, A. Catala and P. Strittmatter, *J. Biol. Chem.*, 1976, **251**, 5095.
60. D. F. O'Brien, L. F. Costa and R. A. Ott, *Biochemistry*, 1977, **16**, 1295.
61. R. Peters and R. J. Cherry, *Proc. Natl. Acad. Sci. USA*, 1982, **79**, 4317.
62. T. M. Fong and M. G. McNamee, *Biochemistry*, 1986, **25**, 830.
63. A. G. Lee, *Biochim. Biophys. Acta*, 1977, **472**, 237.
64. E. K. Rooney and A. G. Lee, *Biochim. Biophys. Acta*, 1983, **732**, 428.
65. A. G. Lee, *Trends Pharmacol. Sci.*, 1982, **1**, 145.
66. R. J. Froud, J. M. East, O. T. Jones and A. G. Lee, *Biochemistry*, 1986, **25**, 7544.
67. O. T. Jones and A. G. Lee, *Pestic. Biochem. Physiol.*, 1986, **25**, 420.
68. O. T. Jones and A. G. Lee, *Biochim. Biophys. Acta*, 1985, **812**, 731.
69. E. K. Rooney, M. G. Gore and A. G. Lee, *Biochemistry*, 1987, **26**, 3688.
70. M. G. Low, *Biochem. J.*, 1987, **244**, 1.
71. J. Deisenhofer, H. Michel and R. Haber, *Trends Biochem. Sci. (Pers. Ed.)*, 1985, **10**, 243.
72. C. J. Brandl, N. M. Green, B. Korczak and D. H. MacLennan, *Cell*, 1986, **44**, 597.
73. E. P. Hoffman, C. M. Knudson, K. P. Campbell and L. M. Kunkel, *Nature (London)*, 1987, **330**, 754.

11.2

Quantitative Analysis of Ligand–Receptor Interactions

*MICHAEL WILLIAMS and MATTHEW A. SILLS

Ciba-Geigy Corporation, Summit, NJ, USA

*Present address: Abbott Laboratories, Abbot Park, IL, USA

11.2.1   INTRODUCTION

Receptors represent one of the major focal points for the study of cell and tissue function and can be studied either directly at the molecular level, or indirectly by observing, for instance, what effect a receptor antagonist can have on overt behavior or function. Between these two 'extremes' (and intermediate positions) there is debate as to which best addresses receptor function in a predictable manner. The discipline of pharmacology is, however, central to the understanding of receptor function, coordinating and integrating data from other scientific disciplines. The maintenance of an objective approach in interpreting data, together with the uniquely human ability to synthesize and deduce, rather than an excessive dependence on technology, is in pharmacology, as in all scientific areas, what leads to tangible advances in knowledge.

As molecular biology reveals more and more of the detailed structure of receptors, a remarkable degree of homology has been revealed in the various peptidic domains of receptors such as the nicotinic cholinergic,[1] β-adrenergic,[2] glycine[3] and GABA-A[4] receptors, receptors for various hormones[5] and associated ion channels.[6] Such knowledge, accrued from the isolation, cloning and sequencing of receptors is anticipated to improve the understanding of receptor function[7] to the extent that it will be easier to design novel chemical entities with improved potential for therapeutic use. At the present time, however, it appears likely that the 'structural detail required for ligand design will . . . . . have to await X-ray crystallography'.[8] As with X-ray crystallography,[9] molecular modeling[10] may also contribute significantly to the elucidation of receptor structure and ligand design.

Receptor function is, however, a biologically oriented process and while these physicochemical techniques may have great potential, they are still some way from the ultimate functionality that is the basis of drug action.[11] For instance, even the relatively simple technique of radioligand binding[12] has been the subject of criticism because of its inherent limitations,[13] *e.g.* the inability to readily differentiate agonists from antagonists. Paradoxically, a major issue has been the inherent limitation of any technique dependent on biological measurements which are circumscribed by the technology available. This has led to two major viewpoints of the process of receptor function.

In the classical approach, modulation of receptor function is measured in terms of a change in animal response. This is often highly empirical. If, for instance, substance P produces a reciprocal hindpaw scratching in rats, then *a priori* any compound producing a similar effect can be described as substance P-like. A logical, albeit somewhat absurd extension of this approach is that since propranolol lowers blood pressure, then any blood-pressure-lowering agent is a β blocker. Based on this approach, the structure–activity relationship derived is descriptive and based on the consequences of receptor-related events.[13] The second, molecular approach also has its limitations. For instance, it may be believed that a receptor has altered characteristics in a given disease state. The assumption can then be made that altering the functionality of the receptor by designing more efficacious agonists, by blocking the effects of endogenous ligands or using ligand replacement therapy could be valid preclinical approaches. In approaching receptor function from a mechanistic perspective, the structure–activity relationship derived is analytical and thus more precise. However, it is not until the desired compound is available that the hypothesis that altered receptor functionality can ameliorate the disease state can be tested. Based on the inherent limitations in these two approaches, it is important, therefore, to consider receptor functionality in terms of a dynamic construct where molecular biological, biochemical and pharmacological (whole tissue/animal) approaches contribute pieces to the final endpoint.

A receptor can be defined as a transductional entity contained within a cell membrane which has the ability to recognize a substance, termed a ligand. A receptor–ligand interaction can then lead to a modification of cell function, and ultimately a change in tissue function. The recognition portion of the receptor, which is often viewed as the receptor *per se*, is linked to its effector *via* a functional unit comprising either a G protein[14] associated with an enzyme and/or ion channel or may be linked

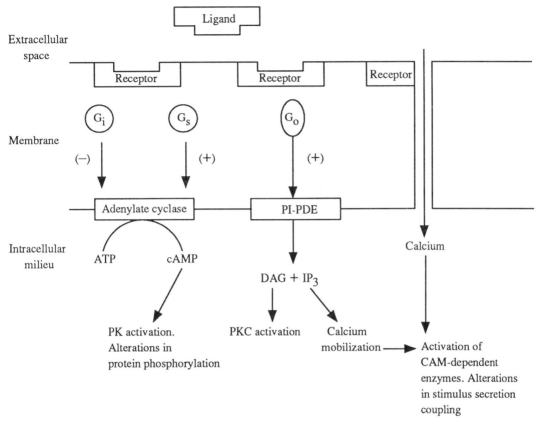

Figure 1 Schematic diagram of a hypothetical receptor and its associated effector components; G_s = stimulatory coupling protein for adenylate cyclase; G_i = inhibitory coupling protein for adenylate cyclase; G_o = coupling protein-mediating receptor effects other than cyclase modulation; PI-PDE = phosphatidyl inositol phosphodiesterase; DAG = diacylglycerol; IP_3 = inositol triphosphate; PK = protein kinase; CAM = calmodulin

directly to an ion channel or an enzyme (Figure 1). In the case of the insulin receptor,[15] it appears that the receptor itself is the enzyme, tyrosine kinase. The functional unit is then responsible for the production of a 'second messenger', the intracellular mediator of the receptor–ligand interaction. This second messenger may be a cyclic nucleotide, an ion, a phospholipid hydrolysis product, the receptor itself or an enzyme-mediated phosphorylation event.[16–20] For the purposes of the present discussion however, the recognition portion of the receptor complex will be referred to as the receptor. The process of ligand binding is, however, only the first step in a sequence of events that contribute to a pharmacological response that can be viewed from a heuristic perspective in two distinct ways: from that of the type of ligand that interacts with a receptor; and from the perspective of how the receptor recognizes the ligand. This presents a potentially hylomorphic distinction between a system where the ligand imposes specificity and function to one where the receptor imposes its innate properties on the ligand.[21] It is important when progressing through the *in vitro*, *in vivo* and whole animal test procedures that are necessary to elucidate the functional characteristics of the receptor–ligand interaction that all approaches to receptor function are considered viable. The understanding of this distinction can considerably enhance the melding process of the various pieces of information to obtain a cohesive and tenable endpoint.

Additional complicating factors in considering the present state of receptor theory relate to receptors for endogenous ligands and binding sites for drugs. The prototypical endogenous drug-like ligands from a receptor perspective were the enkephalins and endorphins.[22] The first 'drug receptor' *per se* was that for the benzodiazepine anxiolytics.[23] Following from these seminal discoveries have come a collection of ephemeral endogenous ligands whose existence has been somewhat questionable, and a number of drug receptors that are either artifactual or actually reveal activity of a drug at a known recognition site. An example of this latter phenomenon is the dibenzocycloalkenimine, MK 801, which, while characterized as a potent anticonvulsant, was inactive in a number of receptor-binding assays.[24] However, when labeled, it displayed a binding pharmacology consistent with the compound being active at phencyclidine PCP-type receptors and acting as a noncompetitive antagonist at the *N*-methyl-D-aspartate receptor.[25]

11.2.2 RECEPTOR THEORY

11.2.2.1 Historical

The initial suggestion that drugs might elicit their therapeutic and pharmacological actions *via* interactions with discrete membrane-associated recognition sites, or receptive substances, on target organs was made at the beginning of the present century,[26,27] based on what, in retrospect, was a minimum of data but has been described as 'prophetic vision'.[28] Despite tremendous technological advances and a continuous refinement in the basic theory, the initial proposals have stood the test of time well and still remain the foundation of what might loosely be called 'receptorology'.

From data on the effects of atropine and pilocarpine on salivation in the cat, Langley, in 1878,[26] proposed the existence of 'nerve ending . . . . substances' with which these drugs formed complexes. Independent studies in the diverse fields of alkaloid dyestuffs and diphtheria toxin immunology[27,29] led Ehrlich to develop the concept of specificity in relation to the interactions of various chemicals with tissues. This was then extended to include affinity and reversibility of such chemical interactions, leading to the postulate of the existence of cell surface recognition sites. Subsequent work led to the famous 'lock and key' hypothesis. The first use of the term 'receptor' has been cited [28] from a paper by Ehrlich in 1900,[30] although the use of the term has also been ascribed to Langley.[7] While further work by the latter and his associate A. V. Hill provided evidence for the chemical nature of the receptor–ligand interaction,[31] it was another decade and a half before Clark's pivotal studies provided evidence for the concept of the occupancy theory.[32]

11.2.2.2 Definitions

Receptors can be classified in terms of their pharmacology, their localization and their function. Ligands on the other hand are described in terms of their efficacy, affinity and selectivity. Efficacy is the ability of a ligand to induce a physiological or pharmacological response in a tissue (*i.e.* contraction) or animal (*i.e.* decrease in core temperature). Affinity relates to the ability of a ligand to bind to a recognition site, or receptor, and the magnitude of various molecular forces that contribute to the physicochemical strength of the interaction. A given ligand may have a low affinity (does not bind especially tightly to its recognition site) but be able to induce a given response in an appropriate test system. This ligand may therefore be equivalent to another ligand that binds with high affinity yet has low intrinsic efficacy and a corresponding reduced ability to induce the given response. In the first case the response evoked is limited by the affinity of the ligand, while in the second the response is finite due to a lack of intrinsic efficacy, which may be a property of either the ligand or the tissue. For instance, a full agonist in one tissue may only be a partial agonist in another tissue because of the degree of coupling between the receptor and the functional components to which it is linked.

Selectivity is the ability of a ligand to elicit a defined response through its ability to bind with greater preference and/or greater efficacy to one recognition site as opposed to another. This concept, and those of efficacy and affinity are discussed in further detail below.

Receptor theory *per se* is related to the Langmuir saturation isotherm and the quantitative use of the law of mass action as described by Michaelis and Menten[33] to describe interactions between enzymes and their substrates. While such a theory provides a good basis for practical studies, it is important to note that much of the controversy surrounding receptor theory arises from the implicit differences between receptors and enzymes. In the latter case, the enzyme is a biological catalyst leading to the formation of a discrete product or products which can be used to quantify and characterize the enzyme. This can be described by the equation

$$\text{Enzyme } + \text{ substrate } \underset{k_{-1}}{\overset{k_{+1}}{\rightleftharpoons}} \text{ ES } \xrightarrow{k_{+2}} \text{ E } + \text{ product} \tag{1}$$

For the receptor interaction, however, no catalytic effect occurs directly as part of the receptor–ligand interaction. Therefore, while ATP may be converted to cAMP *via* the activation of the enzyme adenylate cyclase[16] through the formation of the receptor–ligand complex, the ligand itself remains unchanged. *A priori*, receptor–ligand interactions occur independently of ligand transformation. The equation for this interaction is

$$\text{Receptor } + \text{ ligand } \underset{k_{-1}}{\overset{k_{+1}}{\rightleftharpoons}} \text{ RL } \xrightarrow{k_{+2}} \text{ R } + \text{ effect} \tag{2}$$

Additionally, the mass action law is apparently not synonymous with the Langmuir isotherm at equilibrium since the former is not an equilibrium condition *per se* but rather reflects the rates attendant on the achievement of such an equilibrium,[34] *i.e.* only approximate results not true values are determined.

Because of experimental anomalies relating to the receptor–ligand (RL) interaction, primarily due to the lack of a quantitative relationship between receptor occupancy and tissue response, such concepts as spare receptors and efficacy are used to explain inconsistencies between anticipated receptor occupation and observed results.

A receptor can be quantitatively described by its dissociation constant, or K_d value, a measure of the affinity of the receptor for a given ligand, and its apparent B_{max} value, the density of binding sites on a concentration/weight basis, a measure of the total number of receptors in a tissue. The K_d value has units of concentration, while the B_{max} value is concentration per mg protein. To further ascribe functionality to a discrete molecular entity using biochemical criteria it is necessary to show that the receptor has a geography consistent with a role in cellular communication. The receptor is usually envisaged as a cell surface protein capable of interacting with the cellular milieu and should thus be found in cellular subfractions in which synaptic regions are enriched. Furthermore, there should be a correlation between the distribution of the presumed endogenous ligand for the receptor and the receptor itself. For instance, it is known from histochemical studies that the highest concentrations of dopamine occur in striatal regions of the brain.[35] Accordingly, a similar enrichment in dopamine receptors can be found in this brain area.[36] Finally, for the receptor the structure–activity relationship for a series of compounds, both agonists and antagonists, should be consistent with what is known for functionally related assays.

Receptors recognize ligands with different affinities. The usual measures of ligand affinity under equilibrium conditions are various iterations of the IC_{50}/ED_{50} value, the concentration of ligand required to inhibit/stimulate a particular measure of receptor function. This can be further derived to yield the K_i value, which is discussed further below. Thus ligand binding and response are two distinct entities, determined by the different parameters of affinity and efficacy. The use of the equilibrium binding constant K, where K is equal to k_{-1}/k_{+1} according to equation (2), has been criticized[34] since the technique of measuring affinity by radioligand binding will measure not K, but the effective binding constant K' which is equal to $K/(1 + \beta/\alpha)$ where α and β are defined in the equation

$$R + L \underset{k_{-1}}{\overset{k_{+1}}{\rightleftharpoons}} RL \underset{\alpha}{\overset{\beta}{\rightleftharpoons}} RL^* \tag{3}$$

This theoretical criticism assumes, however, that the interaction of all ligands with their receptor follows the Castillo/Katz concept of isomerization of the RL complex[37] with a dynamic intermediate. The degree of formation of this latter entity and its intrinsic energy, enthalpic or entropic, are thought to be a possible measure of efficacy.

A full agonist is a ligand that can elicit a maximal response in a given effector system (Figure 2a). However, such a ligand need not have high affinity. A partial agonist is a ligand that cannot produce a maximal response because of reduced efficacy (Figure 2b), while an antagonist is a ligand with zero efficacy. By such definition, a partial agonist has a component of action that also has zero efficacy and may also be described as a mixed agonist–antagonist. A new class of receptor ligand, the inverse agonist, has evolved from studies related to the central benzodiazepine receptor complex.[38] An

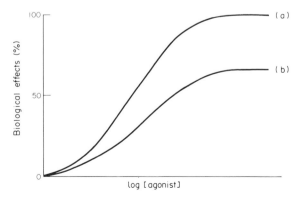

Figure 2 Dose/concentration–response curve; (a) = full agonist; (b) = partial agonist

inverse agonist is a ligand that has negative efficacy in that it has functional actions opposite to those of a full agonist. There is an additional spectrum of activity where, for instance, an inverse agonist can also have antagonist activity (a partial inverse agonist) and other ligands can block the actions of inverse agonists (full antagonists). There is much semantic controversy related to such criteria in that the functional response to a ligand is not only the consequence of the intrinsic properties of the ligand but also the nature of the tissue preparation that is being used for data generation.

A receptor can also be defined according to the type of tissue and the species from which it was derived. This can lead to a somewhat circular situation and considerable confusion when, as noted by Black[13] in the concept of analytical pharmacology, the pharmacological activity of a compound is defined with reference to its actions in a particular tissue. The compound is then used as a tool to define other actions. Thus, actions ascribed to an interaction with the recognition site originally defined are then interpreted in terms of similar, if not identical, RL interactions in other tissues, irrespective of the possibility that in the latter the compound may produce its effects *via* other receptor types. This can contribute to confusion in describing the type of receptor mediating a given response. The classical serotonin-M receptor originally described by Gaddum and coworkers[39] in peripheral tissues has been found, based on the actions of compounds such as MDL 72222, ICS 205930 and odanserin,[40–42] to be similar to the 5-HT$_3$ receptor subtype.

11.2.2.3 Occupancy Theory

In 1926 Clark, in studying the effects of acetylcholine (ACh) in cardiac and abdominal muscle, developed the dose–response (DR) curve (Figure 2) and, from a logarithmic plot, showed that antagonists such as atropine caused a rightward shift in the DR curve (Figure 3). These data led Clark to assume that the biological or functional response to receptor activation was directly proportional to the number of receptors occupied by a given ligand at equilibrium.[32] The equation describing this phenomenon was proposed as

$$E_A/E_M = [RL]/[R]_T \qquad (4)$$

where E_A = fractional response; E_M = maximal response; [RL] = concentration of receptor–ligand complex and $[R]_T$ = total receptor concentration. At equilibrium, $R + L \rightleftharpoons RL$, such that the affinity constant K_A can be defined where $K_A = [RL]/[L][R]$. This is the same equation derived from Langmuir's saturation isotherm, which in turn derives from the law of mass action. Using the Michaelis–Menten derivation,[33] it now became possible to formalize the occupancy theory in the following terms: (i) the RL complex is reversible; (ii) association is a bimolecular and dissociation a monomolecular process; (iii) all receptors of a given type are equivalent and independent of one another; (iv) binding of the ligand to the receptor does not alter the free (F) concentration or the affinity of the receptor for the ligand; (v) the response elicited by receptor occupation is directly

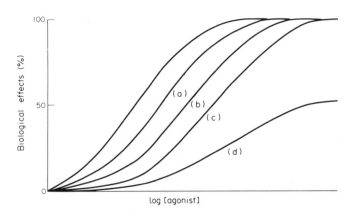

Figure 3   Antagonist effects on dose/concentration–response relationships. Addition of increasing concentrations, (a), (b) and (c), of a competitive antagonist causes a shift to the right of the response curve with the same maximum being obtained. It may be noted that the shifted curves are also parallel. In the presence of a noncompetitive antagonist, (d), a similar rightward shift occurs; the maximum is diminished however, indicating that increasing concentrations of agonist cannot completely overcome the effects of a noncompetitive antagonist

proportional to the number of receptors occupied by the ligand; and (vi) the biological response is dependent on the attainment of an equilibrium between R and L.

Equation (2) can be rearranged to give the equilibrium dissociation constant, K_d, according to the equation

$$K_d = ([R][L])/[RL] \qquad (5)$$

where $K_d = k_{-1}/k_{+1}$, which by analogy with the Michaelis–Menten enzyme derivation[33] is the concentration of the ligand that occupies 50% of the available receptors.

While occupancy theory has inherent limitations related to the inability to define the relative concentrations of free receptor and RL complex, it provides a useful working basis for delineating receptor theory.

Gaddum[43] further developed the antagonist concept by proposing that antagonist ligands occupied the receptor without eliciting a response, thus preventing agonist ligands from producing their effects. Since this interaction is usually competitive in nature, an agonist could then overcome the antagonist effects as its concentration is increased. The generation of a series of DR curves in the presence of fixed, progressive increases in antagonist concentration (Figure 4) allows for the determination of a pA_2 value, the affinity of an antagonist for a receptor, by the method of Schild[44]

$$pA_2 = -\log_{10} K_B \qquad (6)$$

where K_B = the dissociation constant for a competitive antagonist.

Noting that various cholinergic agonists were not all able to produce a maximal response in skeletal muscle even at supramaximal concentrations, Ariens[45] formulated the concept of intrinsic activity. Full antagonists had an intrinsic activity of zero and full agonists a value of unity. Partial agonists and agonist/antagonists could then have intermediate values. Presumably, on this basis, inverse agonists could have an intrinsic activity of -1. By analogy with the Michaelis–Menten equation, where the velocity of an enzyme reaction E is proportional to the concentration of enzyme–substrate complex, for a receptor, E_R is proportional to $[RA]$

$$E_R = \alpha r_0 1 + (K_R/[A]) \qquad (7)$$

where r_0 is the total receptor concentration and K_R is the affinity constant. Drug action is thus a consequence of both K_R and α, the latter being a proportionality constant.

Stephenson[46] approached the issue of partial agonists by introducing the concept of efficacy, a modification of Clark's occupancy theory, which considered the situation where a maximal response could occur when only a small proportion of available receptors on a tissue were occupied. The relationship between tissue response and receptor occupation was therefore not linear. The response was designated as the result of the stimulus (S), which was defined as the product of the fraction of receptors occupied and the efficacy of the ligand. This nonproportionality between receptor occupancy and tissue response has been extensively documented.[47]

Efficacy differs from intrinsic activity in that the latter is described as a proportion of the size of the maximal response (effect = $\alpha[LR]$), where α is the intrinsic activity. The maximal response is implicit in the experimental derivation of the efficacy concept. However, the description of efficacy

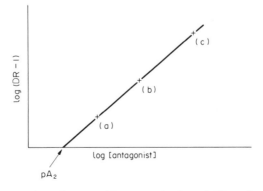

Figure 4 Schild plot. Three concentrations of a competitive antagonist shown in Figure 3 as (a), (b) and (c) are plotted by the method of Schild[44] to yield pA_2, a measure of antagonist activity. With a slope of unity the antagonist is usually competitive, while a slope deviating from unity is indicative of noncompetitive/allosteric behavior. For further discussion, see ref. 131

relies on a relationship between the stimulus S given to a tissue, where $S = \varepsilon K[L]$ and where ε = efficacy, K = equilibrium association constant and $[L]$ = drug concentration. Affinity constants can, however, differ experimentally when efficacy and intrinsic activity definitions are used under similar experimental conditions. Ariens, however, has since modified the initial intrinsic activity theory and has defined intrinsic efficacy to be more equivalent to Stephenson's efficacy concept.[48] Thus the drug response is a function of not only the efficacy of the ligand but also the degree of receptor occupation.

Nickerson, in studying the effects of histamine in guinea pig ileal strips, showed that in the presence of an irreversible competitive antagonist where the number of available histamine receptors was decreased by 99%, a maximal response was still observed.[49] This observation led to the concept of spare receptors such that with an efficacious agonist it was only necessary to occupy a fraction of the receptors (in this particular study, 1%) in a tissue to elicit a maximal response. Furchgott further defined intrinsic efficacy to include the tissue concentration of receptors,[50] a modification that left efficacy as a strictly drug- rather than drug/tissue-related term. This work further reinforced the possibility of a 'receptor reserve' or spare receptors in a tissue, which can be defined as 'the fraction of the total receptor pool not required for a maximal tissue response'.[11] Drug-related responses in a given tissue have been considered, therefore, to depend on four factors:[11] (i) the density of receptors in a given tissue; (ii) the efficiency of the tissue in translating the binding reaction into a tissue response; (iii) the equilibrium dissociation constant of the RL complex; and (iv) the intrinsic efficacy of the drug for the receptor.

However, this still leaves the spare receptor concept as more of a convenient explanation for experimental data that deviate significantly from that predicted using occupancy theory rather than a concept with a biochemical rationale. For instance, if spare receptors for a given agonist are present on a tissue, why should there be changes in receptor number when the agonist input to a given tissue is reduced (supersensitivity) or increased (subsensitivity/tolerance)? It has been argued[51] that for a response that is rapid in onset and termination, the presence of an excess of receptors allows a relatively low affinity agonist, present in low concentrations, to readily produce a tissue response. The low affinity also ensures a rapid dissociation of the agonist from the receptor and a corresponding rapid termination of the physiological response. Kenakin[11] has compared the efficiency of the coupling of receptor activation to that of a power amplifier. Thus receptor occupancy *per se*, as in the case of Nickerson's histamine-mediated responses, is a function not only of the efficacy of the ligand but also of the coupling system(s) and in this respect it is still unknown as to what features of a molecule contribute to efficacy. Is it the ability of an agonist to enhance effector coupling in some manner, by changing a 'loose' coupling state to a 'tight' one? Also, to what extent does the ability of the tissue to respond affect the classification of its intrinsic efficacy? Furthermore, while it is relatively easy to dismiss the usefulness of receptor-binding techniques to contribute data to the debate on the spare receptor concept,[11] it is highly likely that partial agonism in some systems may reflect bioavailability (drug diffusion) issues rather than any intrinsic pharmacological properties of the molecule.

There is still much to be learnt about both the concepts of efficacy and receptor reserve. The ability to design compounds that are endowed with more or less efficacy has yet to be quantified and, within the realm of understanding drug action and the molecular basis of disease etiology, such concepts require more formal physiological validation.

11.2.2.4 Rate Theory

To explain experimental observations such as the persistence of antagonist-mediated effects, the 'fade' of agonist actions where maximal but transient responses occur followed by longer lasting responses of lesser magnitude and agonist-mediated 'block' of their own actions, Paton[52] modified occupancy theory to a more chemically based rate theory. In this theory it is not the number of receptors occupied that determines the response but rather the rate of RL formation, thus the effect E is equal to a proportionality factor θ and the velocity V of the response, where θ reflects the processing of the RL interaction and includes an efficacy component. Thus

$$E \;=\; \theta V_{eq} \tag{8}$$

The rate of RL formation is measured in terms of 'quanta', discrete 'all-or-none' changes in receptor-mediated events within the cell or tissue.

In mathematically comparing equilibrium conditions for occupancy and rate theory situations, Limbird concluded[7] that differences in response are a factor of the dissociation rate constant. Thus if this factor is large a ligand will be an agonist and if small, thus restricting the occurrence of quanta due to occupancy of receptors, an antagonist. However, since the proportionality constant has the self-same limitations as the efficacy factor and may be defined differently for occupancy and rate conditions, one is still left with an intangible element designed to encompass, explain and be expanded to accommodate experimental findings rather than predict them. Thus, both rate and occupancy theories attempt to describe deviations from predicted concentration/dose–response curves in terms of a simple pseudo-first-order, bimolecular reaction involving the interaction of a single ligand L with a single receptor R. Rate theory, as noted, predicts that potency is a function of the affinity of the ligand for the receptor. While rate theory can reasonably explain the experimental data derived by Paton in guinea pig ileum, numerous other examples exist where rate theory is not applicable. For instance, if the efficiency of coupling is a major rate-limiting (or amplifying) step, then the kinetics of the RL response as defined in rate theory may not reflect the tissue response to receptor activation. Rate theory has been described as a 'provocative conceptualization . . . . . with limited applicability'.[7] Given the confusion surrounding the various aspects of occupancy theory described above, such a judgement may be premature, especially when considering that much of the data generated to support either of the various arguments assume instantaneous diffusion of the ligand to its site of action. As noted, the concept of the RL interaction involving only a single receptor and ligand does not readily accommodate either allosteric receptor modulators that influence receptor function by binding to sites adjacent and proximal to the site under study or receptor complexes.

11.2.2.5 Inactivation Theory

Receptor inactivation theory appears to accommodate the major elements of both occupancy and rate theory. Proposed in 1977 by Gosselin,[53] this theory has received scant attention. Unlike the Castillo/Katz model (equation 3), which assumes that the RL interaction leads to an intermediate 'active' state, receptor inactivation theory is based on the premise that following the formation of the RL complex, an inactive form of the receptor, R', occurs according to the schema

$$[R] + [L] \underset{k_{-1}}{\overset{k_{+1}}{\rightleftharpoons}} [RL] \tag{9}$$
$$k_3 \diagdown \quad \diagup k_2$$
$$[R'L]$$

with k_{+1} being the rate of onset, k_{-1} the rate of offset, k_2 the rate of formation of inactive receptor and k_3 the rate constant for regeneration of the active entity. The response elicited is then proportional to the rate of R' formation, which is equal to $k_3[R'L]$, thus being dependent on the number of occupied receptors as well as the rate of R' formation. In this theory, efficacy is a function of the relative magnitudes of k_2 and k_3. As with the rate theory, unequivocal experimental evidence to support the theory appears to be difficult to obtain and, as has been universally agreed,[7,11] under equilibrium conditions it is not possible to distinguish between occupancy, rate and receptor inactivation theories. This is a point of some interest since it assumes that maximal receptor occupancy due to the rapid 'on/off' predicted for a full agonist under the rate theory, the maximal occupancy of receptors in a finite sense predicted from occupancy theory or the rapid regeneration of R from R' predicted from inactivation theory, causes a maximal response. Receptor reserve may therefore appear to have no role in receptor-mediated events under such conditions.

11.2.3 ALLOSTERIC MODULATION AND RECEPTOR COMPLEXES

The considerable evidence for nonlinear concentration–response curves in models of receptor functionality is similar to the enzymological concept of allosterism.[54] The classical studies of Hill on the binding of oxygen to hemoglobin[55] showed that the association of oxygen with each of the four heme moieties occurred in a graded fashion. Binding of the first molecule facilitated binding of the second and so on, such that the saturation curve was steeper than that predicted from mass action kinetics. The binding of oxygen to hemoglobin is an example of positive cooperativity. Allosteric modulators differ from classical ligands by acting at sites distinct from the active site of the receptor. Intrinsic to the concept of allosteric modulators is that binding of the modulating ligand induces a conformational change, which in turn can then facilitate or prevent further ligand association. While Adair[56] and Pauling [57] have contributed significantly to the allosteric theory, the two best-known models are the concerted model of Monod, Wyman and Changeaux,[58] and the Koshland, Nemethy

Table 1 Examples of Allosteric Receptor Models

Concerted model (Monod et al.)

(i)   Receptor is a multicomponent oligomer comprising a finite number of identical subunits
(ii)   These are symmetrically arranged and have a single binding site for the ligand
(iii) Receptor exists in two conformational states—one of which has a preference for ligand
(iv)   Conformational state transition involves a simultaneous shift in state of all subunits
(v)   No hybrids can exist, which implies cooperativity

Sequential model (Koshland et al.)

(i)   Receptor is a multicomponent oligomer with symmetrically arranged protomers, each with a single binding site
(ii)   Protomers can exist in two conformational states—transition is *induced* by the ligand
(iii) Receptor symmetry is lost when ligand binds
(iv)   Hybrid states of the oligomer can be stabilized by protomers
(v)   Stabilization is equivalent to negative cooperativity

---

and Filmer[59] sequential or induced-fit model. As indicated in Table 1, most allosteric models are assumed to contain oligomeric protein units with identical subunits. These oligomers are thought to exist in two states which are in equilibrium in the absence of ligand. Ligand binding can induce a conformational change in the allosteric proteins, moving the equilibrium of the two states to favor that with the higher affinity for the ligand. The assumption is that the shift in the state of the oligomers conforms to a difference in the functionality of the receptor. As with the basis of receptor theory, the extrapolation of enzyme theory to receptors is not without its pitfalls. In the absence of purified, functional receptors it is unlikely that the data generated from receptor studies are of sufficient sophistication to detect subunit interactions within a kinetic framework. Photoinactivation/photoaffinity studies have delineated the subunit structure of the central benzodiazepine receptor, which comprises two α and two β subunits.[60] Further studies using molecular biological techniques have shown that the GABA-binding site associated with this receptor is carried on the β subunit.[61] Despite such studies, it is unclear to what extent this information has aided in the understanding of receptor function. For instance, while the antianxiety actions of the benzodiazepines have been attributed to a distinct receptor subtype designated BZ-1,[23] which has been localized to the cerebellum, and the side effects associated with this class of drug (sedation, muscle relaxation) to a BZ-2-type receptor localized to the hippocampus,[23] monoclonal antibodies to the epitopes of the subunits described have shown neither a difference in the antigenicity of the subunits in the different brain regions nor a differential distribution in the ratio of these subunits.[62]

Similarly, while the nicotinic cholinergic receptor (nAChR) of the *Torpedo electroplax* is the most studied of all neurotransmitter receptors, primarily because of its abundance and the simplicity of the system in which it is found,[63] the information derived from isolation, cloning and sequencing of this receptor[1] has done little at this time to increase understanding of the properties related to ligand recognition. The nAChR comprises several functional peptidic domains termed α, β, γ and δ that surround a voltage-regulated sodium channel by which receptor activation is linked to physiological function. The nAChR therefore does not depend on a second messenger to produce its physiological effects, but rather elicits a change in ion channel conductance by a true allosterically induced change.[64]

Recent studies indicate that allosteric-type receptors are more likely to represent generalized multifunctional complexes akin to the interlinked enzymic pathways discovered in bacteria that form the basis of feedback inhibition theory and the Monod model.[58,65]

11.2.3.1 The Central Benzodiazepine Receptor Complex

The success of the benzodiazepine (BZ) diazepam as an antianxiety agent led to a considerable effort to determine its mechanism of action at the molecular level. It soon became apparent that BZs were able to facilitate the actions of the inhibitory neurotransmitter GABA.[23] The mechanism by which this occurred was unclear until 1977, when a specific binding site for [³H]diazepam was identified.[23] Shortly afterwards it was discovered *in vitro* using radioligand-binding techniques that there was an allosteric interaction between GABA receptors of the A-subtype and the central BZ receptor.[66] Such work has been extrapolated to encompass a receptor complex, comprising a GABA-A receptor, a high affinity central BZ receptor and a chloride channel through which the inhibitory actions of GABA are mediated.[60] Thus, rather than invoking a network of interacting synapses, electrophysiological, biochemical and molecular biological evidence has shown that a functional macromolecule comprising distinct functional units and, as noted, component subunits, is responsible for the therapeutic effects of the anxiolytic diazepam. Within the framework of classical receptor theory and the allosteric theory discussed above, studies of concentration– or dose–response relationships for the effects of diazepam on GABA-mediated neurotransmission processes would not be expected to follow mass action kinetics, especially in light of the fact that dissimilar ligands are responsible for changes in the functional characteristics of the macromolecular complex.

11.2.3.2　The *N*-Methyl-D-Aspartate/Phencyclidine/Glycine Receptor Complex

The observation[67] that dissociative anesthetics such as phencyclidine (PCP) could noncompetitively antagonize the actions of receptors for the excitatory amino acid *N*-methyl-D-aspartate (NMDA) provided the basis for the hypothesis that a macromolecular complex for NMDA and PCP similar to that for the BZ receptor complex might exist. Radioligand binding to the PCP receptor was found to be both glutamate (the endogenous ligand for the NMDA receptor) and magnesium dependent.[68] Other work with the anticonvulsant MK 801[25] and with the amino acid glycine has provided evidence for a NMDA/PCP/glycine receptor complex linked to a cation channel.[69] A zinc-modulated site on the complex has also been described.[70] The relationship between the components appears, however, considerably more complex than that seen for the BZ receptor.[71]

11.2.4　RECEPTOR-LINKED SECOND MESSENGER SYSTEMS (see Chapter 11.4)

While cyclic AMP and, to a lesser extent, cyclic GMP represent the best known second messengers,[16,17,72] calcium[73,74] and phospholipids,[18,75,76] as well as the alterations in protein phosphorylation occurring *via* the activity of several classes of protein kinases and phosphoprotein phosphatases,[20,77] can subserve similar roles. The late addition of these entities to the role of second messengers has been primarily due to technical difficulties in measuring their production and/or changes in occurrence.

In some instances, the ligand for an intracellular receptor can act in a somewhat loose sense as its own second messenger. One mechanism of signal transduction is typified by steroid modulation of cell function.[19] Steroid hormones, due to their small size ($M \sim 300$) and lipophilicity, can cross the cell membrane by simple diffusion. The steroid, depending on its type, can then bind with high affinity to a specific cytosolic protein, analogous to a receptor. The steroid–protein complex can then bind selectively to chromatin in the cell nucleus to regulate the transcription of target genes.[78] This is a highly selective process, often involving less than 1% of the component proteins of a given cell type. The effects of a given steroid hormone are dependent on the cell type activated.[79] The effects of activated steroid receptors on cell function can be twofold: a primary response involving the initial effect of gene transcription and a delayed secondary response where the products of the initial genes transcribed activate other genes.[80]

11.2.5　RECEPTOR DYNAMICS

Receptors are dynamic constituents of the cell being replaced as part of the normal homeostatic regenerative process. Half-lives for receptors can vary between three hours and several days as based on data derived from animal models.[81] Despite evidence for such receptor dynamics, the use of irreversible and quasi-irreversible compounds as therapeutic agents has not met with any degree of acceptance, a fact that may also be attributed to a general lack of selectivity in currently available compounds such as alkylating agents.

11.2.5.1　Pharmacological and Functional Antagonism

In considering receptor dynamics in terms of the consequent alterations in cellular function, the differentiation between pharmacological and functional antagonism is one that may provide a clearer understanding of the distinction between the classical and molecular approaches to the delineation of receptor function. Pharmacological antagonism occurs when an RL interaction is antagonized by a second ligand that modulates a given receptor-mediated event by altering receptor activation. This can occur by either competitive or noncompetitive antagonism at, or in the proximity of, the receptor. A competitive antagonist interacts directly with the receptor in a manner similar to the endogenous ligand. A noncompetitive antagonist influences the RL interaction by binding at a site adjacent to, or overlapping, the receptor and thus indirectly or allosterically alters the nature and consequences of the RL interaction. In the case of functional antagonism, a similar effect can also be observed except that the readout is the result of the interfacing of several distinct mechanisms. For example, if a serotonergic neuronal system impinges on a substance P system, which in turn alters the function of a histamine system, which in turn causes a change in pulmonary function, this final effect can be antagonized pharmacologically by a serotonin antagonist and functionally by either a substance P or histamine antagonist. If the concept of functional antagonism is not readily appreciated, it would be easy to define a histamine antagonist as a serotonin antagonist because, at surface value, both agents produced the same effect. Unfortunately such instances are far from rare.

11.2.5.2   Receptor Desensitization

The increased availability of an endogenous ligand either through medication or due to an alteration in normal function due to some extraneous challenge (usually that associated with a disease state) can lead to a homeostatic change in receptor dynamics that is reflected as a compensatory change in receptor function. Returning to Kenakin's 'power amplifier' concept,[11] when the signal is too intense for normal function, the system needs to be turned down, which can result in a decrease in the number of functional receptors. This may occur either by a change in receptor number, a down-regulation as described below, or some alteration in the coupling state associated with the receptor readout. This latter effect is very subtle and often not easy to measure. Mechanisms that may result in receptor desensitization include: (i) alterations in the phosphorylation state of membrane-associated coupling units, mediated either *via* cyclic nucleotide, calcium or phospholipid modulation of intracellular protein kinase entities,[20] (ii) trans-synaptic regulation of second messenger formation due to the summation of inputs that both positively and negatively regulate G protein coupling to the effector system,[72,82,83] and (iii) receptor internalization or clustering.[7]

11.2.5.3   Receptor Down-regulation

As noted, receptor down-regulation is a mechanism to reduce receptor functionality. Down-regulation can be measured, following chemical or surgical lesioning in animals, by radioligand binding over a range of ligand concentrations to determine the K_d and apparent B_{max} values. Changes in the K_d value, representing alterations in the affinity of the receptor, can theoretically alter receptor functionality by requiring greater concentrations of agonist to elicit a response. Since, however, down-regulation is considered to be a response to excess agonist, this is unlikely to be an effective means to change receptor functionality. A decrease in receptor number is a more tangible response to excess ligand and has been noted in response to many drug treatments.[83] Studies comparing Wistar Kyoto (WKY) rats to the genetically related spontaneously hypertensive (SH) rats have shown many differences in receptor-binding characteristics[84] between the two strains. Which, or how many, of these are responsible for the hypertensive state has yet to be determined. Measurement of receptor number has also represented an important process for determining human disease etiology. Usually performed on post-mortem human samples, the aim is to see what receptors are altered and thus gain clues as to the underlying molecular mechanisms contributing to the disease resulting in death. While receptor changes have been shown to occur in brains from patients with Huntington's chorea,[85] Parkinsonism,[86] schizophrenia,[87] Alzheimer's disease[88] and depression,[89] the markers indicative of a given disease pathology have yet to be unequivocally determined. Ideally, the unambiguous identification of a lesion associated with a given disease and the ability to measure such markers in blood components may make diagonsis easier, as well as providing a means to monitor the effects of drug therapy.

Receptor down-regulation in response to excess ligand, while reliably demonstrated many times in the past decade and a half using radioligand-binding techniques, appears to raise serious questions as to the functional significance of spare receptors. It is possible that what is observed when assessing down-regulation may represent an alteration in the dynamics of receptor turnover. Receptor phosphorylation represents one mechanism for altered receptor function and potential functional down-regulation.[20]

11.2.5.4 Receptor Up-regulation

When an endogenous agonist is available in reduced amounts or is absent, or an antagonist is present for a prolonged period of time (*i.e.* chronically), the opposite effect to down-regulation can occur, namely an increase in receptor number to increase the functionality of receptor activation. In animal models, this increase in functionality can also occur by an increase in receptor affinity (decreased K_d), which increases the likelihood of agonist interacting with receptor. Increased numbers of receptors can occur in Parkinsonism, where the functional dopaminergic input is reduced[90] and in Alzheimer's disease where a decrease in cholinergic neurotransmission is the most pronounced effect.[91] Alterations in receptor coupling may also represent a mechanism for increasing receptor functionality. Again, however, where receptor reserve fits into this schema remains to be determined.

11.2.6 RECEPTOR CLASSIFICATION

To a large extent, the taxonomy of receptors has occurred somewhat serendipitously. As new substances have been found and shown to have biological activity, the nomenclature has arisen as the investigators involved have judged appropriate. Von Euler and Gaddum's substance P was named after the peak obtained in an isolation procedure,[92] while SRSA (slow-reacting substance of anaphylaxis) was a biological extract that was described in terms of its biological effect and subsequently shown to contain a number of products of the arachidonic acid pathways.[93] Often different groups have discovered the same compound under different names. For instance the inflammatory mediator, catabolin, has been found to be interleukin-1.[94] In addition to such serendipity in the naming of the basic substances mediating cellular communication, studies on the cellular effects of these substances and related compounds have led to an arbitrary and confusing system of receptor classification, often without any functional considerations.[95] One example of this 'incoherent'[96] nomenclature is that for dopamine receptors where, to a large extent depending on *in vitro* binding criteria, as many as 20 potential subtypes of receptor were described.[97] These appear to have resolved themselves, however, into two major classes, D_1 and D_2.[98] However, in the field of serotonin (5-HT) recent studies have led to the identification of three major subclasses of receptor termed 5-HT_1, 5-HT_2 and 5-HT_3, which may also have subtypes.[99,100] The identification of at least eight types of 5-HT receptor as compared to the classical M- and D-type 5-HT receptors identified by Gaddum and Picarrelli[39] has catalyzed a move, long overdue,[96] towards creating a more rational receptor classification similar to that used for enzymes.[99,101] While this is not without its problems,[102] especially since, as noted, unlike enzymes, receptors cannot be characterized in terms of their substrate or product, the realization that a system is needed is a major step forward in moving studies of receptor pharmacology from the quaint idiosyncrasies of creative individuals to the more unambiguous and definitive definitions that a committee can provide. The challenge will be to avoid android newspeak along the lines of 'autoreceptor 5.6.5.4'.

The definition of receptors based solely on radioligand-binding criteria is, however, clearly untenable, and yet the precise nature in which effector second messenger systems and substrate proteins for protein kinases can be incorporated into a classification schema remains to be adequately determined to avoid undue complexity and an overinterpretation of experimental data. Ariens has suggested[96] that the term 'acceptor' be used until a binding site is shown to have met the criteria for a receptor.

11.2.6.1 Ligand Selectivity

It is often assumed that a ligand, once identified as either an agonist or antagonist, has ideal selectivity for its receptor.[102] Based on the premise that compound A is a serotonin antagonist in a single system, this compound is then used, often mindlessly, to define any action affected by compound A as serotonergic in nature. An actual example in point is that of cyproheptadine, which has antimuscarinic, antiserotonergic and antihistaminic activities to equal degress as well as an element of calcium antagonist activity[103] but is often referred to as a selective 5-HT receptor antagonist.[102] A similar example is the benzodiazepine tifluadom, which has potent analgesic activity ascribed to interactions with κ-opiate receptors[104] but has in addition been found to be active at peripheral cholecystokinin (CCK) receptors,[105] a finding leading to the suggestion that the analgesic actions of this compound may in fact involve CCK. The issue of 'polypharmic ligands' has been addressed[13,102] with the perhaps general caveat that the problem in specificity lies not with the ligand but with 'an ineffable need to invoke specificity' on the part of the investigator. One way to avoid the overstatement of selectivity is to obtain a full profile of a compound in radioligand-binding assays. However, the limitations of the *in vitro* technique may not prevent surprises occurring in more classical pharmacological test procedures. As further noted by Black,[13] specificity is usually only determined when a pure biochemical test system is used to assess activity. This becomes somewhat reductionistic in that specificity can be predetermined by the choice of ligand, assay system and readout.

11.2.6.2 Tissue Responses

The issue of receptor identification and ligand specificity can be further confounded by the type of tissue studied. Receptor-mediated responses beyond the level of receptor recognition follow a functional path based on the tissue in question. Thus while LTD_4 receptors are present in both the lung and gut,[93] the response which their activation produces will be a function of the tissue rather than the receptor. Similarly, the second messenger mediating the effects of receptor activation will also define the response elicited in the target tissue. The putative neuromodulator adenosine causes vasodilation in the coronary vascular system but in the kidney causes vasoconstriction.[106] Similarly, as already noted, the effects of a given steroid hormone on gene transcription also depend not on the type of receptor but the cell in which the receptor is located.[78] This phenomenon, which is 'phenotypic' in nature, is a result of the effect of the second messenger on the constituent proteins of the cell and cannot, in isolation, be used as a reliable criterion for receptor classification without due consideration of the receptor effecting the change in second messenger production. Given that the second messenger process is an amplification process, the imposition of effector and substrate systems on the recognition unit's pharmacological profile provides an increased complexity of permutations available for receptor classification that may prove unwieldy.

11.2.7 RADIOLIGAND BINDING

11.2.7.1 Basic Concepts

The technique of radioligand binding is one of the most simple and cost effective in the armamentarium of pharmacological experimentation. Like all such techniques, its obviousness belies its inherent difficulties and nuances and is not reflective of the historical events that led to one of the first viable assays, developed by Snyder and Pert in 1973 for the opiate antagonist naloxone.[107] In addition, the simplicity of the technique can lead to a degree of naivity from the classical pharmacologist to the extent that radioligand binding is often referred to by the diminutive of 'grinding and binding'.

The idea of using radiolabeled ligands to 'tag' receptors arose in the 1950s from significant advances in radiochemistry resulting from the Manhattan project and from the biological application of these tools in the study of drug metabolism. Early studies were hampered, however, by the fact that the process of labeling reduced the functional activity and specificity of the ligand. The inability to obtain ligands that were 'hot' enough, *i.e.* to get sufficient radioactivity into a molecule to differentiate binding of the ligand to a receptor from the large amounts of nonspecific binding occurring through the process of absorption, was also a limiting factor. In the 1970s these technical problems were overcome[108] and radioligands with specific activities in the range of 15–90 Ci mmol^{-1} (1 Ci = 3.7×10^{10} Bq) are now in routine use.[12] Isotopes used to label ligands include tritium ([^{3}H]), iodine ([^{125}I]) and sulfur ([^{35}S]). In the case of [^{125}I] a specific activity of 2200 Ci mmol^{-1} can theoretically be achieved. This can facilitate the study of receptors, (i) that are found in very low concentrations in tissues of interest, *i.e.* adenosine receptors in cardiac tissue; and (ii) where the costs of ligands, as in the case of peptides, can be prohibitive. Increasingly, environmental concerns with the use of radiolabeled ligands have directed interest to the evaluation of systems such as ELISA (enzyme-linked immunosorbent assay), which have replaced iodine in many radioimmunoassay systems.

11.2.7.2 Practical Aspects

Receptor–ligand (RL) complexes are formed by the incubation of tissues rich in the receptors under study together with a radioligand of suitable radioactivity, usually 20 Ci mmol^{-1} or greater.[12] The time period for equilibrium to be reached is a function of the receptor being studied, the radioligand used and the incubation conditions. Despite the fact that isoosmotic buffers are often used as incubation media, the procedures used to prepare tissues are usually sufficiently non-physiological that the rationale for returning to a physiological buffer system is often unclear.

Once the RL complex is formed, the unbound radioactivity must be removed to allow determination of the radioactivity bound. This is usually accomplished by one of two methods: centrifugation or filtration under negative pressure.[109] Free radioactivity, that unassociated with tissue, can be removed by washing. Theoretical considerations argue that affinity measurements for RL complexes of ligands with low affinity ($K_d > 20$ nM) and/or a fast dissociation rate cannot be reliably or accurately determined using filtration methodology but rather require the gentler conditions of centrifugation. Filtration requires the active washing of the RL complex, while centrifugation results in the removal of the complex from the reaction milieu. The distinction in deciding which isolation technique to use is not always clear, reflecting some of the mystique of the technique where the predictable does not always work. Thus, assays have been documented where filtration methodology has been used relatively successfully with ligands that have K_d values in the micromolar range. Filtration has obvious advantages over centrifugation, both in terms of equipment costs and sample processing. For centrifugation, the number of samples that can be run is limited by the number of spaces available in a centrifuge rotor. This technique, involving sedimentation of the RL complex, also requires that the complex be dissolved and counted. For filtration, the RL complex is isolated on a filter, which, after drying, can be transferred to a scintillation vial. In typical experiments, many hundreds of samples can be processed by filtration isolation in the time it takes to do a 70–100 sample experiment using centrifugation. The lack of availability of radioligands with receptor affinity sufficient to allow filtration may, however, preclude the use of this technique. Following isolation of the RL complex, radioactivity can be determined by conventional β- or γ-spectrometry.

In addition to binding selectively to sites with pharmacology consistent with the presence of a receptor, radioactivity can also be associated, either by adsorption or sequestration, to sites that are not related to the receptor being studied. In the tissue this can be due to the association of the radioligand with sites on the membranes that are distinct from the receptor, *i.e.* protein sequestration sites. In addition, radioactivity can bind to the filters used for the isolation of tissue or can bind to the test tube in which the centrifugation or binding reaction is performed. This binding is termed the nonspecific binding and can be measured by including in parallel assay tubes with an excess ($> 100 \times$) of an unlabeled ligand specific for a given receptor. Measurement of binding in the absence and presence of this 'specific' agent provides data on total ligand binding and nonspecific binding, respectively. Their difference is the specific binding of the ligand. This is the pharmacologically relevant receptor-associated binding which is used to measure RL interactions. Such binding can vary, for example, between 40 and 98% of total binding, depending on the ligand and tissue source. Working with less than 30% specific binding can severely limit the usefulness of the data derived. Obviously the higher the 'signal-to-noise' ratio, the better the data derived. Nonspecific binding in filtration assays can be reduced by the presoaking of filters in polyethylenimine (PEI), which prevents absorption of radioactivity.[110]

The choice of nonspecific agent can be crucial to the characterization of the receptor to which specific binding occurs. For instance, as already noted, ligands are not necessarily specific and it may be necessary, although not preferable, to mask components of specific binding in what are called 'cocktail' assays. For instance, in striatum, the nonselective adenosine agonist 5'-N-ethylcarboxamidoadenosine (NECA) binds to both A_1 and A_2 subtypes of the adenosine receptor. Nonspecific binding can be determined in the presence of an excess of xanthine–adenosine antagonist[111] or another adenosine analog.[112] However, if a highly selective A_1 ligand, cyclopentyladenosine (CPA), is included at a concentration of 50 nM to selectively block the A_1 component of NECA binding,[111] the assay can then be used to selectively measure A_2 receptors.

In instances where the pharmacology of a receptor is well characterized, there are usually several different structural classes of compounds that interact with the receptor. In such instances it is preferable to use a nonspecific agent that is structurally distinct from the radioligand rather than the corresponding cold ligand. In the case of serotonin$_{1A}$ (5-HT$_{1A}$) receptors, the aminotetralin 8-OH-DPAT (1 nM) can be used as a radioligand with 10 μM 5-HT being used to determine nonspecific binding.[113] Another radioligand, selective for the α_1 adrenoceptor WB 4101, can also be used to label 5-HT$_{1A}$ receptors but in this instance its α_1-adrenergic component can be blocked by the inclusion of 30 nM prazosin, a more selective α_1-adrenergic ligand. The 5-HT ligand lisuride can then be used to measure nonspecific binding.[114] In other binding assays, especially those used for measuring peptide receptors,[115,116] there is rarely a wide range of compounds that can be used to determine nonspecific binding. Thus such binding is measured in an excess of either cold ligand or modified forms of the ligand. This is theoretically incorrect inasmuch as a decrease in total binding can occur, not only due to the blockade of specific binding sites but also due to a phenomenon known as isotope dilution. Inclusion of the cold nonspecific agent reduces the specific activity of the radioligand such that it is possible to have the same total amount of binding occurring, which then appears to be reduced based on the number of counts bound due to a dilution in the radioactivity. For instance, if total binding is 10 000 c.p.m., a 100-fold reduction in specific binding can result in only 100 counts being bound 'nonspecifically'. Thus 9900 c.p.m. appear to be specific. While such assays have serious limitations, they can, however, be useful and in the absence of other nonspecific agents have to be used in this form. For the peripheral CCK receptor, [^{125}I] CCK can be used to label the receptor using a large excess of unlabeled CCK to determine nonspecific binding. Using such an assay, the nonpeptidic CCK antagonist asperlicin was identified[117] and a derivative, L 364 718, labeled to measure peripheral CCK receptors.[118]

Specific binding requires validation before it can be equated with receptor binding. Several criteria for such validation[119] are shown in Table 2. However, even when such criteria are validated, binding need not always be synonymous with receptor-related proteins. The most famous example of this is the stereoselective binding of the opiate antagonist naloxone to talc.[119] Similarly, binding of phencyclidine (PCP) to brain tissue can be confused with nonreceptor-related binding to filter disks.[120,121]

11.2.7.3 Peptide Receptors

In addition to the theoretical concerns related to the nonspecific component of receptor binding, when using peptide radioligands other concerns relate to the lability of the radioligand as well as the nature of equilibrium binding for these entities.[116,122] In addition, there is a marked tendency for peptide radioligands to adsorb to surfaces with which they come in contact. This can affect the assessment of free ligand concentrations as well as lead to overestimates of bound radioactivity. This phenomenon can be circumvented by the inclusion of bovine serum albumin in the assay mixture, which can block these adsorption sites, or by the PEI technique already discussed. To prevent peptide ligand metabolism various inhibitors of proteolysis are used, including bacitracin, leupeptin, phenanthroline and EDTA. These are chosen on an *ad hoc* basis, the process of validating the assay establishing which of these do not deleteriously affect the signal-to-noise ratio for the radioligand. Ideally, the identity of the bound ligand should be authenticated. This is difficult, however, in that the amounts bound can be in the order of 10^{-12} M and sophisticated assay techniques are necessary to measure such small ligand amounts. An additional complication in terms of ligand stability is that the association rate constants for peptide radioligands are often three orders of magnitude below those seen for other types of radioligand.[122] As a consequence, incubation periods which can run for times as great as 5–8 h (as compared to 15 min–2 h for nonpeptide assays) have to be balanced against the instability of the ligand, the stability of the receptor source, possible desensitization of the receptor and pseudoirreversible binding. In a practical sense therefore, some assays are not run to equilibrium to circumvent these problems. Extra caution is then needed in the data evaluation process.

Table 2 Criteria for Identification of Binding Sites as Receptors[119]

(i)	Binding of radioligand to recognition site should be saturable, indicating a finite number of binding sites
(ii)	Binding affinity should be high (K_d value $\sim 10^{-10}$–10^{-8} M), consistent with a potential role as a neurohumoral agent
(iii)	Radioligand binding should be readily reversible, consistent with a physiological action for the termination of ligand action
(iv)	The distribution of binding sites, both between tissues and within the cell/tissue, should be compatible with the proposed physiological role of the natural ligand
(v)	The pharmacology of the binding site should have similar agonist/antagonist properties to those observed for the natural ligand or its analogs in functional test procedures
(vi)	A simultaneous correlation of binding with biological dose/concentration curves in identical tissue preparations should be generated

11.2.7.4 Receptor Sources

In using receptor binding to study receptor function, the choice of tissue source can affect the validity of the data obtained. There is considerable evidence for distinct differences in receptor pharmacology depending on the species used.[12] For instance, adenosine A_1 receptors from calf brain show dramatic differences in their sensitivity to xanthine–adenosine antagonists as compared to human tissues.[123] Furthermore, when the inevitable goal of understanding receptor function is to study disease etiology and design compounds to alleviate or prevent such diseases, it becomes problematic when defined receptor subtypes cannot be identified in human brain samples.[124,125] While species differences in receptor characterization can be a problem, in the case of the spontaneously hypertensive rat or dog open-heart model, the data derived have not precluded a realistic extrapolation of the predictability of drug action to the human species. Such factors should be considered, however, when inconsistent experimental results are obtained or compounds reveal evidence for receptor subtypes that cannot be confirmed in other species or models. Data integration from a variety of sources is the key to understanding receptor function.

The receptor densities in peripheral tissues, as contrasted to brain tissue—the usual source of receptors—are usually very low, reflecting the discrete nature of nerve innervation. As shown by the tissue selectivity of many classes of drugs, the understanding of differences in receptor pharmacology and function between tissues is a major challenge in the area of molecular pharmacology for the next decade.

One way to circumvent low receptor densities is to use radioactive ligands with high specific activity. Another is the use of cell lines rich in a given receptor.[126] The NG 108-15 neuroblastoma cell line can be used to study the characteristics of several neurotransmitter receptors. While the data derived are subject to scrutiny because the cell lines are by their very nature atypical, they are useful and allow for the preparation of receptor-enriched membrane tissue sources without the excessive use of animal tissues. The techniques of molecular biology can considerably facilitate this process by permitting overexpression of the genes for cloned receptors.

11.2.7.5 Autoradiography

Receptors can also be studied using intact tissues by methodology developed by Kuhar and coworkers.[127] A tissue slice, or cell preparation, can be affixed to a conventional histological slide[128] and, using similar techniques to those used for binding in cell homogenates, specific binding can be measured in discrete tissue regions. When the binding reaction is completed, the labeled slides can be juxtaposed to tritium sensitive film, which, following a suitable exposure time (dependent on the amount of radioactivity bound), can be developed and the film read using computer-assisted densitometry. Computerized color enhancement of the films then permits the striking evaluation of differences in receptor densities. While this latter process is dramatic, it is somewhat ephemeral to the process of understanding receptor function *per se* and only recently has this technique been used to assess the quantitative regional and tissue differences in receptor pharmacology—a labor intensive process. Like other binding techniques, receptor autoradiography has its limitations, primarily in relation to removing excess radioactivity from the incubated tissue sections without destroying their architecture and the problem of quenching when using tritium.[128]

11.2.7.6 Receptor Binding in Disease Diagnosis

Studies using conventional radionuclide ligand tracers in human tissues have been restricted to the use of easily accessible body fluids, biopsy samples or post-mortem tissues. The overall aim has been to permit both the detection of receptor abnormalities in various disease states and to detect receptor 'analytes' that would permit disease diagnosis and the titration of drug treatment.

Several groups have, however, carried this approach to the living organism using positron-emission scanning in conjunction with the positron-emitting radionuclides, [^{11}C], [^{18}F], [^{13}N] and [^{15}O].[129] These tracers, due to their very short half-lives (~ 20 min), have to be incorporated into glucose, oxygen or various drugs at a site proximal to the positron-emitting scanning (PET) equipment. Obviously, bioavailability of these substances is a major factor in their use, requiring various correction factors to adjust the specific activity for the tissue region being studied. Using carfentanil, a derivative of the μ-opiate receptor ligand fentanyl, it has been shown that prolonged exercise can reduce the accumulation of [^{11}C]carfentanil, an indication of increased amounts of endogenous enkephalins being released.[130] In the future, with further enhancement of detection systems and a reduction in their cost, the technique of *in vivo* receptor imaging will become increasingly important in medicine.

11.2.8 GENERATION AND ANALYSIS OF RECEPTOR–LIGAND INTERACTIONS

While the techniques in this section relate primarily to analysis of data generated using radioligand binding, they are useful for analysis of other data, especially in conjunction with more general analysis techniques.[131]

11.2.8.1 Saturation Experimentation

Prior to the availability of personal computers and easy access to mainframes, the most common methods used for analysis of receptor-binding data and dose–response curves relied on graphical approaches or procedures amenable to the use of calculators. For saturation experiments, where the amount of ligand specifically bound is determined at varying ligand concentrations, untransformed data can be described in terms of a rectangular hyperbola (Figure 5) similar to that observed for dose–response relationships (Figure 2). Nonspecific binding is a linear function with respect to the concentration of radioligand. The total number of sites, or apparent B_{max},[132] is the amount of binding observed at saturating concentrations of radioligand and is represented by an asymptote to the top of the hyperbola. The K_d value, which is indicative of the affinity of the receptor for the radioligand, is that concentration of ligand at which, by definition,[33] 50% of the total number of receptors can be labeled (Figure 5).

11.2.8.1.1 *Scatchard/Rosenthal plots*

Due to the nonlinearity of radioreceptor saturation curves, both the 'apparent' B_{max} and K_d values can only be approximated from this plot and it has become commonplace to transform and plot saturation data in linear form as a Scatchard or Rosenthal plot. While the Scatchard plot was originally developed[133] to determine the number of binding sites per unit of protein in a defined milieu where the total number of binding sites was known, this was subsequently modified by Rosenthal[134] for situations where the receptor concentration was unknown. Although the designation Rosenthal plot is probably more accurate, the terminology still most commonly used as a generic description is that of the Scatchard plot where B/F is plotted as a function of B

$$\frac{B}{F} = -\frac{1}{K_d}B + \frac{B_{max}}{K_d} \qquad (10)$$

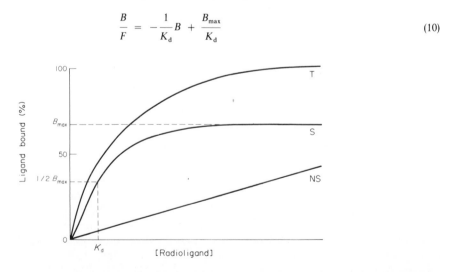

Figure 5 Radioligand saturation curves. Increasing concentrations of radioligand result in increases in radioactivity bound to receptors as indicated on the ordinate. While total (T) and nonspecific (NS) binding are not saturable, their difference, T − NS, represents specific (S) binding to the receptor. This component is saturable. The horizontal asymptote (or maximal specific binding), as indicated, represents an approximation of the receptor B_{max}. The concentration at which half-maximal ($B_{max}/2$) binding occurs is K_d as derived from Michaelis–Menten kinetics (for further discussion, see text)

where B is the amount specifically bound and F represents the amount of free ligand. Using this procedure, the B_{max} value can be obtained from the intercept on the abscissa and the K_d value is obtained from the negative reciprocal of the slope (Figure 6). Other derivations of the basic Scatchard plot include the Eadie–Hofstee[135] and Wolff plots.[136]

In situations where the radioligand binds to a single site, a linear Scatchard plot is generated and reasonable estimates of B_{max} and K_d values can be obtained. Linear Scatchard plots can also be obtained, however, when a nonselective radioligand binds to more than one site with the same affinity. As noted by Klotz,[132,137] it is imperative to employ high enough concentrations of radioligand to ensure that simple, one-site binding following mass action law can occur. While ideally 90% of binding sites should be occupied, necessitating radioligand concentrations 9–10 times that of the anticipated K_d value, 70–80% saturation can be sufficient.[138] The rationale is that a second, low affinity binding site may not be detectable if high enough concentrations of ligand are not used. Even though extrapolation of the line generated using low ligand concentrations may indicate the presence of a single site, the lower affinity site may not be detected due to compression of the data points at high concentrations of radioligand.

Analysis of Scatchard plots to obtain B_{max} and K_d values for simple binding situations, where binding to one component follows mass action law, remains widely employed. Utilization of graphical methods to analyze nonlinear Scatchard plots is more complicated. Concave-downward Scatchard plots, which are not commonly observed, can indicate the presence of positive cooperativity. In this circumstance, the binding of one molecule of radioligand to the receptor can facilitate the subsequent binding of other radioligand molecules. However, a similar shaped plot can be obtained due to artifactual reasons, *e.g.* if equilibrium is not adequately achieved, a common problem when using peptide radioligands as discussed above.

Nonlinear concave-upward Scatchard plots (Figure 7) can be obtained under several conditions. For example, curvilinear plots can occur if the nonspecific binding is improperly defined or if the receptor recognizes the labeled and unlabeled ligands with different affinities.[139] Similarly, curvilinear Scatchard plots may be generated due to the presence of multiple independent receptor sites for which the radioligand has different affinities, and when negative cooperativity occurs, *i.e.* where binding of the radioligand reduces further binding of ligand to the receptor. In the case of receptor complexes, this phenomenon need not occur within the framework of classical allosteric theory (Table 1) but rather may reflect a feedback inhibition-type process.[65] Another possibility is the presence of multiple states of a single receptor population or the existence of two-step, three-component binding. In this instance, the ligand is thought to initially interact with the receptor, which could then interact with the third component. The ternary complex model[140] was proposed in an attempt to characterize the interaction of the β adrenoceptor with agonists and a guanine nucleotide regulatory protein.

One method employed to approximate B_{max} and K_d values for multiple component binding using Scatchard plots has been to draw asymptotes to the two linear components of the curve. However, the values determined in this manner have been found to be poor approximations of the actual values with a considerable element of subjectivity. Another method is to determine the slopes of the

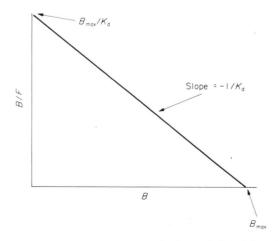

Figure 6 Scatchard transformation of specific binding data. Plotting radioligand bound (B) divided by the free (F) radioligand concentration at equilibrium against B, yields a Scatchard plot with slope $-1/K_d$ and intercepts on the ordinate and abcissa of B_{max}/K_d and B_{max}, respectively

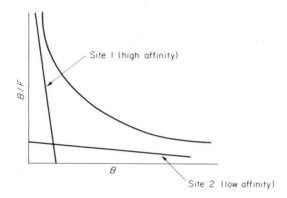

Figure 7 Curvilinear/complex Scatchard plots. When one or more sites or states of a receptor are present, the Scatchard plot (Figure 6) appears curvilinear and can be resolved, by appropriate analysis, into its respective components

curves such that each point on the actual data curve represents the summation of the two linear components.[141] While more accurate than the 'pencil and paper' method, it is quite tedious. Linear regression analysis can also be used to ensure greater objectivity and accuracy. However, this method is incorrect since the nature of the Scatchard plot, involving free ligand (F) on both ordinate and abcissa, is biased towards a regression based on a common variable.[12]

In addition to these issues, there are also several general problems that limit the value of this analysis. These include the problem of error associated with the determination of free ligand concentration F. This error is contributory on both axes due to transformation of the binding data and unequal weight of error. Furthermore, certain ligands, such as the muscarinic cholinergic ligand quinuclidinyl benzilate (QNB), have been found to be affected by 'zone behavior',[142] where most of the ligand added is bound such that the free concentration can be as little as 5% of total counts added.

The free concentration usually can be determined either by subtracting the amount of known radioactivity bound from that added ($F - B$), or by taking an aliquot of the reaction mixture after the termination of the reaction when the tissue has been removed. F can thus be determined directly. This, however, may not be a very accurate measure; for example, given that in a typical experiment approximately 10 000 c.p.m. would be added in a volume of 1 mL and only 2–3% would be expected to bind, *i.e.* 200–300 c.p.m., the opportunity for error in taking μL aliquots is large, as is the successive extrapolation of the molar free concentration of ligand through a series of dilution corrections. In either instance, relatively small changes in the number of counts per minute determined can cause differences in the estimated free concentration that are due to experimental variation rather than any intrinsic property of the receptor. Such factors, together with the increasing complexity of data obtained from saturation experiments with multiple receptor components and the investigation of molecular mechanisms of action (*e.g.* the effect of guanine nucleotides on radioligand binding), require the use of more sophisticated analytical methods which are capable of analyzing untransformed binding data, such as nonlinear regression techniques.

11.2.8.1.2 *The Hill plot*

Another method of determining the K_d value from saturation experiments is the use of the Hill equation[55]

$$B = \frac{B_{max}[L]^n}{K_d' + [L]^n} \tag{11}$$

where n is the Hill coefficient, [L] is the concentration of free ligand and K_d' is the K_d at $n_H = 1$. When transformed, the data can be plotted linearly (Figure 8) as $\log(B/B_{max} - B)$ as a function of $\log[L]$ according to the relationship

$$\log\frac{B}{B_{max} - B} = n\log[L] - \log K_d' \tag{12}$$

The K_d value can be obtained when $\log(B/B_{max} - B) = 0$. A disadvantage of this plot in comparison to the Scatchard plot is that B_{max} values are not attainable.

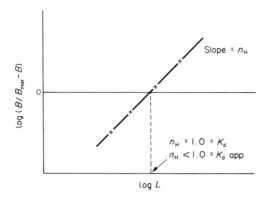

Figure 8 Hill Plot. In the classical Hill plot[31] of saturation binding data, a logarithmic plot of $B/B_{max} - B$ *versus* free ligand concentration, yields the Hill coefficient (n_H) and K_d. The latter determination is a function of the Hill coefficient. When $n_H < 1.0$, negative cooperativity or multiple binding components may occur

11.2.8.2 Competition Experiments

Another common type of binding experiment is the competition experiment, where a fixed concentration of radioligand is incubated in the presence of various concentrations of inhibitor. These experiments are generally employed to study the pharmacology of the receptor. The ability of compounds to inhibit the specific binding of a radioligand can be quantitatively evaluated by determining the IC_{50} value, which is that concentration of inhibitor at which 50% of specific radioligand binding is inhibited. IC_{50} values can be determined by several methods, including visual inspection of plotted data, log–logit analysis or log–probit transformation. In the latter case, data are transformed and logit B, or $\log(B_i/B_0 - B_i)$ is plotted as a function of $\log[I]$ (Figure 9) according to the equation

$$\log \frac{B_i}{B_0 - B_i} = n \log[I] - n \log IC_{50} \tag{13}$$

where B_i represents the amount of ligand bound in the presence of competitor I, B_0 represents the amount of ligand bound in the absence of competitor and n_H represents the pseudo Hill coefficient.

In this analysis, x = IC_{50} value when $\log(B_i/B_0 - B_i) = 0$. The slope of the line, termed the pseudo Hill coefficient or the slope factor n_H, indicates whether binding is simple or complex. Although not a true Hill coefficient, since binding of I is indirectly determined, it is often referred to as the Hill coefficient. Slope factors of one are consistent with binding to one site that follows mass action law. However, slope factors of one can also be obtained when a nonselective compound inhibits the binding of a nonselective ligand that is labeling more than one receptor. Slope factors greater than one may reflect positive cooperativity, whereas n_H may be less than unity for several reasons, including the presence of multiple receptor subtypes, negative cooperativity, multiple interconverting receptor states or two-step, three-component binding (*e.g.* ternary complex formation).[140]

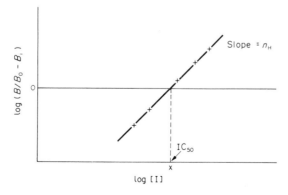

Figure 9 Determination of IC_{50} using the Hill equation. Replotting competition data according to the method of Hill,[31] yields a logarithmic plot with a slope n_H and an intercept approximating the IC_{50} value for that drug

When such complex binding occurs, data analysis needs to be equally sophisticated to resolve binding into individual components.

In determining the IC_{50} value for a compound, it is essential that an adequate number of concentration points and a sufficiently broad range of concentrations be used to derive the most accurate information from this experiment.[143] While IC_{50} values can be derived with three-point competition curves covering the region of 50% inhibition (Figure 10a), such data are at best limited since they allow no evaluation of binding behavior at either end of the competition curve. In this manner, important differences in the biological activity of the competitor that would provide information on the molecular interactions and contribute significantly to knowledge of the physiological activity of the compound would be omitted.

Since the IC_{50} value is a function of the radioligand concentration, Cheng and Prusoff[144] developed a method for generating a K_i value for competing compounds that can then be used to compare the pharmacology of competitive compounds, irrespective of the ligand concentration, according to the equation

$$K_i = \frac{IC_{50}}{1 + [L]/K_d} \tag{14}$$

where [L] represents the ligand concentration and K_d is the affinity of receptor R for L. Several assumptions are made in the derivation of this formula, such that the relationship is only valid when the receptor concentration is much less than the ligand concentration, *i.e.* $[R] < 0.1[L]$. Also, it is assumed that there is only a single class of receptor present that obeys mass action law.

Conversion of an IC_{50} value to a K_i value is particularly important when comparing the pharmacology of a given inhibitor across a range of different binding assays where differences in K_d values and the concentrations of ligand used can give rise to misleading information. For example, in considering the situation where the ability of compound Z to inhibit binding of muscarinic and bradykinin receptor ligands is compared and this compound displays an IC_{50} value of 1 nM for [³H]GNB binding and 0.02 nM $\{2/[1 + (1.0/0.01)]\}$ would be generated for [³H]QNB binding and 2 nM for [³H]bradykinin binding, one would conclude that the compound was twofold selective for the muscarinic cholinergic receptor. However, given that the assay ligand concentrations are 0.06 and 1.0 nM, respectively, and the K_d values for the receptors are 0.06 and 0.01, respectively, a K_i value of 0.5 nM $\{1/[1 + (0.06/0.06)]\}$ would be generated for [³H]bradykinin binding. Rather than compound Z being twofold selective for muscarinic receptors, it would actually be 25-fold selective for bradykinin receptors.

The Cheng–Prusoff relationship makes the assumption that the receptor concentration is much less than the ligand concentration, *i.e.* $[R] \ll 0.1[L]$. Since this assumption is not always valid, other equations have been derived to calculate K_i values when a significant amount of receptor is labeled.

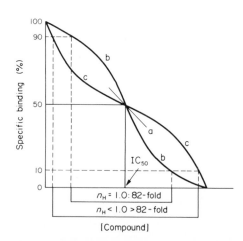

Figure 10 Complex/competition curves. (a) Plotting data close to the 50% point while providing an IC_{50} value can seriously limit the value of the data obtained ignoring any information from the extremes of the competition curve. (b) A more complete inhibition curve for a competitive inhibitor has a Hill value (n_H) of unity, requiring an 82-fold difference in drug concentration to displace from 10–90% of specific binding (90–10% of total binding remaining). (c) For more complex situations, *i.e.* more than one binding site or a noncompetitive competitor, the range of concentrations for achieving the 10–90% inhibition curve is greater than 82-fold

One equation, developed by Linden[145] based on the derivation of Jacobs *et al.*[146] is

$$K_i = \frac{[I]}{1 + \dfrac{[L]}{K_d} + (B_{max}/K_d)\dfrac{(K_d + [L]/2)}{K_d + [L]}} \tag{15}$$

Again, the assumption is made that binding is to one receptor and obeys mass action law.

For the analysis of complex inhibition curves, the methodology prior to the availability of computer programs was extremely limited. In such experiments, the slope of the inhibition curve is usually shallow rather than steep. When binding occurs to one receptor and follows Michaelis–Menten kinetics, 10 to 90% of the radioligand is inhibited over an 82-fold concentration range of inhibitor (Figure 10b). The slope factor under these conditions is unity. When binding is complex, as is the case when a radioligand that binds to two receptor sites with similar affinity is inhibited selectively by a competing drug, the concentration range over which 10 to 90% of the binding is inhibited is greater than 82-fold (Figure 10c). Thus, the shape of the inhibition curve becomes shallower, with the result that the slope factor is less than one.

In those circumstances where a nonselective ligand is inhibited by a selective competing compound, the degree of selectivity of the competing compound and the proportion of receptor subtypes labeled will reflect on the shallowness of the inhibition curve and degree to which n_H differs from unity.[147] A compound that shows a 1000-fold degree of selectivity will inhibit a majority of the binding to one receptor before it begins to inhibit binding to the second receptor. In contrast, a compound that is not very selective will not be able to differentiate very well between the two different receptors. The more selective the compound, the lower the slope factor. With regard to the proportion of receptors labeled, a 50-fold selective compound will exhibit a lower slope factor if the different receptors are present in equal quantities (50:50) rather than the condition where one receptor subtype only encompasses 15% of the total receptor population.

11.2.8.3 Kinetic Experiments

Kinetic binding experiments, in which the rates of association or dissociation of the radioligand are determined, are another type of binding experiment requiring quantitation. Since these are described by nonlinear functions, any degree of quantitation for graphical analysis requires linearization and transformation of the data.

11.2.8.3.1 Dissociation experiments

The amount of ligand bound as a function of time is described by the equation

$$B/B_0 = 1 - \exp(-k_2 t) \tag{16}$$

where B is the amount bound at time t, B_0 is the amount bound at $t = 0$, t is time and k_2 is the dissociation rate constant. Dissociation can be initiated by dilution of the RL complex into a large volume of reaction mixture, which approximates to infinity, or by the addition of a large excess of the nonspecific agent. Logarithmic transformation results in a linear plot from which the rate of dissociation can be determined

$$\ln(B/B_0) = -k_2 t \tag{17}$$

When $\ln(B/B_0)$ is plotted as a function of time, the slope equals $-k_2$ (Figure 11a). Consistent with previous models, this method assumes the presence of one receptor which follows mass action law. When complex binding occurs, a similar problem to that observed with curvilinear Scatchard plots is evident, *i.e.* how to determine two kinetic constants from a curvilinear plot. Concave-downward plots will be generated if positive cooperativity occurs, whereas concave-upward plots will be observed when multiple receptor subtypes, multiple receptor states or negative cooperativity is present. Dissociation kinetic experiments have been used extensively in conjunction with thermodynamic studies to derive evidence for subtypes of the BZ receptor.[23]

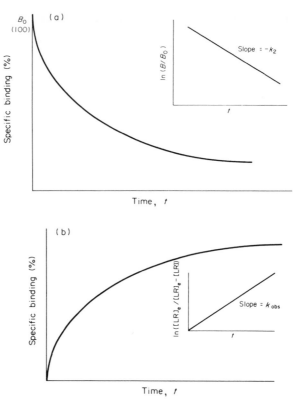

Figure 11   Association/dissociation curves. (a) Dissociation: after a binding reaction has reached equilibrium, dissociation of bound ligand can be initiated by the addition of either an excess of cold displacer or infinite dilution of the reaction mixture. Transformation of the data as indicated in the inset, where B = radioligand bound at time t and B_0 = radioligand bound at time $t = 0$, can yield the dissociation rate constant, k_2. (b) Association: the plot of a fixed concentration of radioligand, usually approximating the K_d value for the receptor derived by saturation analysis, against time, t, can be transformed as indicated in the inset to yield k_{obs} from which, as described in equation (19) of the text, the association rate constant, k_1, can be derived

11.2.8.3.2   *Association experiments*

Another common type of kinetic experiment is the measurement of association, where the rate of formation of the drug–receptor complex is determined as a function of time (Figure 11b). Determination of the association rate constant is not as straightforward as that for the dissociation rate constant. In dissociation experiments, the reaction is regarded as a simple first-order reaction since equilibrium is considered to have been reached and further association has been prevented. In association experiments, steady state rather than equilibrium is reached and consideration of receptor and ligand depletion must be addressed. A second-order reaction describing association can be characterized by the equation

$$\ln\frac{[LR]_e\{[L]_T - ([LR][LR]_e/[R]_T)\}}{[L]_T([LR]_e - [LR])} = k_1t\left(\frac{[L]_T[R]_T}{[LR]_e} - [LR]_e\right) \tag{18}$$

where $[LR]_e$ represents the amount bound at 'equilibrium', $[LR]$ is the amount bound at time t, $[L]_T$ and $[R]_T$ are the total ligand and receptor concentrations, respectively, and k_1 is the association rate constant. If the left side of the equation is plotted as a function of time, k_1 can be derived from the slope.

More commonly, the assumption is made that less than 10% of the ligand is bound during the reaction, such that association can be estimated by a pseudo-first-order reaction, described by the equation

$$\ln\frac{[LR]_e}{[LR]_e - [LR]} = \frac{k_1[L]_T[R]_T}{[LR]_e}t = k_{obs}t \tag{19}$$

where $k_{obs} = k_1 [L]_T + k_{-1}$, from which k_1 can be derived. The value for k_1 can also be determined from the slope of the plot of k_{obs} *versus* [L], where k_{obs} is determined at various ligand concentrations.

A third approach, which has fallen into disfavor due to inherent limitations of accuracy, is to plot the left side of the above equation as a function of time. Using only initial time points and not taking dissociation of the ligand into consideration, a linear relationship is obtained where the slope is equal to k_{obs}.

The above considerations are again only applicable for one-site binding that obeys mass action law. For situations where Michaelis–Menten kinetics are no longer observed, it is virtually impossible to dissect out more than one binding component by these methods.

In addition to determining whether ligand binding is reversible, a practical aspect of kinetic experiments is that they provide an independent assessment of the K_d value determined by saturation experiments, since the K_d value is equal to k_2/k_1.

11.2.8.4 Computer Analysis

Most, if not all, of the currently available packages for computerized analysis of binding data are based on the method of Feldman.[148] These arose from the need for better, more objective and less time consuming 'number-crunching' methods coupled with the increased ease of availability of computers. Besides providing a means of examining untransformed data, which limits the measurement error to a single variable, *i.e.* amount bound, a number of packages provide a graphical representation of the 'best fit' of the mathematical model to the data. Using nonlinear regression analysis, the 'best fit' of the data to a mathematical model is determined through the use of successive iterations. Initially, the errors between the theoretical data points, which are derived from the given binding model, and the actual data points are squared and summed, resulting in the sum of the squares of the residuals (ss_r). In successive iterations, the ss_r is reduced to the point where further iterations result in no further significant reductions in the ss_r (*e.g.* the change in ss_r is less than 0.01%). The ss_r is then computed for successively more complex models, *e.g.* one- *vs.* two-, two- *vs.* three-component models. The resulting ss_r values and values for the degrees of freedom are then used to calculate the F ratio according to the partial F test[149]

$$F = \frac{(ss_1 - ss_2)(df_1 - df_2)}{ss_2/df_2} \tag{20}$$

where ss_1 and ss_2 are the sum of the squares of residuals for the one-component and two-component models, respectively, and df_1 and df_2 are the degrees of freedom for the one- and two-component models, respectively. The F ratio thus provides a statistical measure of whether a two-site model describes the data significantly better than a one-site model.

One feature of computer analysis is that it allows the experimenter to analyze data simultaneously. Besides analyzing experiments individually, several software packages, such as LIGAND[150] and MKMODEL,[151] allow for data from replicate experiments to be analyzed simultaneously to yield one final answer.

For example, in taking a case where four saturation experiments are performed using a radioligand that was not sufficiently selective for two receptor subtypes, two experiments could indicate that a two-component model describes the data significantly better than a one-component model, whereas two other experiments could be described by a one-component model. In such a situation what would be concluded? Analyzing data simultaneously, one answer is obtained, *i.e.* that either a one- or two-component model best describes the data. Simultaneous analysis increases statistical reliability, with the result that there is an increased capability of fitting data to a multicomponent model.[147,152] With regard to the previous example, simultaneous analysis would most likely allow for the detection of two components.

Other characteristics of computer analysis include weighting of data and constraining of parameters. It has been shown that the error associated with ligand binding varies in relation to the ligand concentration in saturation experiments and as a function of inhibitor concentration in competition experiments. Most of the computer analysis packages currently allow for weighting as a function of the reciprocal of the variance. The most accurate method, which is rarely considered, is to determine the weighting function experimentally.[153]

Constraining of experimentally derived parameters such as amount bound or affinity constant is another useful option available in certain computer analysis programs, such as LIGAND. An example is when analysis of a competition binding experiment indicates that greater than 100% of binding occurs, which is probably attributable to improper definition of the top of the binding curve. Since by definition there should be 100% binding, the amount bound can be constrained at 100%.

11.2.8.4.1 Computer analysis of saturation data

The utilization of nonlinear regression computer analysis for saturation experiments has aided in the elucidation of K_d and B_{max} values where more than one binding component is present. Previous methodologies, as mentioned before, are either tedious or represent only approximations of the values. In addition, the analysis of saturation isotherms utilizes equations such that the untransformed binding data are used in the analysis. The general form of the equation that is generally used for saturation analysis is

$$B = \frac{B_{max}}{1 + (K_d/[L])} + N \tag{21}$$

where B is the total amount of ligand bound at concentration $[L]$, B_{max} is the total amount of specific binding, N is the amount of nonspecific binding and K_d is the affinity of the receptor for the radioligand.

For a two-component model

$$B = \frac{B_{max1}}{1 + (K_{d1}/[L])} + \frac{B_{max2}}{1 + (K_{d2}/[L])} + N \tag{22}$$

where B_{max1} and B_{max2} represent the total amount of specific binding to sites 1 and 2, respectively, and K_{d1} and K_{d2} represent the affinity of sites 1 and 2 for the ligand, respectively.

Of the computer packages that are available for analyzing saturation data, all provide a statistical measure of the goodness of fit of the model. Certain packages, such as LIGAND[150] and LUNDON-1,[154] automatically correct for radioligand depletion due to receptor occupancy. Others, such as RS/1[155] and MKMODEL,[151] rely on the user to perform this correction. Whereas LIGAND, MKMODEL and RS/1 allow for the simultaneous analysis of replicate sets of binding data, LUNDON-1 does not.

In deriving saturation data for analysis, it is important that at least 10, and preferably 20, different ligand concentrations be examined to fully characterize binding of the radioligand. When two components of binding are suspected of being present, it is essential that the binding isotherm is well defined at the plateau of the hyperbola, *i.e.* in the region of high radioligand concentrations (Figure 5). If not, two possible outcomes can occur. One is that the second component of binding will appear to be nonsaturable and estimates of B_{max} and K_d for the second component will be overly exaggerated. The second is that the other component will be detected as nonspecific binding.

It is particularly important, therefore, that nonspecific binding be correctly defined. If a wide range of radioligand concentrations are employed, then it may be necessary to examine whether the same concentration of the compound being used to define nonspecific binding should be used at every radioligand concentration. Rather, increasing concentrations of the compound at higher radioligand concentrations may need to be utilized. One of the salient features of this analysis is that it provides a check on the determination of nonspecific binding. Normally, total and nonspecific binding are determined for each concentration of radioligand. Using this method of analysis, the amount of nonspecific binding can also be determined by the computer program directly from total binding. Thus, a comparison can be made between computer-derived and experimentally derived specific binding.

11.2.8.4.2 Computer analysis of competition data

Prior to the development of computer programs which performed nonlinear regression analysis of untransformed data, a computerized method was developed to analyze complex competition data, termed a modified Eadie–Hofstee[135] or 'reverse Scatchard' plot. The amount bound (or percent inhibited) can be plotted as a function of bound/competitor concentration (or percent inhibited/ competitor concentration). Using iterative analysis, two linear lines can then be derived, which yield estimates of the percentage of each receptor subtype present and the IC_{50} value of the competitor for each receptor.[156] The major disadvantage of this procedure is that it is assumed that both receptor components show equal affinity for the radioligand.

Development of nonlinear regression computer analysis has permitted the analysis of complex data from competition experiments.[157,158] Not only can the IC_{50} value of the competitor and the amount of binding to each component at the given radioligand concentration be determined, but slope factors can also be obtained. Initially, to get a general idea for whether a multicomponent analysis will be necessary, the data can be analyzed according to a four-parameter logistic equation

$$B = \frac{B_0 - N}{1 + ([I]/IC_{50})^{n_H}} + N \tag{23}$$

where B is the amount of total binding, B_0 is the amount bound in the absence of inhibitor I, N is the amount of nonspecific binding, and n_H is the slope factor. Depending on how different the value obtained for n_H is from unity will indicate whether a two-site analysis will be required.

For a one-site model, where the K_d value of the radioligand is known, the data are analyzed according to the equation

$$B = \frac{B_{max}}{1 + (K_d/[L])[1 + ([I]/K_i)]} + N \tag{24}$$

where B is the total amount bound at ligand concentration [L], N is the amount of nonspecific binding, [I] is the inhibitor concentration and K_i is the affinity constant for the inhibitor. The data can then be analyzed using a two-site model to determine whether a one- or two-site model better describes the binding data

$$B = \frac{B_{max1}}{1 + (K_{d1}/[L])[1 + ([I]/K_{i1})]} + \frac{B_{max2}}{1 + (K_{d2}/[L])[1 + ([I]/K_{i2})]} + N \tag{25}$$

where B is the total amount bound, B_{max1} and B_{max2} are the maximum number of binding sites for components 1 and 2, respectively, K_{d1} and K_{d2} are the dissociation constants for components 1 and 2, respectively, and K_{i1} and K_{i2} are the affinity constants of the competitor for components 1 and 2, respectively.

In certain instances, the K_d value of the radioligand may not be well defined or it may be inappropriate to determine the K_i value from the IC_{50} value obtained, for example in the situation where multiple states of a receptor may be present. In this instance, data are analyzed according to the equation

$$B = \frac{B_0}{1 + ([I]/IC_{50})} + N \tag{26}$$

where B_0 is the amount bound when [I] = 0 and IC_{50} is the concentration at which specific binding = $0.5(B_0)$. Whether a one- or two-site binding model best describes the data can be determined by analyzing the data according to a two-site model according to the equation

$$B = \frac{B_{01}}{1 + [I]/IC_{50(1)}} + \frac{B_{02}}{1 + [I]/IC_{50(2)}} + N \tag{27}$$

where B_{01} and B_{02} represent the amount of binding to components 1 and 2 in the absence of inhibitor, and $IC_{50(1)}$ and $IC_{50(2)}$ represent the concentration of inhibitor at which 50% of binding is inhibited to components 1 and 2, respectively.

As a general rule, and in particular when analyzing competition binding data by computer, it is essential to adequately define the top and bottom of the inhibition curves. If the top of the inhibition curve is not well defined, the total amount of specific binding may be overestimated since the top of the curve may not be seen to reach a plateau. In comparison, if the bottom portion of the inhibition curve is not adequately defined, the definition of nonspecific binding will be inaccurate and the degree of binding to the low affinity site as well as the IC_{50} value for the competitor will be overestimated. As a minimum, 8–10 data points should be employed for an inhibitor with at least three orders of magnitude difference in the concentration range. For those situations where evidence is derived for the possible existence of more than one binding site interaction, 18–20 point competition curves should be generated over four to five orders of magnitude of concentration. As with data derived by saturation analysis, three or more separate experimental replications are required for data validation.

Most of the current software packages analyze competition experiments. While LIGAND and MKMODEL are capable of analyzing data simultaneously, LUNDON-2 offers the advantage of taking into consideration depletion of radioligand, receptor and inhibitor concentrations, which are normally assumed to change by less than 10%.

11.2.8.4.3 Computer analysis of kinetic experiments

Computer analysis of kinetic binding experiments has not progressed to the same point as analysis of saturation or competition experiments. Nonlinear regression analysis programs, such as RS/1 and MKMODEL, where equations can be entered to generate estimates of the amount bound and the kinetic constants, are generally used.

For dissociation experiments, the equation describing a one-site model is

$$B = B_0 \exp(-k_2 t) \tag{28}$$

where B_0 is the amount of binding at equilibrium ($t = 0$) and k_2 is the dissociation rate constant. For a two-site model, data can be analyzed according to the equation

$$B = B_{01} \exp(-k_{2(1)} t) + B_{02} \exp(-k_{2(2)} t) \tag{29}$$

where B_{01} and B_{02} are the amounts bound to components 1 and 2 at equilibrium and $k_{2(1)}$ and $k_{2(2)}$ are the dissociation rate constants for components 1 and 2, respectively.

For association experiments, computer models that accurately describe the association rate constants for more than one binding component have not been adequately developed. What is currently available are programs describing models of pseudo-first-order reactions for one- and two-components systems. For the one-site model

$$B = B_0 \{1 - \exp[-(k_1 [L]_T + k_2) t]\} \tag{30}$$

where B_0 is the amount bound at equilibrium, k_1 is the association rate constant, $[L]_T$ is the total concentration of free ligand and k_2 is the dissociation rate constant.

For a two-site model

$$B = B_{01} \{1 - \exp[-(k_{1(1)} [L]_T + k_{2(1)}) t]\} + B_{02} \{1 - \exp[-(k_{1(2)} [L]_T + k_{2(2)}) t]\} \tag{31}$$

where B_{01} and B_{02} are the amounts bound to components 1 and 2 at equilibrium, respectively, $k_{1(1)}$ and $k_{1(2)}$ are the association rate constants for components 1 and 2, respectively and $k_{2(1)}$ and $k_{2(2)}$ are the dissociation rate constants for components 1 and 2, respectively, which were determined from the dissociation experiments.

A type of kinetic experiment that has been receiving increased attention is that of competition kinetics.[159-161] In this approach, the kinetics and, in particular, the association rates of a radioligand are compared in the absence and presence of a competitor and can provide information regarding reversibility of a ligand as well as whether a compound is a competitive or noncompetitive inhibitor at the receptor site. In addition, the association and dissociation rate constants of the competitor can be derived. Analysis of this type of experiment is difficult, particularly since no software packages currently exist for this data analysis.

11.2.8.5 Delineation of Independent Multiple Receptors—Sites *Versus* Multiple Interconvertible States

In the analysis of complex binding data, the equations that are generally employed assume that multiple independent receptor sites are present. However, in recent years increasing instances of data inconsistent with these findings have been generated, *i.e.* the data suggest that rather than independent subtypes, interconvertible states of the receptor are present. Results from several types of experiments can differentiate between these two possibilities, as indicated below. A crucial consideration in either case is that all data should be *consistent* with the hypothesis of whether multiple states or subtypes are present.

11.2.8.5.1 Saturation experiments

Certain results from binding experiments can be indicative of whether multiple receptor subtypes or multiple states of a receptor are present. In several systems,[162, 163] for example, an antagonist radioligand yields a B_{max} value greater than that obtained for an agonist radioligand where only one receptor is known to exist. Since these results cannot be readily explained by the presence of multiple receptor subtypes, other explanations were sought, especially in the study of multiple states of the β adrenoceptor. In this system, it has been suggested that when an agonist binds to the receptor, it induces the formation of a high affinity state of the receptor, somewhat similar to the Castillo/Katz model.[37] According to the ternary complex model developed by De Lean *et al.*,[140] the formation of a high affinity ternary complex (HRG) consisting of agonist or hormone (H), receptor (R) and guanine nucleotide regulatory protein (G) is induced by agonists. Antagonists are thought to bind to the receptor, but are unable to induce the formation of the ternary complex. Accordingly, antagonists would bind with a similar high affinity to all receptors, whereas agonists would bind with high affinity to the proportion of receptors involved in ternary complex formation (HRG; those receptors coupled with G), and with low affinity to receptors not coupled (HR). In saturation experiments, whereas radiolabeled antagonists would be seen to bind to all of the receptors, radiolabeled agonists may appear to bind to only a portion of these sites (HRG). Thus, the B_{max} value would appear lower for the radiolabeled agonist.

When multiple binding components are indicated by computer analysis as shown by curvilinear Scatchard plots, it should not automatically be assumed that multiple receptor subtypes are present. Rather, data consistent with either the presence of multiple sites or states should be generated. If multiple subtypes of the receptor are present, the total number of binding sites would be expected to be the same regardless of which radioligand is used. As indicated above, this may not be the case if multiple states are present.

One possible way to discriminate between states and subtypes when multiple components are present is to examine whether inclusion of guanine nucleotides in the binding assay alters binding of the radioligand. Data consistent with the presence of receptor states would reveal that the high affinity state is converted into the low affinity state, with the result that one binding component is now seen. However, the total number of binding sites in the absence *versus* the presence of GTP would be unchanged. For example, saturation studies with the 5-HT agonist [³H]5-HT showed two binding components and a curvilinear Scatchard plot.[164] K_d and B_{max} values for the high and low affinity components were 0.5 nM and 230 fmol per mg protein, and 9 nM and 480 fmol per mg protein, respectively. When these experiments were conducted in the presence of GTP, only a single binding component was detected, with a K_d value of 14 nM and a B_{max} value of 620 fmol per mg protein. These data are consistent with the idea, as in the ternary complex model, that inclusion of GTP converts the high affinity state into the low affinity state since the total number of binding sites remains essentially the same.

If GTP is seen to eliminate the high affinity component, this may be indicative of the presence of multiple states where the K_d value of the low affinity state is so high that binding is not detected. In this circumstance, the B_{max} value would be decreased. Since the ability of GTP to decrease binding could represent competitive inhibition rather than conversion of a high to low affinity state, these types of results must be interpreted cautiously.

Another example of when multiple components of binding from saturation experiments provide evidence for the existence of multiple receptor states is found in experiments examining the binding of [³H]TCP to the PCP receptor.[71] Under normal conditions, well-washed membranes generated a linear Scatchard plot, and computer analysis revealed the presence of one binding component with a K_d value of 110 nM and a B_{max} value of 2700 fmol per mg protein. When magnesium and L-glutamate were included in the binding assay, a curvilinear Scatchard plot was generated. Computer analysis indicated that two components were present, a high affinity component with K_d and B_{max} values of 4 nM and 1100 fmol per mg protein, and a low-affinity component with a K_d of 90 nM and a B_{max} of 1700 fmol per mg protein. Since the total number of binding sites was essentially the same under both conditions and the K_d value of the low affinity component corresponded with that obtained without magnesium or L-glutamate present, the data were consistent with the idea that the inclusion of magnesium and L-glutamate induce a high affinity state of the PCP receptor.

11.2.8.5.2 Competition experiments

When conducting competition experiments, there are several instances where complex binding occurs and it may be unclear whether independent receptor sites or interconvertible receptor states are present. In one situation, a radiolabeled antagonist may be examined where saturation experiments indicate that one component is present and a linear Scatchard plot is generated. In this instance, it would be expected that if one receptor was present, any compound inhibiting binding of the radioligand would generate a steep inhibition curve with a slope factor near unity. However, in many instances,[158,165,166] agonists have been found to produce shallow inhibition curves with slope factors less than one, whereas antagonists produce steep inhibition curves with slope factors equal to one. Furthermore, the percent of high and low affinity components determined vary, depending on which agonist is examined.[158] If receptor subtypes were present, it would be expected that similar proportions of high and low affinity sites would be observed regardless of which agonist, or whether an agonist or antagonist, was examined. In several receptor systems where the receptor is known to be coupled to a guanine nucleotide regulatory protein (G), the addition of guanosine triphosphate (GTP) to the binding assay has been found to produce a rightward shift in the agonist inhibition curves where the plots are now steep with slope factors of one. Antagonist competition curves are unaffected by the inclusion of GTP. If receptor subtypes were truly present rather than multiple states of the receptor, inclusion of GTP should have no effect on the inhibition curves. One explanation that has been derived to explain these data in accordance with the ternary complex model is that agonists bind with high affinity to one of two states of the receptor (generating shallow or two-component inhibition curves), whereas antagonists recognize both states with equal affinity (generating steep inhibition curves). GTP destabilizes the high affinity state of the receptor such that all of the receptor is present in the low affinity form, so that all compounds produce steep inhibition curves, and agonist competition curves appear to shift to the right.

Another situation that can occur is when compounds compete for the binding of a radiolabeled antagonist and shallow inhibition curves are generated by both agonists and antagonists. If receptor subtypes are present, then the percentage of subtypes should be similar regardless of which compound competes for the binding. In this situation, shallow inhibition curves would be generated when a nonselective ligand is inhibited by selective compounds. Nonselective compounds would produce steep inhibition curves in this instance. This represents a classic method of studying receptor subtypes. If possible, a tissue is selected where the proportion of sites is 50:50 (see above). If the percentage of components varies, it could be concluded that multiple states of the receptor are present. One explanation that has been offered to explain such results is that there is a difference in the ability of agonists to induce the formation of the high affinity state of the receptor. In certain systems,[158] this difference is thought to be related to differences in the intrinsic activity of the compound, so that a compound with high intrinsic activity will induce a greater proportion of high affinity states than a compound with lower intrinsic activity.

Another criterion to confirm the presence of subtypes is that the IC_{50} values generated should be similar regardless of the tissue in which the competition experiments are conducted. For example, in receptor systems where interactions between the receptor and the G protein occur, *i.e.* where the receptor is 'coupled' to the G protein, the degree of coupling can vary between tissues such that the IC_{50} value of an agonist for the high affinity component may be lower (higher affinity) in the tissue where receptor and G protein are more tightly coupled.

A third criterion to differentiate between receptor subtypes and states in the above situation involves the use of guanine nucleotides. If the inclusion of GTP in the binding assay is able to change either the percentage of high and low affinity binding components or if the overall IC_{50} value (*i.e.* the IC_{50} value obtained for the one-site fit) is increased, these results suggest the presence of multiple states of the receptor. The lack of effect of GTP indicates either that multiple subtypes are present or that multiple states insensitive to guanine nucleotides exist.

Besides guanine nucleotides, several other types of manipulations can be performed that can alter binding in systems coupled to a G protein. Included among these are the ability of the divalent cation magnesium to enhance binding of a radiolabeled agonist and the effect of *N*-ethylmaleimide (NEM) to reduce agonist affinity, either in saturation or competition experiments. NEM is thought to interact with sulfhydryl bonds and thereby lock the receptor in its low affinity state.[167] Magnesium is thought to interact through a site on the G protein to enhance the coupling of the G protein with the receptor.[168]

For situations where a selective ligand interacts with multiple receptor components, the situations described above can be used as a guideline. However, it must be recognized that binding can be very complex. For example, if the binding of a radiolabeled agonist is inhibited by a competing agonist, both may interact with multiple states of the receptor.

11.2.8.6 Analysis of Multiple States With Equations Describing Multiple Receptor Subtypes

The existence of multiple receptor subtypes *versus* multiple receptor states, as discussed above, is becoming more relevant, particularly when a radiolabeled agonist is employed to characterize a receptor. The question that is beginning to receive increasing attention is whether it is appropriate to characterize binding to multiple interconvertible states of a receptor when the mathematical models used in computer analysis are for multiple independent receptor sites. To address these concerns, several studies have been conducted to evaluate the ternary complex model that was alluded to previously. This model is similar in concept to that of the mobile receptor hypothesis described by Jacobs and Cuatrecasas[169] and the two-step model of RL interactions described by Boeynaems and Dumont.[170] As indicated in Figure 1, a compound not only interacts with the receptor, but the hormone receptor can interact with a third component, which in the ternary complex model is considered as the G protein. The compound can also interact with the precoupled receptor–G protein complex. Experimental results from such studies indicate that this model is not the final solution. In certain systems, such as for the dopamine-D_2 and β-adrenergic receptor, the model accurately describes the data.[140,171] However, the assumptions regarding the availability of G protein are different in the two systems. For example, in the bovine anterior pituitary, the ternary complex model can accurately describe binding to dopamine-D_2 receptors if the assumption is made that the population of receptors exceeds that of the G protein and that there is a high degree of precoupling between the receptor and G protein, particularly in the absence of agonist.[171] In contrast, it appears that the receptor and G protein are present in similar amounts for the β-adrenergic receptor in the frog erythrocyte and little precoupling occurs between the receptor and G protein.[140] Ehlert[172] found that this model adequately described interactions of muscarinic compounds with [^{3}H]N-methylscopolamine in rabbit myocardium if the assumption was made that very little precoupling between receptor and G protein occurred. In contrast, other investigators have reported that the ternary complex model cannot adequately describe the effects of agonists and/or guanine nucleotides.[173,174]

Where does this leave the researcher who is concerned about whether one or two components, much less whether multiple sites or states, are present? Is it necessarily wrong to analyze data using 'incorrect' models? It would seem that a more relevant concern is do we know '*a priori*' which model is relevant, *i.e.* whether multiple states or subtypes are present? In many instances, this is unclear. It would then be more appropriate to use general models, which describe independent binding sites, to characterize the given situation. Once it can be discerned whether multiple receptor subtypes or states are present, it would then be reasonable to examine possible models to more accurately describe the binding data. However, it should be taken into consideration that the affinity constants generated are 'observed' rather than actual values and may not relate to the kinetic parameters (affinity constants) described by the model.

Another consideration is that, at present, there are few alternatives to the independent receptor site models to analyze data, none of which are currently available on computer software packages. One model that has recently been investigated was applied to examine multiple opiate receptor interactions and attempted to consider allosteric interactions of receptor subunits.[175]

Consideration must also be given to the evaluation of whether one binding model is better than another model. At present, the statistics used in determining best 'fits' of a model rely on a comparison of simple (one-site) to complex (two- or three-site) models, *e.g.* F ratio. Since new models may describe data to a similar degree, *i.e.* lower the sum of the square of the residuals to a similar point, a method of comparison needs to be developed.

While the analysis of radioligand-binding data has advanced considerably since the exclusive use of 'pencil and paper' graphics, it is somewhat premature to consider that the present advancements have accomplished all that needs to be done in the analysis of receptor-binding data. A judicious assessment of the usefulness of computerized data analysis within the context of the accuracy of biological test procedures being examined can, in many cases, clarify the extent to which the former can contribute in a logical manner.

11.2.9 NEUROEFFECTORS AND COTRANSMITTERS

Receptor theory deals almost exclusively in terms of a simple interaction of a single ligand with a single receptor, with the role of the former being that of a neurotransmitter.[176] Under such circumstances, as with the simplest of binding models, it is assumed that each effector organ, postsynaptic nerve cell or discrete organelle responds to a single RL activation event. This is often referred to as Dale's law.[177] In many instances, however, especially in the CNS, postsynaptic cells can summate and integrate input from several neurotransmitter inputs, both pre- and post-synaptically, to elicit a final response.

An additional level of complexity in regard to this integrative model occurs when two neuro-effectors are released from a single presynaptic site and where one of these entities functions as a modulator to either facilitate or terminate the actions of the primary neurotransmitter.[178] The situation here is somewhat analogous to the gating mechanism of the transistor and offers a new 'twist' to what is understood as receptor function and how experimentally derived data can be interpreted. The possible misinterpretation of Dale's law[179] may thus have precluded consideration of cotransmitter function until relatively recently.[177,180,181]

A series of possible RL interactions related to cotransmitter function have been documented[182] and are listed in Table 3. Quite obviously, these considerations increase the complexity of the consequences of the RL interaction and, with the additional possibility of receptor-mediated phosphorylation of other receptors,[20] affords a degree of sophistication where, at the molecular level, deviations from mass action kinetics may be anticipated to be the rule rather than the exception. It will be of considerable interest to see where receptor theory and data analysis proceed in the next decade.

11.2.10 MOLECULAR BIOLOGY OF THE RECEPTOR

The advent of the highly sophisticated techniques of molecular biology and the startling leaps forward in the characterization of receptor primary structures have, as indicated in the introduction to this chapter, led to a mandatory incorporation of molecular biology into any research program dealing with the study of receptors. Receptor isolation, cloning and sequencing are therefore the major focus of receptor research, akin to the scaling of Mount Everest.

In practical terms, however, the usefulness of the data obtained from such studies appears to be more applicable to the study of receptor structure rather than function. Thus by offering the ability to clone receptors, molecular biology offers the opportunity to facilitate their study as isolated entities. Incorporation of isolated receptors into frog oocytes has shown that function can be retained.[4] Thus the various factors necessary for receptor functionality can be studied in a defined environment.

While the past history of success in enzyme isolation is often used as an example of what might be achieved by isolating receptors, receptor function is often more related to the association of the receptor recognition unit with membrane proteins and lipids that impart such function. In isolating receptors, very often while the final protein entity of defined molecular weight may have been derived from a tissue source rich in the receptor of interest, there is not always the possibility to demonstrate that the protein is functional. Binding assays can be done using solubilized material to see whether recognition still exists.[6] From cloning, the primary structure of isolated receptors can be determined[1-6] and from matrix analysis, functionality can be provisionally ascribed to residues thought to be adjacent to one another in the native molecule. For instance, in the isolated calcium channel blocker receptor isolated from rabbit skeletal muscle, glutamate residues at positions 87 and 90 in repeat I and aspartate residues at positions 465, 836 and 1151 in repeats II, III and IV have been implicated in high affinity calcium binding.[6] Using site-directed mutagenesis, it will be possible to directly test this hypothesis by analogy with the determination of the binding site of the nicotinic ACh receptor.[183] Ideally, the use of such techniques will allow more information to be derived for building necessary databases to transform molecular modeling from theory to practice. Similarly, raising polyclonal or monoclonal antibodies to either the isolated receptor or its ligand will provide another tool to examine the physiological role of various neuroeffector agents.[184] In addition, where receptor subtypes are thought to exist, their anatomical locale can be studied by antibody labeling as well as autoradiographic techniques.

Table 3 Cotransmitter Situations[182]

(i) Cotransmitter neurons can:
 (a) contain multiple neurotransmitters derived from a common gene coding for a prohormone
 (b) contain multiple neurotransmitters derived from different genes
 (c) contain peptide and nonpeptide neuroeffectors
 (d) contain multiple nonpeptide neuroeffectors

(ii) Postsynaptic interactions can occur when:
 (a) both coeffector agents influence the same receptor on a postsynaptic neuron
 (b) each coeffector influences a different receptor on the postsynaptic neuron
 (c) each coeffector influences a different receptor, each of which is located on a different neuron
 (d) coeffectors modulate the actions of one another at the postsynaptic site

---

11.2.11 THEORETICAL PREDICTION, DATA INTEGRATION AND ANALYTICAL PHARMACOLOGY

Pharmacology is a diverse scientific discipline exemplified by the identification of new compounds that permit the elucidation of receptor function. As a consequence there is, as discussed in the introduction, a discordant interface between classical and molecular pharmacology that often leads to an element of tunnel vision and a chauvinism in the various disciplines that often preclude synergism and objectivity. The discovery of new compounds results in new assay systems that permit the discovery of other new compounds.[185] The technical process by which this occurs is highly empirical. The classical approach, highly dependent on serendipity, has led to drugs such as chlorpromazine and the tricyclic antidepressants.[186] The more pragmatic molecular approach has resulted in the histamine-H_2 blockers,[187] the angiotensin-converting enzyme inhibitors[188] and the HMG CoA (hydroxymethylglutaryl coenzyme A) reductase inhibitors,[189] used in the treatment of ulcers, hypertension and hyperlipidemia, respectively. Thus there are different, albeit equally viable, approaches to the same endpoint and to new therapeutic entities, all of which are successful when viewed retrospectively. When used in a predictive sense, however, the success of these approaches cannot be guaranteed. The identification of *the* successful formula by which drugs could be discovered would no doubt make the business of the pharmaceutical industry a lot less risky.[190] At the same time, however, this formula might limit research in such a manner so as to remove 'the unexpected in science'[191] that fuels discovery.

In reviewing the various methods to study receptor function at the quantitative level, the benefits as well as shortcomings of the various methodologies have been outlined. To a large extent, however, the theoretical aspects that underlie all approaches have intrinsic limitations related to the ability of the experimenter to derive data that match the sophistication of present computational methodologies. Two examples may suffice to illustrate this viewpoint.

The automatic assumption that nonlinear dose–response curves are related to various aspects of efficacy or receptor reserve does not take into account the existence of receptor complexes or an understanding of allosteric and noncompetitive ligand interactions as originally defined in enzyme theory. Similarly, the derivation of Hill coefficients that indicate the potential for receptor/ligand cooperativity and ternary complex formation requires resolution within a practical framework. This is of especial importance when one considers that the experimental expression of such events is often not measurable with currently available technology. For instance, given that neurotransmission is an event established to occur in the millisecond time frame, do radioligand-binding experiments that require from minutes to hours to achieve equilibrium conditions offer knowledge usable to the 'natural' situation other than by an act of faith? The literature attests that even with such limitations this technique, as with many others used in the study of receptor function, does have significant merit and applicability. To reiterate, the integration and interfacing of data from different methodological approaches can allow for a synergism that permits a more rapid and realistic appraisal of receptor function. This in turn can accelerate understanding of receptor function at the molecular level and generate information that can be used in the design of potential new therapeutic entities.

11.2.12 REFERENCES

1. M. Noda, S. Shimizu, T. Tanabe, T. Takai, T. Kayano, T. Ikeda, H. Takahashui, H. Inayama, Y. Kanaoka, N. Minamino, K. Kangawa, H. Matsuo, M. Raftery, T. Hirose, S. Inayama, H. Hayashida, T. Miyata and S. Numa, *Nature (London)*, 1984, **312**, 121.
2. R. A. F. Dixon, B. K. Kobilka, D. J. Strader, J. L. Benovic, H. G. Dohlman, T. Frielle, M. A. Bolanowski, C. D. Bennett, E. Rands, R. E. Diehl, R. A. Mumford, E. E. Slater, I. S. Sigal, M. G. Caron, R. J. Lefkowitz and C. D. Strader, *Nature (London)*, 1986, **321**, 75.
3. G. Grenningloh, A. Rienitz, B. Schmitt, C. Methfessel, M. Zensen, K. Beyreuther, E. D. Gundelfinger and H. Betz, *Nature (London)*, 1987, **328**, 215.
4. P. R. Schofield, M. G. Darlinson, N. Fujita, D. R. Burt, F. A. Stephenson, H. Rodriguez, L. M. Rhee, J. Ramachandran, V. Reale, T. A. Glencorse, P. H. Seeburg and E. A. Barnard, *Nature (London)*, 1987, **328**, 221.
5. A. Ullrich, J. R. Bell, E. Y. Chen, R. Werrara, L. M. Petruzzelli, T. J. Dull, A. Gray, L. Coussens, Y.-C. Liao, M. Tsubokawa, A. Mason, P. W. Seeberg, G. Grunfeld, O. M. Rosen and J. Ramachandran, *Nature (London)*, 1985, **313**, 256.
6. T. Tanabe, H. Takeshima, A. Mikami, V. Flockerzi, H. Takahashi, K. Kanagaw, K. Kojima, H. Matsuo, T. Hirose and S. Numa, *Nature (London)*, 1987, **328**, 313.
7. L. E. Limbird, 'Cell Surface Receptors: A Short Course on Theory and Methods', Nijhoff, Boston, 1986.
8. W. H. M. L. Luyten and S. F. Heinemann, *Annu. Rep. Med. Chem.*, 1987, **22**, 281.
9. P. Loftus, M. Waldman and R. F. Hout, Jr., in 'Drug Discovery and Development', ed. M. Williams and J. B. Malick, Humana Press, Clifton, NJ, 1987, p. 73.
10. P. Gund, T. A. Halgren and G. M. Smith, *Annu. Rep. Med. Chem.*, 1987, **22**, 269.
11. T. P. Kenakin, 'Pharmacological Analysis of Drug Receptor Interaction', Raven Press, New York. 1987.

12. M. Williams and S. J. Enna, *Annu. Rep. Med. Chem.*, 1986, **21**, 211.
13. J. W. Black, in 'Perspectives In Receptor Classification', ed. J. W. Black, D. H. Jenkinson and V. P. Gerskowitch, Liss, New York, 1987, p. 11.
14. A. Gilman, *Cell*, 1984, **36**, 577.
15. O. M. Rosen, *Science (Washington, D.C.)*, 1987, **237**, 1452.
16. G. I. Drummond, 'Cyclic Nucleotides in The Nervous System', Raven Press, New York, 1984.
17. P. J. England and C. P. Downes, in 'Comprehensive Medicinal Chemistry', ed. J. C. Emmett, Pergamon Press, Oxford, 1989, vol. 3, chap. 11.4.
18. M. J. Berridge, *Biochem. J.*, 1984, **220**, 345.
19. B. S. McEwan, *Biochem. Pharmacol.*, 1987, **36**, 1755.
20. P. Greengard, 'Fidia Research Foundation Neuroscience Award Lectures', Liviana Press, Padova, 1986, p. 52.
21. M. Hollenberg, *Trends Pharmacol. Sci.*, 1987, **8**, 196.
22. S. H. Snyder, *Science (Washington, D.C.)*, 1984, **224**, 22.
23. R. F. Squires, *Handb. Neurochem.*, 1984, **6**, 261.
24. B. V. Clineschmidt, M. Williams, J. J. Witoslawski, P. R. Bunting, E. A. Risley and J. A. Totaro, *Drug Dev. Res.*, 1982, **2**, 147.
25. E. H. F. Wong, J. A. Kemp, T. Priestly, A. R. Knight, G. N. Woodruff and L. L. Iversen, *Proc. Natl. Acad. Sci. USA*, 1986, **83**, 7104.
26. J. N. Langley, *J. Physiol. (London)*, 1878, **1**, 339.
27. P. Ehrlich, *Proc. R. Soc. London*, 1900, **55**, 424.
28. P. M. Dean, 'Molecular Foundations of Drug–Receptor Interaction', Cambridge University Press, New York, 1987.
29. P. Ehrlich, in 'The Collected Papers of Paul Ehrlich', ed. F. Himmelweit, Pergamon Press, London, 1956, vol. 1, p. 596.
30. P. Ehrlich and J. Morgenroth, in 'The Collected Papers of Paul Ehrlich', ed. F. Himmelweit, Pergamon Press, London, 1956, vol. 2, p. 205.
31. A. V. Hill, *J. Physiol. (London)*, 1909, **39**, 361.
32. A. J. Clark, 'The Mode of Action of Drugs on Cells', Arnold, London, 1933.
33. L. Michaelis and M. L. Menten, *Biochem. Z.*, 1913, **49**, 333.
34. D. Colquhoun, *Trends Pharmacol. Sci.*, 1985, **6**, 197.
35. A. Carlsson, *Pharmacol. Rev.*, 1959, **11**, 490.
36. I. Creese, D. R. Sibley, M. W. Hamblin and S. E. Leff, *Annu. Rev. Neurosci.*, 1983, **6**, 43.
37. J. del Castillo and B. Katz. *Proc. R. Soc. London, Ser. B*, 1957, **146**, 369.
38. C. Braestrup, R. Smhmiechen, G. Neff, M. Nielsen and E. N. Petersen, *Science (Washington, D.C.)*, 1982, **216**, 1241.
39. J. H. Gaddum and Z. P. Picarrelli, *Br. J. Pharmacol.*, 1957, **12**, 323.
40. J. R. Fozard, *Naunyn-Schmiedeberg's Arch. Pharmacol.*, 1984, **326**, 36.
41. B. P. Richardson, C. Engel, P. Donatsch and P. A. Stadler, *Nature (London)*, 1985, **316**, 126.
42. B. J. Jones, N. J. Oakley and M. B. Tyers, *Br. J. Pharmacol.*, 1987, **90**, 88.
43. J. H. Gaddum, *J. Physiol. (London)*, 1936, **89**, 7.
44. O. Arunlakshana and H. O. Schild, *Br. J. Pharmacol.*, 1959, **14**, 148.
45. E. J. Ariens, *Arch. Int. Pharmacodyn. Ther.*, 1954, **99**, 32.
46. R. P. Stephenson, *Br. J. Pharmacol.*, 1956, **11**, 379.
47. R. F. Furchgott, *Pharmacol. Rev.*, 1955, **7**, 183.
48. J. M. Van Rossum and E. J. Ariens, *Arch. Int. Pharmacodyn. Ther.*, 1962, **136**, 385.
49. M. Nickerson, *Nature (London)*, 1956, **178**, 697.
50. R. F. Furchgott, *Annu. Rev. Pharmacol.*, 1964, **4**, 21.
51. A. Goldstein, L. Aronow and S. M. Kalman, 'Principles Of Drug Action: The Basis of Pharmacology', 2nd edn., Wiley, New York, 1974, p. 82.
52. W. D. M. Paton, *Proc. R. Soc. London, Ser. B*, 1961, **154**, 21.
53. R. E. Goselin, in 'Kinetics Of Drug Action', ed. J. M. Van Rossum, Springer-Verlag, Berlin, 1977, p. 323.
54. J. Westley, 'Enzymic Catalysis', Harper and Row, New York, 1969, p. 177.
55. A. V. Hill, *Biochem. J.*, 1913, **7**, 471.
56. G. S. Adair, *J. Biol. Chem.*, 1925, **63**, 529.
57. L. Pauling, *Proc. Natl. Acad. Sci. USA*, 1935, **21**, 186.
58. J. Monod, J. Wyman and J.-P. Changeaux, *J. Mol. Biol.*, 1965, **12**, 88.
59. D. E. Koshland, G. Nemethy and D. Filmer, *Biochemistry*, 1966, **5**, 365.
60. M. Williams and R. A. Olsen, in 'Receptor Pharmacology and Function', ed. M. Williams, R. A. Glennon and P. B. M. W. M. Timmermans, Dekker, New York, 1988.
61. G. B. Stauber, R. W. Ransom, A. I. Dilber and R. W. Olsen, *Eur. J. Biochem.*, 1987, **167**, 125.
62. P. Haring, C. Stahi, P. Schoch, B. Takacs, T. Staehelin and H. Mohler, *Proc. Natl. Acad. Sci. USA*, 1985, **83**, 4837.
63. J. C. Eccles, 'The Physiology Of Synapses', Academic Press, New York, 1964, p. 66.
64. M. A. Raftery, M. Hunkapiller, C. Strader and L. Hood, *Science (Washington, D.C.)*, 1980, **208**, 1454.
65. M. Dixon and E. C. Webb, 'Enzymes', 3rd edn., Academic Press, London, 1979, p. 614.
66. J. F. Tallman, J. W. Thomas and D. W. Gallager, *Nature (London)*, 1978, **274**, 383.
67. A. N. Anis, S. C. Berry, N. R. Burton and D. Lodge, *Br. J. Pharmacol.*, 1983, **79**, 565.
68. P. Loo, A. Braunwalder, J. Lehmann and M. Williams, *Eur. J. Pharmacol.*, 1986, **123**, 467.
69. J. A. Kemp, *Trends NeuroSci.*, 1987, **10**, 294.
70. S. N. Murphy, I. J. Reynolds, W. Hartwig and R. J. Miller, *Soc. Neurosci. Abstr.*, 1987, **13**, 759.
71. P. S. Loo, A. F. Braunwalder, J. Lehmann, M. Williams and M. A. Sills, *Mol. Pharmacol.*, 1987, **32**, 820.
72. W. J. Kinnier, in 'Receptor Pharmacology and Function', ed. M. Williams, R. A. Glennon and P. B. M. W. M. Timmermans, Dekker, New York, 1988, p. 85.
73. H. Rasmussen, D. B. P. Goodman and A. Tennenhouse, *CRC Crit. Rev. Biochem.*, 1972, **1**, 95.
74. R. J. Miller, *Science (Washington, D.C.)*, 1987, **235**, 46.
75. M. J. Berridge and R. F. Irvine, *Nature (London)*, 1984, **312**, 315.

76. P. W. Majerus, T. M. Connolly, H. Deckmyn, T. S. Ross, T. E. Bross, H. Ishii, V. S. Bansal and D. B. Wilson, *Science (Washington, D.C.)*, 1987, **235**, 1519.
77. M. D. Browning, R. Huganir and P. Greengard, *J. Neurochem.*, 1985, **45**, 11.
78. K. R. Yamamoto and B. N. Alberts, *Annu. Rev. Biochem.*, 1976, **45**, 712.
79. C. R. Kahn, *J. Cell Biol.*, 1976, **70**, 261.
80. B. Attardi and S. Ohno, *Endocrinology (Baltimore)*, 1978, **103**, 760.
81. L. C. Mahan, R. M. McKernan and P. A. Insel, *Annu. Rev. Pharmacol. Toxicol.*, 1987, **27**, 215.
82. A. C. Dolphin, *Trends NeuroSci.*, 1987, **10**, 53.
83. I. Creese and D. R. Sibley, *Annu. Rev. Pharmacol. Toxicol.*, 1981, **21**, 357.
84. R. C. Webb, in 'Cardiovascular Pharmacology', 2nd edn., ed. M. Antonaccio, Raven Press, New York, 1984, p. 239.
85. J. T. Greenamyre, J. B. Penney, A. B. Young, C. D'Amato, S. P. Hicks and I. Shoulson, *Science (Washington, D.C.)*, 1985, **227**, 1496.
86. E. K. Perry, in 'Psychopharmacology, A Third Generation Of Progress', ed. H. Meltzer, Raven Press, New York, 1987, p. 887.
87. T. J. Crow, F. Owen, A. J. Cross, R. Lofthouse and A. Longden, *Lancet*, 1978, **1**, 36.
88. P. J. Whitehouse, in 'Treatment Development Strategies For Alzheimer's Disease', ed. T. Crook, R. Bartus, S. Ferris and S. Gershon, Powley Associates, Madison, CT, 1986, p. 483.
89. S. J. Enna, in 'Receptor Binding In Drug Research', ed. R. A. O'Brien, Dekker, New York, 1986, p. 409.
90. A Carlsson, in 'Psychopharmacology, A Third Generation Of Progress', ed. H. Meltzer, Raven Press, New York, 1987, p. 39.
91. N. R. Cutler, in 'Psychopharmacology, A Third Generation Of Progress', ed. H. Meltzer, Raven Press, New York, 1987, p. 897.
92. U. S. von Euler and J. H. Gaddum, *J. Physiol. (London)*, 1931, **72**, 74.
93. B. Samuelsson, *Science (Washington, D.C.)*, 1983, **220**, 568.
94. J. Saklatvala, L. M. C. Pilsworth, S. J. Sarsfield, J. Gavrilovic and J. K. Heath, *Biochem. J.*, 1984, **224**, 461.
95. J. P. Green, *Trends Pharmacol. Sci.*, 1987, **8**, 90.
96. E. A. Ariens, *J. Recep. Res.*, 1984, **4**, 1.
97. P. Seeman, *Pharmacol. Rev.*, 1981, **32**, 229.
98. J. Kebabian and D. B. Calne, *Nature (London)*, 1979, **277**, 93.
99. J. P. Green and S. Maayani, in 'Perspectives In Receptor Classification', ed. J. W. Black, D. H. Jenkinson and V. P. Gerskowitch, Liss, New York, 1987, p. 237.
100. H. Weinstein, in 'Perspectives in Receptor Classification', ed. J. W. Black, D. H. Jenkinson and V. P. Gerskowitch, Liss, New York, 1987, p. 41.
101. M. Williams, *Trends Pharmacol. Sci.*, 1987, **8**, 251.
102. J. P. Green, *Trends Pharmacol. Sci.*, 1987, **8**, 377.
103. M. Williams and G. E. Martin, *J. Pharm. Pharmacol.*, 1982, **34**, 56.
104. D. Romer, H. H. Busher, R. C. Hill, R. Maurer, T. J. Petcher, H. Zuegner, W. Benson, E. Finner, W. Ilkowski and P. W. Thies, *Nature (London)*, 1982, **298**, 759.
105. R. S. L. Chang, V. J. Lotti, T. B. Chen and M. E. Kegan, *Neurosci. Lett.*, 1986, **72**, 211.
106. P. C. Churchill and A. K. Bidani, in 'The Adenosine Receptors', ed. M. Williams, Humana Press, Clifton, NJ, 1989, in press.
107. C. B. Pert and S. H. Snyder, *Proc. Natl. Acad. Sci. USA*, 1973, **70**, 2243.
108. Y.-P. Wan and S. D. Hurt, in 'Brain Receptor Methodologies, Part A', ed. P. J. Marangos, I. C. Campbell and R. M. Cohen, Academic Press, Orlando, FL, 1984, p. 21.
109. J. Bennett and H. I. Yamamura, in 'Neurotransmitter Receptor Binding', 2nd edn., ed. H. I. Yamamura, S. J. Enna and M. J. Kuhar, Raven Press, New York, 1985, p. 61.
110. R. F. Bruns, K. Lawson-Wendling and T. A. Pugsley, *Anal. Biochem.*, 1983, **132**, 74.
111. R. F. Bruns, G. A. Lu and T. A. Pugsley, *Mol. Pharmacol.*, 1986, **29**, 331.
112. G. A. Stone, M. F. Jarvis, M. A. Sills, B. Weeks, E. A. Snowhill and M. Williams, *Drug Dev. Res.*, 1988, **15**, 31.
113. D. N. Middlemiss and J. Fozard, *Eur. J. Pharmacol.*, 1983, **90**, 151.
114. A. B. Norman, G. Battaglia, A. L. Morrow and I. Creese, *Eur. J. Pharmacol.*, 1985, **106**, 461.
115. R. Quirion and P. Gaudreau, *Neurosci. Biobehav. Rev.*, 1985, **9**, 413.
116. M. Williams, A. Y. Jeng and L. P. Wennogle, in 'Proteins And Peptides As Drugs', ed. P. I. Nadler, Dekker, New York, 1989, in press.
117. R. S. L. Chang, V. J. Lotti, R. L. Monaghan, J. Birnbaum, E. O. Stapley, M. A. Goetz, G. Albers-Schoenberg, A. A. Patchett, T. M. Liesch, O. D. Hensens and J. P. Springer, *Science (Washington, D. C.)*, 1985, **230**, 177.
118. B. E. Evans, K. E. Rittle, M. G. Bock, R. M. DiPardo, R. M. Freidinger, W. L. Whittier, N. P. Gould, G. F. Lundell, C. E. Hominick, D. F. Veber, P. S. Anderson, R. S. L. Chang, V. J. Lotti, D. J. Cerino, T. B. Chen, P. J. King, K. A. Kunkel, J. P. Springer and J. Hirschfield, *J. Med. Chem.*, 1987, **30**, 1229.
119. P. Cuatrecasas and M. Hollenberg, *Adv. Protein Chem.*, 1976, **30**, 251.
120. S. R. Zukin and R. S. Zukin, *Proc. Natl. Acad. Sci. USA*, 1979, **76**, 5372.
121. S. Maayani and H. Weinstein, *Life Sci.*, 1980, **26**, 2011.
122. V. Pliska, *J. Recep. Res.*, 1983, **3**, 227.
123. J. W. Ferkany, H. Valentine, G. A. Stone and M. Williams, *Drug Dev. Res.*, 1986, **9**, 85.
124. D. Hoyer, A. Pazos, A. Probst and J. M. Palacios, *Brain Res.*, 1986, **376**, 85.
125. M. M. Dietl and J. M. Palacios, *Soc. Neurosci. Abstr.*, 1987, **13**, 413.
126. E. El-Fakahany, in 'Receptor Pharmacology and Function', ed. M. Williams, R. A. Glennon and P. B. M. W. M. Timmermans, Dekker, New York, 1988, p. 695.
127. M. J. Kuhar, E. B. De Souza and J. R. Unnerstall, *Annu. Rev. Neurosci.*, 1986, **9**, 27.
128. E. W. Snowhill and C. A. Boast, in 'Quantitative Receptor Autoradiography', ed. C. A. Boast, E. W. Snowhill and C. A. Altar, Liss, New York, 1986, p. 13.
129. H. N. Wagner, *Semin. Nucl. Med.*, 1986, **16**, 51.

130. H. N. Wagner, in 'Quantitative Receptor Autoradiography', ed. C. A. Boast, E. W. Snowhill and C. A. Altar, Liss, New York, 1986, p. 233.
131. R. J. Tallarida and L. S. Jacob, 'The Dose–Response Relationship in Pharmacology', Springer-Verlag, New York, 1979.
132. I. M. Klotz, *Science (Washington, D.C.)*, 1982, **217**, 1247.
133. G. Scatchard, *Ann. N. Y. Acad. Sci.*, 1949, **51**, 660.
134. H. E. Rosenthal, *Anal. Biochem.*, 1967, **20**, 525.
135. B. H. J. Hofstee, *Nature (London)*, 1959, **184**, 1296.
136. D. D. Knightly and N. A. C. Cressie, *J. Steroid Biochem.*, 1980, **13**, 1317.
137. I. M. Klotz, *Trends Pharmacol. Sci.*, 1983, **4**, 253.
138. E. Burgisser, *Trends Pharmacol. Sci.*, 1984, **6**, 142.
139. D. R. Burt, in 'Receptor Binding In Drug Research', ed. R. A. O'Brien, Dekker, New York, 1986, p. 3.
140. A. De Lean, J. M. Stadel and R. J. Lefkowitz, *J. Biol. Chem.*, 1980, **255**, 7108.
141. D. L. Hunston, *Anal. Biochem.*, 1975, **63**, 99.
142. O. H. Straus and A. Goldstein, *J. Gen. Physiol.*, 1943, **26**, 559.
143. M. Williams and P. L. Wood, in 'Neuromethods', ed. A. A. Boulton, G. B. Baker and P. Hrdina, Humana Press, Clifton, NJ, 1986, vol. 4, p. 543.
144. Y.-C. Cheng and W. H. Prusoff, *Biochem. Pharmacol.*, 1973, **22**, 3099.
145. J. Linden, *J. Cyclic Nucleotide Res.*, 1982, **8**, 163.
146. S. Jacobs, K.-J. Chang and P. Cuatrecasas, *Biochem. Biophys. Res. Commun.*, 1975, **66**, 687.
147. A. De Lean, A. A. Hancock and R. J. Lefkowitz, *Mol. Pharmacol.*, 1982, **21**, 5.
148. H. A. Feldman, *Anal. Biochem.*, 1980, **107**, 220.
149. N. R. Draper and H. Smith, 'Applied Regression Analysis', Wiley, New York, 1966.
150. P. J. Munson and D. Rodbard, *Anal. Biochem.*, 1980, **107**, 220.
151. N. H. Wolford, 'MK MODEL: An Extended Least Squares Modelling Program', Elsevier/North Holland, Amsterdam, 1986.
152. A. De Lean, P. J. Munson and D. Rodbard, *Am. J. Physiol.*, 1978, **235**, E97.
153. D. Rodbard, R. H. Lenox, H. L. Wray and D. Rasmeth, *Clin. Chem. (Winston-Salem, N.C.)*, 1976, **22**, 350.
154. J. E. Lundeen and J. H. Gordon, in 'Receptor Binding In Drug Research', ed. R. A. O'Brien, Dekker, New York, 1986, p. 31.
155. RS/1 Release 2 Features, Bolt, Beranek and Newman Software Products Corporation, Cambridge, MA, 1985.
156. K. P. Minneman, L. R. Hegstrand and P. B. Molinoff, *Mol. Pharmacol.*, 1979, **16**, 34.
157. A. A. Hancock, A. L. De Lean and R. J. Lefkotwitz, *Mol. Pharmacol.*, 1979, **16**, 1.
158. R. S. Kent, A. De Lean and R. J. Lefkowitz, *Mol. Pharmacol.*, 1980, **17**, 14.
159. H. J. Motulsky and L. C. Mahan, *Mol. Pharmacol.*, 1984, **25**, 1.
160. G. Schrieber, Y. I. Henis and M. Sokolovsky, *J. Biol. Chem.*, 1985, **260**, 8789.
161. M. L. Contreras, B. B. Wolfe and P. B. Molinoff, *J. Pharmacol. Exp. Ther.*, 1986, **239**, 136.
162. B. B. Hoffman, T. Michel, D. Mullikan-Kilpatrick, R. J. Lefkowitz, M. E. Tolbert, H. Gilman and J. Fin, *Proc. Natl. Acad. Sci. USA*, 1980, **77**, 4569.
163. R. S. L. Chang, V. J. Lotti and T. B. Chen, *Biochem. Pharmacol.*, 1987, **36**, 1709.
164. M. A. Sills, B. B. Wolfe and A. Frazer, *Mol. Pharmacol.*, 1984, **26**, 10.
165. N. R. Zahniser and P. B. Molinoff, *Nature (London)*, 1978, **275**, 453.
166. A. De Lean, H. Ong, J. Gutowska, P. W. Schiller and N. McNicoll, *Mol. Pharmacol.*, 1984, **26**, 498.
167. B. F. Kilpatrick, A. De Lean and M. Carcon, *Mol. Pharmacol.*, 1982, **22**, 298.
168. S. Y. Lech and M. E. Maguire, *Mol. Pharmacol.*, 1982, **22**, 267.
169. S. Jacobs and P. Cuatrecasas, *Biochim. Biophys. Acta*, 1976, **433**, 482.
170. J. M. Boeynaems and J. E. Dumont, *Mol. Cell. Endocrinol.*, 1977, **7**, 33.
171. K. A. Wreggett and A. De Lean, *Mol. Pharmacol.*, 1984, **26**, 214.
172. F. J. Ehlert, *Mol. Pharmacol.*, 1985, **28**, 410.
173. T. W. T. Lee, M. J. Sole and J. W. Wells, *Biochemistry*, 1986, **25**, 7009.
174. H.-M. S. Wong, M. J. Sole and J. W. Wells, *Biochemistry*, 1986, **25**, 6995.
175. C. D. Demoliou-Mason and E. A. Barnard, *J. Neurochem.*, 1986, **46**, 1118.
176. H. F. Bradford, 'Chemical Neurobiology', Freeman, New York, 1986, p. 158.
177. D. D. Potter, E. J. Furshpan and S. C. Landis, *Neurosci. Commun.*, 1981, **1**, 1.
178. G. Campbell, *Annu. Rev. Pharmacol. Toxicol.*, 1987, **27**, 51.
179. E. Costa, 'Fidia Research Foundation Neuroscience Award Lectures', Liviana Press, Podova, 1986, p. i.
180. G. Burnstock, *Neuroscience*, 1976, **1**, 239.
181. M. Hollenberg, in 'Receptor Pharmacology and Function', ed. M. Williams, R. A. Glennon and P. B. M. W. M. Timmermans, Dekker, New York, 1988, p. 1.
182. T. L. O'Donohue, W. L. Millington, G. E. Handelmann, P. C. Contreras and B. M. Chronwall, *Trends Pharmacol. Sci.*, 1985, **6**, 305.
183. M. Mishina, T. Tobimatsu, K. Imoto, K. Tanaka, Y. Fujita, K. Fukada, M. Kuraski, H. Takahashi, Y. Morimoto, T. Hirose, S. Inayama, T. Takhashi, M. Kuno and S. Numa, *Nature (London)*, 1985, **313**, 364.
184. M.-L. Swenberg, S. H. Buck and W. Lovenberg, *Brain Res.*, 1987, **417**, 131.
185. P. M. Laduron, J. E. Leysen, W. Gommeren, P. F. M. Janssen, A. Schoffe, J. Van Dun, P. Van Gompert, M. Verwimp and W. Wouten, *Drug Dev. Res.*, 1986, **8**, 15.
186. P. Deniker, in 'Discoveries In Pharmacology: Psycho- and Neuro-pharmacology', ed. M. J. Parnham and J. Bruinvels, Elsevier, Amsterdam, 1983, vol. 1, p. 163.
187. R. Ganellin, *J. Med. Chem.*, 1981, **24**, 913.
188. D. W. Cushman and M. A. Ondetti, *Prog. Med. Chem.*, 1980, **17**, 43.
189. A. W. Alberts, J. Chen, G. Kuron, V. Hunt, J. Huff, C. Hoffman, J. Rothrock, M. Lopez, H. Joshua, E. Harris, A. Patchett, R. Monaghan, S. Currie, E. Stapley, G. Albers-Schonberg, O. Hensens, J. Hirshfield, K. Hoogsteen, J. Liesch and J. Springer, *Proc. Natl. Acad. Sci. USA*, 1980, **77**, 3957.
190. M. Williams and G. L. Neil, *Prog. Drug Res.*, 1988, **32**, 329.
191. J. W. Black, *Br. J. Clin. Pharmacol.*, 1986, **22**, S5.

11.3

Isolation, Purification and Molecular Biology of Cell Membrane Receptors

MELISSA A. BUCK, CLAIRE M. FRASER and J. CRAIG VENTER

National Institutes of Health, Bethesda, MD, USA

11.3.1 STRUCTURAL AND FUNCTIONAL PROPERTIES OF CELL MEMBRANE PROTEINS

The plasma membrane is a fundamental structural component of all cells. The membrane encases the cytoplasm in prokaryotes and eukaryotes and creates internal compartments in eukaryotic cells in which specific cellular functions are performed. The phospholipid bilayer is a basic structure of biological membranes but the membranes are considerably more complex than a simple bilayer. Generally a substantial amount of protein is associated with the cell membrane. The amount of protein and lipid material varies depending on the specific functions of the cell membrane.

In addition to the structural contribution of the membrane to the cell, the plasma membrane functions as a semipermeable barrier to different nutrients, ions and molecules. Primarily the protein constituents of the membrane are responsible for the transport of molecules across the lipid bilayer of the membrane and determine its catalytic activities.[1] There are two types of proteins associated with cell membranes: those loosely bound, known as peripheral membrane proteins, and those imbedded within the membrane structure, referred to as integral membrane proteins.[2]

In order for a cell to survive and grow it must interact and communicate with other cells and constituents in its environment. Therefore eukaryotic and prokaryotic cells possess proteins, including receptors, that are exposed to the external side of the membrane and monitor the cell's surroundings. Other membrane proteins are necessary for intracellular metabolism and are located on or in the membrane. Some proteins, known as transmembrane proteins, have been found to extend through the bilayer. These membrane proteins, such as the adrenergic and muscarinic cholinergic receptors for example, have groups that protrude from both sides of the membrane; amino acid side chains that lie within the bilayer are largely hydrophobic, while those that interact with the extracellular and intracellular surfaces of the membrane are predominantly hydrophilic.[3] Isolation of various membrane proteins such as receptors that are found in very low concentrations in the cell membrane requires extremely sensitive measures of detection. Specific radioligand binding or photoaffinity labeling of receptors provides a necessary means of monitoring the purification and quantification of the membrane protein obtained.

Advances in molecular cloning and cell transfection and expression of the DNA encoding membrane receptor protein have recently provided the technology to obtain increased levels of receptors. With larger quantities of receptor proteins available, in-depth structural and functional analysis can be performed.

11.3.2 SOLUBILIZATION OF MEMBRANE PROTEINS: AGENTS AND PROCEDURES

Due to the different natures of insertion and attraction that the membrane proteins have for the plasma membrane, a variety of techniques are required for their isolation and purification. The loosely bound peripheral membrane proteins are easily removed from the membrane by mild solubilization treatments. The solubilization of these proteins involves washing the membranes with solutions of high salt concentrations or manipulating the Ca^{2+} and Mg^{2+} ion concentrations of the cell. The complete removal of these ions from the membrane environment or the addition of chelating agents such as EDTA releases the peripheral protein into the solution environment. The complete removal of salt from the membrane suspension disturbs the electrostatic attractive interactions between the peripheral membrane proteins and the membrane and the repulsive forces between the peripheral membrane proteins and the integral membrane proteins.[2] By disturbing these interactions the peripheral proteins can dissociate from the membrane with no tightly bound lipid material attached.

11.3.2.1 Detergents

Solubilization of integral membrane proteins requires much more rigorous treatments of the membrane with agents that can destroy its structural integrity. The integral proteins are often isolated with bound lipid without which they tend to aggregate or precipitate in an aqueous environment. A variety of detergents, either neutral and/or negatively or positively charged species, have been employed for this purpose depending on the composition of the particular membrane and the protein to be isolated. Charged detergents are not recommended when a strict control of ionic strength is required. Ionic detergents interact with hydrophilic and hydrophobic moieties of a protein and alter the protein conformation to such a degree that the biological activity of the protein is lost. The anionic detergents sodium dodecyl sulfate (SDS) and sodium deoxycholate are examples of detergents that denature the integral membrane proteins and render them enzymatically inactive.[4, 5]

The neutral detergents, such as Triton X-100 and Lubrol, solubilize many of the proteins in functionally active forms;[6] however, Triton X-100 and bile salts have been found to strongly inhibit cyclase function.[7] No one detergent has been shown to be universally applicable for receptor solubilization, but 3-cholamidopropyldimethylammonio-1-propane sulfonate (CHAPS), digitonin and octyl glucoside have been found to be the most effective in solubilizing functional receptors.[8] The nature of the neutral detergent interaction with an integral membrane protein probably involves the hydrophobic part of the detergent and the hydrophobic portion of the protein. The detergent substitutes for the fatty acids chains of the membrane phospholipids, releasing the membrane protein in an active form.[9] It is important to keep in mind that the use of any detergent may render the integral membrane protein in an irreversibly denatured form that may not be the desired or functional form. Membrane proteins can be categorized based upon the different degrees of solubilization.

11.3.2.2 Chaotropes and Organics

Another type of solubilizing agents are the chaotropes which disrupt the ordered arrangement of water molecules that surround the membrane. Once the rigid water framework is disturbed, dissociation of the membrane protein from the membrane can be accomplished. Some commonly used chaotropes are urea, guanidinium chloride, sodium iodide and sodium thiocyanate. Organic solvents have also been used separately or in conjunction with detergents or chaotropes to solubilize integral membrane proteins. Alcohols of intermediate carbon chain length have been used to isolate enzymatically active proteins. Basic or acidic solvent systems have been used to solubilize and denature membrane proteins.[2]

In order to optimize the solubilization of integral membrane proteins, a number of factors must be taken into consideration in addition to the detergent or the chaotropic agent. The choice of medium, the initial protein concentration, pH and temperature can affect the recovery and activity of the protein. High ionic strength buffers dissociate complexes more readily by disrupting the electrostatic and intermolecular interactions in the membranes.[10] It is recommended that the initial protein concentration be high when attempts are made to solubilize active receptors in order to maintain their function. Once the integral membrane protein has been solubilized, the further purification of this protein by biochemical techniques requires the presence of the solubilizing agent.

We have previously mentioned that the solubilization of a membrane protein may possibly affect the overall protein conformation, thereby altering receptor affinity for ligand or completely eliminating the ability of a soluble receptor to bind ligands. The effects of solubilization can only be determined by assays on the soluble receptors. A specific means of detecting the membrane protein of interest can be accomplished by using radioligand binding or photoaffinity labeling.

Once a suitable protocol for the solubilization of a membrane receptor has been established, receptor purification may proceed. This can be accomplished using a variety of techniques, such as affinity chromatography, isoelectric focusing, immunoprecipitation, gel electrophoresis, gel exclusion chromatography and high performance liquid chromatography (HPLC). Due to the numerous and often rigorous steps involved with the isolation and purification of membrane proteins, one approach for following the receptor throughout purification is to radiolabel the protein in membranes prior to solubilization. The labeled receptor can then be detected by scintillation or γ counting or by SDS–polyacrylamide gel electrophoresis (SDS-PAGE) and autoradiography. Once the membrane protein is obtained in its purified form, the protein can be structurally and functionally characterized by such techniques as peptide mapping, amino acid sequencing, immunological mapping with monoclonal antibodies and gene cloning.

11.3.3 METHODS FOR ISOLATION AND PURIFICATION OF MEMBRANE RECEPTORS

One requirement for performing detailed structural and functional analysis of any protein is to have the sample of interest in a highly purified form free of contaminating macromolecules. In order to optimize the isolation and purification of membrane proteins, it is necessary to capitalize on the different physical and chemical properties of the membrane and its constituents. In the case of a membrane receptor, one must often devise a method for protein isolation that has no effect on the biological activity of the protein.

11.3.3.1 Affinity Chromatography

Affinity chromatography provides the means for achieving separations which are too difficult or virtually impossible to achieve using less specific techniques. Affinity chromatography relies upon the specific binding capabilities of the membrane proteins as the means of purification.[11] This type of adsorption chromatography involves the use of a bed material with biological affinity for the component to be purified as compared to conventional chromatographic techniques in which the separation depends on physical and chemical differences between substances rather than functions.

Affinity chromatography requires the covalent attachment of a specific ligand to the insoluble column matrix.[12] Sepharose-4B column packing has been successfully used in a number of purification columns. Epoxy activation of Sepharose-4B provides a hydrophilic spacer and an active oxirane group for direct coupling to ligands containing hydroxyl, amino or thiol groups.[13] The spacer arm between the ligand and the column matrix minimizes the steric interference between the protein–ligand complex and the column matrix.

Epoxy-activated Sepharose is produced upon the reaction of bisoxirane with Sepharose. A stable uncharged ether linkage is formed between the spacer arm and the matrix. Buffers containing carbonate, borate or phosphate provide the best elution results on these affinity chromatography columns. Recent studies have combined the purification techniques of affinity chromatography and size-exclusion HPLC to obtain extremely high levels of purified receptors.[14, 15] An example of a purification protocol for isolation of mammalian β-adrenergic receptors is presented in Figure 1. This paradigm combines affinity chromatography, size-exclusion HPLC and SDS–PAGE.

Radioligand binding or photoaffinity labeling is required for detection, quantification and characterization of the purified protein eluted from affinity matrices. The amount of receptor bound to the column is estimated by the difference between the total binding activity loaded onto the column and the total binding activity found in the eluate. Affinity chromatography is capable of achieving high yields and specific purification, providing the binding properties of the proteins are maintained in the detergent media used for the purification and the covalently bound affinity ligands remain attached to the column matrices.[16]

11.3.3.2 Isoelectric Focusing

Isoelectric focusing has often been the method of choice when separating amphoteric proteins. The influence of an electric field on these proteins causes the migration and focusing of a protein at a specific point which corresponds to the isoelectric point (pI) of the protein.[17] Isoelectric focusing

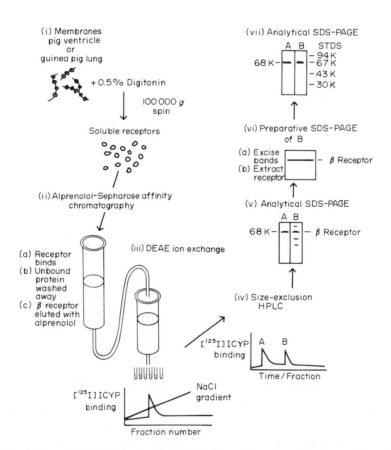

Figure 1 Schematic diagram depicting the steps involved in the purification of mammalian β-adrenergic receptors

involves the use of an ion-exchange support in which the charged proteins are adsorbed onto and selectively eluted using a salt or pH gradient. The gradient is usually formed outside the column and passed over the support to elute the proteins. Sluyterman and co-workers have been able to generate a pH gradient within the column employing the buffering capacity of the column support.[18] Proteins are desorbed when the pH of the gradient is less than the pI of the protein. The protein moves along the column at or near the point in the migrating pH gradient equal to its pI. Since the linear velocity of the mobile phase is greater than the velocity of a particular pH within the gradient, proteins will be focused in the column by this process at their specific pI. However, a disadvantage to isoelectric focusing column chromatography is the long preparation times necessary to develop and recycle a column and the tedious analysis of the procedure.

An alternative method for isoelectric focusing that has been successfully applied to the purification of neurotransmitter receptors is the use of density gradient isoelectric focusing.[17] It provides excellent resolution and concentrates the protein of interest in addition to providing purification. The inclusion of a sucrose density gradient together with a running temperature of 0–4°C increases sample stability. An example of the results obtained from density gradient isoelectric focusing of mammalian β_1- and β_2-adrenergic receptors is presented in Figure 2. As illustrated, this method is sensitive enough to resolve substances with a difference of 0.2 pH units in their isoelectric points. From a procedural standpoint it is best to use a wide pH range between three and 10 when focusing a protein for the first time.[17]

11.3.3.3 Immunoaffinity Chromatography

Immunoaffinity chromatography is a means of membrane protein purification that focuses on the functional properties of a protein. This procedure provides selective precipitation of a specific protein from a complex cellular mixture. Immunoaffinity chromatography involves the use of specific antibodies directed against a given protein.[19] The membrane protein must first be removed from the cell by detergents or chaotropes. In order to have a means of monitoring the protein, the

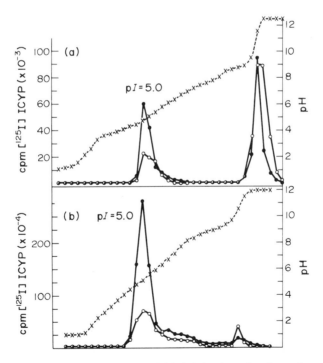

Figure 2 Density gradient isoelectric focusing of (a) radiolabeled dog heart β_1-adrenergic receptor and (b) radiolabeled guinea pig lung β_2-adrenergic receptor. Receptors from the indicated tissues were specifically radiolabeled with the β-receptor antagonist [^{125}I]iodocyanopindolol ([^{125}I]ICYP; ●, total ligand binding; ○, nonspecific ligand binding in the presence of 1 μmol dm^{-3} 1-propranolol) and solubilized from membranes with digitonin. Samples were loaded onto a prefocused isoelectric focusing column and the isoelectric focusing run was performed as described by Lilly.[17] The × illustrates the pH gradient formed across the column. The peak of radioactivity at the basic end of the column represents unbound radioligand that dissociated from the receptor during the experiment

cell can be radiolabeled prior to incubation with antibodies. The membrane protein is bound to a specific antiprotein antibody immobilized on an inert support such as cyanogen bromide-activated Sepharose[19] and can then be washed from the column and analyzed by electrophoresis and autoradiography.

The success of immunoaffinity chromatography critically depends on the formation of an insoluble immune complex between a protein antigen and an antigen-specific monoclonal or polyclonal antibody. The antibody is covalently linked to Sepharose by using the cyanogen bromide-activation method.[20, 21] This isolation procedure requires the column to be equilibrated with a high salt buffer followed by a buffer containing a low percentage of nonionic detergent. The soluble protein antigen is slowly applied to the column to allow for equilibration between antigen and immobilized antibody. The cyanogen bromide-activated Sepharose column is carefully washed with buffer containing detergent to remove protein adsorbed nonspecifically. The antigen is then eluted by using a low pH solution of 0.1 mol dm^{-3} glycine or a high pH solution of 0.1 mol dm^{-3} triethylamine with or without detergent. The antigen can be removed from the column by ligand-specific elution if the antibody is directed to a determinant in the ligand binding site of the receptor and competes with a receptor-specific ligand for receptor binding.

Ligand-specific elution involves much milder conditions of elution allowing for increased protein stability and further proof of the identity of the receptor.[19] This approach was initially applied to the purification of turkey erythrocyte β-adrenergic receptors by Fraser and Venter in 1980 using a monoclonal antibody against the ligand binding site of the receptor (Figure 3).[22] The size of the immunoaffinity-purified turkey erythrocyte β receptor reported in 1980 has recently been confirmed from the cloning and sequence analysis of this protein.[23]

11.3.3.4 Immunoprecipitation

Immunoprecipitation of a radiolabeled antigen can also be performed using monoclonal, polyclonal and autoantibodies. The precipitation method, like immunoaffinity chromatography, is dependent on the formation of an immune complex between the protein antigen and its specific antibody. This method can also be applied in the isolation and purification of unlabeled antigens. The advantages in using antibodies for the isolation and purification of membrane proteins are the high specificity and the high degree of sensitivity of the method to precipitate specific membrane proteins found in low concentrations in the cell membrane. For example, we have utilized monoclonal antibodies to human α_2-adrenergic receptors to specifically precipitate these receptors from a sample of solubilized platelet membranes. Furthermore, we have shown these antibodies to be specific for α_2-adrenergic receptors, with no cross-reactivity for α_1-adrenergic, β_2-adrenergic or muscarinic cholinergic receptors (Figure 4).

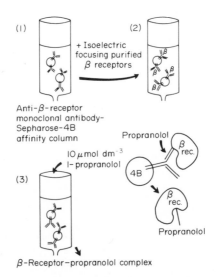

Figure 3 Schematic diagram depicting the steps involved in the immunoaffinity purification of the turkey erythrocyte β-adrenergic receptor using a ligand-binding-site-specific monoclonal antibody

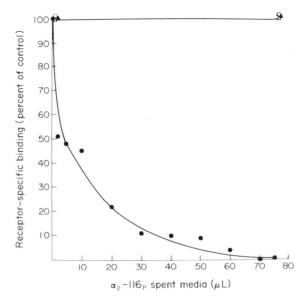

Figure 4 Immunoprecipitation of neurotransmitter receptors using a monoclonal antibody against the human platelet α_2-adrenergic receptor. Digitonin-solubilized receptors were incubated with increasing concentrations of culture medium containing a monoclonal antibody to the human α_2-adrenergic receptor for 16 h at 4 °C: ○, β_2-receptor; △, muscarinic cholinergic receptor; ▲, α_1-receptor; ●, α_2-receptor. An excess of rabbit antimouse Ig was added to the samples and they were incubated for 6 h at 4 °C. Immune complexes were precipitation by centrifugation at 10 000 g × 20 min. The amount of each receptor remaining in the supernate was assayed by ligand binding. These results are expressed as a percentage of the starting receptor concentration

11.3.3.5   Selective Precipitation

Selective precipitation by poly(ethylene glycol) (PEG) or by ammonium sulfate has been used to precipitate free protein or protein–hormone complexes from a mixture of binding proteins and ligands. The carrier protein γ-globulin is essential in the precipitation of solubilized protein.[24] There exist some pH and sensitivity restrictions with the precipitation procedure that limit its usefulness.

11.3.3.6   Two-dimensional Gel Electrophoresis

Another method that provides a means of separating a mixture of proteins is two-dimensional electrophoresis. One-dimensional electrophoretic separation of protein mixtures often lacks sufficient resolution for the isolation of a single protein species. However, two-dimensional gel electrophoresis may greatly enhance membrane protein purification as each dimension is based upon a different physicochemical parameter for separation, such as electrical charge and protein molecular weight. The membrane proteins are first solubilized by one of the various agents mentioned above which renders the proteins in monomeric units. The membrane proteins are then separated in the first dimension by isoelectric focusing according to their isoelectric points in a solution of Triton X-100 and urea. In the second dimension, the proteins are separated according to their molecular weight. The separation is performed using SDS-PAGE according to Laemmli[25] with an acrylamide gel gradient as described by Boschetti *et al.*[26] Two-dimensional gel electrophoresis can be an extremely useful method in combination with new protein microsequencing technology that allows for protein sequence analysis to be performed with a single spot on a two-dimensional gel.[27]

11.3.3.7   Gel Exclusion Chromatography

Gel exclusion chromatography has been employed as a means of purifying a mixture of membrane proteins based on their structural properties of molecular weight and size. A column is packed with inert polymer or polysaccharide beads of varying pore sizes. The lower molecular weight proteins penetrate the beads and are retained longer on the column than the higher molecular weight proteins. The column is calibrated with proteins of known molecular weight. A standard curve is generated using the column elution volumes of the standard proteins *vs.* the logarithm of their molecular weights. While this method can provide a reasonable degree of membrane protein purification, it is not possible to obtain an accurate protein molecular weight for membrane proteins using this technique as the presence of protein-bound detergent results in a gross overestimation of the mass of a protein. As illustrated in Figure 5, size-exclusion chromatography of radiolabeled turkey erythrocyte β_1-adrenergic receptors indicated a Stokes radius of 4.2 nm for the solubilized protein. Application of this technique to the purification of crude solubilized β-adrenergic receptors yielded an approximate fivefold purification.

11.3.3.8 High Performance Liquid Chromatography

Various types of high performance liquid chromatography (HPLC) can be employed depending on the contents of the membrane protein mixture to be separated and the parameters for the separation. Membrane proteins can be resolved from a complex mixture of cellular components by HPLC. The isolation and purification of membrane proteins can be accomplished by employing one of the following types of chromatography: size-exclusion (SE-HPLC), ion-exchange (IE-HPLC), hydrophobic interaction (HI-HPLC) or reverse-phase (RP-HPLC). The advancement in HPLC has provided another means of isolating and purifying membrane proteins by more rapid separation and higher efficiency than gel electrophoresis and isoelectric focusing, and is much less tedious than classic gel exclusion chromatography.

SE-HPLC is mainly employed for separations involving a vast array of proteins of large molecular weight and to remove contaminants and other proteins of lesser molecular weight. It is not uncommon to have size-exclusion columns linked in tandem with the larger pore sized columns, *i.e.* TSK-4000 (Beckman), at the beginning, followed by a smaller pore sized column, *i.e.* TSK-3000 or TSK-2000. This network of columns provides a series of steps for the protein contaminants to be resolved and separated from the protein of interest. Silica-based SE-HPLC columns provide the highest efficiency in the pH range of 2.5 to 7.5. For polymer-based columns, the mobile phase can have a pH as high as 12. Size-exclusion columns allow the separation of low and very high molecular weight proteins (2 kDa–1000 kDa). SE-HPLC can generally separate nonaqueous membrane proteins soluble in organic solvents by using a semirigid column packing material (uSpherogel by Beckman/Altex) that allows for the separation of proteins ranging in molecular weight from 10^2 to

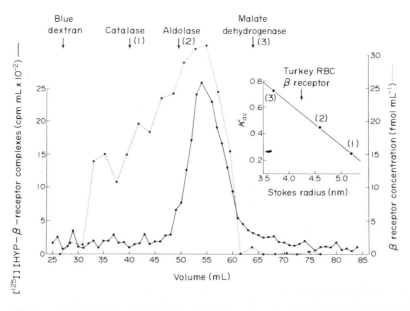

Figure 5 Size-exclusion chromatography of digitonin-solubilized turkey erythrocyte β_1-adrenergic receptors. Turkey erythrocyte β-adrenergic receptors were solubilized from membranes with digitonin and applied to a column containing Sepharose-6B equilibrated in phosphate buffer containing detergent. Fractions were collected and aliquots of each fraction were assayed for the presence of receptor using ligand binding. The column was calibrated with the indicated standards and a standard curve of Stokes radius *vs.* K_{av} was obtained. These data indicate that the digitonin-solubilized turkey erythrocyte receptor has a Stokes radius of 4.2 nm

10^8 Da. An example of SE-HPLC is shown in Figure 6, in which it was utilized as a final step in the purification of the mammalian lung β_2-adrenergic receptor.

In those instances when membrane proteins cannot be distinguished or separated by molecular weight, they may be separated by chromatofocusing,[28] in which proteins are eluted from an ion-exchange column utilizing the increased speed and capacity provided by IE-HPLC. This method allows for the detection of protein heterogeneity not demonstrated by SE-HPLC or by RP-HPLC. In theory, chromatofocusing is the application of isoelectric focusing adapted to IE-HPLC.

Another aspect similar to ion-exchange chromatography is the separation of hydrophobic proteins based on their degree of hydrophobicity and hydrophobic interactions with the column support. The column packing materials have a bonded phase suitable for hydrophobic interaction. An important feature of the mobile phase is the use of a high salt concentration that causes additional hydrophobic residues of the proteins to be exposed by removing water molecules from the protein surfaces. This leads to the association of the protein with apolar groups of the stationary phase. The descending salt gradient allows the protein to rehydrate leading to selective elution and retention of its biological activity.[29] HI-HPLC uses polymer-based columns with propyl, polyether or phenyl groups attached to the stationary phase. Elution of hydrophobic proteins under these conditions in aqueous buffers promotes the retention of the structural integrity of the membrane

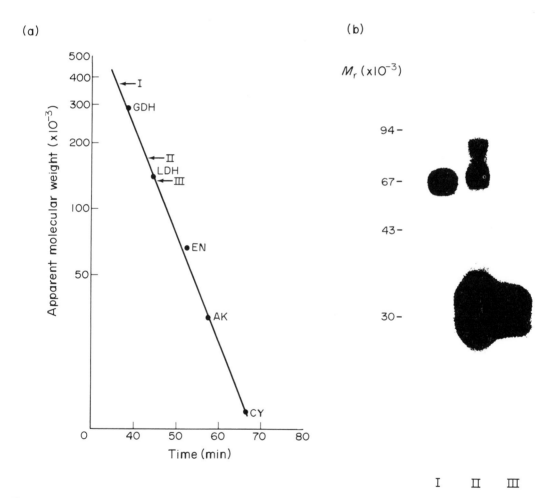

Figure 6 Radioiodination of purified guinea pig lung β_2-adrenergic receptors from SE-HPLC. (a) Affinity-purified guinea pig lung β-adrenergic receptors were chromatographed on one Beckman TSK-3000 and two Beckman TSK-2000 columns linked in series. Fractions were collected and assayed using ligand binding. The arrows, labeled I, II and III, represent fractions containing receptor binding. The position of elution of the standard proteins cytochrome c (CY), adenylate kinase (AK), enolase (EN), lactate dehydrogenase (LDH) and glutamate dehydrogenase (GDH) are also indicated. (b) Radioiodination of proteins in peaks I–III. Proteins in the indicated fractions were radiolabeled with Na[^{125}I] using chloramine T and analyzed with SDS-PAGE according to the method of Laemmli. The relative molecular mass (M_r) of SDS-PAGE markers is indicated on the left of the figure. Peak I contains only a single protein of $M_r = 68\,000$ that represents the purified β_2-adrenergic receptor

protein. The salt gradient chosen for the separation of membrane proteins is dependent upon their hydrophobicity. Normally an ammonium sulfate gradient is sufficient for the separation of proteins of low hydrophobicity; however, sodium sulfate is used when a more discerning salt gradient is required. Some membrane proteins of low hydrophobicity are poorly retained on the column and are difficult to isolate and purify. However, the salt concentration of the gradient can be increased and if necessary the column temperature can also be increased to help retain the protein. The column temperature should not exceed 45 °C in order to prevent loss of the tertiary structures of the proteins.[30] Other gradient manipulations are required when dealing with extremely hydrophobic membrane proteins. The retention problem is reversed; the protein needs to be released more quickly from the column. In this case, the objective is to decrease the retention of the hydrophobic membrane proteins and two alternatives are available. The first is to lower the column temperature which also preserves the native protein structure. The second is to use detergents or organics in the eluant but some of these solubilizing agents tend to be denaturing agents. Also, the chosen agent must not interfere in the detection of the protein, *i.e.* it must not strongly absorb at 214 nm and 280 nm. A recommended detergent is Brij because of its transparency to UV light. The other alternative in dealing with hydrophobic membrane proteins is to employ the RP-HPLC organic solvent elution scheme on the HI-HPLC column. Unfortunately the conventional low-pH reversed-phase chromatography systems are strongly denaturing to the proteins.[30] Therefore, operating under the HI-HPLC conditions favoring the structural and functional preservation of the native protein is recommended whenever possible.

RP-HPLC is another method capable of separating and isolating membrane proteins on the basis of hydrophobicity. RP-HPLC employs the use of silica column material with alkyl silane-bonded groups ranging in carbon length from two to 18. The silica support is restricted in its use due to pH limitations. The organic solvent system requires acidification of the mobile phase by phosphoric, perchloric or trifluoroacetic acids. The phosphoric and perchloric acid groups in the mobile phase can form hydrophilic ion pairs with a protein to increase its polarity and decrease its retention time. This type of acidification is useful when dealing with extremely hydrophobic membrane proteins. Organic acids such as trifluoroacetic acid (TFA) form hydrophobic ion pairs with proteins as well as functioning as a solubilizing agent. TFA forms ion pairs with basic amino acids in the protein and increases its retention time. The organic acids partially denature the protein and increase the number of exposed hydrophobic sites on the protein which can result in a longer retention on the column. Pentafluorobutyric acid also acts as an ion pair which retards the elution of basic polypeptides.

Recently in the literature, RP-HPLC has been used for peptide mapping and amino acid analysis of membrane protein fragments. Once the membrane proteins have been isolated and purified by any of the previously mentioned techniques, the high sensitivity of RP-HPLC is employed to

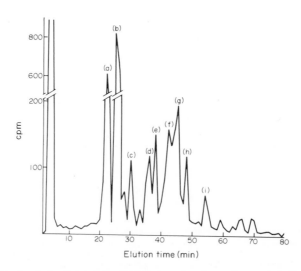

Figure 7   RP-HPLC tryptic digest of radiolabeled guinea pig lung β_2-adrenergic receptors. Guinea pig lung β_2-adrenergic receptors purified as outlined in Figure 1 were radiolabeled with Na[^{125}I] and digested with TPCK-trypsin at an approximate molar ratio of 1:100 for 16 h at 37 °C. The sample was injected onto the HPLC column and was eluted with a linear gradient of 0–65% of 0.1% CF_3CO_2H in MeCN. Fractions were assayed for the presence of radioactivity

purify the proteolytic membrane protein fragments for mapping and analysis purposes. Stone and Williams [31] have obtained reproducible tryptic peptide maps by RP-HPLC on samples of less than 50 pmol of bacteriophage T4 gene 43 protein and accurate amino acid composition analysis on less than 50 ng of the same protein. Higher resolution of the peptides is obtained using column packing of 300 Å pore size. The choice of reverse-phase column is dependent upon the length of the peptide. Columns of C_{18} packing provide better resolution of shorter peptides than columns of C_4 packing material. RP-HPLC has also been utilized in the study of purified hamster and guinea pig lung β_2-adrenergic receptors. Digestion of the radioiodinated guinea pig lung β receptor with trypsin and analysis of the radiolabeled peaks by RP-HPLC revealed nine major peaks of radioactivity, indicating the presence of nine tryptic peptides containing tyrosine (Figure 7).[15]

The use of HPLC has provided a more efficient and rapid means of isolating and purifying membrane proteins compared to open-column chromatography methods. However, limitations are associated with all the purification methods because of the sample amounts that need to be loaded, the hydrophobicity and solubility of the membrane proteins and the ease and reproducibility of the method. These limitations must be considered when determining the optimal method for the isolation and purification of a particular membrane protein sample.

11.3.4 APPROACHES TO THE CHARACTERIZATION OF MEMBRANE RECEPTORS

11.3.4.1 Photoaffinity Labeling

In addition to being an aid in the purification and isolation of membrane proteins, photoaffinity labeling is also a useful method for investigating the chemical structure and mode of action of a protein. This methodology involves covalently and specifically linking a radioligand to the receptor protein. Singer[32] was the first to propose the use of photoaffinity labels to tag membrane proteins. Photoaffinity probes have previously been successfully utilized in adrenergic systems by a number of groups to label ligand-binding subunits of β, α and dopamine receptors. Figure 8 illustrates the use of iodocyanopindolol diazirine (ICYP-D) for photoaffinity labeling of the β-adrenergic receptor.[15] As shown in this figure, a protein that migrates on SDS–polyacrylamide gels with a mobility corresponding to 68 000 is stereoselectively labeled with ICYP-D. Recently, Niznik and co-workers[33] employed a high-affinity radiolabeled photoreactive derivative of spiperone, azido-N-methyl-spiperone, to probe the structure of the dopamine D_2-receptor. This receptor was characterized in both its membrane and soluble state.

Specific labels can provide a means for identifying receptor binding sites and their constituent peptides as well as a means of measuring distance relationships between active and regulatory sites. Polypeptide chains which contribute to a given active site of an enzyme or a ligand binding site of a receptor can be identified by SDS-PAGE analysis or by RP-HPLC if they are specifically labeled with a radioactive photoaffinity label. An example of such information obtained from RP-HPLC analysis of photoaffinity-labeled hamster lung β_2-adrenergic receptors is illustrated in Figure 9. A single major labeled tryptic peak was observed (Figure 9a) while two major labeled cyanogen bromide peaks were observed (Figure 9b). These results suggested that there were two sites of covalent attachment of the photoaffinity label, fairly close to each other and both within a single tryptic peak that contained a methionine residue.[15] There are six tryptic peptides in the hamster lung β receptor sequence that meet these criteria.

Hydrophobic photogenerated reagents, such as nitrenes and carbenes, have been used for labeling parts of membrane proteins that are buried within the lipid bilayer.[34] Nitrenes generated from aryl azides have been used to distinguish intrinsic from extrinsic membrane proteins. Nitrenes have been used to label the membrane protein glycophorin A in or close to the transmembrane hydrophobic sequence.[35] Bayley and Knowles[36] have found carbenes to be more reactive than nitrenes towards carbon–hydrogen bonds in single-bilayer phospholipid vesicles. Goldman and Pober[31] have shown that carbenes generated within the lipid bilayers insert into the saturated fatty acyl chains. The carbene ^{3}H-adamantylidene, generated photochemically within biological membranes from ^{3}H-adamantane diazirine, has been found to label the intrinsic membrane proteins, glycophorin A, human major histocompatibility antigens (HLA-A2 and HLA-B7) and influenza virus hemagglutinin HA_2, in or close to the hydrophobic peptides that are believed to lie within the hydrocarbon region of the lipid bilayer.[34]

The use of photolabeling reagents for membrane proteins requires consideration of which reagent to use in order to obtain the highest specific labeling, the need for scavenger molecules such as 2-mercaptoethanol in cases where adequate levels of labeling cannot be achieved, the affinity of the

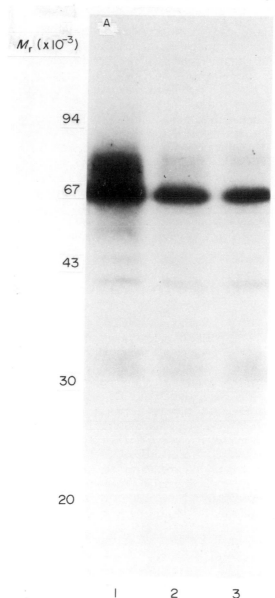

Figure 8   Photoaffinity labeling of guinea pig lung β_2-adrenergic receptors. Membranes were incubated with 250 pmol dm^{-3} iodocyanopindolol diazirine (ICYP-D) alone (lane 1) or with 1 μmol dm^{-3} d-propranolol (lane 2) or 1 μmol dm^{-3} l-propranolol (lane 3) for 60 min at 30 °C in the dark. Samples were diluted, cooled and photolysis was performed by irradiation at 365 nm for 60 min using a 6 W UV light lamp. Samples were analyzed by SDS-PAGE followed by autoradiography. The molecular weight markers are indicated on the left of the figure. The labeled receptor has a mobility corresponding to $M_r = 68\,000$

ligand for the receptor, the specific activity of the radioactive label and its position of attachment. Photoaffinity labeling provides two distinct advantages over affinity labeling. The photolyzable reagents display a greater specificity than affinity labeling under the same conditions and labeling of hydrophobic sites is possible using highly reactive carbenes or nitrenes produced upon photolysis. The use of site-specific photolyzable reagents aids in elucidating the mode of action of the receptor at the molecular level and as a structural probe of the protein. The attachment of other specific labels, such as fluorescent and spin labels, allows the monitoring of conformational changes in the receptor in response to physiological stimuli.

11.3.4.2   Amino Acid Sequencing and Peptide Mapping

Other means of characterizing receptor proteins are by amino acid sequence determination and peptide mapping. As previously mentioned, RP-HPLC technology has helped significantly in

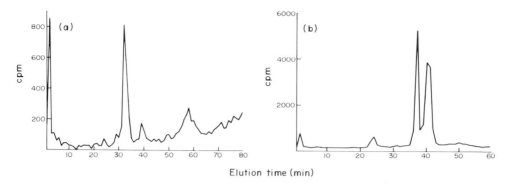

Figure 9 RP-HPLC digest maps of [^{125}I]iodocyanopindolol-labeled hamster lung β-adrenergic receptors. (a) Receptor was digested with trypsin and analyzed as described in the legend of Figure 7. (b) Receptor was reduced with dithiothreitol, carboxymethylated with iodoacetic acid and digested with a 500-fold molar excess of cyanogen bromide. The sample was applied to a RP-HPLC column and eluted with a 0–60% linear gradient of 0.1% CF_3CO_2H in MeCN

improving and advancing these forms of analysis. Peptide mapping has proved to be an extremely useful tool in the structural characterization of the relationships between the receptor domains and their involvement in cell function. Most RP-HPLC peptide mapping of partial or complete proteolytic digestion can be performed on nanomole amounts of protein. If the receptor could be specifically radiolabeled or photolabeled in its native environment, more information related to structural changes due to ligand binding or protein interaction with cellular components could be obtained and analysis could be performed on the picomole level.

11.3.4.3 Monoclonal Antibodies

Monoclonal antibodies have been used as probes of receptor structure and function on cell proteins of low concentration and stability.[37, 38] Monoclonal antibodies can be directed against many parts of a receptor and the site of attachment of the antibody can be determined precisely.[39] The receptor specificity of each monoclonal antibody and the determination of a number of different antigenic determinants is constructive in defining the pathological significance of antireceptor autoantibodies. Numerous studies performed using monoclonal antibodies have advanced receptor research in the areas of molecular homology and antigenic determinants between receptors of different species, clinical applications and structural characterization of receptor subunits. Data derived using monoclonal antibodies to the muscarinic cholinergic receptor provided the first evidence that muscarinic cholinergic and adrenergic receptors displayed structural homology,[40] an idea that has been confirmed from the cloning and sequencing of genes encoding these proteins.[23]

11.3.5 RECOMBINANT DNA TECHNOLOGY IN RECEPTOR STUDIES

Over the past few years, advances in pharmacological, biochemical and molecular biology techniques have promoted the study of membrane receptors using new methods. Previously, it was very difficult to isolate, purify and structurally and functionally analyze receptor proteins because of their extremely low density in the cell membrane. However, the current capabilities for isolating genes encoding neurotransmitter receptors, coupled with methods for cell transfection to obtain high density expression of the protein, should provide the required amounts of protein for elucidating the structure and function of membrane receptors of the nervous and endocrine systems.

11.3.5.1 Construction of cDNA and Genomic Libraries

Recombinant DNA technology has evolved as an excellent method for obtaining the protein sequence encoding a particular receptor. The isolation and selection of a specific receptor gene is made easier if it displays a phenotypic marker. However, this type of selection is rarely found in eukaryotic genes and bacterial sequences. Therefore, it is necessary to screen DNA libraries with hybridization probes derived from specific nucleic acid sequences of the receptor protein or with a specific antibody that recognizes the protein in order to obtain DNA for sequencing studies.

It is important to first decide whether to screen a cDNA or genomic library. The clones isolated from cDNA libraries are derived from cellular mRNA and therefore provide information on the types of receptors expressed in a particular cell or tissue. On the other hand, genomic DNA clones include introns, exons and regulatory domains of a protein. The production of a cDNA or genomic library involves obtaining large numbers of recombinant clones without using large amounts of packaging mixture, vector or DNA insert. The first step involves determining the appropriate ratio of DNA insert to DNA vector. Several test ligations must be performed using varying amounts of insert to a constant amount of vector. It is difficult to estimate the appropriate quantities of each specific DNA when dealing with such small amounts and the degree of uncertainty of completeness of the ligation reaction. By determining the optimal ratio, one can be assured of constructing a library that will be large enough to account for the entire genome.

The optimal cDNA library contains at least one cDNA clone for each mRNA sequence in the cell and expresses the desired mRNA sequence at high levels. The construction of a cDNA library is accomplished by using double-stranded cDNA ligated into phage vector DNA. The ligation product is packaged into phage particles for transformation of the host bacteria. The construction of cDNA libraries has been plagued with numerous problems in the ligation and digestion reactions, but with technological advances and the use of high quality restriction enzymes these problems have been eliminated.

11.3.5.2   Southern and Northern Blot Analysis

A useful technique for analyzing the DNA of positive clones from genomic libraries is Southern blot analysis.[41] This procedure involves the digestion of the DNA of interest and its hybridization with a specific radiolabeled probe. Initially, the DNA is digested by specific restriction enzymes and run on an agarose gel. The DNA is transferred from the gel to a solid support such as a nitrocellulose filter or nylon membrane. After the transfer is complete, the DNA is immobilized onto the solid support by UV irradiation or by baking the filter. The filter is hybridized with a specific probe for detecting homologous DNA of the receptor. The filter is exposed to X-ray film to determine the results by autoradiography.

Northern blot analysis is used to analyze RNA sequences from positive clones from cDNA libraries.[42] The procedure is very similar to Southern blot analysis. After the RNA is transferred to the solid support, it is hybridized to a specific DNA probe of known size and amount. This probe enables the determination of the size and amount of the RNA on the filter. The molecular weight of the RNA can be determined from a standard curve constructed from the logarithmic molecular weights and characteristic mobility on an agarose gel of known denatured RNA species.

Once the receptor gene has been characterized by blot analysis, other functional and genetic characteristics of the gene can be analyzed by transfecting various cell lines with the gene. The elements responsible for regulation of gene expression can be determined by mutating the gene and examining its activity and ligand binding capabilities under a variety of conditions.

11.3.5.3   Cell Transfection

Cell transfection can be accomplished in three different ways: calcium phosphate transfection, diethylaminoethyl- (DEAE-)dextran transfection and electroporation.[19] The first two methods involve attachment of the DNA to the cell surface under specific chemical environmental conditions. The DNA is endocytosed into the cell and expressed and selected under conditions that favor the survival of the cells carrying the specific DNA. Electroporation uses electric currents to open pores in the cell allowing for DNA diffusion into the cell. This procedure can be performed on virtually any type of cell.

The transcription or replication of the transfected gene can be analyzed by harvesting the cell after a few days. This type of transfection is known as transient. However, many experiments require the introduced gene to be integrated into the chromosomal DNA of the cells. Selective markers are used in the formation of these cell lines. This is referred to as permanent or stable transfection. Transfected cells can be analyzed for the presence of the expressed receptor by ligand binding or other functional assays (Figure 10).

Large-scale production of a permanently expressed gene can be achieved by amplification. This involves the use of the selective marker dihydrofolate reductase (DHFR) along with the gene of interest. Addition of increasing amounts of methotrexate to the culture medium results in an increase

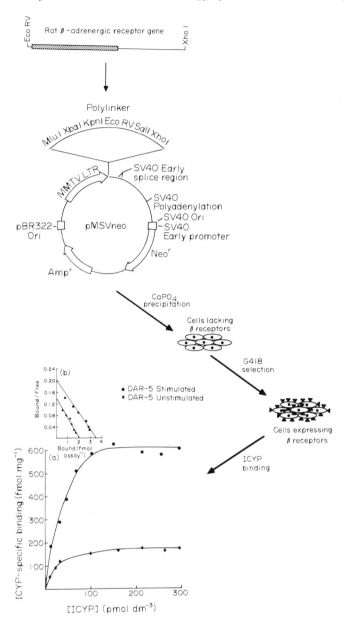

Figure 10 Schematic diagram depicting the steps involved in the production of clonal cell lines permanently expressing neurotransmitter receptors

in the copy number of the gene encoding DHFR as well as any other gene that was coexpressed with the selectable marker.[43] This approach allows for the production of large amounts of a given gene product.

11.3.5.4 Site-directed Mutagenesis

Site-directed mutagenesis is recommended as a means of investigating the function of membrane receptors in relationship to their primary sequence and structure.[19] An oligonucleotide corresponding to the DNA sequence of the receptor is synthesized with a desired sequence change. The oligonucleotide is annealed to a single-stranded circular DNA template. The DNA template has had a small number of its thymine residues replaced by uracil to provide efficient recovery of the mutant. The DNA template is produced within a bacterial strain that is deficient in the enzyme dUTPase, therefore a higher concentration of dUTP is present in the cell and it competes with dTTP for

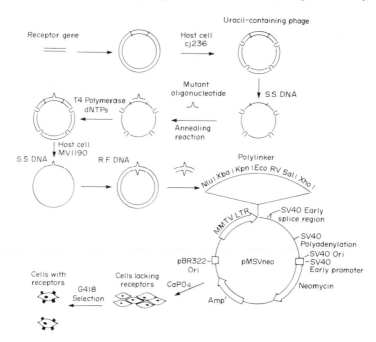

Figure 11 Schematic diagram depicting the steps involved in the production of site-directed mutant receptors using the technique of Kunkel[48]

incorporation into the DNA. The presence of uracil does not inhibit the DNA template in DNA synthesis. The double-stranded hybridization product of the oligonucleotide and the DNA template is used to transfect the cell line (Figure 11). Phage plaques or colonies can be selected by a phenotypic marker or random clones can be selected for DNA sequencing to insure selection of the mutant DNA. The mutant receptor DNA can be expressed and localized in the membrane. Ligand binding studies can be performed to determine the effect of the altered DNA sequence on the function of the receptor.

11.3.6   APPLICATION OF RECOMBINANT DNA TECHNOLOGY

Recent work from the cloning and sequence analysis of genes encoding neurotransmitter receptors of the autonomic nervous system has revealed that the adrenergic and muscarinic cholinergic receptors display considerable amino acid homology[44] even though they exhibit tremendous pharmacological and biochemical diversity (Figure 12). These findings suggest that these receptors may have arisen as a result of gene duplication from a precursor receptor protein.

Site-directed mutagenesis of human β-adrenergic receptors has revealed that the conserved aspartate residues in the second and third transmembrane segments of the receptor are involved in agonist and antagonist binding and receptor activation[45, 46] (Figure 13). Substitution of aspartate residue 79[45] in the second transmembrane segment with asparagine produced a mutant receptor with reduced affinity for isoproterenol, epinephrine and norepinephrine. This mutation also caused the uncoupling of the receptor from stimulatory guanine nucleotide proteins.

The mutation of aspartate residue 130[46] in the third transmembrane segment of the receptor with asparagine resulted in a mutant with normal antagonist binding but an increased affinity for agonists. The mutant receptor did not affect the stimulation of adenylate cyclase. Taken together, these data suggest that the conserved aspartate residues must play a significant role in the structural conformation and function of this receptor.

The advancement and application of recombinant DNA technology will be extremely useful in determining the relationships among the variety of neurotransmitter receptors. An evolutionary relationship between the adrenergic and cholinergic receptors has been proposed.[44, 47] Structural and functional data have been reported revealing conserved regions of receptors involved in binding guanine nucleotide proteins and in adenylate cyclase stimulation. Secondary structural similarities have been found by analysis of the deduced protein sequences from their gene sequences and by

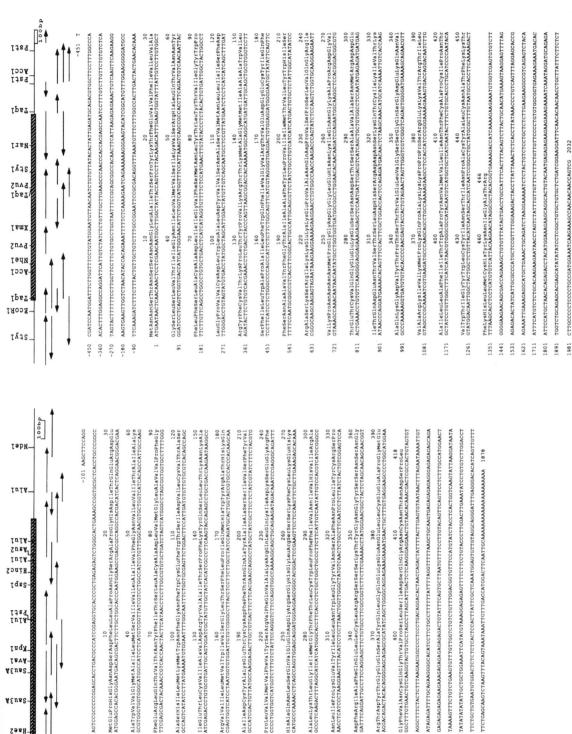

Figure 12 Nucleotide sequence and deduced amino acid sequence of rat cardiac β-adrenergic (a) and muscarinic cholinergic (b) receptors. Partial restriction endonuclease maps and nucleotide sequencing strategies for cDNA clones RHB-DAR (a) and RHB-MF (b) are illustrated. The protein coding regions are marked by stippled boxes. The extent and direction of sequence determinations are indicated by the horizontal arrows. Nucleotide sequences and deduced amino acid sequences of cDNA clones RHB-DAR and RHB-MF are shown

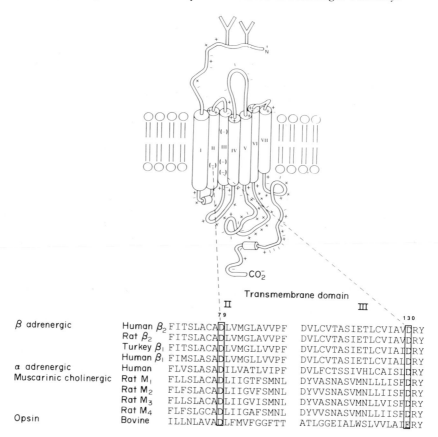

		Transmembrane domain	
		II	III
		7 9	1 3 0
β adrenergic	Human β₂	FITSLACA[D]LVMGLAVVPF	DVLCVTASIETLCVIAV[D]RY
	Rat β₂	FITSLACA[D]LVMGLAVVPF	DVLCVTASIETLCVIAV[D]RY
	Turkey β₁	FITSLACA[D]LVMGLLVVPF	DVLCVTASIETLCVIAI[D]RY
	Human β₁	FIMSLASA[D]LVMGLLVVPF	DVLCVTASIETLCVIAI[D]RY
α adrenergic	Human	FLVSLASA[D]ILVATLVIPF	DVLFCTSSIVHLCAISI[D]RY
Muscarinic cholinergic	Rat M₁	FLLSLACA[D]LIIGTFSMNL	DYVASNASVMNLLLISF[D]RY
	Rat M₂	FLFSLACA[D]LIIGVFSMNL	DYVVSNASVMNLLIISF[D]RY
	Rat M₃	FLLSLACA[D]LIIGVISMNL	DYVASNASVMNLLVISF[D]RY
	Rat M₄	FLFSLGCA[D]LIIGAFSMNL	DYVVSNASVMNLLIISF[D]RY
Opsin	Bovine	ILLNLAVA[D]LFMVFGGFTT	ATLGGEIALWSLVVLA[I]RY

Figure 13 Schematic diagram depicting the presumed tertiary structure of the human β-adrenergic receptor. The primary structure of the human β-adrenergic receptor indicates that the receptor contains seven hydrophobic stretches of amino acids that are presumed to span the bilayer (labeled I–VII). These segments are connected by alternating extracellular and intracellular loops. The amino acid sequence of the second and third transmembrane segments of a number of related receptors is indicated at the bottom of the figure. These domains display considerable amino acid homology. The conserved aspartate residues, enclosed within the stippled boxes, have been shown to be involved in ligand binding and receptor coupling to guanine nucleotide-binding proteins in the human β₂-adrenergic receptor

hydropathy analysis. The extent of structural homology among these proteins has become more apparent with the cloning and sequencing of the receptor genes from a variety of species. A common structural feature proposed for each of these proteins is that they contain seven transmembrane spanning segments.[3] The homology between these receptors supports the theory that neurotransmitter receptors evolved from one common ancestor.

11.3.7 REFERENCES

1. M. H. Saier, Jr. and C. D. Stiles, 'Molecular Dynamics in Biological Membranes', Springer-Verlag, New York, 1975, p. 16.
2. S. J. Singer, *Annu. Rev. Biochem.*, 1974, **43**, 805.
3. A. R. Kerlavage, C. M. Fraser, F.-Z. Chung and J. C. Venter, *Proteins: Struct. Funct. Genet.*, 1986, **1**, 287.
4. T. L. Steck and C. F. Fox, in 'Membrane Molecular Biology', ed. C. F. Fox and A. D. Keith, Sinauer Associates, Stamford, CT, 1972, p. 27.
5. A. Helenius and K. Simons, *Biochim. Biophys. Acta*, 1975, **415**, 29.
6. W. L. Strauss, G. Ghai, C. M. Fraser and J. C. Venter, *Arch. Biochem. Biophys.*, 1979, **196**, 566.
7. A. J. Biotonti, J. Moss, L. M. Hjelmeland and M. Vaughan, *Biochemistry*, 1982, **21**, 3650.
8. L. M. Hjelmeland and A. Chrambach, in 'Receptor Biochemistry and Methodology', ed. J. C. Venter and L. C. Harrison, Liss, New York, 1984, vol. 1, p. 35.
9. O. J. Bjerrum, in 'Membrane Proteins, A Laboratory Manual', ed. A. Azzi, U. Brodbeck and P. Zahler, Springer-Verlag, New York, 1981, p. 13.
10. A. C. Newby, A. C. Chrambach and E. M. Bailyes, in 'Techniques in Lipid and Membrane Biochemistry—Part I', ed. T. R. Hesketh, H. L. Kornberg, J. C. Metcalf, D. H. Northcote, C. I. Pogsone and K. F. Tipton, Elsevier, New York, 1982, vol, B4/I, No. B409, p. 1.
11. P. Cuatrecasas and C. B. Anfinsen, *Annu. Rev. Biochem.*, 1971, **40**, 259.

12. S. D. Flanagan, in 'Receptor Biochemistry and Methodology', ed. J. C. Venter and L. C. Harrison, Liss, New York, 1984, vol. 2, p. 15.
13. 'Affinity Chromatography', Pharmacia Fine Chemicals, Uppsala, Sweden, 1983.
14. J. L. Benovic, R. G. L. Shorr, M. G. Caron and R. J. Lefkowitz, *Biochemistry*, 1984, **23**, 4510.
15. C. M. Fraser, A. R. Kerlavage, A. P. Mariani and J. C. Venter, *Proteins: Struct. Funct. Genet.*, 1987, **2**, 34.
16. A. D. Strosberg, in 'Receptor Biochemistry and Methodology', ed. J. C. Venter and L. C. Harrison, Liss, New York, 1984, vol. 2, p. 1.
17. L. Lilly, B. Eddy, J. Schaber, C. M. Fraser and J. C. Venter, in 'Receptor Biochemistry and Methodology', ed. J. C. Venter and L. C. Harrison, Liss, New York, 1984, vol. 2, p. 77.
18. L. A. E. Sluyterman and J. Wijdenes, *J. Chromatogr.*, 1981, **206**, 441.
19. F. A. Ausubel, R. Brent, R. E. Kingston, D. D. Moore, J. A. Smith, J. G. Seidman and K. Struhl (eds.), 'Current Protocols in Molecular Biology', Greene and Wiley-Interscience, New York, 1987.
20. P. Cuatrecasas, *J. Biol. Chem.*, 1970, **245**, 3059.
21. S. C. March, I. Parikh and P. Cuatrecasas, *Anal. Biochem.*, 1974, **60**, 149.
22. C. M. Fraser and J. C. Venter, *Proc. Natl. Acad. Sci. U.S.A.*, 1980, **77**, 7034.
23. Y. Yarden, H. Rodriguez, S. K.-F. Wong, D. R. Brandt, D. C. May, J. Burnier, R. N. Harkins, E. Y. Chen, J. Ramachandran, A. Ullrich and E. M. Ross, *Proc. Natl. Acad. Sci. U.S.A.*, 1986, **83**, 6795.
24. M. F. El-Refai, in 'Receptor Biochemistry and Methodology', ed. J. C. Venter and L. C. Harrison, Liss, New York, 1984, vol. 1, p. 99.
25. U. K. Laemmli, *Nature (London)*, 1970, **227**, 680.
26. A. Boschetti, E. Sauton-Heiniger and K. J. Clemetson, in 'Membrane Proteins. A Laboratory Manual', ed. A. Azzi, U. Brodbeck and P. Zahler, Springer-Verlag, New York, 1981, p. 3.
27. R. H. Aebersold, R. J. Leavitt, R. A. Saavedra, L. E. Hood and S. B. H. Kent, *Proc. Natl. Acad. Sci. U.S.A.*, 1987, **84**, 6970.
28. G. Wagner and F. E. Regnier, *Anal. Biochem.*, 1982, **126**, 37.
29. S. M. Hyder and J. L. Wittliff, *Biochromatography*, 1987, **2**, 121.
30. 'Bio-Radiations', Bio-Rad, Richmond, CA, 1984, No. 51, p. 3.
31. K. L. Stone and K. R. Williams, *J. Chromatogr.*, 1986, **359**, 203.
32. S. J. Singer, in 'Ciba Foundation Symposium on Molecular Properties of Drug Receptors', ed. R. Porter and M. O'Connor, Churchill, London, 1970, p. 229.
33. H. B. Niznik, D. E. Grigoriadia and P. Seeman, *FEBS Lett.*, 1986, **209**, 71.
34. D. W. Goldman, J. S. Pober, J. White and H. Bayley, *Nature (London)*, 1979, **280**, 841.
35. I. Kahane and C. Gitler, *Science (Washington, D.C.)*, 1978, **201**, 351.
36. H. Bayley and J. R. Knowles, *Methods Enzymol.*, 1977, **46**, 69.
37. T. Maniatis, E. F. Fritsch and J. Sambrook, 'Molecular Cloning: A Laboratory Manual', Cold Spring Harbor, New York, 1982.
38. C. M. Fraser and J. Lindstrom, in 'Receptor Biochemistry and Methodology', ed. J. C. Venter and L. C. Harrison, Liss, New York, 1984, vol. 3, p. 1.
39. W. J. Gullick and J. M. Lindstrom, *Biochemistry*, 1983, **22**, 3312.
40. J. C. Venter, B. J. Eddy, L. M. Hall and C. M. Fraser, *Proc. Natl. Acad. Sci. U.S.A.*, 1984, **81**, 272.
41. E. M. Southern, *J. Mol. Biol.*, 1980, **98**, 503.
42. P. S. Thomas, *Proc. Natl. Acad. Sci. U.S.A.*, 1980, **77**, 5201.
43. J. H. Nunberg, R. J. Kaufman, R. T. Schimke, G. Urlaub and L. A. Chasin, *Proc. Natl. Acad. Sci. U.S.A.*, 1978, **75**, 5553.
44. J. D. Gocayne, D. A. Robinson, M. G. FitzGerald, F.-Z. Chung, A. R. Kerlavage, K.-U. Lentes, J. Lai, C.-D. Wang, C. M. Fraser and J. C. Venter, *Proc. Natl. Acad. Sci. U.S.A.*, 1987, **84**, 8296.
45. F.-Z. Chung, C.-D. Wang, P. C. Potter, J. C. Venter and C. M. Fraser, *J. Biol. Chem.*, 1988, **263**, 4052.
46. C. M. Fraser, F.-Z. Chung, C.-D. Wang and J. C. Venter, *Proc. Natl. Acad. Sci. U.S.A.*, 1988, **85**, 5478.
47. J. C. Venter, U. diPorzio, D. A. Robinson, S. M. Shreeve, J. Y.-W. Lai, A. R. Kerlavage, S. P. Fracek, Jr., K.-U. Lentes and C. M. Fraser, *Prog. Neurobiol. (Oxford)*, 1988, **30**, 105.
48. T. A. Kunkel, *Proc. Natl. Acad. Sci. U.S.A.*, 1985, **82**, 488.

11.4*

Transmembrane Signalling, Second Messenger Analogues and Inositol Phosphates

BARRY V. L. POTTER

Leicester University, UK

* This chapter is based upon articles published in 'Natural Product Reports', The Royal Society of Chemistry, Cambridge, 1990 and 'Transmembrane Signalling, Intracellular Messengers and Implication for Drug Development', ed. S. R. Nahorski, John Wiley & Sons Ltd., Chichester, 1990, with the permission of the respective publishers.

11.4.1 INTRODUCTION

Known signalling pathways by which external stimuli are converted into internal cellular responses are few in number yet regulate a host of physiological and biochemical processes and share similar characteristics. The foundations of the two major transmembrane signalling pathways known today involving mediatory molecules known as 'second messengers' were laid in the 1950s. Some 31 years ago Sutherland and Rall discovered 3',5'-cyclic adenosine monophosphate (cAMP),[1] a molecule now well established as a ubiquitous second messenger.[2] Even before the realization of the importance of cAMP, Hokin and Hokin in 1953 had demonstrated the phenomenon of receptor-mediated phospholipid turnover,[3] but it was not until 1975 that Michell suggested that this was linked to an increase in cytosolic Ca^{2+} concentration.[4] Only after the subsequent realization of the importance of phospholipase C-catalyzed cleavage of phosphatidylinositol 4,5-diphosphate (PIP_2) into the two second messengers inositol 1,4,5-triphosphate (IP_3), which mobilizes intracellular Ca^{2+},[5] and diacylglycerol (DAG), which activates protein kinase C,[6] have these events blossomed into the now well-established polyphosphoinositide signalling pathway of the 1980s[7] and contributed dramatically towards the rapid current upsurge of interest in second messengers.

Since the first reports in 1983–1984 that the cyclitol polyphosphate, D-*myo*-inositol 1,4,5-triphosphate, based on *myo*-inositol,* in combination with diacylglycerol and calcium, acts as a second messenger,[5,8] and is the long-sought-after link between the spatially separated events of receptor stimulation and the mobilization of calcium from intracellular stores, interest in this molecule has been greatly stimulated[7] (for a popular account see ref. 9). This interest has been both academic and industrial. In the former case, it has become clear that this discovery is one of the most significant recent events in cell biology, heralding a new era in our understanding of receptor-coupled aspects of cellular control, and in the latter because receptors which bind such second messengers, enzymes which metabolize them and the generative pathways responsible for their formation are naturally seen by the medicinal chemist as potential targets for rational drug design.

While most of the rapid progress of the last five years in the polyphosphoinositide field has been biological in nature, as testified by the plethora of biological reviews[3,5–7,9–18] and books[19–23] currently available on this topic, it is clear that current and future efforts of the bioorganic and medicinal chemist will underpin long-term efforts related to the molecular details of, and rational pharmacological intervention in, second-messenger-mediated signalling systems. Consequently, significant parallel interests have also been stimulated in the chemical synthesis of analogues which might interfere with the actions or metabolism of these second messengers and thus aid in investigations of their actions or give rise to novel biological effects. Indeed, since the discovery of cAMP more than 600 cAMP analogues have been chemically synthesized[24] and yet only two cAMP antagonists have been identified. By contrast, such efforts are only just beginning for IP_3 and diacylglycerol. First syntheses of *myo*-inositol 1,4,5-triphosphate were reported in 1986–1987 and these have been followed by significant synthetic progress to the extent that essentially all of the problems inherent to inositol phosphate synthesis have now been overcome (Section 11.4.7). However, the complex nature of inositol phosphate metabolism,[18] which is still evolving, is providing regular new targets for synthesis. The focus of current activity must now invariably move towards synthesis of modified inositol phosphates with novel biological properties.

The aim of this review is to attempt a synthesis of both new biological and related chemical progress in this area, focusing on the phosphorylated second messengers, and more specifically upon the more recent advances in the polyphosphoinositide signalling pathway. A completely comprehensive coverage of the biology of recent years is, however, beyond the scope of this article and the reader is referred to the many existing reviews in this area.[5–7,9–23] For a more comprehensive discussion of the regulation of second messenger pathways by phosphodiesterases and protein kinases and their inhibitors, the reader if referred to Chapters 5.5 and 8.7.

---

* All references to inositol refer to the *myo* isomer unless specified.

11.4.2 TRANSMEMBRANE SIGNALLING

Cells are dependent upon each other for the division of labour in a complex organism and communicate with one another by means of chemical signals, which may be hormones, growth factors, neurotransmitters, *etc.* While a lipophilic steroid, for example, can pass readily through the plasma membrane surrounding the cell, the hydrophobic nature of the latter acts as a physical barrier to the flow of information carried by nonlipophilic messengers and a variety of mechanisms have been evolved whereby an external chemical signal can be translated into an internal response in a stimulated cell (Figure 1). These mechanisms are dependent upon the stimulation of cell surface receptors, which span the membrane, and their subsequent coupling to an event, which produces a cascade of biochemical processes culminating in a change in cell behaviour, such as the secretion of a specific enzyme, physical contraction (in the case of muscle cells) or the onset of cell division (Figure 2a).

If only plasma membrane receptors are considered, three distinct types can be recognized (Figure 1). In the first case the receptor is linked to an ion channel, which is normally closed. On receptor activation, the channel opens, thereby allowing cations such as sodium or potassium to flow into or out of the cell. In the second case the receptor is itself an enzyme, a tyrosine kinase, which on activation phosphorylates tyrosine residues in key internal target proteins. Insulin exerts its action in this way as do other growth factors. Finally, there are receptors which are intrinsically neither ion channels nor enzymes. Such receptors are coupled to internal enzymes or ion channels by means of a class of guanosine 5′-triphosphate (GTP) binding transmembrane glycoproteins known as G proteins.[25,26]

Receptors working through G proteins include those for messenger molecules, *e.g.* the β-adrenergic receptor and the muscarinic cholinergic receptor and for light (rhodopsin). On receptor stimulation by an agonist (first messenger) an associated G protein is induced to release a molecule of GDP and bind GTP. In this activated form it can dissociate into subunits, which, in ways that are not yet entirely clear, can activate effector molecules to mediate relese of an internal 'second messenger'. Until recently the most well known and best understood example of this process was the G-protein-regulated production of adenosine 3′,5′-cyclic monophosphate (cAMP) from ATP *via* the effector adenylate cyclase.[27] Since one molecule of effector can produce many molecules of second messenger, a significant amplification of the original signal is achieved. It is now clear that the effector for the phosphoinositide signalling system, polyphosphoinositide phosphodiesterase, a phospholipase C (PLC), interacts with plasma membrane receptors (R), activated by an agonist (A), by means of a stimulatory G protein (G) (Figure 2b).[28]

11.4.3 THE cAMP SIGNALLING SYSTEM

A detailed discussion of the biology of the cAMP signalling system is beyond the scope of this review. The reader is referred to reviews[27,29] and a recent volume dedicated to this pathway.[30] The

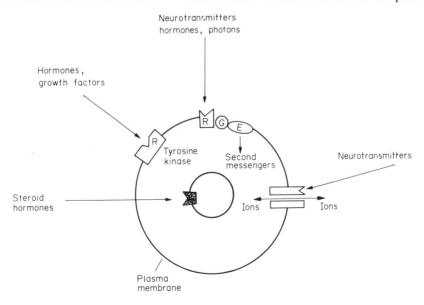

Figure 1 Pathways of transmembrane signalling

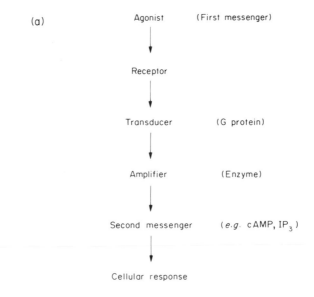

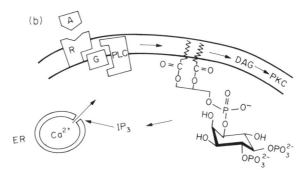

Figure 2   (a) Sequence of events in transmembrane signalling *via* second messengers; (b) receptor-mediated generation of inositol 1,4,5-triphosphate and diacylglycerol in response to agonist stimulation

cAMP signalling pathway is used by many hormones, including epinephrine and glucagon for example, and is characterized by the possession of stimulatory and inhibitory G protein transducers, G_s and G_i, linked respectively to stimulatory and inhibitory membrane receptors, R_s and R_i (Figure 3).[26,27,29,31] The binding of an external signal to R_s stimulates a conformational change which is transmitted to G_s, and induces the release of bound GDP. The binding of GTP to the α subunit of G_s then allows it to dissociate from the β–γ subunit and activate the membrane-associated enzyme adenylate cyclase (AC) to form cAMP from ATP. In a similar fashion the arrival of an external signal at R_i leads to a switching off of adenylate cyclase. Once formed, cAMP participates in the final stages of the pathway by binding to the regulatory subunit (R) of the protein kinase enzyme A-kinase, thus liberating the catalytic subunit (C), which phosphorylates target proteins leading to the overall cellular response.

11.4.3.1   Synthesis of cAMP Analogues

3′,5′-Cyclic AMP is, a nucleotide, possessing fused five- and six-membered ring systems (Figure 4; **1**). While considerable attention has been focused upon chemical modification to determine structure–activity relationships and define interactions between cAMP and cAMP dependent protein kinase, and many purine-modified analogues have been synthesized,[32] analogues prepared by modification of the phosphorus atom are of especial interest and have led to the identification of the only known cAMP antagonists. The phosphorus atom in cAMP is a prochiral centre in the asymmetric environment of a nucleotide and consequently replacement of one of the two peripheral oxygen atoms by another group produces diastereoisomers. Thus, for the phosphorothioates, *e.g.*

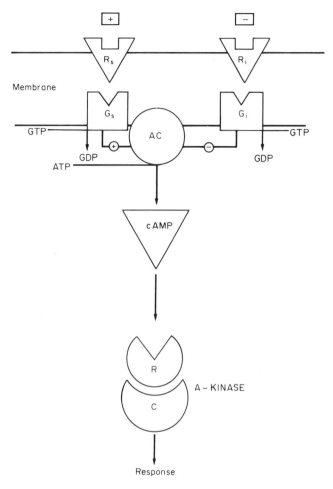

Figure 3 The cAMP signalling pathway

the isomers of cAMPS (**2**) and (**3**), the introduction of a sulfur atom at this centre produces R_p and S_p diastereoisomers[33,34] (**2**) and (**3**) respectively (Figure 4), which can have significantly different properties (Section 11.4.3.2).

The first synthesis of cAMPS was reported in 1974,[35] by a method which has now been improved to give a general preparation of nucleoside 3',5'-cyclic phosphorothioates in which the base-protected nucleoside is phosphorylated and the product cyclized.[36] A simple procedure for the cyclothiophosphorylation of unprotected nucleosides has also been reported,[37] which is particularly applicable to the synthesis of phosphorothioate analogues with modified heterocyclic base moieties. In both these cases the resulting mixture of diastereoisomers must be separated either by ion exchange chromatography, crystallization or reverse phase HPLC. A stereospecific approach has, however, also been devised[38] in which separable diastereoisomeric anilidates can be stereospecifically converted into diastereoisomerically pure isomers of cAMPS. This method has also been used for other cyclic nucleotides,[39] but although stereospecific, requires a multistep synthesis with low overall yields. This route, however, provided a vital reference point by which the absolute configuration of material prepared *via* cyclization syntheses could be correlated. (An X-ray structure of the crystalline R_p-cAMPS has now been reported.[40]) A similar route has also allowed the synthesis of the cAMP phosphorodithioate analogue (cAMPS$_2$; **4**), in which both prochiral oxygens have been replaced by sulfur (Figure 4) from a cyclic thiophosphoranilidate.[38]

cAMP is formed from ATP (**8**) by the enzyme adenylate cyclase. Another, less commonly used, route to phosphorothioate analogues of cyclic nucleotides involves the enzymatic cyclization of one diastereoisomer of the corresponding nucleoside 5'-O-(1-thiotriphosphate) (*e.g.* **9**) with inversion of configuration at phosphorus to the nucleoside 3',5'-cyclic phosphorothioate using the appropriate cyclase (Figure 5). Thus, both adenylate cyclase and guanylate cyclase have been used to prepare the R_p diastereoisomers of cAMPS[41] (from **9**) and cGMPS (**6**)[42] (from **11**) respectively. Disadvantages of

(**1**) X = Y = O, B = A
(**2**) X = O, Y = S, B = A
(**3**) X = S, Y = O, B = A
(**4**) X = Y = S, B = A
(**5**) X = Y = O, B = G
(**6**) X = O, Y = S, B = G
(**7**) X = S, Y = O, B = G

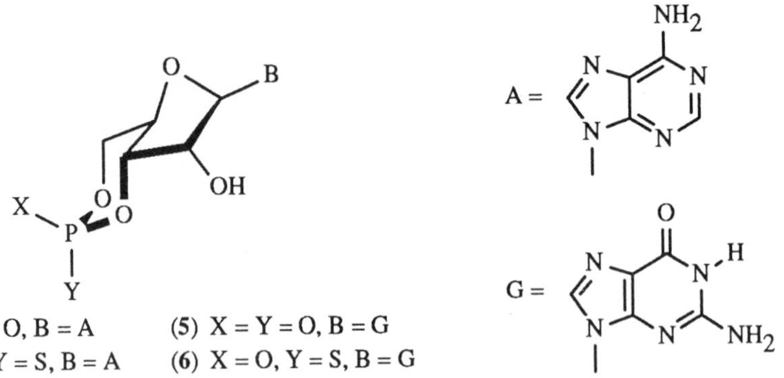

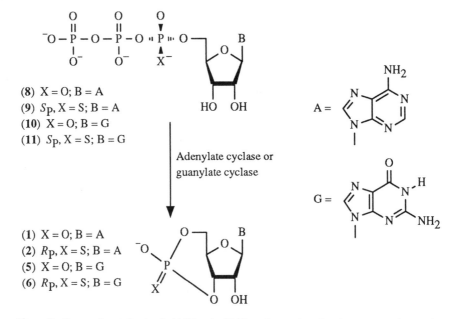

Figure 4 Structures of cAMP, cGMP and their phosphorothioate analogues.

(**8**) X = O; B = A
(**9**) S_P, X = S; B = A
(**10**) X = O; B = G
(**11**) S_P, X = S; B = G

(**1**) X = O; B = A
(**2**) R_P, X = S; B = A
(**5**) X = O; B = G
(**6**) R_P, X = S; B = G

Figure 5 Enzymatic synthesis of cAMP and cGMP analogues by adenylate or guanylate cyclase

this method are that the enzymes are not readily available and, more importantly, that this route only gives access to one diastereoisomer. Reviews have summarized aspects of the synthesis of cAMPS.[33,34]

11.4.3.2 Biology of cAMP Analogues

The breakdown of cyclic nucleotides is catalyzed by specific phosphodiesterases. cAMPS differs from cAMP by virtue of its enhanced metabolic stability, as shown by the very slow hydrolysis of the S_p diastereoisomer by beef heart and rabbit brain cAMP phosphodiesterases.[35] (N.B. It was subsequently discovered that the experiments with these enzymes had been carried out on pure S_p-cAMPS (**3**) and not on a diastereoisomeric mixture as reported.) R_p-cAMPS (**2**) is not a substrate for beef heart cAMP phosphodiesterases;[43] however, both isomers are cleaved by baker's yeast phosphodiesterase with inversion of configuration at phosphorus.[43] Both type I and type II cAMP dependent protein kinases are activated by S_p-cAMPS (**3**) (axial sulfur substitution) but R_p-cAMPS (**4**) (equatorial sulfur substitution) is an antagonist and does not cause release of the catalytic subunit although it binds to the regulatory subunit.[44] The inability of R_p-cAMPS to cause a conformational change in the regulatory subunit has been postulated to be the result of interference of the equatorial sulfur with a hydrogen bond or salt bridge normally between the protein and the agonist (P—S has a much lower affinity for forming H bonds than P—O[40]). Activation of cAMP dependent protein kinase has been observed in hepatocytes, where the phosphorylase kinase–phosphorylase glycogenolytic cascade is affected by S_p-cAMPS, but R_p-cAMPS acts as an antagonist.[45] Glucagon-induced glycogenolysis is also inhibited by R_p-cAMPS.[46] Recently, the phosphorodithioate analogue of cAMP possessing double sulfur substitution at phosphorus, cAMPS$_2$ (4; Figure 4), has also been found to be an antagonist of bovine heart type II cAMP dependent protein kinase, indicating that the most important structural requirement for the dissociation of the holoenzyme is an equatorial exocyclic oxygen.[47] A recent study using purified enzyme has also been reported.[48]

Many reports testify to the ability of cAMPS to mimic the actions of cAMP. Thus, S_p-cAMPS can cause parotid cells to secrete amylase[49] and it has been used to study the cAMP-induced phosphorylation of microtubule-associated protein 2 in brain[50] and hormone-induced steroidogenesis.[51] cAMPS and other analogues have been used to define structure–activity relationships for binding to the cell surface cAMP receptor and chemotaxis in the slime mould *Dictyostelium discoideum*,[52] a system that shows no response with another commonly used lipophilic analogue, dibutyryl cAMP.[53] S_p-cAMPS binds to the *E. coli* cAMP receptor protein as studied by ^{1}H NMR spectroscopy.[54] In investigations of stimulation of lac transcription by cAMP analogues, R_p-cAMPS was found to be *ca.* 600-fold more potent at catabolite repression of β-galactosidase synthetase in *E. coli* than S_p-cAMPS and *ca.* 50-fold more potent than cAMP.[55] S_p-cAMPS inhibits the rate of triacylglycerol synthesis from glycerol and phosphatidylcholine from choline in hepatocytes[56] and the rate of antigen-stimulated release of histamine in mast cells.[57] cAMPS can penetrate cells and has a clear advantage over dibutyryl cAMP, which releases butyric acid on hydrolysis and can thus generate artifacts.[53]

11.4.4 cGMP AS A SECOND MESSENGER

cGMP differs structurally from cAMP in that guanine replaces adenine in the molecule (5; Figure 4). Whilst cGMP appears to possess many of the characteristics of a second messenger, the precise details of its actions are not well understood. cGMP is synthesized from GTP by the enzyme guanylate cyclase, which is usually not linked to a receptor. However, levels of cGMP have been found to increase following stimulation of receptors coupled to polyphosphoinositide hydrolysis,[3,4] and cGMP can activate a protein kinase, G-kinase.[58] A specific role for cGMP in the cell has, however, yet to be established.

Guanosine 3′,5′-cyclic monophosphate (cGMP) is also an important second messenger in vision[59] (for a general review of the molecules of visual excitation see ref. 60). Indeed, it is in the retina, where light is transformed into nerve impulses, that the most complete role for cGMP is currently available[61] and the amplification cascade of vertebrate photoreceptor cells closely resembles the cAMP cascade. Vertebrate photoreceptors, or rod cells in the retina, act as sensory transducers,

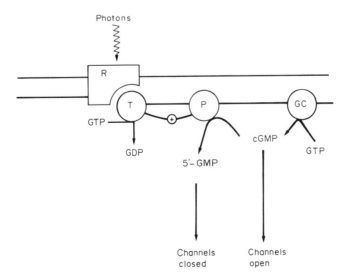

Figure 6   Role of cGMP as a second messenger in vision

where incoming stimuli (photons) at a membrane-spanning receptor (rhodopsin) are coupled to the release of a neurotransmitter by the cell, regulated by changes in the permeability of the plasma membrane to sodium ions.[62] Photoexcited rhodopsin (R), by means of the G protein transducin (T), which is similar to G_s of the cAMP system, triggers an enzymatic amplification cascade resulting in the hydrolysis of cGMP to 5'-GMP by cGMP phosphodiesterase (P) (Figure 6).[63] cGMP has been found to act directly in a highly cooperative fashion[64] on the light sensitive channel of retinal rods, keeping these channels permeable to sodium in the dark. With the activation of cGMP phosphodiesterase the level of cGMP falls steeply and the cation specific channels close, resulting in a plasma membrane hyperpolarization, which is communicated to a synapse and, *via* retinal nerve cells and the optic nerve, ultimately to the brain. Restoration of the dark state is accomplished by deactivation of rhodopsin and regeneration of cGMP by guanylate cyclase. It is worth noting that in the photoreceptors of the crab *Limulus*, injection of inositol 1,4,5-triphosphate can mimic the effect of light,[65-67] whereas cGMP is without effect, indicating possible diversity in visual signal transduction mechanisms.

The most important analogues of cGMP, the diastereoisomers of cGMPS (**6**) and (**7**) (Figure 4) have not yet found wide application. However, they have been used as inhibitors of cyclic phosphodiesterase in rod outer segments[68] and to determine the stereochemical course of the cGMP phosphodiesterase reaction by inversion of configuration at phosphorus.[69]

11.4.5   STEREOCHEMISTRY AND NOMENCLATURE OF INOSITOL DERIVATIVES

11.4.5.1   Stereochemistry and Nomenclature

In 1850 Scherer isolated an optically inactive isomer of cyclohexanehexol from muscle, which he designated 'Inosit'. Later the suffix -ol was added and as other isomers were discovered or synthesized they were also named 'inositols'. There are nine possible isomeric inositols (**12–20**; Figure 7),[70] prefixed: *cis-, epi-, allo-, myo-, muco-, neo-*, D-*chiro-*(+)-, L-*chiro-*(−)- and *scyllo-*. The large range of inositols and derivatives has caused some difficult problems of nomenclature, which have still not been fully resolved. The publication in 1967 of a set of rules known as the '1967 IUPAC Tentative Rules for Cyclitols'[71] has gone a considerable way towards standardization, although difficulties still exist. Some aspects of these rules are outlined below in the treatment of *myo*-inositol. Proposals have been made that the system of stereospecific numbering should be adopted for inositol derivatives,[72] but these have not yet found widespread acceptance. A note on recent attempts to simplify nomenclature and abbreviations has appeared.[73] Additionally, for a simplified discussion of this topic, which attempts to highlight some current stereochemical misconceptions in

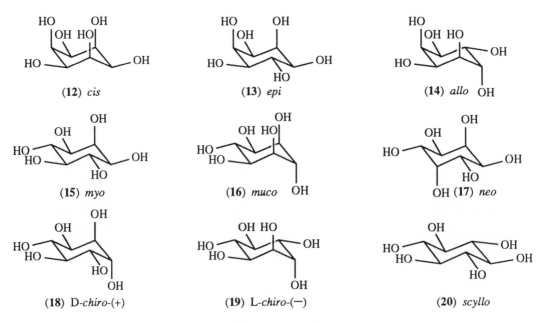

Figure 7   The nine isomers of inositol

the biochemical community, consequent upon the recent attraction to the field of many nonspecialists, the reader is referred to an excellent review.[74]

11.4.5.2 *myo*-Inositol (15)

In the current context of phosphoinositide-generated second messengers we need fortunately only be concerned with the IUPAC rules as applied to *myo*-inositol (Figure 7). *myo*-Inositol (15) is a *meso* compound and consequently possesses a plane of symmetry with five equatorial hydroxyl groups and one axial hydroxyl group. The carbon bearing the axial hydroxyl is numbered C-2 and the other ring carbons can be numbered C-1 to C-6 from a C-1 atom either side of C-2, proceeding around the ring in a clockwise or anticlockwise fashion. According to convention, an anticlockwise numbering gives rise to a substituted inositol with a D prefix and a clockwise numbering an inositol with an L prefix. The choice of prefix is normally determined by giving preference to that which results in the lowest numbering of substituents. Thus, in Figure 8a in (15) the symmetry plane is through C-2 and C-5. Consequently, substitution of one of the symmetry-related pairs of carbon atoms C-1, C-3 and C-4, C-6 gives rise to enantiomers, which must bear a D or L prefix. Substitution of only C-2 or C-5 clearly gives a *meso* product and a prefix is inappropriate. In Figure 8b the enantiomers of the IP_3 metabolite *myo*-inositol 1,4-diphosphate (1,4-IP_2) are shown. The metabolite of the natural product is D-1,4-IP_2 (21), formed by 5-phosphatase action, and its enantiomer is the mirror image L-1,4-IP_2 (22), these numberings being chosen since they are lower in comparison to the other possibilities, namely L-3,6-IP_2 and D-3,6-IP_2 respectively. However, problems can arise with strict adherence to the IUPAC rules, especially when traversing a metabolic pathway, where confusing changes in nomenclature can occur. For example, D-*myo*-inositol 3,4-diphosphate (IUPAC conventional name L-*myo*-inositol 1,6-diphosphate), a product of metabolism of D-*myo*-inositol 1,3,4-triphosphate, is metabolized by phosphatases to the monophosphate L-*myo*-inositol 1-phosphate, although the nonconventional name D-*myo*-inositol 3-phosphate allows more immediate appreciation of the metabolic step occurring. An IUPAC recommendation to allow all biologically relevant compounds of *myo*-inositol to be denoted as D derivatives with the abbreviation Ins has been proposed recently.[75]

11.4.6 BIOCHEMISTRY, ACTIONS AND METABOLISM OF *MYO*-INOSITOL PHOSPHATES

11.4.6.1 Biosynthesis of *myo*-Inositol

Most *myo*-inositol intake in humans is from plants and only a small fraction is biosynthesized. However, *de novo* synthesis is possible in both plants and animals, *via* the isomerization of D-glucose 6-phosphate (23; Figure 9) catalyzed by the enzyme L-*myo*-inositol 1-phosphate synthase (D-*myo*-inositol 3-phosphate synthase). This enzyme has been purified to homogeneity from yeast[76] and its gene regulation studied,[77] but it is most abundant in mammalian testis from which it has also been purified[78,79] and in brain (Section 11.4.6.1).

The reaction catalyzed by L-*myo*-inositol 1-phosphate synthase is shown in Figure 9, and on account of its intrinsic stereochemical interest (a stereospecific ring closure and inosose reduction), its mechanism has been intensively studied, especially using the techniques of isotopic labelling. The participation of oxidized intermediates in this reaction pathway has been implicated for some time, although conclusive proof has not been forthcoming. The intermediacy of L-*myo*-inosose-2 1-phosphate (25) has, however, recently been demonstrated using homogeneous enzyme,[80] although similar proof for 5-ketoglucose 6-phosphate (24) is not yet available. This biosynthetic pathway has been reviewed,[81,82] and stereochemical aspects have been discussed.[74]

Thus, D-glucose 6-phosphate (23) is presumed to be oxidized to 5-ketoglucose 6-phosphate (24) by the NAD^+ dependent oxidoreductase activity of the enzyme (loss of H_A in 23, Figure 9). The aldolase activity then closes the ring in a stereospecific fashion to form L-*myo*-inosose-2 1-phosphate (25). A specific hydrogen from the NADH (H_A) is then retransferred by a stereospecific reduction of the keto group to give L-*myo*-inositol 1-phosphate (D-*myo*-inositol 3-phosphate; 26), which is hydrolyzed to *myo*-inositol (15) by *myo*-inositol-1-phosphatase.

myo-Inositol-1-phosphatase is a particularly interesting enzyme since it hydrolyzes both the D and L isomers of *myo*-inositol 1-phosphate, the L isomer arising *via* the above pathway and the D isomer by the hydrolysis of phosphatidylinositol phospholipids. The enzyme has been purified from rat

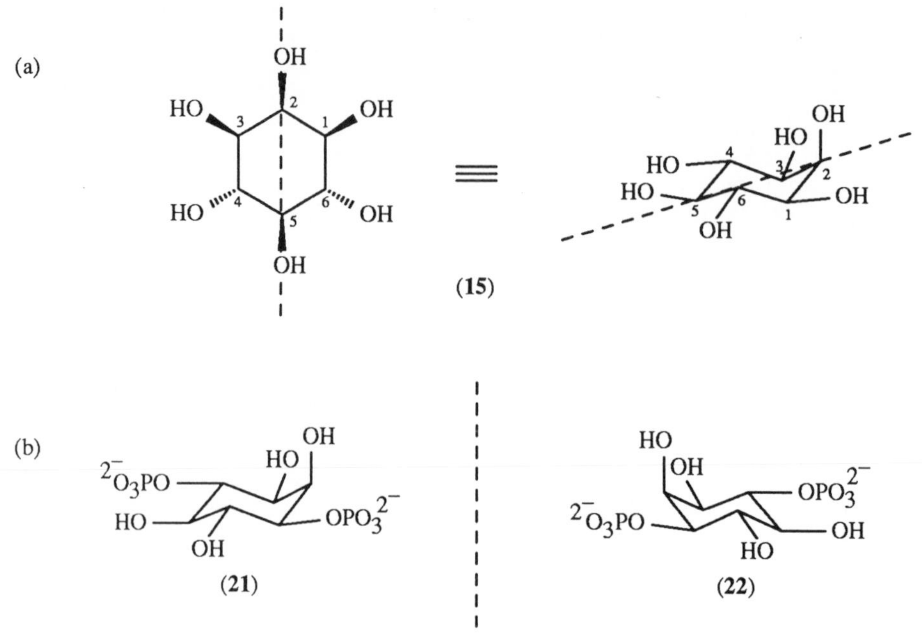

(a)

(15)

(b)

(21)   (22)

Figure 8   (a) *myo*-Inositol; (b) the enantiomers of *myo*-inositol 1,4-diphosphate

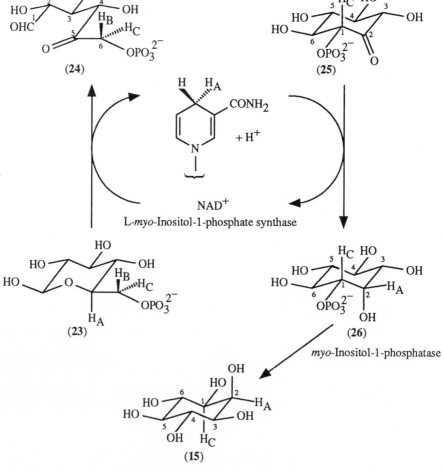

(24)   (25)

+H$^+$

L-*myo*-Inositol-1-phosphate synthase

NAD$^+$

(23)   (26)

myo-Inositol-1-phosphatase

(15)

Figure 9   Biosynthesis of *myo*-inositol

brain[83] and more recently from bovine brain.[84,85] Using enzyme purified to homogeneity it has been shown that this single enzyme dephosphorylates not only D- and L-*myo*-inositol 1-phosphate, but also D- and L-*myo*-inositol 4-phosphate and possibly *myo*-inositol 5-phosphate.[86]

Aside from this lack of specificity, this enzyme is also of considerable current interest on account of its sensitivity to inhibition by the lithium cation. It was observed in 1971 that levels of free *myo*-inositol decreased significantly in the brains of Li^+-treated rats.[87] Li^+ is widely used in the treatment of manic depression, and currently links between the known therapeutic effects of lithium in brain and its noncompetitive inhibition of *myo*-inositol-1-phosphatase are being actively sought. Since the brain does not have access to dietary *myo*-inositol, which cannot cross the blood–brain barrier, the *de novo* biosynthetic pathway *via* D-glucose 6-phosphate is used. If the final stage in this pathway, the dephosphorylation of L-*myo*-inositol 1-phosphate, is blocked by lithium inhibition, the brain is unable to replenish its stores of phosphatidylinositol lipids and the messenger system based on these lipids (Section 11.4.6.2), which is used by neurotransmitters in cell signalling to alter electrical activity, will be unable to operate. This is thought to be particularly important in those cells which are hyperactive, as may be the case in some forms of mania.[88,89] These important aspects have been recently reviewed.[90,91]

Li^+ has also been found to decrease the accumulation of inositol 1,3,4,5-tetraphosphate in stimulated brain slices,[92] suggesting that it may be inhibiting an IP_4 dependent activity. Another recent advance in this area has been the observation that Li^+ at therapeutic concentrations can affect G-protein-receptor coupling, thus suggesting another possible biochemical target for the antimanic and antidepressant effects of this ion.[93,94]

A recent study has shed more mechanistic detail on the inhibition of *myo*-inositol-1-phosphatase by Li^+ ion,[95] which is unusual by virtue of its uncompetitive nature. It was demonstrated that bovine brain *myo*-inositol-1-phosphatase operates *via* a ping-pong mechanism and that the dephosphorylation involves the participation of a phosphoryl–enzyme intermediate. Li^+ is thought to inhibit the second step of the reaction, namely the breakdown of the phosphoryl–enzyme intermediate, possibly by coordination to an attacking active site water molecule with a concomitant decrease in its nucleophilicity. It is clear that a better understanding of the molecular mechanism of Li^+ inhibition will go a long way towards assisting the rational design of mimics with potential antimanic properties.

11.4.6.2 The Phosphatidylinositol Cycle

Less than 10% of the total phospholipid in animal cells is comprised of three *myo*-inositol-containing phosphatides (Figure 10a): phosphatidylinositol (1-(3-*sn*-phosphatidyl)-D-*myo*-inositol; PI; **27**), which comprises over 90% of total lipid and is primarily located in the endoplasmic reticulum, and the polyphosphoinositides: phosphatidylinositol 4-phosphate (PIP; **28**) and phosphatidylinositol 4,5-diphosphate (PIP$_2$; **29**), which together with a small proportion of total PI are located in the inner leaflet of the plasma membrane. Recent findings have, however, provided evidence for new polyphosphoinositides, phosphatidylinositol 3-phosphate (PI-3-P)[96] and probably phosphatidylinositol 3,4,5-triphosphate (PIP$_3$).[97] Of considerable interest here is the observation that the binding of platelet-derived growth factor (PDGF) to the PDGF receptor and stimulation of protein–tyrosine kinase activity can activate a 3′-lipid kinase activity which produces these novel lipids from PI and PIP$_2$ respectively, as well as the previously unidentified PI-3,4-P$_2$.[98] Since PI-3,4-P$_2$ and PIP$_3$ are not present in unstimulated cells, these phospholipids are candidates for mediators of the PDGF mitogenic response. Whilst it has been known for many years that these phospholipids are highly active metabolically and that stimulation of many cell surface receptors results in PI turnover, only recently has a coherent physiological role in relation to their role in cellular Ca^{2+} homeostasis emerged. This was originally stimulated by the seminal review of Michell.[4] The historical development of the 'Phospholipid Effect' and its relevance to current research has been reviewed.[3,99,100]

The structure of PI is shown in Figure 10a. At the *sn*-3-position of diacylglycerol *myo*-inositol is linked *via* its D-1-hydroxy group by a phosphodiester bridge. PI isolated from plants has a different structure to PI from animal sources. In plants the *sn*-2 glycerol carbon is linked to the C_{18} acid linoleic acid (18:2) and the *sn*-1 position is linked to fatty acids of the (16:0), (18:0) or (18:2) form, whereas in animals arachidonic acid (20:4) predominates at C-2 and stearic acid (18:0) at C-1. Aside from the release of the important second messengers inositol 1,4,5-triphosphate and diacylglycerol, the latter is an important but not exclusive source of arachidonate, the precursor of the eicosanoids.[101]

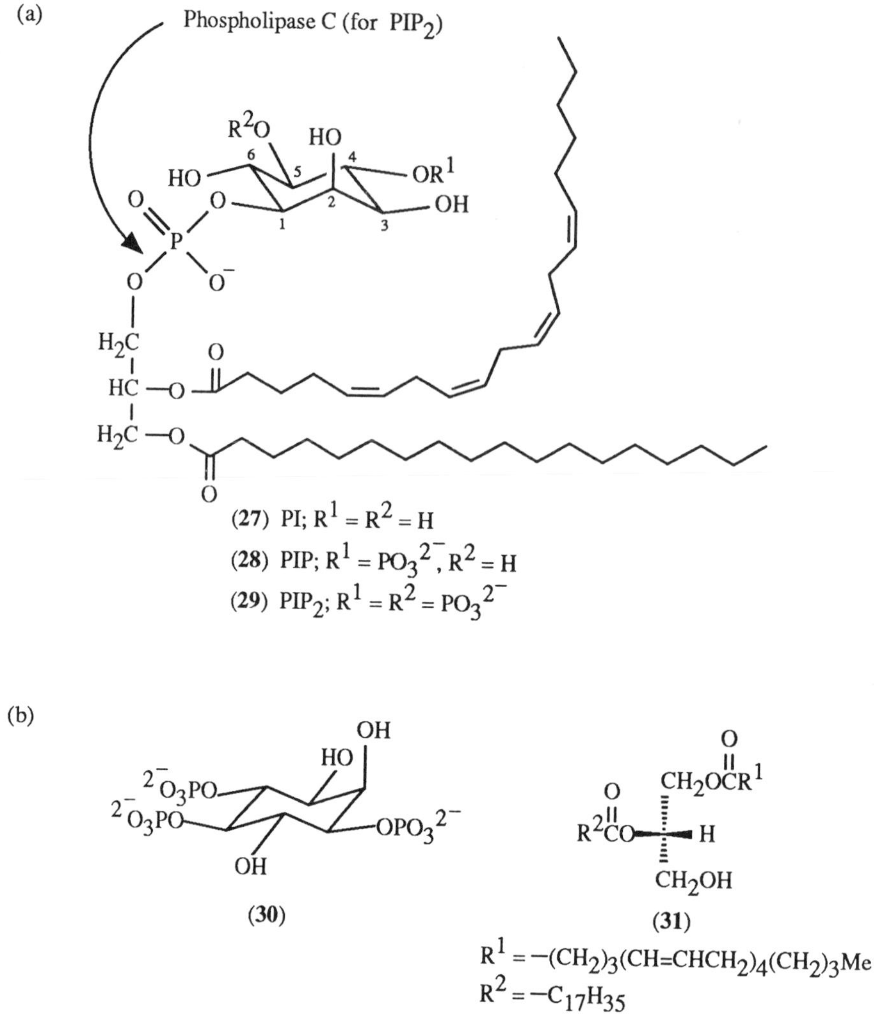

(a)

Phospholipase C (for PIP$_2$)

(27) PI; $R^1 = R^2 = H$
(28) PIP; $R^1 = PO_3^{2-}$, $R^2 = H$
(29) PIP$_2$; $R^1 = R^2 = PO_3^{2-}$

(b)

(30)

(31)

$R^1 = -(CH_2)_3(CH=CHCH_2)_4(CH_2)_3Me$
$R^2 = -C_{17}H_{35}$

Figure 10   (a) Structures of the phosphatidylinositol lipids; (b) structures of D-*myo*-inositol 1,4,5-triphosphate and diacyl-glycerol

PI (**27**) is phosphorylated by a specific kinase (PI kinase) to give the 4-phosphate PIP (**28**), which in turn is phosphorylated by another kinase (PIP kinase) to generate the key lipid, the 4,5-diphosphate PIP$_2$ (**29**). In turn, specific phosphomonoesterases can dephosphorylate PIP and PIP$_2$.[102] Upon receptor activation the associated G protein activates a membrane-bound phosphodiesterase or phosphoinositidase, phospholipase C (the enzyme from platelets has recently been purified,[103] but in general mammalian PLCs have been poorly characterized; an X-ray structure of PLC from *Bacillus cereus* has also been reported[104] and this area has been reviewed [105]), which cleaves PIP$_2$ into two second messengers, *myo*-inositol 1,4,5-triphosphate (**30**) and diacylglycerol (**31**; Figure 10b) which together form a bifurcating signalling pathway.

11.4.6.3   Sites of Action of Inositol 1,4,5-Triphosphate and Diacylglycerol

myo-Inositol 1,4,5-triphosphate diffuses into the cytosol and releases calcium from an internal store *via* a receptor, probably on the endoplasmic reticulum and linked to a Ca^{2+} channel. (For a discussion of another possibility, the newly described discrete smooth-surfaced Ca^{2+}-containing organelle, the 'calciosome', see ref. 106.) The subsequent rise in intracellular Ca^{2+} can be used to activate specialized Ca^{2+}/calmodulin dependent protein kinases or multifunctional Ca^{2+}/cal-modulin dependent protein kinase[107] to elicit the overall cellular response. The inositol 1,4,5-triphosphate receptor has been localized to the endoplasmic reticulum in cerebellar Purkinje cells using immunocytochemical techniques.[108] Progress has been made in the purification to apparent homogeneity of an inositol triphosphate receptor from rat cerebellum[109-111]* (inositol 1,4,5-triphosphate binding to cerebellar membranes is potently inhibited by Ca^{2+} and this may be mediated by a membrane protein 'calmedin',[112] abundant in brain but not in peripheral tissues and not present in the purified receptor, which is Ca^{2+} insensitive) and kinetic studies have shown the opening of Ca^{2+} channels by inositol 1,4,5-triphosphate to be cooperative, involving the binding of at least three molecules of inositol triphosphate.[113] (For an alternative hypothesis, which suggests that a receptor-activated PI kinase could play the same or complementary role as PLC and that hormone-released Ca^{2+}, stored in membranes in a cage formed by the phosphate and carbonyl oxygens of two hydrogen-bonded phospholipid molecules, could be generated by the polyphosphoinositide shuttle, see ref. 114 and a demonstration of the release of membrane-bound Ca^{2+}.[115])

Diacylglycerol activates protein kinase C.[6,116] PKC was identified as the much-sought-after 'receptor' for the tumour-promoting phorbol esters.[117] PKC was originally thought to be a single entity, but it is now clear that a large family of such protein kinase C enzymes exists.[118,119] Diacylglycerol (**31**), which is hydrophobic, and remains in the plane of the membrane, can be metabolized by two major pathways: by a kinase or a lipase. In the first case the fatty acid moieties are conserved and DAG is phosphorylated to phosphatidic acid, which then combines with CMP to form CMP-phosphatidate, which can be coupled to a molecule of *myo*-inositol (**15**) to re-form PI (**27**), to be used once more for signalling (Figure 11). This reaction is catalyzed by the enzyme PI synthetase. In the second case the DAG is hydrolyzed by a lipase to a monoacylglycerol with the release of the eicosanoid precursor arachidonic acid,[101] which is used in prostaglandin synthesis. Structural aspects of the DAG limb of the signalling pathway have been studied using DAG analogues[120] and the structural requirements for PKC activation by lipids have been reviewed.[121]

11.4.6.4 Metabolism of *myo*-Inositol 1,4,5-Triphosphate

A second messenger, once released inside the cell, must be efficiently deactivated metabolically in order to terminate its action and return the cell to a basal state in preparation for a new stimulus. Additionally, metabolites of the second messenger may well have other physiological activities within the cell. These aspects have come under close scrutiny in the past few years and it has become clear that the metabolism of inositol 1,4,5-triphosphate to free inositol, which is then recycled into

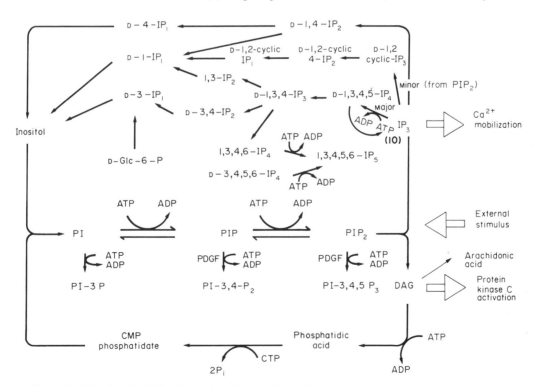

Figure 11 The phosphatidylinositol cycle and metabolism of inositol 1,4,5-triphosphate and diacylglycerol

---

* The inositol 1,4,5-triphosphate cerebellar receptor has now been cloned and sequenced[303] and incorporation of the purified receptor into liposomes has demonstrated that it can mediate Ca^{2+} release in response to inositol 1,4,5-triphosphate.[304]

lipid synthesis, is of considerable complexity, generating many inositol phosphates (Figure 11), which are often very difficult to separate and identify. Only basic features of this aspect of the phosphatidylinositol cycle will be entered into here. For more detail the reader should consult recent reviews.[14,18,122-124]

The initial generation of second messengers *via* the phospholipase C-mediated cleavage of PIP_2 (Figure 10a) is complicated by the fact that *myo*-inositol 1,4,5-triphosphate is not the sole hydrophilic product. Attack of a water molecule on the phosphodiester linkage of PIP_2 gives inositol 1,4,5-triphosphate (**30**) and DAG (**31**), but cleavage may also be accomplished by attack of the 2-hydroxy group at phosphorus, reminiscent of the reaction mechanism for RNAase enzymes, to yield inositol 1,2-cyclic 4,5-triphosphate (**32**; Figure 12), for example in thrombin-stimulated platelets.[125] (The existence of *myo*-inositol 1,2-cyclic monophosphate (**33**), presumably formed by PLC hydrolysis of PI, has been known for some time.[126]) There has been considerable controversy concerning the putative role of this molecule (**32**) in cellular signalling, since initial reports appeared describing its activity in calcium mobilization to be very similar or even greater than that of inositol 1,4,5-triphosphate in platelets and in *Limulus* photoreceptors[127] and in Swiss 3T3 cells.[128] These led to the suggestion that inositol 1,2-cyclic 4,5-triphosphate (**32**) is a second messenger in its own right.[122] This has remained controversial and it has proved impossible to confirm some of the earlier results,[129] casting doubt upon some of the original data. Certainly, inositol 1,2-cyclic 4,5-triphosphate mobilizes intracellular calcium, but is considerably weaker than inositol 1,4,5-triphosphate. A physiological role for the former must now be in doubt and other older data should be reassessed. Indeed, recent reports have demonstrated that the long half-life of inositol 1,2-cyclic 4,5-triphosphate in parotid cells is not compatible with a physiological function in calcium release[130] and its low concentration in some stimulated cells argues against an important messenger role for this compound.[131] It seems possible that chemical opening of the cyclic five-membered ring may have occurred in the samples originally used, resulting in an increase in activity, or that the original material, isolated with considerable difficulty from complex biological mixtures, may have still been contaminated with inositol 1,4,5-triphosphate.

There is, however, no doubt as to the second messenger role for inositol 1,4,5-triphosphate. Two major routes of metabolism have been discovered (Figure 13). It was known for some time that inositol 1,4,5-triphosphate is metabolized by the action of a 5-phosphatase, this being first demonstrated in erythrocytes[132] and subsequently in many other cells.[18] Soluble 5-phosphatase has been highly purified from platelets[133] and to homogeneity from brain.[134] Since the product of the action of this enzyme, *myo*-inositol 1,4-diphosphate (**21**), has no known physiological role in this signalling pathway, it seems clear that this enzyme acts to terminate the calcium mobilization signal. (However, (**21**) has recently been shown to be an allosteric activator of 6-phosphofructo-1-kinase.[135]) D-Inositol 1,4-diphosphate is metabolized to D-inositol 1-phosphate and D-inositol 4-phosphate, with the latter probably being the major product. (This is, however, controversial, see ref. 18.) These monophosphates are subsequently converted to *myo*-inositol, which re-enters the cycle.

The discovery in 1985 of the higher polyphosphate, inositol 1,3,4,5-tetraphosphate (**34**; Figure 13)[36] and later of the 3-kinase enzyme,[137] which has now been purified,[138] added a further complication to the metabolic pathway and speculation about the possible function of this molecule was initiated. Moreover, reports have indicated that in some circumstances (low Mg^{2+}, but see ref. 139) inositol 1,3,4,5-tetraphosphate (**34**) can be a source of inositol 1,4,5-triphosphate, *via* a 3-phosphatase,[140] and indeed, apparent Ca^{2+}-releasing properties of inositol 1,3,4,5-tetraphosphate have now been ascribed to its conversion into inositol 1,4,5-triphosphate in L1210 cells.[141] No unambiguous role for this molecule has, however, yet been elucidated and considerable controversy has been raised by the suggestion that inositol 1,3,4,5-tetraphosphate acts as a second messenger in its own right and may be responsible for mediating the entry of extracellular calcium through

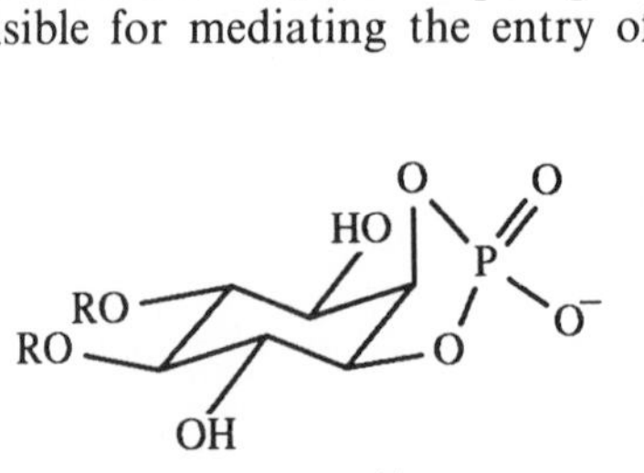

(**32**) $R = PO_3^{2-}$
(**33**) $R = H$

Figure 12

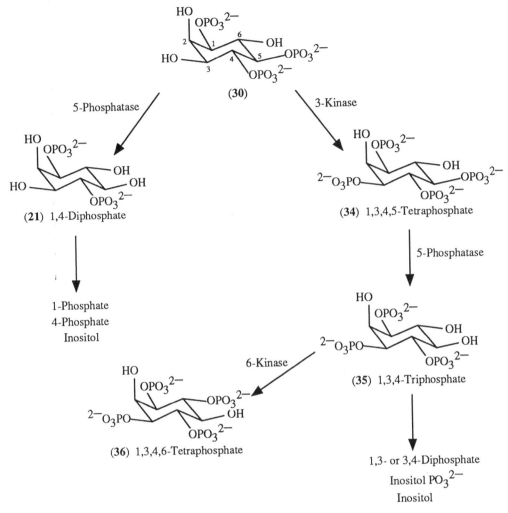

Figure 13   Two major pathways of metabolism for inositol 1,4,5-triphosphate

plasma membrane ion channels. This possibility was raised by the suggestion that inositol 1,3,4,5-tetraphosphate acts synergistically with inositol 1,4,5-triphosphate in raising a fertilization envelope when microinjected into sea urchin eggs.[123,142,143] While this particular aspect remains controversial, in the light of a report that some eggs can be activated in the absence of external calcium and independently of inositol 1,3,4,5-tetraphosphate[144] and that inositol 1,3,4,5-tetraphosphate does not induce Ca^{2+} influx in *Xenopus laevis* oocytes,[145] it does however seem certain that a synergism between inositol 1,3,4,5-tetraphosphate and inositol 1,4,5-triphosphate exists, at least in cells from mouse lacrimal glands.[146,147] In general, it seems more likely that inositol 1,3,4,5-tetraphosphate may have a role to play in mediating communication between different inositol 1,4,5-triphosphate sensitive and insensitive intracellular calcium pools.[123] Such pools have been recently identified and characterized in pancreatic acinar cells.[148] In this sense it is also of interest to note that guanosine 5'-triphosphate (GTP) has been found to mobilize calcium from a functionally different inositol 1,4,5-triphosphate insensitive endoplasmic reticulum store.[149-151] It is possible that inositol 1,3,4,5-tetraphosphate or GTP act as links between these two compartments. A recent report has demonstrated that inositol 1,3,4,5-tetraphosphate induces calcium resequestration in rat liver cells, suggesting a physiological role for this metabolite.[152] Moreover, receptors for inositol 1,3,4,5-tetraphosphate have also been uncovered, in HL-60 cells[153] and in adrenal cortex.[154]

Whatever the function of inositol 1,3,4,5-tetraphosphate, it appears to be metabolized by the same 5-phosphatase as inositol 1,4,5-triphosphate and for which it is a better substrate. However, the situation is complicated by the existence of both soluble and particulate forms of the enzyme and more than one subtype of the former.[155] The type I soluble enzyme cleaves both substrates, but the type I enzyme has a very poor affinity for the tetraphosphate.[134,155] For a discussion of this controversial aspect see ref. 18. The product, inositol 1,3,4-triphosphate (**35**; Figure 13) was also proposed to have a physiological function on the basis of a report that it was a moderately potent mobilizer of intracellular calcium.[128] However, a more recent study[156] has not confirmed this and there is now no strong evidence for a physiological role for this molecule.

The metabolism of D-*myo*-inositol 1,3,4-triphosphate varies between tissues. The products are D-inositol 1,3-diphosphate and/or D-inositol 3,4-diphosphate. These diphosphates are subsequently converted into the monophosphates inositol 1-phosphate and inositol 3-phosphate respectively, and these are ultimately dephosphorylated to inositol.

Other metabolic pathways have also recently emerged. It is now apparent that inositol 1,3,4-triphosphate can be phosphorylated by a 6-kinase to inositol 1,3,4,6-tetraphosphate (**36**).[157,158] It appears that this molecule can be further phosphorylated to inositol 1,3,4,5,6-pentaphosphate. This pentaphosphate can also be synthesized *via* a 3-kinase[159] from a different precursor, D-*myo*-inositol 3,4,5,6-tetraphosphate (L-1,4,5,6-IP$_4$),[160] the source of which is as yet unknown. An NMR study of this molecule, isolated from turkey erythrocytes, has been reported.[161]

Such higher inositol polyphosphates have long been known to be present in plants and in avian erythrocytes,[82,162] where they function to provide phosphate storage and to modulate the oxygen affinity of hemoglobin. Their presence in mammalian cells, however, together with recent observations indicating that these molecules may provide intracellular and extracellular signals in brain[163,164] indicate an exciting future in store for this area,[165] although is seems unlikely that these higher polyphosphates are directly involved in signal transduction. The complex metabolism of inositol 1,4,5-triphosphate is summarized in Figures 11 and 13 and has been extensively reviewed.[18]

11.4.7   SYNTHESIS OF INOSITOL PHOSPHATES

Recognition that D-*myo*-inositol 1,4,5-triphosphate is a second messenger has stimulated intense renewed interest in the chemistry of inositol phosphates. Many inositol phosphates had already been synthesized before this recent revival, and this earlier work is covered in two books.[162,166] In spite of this, some of the older procedures used were not entirely satisfactory. This was especially true for the phosphorylation of polyols, where the presence of vicinal diols makes simultaneous polyphosphorylation difficult and encourages the formation of cyclic five-membered phosphate diesters. (However, for an alternative view, see ref. 167.) Nevertheless, *myo*-inositol 4,5-diphosphate was originally synthesized in 1961 using diphenyl phosphorochloridate as phosphorylating agent.[168]

There are four distinct problems intrinsic to inositol polyphosphate synthesis: first, when using *myo*-inositol as starting material, suitably protected derivatives must be prepared which will facilitate later incorporation of phosphate groups at selected positions; secondly, since the D enantiomer is the natural messenger, such derivatives must be efficiently resolved; thirdly, an efficient phosphorylation strategy is required, which overcomes the difficulties associated with cyclic phosphate formation; and finally the phosphorylated intermediate must be deprotected under conditions which avoid any migration of phosphate groups onto neighbouring hydroxyl groups.

Protection strategies already have a long historical development in this field,[162,166] but several new approaches have been recently described,[169-174] as will become apparent from examination of individual syntheses. These and other strategies have been reviewed.[175] Not all protected inositols prepared to date have yet been converted into inositol phosphates. Resolution has been a problem for a long time. The procedures of Shvets,[176,177] employing orthoesters of D-mannose, used to be the only methods available. Recent work, however, has highlighted the advantages of using diastereoisomeric camphanates, monomenthoxyacetates, menthoxycarbonates, carbamates, acetylmandelates, tartrates, chiral HPLC or GLC columns or even enzymes. The need for resolution of synthetic intermediates in some instances has been overcome by the use of chiral starting inositols derived from D-pinitol and L-quebrachitol,[178] and by the synthesis of optically active protected inositols from D-glucurono-6,3-lactone.[179] A novel route from benzene avoiding *myo*-inositol as starting material has also been devised.[180]

Several NMR studies on inositol phosphates have been reported. Multinuclear NMR has been carried out to confirm the structures and partial conformations of inositol 1,4,5-triphosphate,[181,183] inositol 1,3,4,5-tetraphosphate,[182,183] inositol 1,4,5,6-tetraphosphate,[161] inositol hexaphosphate (phytic acid)[184] and a variety of lower inositol phosphates.[183] The data on phytic acid demonstrate that the conformation of this molecule varies with its degree of protonation. At high pH it possesses one axial phosphate group and five equatorial phosphate groups, whereas between pH 2 and 5 it adopts a conformation with one equatorial phosphate and five axial phosphates, stabilized by intramolecular hydrogen bonding. A ^{1}H NMR study of the polar headgroup conformation of inositol phospholipids has been carried out.[185] ^{1}H NMR resonances of PI, PIP and PIP$_2$ were assigned and rotamer populations around bonds in the polar head groups were calculated.

11.4.7.1   Inositol Analogues

Interest in the synthesis of modified *myo*-inositol analogues stems from the knowledge that *myo*-inositol is taken up by many cells[186-188] and incorporated into PI by the enzyme PI synthetase. The incorporation of synthetic analogues into phosphatidylinositol lipids therefore offers an attractive target for pharmacological intervention in the signalling pathway and the inhibition of the formation or hydrolysis of PIP$_2$. Since a large number of growth stimuli are now known to stimulate inositol lipid hydrolysis,[189] the presentation of fraudulent phospholipid species to the cell, especially those which could not be further phosphorylated, could inhibit phospholipase C or reduce the availability of PIP$_2$, thus affecting cell proliferation *inter alia*. Isosteric fluorinated analogues are particularly attractive in this respect, since the size and electronegativity of fluorine lie between hydrogen and the hydroxyl group. To these ends a number of 1-, 4- and 5-deoxy and 4- and 5-deoxyhalo-cyclitols have been prepared from mono- and di-*O*-cyclohexylidene derivatives of *myo*-inositol.[190] Interestingly, 5-deoxy-*myo*-inositol (**37**) and 5-fluoro-5-deoxy-*myo*-inositol (**38**) were shown to be taken up by L1210 leukaemia cells and incorporated into cellular phospholipid. The latter was shown to be phosphorylated by endogenous PI kinase to the 5-fluoro-5-deoxy-PIP analogue but, not surprisingly, no PIP$_2$ analogue was detected.[191]

Chemoenzymatic methods for the synthesis of selectively protected derivatives of 3-deoxy-*epi*-inositol and 1-deoxy-*scyllo*-inositol have been developed, taking advantage of the preference of *Candida cylindracea* lipase to hydrolyze (*R*) esters with high enantiospecificity.[192]

The synthesis of both enantiomers of 1-fluoro-1-deoxy-*myo*-inositcl (**39**) has been reported[193] and the ability of this molecule to substitute for *myo*-inositol biologically has been indicated. An improved route based upon the direct fluorination of the optically active natural product quebrachitol has been devised[194] and it has been noted that 1-fluoro-1-deoxy-*myo*-inositol is a potent inhibitor of cellular replication in PC12 cells.

11.4.7.2   Inositol Monophosphates

There are four possible simple *myo*-inositol monophosphates: the symmetrical 2-phosphate and 5-phosphate and the two enantiomeric pairs inositol 4(6)-phosphatc and 1(3)-phosphate. Prior to, and after, the demonstration that the hydrolysis of brain phosphoinositides gave

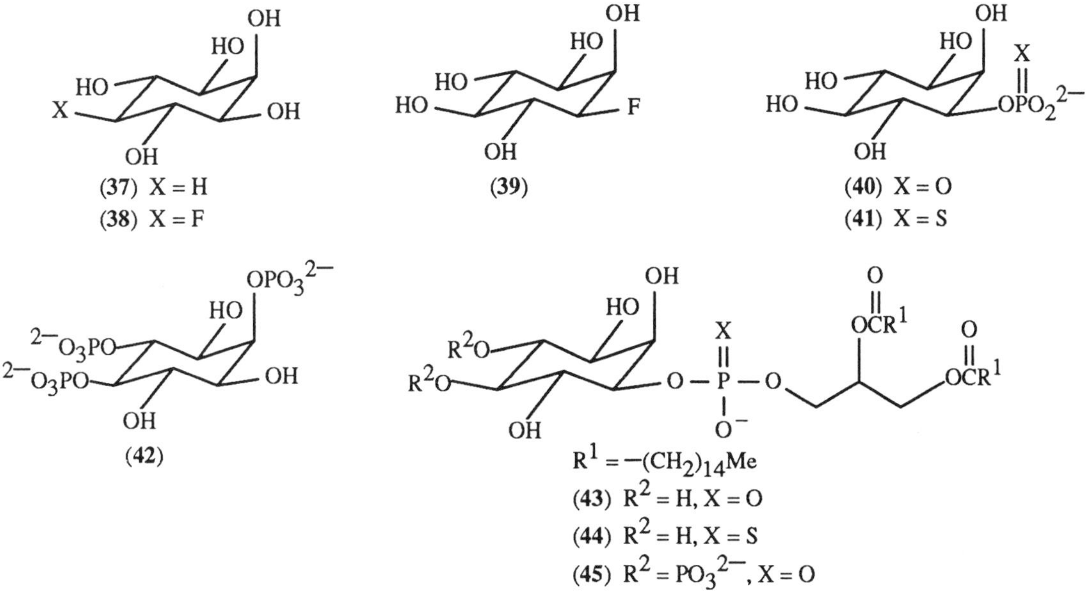

Figure 14

D-(+)-*myo*-inositol 1-phosphate (**40**)[195] there were many syntheses of racemic and optically active *myo* and other inositol monophosphates, which have been well reviewed.[162,175] Syntheses of both racemic and enantiomerically pure *myo*-inositol 1- and 4-phosphates have been reported.[196,197] The resolution of DL-inositol 1-phosphate as the 2,3,4,5,6-penta-*O*-(trimethylsilyl) 1-dimethylphosphate derivative on a chiral GLC column has been described.[196] Another route to the racemic 4-phosphate[197,198] adopts chelation-controlled phosphorylation of the monoanion of a novel orthoformate ester of *myo*-inositol, first described by Lee and Kishi,[199] to give racemic inositol 4-phosphate in high yield.[198,200] Racemic inositol 1-phosphate ± (**40**) has been synthesized[201] and inositol 4-, 5- and 6-phosphates have been prepared using a novel precursor with mixed hydroxyl protection: a cyclohexylidene 1,2-acetal and the tetraisopropyldisiloxane-1,3-diyl group at the 3 and 4 positions.[202]

11.4.7.2.1 *Inositol 1,2-cyclic phosphate*

D-*myo*-Inositol 1,2-cyclic phosphate (**33**) has been synthesized by reaction of the diol 3,4,5,6-tetra-*O*-benzyl-*myo*-inositol with *N*-methylpyridinium phosphorodichloridate followed by catalytic hydrogenation.[203] An unusual approach for the phosphorylation of unprotected *myo*-inositol has been described using reaction with a novel aminobicyclophosphane. Mixtures of inositol 1-phosphate, 2-phosphate and 1,2-cyclic phosphate were obtained and were separated by HPLC.[204]

11.4.7.3 Inositol Diphosphates

Syntheses of inositol 1,3-diphosphate[197,198] and racemic inositol 1,4-diphosphate (**21**)[205] have been reported and pure enantiomers of (**21**) have been prepared by phosphorylation of the appropriate enantiomers of biscyclohexylidene *myo*-inositol, resolved using orthoesters of D-mannose.[206] Similar approaches have been used to prepare optically pure inositol 3,4-diphosphate and 4,5-diphosphate.[206] Other routes have been developed to give the enantiomers of inositol 1,4-diphosphate[207] and racemic inositol 4,5-diphosphate.[208,209]

11.4.7.4 Inositol Triphosphates

11.4.7.4.1 *Inositol 1,4,5-triphosphate*

Most synthetic activity has naturally focused upon inositol 1,4,5-triphosphate (**30**). The first synthesis of optically active D-(−)-inositol 1,4,5-triphosphate was reported by Ozaki *et al.* in 1986.[210] A synthesis of racemic inositol 1,4,5-triphosphate was subsequently reported[211,212] which was dependent upon modified routes to the appropriate precursor.[170,171] Use of resolved D-1,2,4-tri-*O*-benzyl-*myo*-inositol[171] gave the D enantiomer of inositol 1,4,5-triphosphate (**31**) by this method[213] and phosphorylation of the other enantiomeric precursor gave the unnatural L-inositol 1,4,5-triphosphate.[212]

A different approach employed a 1,2-cyclopentylidene acetal, which was first selectively silylated at the 3- and 6-positions and then reacted with 9-chloro-2,7-dibromo-9-phenylxanthene to yield a triol after desilylation, giving racemic inositol 1,4,5-triphosphate after phosphorylation.[214] Optically active inositol 1,4,5-triphosphate was prepared by this route[214] by use of an optically active diol prepared using galactinol[215] as starting material.

Phosphorylation of the tripotassium alkoxide salt of a suitably blocked triol using tetrabenzyl pyrophosphate (**74**),[197,198,216] followed by catalytic hydrogenation and acid treatment, gave the enantiomers of inositol 1,4,5-triphosphate.[197,217]

A short synthesis of racemic inositol 1,4,5-triphosphate has been reported in which 1,4-di-*O*-benzoyl-*myo*-inositol was partially phosphitylated with dimethyl chlorophosphite at low temperature, avoiding the need for protection of an axial 2-hydroxy group.[218]

The use of *N*,*N*-diisopropyl dibenzylphosphoramidite has been suggested for the synthesis of inositol phosphates[219] and has been used to prepare racemic inositol 1,4,5-triphosphate. Optically active D-*myo*-inositol 1,4,5-triphosphate has been synthesized from the intermediate 1,2-cyclohexylidene-3,6-diallyl-*myo*-inositol.[220] A route has been developed for the preparation of inositol 1,4,5-triphosphate using a novel mixed P^{III} and P^{V} phosphorylation approach.[221,222]

An approach to inositol 1,4,5-triphosphate *via* use of the key intermediate D-3,6-di-*O*-benzyl-4,5-bis(dibenzylphosphoryl)-*myo*-inositol has been devised.[203] A chemoenzymatic approach employing the enzyme cholesterol esterase is the keynote of a recent synthesis of D-inositol 1,4,5-triphosphate,[223] in which the optically active diol 1,2:5,6-di-*O*-cyclohexylidene-*myo*-inositol was used as starting material.

The customary starting material for the synthesis of *myo*-inositol phosphates has naturally been *myo*-inositol (**15**), which is cheap and readily available. However, a conceptually different approach, using benzene as starting material, has been provided by Ley,[180] who has used the observation that microbiological oxidation of benzene by *Pseudomonas putida* affords *cis*-1,2-dihydroxycyclohexa-3,5-diene,[224] providing a useful starting material for the synthesis of racemic inositol 1,4,5-triphosphate.

A chiral synthesis of the enantiomers of inositol 1,4,5-triphosphate has been reported[178] starting with the enantiomers of *chiro*-inositol, derived by demethylation of D-pinitol and L-quebrachitol. The ^{3}H-radiolabelled D and L enantiomers of inositol 1,4,5-triphosphate have been synthesized.[225]

11.4.7.4.2 Inositol 1,3,4-triphosphate

Inositol 1,3,4-triphosphate (**35**) has been synthesized from 2,4,5-tri-*O*-benzyl-*myo*-inositol,[226] also available by a different route.[171] This material has also been synthesized from the same precursor by the use of tetrabenzyl pyrophosphate[207,217,228] and *N,N*-diisopropyldibenzyl phosphoramidite.[219]

An approach has also been described to obtain pure enantiomers of inositol 1,3,4-triphosphate and which can be adapted to allow preparation of radiolabelled [^{3}H]-inositol 1,3,4-triphosphate.[229]

11.4.7.4.3 Inositol 2,4,5-triphosphate

1,3,4-Tri-*O*-benzyl-*myo*-inositol has been synthesized and used to prepare racemic inositol 2,4,5-triphosphate (**42**).[207,227] D-3,6-Di-*O*-benzyl-4,5-bis(dibenzylphosphoryl)-*myo*-inositol has also been used for the synthesis of inositol 2,4,5-triphosphate.[203] Prior to this synthesis, the same authors had completed the synthesis of a fully protected, phosphorylated and resolved precursor of D-inositol 2,4,5-triphosphate but without achieving the final deprotection step.[230] This synthesis remains to be completed.

11.4.7.4.4 Inositol 1,2-cyclic 4,5-triphosphate

Only one synthesis of inositol 1,2-cyclic 4,5-triphosphate (**22**) from *myo*-inositol has been reported from the intermediate D-3,6-di-*O*-benzyl-4,5-bis(dibenzylphosphoryl)-*myo*-inositol.[203] Inositol 1,2-cyclic 4,5-triphosphate has, however, also been prepared in low yield from inositol 1,4,5-triphosphate by the action of a water soluble carbodiimide, 1-ethyl-3-(3-dimethylaminopropyl)carbodiimide. The product was isolated from a complex mixture by anion exchange HPLC and was shown to be converted to inositol 1,4,5-triphosphate by acid treatment and to be a substrate for the 5-phosphatase from platelets.[231]

11.4.7.5 Inositol Tetraphosphates

11.4.7.5.1 Inositol 1,3,4,5-tetraphosphate

Racemic inositol 1,3,4,5-tetraphosphate (**34**) was first synthesized from a symmetrical inositol orthoformate.[200] A similar route was adopted by another group[227] and a combined report has now appeared.[198] 2,6-Dibenzyl-*myo*-inositol has also been used as a starting material for P^{III} approaches and was phosphitylated with diisopropylamino(2-cyanoethyl)chlorophosphine[232] or *N,N*-diethyl dibenzylphosphoramidite.[219]

The choice of orthoester protection of *myo*-inositol was a key point of a synthesis which led to both enantiomers of inositol 1,3,4,5-tetraphosphate by two routes,[233] including a novel enantioselective monodeacylation of a symmetrical dibutyrate with porcine liver esterase.

A different approach has been adopted by Meek,[218] who employed a base-catalyzed isomerization of the 1-benzoate group in the readily available *myo*-inositol 1,4-dibenzoate to give, *inter alia*, the required 2,4-dibenzoate, which was phosphorylated and deblocked. Enantiomerically pure D-*myo*-inositol 1,3,4,5-tetraphosphate has also been synthesized by other routes.[220,234]

11.4.7.5.2   Inositol 1,4,5,6-tetraphosphate

Racemic inositol 1,4,5,6-tetraphosphate has been synthesized from the 1,2-*O*-isopropylidene ketal of *myo*-inositol.[218] This product can also be prepared by phosphitylation of the ketal with diisopropylamino(2-cyanoethyl)chlorophosphine.[235]

11.4.7.5.3   Inositol 1,3,4,6-tetraphosphate

The synthesis of inositol 1,3,4,6-tetraphosphate (**36**) has been accomplished utilizing novel protection of inositol with the tetraisopropyldisiloxane-1,3-diyl group.[202]

11.4.8   INOSITOL LIPID SYNTHESIS

Much of the less recent work on phosphatidylinositol lipid and analogue synthesis has been covered in a review.[236] A recent synthesis[237] has addressed a route to 1,2-dipalmitoyl-*sn*-glycer-3-yl-D-*myo*-inositol 1-phosphate (**43**). Different routes to dipalmitoyl analogues of PI and PIP based upon the selective phosphorylation of (+)-2,3:5,6-diisopropylidene-*myo*-inositol have also been reported.[238] The PIP$_2$ phospholipid analogue, 1-*O*-(1,2-di-*O*-palmitoyl-*sn*-glycero-3-phospho)-D-*myo*-inositol 4,5-diphosphate (**45**) has also been synthesized.[239] (The di-*O*-stearoyl phospholipid has been synthesized previously by the Soviet group[176,240,241] and the work of this group in this area has been reviewed,[236,242] including a review of phosphorylation methods.[242])

11.4.9   INOSITOL PHOSPHATE ANALOGUES

Now that the second messenger properties of inositol 1,4,5-triphosphate are well established, attention has turned to the synthesis of inositol phosphate analogues, which are hoped to possess novel biological properties. The first analogue of an inositol phosphate to be reported was the triphosphorothioate (**46**) in which the three phosphate groups of inositol 1,4,5-triphosphate have been replaced by phosphorothioates.[243] Phosphorothioate analogues of nucleotides in particular have proven to be invaluable in studies in mechanistic enzymology and molecular biology[244] and in examining the stereochemistry of enzymatic phosphoryl transfer reactions[33,34] and analogues of established second messengers, cAMP and cGMP have been available for some time. Their use in the inositol phosphate field stems from their resistance to phosphatase-catalyzed degradation.[205] Thus, a similar route to that employed for the synthesis of inositol 1,4,5-triphosphate[211] was adopted, except that the triphosphite hexaester intermediate was oxidized with sulfur in pyridine to the protected triphosphorothioate, which was deblocked using sodium in liquid ammonia to give (**46**). Inositol 1,4,5-triphosphorothioate is active in binding to specific receptor sites[109-111] in brain[245] and hepatocytes[246] and only slightly less potent than inositol 1,4,5-triphosphate. Moreover, it is a potent agonist in releasing intracellular calcium in several systems such as *Xenopus* oocytes,[247] permeabilized Swiss 3T3 cells,[156,247] GH$_3$ cells,[156] hepatocytes,[248] pancreatic acinar cells[148] and mouse lacrimal cells[147] and only three- to four-fold less potent than inositol 1,4,5-triphosphate. However, as expected, it is resistant to 5-phosphatase-catalyzed dephosphorylation[245,248] and can therefore give rise to a sustained calcium transient in cells.[17,248] It is a potent inhibitor of 5-phosphatase,[249,250] but surprisingly is not bound by the 3-kinase and does not compete with inositol 1,4,5-triphosphate for this enzyme.[248,251]

While it is clear that this analogue will be a valuable tool for studies of polyphosphoinositide metabolism, it would be useful to have analogues in which only one specific phosphate group had been replaced by phosphorothioate. In particular, the analogue (**47**), inositol 1,4-diphosphate 5-phosphorothioate would be highly desirable, since it is nearer in structure to inositol 1,4,5-triphosphate, yet maintains the advantages of phosphatase resistance. This analogue has been synthesized by a mixed P^V/P^{III} approach by phosphitylation of a protected 1,4-diphosphate and conversion to blocked 5-phosphorothioate, which was deblocked to give (**47**).[221] This compound behaves in a similar fashion to inositol 1,4,5-triphosphorothioate (**46**) in binding to cerebellar receptors,

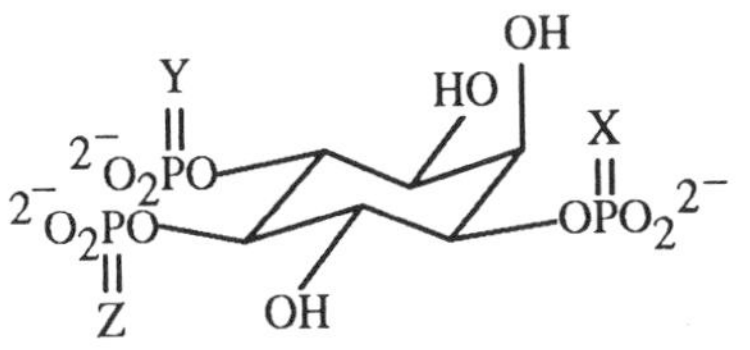

(46) X = Y = Z = S
(47) X = Y = O, Z = S
(48) X = Y = O, Z = ^{35}S
(49) X = O, Y = Z = ^{35}S

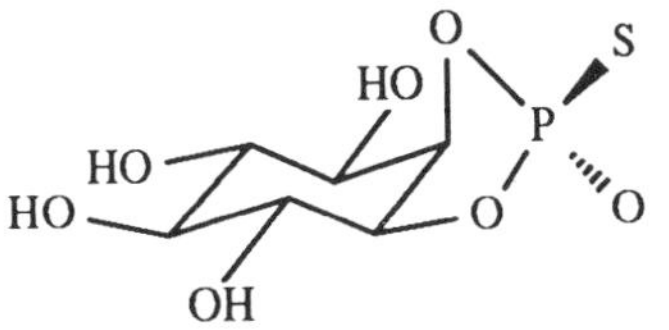

(50)

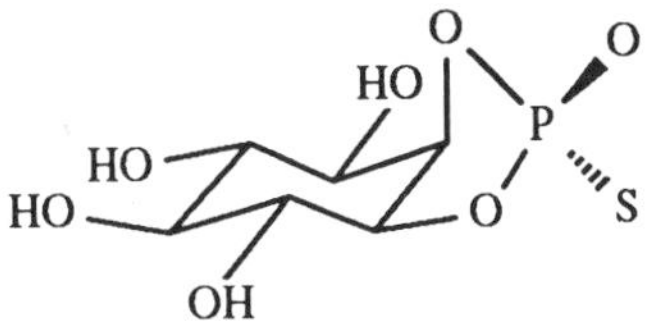

(51)

Figure 15

release of intracellular calcium and inhibition of 5-phosphatase,[222] but is bound by the 3-kinase,[251] suggesting that the presence of the 4-phosphorothioate in inositol 1,4,5-triphosphorothioate may inhibit kinase-mediated phosphorylation of the 3-hydroxy group.

A different approach to the preparation of phosphorothioate analogues of inositol 1,4,5-triphosphate has been adopted by the use of the thiophosphorylation of PI (27) and PIP (28) using kinases in human erythrocyte ghosts and ATPγS.[252] This can naturally be adapted to prepare the highly desirable ^{35}S radioactively labelled material by employing [^{35}S]ATPγS. Thus, incubation of ATPγ^{35}S with erythrocyte ghosts produced ^{35}S-labelled PIP$_2$ lipid analogues, with the ^{35}S label in both the 4- and 5-positions or uniquely in the 5-position. Activation of the phospholipase C with calcium cleaved this modified lipid to give a mixture of inositol 1,4-diphosphate 5[^{35}S]phosphorothioate (48) and inositol 1-phosphate 4,5[^{35}S]-diphosphorothioate (49), which was shown to be resistant to 5-phosphatase.

Since the preparation of these phosphorothioates, other such analogues have appeared. Thus, the synthesis of racemic inositol 1-phosphorothioate (41) has been reported[201] by phosphorylation of 1,2,4,5,6-penta-O-acetyl-*myo*-inositol with thiophosphoryl chloride and quenching of the intermediate thiophosphorochloridate. Also, *endo*-(50) and *exo*-(51) diastereoisomers of the racemic cyclic five-membered 1,2-phosphorothioates have been prepared by thiophosphorylation of racemic 1,4,5,6-tetra-O-acetyl-*myo*-inositol using thiophosphoryl chloride. After quenching with potassium hydroxide, the mixture was separated into *exo* and *endo* diastereoisomers by flash chromatography.[253] A different approach relied upon the monophosphitylation of 1,4,5,6-tetrabenzyl-*myo*-inositol at either the 1- or 2-position, simultaneously, followed by cyclization of the phosphoramidites to the *exo* and *endo* diastereoisomeric cyclic methoxyphosphites, oxidation to the *endo*-(50) and *exo*-(51) cyclic phosphorothioates respectively with sulfur, separation of diastereoisomers and deblocking.[254]

The PI analogue 1,2-dipalmitoyl-*sn*-glycero-3-thiophospho-*myo*-inositol (44) has been synthesized and used to determine the stereochemical course of the cleavage reaction catalyzed by phosphatidylinositol specific PLC.[254]

Starting with PI from yeast, and using semisynthetic methods, a fluorescent PI analogue possessing a *cis*-parinaroyl moiety in the fatty acid part has been synthesized and its properties investigated.[255]

The use of the ammonium salt of benzyl-1*H*-phosphonic acid has been demonstrated in the synthesis of racemic inositol 1,4,5-tri-1*H*-phosphonate (52). Thus, DL-1,2,4-tri-O-benzyl-*myo*-inositol was phosphonylated and the product, after anionic debenzylation, gave the analogue (52).[256] No biological activity of this analogue has, however, yet been reported. Racemic-*myo*-inositol 1-phosphonate has also been synthesized.[257]

A series of synthetic analogues has been synthesized and biologically evaluated by the Merck group.[258] In addition to naturally occurring inositol phosphates and L-inositol 1,4,5-triphosphate (53), inositol 1,3,5-triphosphate (54), racemic 1,2,4-cyclohexane triphosphate (55) and 6-O-methoxyinositol 1,4,5-triphosphate (56) have been prepared. All analogues were found to be full agonists in calcium mobilization in permeabilized bovine aortic smooth muscle cells, but were 100–2000-fold less potent than the natural agonist. The analogues tested were not substrates but quite potent inhibitors of the aortic 5-phosphatase enzyme, even interestingly the 1,3,5-triphosphate

(54), which does not possess a vicinal diphosphate group. However, inhibition of inositol [^{3}H]-1,4,5-triphosphate turnover by the 3-kinase in these analogues was less marked, being some 100–1000-fold less than inositol 1,4,5-triphosphate. Substrate properties were, however, not measured. Thus, it is clear that the 5-phosphatase is relatively nonspecific in its recognition of inositol phosphates, while the 3-kinase and receptor are considerably more selective. L-Inositol 1,4,5-triphosphate (53) was surprisingly only threefold less potent in binding to aortic 5-phosphatase than its enantiomer and natural substrate, D-inositol 1,4,5-triphosphate. This is in excellent agreement with studies on erythrocyte 5-phosphatase using independently synthesized L-inositol 1,4,5-triphosphate.[249]

Synthetic analogues modified at the 2-position have been synthesized and biologically evaluated[259] with respect to their effects upon 5-phosphatase, 3-kinase and the mobilization of intracellular Ca^{2+}. 2-Deoxyinositol 1,4,5-triphosphate (60) and analogues with extra groups at the 2-position inhibited the hydrolysis of 5[^{32}P]inositol 1,4,5-triphosphate with lower K_i values than inositol 1,4,5-triphosphate. The 2-deoxy analogue (60) was as potent as inositol 1,4,5-triphosphate in inhibiting the phosphorylation of [^{3}H]inositol 1,4,5-triphosphate by 3-kinase and was a full agonist for Ca^{2+} release from permeabilized macrophages and some 2.5-fold less potent than inositol 1,4,5-triphosphate itself, indicating that the 2-position can be modified with only slight decreases in activity.

6-O-Methoxy-*myo*-inositol 1,4,5-triphosphate (56) has also been synthesized from benzene as starting material using intermediates obtained by microbiological oxidation.[180] This route is obviously versatile and has been shown to be applicable to the synthesis of a variety of other racemic 6-substituted inositol phosphate analogues such as 6-deoxy- (57), 6-deoxy-6-fluoro- (58) and 6-deoxy-6-methyl-inositol 1,4,5-triphosphate (59).[260] Modification at the 6-position has also been achieved in a different synthesis of D-6-deoxy-*myo*-inositol 1,4,5-triphosphate (59).[261] This analogue is some 100-fold less potent than inositol 1,4,5-triphosphate in releasing intracellular Ca^{2+}.

Inositol phosphate analogues which might be cell permeable would obviously find considerable application. To this end the synthesis of racemic 2,3,6-tributyryl-*myo*-inositol 1,4,5-triphosphate (61) has been addressed[262] by phosphorylation of 1,2,4-tri-O-butyryl-*myo*-inositol. Removal of phosphate protecting groups gave (61). The utility of this molecule, however, remains to be established.

Semisynthetic inositol 1,4,5-triphosphate analogues modified at the 1-position have been prepared and biologically evaluated.[263] These analogues were prepared by chemical modification of the deacylated lipid, *sn*-glycero(3)-1-phospho-D-*myo*-inositol 4,5-diphosphate (62). Mild periodate oxidation gave the glycoaldehyde derivative glycoaldehyde (2)-1-phospho-D-*myo*-inositol 4,5-diphosphate (63). Some of the oxidized material glycolic acid (2)-1-phospho-D-*myo*-inositol 4,5-diphosphate (64) was also produced. Reductive amination of the glycoaldehyde (63) using ethanolamine or octylamine gave N-hydroxyethyl- or N-octyl-2-aminoethanol (1)-1-phospho-D-*myo*-inositol 4,5-diphosphate, (65) and (66) respectively. All of these modified compounds were full agonists in calcium

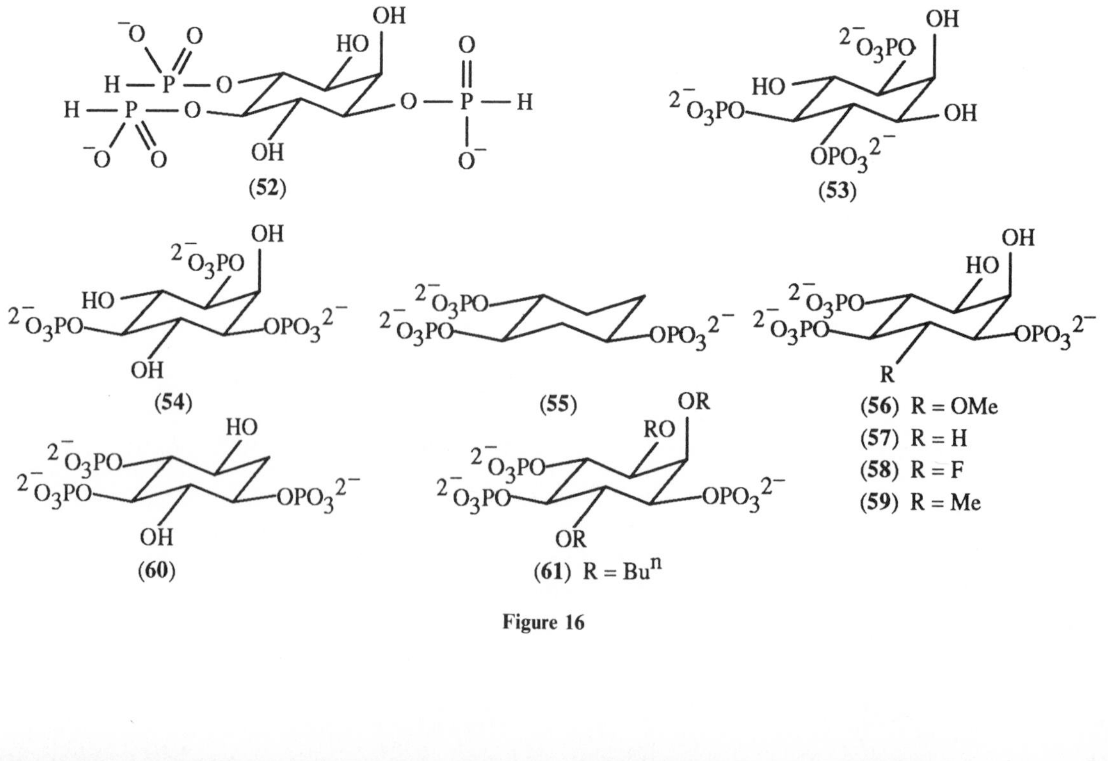

Figure 16

release and with the exception of (**65**) were relatively potent, indicating that the 1-phosphate group of inositol 1,4,5-triphosphate can be modified without or with only minor loss of biological activity. Similar results were obtained when these compounds were tested as inhibitors of aldolase A, an enzyme which has been found to be a potent isomer selective binder of inositol polyphosphates.[264]

In order to aid studies on localization and purification of inositol 1,4,5-phosphate receptors, it is desirable to synthesize photoaffinity analogues of inositol 1,4,5-triphosphate. First steps in this area have been made with the preparation of an aryl azide derivative of inositol 1,4,5-triphosphate.[265] Thus, inositol 1,4,5-triphosphate was coupled to *p*-azidobenzoic acid using *N,N*'-carbonyl-diimidazole. Unfortunately, the site of location of the *p*-azidobenzoic acid moiety was not determined, although hydroxyl group substitution was presumed, and a mixture was used (**67**). However, an irreversible inhibition of inositol 1,4,5-triphosphate-induced calcium release in saponin-permeabilized photoirradiated macrophages was observed, which could be prevented by the presence of a large excess of inositol 1,4,5-triphosphate. More recently, this photoaffinity label has been shown to label three proteins in macrophages.[266]

The photochemically induced release of an active molecule of physiological interest such as ATP, GTP, second messengers or even ions from an inactive precursor has considerable potential for studies in cellular physiology, especially in kinetic measurements, where diffusional delay of agents into tissues is often a limitation. Inactive precursors which yield, on irradiation for example, a free second messenger are known as 'caged' compounds[267,268] and allow time-resolved measurements to be carried out. Esterification of the three phosphate monoester groups of inositol 1,4,5-triphosphate

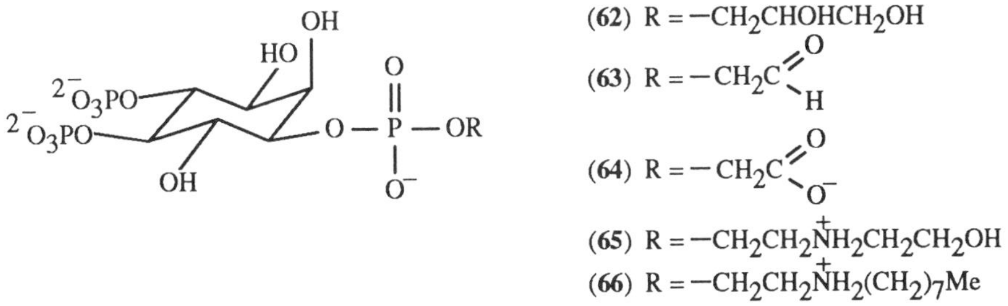

(**62**) $R = -CH_2CHOHCH_2OH$

(**63**) $R = -CH_2C\underset{H}{\overset{O}{\diagup}}$

(**64**) $R = -CH_2C\underset{O^-}{\overset{O}{\diagup}}$

(**65**) $R = -CH_2CH_2\overset{+}{N}H_2CH_2CH_2OH$

(**66**) $R = -CH_2CH_2\overset{+}{N}H_2(CH_2)_7Me$

Figure 17

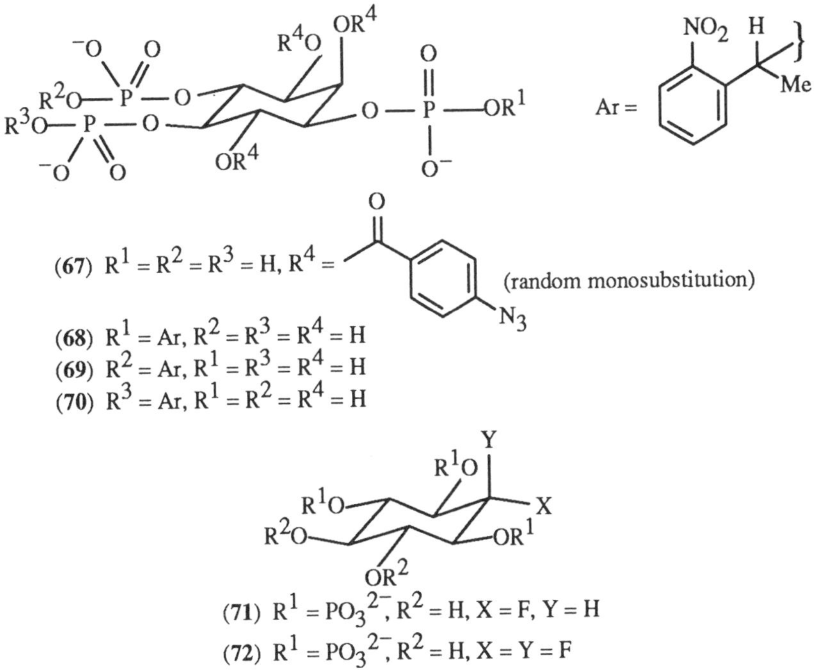

$Ar = $

(**67**) $R^1 = R^2 = R^3 = H, R^4 = $ (random monosubstitution)

(**68**) $R^1 = Ar, R^2 = R^3 = R^4 = H$
(**69**) $R^2 = Ar, R^1 = R^3 = R^4 = H$
(**70**) $R^3 = Ar, R^1 = R^2 = R^4 = H$

(**71**) $R^1 = PO_3{}^{2-}, R^2 = H, X = F, Y = H$
(**72**) $R^1 = PO_3{}^{2-}, R^2 = H, X = Y = F$

Figure 18

with 1-(2-nitrophenyl)diazoethane[269] yields caged inositol 1,4,5-triphosphate[270] as a mixture of singly and multiply caged material. The singly caged material was resolved into P-1 (**68**), P-4 (**69**) and P-5 (**70**) isomers by HPLC. All three compounds released inositol 1,4,5-triphosphate on irradiation. (**68**) was a potent releaser of Ca^{2+} and was a substrate for 5-phosphatase. By contrast, (**69**) and (**70**) were inactive in Ca^{2+} release, were 5-phosphatase resistant and (**70**) was a 3-kinase inhibitor. (**69**) and (**70**) have been used to investigate the role of inositol 1,4,5-triphosphate in excitation–contraction coupling in muscle.[271] The results are consistent with an essential role for this molecule in pharmacomechanical coupling in smooth but not striated muscle.

Fluorinated analogues of racemic inositol 1,3,4-triphosphate have been synthesized from a suitably protected intermediate by reaction with DAST[229] to produce an intermediate with an equatorial 2-fluorine, which was phosphorylated with tetrabenzyl pyrophosphate, followed by deprotection to give the 2-fluoro-2-deoxyinositol 1,3,4-triphosphate analogue (**71**). The 2,2-difluoroinositol 1,3,4-triphosphate (**72**) was synthesized in a similar fashion.

11.4.10   APPLICATIONS OF INOSITOL PHOSPHATE ANALOGUES

Inositol phosphate analogues have not yet been extensively employed in biological investigations, since until recently they had not been widely available. However, it is to be expected that they will have a significant role to play in the future and initial progress has been made. The synthesis of the unnatural L-isomer of inositol 1,4,5-triphosphate (**53**), for example, has enabled the marked stereospecificity of a specific binding site in cerebellum[109–111] to be established[272] as well as the stereospecificity of the receptor controlling Ca^{2+} release.[156,248,258] Other investigations have been carried out using synthetic analogues to examine the structural requirements for binding to and activating the receptor, and for binding to and inhibiting the metabolic enzymes 5-phosphatase[249,258,259] and 3-kinase.[258,259] Such information will be crucial for the future design of enzyme inhibitors and receptor antagonists. The use of photoaffinity labels[265,266] will be invaluable in locating and purifying inositol phosphate receptor sites, and caged compounds[267–271] will find applications in studies on rapid kinetics.

Inositol phosphorothioates are currently finding important applications in studies of the polyphosphoinositide signalling pathway. The phospholipid phosphorothioate (**44**) has been used to investigate the stereochemical course of the PI specific PLC cleavage reaction.[254] Since the demonstration that inositol 1,4,5-triphosphate and inositol 1,3,4,5-tetraphosphate can operate synergistically,[142,143] attention has turned towards identifying a role for the latter polyphosphate. The only system where an apparent synergy has subsequently been identified is in lacrimal acinar cells, where the tetraphosphate was found to be essential in conjunction with inositol 1,4,5-triphosphate in maintaining a Ca^{2+} dependent K^+ current, dependent upon extracellular Ca^{2+}.[146,147] In this system, the triphosphorothioate (**46**) alone gave rise to a single transient response, typical of the triphosphate, but together with the tetraphosphate evoked the same sustained response, confirming that the transient response with inositol 1,4,5-triphosphate was not due to rapid metabolism and that the tetraphosphate was not producing its effect by protecting the former against degradation by the common 5-phosphatase.[147]

Many agonists evoke oscillations in the internal Ca^{2+} concentration of their target cells.[13,273,274] Attention has recently been focused upon identifying the mechanism underlying this phenomenon: one mechanism invokes fluctuating levels of inositol 1,4,5-triphosphate under control of the receptor, giving rise to pulsatile release of Ca^{2+}, and another is based upon a cytoplasmic oscillator involving Ca^{2+} feedback loops and Ca^{2+}-induced Ca^{2+} release, possibly combined with interactions between inositol 1,4,5-triphosphate sensitive and insensitive intracellular Ca^{2+} pools, which may communicate. The triphosphorothioate (**46**) was found to evoke repetitive pulses of Ca^{2+}-activated Cl^- current, similar in amplitude and frequency to the response to acetylcholine in perfused mouse pancreatic acinar cells,[275] thus demonstrating that even at a constant level of this analogue pulsatile Ca^{2+} release is possible and arguing against the receptor-controlled oscillator model[274,276] and any role for metabolism of the triphosphate in generating the Ca^{2+} spikes. In addition, (**46**) has been used to functionally distinguish between such inositol 1,4,5-triphosphate sensitive and insensitive nonmitochondrial Ca^{2+} pools in rat pancreatic acinar cells.[148] (**46**) and (**47**) have also been used as 5-phosphatase inhibitors to inhibit inositol 1,4,5-triphosphate breakdown in electrically permeabilized neuroblastoma cells.[250] Inhibition of metabolism of exogenous [5^{32}P]IP$_3$ breakdown was *ca.* 10 times more potent than effects upon cell-membrane-derived [^{3}H]IP$_3$, indicating compartmentalization of endogenous IP$_3$. (**46**) was found to activate a K^+ conductance in rat hippocampal neurones and inhibit action potential firing,[277] whereas it was impossible to observe any effect with inositol 1,4,5-triphosphate, presumably on account of rapid metabolism, clearly indicating the value of such a nonhydrolyzable analogue.

11.4.11 GLYCOSYL-PHOSPHATIDYLINOSITOL ANCHORS

Glycosylated forms of PI have been recently shown to play important roles in the function of biological membranes by anchoring cell surface membrane proteins (more than 30 to date) of widely different origin and function.[278-281] Until recently, it had been thought that the structural integrity of a membrane was determined by noncovalent interactions between proteins and lipids, and that membrane proteins were anchored in place by sequences of hydrophobic amino acids buried in the lipid bilayer. However, a novel linkage for the hydrophobic attachment of proteins to membranes by phospholipid has now been demonstrated, in which the hydrophobic anchor is the 1,2-diacylglycerol moiety of a PI molecule, covalently linked to a polypeptide chain (a GPI anchor). Thus, the α-carboxyl group of the C-terminal end of a protein is linked *via* an amide bond through an ethanolamine phosphodiester to the 6-hydroxy group of a mannose residue in a branched oligosaccharide, which is glycosidically linked at the C-1 position of a terminal glucosamine residue to PI at the 6-hydroxy of the inositol ring (73). Although in most cases the precise structures have not been determined, certain elements are thought to be generally conserved and most structural work stems from studies on the variant surface glycoprotein of the parasite *Trypanosoma brucei*[282] and rat brain Thy-1 glycoprotein.[283]

Bacterial PI specific PLCs cleave GPI anchors to release the protein in soluble form and release of a protein from the membrane by such an enzyme is considered to be good evidence for the involvement of such anchors, although some proteins have been found to be relatively resistant to PI–PLC release.[279-281] It has been proposed that insulin may mediate some of its actions through

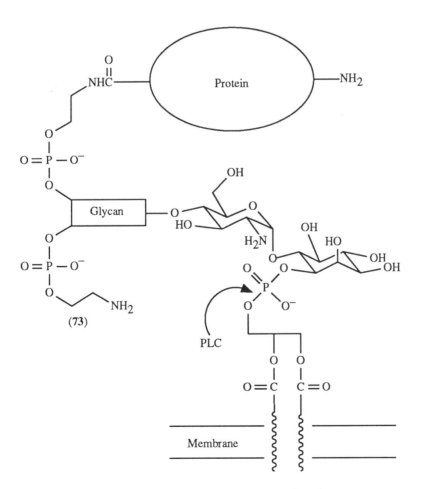

Figure 19 A phosphatidylinositol lipid protein anchor

stimulating glycosyl–PI specific PLC cleavage of an insulin sensitive phosphatidylinositol glycan, structurally similar to the GPI anchor (but lacking ethanolamine and amino acids), to diacylglycerol and soluble glycan–inositol phosphate factors, the latter of which can modulate various metabolic enzymes.[280,284] However, it is as yet still premature to regard inositol phosphate glycans as second messengers of insulin action.

11.4.12   ANALYTICAL METHODS

Many of the biochemical and pharmacological studies of the polyphosphoinositide signalling pathway have depended upon the generation of radiolabelled inositol phosphates in cells or tissue slices incubated with [³H]inositol or [³²P] inorganic phosphate. There are clearly limitations to such methods, the most obvious being that they generally only allow measurement of relative fluxes through metabolic pathways on agonist stimulation and rarely yield absolute mass or concentration data. Moreover, the functional state of a tissue preparation may not resemble that occurring *in vivo* and it is therefore essential to develop methods for accurate mass measurement of inositol phosphates in tissues and in intact animals.

The first such measurement was in thrombin-stimulated platelets and depended upon isolation and dephosphorylation of an inositol phosphate followed by capillary gas chromatographic analysis of the hexatrimethylsilylated derivative.[285] However, inositol phosphate isomers could not be distinguished in this way and now that the metabolism of inositol 1,4,5-triphosphate is clearly so complex this is crucial. This method has been modified to include an HPLC separation step to allow the quantification of isomers in cardiac tissue.[286] Inositol 1,4,5-triphosphate has been extracted and separated by HPLC from other isomers in bradykinin-stimulated MDCK cells, and acid hydrolysis and conversion of the inositol to the hexatrifluoroacetyl derivative allowed quantification by negative ion mass spectrometry.[287] A method has been developed whereby inositol 1,4,5-triphosphate can be separated from interfering 1,3,4-triphosphate isomer in tissue extracts by selective dephosphorylation of the latter by a crude cerebral supernatant in Mg^{2+} free buffer.[288] Two major instrumental analytical methods have also been developed: one involves anion exchange HPLC[289] with on-line enzymatic hydrolysis of the phosphates, using a post column reactor containing immobilized alkaline phosphatase, and molybdate detection of inorganic phosphate.[290] The other method uses a 'metal-dye' detection system involving a dye-based ternary complexometric technique not requiring dephosphorylation, in which tervalent transition metal ions are bound with high affinity to the dye 4-(2-pyridylazo)resorcinol and inositol phosphate polyanions.[291] This method permits picomolar range detection of inositol phosphates.

A sensitive radioreceptor assay method has been developed for inositol 1,4,5-triphosphate assay using a particulate preparation from bovine adrenal cortex[292] and another report has used a similar method to estimate inositol 1,4,5-triphosphate mass in hepatocytes.[293] A radioreceptor method has also been developed using the less sensitive cerebellum receptor.[294] Cellular and extracellular concentrations of inositol 1,4,5-triphosphate in the slime mould *Dictyostelium discoidum* have been measured.[295]

The mass of inositol 1,4,5-triphosphate in squid retina has been estimated using the acidic methanolysis of PIP_2 to incorporate ^{14}C label from [^{14}C]methanol of known specific activity.[296]

11.4.13   INOSITOL 1,4,5-TRIPHOSPHATE ANTAGONISTS

The paucity of chemical agents by which the phosphatidylinositol signalling pathway can be pharmacologically manipulated is underlined by the lack of a simple small molecule inositol 1,4,5-triphosphate antagonist. To aid the design of such a molecule extensive structure–activity studies are required. The receptor which binds inositol 1,4,5-triphosphate is probably linked to a Ca^{2+} channel and binding of at least three molecules of messenger is necessary for channel opening.[113] In the rational search for an agent which possesses high affinity for the receptor, yet does not release Ca^{2+}, it is necessary, if at all possible, to attempt to dissect those structural features of inositol 1,4,5-triphosphate which determine binding affinity from those which trigger opening of the Ca^{2+} ion channel. Many naturally occurring and synthetic inositol phosphates have been found to possess lower binding affinity than inositol 1,4,5-triphosphate for binding sites, which can be correlated with correspondingly lower Ca^{2+}-releasing ability. The ability of an inositol polyphosphate to release Ca^{2+} depends critically upon the positional distribution of phosphate groups around the inositol ring. A rank order of potency to release Ca^{2+} is Ins (1,4,5)P_3 > glycero-Ins

$(4,5)P_2 >$ Ins $(2,4,5)P_3 >$ Ins $(4,5)P_2 \gg$ Ins $(1,4)P_2$. No compound lacking a D-vicinal 4,5-diphosphate grouping has yet been found to release Ca^{2+} (inositol 1,3,4,5-tetraphosphate is surprisingly weak[129,258]). A phosphate group at the D-1 position is thought only to enhance affinity for the receptor. Modifications at the 4,5 locus may be the way to design a molecule which can directly affect channel opening, providing that high binding affinity can be maintained in such an analogue.

At present the only promising lead compounds for the development of a small molecule antagonist are the sulfated polysaccharide macromolecules heparin (**74**) and the similar pentosan polysulfate.[297] Initial indications that heparin could interact with inositol 1,4,5-triphosphate binding sites came from the observation that the cerebellar site first described by Worley *et al.*[109] is sensitive to heparin.[110] Indeed, subsequently the protein representing this site has been significantly purified using heparin–agarose affinity chromatography.[111] Heparin was also found to inhibit inositol 1,4,5-triphosphate-induced Ca^{2+} release in hepatocytes,[299] pancreatic β cells[299] and rat liver microsomes.[300] The potent antagonism of inositol 1,4,5-triphosphate-activated Ca^{2+} release by heparin has recently been demonstrated to be both competitive and reversible, with an affinity of heparin for the binding site of *ca.* 3 nM.[301] It is tempting to presume that the negatively charged sulfate groups of heparin may be interacting directly with those parts of the receptor responsible for binding the phosphate groups of inositol 1,4,5-triphosphate. Heparin is a macromolecule with a molecular weight in excess of 20000 and although fragments of lower molecular weight have been investigated with some success,[301] they are still an order of magnitude away from what could be considered as an inositol 1,4,5-triphosphate analogue. A recent study has shown that both *N*- and *O*-sulfate groups contribute to receptor binding activity, since desulfated heparin was inactive. Also, there is a strong correlation of activity with chain length, since chains of lower length than 18–24 residues were much less active in binding.[297] Clearly, a closer study of the heparin–receptor interaction is essential in the search for structural features which can be incorporated into a small molecule antagonist. Such a molecule would be an invaluable experimental tool and might have therapeutic potential in treatment of certain disease states. It should be noted that the undoubted, if as yet incompletely clarified, importance of inositol 1,3,4,5-tetraphosphate and the discovery of receptors for this molecule[153,154] make additionally the development of an inositol 1,3,4,5-tetraphosphate antagonist also highly desirable.

Other compounds which have been found to affect inositol 1,4,5-triphosphate binding to its receptor include *p*-chloromercuribenzene sulfonate[111] and *p*-hydroxymercuribenzoate,[302] the latter of which was found to inhibit inositol 1,4,5-triphosphate-induced Ca^{2+} release in permeabilized endocrine cells. This is probably the result of decreased binding of inositol 1,4,5-triphosphate to its receptor protein, since protection against such inhibition was conferred by pretreatment with DTT or 2-mercaptoethanol, indicating a role for thiol groups in receptor binding. Perhaps more interesting, however, is the reversible inhibition of inositol 1,4,5-triphosphate-induced Ca^{2+} release exhibited by decavanadate, which has an IC_{50} of 5 µM for inhibition of Ca^{2+} release in RINA2 and PC12 cells.[302] Decavanadate may specifically interact with the inositol 1,4,5-triphosphate receptor protein.

11.4.14 OUTLOOK

Since the first evidence of a second messenger role for inositol 1,4,5-triphosphate, the study of polyphosphoinositide metabolism and its effects has been catapulted from the position of relatively uninspiring backwater to being one of the most rapidly expanding fields at the forefront of modern biology. Equally, this has stimulated a renaissance for inositol phosphate chemistry, which shows no

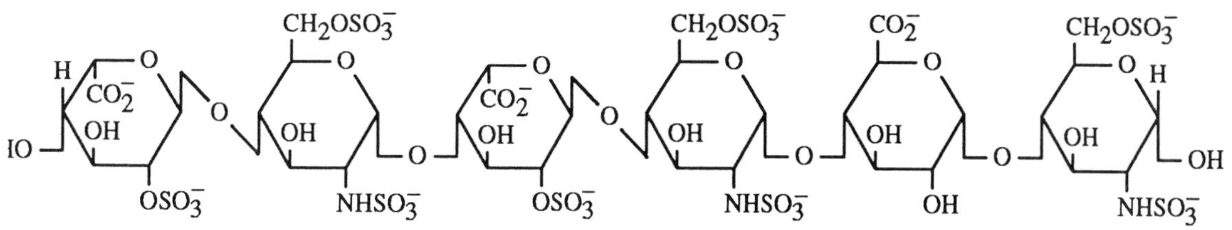

2-Sulfo-α-iduronate   2,6-Disulfoglucosamine   β-Glucuronate

(74)

Figure 20 Structure of heparin polysaccharide

sign of subsiding. Indeed, it is not unrealistic to expect that a significant proportion of future progress in inositol phosphate biology will be underpinned by the current interest in inositol phosphate chemistry. The development of synthetic inositol phosphate analogues with novel biological properties can be envisaged, including antagonists, 'caged' compounds, cell-penetrating compounds, affinity, photoaffinity and spin-labelled inositol phosphate analogues, fluorescent probes and inositol phosphates linked to affinity columns for the purification of receptors and enzymes. Crucial to the success of such ventures will be interdisciplinary collaborations by chemists with cell biologists, biochemists and pharmacologists. If the current pace of progress is maintained, we can expect an exciting future.

ACKNOWLEDGEMENTS

Work in the author's laboratory was supported by the SERC, the Research Corporation Trust, The Wellcome Trust, Merck Sharp & Dohme Research and the Lister Institute of Preventive Medicine. The author acknowledges valuable collaborations with S. R. Nahorski, R. Gigg, A. M. Cooke, M. R. Hamblin, J. McBain, N. J. Noble, J. Strupish, A. L. Willcocks and R. Wojcikiewicz of the Departments of Chemistry and Pharmacology, Leicester University for their experimental contributions to some of the work discussed here. B.V.L.P. is a Lister Institute Fellow.

11.4.15 REFERENCES

1. E. W. Sutherland and T. W. Rall, *J. Biol. Chem.*, 1958, **232**, 1065, 1077.
2. P. Cohen, *Eur. J. Biochem.*, 1985, **151**, 439.
3. L. E. Hokin, *Annu. Rev. Biochem.*, 1985, **54**, 205.
4. R. Michell, *Biochim. Biophys. Acta*, 1975, **415**, 81.
5. M. J. Berridge and R. F. Irvine, *Nature (London)*, 1984, **312**, 315.
6. Y. Nishizuka, *Nature (London)*, 1984, **308**, 693.
7. M. J. Berridge, *Annu. Rev. Biochem.*, 1987, **56**, 159.
8. H. Streb, R. F. Irvine, M. J. Berridge and I. Schulz, *Nature (London)*, 1983, **306**, 67.
9. M. J. Berridge, *Sci. Am.*, 1985, **253**, 124.
10. A. A. Abdel-Latif, *Pharmacol. Rev.*, 1986, **38**, 227.
11. M. J. Berridge, *J. Exp. Biol.*, 1986, **124**, 323.
12. M. J. Berridge, *Biochim. Biophys. Acta*, 1987, **907**, 33.
13. M. J. Berridge and R. F. Irvine, *Nature (London)*, 1989, **341**, 197.
14. P. W. Majerus, T. M. Connolly, V. S. Bansal, R. C. Inhorn, T. S. Ross and D. L. Lips, *J. Biol. Chem.*, 1988, **263**, 3051.
15. S. R. Nahorski, *Trends Neurosci.*, 1988, **11**, 444.
16. G. W. Mayr, *Boehringer Mannheim Biochemica*, 1987, Topics in Biochemistry.
17. S. R. Nahorski and B. V. L. Potter, *Trends Pharmacol. Sci.*, 1989, **10**, 139.
18. S. B. Shears, *Biochem. J.*, 1989, **260**, 313.
19. J. E. Bleasdale, J. Eichberg and G. Hauser (eds.), 'Inositol and Phosphoinositides: Metabolism and Regulation', Humana Press, Clifton, NJ, 1985.
20. P. Cohen and M. D. Houslay (eds.), 'Molecular Mechanisms of Transmembrane Signalling', Elsevier, Amsterdam, 1985.
21. J. W. Putney, Jr., 'Phosphoinositides and Receptor Mechanisms', Liss, New York, 1986.
22. M. J. Berridge and R. H. Michell (eds.), 'Inositol Lipids and Transmembrane Signalling', The Royal Society, London, 1988.
23. R. H. Michell, A. H. Drummond and C. P. Downes, 'Inositol Lipids and Cell Signalling', Academic Press, London, 1989.
24. J. P. Miller, in 'Cyclic 3',5' Nucleotides: Mechanism of Action', ed. H. Cramer and G. Schulz, Wiley, London, 1978, p. 77.
25. E. J. Neer and D. Clapham, *Nature (London)*, 1988, **333**, 129.
26. A. G. Gilman, *Annu. Rev. Biochem.*, 1987, **56**, 615.
27. A. Levitzki, *Trends Biochem. Sci.*, 1988, **13**, 298.
28. S. Cockroft, *Trends Biochem. Sci.*, 1987, **12**, 75.
29. M. Schramm and Z. Selinger, *Science (Washington D.C.)*, 1984, **225**, 1350.
30. J. D. Corbin and R. A. Johnson, *Methods Enzymol.*, 1988, **159**.
31. A. Levitzki, *Physiol. Rev.*, 1986, **66**, 819.
32. B. Jastorff, J. Hoppe and M. A. Morr, *Eur. J. Biochem.*, 1979, **101**, 555.
33. F. Eckstein, *Angew. Chem., Int. Ed. Engl.*, 1983, **22**, 423.
34. F. Eckstein, *Annu. Rev. Biochem.*, 1985, **54**, 367.
35. F. Eckstein, L. P. Simonson and H.-P. Baer, *Biochemistry*, 1974, **13**, 3806.
36. F. Eckstein and U. Kutzke, *Tetrahedron Lett.*, 1986, **27**, 1657.
37. H.-G. Genieser, W. Dostman, U. Bottin, E. Butt and B. Jastorff, *Tetrahedron Lett.*, 1988, **29**, 2803.
38. J. Baraniak and W. J. Stec, *J. Chem. Soc., Perkin Trans. 1*, 1987, 1645.
39. W. J. Stec, *Acc. Chem. Res.*, 1983, **16**, 411.
40. W. Hinrichs, M. Steifa, W. Saenger and F. Eckstein, *Nucleic Acids Res.*, 1987, **15**, 4945.
41. F. Eckstein, P. J. Romaniuk, W. Heideman and D. R. Storm, *J. Biol. Chem.*, 1981, **256**, 9118.
42. P. D. Senter, F. Eckstein, E. Muelsch and E. Boehme, *J. Biol. Chem.*, 1983, **258**, 6741.
43. R. L. Jarvest, G. Lowe, J. Baraniak and W. J. Stec, *Biochem. J.*, 1982, **203**, 461.

44. L. H. Parker Bothelo, J. D. Rothermel, R. V. Coombs and B. Jastorff, *Methods Enzymol.*, 1988, **159**, 159.
45. J. D. Rothermel, W. J. Stec, J. Baraniak, B. Jastorff and L. H. Parker Bothelo, *J. Biol. Chem.*, 1983, **258**, 12 125.
46. J. D. Rothermel, B. Jastorff and L. H. Parker Bothelo, *J. Biol. Chem.*, 1984, **259**, 8151.
47. L. H. Parker Bothelo, L. C. Webster, J. D. Rothermel, J. Baraniak and W. J. Stec, *J. Biol. Chem.*, 1988, **263**, 5301.
48. J. D. Rothermel and L. H. Parker Bothelo, *Biochem. J.*, 1988, **251**, 757.
49. F. Eckstein, S. Eimerl and M. Schramm, *FEBS Lett.*, 1976, **64**, 92.
50. C. Richter-Landsberg and B. Jastorff, *J. Neurochem.*, 1985, **45**, 1218.
51. K. M. McMasters, D. M. Anderson, L. H. Parker Bothelo, G. J. McDonald and W. R. Moyle, 'Advances in Gene Technology', ICSU Short Reports, 1986, vol. 4, p. 228.
52. P. J. M. Van Haastert and E. Kien, *J. Biol. Chem.*, 1983, **258**, 9636.
53. F. Ito and J. Y. Chou, *J. Biol. Chem.*, 1984, **259**, 2526.
54. A. M. Gronenborn and G. M. Clore, *Biochemistry*, 1982, **21**, 4040.
55. H.-G. Scholuebbers, P. H. van Knippenberg, J. Baraniak, W. J. Stec, U. Morr and B. Jastorff, *Eur. J. Biochem.*, 1984, **138**, 101.
56. S. L. Pelech, P. H. Pritchard, D. N. Brindley and D. E. Vance, *Biochem. J.*, 1983, **216**, 129.
57. F. Eckstein and J. C. Foreman, *FEBS Lett.*, 1978, **91**, 182.
58. N. D. Goldberg and M. K. Haddox, *Annu. Rev. Biochem.*, 1977, **46**, 823.
59. R. L. Volle and L. F. Quenzer, *Fed. Proc., Fed. Am. Soc. Exp. Biol.*, 1983, **42**, 3099.
60. L. Stryer, *Sci. Am.*, 1987, **255**, 42.
61. L. Stryer, *Annu. Rev. Neurosci.*, 1986, **9**, 87.
62. E. E. Fersenko, S. S. Kolesnikov and A. L. Lyubarsky, *Nature (London)*, 1985, **313**, 310.
63. M. Chabre, *Annu. Rev. Biophys. Chem.*, 1985, **14**, 331.
64. A. L. Zimmerman and D. A. Baylor, *Nature (London)*, 1986, **321**, 70.
65. J. E. Brown, L. J. Rubin, A. J. Ghalayni, A. L. Tarver, R. F. Irvine, M. J. Berridge and R. E. Anderson, *Nature (London)*, 1984, **311**, 160.
66. A. Fein, R. Payne, D. M. Corson, M. J. Berridge and R. F. Irvine, *Nature (London)*, 1984, **311**, 157.
67. R. Payne, B. Walz, S. Levy and A. Fein, *Philos. Trans. R. Soc. London, Ser. B*, 1988, **320**, 359.
68. A. L. Zimmerman, G. Yamanaka, F. Eckstein, D. A. Baylor and L. Stryer, *Proc. Natl. Acad. Sci. USA*, 1985, **82**, 8813.
69. F. Eckstein, J. W. Karpen, J. M. Critchfield and L. Stryer, *J. Biol. Chem.*, 1988, **263**, 14 080.
70. L. Bouveault, *Bull. Soc. Chim. Fr.*, 1894, **11**, 144.
71. *IUPAC Information Bulletin*, 1968, **32**, 51.
72. B. A. Klyashchitskii, V. I. Shvets and N. A. Preobrazhenskii, *Chem. Phys. Lipids*, 1969, **3**, 393.
73. R. H. Michell and M. J. Berridge, *Philos. Trans. R. Soc. London, Ser. B*, 1988, **320**, 237.
74. R. Parthasarathy and F. Eisenberg, Jr., *Biochem. J.*, 1986, **235**, 313.
75. *Biochem. J.*, 1989, **258**, 1.
76. T. F. Donahue and S. A. Henry, *J. Biol. Chem.*, 1981, **256**, 7077.
77. J. P. Hirsch and S. A. Hewy, *Mol. Cell. Biol.*, 1986, **6**, 3320.
78. T. Maeda and F. Eisenberg, Jr., *J. Biol. Chem.*, 1980, **255**, 8458.
79. L. A. Mauck, Y.-H. Wong and W. R. Sherman, *Biochemistry*, 1980, **19**, 3623.
80. F. Eisenberg, Jr. and T. Maeda, in 'Inositol and Phosphoinositides: Metabolism and Regulation', ed. J. E. Bleasdale, J. Eichberg and G. Hauser, Humana Press, Clifton, NJ, 1985, p. 3.
81. F. A. Loewus, *Recent Adv. Phytochem.*, 1974, **8**, 179.
82. F. A. Loewus and M. W. Loewus, *Annu. Rev. Plant Physiol.*, 1983, **34**, 137.
83. K. Takimoto, M. Okada, Y. Matsuda and H. Nakagawa, *J. Biochem. (Tokyo)*, 1985, **98**, 363.
84. P. V. Attwood, J.-B. Ducep and M.-C. Chanal, *Biochem. J.*, 1988, **253**, 387.
85. J. L. Meek, T. J. Rice and E. Anton, *Biochem. Biophys. Res. Commun.*, 1988, **156**, 143.
86. N. S. Gee, C. I. Ragan, K. J. Watling, S. Aspley, R. G. Jackson, G. G. Reid, D. Gani and J. K. Shute, *Biochem. J.*, 1988, **249**, 883.
87. J. H. Allison and M. A. Stewart, *Nature (London)*, 1971, **233**, 267.
88. M. J. Berridge, C. P. Downes and M. R. Hanley, *Biochem. J.*, 1982, **206**, 587.
89. W. R. Sherman, L. Y. Munsell, B. G. Gish and M. P. Honchar, *J. Neurochem.*, 1985, **44**, 798.
90. W. R. Sherman, in 'Inositol Lipids in Cell Signalling', ed. R. H. Michell, A. H. Drummond and C. P. Downes, Academic Press, London, 1989, p. 39.
91. A. H. Drummond, *Trends Pharmacol. Sci.*, 1987, **8**, 129.
92. I. H. Batty and S. R. Nahorski, *Biochem. J.*, 1987, **247**, 797.
93. S. Avissar, G. Schreiber, A. Danon and R. H. Belmaker, *Nature (London)*, 1988, **331**, 440.
94. A. H. Drummond, *Nature (London)*, 1988, **331**, 388.
95. J. K. Shute, R. Baker, D. C. Billington and D. Gani, *J. Chem. Soc., Chem. Commun.*, 1988, 626.
96. M. Whitman, C. P. Downes, M. Keeler, T. Keller and L. Cantley, *Nature (London)*, 1988, **332**, 644.
97. A. E. Traynor-Kaplan, A. L. Harris, B. L. Thompson, P. A. Taylor and L. A. Sklar, *Nature (London)*, 1988, **334**, 353.
98. K. R. Auger, L. A. Serunian, S. P. Soltoff, P. Libby and L. C. Cantley, *Cell*, 1989, **57**, 167.
99. J. N. Hawthorne, *Biochem. Soc. Trans.*, 1988, **16**, 657.
100. S. K. Fisher, L. A. A. van Rooijen and B. W. Agranoff, *Trends Biochem. Sci.*, 1984, **9**, 53.
101. W. L. Smith, *Biochem. J.*, 1989, **259**, 315.
102. M. Sakon, J. Kambayashi, T. Tsujinaka and T. Mori, *Biochem. Int.*, 1988, **16**, 639.
103. Y. Banno, Y. Yada and Y. Nozawa, *J. Biol. Chem.*, 1988, **263**, 11 459.
104. E. Hough, L. K. Hansen, B. Birknes, K. Jynge, S. Hansen, A. Hordvik, C. Little, E. Dodson and Z. Derwenda, *Nature (London)*, 1989, **338**, 357.
105. C. Little, *Biochem. Soc. Trans.*, 1989, **17**, 271.
106. P. Volpe, K.-H. Krause, H. Sadarnitsu, F. Zorgato, T. Pozzan, J. Meldolesi and P. D. Lew, *Proc. Natl. Acad. Sci. USA*, 1988, **85**, 1091.
107. H. Schulman and L. L. Lou, *Trends Biochem. Sci.*, 1989, **14**, 62.
108. C. A. Ross, J. Meldolesi, T. A. Milner, T. Satoh, S. Supattapone and S. H. Snyder, *Nature (London)*, 1989, **339**, 468.

109. P. F. Worley, J. M. Baraban, J. S. Colvin and S. H. Snyder, *Nature (London)*, 1987, **325**, 159.
110. P. F. Worley, J. N. Baraban, S. Supattapone, V. S. Wilson and S. H. Snyder, *J. Biol. Chem.*, 1987, **262**, 12 132.
111. S. Supattapone, P. F. Worley, J. M. Baraban and S. H. Snyder, *J. Biol. Chem.*, 1988, **263**, 1530.
112. S. K. Danoff, S. Supattapone and S. H. Snyder, *Biochem. J.*, 1988, **254**, 701.
113. T. Meyer, D. Holowka and L. Stryer, *Science (Washington D.C.)*, 1988, **240**, 653.
114. H. Brockerhoff, *Chem. Phys. Lipids*, 1986, **39**, 83.
115. V. P. S. Chauhan and H. Brockerhoff, *Biochem. Biophys. Res. Commun.*, 1986, **136**, 288.
116. U. Kikkawa and Y. Nishizuka, *Annu. Rev. Cell. Biol.*, 1986, **2**, 149.
117. M. Castangna, Y. Takai, K. Kaibuchi, K. Sano, U. Kikkawa and Y. Nishizuka, *J. Biol. Chem.*, 1982, **257**, 7847.
118. Y. Nishizuka, *Science (Washington D.C.)*, 1986, **233**, 305.
119. Y. Nishizuka, *Nature (London)*, 1988, **334**, 661.
120. B. R. Ganong, C. R. Loomis, Y. A. Hannun and R. M. Bell, *Proc. Natl. Acad. Sci. USA*, 1986, **83**, 1184.
121. R. Rando, *FASEB J.*, 1988, **2**, 2348.
122. P. W. Majerus, T. M. Connolly, H. Deckmyn, T. S. Ross, T. E. Bross, H. Ishii, V. S. Bansal and D. B. Wilson, *Science (Washington D.C.)*, 1986, **234**, 1519.
123. R. F. Irvine, R. M. Moor, W. K. Pollock, P. M. Smith and K. A. Wreggett, *Philos. Trans. R. Soc. London, Ser. B*, 1988, **320**, 281.
124. C. P. Downes, *Biochem. Soc. Trans.*, 1989, **17**, 259.
125. H. Ishii, T. M. Connolly, T. E. Bross and P. W. Majerus, *Proc. Natl. Acad. Sci. USA*, 1986, **83**, 6397.
126. R. M. C. Dowson, N. Freinkel, F. B. Jungalwala and N. Clarke, *Biochem. J.*, 1971, **122**, 605.
127. D. B. Wilson, T. M. Connolly, T. E. Bross, P. W. Majerus, W. R. Sherman, A. N. Tyler, L. J. Rubin and J. E. Brown, *J. Biol. Chem.*, 1985, **260**, 13 496.
128. R. F. Irvine, A. J. Letcher, D. J. Lander and M. J. Berridge, *Biochem. J.*, 1986, **240**, 301.
129. A. L. Willcocks, J. Strupish, R. F. Irvine and S. R. Nahorski, *Biochem. J.*, 1989, **257**, 297.
130. A. R. Hughes, T. Takemura and J. W. Putney, *J. Biol. Chem.*, 1988, **263**, 211.
131. N. S. Wong, C. J. Barker, S. B. Shears, C. J. Kirk and R. H. Michell, *Biochem. J.*, 1988, **252**, 1.
132. C. P. Downes, M. C. Mussat and R. H. Michell, *Biochem. J.*, 1982, **203**, 169.
133. T. M. Connolly, V. S. Bansal, T. E. Bross, R. F. Irvine and P. W. Majerus, *J. Biol. Chem.*, 1987, **262**, 2146.
134. C. A. Hansen, R. A. Johanson, M. T. Williamson and J. R. Williamson, *J. Biol. Chem.*, 1987, **262**, 17 319.
135. G. W. Mayr, *Biochem. J.*, 1989, **259**, 463.
136. I. H. Batty, S. R. Nahorski and R. F. Irvine, *Biochem. J.*, 1985, **232**, 211.
137. R. F. Irvine, A. J. Letcher, J. P. Heslop and M. J. Berridge, *Nature (London)*, 1986, **320**, 631.
138. R. A. Johanson, C. A. Hansen, and J. R. Williamson, *J. Biol. Chem.*, 1988, **263**, 7465.
139. D. Hoeer, A. Kwiatowski, C. Seib, W. Rosenthal, G. Schultz and E. Oberdisse, *Biochem. Biophys. Res. Commun.*, 1988, **154**, 668.
140. C. Doughney, M. A. McPherson and R. L. Dormer, *Biochem. J.*, 1988, **251**, 927.
141. P. J. Cullen, R. F. Irvine, B. J. Drobak and A. P. Dawson, *Biochem. J.*, 1989, **259**, 931.
142. R. F. Irvine and R. M. Moor, *Biochem. J.*, 1986, **240**, 917.
143. R. F. Irvine and R. M. Moor, *Biochem. Biophys. Res. Commun.*, 1987, **146**, 284.
144. I. Crossley, K. Swann, E. Chambers and M. Whitaker, *Biochem. J.*, 1988, **252**, 257.
145. P. M. Snyder, K. H. Krause and M. J. Welsh, *J. Biol. Chem.*, 1988, **263**, 11 048.
146. A. P. Morris, D. V. Gallacher, R. F. Irvine and O. H. Petersen, *Nature (London)*, 1987, **330**, 653.
147. L. Changya, R. F. Irvine, D. V. Gallacher, B. V. L. Potter and O. H. Petersen, *J. Membr. Biol.*, 1989, **109**, 85.
148. F. Thevenod, M. Dehlinger-Kremer, T. P. Kemmer, A. L. Christian, B. V. L. Potter and I. Schulz, *J. Membr. Biol.*, 1989, **109**, 173.
149. V. Henne, A. Piiper and H.-D. Soeling, *FEBS Lett.*, 1987, **218**, 153.
150. J. M. Mullaney, M. Yu, T. K. Ghosh and D. L. Gill, *Proc. Natl. Acad. Sci. USA*, 1988, **85**, 2499.
151. T. K. Ghosh, J. M. Mullaney, F. I. Tarazi and D. L. Gill, *Nature (London)*, 1989, **340**, 236.
152. T. D. Hill, N. M. Dean and A. L. Boynton, *Science (Washington, D.C.)*, 1989, **242**, 1176.
153. P. G. Bradford and R. F. Irvine, *Biochem. Biophys. Res. Commun.*, 1987, **149**, 680.
154. P. Enyedi and G. H. Williams, *J. Biol. Chem.*, 1988, **263**, 7940.
155. C. Erneux, M. Lemos, B. Verjans, P. Vanderhaegen, A. Delvaux and J. E. Dumont, *Eur. J. Biochem.*, 1989, **181**, 317.
156. J. Strupish, A. M. Cooke, B. V. L. Potter, R. Gigg and S. R. Nahorski, *Biochem. J.*, 1988, **253**, 901.
157. S. B. Shears, J. B. Parry, E. K. Tang, R. F. Irvine, R. H. Michell and C. J. Kirk, *Biochem. J.*, 1987, **246**, 139.
158. T. Balla, G. Guillemette, A. J. Baukal and K. J. Catt, *J. Biol. Chem.*, 1987, **262**, 9952.
159. L. R. Stephens, P. T. Hawkins, A. J. Morris and C. P. Downes, *Biochem. J.*, 1988, **249**, 283.
160. L. R. Stephens, P. T. Hawkins, A. J. Morris and C. P. Downes, *Biochem. J.*, 1988, **249**, 271.
161. G. W. Mayr and W. Dietrich, *FEBS Lett.*, 1987, **213**, 278.
162. D. J. Cosgrove, 'Inositol Phosphates, Their Chemistry, Biochemistry & Physiology', Elsevier, Amsterdam, 1980.
163. M. Vallejo, T. R. Jackson, S. L. Lightman and M. R. Hanley, *Nature (London)*, 1987, **330**, 656.
164. M. R. Hanley, T. R. Jackson, M. Vallejo, S. I. Patterson, O. Thastrup, S. Lightman, J. Rogers, G. Henderson and A. Pini, *Philos. Trans. R. Soc. London, Ser. B*, 1988, **320**, 381.
165. D. Carpenter, M. R. Hanley, P. T. Hawkins, T. R. Jackson, L. R. Stephens and M. Vallejo, *Biochem. Soc. Trans.*, 1989, **17**, 3.
166. T. Posternak, 'The Cyclitols', Holden-Day, San Francisco, 1965.
167. K.-L. Yu, K.-Y. Ko and B. Fraser-Reid, *Synth. Commun.*, 1988, **18**, 465.
168. S. J. Angyal and M. E. Tate, *J. Chem. Soc.*, 1961, 4122.
169. J. Gigg, R. Gigg, S. Payne and R. Conant, *Carbohydr. Res.*, 1985, **142**, 132.
170. J. Gigg, R. Gigg, S. Payne and R. Conant, *J. Chem. Soc., Perkin Trans. 1*, 1987, 423.
171. J. Gigg, R. Gigg, S. Payne and R. Conant, *J. Chem. Soc., Perkin Trans. 1*, 1987, 1757.
172. J. Gigg, R. Gigg, S. Payne and R. Conant, *J. Chem. Soc., Perkin Trans. 1*, 1987, 2411.
173. P. J. Garegg, T. Iversen, R. Johansson and B. Lindberg, *Carbohydr. Res.*, 1984, **130**, 322.
174. P. J. Garegg, B. Lindberg, I. Kvarnstrom and S. C. T. Svensson, *Carbohydr. Res.*, 1985, **139**, 209.

175. D. C. Billington, *Chem. Soc. Rev.*, 1989, **18**, 83.
176. V. I. Shvets, A. E. Stephanov, V. N. Krylova and P. V. Gulak, 'Myo-inositol and Phosphoinositides', Nauka Publishing House, Moscow, 1987.
177. A. E. Stephanov and V. I. Shvets, *Chem. Phys. Lipids*, 1979, **25**, 247.
178. W. Tegge and C. E. Ballou, *Proc. Natl. Acad. Sci. USA*, 1989, **86**, 94.
179. Y. Watanabe, M. Mitani and S. Ozaki, *Chem. Lett.*, 1987, 123.
180. S. V. Ley and F. Sternfeld, *Tetrahedron Lett.*, 1988, **29**, 5305.
181. J. C. Lindon, D. J. Baker, R. D. Farrant and J. M. Williams, *Biochem. J.*, 1986, **233**, 275.
182. J. C. Lindon, D. J. Baker, J. M. Williams and R. F. Irvine, *Biochem. J.*, 1987, **244**, 591.
183. S. Cerdan, C. A. Hansen, R. Johanson, T. Inubushi and J. R. Williamson, *J. Biol. Chem.*, 1986, **261**, 14 676.
184. J. Emsley and S. Niazi, *Phosphorus Sulfur*, 1981, **10**, 401.
185. T. Shibata, J. Uzawa, Y. Sugiura, K. Hayashi and T. Takizawa, *Chem. Phys. Lipids*, 1984, **34**, 107.
186. J. D. Moyer, N. Malinowski, E. A. Napier and J. Strong, *Biochem. J.*, 1988, **254**, 95.
187. R. Spector, *Neurochem. Res.*, 1988, **13**, 785.
188. M. D. Tuersley, L. Best and S. Tomlinson, *J. Neurochem.*, 1988, **51**, 1610.
189. M. J. Berridge, *Biochim. Biophys. Acta*, 1987, **907**, 33.
190. C. Jiang, J. D. Moyer and D. C. Baker, *J. Carbohydr. Chem.*, 1987, **6**, 319.
191. J. D. Moyer, O. Reizes, A. Surender, C. Jiang, N. Malinowski and D. C. Baker, *Mol. Pharmacol.*, 1988, **33**, 683.
192. H. Hoenig, P. Senfer-Wasserthal, A. E. Stuetz and E. Zenz, *Tetrahedron Lett.*, 1989, **30**, 811.
193. A. P. Kozikowski, Y. Xia and J. M. Rusnak, *J. Chem. Soc., Chem. Commun.*, 1988, 1301.
194. A. P. Kozikowski, A. H. Fauq and J. M. Rusnak, *Tetrahedron Lett.*, 1989, **30**, 3365.
195. L. I. Pizer and C. E. Ballou, *J. Am. Chem. Soc.*, 1959, **81**, 915; 1960, **82**, 3333.
196. A. L. Leavitt and W. R. Sherman, *Carbohydr. Res.*, 1982, **103**, 203.
197. D. C. Billington, R. Baker, J. Kulagowski and I. M. Mawer, *J. Chem. Soc., Chem. Commun.*, 1987, 314.
198. D. C. Billington, R. Baker, J. J. Kulagowski, I. M. Mawer, J. P. Vacca, S. J. de Solms and J. R. Huff, *J. Chem. Soc., Perkin Trans. 1*, 1989, 1423.
199. H. W. Lee and Y. Kishi, *J. Am. Chem. Soc.*, 1985, **50**, 4402.
200. D. C. Billington and R. Baker, *J. Chem. Soc., Chem. Commun.*, 1987, 1011.
201. T. Metschies, C. Schulz and B. Jastorff, *Tetrahedron Lett.*, 1988, **29**, 3921.
202. Y. Watanabe, M. Mitani, T. Morita and S. Ozaki, *J. Chem. Soc., Chem. Commun.*, 1989, 482.
203. Y. Watanabe, T. Ogasawara, H. Nakahira, T. Matsuki and S. Ozaki, *Tetrahedron Lett.*, 1988, **29**, 5259.
204. B. Duthu, D. Honalla and R. Wolf, *Can. J. Chem.*, 1988, **66**, 2965.
205. M. R. Hamblin, J. S. Flora and B. V. L. Potter, *Biochem. J.*, 1987, **246**, 771.
206. V. N. Krylova, N. I. Kobel'kova, G. F. Olenik and V. I. Shvets, *Zh. Org. Khim.*, 1980, **16**, 62.
207. J. P. Vacca, S. J. de Solms, J. R. Huff, D. C. Billington, R. Baker, J. Kulagowski and I. Mawer, *Tetrahedron*, 1989, **45**, 5679.
208. M. R. Hamblin, R. Gigg and B. V. L. Potter, *J. Chem. Soc., Chem. Commun.*, 1987, 626.
209. M. R. Hamblin, R. Gigg and B. V. L. Potter, *Biochem. Soc. Trans.*, 1987, **15**, 415.
210. S. Ozaki, Y. Watanabe, T. Ogasawara, Y. Kondo, N. Shiotani, H. Nishii and T. Matsuki, *Tetrahedron Lett.*, 1986, **27**, 3157.
211. A. M. Cooke, R. Gigg and B. V. L. Potter, *Tetrahedron Lett.*, 1987, **28**, 2305.
212. A. M. Cooke, R. Gigg and B. V. L. Potter, *Biochem. Soc. Trans.*, 1987, **15**, 904.
213. A. M. Cooke, R. Gigg and B. V. L. Potter, unpublished work.
214. C. B. Reese and J. G. Ward, *Tetrahedron Lett.*, 1987, **28**, 2309.
215. A. E. Stephanov, B. A. Klyashchitskii, V. I. Shvets and R. P. Evstigneeva, *Bioorg. Khim.*, 1976, **2**, 1627.
216. H. Watanabe, H. Nakahira, M. Buyna and S. Ozaki, *Tetrahedron Lett.*, 1987, **28**, 4179.
217. J. P. Vacca, S. J. de Solms and J. R. Huff, *J. Am. Chem. Soc.*, 1987, **109**, 3478.
218. J. L. Meek, F. Davidson and F. W. Hobbs, Jr., *J. Am. Chem. Soc.*, 1988, **110**, 2317.
219. K.-L. Yu and B. Fraser-Reid, *Tetrahedron Lett.*, 1988, **29**, 979.
220. C. A. Dreef, R. J. Tuinman, C. J. J. Elie, G. A. van der Marel and J. H. van Boom, *Recl. Trav. Chim. Pays-Bas*, 1988, **107**, 395.
221. A. M. Cooke, N. J. Noble, S. Payne, R. Gigg and B. V. L. Potter, *J. Chem. Soc., Chem. Commun.*, 1989, 269.
222. A. M. Cooke, N. J. Noble, R. Gigg, A. L. Willcocks, J. Strupish, S. R. Nahorski and B. V. L. Potter, *Biochem. Soc. Trans.*, 1989, **16**, 992.
223. Y.-C. Liu and C.-S. Chen, *Tetrahedron Lett.*, 1989, **30**, 1617.
224. S. V. Ley and F. Sternfeld, *Tetrahedron Lett.*, 1987, **28**, 225.
225. J. F. Marecek and G. D. Prestwich, *J. Labelled Comp. Radiopharm.*, 1989, **27**, 917.
226. C. E. Dreef, G. A. van der Marel and J. H. van Boom, *Recl. Trav. Chim. Pays-Bas*, 1987, **106**, 161.
227. S. J. de Solms, J. P. Vacca and J. R. Huff, *Tetrahedron Lett.*, 1987, **28**, 4503.
228. S. Ozaki, M. Kohno, H. Nakahira, M. Bunya and Y. Watanabe, *Chem. Lett.*, 1988, 77.
229. M. F. Boehm and G. D. Prestwich, *Tetrahedron Lett.*, 1988, **29**, 5217.
230. Y. Watanabe, T. Ogasawara, N. Shiotani and S. Ozaki, *Tetrahedron Lett.*, 1987, **28**, 2607.
231. R. J. Auchus, S. L. Kaiser and P. W. Majerus, *Proc. Natl. Acad. Sci. USA*, 1987, **84**, 1206.
232. A. M. Cooke, D. C. Billington and B. V. L. Potter, unpublished work.
233. G. Baudin, B. I. Glaenzer, K. S. Swaminathan and A. Vasella, *Helv. Chim. Acta*, 1988, **71**, 1367.
234. S. Ozaki, Y. Kondo, H. Nakahira, S. Yamaoka and Y. Watanabe, *Tetrahedron Lett.*, 1987, **28**, 4691.
235. M. R. Hamblin, L. R. Stephens and B. V. L. Potter, unpublished work.
236. R. Gigg, *Chem. Phys. Lipids*, 1980, **26**, 287.
237. J. G. Ward and R. C. Young, *Tetrahedron Lett.*, 1988, **29**, 6013.
238. M. Jones, K. K. Rana, J. G. Ward and R. C. Young, *Tetrahedron Lett.*, 1989, **30**, 5353.
239. C. E. Dreef, C. J. J. Elie, F. Hoogerhout, G. A. van der Marel and J. H. van Boom, *Tetrahedron Lett.*, 1988, **29**, 6513.
240. V. N. Krylova, N. P. Gornaeva, V. I. Shvets and R. P. Evstigneeva, *Dokl. Akad. Nauk SSSR*, 1979, **246**, 339.
241. V. N. Krylova, A. I. Lyutik, N. P. Gornaeva and V. I. Shvets, *Zh. Obshch. Khim.*, 1981, **51**, 210.

242. A. E. Stephanov and V. I. Shvets, *Chem. Phys. Lipids*, 1986, **41**, 1.
243. A. M. Cooke, R. Gigg and B. V. L. Potter, *J. Chem. Soc., Chem. Commun.*, 1987, 1525.
244. F. Eckstein and G. Gish, *Trends Biochem. Sci.*, 1989, **14**, 97.
245. A. L. Willcocks, B. V. L. Potter, A. M. Cooke and S. R. Nahorski, *Eur. J. Pharmacol.*, 1988, **155**, 181.
246. D. Nunn, B. V. L. Potter and C. W. Taylor, *Biochem. J.*, 1990, in press.
247. C. W. Taylor, M. J. Berridge, A. M. Cooke and B. V. L. Potter, *Biochem. Biophys. Res. Commun.*, 1988, **150**, 626.
248. C. W. Taylor, M. J. Berridge, A. M. Cooke and B. V. L. Potter, *Biochem. J.*, 1989, **259**, 645.
249. A. M. Cooke, S. R. Nahorski and B. V. L. Potter, *FEBS Lett.*, 1989, **242**, 373.
250. R. Wojcikiewicz, A. M. Cooke, B. V. L. Potter and S. R. Nahorski, *J. Biol. Chem.*, 1989, submitted.
251. J. McBain, S. R. Nahorski and B. V. L. Potter, unpublished results.
252. P. Folk, E. Kmonickova, L. Krpejsova and A. Strunecka, *J. Labelled Comp. Radiopharm.*, 1988, **25**, 793.
253. C. Schulz, T. Metschies and B. Jastorff, *Tetrahedron Lett.*, 1988, **29**, 3919.
254. G. Lin and M.-D. Tsai, *J. Am. Chem. Soc.*, 1989, **111**, 3099.
255. P. Somerharju and K. W. A. Wirtz, *Chem. Phys. Lipids*, 1982, **30**, 81.
256. C. E. Dreef, G. A. van der Marel and J. H. van Boom, *Recl. Trav. Chim. Pays-Bas*, 1987, **106**, 512.
257. J. J. Kulagowski, *Tetrahedron Lett.*, 1989, **30**, 3869.
258. M. A. Polokoff, G. H. Bencen, J. P. Vacca, J. de Solms, S. D. Young and J. R. Huff, *J. Biol. Chem.*, 1988, **263**, 11 922.
259. M. Hirata, Y. Watanabe, T. Ishimatsu, T. Ikebe, Y. Kimura, K. Yamaguchi, S. Ozaki and T. Koga, *J. Biol. Chem.*, 1990, in press.
260. S. V. Ley, M. Parra, A. J. Readgrave, F. Sternfeld and A. Vidal, *Tetrahedron Lett.*, 1989, **30**, 3557.
261. S. D. Gero, personal communication.
262. W. Tegge, Ph.D. Thesis, University of Bremen, 1986.
263. V. Henne, G. W. Mayr, B. Grabowski, B. Koppitz and H.-D. Soeling, *Eur. J. Biochem.*, 1988, **174**, 95.
264. B. Koppitz, F. Vogel and G. W. Mayr, *Eur. J. Biochem.*, 1986, **161**, 421.
265. M. Hirata, T. Sasaguri, T. Hamachi, T. Hashimoto, M. Kukita and T. Koga, *Nature (London)*, 1985, **317**, 723.
266. T. Ishimatsu, Y. Kimura, T. Ikebe, K. Yamaguchi, T. Koga and M. Hirata, *Biochem. Biophys. Res. Commun.*, 1988, **155**, 1173.
267. J. H. Kaplan and A. P. Somlyo, *Trends Neurosci.*, 1989, **12**, 54.
268. J. A. McCray and D. R. Trentham, *Annu. Rev. Biophys. Chem.*, 1989, **18**, 239.
269. J. W. Walker, G. P. Reid, J. A. McCray and D. R. Trentham, *J. Am. Chem. Soc.*, 1988, **110**, 7170.
270. J. W. Walker, J. Feeney and D. R. Trentham, *Biochemistry*, 1989, **28**, 3272.
271. J. W. Walker, A. V. Somlyo, Y. E. Goldman, A. P. Somlyo and D. R. Trentham, *Nature (London)*, 1987, **327**, 249.
272. A. L. Willcocks, B. V. L. Potter, A. M. Cooke and S. R. Nahorski, *Biochem. Biophys. Res. Commun.*, 1987, **146**, 1071.
273. T. J. Rink and R. Jacob, *Trends Neurosci.*, 1989, **12**, 43.
274. M. J. Berridge, P. H. Cobbold and K. S. R. Cuthbertson, *Philos. Trans. R. Soc. London, Ser. B*, 1988, **320**, 325.
275. M. Wakui, B. V. L. Potter and O. H. Petersen, *Nature (London)*, 1989, **339**, 317.
276. T. Meyer and L. Stryer, *Proc. Natl. Acad. Sci. USA*, 1988, **85**, 5051.
277. M. McCarren, B. V. L. Potter and R. Miller, *Neuron*, 1989, **3**, 461.
278. M. G. Low, M. A. J. Ferguson, A. H. Futerman and I. Silman, *Trends Biol. Sci.*, 1986, **11**, 212
279. M. G. Low, *Biochem. J.*, 1987, **244**, 1.
280. M. G. Low and A. R. Saltiel, *Science (Washington, D.C.)*, 1988, **239**, 268.
281. M. A. J. Ferguson and A. F. Williams, *Annu. Rev. Biochem.*, 1988, **57**, 285.
282. M. A. J. Ferguson, S. W. Homans, R. A. Dwek and T. W. Rademacher, *Science (Washington, D.C.)*, 1988, **239**, 753.
283. S. W. Homans, M. A. J. Ferguson, R. A. Dwek, T. W. Rademacher, R. Anand and A. F. Williams, *Nature (London)*, 1988, **333**, 269.
284. A. R. Saltiel, D. G. Osterman, J. C. Darnell, L. R. Sorbara-Cazan, B. L. Chan, M. G. Low and P. Cuatrecasas, *Philos. Trans. R. Soc. London, Ser. B*, 1988, **320**, 345.
285. S. E. Rittenhouse and J. P. Sassoon, *J. Biol. Chem.*, 1986, **260**, 8657.
286. G. P. Heathers, P. B. Corr and L. J. Rubin, *Biochem. Biophys. Res. Commun.*, 1988, **156**, 485.
287. D. Portilla and A. R. Morrison, *Biochem. Biophys. Res. Commun.*, 1986, **140**, 644.
288. E. D. Kennedy, I. H. Batty, E. R. Chilvers and S. R. Nahorski, *Biochem. J.*, 1989, **260**, 283.
289. J. L. Meek and F. Nicoletti, *J. Chromatogr.*, 1986, **351**, 303.
290. J. L. Meek, *Proc. Natl. Acad. Sci. USA*, 1986, **83**, 4162.
291. G. W. Mayr, *Biochem. J.*, 1988, **254**, 585.
292. R. A. J. Challiss, I. H. Batty and S. R. Nahorski, *Biochem. Biophys. Res. Commun.*, 1988, **157**, 684.
293. S. Palmer, K. T. Hughes, D. Y. Lee and M. J. O. Wakelam, *Cell Signalling*, 1989, **1**, 147.
294. D. S. Bredt, R. J. Mourey and S. H. Schneider, *Biochem. Biophys. Res. Commun.*, 1989, **159**, 976.
295. P. J. van Haastert, *Anal. Biochem.*, 1989, **177**, 115.
296. J. E. Brown, M. Rudnick, A. J. Letcher and R. F. Irvine, *Biochem. J.*, 1988, **253**, 703.
297. M. A. Jones, M. D. Bootman, B. F. Higgins, D. A. Lane, G. F. Pay and U. Lindahl, *FEBS Lett.*, 1989, **252**, 105.
298. T. D. Hill, P.-O. Berggren and A. L. Boynton, *Biochem. Biophys. Res. Commun.*, 1987, **149**, 897.
299. T. Nilsson, J. Zwiller, A. L. Boynton, and P.-O. Berggren, *FEBS Lett.*, 1988, **229**, 211.
300. P. J. Cullen, J. G. Comerford and A. P. Dawson, *FEBS Lett.*, 1988, **228**, 57.
301. T. K. Ghosh, P. S. Eis, J. M. Mullaney, C. L. Ebert and D. L. Gill, *J. Biol. Chem.*, 1988, **263**, 11 075.
302. E. J. Foehr, J. Scott, G. Ahnert-Hilger and M. Gratzl, *Biochem. J.*, 1989, **262**, 83.
303. T. Furuichi, S. Yoshikawa, A. Miyawaki, A. Wada, N. Maeda and K. Mikoshiba, *Nature (London)*, 1989, **342**, 32.
304. C. D. Ferris, R. L. Iluganis, S. Supattapore and S. H. Snyder, *Nature (London)*, 1989, **342**, 87.

12.1

α-Adrenergic Receptors

PIETER B. M. W. M. TIMMERMANS, ANDREW T. CHIU and
MARTIN J. M. C. THOOLEN

E. I. du Pont de Nemours & Co., Wilmington, DE, USA

12.1.1   INTRODUCTION

α-Adrenergic receptors play a pivotal role in the regulation of a variety of physiological processes, particularly within, but not limited to, the cardiovascular system. The last decade has seen a renaissance of interest in α-adrenergic receptors, their physiological relevance, classification and second messenger systems. The in-depth knowledge arising from this research is leading towards the development of agonists and antagonists, highly selective for the various subtypes of α-adrenergic receptors and with possible therapeutic value.

The recent interest and intense research into α-adrenergic receptors has been spurred by a number of factors. These include, for instance, the observation that centrally located α-adrenoceptors are the main target for the antihypertensive drugs α-methylDOPA (**1**), clonidine (**2**) and guanfacine (**3**), the distinction between pre- and post-synaptic α-adrenergic receptors, and the establishment of the generally accepted subdivision of α-adrenoceptors into two main classes, *i.e.* α_1 and α_2 subtypes. Research has been stimulated further by the introduction of new more selective compounds, the detection and characterization of novel locations and functions of α-adrenergic receptors, and the easy accessibility of test systems such as radioligand binding assays. It has invariably been observed that increased knowledge of receptors and their subtypes, locations and functions has led to the successful development of clinically relevant and interesting compounds and therapeutically valuable drugs.

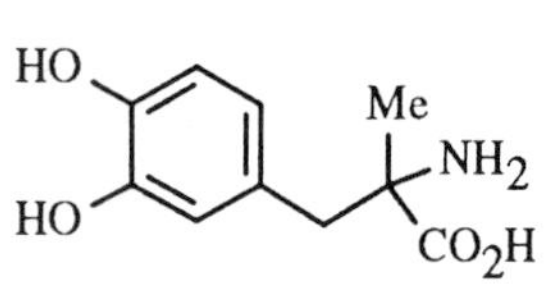

It is the purpose of this chapter to provide a comprehensive overview of the classification, location and physiological relevance of α-adrenergic receptors as well as the structure–activity relationships of α-adrenergic agonists and antagonists.

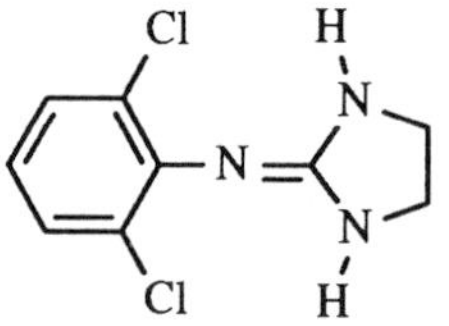

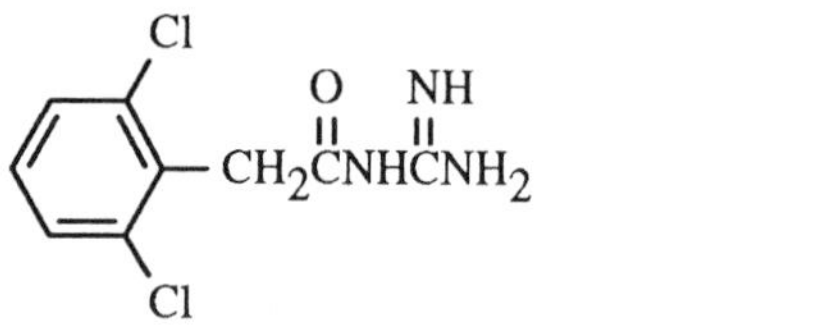

12.1.2   α-ADRENERGIC NEUROTRANSMISSION

The aim of this section is to provide a concise and pertinent description of the morphological, physiological and biochemical processes controlling sympathetic postganglionic noradrenergic neurotransmission. For more detailed descriptions, the reader may refer to the reviews by Starke,[1] Langer[2] and Gothert.[3] A diagrammatic model of a peripheral noradrenergic synapse is shown in Figure 1. The evidence accumulated so far indicates that the noradrenergic neurons in the central nervous system (CNS) exhibit similar physiological and biochemical modulation to those in the peripheral sympathetic nervous system. Therefore, examples derived from the peripheral system are used here.

12.1.2.1   Biosynthesis

The precursor of the noradrenergic neurotransmitter norepinephrine (**4**), *i.e.* the amino acid L-tyrosine (**5**), is taken up into the axoplasm by an active transport process. As shown diagrammatically in Figure 1, the intraneuronal synthesis of norepinephrine begins with conversion of L-tyrosine to L-3,4-dihydroxyphenylalanine (**6**; L-DOPA). This reaction is catalyzed by the enzyme tyrosine hydroxylase and is the rate-limiting step in norepinephrine synthesis. Once L-DOPA is formed, it is rapidly decarboxylated to the corresponding amine, dopamine (**7**), by a decarboxylase found in the cytoplasm of the monoamine neurones in both the peripheral and the central nervous system as well as extraneuronally. Since it catalyzes the decarboxylation of several other aromatic

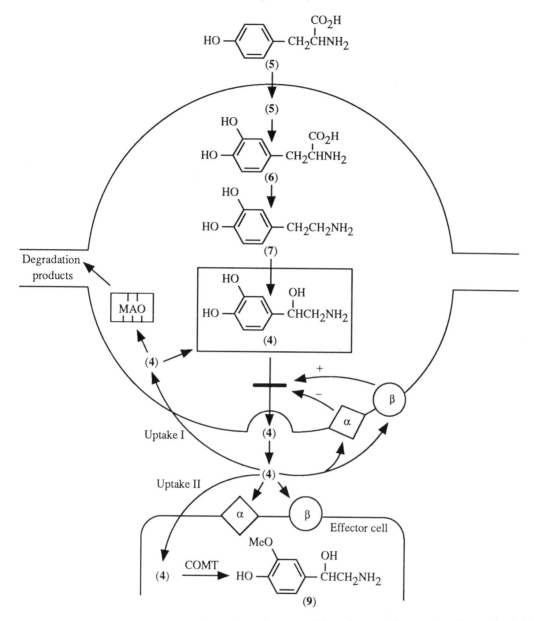

Figure 1 Diagrammatic model of a peripheral noradrenergic synapse. The various steps in transmitter (**4**; norepinephrine) biosynthesis are shown in the center. Also shown are the pre- and post-synaptic sites of action of norepinephrine as well as its inactivation after release. For discussion see text. COMT = catechol *O*-methyltransferase, MAO = monoamine oxidase

amino acids, it is best referred to as aromatic amino acid decarboxylase. Dopamine, synthesized in the axoplasm, is actively taken up into the storage granule in which a Cu^{2+}-containing protein, dopamine β-hydroxylase (DBH), converts dopamine into norepinephrine. Greater detail on the biosynthetic pathway can be found in a review by Henning.[4] The enzymatic step responsible for the conversion of (**4**) into epinephrine (**8**) is effected by the enzyme phenylethanolamine *N*-methyltransferase (PNMT). The highest PNMT concentration is present in the adrenal medulla but PNMT activity is also found in the brain.

(**4**) HO—(ring)—CH(OH)CH$_2$NH$_2$, with HO on ring

(**8**) HO—(ring)—CH(OH)CH$_2$NHMe, with HO on ring

12.1.2.2 Storage

The catecholamines synthesized or taken up by the nerve terminals are stored in the storage granules, which concentrate catecholamines in high concentrations through an active uptake process.[5] The storage prevents newly synthesized transmitter from diffusing out of the neuron or from destruction by the intraneuronally located mitochondrial enzyme monoamine oxidase (MAO). The granules serve as a depot transmitter that may be released upon stimulation by action potentials.

12.1.2.3 Release

The exact mechanisms underlying the release of catecholamines from nerve terminals are far from clear. Our current concept depicts the following events. On arrival of the action potential at the varicosity, Ca^{2+} ions entering the nerve terminals trigger the fusion of storage vesicles with the neuronal membrane, partially liberating its contents (chromogranin, ATP, DBH and catecholamines) by exocytosis. There is evidence of preferential release of newly synthesized catecholamines.[6]

12.1.2.4 Inactivation

The norepinephrine released into the synapse activates postsynaptic α- or β-adrenergic receptors located on the membranes of the target organ cells as well as presynaptic receptors located on the nerve terminals (see Section 12.1.2.6). Termination of the effects of the transmitter is brought about principally by its reuptake into the neuron, a process generally referred to as Uptake I, but also through metabolism and diffusion from the synaptic region. Metabolic degradation of catecholamines is effected by MAO and catechol *O*-methyltransferase (COMT). MAO is primarily localized in the mitochondria of the neuron and oxidatively deaminates catecholamines and other biogenic amines. The levels of free catecholamines in the neuronal axoplasm are controlled by MAO and uptake into the storage granules. COMT is found in the cytoplasm of most cells and has been suggested to function largely extraneuronally. Norepinephrine taken into the postsynaptic nonneuronal cells (Uptake II) is degraded by COMT to normetanephrine (9; Figure 1). During physiological rates of nerve activity the combined efficiency of the catabolizing enzymes and, in particular, the membrane pump is quite sufficient to prevent overflow of catecholamines from the synapse.

The physiological importance of neuronal uptake in regulating the intrasynaptic concentration of norepinephrine is inversely related to the width of the synaptic gap: the narrower the gap the more important is neuronal uptake in regulating the concentration of the neurotransmitter. It appears that the width of the synaptic gap is also important for the negative feedback mechanism that regulates norepinephrine release.[7] Thus, organs with narrow synaptic gaps exhibit greater presynaptic feedback inhibition of norepinephrine release (see Section 12.1.2.6).

12.1.2.5 Cotransmitters

Numerous examples of the coexistence of two or more neuroactive substances in a single neuron are found. Evidence now suggests that, in particular, the coexistence of classic neurotransmitters with neuropeptides in the same neuron may be a very common occurrence.[8] Norepinephrine has long been known to coexist with somatostatin in the peripheral nervous system and with enkephalin in the peripheral and central nervous systems.[9] Thus, the sympathetic neurons not only contain and release norepinephrine as well as epinephrine (the latter originates from the adrenal medulla and is taken up into the neuron from the extracellular space) but also ATP[10] and a host of other peptides. However, the physiological function of the coexistence of the neurotransmitter with other (co)transmitters remains unclear and is beyond the scope of this chapter. The reader should refer to the references cited above for more details.

12.1.2.6 Modulation of α-Adrenergic Neurotransmission

It has long been assumed that the functions of noradrenergic nerve endings were limited to the synthesis, storage, release and inactivation of norepinephrine. It has now become clear that not only innervated target cells and the cell body and dendrites of a nerve cell are endowed with receptors, but that nerve terminals also contain receptors which are thought to play a pivotal role in the modulation of neurotransmission.[1,2,11,12] These receptors on the axon terminals which are localized before the synaptic cleft are termed presynaptic receptors.

Presynaptic α-adrenergic receptors situated at the noradrenergic nerve terminals (see Figure 1) have been extensively studied.[1,2,11,12] The excitation of the presynaptic α-adrenergic receptors by an agonist, *i.e.* either the endogenous neurotransmitter norepinephrine or a synthetic α-adrenergic agonist, inhibits the release of norepinephrine from the terminal per nerve impulse. Consequently, as the concentration of norepinephrine present in the synaptic cleft reaches a threshold, it activates these presynaptically located α-adrenergic receptors, thereby triggering a negative feedback mechanism on its own release (autoinhibition). In contrast, antagonists of presynaptic α-adrenergic receptors generally enhance the stimulation-evoked release of the neurotransmitter norepinephrine. From a comparison of the relative activities of agonists and antagonists, ample experimental evidence has become available showing that the prejunctionally located α-adrenergic receptors which inhibit norepinephrine release are distinguished from the postsynaptically situated α-adrenergic receptors mediating smooth muscle contraction (see Section 12.1.4). According to the currently accepted classification of α-adrenergic receptors (see Section 12.1.4), α_1-adrenergic receptors are mainly found at postsynaptic sites, whereas adrenergic receptors of the α_2 subclass are found at pre- as well as post-junctional locations.

Various mechanisms have been proposed for the link between presynaptic α_2-adrenergic receptor activation and inhibition of norepinephrine release in which a pivotal role for Ca^{2+} has been established.[1,13] More recent data implicate inhibition of adenylate cyclase with receptor activation and subsequent attenuation of transmitter release.[14] Promotion of K^+ conductance is a currently discussed ionic basis of presynaptic α_2-adrenergic-receptor-stimulation-induced inhibition of norepinephrine release.[15] Furthermore, a role for protein kinase C has been suggested in the exocytotic release of norepinephrine from sympathetic nerve endings.[16] Finally, there are other presynaptic α_2-adrenergic receptors which may control the firing rate of a neuron. These events are probably exerted by receptors located not only on the nerve terminals but rather on the soma and/or the dendrites (see Section 12.1.5).[17] They are activated by the respective transmitter released either from recurrent axon collaterals to the cell body of the same neuron or by axons of other neurons which release the same transmitter. The most obvious function of presynaptic receptors is mediation of the effect of transmitter secreted from adjacent axon terminals. In many tissues, postganglionic sympathetic and parasympathetic fibers lie in close proximity.[1,2,11,12]

Although less well-established as a modulatory mechanism in sympathetic neurotransmission, presynaptic β-adrenergic receptors have been associated with facilitation of stimulation-evoked release of norepinephrine (Figure 1).[1-3,11,12,18] Thus, the cotransmitter epinephrine may activate facilitatory presynaptic β-adrenergic receptors and initiate a positive feedback regulation of transmitter release.

12.1.3 *IN VITRO* AND *IN VIVO* BIOLOGICAL ASSAYS

The current understanding of α-adrenergic receptors and their roles in noradrenergic neurotransmission has been reached through studies using a variety of *in vitro* and *in vivo* test procedures. Representative methods and biological systems, referred to later in this chapter, are described here.

12.1.3.1 Radioligand Binding Studies

Experimental designs using selective radiolabeled ligands have supported the concept of α_1- and α_2-adrenergic receptors and significantly extended our knowledge of the occurrence and distribution of both subclasses.[19-23] A host of selective ligands has become commercially available. The affinity of (synthetic) agonists and antagonists for α_2- and/or α_1-adrenergic receptors can be estimated in radioligand displacement studies. It should be stressed that radioligand displacement studies only provide information about the affinity of a compound for a particular receptor, and do not allow a distinction between agonistic or antagonistic properties of the displacer. The ability of agonists, and in particular antagonists, to displace radioactive markers from α_1- and α_2-adrenergic receptor sites has been shown to correlate satisfactorily with their affinities determined in functional tests.[24]

12.1.3.2 *In Vivo* Animal Studies

In vivo postjunctional vascular α-adrenergic receptors are studied using whole animal preparations in which the vasoconstriction induced by α-adrenergic receptor agonists is measured *via* the resulting increase in diastolic arterial pressure. Most commonly used is the pithed rat, in which the spinal cord has been destroyed by introduction of a metal rod. This procedure allows study of the effect of vasoconstrictor agents on the peripheral circulation without interference from any nervous reflexes or central regulation. Since both α_1- and α_2-adrenergic receptors are located postjunctionally on vascular smooth muscle, both subtypes can be studied using selective agonists and antagonists. This model also provides an opportunity to investigate presynaptic α_2-adrenergic receptors in the circulation. Thus, by selective electrical stimulation of specific portions of the pithing rod, the sympathetic nerves innervating the heart or vasculature may be activated to release norepinephrine and increase heart rate or diastolic pressure. Stimulation of prejunctional α_2-adrenergic receptors will diminish these effects, whereas α_2-adrenergic blockers may increase them.[1-3] Centrally located α_2-adrenergic agonist receptors play an important role in regulation of the peripheral circulation as well as in regulating the state of vigilance (see Section 12.1.8). α_2-Adrenergic agonists capable of penetrating the blood–brain barrier cause reduction of blood pressure and heart rate upon systemic administration to animals and man and cause sedation, expressed as an increase in the barbiturate-induced loss of fighting reflex, in mice and rats and as sleep in 1–2-day-old chicks.[25] The effects are reversed by α_2-adrenoceptor antagonists.[25]

12.1.3.3 *In Vitro* Functional Studies

Unfortunately, most isolated vascular tissues *in vitro* do not allow the study of postjunctional α_2-adrenergic receptors. With the exception of the dog and rabbit isolated saphenous veins, the rat tail artery and some cerebral vessels, α_2-adrenergic receptors have not been demonstrated to be present postjunctionally in isolated vascular or other smooth muscle preparations. Nevertheless, postjunctional α_1-adrenergic receptors are readily studied in isolated aortic, pulmonary arterial or other vascular smooth muscle from rats, rabbits, guinea pigs and other animals. Other useful smooth muscle preparations include the rat isolated vas deferens and anococcygeus muscle. Contractions elicited by α_1-adrenergic receptor agonists are selectively antagonized by α_1-adrenergic receptor antagonists, and the affinities of antagonists may be assessed in a quantitative manner using Schild analysis, resulting in pA_2 values[26] (see Volume 3, Chapter 11.2). Not only does the pA_2 value provide a measure of the affinity of a particular antagonist, it is also a powerful tool in the characterization of various α-adrenergic receptor subtypes (see Section 12.1.4). Presynaptic α_2-adrenergic receptors are accessible in these organs by electrical field stimulation or KCl-induced release of norepinephrine. The resulting contractions can be inhibited by stimulation of prejunctional α_2-adrenergic receptors with selective agonists. Peripheral presynaptic α_2-adrenergic (hetero-) receptors are located on the cholinergic nerve terminals innervating the ileum, and the isolated transmurally electrically stimulated guinea pig ileum has been shown to be a valuable screening test system for these receptors.[27]

Centrally located prejunctional α_2-adrenergic receptors are studied *in vitro* by measuring the release of radiolabeled neurotransmitters upon stimulation. The neurotransmitter release can be inhibited by α_2-adrenergic receptor agonists and enhanced by α_2-adrenergic receptor antagonists. Distinction between prejunctional auto- and hetero-receptors (see Section 12.1.4) is made by studying the release of [^{3}H]norepinephrine and other radiolabeled transmitters, respectively.[1-3] For more details on *in vitro* methods for studying α-adrenergic receptor agonists and antagonists the reader should refer to the review by Doxey and Roach.[27]

12.1.4 CLASSIFICATION OF α-ADRENERGIC RECEPTORS

12.1.4.1 Subdivision into α_1 and α_2 Types

The α and β classification of adrenergic receptors was originally proposed by Ahlquist[28] to explain the actions of six sympathomimetic amines. The subsequent subdivision of β-adrenergic receptors into β_1 and β_2 types, as demonstrated originally by Furchgott[29] and Lands *et al.*,[30] is generally accepted and therapeutically relevant. Initially, the classification of α-adrenergic receptors into α_1 and α_2 subtypes paralleled the discovery and establishment of the concept of presynaptic regulation of neurotransmitter release (see Section 12.1.2.6). α-Adrenergic receptors located presynaptically on nerve terminals and regulating the release and synthesis of neurotransmitters were designated α_2, whereas those located postsynaptically on target organs and mediating a biological response upon stimulation (*e.g.* vasoconstriction) were called α_1-adrenergic receptors.[1] The distinction between pre- and post-synaptic α-adrenergic receptors is strongly supported by the differences in affinities and selectivities of a large array of α-adrenergic agonists and antagonists.[1,2] Figure 2 illustrates the different selectivities for a number of α-adrenergic agonists and antagonists. The pre- and post-synaptic ratios vary about five-hundredfold for agonists and the affinity ratios differ more than a thousandfold for antagonists.[1] Prazosin (**10**) has been shown to be a highly selective antagonist of postjunctional α-adrenergic receptors, while yohimbine (**11**) and rauwolscine (**12**) preferentially block prejunctional α-adrenergic receptors. Methoxamine (**13**) and phenylephrine (**14**) were identified as preferential agonists for postjunctional α-adrenergic receptors, whereas α-methylnorepinephrine (**15**) and tramazoline (**16**) acted as relatively selective presynaptic α-adrenergic receptor agonists. These observations, together with the obvious differences in location and function, led Langer[2] to propose that the postsynaptic α-adrenergic receptors be nominated α_1 and the presynaptic type α_2.

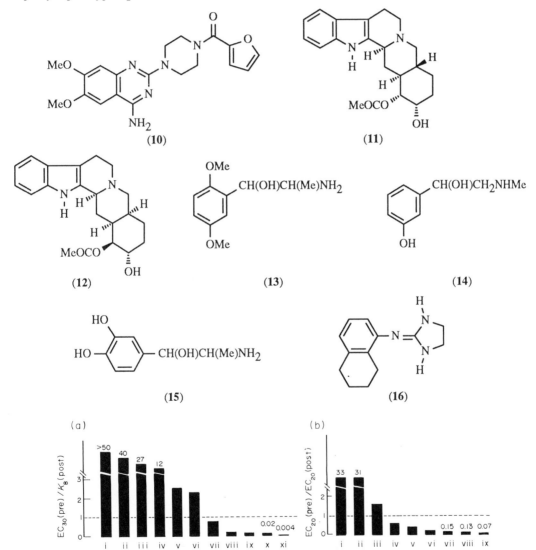

Figure 2 Pre/postsynaptic selectivity ratios for various α-adrenergic antagonists (a) and agonists (b) established in the rabbit isolated pulmonary artery. (a) EC_{30} (pre) = concentration facilitating [³H]norepinephrine release by 30% (presynaptic effect); K_B(post) = antagonism against phenylephrine- and norepinephrine-induced contraction (postsynaptic effect); i, prazosin; ii, corynanthine; iii, clozapine; iv, azapetine; v, phentolamine; vi, mianserin; vii, piperoxan; viii, tolazoline; ix, dihydro-ergotamine; x, yohimbine; xi, rauwolscine. (b) EC_{20}(pre) = concentration inhibiting [³H]norepinephrine overflow by 20% (presynaptic effect); EC_{20}(post) = concentration inducing 20% of the maximal contraction (postsynaptic effect); i, methoxamine; ii, phenylephrine; iii, norepinephrine; iv, epinephrine; v, naphazoline; vi, oxymetazoline; vii, clonidine; viii, α-methyl-norepinephrine; ix, tramazoline. Most of the above-mentioned compounds are treated separately in the course of this chapter
(data compiled from ref. 1)

However, the discovery of α-adrenergic receptors outside noradrenergic terminal axons, on some organelles lacking synapses and even at postsynaptic sites with the general characteristics of those found presynaptically necessitated revision and refinement of this classification. For instance, the selective α_2-adrenergic agonist B-HT 933 (**17**; azepexole) was shown to increase diastolic arterial pressure after intravenous injection in pithed rats *via* stimulation of postjunctional vascular α-adrenergic receptors; this response was inhibited by yohimbine but not by prazosin.[31] The existence and functionality of postjunctional vascular α_2-adrenergic receptors has since been established unequivocally by a large number of *in vivo* as well as *in vitro* studies in various species including man.[13] Figure 3 illustrates the selectivity of a number of α-adrenoceptor antagonists for postjunctional vascular α_1- and α_2-adrenergic receptors.

$$Et-N \begin{array}{c} \diagup \\ \diagdown \end{array} \cdots \begin{array}{c} N \\ \diagdown \\ O \end{array} \cdots NH_2$$

(**17**)

Similarly, platelet aggregation is initiated by stimulation of α_2-adrenergic receptors located on the platelet membrane.[32] Therefore, anatomical location has been abandoned as the classifying criterion of α-adrenergic receptors. The designation α_1 or α_2 is now exclusively based upon the drug selectivities of the α-adrenergic receptor in question, irrespective of its function or anatomical position.

A large number of α-adrenergic receptor agonists and antagonists with various degrees of selectivity for α_1- or α_2-adrenergic receptors are currently available. Among these, several display high selectivity for either type and are indispensable tools for the study and identification of α-adrenergic receptors and additional selective agonists/antagonists. The structure–activity relationships for these classes of compounds are discussed in Sections 12.1.6 and 12.1.7.

Signal transduction after α_1-adrenergic receptor activation involves an increase in the intracellular free Ca^{2+} concentration. The α_1-adrenergic-receptor-coupled event is presumably activation of a plasma membrane phospholipase C which hydrolyzes phosphatidylinositol 4,5-biphosphate (PIP_2) generating two second messenger molecules, *i.e.* inositol 1,4,5-triphosphate (IP_3) and 1,2-diacylglycerol (DG). IP_3 may be responsible for the intracellular mobilization of Ca^{2+}. DG activates protein kinase C (PKC) leading to protein phosphorylation and possibly opening of a slow Ca^{2+} channel.[33] α_2-Adrenergic receptors in general are believed to be coupled to adenylate cyclase in an inhibitory manner in that stimulation results in inhibition of cAMP production or directly opens a slow Ca^{2+} channel to allow influx of extracellular Ca^{2+} (see Volume 3, Chapter 11.4).[13,34]

The α_1- (hepatic plasma membranes) and α_2-adrenergic receptors (platelets) have been solubilized in an active form. The α_1-adrenergic receptor has been purified to apparent homogeneity and contains a major subunit of approximately 80 kDa. Progress in the purification and reconstitution of the α_2-adrenergic receptor has been affected by the lack of suitable affinity labels.[35]

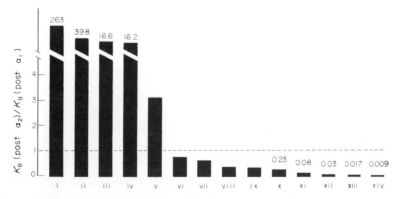

Figure 3 Selectivity ratios of α-adrenergic receptor antagonists for postsynaptic α_1- and α_2-adrenergic receptors. The ratio K_B(post α_2)/K_B(post α_1) resulted from antagonism against α_2- and α_1-adrenergic-receptor-induced vasoconstriction in pithed rats, respectively. i, prazosin; ii, clozapine; iii, corynanthine; iv, azapetine; v, phentolamine; vi, tolazoline; vii, mianserin; viii, piperoxan; ix, dihydroergotamine; x, idazoxan; xi, yohimbine; xii, Wy 26703; xiii, imiloxan; xiv, rauwolscine. Most of the above-mentioned compounds are treated separately in the course of this chapter (data compiled from refs. 49, 165 and 352)

12.1.4.2 Heterogeneity of α₁- and α₂-Adrenergic Receptors

Although the classification criteria for α-adrenergic receptors are relatively sharply defined, heterogeneity still exists in the affinities for agonists and antagonists among α₁- and α₂-adrenergic receptors from different organs and species.

12.1.4.2.1 Heterogeneity of α₁-adrenergic receptors

Analysis of α antagonist potency, expressed as pA_2, at α₁-adrenergic receptors in isolated tissues from a variety of species has suggested that postjunctional α₁-adrenergic receptors are heterogeneous. As reviewed by Flavahan and Vanhoutte,[36] a range of pA_2 values for prazosin (10) and yohimbine (11) on postjunctional α₁-adrenergic receptors on various isolated blood vessels have been reported. Although in each isolated vessel the α-adrenergic receptor mediating vasoconstriction was unequivocally identified as α₁ because of the much higher (three-hundred- to thousandfold) affinity for prazosin than for yohimbine, the architectures of the α₁-adrenergic receptors on rat aorta, guinea pig aorta, rabbit aorta, rabbit pulmonary artery and rat mesenteric artery are not identical. Similarly, Ruffolo *et al.*[37] reported a range of pA_2 values for yohimbine against norepinephrine (4) in isolated aortas from rat, guinea pig, hamster, cat, dog and rabbit (Figure 4), showing heterogeneity among these populations of α₁-adrenergic receptors.

In cat mesenteric arteries, norepinephrine-induced contractions can be blocked competitively by both prazosin and rauwolscine (12), prazosin being only twenty times more potent than rauwolscine, in contrast to much higher ratios found in rat aorta and other tissues with a 'classical' α-adrenergic receptor population.[38] Similarly, in dog splenic artery, prazosin is only 10 times more potent than rauwolscine against norepinephrine, while the difference is only threefold in dog splenic vein.[39]

Comparison of the relative potencies or affinities of agonists in different receptor systems can be an important tool for receptor classification. Most studies have shown that agonist and antagonist potencies correlate reasonably well when compared at different α-adrenergic receptor sites, such as vascular contraction and displacement of [³H]WB 4101 (18) binding to brain homogenates[40] or blockade of phenylephrine-induced pressor responses in pithed rats and displacement of [³H]prazosin from central binding sites.[41] However, de Jonge *et al.*[42] found that the central binding affinity of *meta*-substituted imidazolidines to α₁-adrenergic receptor sites (IC_{50}) did not correlate with peripheral α₁-adrenergic receptor agonist potency as pressor agents in pithed rats (pD_2). Such a discrepancy could possibly be explained by differences in efficacy and/or receptor reserve among the agonists. However, all compounds investigated were partial agonists with comparable efficacy. Hence, these data point towards heterogeneity between central and peripheral α₁-adrenergic receptors. Similarly, no correlation was found between the pD_2 values for a series of α₁-adrenergic agonists on rat isolated aorta, guinea pig isolated aorta and rat isolated anococcygeus muscle, illustrating the different architectures of these three populations of α₁-adrenergic receptors.[43]

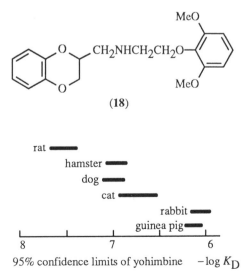

Figure 4 Mean $-\log K_B$ values and 95% confidence limits for yohimbine (11) in aortas from six mammalian species (reproduced from ref. 37 by permission of Williams & Wilkins Co.)

Using radioligand binding techniques, various authors have shown that differences exist in the equilibrium constants of antagonists and agonists for α_2-adrenergic receptors from various origins. Bylund[44] has reviewed much of the available data and found that prazosin (10) generally has a higher affinity for α_2-adrenergic receptors in tissues from rodents such as rat and guinea pig, while a lower affinity was found for α_2-adrenergic receptors in tissues from non-rodent species such as dog, cat, pig and man. Conversely, a five to 10 times higher affinity of [³H]yohimbine (11) for α_2 binding sites from non-rodent compared to rodent tissues was found, while oxymetazoline (19) was also more potent in non-rodent species. A definition of α_2-adrenergic receptor subtypes was proposed with prazosin having a lower affinity ($K_i = 200–300$ nmol dm^{-3}) at α_2A receptors and a higher affinity ($K_i = 5–10$ nmol dm^{-3}) at α_2B receptors. Using this definition, the human platelet appears to have only the α_2A subtype, while all the receptors in the neonatal rat lung are of the α_2B subtype. Roughly equal amounts of α_2A and α_2B receptors were found in rat brain, while in the rat submandibulary gland about 85% of the receptors are α_2A.

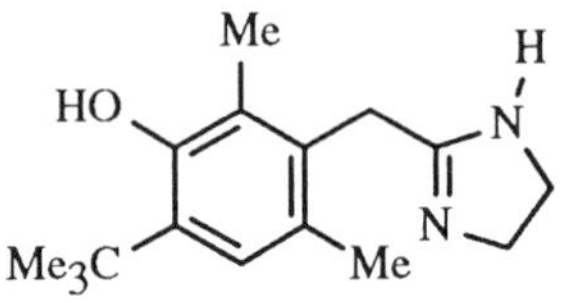

(19)

Dickinson *et al.*[45] compared [³H]yohimbine binding to membrane preparations of human colon, cerebral cortex, kidney, spleen and platelets with binding to preparations of rabbit spleen, kidney and cortex, rat cerebral cortex and cat spleen. The equilibrium dissociation constants of [³H]yohimbine ranged from 1.6 to 2.6 nmol dm^{-3} in human tissues and from 5.1 to 9.4 nmol dm^{-3} for the animal tissues. Binding to all tissues was displaced by drugs in the order of potency yohimbine > phentolamine (20) > prazosin, indicating the α_2-adrenergic character of the labeled sites. Whilst phentolamine and corynanthine (21) possessed similar affinities for all α_2-adrenergic receptor sites investigated, prazosin and idazoxan (22) exhibited differential potencies of α_2-adrenergic receptor binding sites in certain species, illustrating heterogeneity and the possible existence of a spectrum of α_2-adrenergic receptors in various species. Similarly, Alabaster *et al.*[46] found differences in the relative affinities of a series of α-adrenergic antagonists for α_2-adrenergic receptors in rat brain and rabbit spleen membranes, in rat left atrium, rat and rabbit vas deferens and rabbit and dog saphenous vein preparations, and concluded that α_2-adrenergic receptors are a heterogeneous population, different subgroups being more apparent between species rather than between tissue types or location.

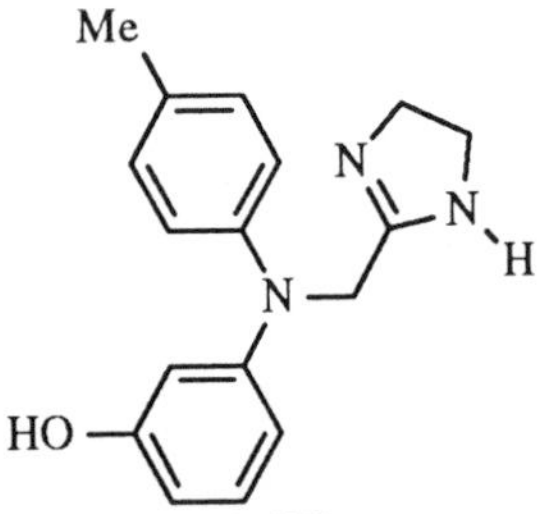

(20) 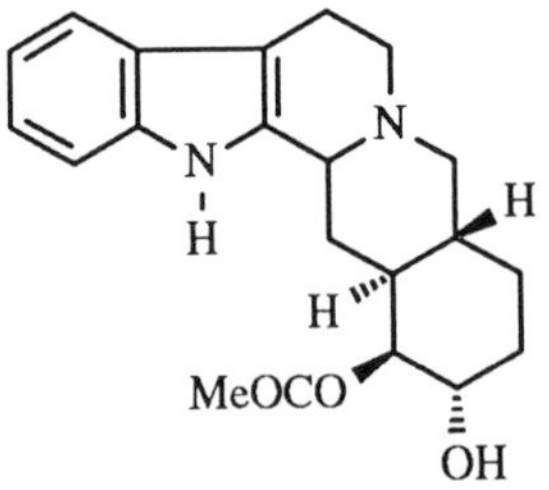   (21) 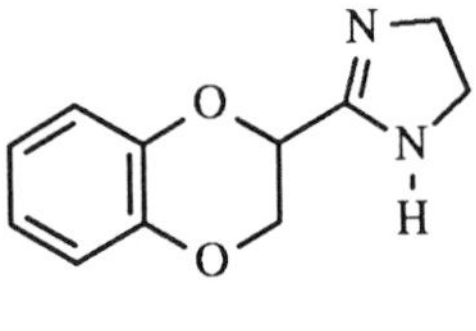   (22)

Using two homologous series of binuclear ligands, diacrines and diquinolines, Adams *et al.*[47] showed that the chain-length dependence of affinity of both types of compounds were similar for [³H]prazosin binding in rat brain and kidney membranes, while marked differences were found between the affinity profiles for central and peripheral α_2-adrenergic receptors labeled with [³H]rauwolscine.

($\pm$)-Idazoxan (22) has been identified as a highly potent and selective antagonist at peripheral[48,49] and central[49–51] α_2-adrenergic receptors. In the rat vas deferens, ($-$)-idazoxan was found to be three times more potent than the ($+$) isomer at antagonizing the receptor-induced inhibition of the electrically evoked contractions.[52] In contrast, ($+$)-idazoxan was found to be more potent than the (−) isomer in antagonizing central α_2-adrenergic-receptor-induced sleep in 24- to 48-hour-old chicks. Since the physicochemical properties of (−)- and (+)-idazoxan are very similar and brain penetration of both isomers should be identical, these data suggest differences between central and peripheral α_2-adrenergic receptor populations.[52]

The effects of stereoisomers of mianserin (23), an antidepressant with α_2-adrenergic-receptor-blocking properties, on KCl-induced [³H]norepinephrine and [³H]serotonin release from rat hypothalamic and cortical synaptosomes have been studied.[53,54] (+)-Mianserin and the racemate antagonized the α_2-adrenergic-receptor-mediated inhibitory effects of norepinephrine on both [³H]norepinephrine and [³H]serotonin release, while (−)-mianserin antagonized the inhibitory effect of noradrenaline on [³H]norepinephrine release only. These data indicate that (−)-mianserin discriminates between α_2-adrenergic receptors regulating release of norepinephrine (α_2 auto-receptors) and those regulating serotonin release (α_2 heteroreceptors) and suggest the existence of differences between these two subtypes in rat brain.

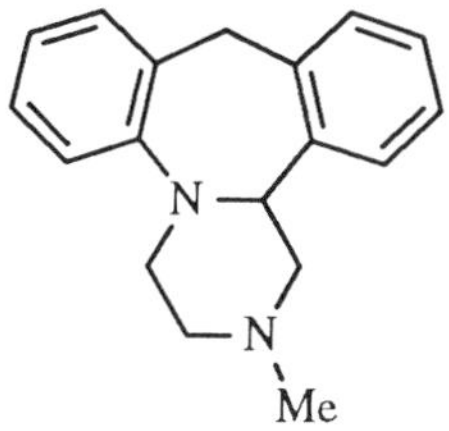

(23)

Very recently, evidence has been put forward in support of a differentiation between pre- and post-junctional α_2-adrenergic receptors. Hieble et al.[55] and Ruffolo et al.[56] have reported that the newly synthesized α-adrenergic receptor antagonist SK & F 104078 (24) is a potent competitive antagonist of postjunctional α_2-adrenergic receptors in dog and rabbit saphenous veins, dog saphenous artery and human platelets, whereas the compound was inactive as an antagonist of prejunctional α_2-adrenergic receptors in atria from dog, guinea pig, rabbit and rat, as well as in guinea pig ileum. Likewise, SK & F 104078 has the ability to block postjunctional arterial α_2-adrenergic receptors in vivo in the pithed rat at doses that do not inhibit prejunctional α_2-adrenergic receptors in the same model. These data suggest that pre- and post-junctional α_2-adrenergic receptors may not represent one homogeneous class, but may be subtypes of the α_2-adrenergic receptor possibly differentiated by SK & F 104078.[55,56]

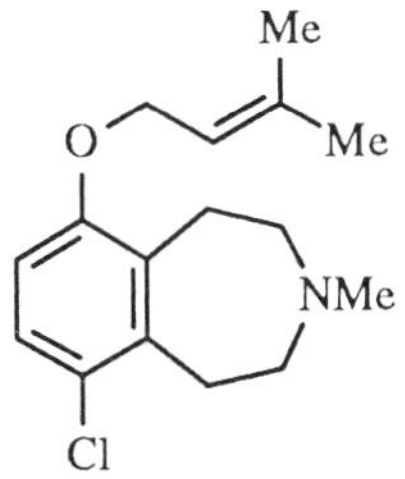

(24)

As summarized above, sufficient evidence has accumulated thus far to accept that heterogeneity exists in the α_1- and α_2-adrenergic receptor subclasses. However, it is premature to propose a generally acceptable further subdivision of α-adrenergic receptors beyond the α_1/α_2 classification, which has proven to be consistent throughout various species and organs. In many cases it remains unclear whether observed differences in affinity of agonists and antagonists for different α_1- and α_2-adrenergic receptors are the result of differences in the recognition sites or in the architecture of the environment surrounding the receptors. However, the observed heterogeneity in the subclasses may provide ground for the development of new selective agents as therapeutics.

12.1.5 DISTRIBUTION AND LOCALIZATION OF α-ADRENERGIC RECEPTORS

12.1.5.1 Pre- and Post-synaptic α-Adrenergic Receptors

Figure 5 displays a more detailed illustration of the localization of α-adrenergic receptors in a peripheral sympathetic neuroeffector junction. α_1-Adrenergic receptors are primarily located post-

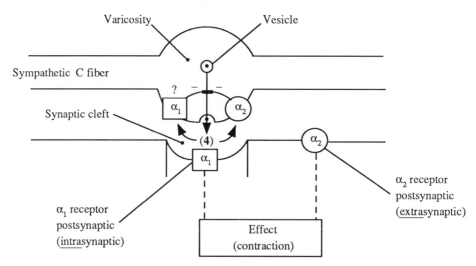

Figure 5 Pre- and post-junctional α-adrenergic receptors of a noradrenergic synapse. Norepinephrine (**4**) released from the varicosity stimulates postsynaptic α_1-adrenergic receptors situated at the target organ. Presynaptic α_2-adrenergic receptors located at the varicosity membrane control a negative feedback of the release of transmitter norepinephrine. The presence and functionality of a small population of presynaptic α_1-adrenergic receptors is still a matter of debate. Postsynaptically and extrasynaptically located α_2-adrenergic receptors would be activated by exogenously applied or circulating norepinephrine. For details, see text

junctionally on target cells. Prejunctionally, the α-adrenergic receptors are primarily of the α_2 subtype. Stimulation of postjunctionally located α_1-adrenergic receptors gives rise to a biological response, while activation of prejunctionally located α_2-adrenergic receptors inhibits norepinephrine release (see Section 12.1.2.6). However, α_2-adrenergic receptors are also found postsynaptically on vascular effector cells, and initiate vasoconstriction upon stimulation. Figure 6 illustrates the vasopressor effects of the selective α_2-adrenergic receptor agonist B-HT 920 (**25**) and the α_1 agonist methoxamine (**13**) in pithed rats. The response to B-HT 920 is preferentially blocked by yohimbine (**11**) but not by prazosin (**10**), while prazosin selectively inhibits the vasoconstriction to methoxamine.[57]

$$\text{CH}_2 = \text{—} \text{N} \text{—} \begin{array}{c} \text{N} \\ \text{S} \end{array} \text{—NH}_2$$

(**25**)

Some evidence has been presented in favor of the presence of a population of presynaptic α_1-adrenergic receptors. Kobinger and Pichler[58] found that the selective α_1-adrenergic agonist St 587 (**26**) inhibited the increase in heart rate induced by electrical stimulation of the spinal cord in pithed rats. This neuroinhibitory effect was blocked by prazosin (**10**) and much less effectively by yohimbine (**11**). In addition, prazosin was shown to partially block the inhibitory effects of clonidine (**2**) in the dog cardioaccelerator nerve preparation, while the α_1-selective agonist methoxamine (**13**) had a weak inhibitory effect by itself.[59] In the isolated rat atrium, prazosin and idazoxan (**22**) were equipotent in producing a potentiation of stimulus-evoked transmitter release. Neither antagonist was as effective as the non-selective α-adrenergic receptor blocker phentolamine (**20**), but the combination of prazosin and idazoxan was indistinguishable from phentolamine.[60] These data suggest a contribution of α_1-adrenergic receptors in presynaptic regulation of transmitter release in some preparations. α_1-Adrenergic receptors may also be located on atrial cholinergic nerve terminals: Flavahan and McGrath[61] have found that the selective α_1-adrenergic receptor agonists amidephrine (**27**) and phenylephrine (**14**) produced a negative chronotropic response in pithed rats. This was postulated to result from activation of neuronal α_2-adrenergic receptors on atrial preganglionic terminals mediating an increase in acetylcholine release, since the effect was abolished by tetrodotoxin, prazosin, corynanthine (**21**) and WB 4101 (**18**) and potentiated by neostygmine, suggesting a contribution of α_1-adrenergic receptors to prejunctional modulation of acetylcholine release. Verplancken *et al.*[62] demonstrated a neuroinhibitory effect of phenylephrine and methoxamine in the isolated rat gastric fundus. It should be noted, however, that these isolated reports on

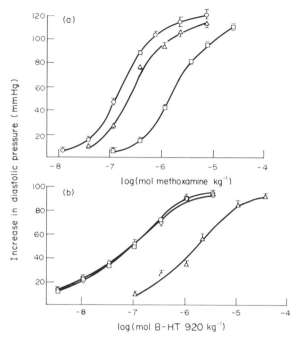

Figure 6 Log(dose)–vasopressor response curves of (a) the α_1-adrenergic receptor agonist methoxamine (**13**) and (b) the α_2-adrenergic receptor agonist B-HT 920 (**25**) with respect to the increase in diastolic pressure in pithed normotensive rats after pretreatment (intravenous, 15 min) with saline ($\bigcirc$), yohimbine ($\triangle$, 1 mg/kg) or prazosin ($\square$, 0.1 mg kg^{-1}). Symbols represent mean values $\pm$SEM ($n = 5$–7, modified after ref. 57). The data show that distinctly different populations of postsynaptic α_1- and α_2-adrenergic receptors can initiate vasoconstriction

α_1-adrenergic-receptor-mediated modulation of noradrenergic and cholinergic neurotransmission contrast with a vast body of evidence linking prejunctional α_2-adrenergic receptors with feedback regulation of neurotransmitter release and synthesis.[1,2,11,12] Therefore, although in certain tissues prejunctional α_1-adrenergic receptors may be present, the physiological or pharmacological relevance of prejunctional α_1-adrenergic receptor activation is probably minor.

(**26**)   (**27**)

12.1.5.2 Presynaptic α_2-Adrenergic Receptors: Auto- and Hetero-receptors

Presynaptic receptors on a particular neuron which are activated by its own neurotransmitter are called autoreceptors. These receptors must be distinguished from presynaptic heteroreceptors which are activated by transmitters released from neighboring nerve terminals or by blood-borne substances. Presynaptic heteroreceptors may be considered postsynaptic with respect to these transmitters. An autoreceptor role can also be played by somadendritic receptors on the same neuron. In this case the somadendritic receptors are considered presynaptic with respect to this transmitter. Figure 7 provides a schematic representation of prejunctional auto, hetero, somadendritic and postjunctional α-adrenergic receptors. Numerous investigations have shown that inhibitory presynaptic α_2-adrenergic auto- and hetero-receptors mediating a negative feedback loop play a role in the fine regulation of the release of norepinephrine and other transmitters, respectively, in the central nervous system and in the periphery, whereas somadendritic α_2-adrenergic receptors inhibit the firing.[3]

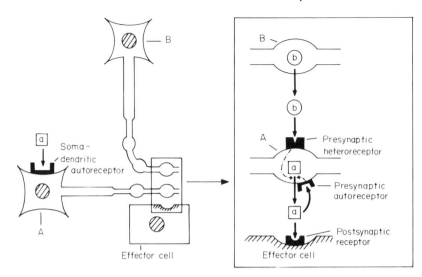

Figure 7 Schematic representation of the localization of α-adrenergic receptors in the periphery or central nervous system. Presynaptic auto- and hetero-receptors for norepinephrine (**4**) are located on neuron A which releases neurotransmitter ⓐ and which innervates an effector cell endowed with postsynaptic receptors. If neuron A is noradrenergic, then the presynaptic α-adrenergic receptors are called autoreceptors. In case neuron A releases a neurotransmitter other than norepinephrine, then the presynaptic α-adrenergic receptors may be activated by norepinephrine ⓑ released by neighboring noradrenergic neuron B and are called heteroreceptors. Presynaptic auto- and hetero-receptors on the varicosity of neuron A modulate the release and synthesis of the particular neurotransmitter (broken arrows). The somadendritic autoreceptors of norepinephrine on the cell body of neuron A in the CNS influence impulse generation (modified after Gothert[3])

12.1.5.3 Intra- and Extra-synaptic α-Adrenergic Receptors

Stimulation of vascular α_1- as well as α_2-adrenergic receptors induces a vasoconstrictor response (see Figure 6). The question as to the physiological or pharmacological correlates for this differentiation has prompted Ariens and Simonis[63] to suggest that the α_2-adrenergic receptors are predominantly epinephrinergic in nature and located extrajunctionally, whereas the α_1-adrenergic receptors are predominantly norepinephrinergic in nature and located postsynaptically in the sympathetic terminal junction. It has been shown that the vasoconstriction in pithed rats induced by spinal cord stimulation or exogenously applied norepinephrine is differentially influenced by selective α-adrenergic receptor blockers, prazosin (**10**) being more effective in inhibiting responses to spinal cord stimulation, while rauwolscine (**12**) is more potent in blocking the vasoconstriction resulting from intravenous norepinephrine.[64,65] Stimulation of the adrenal medulla in pithed rats produced a vasopressor response which consisted of summating α_1- and α_2-adrenergic-receptor-mediated components and was found to be identical to the effect of intravenous epinephrine. In addition, as shown in Figure 8, the pressor responses elicited by sympathetic nerve stimulation in the dog were markedly antagonized by prazosin, while rauwolscine rendered the effects of intravenous norepinephrine sensitive to prazosin blockade.[67] Further studies *in vivo* and *in vitro* showed that prazosin was more effective in blocking the responses to norepinephrine released by nerve stimulation than in antagonizing the same end organ effect brought about by exogenously applied norepinephrine.[68] Wilffert *et al.*[65] showed that the pressor effects of norepinephrine released through ganglionic stimulation with 1,1-dimethyl-4-phenylpiperazine (DMPP) in pithed rats were affected by rauwolscine only at the higher doses of the ganglionic stimulant. After bilateral adrenalectomy, however, rauwolscine was no longer effective, whereas prazosin invariably exerted a pronounced inhibitory effect. These data support the concept that postsynaptic vasoconstrictor α_1-adrenergic receptors are part of the synapse or at least are located close to the nerve terminal, and that the corresponding α_2-adrenergic receptors have a predominant extrasynaptic location or are at least located further away from the terminal. However, the hypothesis that vascular postsynaptic α_1-adrenergic receptors are innervated in contrast to postsynaptic α_2-adrenergic receptors, which then should be considered hormone receptors, may be an oversimplification. There is increasing evidence that postsynaptic α_2-adrenergic receptors can be involved to a significant or even predominant degree in the vasoconstriction due to sympathetic nerve stimulation. Some examples are the tail artery of spontaneously hypertensive and Sprague–Dawley normotensive rats,[69,70] dog[71] and human[72] saphenous veins, dog (poststenotic) coronary[73] and femoral[74,75] vascular beds

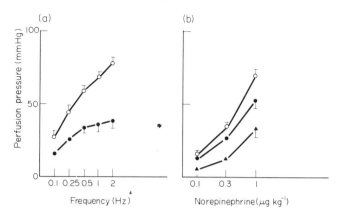

Figure 8 Effect of prazosin (**10**) on the hindlimb perfusion pressor responses to lumbar sympathetic stimulation; (b) effect of prazosin and rauwolscine (**12**) on responses to exogenous norepinephrine (**4**) in anesthetized dogs: ○, control; ●, prazosin ($10\,\mu g\,kg^{-1}$); ▲, prazosin and rauwolscine ($10\,\mu g\,kg^{-1}$). The effects of norepinephrine were obtained in ganglion- and β-adrenergic-receptor-blocked animals (modified after ref. 67)

and the rabbit renal vasculature.[76] Indications for neuronally activated postsynaptic vascular α_2-adrenergic receptors were also obtained in the pithed rat using the indirectly acting sympathomimetic agent tyramine.[77] It is possible that these α_2-adrenergic receptors are activated *via* stimulation of ganglionic muscarinic M_2-receptors.[78] As an alternative hypothesis for the extrasynaptic location of vascular α_2-adrenergic receptors, it has been proposed that activation of ganglionic nicotinic and muscarinic M_1-receptors would lead to activation of the varicosities nearest to the nerve terminal. On the other hand, activation of ganglionic muscarinic M_2-receptors may lead to additional release of neurotransmitter from the more distantly located varicosities, thereby activating α_2-adrenergic receptors (see Figure 9). However, additional evidence is required to firmly support and possibly generalize this concept.

α-Adrenergic receptors are found in a wide variety of tissues in mammalian organisms. Table 1 summarizes the distribution of α_1- and α_2-adrenergic receptors in various organs, together with a short description of the biological consequences of stimulation of these receptors. A detailed overview of the function and physiology of α_1- and α_2-adrenergic receptors is given in Section 12.1.8.

12.1.6 STRUCTURE–ACTIVITY RELATIONSHIPS OF α-ADRENERGIC RECEPTOR AGONISTS

α-Adrenergic receptor agonists can be divided into two major classes: the β-phenethylamines, which include compounds such as norepinephrine (**4**), phenylephrine (**14**) and methoxamine (**13**);

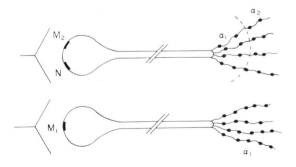

Figure 9 Schematic representation of sympathetic ganglia with their postganglionic neuron terminating in the vascular wall. The nicotine (N), muscarine-1 (M_1) and muscarine-2 (M_2) receptors are located on the cell body of the ganglia. It is suggested that the varicosities of the ganglion endowed with both nicotine and M_2 receptors can roughly be divided over two regions. In the vascular wall the more proximal varicosities interfere predominantly with postsynaptic α_1-adrenergic receptors and the more distant ones with postjunctional α_2-adrenergic receptors. A stimulus initiated by activation of the ganglionic nicotine receptors may reach the varicosities in the proximal area, whereas stimulation of the ganglionic M_2 receptors may give rise to a stimulus which reaches the varicosities in the more distant region. Excitation of M_1 receptors elicits activation of postsynaptic α-adrenergic receptors only. Note that M_1 and nicotine receptors mediate the activation of different populations of α_1-adrenergic receptors. This concept is based on data obtained in pithed rats[77,78]

Table 1   Distribution, Localization and Functions of α_1- and α_2-Adrenergic Receptors

Type	Organ/tissue (location)	Activation causes
α_1	Blood vessels (postsynaptic)	Contraction
	Smooth muscle (postsynaptic)	Contraction
	Heart (postsynaptic)	Positive inotropy/chronotropy (negative chronotropy)
	Eye (postsynaptic)	Mydriasis, ocular hypertension
	Liver (postsynaptic)	Glycogen phosphorylase activation
	CNS (postsynaptic)	Stimulation, inhibition of baroreceptor afferent inputs
	Sympathetic neurons (presynaptic?)	Inhibition of noradrenaline release (?)
α_2	Sympathetic, cholinergic and serotonergic neurons (presynaptic)	Inhibition of noradrenaline, acetylcholine and serotonin release
	CNS (postsynaptic)	Hypotension, bradycardia
	Sympathetic ganglia	Hyperpolarization
	Somadendrites in CNS	Inhibition of firing
	Platelets	Aggregation
	Fat cells	Inhibition of lipolysis
	Pancreatic islets	Inhibition of insulin secretion
	Blood vessels (postsynaptic)	Contraction
	Eye	Ocular hypotension
	Intestinal epithelial cells	Inhibition of intestinal secretions

and the imidazoli(di)nes and related structures, which include compounds such as clonidine (**2**), naphazoline (**28**) and oxymetazoline (**19**). In discussing the structure–activity relationships of α-adrenergic receptor agonists it is important to realize that one must deal with structure–activity relationships for β-phenethylamines *vs.* imidazoli(di)nes, α_1- *vs.* α_2-adrenergic receptors and affinity *vs.* efficacy, in addition to any and all combinations and permutations of these factors.[79] Although the structure–selectivity relationships in α_1- and α_2-adrenergic receptor agonists are virtually unknown and unexplored, it has become obvious that the imidazoli(di)nes and β-phenethylamines possess several marked differences in their structural demands for α-adrenergic receptor agonist activity, whereby the α_1- and α_2-adrenergic receptors show different requirements. Occupation and activation of α_1- and α_2-adrenergic receptors also exhibit different structural requirements.[79] In addition to these two major groups of α-adrenergic receptor stimulants, numerous miscellaneous structures which are difficult to fit into either class have been designed.

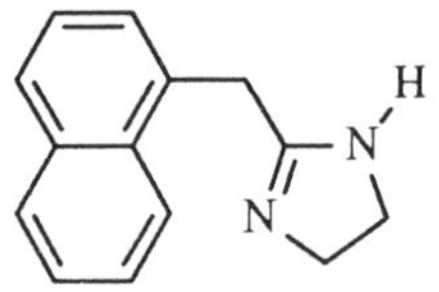

(28)

12.1.6.1   Conformational Requirements of α-Adrenergic Receptor Agonists

The most active enantiomer of norepinephrine (**4**) and other β-phenethylamines at α_1- and α_2-adrenergic receptors is the $(R)(-)$ isomer. Theoretical calculations indicate that the preferred conformation of $(R)(-)$-norepinephrine in solution is the extended *trans* conformation,[80,81] in which the amino and phenyl groups are at a dihedral angle of 180° to one another. X-Ray crystallographic studies of $(-)$-norepinephrine in the solid state show that, in this state as in solution, the preferred conformation is the extended *trans* form.[82] Limited amounts of data are available which establish the most active conformation of sympathomimetic amines interacting with α-adrenergic receptors. The use of conformationally restricted analogs has strongly suggested, however, that the extended *trans* conformation, which is the highly preferred conformation in solution and in the solid state, is also the conformation preferred by α_1- and α_2-adrenergic receptors.[83–85]

Following Pullman *et al.*[81,86] and Wermuth *et al.*,[87] Hoefke[88] has proposed that the imidazolidine clonidine (**2**) can assume a conformation that mimics two critical distances of norepinephrine with the phenyl and imidazoline rings perpendicular. The distance from the center of the phenyl ring to the distant $\overset{+}{N}H$ is 5.0–5.1 Å, while the distance from the bridge nitrogen to this distant $\overset{+}{N}H$ is 1.28–1.36 Å. These distances compare favorably with 5.1–5.2 Å and 1.2–1.4 Å, respectively, for norepinephrine (Figure 10). X-Ray crystallographic studies of clonidine hydrochloride in the solid phase also show a nearly perpendicular arrangement (75°) between phenyl and imidazolidine rings.[89,90] CNDO/2 calculations of clonidine base have suggested that this interplanar angle may not be 90°.[90] However, UV photoelectron spectroscopy in solution and CNDO/s calculations resulted in 90° for this angle.[92]

12.1.6.2 Stereochemical Requirements of α-Adrenergic Receptor Agonists

The natural sympathetic neurotransmitter norepinephrine (4) contains an asymmetric center located at the β carbon atom of the aliphatic side chain. In a variety of adrenergic test systems $(R)(-)$-norepinephrine has invariably been shown to be more potent than the $(S)(+)$ isomer or the deoxy derivative. In their now classical hypothesis, Easson and Stedman[93] have provided an explanation for these quantitative differences by proposing a three-point attachment of norepinephrine to what was then called the 'adrenergic receptor'. The points of interaction included the basic nitrogen of the amine function, the substituted phenyl moiety and the hydroxyl group of the β carbon atom. Only for the $(R)(-)$ isomer of norepinephrine would these three groups be in the ideal stereochemical conformation for interaction with the 'adrenergic receptor'. In the less active $(S)(+)$ isomer, the hydroxyl group would be in a position away from its attachment site, and the activity would be similar to the deoxy derivative. Thus, in general, the Easson–Stedman hypothesis predicts the order of activity for phenethylamines with asymmetry at the β carbon atom to be $(R)(-) > (S)(+) = $ deoxy. A number of studies have confirmed this original hypothesis, using various test systems for α-adrenergic receptors.[94] After the subclassification of α-adrenergic receptors into α_1 and α_2 subtypes, the significance of the Easson–Stedman hypothesis has been shown to be valid for the interaction of phenethylamines with both α-adrenergic receptor classes.[94] Figure 11 summarizes these findings for norepinephrine.

It has been suggested that α_1- and α_2-adrenergic receptors differ with respect to the stereochemical requirements for phenethylamines with asymmetry located at the α carbon atom. For both the $(S)(+)$ and $(R)(-)$ isomers of α-methyldopamine (29), the Easson–Stedman hypothesis correctly predicts the potency at α_1-adrenergic receptors to be equal to dopamine (7), since these compounds lack the β-hydroxyl group and would interact with the α_1-adrenergic receptor *via* a two-point interaction only.[94,95] However, the much higher potency observed for $(S)(+)$-α-methyldopamine over $(R)(-)$-α-methyldopamine at α_2-adrenergic receptors indicates that a third recognition site for the α-methyl group is present on the α_2- but not on the α_1-adrenergic receptor.[94,95] Results obtained with the four stereoisomers of α-methylnorepinephrine (15) have provided further support for such an additional α-methyl recognition site on α_2- but not on α_1-adrenergic receptors.[94]

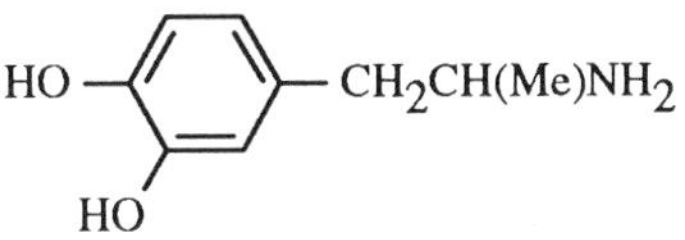

$$HO-\text{(ring)}-CH_2CH(Me)NH_2$$

(29)

The Easson–Stedman hypothesis does not hold true for imidazoli(di)nes. For example, for isomers of 2-(3,4, α-trihydroxybenzyl)imidazoline (30), in which the chiral center corresponds to the β carbon atom in phenethylamines, and the deoxy analog the rank order of potency at α_1- and α_2-adrenergic

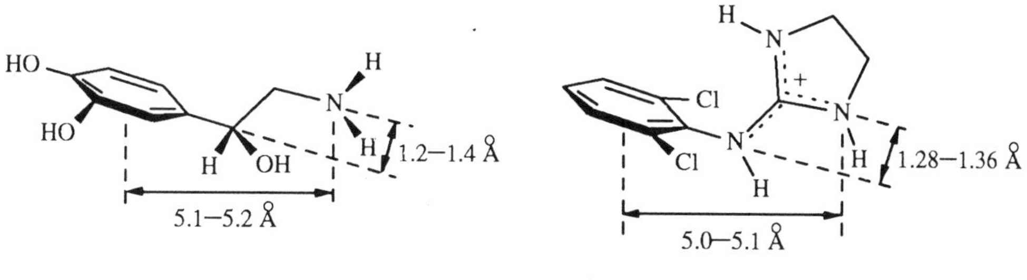

Figure 10 Proposed conformations of norepinephrine (4) and clonidine (2) for interaction with α-adrenergic receptors (see refs. 81 and 86–88)

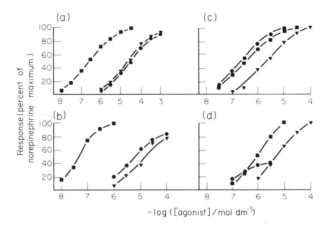

Figure 11 Differences in the applicability of the Easson–Stedman hypothesis to the α_1- and α_2-adrenergic effects of phenethylamines and imidazolines. Illustrated are (a) the α_1- (guinea pig aorta) and (b) the α_2- (field-stimulated guinea pig ileum) adrenergic effects of the stereoisomers of norepinephrine (4) and the corresponding deoxy derivative, dopamine (7); and (c) the α_1- (guinea pig aorta) and (d) the α_2- (field-stimulated guinea pig ileum) adrenergic effects of the stereoisomers of 2-(3,4,α-trihydroxybenzyl)imidazoline and the corresponding deoxy derivative. ■, $(R)(-)$; ▼, $(S)(+)$; ●, deoxy (modified after ref. 353)

receptors was deoxy $\geq (R)(-) > (S)(+)$.[94] In addition, the activity ratios of the $(-)$ and $(+)$ isomers of imidazolines are rather small (five- to ten-fold) in contrast to phenethylamines, where one-hundred- to five-hundred-fold differences between the potency of optical isomers are found (Figure 11).[94] These results suggest that the imidazolines may bind to the α-adrenergic receptor *via* a two-point attachment involving only the phenyl ring and one nitrogen atom of the imidazoline nucleus.

(30)

12.1.6.3 Structure–Activity Relationships in α-Adrenergic Receptor Agonists

12.1.6.3.1 *Phenethylamines*

The substituent at the phenyl ring of β-phenethylamines which has the greatest impact on the α-adrenergic receptor agonist activity is clearly the hydroxyl group.[79] The 3,4-dihydroxy-substituted molecules are always the most potent α_1- and α_2-adrenergic receptor agonists in series derived from either norepinephrine (4), epinephrine (8) or α-methylnorepinephrine (15). Among monophenolic congeners the highest potency always resides in the *meta*-substituted derivative, whereas the *para*-substituted analog is always much weaker. Compounds without hydroxyl substitution are extremely weak α-adrenergic receptor stimulants. At α_1-adrenergic receptors this decrease in potency is largely due to diminished affinity, whereas at α_2-adrenergic receptors this is mainly caused by a decrease in efficacy.[79]

Substitution of both hydroxyl groups in epinephrine by fluorine or chlorine has been found to reduce potency at α_1-adrenergic receptors.[79] Replacement of the 3-hydroxyl group by a sulfonamido functionality retains α_1-adrenergic receptor agonist activity, but abolishes it when performed at the 4-position.[96] This is consistent with the observation mentioned above that the *meta* position is more important than the *para* for agonist activity.

The important role of the hydroxyl group at the β carbon of the phenethylamines has been touched upon earlier with the Easson–Stedman hypothesis (see Section 12.1.6.2). Substitution at the α carbon atom with a methyl group significantly reduces agonist activity at α_1-adrenergic receptors, but increases the potency at α_2-adrenergic receptors. This increase results from an increase in affinity as well as in efficacy.[79]

Norepinephrine is a less potent α-adrenergic receptor agonist than its *N*-methyl analog epinephrine. As higher normal and branched alkyl substitutions are made, α_1-adrenergic receptor agonist activity decreases and is virtually absent for any form of *N*-butyl substitution (Table 2).[97] The decrease in α_1-adrenergic receptor agonist activity is accompanied by a diminution in both affinity and efficacy. Significant affinity is again found for compounds bearing (phenyl-containing) bulkier groups (Table 2). Agonist activity has returned for dobutamine (31), which behaves as an agonist at α_1-adrenergic receptors *in vivo* and *in vitro*.[98,99]

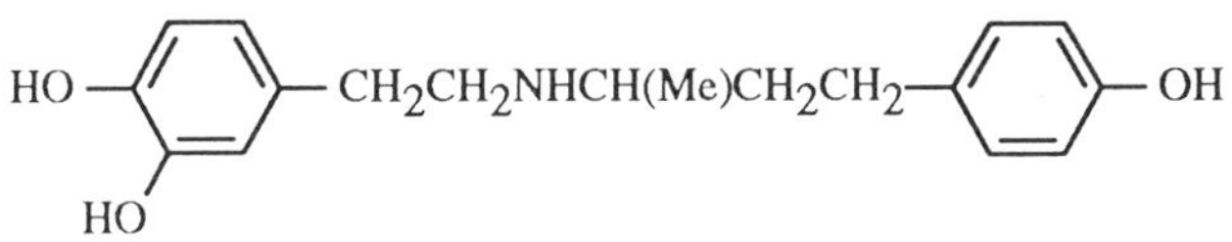

HO—⟨⟩—$CH_2CH_2NHCH(Me)CH_2CH_2$—⟨⟩—OH, HO

(31)

12.1.6.3.2 *Imidazoli(di)nes*

Originally, the interest in designing drugs stimulating α-adrenergic receptors was driven by their potential application as nasal decongestants. For example, the classic imidazoline derivatives such as naphazoline (28), xylometazoline (32), tramazoline (16), oxymetazoline (19) and tetrahydrozoline (33) were developed for exactly this purpose long before the subdivision of α-adrenergic receptors into α_1 and α_2 subclasses was even thought of. In fact, these agonists later turned out to be mixed agonists at α_1- and α_2-adrenergic receptors, as are the endogenous catecholamines norepinephrine (4) and epinephrine (8).

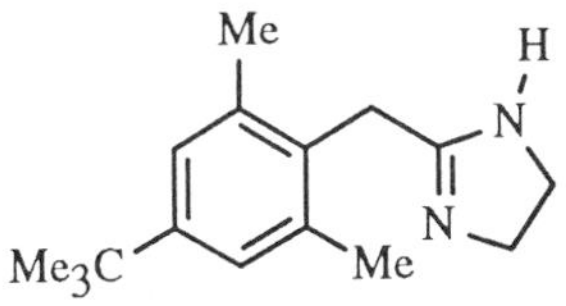

(32) 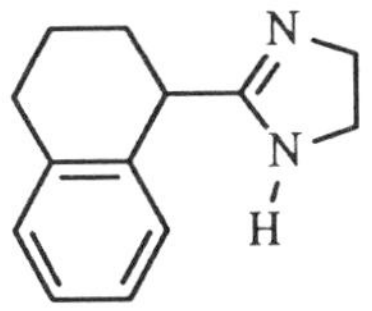   (33)

A strong impetus to the research on α-adrenergic receptors and the drugs interacting with them has been the recognition that centrally acting antihypertensive agents, such as clonidine (2) and α-methylDOPA (1), exert this action by virtue of their interference with α-adrenergic receptors in the CNS.

Although in 1962 the purpose of synthesizing clonidine was to develop a novel nasal decongestant, the more or less accidental discovery of its potent antihypertensive properties has led to the synthesis of a large number of derivatives, mainly at the research laboratories of C. H. Boehringer Sohn (Ingelheim, FRG) by Stahle and co-workers. In the search for similar molecules, compounds more or less related to the fundamental structure of clonidine have been developed subsequently by several companies. The most important of these are summarized in Table 3.[100,101] Some of these structures will be discussed separately in the course of this section. Studies aimed at elucidating the (quantitative) structure–activity relationships of imidazoli(di)nes have dealt mainly with three areas of structural modification, as shown in Figure 12 for a molecule of clonidine, *i.e.* modification of the aromatic portion (A), the bridge (B) and the imidazolidine moiety (C).

The structural modification involving enlargement of the five-membered (imidazolidine) ring of clonidine into a six-, seven- or eight-membered nucleus has been shown to produce a pronounced

Table 2 α_1-Adrenergic Receptor Agonist Activity of
some N-Substituted Phenethylamines[97]

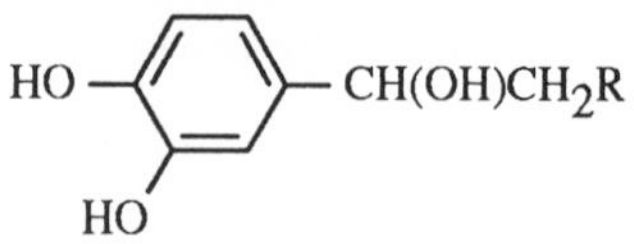

HO—⟨benzene ring⟩—CH(OH)CH$_2$R
HO

R	IA^a	pD_2^a	pA_2^a
NH$_2$	1.0	5.4	
NHMe	1.0	5.7	
NHEt	0.9	5.2	
NHPr^n	0.3	3.3	
NHCHMe$_2$	0.6	3.0	
NHCH$_2$CHMe$_2$	0	<3	
NHBu^n	0	<3	
NHCH(Me)Et	0	<3	
NHCH(Me)CH$_2$Ph	0		4.4
NHCMe$_2$CH$_2$Ph	0		5.9

^{a} Rat vas deferens.

decrease (about a hundredfold) in hypotensive (α_2-adrenergic receptor mediated) and vasoconstrictor (α_1-adrenergic receptor mediated) activities.[88,100,101] Different five-membered mono- or bicyclic hetero ring systems are tolerated for high α_1- and α_2-adrenergic receptor agonist activity. For example, compound 44-549 (**34**)[102] and ICI 106270 (**35**)[103] are as potent as clonidine. Also, an oxazolidine moiety as in Bay c 6014 (**36**) provides high α-adrenergic-receptor agonist potency, but six-membered heterocyclic rings, such as found in the α_2-adrenergic-receptor-selective stimulant xylazine (**37**; see below), invariably reduce potency.[100] The imidazolidine ring of clonidine has been structurally altered by ring-closure reactions into annellated bicyclic structures. The hypotensive activity of these clonidine derivatives was distinctly diminished, some structures within the imidazo[1,2-a][1,3,5]triazine series excepted.[88,100,101] Recently an imidazole derivative, M 6434 (**38**), has been reported to be a potent vasoconstrictor following intravenous as well as oral administration.[104] The compound has been characterized to be a full α_1-adrenergic receptor agonist and a partial α_2-adrenergic receptor stimulant with some preference for the former subtype.[105]

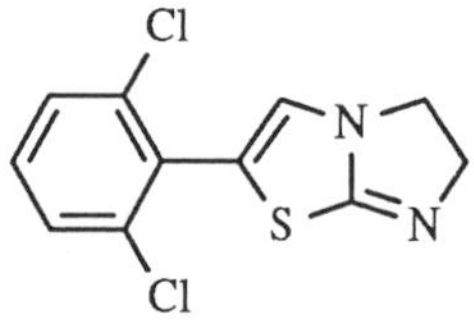

(34) 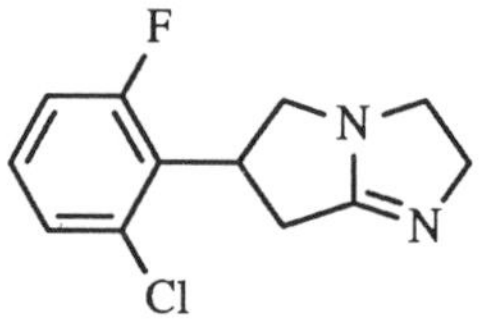   (35) 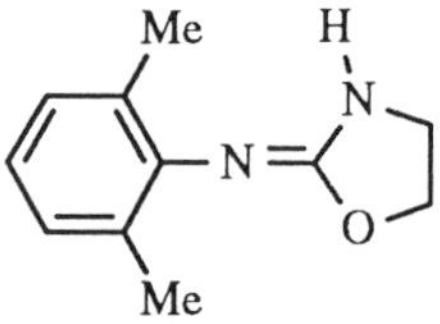   (36)

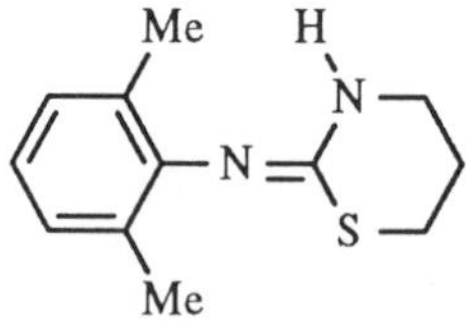

(37) 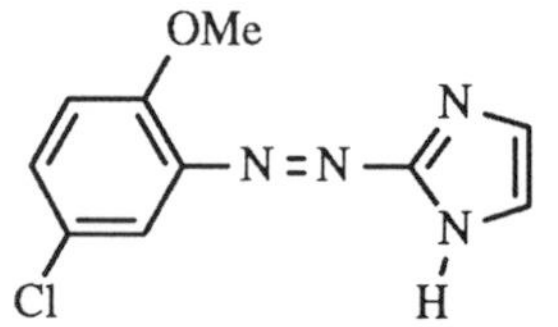   (38)

Radioligand binding studies using [³H]clonidine to label α_2-adrenergic receptors have shown that substitution of an imidazoli(di)ne nitrogen atom destroys affinity, as does opening of the five-membered ring[106] and interconnecting the two ring systems, as achieved in (**39**), thereby forcing the molecule into a nearly planar structure.[100]

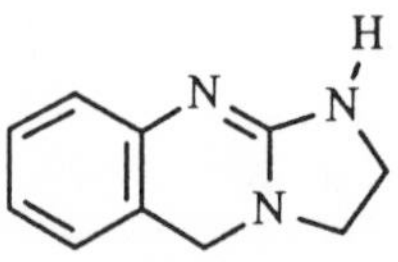

(39)

Table 3 Collection of Clonidine-like Hypotensive Agents Developed as Potential Antihypertensive Drugs[101]

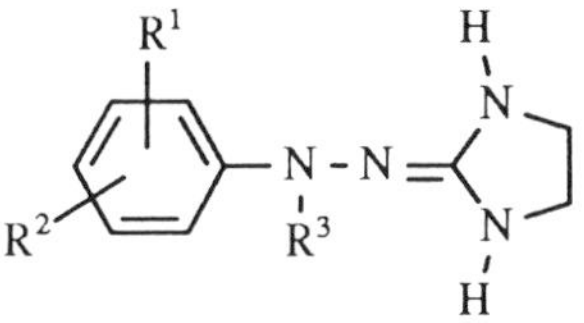

Ciba 1966

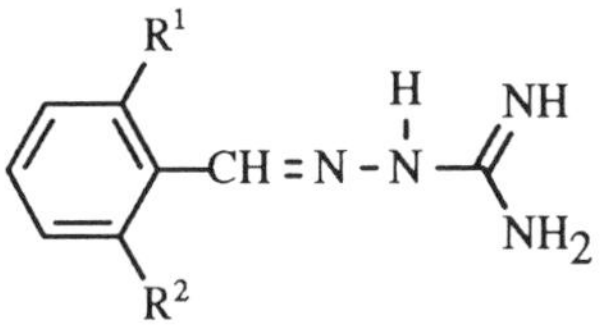

Wyeth 1969

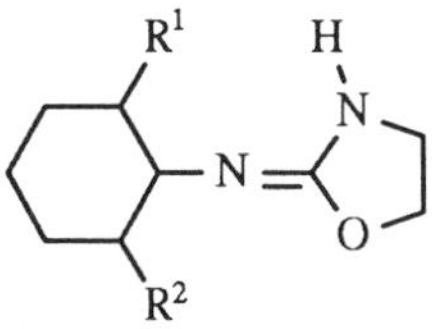

Bayer 1966

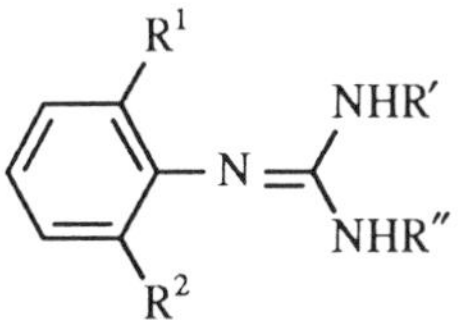

Seperic 1971

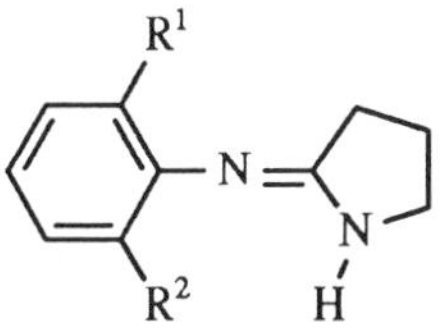

Bayer 1967; Searle 1971

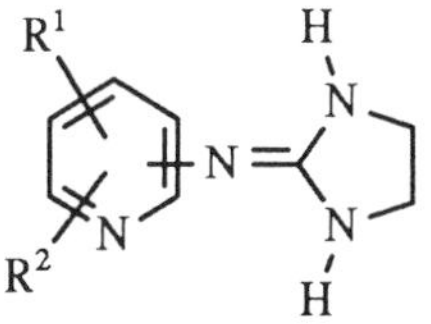

Beecham 1969

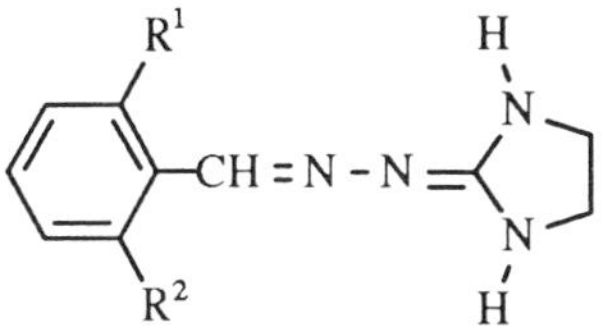

Sandoz 1967

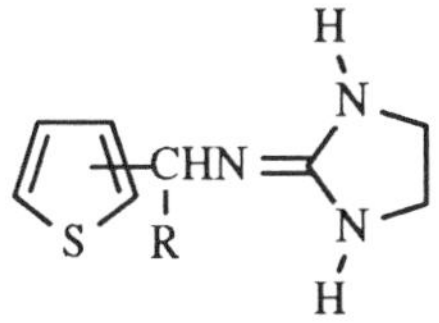

Sumitomo 1969; Ciba-Geigy 1970

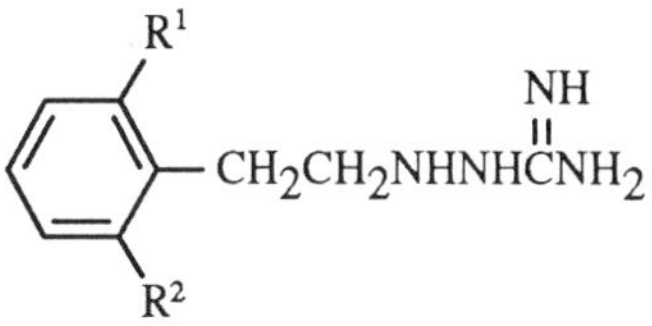

Wander 1965

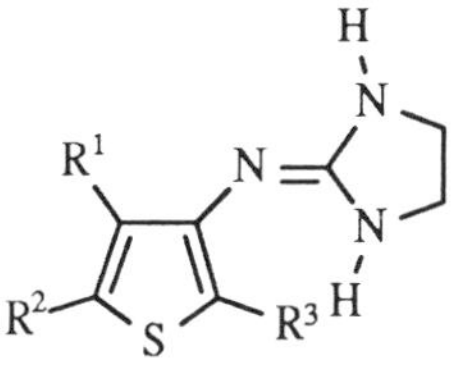

Hoechst 1969

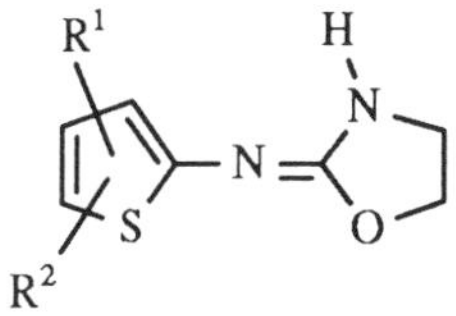

Du Pont 1970

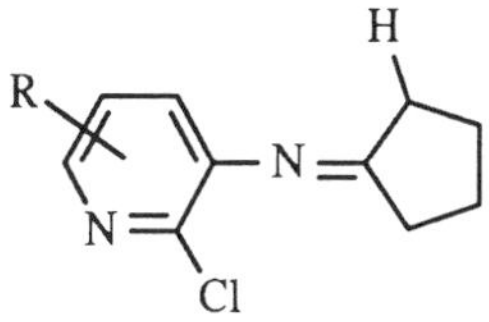

Searle 1971

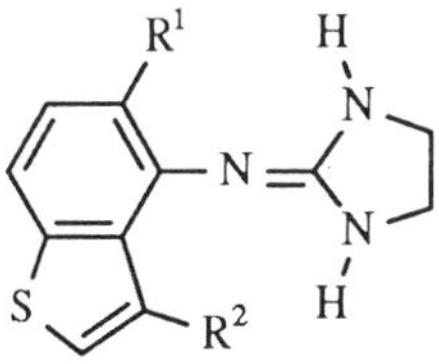

Pfizer 1970

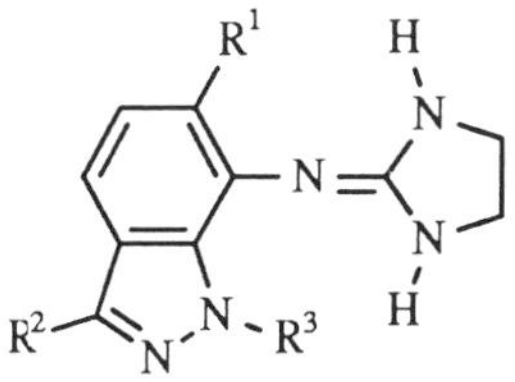

Wander 1971

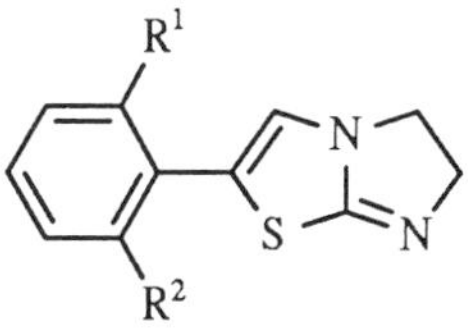

Sandoz 1969

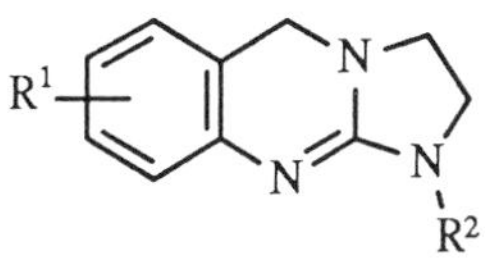

Smith Kline & French 1969

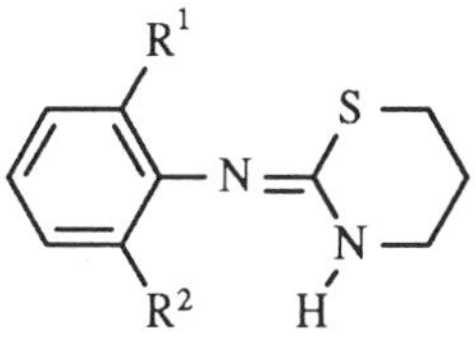

Bayer 1962

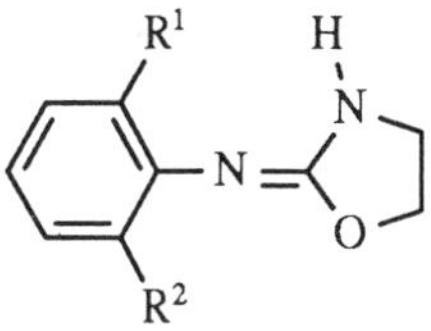

Du Pont 1965; Bayer 1966;
Lab Daussee 1958

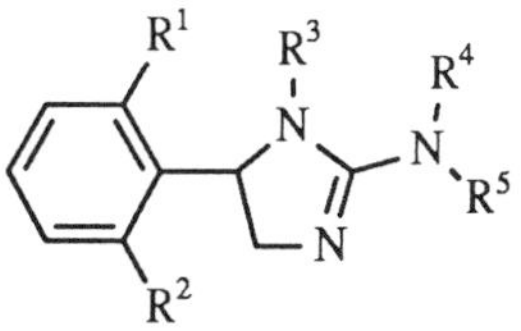

Mead Johnson 1972; Bristol Myers 1971

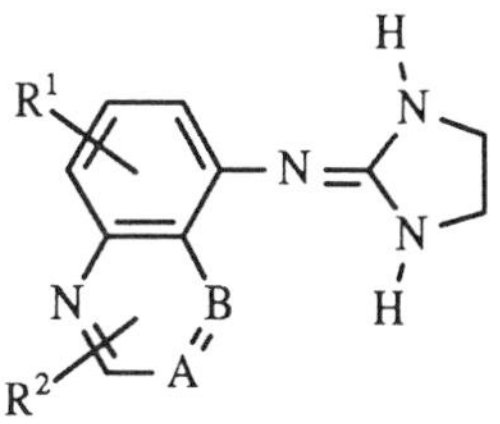

Pfizer 1972
(A = B = N = CH or CH = N)

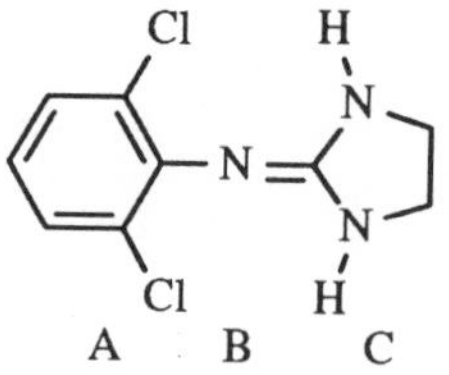

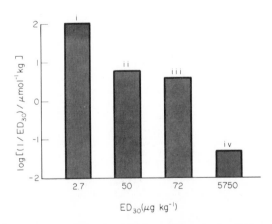

Figure 12 Subdivision of the molecule of clonidine (**2**) into three fundamental structural units accessible to chemical modification

Replacement of the bridging nitrogen of clonidine by other ring junctions is accompanied by a decrease in central hypotensive α_2-adrenergic-receptor-induced activity.[107] This is illustrated in Figure 13, where the methylene, oxygen and sulfur analogs of clonidine exhibit but moderate hypotensive activity. For α_1-adrenergic receptor agonist activity a methylene bridge may substitute for the nitrogen bridge with no significant loss of potency.[79] Extension of the bridge between phenyl and imidazolidine rings also produces molecules with a loss of hypotensive activity. This diminution is particularly great when the ring junction exceeds three atoms.[100] An exception is the non-selective agonist lofexidine (**40**) which is as potent as clonidine (**2**).[108]

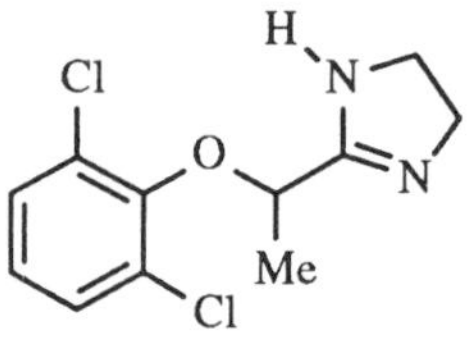

(40)

Lofexidine is one of the few imidazolines with an asymmetric center and its isomers have been characterized with respect to their interaction with α-adrenergic receptors.[109] Various *in vivo* and *in vitro* experiments showed that the α_1- and α_2-adrenergic receptor agonist activity of lofexidine predominantly resides in the $(-)$ isomer. However, the isomeric activity ratio of about twentyfold is higher than normally found for other imidazoli(di)nes (see above). It seems obvious that the two-atom bridge in lofexidine should explain this finding, but the reason has not been further explored.[109]

Figure 13 Central α_2-adrenergic-receptor-mediated hypotensive activity of some bridge analogs of clonidine (**2**). Hypotensive activity was determined after intravenous injections into anesthetized rats. The logarithm of the reciprocal dose (μmol kg^{-1}) required to decrease the mean arterial pressure by 30% of the initial value is given on the ordinate. i, X $=$ —N==; ii, X = —S—; iii, X = —CH$_2$—; iv, X = —O— (modified after ref. 100)

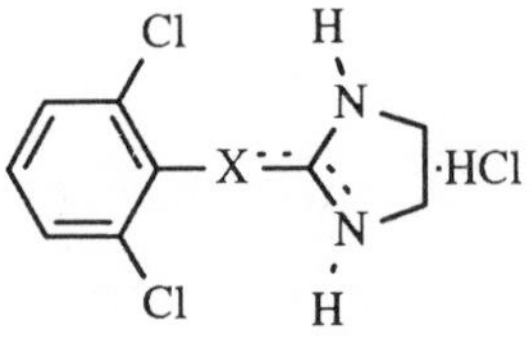

Whereas hydroxylation of the β carbon atom in phenethylamines greatly enhances the α-adrenergic receptor agonist potency (see above), it has a deleterious effect in imidazolines. Hydroxylation of the methylene bridge analog of clonidine[110] as well as hydroxyl substitution of the alkyl bridge in arylalkylimidazole derivatives[111] has been reported to markedly reduce α-adrenergic receptor agonist activity. On the other hand, methyl substitution, as exemplified by lofexidine (see above) and recently shown for some arylalkylimidazoles,[111] does not negatively influence α-adrenergic receptor agonist activity. The detrimental effect of hydroxylation of the carbon bridge in phenylalkylimidazolines/imidazoles supports the hypothesis that the interaction of these compounds with α_1- and α_2-adrenergic receptors is different from that of the phenethylamines (see above). However, the alkyl bridge seems to contribute directly to the binding process.[111]

Clonidine-like substances displaying α_1-adrenergic-(vasoconstriction) and α_2-adrenergic-(hypotension) receptor-stimulatory activities have been found in a chemical class which may be called 'open-ring imidazolidines'.[100] The best-known molecules possess a structure consisting of a 2,6-dichlorophenyl moiety connected to a guanidine portion *via* a two-atom bridge. Guanabenz (**41**) and guanfacine (**3**) are centrally acting hypotensive drugs with a similar mode of action to clonidine.[112,113]

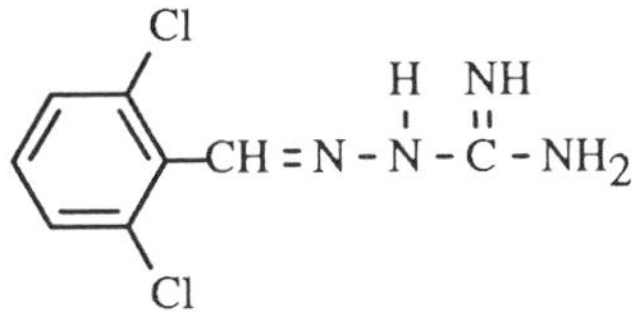

(**41**)

Several compounds related to clonidine (**2**), in which the major structural difference is found in the aromatic (phenyl) nucleus, have been evaluated for α-adrenergic-receptor-stimulatory properties with the aim of developing useful antihypertensives. The 2,6-dichlorophenyl moiety of clonidine has been replaced by a substituted thiophene ring in tiamenidine (**42**), which is somewhat less potent than clonidine in lowering arterial pressure.[114] In the experimental compound Bay a 6781 (**43**) it is notable that a non-aromatic cyclohexyl moiety can replace the phenyl ring in clonidine. This derivative is a centrally acting hypotensive drug which is as potent as clonidine at least in animals.[100,115] An aromatic ring structure is apparently not a prerequisite for stimulating α_1- or α_2-adrenergic receptors, inasmuch as the oxazolidine S3341 (**44**) has been found to possess central α_2-adrenergic-receptor-mediated antihypertensive properties.[116] S3341 has been characterized as a non-selective α_1-/α_2-adrenergic receptor agonist, less potent than clonidine as an antihypertensive but with a similar mechanism of action.[116] S3341 (rilmenidine) has been approved very recently for marketing in France as Hyperium. A quinoxaline system is found in the experimental compound UK-14,304 (**45**), which is also a centrally acting hypotensive agent through stimulation of α-adrenergic receptors.[100] UK-14,304 was subsequently identified as a highly selective stimulant of α_2-adrenergic receptors (see below).[57] Moxonidine (**46**) is one of the latest products of the search for clonidine-like antihypertensive drugs. This pyrimidine derivative is a full agonist of α_1- and α_2-adrenergic receptors *in vitro* and possesses pronounced antihypertensive properties.[117]

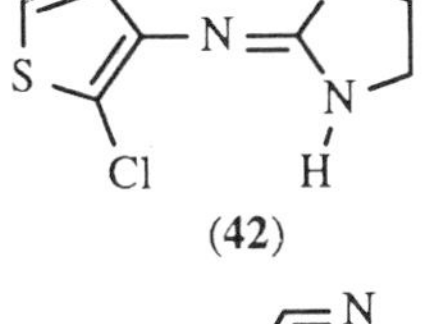

(**42**) 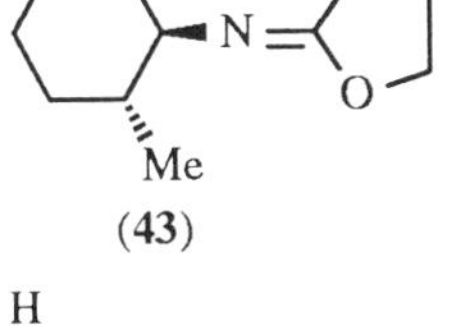   (**43**) 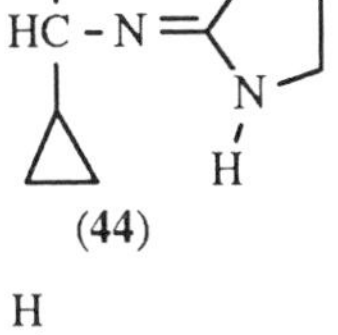   (**44**)

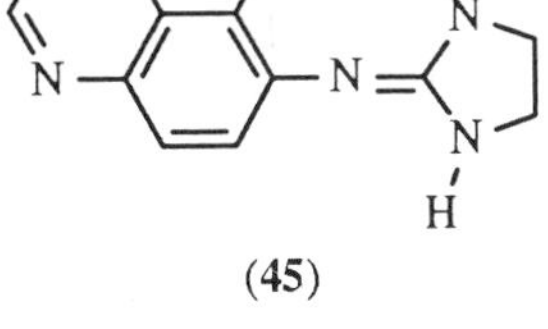

(**45**) 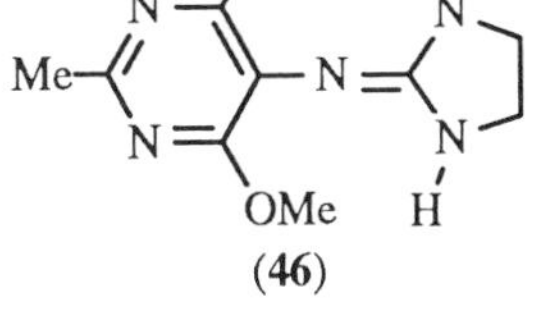   (**46**)

The compounds differing in substitution at the phenyl ring of clonidine (**2**) represent an extensive group of derivatives which have been employed to explore the structure–activity relationships. The available data have been compiled and reviewed.[100] Upon alteration of the 2,6-disubstitution pattern of the chlorine groups in clonidine into other substitution patterns (2,5-, 2,4-, 2,3-, 3,4- and 3,5-) hypotensive activity is diminished.[100] Although less potent than clonidine, the relatively high activity of the 2,3-dichloro analog and in general all 2,3-disubstituted congeners is worth mentioning.[88,100,101] Any substitution at the 4-position of the phenyl ring in clonidine has led to derivatives of which the hypotensive activity is decreased compared to that of the parent compound (= clonidine). Five examples are given in Figure 14.[100] It should be added, however, that 4-hydroxy- and in particular 4-amino-clonidine are potent non-selective α_1-/α_2-adrenergic receptor agonists.[118] In fact, 4-amino[^{3}H]clonidine is a very useful probe for labeling α_2-adrenergic receptors.[119] However, their hypotensive activity is much less than that of clonidine due to their moderate lipophilicity.

As for the phenethylamines, 3,4-dihydroxyl substitution also produces the most potent α_1- and α_2-adrenergic receptor agonists in the imidazoli(di)ne series. This applies to (phenylimino)imidazolidines as well as to benzylimidazolines.[79] However, the aromatic hydroxyl groups of the imidazoli(di)nes affect predominantly efficacy and not affinity.

The effects of a limited number of halogen- and alkyl-substituted (phenylimino)imidazolidines have been studied on α_1- and α_2-adrenergic receptors under well-defined *in vitro* conditions.[120-124] To summarize the findings, in monosubstituted (phenylimino)imidazolidines, the activity on both α_1- and α_2-adrenergic receptors is particularly high for *ortho*-substituted molecules, and the effects of chlorine, bromine, methyl and ethyl substituents are about equivalent. Disubstitution with halogen or alkyl groups has been found to enhance activity at α_1- and α_2-adrenergic receptors, where a 2,6-disubstitution pattern provides the greatest activity, but 2,3-, 2,4- and 2,5-disubstituted analogs are also still appreciably potent. Again, only minor differences exist between chlorine, bromine, methyl and ethyl and any combination of these substituents. In fact, most disubstituted (phenylimino)-imidazolidines have about the same *in vitro* activity at α_1- and α_2-adrenergic receptors. This is in marked contrast to the phenethylamines which vary dramatically in α_1- and α_2-adrenergic receptor agonist activity depending on the substitution pattern (see above).

It should be kept in mind that although no marked changes in α_1- and α_2-adrenergic receptor agonist activity are observed at the receptor level when various halogen- and alkyl-substituted (phenylimino)imidazolidines are studied, these compounds show very pronounced differences in centrally induced α_2-adrenergic-receptor-mediated hypotensive activities (see above). This is obviously due to the marked differences in distribution properties which heavily depend on the lipophilicity of the compounds. For this reason, halogen-substituted congeners (see clonidine) have always provided better candidates for antihypertensive drugs than alkyl-substituted derivatives.

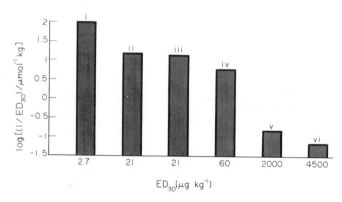

Figure 14 Effect of various substituents in the *para* position of the clonidine (**2**) molecule on hypotensive activity. Hypotensive activity was determined after intravenous injections into anesthetized rats. The logarithm of the reciprocal dose (μmol kg^{-1}) required to decrease the mean arterial pressure by 30% of the initial value is given at the ordinate. i, X = 2,6-dichloro; ii, X = 2,4,6-trichloro; iii, X = 2,6-dichloro-4-methyl; iv, X = 4-bromo-2,6-dichloro; v, X = 2,6-dichloro-4-methoxy; vi, X = 2,6-dichloro-4-nitro (modified after ref. 100)

12.1.6.4 Quantitative Structure–Activity Relationships in Clonidine-like Imidazolidines

Quantitative correlations between the peripheral hypertensive activity of 22 phenyl-substituted imidazolidines and their physicochemical parameters have been presented by Rouot et al.[125,126] The potency of the compounds to increase arterial pressure was expressed as pD_2 obtained from log dose–response curves following intravenous injections into pithed rats. The authors considered that the stimulation of the vascular α-adrenoceptors is brought about by the protonated imidazolidine. Therefore, in their equations they used the pD_2 values corrected for ionization at pH = 7.4. With respect to the steric constant E_s, a partial summation over certain positions at the phenyl ring was studied, e.g. E_s-2,6. The E_s-2 was attributed to the smaller substituent, whereas E_s-6 referred to the larger group at the *ortho* position.

The study pointed out the involvement of steric features of the substituents attached at both *ortho* positions (equation 1)

$$pD_2 = -0.82(\pm 0.17)(E_s\text{-}2,6)^2 - 2.08(\pm 0.45)E_s\text{-}2,6 - 1.28(\pm 0.42)E_s\text{-}2 - 0.48(\pm 0.22)F + 6.11 \tag{1}$$

$$n = 17, \quad r = 0.96, \quad F = 35.8, \quad s = 0.22$$

Equation (1) also contains the summation of the inductive component of the electronic effect of all the substituents attached to the phenyl ring, F. It was found that replacing E_s-2 by E_s-6 yielded identical levels of significance. The authors have explained their results by suggesting that the variance in pD_2 does not solely depend on the steric bulk at the *ortho* position, but is also determined by the distribution of the substituents on both *ortho* positions. The steric dimensions of the 4-position apparently do not play an important role in the vasoconstrictor activity, since the inclusion of an additional E_s-4 term did not improve the correlation. However, its electronic effect is incorporated in F. Four compounds were synthesized to test the validity of equation (1) and the calculated and observed α-adrenergic-receptor-mediated vasopressor potencies agreed very well.[125,126] At present, it is difficult to judge the general applicability/validity of equation (1) in predicting the vasoconstrictor activity of imidazolidines, since later findings showed that a mixed population of distinct α_1- and α_2-adrenergic receptors is mediating this response (see Section 12.1.5). However, the non-selectivity towards α_1- and α_2-adrenergic receptors of the agonists involved in this study may explain the high level of significance of equation (1).

The effects of clonidine (2), oxymetazoline (19) and 13 substituted (phenylimino)imidazolidines have been studied and compared on α_1-adrenergic receptors in guinea pig and rabbit aorta and on (presynaptic) α_2-adrenergic receptors in guinea pig atria.[127] In the aorta all compounds were found to be partial agonists and the agonist activity (pD_2 corrected for ionization) correlated best with the pK_a of the molecules (equation 2).

$$pD_2 = 1.17(\pm 0.16)\,pK_a - 3.30(\pm 1.45) \tag{2}$$

$$n = 13, \quad r = 0.91, \quad F = 54.50, \quad s = 0.65$$

The observation that the variance in pD_2 of clonidine-like imidazolidines at α-adrenergic receptors can be explained at least partly on the basis of the difference in degree of dissociation of the compounds has been reported previously.[123] The ability to inhibit pendular movements in rabbit isolated intestine *via* activation of α-adrenergic receptors was found to correlate best with pK_a (equation 3).

$$pD_2 = 0.362\,pK_a + 2.088 \tag{3}$$

$$n = 11, \quad r = 0.837, \quad s = 0.242$$

Quantitative relationships have been calculated mathematically, comprising correlations between central hypotensive activity (mediated by stimulation of α_2-adrenergic receptors) and the molecular structure of 27 (phenylimino)imidazolidines, structurally related to clonidine (2).[128] The quantitation of the hypotensive activity was achieved by pED_{30}, where ED_{30} is the dose (μmol kg^{-1}), corrected for ionization, connected with a response of a 30% decrease in mean arterial pressure following intravenous administration to anesthetized rats. A large number of independent variables were examined: seven Hammett-type electronic parameters, eight molecular orbital indices, lipophilicity and various steric constants. After intravenous administration, a certain amount of the dose injected will eventually reach the CNS. This limited amount of substance interacts with the central α_2-adrenergic receptors which finally leads to a hypotensive response. For this reason the central hypotensive activity (pED_{30}) of the imidazolidines is determined by the actual receptor interaction and the processes providing the concentration in the brain. The best equation obtained by stepwise regression was equation (4).

$$pED_{30} = -0.00032(\pm 0.00008)(\Sigma Par)^2 + 0.105(\pm 0.03)\Sigma Par - 0.695(\pm 0.17)\Delta pK_a + 5.333(\pm 1.89)HOMO(P)$$

$$+ 6.752(\pm 2.25)EE(P) + 2.494 \tag{4}$$

$$n = 27, \quad r = 0.952, \quad F = 40.34, \quad s = 0.341$$

ΣPar stands for the sum of the parachor value of the substituent(s) and is defined as the product of the substituent effect on the molecular volume and the fourth root of the surface tension. ΔpK_a refers to the substituent effect on the dissociation of the imidazolidines in water. HOMO(P) is the energy of the highest occupied molecular orbital of the protonated species and EE(P) corresponds to its lowest π-electronic excitation energy.

It can be anticipated that the parachor represents an independent variable containing lipophilic as well as steric properties of the phenyl-attached substituents. The appearance of ΔpK_a in equation (4) has been ascribed to its profound influence on the lipophilicity of these imidazolidines, since the degree of dissociation depends heavily on the pK_a of the molecule.[128] Additionally, it may also reflect electronic effects playing a part in the interaction between imidazolidine and the central (hypotensive) α_2-adrenergic receptors. The partial correlation of the excitation energy (EE) in combination with the HOMO energy, an index of electron donor ability, has been interpreted as an indication that a charge-transfer complex is formed at the receptor site.[128] Equation (4) accounts for 90% of the variances in pED_{30} and all compounds were predicted within two standard deviations. Because of the rather large ratio of examined variables to observations, the validity of equation (4) has to be regarded with caution.[129]

Although equation (4) suggests that the hypotensive activity of the compounds is expressed adequately in terms of overall molecular properties, it lacks the detailed characteristics of the mechanism of interaction of these drugs with the α_2-adrenergic receptor. This is obviously due to the fact that in addition to the actual receptor engagement the 'kinetics' also need to be accounted for. Consequently, in order to study those structural properties of the compounds essential to this receptor interaction it is necessary to remove these distribution effects. The separation of the transport kinetics from the receptor occupation was achieved by determining the (rat) brain concentrations of the compounds at the moment of maximal decrease in mean arterial pressure.[130] The tendency of the imidazolidines to accumulate into the (rat) brain, $\log(C_{brain}/C_{i.v.})$, could be represented by a most significant parabolic relationship in the (octanol/aqueous buffer, pH = 7.4) partition coefficient, $\log P'$ (Figure 15).[130] For all the member imidazolidines this relationship was employed to calculate the brain concentration (nmol g^{-1} of brain tissue w.w.) associated with a decrease in mean arterial pressure by 30%, $ED_{30}(C)$. This biological variable is independent of distributing effects. Equation (5) resulted from stepwise regression analysis and omission of two *meta*-substituted compounds.

$$pED_{30}(C) = -0.439(\pm 0.10)(\Sigma E_s)^2 - 1.939(\pm 0.48)\Sigma E_s + 2.180(\pm 0.91)\Sigma R$$

$$+ 4.719(\pm 1.40)HOMO(P) + 6.249(\pm 1.64)EE(P) + 7.190 \tag{5}$$

$$n = 25, \quad r = 0.965, \quad F = 50.78, \quad s = 0.262$$

Equation (5) explains 93% of the variance in blood-pressure-lowering activity. In Figure 16 the hypotensive activities calculated according to equation (5) are plotted against the ones actualy determined with the aid of animal experiments.[128] It can be seen from this figure that equation (5) provides calculated activities which agree well with the experimental ones. The hypotensive activity of the clonidine-like drugs at the central α_2-adrenergic receptor level is expressed in terms of the resonance contribution of the phenyl-attached substituents to the overall electronic effects, ΣR, a parabolic dependence on the overall steric properties of the same substituents, ΣE_s, and the two quantum chemical parameters HOMO(P) and EE(P) already mentioned above. In an alternative equation it was shown that $-\Sigma F$ substituted for ΣR and $^qC_8(P)$, *i.e.* the π-electron charge density at the guanidine carbon atom in the protonated species, substituted for HOMO(P) to give equal statistics as for equation (5).[128]

Equation (5) and similar correlations have been translated into a hypothetical working model in an attempt to provide an insight into the mode of interaction between clonidine-like drugs and the central α_2-adrenergic receptor. The major aspects of this hypothetical model of interaction are illustrated in Figure 17.[128]

The model suggests a receptor site which has the ability of accepting electrons from an electron-donating drug. The aromatic phenyl ring of the agonist possibly interacts by means of electron

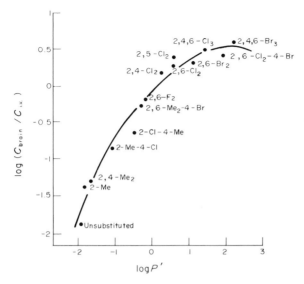

Figure 15 Dependence of the ability to accumulate into the brain of rats, $\log(C_{\text{brain}}/C_{\text{i.v.}})$, on lipophilicity, $\log P'$, for clonidine (**2**; 2,6-dichloro) and structurally related imidazolidines (modified after ref. 130). The relationship is mathematically expressed by

$$\log(C_{\text{brain}}/C_{\text{i.v.}}) = -0.133(\log P')^2 + 0.574\log P' - 0.094$$

$$n = 14, \quad r = 0.987, \quad s = 0.139, \quad F = 211.83\,(p < 0.001)$$

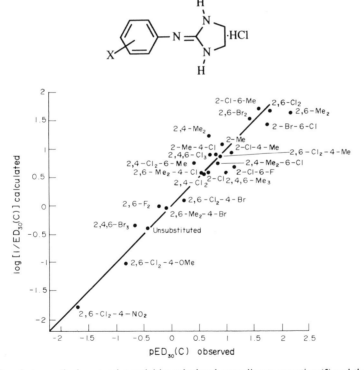

Figure 16 Comparison between the hypotensive activities calculated according to equation (5) and those determined with the aid of animal experiments for clonidine (**2**; 2,6-dichloro) and 24 structurally related imidazolidines (reproduced from ref. 128 by permission of the American Chemical Society)

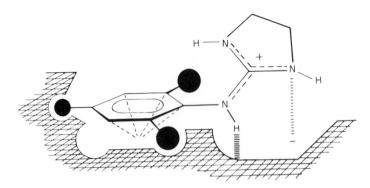

Figure 17 Hypothetical working model illustrating the proposed mode of interaction between clonidine-like imidazoli-(di)nes and the central α_2-adrenergic receptor, leading to a centrally mediated hypotensive effect. The model has been constructed from the results of quantitative structure–activity relationship studies. For explanation see text (reproduced from ref. 128 by permission of the American Chemical Society)

donation with an electron-deficient area of the receptor. Another type of interaction may be an electrostatic one, accomplished between a negatively charged site at the receptor and a positively charged nitrogen atom of the drug. Resonance interaction between the aromatic portion and the imidazolidine moiety of the drug is not permitted for an intimate interaction. Interaction of this type will dissipate the positive charge in the case of electron-donating substituents, whereas electron-withdrawing groups will hinder the electron donation to the receptor. A third type of interaction has been proposed in the form of hydrogen-bond formation in which the bridge acts as the hydrogen donor. However, this does not seem to be of great importance, since for other potent centrally acting α-adrenergic hypotensive drugs the formation of such a hydrogen bond is not possible (*e.g.* lofexidine; **40**). In fact, imidazoli(di)nes like clonidine are presently believed to interact with α_1- and α_2-adrenergic receptors *via* a two-point attachment (see Section 12.1.6.2).

Rather stringent demands are made upon the steric bulk of the substituents attached to the phenyl ring. Probably one side only of the phenyl ring determines the major fit with the receptor. A double *ortho*-substitution is necessary with rather bulky groups to keep the imidazolidine ring in the most favorable (perpendicular) orientation.

Although *meta*-substituted compounds were omitted in the generation of equation (5), it should be noted that it was only 2,5-disubstitution which could not be accounted for. The 2,3-dichloro analog fitted perfectly in the regression.[128] Based on this observation, it has been predicted that an additional 3-substituent can be tolerated in the molecule of clonidine without loss of activity.[100] The subsequent synthesis and testing of the 2,3,6-trichloro and the 2,3-dichloro-6-methyl derivatives of clonidine has proven that this suggestion is correct.[131,132] The 2,3,6-trichloro analog is approximately three times more effective than clonidine (**2**) in reducing mean arterial pressure of anesthetized rats following intravenous administration. This particular derivative is presently the most potent hypotensive clonidine congener.[130,131]

12.1.6.5 α_1-Adrenergic Receptor Agonists

(+)-*erythro*-Methoxamine **(13)**,[57,133] (−)-phenylephrine **(14)**,[57,133,134] (−)-amidephrine **(27)**,[135,136] (+)- and (−)-SK & F 89478 **(47)**,[137] St 587 **(26)**,[138] Sgd 101/75 **(48**; indanidine)[139] and cirazoline **(49)**[57] fulfill the criteria for selective α_1-adrenergic receptor stimulants. For example, they all increase diastolic pressure in mammals including man and this effect is most sensitive to blockade by prazosin **(10)**, with yohimbine **(11)** and rauwolscine **(12)** being much less effective.

(47)   (48)   (49)

Limited work has been done on the systematic investigation of the structure–selectivity relationships in α_1-adrenergic receptor agonists. Within a series of phenylethylamines related to methoxamine it has been observed that for open-chain compounds, such as methoxamine, in which the amine-containing portion is free to adopt numerous conformations, a hydroxyl group is mandatory for direct α_1-adrenergic-receptor-stimulatory activity.[140] When the hydroxyl group is removed, activity is markedly reduced unless the amine is incorporated into a more sterically defined structure. The authors[140] concluded that in order for a phenylethylamine to be active as an α_1-adrenergic receptor agonist it should have a β nitrogen in a fully extended conformation relative to a substituted phenyl ring. Optimum potency is found for compounds possessing this nitrogen exocyclic to a saturated six-membered ring.[140] Within those 2-aminotetralins, substituent alterations on the ring, as well as on the nitrogen, change the α_1-adrenergic receptor agonist activity by over three orders of magnitude, producing optimum activity when substituents were placed at both the 5- and 8-positions.[141] Table 4 shows the influences of various substituents in these two positions.[141] The structure which has an (S)-methyl at the 5-position (47; SK & F 89748) has been found to be the most potent agonist in this series. The ($-$) isomer of SK & F 89748 is approximately five times more potent than the ($+$) isomer.[137]

In contrast to Sgd 101/75 (48) and cirazoline (49), for which the selective α_1-adrenergic-receptor-stimulatory activity was identified accidentally, the selection of St 587 (26) as a preferential stimulant of α_1-adrenergic receptors was a more rational process. Linear regression analysis showed that within a series of 16 2,3- and 2,5-disubstituted phenyl(imino)imidazolidines 67% ($= r^2$) of the variance in the centrally mediated α_2-adrenergic-receptor-induced hypotensive activity (pC_{20}) could be explained by Taft's steric parameter of the substituent at the 5-position, E_s-5 (equation 6).[142] As expected, inclusion of lipophilicity ($\log P'$) into this equation to account for the brain penetration of the compounds significantly improved this correlation (equation 7).

$$pC_{20} = 1.50E_s\text{-}5 + 5.56 \tag{6}$$

$$n = 16, \quad r = 0.82, \quad F = 28.9, \quad s = 0.55$$

$$pC_{20} = 1.29E_s\text{-}5 + 0.51\log P' + 5.50 \tag{7}$$

$$n = 16, \quad r = 0.90, \quad F = 28.8, \quad s = 0.43$$

In addition, for a similar series of phenyl(imino)imidazolidines, intrinsic activity (IA) at cardiac presynaptic α_2-adrenergic receptors was found to be linearly correlated with E_s-5 (equation 8).[143]

$$IA = 0.57E_s\text{-}5 + 0.13 \tag{8}$$

$$n = 8, \quad r = 0.98, \quad F = 119.22, \quad s = 0.29$$

Table 4 α-Adrenergic Receptor Agonist Activity of 5,8-Disubstituted 2-Aminotetralins[141]

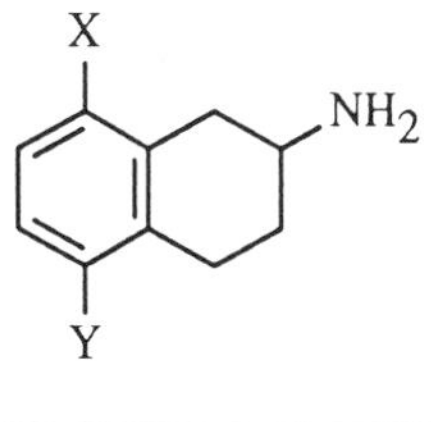

X	Y	EC_{50} (nmol dm^{-3})[a]
H	H	> 30 000
H	OMe	2200
OMe	H	1700
Cl	OMe	230
Me	Me	10 000
OMe	OMe	120
OMe	SMe	12 (47; SK&F 89748)
Methoxamine (13)		720

[a] EC_{50} = 50% of maximum contraction to norepinephrine (4) in rabbit ear artery.

The regression equations (6–8) indicate that increasing steric bulk at the 5-position of these phenyl(imino)imidazolidines decreases the ability of these compounds to stimulate α_2-adrenergic receptors. Apparently, activation of α_2-adrenergic receptors cannot be accomplished when a relatively bulky substituent is present at the 5-position of the phenyl moiety. Subsequent studies showed that such substitution at the 5-position did not affect the ability of these compounds to activate α_1-adrenergic receptors, pointing to a distinct structural difference between α_1- and α_2-adrenergic receptors.[144]

Based on the observations discussed above, that increasing steric dimensions at the 5-position favor α_1-adrenergic receptor agonist activity in phenyl(imino)imidazolidines, St 587 (26), possessing the bulky trifluoromethyl group, was added to the series and found most selective in stimulating α_1-adrenergic receptors.[138] This particular imidazolidine derivative completely lacks agonistic activity at α_2-adrenergic receptors.[138] The combination of α_1-adrenergic receptor agonist selectivity and pronounced lipophilicity has made St 587 (26) a valuable tool in characterizing various α_1-adrenergic receptor populations.

It should be cautioned that although the above-mentioned compounds discriminate as agonists between α_1- and α_2-adrenergic receptors in favor of the former subtype, they are unable to distinguish between both classes as far as (binding) affinity is concerned.[137] As shown in Figure 18, for these selective α_1-adrenergic receptor agonists a highly significant linear relationship can be derived between binding affinity for α_1- and α_2-adrenergic receptors.[137] In fact, cirazoline (49) has been shown to possess potent α_2-adrenergic-receptor-blocking activity.[145]

Recently, the 2,5- and 3,5-dimethoxy-substituted derivatives of tolazoline (50) were reported to produce vasopressor responses that were attenuated by the α_1-adrenergic receptor blocker prazosin (10), but were not affected by the α_2-adrenergic receptor antagonist yohimbine (11), each applied in selective doses.[146] Neither of the tolazoline analogs produced an α_2-adrenergic-receptor-mediated inhibition of neurogenic tachycardia.[146] The data indicate that 2,5- and 3,5-dimethoxytolazoline are highly selective α_1-adrenergic receptor agonists and may be, additionally, useful tools with which to probe α_1-adrenergic receptors.

(50)

12.1.6.6 α_2-Adrenergic Receptor Agonists

A variety of chemical structures are currently available which selectively stimulate pre- and post-synaptic α_2-adrenergic receptors. Originally, B-HT 933 (17; azepexole) was introduced as a centrally acting antihypertensive drug pharmacologically related, but structurally unrelated, to the imidazoli-

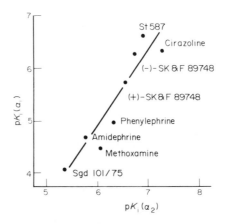

Figure 18 Relationship ($r = 0.93$) between binding affinity for α_1-adrenergic-receptor-like binding sites in rat brain membranes identified by [³H]prazosin, $pK_i(\alpha_1)$, and binding affinity for α_2-adrenergic-receptor-like binding sites characterized by [³H]clonidine, $pK_i(\alpha_2)$, for the currently available selective agonists of α_1-adrenergic receptors (modified after ref. 137)

dine clonidine (**2**).[147] Shortly thereafter B-HT 920 (**25**; alefexole) was reported to share these properties with B-HT 933 at higher potency.[148] It was subsequently found that both B-HT 933 and B-HT 920 were highly selective agonists of α_2-adrenergic receptors, virtually lacking affinity for the α_1-adrenergic receptor subtype.[57,149] B-HT 958 (**51**) is a selective but partial α_2-adrenoceptor agonist of relatively moderate potency.[150] It should be added that B-HT 958, and in particular B-HT 920, exhibit strong D_2-dopamine receptor agonist activity, which complicates their use as selective tools to identify α_2-adrenoceptors.[151]

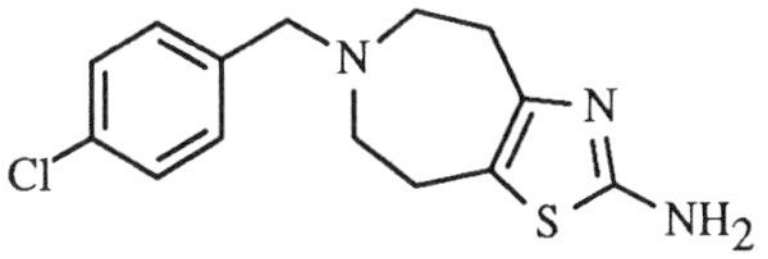

(**51**)

High preference towards stimulation of α_2-adrenergic receptors is further found for UK-14,304 (**45**),[57] xylazine (**37**),[152] TL-99 (**52**),[153] M-7 (**53**),[154] DP-6,7-ADTN (**54**)[155] as well as some *exo* isomers of 2-amino-6,7-dihydroxybenzonorbornene (**55**).[85] It is fair to say that as yet there has been no rationale developed for the design of selective agonists of α_2-adrenergic receptors. All the drugs mentioned in this section have been found accidentally. Consequently, the structure–activity/selectivity relationships are largely unexplored.

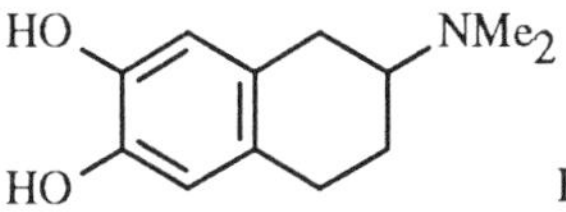

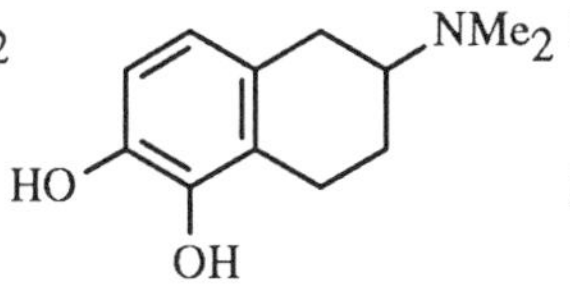

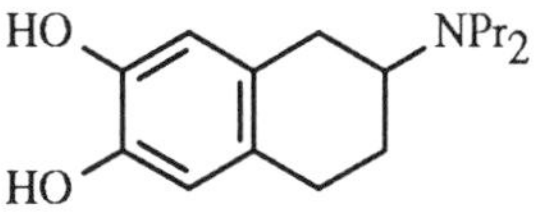

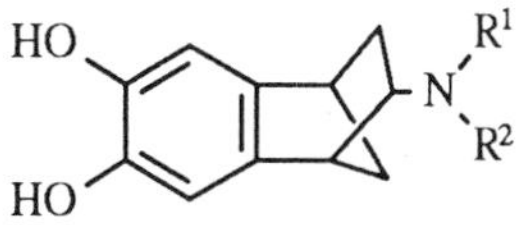

(**52**)   (**53**)   (**54**)   (**55**) R^1, R^2 = H or Me

The experimental data reported for medetomidine (**56**) and MVP 295 (**57**) suggest that they are lipophilic, potent and selective α_2-adrenergic-receptor agonists.[156,157] The veterinary antinociceptive and sedative compound detomidine (**58**) is also α_2-adrenergic-receptor selective and stimulates α_1-adrenergic receptors at higher doses only.[158] Medetomidine (**56**) is undergoing clinical trials as a veterinary sedative/analgesic, where its advantages are expected to be its potency, selectivity and rapid reversibility by subsequent treatment with antagonist. It has been speculated that low doses may be useful in human patients with anxiety and panic attacks.[159]

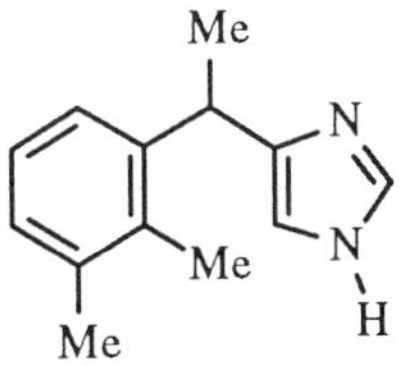

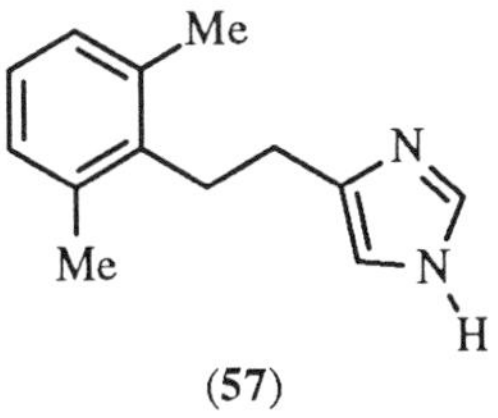

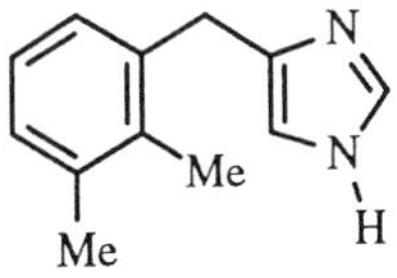

(**56**)   (**57**)   (**58**)

Aganodine (**59**; BDF 7570) has been reported as a very selective α_2-adrenergic receptor agonist with extremely high affinity for this subclass of α-adrenergic receptor in radioligand binding experiments.[160] Interestingly, agonidine does not cross the blood–brain barrier and exerts only peripheral α_2-adrenergic-receptor-stimulating properties.[161]

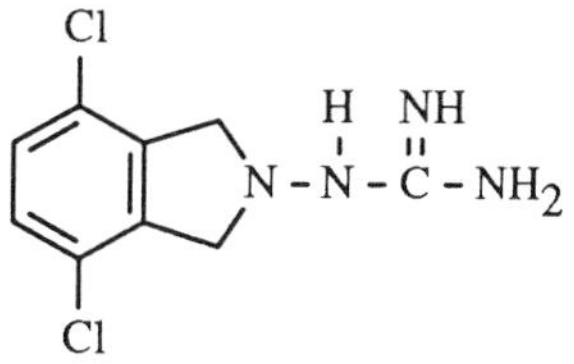

(**59**)

12.1.7 STRUCTURE–ACTIVITY RELATIONSHIPS OF α-ADRENERGIC RECEPTOR ANTAGONISTS

The more classical antagonists of α-adrenergic receptors, tolazoline (**50**), phentolamine (**20**) and piperoxan (**60**), have been recognized as non-selective for either subtype. As a general class, the 2-alkylamino-1,4-benzodioxanes, of which piperoxan (**60**) is one of the oldest representatives,[162] possess affinity for α-adrenergic receptors. This latter agent has remained an important pharmacological tool, being a competitive antagonist of α₁- and α₂-adrenergic receptors with a slight preference for the α_2 subtype.[163–165] Substitution of the benzodioxane nucleus with 6-methyl or 7-chloro decreased the affinity for both α₁- and α₂-adrenergic receptors by about tenfold.[166] Introduction of a methoxy substituent at the chiral 2-position caused a dramatic loss of affinity for both α-adrenergic receptor subtypes.[167]

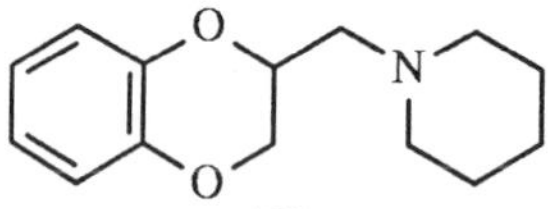

(60)

Phentolamine (**20**) is a potent and competitive, but also non-selective, antagonist of α-adrenergic receptors.[163–165] It appears that in a 2-(aminomethyl)imidazoline series, arylcyclohexyl or diaryl substitution on nitrogen produces non-selective α-adrenergic receptor antagonists.[168] Although monoaryl derivatives generally appear to be α₁-adrenergic receptor agonists, activity at the α₂-adrenergic receptor is more difficult to predict. For example, 3-hydroxyl and 2-chloro substituents produced α₂-adrenergic receptor agonists, whereas the corresponding 4-methyl derivative is an α₂-adrenergic receptor antagonist.[168]

Phenoxybenzamine (**61**), like related β-haloalkylamines, impairs responses induced by stimulation of α-adrenergic receptors as well as of several other receptor types. It has been suggested that phenoxybenzamine acts by directly alkylating the receptor site.[169] Numerous studies *in vivo* and *in vitro* have since shown that phenoxybenzamine is more potent in inactivating α₁- than α₂-adrenergic receptors.[164,170,171] Although phenoxybenzamine is considered α₁-adrenergic-receptor selective, its selectivity is less pronounced than that of, for example, prazosin (**10**).

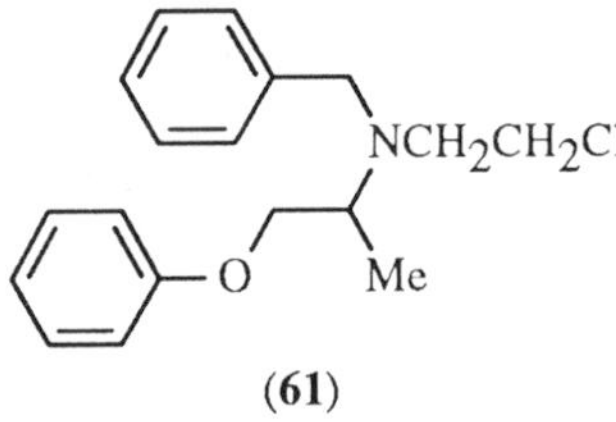

(61)

The irreversible non-selective α-adrenergic receptor antagonist benextramine (**62**) is thought to react with α-adrenergic receptors by a disulfide interchange reaction with sulfhydryl groups on the receptors.[172,173] Its mechanism of action is different from that of phenoxybenzamine.[173]

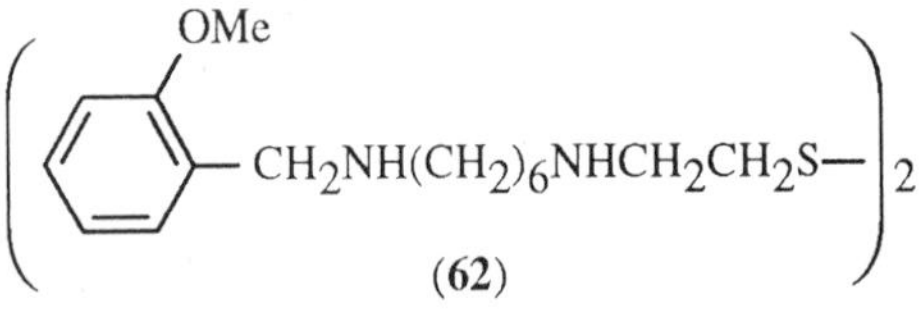

(62)

More recently, the substituted 2-(phenylimino)imidazolidine, FR 35447 (**63**), has been reported to block pre- and post-synaptic α₁- and α₂-adrenergic receptors with a potency and selectivity comparable to phentolamine (**20**).[174]

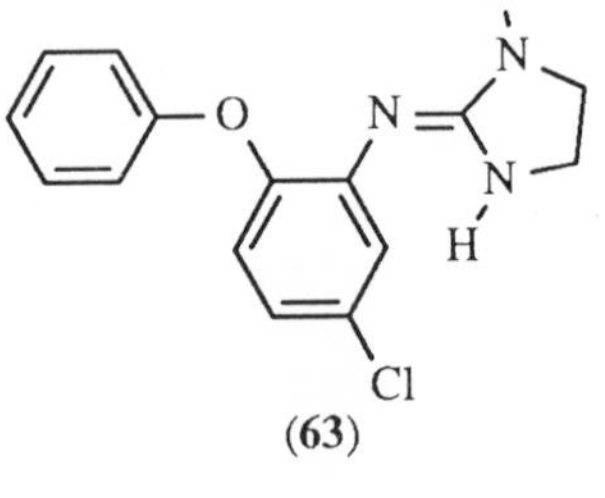

(63)

12.1.7.1 α₁-Adrenergic Receptor Antagonists

A variety of structures show blocking selectivity towards α₁-adrenergic receptors. The anti-hypertensive agent prazosin (**10**) is, to date, the α₁-adrenergic receptor antagonist possessing the highest potency as well as selectivity.[164,165,175] In addition, corynanthine (**21**), a diastereoisomer of the α₂-adrenergic-receptor-selective blocker yohimbine (**11**), an indole alkaloid, selectively interferes with α₁-adrenergic receptors.[164,165,176,177]

The basic structure of prazosin has been a lead for other selective α₁-adrenergic receptor antagonists, such as terazosin (**64**), doxazosin (**65**) and trimazosin (**66**).[175] The onset of the antihypertensive activity and the elimination half-life of doxazosin is longer than that of prazosin.[178] Trimazosin clearly has lower affinity for α₁-adrenergic receptors than prazosin, but it also blocks phosphodiesterase, thus enhancing its potency as an antihypertensive agent.[179] Other quinazoline derivatives, such as UK-18,596 (**67**)[180] or H3088 (**68**),[181] bunazosin (**69**)[182] and alfuzosin (**70**)[183] preferentially interact with α₁-adrenergic receptors with varying degrees of affinity.

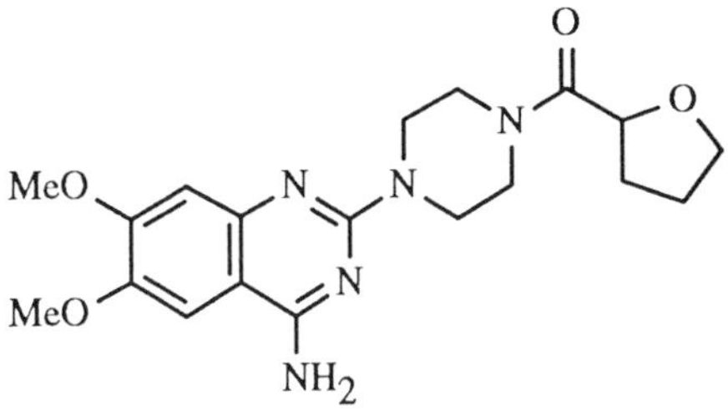

(**64**)

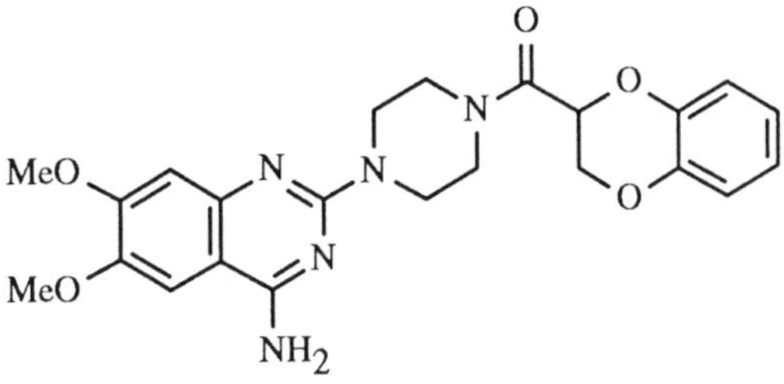

(**65**)

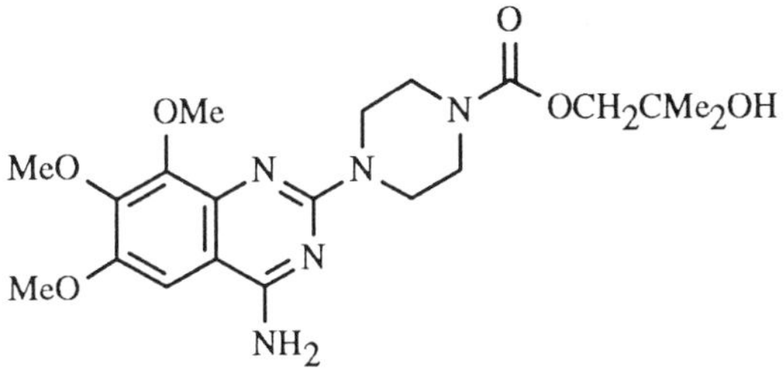

(**66**)

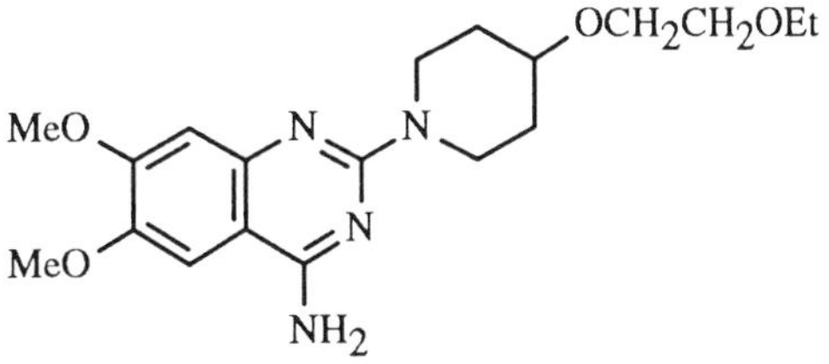

(**67**)

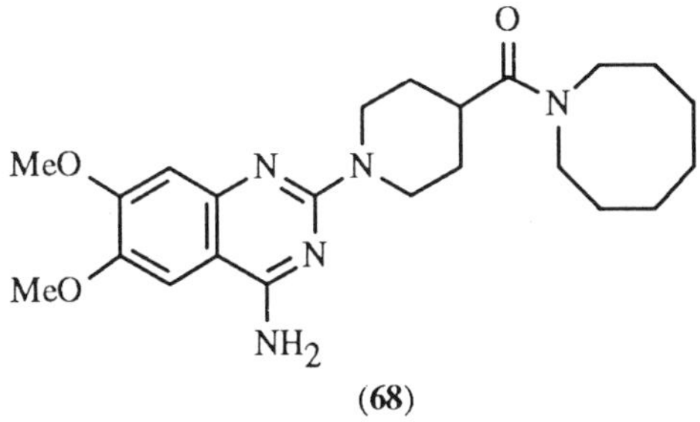

(**68**)

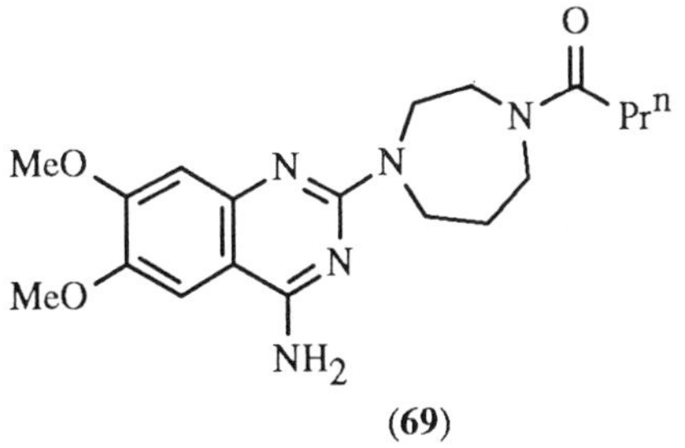

(**69**)

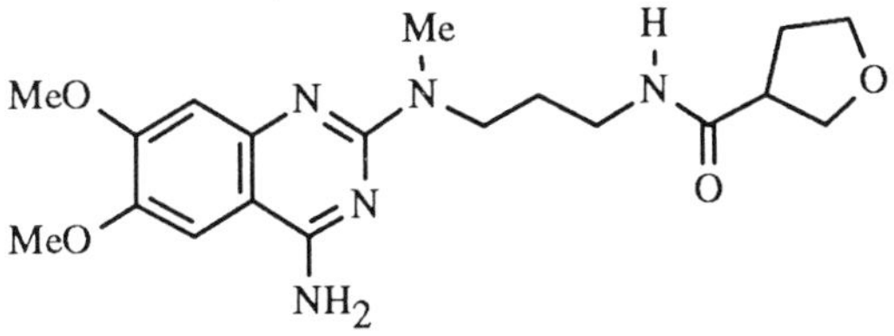

(**70**)

Prazosin-like quinazolines are weak bases that accept a proton at N-1. The presence of the 4-amino group is very important for its α₁-adrenergic receptor affinity. Upon replacement of the 4-amino by a 4-methyl group, affinity is lost (a personal observation by the authors). Requirements for high α₁-adrenergic receptor affinity appear to be a positive charge and appropriate bulk/lipophilicity at opposite sides of this charge. The furoylpiperazine moiety in prazosin (**10**) can be replaced by a piperidine group having various substituents, without loss of affinity. However, the nature of the substituent profoundly affects the duration of action *in vivo*.[184]

It was found that substitution of aralkyl groups at the nitrogen atom of phenethanolamines led to β-adrenergic receptor antagonists with additional α_1-adrenergic-receptor-blocking activity.[185,186] For example, labetalol (71) has been shown to exert a non-selective β-adrenergic and a selective α_1-adrenergic receptor blockade.[187,188] More recently, a series of arylethanolamines derived from benzenesulfonamide were shown to possess α- and β-adrenergic-receptor-blocking activities.[189] However, these analogs, such as amosulalol (72), differ from labetalol in the ratio of their α- to β-adrenergic-receptor-blocking effect, being more potent at α_1-adrenergic receptors while labetalol is more potent at β_1-adrenergic receptors.[190]

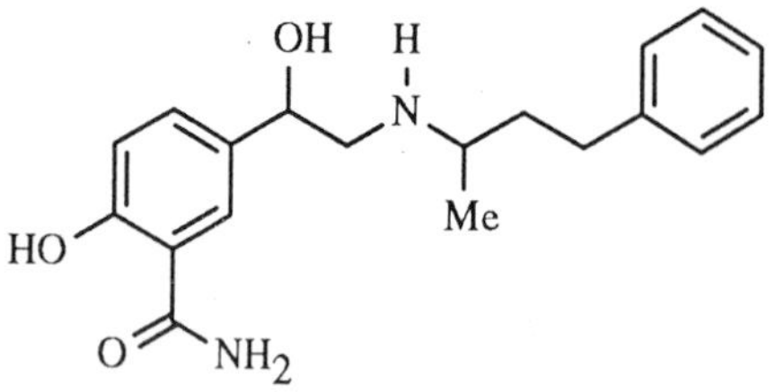

(71) 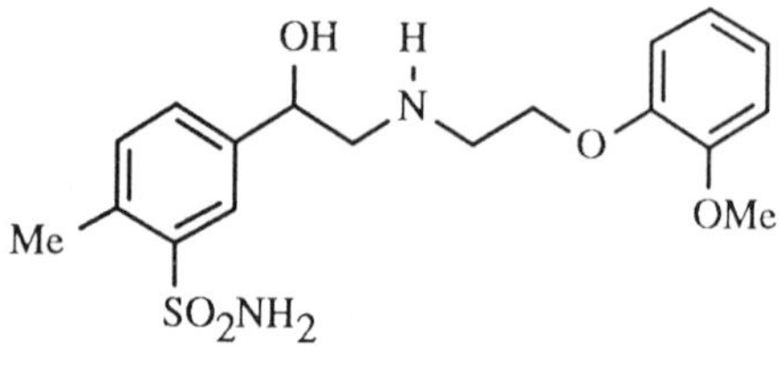   (72)

Benzodioxanes represent one of the oldest groups of competitive antagonists of α_1-adrenergic receptors.[162] WB 4101 (18) is the best-known example. In WB 4101-like molecules a di*ortho* substitution with methoxy groups yields high affinity for α_1-adrenergic receptors.[166,191] Replacement by methyl groups decreases affinity to the level of the non-methoxylated molecule. Repositioning of a methoxy group to the *meta* or *para* position reduces potency, but introduction of an hydroxyl functionality increases potency. The oxygen atom in the side chain does not appear to be essential for affinity, although the distance between the benzodioxane and the 2,6-dimethoxyphenyl nuclei is important. The benzodioxane moiety itself may not be critical for high affinity either,[192] and substitution of the oxygen at the 4-position in this ring system with a sulfur has recently yielded a more potent and selective α_1-adrenergic receptor antagonist.[193] The importance of the secondary amino structure in the side chain is emphasized by the dramatic loss of affinity for α_1-adrenergic receptors upon alkylation.[166]

A number of substituted phenylpiperazines have been reported to possess antihypertensive activity in which blockade of vascular postsynaptic α_1-adrenergic receptors presumably plays a major role. Urapidil (73) is an effective hypotensive agent and as such its mechanism of action is thought to involve antagonism of α_1-adrenergic receptors as well a stimulation of presynaptic and central α_2-adrenergic receptors.[194,195] However, the (minor) central hypotensive action of urapidil is not blocked by yohimbine.[196] In fact, the ability of urapidil to stimulate α_2-adrenergic receptors has been refuted.[197]

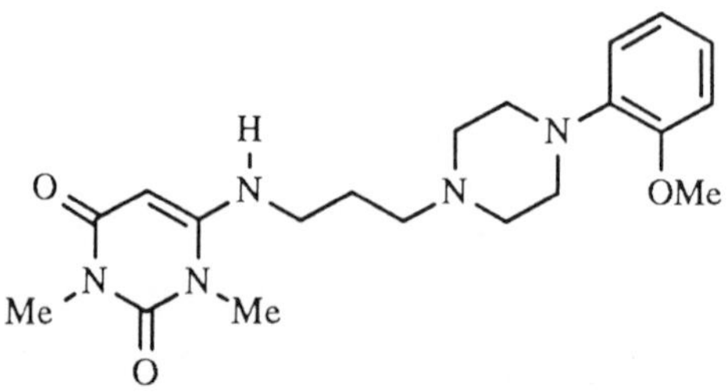

(73)

The phenylpiperazine derivatives AR-C 239 (74) and SGD-1534 (75) have long-lasting antihypertensive effects when given orally.[198,199] Both agents possess a peripheral α_1-adrenergic-receptor-blocking action which is presumably responsible for their blood-pressure-lowering effect.[200] SGD-1534 has been advocated to be more potent and more selective in blocking postsynaptic α_1-adrenergic receptors than α_2-adrenergic receptors when compared to prazosin (10).[201]

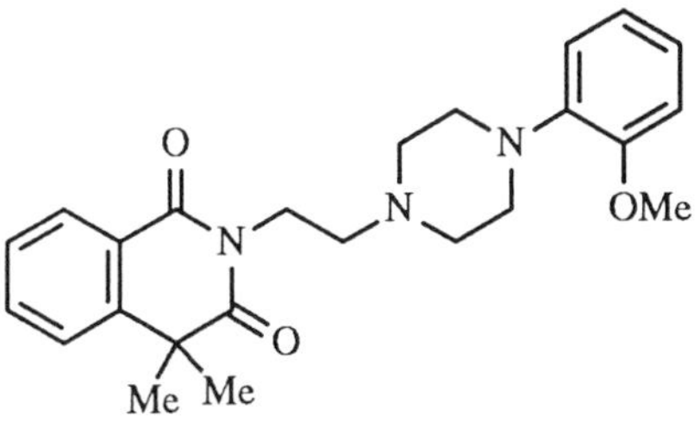

(74)

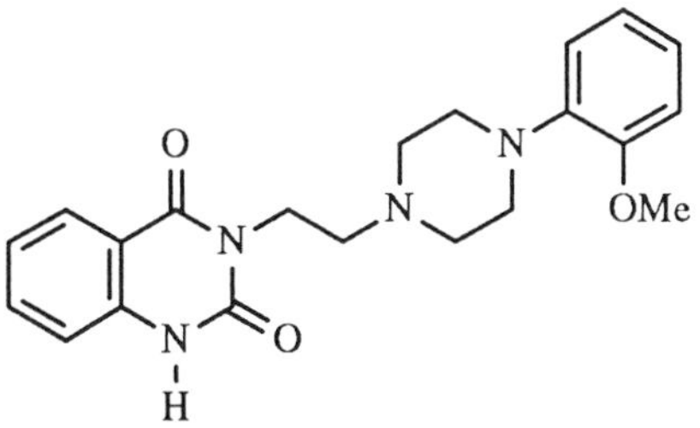

(75)

CI-926 (**76**) is a new orally effective antihypertensive agent in several animal models of hypertension.[202] The profile of CI-926 suggests that its antihypertensive effect is due to blockade of α_1-adrenergic receptors, but that interaction at other receptors may also contribute to this activity.

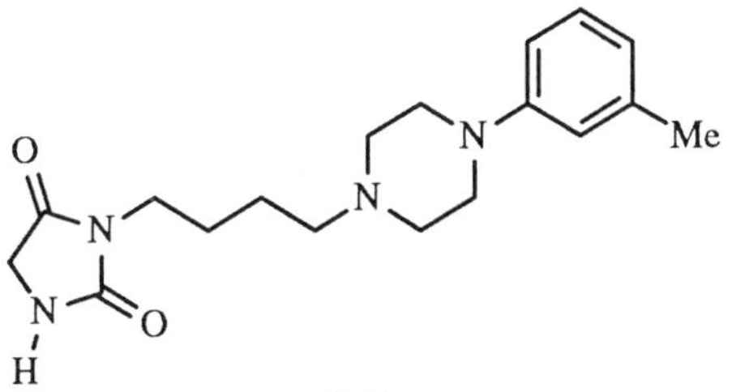

(76)

Finally, some miscellaneous structures are worth mentioning. By virtually lacking affinity for α_2-adrenergic receptors they exert selective blockade of the α_1 subtype, although they also possess other properties. Tibalosine (**77**) has been reported to lower arterial pressure mainly by selective interference with vascular α_1-adrenergic receptors.[203] However, a central mode of action has also been suggested for this compound.[204] Although ketanserin (**78**) is a most selective serotonin (5-HT$_2$) receptor antagonist,[205] it also exhibits significant selective affinity for α_1-adrenergic receptors.[206,207] BE 2254 (**79**; HEAT) and some of its derivatives act as rather selective antagonists of postsynaptic α_1-adrenergic receptors.[208] [^{125}I]BE 2254 proved to be a very useful radioligand for α_1-adrenergic receptors.[209] Indoramin (**80**) is a clinically effective antihypertensive agent; it selectively interferes with vascular α_1-adrenergic receptors and possesses a myocardial-membrane-stabilizing effect.[210]

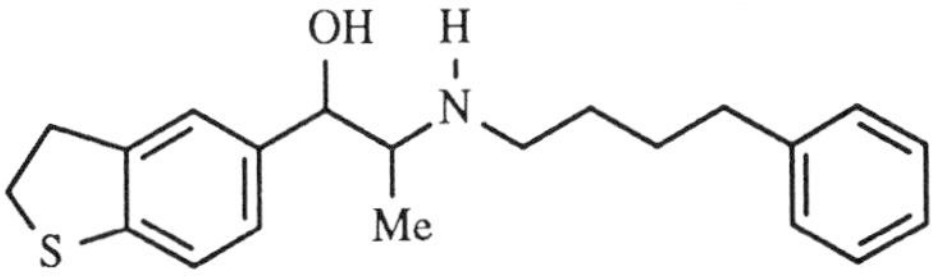

(77)

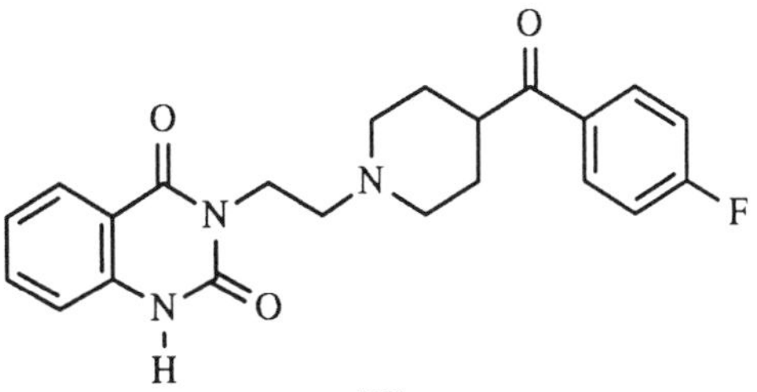

(78)

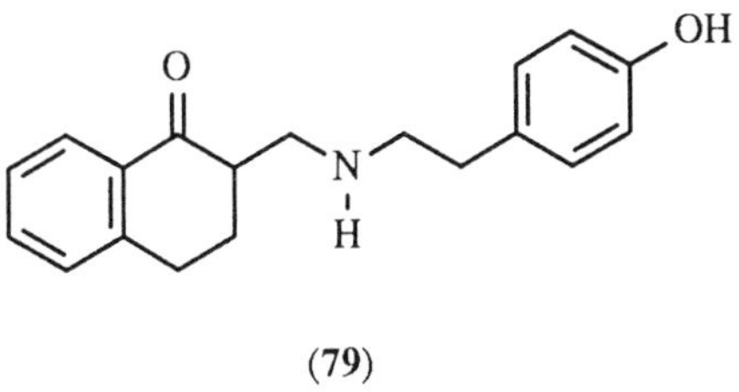

(79)

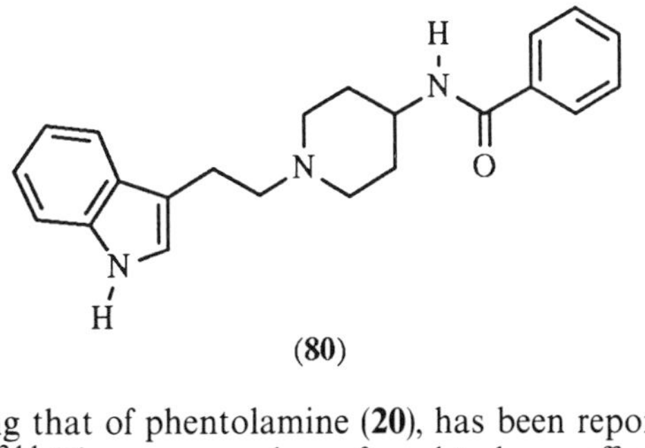

(80)

α-Adrenergic-receptor-blocking activity, exceeding that of phentolamine (**20**), has been reported for the benzimidazolinone derivative, KF-4307 (**81**).[211] The compound was found to be an effective orally active antihypertensive agent, possibly mediating its effect through antagonism of vascular α_1-adrenergic receptors. In addition, a CNS component contributing to the cardiovascular effects of

KF-4307 has been suggested. Interestingly, the methoxy analog, KF-4942 (**82**), did not produce a centrally mediated hypotensive response and also lacked affinity for presynaptic α_2-adrenergic receptors.[212] Thus KF-4942 was concluded to be an agent with properties similar to prazosin (**10**). The pronounced hypotensive effect of R 28935, the racemic mixture of the benzimidazolone (**83**), is of CNS origin and stereospecific, since the *threo* form, R 28914 (**84**), is much less potent.[213] Although central α_1-adrenergic receptors have been suggested as playing a role in the mechanism of action of R 28935, it lacks α_1-adrenergic-receptor-stimulatory activity and its affinity for this α-adrenergic receptor type is but moderate.[213]

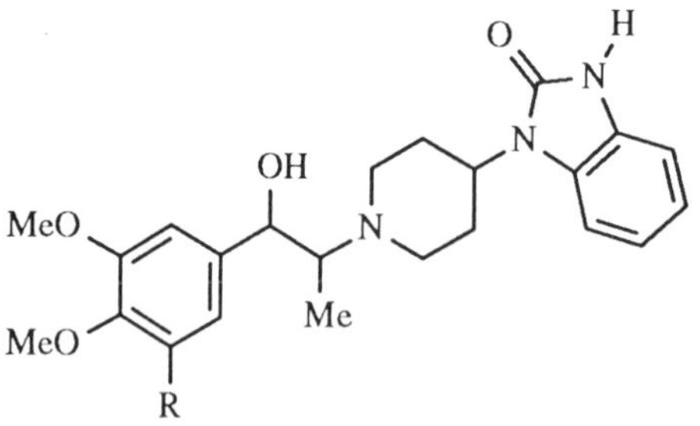

(**81**) R = H
(**82**) R = OMe

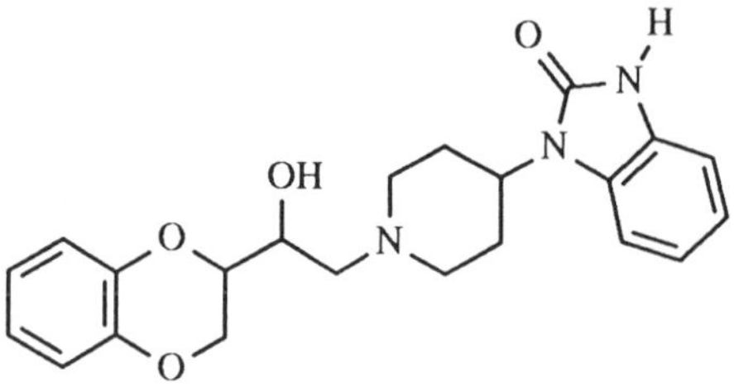

(**83**) *Erythro* = R 28935
(**84**) *Threo* = R 28914

12.1.7.2 α_2-Adrenergic Receptor Antagonists

Numerous structurally different compounds have been identified and designed as selective antagonists of α_2-adrenergic receptors. The indole alkaloid yohimbine (**11**) preferentially antagonizes α_2-adrenergic receptors and has long been of considerable interest as a pharmacological tool.[164,165,176,177] The pharmacology of yohimbine in relation to the physiology of α_2-adrenergic receptors has been reviewed in detail.[214] The diastereoisomer rauwolscine (**12**; α-yohimbine) shows even greater selectivity for α_2-adrenergic receptors.[164,165,176,177]

Studies concerning the structure–affinity relationships for yohimbine and related diastereoisomers suggest that the indole nucleus, the nitrogen atom N-4, and the carbomethoxy substituent at C-16 constitute the critical binding sites at α-adrenergic receptors and that planarity of rings A, B, C and D are a prerequisite for α-adrenergic receptor affinity.[215–217] In addition, those compounds in which the carbomethoxy group lies in the plane of the aromatic nucleus and N-4, as in yohimbine (**11**) and rauwolscine (**12**) (Figure 19), exhibit a preference for α_2-adrenergic receptors.[216] In the case of corynanthine (**21**), on the other hand, the β-oriented ester substituent cannot achieve coplanarity with the two other postulated binding sites (Figure 19) and selectivity for α_1-adrenergic receptors results.[216] Deletion of the C-17 hydroxy substituent in yohimbine has been found to cause no significant change in affinity for α_2-adrenergic receptors, but substantially increased the affinity for α_1-adrenergic receptors.[218] Epimerization at this position to give β-yohimbine, on the other hand, has relatively minor effects on the affinity for either α_1- or α_2-adrenergic receptors.[219]

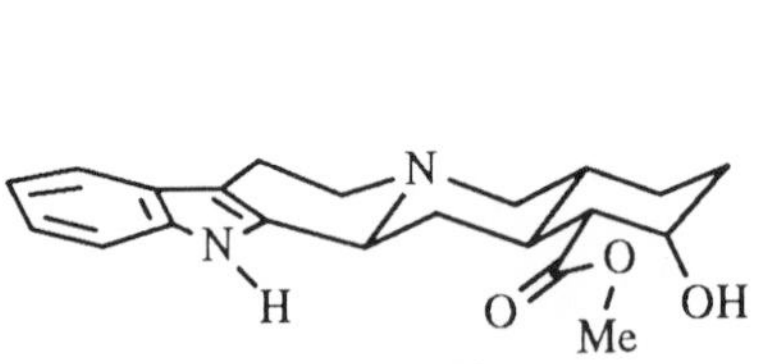

(**11**) Yohimbine

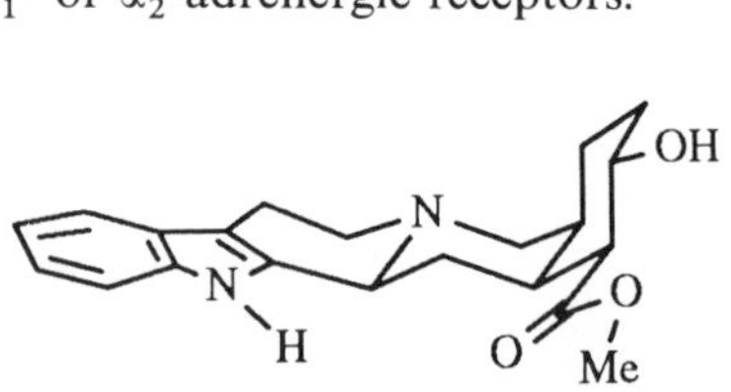

(**12**) Rauwolscine

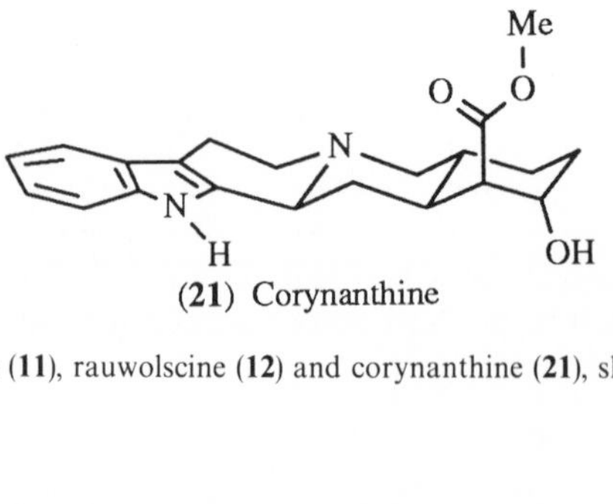

(**21**) Corynanthine

Figure 19   Structures of yohimbine (**11**), rauwolscine (**12**) and corynanthine (**21**), showing the different configurations

Yohimbine and (dia)stereoisomers also possess significant serotonergic-blocking properties.[214,220] This is most likely due to the indolamine substructure which is shared by serotonin. In fact, the potency order of the yohimbine diastereoisomers as α_2-adrenergic receptor antagonists closely resembles that as serotonin receptor antagonists.[164,217]

The rationale behind the design of idazoxan (**22**) has been to improve the affinity of the weak α_2-adrenergic receptor blocker fenmetazole (**85**)[221] by combining its structural features with those of the potent but non-selective α-adrenergic receptor antagonist piperoxan (**60**).[222] Idazoxan is currently recognized as one of the most potent and selective α_2-adrenergic receptor antagonists (see Table 5).[223,224] The discovery of idazoxan has led to the synthesis and pharmacological evaluation of a large number of derivatives. It was found that even minor modifications of the benzodioxane–imidazoline structure could greatly reduce α_2-adrenergic-receptor-blocking activity and could also dramatically change the α_2/α_1 selectivity profile.[222] More recently, the observation has been made that the selectivity and potency of this class of compounds is markedly enhanced by certain substituents located at the 2-position of the benzodioxane ring.[225] Table 5 lists some selected examples. Similar structure–activity relationships apply to the congeneric dihydrobenzofuran series.[226]

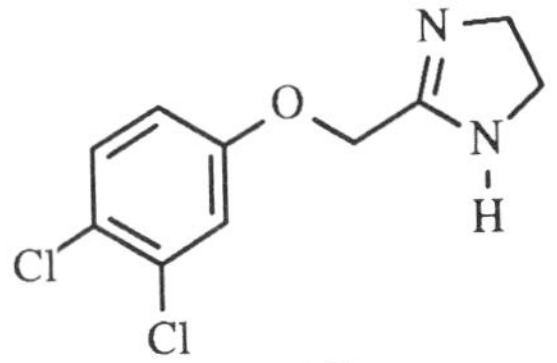

(85)

Although imiloxan (**86**) is 30 to 100 times less potent than idazoxan, it shows a high degree of selectivity in blocking α_2-adrenergic receptors.[224,227] Imiloxan turned out to be the most selective compound from a large series of 1-alkylimidazoles.[228] Several members of a series of 1-(2-pyridinyl)piperazines were found to be potent and selective antagonists of α_2-adrenergic receptors. In various assays, the 3-fluoro analog (**87**) showed enhanced or comparable potency and selectivity when compared with rauwolscine (**12**).[229] BDF 6143 (**88**) represents another chemical entity possessing preference for antagonizing α_2-adrenergic-receptor-mediated effects.[230] Although BDF 6143 is a potent α_2-adrenergic receptor antagonist, it can also act as a (partial) α_1-adrenergic receptor agonist.[231]

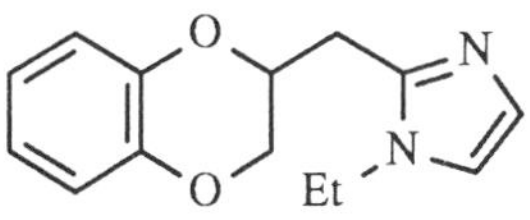

(86) 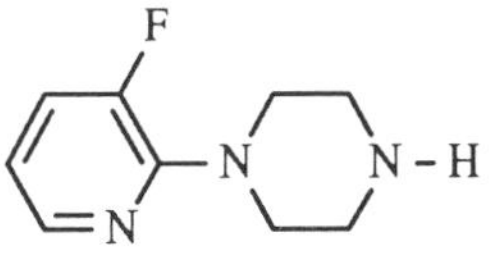   (87) 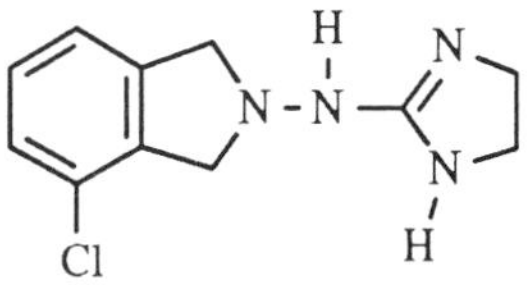   (88)

Extreme α_2-adrenergic-receptor-blocking selectivity has been identified for some benzoquinolizines, such as Wy 25309 (**89**), Wy 26392 (**90**) and Wy 26703 (**91**), exceeding that of yohimbine (**11**).[232,233] It may be added that these benzoquinolizines, like yohimbine (see above), also antagonize serotonergic receptors.[234] The benzofuroquinolizine L-654,284 (**92**) is also a highly potent and selective antagonist of α_2-adrenergic receptors.[235] When tested in several *in vivo* and *in vitro* models for α_2-adrenergic receptor antagonist activity and compared to several reference agents, L-654,284 was generally a more potent α_2-adrenergic receptor antagonist than idazoxan (**22**) with comparable α_2/α_1 selectivity and was several times more potent and α_2-selective than Wy 26703 or yohimbine. In addition, L-654,284 showed better oral bioavailability than idazoxan or Wy 26703.[235] Results of minimum energy conformation calculations and consideration of the potential hydrogen-bond-accepting properties of the sulfonyl oxygens in L-654,284 have led to the suggestion that spirocyclic compounds such as (**93**) would show improved affinity for the α_2-adrenergic receptor.[236] L-657,743 (**93**; $n = 2$) is reported to have considerably higher α_2-adrenergic receptor antagonist potency, α_2/α_1-adrenergic-receptor-blocking selectivity and α_2-adrenoceptor specificity (*i.e. vs.* dopaminergic and serotonergic receptors) than yohimbine.[237]

Table 5 α-Adrenergic Receptor Selectivity Ratios of
Idazoxan (**22**) and some Derivatives

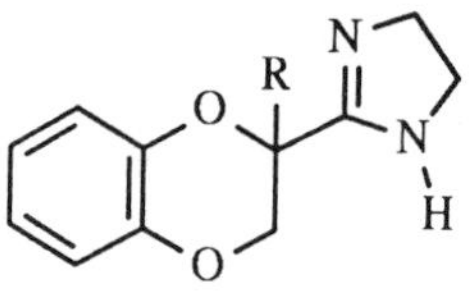

R	α_2/α_1[a]	
	In vitro[b]	*In vivo*[c]
H (**22**; idazoxan)	151	58
Me	457	127
Et	195	131
Pr^n	229	90
Isopropenyl	617	120
OMe	316	—
OEt	151	—
Yohimbine (**11**)	50	22

[a] Antilogarithm of the difference between pA_2 values. [b] α_2 = pA_2 *vs.* UK-14,304 (**45**), rat vas deferens; α_1 = pA_2 *vs.* noradrenaline (**4**), rat anococcygeus muscle. [c] α_2 = twofold shift *vs.* UK-14,304 (**45**), pithed rat, cardiac presynaptic; α_1 = twofold shift *vs.* cirazoline (**49**), pithed rat, vascular postsynaptic.

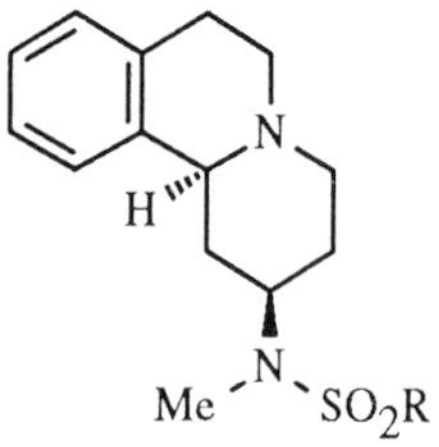

(**89**) R = isobutyl
(**90**) R = *n*-propyl
(**91**) R = methyl

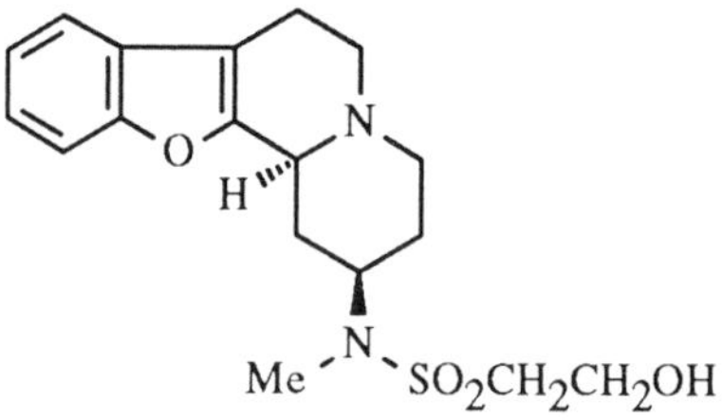

(**92**)

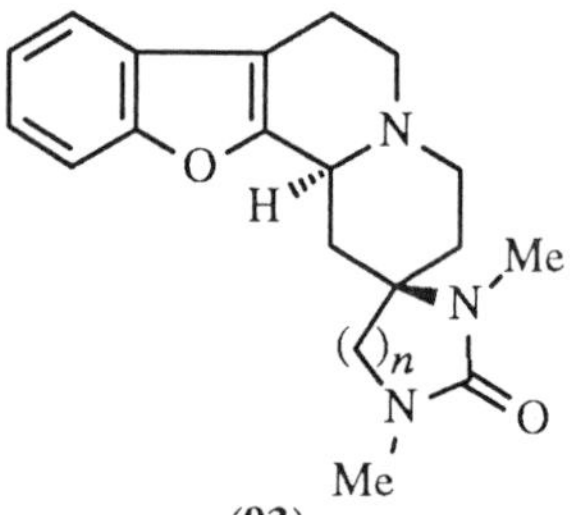

(**93**)

The selectivity and specificity of CH-38083 (**94**) for α-adrenergic receptors have been studied and compared with those of yohimbine and idazoxan in peripheral tissues and in the CNS.[238] The results obtained classify CH-38083 as a potent and highly selective antagonist of both peripheral and central α$_2$-adrenergic receptors. Unlike yohimbine and some other α$_2$-adrenergic receptor antagonists (see above), CH-38083 lacks affinity for serotonergic receptors.[238]

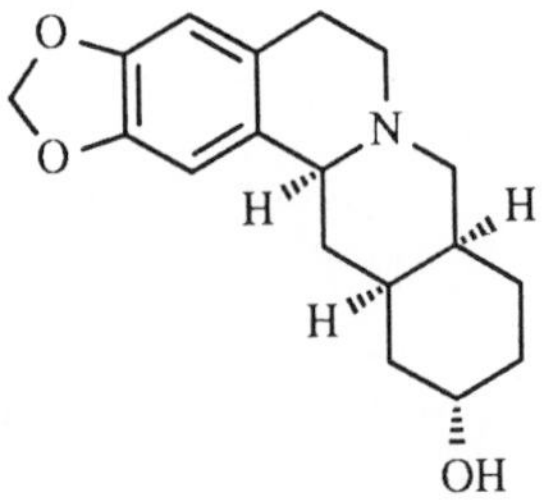

(**94**)

Midaglizole (**95**; DG-5128) was first shown to be an orally effective hypoglycemic and insulin secretagog *in vitro* and *in vivo*, based on antagonism of α$_2$-adrenergic receptors.[239] Subsequently, midaglizole was shown to be a selective α$_2$-adrenergic receptor antagonist, although with relatively low affinity.[240,241] Recently, midaglizole has been found to be clinically effective for non-insulin-dependent diabetes mellitus.[242]

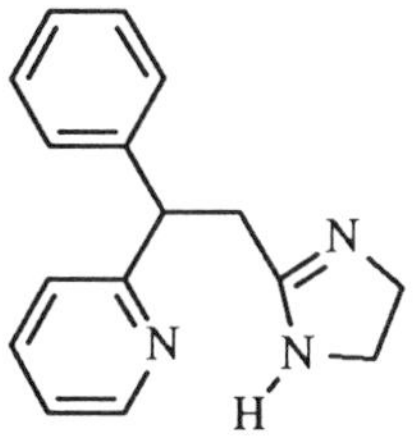

(95)

Examination of three chemical classes of cyclized phenethylamines, the 2-aminoindans, tetra-hydroisoquinolines and 3-benzazepines, showed that all three classes had affinity for the α_2-adrenergic receptor, and that chlorine substitution enhanced α_2-adrenergic receptor affinity by at least an order of magnitude (see Table 6).[243] The chlorinated benzazepine SK & F 86466 (96) in particular showed a high preference for antagonizing α_2-adrenergic-receptor-mediated effects and has been used successfully as a tool for identifying α_2-adrenergic receptors.[244]

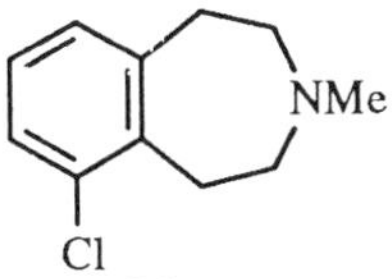

(96)

Very recently, two derivatives of SK & F 86466 bearing an alkenyloxy substituent in the 9-position were reported to possess enhanced affinity for postsynaptic α_2-adrenergic receptors over presynaptic α_2-adrenergic receptors.[245] As illustrated by Table 7, 9-substitution enhances the affinity of SK & F 86466 for both central and peripheral α_1-adrenergic receptors. Postjunctional α_2-adrenergic receptor affinity is essentially unaffected, while the affinity for the prejunctional neuroinhibitory α_2-adrenergic receptor is markedly decreased. Hence, a compound such as SK & F 104078 (24) has selective agonist activity at post- (α_1 and α_2) vs. pre-junctional (α_2) α-adrenergic receptors.[245]

12.1.8 PHYSIOLOGY AND PHARMACOLOGY OF α-ADRENERGIC RECEPTORS IN ANIMALS AND MAN

Table 1 displays the occurrence of α_1- and α_2-adrenergic receptors in various organ systems and summarizes the physiological consequences of stimulation or antagonism (see Section 12.1.5.3). In the present section, the physiology and pharmacology of α-adrenergic receptors is reviewed. For

Table 6 Affinity for α-Adrenergic Receptors of some Cyclized Phenethylamines (i–iv)[238]

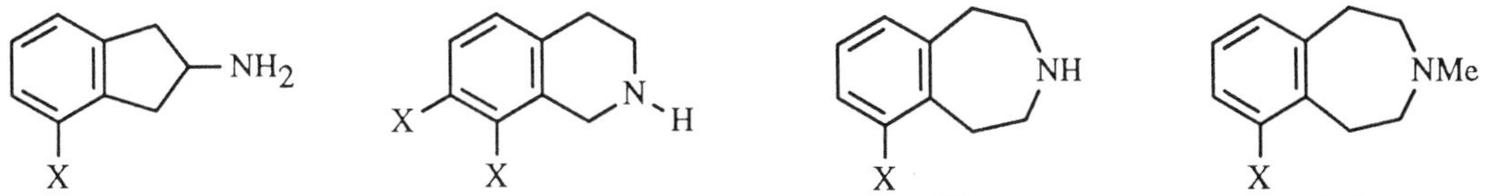

(i)   (ii)   (iii)   (iv)

| | K_B (nmol dm^{-3})^a | | | | | | | |
| | (i) | | (ii) | | (iii) | | (iv) | |
X	α_1	α_2	α_1	α_2	α_1	α_2	α_1	α_2
H	—	>3000	—	3100	16 500	100	—	—
Cl	7500	350	6000	380	730	18	900	17
							(96; SK&F 86466)	

^{a} $K_B(\alpha_1)$: vs. norepinephrine-induced contraction (rabbit ear artery); $K_B(\alpha_2)$: vs. B-HT 920-induced inhibition (guinea pig atrium).

Table 7 Affinity for α-Adrenergic Receptors of 9-Alkenyloxy Derivatives of SK&F 86466 (**96**)[240]

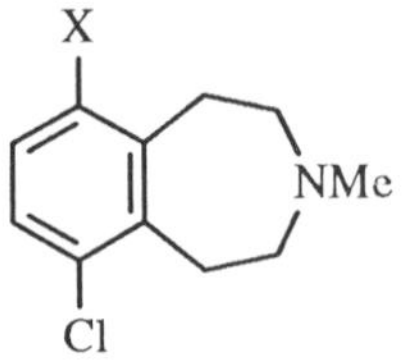

	X	α_1 (nmol dm^{-3})		α_2 (nmol dm^{-3})	
		$K_B{}^a$	$K_i{}^b$	$K_B(pre)^c$	$K_B(post)^d$
SK & F 86466 (**96**)	H	600	432	17	42
SK & F 101253	—OCH$_2$CH=CH$_2$	150	146	900	54
SK & F 104078 (**24**)	—OCH$_2$CH=CMe$_2$	155	157	>10 000	76

[a] *Vs.* norepinephrine-induced contractions (rabbit aorta). [b] Inhibition of [^{3}H]prazosin (**10**) binding (brain membranes). [c] *Vs.* B-HT 920-induced inhibition (guinea pig atrium). [d] *Vs.* B-HT 920-induced contraction (dog saphenous vein).

easy reference, Table 8 summarizes the drugs dealt with in this chapter, their selectivity for α_1- or α_2-adrenergic receptor subtypes and their use or currently projected use as therapeutic agents. In addition, all compounds which are currently not under development as therapeutic agents, but may be used as research tools, are included in Table 8.

The regulation of cardiovascular function by α-adrenergic receptors takes place at various levels, *i.e.* arterial, venous, cardiac, central and peripheral autonomic nervous system and renal. The interplay between these levels allows for fine-tuned regulatory mechanisms, which will be dealt with separately in this section.

12.1.8.1 Peripheral Arterial α-Adrenergic Receptors

As described in Section 12.1.4, α_1- as well as α_2-adrenergic receptors are located on the vascular smooth muscle cell membranes, where, upon stimulation by appropriate agonists, they mediate vasoconstriction. The occurrence of α_1/α_2-adrenergic receptors throughout the arterial vascular bed is not uniform. Table 9 summarizes which α-adrenergic receptor subtype mediates vasoconstriction in different vascular beds from different mammalian species.

The simultaneous occurrence of both receptor subtypes on vascular smooth muscle makes it conceivable that α_1- as well as α_2-adrenergic receptors can contribute to the maintenance of peripheral arterial tone and may play a role in the increased peripheral resistance seen in hypertension. In about one-third of patients with essential hypertension, plasma epinephrine concentrations (a more attractive marker for human peripheral sympathetic activity[246]) were found to be elevated over normotensive controls at rest and during stress.[246] It may be perceived that elevated plasma epinephrine concentrations may contribute to elevated peripheral resistance in essential hypertension indirectly through facilitation of norepinephrine release *via* stimulation of prejunctional β_2-adrenergic receptors (see Section 12.1.2.6) and directly through stimulation of postjunctional α_1- and α_2-adrenergic receptors. Drugs acting as selective antagonists at vascular postjunctional α_1-adrenergic receptors are now frequently used in the therapy of high blood pressure, prazosin (**10**) being the most common drug. Selective blockade of peripheral vascular α_1-adrenergic receptors leads to an effective antihypertensive action with a decrease in peripheral resistance that is not accompanied by reflex tachycardia.[247] However, the possibility of orthostatic hypotension after the onset of prazosin therapy (first dose effect) must be recognized.[247] The effectiveness of prazosin in the chronic therapy of hypertension may partly be due to its lack of affinity for α_2-adrenergic receptors: blockade of presynaptic α_2-adrenergic receptors could increase the neuronal release of norepinephrine and thus counteract the vasodilatation and facilitate tachycardia.[248]

In contrast to α_1-adrenergic receptors, postjunctional vascular α_2-adrenergic receptors have not been established yet as a target for antihypertensive therapy. There is some evidence suggestive of a role for postjunctional vascular α_2-adrenergic receptors in the pathogenesis and maintenance of

Table 8 Drugs in Current Use as Agonists or Antagonists at α-Adrenergic Receptors

Compound	Selectivity	Therapeutic use	Projected use	Structure
Agonists				
Epinephrine	α_1/α_2	Vasoconstrictor		(8)
Norepinephrine	α_1/α_2	Vasoconstrictor		(4)
α-MethylDOPA (α-methyl-norepinephrine)	$\alpha_2 > \alpha_1$	Centrally acting anti-hypertensive		(1/15)
Clonidine	α_1/α_2	Centrally acting anti-hypertensive, anti-withdrawal agent	Stimulation of growth hormone	(2)
Guanfacine	α_1/α_2	Centrally acting anti-hypertensive		(3)
Azepexole	α_2		Centrally acting antihyper-tensive, ocular hypotensive	(17)
Alefexole	α_2			(25)
Lofexidine	α_1/α_2		Antiwithdrawal agent	(40)
Xylazine	$\alpha_2 > \alpha_1$	Veterinary tranquillizer		(37)
Guanabenz	$\alpha_2 > \alpha_1$	Centrally acting anti-hypertensive		(41)
Rilmenidine	$\alpha_2 > \alpha_1$	Centrally acting anti-hypertensive		(44)
UK-14,304	α_2			(45)
Phenylephrine	α_1	Vasoconstrictor		(14)
Methoxamine	α_1			(13)
Cirazoline	α_1			(49)
Tramazoline	α_1/α_2	Decongestant		(16)
Oxymetazoline	α_1/α_2	Decongestant		(19)
Xylometazoline	α_1/α_2	Decongestant		(32)
Tetrahydrozoline	α_1/α_2	Vasoconstrictor		(33)
Naphazoline	α_1/α_2	Decongestant		(28)
Amidephrine	α_1			(27)
St 587	α_1			(26)
Indanidine	α_1			(48)
SK&F 89748	α_1			(47)
Tiamenidine	α_1/α_2			(42)
Moxonidine	α_1/α_2		Antihypertensive	(46)
TL-99	α_2			(52)
M-7	α_2			(53)
DP-6,7-ADTN	α_2			(54)
Medetomidine	α_2		Veterinary sedative anxiolytic	(56)
MVP 295	α_2			(57)
Detomidine	α_2	Veterinary sedative		(58)
44-549	α_1/α_2			(34)
ICI 106270	α_1/α_2			(35)
Bay c 6014	α_1/α_2			(36)
M 6434	$\alpha_1 > \alpha_2$			(38)
Aganodine	α_2			(59)
Antagonists				
Tolazoline	α_1/α_2			(50)
Phentolamine	α_1/α_2	Antihypertensive		(20)
Piperoxan	α_1/α_2			(60)
Phenoxybenzamine	$\alpha_1 > \alpha_2$	Antihypertensive		(61)
Benextramine	α_1/α_2			(62)
FR 35447	α_1/α_2			(63)
Prazosin	α_1	Antihypertensive		(10)
Terazosin	α_1	Antihypertensive		(64)
Doxazosin	α_1	Antihypertensive		(65)
Trimazosin	α_1	Antihypertensive		(66)
Bunazosin	α_1		Antihypertensive	(69)
Alfuzosin	α_1		Antihypertensive	(70)
Corynanthine	α_1			(21)
UK-18,596	α_1			(67)
H3088	α_1			(68)
Labetalol	$\alpha_1 (\beta_1/\beta_2)$	Antihypertensive		(71)
Amosulalol	$\alpha_1 (\beta_1/\beta_2)$		Antihypertensive	(72)
WB 4101	α_1			(18)
Urapidil	$\alpha_1 (\beta_1)$	Antihypertensive		(73)
AR-C 239	α_1			(74)
SGD-1534	α_1			(75)

Table 8 (*Contd.*)

Compound	Selectivity	Therapeutic use	Projected use	Structure
CI-926	α_1			(76)
Tibalosine	α_1	Antihypertensive		(77)
Ketanserin	α_1 (5-HT$_2$)		Antihypertensive, antipsychotic	(78)
BE 2254 (HEAT)	α_1			(79)
Indoramin	α_1	Antihypertensive		(80)
Yohimbine	α_2		Antiimpotence	(11)
Rauwolscine	α_2			(12)
Idazoxan	α_2		Antidepressant	(22)
Fenmetazole	α_2			(85)
Imiloxan	α_2			(86)
Wy 25309/26392/26703	α_2			(89/90/91)
L-654,284	α_2			(92)
L-657,743	α_2		Antidepressant	(93)
CH-38083	α_2		Antidepressant	(94)
Midaglizole	α_2		Antidiabetic	(95)
BDF 6143	α_2			(88)
Mianserin	α_2	Antidepressant		(23)
SK&F 86466	α_2			(96)
SK&F 104078	α_1/α_2 (postjunctional)		Antihypertensive	(24)

Table 9 Distribution of α-Adrenergic Receptors in Various Vascular Beds

Vascular bed	Species	α-Adrenergic receptor subtype	Ref.
Whole animal (blood pressure)	Anesthetized dog	$\alpha_1 + \alpha_2$	354, 355
	Pithed dog	$\alpha_1 + \alpha_2$	356
	Conscious dog	$\alpha_1 + \alpha_2$	260
	Anesthetized cat	$\alpha_1 + \alpha_2$	357
	Pithed cat	$\alpha_1 + \alpha_2$	257, 357
	Pithed rat	$\alpha_1 + \alpha_2$	215
	Pithed rabbit	$\alpha_1 + \alpha_2$	358
	Conscious rabbit	$\alpha_1 + \alpha_2$	359
Venous capacitance vessels	Pithed rat	$\alpha_1 + \alpha_2$	257
	Pithed cat	α_1	257
	Anesthetized dog	α_1	258
	Conscious dog	$\alpha_1 + \alpha_2$	260, 262
	Anesthetized dog	$\alpha_1 + \alpha_2$	261
Coronary circulation	Anesthetized dog	$\alpha_1 + \alpha_2$	266–268, 270
	Isolated guinea pig heart	$\alpha_1 + \alpha_2$	269
Mesenteric circulation	Pithed rat	$\alpha_1 + \alpha_2$	360
	Anesthetized dog	$\alpha_1 + \alpha_2$	361
	Anesthetized cat	$\alpha_1 + \alpha_2$	329
Renal vasculature	Anesthetized rat	α_1	328
	Pithed rat	α_1	362
	Anesthetized cat	α_1	329
	Anesthetized dog	α_1	330
	Anesthetized rabbit	$\alpha_1 + \alpha_2$	331
	Human (hypertensive)	$\alpha_1 + \alpha_2$	332
Pulmonary circulation	Anesthetized dog	$\alpha_1 + \alpha_2$	263, 265
	Anesthetized cat	$\alpha_1 + \alpha_2$	264
Muscular	Anesthetized dog (femoral)	$\alpha_1 + \alpha_2$	74, 330, 354
	Anesthetized cat (femoral)	$\alpha_1 + \alpha_2$	74
	Anesthetized rabbit	$\alpha_1 + \alpha_2$	363
	Anesthetized rat (hindquarters)	$\alpha_1 + \alpha_2$	364
	Human (forearm)	$\alpha_1 + \alpha_2$	253, 365

hypertension. Sawyer *et al.*[249] demonstrated that vascular postjunctional α_2-adrenergic receptors are possibly involved in the control of blood pressure in intact anesthetized spontaneously hypertensive rats, but not following adrenal demedullation, suggesting that circulating catecholamines are responsible for these α_2-receptor-mediated pressor effects. However, the role of vascular postjunctional α_2-adrenergic receptors in man is controversial. Both prazosin (**10**)[250] and yohimbine (**11**)[251] have been reported to produce a more pronounced vasodilatation in the forearm vasculature of hypertensive patients compared to normotensive controls. Such an increased sensitivity was not demonstrated for the non-selective α-adrenergic receptor blocker phentolamine (**20**).[252] Jie *et al.*[253] could not confirm the earlier results obtained with yohimbine.[251] However, norepinephrine and epinephrine as well as the selective α_2-adrenergic agonist B-HT 933 (**17**) produced a more pronounced vasoconstriction in the human forearm of essential hypertensive patients than in normotensive controls.[253] No preference was found for either the α_1- or α_2-adrenergic receptor in the greater response of hypertensive patients.[253] Nevertheless, selective α_2-adrenergic receptor antagonists such as rauwolscine have been shown to reduce blood pressure in spontaneously hypertensive rats.[249] In addition, the selective α_2-adrenergic receptor blocker SK&F 86466 (**96**)[254,255] has been reported to exert a blood-pressure-lowering effect in anesthetized DOCA-salt, renal and spontaneously hypertensive rats, but much less in anesthetized normotensive and renal hypertensive rats.[254] In addition, SK&F 86466 dose-dependently reduced blood pressure in conscious DOCA-salt hypertensive rats, concurrent with a reflex increase in heart rate.[255] Conceivably, the blockade of prejunctional α_2-adrenergic receptors in the heart will contribute to the observed tachycardia. As reported recently,[55,56] the α-adrenergic blocker SK&F 104078 (**24**) selectively antagonizes postjunctional α_2-adrenergic receptors over prejunctional ones. It is plausible that compounds such as SK&F 104078 may prove to be important tools in identifying the postjunctional vascular α_2-adrenergic receptor as an attractive target for antihypertensive therapeutics.

12.1.8.2 Venous α-Adrenergic Receptors

Although the presence of venous postjunctional α_2-adrenergic receptors has convincingly been demonstrated in isolated veins,[256] the relative contribution of α_1- and α_2-adrenergic receptors in the regulation of venous tone has been subject to debate.

Selective α_1-adrenergic receptor agonists have been reported to increase cardiac output in anesthetized rats,[257] cats[257] and dogs,[258] while selective α_2-adrenergic receptor stimulation increased cardiac output in rats only,[257,258,259] possibly reflecting different contributions of α_1/α_2-adrenergic receptors on venous capacitance and venous return. Conversely, Woodman and Vatner[260] found no evidence for major differences between the actions of the α-adrenergic receptor subtypes on the venous circulation of conscious dogs. Elsner *et al.*[261] demonstrated that the α_2-adrenergic receptor agonist UK-14,304 (**45**), as well as the α_1 agonist methoxamine (**13**), lowered venous compliance and increased central venous pressure in anesthetized dogs, and concluded that postsynaptic α_2-adrenergic receptors, in addition to α_1-adrenergic receptors, are functional in the venous system *in vivo* and contribute substantially to the humoral regulation of venous tone. Similar findings were reported for conscious dogs.[262] Therefore, it appears that both α-adrenergic receptor subtypes play a role in venous capacitance regulation, but the physiological correlates are as yet unclear. The orthostatic hypotension that may accompany antihypertensive therapy with prazosin and other sympatholytic agents is possibly related to diminished α_1-adrenergic venous tone.[247]

12.1.8.3 Pulmonary Vascular α-Adrenergic Receptors

The pulmonary circulation represents a critical vascular bed in certain disease states such as pulmonary hypertension, adult respiratory distress syndrome and congestive heart failure, in which pulmonary resistance is abnormally elevated. Both postjunctional α_1- and α_2-adrenergic receptors have been shown to mediate pulmonary vasoconstriction in dogs[263] and cats[264] and have been suggested to play an important role in the increase in pulmonary capillary wedge pressure observed in congestive heart failure patients treated with dopamine.[263,265] Since the pulmonary vasoconstriction to tyramine in dogs was more effectively blocked by prazosin (**10**) than by yohimbine (**11**), it appears that postjunctional pulmonary α_1-adrenergic receptors are located predominantly at the vascular neuroeffector junction and that α_2-adrenergic receptors are extrasynaptic in location.[263] As yet, the role of α-adrenergic receptors in the pathophysiology of pulmonary hypertension is unknown.

12.1.8.4 α-Adrenergic Receptors in the Coronary Circulation

Both postjunctional vascular α_1- and α_2-adrenergic receptors have been identified in coronary arteries of dogs[266-268] and guinea pigs.[269] Holtz *et al.*[266] demonstrated that the reduction of coronary blood flow elicited by exogenously applied norepinephrine in dogs is antagonized to a greater degree by rauwolscine (**12**) than by prazosin (**10**), thus suggesting a more prominent role for α_2-adrenergic receptors in the regulation of coronary blood flow. The presence of α_1-adrenergic receptors on large epicardial coronary arteries has been demonstrated,[267] whereas α_2-adrenergic receptors appear to be located primarily on the smaller resistance vessels of the coronary bed.[266,267] Kopia *et al.*[268] found that the selective α_2-adrenergic receptor antagonist idazoxan (**22**) was also more effective than prazosin in blocking the coronary vasoconstriction to sympathetic nerve stimulation in dogs and suggested that postjunctional α_2-adrenergic receptors in the coronary circulation are predominantly innervated, with α_1-adrenergic receptors being innervated to a lesser degree. The role of α_1- and α_2-adrenergic receptors in the regulation of blood flow in underperfused coronary vascular beds is unclear. Sympathetic nerve stimulation was found insufficiently effective to overcome the distal vasodilatation evoked by application of a severe coronary artery stenosis in dogs.[268] On the other hand, intracoronary administration of B-HT 920 (**25**) in dogs was reported to increase coronary resistance to the same extent before and after exhaustion of coronary dilator reserve by a severe stenosis in dogs.[270]

12.1.8.5 α-Adrenergic Receptors in the Central Nervous System

Although receptor binding studies show an abundance of α_1- and α_2-adrenergic receptor binding sites in the brain of mammalian species, including man, the precise physiological role of α_1- and α_2-adrenergic receptors in the CNS is far from being understood. However, central α_2-adrenergic receptors have been identified as targets for antihypertensive drugs such as clonidine (**2**) and possibly for antidepressant drugs such as mianserin (**23**) and idazoxan (**22**).

It is generally accepted that the centrally mediated hypotension and bradycardia elicited by clonidine, guanfacine (**3**) and α-methylDOPA (**1**) is the result of stimulation of α_2-adrenergic receptors located in the pontomedullary region of the brain.[271,272] This mechanism of action is firmly supported by the findings that selective α_2-adrenergic receptor antagonists such as yohimbine (**11**), rauwolscine (**12**) and idazoxan are effective blockers of the hypotension induced by clonidine and related compounds, that all lipophilic α_2-adrenergic receptor agonists such as B-HT 920 (**25**), B-HT 933 (**17**), UK-14,304 (**45**), guanabenz (**41**) and xylazine (**38**) all produce a centrally induced hypotensive effect and that the lipophilic selective α_1-adrenergic receptor agonists such as cirazoline (**49**) and St 587 (**26**) clearly lack such hypotensive activity.[271] Stimulation of central α_2-adrenergic receptors gives rise to a decrease in peripheral sympathetic outflow in animals and man,[273-282] resulting in a reduction of vascular sympathetic tone and a reduction in arterial pressure. In addition, a centrally induced facilitation of vagus reflex activity as well as stimulation of cardiac prejunctional α_2-adrenergic receptors have been identified as mechanisms contributing to the bradycardiac effects of α_2-adrenergic receptor agonists.[283,284] Various brain sites have been proposed as the primary target for centrally acting antihypertensives.[285] Among them, the nucleus tractus solitarii and the lateral reticular nucleus, both pontomedullary sites, have the most support from experimental evidence: destruction of either nucleus in animals eliminates the hypotensive effects brought about by systemically administered clonidine[285-287] and microinjections of clonidine are the most effective in reducing blood pressure in these nuclei.[271,285,288]

The question of the pre- or post-junctional location of the central α_2-adrenergic receptors mediating hypotension is as yet not conclusively answered. Support for a presynaptic location is given by the observation that one of the most prominent central effects of clonidine and related compounds is a decrease in norepinephrine turnover and synthesis rate.[289,290] On the other hand, depletion of norepinephrine in the brain by reserpine or 6-hydroxydopamine and subsequent inhibition of synthesis did not reduce clonidine's, depressant effect on sympathetic nerve activity nor did it reduce its vagally induced bradycardia.[271,291,292] Consequently, central endogenous nor-epinephrine is apparently not required for the cardiovascular response to clonidine, indicating a postsynaptic location of the α_2-adrenergic receptors involved.

An additional site where α-adrenergic receptors may interfere with blood pressure control may be the spinal cord. Kubo *et al.*[293] demonstrated that clonidine (**2**), guanabenz (**41**) and B-HT 920 (**25**), but not St 587 (**26**), reduced blood pressure after intrathecal injection at the T6–T7 level in anesthetized rats. Yohimbine (**11**) caused an increase in blood pressure, while only a weak hypotensive effect occurred after intrathecal injection of prazosin (**10**). These data are indicative of a role for spinal α_2-adrenergic receptors in blood pressure control. Endogenous catecholamines appear to activate these α_2-adrenergic receptors tonically.[293]

Sedation is a prominent side effect of antihypertensive therapy using centrally acting α_2-adrenergic receptor agonists. The involvement of α_2-adrenergic receptors in these sedative effects has been proposed.[294] Depletion of catecholamines and/or destruction of noradrenergic neurons prevented the sedation produced by clonidine (**2**) and B-HT 933 (**17**) in rats, pointing towards a possible presynaptic location of the α_2-adrenergic receptors mediating this effect.[295,296] In addition, central presynaptic α_2-adrenergic receptors have been suggested as playing a role in the antinociceptive and antiwithdrawal effects of clonidine.[297,298] Furthermore, central α_2-adrenergic receptors have been associated with anxiety, learning and memory, depression, thermoregulation, schizophrenia, hunger drives, dementia, psychoses and control of growth hormone and ACTH release.[297-300] Despite the incomplete understanding of the exact role of central α_2-adrenergic receptors in neurological disorders, α_2-adrenergic receptor antagonists are being studied as antidepressants. Phenoxybenzamine (**61**) and yohimbine (**11**) are synergistic with several antidepressants in decreasing β-adrenoceptor density in rat cerebral cortex, indicating that combined administration of α_2-adrenergic receptor blockers with other antidepressants may provide a more rapid onset of the therapeutic effect.[301-304] The antidepressant effects of mianserin (**23**) have been suggested to stem partly from its activity as an α_2-antagonist.[298,299] The potential for α_2-adrenergic antagonists as antidepressants is being investigated clinically with idazoxan (**22**), which reduced Hamilton scores by approximately 50% in a small four-week open trial with mainly severely depressive patients.[305]

Clonidine (**2**) and related α_2-adrenergic receptor agonists suppress narcotic withdrawal signs in animals and man.[306,307] Stimulation of presynaptic α_2-autoreceptors inhibits the firing of the locus ceruleus through reduction of norepinephrine release.[308] A similar mechanism may underly the effectiveness of clonidine in the treatment of alcohol[309] and smoking[310] withdrawal syndromes.

Human anxiety is associated with an enhanced noradrenergic activity in the CNS.[311,312] The reported beneficial effects of clonidine (**2**) as an antianxiety agent in humans may result from its inhibitory effect on norepinephrine release by stimulation of α_2-adrenergic receptors.[313,314] The observation that yohimbine has anxiogenic properties is in agreement with this hypothesis.[315]

12.1.8.6 Myocardial α-Adrenergic Receptors

The existence of myocardial α-adrenergic receptors mediating positive inotropic and chronotropic effects of adrenergic agents is well established in various mammalian species including man.[316,317] Phenylephrine (**14**) has been shown to evoke an α-adrenergic-receptor-mediated inotropic response in human atria[318] and human ventricle.[319] Skomedal et al.[320] demonstrated that myocardial α-adrenergic receptors contribute to the inotropic response to norepinephrine in human atria, although the β-adrenergic-receptor-mediated effects were clearly dominant. Thus, myocardial α-adrenergic receptors may have a functional role in the response to norepinephrine. Although the inotropic α-adrenergic receptor has not been characterized unequivocally, the effects of phenylephrine point towards an α_1 character. Also, Muntz et al.[321] did not observe any [^{3}H]rauwolscine labeling in rat heart using quantitative autoradiography.

α-Adrenergic antagonists such as phentolamine (**20**), prazosin (**10**) and yohimbine (**11**) exhibit an antiarrhythmic effect in animals subjected to coronary artery occlusion and reperfusion.[322,323] Radioligand binding studies have indicated that the density of α_1-adrenergic receptors significantly increases in ischemic myocardial tissue.[324] It has been shown that prazosin reduced the extent of myocardial damage due to coronary artery occlusion and reperfusion in dogs, indicating that myocardial α_1-adrenergic receptors may play a role in ischemic myocardial damage.[325]

12.1.8.7 Renal α-Adrenergic Receptors

There is abundant evidence for a dense noradrenergic innervation of the various components of the mammalian kidney, not only the afferent and efferent arterioles and the juxtaglomerular apparatus, but all portions of the nephron including the collecting duct. The bulk of the evidence from renal denervation or renal nerve stimulation studies indicates that neuronal control of renal excretory functions is mediated *via* α-adrenergic receptors.[326,327] Radioligand binding studies have shown the presence of α_1- and α_2-adrenergic receptors in the kidney, with α_2 receptors predominating numerically over α_1 receptors. With respect to the renal vasculature, a predominant role for postjunctional α_1-adrenergic receptors in renal vasoconstriction has been established in rats, cats and dogs.[328-330] In rabbit and human renal vasculature there appears to be a role for α_2-adrenergic receptors as well.[331,332] Both α_1- and α_2-adrenergic receptors have been implied in the regulation of renal excretory function. Renal nerve stimulation results in antidiuresis and antinatriuresis, an effect apparently mediated *via* renal tubular α_1-adrenergic receptors in dogs,[333] rabbits[334] and rats[335] since these effects are more effectively blocked by prazosin (10) than by yohimbine (11).[333-335] Although renal α_2-adrenergic receptors are more abundantly present, their physiological role and contribution to the pathophysiology of hypertension is quite unclear. DiBona and Sawin[336] did not observe significant effects of α_2-adrenergic receptor stimulation or blockade on renal hemodynamics of excretory function in anesthetized spontaneously hypertensive or normotensive rats.

However, clonidine (2) and guanfacine (3) have been shown to increase sodium and water excretion in whole animals[337,338] and isolated rat kidneys.[335] Gellai and Ruffolo[339] demonstrated that intravenous infusion of B-HT 933 (17) significantly increased urinary excretion of water and sodium in conscious normotensive rats. Potassium and urea excretion were not altered. Urine osmolality decreased during B-HT 933 infusion, suggesting a possible interaction between α_2-receptors and the vasopressin system. These studies suggested that α_2-adrenergic receptors in rats modulate reabsorption of water and sodium at the site of the renal nephron. The hypothesis has been forwarded that α_1- and α_2-adrenergic receptors play separate roles in the handling of water and sodium: renal nerve stimulation potentiates tubular water and sodium reabsorption *via* innervated α_1-adrenergic receptors while extrasynaptically located α_2-adrenergic receptors, stimulated by circulating catecholamines, mediate the opposite effects.[337,338]

In genetically hypertensive rats, renal α_1- as well as α_2-adrenergic receptor density is increased over normotensive controls.[340] In addition, α_2-receptor density is augmented further with high salt diets.[341] It is as yet unclear whether these observed increases in renal α-receptor density are part of the pathogenetic mechanism of hypertension or a reflection of compensatory mechanisms in response to changes in the interior milieu. An in-depth discussion on the possible role of renal α_2-adrenergic receptors in hypertension may be found elsewhere.[341]

12.1.8.8 Ocular α-Adrenergic Receptors

The effects of α-adrenergic drugs on intraocular pressure are rather complex. Norepinephrine (4), phenylephrine (14) and clonidine (2) have all been reported to reduce intraocular pressure after topical application.[342] In conscious rabbits, selective stimulation of α_1-adrenergic receptors induces a transient elevation of intraocular pressure, accompanied by mydriasis and followed by ocular hypotension, whereas selective stimulation of the α_2 subtype causes a marked ocular hypotensive response only.[342] However, selective α_2-adrenergic receptor blockade has also been reported to result in ocular hypotension in rabbits with intact sympathetic innervation to the eye.[343,344] The initial rise in ocular pressure by α_1-adrenergic receptor agonists has convincingly been attributed to stimulation of α_1-adrenergic receptors on extraocular muscles, resulting in contraction.[345,346] The therapeutic relevance of ocular α_2-adrenergic receptors remains to be established.

12.1.8.9 Miscellaneous

Apart from the localizations described above, α_2-adrenergic receptors are also present on platelets (α_2), where stimulation gives rise to platelet aggregation. Furthermore, α_2-adrenergic receptors mediate inhibition of insulin release from pancreatic islets, inhibit lipolysis in fat cells and stimulate growth hormone release from the adenohypophysis.[248,301] As alluded to earlier (see Section 12.1.7.2), midaglizole (95) is the first example of a selective α_2-antagonist being developed as an antidiabetic drug.

α_1-Adrenergic receptors on liver cell membranes activate glycogen phosphorylase.[248] A population of α_2-adrenergic receptors possibly of importance for the regulation of vascular reactivity was recently identified on vascular endothelial cells. Removal of endothelium enhances the sensitivity of a variety of isolated mammalian vessels to the contractile effects of norepinephrine.[347] These effects could be attributed to stimulation of endothelial α_2-adrenergic receptors, which would release endothelial-derived relaxing factor, thus counteracting the vasoconstriction brought about by stimulation of vascular smooth muscle α-adrenergic receptors.[345] The physiological relevance of this vasorelaxant mechanism is unclear.

In the urogenital system, α-adrenergic receptors are located in the bladder, where α_1-receptors primarily mediate bladder contraction and a mixed population of α_1/α_2 receptors can contract the urethra.[348,349] In the prostate, α_1-adrenergic receptors mediate contraction.[350] In human prostate hypertrophy, the density of α_1-adrenergic receptors increases, which may contribute to the urinary bladder obstruction commonly seen in prostate hypertrophy.[365] Selective α_1-adrenergic receptor antagonists are therapeutically employed to alleviate this obstruction.[350,365]

Finally, the inhibitory effects of α_2-adrenergic receptor agonists on intestinal motility suggests a therapeutic approach for the treatment of excessive gastrointestinal motility and diarrhea.[351]

12.1.9 CONCLUDING REMARKS

α-Adrenergic receptors have proven to be attractive targets for drugs, especially in the treatment of cardiovascular diseases such as hypertension. As our understanding of the physiological role of the various subtypes of α-adrenergic receptors increases, new indications for drugs acting *via* α-adrenergic receptors will undoubtedly be found.

The identification and characterization of α-adrenergic subtypes has contributed very considerably to the development of therapeutic strategies. It is to be expected that a detailed knowledge of the often well-concealed differences between α-adrenergic receptor subtypes in different tissues, as well as understanding the structure–activity relationships of α-adrenergic receptor agonists and antagonists, will yield new organ-selective compounds and valuable new drugs. Areas in which α-adrenergic receptor agonists or antagonists may play a future role as therapeutic agents include the effects mediated by vascular postjunctional α_2-adrenergic receptors in hypertension, α-adrenergic receptors in the pulmonary circulation and in the renal control of body fluids, CNS diseases such as depression and drug or alcohol dependence and impaired growth due to inadequate growth hormone release. The widespread progress into these important therapeutic modalities should be considered the most valuable pay-off of the renaissance of interest into α-adrenergic receptors during the last decade.

12.1.10 REFERENCES

1. K. Starke, *Annu. Rev. Pharmacol. Toxicol.*, 1981, **21**, 7.
2. S. Z. Langer, *Pharmacol. Rev.*, 1981, **32**, 377.
3. M. Gothert, *Arzneim.-Forsch.*, 1985, **35**, 1909.
4. M. Henning, in 'Handbook of Hypertension', ed. P. A. van Zwieten, Elsevier, Amsterdam, 1984, vol. 3, p. 154.
5. J. R. Cooper, F. E. Bloom and R. H. Roth, in 'The Biochemical Basis of Neuropharmacology', Oxford University Press, Oxford, 1978, p. 1.
6. N. E. Anden, A. Carlsson and J. Haggendal, *Annu. Rev. Pharmacol.*, 1969, **9**, 119.
7. S. Z. Langer, M. A. Enero, E. Adler-Graschinsky, M. L. Dubocovich and S. M. Celuch, in 'Proceedings of Symposium on Central Action of Drugs in the Regulation of Blood Pressure', ed. D. S. Davies and J. L. Reid, Pitman Medical, Tunbridge Wells, 1975, p. 133.
8. C. J. Pazoles and J. L. Ives, *Annu. Rep. Med. Chem.*, 1985, **20**, 51.
9. J. M. Lundberg and T. Hokfelt, *Trends NeuroSci. (Pers. Ed.)*, 1983, **6**, 325.
10. C. Su, *Annu. Rev. Pharmacol. Toxicol.*, 1983, **23**, 397.
11. T. C. Westfall, *Physiol. Rev.*, 1977, **57**, 659.
12. E. S. Vizi, *Prog. Neurobiol. (Oxford)*, 1979, **12**, 181.
13. P. B. M. W. M. Timmermans and P. A. van Zwieten, *J. Med. Chem.*, 1982, **25**, 1389.
14. A. N. M. Schoffelmeer and A. H. Mulder, *Naunyn-Schmiedeberg's Arch. Pharmacol.*, 1983, **323**, 188.
15. T. M. Egan, G. Henderson, R. A. North and J. T. Williams, *Br. J. Pharmacol.*, 1983, **78**, 3P.
16. J. M. Baraban, R. J. Gould, S. J. Peroutka and A. H. Snyder, *Proc. Natl. Acad. Sci. U.S.A.*, 1985, **82**, 604.
17. G. K. Aghajanian and J. M. Cedarbaum, in 'Catecholamines: Basic and Clinical Frontiers', ed. E. Usdin, I. J. Kopin and J. Barchas, Pergamon Press, Oxford, 1979, vol. 1, p. 619.
18. H. Majewski and M. J. Rand, *Trends Pharmacol. Sci.*, 1984, **5**, 500.
19. C. L. Wood, C. D. Arnett, W. R. Clarke, B. S. Tsai and R. J. Lefkowitz, *Biochem. Pharmacol.*, 1979, **28**, 1277.
20. D. C. U'Prichard and S. H. Snyder, *Life Sci.*, 1979, **24**, 79.
21. B. B. Hoffman and R. J. Lefkowitz, *N. Engl. J. Med.*, 1980, **302**, 1390.
22. H. Glossmann, R. Hornung and P. Presek, *J. Cardiovasc. Pharmacol.*, 1980, **2** (Suppl.), S303.
23. D. B. Bylund and D. C. U'Prichard, *Int. Rev. Neurobiol.*, 1983, **24**, 343.
24. K. Starke, *Rev. Physiol. Biochem. Pharmacol.*, 1981, **88**, 199.
25. P. B. M. W. M. Timmermans, in 'Handbook of Hypertension', ed. P. A. van Zwieten, Elsevier, Amsterdam, 1984, vol. 3, p. 102.
26. O. Arunlakshana and H. O. Schild, *Br. J. Pharmacol. Chemother.*, 1959, **14**, 418.
27. J. C. Doxey and A. G. Roach, *J. Auton. Pharmacol.*, 1980, **1**, 73.
28. R. P. Ahlquist, *Am. J. Physiol.*, 1948, **153**, 586.
29. R. F. Furchgott, *Ann. N. Y. Acad. Sci.*, 1967, **137**, 553.

30. A. M. Lands, A. Arnold, J. P. McAuliff, F. P. Luduena and T. G. Brown, *Nature (London)*, 1967, **214**, 597.
31. P. B. M. W. M. Timmermans and P. A. van Zwieten, *Eur. J. Pharmacol.*, 1980, **63**, 199.
32. B. B. Hoffman and R. J. Lefkowitz, *Annu. Rev. Pharmacol. Toxicol.*, 1980, **20**, 581.
33. J. H. Exton, *Am. J. Physiol.*, 1985, **248**, E633.
34. K. H. Jacobs, *J. Cardiovasc. Pharmacol.*, 1985, **7**, S109.
35. C. J. Homcy and R. M. Graham, *Circ. Res.*, 1985, **56**, 635.
36. N. A. Flavahan and P. M. Vanhoutte, *Trends Pharmacol. Sci.*, 1986, **7**, 347.
37. R. R. Ruffolo, J. R. Waddell and E. L. Yaden, *J. Pharmacol. Exp. Ther.*, 1982, **221**, 309.
38. T. V. C. Skarby, K. E. Andersson and L. Edvinsson, *Acta Physiol. Scand.*, 1983, **117**, 63.
39. J. P. Hieble and D. F. Woodward, *Naunyn-Schmiedeberg's Arch. Pharmacol.*, 1984, **328**, 44.
40. J. P. Hieble, H. M. Sarau, J. J. Foley, R. M. DeMarinis and P. G. Pendleton, *Naunyn-Schmiedeberg's Arch. Pharmacol.*, 1982, **318**, 267.
41. P. B. M. W. M. Timmermans, F. Karamat Ali, H. Y. Kwa, A. M. C. Schoop, F. D. Slothorst-Grisdijk and P. A. van Zwieten, *Mol. Pharmacol.*, 1981, **20**, 295.
42. A. De Jonge, P. B. M. W. M. Timmermans and P. A. van Zwieten, *J. Pharmacol. Exp. Ther.*, 1983, **226**, 565.
43. E. Vila, M. J. M. C. Thoolen, J. J. Beckeringh, P. B. M. W. M. Timmermans and P. A. van Zwieten, *Eur. J. Pharmacol.*, 1985, **106**, 97.
44. D. B. Bylund, *Pharmacol., Biochem. Behav.*, 1985, **22**, 835.
45. K. E. J. Dickinson, R. M. McKernan, C. M. M. Miles, K. S. Leys and P. S. Sever, *Eur. J. Pharmacol.*, 1986, **120**, 285.
46. V. A. Alabaster, R. F. Keir and C. J. Peters, *Br. J. Pharmacol.*, 1986, **88**, 607.
47. A. Adams, B. Jarrott, W. A. Denny and L. P. G. Wakelin, *Eur. J. Pharmacol.*, 1986, **127**, 27.
48. C. B. Chapleo, J. C. Doxey, P. L. Meyers and A. G. Roach, *Br. J. Pharmacol.*, 1981, **74**, 942P.
49. P. B. M. W. M. Timmermans, J. Q. Qian, R. R. Ruffolo and P. A. van Zwieten, *J. Pharmacol. Exp. Ther.*, 1984, **228**, 739.
50. P. W. Dettmar, A. G. Lynn and I. F. Tulloch, *Neuropharmacology*, 1983, **22**, 729.
51. J. C. Doxey, A. G. Roach, D. A. Strachan and N. K. Virdee, *Br. J. Pharmacol.*, 1984, **83**, 713.
52. H. Dabire, P. Mouille and H. Schmitt, *Eur. J. Pharmacol.*, 1983, **86**, 83.
53. V. J. Nickolson, J. H. Wierenga and A. M. L. van Delft, *Naunyn-Schmiedeberg's Arch. Pharmacol.*, 1982, **303**, 193.
54. M. Raiteri, G. Maura, A. Gemignani and A. Pittaluga, *Naunyn-Schmiedeberg's Arch. Pharmacol.*, 1983, **322**, 180.
55. J. P. Hieble, A. C. Sulpizio, A. J. Nichols, R. M. DeMarinis, F. R. Pfeiffer, P. G. Lavanchy and R. R. Ruffolo, *J. Hypertens.*, 1986, **4** (Suppl. 6), S189.
56. R. R. Ruffolo, A. C. Sulpizio, A. J. Nichols, R. M. DeMarinis and J. P. Hieble, *Naunyn-Schmiedeberg's Arch. Pharmacol.*, 1987, **336**, 415.
57. J. C. A. van Meel, A. de Jonge, P. B. M. W. M. Timmermans and P. A. van Zwieten, *J. Pharmacol. Exp. Ther.*, 1981, **219**, 760.
58. W. Kobinger and L. Pichler, *Eur. J. Pharmacol.*, 1982, **82**, 203.
59. J. M. Kitzen, M. A. Schwenkler, J. Fiore-Miele, L. D. Hewllyer and J. Moeller, *Pharmacologist*, 1983, **25**, 194.
60. D. F. Story, C. A. Stanford-Starr and M. J. Rand, *Clin. Sci.*, 1985, **68** (Suppl. 10), 111s.
61. N. A. Flavahan and J. C. McGrath, *Br. J. Pharmacol.*, 1982, **77**, 319.
62. P. A. Verplancken, R. A. Lefebvre and M. G. Bogaert, *J. Pharmacol. Exp. Ther.*, 1984, **231**, 404.
63. E. J. Ariens and A. M. Simonis, *Biochem. Pharmacol.*, 1983, **32**, 1539.
64. I. Yamaguchi and I. J. Kopin, *J. Pharmacol. Exp. Ther.*, 1980, **214**, 762.
65. B. Wilffert, P. B. M. W. M. Timmermans and P. A. van Zwieten, *J. Pharmacol. Exp. Ther.*, 1982, **221**, 762.
66. N. A. Flavahan, T. L. Grant, J. Greig and J. C. McGrath, *Br. J. Pharmacol.*, 1985, **86**, 265.
67. S. Z. Langer, R. Massingham and N. B. Shepperson, *Clin. Sci.*, 1980, **214**, 275.
68. S. Z. Langer and P. E. Hicks, *J. Cardiovasc. Pharmacol.*, 1984, **6**, S547.
69. I. C. Medgett, P. E. Hicks and S. Z. Langer, *J. Pharmacol. Exp. Ther.*, 1984, **231**, 159.
70. I. C. Medgett, *Eur. J. Pharmacol.*, 1985, **108**, 281.
71. N. A. Flavahan, T. J. Rimele, J. P. Cooke and P. M. Vanhoutte, *J. Pharmacol. Exp. Ther.*, 1987, **240**, 589.
72. J. R. Docherty and L. Hyland, *Br. J. Pharmacol.*, 1985, **84**, 573.
73. M. Saeed, J. Holtz, D. Elsner and E. Bassenge, *J. Cardiovasc. Pharmacol.*, 1985, **7**, 167.
74. J. C. Gardiner and C. J. Peters, *Eur. J. Pharmacol.*, 1982, **84**, 189.
75. D. Elsner, M. Saeed, O. Sommer, J. Holtz and E. Bassenge, *Hypertension (Dallas)*, 1985, **6**, 915.
76. I. F. A. Heese and E. J. Johns, *J. Auton. Pharmacol.*, 1984, **4**, 145.
77. B. Wilffert, M. A. M. Gouw, A. de Jonge, P. B. M. W. M. Timmermans and P. A. van Zwieten, *J. Pharmacol. Exp. Ther.*, 1982, **223**, 219.
78. B. Wilffert, D. Davidesko, P. B. M. W. M. Timmermans and P. A. van Zwieten, *J. Pharmacol. Exp. Ther.*, 1983, **226**, 855.
79. R. R. Ruffolo, in 'Adrenergic Receptors and Catecholamine Action', ed. G. Kunos, Wiley, New York, 1983, part B, p. 1.
80. L. B. Kier, *J. Pharmacol. Exp. Ther.*, 1968, **164**, 75.
81. J. L. Cumbeils, Ph. Courriere and B. Pullman, *J. Med. Chem.*, 1972, **15**, 453.
82. D. Carlstrom, R. Bergin and G. Falkenberg, *Q. Rev. Biophys.*, 1973, **3**, 257.
83. P. W. Erhardt, R. J. Corcynski and W. G. Anderson, *J. Med. Chem.*, 1979, **22**, 907.
84. R. R. Ruffolo, K. S. Anderson and D. D. Miller, *Mol. Pharmacol.*, 1982, **21**, 259.
85. P. E. Hicks, C. Waldron, P. Burn and P. A. Crooke, *J. Pharm. Pharmacol.*, 1983, **35**, 94.
86. B. Pullman, J. L. Coubeils, P. Courriere and J. P. Gervois, *J. Med. Chem.*, 1972, **15**, 17.
87. C. J. Wermuth, J. Schwartz, J. Leclerc, J. P. Garnier and B. Rouot, *Clin. Ther.*, 1973, **1**, 115.
88. W. Hoefke, *ACS Symp. Ser.*, 1979, **27**, 27.
89. V. Cody and G. T. DiTitta, *J. Mol. Struct.*, 1979, **9**, 33.
90. G. Byre, A. Mostad and C. Romming, *Acta Chem. Scand., Ser. B*, 1976, **30**, 843.
91. C. M. Meerman-van Benthem, K. van der Meer, J. J. Mulder, P. B. M. W. M. Timmermans and P. A. van Zwieten, *Mol. Pharmacol.*, 1975, **11**, 667.
92. A. P. de Jong and H. van Dam, *J. Med. Chem.*, 1980, **23**, 889.
93. L. H. Easson and E. Stedman, *Biochem. J.*, 1933, **27**, 1257.
94. R. R. Ruffolo, in 'Stereochemistry and Biological Activity of Drugs', ed. E. J. Ariens, W. Soudijn and P. B. M. W. M. Timmermans, Blackwell, Oxford, 1983, p. 103.

95. R. R. Ruffolo and J. E. Waddell, *Life Sci.*, 1982, **31**, 2999.
96. A. A. Larsen, W. A. Gould, H. R. Roth, W. T. Comer, R. H. Uloth, K. W. Dungan and P. M. Lish, *J. Med. Chem.*, 1967, **10**, 462.
97. P. Pratesi and E. Grana, *Adv. Drug Res.*, 1965, **2**, 127.
98. T. P. Kenakin, *J. Pharmacol. Exp. Ther.*, 1981, **216**, 210.
99. R. R. Ruffolo and E. L. Yaden, *J. Pharmacol. Exp. Ther.*, 1983, **224**, 46.
100. P. B. M. W. M. Timmermans, W. Hoefke, H. Stahle and P. A. van Zwieten, *Prog. Pharmacol.*, 1980, **3** (1), 1.
101. H. Stahle, in 'Proceedings of the 4th International Symposium on Medicinal Chemistry', ed. J. Maas, Elsevier, Amsterdam, 1974, p. 75.
102. P. B. M. W. M. Timmermans and P. A. van Zwieten, *Pharmacology*, 1978, **16**, 106.
103. R. R. Ruffolo, E. L. Yaden, P. B. M. W. M. Timmermans, P. A. van Zwieten and M. D. Hynes, *J. Pharmacol. Exp. Ther.*, 1984, **229**, 58.
104. H. Ohnishi, K. Yanaguchi, M. Satoh, M. Obata, A. Yemura, Y. Toyonaka and Y. Suzuki, *Arzneim.-Forsch.*, 1981, **31**, 1425.
105. M. Sato, I. Muramatsu and M. Funiwana, *Blood Vessels*, 1984, **21**, 246.
106. R. J. Summers, B. Jarrott and W. J. Louis, *Eur. J. Pharmacol.*, 1980, **66**, 233.
107. P. B. M. W. M. Timmermans and P. A. van Zwieten, *Eur. J. Med. Chem.—Chim. Ther.*, 1980, **15**, 323.
108. E. Graf, I. S. Doppelfeld and G. Prop, *Arzneim.-Forsch.*, 1982, **32**, 941.
109. B. Wilffert, M. J. Mathy, H. D. Batink, A. de Jonge, M. J. M. C. Thoolen, G. Prop, E. Graf, P. B. M. W. M. Timmermans and P. A. van Zwieten, *Arch. Int. Pharmacodyn. Ther.*, 1985, **273**, 18.
110. R. R. Ruffolo, P. B. M. W. M. Timmermans and P. A. van Zwieten, *J. Auton. Pharmacol.*, 1983, **3**, 185.
111. J. M. Savola, *Naunyn-Schmiedeberg's Arch. Pharmacol.*, 1986, **334**, 423.
112. T. Baum, A. T. Shropshire, G. Rowles, R. van Pelt, S. P. Fernandez, D. K. Eckfeld and M. I. Gluckman, *J. Pharmacol. Exp. Ther.*, 1970, **171**, 276.
113. G. Scholtysik, H. Lauener, E. Eichenberger, H. Burki, R. Saltzmann, E. Muller-Schweinitzer and R. Waite, *Arzneim.-Forsch.*, 1975, **25**, 1483.
114. E. Lindner and J. Kaiser, *Arch. Int. Pharmacodyn. Ther.*, 1974, **211**, 305.
115. F. Jacobs, U. Werner and H. J. Schumann, *Arzneim.-Forsch.*, 1972, **22**, 1124.
116. P. A. van Zwieten, M. J. M. C. Thoolen, F. A. M. Jonkman, B. Wilffert, A. de Jonge and P. B. M. W. M. Timmermans, *Arch. Int. Pharmacodyn. Ther.*, 1986, **279**, 130.
117. J. Bergerhausen, *Naunyn-Schmiedeberg's Arch. Pharmacol.*, 1985, **328**, R80.
118. G. Leclerc, B. Rouot, J. Schwartz, J. Velly and C. G. Wermuth, *Br. J. Pharmacol.*, 1980, **71**, 5.
119. B. Rouot and S. H. Snyder, *Life Sci.*, 1979, **25**, 769.
120. A. P. de Jong and W. Soudijn, *Eur. J. Pharmacol.*, 1981, **69**, 175.
121. B. Jarrott, R. J. Summers, A. J. Culvenor and W. J. Louis, *Circ. Res.*, 1980, **46** (Suppl. I), I-15.
122. J. P. Hieble and R. J. Pendleton, *Naunyn-Schmiedeberg's Arch. Pharmacol.*, 1979, **309**, 217.
123. H. A. J. Struyker Boudier, J. de Boer, G. Smeets, E. J. Lien and J. van Rossum, *Life Sci.*, 1975, **17**, 377.'
124. R. R. Ruffolo, J. E. Waddell and E. L. Yaden, *J. Pharmacol. Exp. Ther.*, 1980, **213**, 267.
125. B. Rouot, G. Leclerc, C. G. Wermuth, F. Miesch and J. Schwartz, *J. Med. Chem.*, 1976, **19**, 1049.
126. B. Rouot, G. Leclerc, C. G. Wermuth, F. Miesch and J. Schwartz, *J. Pharmacol.*, 1977, **8**, 95.
127. I. C. Medgett and M. W. McCulloch, *Clin. Exp. Pharmacol. Physiol.*, 1983, **10**, 395.
128. P. B. M. W. M. Timmermans and P. A. van Zwieten, *J. Med. Chem.*, 1977, **20**, 1636.
129. J. G. Topliss and R. P. Edwards, *J. Med. Chem.*, 1979, **22**, 1238.
130. P. B. M. W. M. Timmermans, A. Brands and P. A. van Zwieten, *Naunyn-Schmiedeberg's Arch. Pharmacol.*, 1977, **300**, 217.
131. P. B. M. W. M. Timmermans, A. de Jonge, P. A. van Zwieten, J. J. J. de Boer and W. N. Speckamp, *J. Med. Chem.*, 1982, **25**, 1122.
132. A. de Jonge, P. B. M. W. M. Timmermans and P. A. van Zwieten, *Br. J. Pharmacol.*, 1983, **78**, 479.
133. K. Starke, T. Endo and H. D. Taube, *Naunyn-Schmiedeberg's Arch. Pharmacol.*, 1975, **291**, 55.
134. P. B. M. W. M. Timmermans, H. Y. Kwa and P. A. van Zwieten, *Naunyn-Schmiedeberg's Arch. Pharmacol.*, 1979, **310**, 189.
135. N. A. Flavahan and J. C. McGrath, *Br. J. Pharmacol.*, 1981, **72**, 585P.
136. M. J. Mathy, H. N. Doods, M. J. M. C. Thoolen, B. Wilffert, A. de Jonge, P. B. M. W. M. Timmermans and P. A. van Zwieten, *J. Auton. Pharmacol.*, 1983, **3**, 249.
137. P. B. M. W. M. Timmermans, M. J. Mathy, H. M. Doods, M. J. M. C. Thoolen, A. de Jonge, B. Wilffert, P. A. van Zwieten, R. M. DeMarinis, J. Lafferty, R. A. Marcia and W. D. Matthews, *Eur. J. Pharmacol.*, 1984, **101**, 45.
138. A. de Jonge, J. C. A. van Meel, P. B. M. W. M. Timmermans and P. A. van Zwieten, *Life Sci.*, 1981, **28**, 2000.
139. M. J. Mathy, M. J. M. C. Thoolen, P. B. M. W. M. Timmermans and P. A. van Zwieten, *Br. J. Pharmacol.*, 1984, **81**, 255.
140. R. M. DeMarinis, W. M. Bryan, D. H. Shah, J. P. Hieble and R. G. Pendleton, *J. Med. Chem.*, 1981, **24**, 1432.
141. R. M. DeMarinis, D. H. Shah, R. F. Hall, J. P. Hieble and R. G. Pendleton, *J. Med. Chem.*, 1982, **25**, 136.
142. A. de Jonge, P. B. M. W. M. Timmermans and P. A. van Zwieten, *J. Pharmacol. Exp. Ther.*, 1982, **222**, 705.
143. A. de Jonge, P. N. Santing, P. B. M. W. M. Timmermans and P. A. van Zwieten, *J. Auton. Pharmacol.*, 1981, **1**, 377.
144. A. de Jonge, P. B. M. W. M. Timmermans and P. A. van Zwieten, *J. Pharmacol. Exp. Ther.*, 1983, **226**, 585.
145. R. R. Ruffolo and J. E. Waddell, *J. Pharmacol. Exp. Ther.*, 1982, **222**, 29.
146. R. R. Ruffolo and K. Messick, *J. Pharmacol. Exp. Ther.*, 1985, **232**, 94.
147. W. Kobinger and L. Pichler, *Naunyn-Schmiedeberg's Arch. Pharmacol.*, 1977, **300**, 39.
148. L. Pichler and W. Kobinger, *J. Cardiovasc. Pharmacol.*, 1981, **3**, 269.
149. P. B. M. W. M. Timmermans and P. A. van Zwieten, *Naunyn-Schmiedeberg's Arch. Pharmacol.*, 1980, **313**, 17.
150. B. Wilffert, P. N. M. van Heiningen, M. J. Mathy, H. D. Batink, A. de Jonge, M. J. M. C. Thoolen, P. B. M. W. M. Timmermans and P. A. van Zwieten, *Naunyn-Schmiedeberg's Arch. Pharmacol.*, 1984, **327**, 90.
151. N. E. Anden, H. Nilsson, E. Ros and R. Thornstrom, *Acta Pharmacol. Toxicol.*, 1983, **52**, 51.
152. J. R. Docherty and J. C. McGrath, *Naunyn-Schmiedeberg's Arch. Pharmacol.*, 1980, **312**, 107.
153. P. E. Hicks and C. Waldron, *Br. J. Pharmacol.*, 1980, **74**, 254P.
154. G. M. Drew, *Eur. J. Pharmacol.*, 1980, **65**, 85.

155. P. B. M. W. M. Timmermans, M. J. Mathy, B. Wilffert, H. O. Kalkman, G. Smit, D. Dijkstra, A. S. Horn and P. A. van Zwieten, *Eur. J. Pharmacol.*, 1984, **97**, 55.
156. J. M. Savola, H. Ruskoaho, J. Puurunen, J. S. Salonen and N. T. Karki, *J. Auton. Pharmacol.*, 1986, **5**, 275.
157. H. Ruskoaho, J. M. Savola, S. Kaipiainen, J. Puurunen and N. Karki, *Naunyn-Schmiedeberg's Arch. Pharmacol.*, 1983, **322**, 279.
158. J. M. Savola, H. Ruskoaho, J. Puurunen and N. T. Karki, *Eur. J. Pharmacol.*, 1985, **118**, 69.
159. F. MacDonald, V. Saano, R. Virtanen and R. Lammintausta, *Fed. Proc., Fed. Am. Soc. Exp. Biol.*, 1987, **46** (3), 699.
160. I. B. Armah, *Naunyn-Schmiedeberg's Arch. Pharmacol.*, 1985, **328** (Suppl.), R 80.
161. P. Jacobitz and E. Hofferber, *Naunyn-Schmiedeberg's Arch. Pharmacol.*, 1985, **328** (Suppl.), R 80.
162. C. Melchiorre and B. Belleau, in 'Adrenoceptors and Catecholamine Action', ed. G. Kunos, Wiley, New York, 1981, part A, p. 181.
163. E. Borowski, K. Starke, H. Ehrl and T. Endo, *Neuroscience*, 1977, **2**, 285.
164. J. C. Doxey, C. F. C. Smith and J. M. Walker, *Br. J. Pharmacol.*, 1977, **60**, 91.
165. P. B. M. W. M. Timmermans, J. C. A. van Meel and P. A. van Zwieten, *J. Auton. Pharmacol.*, 1980, **1**, 53.
166. P. B. M. W. M. Timmermans, J. E. van Kemenade, H. D. Batink and P. A. van Zwieten, *Pharmacology*, 1983, **26**, 258.
167. M. R. Stillings, C. D. England and C. F. C. Smith, in 'Proceedings of VIIIth International Symposium on Medicinal Chemistry', ed. R. Dahlbom and J. L. G. Nilsson, Swedish Pharmaceutical Press, Stockholm, 1985, vol. 1, p. 112.
168. W. S. Saari, W. Halczenko, W. C. Randall and V. J. Lotti, *J. Med. Chem.*, 1983, **26**, 1769.
169. R. F. Furchgott and P. Burzstyn, *Ann. N.Y. Acad. Sci.*, 1967, **144**, 882.
170. J. W. Constantine, W. Lebel and R. Archer, *Eur. J. Pharmacol.*, 1982, **85**, 325.
171. K. P. Minneman, *Eur. J. Pharmacol.*, 1983, **94**, 171.
172. C. Melchiorre and B. Belleau, in 'Adrenoceptors and Catecholamine Action', ed. G. Kunos, Wiley, New York, 1981, part A, p. 181.
173. B. G. Benfey, *Trends Pharmacol. Sci.*, 1982, **3**, 470.
174. T. Kamitani, M. Katamoto, K. Tsujioka, T. Terai, M. Ohtsuka, T. Ono, H. Kikuchi and S. Kumada, *Jpn. J. Pharmacol.*, 1985, **39**, 251.
175. P. B. M. W. M. Timmermans and P. A. van Zwieten, in 'Handbook of Hypertension', ed. P. A. van Zwieten, Elsevier, Amsterdam, 1984, vol. 3, p. 239.
176. R. Weitzell, T. Tanaka and K. Starke, *Naunyn-Schmiedeberg's Arch. Pharmacol.*, 1979, **308**, 127.
177. N. B. Shepperson, N. Duval, R. Massingham and S. Z. Langer, *J. Pharmacol. Exp. Ther.*, 1981, **219**, 540.
178. V. A. Alabaster and M. J. Davey, *Br. J. Pharmacol.*, 1986, **21**, 9S.
179. J. W. Constantine, W. Lebel and R. Weeks, *J. Cardiovasc. Pharmacol.*, 1984, **6**, 142.
180. P. B. M. W. M. Timmermans, H. Y. Kwa, F. Karamat Ali and P. A. van Zwieten, *Arch. Int. Pharmacodyn. Ther.*, 1980, **245**, 218.
181. L. Eriksson, H. Karppanen, E. Honkanen and U. M. Kokkonen, *Acta Pharmacol. Toxicol.*, 1984, **54**, 158.
182. T. Kawasaki, K. Uezono, I. Abe, S. Nakamura, M. Ueno, N. Kawazoe and T. Amae, *Eur. J. Clin. Pharmacol.*, 1981, **20**, 399.
183. I. Cavero, F. Lefevre-Borg and Ph. Manoury, *Br. J. Pharmacol.*, 1984, **81**, 13P.
184. E. Honkanen, A. Pippuri, P. Kairisalo, P. Norc, H. Karppanen and I. Paakkari, *J. Med. Chem.*, 1983, **26**, 1433.
185. D. Cambridge, M. J. Davey and R. Massingham, *Br. J. Pharmacol.*, 1977, **59**, 514P.
186. J. E. Clifton, I. Collins, P. Hallett, D. Hartley, L. H. C. Lunts and P. D. Wicks, *J. Med. Chem.*, 1982, **25**, 670.
187. G. M. Drew, *Br. J. Pharmacol.*, 1978, **64**, 292.
188. R. T. Brittain, G. M. Drew and G. P. Levy, *Br. J. Pharmacol.*, 1981, **73**, 282P.
189. T. Fujikura, K. Niigata, S. Hashimoto, K. Imai and T. Takenaka, *Chem. Pharm. Bull.*, 1982, **30**, 4092.
190. M. Asano, H. Haskimoto and M. Nakashima, *Arch. Int. Pharmacodyn. Ther.*, 1983, **262**, 34.
191. H. Kapur, B. Rouot and S. H. Snyder, *Eur. J. Pharmacol.*, 1979, **57**, 317.
192. C. Melchiorre, D. Giardina, P. Gallucci and L. Brasili, *J. Pharm. Pharmacol.*, 1982, **34**, 683.
193. C. Melchiorre, L. Brasili, D. Giardina, M. Pigini and G. Strappaghetti, *J. Med Chem.*, 1984, **27**, 1536.
194. M. Eltze, *Eur. J. Pharmacol.*, 1979, **59**, 1.
195. W. Schoetensack, E. G. Bruckshen and K. Zech, in 'New Drugs Annual: Cardiovascular Drugs', ed. A. Scriabine, Raven Press, New York, 1983, p. 19.
196. P. A. van Zwieten, M. J. Mathy and M. J. M. C. Thoolen, *J. Pharm. Pharmacol.*, 1985, **37**, 810.
197. R. Zelis, *J. Pharmacol. Exp. Ther.*, 1986, **237**, 746.
198. P. Mouille, A. M. Huchet, J. Chelly, B. Lucet, M. F. Doursout and H. Schmitt, *J. Cardiovasc. Pharmacol.*, 1980, **2**, 175.
199. H. Nabata, J. Aono, N. Ishizuka and K. Sakai, *Arch. Int. Pharmacodyn. Ther.*, 1985, **277**, 104.
200. J. Aono, H. Nabata, N. Ishizuka and K. Sakai, *Arch. Int. Pharmacodyn. Ther.*, 1985, **277**, 126.
201. J. Imagawa and K. Sakai, *Eur. J. Pharmacol.*, 1986, **131**, 257.
202. M. J. Ryan, F. A. Bjork, D. M. Cohen, L. L. Coughenour, T. C. Major, N. P. Mathias, T. E. Mertz, B. J. Olszweski, R. M. Singer, D. B. Evans and H. R. Kaplan, *J. Pharmacol. Exp. Ther.*, 1986, **238**, 473.
203. J. Q. Qian, M. J. Mathy, M. J. M. C. Thoolen, P. B. M. W. M. Timmermans and P. A. van Zwieten, *Arch. Int. Pharmacodyn. Ther.*, 1983, **266**, 264.
204. P. Chatelain, M. Claeys, W. van Dorsser and J. Roba, *Arch. Int. Pharmacodyn. Ther.*, 1984, **268**, 271.
205. J. M. van Neuten, P. A. J. Janssen, J. van Beek, R. Xhonneux, T. J. Verbeuren and P. M. Vanhoutte, *J. Pharmacol. Exp. Ther.*, 1981, **218**, 217.
206. J. R. Fozard, *J. Cardiovasc. Pharmacol.*, 1982, **4**, 829.
207. H. O. Kalkman, P. B. M. W. M. Timmermans and P. A. van Zwieten, *J. Pharmacol. Exp. Ther.*, 1982, **222**, 227.
208. M. Gothert, C. Dieckhofer and J. Nolte, *J. Cardiovasc. Pharmacol.*, 1983, **5**, 13.
209. G. Engel and D. Hoyer, *Eur. J. Pharmacol.*, 1981, **73**, 221.
210. J. L. Archibald, *Br. J. Clin. Pharmacol.*, 1981, **12**, 45S.
211. Y. Kasuya, J. Kurihara and H. Kato, *Arzneim.-Forsch.*, 1983, **33**, 557.
212. A. Karasawa, K. Shuto, K. Kubo, Y. Kasuya, M. Hashikami and K. Shigenobu, *Arch. Int. Pharmacodyn. Ther.*, 1983, **261**, 278.
213. P. B. M. W. M. Timmermans, in 'Stereochemistry and Biological Activity of Drugs', ed. E. J. Ariens, W. Soudijn and P. B. M. W. M. Timmermans, Blackwell, Oxford, 1983, p. 161.

214. M. R. Goldberg and D. Robertson, *Pharmacol. Rev.*, 1983, **35** (2), 143.
215. J. C. McGrath, *Biochem. Pharmacol.*, 1982, **31**, 467.
216. N. Ferry, M. Goodhardt, J. Hanoune and T. Sevenet, *Br. J. Pharmacol.*, 1983, **78**, 359.
217. G. A. Lambert, W. J. Lang, E. Friedman, E. Meller and S. Gershon, *Eur. J. Pharmacol.*, 1978, **49**, 39.
218. J. J. Baldwin, J. R. Huff, W. C. Randall, J. P. Vacca and M. M. Zrada, *Eur. J. Med. Chem.—Chim. Ther.*, 1985, **20**, 67.
219. K. Starke, *Rev. Physiol. Biochem. Pharmacol.*, 1981, **88**, 199.
220. A. J. Kaumann, *Naunyn-Schmiedeberg's Arch. Pharmacol.*, 1983, **329**, 149.
221. *Drugs of the Future*, 1976, **1**, 239.
222. C. B. Chapleo, P. L. Myers, R. C. M. Butler, J. C. Doxey, A. G. Roach and C. F. C. Smith, *J. Med. Chem.*, 1983, **26**, 823.
223. J. C. Doxey, A. C. Lane, A. G. Roach and N. K. Virdee, *Naunyn-Schmiedeberg's Arch. Pharmacol.*, 1984, **325**, 136.
224. P. B. M. W. M. Timmermans, J. Q. Qian, R. R. Ruffolo and P. A. van Zwieten, *J. Pharmacol. Exp. Ther.*, 1984, **228**, 739.
225. J. C. Doxey, A. G. Roach, D. A. Strachan and N. K. Virdee, *Br. J. Pharmacol.*, 1984, **83**, 713.
226. C. B. Chapleo, P. L. Myers, R. C. M. Butler, J. A. Davis, J. C. Doxey, S. D. Higgins, M. Myers, A. G. Roach, C. F. C. Smith, M. R. Stillings and A. P. Welbourn, *J. Med. Chem.*, 1984, **27**, 570.
227. A. D. Michel, S. R. Nahorski and R. L. Whiting, *Br. J. Pharmacol.*, 1981, **74**, 845P.
228. J. M. Caroon, R. D. Clark, A. F. Kluge, R. Olah, D. B. Repke, S. H. Unger, A. D. Michel and R. L. Whiting, *J. Med. Chem.*, 1982, **25**, 666.
229. W. S. Saari, W. Halczenko, S. W. King, J. R. Huff, J. P. Guare, C. A. Hunt, W. C. Randall, P. S. Anderson, V. J. Lotti, D. A. Taylor and B. V. Clineschmidt, *J. Med. Chem.*, 1983, **26**, 1696.
230. I. B. Armah, D. R. Ferry and H. Glossmann, *Br. J. Pharmacol.*, 1983, **78**, 151P.
231. J. R. Docherty, M. Gothert, C. Dieckhofer and K. Starke, *Arzneim.-Forsch.*, 1982, **32**, 1534.
232. N. Lattimer, K. F. Rhodes, T. J. Ward, J. F. Waterfall and J. F. White, *Br. J. Pharmacol.*, 1982, **75**, 154P.
233. P. M. Paciorek, V. Pierce, N. B. Shepperson and J. F. Waterfall, *Br. J. Pharmacol.*, 1984, **82**, 127.
234. N. Lattimer, R. P. McAdams, K. F. Rhodes, S. Sharma, S. J. Turner and J. F. Waterfall, *Naunyn-Schmiedeberg's Arch. Pharmacol.*, 1984, **327**, 312.
235. D. J. Pettibone, B. V. Clineschmidt, V. J. Lotti, G. E. Martin, J. R. Huff, W. C. Randall, J. Vacca and J. J. Baldwin, *Naunyn-Schmiedeberg's Arch. Pharmacol.*, 1986, **333**, 110.
236. P. S. Anderson, J. J. Baldwin, B. V. Clineschmidt, S. J. deSolms, J. P. Guare, C. A. Hunt, V. J. Lotti, D. J. Pettibone, W. C. Randall, Y. Sakurai, W. M. Sanders, J. P. Vacca and S. D. Young, 191st ACS National Meeting, New York, April 13–18, 1986, abstract no. 56.
237. D. J. Pettibone, B. V. Clineschmidt, V. J. Lotti, J. J. Baldwin, J. R. Huff, W. C. Randall, J. Vacca and S. D. Young, *Naunyn-Schmiedeberg's Arch. Pharmacol.*, 1987, **336**, 169.
238. E. S. Vizi, L. G. Harsing, J. Gaal, J. Kapocsi, S. Bernath and G. T. Somogyi, *J. Pharmacol. Exp. Ther.*, 1986, **238**, 701.
239. K. Kamada, S. Ono and Y. Abiko, *Arzneim.-Forsch.*, 1982, **32**, 39.
240. I. Muramatsu, M. Oshita and K. Yamanaka, *J. Pharmacol. Exp. Ther.*, 1983, **227**, 194.
241. K. Yamanaka, S. Kigoshi and I. Muramatsu, *Eur. J. Pharmacol.*, 1985, **106**, 625.
242. S. Kawazu, M. Suzuki, K. Negishi, J. Ishi, H. Sando, H. Katagiri, Y. Kanazawa, S. Yamanouchi, Y. Akanuma, H. Kajinuma, K. Suzuki, K. Watanabe, T. Itoh, T. Kobayashi and K. Kosaka, *Diabetes*, 1987, **36**, 221.
243. J. P. Hieble, J. M. Roesler, P. J. Fowler, W. D. Matthews and R. M. DeMarinis, in 'Vascular Neuroeffector Mechanisms', ed. J. A. Bevan, T. Godfraind, R. A. Maxwell, J. C. Stoclet and M. Worcel, Elsevier, Amsterdam, 1985, p. 159.
244. R. M. DeMarinis, J. P. Hieble and W. D. Matthews, *J. Med. Chem.*, 1983, **26**, 1213.
245. R. Daly, D. Ashton, A. Sulpizo and J. P. Hieble, *Fed. Proc., Fed. Am. Soc. Exp. Biol.*, 1987, **46** (3), 701.
246. F. R. Buhler, P. Bolli, F. W. Amann, P. Erne and W. Kiowski, *J. Cardiovasc. Pharmacol.*, 1984, **6**, S753.
247. J. L. Reid and J. Vincent, *Cardiology*, 1986, **73**, 164.
248. S. Z. Langer, N. Duval and R. Massingham, *J. Cardiovasc. Pharmacol.*, 1985, **7** (Suppl. 8), S1.
249. R. Sawyer, P. Warnock and J. R. Docherty, *J. Cardiovasc. Pharmacol.*, 1985, **7**, 809.
250. F. W. Amann, P. Bolli, W. Kiowski and F. R. Buhler, *Hypertension (Dallas)*, 1981, **3** (Suppl. 1), 119.
251. P. Bolli, P. Erne, W. Kiowski, F. W. Amann and F. R. Buhler, *Clin. Sci.*, 1985, **68** (Suppl. 10), 141s.
252. W. Kiowski, P. van Brummelen and F. R. Buhler, *Clin. Sci.*, 1979, **57**, 177s.
253. K. Jie, P. van Brummelen, P. Vermey, P. B. M. W. M. Timmermans and P. A. van Zwieten, *J. Cardiovasc. Pharmacol.*, 1986, **8**, 190.
254. J. P. Hieble, R. M. DeMarinis, P. J. Fowler and W. D. Matthews, *J. Pharmacol. Exp. Ther.*, 1986, **236**, 90.
255. J. M. Roessler, J. P. McCafferty, R. M. DeMarinis, W. D. Matthews and J. P. Hieble, *J. Pharmacol. Exp. Ther.*, 1986, **236**, 1.
256. S. Z. Langer and P. E. Hicks, *J. Cardiovasc. Pharmacol.*, 1984, **6** (Suppl. 4), S547.
257. H. O. Kalkman, M. J. M. C. Thoolen, P. B. M. W. M. Timmermans and P. A. van Zwieten, *J. Pharm. Pharmacol.*, 1984, **36**, 265.
258. P. Zandberg, P. B. M. W. M. Timmermans and P. A. van Zwieten, *J. Cardiovasc. Pharmacol.*, 1984, **6**, 256.
259. M. Gerold and G. Haeusler, *Naunyn-Schmiedeberg's Arch. Pharmacol.*, 1983, **322**, 29.
260. O. L. Woodman and S. F. Vatner, *J. Pharmacol. Exp. Ther.*, 1986, **237**, 86.
261. D. Elsner, D. J. Steward, O. Sommer, J. Holtz and E. Bassenge, *Hypertension (Dallas)*, 1986, **8**, 1003.
262. S. Algeo, C. P. Appleton, G. V. Martin, R. W. Lee, R. Mulkey, M. Olajos and S. Goldman, *J. Cardiovasc. Pharmacol.*, 1985, **7**, 1055.
263. R. J. Shebushki, T. Fujita and R. R. Ruffolo, *J. Pharmacol. Exp. Ther.*, 1986, **238**, 217.
264. A. L. Hyman and P. J. Kadowitz, *Am. J. Physiol.*, 1985, **249**, H891.
265. C. V. Leier, P. T. Heban, P. Huss, C. A. Bush and R. P. Lewis, *Circulation*, 1978, **58**, 466.
266. J. Holtz, M. Saeed, O. Sommer and E. Bassenge, *Eur. J. Pharmacol.*, 1982, **82**, 199.
267. G. Heusch, A. Deussen, J. Schipke and V. Thamer, *J. Cardiovasc. Pharmacol.*, 1984, **6**, 961.
268. G. A. Kopia, L. J. Kopaciewicz and R. R. Ruffolo, *J. Pharmacol. Exp. Ther.*, 1986, **239**, 641.
269. N. Decker and J. Schwartz, *J. Pharmacol. Exp. Ther.*, 1985, **232**, 251.
270. A. Deussen, G. Heusch and V. Thamer, *Eur. J. Pharmacol.*, 1985, **115**, 147.
271. P. B. M. W. M. Timmermans, in 'Handbook of Hypertension', ed. P. A. van Zwieten, Elsevier, Amsterdam, 1984, vol. 3, p. 102.
272. H. Schmitt, in 'Antihypertensive Agents', ed. F. Gross, Springer-Verlag, Berlin, 1977, p. 299.

273. H. Schmitt, H. Schmitt, J. R. Boissier and J. F. Guidicelli, *Eur. J. Pharmacol.*, 1967, **2**, 147.
274. H. Schmitt, H. Schmitt, J. R. Boissier, J. R. Guidicelli and J. Fichelle, *Eur. J. Pharmacol.*, 1968, **2**, 340.
275. G. Haeusler, *Naunyn-Schmiedeberg's Arch. Pharmacol.*, 1973, **278**, 231.
276. G. Tauberger and P. Kuhn, *Naunyn-Schmiedeberg's Arch. Pharmacol.*, 1971, **268**, 33.
277. T. Baum, A. T. Shropshire and L. L. Varner, *J. Pharmacol. Exp. Ther.*, 1972, **182**, 135.
278. T. Baum and A. T. Shropshire, *Eur. J. Pharmacol.*, 1976, **37**, 31.
279. T. Baum and A. T. Shropshire, *Neuropharmacology*, 1970, **9**, 305.
280. R. Waite, in 'Recent Advances in Hypertension', ed. P. Milliez and M. Safar, Boehringer, Ingelheim am Rheim, 1975. p. 27.
281. B. B. Wallin and M. Frisk-Holmberg, *Hypertension (Dallas)*, 1981, **3**, 340.
282. M. Laubie and H. Schmitt, *Prog. Brain Res.*, 1977, **47**, 337.
283. A. M. Huchet, J. Chelly and H. Schmitt, *Eur. J. Pharmacol.*, 1981, **71**, 455.
284. A. de Jonge, P. B. M. W. M. Timmermans and P. A. van Zwieten, *Naunyn-Schmiedeberg's Arch. Pharmacol.*, 1981, **317**, 8.
285. R. A. Gillis, P. J. Gatti and J. A. Quest, *J. Cardiovasc. Pharmacol.*, 1985, **7** (Suppl. 8), S38.
286. Z. Sreniawski, W. Kostowski and E. Widy-Tyszkiewicz, *Pol. J. Pharmacol. Pharm.*, 1976, **28**, 605.
287. J. Lypski, J. Przybylski and E. Solnika, *Eur J. Pharmacol.*, 1976, **38**, 19.
288. P. Zandberg, W. de Jong and D. de Wied, *Eur. J. Pharmacol.*, 1979, **55**, 43.
289. N. E. Anden, M. Grabowska and U. Strombom, *Naunyn-Schmiedeberg's Arch. Pharmacol.*, 1976, **292**, 43.
290. O. Curet, T. Dennis and B. Scvatton, *J. Pharmacol. Exp. Ther.*, 1987, **240**, 327.
291. W. Kobinger, *Rev. Physiol. Biochem. Pharmacol.*, 1978, **81**, 39.
292. G. L. Haeusler, *J. Cardiovasc. Pharmacol.*, 1982, **4**, S72.
293. T. Kubo, J. Nagura and Y. Misu, *J. Pharmacol. Exp. Ther.*, 1987, **240**, 298.
294. P. B. M. W. M. Timmermans, A. M. C. Schoop, H. Y. Kwa and P. A. van Zwieten, *Eur. J. Pharmacol.*, 1981, **70**, 7.
295. I. Zebrowska-Lupina, E. Przegalinski, M. Sloniec and Z. Kleinrock, *Naunyn-Schmiedeberg's Arch. Pharmacol.*, 1977, **297**, 227.
296. L. Pichler and W. Kobinger, *Naunyn-Schmiedeberg's Arch. Pharmacol.*, 181, **317**, 180.
297. H. Lal and S. Fielding (eds.), 'Psychopharmacology of Clonidine', Liss, New York, 1981, p. 1.
298. S. Fielding, T. C. Spaulding and H. Lal, in 'Psychopharmacology of Clonidine', ed. H. Lal and S. Fielding, Liss, New York, 1981, p. 226.
299. I. Gil-Ad, E. Topper and Z. Zaron, *Lancet*, 1979, **2**, 278.
300. G. R. van Loon, U. Scapagnini, G. P. Moberg and W. F. Ganong, *Endocrinology (Baltimore)*, 1971, **89**, 1464.
301. F. T. Crews, S. M. Paul and F. K. Goodwin, *Nature (London)*, 1981, **290**, 787.
302. T. Reisine, R. Johnson, R. Ursillo and H. I. Yamamura, *Biochem. Pharmacol.*, 1982, **31**, 63.
303. J. A. Scott and F. T. Crews, *J. Pharmacol. Exp. Ther.*, 1983, **224**, 640.
304. J. M. Goldstein, L. C. Knobloch and J. M. Malik, *Fed. Proc., Fed. Am. Soc. Exp. Biol.*, 1984, **43**, 941.
305. D. I. Crossley, '9th International Congress on Pharmacology, London', 1984, Abstract no. 1724P.
306. W. Hoefke and H. M. Jennewein, in 'Psychopharmacology of Clonidine', ed. H. Lal and S. Fielding, Liss, New York, 1981, p. 75.
307. M. S. Gold, D. E. Redmond and H. D. Kleber, *Lancet*, 1978, **1**, 599.
308. H. Lal and S. Fielding, *Trends Pharmacol. Sci.*, 1983, **4**, 70.
309. J. A. Steiner, A. J. Wilkins and W. Jenkins, *Br. J. Clin. Pharmacol.*, 1983, **15**, 583P.
310. A. H. Glassman, W. K. Jackson, B. T. Walsh, S. P. Roose and B. Rosenfeld, *Science (Washington, D.C.)*, 1984, **226**, 864.
311. D. E. Redmond and Y. H. Huang, *Life Sci.*, 1979, **25**, 2149.
312. R. Hoehnsaric, A. F. Merchant, M. L. Keyser and V. K. Smith, *Arch. Gen. Psychiatry*, 1981, **38**, 1278.
313. D. E. Redmond, *Trends Pharmacol. Sci.*, 1982, **3**, 477.
314. D. S. Charney, G. R. Heninger, D. E. Sternberg, K. M. Hafstad, S. Giddings and D. H. Landis, *Arch. Gen. Psychiatry*, 1982, **32**, 290.
315. D. S. Charney, G. R. Heninger and D. E. Redmond, *Life Sci.*, 1983, **33**, 19.
316. H. Scholtz, in 'Handbook of Experimental Pharmacology', ed. L. Szekeres, Springer-Verlag, Berlin, 1980, vol. 54/I, part I, p. 651.
317. B. G. Benfey, *Life Sci.*, 1982, **21**, 101.
318. H. J. Schumann, M. Endo and J. Wagner, *Naunyn-Schmiedeberg's Arch. Pharmacol.*, 1974, **284**, 13374.
319. A. Mugge, R. Bruckner, W. Meyer, W. Schmitz and H. Scholtz, *Naunyn-Schmiedeberg's Arch. Pharmacol.*, 1983, **324** (Suppl.), 130.
320. T. Skomedal, H. Aass, J. Osnes, N. B. Fjeld, G. Klingen, A. Langslet and G. Semb, *J. Pharmacol. Exp. Ther.*, 1985, **233**, 441.
321. K. H. Muntz, L. Meyer, S. Gadol and T. A. Calianos, *J. Pharmacol. Exp. Ther.*, 1986, **236**, 542.
322. A. Leimdorfer, *Am. J. Physiol.*, 1952, **171**, 742.
323. P. B. Corr and W. A. Crawford, *Am. Heart J.*, 1981, **102**, 605.
324. P. B. Corr, J. A. Shayman, J. B. Kramer and R. J. Kipnis, *J. Clin. Invest.*, 1981, **67**, 1232.
325. A. D. Sharma and P. B. Corr, in 'α-Adrenoceptor Blockers in Cardiovascular Disease', ed. H. Refsum and O. D. Mjos, Churchill Livingstone, New York, 1985, p. 249.
326. E. Bello-Reuss, R. E. Colindres, E. Pastoriza-Munoz, R. A. Mueller and C. W. Gottschalk, *J. Clin. Invest.*, 1975, **56**, 208.
327. G. F. DiBona and L. L. Sawin, *Am. J. Physiol.*, 1983, **245**, F322.
328. P. W. Wolff, F. A. Gesek and J. W. Strandhoy, *Fed. Proc., Fed. Am. Soc. Exp. Biol.*, 1985, **44**, 7692.
329. G. M. Drew and S. B. Whiting, *Br. J. Pharmacol.*, 1979, **67**, 207.
330. P. T. Horn, J. D. Kohl, J. J. Listinsky and L. I. Goldberg, *Naunyn-Schmiedeberg's Arch. Pharmacol.*, 1982, **318**, 166.
331. I. F. A. Hesse and E. J. Johns, *J. Auton. Pharmacol.*, 1984, **4**, 145.
332. P. W. de Leeuw, P. N. van Es, P. Vermey and W. H. Birkenhager, *Hypertension (Dallas)*, 1986, **8**, 836.
333. J. L. Osborn, H. Holdaas, M. D. Thames and G. F. DiBona, *Circ. Res.*, 1983, **53**, 298.
334. I. F. A. Hesse and E. J. Johns, *Br. J. Pharmacol.*, 1984, **84**, 715.
335. D. D. Smyth, S. Umemura and W. A. Pettinger, *Circ. Res.*, 1985, **57**, 304.
336. G. F. DiBona and L. L. Sawin, *Hypertension (Dallas)*, 1987, **9**, 41.
337. U. B. Olson, *Eur. J. Pharmacol.*, 1976, **36**, 95.

338. J. W. Strandhoy, M. Morris and V. M. Buckalew, *J. Pharmacol. Exp. Ther.*, 1982, **221**, 347.
339. M. Gellai and R. R. Ruffolo, *J. Pharmacol. Exp. Ther.*, 1987, **240**, 723.
340. A. Sanchez, M. J. Vidal, R. Martinez-Sierra and J. Saiz, *J. Pharmacol. Exp. Ther.*, 1986, **237**, 972.
341. W. A. Pettinger, *Hypertension (Dallas)*, 1987, **9**, 3.
342. H. C. Innemee, A. de Jonge, J. C. A. van Meel, P. B. M. W. M. Timmermans and P. A. van Zwieten, *Naunyn-Schmiedeberg's Arch. Pharmacol.*, 1981, **316**, 294.
343. W. D. Matthews, A. Sulpizio, P. J. Fowler, R. DeMarinis, J. P. Hieble and M. V. W. Bergamini, *Curr. Eye Res.*, 1984, **3**, 737.
344. E. Duzman, M. V. W. Bergamini, H. Mizoguchi and W. D. Matthews, in 'Recent Advances in Glaucoma', ed. U. Ticho and R. David, Elsevier, Amsterdam, 1984, p. 195.
345. H. C. Innemee and P. A. van Zwieten, *Albrecht von Graefes Arch. Klin. Exp. Ophthalmol.*, 1978, **207**, 149.
346. J. M. Rowland and D. E. Potter, *Ophthalmic Res.*, 1980, **12**, 221.
347. V. Miller and P. M. Vanhoutte, *Eur. J. Pharmacol.*, 1985, **118**, 123.
348. G. Tsujimoto, P. V. Timmis and B. B. Hoffman, *J. Pharmacol. Exp. Ther.*, 1986, **236**, 384.
349. S. Ueda, N. Satake and S. Shibata, *Eur. J. Pharmacol.*, 1984, **103**, 249.
350. M. Caine, *Fed. Proc., Fed. Am. Soc. Exp. Biol.*, 1986, **45**, 2604.
351. N. S. Docherty and A. A. Hancock, *J. Pharmacol. Exp. Ther.*, 1983, **225**, 269.
352. C. Korstanje, H. N. Doods, A. de Jonge, M. J. M. C. Thoolen, B. Wilffert, P. B. M. W. M. Timmermans and P. A. van Zwieten, *J. Auton. Pharmacol.*, 1984, **4**, 287.
353. R. R. Ruffolo, P. J. Rice, P. N. Patil, A. Hamada and D. D. Miller, *Eur. J. Pharmacol.*, 1984, **4**, 287.
354. S. Z. Langer, N. B. Shepperson and R. Massingham, *Clin. Sci.*, 1980, **59**, 225s.
355. S. Z. Langer and N. B. Shepperson, *J. Cardiovasc. Pharmacol.*, 1982, **4**, 8.
356. J. W. Constantine, D. Gunnel and R. A. Weeks, *Eur. J. Pharmacol.*, 1980, **66**, 281.
357. P. B. M. W. M. Timmermans, M. J. M. C. Thoolen, M. J. Mathy, B. Wilffert, A. de Jonge and P. A. van Zwieten, *Eur. J. Pharmacol.*, 1983, **96**, 187.
358. J. C. McGrath, N. A. Flavahan and C. E. McKean, *J. Cardiovasc. Pharmacol.*, 1982, **4**, 101.
359. C. A. Hamilton and J. L. Reid, *Cardiovasc. Res.*, 1982, **16**, 118.
360. C. Richer, F. Lefevre-Borg, J. Lechaire, C. Gomeni, R. Gomeni, J. F. Giudicelli and I. Cavero, *J. Pharmacol. Exp. Ther.*, 1987, **240**, 944.
361. N. B. Shepperson, N. Duval and S. Z. Langer, *Eur. J. Pharmacol.*, 1982, **81**, 627.
362. C. J. Waldron and P. E. Hicks, *J. Auton. Pharmacol.*, 1985, **5**, 333.
363. H. Madjar, J. R. Docherty and K. Starke, *J. Cardiovasc. Pharmacol.*, 1980, **2**, 619.
364. W. Kobinger and L. Pichler, *Eur. J. Pharmacol.*, 1981, **76**, 101.
365. W. Kiowski, U. L. Huethen, R. Ritz and F. Buhler, *Clin. Pharmacol. Ther.*, 1983, **34**, 565.
366. S. Yamada, N. Ashizawa, H. Udhijama, K. Nakayama, E. Hayashi and K. Honda, *J. Pharmacol. Exp. Ther.*, 1987, **242**, 326.

12.2

β-Adrenergic Receptors

BRIAN G. MAIN

ICI Pharmaceutical Division, Alderley Park, UK

12.2.1 INTRODUCTION

Adrenoceptors play a vital role in the control of the autonomic nervous system. Ahlquist's discovery[1] that the adrenergic system could be divided into two branches, named α and β, clarified greatly the ways in which the neurotransmitters adrenaline and noradrenaline controlled bodily function, particularly in the cardiovascular system, and this classification was made more complete by Lands dividing the β-system further into β_1 and β_2.[2]

The first successful drugs were β-agonists and β-antagonists designed to treat asthma and angina pectoris, respectively, but they were also found to be effective treatments for such diverse diseases as hypertension, glaucoma, heart failure, anxiety and obesity, these results being totally unexpected. The realization of these properties caused the pharmaceutical industry to expend a great deal of research effort into drugs with various profiles, and now literally dozens of β-adrenoceptor agonists, partial agonists and antagonists are available clinically for various indications.

On the academic side attention focussed more on trying to gain understanding of the structure and cellular mode of action of β-receptors and has culminated in the isolation, characterization and, recently, cloning of the receptors from various tissues, including human.

The aim of this chapter is to discuss the isolation and structure of the β-adrenoceptor in terms of its components, coupling and chemical identity, and then to describe the structure–activity relationships of drugs which bind to the receptor. A review of the clinical studies in each therapeutic area is then presented.

12.2.2 STRUCTURE OF THE CATECHOLAMINE NEUROTRANSMITTERS AND CLASSIFICATION OF ADRENERGIC RECEPTOR SUBTYPES

There are three catecholamine neurotransmitters, dopamine (1), adrenaline (2) and noradrenaline (3), the last two being referred to as epinephrine and norepinephrine in the USA. Dopamine is achiral but the others occur naturally in the $R(-)$ form shown, the $S(+)$ isomers being relatively inert. Noradrenaline is the transmitter released at nerve endings by stimulation of adrenergic nerves while adrenaline is a circulating hormone released by the adrenal gland in response to stress. The formation, distribution and metabolism of catecholamines is described in more detail in Chapter 12.1.

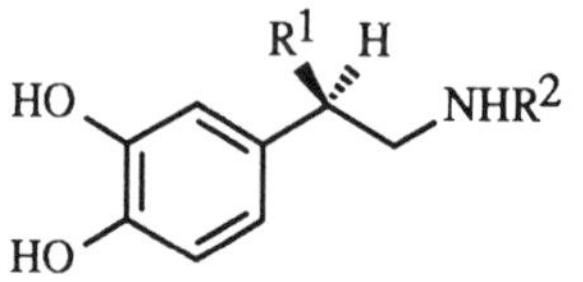

$$\textbf{(1)} \ R^1 = H, R^2 = H$$
$$\textbf{(2)} \ R^1 = OH, R^2 = Me$$
$$\textbf{(3)} \ R^1 = OH, R^2 = H$$

Catecholamines induce a variety of biological responses in mammalian systems, mainly in smooth muscle, the central nervous system (CNS) and the control of metabolism.[3] A number of synthetic analogues have been known for many years which exhibit some of the biological properties of the natural neurotransmitters but, and this has caused much frustration, each of these is subtly different from the others and it became impossible to define accurately the properties of a 'typical adrenergic agonist'. For example, noradrenaline accelerates heart rate and constricts blood vessels in situations where adrenaline accelerates heart rate while relaxing blood vessels.

It was not until 1948 that the first order was introduced into this miscellany of actions by Ahlquist,[1] who examined the effects of a series of catecholamine-mimetic (often termed sympathomimetic) amines on a variety of adrenergic responses. The observed potencies fell into two distinct groups and Ahlquist concluded that two different receptors must be present in the adrenergic nervous system, and named them alpha (α) and beta (β). α-Agonists generally cause constriction of smooth muscle and β-agonists relaxation, with the notable exception of cardiac muscle where β-agonists cause an increase in both the rate and force of contraction. The effects of adrenergic agonists are due, therefore, to the balance of α- and β-properties which they possess, hence the predominantly α-agonist noradrenaline causes vasoconstriction, while the more β-agonist adrenaline causes vasodilation. Both amines increase heart rate due to their β-properties, α-agonists having no effect on atrial muscle.

In 1967 Lands and co-workers[2] clarified the situation still further when, in a similar manner to Ahlquist, they compared the potencies of a number of β-adrenergic agonists on lipolysis, cardiac stimulation, bronchodilation and vasodilation. The drugs fell into two clear classes, which had greater potency either on the heart and lipolysis or on the lungs and blood vessels. Lands concluded that β-receptors existed in two types which he designated β_1 (acting on the heart and adipose tissue) and β_2 (in the lungs and blood vessels). This explained most experimental observations and, in a further paper,[4] Lands' group expanded the classification by the study of the same series of drugs in other tissues. Collier and Dornhorst[5] demonstrated, two years later, the existence of the two receptor subtypes in man and the hypothesis gained increasing acceptance until the early 1970s when papers began to appear suggesting that Lands's β_1/β_2 concept was an oversimplification.

The first report came from a Swedish group[6] who demonstrated that both β_1- and β_2-receptors were present in cardiac atrial tissue, though not in ventricle (β_1 only) and, incidentally, gave expression to the idea of a 'force selective' β-stimulant. This paper was followed by many others from both pharmacological and biochemical research groups suggesting that tissues may contain not one subtype of β-receptor, but a *preponderance* of that subtype. Hence atrial tissue contains an excess (4:1) of β_1-receptors[7] while bronchial tissue contains an excess (3:1) of β_2-receptors,[8] suggesting that absolute tissue selectivity of drug action by β_1- or β_2-specific ligands is unattainable. These results were confirmed by Brodde *et al.*[9] in human right atrium (ratio 4:1) and Heitz *et al.*[10a] in human left atrium and ventricle (ratio approx. 2:1 in each case). A recent paper[10b] suggests that the bovine coronary artery contains a homogeneous population of β_1-receptors, one of the few such cases.

Following Ariëns and Simonis's hypothesis[11] that separate β-receptors might exist for neurotransmitter noradrenaline (β-T) and hormonal adrenaline (β-H), Bryan *et al.*[12] studying rat, guinea pig and cat atria, suggested that β_1-receptors are 'innervated' β-receptors (β-T) and β_2-receptors are 'hormonal' receptors (β-H). This is an interesting idea to explain the reasons for two receptor subtypes being present in one tissue. For a more detailed discussion of this topic the reader is referred to a review by Molinoff.[13]

It should be remembered that demonstrating the presence of a receptor subtype in a tissue by radioligand binding does not demonstrate that this subtype has functional significance. Biological response in an isolated tissue is a result of receptor occupancy and receptor–response coupling, while in a whole animal this response may be masked by various reflex systems. It is also important to note that β_1/β_2 receptor ratios vary markedly between species and so the direct transference of a result from even an *in vivo* experiment to man should be attended by extreme caution. For most practical purposes the classification laid out in Lands papers[2,4] holds true.

The β-receptor subtypes present in various tissues are shown in Table 1. Ref. 14 provides useful reading on this topic.

A second complication of the simple $\alpha/\beta_1/\beta_2$ theory came with the discovery[15] of compounds which act on brown adipose tissue (BAT or 'brown fat') in a manner which, though demonstrably β-adrenergic in nature, corresponds to neither β_1- nor β_2-selectivity (see Section 12.2.7.6).

In a series of papers Arch and co-workers[16a] described this BAT receptor as an 'atypical β-receptor'—often referred to in conversation, though not yet in print, as a β_3-receptor. While

Table 1 Effects of Adrenoceptor Agonists on Various Tissues

Tissue	Effect	α	Receptor type β_1	β_2
Heart	Rate	—	Increase	Increase
	Force of contraction	—	Increase	
	Coronary blood vessels	Constriction	Dilation	Dilation
Blood vessels	Vascular tone	Constriction	—	Dilation
Lung	Bronchial muscle tone	—	?	Relaxation
Uterus	Uterine muscle tone	Constriction	—	Relaxation
Pancreas	Insulin release	Inhibition?	—	Stimulation
Muscle and liver	Glycogenolysis	Stimulation?	—	Stimulation
Adipose tissue (white)	Lipolysis	—	Stimulation	—
Adipose tissue (brown)	Calorigenesis	—	Stimulation?	—
Skeletal muscle	Tension	—	—	Decrease
Intestine	Smooth muscle tone	Relaxation	Relaxation	Relaxation
Kidney	Renin release	—	Increase	—
Salivary gland	Secretion	—	Increase	—
Urinary bladder	Muscle tone	—	—	Relaxation

this receptor is not fully characterized at present, the large amount of current research in this area suggests that it soon will be. Early stages of biochemical characterization suggest the receptor to be a β_1 subtype.[16b]

In addition to the postsynaptic receptors mentioned above it has been known for some years that prejunctional β-receptors exist.[17] Activation of these receptors facilitates release of noradrenaline when the nerves are stimulated, and therefore augments the normal response. These presynaptic receptors are probably mainly of the β_2-type, although some β_1-systems are known, and Rand and Majewski[18] have developed an interesting hypothesis suggesting that they may be involved in the development of hypertension.

They suggest that stress-induced adrenaline release causes uptake of adrenaline into sympathetic nerve terminals which then, on stimulation of the nerve, is coreleased with noradrenaline and, by stimulation of presynaptic β-receptors, causes more noradrenaline to be released, causing excessive vasoconstriction. Over long periods this could lead to hypertension, and indeed it does so in rats which are treated chronically with adrenaline. Presynaptic β-receptors have been reviewed by Misu and Kubo[19a] and by Borkowski.[19b]

12.2.3 CELLULAR ACTIONS OF CATECHOLAMINES AT β-RECEPTORS

12.2.3.1 β-Receptor Coupling

In 1967 Robison, Butcher and Sutherland proposed that occupation of β-receptors by catecholamines caused activation of the enzyme adenylate cyclase (AC).[20] The cyclic adenosine monophosphate (cAMP) produced was a 'second messenger', amplifying the effect and initiating a biochemical cascade which led, ultimately, to an observable biological response such as the contraction of cardiac muscle. This process could be illustrated by the simple model shown in Figure 1, where the receptor R is directly linked to the catalytic unit, C, of the adenylate cyclase. The link between β-receptor and AC is now accepted universally but continued study has shown that the simple model is inadequate, and more complete models have been devised to accommodate new concepts such as the role of guanine nucleotide regulating proteins and receptor desensitization.

In the mid 1970s it became apparent that in addition to the receptor unit R and catalytic unit C a third protein was present. This is the guanine nucleotide regulatory protein G, first isolated by Pfeuffer and Helmreich,[21] which acts as a shuttle, linking activated R to C. It should be noted that many early papers term this protein N protein. Binding of an agonist to the R protein causes a conformational change (to R*) which enables it to bind, in the presence of GTP, to G protein. This activated complex then binds to C and enzymic activity is produced. Inactivation is caused by hydrolysis of the GTP to GDP, causing collapse of the complex and a return to the starting state, R. Binding of antagonists to R does not cause the conformational change necessary to bind G protein, and activation of the C unit cannot occur. The exact mechanism by which these changes occur is not known, but the evidence has been reviewed by a number of authors.[22-24]

Since this time a still more complete (and complex) picture has emerged with the discovery that G protein has three subunits (α, β, γ) and also that in parallel with the stimulatory situation described

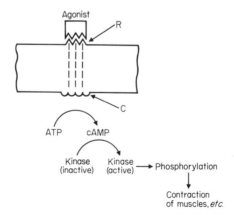

Figure 1 An early model of β-receptor coupling

above (the components are now termed R_s, R_s^*, G_s) there exists an inhibitory receptor R_i (*e.g.* α_2 or opiate receptors) coupling through an inhibitory G_i to the same catalytic unit. The only difference between G_s and G_i is in the α unit (α_s and α_i), the β and γ units being identical in each case. The current view of the system is depicted in Figure 2. Combination of agonist and receptor causes the conformational change to R^* and, in the presence of GTP and magnesium ion, interaction of the receptor with the G_s complex occurs, forming a ternary complex $R^*\beta\gamma$ and liberating the α_s.GTP unit which binds to, and activates, the catalytic unit C by forming a trimer α_s.GTP.C. Hydrolysis of the GTP to GDP releases α_s which then recombines with its β and γ units to release R^* which may then dissociate back to R. The whole system is a series of equilibria which, in the presence of sufficient GTP, *etc.*, is controlled by the concentration of agonist. An exactly analogous situation occurs when an inhibitory receptor is activated, but the α_i.GTP.C complex is incapable of catalyzing the hydrolysis of ATP.

It is difficult to state clearly where this model was first proposed, as it seems to have arisen by steady evolution from earlier models. For example Shorr, Lefkowitz and Caron[25] quote eleven papers reviewing the area, and several other reviews[26, 27] should probably be included in this list from the period 1980–4, illustrating the gradual refinement of the model. Recently Levitzki[28] has reviewed the current state of knowledge.

12.2.3.2 β-Receptor Desensitization

Prolonged exposure of β-receptors to β-agonists causes progressive loss of biological effect, a process known as desensitization (see Chapter 11.2). Though this is very marked in the biochemical situation, in man it is evident only when tolerance develops to β-agonists inhaled for the relief of asthma, and in the reduced effect of β-agonists on the hearts of patients suffering chronic heart failure.[29]

When exposure of a cell to an agonist causes loss of responsiveness to just that agonist the desensitization is termed homologous; when responsiveness to other AC-coupled receptors is lost as well then it is termed heterologous. Both types are known with β-receptors, although the former is more usual. An excellent review of this topic is available.[30] The first stage of homologous desensitization is the 'clustering' or local sequestration of agonist-bound β-receptors in a compartment of the cell which is out of contact with the catalytic unit of AC.[31, 32] This stage is reversible, but, recently, a cytosolic enzyme, β-adrenergic receptor kinase (β-ARK) has been discovered[33] which phosphorylates the receptor irreversibly. β-ARK is translocated from the cytosol to the plasma membrane when β-agonist is present, and will not phosphorylate the receptor unless this agonist is present. The enzyme has been partially purified[34] and shown to phosphorylate solely on serine; unlike all other biological actions stimulated by β-agonists this phosphorylation is cAMP independent.[35]

This desensitization causes physical loss of β-receptors and β-receptor density in the membrane is reduced markedly; the effect can be prevented by pretreatment with β-antagonists. In an interesting paper on the thermal and enzymic stability of β-receptors Baker and Potter[36] showed that there are

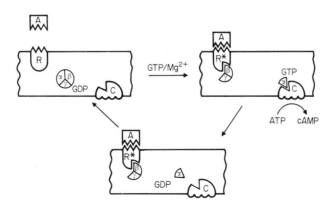

Figure 2 A more recent model of β-receptor coupling

three distinct physical forms of the receptor: agonist occupied, antagonist occupied and unoccupied. It is only the first of these that can be desensitized.

12.2.3.3 Purification of the Components of the β-Receptor Complex

Major efforts have been made to isolate, purify and characterize the components of the β-receptor/AC complex, and these have culminated recently in considerable success. Pfeuffer's group[37] have isolated AC from rabbit myocardial membranes, achieving a 60 000-fold purification to what appears to be two proteins, one of M_r 150 000 which corresponds to the catalytic unit itself, and one of M_r 42 000 which they believe to be the α_s subunit of the associated G_s protein. The components of G_s and G_i protein have been isolated; α_s has an M_r of 45 000, while that of α_i is 41 000; the β unit is slightly smaller (M_r 35 000), while the third protein γ has an M_r of only 10 000. The properties of G proteins have been reviewed by Gilman.[38]

The purification of the β-receptor unit R has been achieved in a number of systems, using the techniques of solubilization with digitonin, HPLC, and affinity chromatography using alprenolol coupled to sepharose.[39,40] The first successful isolation was the β_2-receptor from frog erythrocytes;[41] it is a single protein of M_r 58 000. The β_1-receptor from turkey erythrocytes was partially purified in 1977,[40] and then purified to homogeneity in 1982;[42] it comprises two proteins M_r 40 000 and 45 000 (in a ratio of *ca.* 3:1) which have identical binding properties. This was demonstrated by pre-incubation with the ^{125}I-labelled photoaffinity β-ligand *p*-azidobenzylcarazolol, when both of the isolated proteins were shown to carry the radiolabel. The chemistry of this useful probe was published in 1983.[43]

The properties of the β-receptor isolated from various species are listed in a review by Shorr *et al.*[25] The most relevant data, of course, are those from human: β_1-receptors have been isolated from cardiac muscle[44] and from placenta;[45a, b] the former contains a single polypeptide M_r 62 000 and the latter contains two peptides M_r 65 000 and 54 000.

One convincing way of demonstrating that the proteins isolated are indeed the true components of the β-receptor complex is to recombine the elements of the system and regenerate AC activity. Pure β-receptor polypeptide from several sources was inserted into phospholipid vesicles and fused with *Xenopus laevis* erythrocyte cells which contain the G_s and C units but have no β-receptors.[46] Responsiveness was restored, and this displayed the usual specificity for β-agonists.

A joint group from Jerusalem and Wurzburg went one stage further when they used purified C unit from bovine brain and rabbit heart, G_s from rabbit liver and turkey erythrocytes, and β-receptor protein from turkey erythrocytes.[47] Fusion of the three components led again to AC activity. Receptor reconstitution studies have been reviewed by Lefkowitz *et al.*[48] and by Levitzki.[49]

Recently the mammalian β_2-receptor gene has been cloned and the primary amino acid sequence determined on the purified receptor protein produced.[50a, b] Some aspects of tertiary structure have been deduced, indicating seven hydrophobic regions which would reside in the plasma membrane, two sites of *N*-glycosylation near the amino terminus on the outside of the cell, and a serine and threonine-rich carboxy terminus on the inside.[51a] These and further studies[51b] suggest considerable homology between β-adrenergic, muscarinic and rhodopsin receptors.

12.2.4 ASSAYS FOR β-RECEPTOR ACTIVITY

When considering β-receptor activity only two basic measurements are important: potency (affinity) and degree of agonism. From these a third parameter may be derived—selectivity, the ratio of potencies for different receptors. A third relevant measurement, though less important, is the lipophilicity of a ligand; this is usually defined as 'log P'—the log of the partition coefficient of the ligand between octan-1-ol and water; it may also be calculated (see Chapter 18.7).

The greatest problems encountered when measuring the properties of β-adrenoceptor ligands are the effects of the various reflex mechanisms which counter the direct actions of the drug,[52] and the effect of interspecies variation. This variation is profound, and is noted most particularly when measuring degree of agonism (*e.g.* prenalterol is a full agonist in the cat,[53] but a partial agonist in the dog[54]), and when considering β_1/β_2 selectivity (*e.g.* salbutamol is 100-fold β_2/β_1 selective in the guinea pig, but only seven-fold in the cat[55]).

The critical parameters may be determined in three types of system: purely biochemical, *e.g.* a receptor binding assay; *in vitro*, in an isolated organ; or *in vivo*, in animal models with varying degrees of sophistication. These options will be considered briefly, and listed in Table 2.

Table 2 Biological Tests for the Evaluation of β-Receptor Ligands

Type	Description of test	Ref.
In vitro (biochemical)	(i) Displacement of ^{3}H-alprenolol binding from canine myocardial membranes (β_1)	65
	(ii) As above, using rat lung membranes (β_2)	66
	(iii) cAMP production	67
In vitro (tissue bath)	(i) Increase in rate and force of contraction of guinea pig atria (β_1) and relaxation of guinea pig tracheal chains (β_2) by β-agonists	68
	(ii) Reversal of the above effects caused by noradrenaline (β_1) or fenoterol (β_2), by β-antagonists	58
	(iii) Decrease in tension of cat soleus muscle by β_2 agonists	63
In vivo	(i) Increase in heart rate (HR) of catecholamine-depleted rats by β_1 (partial) agonists	59
	(ii) Increase in HR and reduction in hind limb perfusion pressure in the reserpinized, vagotomized cat, measuring β_1 and β_2 affinity and partial agonism	60
	(iii) Similar to (ii) using the reserpinized, denervated, anaesthetized dog	61
	(iv) Reversal of isoprenaline-induced tachycardia and reduction of blood pressure in the vagotomized cat by β-antagonists	59
	(v) Reversal of AcCh-induced bronchospasm in the guinea pig, by β_2-agonists	62

12.2.4.1 *In Vitro* Assays

12.2.4.1.1 *Biochemical assays*

The advent of radiolabelled ligands, in particular ^{3}H-dihydroalprenolol,[56] led to the establishment of assays which measure the ability of ligands to displace these radiolabels from membrane fractions containing β-receptors. Reversible binding and stereospecificity may be demonstrated in these systems; they give useful estimates of affinity, but no indication of agonist or antagonist status and, obviously, can give no information on any aspect of metabolism (*e.g.* 'prodrugs' will be inactive). As stimulation of β-receptors causes an increase in cAMP production this may be used as a measure of agonist potency.[57]

12.2.4.1.2 *Tissue bath assays*

These convenient assays measure directly the effect of an agonist on a target organ having the appropriate β_1/β_2 selectivity, a subject reviewed by Molinoff.[13] Conversely, antagonism of the effect of a standard agonist in these systems may be measured.

In view of the mixed populations of β_1- and β_2-receptors found in some tissues O'Donnell and Wanstall[58] have recommended that for the best estimates of potency (and therefore selectivity) β_1-agonists such as noradrenaline should be used for measuring antagonism in β_1-tissues (*e.g.* atria), while β_2-agonists such as fenoterol should be used in β_2-systems (*e.g.* uterus). This seems a very sensible suggestion.

12.2.4.2 *In Vivo* Assays

Models vary in complexity depending on the degree to which reflex systems have been neutralized or suppressed. Administration of a β-agonist to an animal which, simply, has been anaesthetized gives no useful information whatsoever, as the existing heart rate and blood pressure vary widely between individual animals. Vagotomy abolishes the parasympathetic reflex,[59] catecholamine depletion reduces the sympathetic reflex,[60] while both of these coupled with section of the sympathetic nerves and perfusion of an artery at constant flow gives a virtually isolated β_1- and β_2-system *in vivo*.[61]

β_2-Effects in pulmonary systems are often measured by the ability of β_2-agonists to reverse the severe bronchospasm induced by administration of histamine or acetylcholine.[62] The very low bronchial tone observed in control animals makes the assay less sensitive to reflex effects than in models measuring blood pressure.

Three final assays worthy of mention are partial agonism in the catecholamine depleted rat (β_1),[59] tremor in the cat soleus muscle (β_2),[63] and non-shivering thermogenesis in the 'cafeteria-fed' rat

('β_3'), where β-agonists induce, acutely, an increase in thermogenesis and, chronically, a loss in weight.[64] The most common primary assay for β_2-bronchodilators has been the isolated guinea pig tracheal chain preparation. This has some intrinsic tone and the ability of a β_2-agonist to cause relaxation may be measured readily, and a pD_2 value calculated.[68]

β_1-Agonism is usually quantified by measuring heart rate response in isolated guinea pig atrium, and, therefore, from the above pD_2 values a value for β_1/β_2 selectivity may be computed.[68]

Generally, β-antagonist parameters have been measured in an anaesthetized, vagotomized cat, in which tachycardia and hypotension in response to isoprenaline injection are measured.[60] The antagonism of these responses by a test substance enables potency and selectivity to be calculated. Similar values may be obtained *in vitro* using guinea pig atrial and tracheal responses to isoprenaline.[58]

Details and references for all these tests are displayed in Table 2.

12.2.5 CHEMICAL STRUCTURE OF THE MAJOR CLASSES OF β-ADRENERGIC LIGANDS

The main classes of β-adrenergic ligand are based on the structure of three important neurotransmitters, dopamine (**1**), adrenaline (**2**) and noradrenaline (**3**).

Dopamine possesses α-, β_1- and β_2-agonist properties, but despite this lack of selectivity it has been used as a cardiac stimulant in the treatment of heart failure.[69] As it is only active after parenteral administration, attempts have been made to introduce sufficient stability into the molecule to enable the derivatives to be administered orally and maintain an adequate duration of action. One such derivative is ibopamine (**4**),[70] the diisobutyryl ester prodrug of *N*-methyldopamine (epinine). This drug is, indeed, active orally, though the duration of action is rather short.[71] Aspects of the pharmacology, metabolism and clinical investigation of ibopamine have been reported in a special issue of 'Arzneimittel-Forschung.'[72]

Modification of the structure of dopamine by addition of a *p*-hydroxyphenylbutylamine side chain causes loss of most of the α- and β_2-effects, and dobutamine (**5**)[73] is a short-acting β_1-stimulant which is inactive orally and which, therefore, has been developed for i.v. infusion in the hospital situation where short term cardiac stimulation is required,[74,75] mainly for support in the heart failure situation. The claims for β_1-selectivity have been challenged,[76] but dobutamine is still used widely in situations where cardiac stimulation is required acutely, but without the concomitant vasodilation caused by isoprenaline.

The final class of dopamine-related drugs contain the phenethylamine unit as part of a tetrahydroisoquinoline ring system. Thus trimetoquinol (**6**) is a non-selective β-agonist,[77,78] while the dichloro analogue (**7**) is a moderately potent β-antagonist.[79] The fully aromatic isoquinolines (**8**) are also claimed to be β-antagonists.[80]

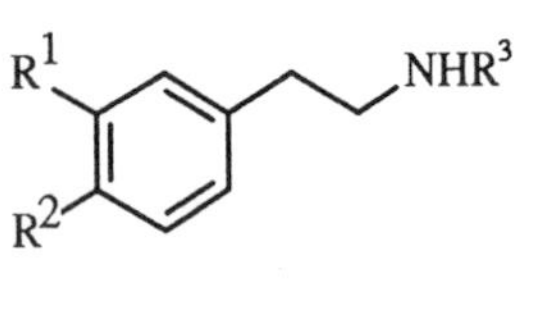

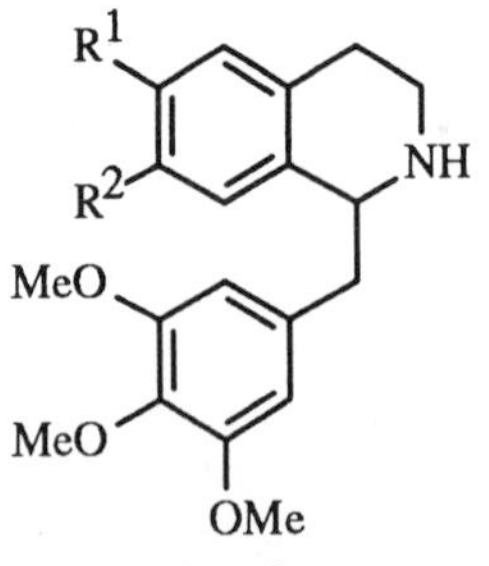

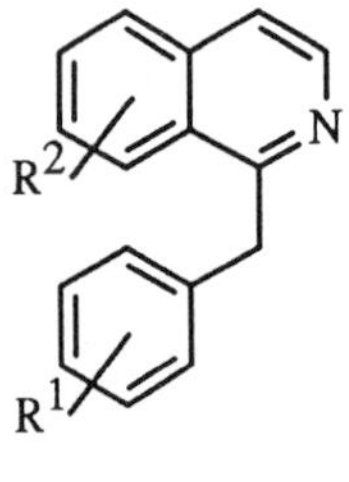

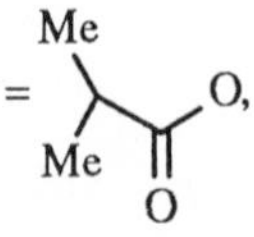

(**4**) $R^1 = R^2 = $ [Me, Me, O] structure, $R^3 = $ Me

(**5**) $R^1 = R^2 = $ OH, $R^3 = $ [Me structure with OH]

(**6**) $R^1 = R^2 = $ OH

(**7**) $R^1 = R^2 = $ Cl

(**8**) $R^1 = $ alkoxy, $R^2 = $ halogen

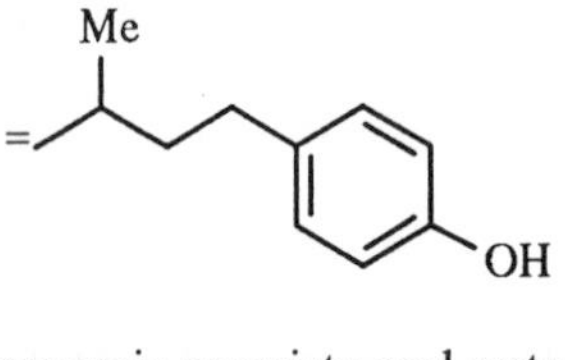

The majority of β-adrenergic agonists and antagonists are related chemically to the arylethanolamine structure of (nor)adrenaline. Increasing the size of the nitrogen substituent from hydrogen (noradrenaline) through methyl (adrenaline) to isopropyl (isoprenaline; **9**) causes progressive loss of α-stimulant activity, isoprenaline being a virtually pure β-stimulant.[81] In 1958 Mills, of the Eli Lilly Company, prepared an analogue, dichlorisoprenaline (DCI, **10**), which proved to be pivotal in the development of both β-agonists and antagonists. Powell and Slater,[82] and then Moran and Perkins[83] showed that DCI is a partial β-agonist, causing direct cardiac stimulation while also antagonizing the stimulant effects of catecholamines. DCI has a far longer duration of action than isoprenaline (which is 3-*O*-methylated by catechol-*O*-methyl transferase, COMT), and hence it offered medicinal chemists the scope for producing a useful drug.

By maintaining one of the catechol hydroxyl groups, β-agonists were developed for the treatment of heart failure and asthma, while by preparing non-phenols, as in DCI, β-antagonists were developed for the treatment of cardiac disease. For convenience SAR will now be discussed in Sections 12.2.6 and 12.2.7), dealing with β-agonists, β-antagonists and partial β-agonists.

12.2.6 β-AGONISTS

Bronchial asthma is characterized by breathlessness resulting from constriction of the airways.[84] One means of relieving this distressing condition is the utilization of the bronchodilating effects of β-agonists ($β_2$-effect), and it is to this end that most β-agonist research has been directed.

Isoprenaline (isoproterenol in the USA) (**9**) is an effective, though short acting, bronchodilator,[85] its use being limited severely by the potent cardiac and vascular properties which it also possesses. DCI (**10**) is a longer acting, orally effective derivative, whose usefulness is also limited by its cardiac effects (see Section 12.2.5). In the 1960s concerted efforts were made to produce drugs which maintained the duration and stability of DCI but which lacked the cardiac effects. Although the situation was not appreciated at first, the challenge was, in fact, to produce a $β_2$-agonist without $β_1$-effects.

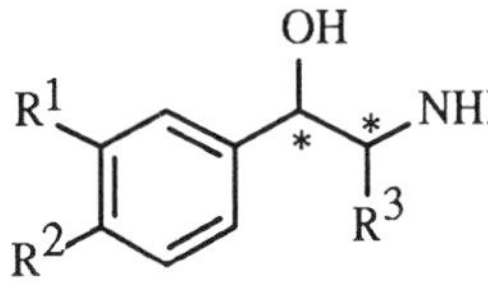

(**9**) $R^1 = R^2 = OH$, $R^3 = H$, $R^4 = Pr^i$

(**10**) $R^1 = R^2 = Cl$, $R^3 = H$, $R^4 = Pr^i$

(**11**) $R^1 = R^2 = OH$, $R^3 = $ alkyl, $R^4 = Pr^i$

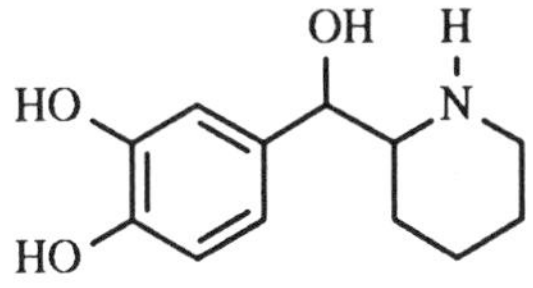

(**12**)

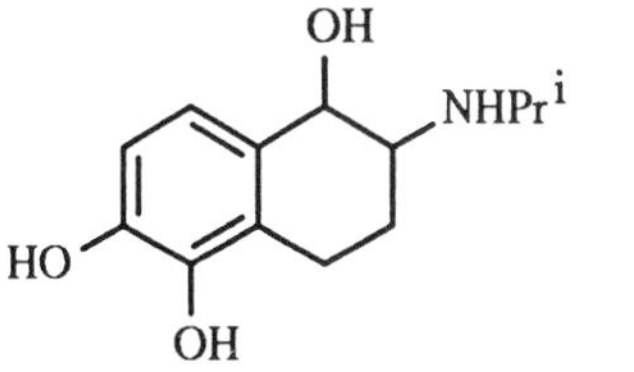

(**13**)

Isoprenaline possesses three key structural units: an aromatic (catechol) ring, an ethanol group and a secondary amine. All were shown to be essential, and early work established that chirality at the benzylic carbon atom is crucial, in all cases the $R(-)$ isomer possessing the β-adrenergic activity,[86,87] as discussed as long ago as 1933.[88] Bulky amino substituents suppress α- and augment β-adrenergic activity,[81,84,89] isopropyl and *t*-butyl groups being particularly favourable. Pratesi *et al.*[89] have attempted to explain this by estimating the pK_a values, steric volume (*E*) and lipophilicity (Hansch π value) of the nitrogen substituent in a series of catecholamines. The results suggest that activity may be estimated solely from the steric volume parameter, as described by the regression equations (1) and (2), in which *E* is the van der Waals molecular volume.

$$pD_2(\text{trachea}) = 5.99 + 1.87E - 0.45E^2 \quad (R^2 = 0.977, \quad n = 221) \tag{1}$$

$$pD_2(\text{atria}) = 6.64 + 3.24E - 1.09E^2 \quad (R^2 = 0.955, \quad n = 100) \tag{2}$$

From these equations it may be seen that peak activity arises with isopropyl substitution in the atria (*E* = 1.5), and *t*-butyl substitution in the trachea (*E* = 2.2).

Substitution at the α-carbon atom of the ethanol unit has given compounds (**11**) with varying potency and selectivity. Lands *et al.*[90] reported that α-ethylisoprenaline (isoetharine) was a potent β-stimulant, while α-methyl and α-propyl derivatives were not, while Lands and Brown,[91] Barlow[92] and Triggle[93] reported a decrease of adrenergic activity with α-substitution. The stereochemistry of the two centres {marked * in structure (**11**)} is vital, for example only the (−) *erythro* isomer of isoetharine has β-agonist activity.[94]

Derivatives have been prepared where α-substituents have been incorporated into rings: rimiterol (**12**)[95] and the hydroxyamino tetralins (**13**)[96] both possess potent β-stimulant activity, the former being selective for β_2-receptors.[97]

The major research effort has been devoted to studies of the substitution of the aromatic ring. Catecholamines are rapidly metabolized; catechol-*O*-methyltransferase (COMT) methylates the hydroxyl group *meta* to the side chain[98] and, on oral dosing, the catechol group is readily sulfated in the gut, preventing absorption.[99] Three groups made attempts to circumvent this metabolism; the Boehringer workers prepared the isomer of isoprenaline, orciprenaline (**14**),[100] which was not a substrate for COMT, and which was active orally, though it had no selectivity for the lung. Lands' paper on β_1/β_2 receptor subtypes[3] prompted a Swedish group to investigate the SAR of amino substitution in the orciprenaline series[101] and they showed that while increasing the bulk of this amino group decreased potency on the guinea pig atrium (β_1), potency in the tracheal (β_2) preparation increased from isopropyl to *t*-butyl before declining with further substitution.

This meant that the *selectivity* was greater for the *t*-butyl compound, named subsequently terbutaline (**15**)—the first β_2-selective agonist; this selectivity arises from both an increase in β_2-potency and a decrease in β_1-potency. A very similar profile of activity was observed in a series of cycloalkylamines, where the cyclobutylamino compound was as selective as terbutaline. These selectivities are represented in Figure 3 and parallel exactly the results in the catecholamine series mentioned previously.[89] Extension of this work by the synthesis of terbutaline derivatives containing dobutamine-like side chains gave a very β_2-selective compound, fenoterol (**16**).[102]

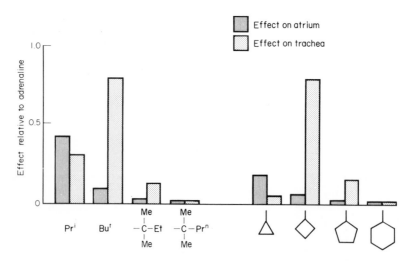

(**14**) R = Pr[i]   (**16**) R =
(**15**) R = Bu[t]

A second approach to the avoidance of COMT inactivation was made by a group from Mead-Johnson when they attempted to mimic the susceptible *meta* hydroxyl group by the incorporation of a methane sulfonamide moiety (pK_a 8.35). The result, soterenol (**17**),[103] was a potent β_2-agonist which is not a substrate for COMT. The isomer (**18**) was not active, indicating the importance of the *para* hydroxyl group.[104]

At around the same time a group at Allen and Hanbury attempted to block the effects of COMT by interposing a methylene group between the *meta* hydroxyl group and the aromatic ring of

Figure 3   The effect on β_1/β_2 selectivity of varying the isopropyl group of orciprenaline (**14**) (reproduced from ref. 101 by permission of the authors)

isoprenaline.[105] They prepared a series of saligenin derivatives, many of which were potent, selective, β_2-stimulants. Of these AH 3365, salbutamol (albuterol in the USA) (19) was selected,[106] and this is now the leading drug in the area of β_2-selective bronchodilators, being active intravenously, by inhalation, and orally. The positional isomer of salbutamol (20) is, as with soterenol, inactive as a β-stimulant;[107] and only the *R* isomer of salbutamol is a β-agonist.[108]

Salbutamol is unaffected by COMT, and is sulfated to a lesser extent than isoprenaline. With terbutaline and soterenol it established that β_2-selective agonists could be made that were long acting, and were effective treatments for asthma.[84,109] The main problems with such agents are the β_2-mediated vasodilation, which may cause reflex tachycardia, and a skeletal muscle tremor which is also a β_2-receptor response; both may be reduced by administering the drug directly into the lung by aerosol. Some efforts have been made to separate bronchial from vascular and skeletal muscle effects, but without real success, suggesting that the receptors are identical.

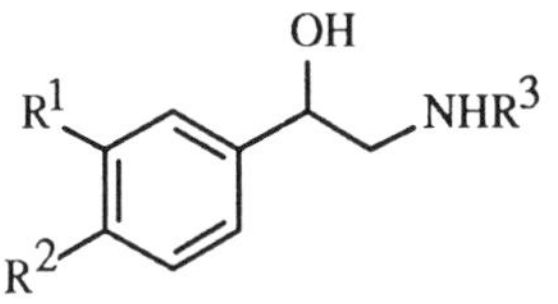

(17) $R^1 = MeSO_2NH$, $R^2 = OH$, $R^3 = Pr^i$
(18) $R^1 = OH$, $R^2 = MeSO_2NH$, $R^3 = Pr^i$
(19) $R^1 = CH_2OH$, $R^2 = OH$, $R^3 = Bu^t$
(20) $R^1 = OH$, $R^2 = CH_2OH$, $R^3 = Bu^t$
(21) $R^1 = CMe_2OH$, $R^2 = OH$, $R^3 = Bu^t$

(22) $R^1 = NHC(O)$—C$_6$H$_4$—OH, $R^2 = OH$, $R^3 = Bu^t$
(23) $R^1 = NHCHO$, $R^2 = OH$, $R^3 = Bu^t$
(24) $R^1 = CH_2NHSO_2Me$, $R^2 = OH$, $R^3 = Bu^t$
(25) $R^1 = CH_2SO_2Me$, $R^2 = OH$, $R^3 = Bu^t$
(26) $R^1 = NHSO_2NMe_2$, $R^2 = OH$, $R^3 = Bu^t$
(27) $R^1 = NH_2$, $R^2 = OH$, $R^3 = Bu^t$

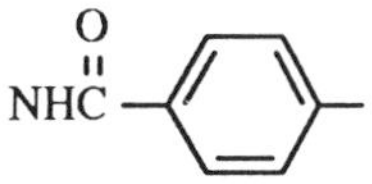

The successful modification of the isoprenaline structure to salbutamol prompted much research into the SAR. The question could be posed: what is the catechol group actually doing? Lunts[109] lists several possibilities for the parameters significant in a *meta* substituent: (i) size; (ii) electronic effects; (iii) capacity to form hydrogen bonds (donor or acceptor); (iv) acidity; (v) ability to chelate metals (assisted by a *para* hydroxyl group); and (vi) capacity to form a redox system (in conjunction with a *para* hydroxyl group).

Many analogues have been made which attempt to address these possibilities, but the results have been equivocal. In particular, branching of the benzyl alcohol group (21) causes a reduction in activity,[107] though other bulky chains may be accommodated, *e.g.* (22).[110] Hydrogen-bond-donating groups (19, 23, 24)[106,111,112] and accepting groups (25)[113] may be tolerated, as may be acidic (26)[111] or basic groups (27).[111] Most, if not all, of the compounds could form metal chelates with ions such as Mg^{2+}, and this may be the role of the catechol, or catechol surrogate, group. The potent activity of quinterenol (28),[114] a derivative of the chelating agent oxine (29), is strong supporting evidence for this.

A number of other aryl ethanolamine β-agonist structures deserve mention. Procaterol (30)[115] is very potent, and here the *meta* substituent is incorporated into a carbostyril ring, which can exist in the keto or enol form. The aromatic ring of salbutamol has been replaced by a pyridine system, pirbuterol (31)[116] being approximately equipotent. The only non-phenols worthy of mention are clenbuterol (32),[117,118] an interesting long lasting, orally effective drug which is β_2-selective in terms of agonism, but which shows β_1-antagonism at high doses, and the related compound mabuterol (33).[119,120a]

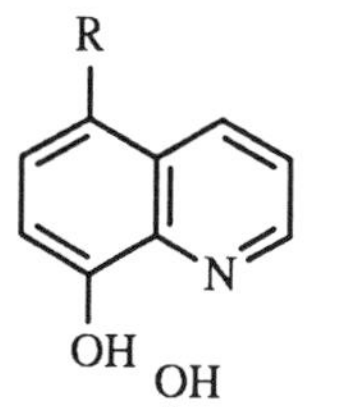

(28) R = CH(OH)CH$_2$NHPr^i
(29) R = H

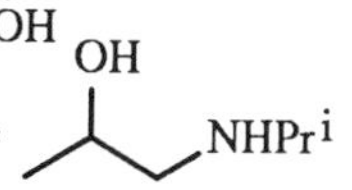

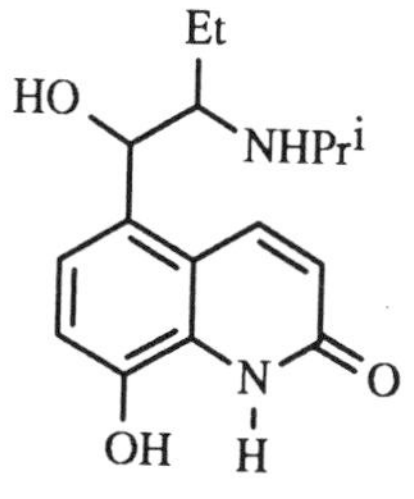

(30)

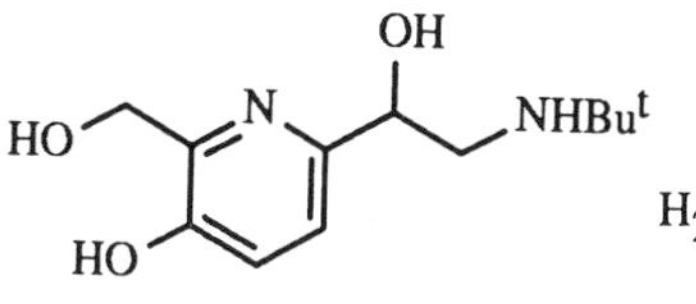

(31)

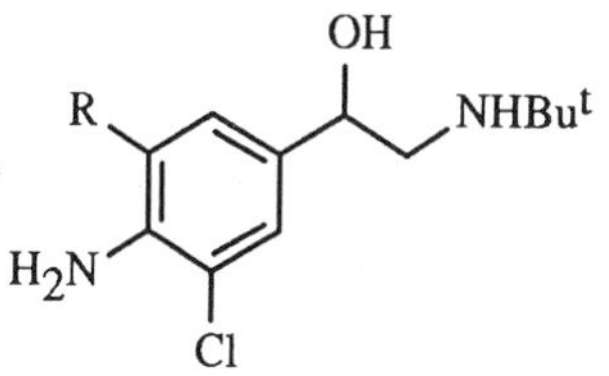

(32) R = Cl
(33) R = CF$_3$

These last two compounds also question the role of the catechol group in the catecholamines, as the *meta* substituents (Cl, CF_3) have no hydrogen bond donor or acceptor properties, are not acidic or basic, and cannot form a chelate! DCI is a potent partial agonist and full agonist properties have been seen in unsubstituted compounds,[54] while sotalol (36) exhibits no agonism. It must be true to say that the exact function of the (substituted) aryl ring has not been determined at present.

A final way of circumventing the metabolic destruction of isoprenaline is the masking of the catechol hydroxyl groups by substituents which are slowly removed by plasma esterases to regenerate the parent catecholamine. The best known of these 'prodrugs' is bitolterol (34), the pharmacology and therapeutic effects of which have been reviewed recently.[120b] Administration of bitolterol by aerosol produces long lasting (up to eight hours) bronchodilation, and larger trials are underway currently.

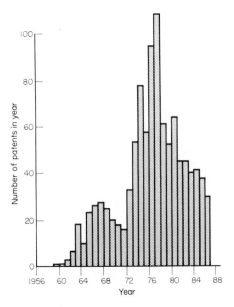

(34)

Perusal of the references listed for this section of the chapter would suggest that the most active phase of β_2-agonist research is well past, and this is confirmed by looking at the number of relevant patent applications from 1960 to date (Figure 4). During this period potent, long-acting, selective β_2-agonists have been developed which, particularly when dosed by inhalation, provide bronchodilation with a minimum of side effects. The SAR has been reviewed in much detail,[55,84,109,121-123] and clinical papers will be discussed in Section 12.2.8.1.

12.2.7 β-ANTAGONISTS

Anginal patients suffer from severe chest pain on exercise. Exercise requires the heart to work harder and supply more blood to the muscles; to perform this work the heart muscle itself requires more oxygen and nutrients from the blood supplying it *via* the coronary arteries. If these arteries are

Figure 4 Frequency of patenting new β-agonists

constricted either by atheromatous deposits or by a vascular spasm then the myocardial muscle becomes ischaemic and, as a result, intense pain is caused which subsides only on resting.[124]

Early attempts to treat angina with vasodilators failed because these drugs dilated *all* the blood vessels, thus diverting blood through healthy arteries (the 'coronary steal' syndrome).[125] The exception is glyceryl trinitrate, a very short-acting compound (dosed sublingually) which appears to dilate coronary vessels fairly selectively and which relieves distress acutely. In the late 1950s Black, in the ICI laboratories, conceived the idea that since the increase in heart rate on exercise was caused mainly by catecholamine stimulation of β-adrenoceptors then a β-receptor antagonist or 'β-blocker' should prevent the heart rate rising to levels where ischaemia would occur, and hence be an effective treatment for angina.[126]

12.2.7.1 Non-selective β-Antagonists

As mentioned in Section 12.2.5, DCI (**10**) played a pivotal role in the discovery of both β-agonists and antagonists. Black's colleague, Stephenson, mimicked some of the aspects of DCI by forming the naphthalene pronethalol (**35**), a compound which retained the β-antagonist properties of DCI but which exhibited far less agonism. Pronethalol was effective clinically in the treatment of angina pectoris[127] and some arrhythmias,[128] and there was unexpected evidence of antihypertensive activity.[129] However, before much more clinical work could be done, thymic tumours were found in mice treated with pronethalol[130] and the drug was withdrawn.

The SAR of arylethanolamine β-antagonists shows similarity to that of the $β_2$-agonists described in Section 12.2.6. Bulky secondary amine substituents are preferred, particularly isopropyl and *t*-butyl,[131] and a secondary alcohol having the $R(-)$ configuration is essential.[132] The naphthalene ring may be replaced by a substituted benzene, though simple groups do not give very potent compounds, with the exception of some chloro and methoxy analogues,[133,134] which show extensive agonism. A group from Mead-Johnson, however, utilized methanesulfonamide as a phenol mimic and obtained a relatively potent β-antagonist, sotalol (**36**),[135] the *meta* isomer (**37**) being a partial agonist. It is not at all clear why sotalol should have this biological profile, as one might expect it to show a high degree of agonism. The pK_a value (8.3) of the sulfonamide is so low, however, that the molecule must exist largely in the zwitterionic form, thus diminishing the possibility of hydrogen bond donation in this position. As a result of this ionization sotalol is an extremely hydrophilic compound. It is the only commercially successful pure β-antagonist to emerge from the arylethanolamine series.

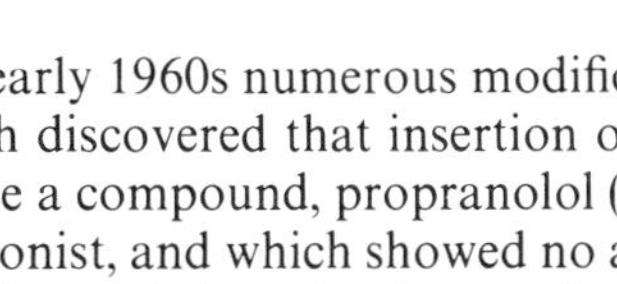

(35)

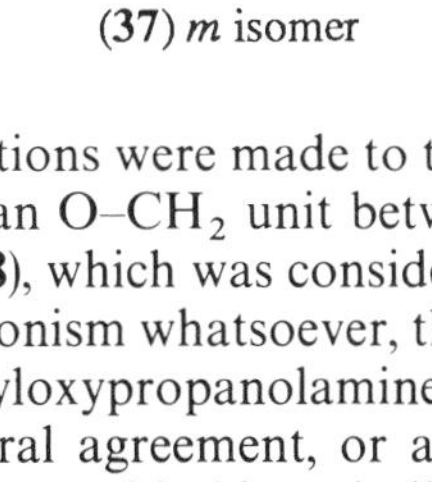

(36) *p* isomer
(37) *m* isomer

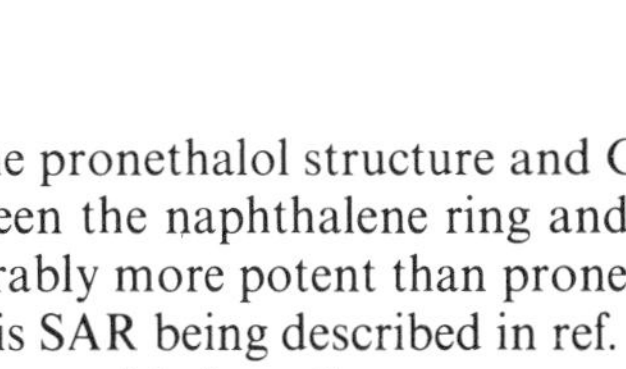

(38)

In the early 1960s numerous modifications were made to the pronethalol structure and Crowther and Smith discovered that insertion of an O–CH_2 unit between the naphthalene ring and the side chain gave a compound, propranolol (**38**), which was considerably more potent than pronethalol as a β-antagonist, and which showed no agonism whatsoever, this SAR being described in ref. 136. The reason why arylethanolamines and aryloxypropanolamines can bind to the same receptor has caused much discussion. There is general agreement, or at least a general assumption, that the ethanolamine fragments of the molecule must bind in a similar manner, and this is supported by the close correlation in the SAR of this part of the molecule in both series. The β-naphthyl isomer of propranolol, which one would expect to be more active as it is the direct analogue of pronethalol, has only one tenth of the activity, about the same as pronethalol, and this may be explained either by postulating puckering of the chain, which is unlikely, or by the notion of the —OCH_2— unit binding to the same site as one of the aryl rings of pronethalol.[137]

Propranolol was shown to be an effective anti-anginal agent[138] and, perhaps more importantly, the antihypertensive effects suggested for pronethalol were amply confirmed.[139] Hypertension is now the major clinical application for β-antagonists, though over the years they have also found application in the treatment of migraine, anxiety, tremor, obesity and glaucoma (see Section 12.2.8).

The discovery of propranolol prompted the synthesis of many thousands of compounds containing an aryloxypropanolamine nucleus (**39**). The SAR has been reviewed many times, most comprehensively by Phillips,[121] but it is summarized below.

The essential features of the series are (referring to structure **39**): (i) an aromatic or heterocyclic ring; (ii) an oxypropanol unit containing the secondary alcohol in the *S* configuration;[132,140] and (iii) a secondary amine bearing at least a two-carbon substituent R^2.

Replacement of the oxymethylene unit by CH_2,[136] OCH_2CH_2,[136] NCH_2,[141] SCH_2,[141] $OCHMe$[142] or $OCMe_2$,[142] causes considerable or complete loss of activity in all cases, and substitution of the α, β, or γ carbon atoms usually causes a loss of potency,[142] although some α-alkyl derivatives retain $β_2$-antagonist activity (Section 12.2.7.3).

Beyond these general 'rules' the aryloxypropanolamine SAR is very tolerant, biological inactivity being fairly difficult to achieve. When considering aryl substitution the trend in potency is *ortho > meta > para*,[143–145] whether the substituent is electron donating or withdrawing, the loss of potency due to *para* substitution being slightly greater in $β_2$-systems. Two *ortho* substituents cause almost complete loss of activity. The degree of agonism exhibited by β-antagonists depends markedly on the substitution in the aromatic ring. Hydroxyl substituents give full or partial agonists (Section 12.2.7.5) but for non-phenols *ortho* substituents, in particular, exert a profound effect. There is a large amount of steric freedom in this position, as is evinced by bornaprolol (**40**)[146] and penbutolol (**41**),[147] but the larger the group the less partial agonism is exhibited. This fact was known for a long time, but attempts were made to quantify it by Richards *et al.*[148] in terms of the prevalence of a minor side chain conformer, and later by Main,[149] using Taft's steric parameter as a measure of molecular size.

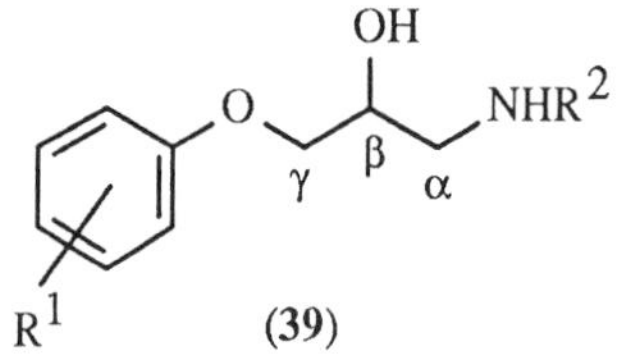

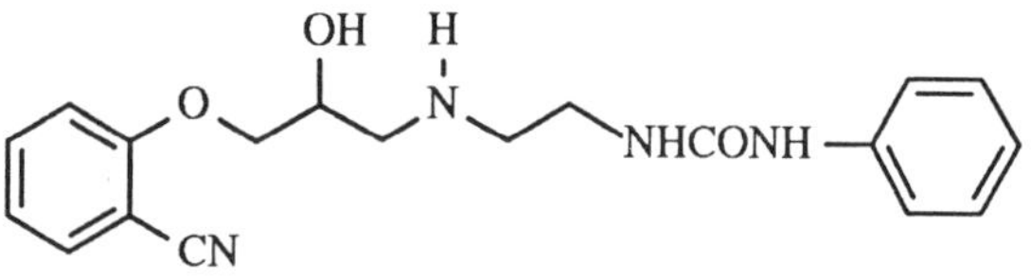

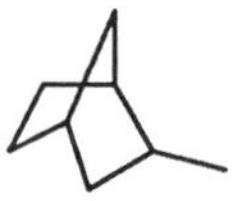

The first group plotted the percentage occurrence of a minor *gauche* conformer of a series of *ortho*-substituted aryloxypropanolamines against the degree of agonism shown by the molecules, and obtained a linear plot suggesting that this conformer was responsible for agonism and that bulky *ortho* substituents hindered its formation. When applied to the corresponding arylethanolamine series, however, a similar correlation did not exist.

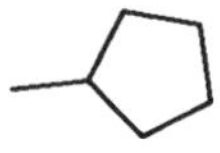

Main approached the situation more empirically, and showed that by plotting Taft's steric factor, E_s, against degree of agonism a straight line could be obtained using several different series of compounds, and this also applied to arylethanolamines. This suggested, simply, that bulky *ortho* substituents hindered binding in a manner which would lead to the expression of agonism.

It must be pointed out that if partial agonism is scaled on a 0–100% of isoprenaline maximum rating then the compounds discussed will fall into the 0–15% range, *i.e.* even the most powerful partial agonists in this group will cause a fall in heart rate when dosed to a patient, as the normal range of sympathetic tone in man appears to be around 20–30% on this scale. If ICI 89406 (**42**) is used as a reference, this has 30% agonism (ICI internal data) and exhibits no effect on *resting* heart rate in man.[150]

Many heteroaromatic systems have been incorporated into β-blockers, one of the earliest being pindolol (**43**).[151] Timolol (**44**)[152] and tazolol (**45**)[153] are examples of β-antagonists where the oxypropanolamine unit is linked directly to a heterocyclic ring.

Prediction of the degree of agonism in these case is virtually impossible, timolol is a pure antagonist and tazolol a potent partial agonist. Although heterocyclic, carteolol (**46**)[154] is probably best considered as a disubstituted phenoxypropanolamine. The properties of all the β-antagonists described above (and those mentioned later) have been collected in a review.[155]

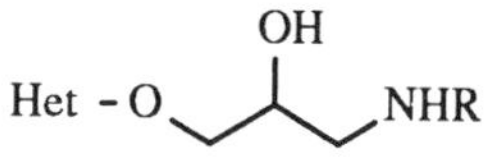

Het $-$O$\diagdown\diagup$$\underset{\text{OH}}{\diagup}$$\diagup$NHR

(43) Het = 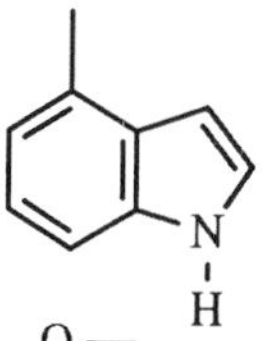 , R = Pr^i

(45) Het =  , R = Pr^i

(44) Het = 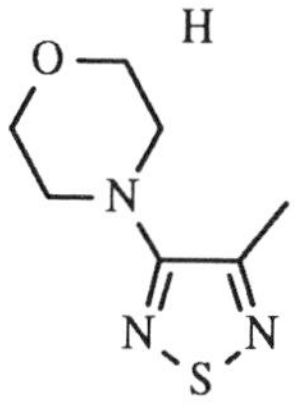 , R = Bu^t

(46) Het = 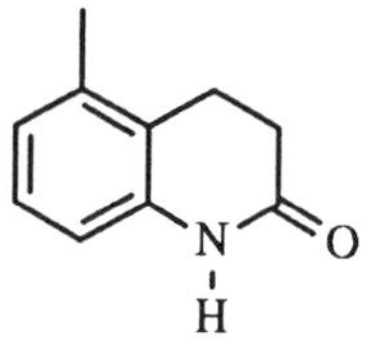 , R = Bu^t

12.2.7.2 β_1-Selective Antagonists

Para-substituted aryloxypropanolamines have a slight tendency towards β_1-selectivity; when this *para* substituent contains an amidic group, activity at β_2-receptors is lowered dramatically, as was found with practolol (**47**).[156] Practolol is a cardioselective β-antagonist with weak partial agonism,[157] the main advantage of this selectivity being a relative freedom from the potential bronchospasm which asthmatics experience when (β_2) bronchodilation is withdrawn by β-blockade with, for example, propranolol. The reason for cardioselectivity is not clear, early suggestions were that it was a distribution phenomenon, practolol being relatively hydrophilic, but this was shown to be untenable by Coleman and Somerville[158] when they compared the *meta* and *para* isomers of practolol, which are equally hydrophilic, and showed that only practolol was cardioselective. This held also for a number of other isomer pairs.

It is very important to note that with practolol isomers, as with other selective *versus* non-selective pairs of compounds, β_1-selectivity is achieved by a reduction in β_2-activity rather than any 'extra' β_1-potency, *i.e.* groups have been introduced which prevent binding to β_2-receptors.

There are two classes of *para* substituent which impart cardioselectivity: amides (sulfonamides) and ethers. The property is possessed by amides of various types, for example the three isomers of practolol (**47**), (**48**)[159] and (**49**)[160,161] (atenolol). Ureas (talinolol, **50**),[162] (**51**)[163] and sulfonamides (**52**)[164] are also cardioselective; all the compounds where the amide is linked directly to the aromatic ring are weak partial agonists, while those having the amide separated from the ring exhibit no agonism. *Para* amides in compounds with another *ortho* substituent also maintain cardioselectivity, *e.g.* acebutolol (**53**)[165] and celiprolol (**54**).[166a,b]

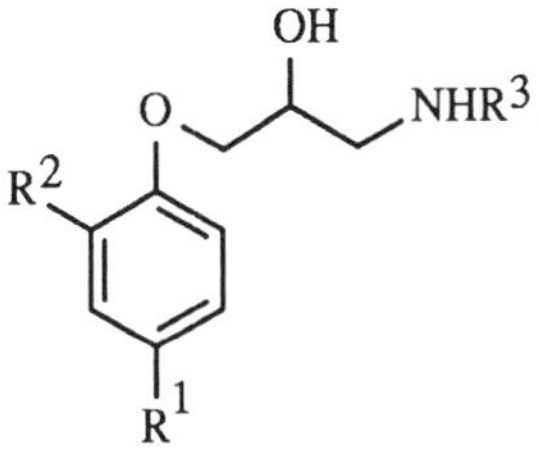

(47) R^1 = AcNH,   R^2 = H, R^3 = Pr^i (51) R^1 = CH$_2$NHCONHMe,   R^2 =H, R^3 = Pr^i
(48) R^1 = CONHMe,   R^2 = H, R^3 = Pr^i (52) R^1 = NHSO$_2$Me,   R^2 = H, R^3 = Pr^i
(49) R^1 = CH$_2$CONH$_2$,   R^2 = H, R^3 = Pr^i (53) R^1 = NHCOEt,   R^2 = COMe, R^3 = Bu^t
   (54) R^1 = NHCONEt$_2$,   R^2 = COMe, R^3 = Bu^t
(50) R^1 = NHCONH$-$, R^2 = H, R^3 = Bu^t

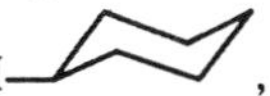

The first ether to demonstrate cardioselectivity was metoprolol (**55**),[167,168] and this has been followed by many others: cicloprolol (**56**),[169] H87/07 (**57**),[167] betaxolol (**58**),[170] and bisoprolol (**59**)[171a,b] are all β_1-selective and, as with the amides, those compounds with a second ether group next to the aromatic ring have partial agonist properties while those with an interposed methylene group have not. The cardioselectivity of the various amides and ethers suggests that the appropriate positioning of a hydrogen bond acceptor group is essential, and that this positioning is even more critical if partial agonism is to be avoided. Nilsson and co-workers[60] have published an interesting paper in which they evaluate the effect of the position of the ether oxygen.

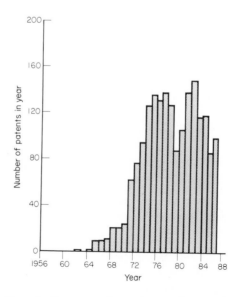

(55) R = CH$_2$CH$_2$OMe   (58) R = CH$_2$CH$_2$O⟨cyclopropyl⟩   (60)
(56) R = OCH$_2$CH$_2$O⟨cyclopropyl⟩
(57) R = OCH$_2$CH$_2$OMe   (59) R = CH$_2$OCH$_2$CH$_2$OPr^i

Atenolol and metoprolol have no agonist properties and are the world leaders in sales of cardioselective β-antagonists, particularly in the field of hypertension. It is perhaps surprising that two molecules with such different structures and physical properties should behave so similarly, but the difference in lipophilicity certainly shows that cardioselectivity cannot be a distribution phenomenon (log P atenolol = 0.23, log P metoprolol = 2.15).[172] The SAR of cardioselective β-blocking drugs has been reviewed by Smith.[173] One anomaly should be mentioned at this stage, cetamolol (60)[174a,b] is the only example known of a cardioselective compound possessing an *ortho* amide substituent which has reached the clinic.

If one compares the number of new β-blocking drugs per year over the past twenty years (Figure 5) it is apparent that, unlike the corresponding β$_2$-agonists (Figure 4), interest is still strong. The first peak in patent activity occurs in the mid 1970s when the cardioselectivity of practolol, metoprolol and atenolol was demonstrated, and the second, which is not yet finished, is due to the continued search for more cardioselective, or even cardiospecific compounds. This has concentrated on two areas, the *para* substitution of the aromatic ring, and elaboration of the amino side chain, and has resulted in a family of extremely cardioselective drugs. A series of bis-linked ethers (61) was prepared by Hoffmann-La Roche workers.[175] When this link was in the 2,2′ position β$_2$-selective compounds were produced, while 4,4′ linking produced β$_1$-selectivity; 3,3′ linked compounds were not markedly selective. The extension of this work to compounds containing the same 4,4′ link, two

Figure 5 Frequency of patenting new β-antagonists

aryl rings, and only one oxypropanolamine side chain (*e.g.* **62**, flusoxolol) gave compounds which were extremely cardioselective.[176]

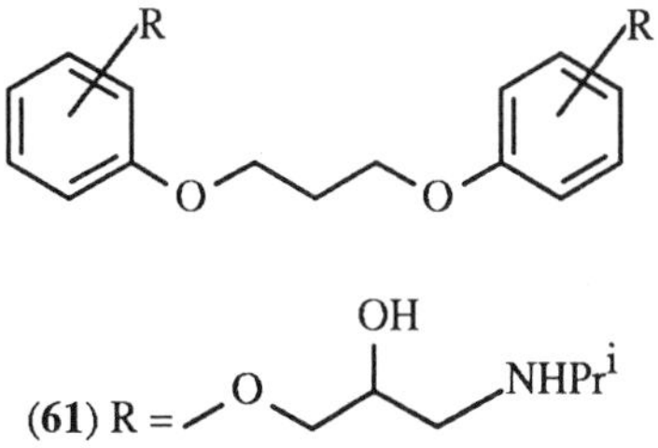

(**61**) R = [structure showing O with OH and NHPr^i side chain]

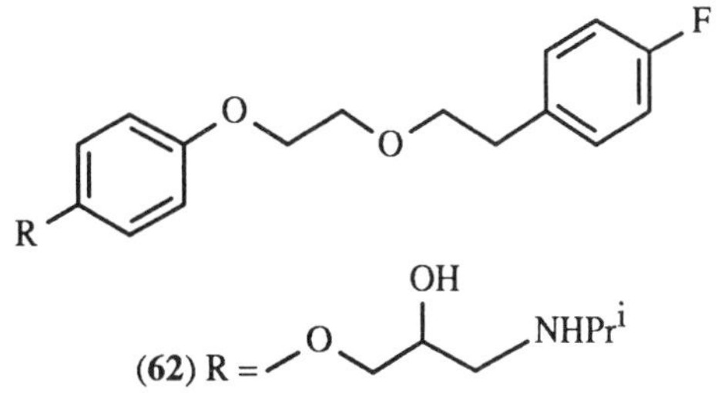

(**62**) R = [structure showing O with OH and NHPr^i side chain]

The use of a *p*-2-quinazolonyl substituent by Thomae workers[177] gave HX-CH44BS (**63**), a β-antagonist with 800-fold β_1-selectivity *in vitro*, and Merck workers developed a series of *p*-2-imidazolyl compounds (**64**) with β_1/β_2 potency ratios in the thousands.[178] These latter compounds showed some degree of agonism, and the group made a number of modifications to try and remove this, the most successful being the introduction of a methylene spacer between the two rings,[179] a ploy which works also with amides and ethers, as mentioned previously. Despite a great deal of detailed probing by the Merck group the exact role of the imidazole group could not be defined, though they suggested that the acidity of the N–H proton may be important in conferring agonism to the compounds. Compound (**65**) is potent in antagonizing β_1-responses, but has virtually no effect on β_2-responses (β_1/β_2 ratio > 2000 *in vivo*, > 9000 *in vitro*). Again β_1-selectivity is attained by a loss of β_2 rather than a gain in β_1 affinity.

The cardioselectivity induced by using a 3,4-dimethoxyphenethyl substituent was first described by Hoefle *et al.* in the synthesis of bevantolol (**66**).[180–182b] Rzeszotarski *et al.*[183,184] have compared several series of compounds containing this group with standard β-blockers and confirmed the effect shown by Hoefle (in this case using *in vitro* data only).

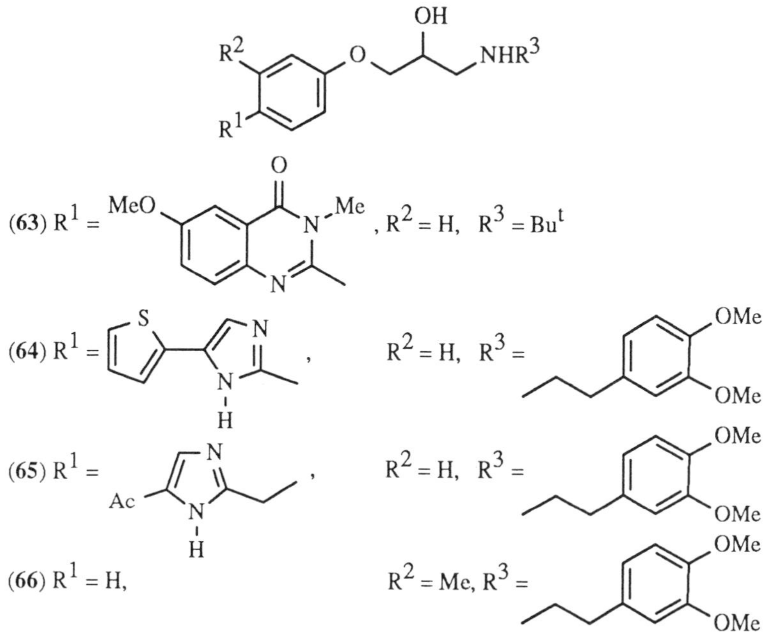

(**63**) $R^1 =$ [MeO quinazolinone structure], $R^2 =$ H, $R^3 =$ Bu^t

(**64**) $R^1 =$ [thiophene-imidazole structure], $R^2 =$ H, $R^3 =$ [3,4-dimethoxyphenethyl structure, OMe, OMe]

(**65**) $R^1 =$ [Ac imidazole structure], $R^2 =$ H, $R^3 =$ [3,4-dimethoxyphenethyl structure, OMe, OMe]

(**66**) $R^1 =$ H, $R^2 =$ Me, $R^3 =$ [3,4-dimethoxyphenethyl structure, OMe, OMe]

Just prior to the publication of the bevantolol structure, a group from Pfizer[185] described a series of cardioselective compounds which contained aryloxyalkylamino side chains, and one of these, tolamolol (**67**), was taken into man where the animal pharmacology was confirmed though the compound was soon withdrawn due to toxicity (mammary tumours). In this paper the amide group was seen to be important while the ether linkage was, by inference, just a linking group. Smith and Tucker showed, however, that even phenoxyethylamino (**68**) and alkoxyethylamino compounds (**69**)[186] were cardioselective, as were their thioether counterparts (**70**, **71**).[187] These results suggested the importance of hydrogen bond acceptor properties in this part of the aryloxypropanolamine structure and, indeed, Smith and co-workers demonstrated that amidic substituents, which are powerful hydrogen bond acceptors, produced very potent and cardioselective drugs (**72**),[188-190] this effect being present also in arylethanolamine structures.[191] In all these compounds the amide groups in the usual aryl ring are not necessary for cardioselectivity, as may be seen by the structures of the cardioselective drugs epanolol (**73**)[192a,b] and primidolol (**74**).[193]

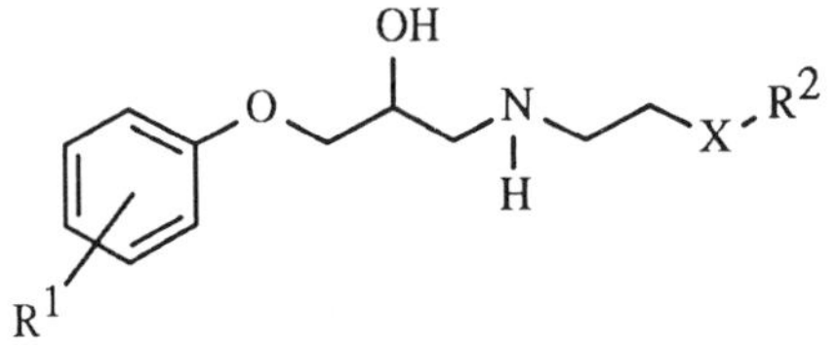

(**67**) R^1 = 2-Me,   X = O, R^2 = —⟨benzene⟩—CONH$_2$

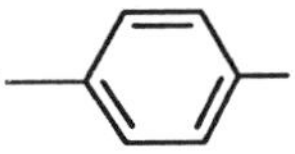

(**68**) R^1 = variety of substituents, X = O, R^2 = aryl
(**69**) R^1 = variety of substituents, X = O, R^2 = alkyl
(**70**) R^1 = variety of substituents, X = S, R^2 = aryl
(**71**) R^1 = variety of substituents, X = S, R^2 = alkyl
(**72**) R^1 = variety of substituents, X = amide, R^2 = aryl/alkyl

(**73**) R^1 = 2-CN,   X = NHCO, R^2 = —CH$_2$—⟨benzene⟩—OH

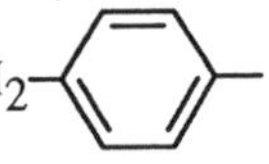

(**74**) R^1 = 2-Me,   X =

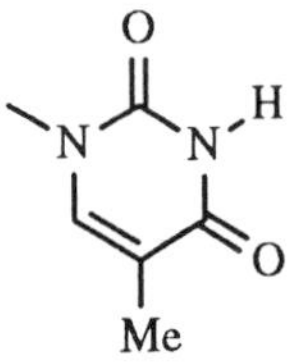

As will have been noted during the above discussion, the competition to produce improved β-blockers is intense. Mitchell, the editor of the International Journal of Cardiology, has written a very appropriate editorial. It is entitled 'Me-too-olol—why do they do it?'[194] and provides much food for thought; there is little doubt that, though individual discoveries produce only small incremental improvements in biological profile, overall, current β-blockers offer a large improvement over pronethalol, the prototype.

12.2.7.3 β$_2$-Selective Antagonists

As mentioned in Section 12.2.6, α-substituted catecholamines such as isoetharine are potent β-stimulants. There is some evidence of β-antagonism in non-phenolic analogues and some, particularly butoxamine (**75**),[195] have been shown to block β$_2$-vascular responses without affecting β$_1$-responses. Butoxamine, however, lacks both potency and a high degree of selectivity.

In the aryloxypropanolamine series the effects of α-methyl substitution are not consistent, and are not always described clearly. These compounds possess four isomers, (±) *threo* (**76**) and (±) *erythro* (**77**), a fact which many papers ignore, the actual nature of the drug used being undefined. For example, both Levy[196] and Fitzgerald and O'Donnell[197] describe the pharmacology of 'α-methyl propranolol', coming to different conclusions regarding selectivity, but they may have been using different isomers. Todd[198] clarified the situation with a comparison of the two isomers with propranolol, showing β$_2$/β$_1$ ratios of 1.3, 9 and 15 respectively for propranolol and its *threo*- and *erythro*-α-methyl isomers.

(**75**)

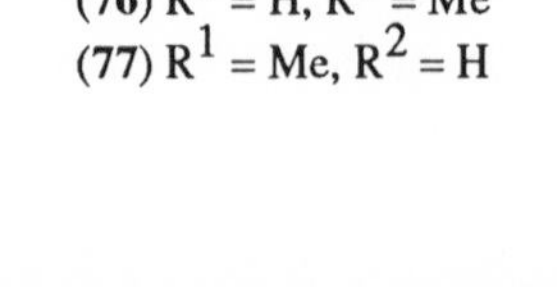

(**76**) R^1 = H, R^2 = Me
(**77**) R^1 = Me, R^2 = H

In several α-methyl analogues Lemke *et al.*[199] found no β-adrenergic activity while Tucker[200] prepared a series of 4-acylamino-substituted compounds (mainly *threo* isomers) which contained $β_1$-, $β_2$- and non-selective examples, indicating that simple introduction of an α-methyl group does not provide $β_2$-selectivity.

The *threo* and, particularly, the *erythro* isomer (ICI 118551) of the indane derivative (**78**) are very selective for $β_2$-receptors,[201] the latter exhibiting a $β_2/β_1$ ratio of more than 100 *in vitro* and 250 *in vivo*,[202] findings that have been confirmed in man.[203] Compounds such as ICI 118551 have two utilities, firstly as a biological tool,[204] but mainly to investigate clinically whether the non-cardiac benefits achieved by non-selective β-antagonists such as propranolol can be realized by a $β_2$-selective agent which has no cardiac effects. The most likely areas are tremor, anxiety and migraine, where cardiac β-blockade is undesirable. ICI 118551 has been shown, recently, to be effective in the treatment of essential tremor,[205] anxiety associated with public speaking,[206] and, perhaps surprisingly, hypertension.[207]

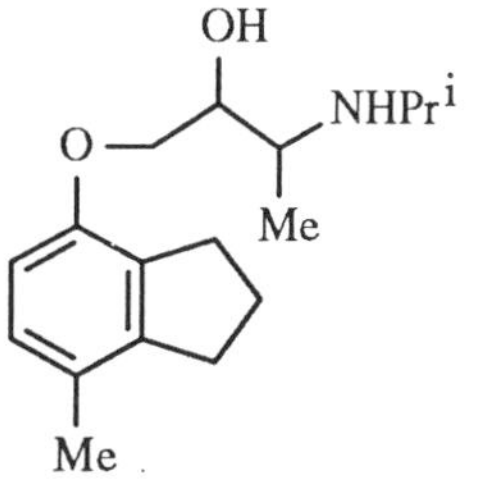

(**78**)

Spirendolol (LI 32468) (**79**), an indanone derivative, has also been used to treat tremor without producing cardiac β-blockade,[208] but very little data have been published on this compound. $β_2$-Selectivity has been reported for the benzimidazole (**80**)[209] and the tricycle (**81**),[210] while there are conflicting reports concerning carazolol (**82**); as discussed by O'Donnell and co-workers,[211] the $β_2$-selectivity is probably poor though the compound is very potent.

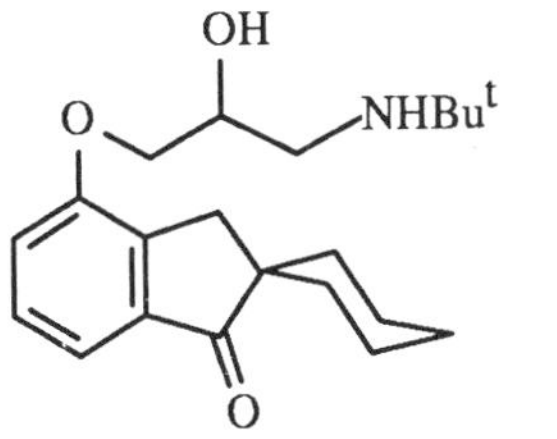

(**79**) 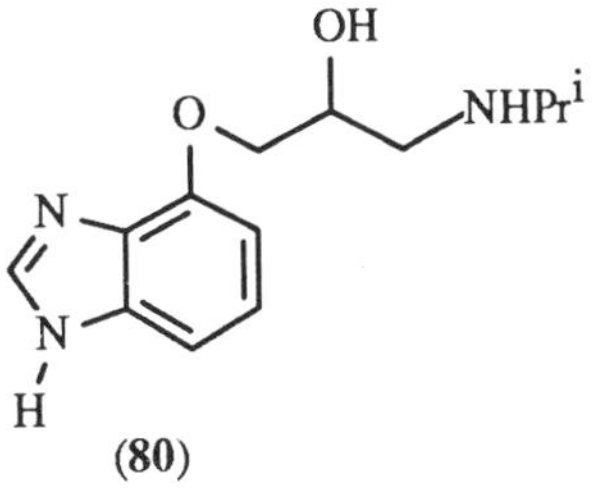   (**80**)

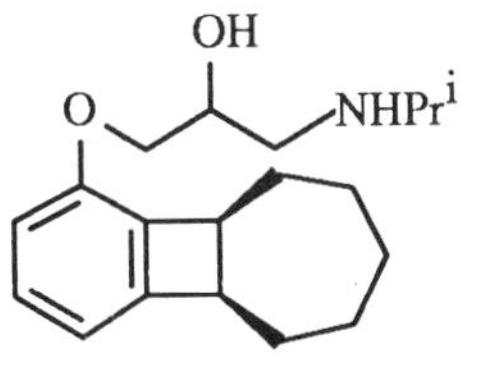

(**81**) 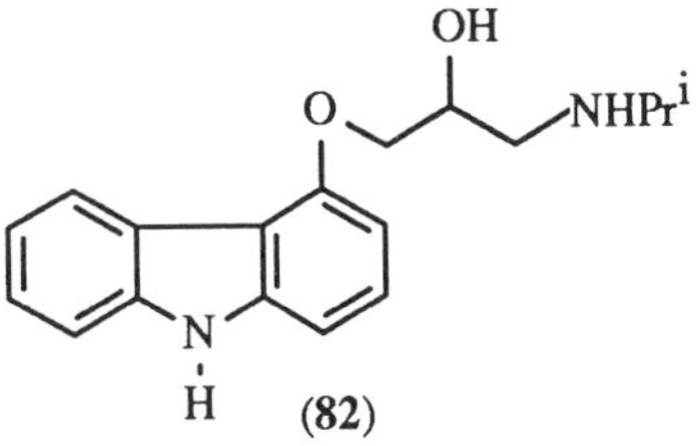   (**82**)

Controversy also surrounds the selectivity of an interesting series of compounds which contain an oximinoether link between the aryl system and the propanolamine chain (**83**). The best known of these, a fluorenone derivative IPS 339 (**84**), was originally stated to have a $β_2/β_1$ selectivity ratio of 155 *in vitro* and 26 *in vivo*,[212, 213] and high $β_2$-potency (pA_2 9.2, trachea). Other workers have failed to reproduce this selectivity, finding ratios of only 2 or 3 in their systems.[214-216] Several subsequent papers from the French group have examined the SAR of oxime ethers,[217,218] and β-antagonist activity has even been found in purely aliphatic systems.[219] One of these compounds, falintolol (**85**), has been taken into the clinic for the treatment of glaucoma.[220] Some studies have been carried out aimed at explaining how these oximes can interact with β-receptors in the same way as aryloxypropanolamines, and also why the *R* and *S* isomers are equiactive.[214,221,222]

OH

$$R^1 \diagdown_{R^2}\!\!=\!N^{-O}\!\diagup\!\diagdown\!\diagup\!^{NHR^3}$$

(83)

OH

$$\text{(fluorenylidene)}=N^{-O}\!\diagup\!\diagdown\!\diagup\!^{NHBu^t}$$

(84)

(85) $R^1 = \triangleright\!\!-\!\!-$, $R^2 = Me$, $R^3 = Bu^t$

From the aforegoing discussion of the SAR of aryloxypropanolamine β-antagonists one may, perhaps, prepare a summary such as that shown in Figure 6. The hatched areas show regions of steric freedom, and the groups X and Y contain a hydrogen bond acceptor unit such as an ether or amide carbonyl oxygen atom. Studies using NMR,[223,224] X-ray[225] and calculation[148] have shown the preferred conformation of the chain to have the aryloxymethyl group and the ammonium group antiperiplanar, in the same manner as the aryl and ammonium groups in catecholamines.[123,225]

12.2.7.4 β-Antagonists with Additional Properties

Hypertension is often treated by a combination of drugs, commonly a vasodilator plus a β-blocker. In addition to the hypotensive actions of both therapies, β-blockade attenuates any reflex tachycardia resulting from the vasodilation. A number of groups have attempted to incorporate both biological activities into one molecular structure, either by producing obvious hybrids or by making compounds which possess both properties but are not just two linked pharmacophores. The advantages are seen to be common metabolism, less tablets per patient per day, and hence greater patient compliance. The disadvantages are that the combination is fixed while individual patients would benefit from individually titrated combinations, and also that to achieve both activities in one molecule some compromises may have to be made, for example cardioselective β-blockade may be lost.

An example of this is prizidolol (**86a**), where a phenyl pyridazinyl hydrazine vasodilator and an *ortho*-substituted aryloxypropanolamine β-blocker are both present.[226a] Prizidolol is as potent as propranolol, is an effective vasodilator, this activity residing with both isomers,[226b] and lowers blood pressure in hypertensive patients.[227] It also has partial agonist properties and is not cardioselective, while the ideal drug would probably be a pure cardioselective antagonist. Prizidolol has been withdrawn due to side effects.[228a] Recently a cardioselective analogue of prizidolol has been introduced, SKF 95018 (**86b**), a combination of a pyridazinone vasodilator and the β1-antagonist betaxolol.[228b-d]

Workers at the Welcome laboratories have hybridized the β-blocker pindolol and the angiotensin-converting-enzyme inhibitor enalapril. The hybrid, BW-A575C (**86c**), expresses both activities,

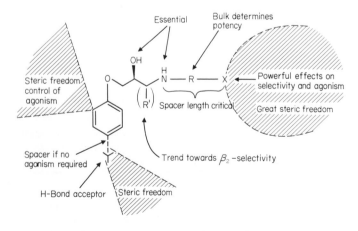

Figure 6   Summary of the SAR of aryloxypropanolamines

potency as an enzyme inhibitor being two to ten times greater than as a β-receptor antagonist.[228e,f] There is no indication of whether the β-blockade is β_1-selective.

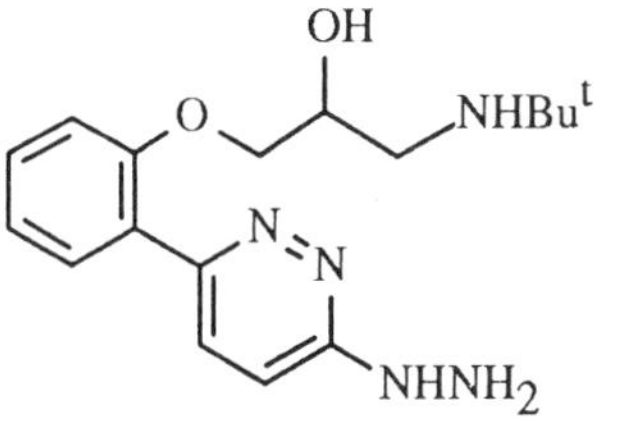

(86a) 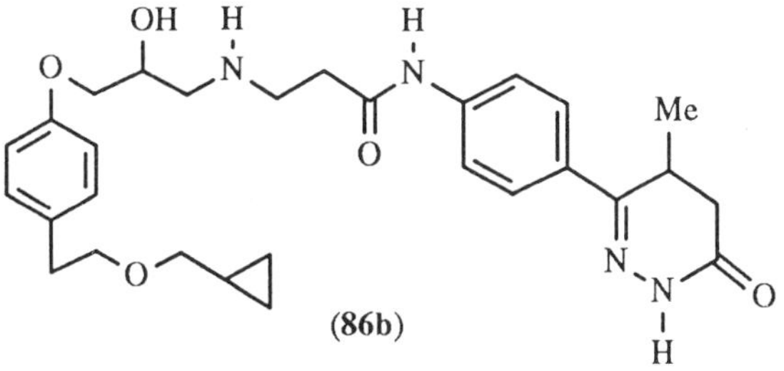   (86b)

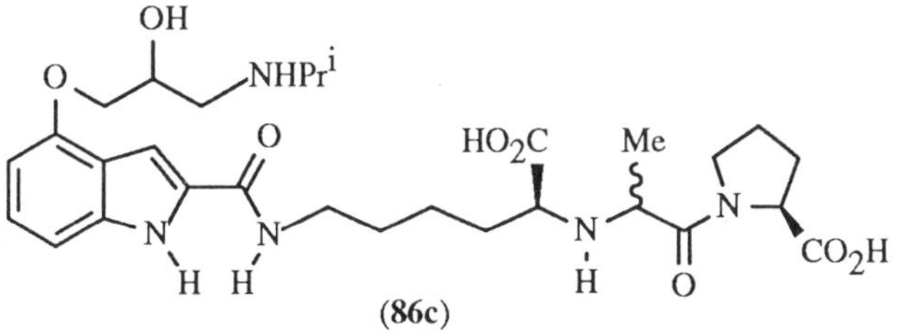

(86c)

Combining vasodilator α-blockers with β-blockers has been a fruitful source of combination drugs. The best known is labetalol (**87**) which utilizes an arylethanolamine β-blocker with an α-blocking phenylbutylamine side chain.[229-232] Labetalol is more potent at the β-receptor than the α-receptor in man, and is sold as a mixture of the four possible isomers (1:1 mixture of two racemates), but the four isomers have been prepared separately,[229,233] the *R,R*-isomer being the most potent at β-receptors and the *R,S*-isomer at α-receptors. The *R,R*-isomer (Sch 19927) is in the clinic. Other α-β blocker molecules are medroxalol (**88**),[234] isoxaprolol (**89**)[235] and arotinolol (**90**).[236]

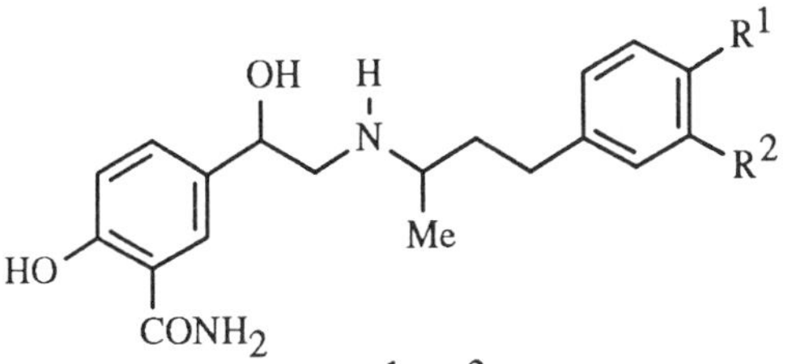

(87) $R^1 = R^2 = H$

(88) $= R^1 + R^2 = $

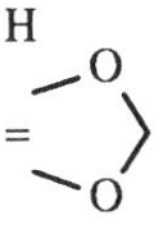

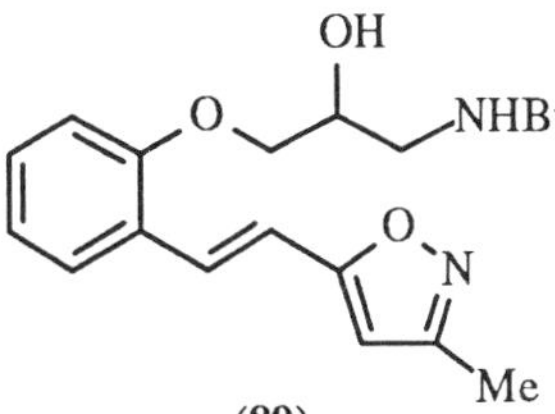

(89)

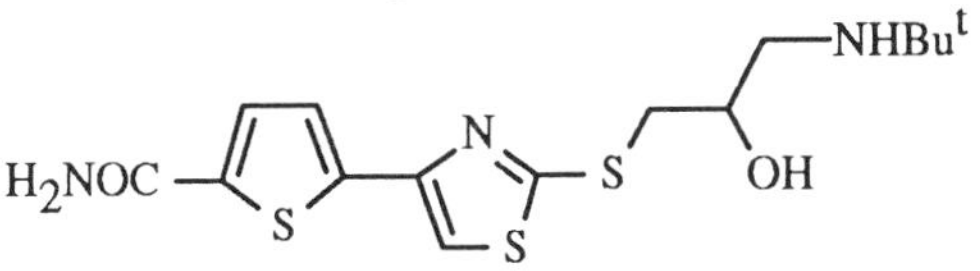

(90)

Though the nitrite ester K-351 (**91**) is a vasodilator and a β-blocker[237] it probably is not a true combination molecule, as it is likely that the drug will need to hydrolyze to nitrite ion for vasodilation to occur.

A considerable amount of work on vasodilator/β-blockers has been carried out by Baldwin's group in the Merck Laboratories. In what they termed the 'symbiotic approach' to drug design incremental modification of (**92**), a compound whose vasodilation was due to β_2-agonism, led to MK 761 (**93**) a non-adrenergic vasodilator with potent β-antagonist properties.[238] Unfortunately, clinical studies had to be terminated due to teratogenicity in rabbits. In a subsequent paper isoelectronic analogues of MK 761 were studied, only the thiazole (**94**) being anywhere comparable.[239] Variation of the MK 761 side chain demonstrated that the vasodilation was not due to α-blockade,[240] and the mechanism is still unknown.

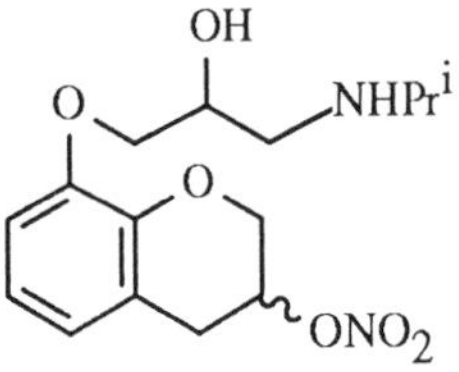

(91) 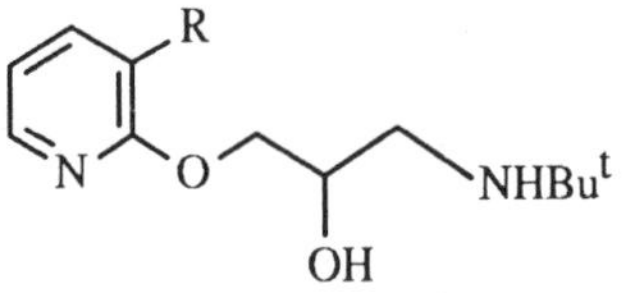   (92) R =   (94)

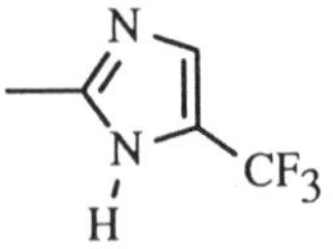

(93) R = CN

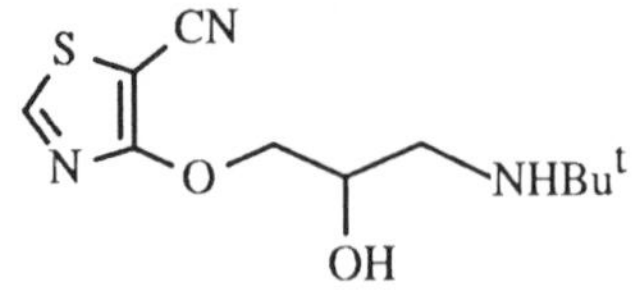

β-Antagonists may be of considerable use in the immediate post-myocardial infarction situation, but if the cardiac depression which they produce is intolerable to the patient then their long duration of action means that it may be dangerous to use them; hence an 'additional property' in this situation would be rapid metabolism/short duration of action. The American Critical Care group have attempted to introduce metabolic lability into β-blockers by incorporating ester groups into the aryloxypropanolamine skeleton, hydrolysis (by plasma esterases) of which would lead to inactive compounds.

Putting the ester into the amine side chain (95) or next to the aromatic ring (96, $n = 0$) gave compounds which were too stable,[241, 242] while extending the methylene link in (96) gave moderately potent cardioselective β-blockers such as esmolol (96, $n = 2$).[242-244] The most recent compound to be developed is flestolol (97: ACC 9089),[245,246a,b] where the —OCH_2— group of aryloxypropanolamines is replaced by a —$C(O)OCH_2$— group. Flestolol is a potent, non-selective β-blocker which gives rapid establishment of β-blockade on infusion, with rapid recovery on ceasing the infusion (80% recovery in 17 minutes). These compounds should find considerable utility in the hospital situation.

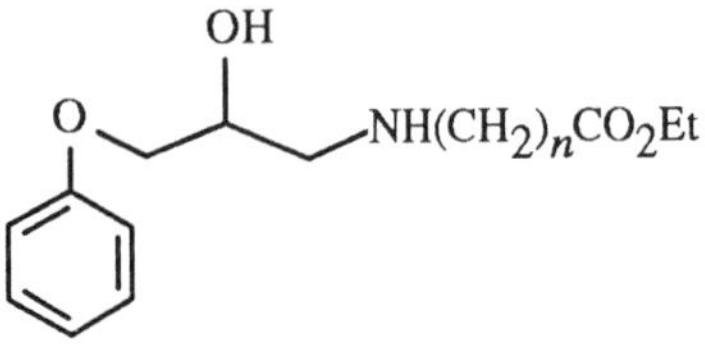

(95) 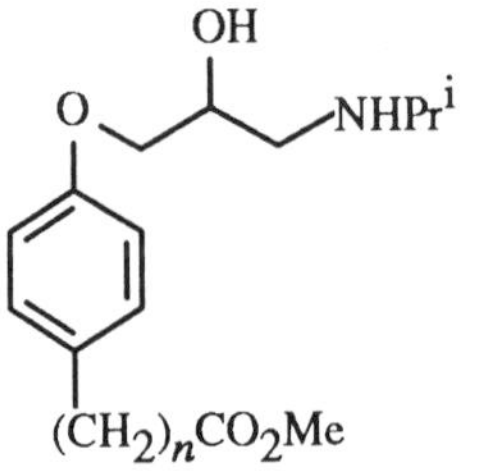   (96) 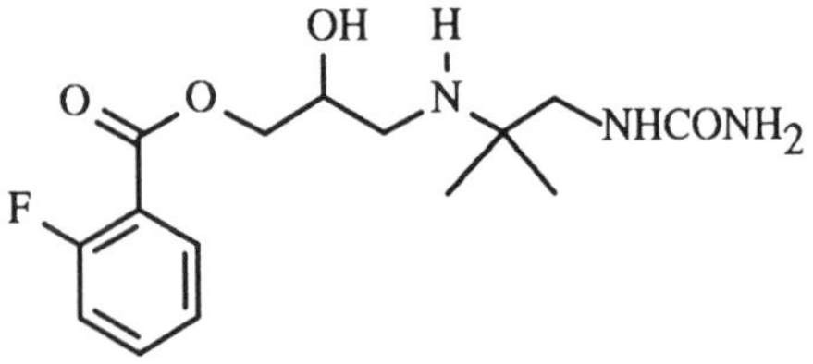   (97)

12.2.7.5 Partial β-Agonists

Isoprenaline is a full β-agonist with slight $β_2$-selectivity. The corresponding aryloxypropanolamine (98) has very similar properties, though the compound is now slightly $β_1$-selective,[247,248] and extension of this by the use of a dimethoxyphenethyl side chain (99) improved this selectivity.[249] However, such compounds are still very unstable and short acting and they have achieved no clinical use. Removal of either of the hydroxyl groups gives partial agonists[54] which are stable, long lasting and orally effective.

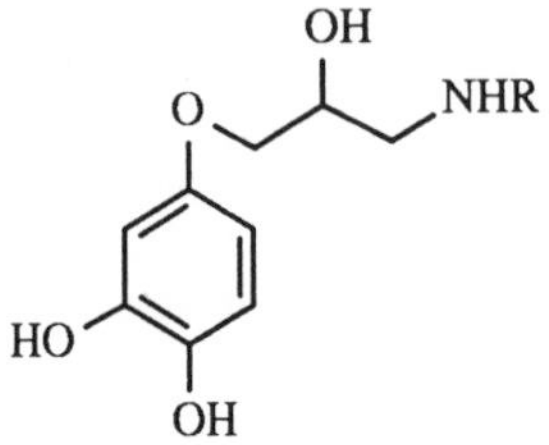

(98) R = Pr^i (99) R =

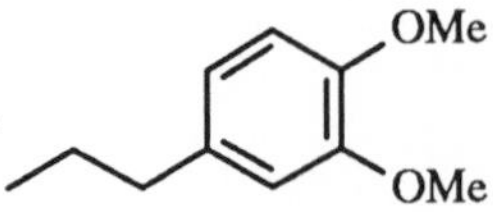

It is important at this stage to put the degree of agonism into perspective. It is well known that full agonists have a high receptor reserve, and isoprenaline, for example, only needs to occupy 5–10% of the receptors in an organ to achieve a full biological response. Partial agonists, however, have a low, or no, receptor reserve and will need to occupy virtually all of the receptors to exert their full effect.[250,251] It follows, therefore, that β-antagonists with some partial agonism, *e.g.* practolol, oxprenolol, are in fact, very weak β-agonists indeed, and dosing these drugs to patients causes a drop in cardiac output though this is less than that seen with propranolol or metoprolol. The exact level of partial agonism that will cause no change in resting cardiac parameters is hard to define but, as mentioned in Section 12.2.7.1, ICI 89406 (**42**) appears to possess approximately this level of agonism.[150] Figure 7 attempts to locate, roughly, some of the known drugs relative to isoprenaline (as 100%) to aid the following discussion.

The first of the monophenolic aryloxypropanolamines to reach the clinic was prenalterol (**100**), a partial agonist with modest $β_1$-selectivity.[252] Prenalterol has been studied intensively as a cardio-tonic for the treatment of chronic heart failure; it is effective in volunteers[253] and in patients after acute dosing,[254,255] but after prolonged treatment the haemodynamic effects decline[256,257] and no long term benefit on morbidity or mortality has been reported. The oral dosage form of the drug has therefore been withdrawn, though it is still available for hospital use intravenously. The pharma-cology, pharmacokinetics and clinical studies of prenalterol have been reviewed.[258]

The arylethanolamine analogue (**101**) of prenalterol has similar selectivity but is nearly a full agonist;[54] two analogues have been studied clinically, butopamine (**102**) and denopamine (**103**). Butopamine has been studied in congestive heart failure (intravenously) and did show an inotropic response, though accompanied by a considerable increase in heart rate.[259] Denopamine has been studied *in vitro*,[260] *in vivo*[261] and in man.[262] It is potent, long lasting and orally active and produces a positive inotropic effect in patients with congestive heart failure[262] after acute dosing. No chronic dosing studies have been published yet.

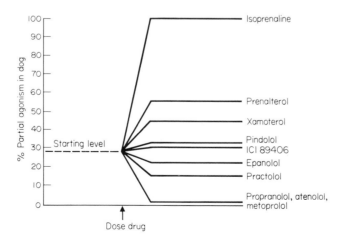

(100) $n = 1$
(101) $n = 0$

(102) R =
(103) R =

Figure 7 Partial agonism of known drugs

Extension of the β-antagonist work on acylaminoalkylamines (Section 12.2.7.2) into phenolic compounds produced potent partial β-agonists (**104**) with a β_1-selectivity comparable to prenalterol or denopamine,[54] this selectivity being maximal with ureas (**105**). The exact nature of the amide or urea group had a profound effect upon both selectivity and the degree of agonism, as is shown in Table 3. Very simple modifications of urea substitution varied agonism between 30 and 90% of isoprenaline, while introduction of an extra *N*-alkyl substituent totally abolished β_2-agonism. The optimum compound xamoterol (**106**; ICI 118587) was selected for development.[61] Xamoterol is cardiotonic in healthy volunteers[263] and heart failure patients.[264] Numerous clinical trials have demonstrated long term benefit[265,266] (up to four years dosing), and possibly this lack of tachyphyl-laxis is due to the extreme (>250:1) β_1-selectivity of xamoterol as an agonist; prenalterol, on the other hand, causes some vasodilation and hence possibly reflex tachycardia *via* release of noradrenaline.

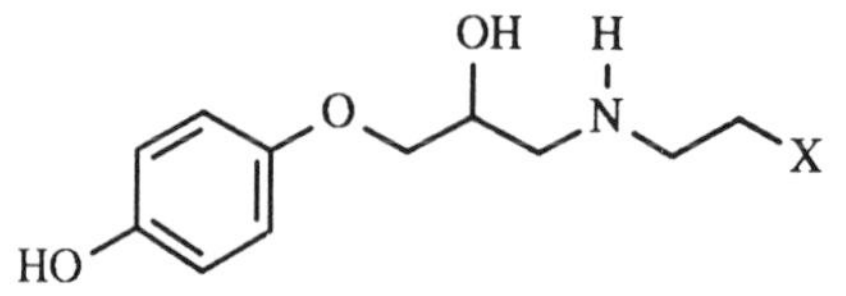

(**104**) X = NHCOR   (**106**) X = NHCON⟨morpholine⟩
(**105**) X = NHCONHR

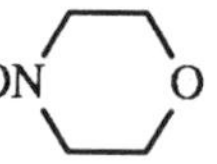

Partial agonists such as prenalterol or xamoterol exert a stabilizing effect on the cardiovascular system of patients, causing stimulation when sympathetic tone is low (*e.g.* at rest, or during low levels of activity) and β-blockade when tone is high due to stress or excessive exercise.

Some non-phenols possess sufficient (partial) agonism to be used as cardiotonics in the treatment of heart failure. Pindolol (**43**) has been tried, but showed no benefit,[267] presumably because its agonism is not quite sufficient. Cicloprolol (**55**) is a cardioselective compound, and its degree of agonism appears to lie between that of pindolol and xamoterol.[169,268,269a,b] The wide variation in degree of agonism in the xamoterol series led to the synthesis of non-phenolic analogues, and some of these were potent β_1-partial agonists,[149] for example the benzylurea (**107**).

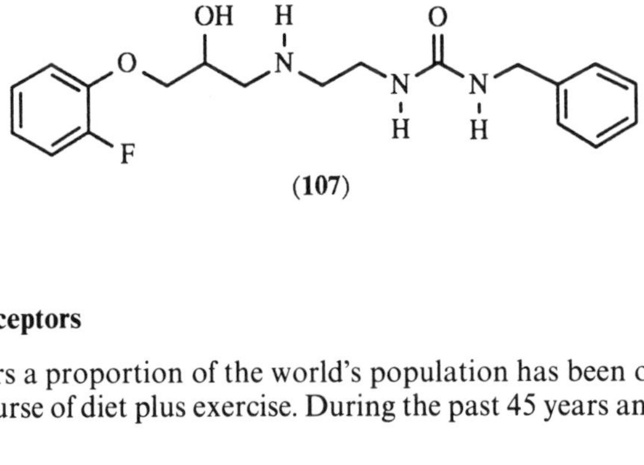

(**107**)

12.2.7.6 Atypical β-Receptors

For thousands of years a proportion of the world's population has been obese, and treatment has followed the obvious course of diet plus exercise. During the past 45 years anorexia has been induced

Table 3 Effect of Various Amidic Substitutions in Structure (**104**) on Partial Agonism and Selectivity

Nature of X (**104**)	Partial agonism (as % isoprenaline)	β_1/β_2 Selectivity
NHCOCH$_2$Ph	40	3.3
NHCONHCH$_2$Ph	80	4.1
NHCONHPh	52	2.8
NHSO$_2$NHPh	92	3.0
NHCONH$_2$	92	1.7
NHCONMe$_2$	29	>40
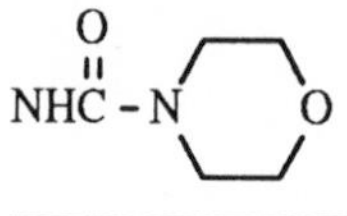 NHC(=O)-N⟨morpholine⟩	43	>250

artificially by treatment with CNS stimulants such as amphetamines,[270] though this does not address the basic cause of the condition.

Recent experiments[271] suggest that obesity may, in some part, be due to the inability of a subject's brown adipose tissue (BAT) to metabolize efficiently the food intake in a calorific manner (nonshivering thermogenesis). BAT, usually situated in the neck or upper abdomen, hydrolyzes triglycerides to glycerol and free fatty acids with the liberation of much heat, and hence exerts an anti-obesity effect.

The lipolysis is controlled by the adrenergic nervous system, but the receptor subtype responsible is by no means clear, with various literature reports claiming it to be β_1,[272,273] or β_2.[274]

In 1984 Arch, and his co-workers from Beecham, published work on a series of arylethanolamines (108) which exhibited anti-obesity activity.[15] They suggested that neither β_1 nor β_2 was an adequate descriptor of the receptor subtype involved and, in a separate paper, Wilson *et al.*[16] studied the effects of a series of β-agonists and antagonists on atrial rate (β_1), uterine tension (β_2) and lipolysis in the rat and concluded that while prenalterol and practolol were clearly selective for β_1 and fenoterol, salbutamol and ICI 118551 selective for β_2-receptor mediated effects, BRL 28410 (109), 35113 (110), and 35135 (111) were selective for the lipolytic response. Wilson *et al.* classified these as 'atypical β-receptors', and the same phrase was also used by Nahorski's group[275] when they examined lipolysis stimulated by noradrenaline or fenoterol in rat adipocytes, and the antagonism of the effect by betaxolol, ICI 118551, and propranolol.

BRL 26830 (112) is believed to be a prodrug, the active species being the corresponding acid BRL 28410. All of the compounds are racemic mixtures of the *R,R* and *S,S* diastereoisomers. Beecham workers have published a detailed account[276] of the antihyperglycaemic effects which are also seen with BRL 26830.

Currently a number of groups are working towards even more selective agents which would produce anti-obesity effects with less risk of CNS or other side effects. The only published data at present concerns the BRL compounds and a Roche compound (Ro 16-8714), which is a tertiary amine of unusual structure (113). The anti-obesity and antihyperglycaemic effects of this latter compound are documented in detail[277] and the inference is made that the activity is similar to the BRL compounds, but a detailed β-receptor subtype profile has not been published.

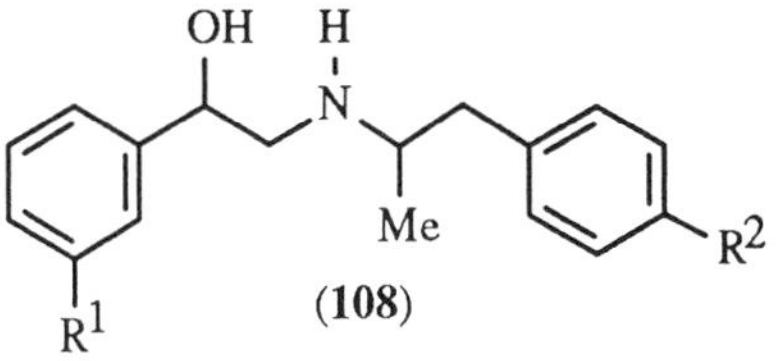

(109) R^1 = H, R^2 = CO_2H
(110) R^1 = CF_3, R^2 = CO_2H
(111) R^1 = Cl, R^2 = OCH_2CO_2Me
(112) R^1 = H, R^2 = CO_2Me

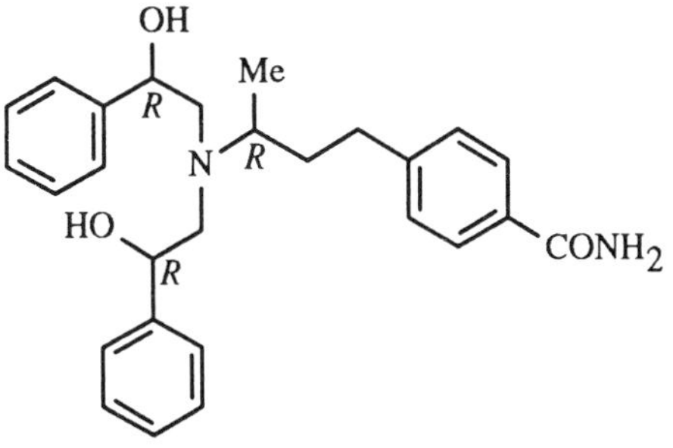

(108)

(113)

References 271–277 provide adequate details of the methods employed to measure lipolytic and anti-obesity effects.

12.2.7.7 Quantitative SAR

In the β-adrenergic field QSAR has been used surprisingly little until recently. A number of successful analyses have been carried out, but the results only apply to strictly limited series of compounds, and do not transfer out of these series. General principles of QSAR are covered in Part 18 in Volume 4 of this work, and the early work relating to β-blockers has been reviewed,[278] Table 4 containing some examples of these QSAR studies.

Since this review[278] a series of very careful studies has been carried out during the course of a thesis by IJzerman, at the University of Amsterdam, in which he corrects the potency figures by allowing for the fraction of molecules which are in the cationic form at the test pH. In several series of aryloxypropanolamine antagonists good regression equations are obtained,[279] relating log P and Austel's steric branching parameter,[280] S_b, to β_1 and β_2 affinity and selectivity in bovine left ventricle and trapezius muscle respectively. Unlike many other studies the structures, in this case,

Table 4 Examples of QSAR Studies

Structure	Parameter	Biological activity	Ref.
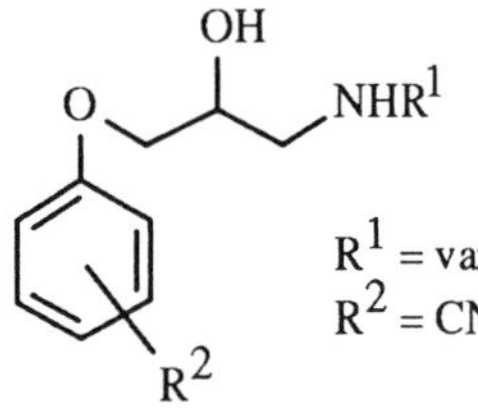 OH, O, NHR^1; R^1 = various alkyl, R^2 = CN, alkyl; R^2	log P (octanol) (Hansch)	Cardiac depression	283
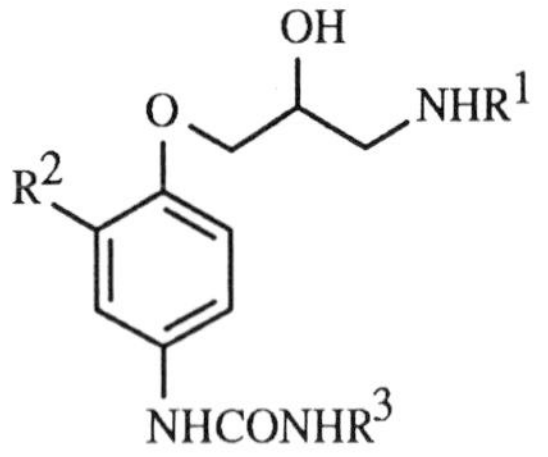 OH, O, NHR^1, R^2, NHCONHR^3	π, σ (Free–Wilson)	Cardiac potency	284
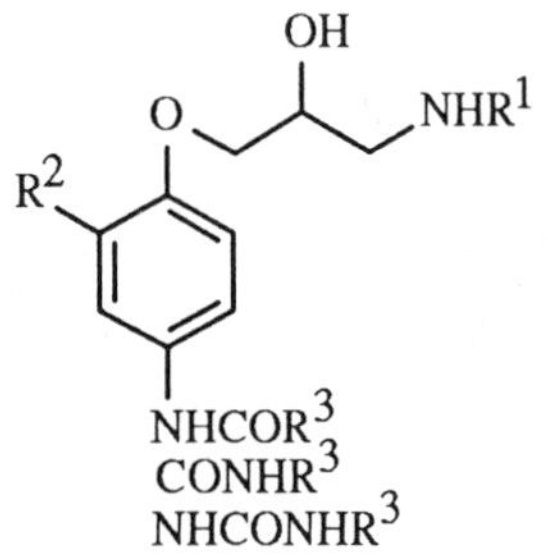 OH, O, NHR^1, R^2, NHCOR^3 CONHR^3 NHCONHR^3	π, σ (Hansch)	Cardiac potency	285
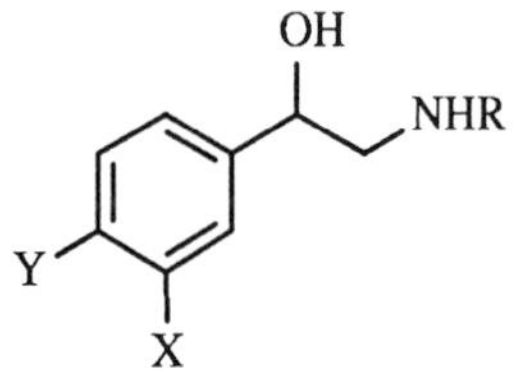 OH, NHR, Y, X	π, pK_a (SIMCA)	Cardiac potency	286
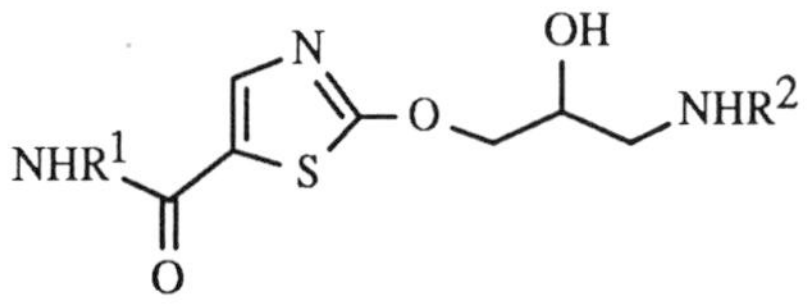 N, OH, O, NHR^2, NHR^1, S, O	'molecular fit' of R and R′	Cardiac potency	287
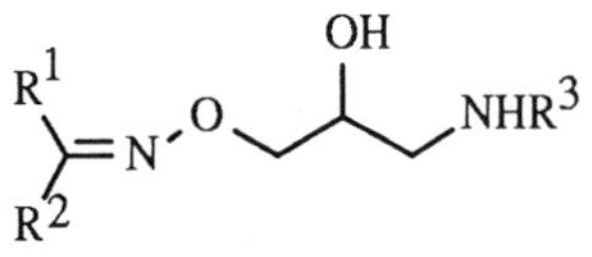 R^1, N–O, OH, NHR^3, R^2	π, σ, f, E_s, parachor	Cardiac potency	212
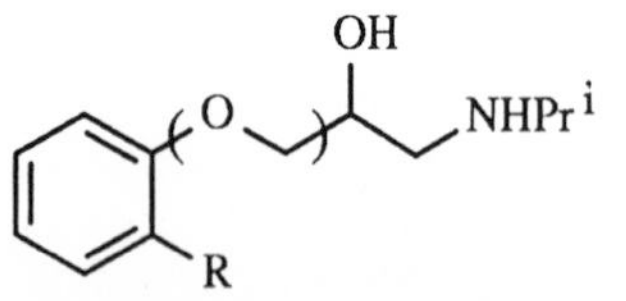 OH, O, NHPr^i, R	E_s	Partial agonism	148, 149

are varied and include, for example, practolol, betaxolol and alprenolol. Similar studies[281,282] were carried out on a series of arylethanolamines, in terms of both affinity and degree of agonism, leading to the conclusion that while log P and S_b were relevant in both cases, aryloxypropanolamine affinity was more reliant on log P, while S_b was dominant in arylethanolamines.

12.2.8 CLINICAL STUDIES WITH β-AGONISTS AND ANTAGONISTS

During the following discussion of the uses of β-adrenoceptor ligands a number of parameters controlling the overall biological profile will be mentioned, among them potency, degree of agonism, selectivity for different receptor subtypes, lipophilicity and pharmacokinetics. β-Agonists and antagonists are, in general, potent compounds; it is unlikely that lack of potency will ever be a problem and one can assume that in all cases adequate blood levels are achievable with an acceptably small dose. Degree of agonism and selectivity will be discussed in detail later, but lipophilicity, metabolism and pharmacokinetics are more conveniently discussed in general terms at this stage.

Lipophilicity affects three main aspects of clinical pharmacology: lipophilic β-blockers show cardiac depression at high doses, due to a direct membrane effect. Though some compounds such as nadolol (**114**) have been designed to circumvent this[288] it is probably true to say that, at normal therapeutic doses, the 'membrane stabilizing activity' (often termed msa) of lipophilic β-blockers is irrelevant.

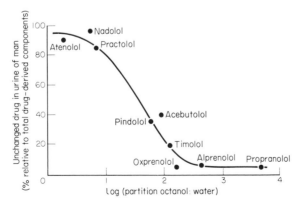

(**114**)

Lipophilic compounds penetrate the 'blood–brain' barrier into the CNS to a greater extent than hydrophilic ones, and they appear to produce a greater incidence of CNS-related side effects. For example atenolol ($\log P = 0.23$) has about 1/30 of the brain/plasma concentration ratio of propranolol ($\log P = 3.65$) or metoprolol ($\log P = 2.15$) and exhibits a lower frequency of CNS-related side effects (drowsiness, vivid dreams, *etc.*).[289]

Lipophilic compounds are also metabolized more rapidly in the liver than hydrophilic ones which are, in fact, excreted unchanged in the urine. Figure 8 is reproduced from a comprehensive review by Bourne.[290] This means that much pharmaceutical research has been necessary to provide the now common 'once a day' dosage formulation for lipophilic β-blockers.

β-Antagonists may be metabolized by two routes; the first, which is general, is shown in Figure 9, while the more specific routes are covered in Bourne's review.[290] Metabolism is also discussed in the reviews of Giudicelli and Witchitz[172] and Regårdh.[291,292a]

A recent review[292b] discusses the pharmacokinetic implications of dosing racemic drugs, showing that a number of stereoselective enzymes and transport proteins govern the differential rates of distribution and metabolism of the two enantiomers of β-blockers. This has obvious implications when deciding between enantiomers and racemates of new potential development drugs.

Catecholamines are, as mentioned previously (Section 12.2.6), rapidly metabolized by 3-*O*-methylation and by sulfation in the gut,[99] hence most bronchodilator β₂-stimulants of clinical

Figure 8 The effect of lipophilicity on the degree of metabolism of β-blocking drugs (reproduced from ref. 290 by permission of the author and John Wiley and Sons Ltd.)

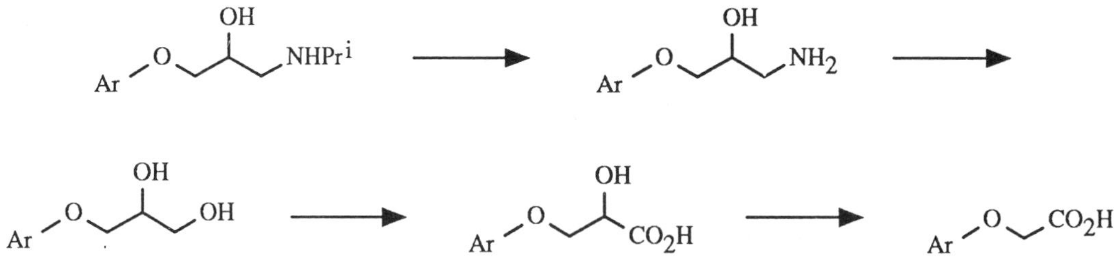

Figure 9 Common metabolism of aryloxypropanolamines

importance lack the catechol moiety. Many of these compounds, such as salbutamol, fenoterol and terbutaline are excreted unchanged in man,[84] or as sulfate esters or glucuronides[293] when dosed orally.

There is not space in this chapter to discuss clinical aspects of β-agonists and antagonists in great detail, nor would it be appropriate to do so. A brief discussion of each of the major disease areas follows, accompanied by relevant reviews for further reading.

12.2.8.1 Asthma

Selective β_2-stimulants are effective bronchodilators, useful for the treatment of asthma. After oral dosing, tachycardia, hypotension, muscle tremor and metabolic effects (insulin release, *etc.*) are frequent side effects,[294,295] all of which are direct β_2-effects, with the exception of the tachycardia which is a reflex to the fall in blood pressure caused by the vasodilation.[296] These effects are lessened by the use of aerosol dosing, the total dose being much reduced by this means, even 20–80 fold by metered dose inhalation.[297] Oral dosing is still used to some extent, particularly in children and the elderly, where mastery of correct inhaler technique is difficult, or where abuse of inhalers is suspected.[298] For some time toxic effects of the freon propellant used in inhalers was suspected,[299] but this is, as yet, unproven.

Salbutamol (albuterol) is the prototypic β-stimulant bronchodilator, against which all others are ranked, and it has been the subject of many reviews[300,301] since early studies demonstrated its efficacy.[302,303] Terbutaline,[304] fenoterol[305] and the non-phenol clenbuterol,[306] are used widely, and the use of these and other β_2-agonists in the treatment of asthma has been reviewed.[307–309]

12.2.8.2 Angina

Since early studies demonstrated the efficacy of pronethalol in the treatment of angina pectoris[127] β-blockers have been used as first-line therapy in this condition. As dozens of β-blockers are now available clinically there has been much debate about the relative merits of ancillary properties such as partial agonism, selectivity and lipophilicity. Partial agonism has been claimed to provide some protection against bronchoconstriction,[310,311] but this claim is disputed;[312] it should also lessen the degree of bradycardia observed in patients at rest, but it is arguable whether the small degree of agonism possessed by current β-blockers makes much difference except in the elderly, who are particularly sensitive to this type of bradycardia.

As anginal patients have differing heart rate thresholds for pain it follows that pure β-antagonists should suppress heart rate below this threshold in a larger number of patients than antagonists with partial agonist activity;[313] this effect is, again, quite small, and difficult to quantify. The relevance of partial agonism has been reviewed by several authors.[314–316b]

The potential advantages of cardioselectivity and hydrophilicity (lack of lipophilicity) relate purely to side effects. Non-selective β-blockers do precipitate bronchospasm in asthamatic patients and β_1-selective compounds are less likely to do so,[317,318] though this safety margin is by no means absolute, and if bronchospasm does occur it is easier to reverse with, for example, salbutamol than when a non-selective β-blocker has been used.[319] Hydrophilic compounds penetrate the CNS poorly, and less side effects of CNS origin are noted.[320–322] The ideal drug would probably be cardioselective and hydrophilic, the question of partial agonism being more controversial. Numerous reviews are available covering the treatment of angina with β-blockers,[323–326b] and the properties of a selection of common β-blockers are summarized in Table 5, and in more detail in ref. 155.

Table 5 Properties of Some Common β-Blockers and Partial Agonists

Name	β_1-Selectivity	Partial agonism	Lipophilicity	Log P
Acebutolol	+	+	+	1.87
Alprenolol	−	+	+ +	2.61
Atenolol	+	−	low	0.23
Betaxolol	+	−	+	
Bevantolol	+	−	+ +	
Cicloprolol	−	+	+	
Epanolol	+	+	low	0.87
Labetalol	−(.+α)	−	+	
Metoprolol	+	−	+	2.15
Nadolol	−	−	low	0.71
Oxprenolol	−	+	+	2.18
Pindolol	−	+	+	1.75
Practolol	+	+	low	0.79
Prenalterol	−	+ +	+	1.1
Propranolol	−	−	+ +	3.65
Sotalol	−	−	low	−0.79
Timolol	−	−	+	2.1
Xamoterol	+	+ +	low	0.03

12.2.8.3 Hypertension

Since the early, unexpected, findings of the antihypertensive effects of pronethalol[129] and propranolol,[139] hypertension has become the major use for β-blocking drugs. They are used either alone or in combination with vasodilators or diuretics and appear to be successful in around 60–80% of patients, with better results in white compared to black, and younger compared to older patients.[327,328]

Cardioselectivity and the presence or absence of partial agonism make no difference to the antihypertensive effect unless the degree of agonism is above that of pindolol[329]; epanolol[330] and xamoterol[331] do not lower blood pressure in hypertensive patients. Apart from this, cardio-selectivity, partial agonism, lipophilicity and frequency of dosing are factors which govern side effects, quality of life and patient compliance.[332] This latter factor is of great importance as patients with mild, or even moderate, hypertension may feel no ill effects, and they are unlikely to continue a course of long term medication which makes them feel worse.

There is no doubt that moderate–severe hypertension is associated with a decrease in life expectancy, but large studies on the effects of treating mild hypertension {diastolic pressure below 110 mmHg (15 kN m^{-2})} were not available until 1985.[333] Results showed only a small benefit, mainly in terms of the prevention of strokes, and this emphasizes the need for side-effect-free therapy.

Despite intensive study the mechanism by which β-blockers lower blood pressure is not known, partly because no good laboratory model of hypertension has been developed. β-Blockers will reduce the release of renin in the kidney (β_1-effect), and hence lower blood levels of angiotensin, a very potent vasoconstrictor. The correspondence of the 60% of patients treated successfully by β-blockers and the 60% treated successfully by angiotensin-converting-enzyme (ACE) inhibitors points to this mechanism being correct, but there is not a good correlation between the fall in blood pressure and circulating renin levels. This theory has been discussed many times,[334,335] and current opinion seems to be against this being the whole truth, though it is probably an important factor.[336,337]

CNS mechanisms have been proposed for the hypotensive actions of β-blockers, but studies with atenolol and metoprolol argue against this.[338,339] A third possibility is that blockade of presynaptic β-receptors is responsible, as discussed in Section 12.2.2.[18,340]

Labetalol is the best known vasodilator/β-blocker combination drug. As stated in Section 12.2.7.4 it is an effective antihypertensive agent though whether it is more effective than a pure β-blocker is open to debate. A supplement of the British Journal of Clinical Pharmacology is devoted to this compound.[341]

Numerous reviews on aspects of β-blockers in the treatment of hypertension have been published, and some are highlighted here.[342–344]

12.2.8.4 Arrhythmias and Post-myocardial Infarction Prophyllaxis

Every year millions of people are admitted to hospital suffering from acute myocardial infarction, and 12 to 18% of these will die in the hospital.[345] During the year subsequent to their release from hospital a disproportionate number of these patients will die, usually suddenly. β-Blockers are used increasingly in these patients, and are lowering the death rate markedly.

The first successful trial was with practolol[346] and, subsequently, large trials with timolol in Norway,[347] propranolol in the USA,[348] and metoprolol in Sweden[349a] have confirmed that mortality is reduced by treatment with β-blockers one to four weeks after infarction, and continuing for one to two years. Extension of this metoprolol trial to a two to seven year follow-up suggests that, providing no adverse effects are seen, it is beneficial to continue the drug treatment for several years after the infarction.[349b] These are the only trials that have shown statistically significant benefit, though smaller trials mostly show a similar trend, as reviewed by Frishman *et al.*,[345,350] and Wilhelmsson and Vedin.[351,352] The case for early intervention (from hours to several days) is less clear. In very large trials both metoprolol[353] and atenolol[354] reduced mortality over two weeks, although the difference was not quite statistically significant for metoprolol. Other trials have produced positive, negative and neutral results as reviewed by Vedin and Wilhelmsson.[355]

The mode of action of β-blockers in these trials is also uncertain. Antiarrhythmic effects[356] and limitation of infarct development[357] have both been suggested, and the evidence is reviewed in a number of articles.[358-361a] A French group have recently reviewed the general topic of β-blockers as antiarrhythmics.[361b] Sotalol has a different antiarrhythmic profile to other β-blockers, exhibiting class III as well as the usual class II activity (Harrison's modification[361c] of the Vaughan Williams classification). Sotalol's antiarrhythmic profile has been reviewed.[361d]

12.2.8.5 Congestive Heart Failure

Congestive heart failure (CHF) is a widespread disease with a poor prognosis. The aetiology is discussed in a recent review,[362] and there are numerous articles reviewing the various recent advances in drug therapy—vasodilators and adrenergic or non-adrenergic inotropic agents.[363,364] Trials in heart failure are notoriously difficult to assess, and this is discussed, rather amusingly, in an editorial by Packer.[365]

In heart failure cardiac β-receptors are down-regulated, while the cardiac β_2-receptors (which respond to adrenaline) are not,[366] hence the heart is abnormally unresponsive to β_1-effects, and sensitive to β_2-effects. A number of β-agonists and partial agonists have been used as cardiotonic and/or vasodilator agents in the treatment of CHF; full β_1 or β_1/β_2 agonists have a limited use in the hospital situation only, while β_1-partial agonists and β_2-agonists have been used chronically. Dopamine[69] and dobutamine[367] improve cardiac function on infusion and recently the prodrug ibopamine has been used orally to gain long term benefit.[72]

The first partial agonist to be used was prenalterol, and trials of acute dosing in chronic heart failure were very promising. Marked cardiotonic effects were noted,[254,368] and pulmonary end-diastolic pressure fell, these effects still being present after one month's dosing.[255] Prolonged dosing, however, revealed the development of tachyphyllaxis,[256,257,369] and in some trials ventricular arrhythmias were seen.[370] The drug has been withdrawn from development as an oral formulation.

The other partial agonist which has been studied widely is xamoterol, an extremely β_1-selective compound. Xamoterol is cardiotonic in volunteers[263] and patients[264] both acutely and after chronic dosing up to four years, and in these long term trials improvement in exercise tolerance and reduction of dyspnoea and oedema have been maintained,[265,266,371,372] and the number of anginal attacks were reduced.[373] No arrhythmogenic affects have been noted, and this could be due to the absence of β_2-agonist properties with this drug. The β_1-selectivity of xamoterol as an antagonist has been demonstrated in a recent trial comparing it with atenolol in asthmatic patients, where xamoterol produced very little bronchoconstriction.[374]

Denopamine is claimed to be a partial β_1-agonist,[262] though published data do not make it entirely clear how much β_2-agonism is present. It is cardiotonic in CHF patients,[375] but no long term trials have been reported.

β_2-Agonists have been used in the treatment of heart failure,[376] especially when it is severe, the vasodilator effects causing a reduction of cardiac filling pressure (preload). Salbutamol[377,378] and pirbuterol[379,380a] are the two agonists which have been studied most, and though acute haemodynamic responses are favourable the side effects and lack of improvement in exercise performance after chronic dosage suggest that these drugs will not be effective long term therapies. Recently a pure β-antagonist (metoprolol) has been used in CHF, with some success providing the antagonist is introduced very gradually.[380b] Shanes has discussed the appropriateness of this treatment.[380c] Current and future therapy of CHF is covered in recent reviews.[381-384]

12.2.8.6 Migraine

Since the serendipitous discovery that propranolol reduced the occurrence of migraine attacks in patients undergoing antihypertensive therapy,[385] many controlled trials have been undertaken. The efficacy of propranolol has been confirmed,[386] but, unlike many of the other clinical aspects of β-blockers, in this case the lack of partial agonism does seem to be important as propranolol, timolol and nadolol (β_1/β_2 no agonism), metoprolol and atenolol (β_1 no agonism) are all effective while oxprenolol, alprenolol and pindolol (β_1/β_2 partial agonists) and acebutolol (β_1 partial agonist) are not.[387,388] This statement should be read with caution, as migraine trials are very difficult to carry out and the results of some smaller trials may be open to question, a topic discussed by Tfelt-Hansen.[388]

β-Blockers have a prophylactic action, and are ineffective if taken once an attack has started. There is some evidence that their effectiveness increases with the period of dosing, patients who have received therapy for one year experiencing greater benefit than they (the same patients) did after three months.[389]

A number of mechanisms have been proposed for the antimigraine effects of β-blockers but none has achieved wide acceptance. Some of these are discussed in reviews[390-393] and recently a supplement in Cephalagia was devoted entirely to the topic.[394]

12.2.8.7 Anxiety and Tremor

β-Blockers attenuate some of the clinical manifestations of anxiety, particularly muscular tremor and tachycardia (palpitations). As these symptoms themselves reinforce the anxiety, breaking the cycle will also reduce the psychological symptoms, though these drugs do not seem to act on them directly.[395] In many stressful situations, where anxiety affects performance, β-blockers produce a marked improvement. Examples of this are rally car driving, public speaking, solo instrument playing and examination stress;[396,397] reaction times are not impaired.[398a] Propranolol and atenolol have been compared recently, with advantage, to placebo,[398a] and Peet has reviewed this and other evidence.[398b]

It is probable that blockade of skeletal muscle response plays an important part in the anxiolytic process (a β_2-response) though reduction of tachycardia will be of equal benefit (β_1-response). β-Blockers are also an effective treatment for essential tremor unaccompanied by anxiety symptoms; the evidence for the β_2-nature of this response has been reviewed,[399] and it is supported by the effectiveness of the β_2-selective antagonists ICI 118551,[205] and spirendolol.[208,400]

12.2.8.8 Glaucoma

Glaucoma is a serious eye disease in which intra-ocular pressure is elevated. In 1967 it was found that systemic propranolol lowered the pressure,[401] but the drug is too irritant when applied topically to be used in this way, and opthalmologists are, understandably, reluctant to use potent cardiac drugs orally. Many other β-blockers, both cardioselective and non-selective, will lower intra-ocular pressure but timolol is by far the most widely used, as it is potent and non-irritant.[402] β-Blockers are absorbed into the systemic circulation remarkably well after instillation into the eye, and, though plasma levels are far below the normal cardiovascular therapeutic range, bradycardia, hypotension and bronchospasm have occasionally been reported.[403]

Levobunolol[404] and betaxolol[405] have both been studied in chronic trials against timolol. Both trials suggest that the drugs are equiactive and have similar side effects, though the cardioselectivity of betaxolol is claimed as an advantage. Falintolol is one of the newer β-blockers to be examined for the treatment of glaucoma.[220a,b]

β-Blockers may possibly work by decreasing the production of aqueous humour, but it is confusing that β-*agonists* are also useful treatments for glaucoma, adrenaline being one of the standard agents. Terbutaline has been found active,[406] and, recently, its prodrug ibuterol has been shown to be one hundred times as potent,[407] though tachyphyllaxis develops rapidly. The actions of β-antagonists in the treatment of glaucoma have been reviewed by Hitchins.[408]

12.2.8.9   Other Indications for β-Blockers

Numerous clinical findings with β-blockers, particularly propranolol, point to new uses for this class of drugs, though efficacy is not proven satisfactorily in these areas at present. Intravaginal use of propranolol or its $R(+)$ isomer causes effective contraception, due to inhibition of sperm motility;[409] this does not imply a reduction in fertility in males dosed systemically with propranolol for other indications, as a contraceptive concentration could never be achieved by this means. Early reports of the successful treatment of schizophrenia[410] were not confirmed; propranolol causes a reduction in the rate of phenothiazine metabolism, and the effect was shown to be due to increased phenothiazine blood levels.[411a]

The effects of β-blocking drugs on blood lipid levels have been reviewed by Wolinsky.[411b]

12.2.8.10   Side Effects

β-Agonists and antagonists have a relatively acceptable spectrum of side effects, and the antagonists, in particular, have a high therapeutic ratio. The main side effects of β_2-agonists relate directly to their pharmacology;[412] vasodilation, muscle tremor and some metabolic effects are caused directly by stimulation of β_2-receptors, and hence the only way of avoiding them is by using the minimum dose and administering directly into the target organ, *i.e.* the lungs.[300, 413] Tachycardia may be caused either reflexly, due to the fall in blood pressure, or directly by stimulation of β_1-receptors if the dose used is high enough to exceed selectivity. These high doses can be achieved if aerosol dosage is used excessively, leading to tachyphyllaxis of bronchial β-receptors, and a further subsequent increase in aerosol usage in an attempt to overcome the tachyphyllaxis.

The side effects seen with β-antagonists are due mainly to the pharmacology of β-blockade. Bronchospasm induced in asthmatics has been mentioned previously (Section 12.2.7.2), and some patients may experience bradycardia or hypotension due to over-response to the normal β-blocking effects. In susceptible patients, heart failure may be precipitated by blockade with pure β-antagonists, and β-blockers which exhibit partial agonism are claimed to be superior in this respect.[414, 415]

CNS-related side effects occur in some patients on β-blocker therapy, particularly with the more lipophilic drugs; these effects include sedation, depression and vivid dreams.[416]

It appears that long term treatment of patients with β-blockers causes up-regulation of β-receptors, and hence when β-blocker therapy is withdrawn abruptly there is an enhanced β-receptor sensitivity which may precipitate an increase in heart rate and blood pressure (β-blocker-withdrawal syndrome). This has been discussed many times,[417–419] and the concensus view is that, if possible, β-blockers should be withdrawn gradually, not suddenly.

The one drug that has caused side effects unrelated to β-blockade is practolol, which produced an occulo-muculo-cutaneous syndrome, involving damage to eyes, skin, ears and the pericardial, pleural and peritoneal membranes[420–422] in a small number of patients, leading to withdrawal of the drug. The reasons for this toxicity are still not known, and no animal model has been found which reproduces it. No other β-blockers have been found that exhibit this form of toxicity. Though side effects are mentioned in many articles and reviews on β-agonists and antagonists,[307,309,323,324,343] the data have not been reviewed comprehensively with the exception of the withdrawal syndrome.[417]

12.2.9   PROFILES OF MAJOR β-ADRENERGIC DRUGS

12.2.9.1   Propranolol

Propranolol was discovered at the ICI laboratories in England in 1962. First developed as an antianginal agent[138] it has been shown to be effective in the treatment of hypertension,[139] anxiety,[397] tremor,[423] arrhythmia[356] and migraine.[386] Following myocardial infarction propranolol reduces death rate[348] if dosed from about two weeks after the event. Although propranolol reduces intraocular pressure in glaucoma patients it is too irritant to apply topically, and this is not a major indication.

Propranolol is contra-indicated in patients who have asthma, uncompensated heart failure, or A–V block. Apart from these cases, propranolol is usually well tolerated, the most common side effects being hypotension, cold extremities, vivid dreams and muscular fatigue. The clinical experience with propranolol is collected in a number of reviews.[323,424–426] This last reference[426] also contains reviews of a number of other β-blockers.

12.2.9.2 Atenolol

Atenolol (ICI) was the first cardioselective (β_1) β-blocker which showed no agonism. It is hydrophilic, hence having a reduced incidence of CNS side effects (*e.g.* vivid dreams),[320] and has been shown to be effective in the treatment of angina,[427] hypertension,[428] anxiety[429] and migraine.[386] It has shown benefit when dosed soon after myocardial infarction.[354] Dosage is usually 100 mg, once daily, with similar contra-indications and side effects to propranolol, except for a reduced incidence of CNS-related effects. It has a greater safety margin in asthmatic patients.[318] The clinical aspects of atenolol have been reviewed.[323,430,431]

12.2.9.3 Metoprolol

Metoprolol (Astra/Hassle) is a β-blocker with similar cardiovascular properties to atenolol, including once daily dosing (200 mg). Being more lipophilic it shows more CNS side effects,[320] but is similarly safer in asthmatic patients. Metoprolol is an effective treatment for hypertension, angina, migraine and post-myocardial infarction, as illustrated in a number of reviews.[432,433]

12.2.9.4 Labetalol

Labetalol (Glaxo) combines non-selective β- with α-blockade, and is used in the treatment of hypertension,[232] dosage being 100–200 mg b.i.d. Labetalol is a mixture of four isomers, which are produced in a fixed ratio by the synthetic method used. Clinical work has been reviewed.[231,232,434]

12.2.9.5 Salbutamol

Salbutamol (Glaxo) was the prototypic β_2-agonist, developed for the treatment of asthma. It is available for oral dosing (2 × 8 mg per day) or as an aerosol (100 μg one or two times per day), the latter giving less side effects due to systemic absorption.[296] It has an immediate bronchodilating effect, offering acute relief during an asthma attack, and is often used in combination with steroids for prophylactic treatment. The adverse reactions are fine tremor, nervous tension or hypotension due to β_2-stimulation.[299,300]

The β_2-mediated vasodilation is the basis for trials that have taken place in heart failure patients.[377,378] Though acute haemodynamic benefit is observed, long term treatment has caused tachyphyllaxis. Many reviews cover the actions of this drug.[299,300,435,436]

12.2.9.6 Other Drugs

Clinical studies with most of the common β-adrenergic drugs have been reviewed, and the appropriate references are shown below: acebutolol,[437] alprenolol,[437] betaxolol,[437] bevantolol,[181,438,439] bisoprolol,[171b,440] bitolterol,[120b] bopindolol,[437] bunitrolol,[437] celiprolol,[166b] cetamolol,[437] dobutamine,[74] epanolol,[441] esmolol,[442] flestolol,[437] formoterol,[112] ibopamine,[72,443] indenolol,[437] mepindolol,[437] moprolol,[437] pafenolol,[437] practolol,[157] prenalterol,[437] sotalol,[444] talinolol,[162] xamoterol.[445]

12.2.10 APPENDIX—POTENCY OF β-AGONISTS AND ANTAGONISTS

Tables 6 and 7 contain values of *in vitro* potencies and selectivities for a variety of β-agonists and antagonists which have been selected from the references cited in this chapter. The tables are not exhaustive and values for different compounds are not strictly comparable as they are extracted from different papers. The original source should be consulted in each case before definite conclusions can be reached, but the tables are qualitatively correct. Further qualitative comparisons are presented in ref. 155.

Table 6 *In Vitro* Potency of β-Agonists

Substance	β_2-Potency[a]	β_1-Potency[b]	Ratio β_2/β_1	Ref.
Adrenaline	7.1	7.2 (EC_{50})	0.8	89
Clenbuterol	9.0	8.4 (EC_{25})	4	124
Fenoterol	8.7	7.3 (EC_{50})	25	68
Isoprenaline	8.1	8.6 (EC_{50})	0.3	68
Mabuterol	8.0	not det.	—	119
Noradrenaline	6.0	7.0 (EC_{50})	0.1	89
Orciprenaline	7.0	6.6 (EC_{50})	2.5	68
Pirbuterol	9.4	7.1 (EC_{25})	200	124
Procaterol	8.0	9.7 (EC_{25})	0.02	115
Quinterenol	7.1	<5 (EC_{25})	>100	124
Salbutamol	7.6	7.0 (EC_{25})	4	115
Soterenol	8.4	8.9 (EC_{25})	0.3	111
Terbutaline	7.1	5.4 (EC_{50})	50	68

[a] log EC_{50} on isolated guinea pig trachea. [b] log EC_{25} or EC_{50} on isolated guinea pig atria.

Table 7 *In Vitro* Potency of β-Antagonists

Substance	β_1-Potency[b]	β_2-Potency[a]	Ratio β_1/β_2	Ref.
Alprenolol	8.1	8.0	1.3	180
Atenolol	6.5	4.3	40	160
Arotinolol	8.6	8.4	1.6	236
Betaxolol	8.8	7.0	60	178
Bevantolol	7.9	6.4	21	180
Bisoprolol	7.5	6.7	6.3	171b
Bunolol	9.7	not det.	—	288
Carazolol	9.6	10.0	4.0	211
Celiprolol	8.0	6.8	16	166b
Cicloprolol	7.9	6.1	60	169
Esmolol	6.7	5.2	32	242
Falintolol	8.0	7.9	1.3	222
HX-CH44BS	7.4	*ca.* 5	320	177
ICI118551	7.2	9.3 (uterus)	0.008	202
IPS339	7.0	9.2	0.006	213
Labetalol	8.3	8.1	1.3	230
Metoprolol	7.8	6.8	11	178
Nadolol	7.0	not det.	—	288
Oxprenolol	7.9	8.6	1.6	236
Pindolol	8.7	8.7	1	236
Prizidolol	7.2	not det.	—	226b
Practolol	6.5	4.3	158	160
Propranolol	8.3	8.5	0.8	160
Talinolol	6.0	4.3	50.0	162
Timolol	9.4	9.6	0.7	178

ACKNOWLEDGEMENT

The author would like to express his thanks to the many people in ICI Pharmaceuticals who have offered help and advice during the preparation of this manuscript.

12.2.11 REFERENCES

1. R. P. Ahlquist, *Am. J. Physiol.*, 1948, **153**, 586.
2. A. M. Lands, A. Arnold, J. P. McAuliff, F. P. Luduena and T. G. Brown, Jr., *Nature (London)*, 1967, **214**, 597.
3. Various authors, *Handb. Exp. Pharmakol.*, 1972, **33**, 1.
4. A. M. Lands, F. P. Luduena and H. J. Buzzo, *Life Sci.*, 1967, **6**, 2241.
5. J. G. Collier and A. C. Dornhorst, *Nature (London)*, 1969, **223**, 1283.
6. E. Carlsson, B. Åblad, A. Brändström and B. Carlsson, *Life Sci.*, 1972, **11**(part 1), 953.

7. A. Hedberg, K. P. Minneman and P. B. Molinoff, *J. Pharmacol. Exp. Ther.*, 1980, **212**, 503.
8. T. H. Morris and A. J. Kaumann, *Naunyn-Schmiedeberg's Arch. Pharmacol.*, 1984, **327**, 176.
9. O.-E. Brodde, K. Karad, H.-R. Zerkowski, N. Rohm and J. C. Reidemeister, *Circ. Res.*, 1983, **53**, 752.
10. (a) A. Heitz, J. Schwartz and J. Velly, *Br. J. Pharmacol.*, 1983, **80**, 711; (b) R. E. Purdy, G. L. Stupecky and P. R. Coulombe, *J. Pharmacol. Exp. Ther.*, 1988, **245**, 67.
11. E. J. Ariëns and A. M. Simonis, in 'Beta-Adrenoceptor Blocking Agents', ed. P. R. Saxena and R. P. Forsyth, North Holland, Amsterdam, 1976, p. 3.
12. L. J. Bryan, J. J. Cole, S. R. O'Donnell and J. C. Wanstall, *J. Pharmacol. Exp. Ther.*, 1981, **216**, 395.
13. P. B. Molinoff, *Drugs*, 1984, **28** (Suppl. 2), 1.
14. A. Arnold, *Handb. Exp. Pharmakol.*, 1980, **54** (1), 63.
15. J. R. S. Arch, A. T. Ainsworth, M. A. Cawthorne, V. Piercy, M. V. Sennitt, V. E. Thody, C. Wilson and S. Wilson, *Nature (London)*, 1984, **309**, 163.
16. (a) C. Wilson, S. Wilson, V. Piercy, M. V. Sennitt and J. R. S. Arch, *Eur. J. Pharmacol.*, 1984, **100**, 309; (b) P. Muzzin, C. Colomb, J.-P. Giacobino, J. C. Venter and C. M. Frazer, *J. Recept. Res.*, 1988, **8**, 713.
17. S. Z. Langer, *Pharmacol. Rev.*, 1981, **32**, 337.
18. M. J. Rand and H. Majewski, *Clin. Exp. Hypertens., Part A*, 1984, **6**, 347.
19. (a) Y. Misu and T. Kubo, *Trends Pharmacol. Sci.*, 1983, 506; (b) K. R. Borkowski, *J. Auton. Pharmacol.*, 1988, **8**, 153.
20. G. A. Robison, R. W. Butcher and E. W. Sutherland, *Ann. N. Y. Acad. Sci.*, 1967, **139**, 703.
21. T. Pfeuffer and E. J. M. Helmreich, *J. Biol. Chem.*, 1975, **250**, 867.
22. R. J. Lefkowitz, *Annu. Rep., Med. Chem.*, 1980, **15**, 217.
23. L. E. Limbird, D. M. Gill and R. J. Lefkowitz, *Proc. Natl. Acad. Sci. USA*, 1980, **77**, 775.
24. A. Levitzki, in 'Topics in Molecular Pharmacology', ed. A. S. V. Burgen and G. C. K. Roberts, Elsevier/North-Holland Biomedical Press, Amsterdam, 1981, p. 23.
25. R. G. L. Shorr, R. J. Lefkowitz and M. G. Caron, in 'Enzymes of Biological Membranes', ed. A. N. Martonosi, 2nd edn., Plenum, New York, vol. 2, 1985, p. 399.
26. R. J. Lefkowitz, M. G. Caron and G. L. Stiles, *N. Engl. J. Med.*, 1984, **310**, 1570.
27. J. Codina, J. Hildebrandt, T. Sunyer, R. D. Sekura, C. R. Manclark, R. Iyengar and L. Birnbaumer, *Adv. Cycl. Nucl. Protein Phosphor. Res.*, 1984, **17**, 111.
28. A. Levitzki, *Physiol. Rev.*, 1986, **66**, 819.
29. J. A. Heinsimer and R. J. Lefkowitz, *Hosp. Pract.*, 1983, **18**, 103.
30. T. K. Harden, *Pharmacol. Rev.*, 1983, **35**, 5.
31. D. R. Sibley and R. J. Lefkowitz, *Nature (London)*, 1985, **317**, 124.
32. R. H. Strasser, R. A. Cerione, J. Codina, M. G. Caron and R. J. Lefkowitz, *Mol. Pharmacol.*, 1985, **28**, 237.
33. J. L. Benovic, R. H. Strasser, M. G. Caron and R. J. Lefkowitz, *Proc. Natl. Acad. Sci. USA*, 1986, **83**, 2797.
34. R. H. Strasser, J. L. Benovic, M. G. Caron and R. J. Lefkowitz, *Proc. Natl. Acad. Sci. USA*, 1986, **83**, 6362.
35. R. H. Strasser, D. R. Sibley and R. J. Lefkowitz, *Biochemistry*, 1986, **25**, 1371.
36. S. P. Baker and L. T. Potter, *Biochem. Pharmacol.*, 1981, **30**, 3361.
37. E. Pfeuffer, R.-M. Dreher, H. Metzger and T. Pfeuffer, *Proc. Natl. Acad. Sci. USA*, 1985, **82**, 3086.
38. A. G. Gilman, *Cell*, 1984, **36**, 577.
39. M. G. Caron, Y. Srinivasan, J. Pitha, K. Kociolek and R. J. Lefkowitz, *J. Biol. Chem.*, 1979, **254**, 2923.
40. G. Vauquelin, P. Geynet, J. Hanoune and A. D. Strosberg, *Proc. Natl. Acad. Sci. USA*, 1977, **74**, 3710.
41. R. G. L. Shorr, R. J. Lefkowitz and M. G. Caron, *J. Biol. Chem.*, 1981, **256**, 5820.
42. R. G. L. Shorr, M. W. Strohsacker, T. N. Lavin, R. J. Lefkowitz and M. G. Caron, *J. Biol. Chem.*, 1982, **257**, 12341.
43. S. L. Heald, P. W. Jeffs, T. N. Lavin, P. Nambi, R. J. Lefkowitz and M. G. Caron, *J. Med. Chem.*, 1983, **26**, 832.
44. G. L. Stiles, R. H. Strasser, T. N. Lavin, L. R. Jones, M. G. Caron and R. J. Lefkowitz, *J. Biol. Chem.*, 1983, **258**, 8443.
45. (a) S. W. Bahouth, L. K. Kelley, C. H. Smith, L. Lautens, A. Ruoho and C. C. Malbon, *Fed. Proc., Fed. Am. Soc. Exp. Biol.*, 1985, **44**, 1795; (b) S. W. Bahouth and C. C. Malbon, *Biochem.*, 1987, **248**, 557.
46. R. A. Cerione, B. Strulovici, J. L. Benovic, R. J. Lefkowitz and M. G. Caron, *Nature (London)*, 1983, **306**, 562.
47. D. Feder, M.-J. Im, H. W. Klein, M. Hekman, A. Holzhöfer, C. Dees, A. Levitzki, E. J. M. Helmreich and T. Pfeuffer, *EMBO J.*, 1986, **5**, 1509.
48. R. J. Lefkowitz, R. A. Cerione, J. Codina, L. Birnbaumer and M. G. Caron, *J. Membr. Biol.*, 1985, **87**, 1.
49. A. Levitzki, *Biochim. Biophys. Acta*, 1985, **822**, 127.
50. (a) R. A. F. Dixon, B. K. Kobilka, D. J. Strader, J. L. Benovic, H. G. Dohlman, T. Frielle, M. A. Bolanowski, C. D. Bennett, E. Rands, R. E. Diehl, R. A. Mumford, E. E. Slater, I. S. Sigal, M. G. Caron, R. J. Lefkowitz and C. D. Strader, *Nature (London)*, 1986, **321**, 75; (b) H. G. Dohlman, M. G. Caron, C. D. Strader, N. Amlaiky and R. J. Lefkowitz, *Biochemistry*, 1988, **27**, 1813.
51. (a) R. J. Lefkowitz, J. L. Benovic, B. Kobilka and M. G. Caron, *Trends Pharmacol. Sci.*, 1986, **7**, 444; (b) H. G. Dohlman, M. G. Caron and R. J. Lefkowitz, *Biochemistry*, 1987, **26**, 2657.
52. E. M. Scott, *J. Auton. Pharmacol.*, 1983, **3**, 113.
53. A. Hedberg, E. Carlsson, E. Fellenius and B. Lundgren, *Naunyn-Schmiedeberg's Arch. Pharmacol.*, 1982, **318**, 185.
54. J. J. Barlow, B. G. Main and H. M. Snow, *J. Med. Chem.*, 1981, **24**, 315.
55. R. T. Brittain, D. Jack and A. C. Ritchie, *Adv. Drug Res.*, 1970, **5**, 197.
56. R. J. Lefkowitz, C. Mukherjee, M. Coverstone and M. G. Caron, *Biochem. Biophys. Res. Commun.*, 1974, **60**, 703.
57. R. A. Burges and K. J. Blackburn, *Nature (London), New Biol.*, 1972, **235**, 249.
58. S. R. O'Donnell and J. C. Wanstall, *Naunyn-Schmiedeberg's Arch. Pharmacol.*, 1979, **308**, 183.
59. A. M. Barrett and J. Carter, *Br. J. Pharmacol.*, 1970, **40**, 373.
60. K. Lövgren, A. Hedberg and J. L. G. Nilsson, *J. Med. Chem.*, 1981, **24**, 451.
61. A. Nuttall and H. M. Snow, *Br. J. Pharmacol.*, 1982, **77**, 381.
62. H. Konzett and R. Rössler, *Naunyn-Schmiedeberg's Arch. Pharmakol. Exp. Path*, 1940, **195**, 71.
63. W. C. Bowman and M. W. Nott, *Br. J. Pharmacol.*, 1970, **38**, 37.
64. J. R. S. Arch and A. T. Ainsworth, *Am. J. Clin. Nutr.*, 1983, **38**, 549.
65. R. W. Alexander, L. T. Williams and R. J. Lefkowitz, *Proc. Natl. Acad. Sci. USA*, 1975, **72**, 1564.
66. D. C. U'Prichard, D. B. Bylund and S. H. Snyder, *J. Biol. Chem.*, 1978, **253**, 5090.

67. A. J. Coleman and A. R. Somerville, *Br. J. Pharmacol.*, 1977, **59**, 83.
68. S. R. O'Donnell and J. C. Wanstall, *Br. J. Pharmacol.*, 1974, **52**, 407.
69. S. I. Rajfer and L. I. Goldberg, *Eur. Heart J.*, 1982, **3** (Suppl. D), 103.
70. C. Casagrande, F. Santangelo, C. Saini, F. Doggi, F. Gerli and O. Cerri, *Arzneim.-Forsch.*, 1986, **36**, 291.
71. J. H. Ren, D. V. Unverferth and C. V. Leier, *J. Cardiovasc. Pharmacol.*, 1984, **6**, 748.
72. Various authors, *Arzneim.-Forsch.*, 1986, **36**, 285.
73. R. R. Tuttle and J. Mills, *Circ. Res.*, 1975, **36**, 185.
74. C. V. Leier and D. V. Unverferth, *Ann. Intern. Med.*, 1983, **99**, 490.
75. K. Chatterjee, R. Bendersky and W. W. Parmley, *Eur. Heart J.*, 1982, **3** (Suppl. D), 107.
76. C. Maccarrone, E. Malta and C. Raper, *J. Cardiovasc. Pharmacol.*, 1984, **6**, 132.
77. E. Yamato, M. Hirakura and S. Sugasawa, *Tetrahedron, Suppl.*, 1966, **8** (part 1), 129.
78. Y. Iwasawa and A. Kiyomoto, *Jpn. J. Pharmacol.*, 1967, **17**, 143.
79. C. Kaiser, H.-J. Oh, B. J. Garcia-Slanga, A. C. Sulpizio, J. P. Hieble, J. E. Wawro and L. I. Kruse, *J. Med. Chem.*, 1986, **29**, 2381.
80. C. Kaiser and L. I. Kruse, *Eur. Pat.*, 0 210 827 (1987) (*Chem. Abstr.*, 1987, **106**, 138 270b).
81. P. Pratesi and E. Grana, *Adv. Drug Res.*, 1965, **2**, 127.
82. C. E. Powell and I. H. Slater, *J. Pharmacol. Exp. Ther.*, 1958, **122**, 480.
83. N. C. Moran and M. E. Perkins, *J. Pharmacol. Exp. Ther.*, 1958, **124**, 223.
84. R. T. Brittain, C. M. Dean and D. Jack, *Pharmacol. Ther., Part B*, 1976, **2**, 423.
85. H. Konzett, *Arch. Exp. Pathol. Pharmakol.*, 1940, **197**, 27.
86. P. N. Patil, J. B. LaPidus and A. Tye, *J. Pharm. Sci.*, 1970, **59**, 1205.
87. C. K. Buckner and P. N. Patil, *J. Pharmacol. Exp. Ther.*, 1971, **176**, 634.
88. L. H. Easson and E. Stedman, *Biochem. J.*, 1933, **27**, 1257.
89. P. Pratesi, L. Villa and E. Grana, *Il Farmaco Ed. Sci.*, 1975, **30**, 315.
90. A. M. Lands, F. P. Luduena, J. O. Hoppe and I. H. Oyen, *J. Am. Pharm. Assoc.*, 1958, **47**, 744.
91. A. M. Lands and T. G. Brown, Jr., in 'Drugs Affecting the Peripheral Nervous System', ed. A. Burger, Dekker, New York, 1967, vol. I, p. 399.
92. R. B. Barlow, in 'Introduction to Chemical Pharmacology', 2nd edn., Wiley, New York, 1964.
93. D. J. Triggle, in 'Medicinal Chemistry', ed. A. Burger, 3rd edn., Wiley, New York, 1970, chap. 46.
94. M. J. Mardle, H. Smith, B. A. Spicer and R. H. Poyser, *J. Med. Chem.*, 1974, **17**, 513.
95. G. H. Sankey and K. D. E. Whiting, *J. Heterocycl. Chem.*, 1972, **9**, 1049.
96. M. Nishikawa, M. Kanno, H. Kuriki, H. Sugihara, M. Motohashi, K. Itoh, O. Miyashita, Y. Oka and Y. Sanno, *Life Sci.*, 1975, **16**, 305.
97. J. L. H. Laity, *J. Pharm. Pharmacol.*, 1971, **23**, 633.
98. E. W. Blackwell, R. H. Briant, M. E. Conolly, D. S. Davies and C. T. Dollery, *Br. J. Pharmacol.*, 1974, **50**, 587.
99. C. F. George, E. W. Blackwell and D. S. Davies, *J. Pharm. Pharmacol.*, 1974, **26**, 265.
100. A. Engelhardt, W. Hoefke and H. Wick, *Arzneim.-Forsch.*, 1961, **11**, 521.
101. J. Bergman, H. Persson and K. Wetterlin, *Experientia*, 1969, **25**, 899.
102. S. R. O'Donnell, *Eur. J. Pharmacol.*, 1970, **12**, 35.
103. A. A. Larsen and P. M. Lish, *Nature (London)*, 1964, **203**, 1283.
104. A. A. Larsen, W. A. Gould, H. R. Roth, W. T. Comer, R. H. Uloth, K. W. Dungan and P. M. Lish, *J. Med. Chem.*, 1967, **10**, 462.
105. D. Hartley, D. Jack, L. H. C. Lunts and A. C. Ritchie, *Nature (London)*, 1968, **219**, 861.
106. R. T. Brittain, J. B. Farmer, D. Jack, L. E. Martin and W. T. Simpson, *Nature (London)*, 1968, **219**, 862.
107. D. T. Collin, D. Hartley, D. Jack, L. H. C. Lunts, J. C. Press, A. C. Ritchie and P. Toon, *J. Med. Chem.*, 1970, **13**, 674.
108. D. Hartley and D. Middlemiss, *J. Med. Chem.*, 1971, **14**, 895.
109. L. H. C. Lunts, in 'Medicinal Chemistry', ed. S. M. Roberts and B. J. Price, Academic Press, London, 1985, p. 49.
110. K. Murase, T. Mase, H. Ida, K. Takahashi and M. Murakami, *Chem. Pharm. Bull.*, 1977, **25**, 1368.
111. C. Kaiser, D. F. Colella, M. S. Schwartz, E. Garvey and J. R. Wardell, Jr., *J. Med. Chem.*, 1974, **17**, 49.
112. K. Tasaka, *Drugs Today*, 1986, **22**, 505.
113. C. Kaiser, M. S. Schwartz, D. F. Colella and J. R. Wardell, Jr., *J. Med. Chem.*, 1975, **18**, 674.
114. A. Scriabine, P. F. Moore, L. C. Iorio, I. M. Goldman, W. K. McShane and K. D. Booher, *J. Pharmacol. Exp. Ther.*, 1968, **162**, 60.
115. S. Yoshizaki, K. Tanimura, S. Tamada, Y. Yabuuchi and K. Nakagawa, *J. Med. Chem.*, 1976, **19**, 1138.
116. S. N. Steen, I. Ziment and J. S. Thomas, *Curr. Ther. Res.*, 1974, **16**, 1077.
117. J. Keck, G. Krüger, K. Noll and H. Machleidt, *Arzneim.-Forsch.*, 1972, **22**, 861.
118. G. Engelhardt, *Arzneim.-Forsch.*, 1972, **22**, 869.
119. T. Murai, T. Maejima, K. Sanai and E. Osada, *Arzneim.-Forsch.*, 1984, **34**(II), 1633.
120. (a) E. Osada, T. Murai, Y. Ishizaka and K. Sanai, *Arzneim.-Forsch.*, 1984, **34**(II), 1641; (b) H. A. Friedel and R. N. Brogden, *Drugs*, 1988, **35**, 22.
121. D. K. Phillips, *Handb. Exp. Pharmakol.*, 1980, **54**, 3.
122. D. J. Triggle, in 'Medicinal Chemistry', ed. A. Burger, 4th edn. Wiley-Interscience, New York, 1981, pp. 225–283.
123. C. Kaiser, in 'Drugs Affecting the Respiratory System', ed. D. L. Temple, American Chemical Society, Washington, 1980, pp. 251–283.
124. D. J. Weatherall, J. G. G. Ledingham and D. A. Warrell (eds.), 'Oxford Textbook of Medicine', Oxford University Press, Oxford, 1983, vol. 2, p. 13.1165.
125. L. C. Becker, *Circulation*, 1978, **57**, 1103.
126. J. W. Black and J. S. Stephenson, *Lancet*, 1962, **2**, 311.
127. G. A. O. Alleyne, C. J. Dickinson, A. C. Dornhorst, R. M. Fulton, K. G. Green, I. D. Hill, P. Hurst, D. R. Laurence, T. Pilkington, B. N. C. Prichard, B. Robinson and M. L. Rosenheim, *Br. Med. J.*, 1963, **2**, 1226.
128. J. P. P. Stock and N. Dale, *Br. Med. J.*, 1963, **2**, 1230.
129. B. N. C. Prichard, *Br. Med. J.*, 1964, **1**, 1227.
130. G. E. Paget, *Br. Med. J.*, 1963, **2**, 1266.

131. R. Howe, A. F. Crowther, J. S. Stephenson, B. S. Rao and L. H. Smith, *J. Med. Chem.*, 1968, **11**, 1000.
132. R. Howe and B. S. Rao, *J. Med. Chem.*, 1968, **11**, 1118.
133. B. Levy and R. P. Ahlquist, *J. Pharmacol. Exp. Ther.*, 1960, **130**, 334.
134. A. M. Hjort, L. O. Randall and E. J. De Beer, *J. Pharmacol. Exp. Ther.*, 1948, **92**, 283.
135. R. H. Uloth, J. R. Kirk, W. A. Gould and A. A. Larsen, *J. Med. Chem.*, 1966, **9**, 88.
136. A. F. Crowther and L. H. Smith, *J. Med. Chem.*, 1968, **11**, 1009.
137. G. M. Donné-Op Den Kelder, G. J. Bijloo and T. Bultsma, *Eur. J. Med. Chem.*, 1986, **21**, 475.
138. J. Hamer, T. Grandjean, L. Melendez and G. E. Sowton, *Br. Med. J.*, 1964, **2**, 720.
139. B. N. C. Prichard and P. M. S. Gillam, *Br. Med. J.*, 1964, **2**, 725.
140. R. Howe and R. G. Shanks, *Nature (London)*, 1966, **210**, 1336.
141. G. Ferrari, R. Ferrini and C. Casagrande, *Boll. Chim. Farm.*, 1968, **107**, 234.
142. R. Howe, *J. Med. Chem.*, 1969, **12**, 642.
143. A. F. Crowther, D. J. Gilman, B. J. McLoughlin, L. H. Smith, R. W. Turner and T. M. Wood, *J. Med. Chem.*, 1969, **12**, 638.
144. E. J. Mylecharane and C. Raper, *Eur. J. Pharmacol.*, 1974, **29**, 93.
145. A. M. Barrett and J. L. Wale, *Eur. J. Pharmacol.*, 1970, **12**, 372.
146. G. Le Fur, P. H. Schmelck, P. Geynet, J. Hanoune and A. Uzan, *Life Sci.*, 1978, **23**, 1841.
147. G. Härtfelder, H. Lessenich and K. Schmitt, *Arzneim.-Forsch.*, 1972, **22**, 930.
148. W. G. Richards, R. Clarkson and C. R. Ganellin, *Philos. Trans. R. Soc. London, Ser. B*, 1975, **272**, 75.
149. B. G. Main, *J. Chem. Technol. Biotechnol.*, 1982, **32**, 617.
150. T. L. Svendsen, O. J. Hartling, J. Trap-Jensen, A. McNair and J. Bliddal, *Clin. Pharmacol. Ther.*, 1981, **29**, 711.
151. J.-F. Giudicelli, H. Schmitt and J. R. Boissier, *J. Pharmacol. Exp. Ther.*, 1969, **168**, 116.
152. A. Scriabine, M. L. Torchiana, J. M. Stavorski, C. T. Ludden, D. H. Minsker and C. A. Stone, *Arch. Int. Pharmacodyn. Ther.*, 1973, **205**, 76.
153. G. Vauquelin, M. L. Lacombe, G. Guellaen, A. D. Strosberg and J. Hanoune, *Biochem. Pharmacol.*, 1976, **25**, 2605.
154. K. Nakagawa, N. Murakami, S. Yoshizaki, M. Tominaga, H. Mori, Y. Yabuuchi and S. Shintani, *J. Med. Chem.*, 1974, **17**, 529.
155. B. G. Main and H. Tucker, *Prog. Med. Chem.*, 1985, **22**, 121.
156. A. F. Crowther, R. Howe and L. H. Smith, *J. Med. Chem.*, 1971, **14**, 511.
157. A. M. Barrett, *Postgrad. Med. J., Suppl.*, 1971, **47**, 7.
158. A. J. Coleman, D. S. Paterson and A. R. Somerville, *Biochem. Pharmacol.*, 1979, **28**, 1011.
159. L. H. Smith, *J. Med. Chem.*, 1976, **19**, 1119.
160. A. M. Barrett, J. Carter, J. D. Fitzgerald, R. Hull and D. Le Count, *Br. J. Pharmacol.*, 1973, **48**, 340P
161. J. D. Harry, M. F. Knapp and R. J. Linden, *Br. J. Pharmacol.*, 1974, **51**, 169.
162. K.-O. Haustein, H. Fiehring, G. Oltmanns and K. Femmer, *Int. J. Clin. Pharmacol. Biopharm.*, 1979, **17**, 465.
163. L. H. Smith, *J. Med. Chem.*, 1977, **20**, 705.
164. L. H. Smith, *Int. Congr. Symp. Ser.—R. Soc. Med.*, 1980, **19**, 93.
165. K. R. H. Wooldridge, *Experientia*, 1972, **28**, 1404.
166. (a) R. D. Smith and P. S. Wolf, in 'New Drugs Annual: Cardiovascular Drugs', ed. A. Scriabine, Raven Press, New York, 1984, vol. 2, p. 19; (b) J. G. Riddell, R. G. Shanks and R. N. Brogden, *Drugs*, 1987, **34**, 438.
167. B. Åblad, E. Carlsson and L. Ek, *Life Sci.*, 1973, **12** (part I), 107.
168. B. Johansson, *Eur. J. Pharmacol.*, 1973, **24**, 194.
169. I. Cavero, F. Lefèvre-Borg and P. Manoury, *Br. J. Pharmacol.*, 1979, **84** (Suppl.), 31P.
170. J. P. Boudot, I. Cavero, S. Fénard, F. Lefèvre-Borg, P. Manoury and A. G. Roach, *Br. J. Pharmacol.*, 1979, **66**, 445P.
171. (a) H.-J. Schliep and J. Harting, *J. Cardiovasc. Pharmacol.*, 1984, **6**, 1156; (b) Various authors, *J. Cardiovasc. Pharmacol.*, 1986, **8** (Suppl. 11), S1.
172. J. F. Giudicelli and S. Witchitz, *Sem. Hop.*, 1983, **59**, 2395.
173. L. H. Smith, *J. Appl. Chem. Biotechnol.*, 1978, **28**, 201.
174. (a) G. Beaulieu, J. Jaramillo and J. R. Cummings, *Can. J. Physiol. Pharmacol.*, 1984, **62**, 302; (b) T. J. Rimele, D. E. Henry, F. R. Giesa, S. K. Buckley, G. Geiger, R. J. Heaslip, D. K. H. Lee and D. Grimes, *J. Cardiovasc. Pharmacol.*, 1988, **12**, 208.
175. R. W. Kierstead, A. Faraone, F. Mennona, J. Mullin, R. W. Guthrie, H. Crowley, B. Simko and L. C. Blaber, *J. Med. Chem.*, 1983, **26**, 1561.
176. P. J. Machin, D. N. Hurst, R. M. Bradshaw, L. C. Blaber, D. T. Burden, A. D. Fryer, R. A. Melarange and C. Shivdasani, *J. Med. Chem.*, 1983, **26**, 1570.
177. J. W. Daemmgen, G. Engelhardt and H. Pelzer, *Arzneim.-Forsch.*, 1985, **35** (I), 383.
178. J. J. Baldwin, G. H. Denny, R. Hirschmann, M. B. Freedman, G. S. Ponticello, D. M. Gross and C. S. Sweet, *J. Med. Chem.*, 1983, **26**, 950.
179. J. J. Baldwin, M. E. Christy, G. H. Denny, C. N. Habecker, M. B. Freedman, P. A. Lyle, G. S. Ponticello, S. L. Varga, D. M. Gross and C. S. Sweet, *J. Med. Chem.*, 1986, **29**, 1065.
180. M. L. Hoefle, S. G. Hastings, R. F. Meyer, R. M. Corey, A. Holmes and C. D. Stratton, *J. Med. Chem.*, 1975, **18**, 148.
181. Symposium in *Am. J. Cardiol.*, 1986, **58**, 1E–40E.
182. (a) I. D. Dukes and E. M. Vaughan Williams, *Br. J. Pharmacol.*, 1985, **84**, 365; (b) H. R. Kaplan, *Am. J. Cardiol.*, 1986, **58**, 3E.
183. W. J. Rzeszotarski, R. E. Gibson, W. C. Eckelman and R. C. Reba, *J. Med. Chem.*, 1979, **22**, 735.
184. W. J. Rzeszotarski, R. E. Gibson, D. A. Simms, E. M. Jagoda, J. N. Vaughan and W. C. Eckelman, *J. Med. Chem.*, 1983, **26**, 644.
185. J. Augstein, D. A. Cox, A. L. Ham, P. R. Leeming and M. Snarey, *J. Med. Chem.*, 1973, **16**, 1245.
186. L. H. Smith and H. Tucker, *J. Med. Chem.*, 1977, **20**, 1653.
187. H. Tucker and J. F. Coope, *J. Med. Chem.*, 1978, **21**, 769.
188. M. S. Large and L. H. Smith, *J. Med. Chem.*, 1982, **25**, 1286.
189. M. S. Large and L. H. Smith, *J. Med. Chem.*, 1983, **26**, 352.
190. M. S. Large and L. H. Smith, *J. Med. Chem.*, 1982, **25**, 1417.
191. M. S. Large and L. H. Smith, *J. Med. Chem.*, 1980, **23**, 112.

192. (a) H. J. Smith, S. E. Halliday, D. C. N. Earl and D. Stribling, *J. Pharmacol. Exp. Ther.*, 1983, **226**, 211; (b) A. J. Bilski, S. E. Hadfield and J. L. Wale, *J. Cardiovasc. Pharmacol.*, 1988, **12**, 227.
193. E. Saltvedt and P. Fauchald, *Curr. Med. Res. Opin.*, 1980, **6**, 528.
194. J. R. A. Mitchell, *Int. J. Cardiol.*, 1984, **5**, 141.
195. B. Levy, *J. Pharmacol. Exp. Ther.*, 1966, **151**, 413.
196. B. Levy, *Br. J. Pharmacol.*, 1973, **49**, 514.
197. J. D. Fitzgerald and S. R. O'Donnell, *Clin. Exp. Pharmacol. Physiol.*, 1978, **5**, 579.
198. M. H. Todd, *Pharmacologist*, 1976, **18**, 138.
199. T. L. Lemke, M. B. Cramer, S. W. Adamski, C. A. Pedone and G. Brooker, *J. Med. Chem.*, 1981, **24**, 1211.
200. H. Tucker, *J. Med. Chem.*, 1981, **24**, 1364.
201. A. J. Bilski, S. Dorries, J. D. Fitzgerald, R. Jessup, H. Tucker and J. Wale, *Br. J. Pharmacol.*, 1980, **69**, 292P.
202. A. J. Bilski, S. E. Halliday, J. D. Fitzgerald and J. L. Wale, *J. Cardiovasc. Pharmacol.*, 1983, **5**, 430.
203. D. Fitzgerald, T. Gumbrielle and J. D. Harry, *Br. J. Clin. Pharmacol.*, 1982, **13**, 586P.
204. S. R. O'Donnell and J. C. Wanstall, *Life Sci.*, 1980, **27**, 671.
205. H. Teräväinen, J. Huttunen and T. A. Larsen, *Acta Neurol. Scand.*, 1986, **74**, 34.
206. I. M. James, W. Burgoyne and D. T. Greenwood, *Coll. Int. Neuro-Psychopharmacol.*, *15th*, Puerto Rico, 1986, Abstract 141.
207. H. H. Vincent, A. J. Man in 't Veld, F. Boomsma, F. Derkx and M. A. D. H. Schalekamp, *J. Hypertens.*, 1985, 3(Suppl. 3), S247; *J. Hypertens.*, 1987, **9**, 198.
208. L. J. Findley and L. Cleeves, *Lancet*, 1984, **1**, 856.
209. C. R. Crooks, J. Wright, P. S. Callery and J. E. Moreton, *J. Med. Chem.*, 1979, **22**, 210.
210. M.-C. Carre, A. Youlassani, P. Caubere, A. Saint-Aubin-Floch, M. Blanc and C. Advenir, *J. Med. Chem.*, 1984, **27**, 792.
211. B. Costin, S. R. O'Donnell and J. C. Wanstall, *J. Pharm. Pharmacol.*, 1983, **35**, 590.
212. G. Leclerc, A. Mann, C.-G. Wermuth, N. Bieth and J. Schwartz, *J. Med. Chem.*, 1977, **20**, 1657.
213. J. L. Imbs, F. Miesch, J. Schwartz, J. Velly, G. Leclerc, A. Mann and C.-G. Wermuth, *Br. J. Pharmacol.*, 1977, **60**, 357.
214. J. J. Baldwin, D. E. McClure, D. M. Gross and M. Williams, *J. Med. Chem.*, 1982, **25**, 931.
215. K. P. Minneman, A. Hedberg and P. B. Molinoff, *J. Pharmacol. Exp. Ther.*, 1979, **211**, 502.
216. S. R. O'Donnell and K. Walduck, *J. Pharm. Pharmacol.*, 1981, **33**, 223.
217. N. Amlaiky, G. Leclerc, N. Decker and J. Schwartz, *Eur. J. Med. Chem.—Chim. Ther.*, 1983, **18**, 437.
218. N. Amlaiky, G. Leclerc, N. Decker and J. Schwartz, *Eur. J. Med. Chem.*, 1984, **19**, 341.
219. M. Bouzoubaa, G. Leclerc, N. Decker, J. Schwartz and G. Andermann, *J. Med. Chem.*, 1984, **27**, 1291.
220. (a) Anon., *Drugs Future*, 1984, **9**, 510; (b) J. Himber, V. L. Sallee, G. Andermann, M. Bouzoubaa, G. Leclerc and L. DeSantis, *J. Ocular Pharmacol.*, 1987, **3**, 111.
221. B. Macchia, A. Balsamo, A. Lapucci, A. Martinelli, F. Macchia, M. C. Breschi, B. Fantoni and E. Martinotti, *J. Med. Chem.*, 1985, **28**, 153.
222. M. Bouzoubaa, G. Leclerc, S. Rakhit and G. Andermann, *J. Med. Chem.*, 1985, **28**, 896.
223. J. Zaagsma, *J. Med. Chem.*, 1979, **22**, 441.
224. T. Jen and C. Kaiser, *J. Med. Chem.*, 1977, **20**, 693.
225. J. Dangoumau, Y. Barrans and M. Cotrait, *J. Pharmacol.*, 1973, **4**, 5.
226. (a) E. M. Taylor, A. M. Roe and R. A. Slater, *Clin. Sci.*, 1979, **57** (Suppl.), 433S; (b) R. J. Eden, D. A. A. Owen and E. M. Taylor, *Br. J. Pharmacol.*, 1983, **78** (Suppl.), 34P.
227. L. Andrén, L. Hansson and A. Svensson, *J. Cardiovasc. Pharmacol.*, 1983, **5**, 898.
228. (a) Anon., *Scrip*, 1984, **867**, 16; (b) G. T. G. Swayne, D. A. A. Owen, E. M. Taylor, R. J. Eden, R. A. Slater and W. Howson, *Arch. Int. Pharmacodyn. Ther.*, 1987, **289**, 251; (c) R. A. Slater, W. Howson, G. T. G. Swayne, E. M. Taylor and D. R. Reavill, *J. Med. Chem.*, 1988, **31**, 345; (d) W. Howson, J. Kitteringham, J. Mistry, M. B. Mitchell, R. Novelli, R. A. Slater and G. T. G. Swayne, *J. Med. Chem.*, 1988, **31**, 352; (e) G. W. Hardy, D. Bull, H. T. Jones, G. Mills and G. Allan, *Tetrahedron Lett.*, 1988, **29**, 799; (f) D. Cambridge, G. Allan, G. W. Hardy, M. J. Mollenfant, A. Ford and P. L. Oliver, *J. Cardiovasc. Pharmacol.*, 1987, **10** (Suppl. 11), S64.
229. J. E. Clifton, I. Collins, P. Hallett, D. Hartley, L. H. C. Lunts and P. D. Wicks, *J. Med. Chem.*, 1982, **25**, 670.
230. R. T. Brittain and G. P. Levy, *Br. J. Clin. Pharmacol.*, 1976, **3** (Suppl.), 681.
231. R. N. Brogden, R. C. Heel, T. M. Speight and G. S. Avery, *Drugs*, 1978, **15**, 251.
232. E. P. McCarthy and S. S. Bloomfield, *Pharmacotherapy (Carlisle, Mass.)*, 1983, **3**, 193.
233. E. H. Gold, W. Chang, M. Cohen, T. Baum, S. Ehrreich, G. Johnson, N. Prioli and E. J. Sybertz, *J. Med. Chem.*, 1982, **25**, 1363.
234. J. M. Grisar, G. P. Claxton, T. M. Bare, R. C. Dage, H. C. Cheng and J. K. Woodward, *J. Med. Chem.*, 1981, **24**, 327.
235. A. Franke, F.-F. Frickel, J. Gries, D. Lenke, R. Schlecker and P. D. Thieme, *J. Med. Chem.*, 1981, **24**, 1460.
236. A. Miyagishi, H. Nakahara and Y. Hara, *Arch. Int. Pharmacodyn. Ther.*, 1984, **271**, 249.
237. Y. Uchida, M. Nakamura, S. Shimizu, Y. Shirasawa and M. Fujii, *Arch. Int. Pharmacodyn. Ther.*, 1983, **262**, 132.
238. J. J. Baldwin, W. C. Lumma, Jr., G. F. Lundell, G. S. Ponticello, A. W. Raab, E. L. Engelhardt, R. Hirschmann, C. S. Sweet and A. Scriabine, *J. Med. Chem.*, 1979, **22**, 1284.
239. J. J. Baldwin, E. L. Engelhardt, R. Hirschmann, G. S. Ponticello, J. G. Atkinson, B. K. Wasson, C. S. Sweet and A. Scriabine, *J. Med. Chem.*, 1980, **23**, 65.
240. D. E. McClure, J. J. Baldwin, W. C. Randall, T. F. Lyon, K. Mensler, C. F. Lundell, A. W. Raab, D. Gross, E. A. Risley, C. S. Sweet and M. Williams, *J. Med. Chem.*, 1983, **26**, 649.
241. P. W. Erhardt, C. M. Woo, R. J. Gorczynski and W. G. Anderson, *J. Med. Chem.*, 1982, **25**, 1402.
242. P. W. Erhardt, C. M. Woo, W. G. Anderson and R. J. Gorczynski, *J. Med. Chem.*, 1982, **25**, 1408.
243. R. J. Gorczynski, V. S. Murthy and T.-F. Hwang, *J. Cardiovasc. Pharmacol.*, 1984, **6**, 1048.
244. R. J. Gray, T. M. Bateman, L. S. C. Czer, C. M. Conklyn and J. M. Matloff, *J. Am. Coll. Cardiol.*, 1985, **5**, 1451.
245. R. J. Gorczynski and A. Vuong, *J. Cardiovasc. Pharmacol.*, 1984, **6**, 555.
246. (a) V. S. Murthy, T.-F. Hwang, L. B. Rosen and R. J. Gorczynski, *J. Cardiovasc. Pharmacol.*, 1987, **9**, 72; (b) R. Achari, D. Drissel, J. D. Hulse, V. Bell, P. Turlapati, A. Laddu and W. L. Matier, *J. Clin. Pharmacol.*, 1987, **27**, 60.
247. B. Åblad, M. Brögard and H. Corrodi, *Acta Pharm. Suec.* 1970, **7**, 551.
248. H. Dowd, G. S. Keh and C. Raper, *Br. J. Pharmacol.*, 1977, **60**, 197.

249. C. Raper, G. A. McPherson and D. Iakovidis, *Eur. J. Pharmacol.*, 1978, **52**, 241.
250. R. P. Stephenson, *Br. J. Pharmacol.*, 1956, **11**, 379.
251. J. M. Van Rossum and E. J. Ariëns, *Arch. Int. Pharmacodyn. Ther.*, 1962, **136**, 385.
252. E. Carlsson, C.-G. Dahlöf, A. Hedberg, H. Persson and B. Tångstrand, *Naunyn-Schmiedeberg's Arch. Pharmacol.*, 1977, **300**, 101.
253. A. Weiss, B. Pfister, P. Imhof, P. H. Degan, D. Burckhardt and U. C. Dubach, *Eur. J. Clin. Pharmacol.*, 1980, **18**, 383.
254. N. A. Awan, K. E. Needham, M. K. Evenson, A. Win and D. T. Mason, *Am. Heart J.*, 1981, **101**, 158.
255. D. N. Sharpe and R. Coxon, *Eur. J. Clin. Pharmacol.*, 1983, **25**, 539.
256. H. Lambertz, J. Meyer and R. Erbel, *Circulation*, 1984, **69**, 298.
257. B. E. Strauer, I. Bohn, B. Hahn, A. Kment and U. Motz, *J. Cardiovasc. Pharmacol.*, 1984, **6**, 491.
258. M. J. Kendall, R. M. Goodfellow and S. Westerling, *J. Clin. Hosp. Pharm.*, 1982, **7**, 107.
259. M. J. Thompson, P. Huss, D. V. Unverferth, A. Fasola and C. V. Leier, *Clin. Pharmacol. Ther.*, 1980, **28**, 324.
260. K. Naito, T. Nagao, M. Otsuka, S. Harigaya and H. Nakajima, *Jpn. J. Pharmacol.*, 1985, **38**, 235.
261. T. Nagao, T. Ikeo, M. Sato, H. Nakajima and A. Kiyomoto, *Adv. Pharmacol. Ther., Proc. Int. Congr., 8th*, Tokyo, 1981 (Pub. 1982), p. 921.
262. M. Kino, Y. Hirota, S. Yamamoto, K. Sawada, M. Moriguchi, M. Kotaka, S. Kubo and K. Kawamura, *Am. J. Cardiol.*, 1983, **51**, 802.
263. G. Jennings, A. Bobik, C. Oddie and R. Restall, *Clin. Pharmacol. Ther.*, 1984, **35**, 594.
264. M. F. Rousseau, H. Pouleur and M.-F. Vincent, *Am. J. Cardiol.*, 1983, **51**, 1267.
265. K. J. Beatt, S. Saltissi, P. J. Kertes, P. C. Adams and D. G. Julian, *Circulation*, 1985, **72** (Suppl. 3), 473, Abstract 1890.
266. M. F. Rousseau, C. Hanet, J. Etienne, C. van Eyll and H. Pouleur, *Abstr. Int. Symp. Left Ventricular Dysfunction*, Jerusalem, Israel, 1985, p. 22.
267. P. F. Binkley, A. Al-Awwa, R. Lewe and C. V. Leier, *Clin. Res.*, 1986, **34**, 889A.
268. H. Pouleur, H. Van Mechelen, H. Balasim, M. F. Rousseau and A. A. Charlier, *J. Cardiovasc. Pharmacol.*, 1984, **6**, 720.
269. (a) J. G. Riddell, P. M. McCaffrey and R. G. Shanks, *Acta Pharmacol. Toxicol.*, 1986, **59** (Suppl. 5), 61; (b) P. E. Hicks, I. Cavero, P. Manoury, F. LeFèvre-Borg and S. Z. Langer, *J. Pharmacol. Exp. Ther.*, 1987, **242**, 1025.
270. J. G. Douglas and J. F. Munro, *Pharmacol. Ther.*, 1982, **18**, 351.
271. N. J. Rothwell and M. J. Stock, *Nature (London)*, 1979, **281**, 31.
272. B. E. Levin and A. C. Sullivan, *J. Pharmacol. Exp. Ther.*, 1986, **236**, 681.
273. M. Frisk-Holmberg and J. Östman, *J. Pharmacol. Exp. Ther.*, 1977, **200**, 598.
274. S. R. Jolly, J. J. Lech and L. A. Menahan, *Biochem. Pharmacol.*, 1978, **27**, 1885.
275. D. Bojanic, J. D. Jansen, S. R. Nahorski and J. Zaagsma, *Br. J. Pharmacol.*, 1985, **84**, 131.
276. M. V. Sennitt, J. R. S. Arch, A. L. Levy, D. L. Simson, S. A. Smith and M. A. Cawthorne, *Biochem. Pharmacol.*, 1985, **34**, 1279.
277. M. K. Meier, L. Alig, M. E. Bürgi-Saville and M. Müller, *Int. J. Obes.*, 1984, **8** (Suppl.), 215.
278. S. H. Ungar, in 'Quantitative Structure–Activity Relationships of Drugs', ed. J. G. Topliss, Academic Press, New York, 1983, p. 177.
279. A. P. IJzerman, R. Dorlas, G. H. J. Aué, T. Bultsma and H. Timmerman, *Biochem. Pharmacol.*, 1985, **34**, 2883.
280. V. Austel, E. Kutter and W. Kalbfleisch, *Arzneim.-Forsch.*, 1979, **29**, 585.
281. A. P. IJzerman, G. H. J. Aué, T. Bultsma, M. R. Linshoten and H. Timmerman, *J. Med. Chem.*, 1985, **28**, 1328.
282. A. P. IJzerman, T. Bultsma and H. Timmerman, *J. Med. Chem.*, 1986, **29**, 549.
283. D. Hellenbrecht, K.-F. Müller and H. Grobecker, *Eur. J. Pharmacol.*, 1974, **29**, 223.
284. P. A. Borea, A. Bonora, V. Bertolasi and G. Gilli, *Arzneim.-Forsch.*, 1980, **30**(II), 1613.
285. R. H. Davies, *Int. J. Quantum Chem., Quantum Biol. Symp.*, 1977, **4**, 413.
286. W. J. Dunn, III, S. Wold and Y. C. Martin, *J. Med. Chem.*, 1978, **21**, 922.
287. S. H. Ungar, in 'Drug Design', ed. E. J. Ariëns, Academic Press, New York, 1980, vol. 9, p. 48.
288. M. E. Condon, C. M. Cimarusti, R. Fox, V. L. Narayanan, J. Reid, J. E. Sundeen and F. P. Hauck, *J. Med. Chem.*, 1978, **21**, 913.
289. J. M. Cruickshank, G. Neil-Dwyer, M. M. Cameron and J. McAinsh, *Clin. Sci.*, 1980, **59**, 4535.
290. G. R. Bourne, *Prog. Drug Metab.*, 1981, **6**, 77.
291. C. C. Regårdh, *Acta Med. Scand., Suppl.*, 1982, **665**, 49.
292. (a) S. Pfeifer and C. Zimmer, *Pharmazie*, 1975, **10**, 625; (b) T. Walle, J. G. Webb, E. E. Bagwell, U. K. Walle, H. B. Daniell and T. E. Gaffrey, *Biochem. Pharmacol.*, 1988, **37**, 115.
293. L. E. Martin, J. C. Hobson, J. A. Page and C. Harrison, *Eur. J. Pharmacol.*, 1971, **14**, 183.
294. R. M. Sly *et al.*, *J. Allergy Clin. Immunol.*, 1985, **75**, 443.
295. H. S. Nelson, *J. Allergy Clin. Immunol.*, 1986, **77**, 771.
296. G. J. J. Teule and P. A. Majid, *Thorax*, 1980, **35**, 536.
297. Editorial, *Lancet*, 1981, **1**, 23.
298. H. F. Pratt, *Clin. Allergy*, 1982, **12**, 203.
299. C. T. Dollery, F. M. Williams, G. H. Draffan, G. Wise, H. Sahyoun, J. W. Paterson and S. R. Walker, *Clin. Pharmacol. Ther.*, 1974, **15**, 59.
300. R. C. Ahrens and G. D. Smith, *Pharmacotherapy*, 1984, **4**, 105.
301. S. Larsson and N. Svedmyr, *Am. Rev. Respir. Dis.*, 1977, **116**, 861.
302. W. T. Simpson, *Postgrad. Med. J., Suppl.*, 1971, **47**, 35.
303. J. W. Paterson, *Postgrad. Med. J., Suppl.*, 1971, **47**, 38.
304. H. Formgren, *Scand. J. Respir. Dis.*, 1975, **56**, 321.
305. N. Svedmyr, *Pharmacotherapy*, 1985, **5**, 109.
306. Y. Salorinne, B. Stenius, P. Tukiainen and H. Poppius, *Eur. J. Clin. Pharmacol.*, 1975, **8**, 189.
307. N. Svedmyr and B. G. Simonsson, *Int. Encycl. Pharmacol. Ther.*, 1981, **104**, 657.
308. R. T. Brittain, C. M. Dean and D. Jack, *Int. Encycl. Pharmacol. Ther.*, 1981, **104**, 613.
309. S. S. Chu, *Drugs Today*, 1984, **20**, 439.
310. V. M. S. Oh, C. M. Kaye, S. J. Warrington, E. A. Taylor and J. Wadsworth, *Br. J. Clin. Pharmacol.*, 1978, **5**, 107.
311. W. J. Louis, J. J. McNeil, B. Jarrott and O. H. Drummer, *Am. J. Cardiol.*, 1983, **52**, 104A.

312. W. H. Perks, S. S. Chatterjee, R. S. Croxson and J. M. Cruickshank, *Br. J. Clin. Pharmacol.*, 1978, **5**, 101.
313. J. D. Harry, *Int. J. Clin. Pharmacol. Res.*, 1982, **2**, 191.
314. D. G. McDevitt, *Drugs*, 1983, **25**, 331.
315. W. J. Louis and J. J. McNeil, *Br. J. Clin. Pharmacol.*, 1982, **13**, 317S.
316. (a) P. A. van Zwieten (ed.), *J. Cardiovasc. Pharmacol.*, 1983, **5** (Suppl. 1); (b) R. J. Northcote, *Int. J. Cardiol.*, 1987, **15**, 133.
317. R. Powles, E. Shinebourne and J. Hamer, *Thorax*, 1969, **24**, 616.
318. P. B. S. Decalmer, S. S. Chatterjee, J. M. Cruickshank, M. K. Benson and G. M. Stirling, *Br. Heart J.*, 1978, **40**, 184.
319. H. Formgren, *Br. J. Clin. Pharmacol.*, 1976, **3**, 1007.
320. J. R. Cove-Smith and C. A. Kirk, *Eur. J. Clin. Pharmacol.*, 1985, **28** (Suppl.), 69.
321. T. A. Betts and C. Alford, *Eur. J. Clin. Pharmacol.*, 1985, **28** (Suppl.), 65.
322. W. P. Koella, *Eur. J. Clin. Pharmacol.*, 1985, **28** (Suppl.), 55.
323. J. M. Cruickshank and B. N. C. Prichard, 'β-Blockers in Clinical Medicine', Churchill Livingstone, Edinburgh, 1987.
324. B. N. C. Prichard, C. W. I. Owens and J. Tuckman, *Handb. Exp. Pharmacol.*, 1980, **54**, 559.
325. J. G. Gerber and A. S. Nies, *Ann. Rev. Med.*, 1985, **36**, 145.
326. (a) W. H. Frishman and M. Teicher, *Cardiology*, 1985, **72**, 280; (b) L. H. Opie, E. H. Sonnenblick, N. M. Kaplan and U. Thadani, in 'Drugs for the Heart', ed. L. H. Opie, Grune and Stratton, London, 1987, chapter 1.
327. D. W. Richardson, J. Freund, A. S. Gear, H. P. Mauck and L. W. Preston, *Circulation*, 1968, **37**, 534.
328. F. R. Bühler, F. Burkart, F. E. Lutold, M. Kung, G. Marbet and M. Pfisterer, *Am. J. Cardiol.*, 1975, **36**, 653.
329. J. D. Fitzgerald, *Clin. Exp. Hypertens.*, 1982, **A4**, 101.
330. B. Dahlöf, M. Danielson, O. Andersson, T. Thulin, P. Öhman, C. Mörlin, J. Boberg, B. E. Karlberg, S. Jern and L. Hansson, *Br. J. Clin. Pharmacol.*, 1984, **18**, 831.
331. G. Leonetti, L. Sampieri, C. Cuspidi, L. Terzoli, L. Rupoli, M. Fruscio, R. Gradnik and A. Zanchetti, *J. Hypertens.*, 1985, **3** (Suppl. 3), S243.
332. A. J. Man in't Veld and M. A. D. H. Schalekamp, *Eur. Heart J.*, 1983, **4** (Suppl. D), 31.
333. Medical Research Council Working Party, *Br. Med. J.*, 1985, **291**, 97.
334. F. R. Bühler, in 'Frontiers in Hypertension Research', ed. J. H. Laragh, F. R. Bühler and D. W. Seldin, Springer-Verlag, New York, 1981, p. 423.
335. J. Conway, *Eur. Heart J.*, 1983, **4** (Suppl. D), 43.
336. A. J. Man in't Veld and M. A. D. H. Schalekamp, *J. Pharmacol.*, 1983, **14** (Suppl. II), 69.
337. M. A. van Baak, H. A. J. Struyker Boudier and J. F. M. Smits, *Clin. Exp. Hypertens., Part A*, 1985, **7**, 1.
338. P. A. van Zwieten and P. B. M. W. M. Timmermans, *Eur. J. Clin. Pharmacol.*, 1985, **28** (Suppl.), 13.
339. A. D. Struthers and C. T. Dollery, *Eur. J. Clin. Pharmacol.*, 1985, **28** (Suppl.), 3.
340. H. Majewski, M. W. McCulloch, M. J. Rand and D. F. Story, *Br. J. Pharmacol.*, 1980, **71**, 435.
341. Various authors, *Br. J. Clin. Pharmacol.*, 1976, **3** (Suppl. 3), 681.
342. D. G. McDevitt, in 'Frontiers in Hypertension Research', ed. J. H. Laragh, F. R. Bühler and D. W. Seldin, Springer-Verlag, New York, 1981, p. 473.
343. A. J. Scriven and P. J. Lewis, *Pharmacol. Ther.*, 1983, **20**, 95.
344. J. D. Fitzgerald, *Handb. Hypertens.*, 1984, **3**, 249.
345. W. H. Frishman, J. Ruggio and C. Furberg, *Postgrad. Med.*, 1985, **78**, 40.
346. Practolol International Study Group, *Br. Med. J.*, 1977, **2**, 419.
347. Norwegian Multicentre Study Group, *N. Engl. J. Med.*, 1981, **304**, 801.
348. β-Blocker Heart Attack Trial Research Group, *J. Am. Med. Assoc.*, 1982, **247**, 1707.
349. (a) A. Hjalmarson, D. Elmfeldt, J. Herlitz, S. Holmberg, I. Málek, G. Nyberg, L. Rydén, K. Swedberg, A. Vedin, F. Waagstein, A. Waldenström, J. Waldenström, H. Wedel, L. Wilhelmsen and C. Wilhemsson, *Lancet*, 1981, **2**, 823; (b) G. Olsson, A. Odén, L. Johansson, A. Sjögren and N. Rehnqvist, *Eur. Heart J.*, 1988, **9**, 365.
350. W. H. Frishman, C. D. Furberg and W. T. Friedewald, *N. Engl. J. Med.*, 1984, **310**, 830.
351. C. Wilhelmsson and A. Vedin, *Am. J. Cardiol.*, 1983, **52**, 108A.
352. J. A. Vedin and C. E. Wilhelmsson, *Annu. Rev. Pharmacol. Toxicol.*, 1983, **23**, 29.
353. The MIAMI Trial Research Group, *Eur. Heart J.*, 1985, **6**, 199.
354. ISIS Trial Research Group, *Lancet*, 1986, **2**, 57.
355. A. Vedin and C. Wilhelmsson, *Prog. Drug Res.*, 1986, **30**, 71.
356. B. N. Singh and D. E. Jewitt, *Drugs*, 1974, **7**, 426.
357. J. Herlitz and Å. Hjalmarson, *Eur. Heart J.*, 1986, **7**, 916.
358. R. M. Norris, *J. Mol. Cell Cardiol.*, 1986, **18** (Suppl. 4), 99.
359. Z. G. Turi and E. Braunwald, *J. Am. Med. Assoc.*, 1983, **249**, 2512.
360. Various authors, *Circulation*, 1983, **67** (Suppl. 1), I-1.
361. (a) W. H. Frishman, S. Charlap and M. Moser, in 'Beta Blockers in the Treatment of Cardiovascular Disease', ed. J. B. Kostis and E. A. De Felice, Raven Press, New York, 1984, p. 155; (b) P. Coumel, J.-F. Leclerc and B. Escoubet, *Eur. Heart J.*, 1987, **8** (Suppl. A), 41; (c) D. C. Harrison, *Am. J. Cardiol.*, 1985, **50**, 185; (d) P. F. Nestico, J. Morganroth and L. N. Horowitz, *Drugs*, 1988, **35**, 286.
362. L. Werkö, *Acta Med. Scand.*, 1987, **221**, 3.
363. P. W. Erhardt, *J. Med. Chem.*, 1987, **30**, 231.
364. S. H. Kubo and R. J. Cody, *Primary Cardiology*, 1986, **12**, 208.
365. M. Packer, *J. Am. Coll. Cardiol.*, 1987, **9**, 433.
366. M. R. Bristow, R. Ginsburg, V. Umans, M. Fowler, W. Minobe, R. Raşmussen, P. Zera, P. Menlove, P. Shah, S. Jamieson and E. B. Stinson, *Circ. Res.*, 1986, **59**, 297.
367. C. V. Leier, J. Webel and C. A. Bush, *Circulation*, 1977, **56**, 468.
368. Å. Hjalmarson, N. Abelardo and E. Waagstein, *Eur. Heart J.*, 1982, **3** (Suppl. D), 115.
369. G. S. Roubin, C. Y. P. Choong, S. Devenish-Meares, N. N. Sadick, P. J. Fletcher, D. T. Kelly and P. J. Harris, *Circulation*, 1984, **69**, 955.
370. P. C. Kirlin, B. Pitt and B. R. Lucchesi, *Acta Med. Scand.*, 1982, **212** (Suppl. 569), 263.
371. H. Pouleur, P. Cheron, F. Lavenne, A. A. Charlier and M. F. Rousseau, *Proc. Cardiovasc. Pharmacother. Int. Symp. Geneva*, 1985, abstract 453.

372. A. O. Molajo and D. H. Bennett, *Br. Heart J.*, 1985, **54**, 17.
373. S. Sasayama, S. Yokawa, M. Akiyama, M. Mikawa and O. Sakai, *Jpn. Circ. J.*, 1987, **50**, 636.
374. J. W. J. Lammers, M. E. T. M. Müller, H. T. M. Folgering and C. L. A. van Herwaarden, *Br. J. Clin. Pharmacol.*, 1986, **22**, 595.
375. J. Thormann, W. Kramer, M. Kindler, H. Neuss, H. Bahawar and M. Schlepper, *Am. Heart J.*, 1985, **110**, 426.
376. R. Canepa-Anson, J. R. Dawson, W. S. Frankl, P. Kuan, G. C. Sutton, S. Reuben and P. A. Poole-Wilson, *Eur. Heart J.*, 1982, **3** (Suppl. D), 129.
377. P. D. V. Bourdillon, J. R. Dawson, R. A. Foale, A. D. Timmis, P. A. Poole-Wilson and G. C. Sutton, *Br. Heart J.*, 1980, **43**, 206.
378. J. D. Stephens, S. O. Banim and R. A. J. Spurrell, *Br. Heart J.*, 1980, **43**, 220.
379. N. A. Awan, M. K. Evenson, K. E. Needham, T. O. Evans, J. Hermanovich, C. R. Taylor, E. Amsterdam and D. T. Mason, *Circulation*, 1981, **63**, 96.
380. (a) B. Sharma, J. Hoback, G. S. Francis, M. Hodges, R. W. Asinger, J. N. Cohn and C. R. Taylor, *Am. Heart J.*, 1981, **102**, 533; (b) R. S. Engelmeier, J. B. O'Connell, P. J. Scanlon and R. M. Gunnar, *Primary Cardiology*, 1987, **13**, 25; (c) J. G. Shanes, *Circulation*, 1987, **76**, 971.
381. K. T. Weber, V. Andrews, J. S. Janicki and N. Reicheck, *Circulation*, 1981, **64**, IV-307.
382. K. J. Klamerus, *Clin. Pharm.*, 1986, **5**, 481.
383. A. R. Lorimer and W. S. Hillis, in 'Cardiovascular Disease', Springer-Verlag, Berlin, 1985, pp. 151–174.
384. C. D. Furberg and S. Yusuf, *Adv. Cardiol.*, 1986, **34**, 124.
385. R. Rabkin, D. P. Stables, N. W. Levin and M. M. Suzman, *Am. J. Cardiol.*, 1966, **18**, 370.
386. K. Weerasuriya, L. Patel and P. Turner, *Cephalagia (Oslo)*, 1982, **2**, 33.
387. B. Åblad and C. Dahlöf, *Cephalagia (Oslo)*, 1986, **6** (Suppl. 5), 7.
388. P. Tfelt-Hansen, *Cephalagia (Oslo)*, 1986, **6** (Suppl. 5), 15.
389. J. A. Rosen, *Ann. Neurol.*, 1983, **13**, 92.
390. B. Dubois and M. G. Bousser, *Therapie*, 1985, **40**, 407.
391. J. W. Lance, *Med. J. Aust.*, 1986, **144**, 85.
392. T. J. Steiner and R. Joseph, *Postgrad. Med. J.*, 1984, **60** (Suppl. 2), 56.
393. P. Turner, *Postgrad. Med. J.*, 1984, **60** (Suppl. 2), 51.
394. *Cephalagia (Oslo)*, 1986, **6** (Suppl. 5).
395. P. Turner, in 'Recent Advances in Clinical Pharmacology', ed. P. Turner and D. C. Shand, Churchill Livingstone, Edinburgh, 1983, vol. 3, p. 223.
396. D. Panizza and M. Lecasble, *Eur. J. Clin. Pharmacol.*, 1985, **28** (Suppl.), 97.
397. L. Patel and P. Turner, *Med. Res. Rev.*, 1981, **1**, 387.
398. (a) P. van Rooy, D. P. Myburgh and A. J. Cilliers, *Eur. J. Clin. Pharmacol.*, 1985, **28** (Suppl.), 105; (b) M. Peet, *Postgrad. Med. J.*, 1988, **64** (Suppl. 2), 45.
399. Anon., *Lancet*, 1983, **2**, 1234.
400. L. Cleeves and L. J. Findley, *J. Neurol., Neurosurg. Psychiatry*, 1984, **47**, 976.
401. C. I. Phillips, G. Howitt and D. J. Rowlands, *Br. J. Ophthalmol.*, 1967, **51**, 222.
402. R. P. LeBlanc, N. E. Saheb and G. Krip, *Can. J. Ophthalmol.*, 1985, **20**, 128.
403. W. H. Frishman, *N. Engl. J. Med.*, 1981, **305**, 500.
404. The Levobunolol Study Group, *Ophthalmology (Rochester, Minn.)*, 1985, **92**, 1271.
405. D. P. Berry, Jr., E. M. Van Buskirk and M. B. Shields, *Arch. Ophthalmol. (Chicago)*, 1984, **102**, 42.
406. D. E. Potter and J. M. Rowland, *Exp. Eye Res.*, 1978, **27**, 615.
407. T. L. Phipps, D. E. Potter and J. M. Rowland, *J. Ocular Pharmacol.*, 1986, **2**, 225.
408. R. A. Hitchings, *Br. Med. J.*, 1982, **285**, 84.
409. J. Zipper, R. G. Wheeler, D. M. Potts and M. Rivera, *Br. Med. J.*, 1983, **287**, 1245.
410. A. Atsmon, I. Blum, M. Steiner, A Latz and H. Wijsenbeek, *Psychopharmacologia*, 1972, **27**, 249.
411. (a) M. Peet, D. N. Middlemiss and R. A. Yates, *Br. J. Psychiatry*, 1981, **138**, 112; (b) H. Wolinsky, *Clin. Cardiol.*, 1987, **10**, 561.
412. V. Grassi, S. Daniotti, M. Schiassi, M. Dottorini and C. Tantucci, *Int. J. Clin. Pharmacol. Res.*, 1986, **6**, 93.
413. G. Thiringer and N. Svedmyr, *Scand. J. Respir. Dis.*, 1976, **57**, 17.
414. P. A. van Zwieten and P. B. M. W. M. Timmermans, *J. Cardiovasc. Pharmacol.*, 1983, **5**, S1.
415. J. M. Cruickshank, *Am. Heart J.*, 1980, **100**, 160.
416. R. V. Lewis, P. R. Jackson and L. E. Ramsay, *Eur. J. Clin. Pharmacol.*, 1985, **28** (Suppl.), 93.
417. R. E. Rangno, in 'Beta Blockers in the Treatment of Cardiovascular Disease', ed. J. B. Kostis and E. A. De Felice, Raven Press, New York, 1984, p. 275.
418. B. N. C. Prichard, B. Tomlinson, R. J. Walden and P. Bhattacharjee, *J. Cardiovasc. Pharmacol.*, 1983, **5**, S56.
419. J. A. Oates, D. Robertson, A. J. J. Wood and R. L. Woosley, in 'Cardiac Therapy', ed. M. R. Rosen and B. F. Hoffman, Martinus Nijhoff, The Hague, 1983, p. 145.
420. R. H. Felix, F. A. Ive and M. G. C. Dahl, *Br. Med. J.*, 1974, **4**, 321.
421. A. J. Marshall, H. Baddeley, D. W. Barritt, J. D. Davies, R. E. J. Lee, T. S. Low-Beer and A. E. Read, *Q. J. Med.*, 1977, **46**, 135.
422. J. T. Nicholls, in 'Medicopharmaceutical Forum No. 7', R. Doll, 1978, Medico-Pharmaceutical Forum, Wimpole Street, London.
423. S. Calzetti, L. J. Findley, S. Perucca and A. Richens, *J. Neurol., Neurosurg. Psychiatry*, 1983, **46**, 393.
424. Various authors, *Clinician*, 1984, **2** (Suppl. 2).
425. B. I. Hoffbrand, R. G. Shanks and I. Brick (eds.), *Postgrad. Med. J.*, 1976, **52** (Suppl. 4).
426. A. Schneeweiss, 'Drug Therapy in Cardiovascular Diseases', Lea and Febiger, Philadelphia, 1986, p. 317.
427. E. Sowton, *Postgrad. Med. J.*, 1977, **53** (Suppl. 3), 90.
428. L. Hansson, A. Westerlund, H. Aberg and B. E. Karlberg, *Eur. J. Clin. Pharmacol.*, 1976, **9**, 361.
429. P. Saul, B. P. Jones, K. G. Edwards and J. A. Tweed, *Eur. J. Clin. Pharmacol.*, 1985, **28** (Suppl.), 109.
430. B. I. Hoffbrand (ed.), *Postgrad. Med. J.*, 1977, **53** (Suppl. 3).
431. A. Schneeweiss, 'Drug Therapy in Cardiovascular Diseases', Lea and Febiger, Philadelphia, 1986, p. 371.

432. R. N. Brogden, R. C. Heel, T. M. Speight and G. S. Avery, *Drugs*, 1977, **14**, 321.
433. J. Koch-Weser, *N. Engl. J. Med.*, 1979, **301**, 698.
434. A. Schneeweiss, 'Drug Therapy in Cardiovascular Diseases', Lea and Febiger, Philadelphia, 1986, p. 386.
435. A. Schneeweiss, 'Drug Therapy in Cardiovascular Diseases', Lea and Febiger, Philadelphia, 1986, p. 482.
436. *Postgrad. Med. J.*, 1971, **47** (Suppl. 8).
437. A Schneeweiss, 'Drug Therapy in Cardiovascular Diseases', Lea and Febiger, Philadelphia, 1986.
438. E. M. Vaughan Williams, *J. Clin. Pharmacol.*, 1987, **27**, 450.
439. W. H. Frishman, R. J. Goldberg and P. Benfield, *Drugs*, 1988, **35**, 1.
440. B. N. C. Prichard, *Eur. Heart J.*, 1987, **8** (Suppl. M), 121.
441. J. Erikssen, A. Rollag and J. E. Otterstad, *Acta Med. Scand.*, 1988, **223**, 35.
442. P. Benfield and E. M. Sorkin, *Drugs*, 1987, **33**, 392.
443. J. M. Henwood and P. A. Todd, *Drugs*, 1988, **36**, 11.
444. B. N. Singh, P. Deedwania, K. Nademanee, A. Ward and E. M. Sorkin, *Drugs*, 1987, **34**, 311.
445. R. Furlong and R. N. Brogden, *Drugs*, 1988, **36**, 455.

12.3

Dopamine Receptors

ALAN. S. HORN

University of Groningen, The Netherlands

12.3.1 INTRODUCTION

Dopamine (DA) was first synthesized in 1910, but its pharmacological properties were largely ignored due to the fact that its sympathomimetic actions are weaker than those of adrenaline and noradrenaline. In 1938, it was shown that DA occurred in human urine and a year later Blaschko[1] proposed that L-DOPA (3,4-dihydroxyphenylalanine) and DA were intermediates in the biosynthesis of noradrenaline and adrenaline from L-tyrosine.

In the late 1950s, it was demonstrated by several groups that DA occurs in the mammalian brain. At this time, Carlsson *et al.*[124] showed that L-DOPA was able to reverse the sedation induced by reserpine in animals. The high concentration of DA in the neostriatum was also reported around this time. The fact that Parkinsonian patients were found to have a more or less total depletion of DA in the corpus striatum led to attempts to treat this condition by administration of L-DOPA. After initial frustrations, this therapy has now come into widespread use.

The second area in which DA has played a role in the last 30 years is in the increase in our understanding of the neurochemical basis of schizophrenia and the actions of antipsychotic drugs, which are now known to be able to block DA receptors.

A third development, which is of more recent origin, is the classification of DA receptors into various types, *i.e.* D-1 and D-2 and autoreceptors, and the recognition of the importance of peripheral DA receptors. The synthesis of various new agonists and antagonists that are selective for these receptors has increased the clinical impact of drugs acting on dopaminergic systems.

Clearly, DA has played a very important role in the development of neuropsychopharmacology and it is likely that this will continue to be the case in the coming years. Anden has even gone as far as to say that 'It is not unlikely that we now know more about DA than about any other neurotransmitter'.[1]

Although an attempt has been made to cover as many topics as possible in the space available, no claim is made that this is a truly comprehensive review of the medicinal chemistry of DA. Such an endeavour would require its own volume rather than just one chapter.

For a general introduction to the field of DA research, *i.e.* both the pharmacology and medicinal chemistry, the reader is referred to refs. 1–8.

12.3.2 BIOSYNTHESIS AND METABOLISM OF DOPAMINE

12.3.2.1 Tyrosine Hydroxylase

Dopamine is formed from L-tyrosine *via* the pathway illustrated in Scheme 1. Tyrosine is obtained from the diet, or it can be synthesized in the liver from L-phenylalanine.[1-3]

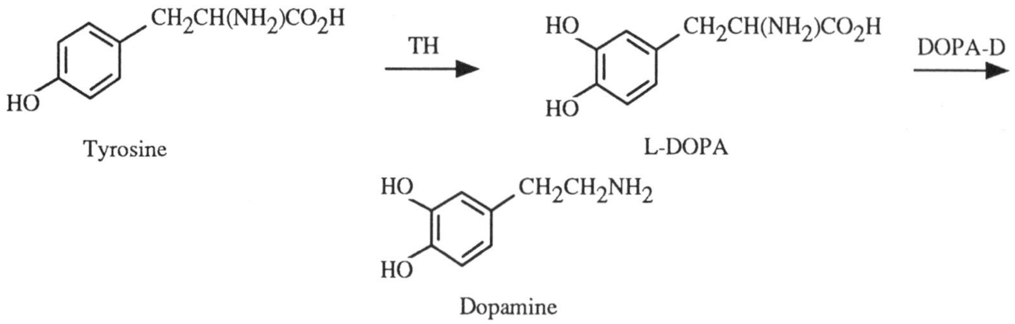

Scheme 1 The biosynthesis of dopamine; TH = tyrosine hydroxylase, DOPA-D = DOPA decarboxylase

These two precursors are present in the blood and the CNS at a concentration of about 5×10^{-5} mol L^{-1}. Tyrosine is accumulated in DA-containing cells by an active transport process. The rate-limiting step in the biosynthesis of DA is the conversion of tyrosine to 3,4-dihydroxyphenylalanine (DOPA) by the enzyme tyrosine hydroxylase (TH). This enzyme displays a fairly high degree of substrate specificity and requires a tetrahydropteridine cofactor. It does not appear to be associated with a particular subcellular organelle and there is strong evidence that, in most tissues, the enzyme exists in a soluble form. As this is the rate-limiting step in the biosynthetic pathway, manipulation of DA levels can be readily achieved by interfering with this enzyme. A number of substrate analogues have been used for this purpose.

Regulation of the biosynthesis of DA occurs at the level of tyrosine hydroxylase activation. Under normal conditions, this enzyme is completely saturated with L-tyrosine. High intraneuronal concentrations of DA inhibit tyrosine hydroxylase by end-product inhibition. Increased impulse flow in DA-containing neurons leads to the synthesis of increased amounts of DA. It has been shown that this is due to an activation of tyrosine hydroxylase, *i.e.* a change in the kinetic properties of the enzyme, whereby it has an increased affinity for the substrate, L-tyrosine, and the cofactor, and a decreased affinity for the end-product inhibitor, DA.

It is of interest that a cessation of impulse flow also leads to a rapid increase in DA accumulation. This appears to be due to a decrease in the release of DA, coupled with a marked increase in DA biosynthesis. The finding that tyrosine hydroxylase activity is increased when endogenous levels of DA are high seems unusual, bearing in mind the end-product inhibition normally brought about by DA. Thus, it appears that blockade of impulse flow leads to a change in the physical properties of the enzyme, *i.e.* it has a decreased sensitivity to inhibition by DA. It has been shown that the decreased affinity for DA is much greater than that observed following electrical stimulation.

On the basis of the above findings, Carlsson[9] postulated the existence of presynaptic autoreceptors for DA, whose function is to modulate DA synthesis. Cessation of activity in DA axons leads to a drop in DA release, which results in a reduced negative feedback inhibition of DA synthesis due to a reduction in the stimulation of the DA sensitive autoreceptors. This leads to an increase in the accumulation of DA and DOPA. In addition, the kinetic activation of tyrosine hydroxylase, resulting from impulse flow blockade, can be completely reversed by concurrent administration of a DA agonist.

12.3.2.2 DOPA Decarboxylase

This enzyme is not specific for the substrate DOPA; it will act on a wide range of aromatic acids and is more correctly called aromatic L-amino acid decarboxylase.[1] The enzyme is not associated with any specific particulate fraction, and the decarboxylation of L-DOPA to DA occurs in the cytoplasm.

The newly synthesized DA is then taken up into the vesicles, located in the nerve endings, where it is stored in a complex with chromogranins, divalent ions, *i.e.* magnesium and calcium, and ATP. There is also evidence for the existence of a soluble or free storage pool of DA in the cytoplasm, which plays a role in controlling DA synthesis by affecting the activity of tyrosine hydroxylase.

12.3.2.3 Metabolism and its Significance in Drug Action

The release of DA from nerve endings occurs *via* exocytosis and is calcium dependent. The main pathways involved in its metabolism are shown in Scheme 2. The two enzymes monoamine oxidase

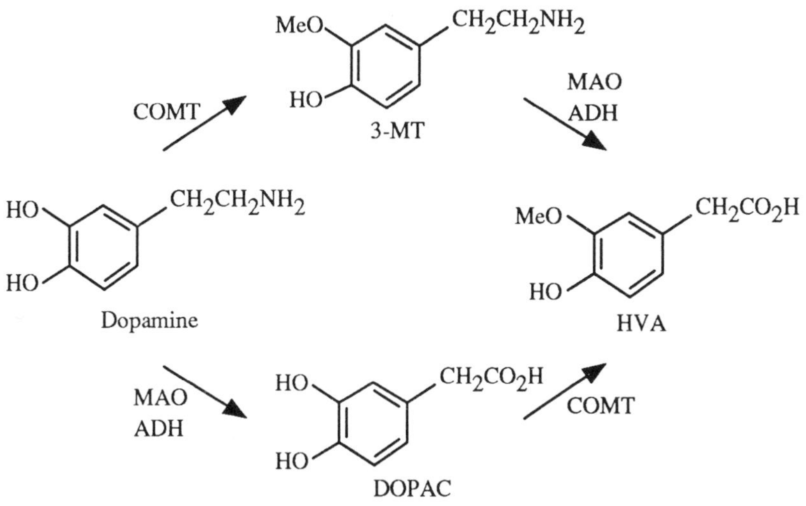

Scheme 2 The metabolism of dopamine by COMT (catechol *O*-methyltransferase); MAO (monoamine oxidase) and ADH (aldehyde dehydrogenase)

(MAO) and catechol *O*-methyltransferase (COMT) convert DA to the compounds 3,4-dihydroxyphenylacetic acid (DOPAC), homovanillic acid (HVA) and 3-methoxytyramine (3-MT), which are the main products of DA metabolism in the brain.[1,10] MAO is associated with the outer layer of mitochondria and occurs in multiple forms (A and B), which have different substrate specificities. The fact that chemical or electrolytic lesions of DA pathways in the striatum do not significantly affect COMT activity is indicative of a nonspecific localization of this enzyme. It is a cytoplasmic enzyme that is free or loosely bound to membranes in the cytoplasm of the cell. The location of MAO is controversial; however, there are strong indications that its predominant location is extraneuronal. DOPAC and HVA are often considered to be intraneuronal and extraneuronal metabolites of DA, respectively; nevertheless not all authors agree on this interpretation. In contrast, there seems to be an agreement in the literature that changes in 3-MT formation do reflect the release of DA.

Many psychotropic drugs have been shown to affect the accumulation of DOPAC, HVA and 3-MT in brain tissue.[1] In the case of amphetamine, the picture is complicated and the effects are dose dependent. The situation with DA agonists is more consistent, *i.e.* DOPAC and HVA levels are decreased, whilst, in general, DA levels are not significantly affected. DA antagonists, the neuroleptics, produce the opposite effect, *i.e.* DOPAC and HVA levels rise and DA levels again are hardly affected.

12.3.3 NEUROANATOMY OF DOPAMINE PATHWAYS IN THE BRAIN

Our knowledge of the neuronal organization of DA systems in the CNS is based on various techniques, of which fluorescence histochemistry has probably made the largest overall contribution.[1] The central DA-containing neurons can be divided into seven systems, as outlined in Table 1. For a detailed discussion of these systems, the reader is referred to the work of Lindvall.[1]

12.3.4 DISTRIBUTION OF DOPAMINE

For detailed information, the reader is referred to chapters in the reference work by Horn *et al.*[1]

12.3.4.1 Individual Brain Regions

Using the very sensitive radioenzymatic methods of measuring DA in small amounts of brain tissue, it has been possible to measure the DA content of more than 100 individual brain regions in the rat.[1] A summary of some of these findings is given in Table 2.

Table 1 Central Dopaminergic Projection Systems[1]

		Cells of origin	Projections
(i)	The mesostriatal system	Substantia nigra	nc. Caudatus-putamen; probably also globus pallidus nc. Accumbens
		Ventral tegmental area	
(ii)	The mesocortical system	Substantia nigra and ventral tegmental area	*Allocortical subdivision:* olfactory tubercle, septum, interstitial nucleus of the stria terminalis, amygdala; probably also the piriform cortex
			Neocortical subdivision: suprarhinal cortex, pregenual and supragenual anteromedial cortex, ventral entorhinal cortex
(iii)	The periventricular system	Mesencephalic periaqueductal gray and periventricular gray of caudal thalamus	Periaqueductal gray, medial thalamus and hypothalamus
(iv)	The incertohypothalamic system	Zona incerta and periventricular hypothalamus	Zona incerta, anterior medial preoptic and periventricular hypothalamus, septum
(v)	The tuberohypophyseal system	Arcuate and periventricular hypothalamic nuclei	Median eminence, pars nervosa and pars intermedia of the pituitary
(vi)	The periglomerular dopamine neurons	Olfactory bulb	Dendritic processes into olfactory glomeruli
(vii)	The retinal dopamine system	Mainly in the inner nuclear layer of the retina	Local dendritic projections

12.3.4.2 Peripheral Nervous Tissue

In the dog (*Canis familiaris*), the following concentrations of DA (g per g tissue) have been reported:[1] superior cervical ganglion, 2.00; inferior cervical ganglion, 0.80; stellate ganglion, 1.53; sympathetic chain, 0.17; cardiac nerve, 0.78; and splenic nerve, 0.45.

12.3.4.3 Peripheral Organs

In the rat (*Rattus norvegicus*), the following concentrations of DA (g per g tissue) have been reported:[1] whole heart, 0.03; lung, 0.18; kidney, 0.03; spleen, 0.02; and liver, 0.03.

12.3.5 THE CHEMISTRY OF DOPAMINE

Dopamine was first synthesized by demethylating 3,4-dimethoxyphenethylamine with concentrated HCl. It is available as the HCl (m.p. = 241–243°C) or HBr salt (m.p. = 218–220° C). Even in the salt form, however, it is sensitive to air and light. The oxidative sensitivity of DA has been widely investigated. The nature of the various oxidation and cyclization products is shown in Scheme 3. The pK_a values of DA are 9.06, 10.60 and 12.05. The $\log P$ (1-octanol/buffer pH 7.4) is -2.36. Further details on the chemistry of DA can be found in the review chapter by Grol.[1]

12.3.6 THE BIOANALYSIS OF DOPAMINE AND ITS METABOLITES

In the past, the most important methods for the determination of DA in biological samples were based on fluorimetry, GLC, mass fragmentography and radioenzymatic assays.[1] The technique which has largely replaced the above methods is high performance liquid chromatography (HPLC), coupled with electrochemical detection.[11] Dopamine is ideally suited to this technique because it is sensitive to electrochemical oxidation and this also applies to several of its metabolites. This technique was introduced around 1972 and now predominates the field. The sensitivity is in the low picogram range.

Table 2 Dopamine in the Brain of the Rat (pg per μg protein)

Telencephalon		*Diencephalon*	
Frontal cortex	1.04	Habenula	4.97
Cingulate cortex	0.91	Nucleus praeopticus medialis	12.33
Parietal cortex	0.84	Zona incerta	5.50
Piriform cortex	2.86	Nucleus subthalamicus	5.28
Entorhinal cortex	2.41	Nucleus interstitialis striae medullaris	13.38
Hippocampus	0.36	Nucleus suprachiasmatis	7.57
Nucleus caudatus	70.53	Nucleus supraopticus	6.84
Globus pallidus	39.62	Nucleus paraventricularis	8.79
Nucleus accumbens	87.17	Nucleus periventricularis	10.92
Olfactory lobe	2.79	Nucleus hypothalamicus anterior	4.55
Olfactory tubercle	94.56	Nucleus arcuatus	17.14
Nucleus tractus diagonalis	32.57	Eminentia mediana	57.99
Medial forebrain bundle (rostral)	51.34	Nucleus ventromedialis	5.10
Nucleus interstitialis striae terminalis	19.09	Nucleus dorsomedialis	10.01
Nucleus spetalis dorsalis	8.13	Nucleus periformicalis	6.21
Nucleus spetalis lateralis	21.35	Medial forebrain bundle (caudal)	7.59
Intermediate septal nucleus	14.54	Nucleus hypothalamicus posterior	7.18
Nucleus septalis medialis	8.57	Nucleus premammillaris ventralis	3.80
Nucleus septalis fimbrialis	4.34	Nucleus premammillaris dorsalis	4.04
Nucleus tractus olfactorius lateralis	8.19	Nucleus mammillaris medialis	4.27
Nucleus amygdaloideus medialis	7.51	Nucleus mammillaris lateralis	2.74
Nucleus amygdaloideus centralis	15.01	Nucleus anterior ventralis thalami	1.20
Nucleus amygdaloideus lateralis	17.48	Nucleus medialis thalami	1.02
Nucleus amygdaloideus corticalis	4.82	Nucleus ventralis thalami	0.24
Nucleus amygdaloideus basalis	7.65	Nucleus reticularis thalami	n.d.
Nucleus amygdaloideus medialis posterior	1.37	Nucleus posterior thalami	2.27
Nucleus amygdaloideus posterior	1.56	Midline thalamic nuclei	4.00
		Corpus geniculatum mediale	2.25
		Corpus geniculatum laterale	0.98
Mesencephalon		*Medulla oblongata*	
Nucleus ruber	5.76	Nucleus raphe magnus	1.18
Substantia nigra zona compacta (A9)	5.36	Nucleus motorius n. facialis	1.64
Substantia nigra zona reticularis	4.94	Nucleus tractus spinalis n. trigemini	2.63
Substantia nigra pars lateralis (A8)	7.76	Nucleus vestibulares (lateral and medial)	0.94
Colliculus superior	1.12	Nucleus cochleares (dorsal and ventral)	0.58
Colliculus inferior	0.40	Nucleus reticularis gigantocellularis	1.11
Substantia grisea centralis, pars dorsalis	4.68	Nucleus reticularis parvocellularis	1.62
Substantia grisea centralis, pars ventralis	3.95	Nucleus reticularis medullae oblongatae (ventral)	1.92
Nucleus raphe dorsalis	5.75	Nucleus reticularis lateralis (A1)	3.27
Nucleus interpeduncularis	8.87	Nucleus tractus solitarii (rostral)	3.20
Area tegmentalis ventralis (Tsai) (A10)	22.43	A2 region	7.28
Nucleus cuneiformis (A7)	2.91	Nucleus commissuralis	10.08
		Nucleus motorius n. hypoglossi	2.53
		Inferior olive	0.85
The Pons		*Cerebellum*	
Nuclei pontis	1.37	Cortex	0.17
Nucleus reticularis pontis	1.39	Nuclei	0.82
Nucleus tegmentalis dorsalis	2.99		
Locus coeruleus (A6)	16.72	*Spinal cord*	
Nuclei parabrachiales	1.65	'Lateral spinal cord'	2.40
A5 region	1.79		
Superior olive	1.12		

12.3.7 THE CLASSIFICATION OF DOPAMINE RECEPTORS

Up until the end of the 1960s, there was apparently no need to postulate the existence of more than one type of DA receptor. During the 1970s, however, several workers, on the basis of various techniques, suggested the existence of multiple DA receptors.

12.3.7.1 DAe/DAi Receptors

The first real attempt to collate and integrate these results into a new theory of DA receptor types, was the work of Cools and van Rossum[12] in 1976. They suggested the existence of two types of DA

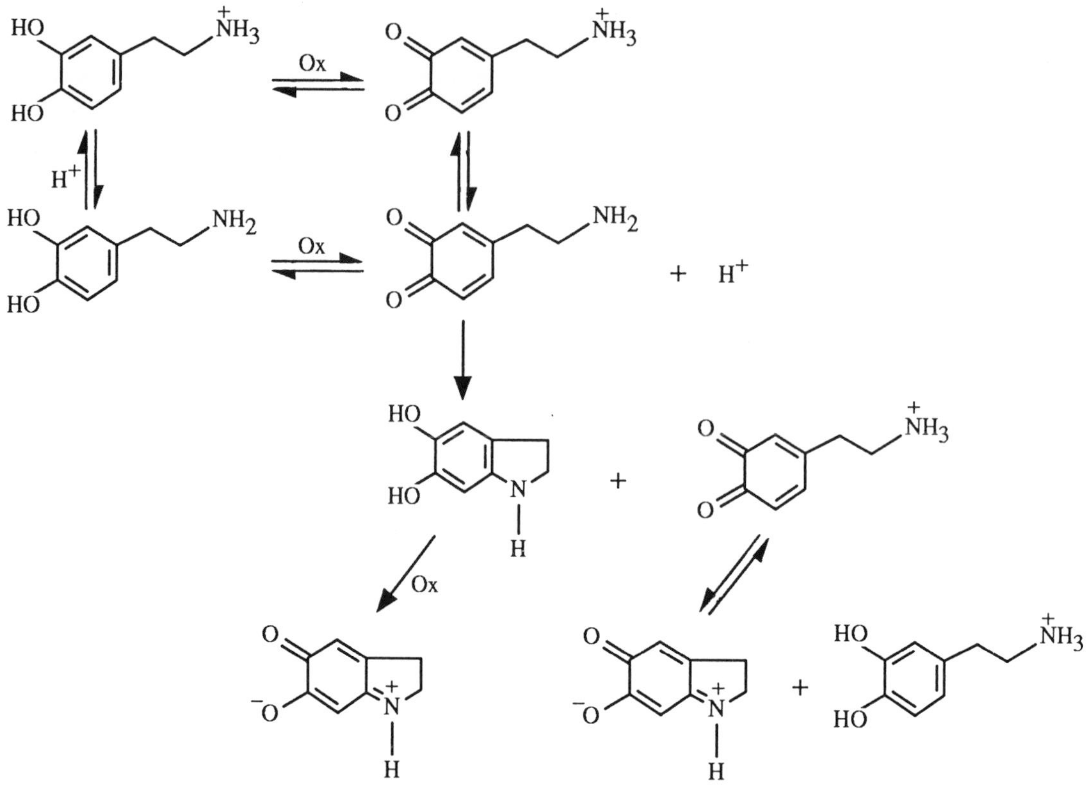

Scheme 3 The oxidation and cyclization of dopamine

receptors, *i.e.* the DAi and DAe types, which were responsible for inhibitory and excitatory effects, respectively. Although this theory attracted some attention, notably in behavioural and clinical circles, it has subsequently been shown to be incorrect by the fact that the key compound, 3,4-dihydroxyphenylimino-2-imidazolidine (DPI; **63**, see Section 12.3.11.17), which was claimed to be a selective DAi agonist, is virtually inactive in almost all standard tests of dopaminergic activity. DPI is in fact a mixed α_1/α_2 agonist.[13]

12.3.7.2 Autoreceptors for DA

In 1972, on the basis of results obtained following axotomy of rat brain nigrostriatal dopamine fibres and its influence on tyrosine hydroxylase activity, Kehr *et al.*[14] suggested the existence of presynaptic dopamine receptors. This concept was expanded in articles by Carlsson[9] and Roth *et al.*[15a] This idea was based on a similar concept which had arisen from neurophysiological studies of receptors located on the nerve terminals of noncatecholaminergic neurons. As it is now known that these receptors are not just restricted to the synapse, but are widely distributed over the neuron,

Table 3 Properties of Nigrostriatal and Mesolimbic Dopamine Autoreceptors

(i)	Nerve terminal autoreceptors modulate the impulse-induced alterations in synthesis and release of dopamine
(ii)	Cell body/dendritic autoreceptors regulate the physiological activity (firing rate) of the dopamine cell
(iii)	In any given dopamine system, autoreceptors are either present on, or absent from, both the nerve terminals and cell bodies/dendrites
(iv)	Within any given dopamine system, nerve terminal and cell body/dendritic autoreceptors appear to have similar or identical pharmacological properties
(v)	Nerve terminal autoreceptors on the mesolimbic dopamine neuron appear to be more sensitive to dopamine agonists than are autoreceptors on nigrostriatal nerve terminals
(vi)	Autoreceptors differ from postsynaptic dopamine receptors in their pharmacological responsiveness (for example, the enhanced sensitivity of autoreceptors to dopamine agonists)
(vii)	The responsiveness of autoreceptors is altered, following chronic exposure to dopamine agonists and antagonists

the term 'autoreceptor' is probably more accurate. Autoreceptors are thought to control the synthesis and release of DA; the evidence for this suggestion is based on neuropharmacological, electrophysiological and behavioural studies. It has been shown that DA autoreceptors on nigral cell bodies and dendrites are 6–10 times more sensitive to the inhibitory effects of DA agonists than are postsynaptic DA receptors located on cells in the caudate nucleus.[16] This differential sensitivity is thought to be due either to a generally higher responsiveness of these receptors or a higher percentage of 'spare' receptors. A summary of some of the properties of these receptors is given in Table 3.

12.3.7.3 D-1 and D-2 DA Receptors

A landmark in DA receptor research was the demonstration by various research groups in the early 1970s that DA is able to stimulate adenylate cyclase activity in neural tissue.[1] For the first time researchers were able to investigate the properties of a DA receptor in a simple *in vitro* system. However, although various agonists and antagonists displayed the expected activity, several dopaminergic ergots, while being able to stimulate DA receptors in the pituitary gland, produced an inhibition of the action of DA in neural tissue. It was therefore suggested that increased cAMP production was associated with D-1 activity and that the other DA receptors (D-2) were not positively linked to this enzyme.[17]* Subsequently, it was shown that stimulation of the D-2 receptor leads to an inhibition of adenylate cyclase activity.[18] Very recently, it has been reported that D-2 receptor stimulation leads to a decrease in the level of inositol triphosphate in rat striatal slices.[19]

A further important development in the area of *in vitro* studies on DA receptors was the demonstration in 1975 by Seeman *et al.*[20] of the existence of specific binding sites using [^{3}H]haloperidol. In the following five years, examination of the binding of various radioactive ligands to the DA receptor led to a classification involving four possible binding sites for DA, *i.e.* D_1, D_2, D_3 and D_4.[21] The difficulties surrounding the various nomenclatures at that time have been reviewed by several authors.[22,23]

The above problems of DA receptor classification have been clarified by the finding that the D_3 and D_4 binding sites are high affinity states of the D_1 and D_2 receptors, respectively.[24] Thus, the general consensus is that there are two DA receptors (D_1 and D_2), which can both occur in high and low affinity states (see Scheme 4).

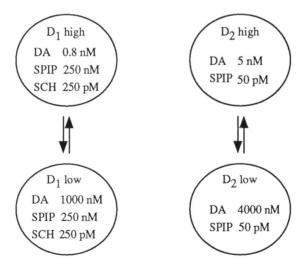

Scheme 4 Dopamine receptors can be divided into two forms, D_1 and D_2, both of which occur in high and low affinity states. Dissociation constants (K values) for dopamine (DA) and the DA receptor antagonists spiperone (SPIP) and SCH23390 (SCH) at D_1 and D_2 DA receptors, respectively, are shown[2]

---

* Currently in the literature there is an interchangeable use of the terms D-1/D-2 and D_1/D_2. The former terminology was used in the original review article[17] and the latter nomenclature arose from radioligand-binding studies. The preference in this chapter will be given to the former terms.

12.3.7.4 Peripheral DA Receptors: DA_1 and DA_2

At the time that efforts were being made to clarify the classification of DA receptors in the CNS, similar activities were being carried out in the peripheral nervous system. At least two distinct subtypes of peripheral DA receptor have been identified to date, *i.e.* the vascular receptor DA_1, which mediates vasodilation, and the neuroinhibiting receptor DA_2, which modulates release of neurotransmitter from the sympathetic nerve terminals.[25] It is generally felt that the DA_1 and DA_2 receptors are more or less identical to the D-1 and D-2 receptors in the CNS. However, although this subdivision explains most of the pharmacology of DA receptors in the periphery, there are certain inconsistencies which have led some authors to suggest that there may be grounds for a further division into two subtypes within each receptor class.[26] The medicinal chemistry and pharmacology of peripheral DA receptors have been reviewed by various authors[27-29] (see also Chapter 12.4).

12.3.8 THE EVALUATION OF DOPAMINERGIC ACTIVITY IN THE CENTRAL NERVOUS SYSTEM

The early methods of evaluating the interaction of drugs with the dopaminergic system in the CNS consisted of *in vivo* neuropharmacology, fluorescence histochemistry and various behavioural tests.[1-3] Since the beginning of the 1970s, these techniques have been supplemented with several *in vitro* methods. Through the use of these tests, it is now possible to obtain a classification of DA agonists and antagonists for D-1/D-2 and pre- and post-synaptic selectivities. The test systems can be conveniently divided into *in vitro* and *in vivo* methodologies.

12.3.8.1 *In Vitro* Assays

12.3.8.1.1 *The* in vitro *binding of [^{3}H]agonists and [^{3}H]antagonists*

The first successful report of *in vitro* binding to DA receptors was that of Seeman *et al.*,[20] in 1975, using [^{3}H]haloperidol and (+)-butaclamol. The use of the latter stereoisomer enabled these workers to distinguish between specific and nonspecific binding of [^{3}H]haloperidol. Since this initial report, more than 20 other radioactive ligands have been used to investigate DA receptors.[21] Currently, the ligands of choice for labelling the D-1 and D-2 receptors are [^{3}H]SCH23390 (**130**) and [^{3}H]spiperone (**111**), respectively. The recently introduced radioligand [^{3}H]N0437 (**17**) is one of the most selective D-2 agonists currently available.[30] Radioligand-binding studies, with one of the above labels, provide the easiest and most rapid answer regarding the possible dopaminergic activity of a new compound, and the method is used worldwide. The scope of this method has been reviewed recently.[31]

Radioligand binding has also been very useful in the field of receptor autoradiography, where it is possible to visualize the anatomical localization of D-1 and D-2 receptors.[32]

12.3.8.1.2 *D-1 adenylate cyclase*

The enzyme adenylate cyclase catalyzes the formation of cAMP from ATP. A form of the enzyme that is sensitive to DA is located in various DA rich brain areas.[1] This was the basis for the original definition of the D-1 form of the DA receptor.[17] The discovery of this functional *in vitro* model of the DA receptor was an important development because it meant that various DA agonists and antagonists could be examined in a simple brain homogenate system. There have been many reports on the SAR of compounds acting on the dopaminergic system using this model.[1,5,33] Although, after the initial enthusiasm, some doubts were raised as to the significance of this receptor,[4] it is now becoming clear that it does play an important role in behaviour. This has been mainly due to the development of specific D-1 antagonists, most notably SCH23390 (**130**) (see Section 12.3.11.14). In the early days, the corpus striatum of the rat was mainly used for this assay; currently the retina of the carp is usually employed due to several practical advantages it possesses.

12.3.8.1.3 *Inhibition of prolactin release*

Release of prolactin from the anterior pituitary is under the control of the hypothalamus.[1,3] Dopamine released from tuberoinfundibular nerve endings, in the median eminence, inhibits this release. This inhibitory effect can be studied *in vitro* in the isolated pituitary, in cultured anterior pituitary cells or in cultures enriched in lactotrophs (*i.e.* prolactin-secreting cells).[4] The system can also be used to study DA antagonists. The receptor involved is of the D-2 type and it is negatively coupled to adenylate cyclase. One advantage of using this tissue, rather than the striatum, is that the receptor population is probably purely D-2 and by definition postsynaptic.

12.3.8.1.4 *Inhibition of the* in vitro *release of [³H]DA*

When DA-rich brain slices are incubated with [³H]DA and then superfused with a suitable physiological medium, radioactivity, representing DA release, is eluted following electrical or potassium stimulation.[3,4] DA agonists have been shown to inhibit this process in a concentration dependent and stereoselective manner. It can also be stereoselectively blocked by DA antagonists. There is good evidence that this presynaptic effect is mediated by D-2 receptors.

12.3.8.1.5 *Inhibition of the* in vitro *release of [¹⁴C]ACh*

There is convincing data that DA nerve terminals in the striatum project onto dendritic spines of striatal cholinergic neurons. Thus, it is known that DA agonists increase striatal acetylcholine (ACh) concentrations and decrease acetylcholine turnover, and that neuroleptics produce the opposite effects. It has also been shown that *in vitro* DA agonists inhibit the stimulation-evoked overflow of radioactivity when striatal slices are preincubated with [¹⁴C]choline, which is converted to [¹⁴C]acetylcholine.[3,4] The inhibition by DA agonists and antagonists is stereoselective. The receptor mediating this postsynaptic effect is of the D-2 variety.

This model and the previous one are very useful functional models of the D-2 receptor. In contrast, however, to results reported in *in vivo* pre- and post-synaptic models, it has usually been found that there are no striking differences between the potencies for drugs in these two *in vitro* models. The reason for this is not clear, although it could be due to the 'semiphysiological' state of the tissue under study, *i.e.* the firing rate of the neurons may be adversely affected in the *in vitro* situation.

12.3.8.1.6 *Effects of drugs on [³H]DA uptake* in vitro

Various drugs which act on the CNS such as cocaine, the amphetamine group and certain anticholinergics have a potent inhibitory effect on the neuronal reuptake of DA.[1] Through an inhibition of the uptake of DA, these drugs are able to exert an indirect stimulating effect on DA receptors. The *in vitro* methods that are used to study this effect are as easy to perform as the radioligand-binding techniques.

12.3.8.1.7 **In vitro *tyrosine hydroxylase activity***

As discussed earlier, it is known that tyrosine hydroxylase (TH), the rate-limiting enzyme in DA biosynthesis, is subject to feedback regulation by DA autoreceptors.[1,3] It has been demonstrated *in vitro* in brain slices and synaptosomers that DA agonists decrease and DA antagonists increase TH activity.

However, the situation is complicated by the fact that certain congeners of DA can be accumulated by the nerve ending, which can lead to a direct inhibition of TH. This has been shown by the fact that certain compounds having an inhibitory effect on TH are sensitive to the presence of a DA uptake inhibitor. Potencies obtained for DA agonists in this system are markedly lower than those found in other *in vitro* tests related to the DA autoreceptor. Taking all factors into account, this is not a method of first choice to evaluate dopaminergic activity.

12.3.8.2 *In Vivo* Assays

12.3.8.2.1 *Effects on DA metabolism*

One of the most useful *in vivo* tests for evaluating DA agonistic or antagonistic activity is that of studying the effects of a drug on the striatal levels of the DA metabolites HVA and DOPAC. It has already been pointed out that agonists produce a fall in these levels, whilst the opposite effect is seen with neuroleptics (see Section 12.3.2.3). Two of the main advantages of this method are that it is sensitive and it does not require any sort of pharmacological pretreatment of the animals.

This effect is probably mediated *via* a combination of auto and postsynaptic DA receptors. However, it has been shown, through lesion studies, that postsynaptic receptors are not essential in this respect.[34]

12.3.8.2.2   DA turnover, the α-MPT model

The decline of DA levels after inhibition of its biosynthesis by the tyrosine hydroxylase inhibitor, α-methyl-*p*-tyrosine (α-MPT), has been taken as a measure of the utilization of DA.[1] DA agonists have been found to reduce, whereas DA antagonists enhance, the rate of DA disappearance after treatment with α-MPT. These results are thought to be due to an influence on the impulse flow-regulated release of DA, since direct influences upon the DA synthesis rate are probably eliminated after treatment with α-MPT. This comparatively simple test system has the additional advantage that, in one experiment, the possible effects on noradrenaline utilization can also be examined. This can provide valuable information on the receptor selectivity of a new drug.[35]

12.3.8.2.3   γ-Butyrolactone model

Administration of γ-butyrolactone (GBL) to rats leads to a reversible chemical lesion of the nigrostriatal neurons. When the impulse flow from the cell body to the nerve terminal is inhibited, the influences of postsynaptic receptors and also autoreceptors on the DA cell body, and on DA turnover, are removed and one can study the effects on autoreceptors located on the DA-containing nerve terminals.[1,2] GBL treatment leads to an increase in DA and DOPA accumulation. This is thought to be due to a sudden lack of inhibitory control of released DA on DA synthesis. These increases in DA and DOPA levels can be antagonized by DA agonists, and the latter effect can in turn be inhibited by DA antagonists. This is one of the best *in vivo* models for establishing a selective action on DA autoreceptors.

12.3.8.2.4   Striatal ACh concentrations

DA receptor agonists cause a blockade of striatal acetylcholine (ACh) release and a subsequent increase in the levels of striatal ACh.[36] Lesion studies indicate that these receptors (D-2 type) are localized on striatal neurons.

It has been reported that some DA receptor agonists, in low doses, produce a decrease in striatal ACh concentrations. This is thought to be a reflection of the selective activation of DA auto-receptors.[37]

12.3.8.2.5   In vivo receptor binding

Using suitable potent and selective DA receptor ligands, either agonists or antagonists, it is possible to label DA receptors *in vivo*. This is generally done with tritiated forms of the drugs,[38] but recently it has been shown that with 5,6-dihydroxy-2-(*N*,*N*-di-*n*-propylamino)tetralin (13) this is not necessary due to the development of a very sensitive method for its determination.[39] The interactions of various psychotropic drugs with DA receptors can be investigated in this manner. A distinct advantage of *in vivo* binding as compared to the *in vitro* method is that it is studied under true physiological conditions. In addition, one can study receptor binding and behavioural effects simultaneously in one experiment.

12.3.8.2.6   In vivo brain dialysis

This technique, which was introduced in 1982, consists of stereotaxically implanting a small dialysis tube into the brain of a rat and then perfusing the tube with a Ringer solution. The small molecules (neurotransmitters and metabolites) which dialyze through the membrane can be measured in the dialysate by the use of HPLC techniques. The influences of dopamine agonists and antagonists on DA and its metabolites can therefore be readily examined. The scope of this technique has been reviewed.[136]

12.3.8.2.7 Locomotor activity

The locomotor activity of rodents can be influenced by DA receptor agonists in various ways. Activity measured in motility cages may be decreased or increased depending on the dose administered, the time of measurement after injection, the habituation to the cage, *etc.* A consistent finding is that low doses of agonists reduce motility, whereas increasing the dose facilitates motility.[1,9] The latter effect, however, is often masked by the appearance of stereotyped behaviour, *i.e.* sniffing, biting, licking, gnawing, *etc.* Increased locomotor activity and stereotyped behaviour are thought to be due to postsynaptic receptor stimulation, whilst hypomotility is considered to be caused by an interaction with DA autoreceptors. Caution should be exercised in assuming that a reduction in locomotor activity is always caused by DA autoreceptor activity, as it is known that α_2 agonists also cause this effect.[40]

12.3.8.2.8 Turning behaviour

DA agonists produce turning behaviour, or asymmetrical postures, after unilateral injection in the striatum, or after systemic administration in animals with unilateral lesions in the nigrostriatal pathway or the striatum.[1] The rotation is directed away from the side of higher dopaminergic activity. Following a lesion or ablation of the striatum, the turning is ipsiversive, *i.e.* towards the side of the lesions due to the virtual inactivity of DA receptors on the lesioned side. This can be achieved by various methods, *i.e.* unilateral injection of a 25% KCl solution, which depolarizes the striatal nerve cells making them unresponsive, by unilateral caudectomy and also by hemitransection.

Lesions following the administration of the neurotoxin 6-hydroxy-DA result in an animal model in which directly acting DA agonists induce turning which is contraversive, *i.e.* away from the side of the lesion due to the fact that these receptors have become supersensitive.[1] The number of rotations that a rat makes following the injection of a DA agonist can be quantitated with the aid of commercially available apparatus.

12.3.8.2.9 Reversal of reserpine-induced hypomotility

In addition to the depletion of monoamines, reserpine administration to rodents leads to a pronounced and long-lasting hypomotility.[1] This effect can be reversed by the administration of DA agonists.[35] This test is thought to reflect postsynaptic dopaminergic activity.

12.3.8.2.10 The MPTP-lesioned monkey model

It is known that in both humans and certain monkeys, the compound 1-methyl-4-phenyl-1,2,3,6-tetrahydropyridine (**1**; MPTP) acts as a selective neurotoxin, whose administration leads to a Parkinson-like syndrome.[41] It is considered by many neurologists to be the best animal model of Parkinson's disease currently available and it has made the screening of potential new DA receptor agonists much easier and more effective. The precise mode of action of this compound is not fully understood; however, it is known that MPTP must be converted to an active metabolite in order to bring about its effects.

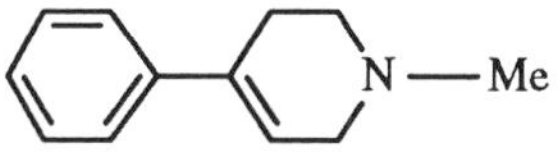

(**1**)

To date it has been shown that D-2 agonists are effective in ameliorating the syndrome caused by this neurotoxin, whilst the currently available D-1 agonists are ineffective.[42]*

---

* Temlett *et al.*[143] have recently shown that the D-1 agonist CY 208-243 is active in the MPTP-lesioned monkey model.

The discovery of the actions of MPTP on nigrostriatal neurons has been the most important development in the area of Parkinson's disease research since the detection of low levels of DA in the basal ganglia of victims and the subsequent use of L-DOPA.[1] It has provided a new impetus to research on the possible biochemical causes of this disease.

12.3.8.2.11 The interaction of D-1 and D-2 receptors in vivo

Prior to 1983 and the discovery of the selective D-1 antagonist SCH23390 (**130**),[43] the significance of D-1 receptors in relation to DA-mediated effects was unclear.[44] However, the development of potent and selective D-1 and D-2 agonists and antagonists in recent years has increased our understanding of the possible roles of these receptors and, perhaps more importantly, their mutual interactions. By examining these agents in various *in vivo* test systems mentioned above, it has become clear that the most striking behavioural effects of D-1 receptor stimulation occur when the D-2 receptor is also being stimulated.[45-47] In normal animals, *i.e.* those animals that have not had their receptor sensitivities changed, all unconditioned behaviour appears to depend upon the simultaneous stimulation of D-1 and D-2 receptors. Thus, the old view that D-2 receptors alone were responsible for producing changes in behaviour following administration of nonselective DA agents and endogenous DA was probably an oversimplification. The possible clinical significance of these concepts has been commented upon.[45,46]

12.3.9 THE EVALUATION OF DOPAMINERGIC ACTIVITY IN THE PERIPHERAL NERVOUS SYSTEM

As already mentioned in Section 12.3.7.4, there is evidence for at least two types of peripheral DA receptors, *i.e.* DA_1 and DA_2. The postsynaptic DA_1 receptors are located on vascular smooth muscles of blood vessels, as well as sites in the kidney, and their stimulation causes vasodilation, inhibition of aldosterone release and sodium and water reabsorption. The neuronal DA_2 receptors are located at various sites within the sympathetic nervous system and their activation leads to inhibition of sympathetic activity.

The effects of DA agonists and antagonists on DA_1 receptors can be examined using the dog mesenteric vascular bed *in vivo* and the rabbit splenic artery *in vitro*.[26] Activity at DA_2 receptors can be determined by using the cat heart *in vivo* and the rabbit isolated rectococcygens muscle *in vitro*. It is known that DA produces a relaxation of vascular smooth muscle by a direct action, whilst it reduces the responses of the heart and the rectococcygens muscle to nerve stimulation by inhibiting the release of noradrenaline and acetylcholine, respectively.

Other vascular preparations that can be used *in vitro* to study the actions of DA agonists and antagonists are the renal, mesenteric, coronary and cerebral arteries of the dog, the mesenteric artery of the rabbit, the cerebral artery of the rat and the perfused kidney of the rat.[137]

The test systems which have been used to study dopaminergic activity at peripheral receptors have been reviewed by several authors,[2,25,29,48,137] to whose work the interested reader is referred. This topic is also covered in Chapter 12.4.

12.3.10 ISOLATION AND CHARACTERIZATION OF DA RECEPTORS

The isolation and determination of the amino acid compositions of the D-1 and D-2 receptors is a logical next step in the development of our understanding of how these entities function at the molecular level. Before the introduction of cloning techniques in receptor research in the 1980s, the difficulties in this area appeared to be very formidable. The main problem was one of tissue source, *i.e.* unlike the situation with the acetylcholine receptor in the *Electrophorus*,[49] there is no known tissue which is comparably rich in DA receptors. This problem has been more or less eliminated by the introduction of molecular cloning techniques, whose application has led to the unravelling of the amino acid sequence of the β_2 adrenergic and M_2 cholinergic receptors.[50]

The main rate-limiting step that remained, once the problem of tissue source had been solved, was that of finding a suitable affinity chromatographic system for the isolation of the receptor from suitable solubilized solutions. To date, three groups have published their findings in the area of the D-2 receptor. Senogles *et al.*[51] solubilized the anterior pituitary D-2 receptor using digitonin and achieved a 1000-fold purification using a derivative of spiperone attached to a Sepharose 4B column.

However, in order to observe eluted receptor-binding activity, reconstitution into phospholipid vesicles was necessary. Ramwani and Mishra[52] achieved solubilization of the bovine striatal D-2 receptor using cholic acid and sodium chloride. A 2000-fold purification was obtained following affinity chromatography on a Sepharose CL-6B column containing covalently bound haloperidol. The highest purification reported to date, 5000-fold, was achieved by Bosker *et al.*,[53] who also solubilized the D-2 receptor from bovine striatum with digitonin. The chromatographic purification consisted of passage over a wheat-germ lectin agarose column, followed by two cycles of affinity chromatography using Sepharose CL-4B as the solid phase and *p*-amino-N0437 as the covalently bound ligand. This approach was novel in the sense that a dopamine agonist rather than an antagonist was used. A major band at $M_R = 95\,000$ was found on an SDS gel. As in other areas of receptor research, photoaffinity labels[54] have played an important role in our understanding of the molecular characteristics of the D-2 receptor. Most of these ligands have an aromatic azido group as the active moiety[55-59] (2a–e). Of the various compounds available, two deserve special mention, *i.e.* [^{125}I] *N*-(*p*-azidophenethyl)spiperone ([^{125}I]N$_3$-NAPS; **2a**)[55] and [^{3}H]azidomethylspiperone ([^{3}H]AMS; **2b**).[56] Studies with [^{125}I]N$_3$-NAPS have shown that the M_R of the D-2 receptor is probably 94 000. This figure was obtained in a variety of tissues and animal species.

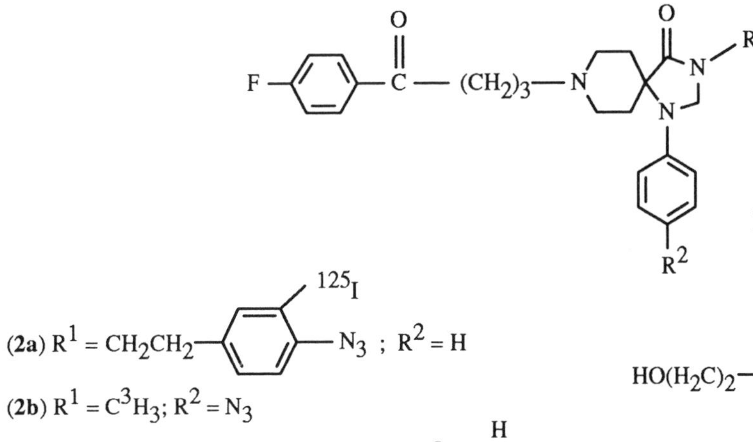

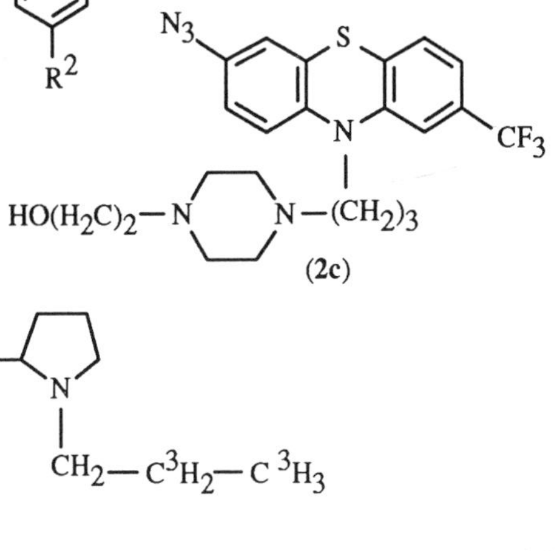

(2a) $R^1 = CH_2CH_2-$ ... $-N_3$; $R^2 = H$

(2b) $R^1 = C^3H_3$; $R^2 = N_3$

(2c)

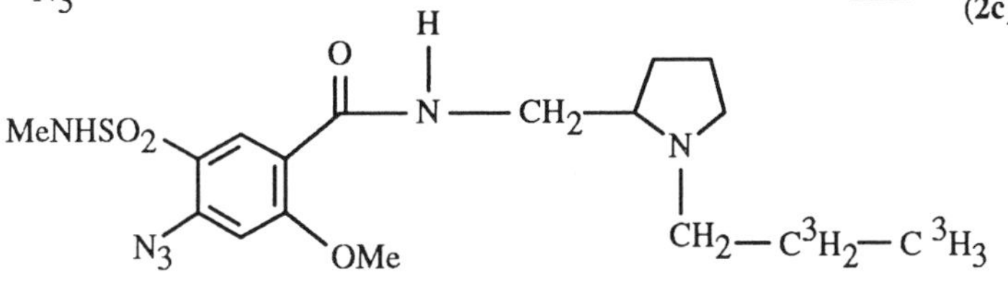

(2d)

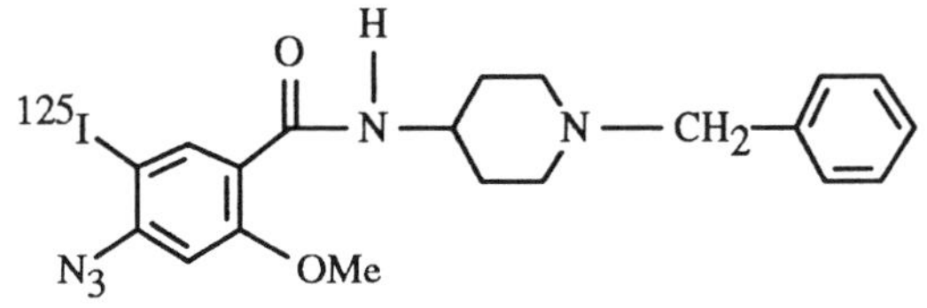

(2e)

A similar value was also obtained using [^{3}H]AMS. This compound is of particular interest because it is now commercially available. Studies with [^{3}H]-7-azidofluphenazine[57] ([^{3}H]-7-AF; **2c**) indicate that the D-2 receptor has a M_R of 92 000. The report by Redouane *et al.*[58] deviates from the above estimations in yielding a M_R value of 85 000, based on the use of [^{3}H]azidosulpride (**2d**). The authors suggest that this may be due to different experimental conditions for SDS-PAGE.

Thus, the majority of the above studies indicate that the M_R of the D-2 receptor is around 94 000. However, different conclusions were reached by Gredal and Nielsen[60,61] using radiation inactivation techniques. They suggest that the target size of the [^{3}H]NPA agonist-binding site is 81 000 Da, whilst that for [^{3}H]spiperone was 137 000 Da. In the case of the D-1 receptor, they report a value of 132 800 Da for the agonist site and 79 000 Da for the antagonist-binding unit.

At the present time, the D-2 receptor is receiving far more attention than the D-1 site, and not surprisingly our knowledge of the molecular properties of the former receptor is much more extensive. It is fairly safe to predict that within a couple of years, information on the amino acid sequence of the D-2 receptor should be known,* and similar information on the D-1 receptor should follow quite soon after.

12.3.11 STRUCTURE–ACTIVITY RELATIONSHIPS OF DA AGONISTS

Until recently, the main interest in developing new DA agonists was for the treatment of Parkinson's disease,[1] *i.e.* as an alternative therapy which might avoid some of the problems encountered with L-DOPA. The massive depletion of DA in these patients and the resulting dysfunction of the dopaminergic nigrostriatal system have been extensively reviewed[1,3,62] and will not be dealt with further in this chapter. The development of L-DOPA therapy and its current status have also been the subjects of many review articles.[1,3,62]

Interest in the development of new and selective DA agonists[3-6] arose as a result of our increasing understanding of the intricacies of DA receptor types, *e.g.* DA autoreceptors[9,15,16] and peripheral DA receptors.[25-29] It has been suggested[8,63] that if one could develop a selective DA autoreceptor agonist, it could possibly be used in schizophrenia due to its ability to reduce DA synthesis and release (see Sections 12.3.2.1 and 12.3.7.2). This suggestion is based on the hypothesis that in schizophrenia one is dealing with a hyperactive dopaminergic system, possibly in the limbic cortex.[64]

Peripheral DA receptors, of the DA_1 and DA_2 types, are of practical interest because of possible applications in cardiovascular therapy in such areas as hypertension, congestive heart failure, angina pectoris and acute renal failure.[27-29]

In this section, the SAR of the DA agonists is dealt with under 16 separate chemical classes and a small miscellaneous group. The reader should bear in mind the fact that much work was done before the emergence of the idea of two DA receptors. Many of the conclusions regarding SAR therefore refer to *general* dopaminergic activity rather than specific D-1 and D-2 activities. For references to the original studies, one should consult the review articles by Kaiser and Jain,[5] Cannon,[6] Carlsson and Nilsson,[8] Katerinopoulos and Schuster[65] and Weinstock *et al.*[66]

12.3.11.1 Phenylethylamines

In general, shortening or lengthening the two-carbon side chain between the aromatic nucleus and nitrogen atom or the introduction of α or β substituents all lead to a pronounced decrease or complete loss of activity. Except for epinine (*N*-methyldopamine; 3), all other *N*-monosubstituted DA analogues are either less active or inactive. The so-called '*N*-propyl effect'[4,8] is seen in various tertiary amines of DA. Thus, if one of the substituents on the nitrogen is an *n*-propyl group, there is usually quite a high degree of activity. It is of interest that this effect is also encountered in other DA agonist series. It is not simply related to lipophilicity and it has been suggested that the receptor has a hydrophobic binding site with a unique geometry to accommodate this group.

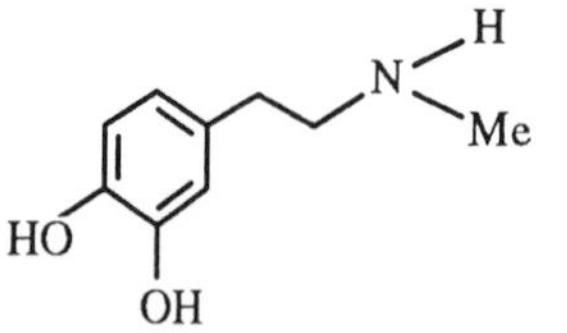

(3) 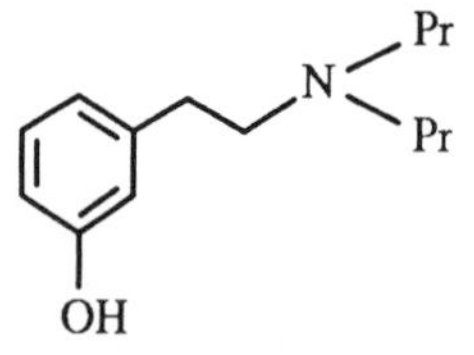   (4)

It is known that a catechol group is not necessary for high D-2 dopaminergic activity, and both *m*-tyramine and *N,N*-di-*n*-propyl-*m*-tyramine (4) display dopaminergic activity, the latter compound being quite potent. A further advantage these compounds possess is that they are not substrates for

---

* Bunzow *et al.*[142] have reported on the amino acid sequence of the dopamine D-2 receptor in rat brain. The sequence shows a high degree of similarity with other G-protein-coupled receptors.

Table 4 Ability of Dopamine Derivatives to Stimulate DA Sensitive Adenylate
Cyclase from Rat Caudate Nucleus[5]

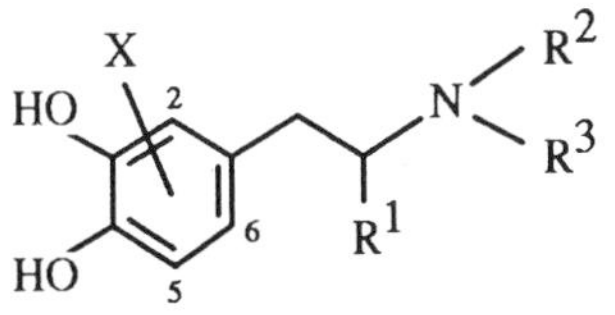

R^1	R^2	R^3	X	Relative activity,[a] adenylate cyclase in rat caudate
H	H	H	H	1.0
H	Me	H	H	0.9
H	Me	Me	H	0.6
H	Me	Me_2^+	H	b
H	Et	H	H	0.025
H	Et	Et	H	0.075
H	Pr^n	H	H	0.025
H	Pr^i	H	H	b
H	Pr^i	Me	H	0.018
H	H	H	2-Me	1.09[c]
H	H	H	6-Me	0.01
H	H	H	2-Ph	0.06
Me	H	H	2-Me	0.02
Me	H	H	2-Ph	b
Me	H	H	6-Me	b
Me	H	H	H	0.01
H	Me	Me	2-Me	0.58
H	Me	Me	2-Ph	b
H	Me	Me	5-Me	b
H	Me	Me	6-Me	0.01
Me	Me	Me	2-Me	0.01
Me	Me	Me	2-Ph	b
Me	Me	Me	5-Me	b
Me	Me	Me	6-Me	b

[a] Potency relative to DA, which is arbitrarily assigned a value of 1. Unless otherwise noted all values have significance of $p < 0.05$. [b] No measurable activity at 100 μM. [c] Not significantly different from 1.0.

COMT. However, it is surprising that the 3,5 positional isomer of *N,N*-di-*n*-propyldopamine is inactive as a DA agonist.

Introduction of substituents into the aromatic ring has not led to a large increase in activity and, in most cases, there is usually a loss of potency. In a series of binding studies, the three mono-fluorodopamines were equipotent with DA in displacing [^{3}H]spiperone, whilst the 2- and 6-fluoro analogues were less potent than their 5-fluoro isomer in displacing [^{3}H]apomorphine. The effects of various substituents on the D-1 activity of DA analogues are shown in Table 4.

12.3.11.2 3-Phenylpiperidines

If one cyclizes one of the *n*-propyl groups of the DA agonist *N,N*-di-*n*-propyl-*m*-tyramine onto the β-position in the side chain, the end result is the formation of the 3-phenylpiperidines of which 3-(3-hydroxyphenyl)-*N*-*n*-propylpiperidine (3-PPP; **5**) is the best known example.

This group of compounds, originally introduced by Carlsson and coworkers,[8] has received much attention in recent years for two reasons. It was found that racemic 3-PPP had a selective action on DA autoreceptors in the CNS and it was suggested that it might have an application in the treatment of schizophrenia. Further interest in this compound was generated when it was discovered that (+)-3-PPP acted as an agonist at autoreceptor and postsynaptic sites, whereas the (−) enantiomer was an autoreceptor agonist and a postsynaptic antagonist (see Section 12.3.13).

SAR studies[67] have shown that ring homologues of 3-PPP, *i.e.* the pyrrolidine (**6**) and azepine (**7**) derivatives, are much less active or inactive, respectively. Incorporation of an ethylene bridge (**8**) into

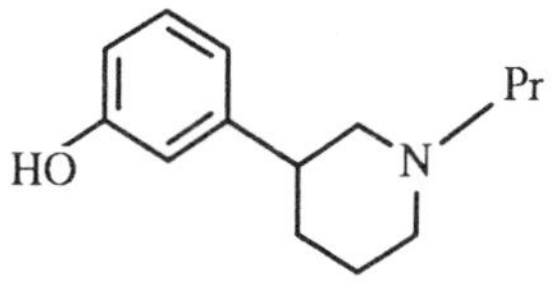

(5) 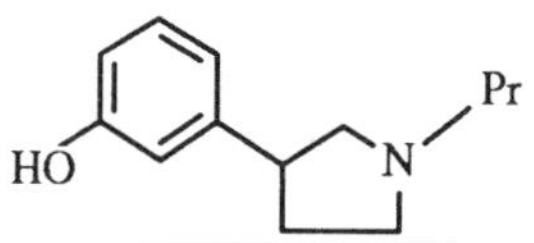   (6) 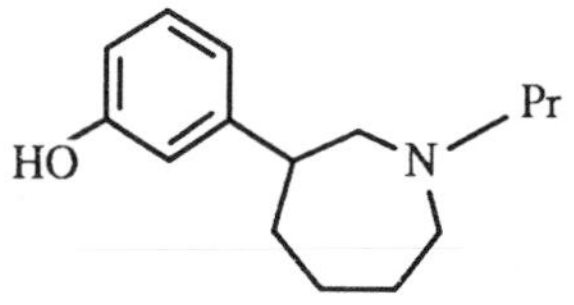   (7)

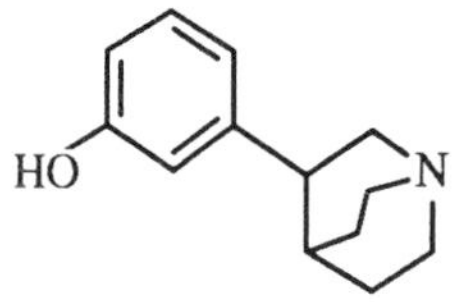

(8) 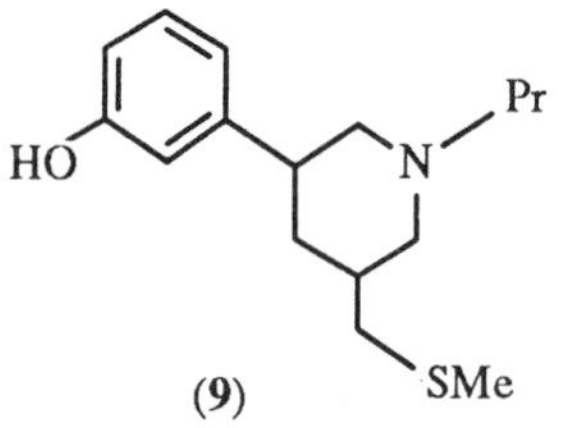   (9)

the piperidine ring (*i.e.* a quinuclidine system) is also detrimental. This is also true for the catechol analogue of 3-PPP, which lacks autoreceptor selectivity.

A 5-methylthiomethyl analogue (**9**) of 3-PPP, structurally related to pergolide, was much less active than the latter compound. It was found that within the *N*-substituted 3-hydroxypiperidines, all compounds in the (*R*) series, and the (*S*) enantiomers with N groups larger than propyl, appeared to be pre- and post-synaptic receptor agonists. The (*S*) enantiomers with ethyl and *N*-Pr^n substituents exhibited presynaptic agonist and postsynaptic antagonistic effects.

The neuropharmacology of 3-PPP has been extensively reviewed by Clark *et al.*[68]

12.3.11.3   2-Aminotetralins

Interest in the 2-aminotetralins (2-ATNs) as possible DA agonists arose in 1971 when Pinder *et al.*[69] made the suggestion that this was the active dopaminergic pharmacophore in apomorphine (see Section 12.3.11.9). As a result, 6,7-dihydroxy-2-aminotetralin (**10**) (also originally referred to as 2-amino-6,7-dihydroxy-1,2,3,4-tetrahydronaphthalene or ADTN), a compound first prepared by Thrift[70] in 1967, was resynthesized and tested for dopaminergic activity by Woodruff *et al.*[71] Although inactive following intraperitoneal (i.p.) injection, the compound was found to be as potent as DA following intracerebral administration. Various improvements on the original synthesis of this compound have been reported.

The isomeric 5,6-dihydroxy-2-aminotetralin (**11**) was synthesized by Cannon *et al.* in 1972,[72] and McDermed *et al.* in 1975.[73] The structural relationship to apomorphine was stressed. Although both isomers are potent DA agonists, in several tests the 6,7 isomer is more active. However, in inducing stereotypy in rats following injection into the nucleus accumbens, the 5,6 isomer is 100 times more potent than the 6,7 compound. This may be due to the fact that the 6,7 isomer is a much better substrate for COMT.[138]

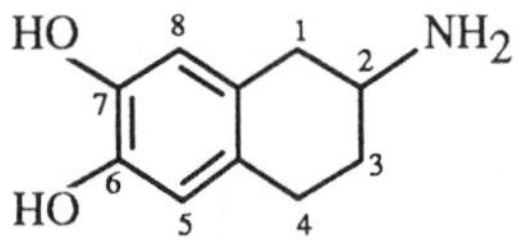

(10) 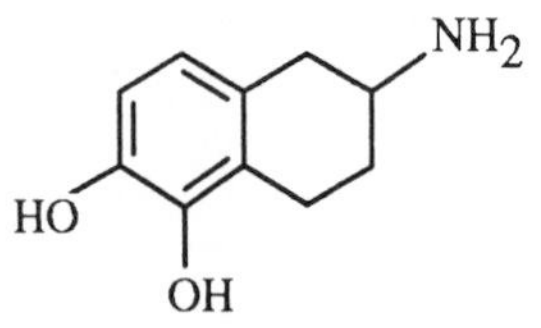   (11)

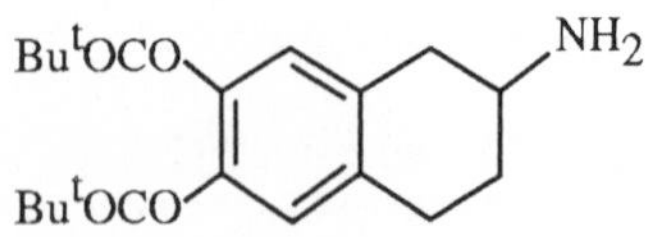

(12) 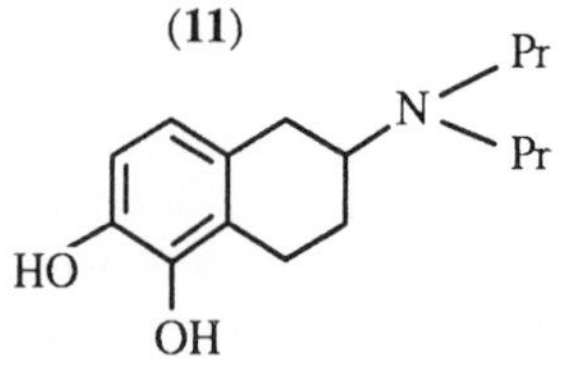   (13)

One of the main problems with these two compounds was their very limited ability to pass through the blood–brain barrier. Horn *et al.*[74] were able to show that this could be improved by preparation of various prodrug esters, *e.g.* the dipivaloyl derivative (**12**). The limited ability of the parent compounds to pass into the brain is partly due to their being good substrates for COMT.

The *N,N*-disubstituted 2-ATNs differ in activity as compared to their parent primary amines. In general, the 5,6 isomer of the *N,N*-disubstituted compounds is more potent than the 6,7 compound. This has been rationalized as being due to a difference in the mode of binding at the receptor. Once again, however, metabolic effects play a role. Of the catechol derivatives that have so far been tested, 5,6-dihydroxy-2-(*N,N*-di-*n*-propylamino)tetralin (**13**) has been shown to be the most potent compound. It has been successfully used to label DA receptors *in vivo*[39] and *in vitro*.[75]

The other catechol analogue requiring special mention is 6,7-dihydroxy-2-(dimethylamino)tetralin (TL-99; **14**). Initially, it was claimed that this compound was a selective DA autoreceptor agonist. Subsequently, however, it was found that it had significant postsynaptic activity and that part of its supposed autoreceptor selectivity was due to actions at α_2 adrenergic receptors.[40]

As in the phenylethylamine series, the resorcinolic 5,7-dihydroxy substitution pattern led to compounds that were, in general, less active than the catechols.

The monohydroxylated analogues of this group show a more or less consistent pattern of activity. The 5-OH isomer is the most active, followed by the 7-OH and finally the 6-OH. It is of interest that some 7-OH analogues exhibit enhanced selectivity for the DA autoreceptor. The discovery of the serotonergic actions of 8-hydroxy-2-(*N,N*-di-*n*-propylamino)tetralin (**15**) was unexpected and most interesting.[8]

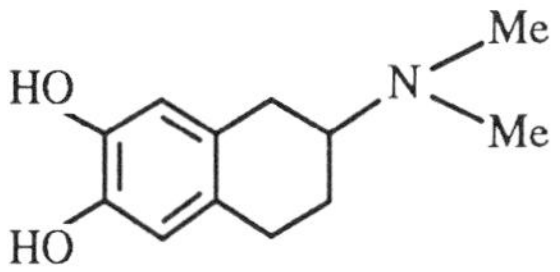

(14) 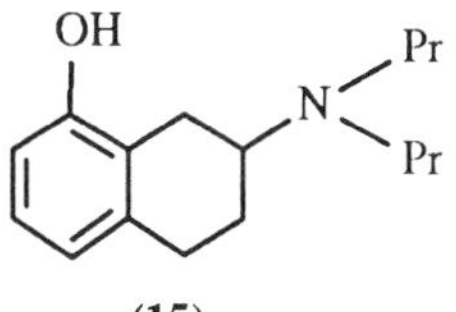   (15)

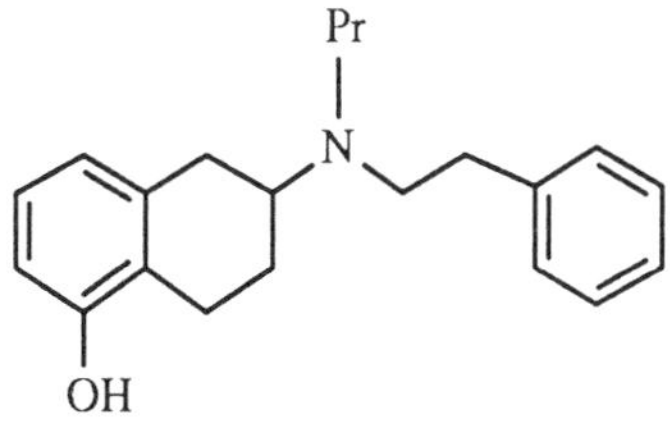

(16) 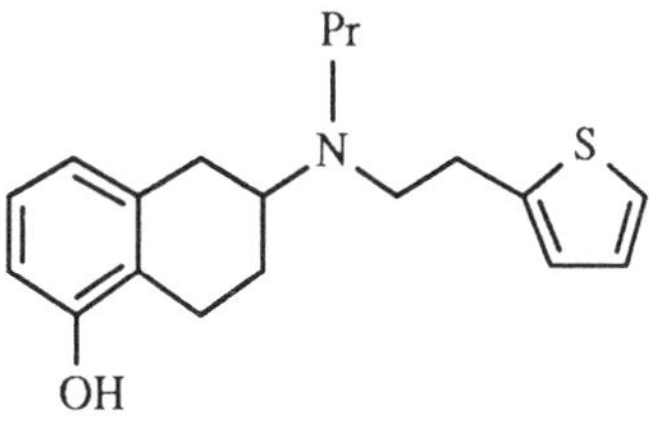   (17)

The 5-OH-ATNs have produced some of the most potent and useful DA agonists so far synthesized. Thus, extensive *in vivo* and *in vitro* studies have shown that N-0434[35] (**16**) and N-0437[30,35] (**17**) are two of the most potent and selective D-2 agonists currently available.[144] It has been suggested that the high D-2 selectivity exhibited by these compounds may be due to the binding of the *N*-ethylaryl moiety to a site outside the one occupied by the primary amine group of DA. A derivative of the former compound has already been mentioned in connection with successful studies on the isolation of the D-2 DA receptor.[53] N-0437 is of interest because it is the first example of a 2-ATN derivative, which has reached the stage of clinical evaluation for the treatment of Parkinson's disease.

In a series of ring-halogenated mono- and di-OH-ATN analogues, the 8-chloro and 8-fluoro-6,7-dihydroxy derivatives were found to be selective D-1 agonists. However, 6,7-dihydroxy-8-chloro-*N*-(4-hydroxyphenylethyl)-*N*-propyl-ATN (**18**) was found to have marked D-2 activity. Replacement of the 6- or 7-OH group by a halogen atom reduced the dopaminergic activity. The other aromatic ring derivatives that have been investigated are analogues of 5-hydroxy-6-methyl-2-aminotetralin (**19**), which are found to retain DA-like activity. It is thought that a metabolite might be responsible for some of the activity.

Studies on conformationally more rigid analogues of the 2-ATNs, such as (**20**), have, in general, been disappointing regarding the pharmacological potencies that were obtained.

An oxygen isostere of 6,7-dihydroxy-2-aminotetralin, *i.e.* 6,7-dihydroxy-3-chromanamine (**21**) was found to have *in vivo* activity similar to that of the parent compound, but its *in vitro* activity was much less. In contrast, 8-hydroxy-*N,N*-dipropyl-3-chromanamine (**22**) was found to possess potent DA-like activity both *in vitro* and *in vivo*.[76]

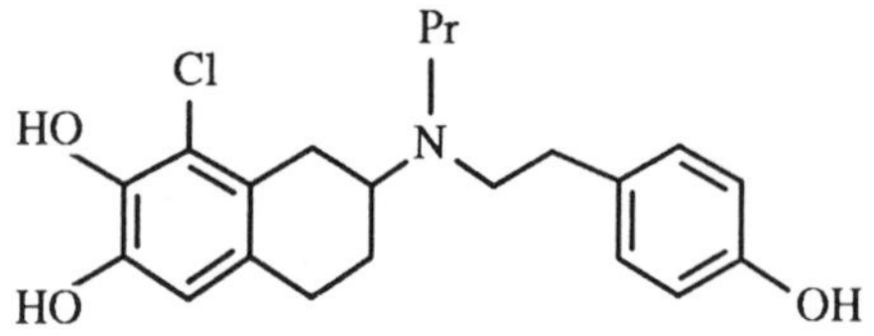

(18)

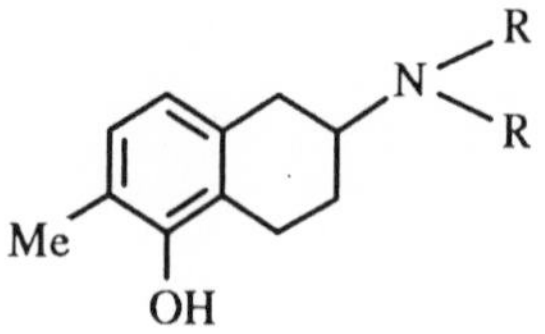

(19)

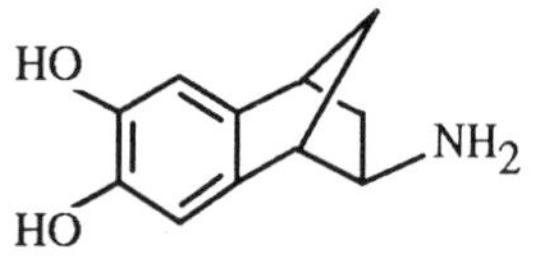

(20)

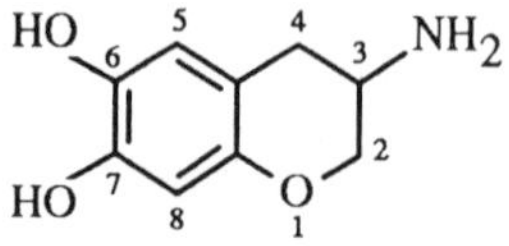

(21)

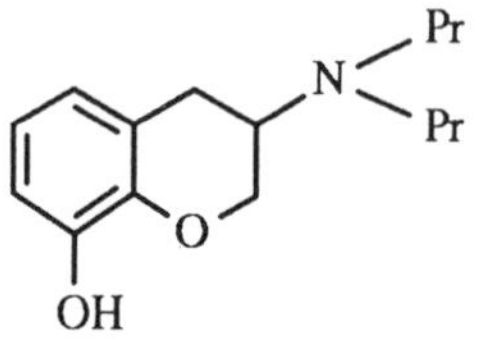

(22)

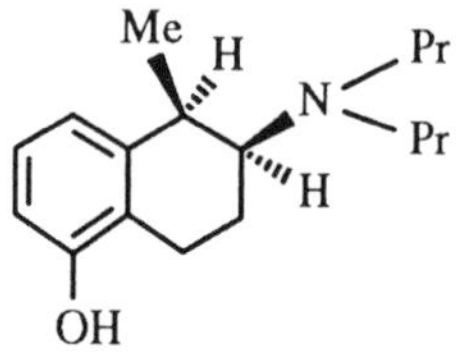

(23)

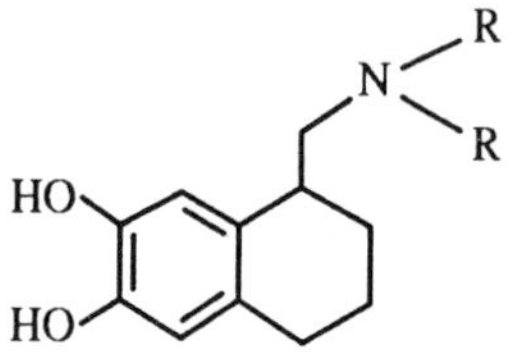

(24)

Introduction of a methyl group at the 1 position has produced some interesting compounds. Thus, it has been shown that $(1R,2S)$-$(-)$-*cis*-5-hydroxy-1-methyl-2-$(N,N$-di-*n*-propylamino)tetralin (**23**) and its methyl ether are DA agonists acting preferentially on DA autoreceptors, while the corresponding $(1S,2R)$-$(+)$ enantiomers exhibit antagonistic actions.

Regarding other substituents at the 1 position, it is of interest that 1-aminomethyl-6,7-dihydroxy-ATNs (**24**) show only very weak DA-like activity; this was also found to be true for the 1-keto analogue.

12.3.11.4 2-Aminoindans

4,5-Dihydroxy-2-aminoindan and the *N*-methyl and *N,N*-dimethyl analogues (**25**) were found to be much weaker emetics in dogs than the corresponding 2-aminotetralins.[6,65] In contrast, the *N,N*-diethyl and *N,N*-dipropyl compounds were found to be violent emetics. Members of the 5,6-dihydroxy series were not very active as DA agonists. All the above mentioned compounds exhibited only weak activity against [^{3}H]spiperone and [^{3}H]-A-6,7-DTN binding to calf caudate homogenates.

In the monophenolic series, the *N,N*-dipropyl-4-OH analogue was more potent than the 5-OH isomer in various biochemical and behavioural tests. Compounds lacking phenolic groups also display some dopaminergic activity *in vivo*; however, it has been suggested that this may be due to metabolic activation.

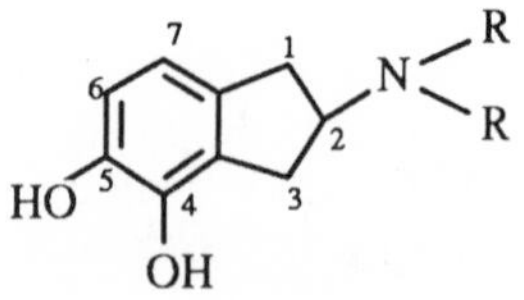

(25)

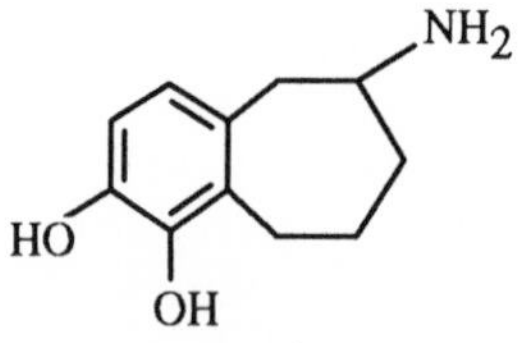

(26)

12.3.11.5 Benzocycloheptenes

1,2-Dihydroxy-6-aminobenzocycloheptene (**26**) and its mono- and di-*N*-propyl derivatives, as well as the resorcinol analogue 1,3-dihydroxy-6-aminobenzocycloheptene, were all found to be more or less inactive as DA agonists.[65]

12.3.11.6 Octahydrobenzo[*g*]quinolines

This group of DA agonists can be looked upon as apomorphine analogues lacking a non-catecholic aromatic ring.[6,65] The B/C rings can be either *cis*- or *trans*-fused and dopaminergic activity generally resides in the *trans* series. In various tests of dopaminergic activity, the 6,7-dihydroxy compounds (27) were found to be more potent than the isomeric 7,8 analogues. An *N*-propyl group was important for high DA-like activity.

Introduction of substituents in the 6-OH isomer at the 3 position, *i.e.* *N,N*-diethyl-*N*-sulfonamide (28) or 3-methylthiomethyl by analogy with CQ-32084 and pergolide, respectively, led to potent compounds having a long duration of action and good oral activity.

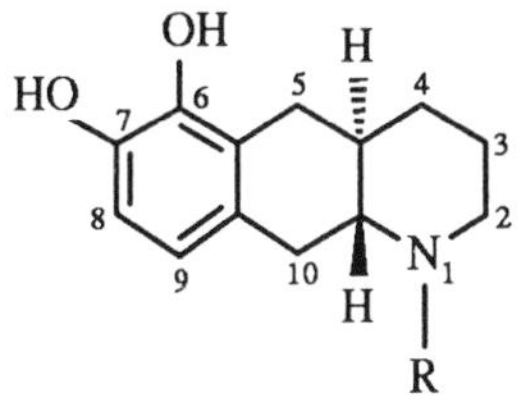

(27) 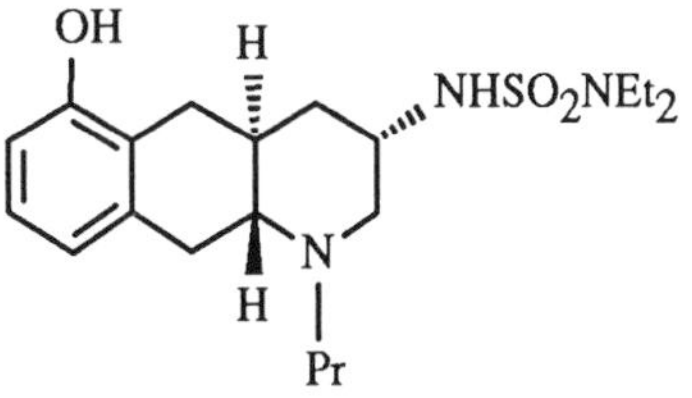   (28)

12.3.11.7 Octahydrobenzo[*f*]quinolines

The SAR of this group of compounds is similar to that discussed above for the [*g*] series.[6,65] The monophenolic 7-, 8- and 9-OH-*N*-propyl derivatives (29) all exhibited dopaminergic activity. By analogy with the 2-aminotetralins, the 10-OH compound showed 5-HT-like activity.

Due to difficulties involved in the preparation of the active *trans* isomers of these compounds, the isosteric ring system containing an oxygen atom, *i.e.* hexahydronaphth[1,2-*b*]-4*H*-1,4-oxazine, has been prepared by several groups.[77,78] The *trans*-*N*-propyl analogue (N0500; 30) was found to be a very potent and selective D-2 agonist. The (+) enantiomer of this compound (PHNO) has been found to be active in cases of Parkinson's disease.[79]

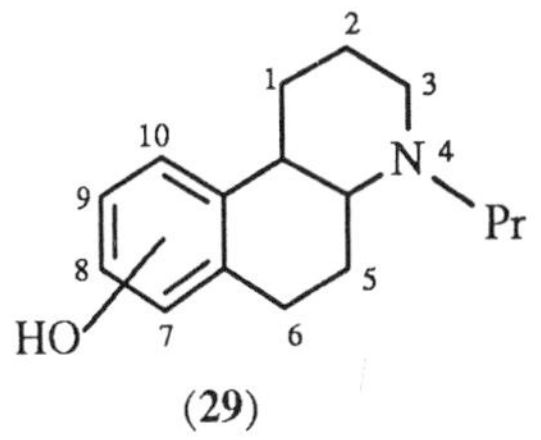

(29) 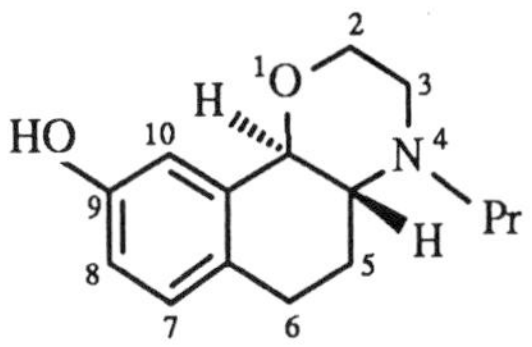   (30)

12.3.11.8 Octahydrobenz[*h*]isoquinolines

The 8,9-dihydroxy analogue as well as its *N*-methyl, ethyl and propyl derivatives (31) were synthesized and tested for their ability to inhibit the response of the cardioaccelerator nerve in cats to electrical stimulation.[6,65] All of these compounds exhibited only very low activity. It was suggested that the steric bulk of carbon atoms 5 and 6 prevented optimal interaction with the DA receptor.

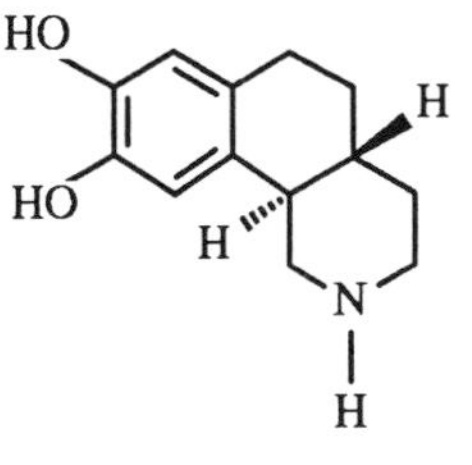

(31) 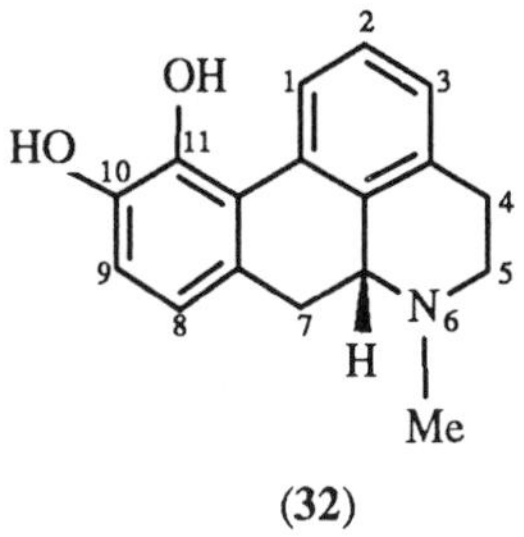   (32)

12.3.11.9   Aporphines

The aporphine derivative apomorphine (**32**) is the most widely studied DA agonist[6,8,65] and it was in fact the first synthetic compound which was shown to have potent direct effects on DA receptors. Even now, with a great variety of DA agonists from which to choose, the neuropharmacologist still often relies on apomorphine as the 'standard' DA agonist. The SAR of this group of compounds has been thoroughly investigated and previous approaches to the synthesis of various aporphines have been improved and the total synthesis of some apomorphine analogues has been reported.

The most salient features of the structural requirements for dopaminergic activity in the aporphine series can be dealt with under the following headings:

(i) *Chirality factor*   The most potent aporphines possess the (*R*) configuration at carbon atom 6a (**32**).

(ii) *Hydroxyl groups*   A comparison of the 11-, 10- and 8-monohydroxy-*N*-*n*-propyl-noraporphines shows clearly that the OH group at the 11 position is of prime importance. This conclusion is also supported by the greater activity of 2,11-dihydroxyaporphine, as compared to the 2,10 isomer. The 11-hydroxyl group corresponds to the *meta* position in DA and the 5-hydroxyl group in the 2-aminotetralin series. As in other series of DA agonists, the methoxy analogues are less active than the free phenols.

(iii) *Nitrogen substituents*   The situation here is very similar to that seen with the 2-amino-tetralins, *i.e.* small-size *N*-alkyl substitution yields maximal dopaminergic activity. Except for emesis, the *N*-propyl analogue of norapomorphine was found to have the highest potency in various tests.

(iv) *Ring alterations*   It has been reported that the catecholic A ring of apomorphine can be replaced by a pyrrole or a pyrazole ring (**33**), with retention of activity. Expansion of the B ring by one carbon atom leads to a loss of activity, whilst elimination of one carbon to form a 5-membered ring leads to a potent, orally active agonist with a long duration of action. Pharmacological evaluation of various ring-opened segments of apomorphine have shown that the compounds were either inactive or, at best, weakly active.

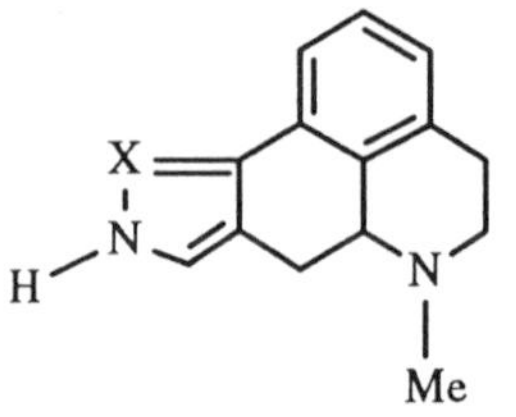

(**33a**) X = CH
(**33b**) X = N

12.3.11.10   Ergot Derivatives

Many of the compounds in this group are derivatives of lysergic acid (**34a**) or ergoline structures (**34b**). The 8 position in the D ring is where a wide variety of groups have been introduced. The effects of halogenation at the 2 position and reduction of the 9,10 double bond have also been investigated in detail.[5,6,8] The main characteristic of this group of compounds is their wide pharmacological activity. In addition, they act not only as DA agonists but also on serotonin and adrenergic receptors. They produce hallucinogenic, vasoconstrictor and oxytocic effects.

The compounds having dopaminergic activity which have been most widely studied include bromocriptine (**35**), lisuride (**36**), lergotrile (**37**) and pergolide (**38**). The first three compounds are D-2 agonists but act as antagonists of the DA sensitive adenylate cyclase (D-1) system. In contrast, pergolide is an agonist at both D-1 and D-2 receptors. Although studies on the effects of varying the substituent at N-6 have not been as thorough as in other groups of DA agonists, it has been shown with pergolide that the order of activity is *n*-propyl > ethyl > methyl. A detailed SAR analysis of the best-studied member of this group, bromocriptine, has led the Sandoz researchers[8] to make the following general conclusions. Studies on the replacement of the pyrrole, indole or benzene rings show that the presence of an aromatic ring system is necessary. A tertiary basic nitrogen atom separated from the aromatic nucleus by two carbon atoms in a given conformation is essential. A prerequisite for DA-like activity in this series is a *trans* junction of the rings C and D. In general, the variation in potency following N-6-alkyl substitution is very similar to that found in the aporphine series. A hydrogen atom at position 1 is not essential for activity. In contrast to the peptide series (*e.g.* bromocriptine), halogenation at position 2 does not yield higher activity, but may still favourably influence unwanted side effects. Regarding the nature and stereochemical requirements of substituents in position 8 or the double bond in positions 8, 9 or 10, it is difficult to make generalizations. However, in certain cases an axial 8 substituent may bring about higher activity than the 8 epimer.

A research group at Schering[8] have shown that reduction of the 9,10 double bond in lisuride yields *trans*-dihydrolisuride (TDL, **39**), which has mixed agonist/antagonist properties.

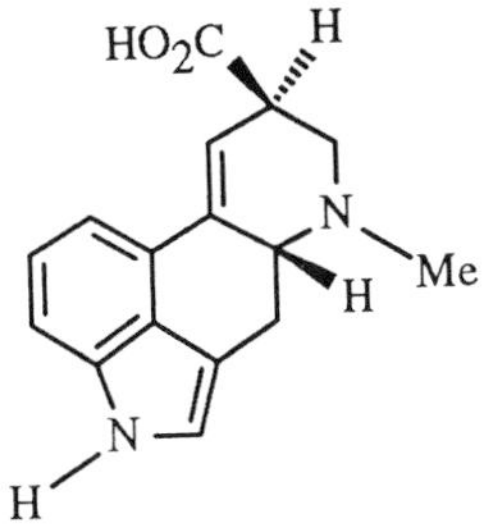

(34a)

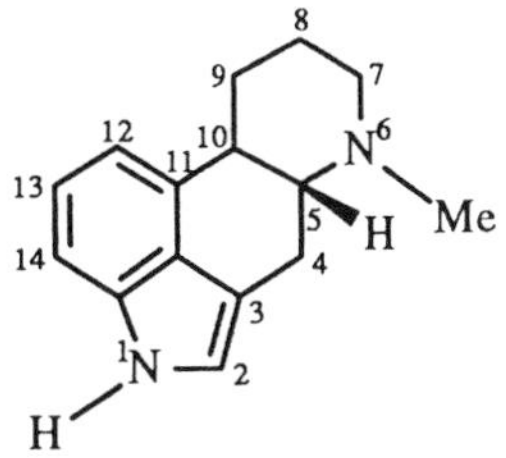

(34b)

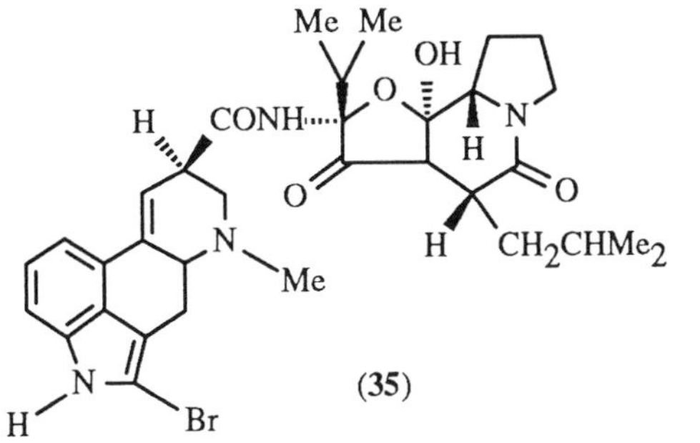

(35)

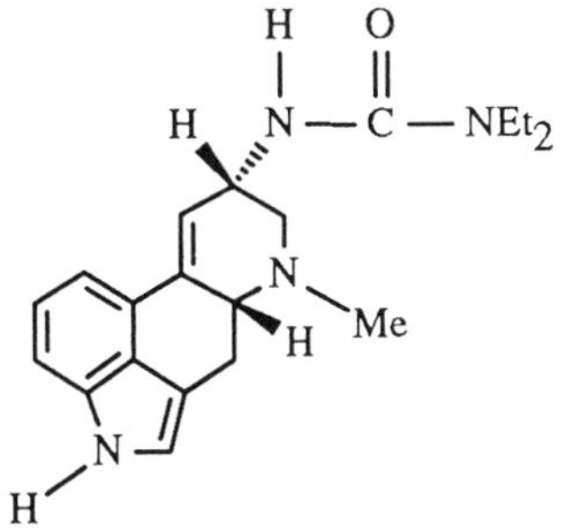

(36)

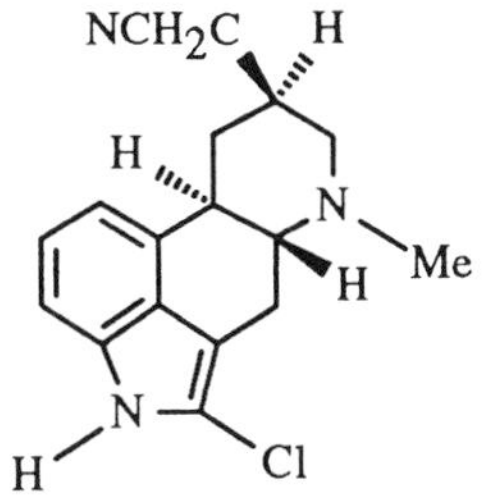

(37)

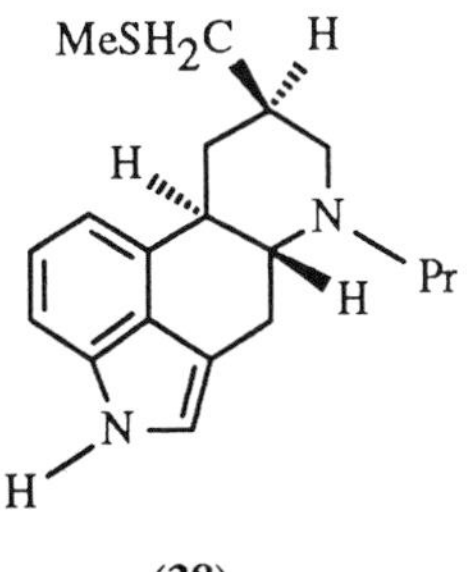

(38)

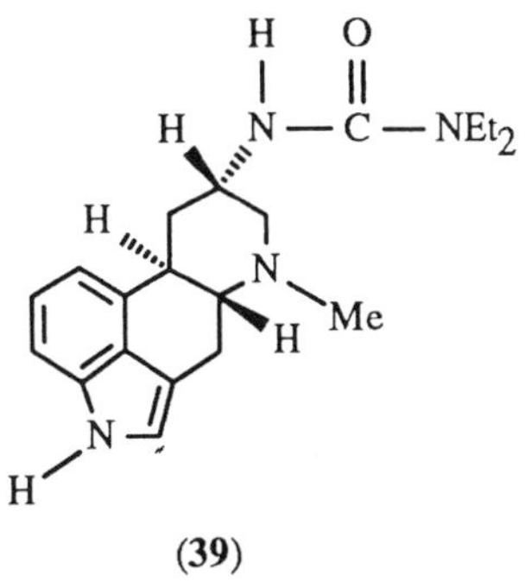

(39)

12.3.11.11 Ergoline-type Analogues

Replacement of the carbon atom at position 9 by an oxygen yields the oxaergolines, which are a group of compounds displaying high dopaminergic activity.[5,6] 6-Ethyl-9-oxaergoline (EOE; **40**) showed activity equal to or greater than that of apomorphine in several tests of DA-like activity, the activity being found mainly in the (−) enantiomer. The 6-*n*-propyl analogue (RU 29717; **41**) has dopaminergic activity which is comparable to pergolide in a variety of tests. A series of C ring homologues of the oxaergolines were generally less potent than the parent compounds.

Other tetracyclic ring systems related to the ergoline system, containing the pyrrolo[3,2,1-*gh*]-4,7-phenanthroline (**42**) and 2-azaergolines (**43**), were essentially devoid of DA agonistic activity. There is an interesting controversy in the literature as to whether the rigid phenethylamine (**44a**) or pyrrolethylamine (**44b**) portion of the ergolines is responsible for their dopaminergic activity.[5,6,8,106] As a result of attempting to clarify this problem a group at Eli Lilly[8] have prepared various ergoline partial structures (**45**), which were found to be potent DA agonists. In addition, they exhibited stereoselectivity with the laevorotatory enantiomers having nearly all the activity. The (−) enantiomer of compound (**45a**) is referred to as quinpirole.

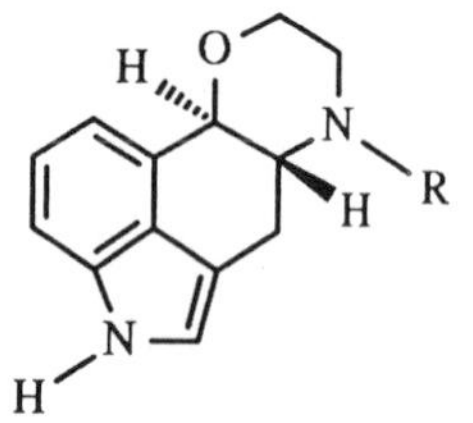

(**40**) R = Et; EOE
(**41**) R = Pr^n; RU 29717

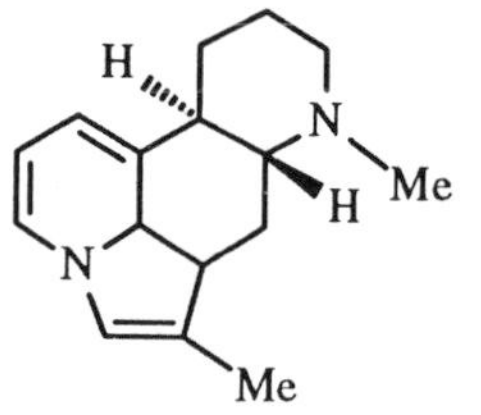

(**42**)

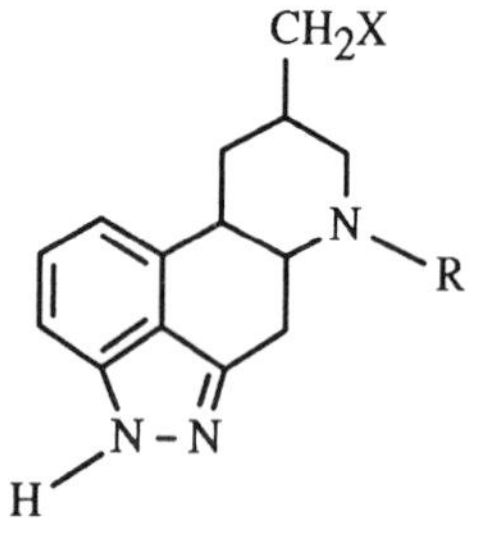

(**43**)

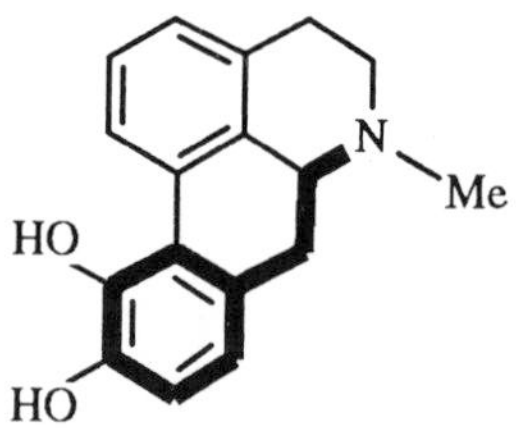

(**44a**)

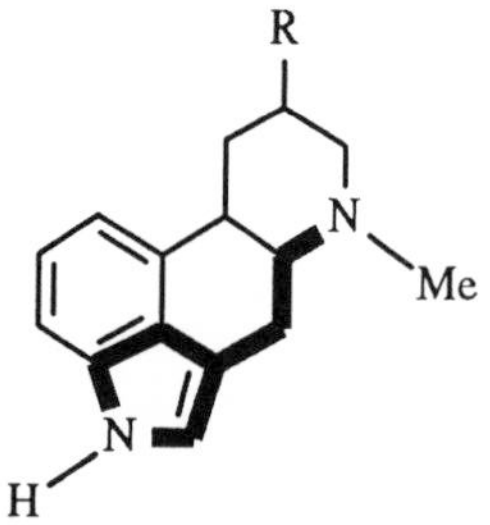

(**44b**)

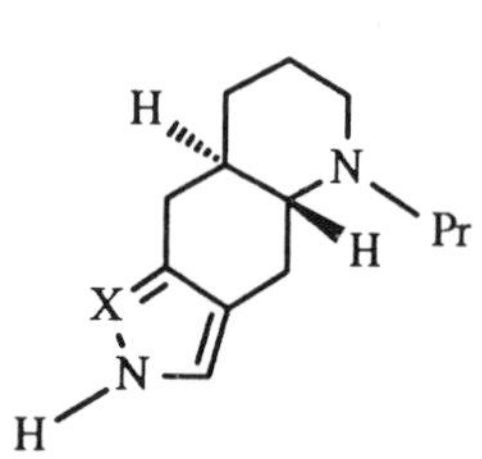

(**45a**) X = N
(**45b**) X = CH

12.3.11.12 Indole Analogues

Attachment of an *N,N*-dipropylaminoethyl side chain to the 4 position of the indole nucleus (**46**) leads to a compound displaying selective DA autoreceptor activity, whose pharmacology resembled that of lergotrile.[5,6] That one is not restricted to a two-carbon atom side chain in these analogues is shown by the activity of EMD 23448 (**47**), which has selective DA autoreceptor activity. It could be of interest to learn something about the preferred receptor conformation of this molecule.

A series of secoergolines, *i.e.* 4-(3-piperidinyl)indoles (**48**) have been prepared and are characterized by the lack of significant DA-like activity *in vitro* although many were able to elicit a decrease in plasma prolactin levels, which may be due to metabolic activation. It is of interest that the order of activity for N substitution of the piperidine is hydrogen > *n*-propyl > methyl > ethyl. The most potent member of the series was RU 27251 (**48a**), which demonstrated enantioselectivity,

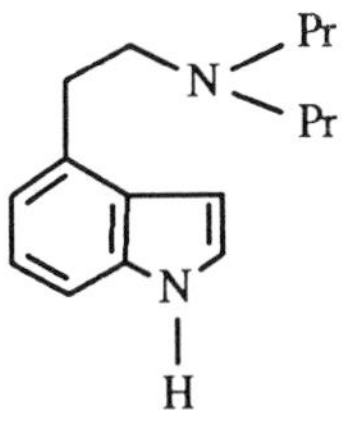

(46) 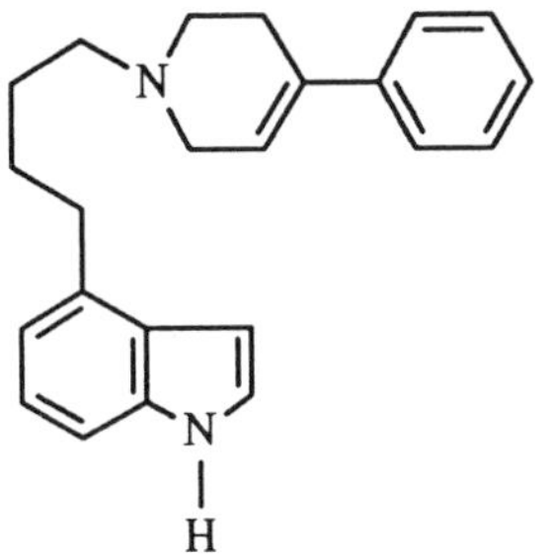　　　　　(47) 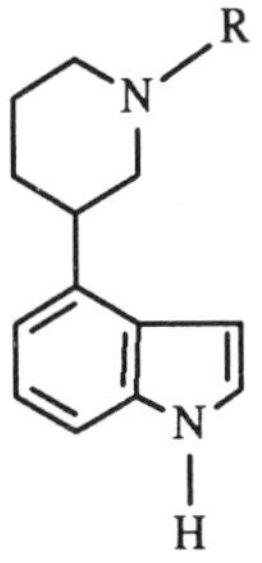　　　　　(48a) R = H; RU 27251

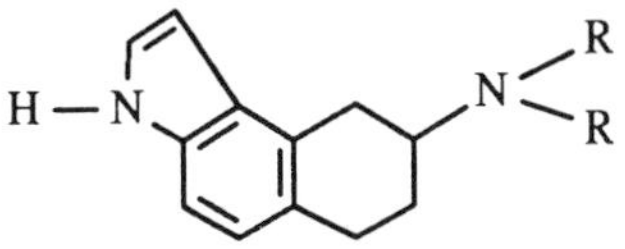

(49) 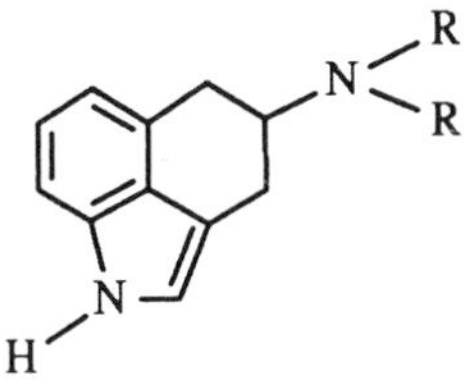　　　　　(50) R = H, Me, Pr 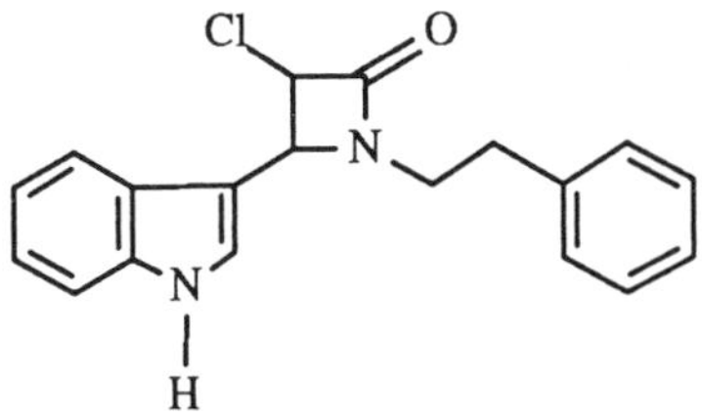　　　　　(51)

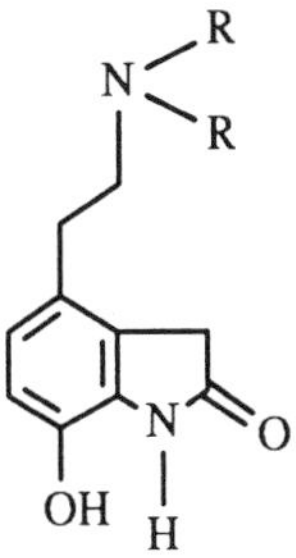

(52a) R = H; SK & F-88827
(52b) R = Pr; SK & F-89124

i.e. the (*R*) enantiomer was more active than the (*S*) isomer. The 4-(3-pyrrolidinyl)- and 4-(3,4-dihydropyrrolyl)-indoles lacked DA-like activity.

A good example of indole–phenol bioisosterism is afforded by the synthesis of a series of 3*H*-benz[*e*]indol-8-amines (49). The *N*,*N*-di-*n*-propyl and *N*,*N*-dimethyl analogues were potent and orally active dopaminergic agents.[80]

4-Aminobenz[*cd*]indole (50) showed marked dopaminergic activity in various tests with the exception of the D-1-related, DA-sensitive adenylate cyclase. In a series of 4-amino *N*-substituted analogues, the order of potency was *n*-propyl > methyl > hydrogen. In a homologous series of cyclohept[*cd*]indolamines, only weak dopaminergic activity was seen.[5]

The substituted 4-indolylazetidinone (51), which bears little structural resemblance to DA, was reported to produce dopaminergic actions.[5]

The indolones SKF-88827 and SKF-89124 (52) have been shown to possess DA$_2$ activity in assays of peripheral drug action.[29]

12.3.11.13 Aminothiazoles

Additional evidence for the idea that neither catecholic nor phenolic hydroxyl groups are an absolute requirement for potent dopaminergic activity was provided by Anden *et al.*,[81] who showed that the aminothiazoloazepine derivative BHT920 (53) is a selective autoreceptor agonist. Initial results obtained with schizophrenic patients appeared to be very promising.[82] The aminothiazole ring has been incorporated into several known DA agonists such as apomorphine, octahydro-benzo[*g*]quinolines and the 2-aminotetralins.[83] An analogue of the latter group, (−)-2-amino-6-propyltetrahydrobenzothiazole (54), was found to be one of the most potent compounds of the group, whose profile was that of a selective autoreceptor agonist.

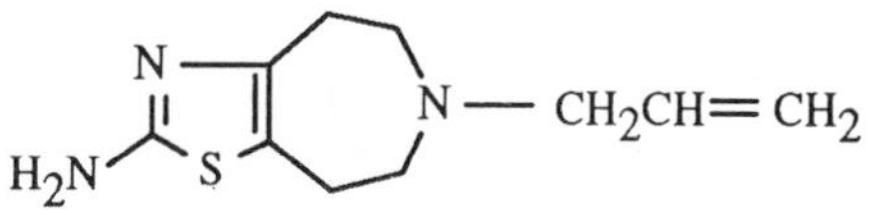

(53) 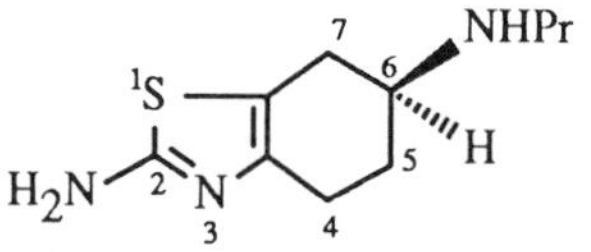   (54)

12.3.11.14 3-Benzazepine Derivatives

This group of compounds is of particular interest because it provided the first selective D-1 agonist, SKF 38393 (**55**). The chemistry and pharmacology of these compounds has been extensively reviewed.[5,6,66] Pharmacological studies of a large number of compounds, by a group at SK&F in the USA, have led to the following generalizations regarding the basic ring system: (i) dopaminergic activity is greatly increased by a 1-phenyl substituent; (ii) the 7,8-catecholic grouping is essential; (iii) further substitution of the tetrahydroazepine ring, at positions 1, 2, 4 or 5, generally abolishes activity; (iv) introduction of a halogen atom at position 6 increases potency; (v) substitution on the nitrogen atom with allyl or methyl groups increases D-2 receptor activity, or it may lead to an antagonist; (vi) introduction of small groups at position 9 generally decreases efficacy, and larger groups can produce antagonists; (vii) substitution of the 1-phenyl ring produces variable effects (*meta* > *para* > *ortho*); and (viii) replacement of the 1-phenyl group by aryl, alkyl or cycloalkyl groups generally decreases or abolishes activity.

The above conclusions were based on studies using the 6-OH-DA-lesioned rat model, effects on the DA sensitive adenylate cyclase and for their ability to decrease renal vascular resistance in dogs.

Of the various compounds synthesized to date, SKF 82526 (fenoldopam; **56**), has gone furthest in development. It is a selective peripheral DA$_1$ agonist, which, due to its polarity, has limited access to the brain. It has been examined clinically for the treatment of essential hypertension and has been shown to produce an acute hypotensive action in humans.

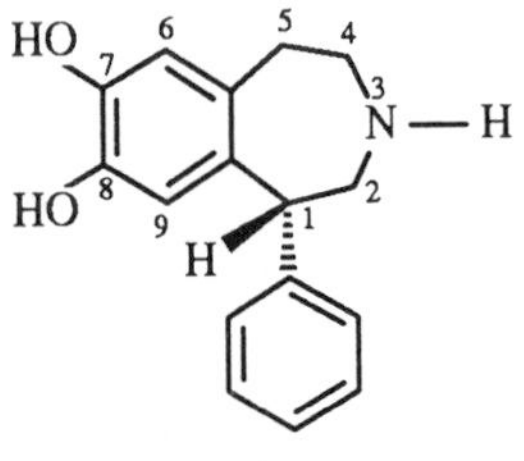

(55) 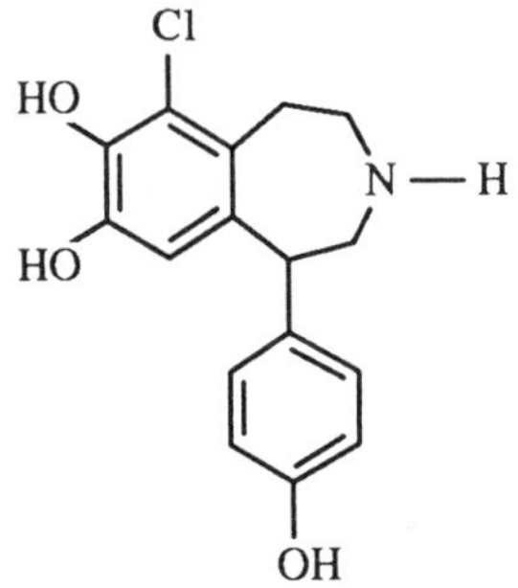   (56)

12.3.11.15 Piperazine Analogues

A number of compounds containing the piperazine nucleus have been found to possess DA-like activity.[5,6] One of the best examples is piribedil (**57**) whose pharmacology has been reviewed in detail. The suggestion that this compound is metabolized *in vivo* to a catecholic analogue is interesting but its validity is uncertain. The fact that a number of related piperazine compounds, *e.g.* (**58**), also show dopaminergic activity but cannot be converted to a catechol-containing product can serve to invalidate the aforementioned idea.

The SAR of a series of troponylpiperazines has been published,[5,6] of which AY-27110 (ciladopa; **59**), was the most interesting.

The 2-pyrimidylpiperazine analogue, buspirone (**60**), has been classified by some workers as a DA agonist, whilst others cite results indicating that it may be a selective antagonist at presynaptic DA receptors.[6]

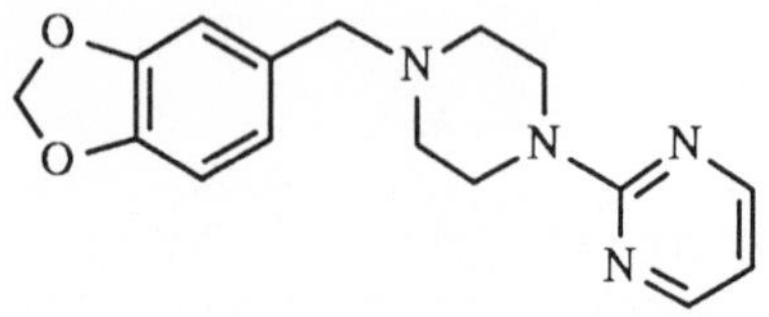

(57) 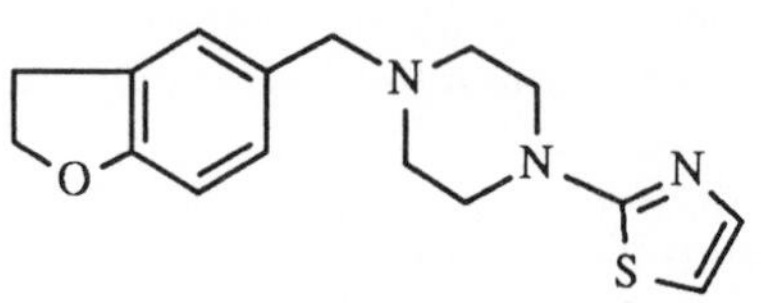   (58)

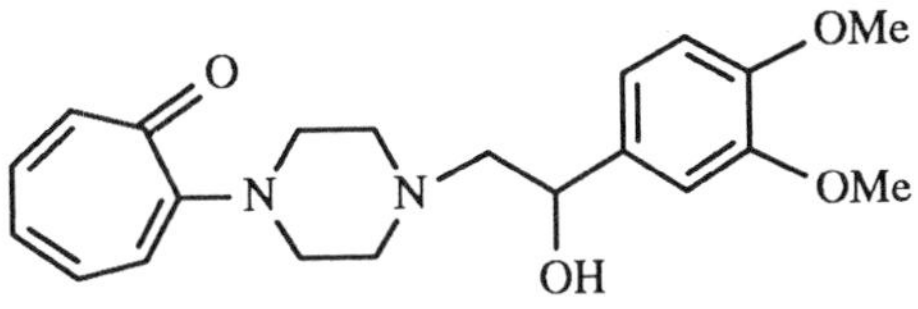

(59)

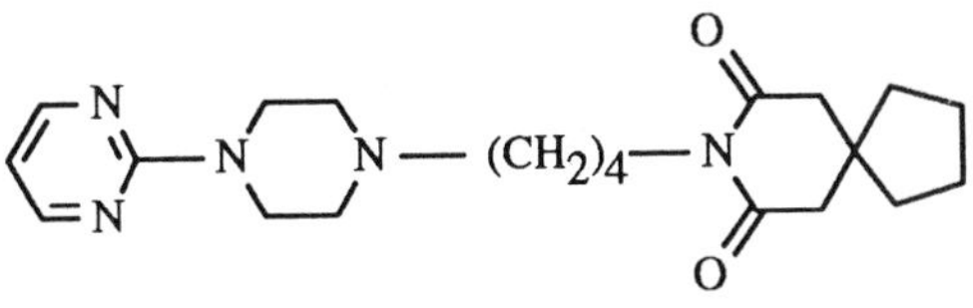

(60)

12.3.11.16 Tetrahydroisoquinoline Derivatives

The three simple tetrahydroisoquinoline (THQ) analogues, shown in (61), are inactive as DA agonists.[6] This is probably due to their conformation resembling the *gauche* form of DA rather than the antiperiplanar or *trans* conformation (see Section 12.3.14).

The THQ derivative, nomifensine (62), displays DA agonistic effects in various models. The 3',4'-catechol analogue of nomifensine is active in the adenylate cyclase model and is also active following injection into the nucleus accumbens of the mouse. It has been shown that the D-1 activity of the latter compound resides almost exclusively in the (S) enantiomer.

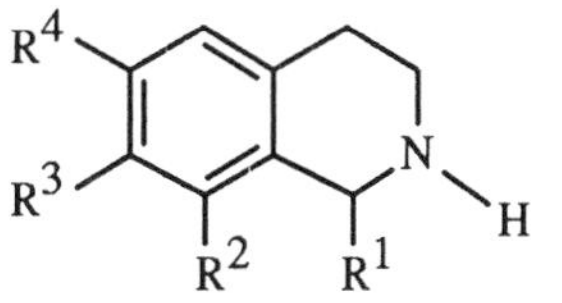

(61)

$R^1, R^2 = H; R^3, R^4 = OH$
$R^1 = Me; R^2, R^3 = OH; R^4 = H$
$R^1 = Me; R^2 = H; R^3, R^4 = OH$

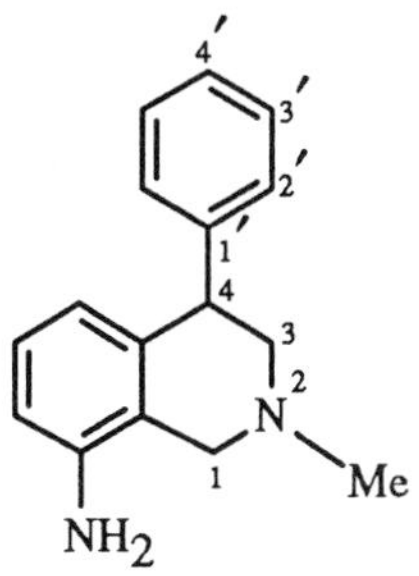

(62)

Various other derivatives of nomifensine have been prepared and shown to have DA-like activities.

12.3.11.17 Miscellaneous Compounds

Various compounds having widely varying structures have been reported to exhibit dopaminergic actions in various *in vitro* and *in vivo* models.[5,6,65] However, no attempt will be made to list all of the compounds that have been reported to have dopaminergic activity.

The imidazolidine derivative, DPI (63), was claimed to produce selective stimulation of DAi receptors.[12] However, a review of the literature shows that this compound is better described as a mixed α_1/α_2 agonist rather than as a DA agonist.[13]

A series of 2-aminoquinazoline derivatives (64) has been prepared, using the 2-aminotetralins as a template. Their inactivity in causing vasodilation in the canine renal artery was thought to be due to the higher base strength of these compounds, as compared to DA. Certain aminomethylbenzocyclobutane derivatives (65) have been identified as dopaminergic agonists, in particular the N,N-di-n-propyl-3,4- and -4,5-dihydroxy derivatives.

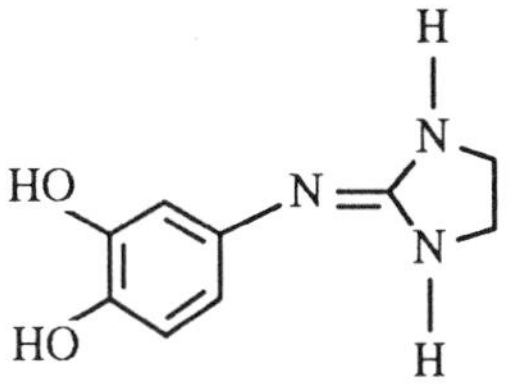

(63)

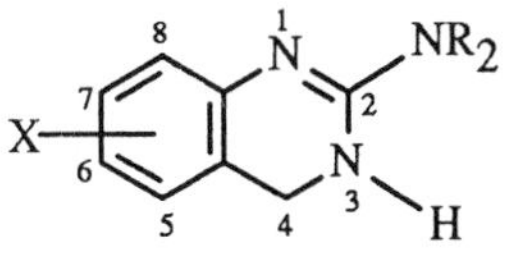

(64a) X = 5,6-(OH)$_2$; R = H, Me, Pr
(64b) X = 6,7-(OH)$_2$; R = H, Me, Pr

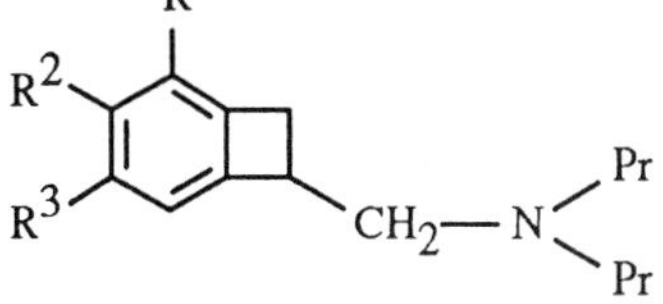

(65a) $R^1, R^2 = OH; R^3 = H$
(65b) $R^1 = H; R^2, R^3 = OH$

In a series of cyclobutane analogues, the *trans* isomers were more potent than the *cis* compounds in binding studies. However, their potency was lower than that of DA.

It is of interest that neither the *cis* nor the *trans* isomer of the cyclopropane analogue of DA (**66**) showed any dopaminergic agonistic or antagonistic activity. Even the *N,N*-di-*n*-propyl derivative of the *trans* isomer only exhibited weak DA-like activity. The general inactivity of these compounds is thought to be due to the extra bulk of the CH_2 group of the cyclopropane ring.

Moragues and coworkers[84] synthesized a series of piribedil congeners based upon 4-aminopiperidine. The compound shown in (**67**) was found to most closely resemble piribedil pharmacologically.

The pyrazole compound, EMD 25004 (**68**), caused rotational activity in 6-OH-DA-lesioned rats, yet it does not induce stereotypy.

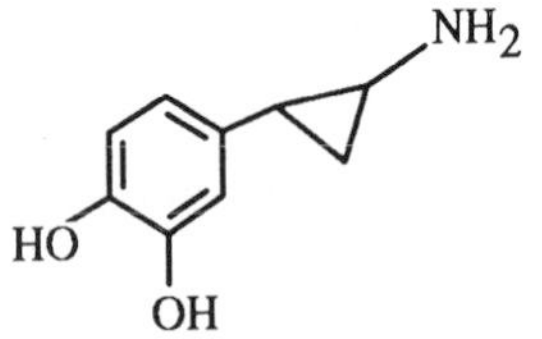

(66)

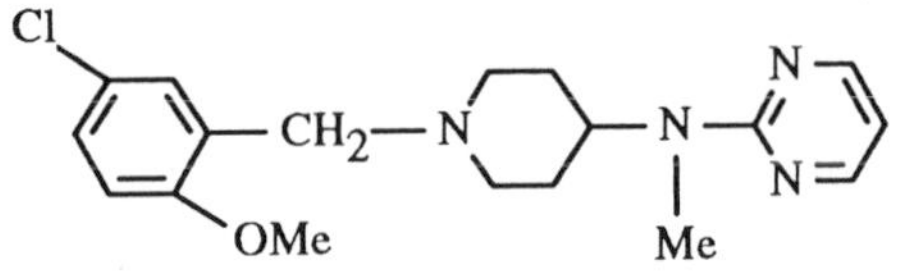

(67)

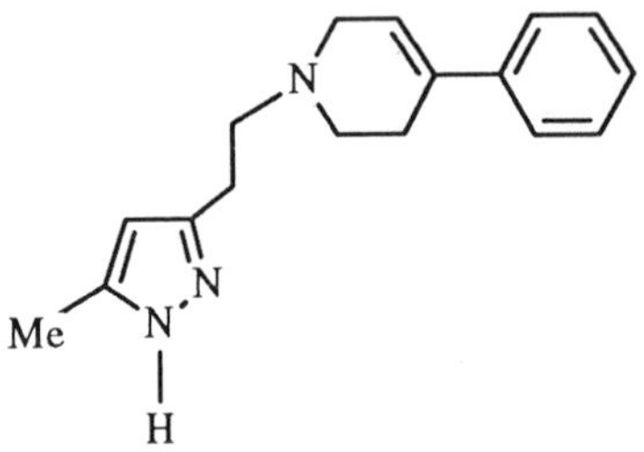

(68)

12.3.11.18 The Significance of the Charge on the Nitrogen Atom of DA Agonists

In previous sections, we have seen that a catecholic or phenolic function is not required for dopaminergic activity. Recently, it has also been shown that the nitrogen atom in DA agonists can be replaced by sulfur if it is permanently charged.[85,86] Thus (**69**) and (**70**), the latter being based on the 2-aminotetralins, were both found to possess direct dopaminergic agonist activity. It has therefore been reasoned that DA agonists probably bind to their receptors through the charged, rather than the nonprotonated, nitrogen atom. This has been supported by the fact that the introduction of a second oxygen atom at the 6 position in (**30**) leads to a compound (**71**), that is only protonated to the extent of 2% at physiological pH, and which is almost inactive as a DA agonist.[87] It has been estimated that the protonated form of apomorphine is about 20 times more active at D-1 and D-2 receptors than the uncharged species.[139]

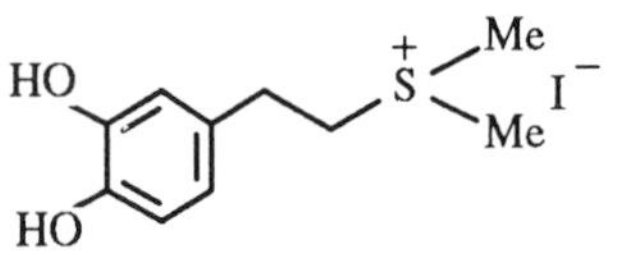

(69)

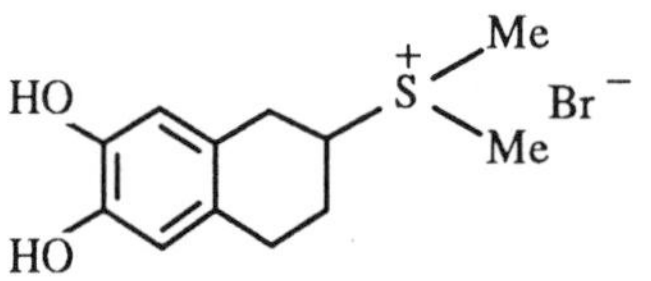

(70)

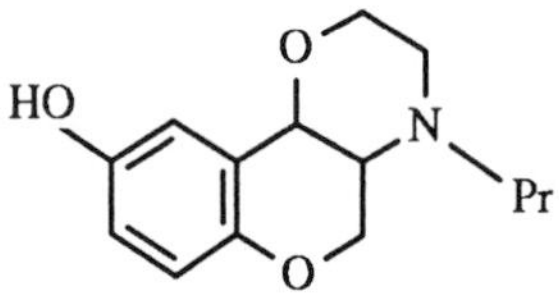

(71)

Similar studies with neuroleptic analogues have shown that these compounds interact with their receptor *via* the protonated form of the species.[88] It has therefore been concluded that both agonists and antagonists have a common site of action.

12.3.12 STRUCTURE–ACTIVITY RELATIONSHIPS OF DA ANTAGONISTS

From the discovery of the antipsychotic activity of chlorpromazine (**72a**) in the 1950s, until the present day, the interest in DA antagonists has been focussed around their use in treating schizophrenia.[1,7] In fact, the use of these compounds to treat this disease was one of the cornerstones of the 'dopamine hypothesis' of schizophrenia.[63,64]

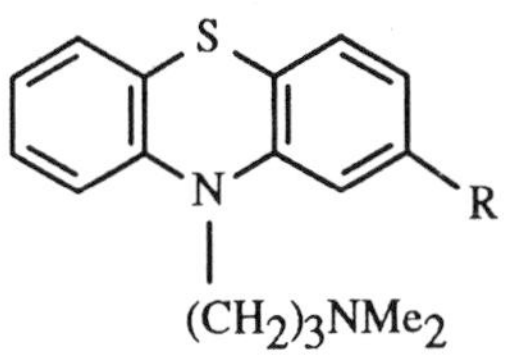

(72a) R = Cl
(72b) R = CF$_3$

These compounds have been divided into 10 separate chemical classes. The caveat mentioned in Section 12.3.11 is also applicable here, *i.e.* much of the work described in this section was done before the division of DA receptors into the D-1 and D-2 types. Most neuroleptics block both D-1 and D-2 receptors. References to the original literature can be found in the review article by Kaiser and Setler.[7]

12.3.12.1 Phenothiazine Derivatives

The SAR of the phenothiazines has been the subject of numerous extensive review articles and only the most salient points will be covered in this section.[7,89] The neuroleptic activity is qualitatively and quantitatively dependent on the nature of the side chain, the amino group and the substituents on the aromatic nucleus.

12.3.12.1.1 *The alkyl side chain*

A three carbon atom separation of the basic nitrogen atom in the side chain and the nitrogen of the nucleus is required for maximum potency. The lower homologue of chlorpromazine (**72a**) has only about one-fifth of its activity in the conditioned avoidance response (CAR) test.[7] Introduction of alkyl groups into the 1, 2 or 3 positions of the side chain generally leads to a decrease in activity, although this effect is sometimes small and inconsistent. Nevertheless, three phenothiazines having a methyl group in the 2 position of the side chain, *i.e.* cyamepromazine (**73a**), ethylisobutrazine (**73b**) and levomepromazine (**73c**), have been in clinical use.

Cyclization of the basic nitrogen atom back onto the side chain generally decreases activity. However, two compounds, thioridazine (**74a**) and mesoridazine (**74b**), which have a piperidine ring incorporated into the side chain have been used clinically.

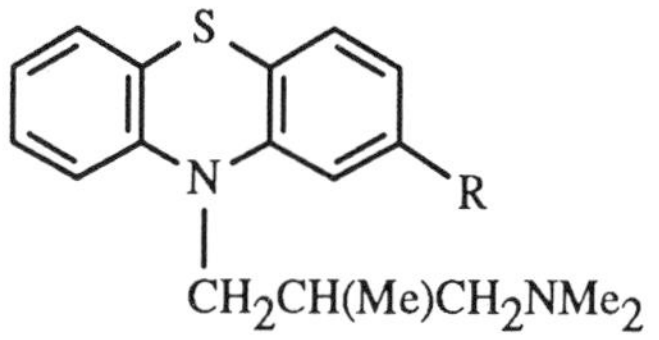

CH$_2$CH(Me)CH$_2$NMe$_2$

(73a) R = CN
(73b) R = Et
(73c) R = OMe

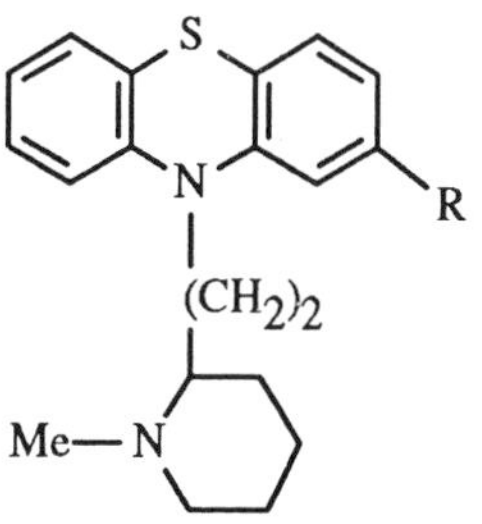

(74a) R = SMe
(74b) R = SOMe

12.3.12.1.2 *The basic amino group*

Maximum neuroleptic activity is associated with derivatives having a tertiary amino function. The secondary amine analogue of chlorpromazine (**72a**) has about half the activity of the parent compound. The primary amine is much less potent than chlorpromazine in a number of tests. In general, substitution of the basic nitrogen atom with larger alkyl groups decreases neuroleptic potency. In the 2-trifluoromethylphenothiazine group (Table 5), the pyrrolidinyl and piperidinyl analogues are slightly less potent than triflupromazine, whilst incorporation of a 4-methyl-1-piperazinyl, *e.g.* trifluoperazine (**75a**), or 4-(2-hydroxyethyl)-1-piperazinyl group, *e.g.* fluphenazine

Table 5 Influence of Modification of the Basic Amino Group on the Neuroleptic Potency of Some Phenothiazine Derivatives[7]

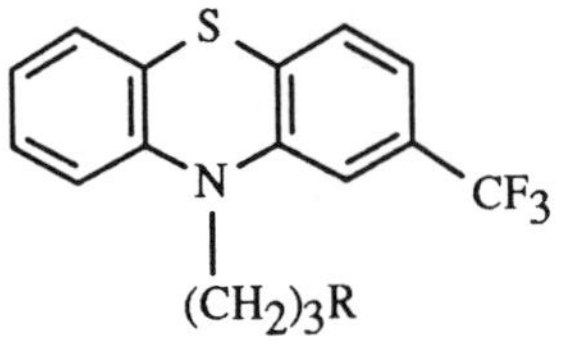

R	CI[a]	R	CI[a]
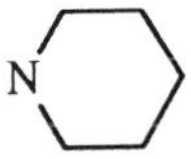 (piperidinyl)	1.9	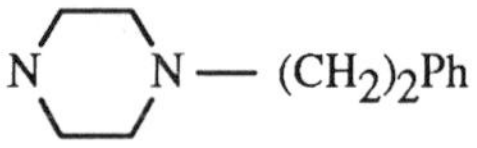 N—N—(CH$_2$)$_2$Ph	3.0
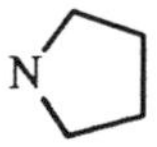 (pyrrolidinyl)	2.1	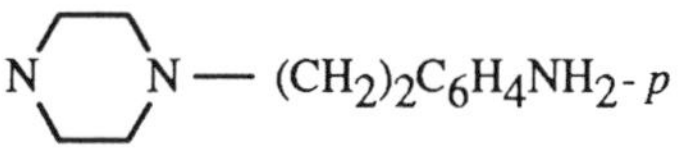 N—N—(CH$_2$)$_2$C$_6$H$_4$NH$_2$-p	9.0
N(Me)$_2$	2.4	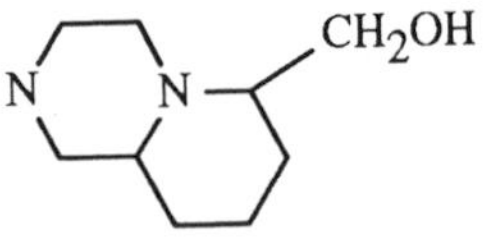 (octahydroquinolizinyl)CH$_2$OH	ca. 9
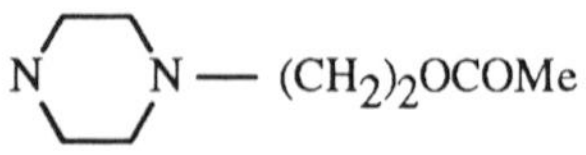 N—N—(CH$_2$)$_2$OCOMe	23.0	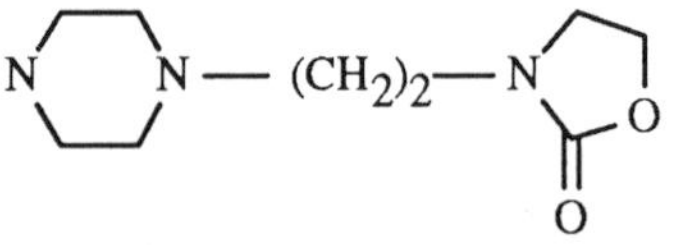 N—N—(CH$_2$)$_2$—N(succinimidyl)	24.8

[a] Chlorpromazine indexes (CIs) were determined by dividing the ED$_{50}$ (the oral dose of free base administered at time of peak activity effective in preventing 50% of rats from responding to a conditioned stimulus) for chlorpromazine, *i.e.* 9.9 mg kg^{-1}, in a conditioned escape response test, by that of the indicated phenothiazine derivative.

(75b), leads to a large increase in activity. This potency-enhancing effect of a 2-hydroxyethyl group is also seen with 4-substituted piperidinylpropylphenothiazines such as the compound shown in (76), which has a pharmacological profile that is similar to that of fluphenazine (75b). Various long chain fatty acid ester derivatives of these 2-hydroxyethyl analogues find clinical utility as depot neuroleptics, when they are injected subcutaneously (s.c.) or intramuscularly (i.m.) in solution in an oil.

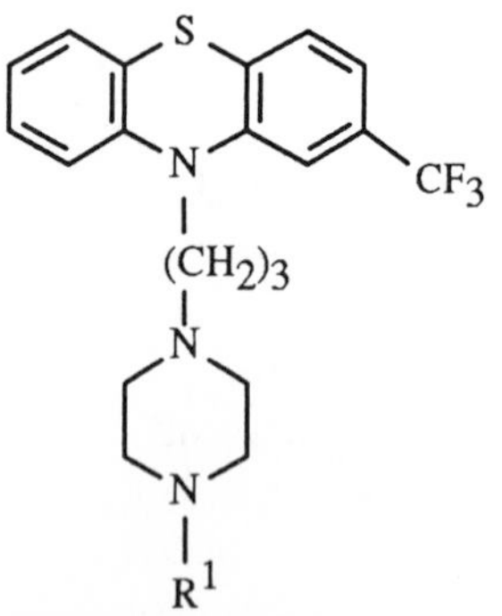

(75a) R^1 = Me
(75b) R^1 = (CH$_2$)$_2$OH

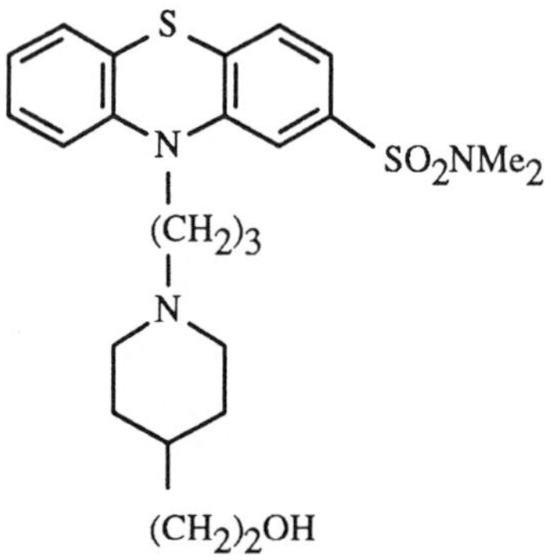

(76)

12.3.12.1.3 Phenothiazine ring substituents

The influence of substituents in the aromatic nucleus has been investigated quite extensively since it became apparent that potency is influenced, both quantitatively and qualitatively, by their nature and location. The compounds in Table 6 are listed in a very rough approximation of increasing

Table 6 Chlorpromazine Indexes (CIs)[a] for Ring-monosubstituted Derivatives of 10-(3-Dimethylamino-propyl)phenothiazines[7]

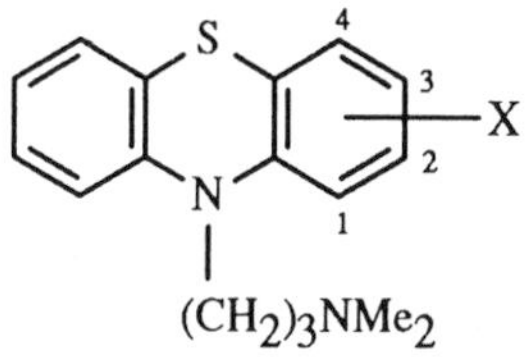

X	CI[a]	X	CI[a]	X	CI[a]	X	CI[a]
1-OH	0.02	2-MeO	0.5	3-CF$_3$	0.43	2-C(=NOH)Me	0.83
2-OH	0.025	2-CONHNH$_2$	0.07	2-CO$_2$Me	0.49	2-Cl	1.0
3-OH	0.13	3-Cl	0.18	2-Pr^{n}CO	2.0	2-SMe	1.0
4-OH	~0.4	2-CHMe$_2$	0.32	2-EtCO	~2.0	2-SCF$_3$	1.0
4-CF$_3$	<0.06	2-Me	0.28	2-MeCO	0.6	2-CF$_3$	2.4
4-Cl	<0.08	3-CMe$_3$	~1	2-SO$_2$Me	0.7	2-CF$_3$SO$_2$	2.4
H	0.4	2-CMe$_3$	0.18				

[a] CIs were determined by dividing the ED value (mg kg^{-1}) for chlorpromazine, by that of the test compound. The results are based on various test systems. For further details, see ref. 7.

neuroleptic potency. In general, with a few exceptions, neuroleptic potency increases in the following order of ring position: 1 < 4 < 3 < 2. Based on data published by various workers, it has been found that for substitution at the 2 position, potency increases in approximately the following order: OH < H ≈ OMe ≈ CONHNH$_2$ < CN < Pr^i < Me < Bu^t ≈ CO$_2$Me ≈ Pr^{n}CO ≈ EtCO < MeCO ≈ SO$_2$Me ≈ C(=NOH)Me < Cl ≈ SMe ≈ S(O)Me ≈ Br ≈ SCF$_3$ < SO$_2$NMe$_2$ < SO$_2$CF$_3$ ≈ CF$_3$.

Although it has been suggested that the potency-enhancing effect of the 2 substituent may be proportional to its electron-withdrawing character, several exceptions are known, *e.g.* the electron-releasing alkyl groups. It has also been hypothesized that the 2 substituent may have some influence on the conformation of the side chain. This is probably unlikely, however, and a more plausible explanation is that it has a local effect at the receptor site on the binding of the molecule.[90]

In general, di- or tri-substitution of the phenothiazine nucleus both lead to a loss in activity.

12.3.12.1.4 Effects of aromatic ring replacement

Replacement of one aromatic nucleus by either a pyridine or thiophene ring has been investigated by several groups. Of the four possibilities for annelation of the pyridine ring, the 1-azapheno-thiazines are the most active group. Prothiopendyl (77) is more potent than promazine, and has about one-fifth of the activity of chlorpromazine. Clinically, it is said to exhibit sedative hypnotic and possible antipsychotic activity.

In the thiophene series, compounds having the same substituents and side chain with the thiophene moiety in 2,3 (78) and 3,4 annelations (79) have neuroleptic properties, whereas those with a 3,2 annelation are more or less inactive.

4-Aminoalkyl-2-phenyl-1,4-benzothiazines (80) and their 3-phenyl isomers (81), which have a freely rotating aromatic ring, are essentially inactive as neuroleptics.

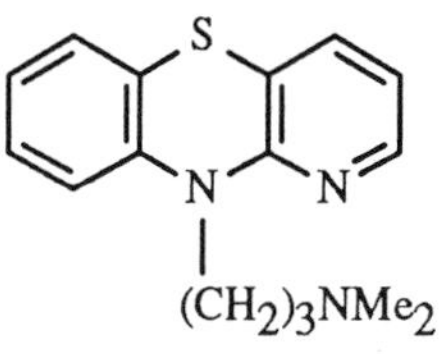

(77)

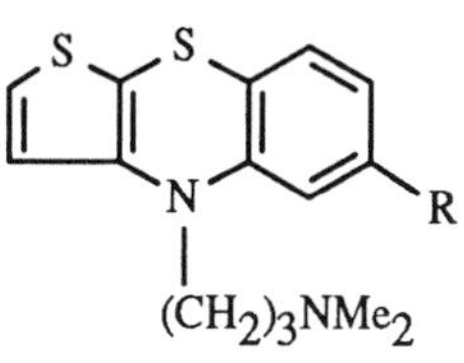

(78) R = H, Cl, CF$_3$

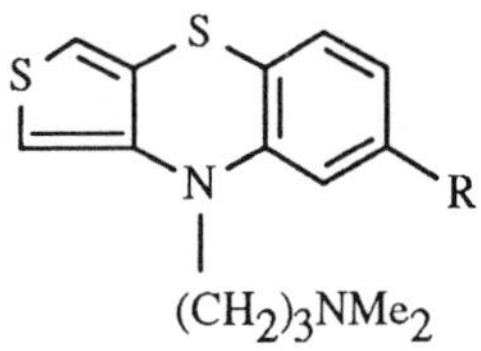

(79) R = H, Cl, CF$_3$

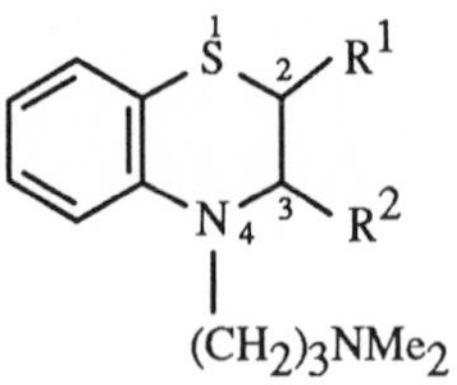

(80) R^1 = Ph; R^2 = H
(81) R^1 = H; R^2 = Ph

12.3.12.1.5 Replacement of nitrogen and sulfur by other heteroatoms in the tricyclic nucleus

In general, the phenoxazine analogues (82) are less active than the corresponding phenothiazine derivatives. The phenoxazine analogue of chlorpromazine, has only about 4% of the activity of the parent drug. The SARs for both series are similar. The neuroleptic potency of the phenoselenazines (83) is intermediate between the phenothiazine and phenoxazine series.

In the case of the acridan analogues, there are two possibilities with regard to the attachment of the side chain, *i.e.* at the 10 (84a) or 9 position (84b) of the nucleus. The potency and SAR of the 10-aminoalkylacridans are similar to those of the corresponding phenoselenazines. In general, the 9-aminopropylacridans are more potent than their 10-substituted isomers.

Analogues in which the nitrogen atom is replaced by phosphorus, *i.e.* the phenothiaphosphine derivatives (85), show only very weak activity.

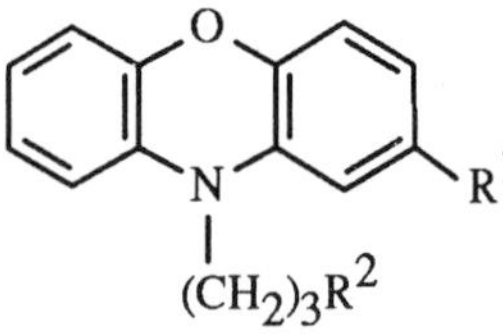

(82)

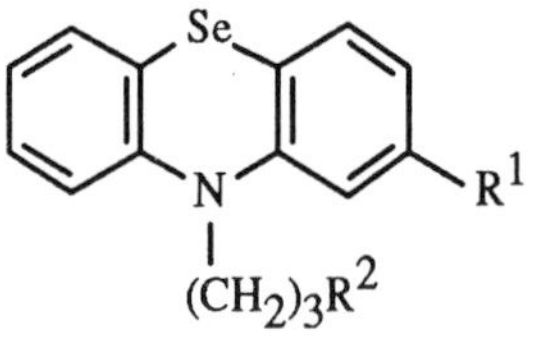

(83)

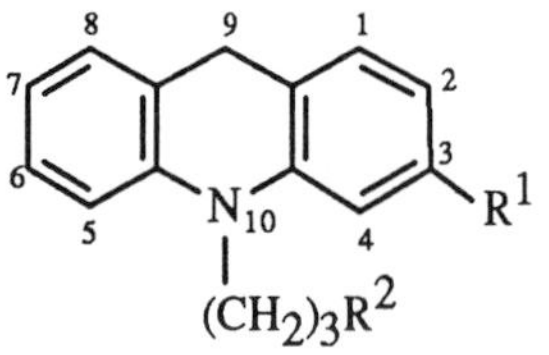

(84a)

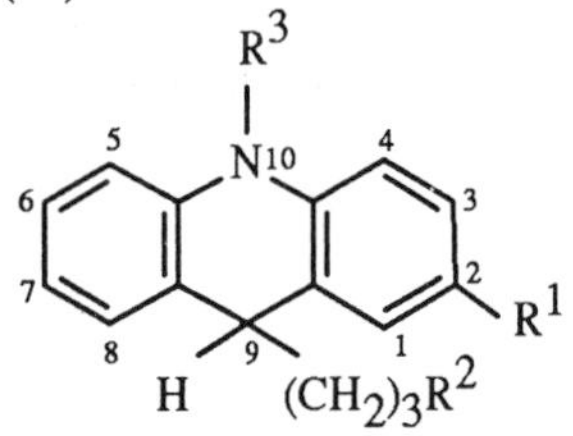

(84b)

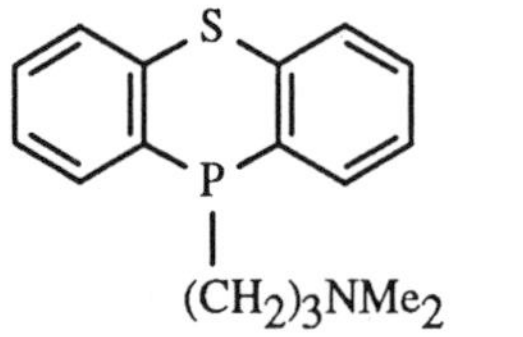

(85)

12.3.12.2 Thioxanthene Derivatives

The SAR of the 9-aminoalkylated thioxanthenes (86) is similar to their phenothiazine counterparts; however, the latter compounds are usually less potent.[7] Similar considerations also apply to the 9-(3-aminopropylidene)-substituted thioxanthenes (87), although these compounds are usually more potent than their saturated analogues.

When one of the aromatic rings contains a substituent, these compounds then exist as *cis/trans* geometric isomers (88a, b). The *cis* or *Z* form (88a) is 5–40 times more potent as a neuroleptic than the *trans* or *E* isomer (88b).

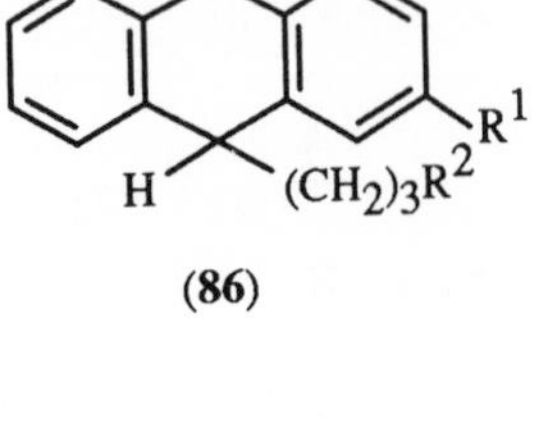

(86)

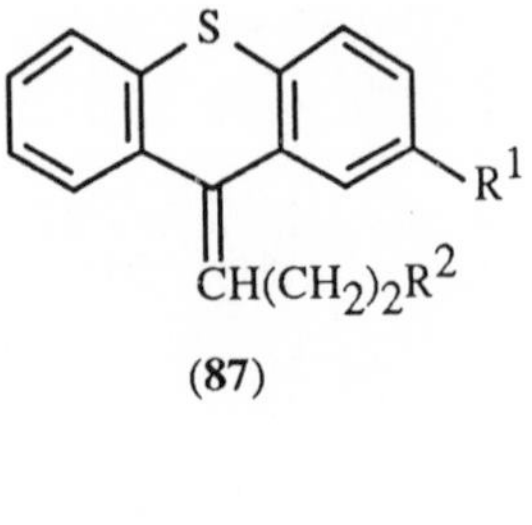

(87)

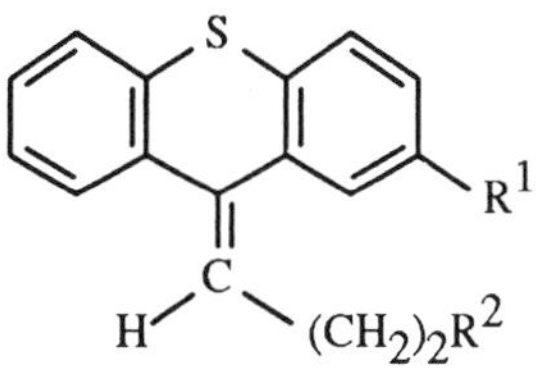

(88a)

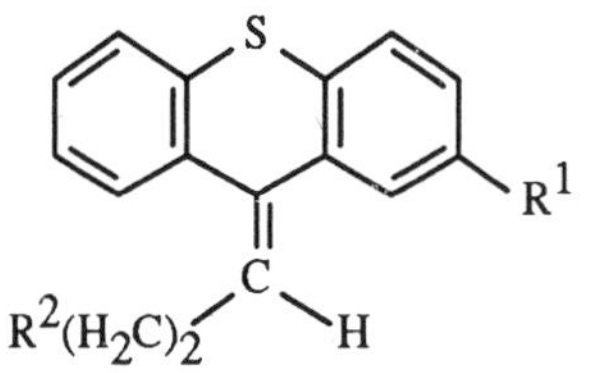

(88b)

Similar isosteric changes have been made in the thioxanthene series as were encountered with the phenothiazines. The selenoxanthene derivatives are generally less potent than their corresponding thioxanthene analogues. The SARs are generally similar for xanthene and thioxanthene derivatives. In the case of the anthracene and dihydroanthracene analogues, the latter compounds are much more potent neuroleptics than the former.

12.3.12.3 Tricyclic Neuroleptics with a Central Seven-membered Ring

Although compounds having a 6-7-6 tricyclic ring system composition usually display a predominance of antidepressant activity, there are various examples of neuroleptic activity in this group.[7]

12.3.12.3.1 *Dibenz[b,e]oxepins and related ring systems*

In a series of 11-aminopropylidene derivatives of dibenzoxepin (89) having various 2 substituents, the chloro analogue was found to be pharmacologically identical to chlorpromazine. Due to the presence of the oxygen heteroatom, as well as the 2 substituent and the double bond in the side chain, there are four stereoisomers. The neuroleptic activities of these compounds are shown in Table 7. It is of interest that the relationship of the side chain to the 2 substituent is of greater importance than its disposition relative to the oxygen atom. The analogue pinoxepin (90), which corresponds in structure to the phenothiazine perphenazine, also has a very similar pharmacological profile to the parent compound. In the clinic, it displays potent antipsychotic–sedative activity.

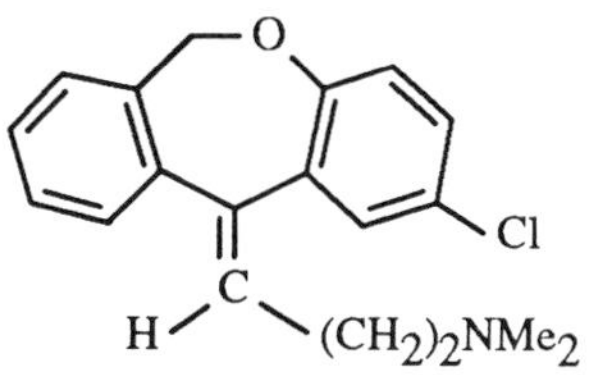

(89)

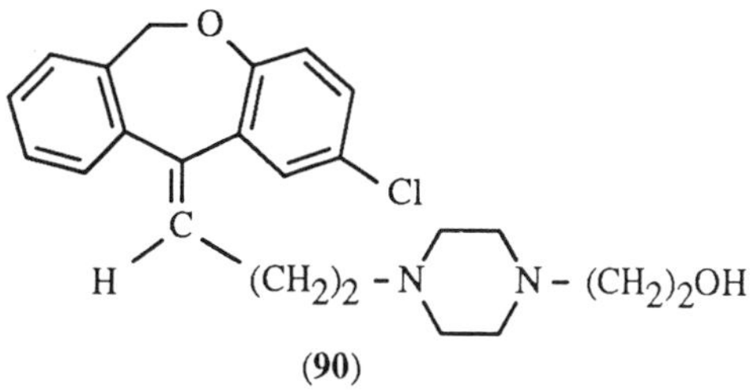

(90)

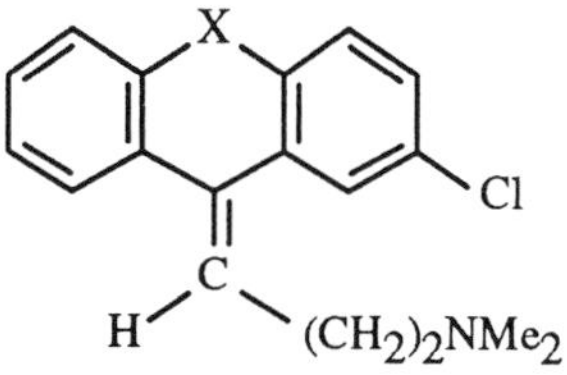

(91a) X = CH=CH
(91b) X = CH₂—CH₂

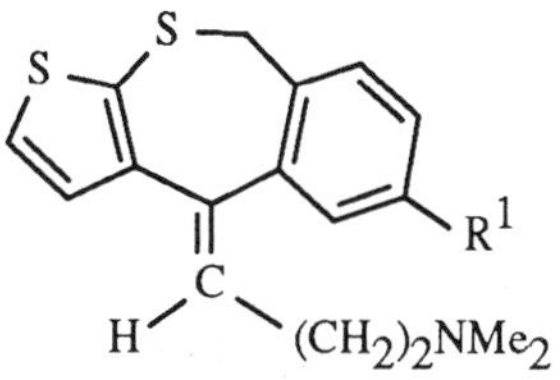

(92a) R¹ = H
(92b) R¹ = Cl

In general, dibenzocycloheptatrienes (91a) are more potent neuroleptics than their reduced analogues (91b).

Analogues of the dibenzo[*b,e*]thiepin system, such as dithiaden (92a) and its 6-chloro derivative (92b), have significant neuroleptic activity.

Table 7 Chlorpromazine Indexes (CIs)[a] for 2- and 9-Substituted (E)- and (Z)-Dimethylaminopropylidene-dibenz[b,e]oxepins[7]

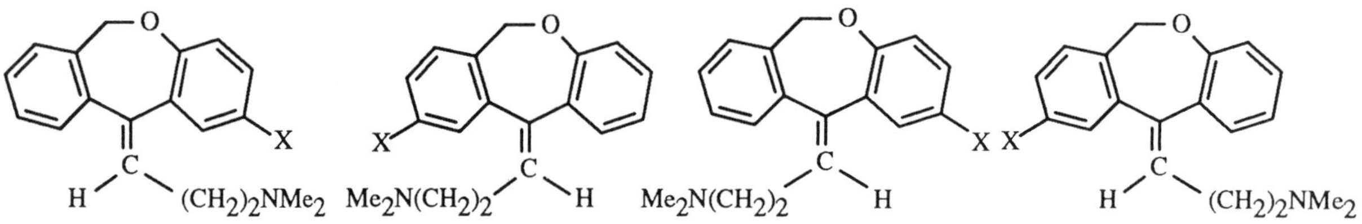

X		CI value		
Cl	1.0[a]	0.27	0.10	<0.10
MeO	0.45	0.20	0.10	<0.10

[a] CIs were determined by dividing the ED_{50} (4 mg kg^{-1}) in a rat CAR test for the (Z)-2-chloro derivative (equipotent with chlorpromazine), by similarly derived value for the test compound.

12.3.12.3.2 Dibenz[b,e][1,4]oxazepines and related ring systems

These compounds may be viewed as phenothiazine analogues, in which the sulfur atom has been replaced by two other bridging atoms (93). In the case of the dibenz[b,e][1,4]oxazepines having a hydroxyethylpiperazinylpropyl side chain and a chloro or trifluoromethyl group at position 7 or 3, they display potent neuroleptic activity at high doses and antianxiety activity at lower doses.

Where the bridging link is an ethylene group, clinically useful compounds have been developed, such as carpipramine (94) and 3-chlorocarpipramine (95) and related compounds. Although the former compound does not show pronounced neuroleptic activity in animals, it is effective in the treatment of chronic schizophrenia. 3-Chlorocarpipramine is marketed in Japan as a combined antipsychotic–antidepressant.

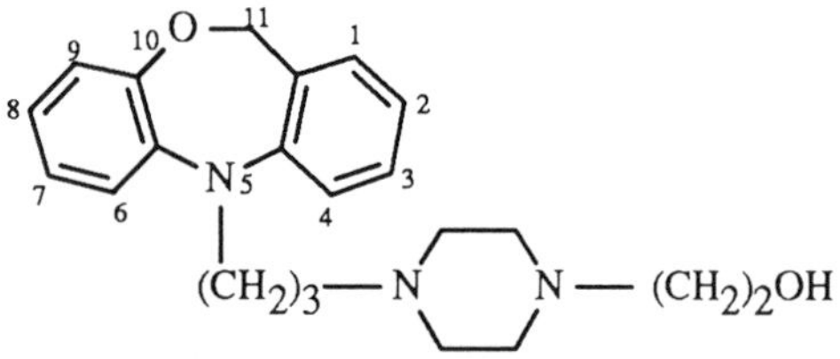

(93)

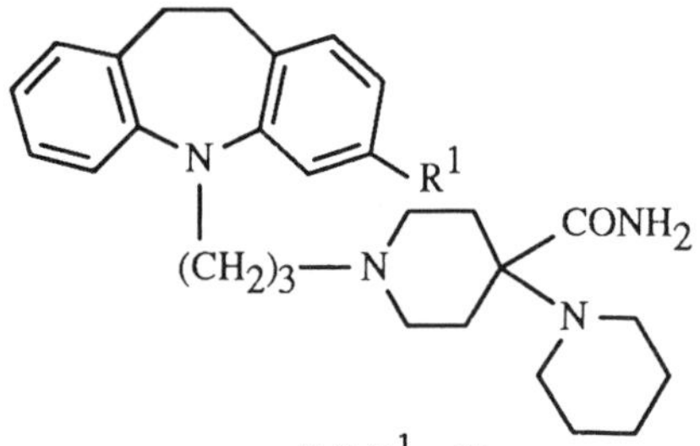

(94) R^1 = H
(95) R^1 = Cl

12.3.12.3.3 Dibenzo[b,f]thiepins and related compounds

The prototype of this series is perathiepin (96a). This group of compounds is the most extensively studied series of tricyclic neuroleptics, next to the phenothiazines. In the rotating rod test, this compound is three times as active as chlorpromazine. The 8-chloro-substituted analogue, octoclothepin (96b), is almost 10 times more potent than chlorpromazine in the same test. The influence of nuclear substitution on neuroleptic activity has been examined extensively. A QSAR study of 18 analogues of perathiepin substituted in the 8 position showed that, not surprisingly, there were some parallels with the 2-substituted phenothiazines. The order of activity for analogues having a methoxyl group at various positions is $8 \gg 2 \approx 6 > 7$.

The most useful compounds that have been developed, following the studies on variations in the nature of the basic amino side chain, are the hydroxyalkyl derivatives of the piperazine group, e.g. noroxyclothepin (97a), oxyclothepin (97b), oxymetothepin (97c) and oxyprothepin (97d). The latter compound is effective in manic and schizophrenic syndromes. As with the phenothiazines, long chain fatty acid esters have been prepared and are in use as depot neuroleptics.

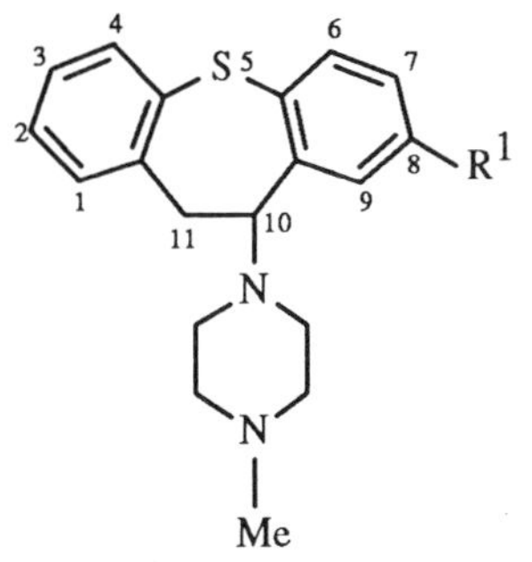

(96a) R^1 = H
(96b) R^1 = Cl

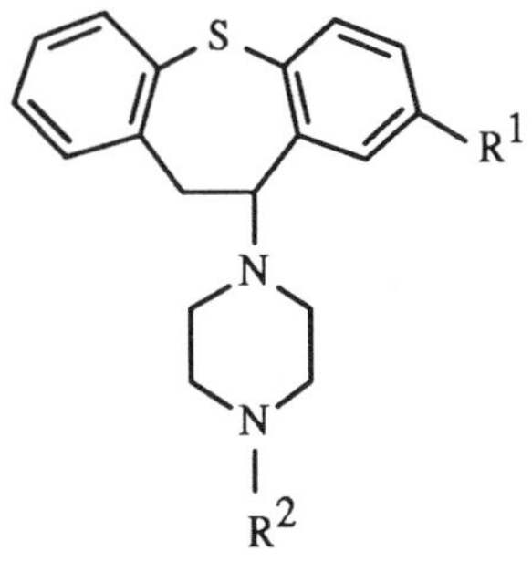

(97a) R^1 = Cl; R^2 = (CH$_2$)$_2$OH
(97b) R^1 = Cl; R^2 = (CH$_2$)$_3$OH
(97c) R^1 = OMe; R^2 = (CH$_2$)$_3$OH
(97d) R^1 = SMe; R^2 = (CH$_2$)$_3$OH

12.3.12.3.4 Dibenzo[b,f][1,4]thiazepines and related compounds

In the general formula shown in (98), the order of decreasing potency in the rat catalepsy test for R^1 = Cl or Me, is X = O > S > CH$_2$ > NH $\gg$ SO $\gg$ SO$_2$. Certain 11-piperazinyl analogues of dibenzo[b, f][1, 4]thiazepine, *i.e.* clotiapine (R^1 = 2-Cl, X = S) and metiapine (R^1 = 2-Me, X = S); dibenz[b, f][1, 4]oxazepine, *i.e.* loxapine (R^1 = 2-Cl, X = O) and its *N*-demethyl analogue amoxepin; dibenzo[b, e][1, 4]diazepines, *i.e.* clozapine (R^1 = 8-Cl, X = NH) and dibenzo[b, e][1, 4]morphanthridine, *i.e.* perlapine (R^1 = H, X = CH$_2$), have either been studied in the clinic or have been marketed for antipsychotic use.

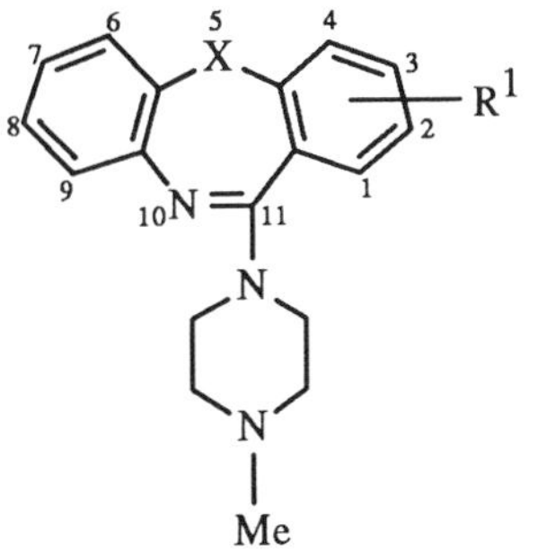

(98)

In general, for neuroleptic activity a substituent at the 2 position is required. The rank order of potency for antagonism of apomorphine in the rat, for groups at this position, is very similar to that seen in other tricyclic series.

One of the most interesting compounds of this group is clozapine. In spite of the fact that it is inactive in causing catalepsy or inhibiting apomorphine-induced stereotypy in rats, it is clinically active as an antipsychotic agent. The main point of interest with this compound is that it produces only a low incidence of extrapyramidal side effects. As in other tricyclic neuroleptic series, the nature of the side chain amino group is of great importance. Thus ring-opened or piperidinyl analogues are inactive as are other analogues in which the basic character of the nitrogen atom of the piperazine ring furthest from the nucleus is changed. In addition, replacement of one of the aromatic rings by a thiophene or pyridine ring generally leads to an inactive compound.

12.3.12.4 Benzocycloheptapyridoisoquinolines

The parent compound of this group is 1*H*-benzo[6,7]cyclohepta[1,2,3-*de*]pyrido[2,1-*a*]isoquinoline (99), which is known as taclamine. This compound, in the form of the *trans* isomer, produces antianxiety rather than neuroleptic effects in animals.[7]

Various 3-tertiary alcohol derivatives (**100**) have been examined for neuroleptic activity. It has been shown that the latter actions are dependent on the relative configurations at positions 3, 4a and 13b. The *trans/trans* configuration is essential for activity. In general, potency increases with increasing size and branching of the 3-alkyl substituent. Racemic butaclamol ($R = Bu^t$) is almost as potent as fluphenazine in antagonizing the effects of amphetamine. Although butaclamol is a clinically effective antipsychotic, it has not yet reached the market. As previously mentioned (see Section 12.3.8.1.1), it provided the breakthrough in early studies on the binding of ^3H neuroleptics to DA receptors *in vitro*.[21]

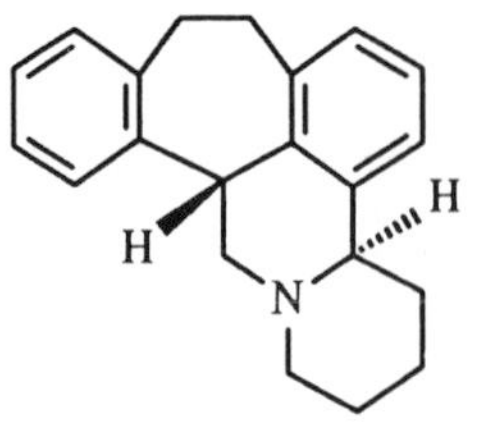

(99) 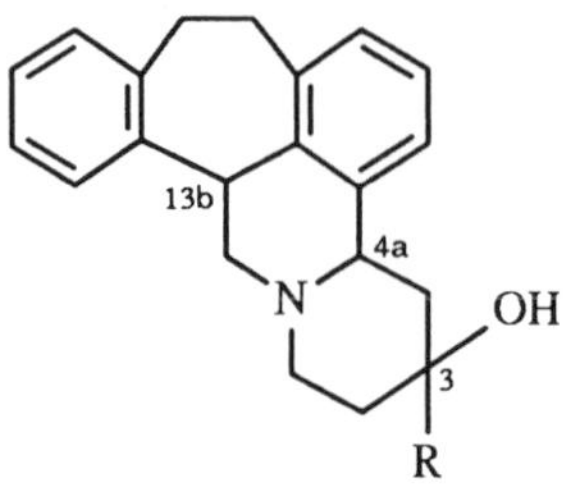   (100)

12.3.12.5 Butyrophenones and Related Compounds

These compounds have been extensively studied[91] since the first report on the neuroleptic activity of haloperidol (**101**) in 1958, by Janssen and coworkers. In excess of 5000 compounds of this general class have been prepared and tested, and more than 20 have been evaluated for antipsychotic activity in humans.[7]

The general structure for this group of neuroleptics is shown in (**102**). The aryl group is optimally a 4-fluorophenyl; this is followed by a carbonyl function, which connects to an unbranched propylene bridge, which, in its turn, carries a terminal amino function. The latter group is where the greatest variation in the molecule is possible, for example 4-substituted piperidinyl, tetrahydropyridyl or piperazinyl groups all lead to highly potent compounds. The above four molecular components of the butyrophenones will now be examined separately.

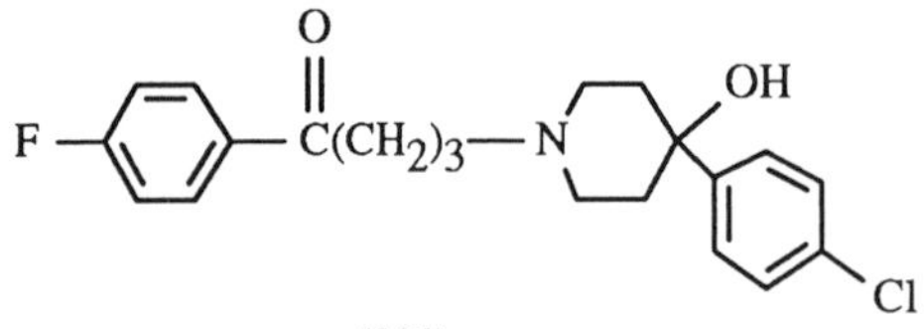

(101) 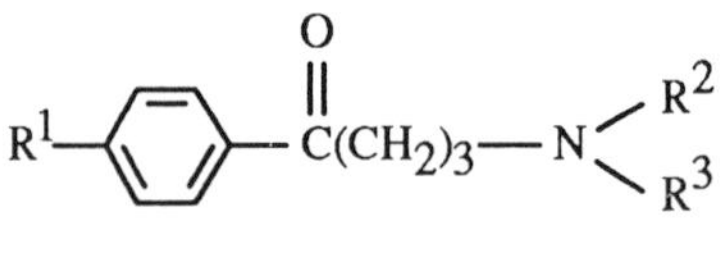   (102)

12.3.12.5.1 The aryl group

Apparently, in nearly all analogues so far examined, the *p*-fluoro substituent produces maximum neuroleptic activity. In fact, anisoperidone (*p*-methoxy; **103**) is one of the few compounds of this class not having a *p*-fluoro atom which has been examined clinically as an antipsychotic.

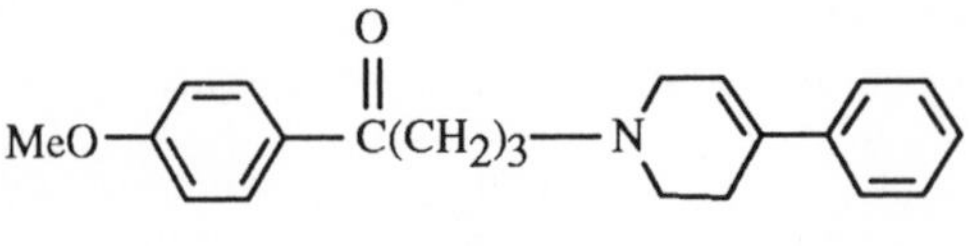

(103)

12.3.12.5.2 The carbonyl group

Modifications of this function lead, in general, to a large decrease of neuroleptic activity. Thus, in the azaspiranylbutyrophenone (**104**), the replacement of the carbonyl group X by CHOH, O, S or SO_2 all lead to a decrease or loss in neuroleptic potency.

It is of interest, however, that when the carbonyl group is replaced by a heterocyclic double bond, such as in the thianaphene analogue in (**105**), the resulting compound has neuroleptic activity comparable to chlorpromazine. In a somewhat similar manner, a benzofuran derivative (**106**) has also been shown to have neuroleptic activity, which is also reflected in its clinical efficiency. It has also been shown that it is possible to incorporate the carbonyl group into an oxazolone ring (**107**) and retain neuroleptic activity.

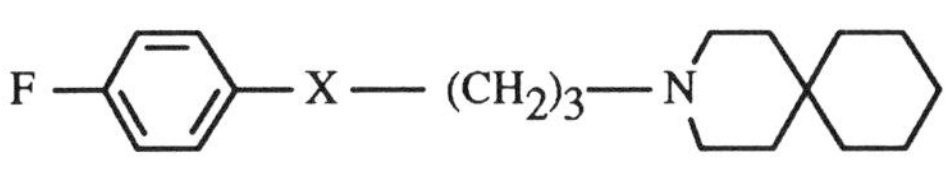

(**104**)

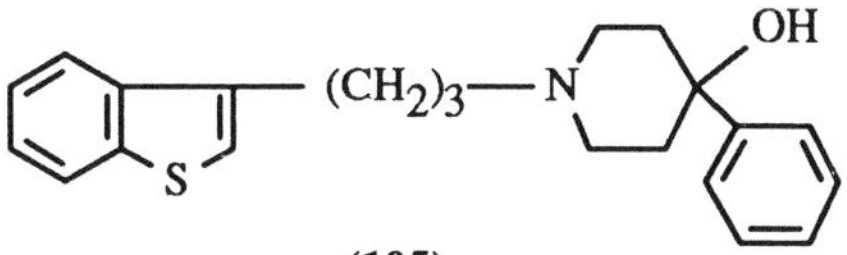

(**105**)

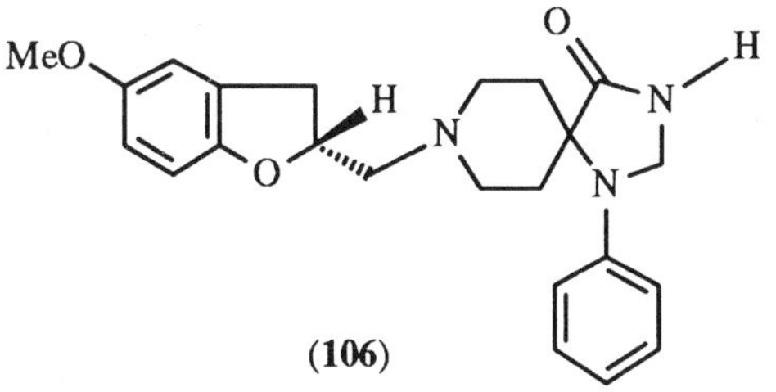

(**106**)

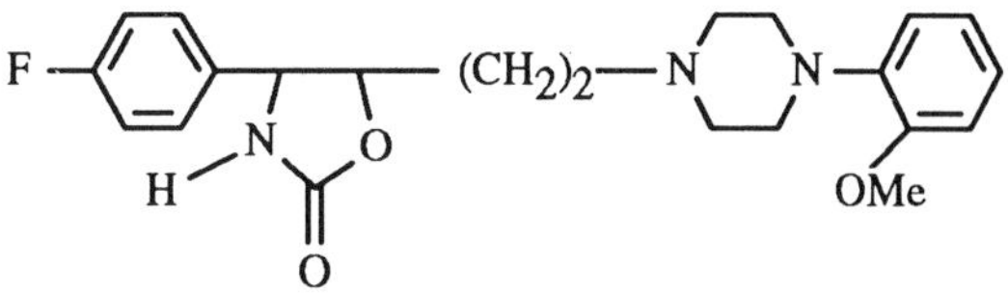

(**107**)

12.3.12.5.3 The propylene chain

In general, lengthening, shortening or branching of the three-carbon chain of the butyrophenones decreases neuroleptic activity. However, certain changes in this chain have resulted in retention of activity. In the case of the cyclopropylmethyl analogue (**108**), the *trans* isomer was equipotent with trifluperidol. Where the chain was incorporated into a piperidine ring (**109**), the compound displayed activity intermediate between that of chlorpromazine and haloperidol in certain tests.

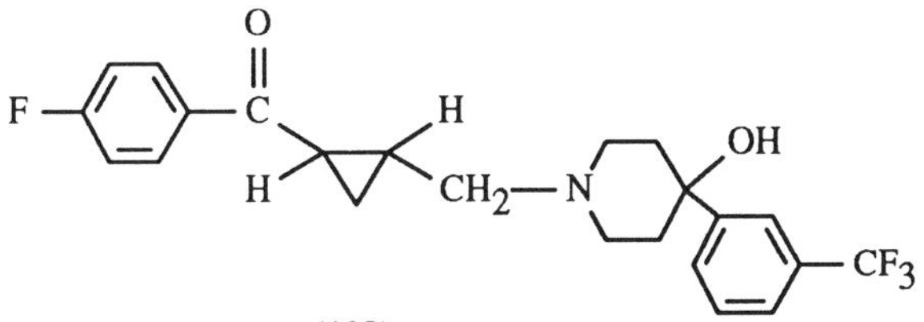

(**108**)

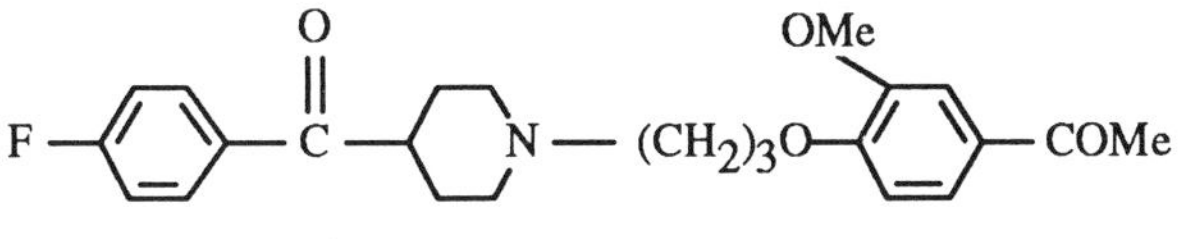

(**109**)

12.3.12.5.4 The basic amino function

As mentioned in Section 12.3.12.5, this is a part of the molecule where considerable variation is possible. Maximum activity is usually associated with various cyclic amines and antipsychotic activity has been described for only a few analogues in which the basic nitrogen atom is not part of a ring, one example being shown in (**110**).

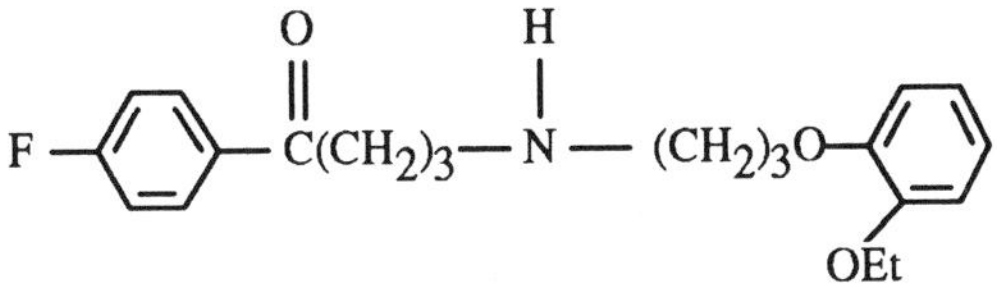

(**110**)

(i) 4-Piperidinyl analogues

In the case of the 4-piperidinylbutyrophenones, maximum activity is associated with analogues having a substituent at position 4. Compounds with groups at the 2 or 3 positions are much less active. Although simple alkyl substitution at position 4 is not very effective, attachment of a spirocarbocyclic system at this position significantly increases activity — the best known example being spiperone (**111**). Other groups at the 4 position which are associated with high potency are an alcoholic hydroxyl, a substituted benzoyl, a tertiary carboxamide or an amino group.

Neuroleptic potency is associated with 4,4-disubstituted piperidines, such as 4-aryl-4-hydroxy. Examples in this group are haloperidol (**101**), trifluperidol (**112a**) and methylperidol (**112b**).

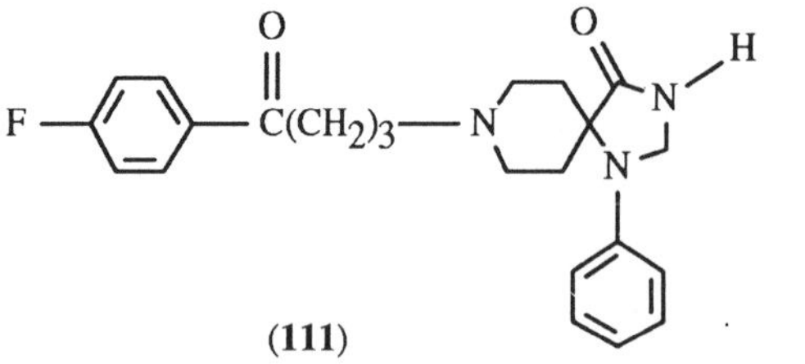

(**111**)

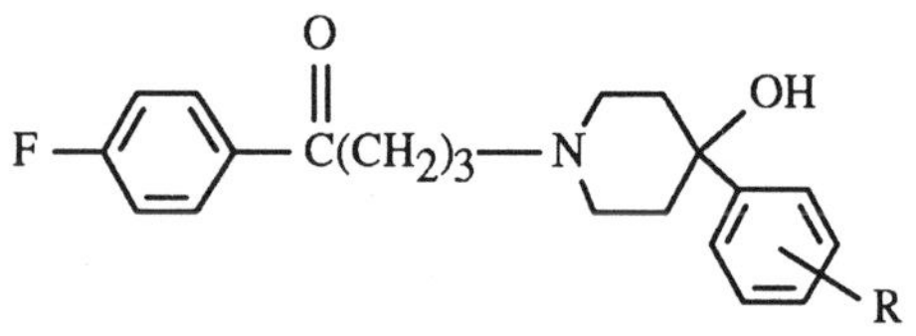

(**112a**) R = *m*-CF$_3$
(**112b**) R = *p*-Me

(ii) 4-(1,2,3,6-Tetrahydropyridyl) analogues

Of the many compounds of this class that have been studied, two, *i.e.* droperidol (**113**) and anisoperidone (**103**), are clinically effective as antipsychotics.

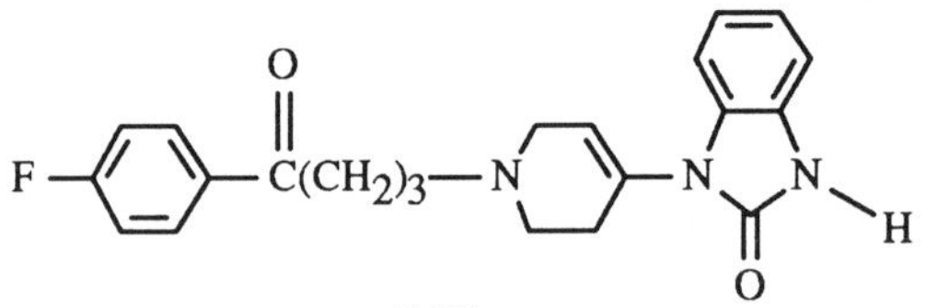

(**113**)

(iii) 4-Piperazinylbutyrophenones

Among butyrophenones containing a 4-piperazinyl group, high neuroleptic activity is associated with an aromatic group in the 4 position of the piperazine ring, *e.g.* butopipazone (**114**). Activity is further enhanced by the presence of an *o*-methoxy group in this aromatic nucleus.

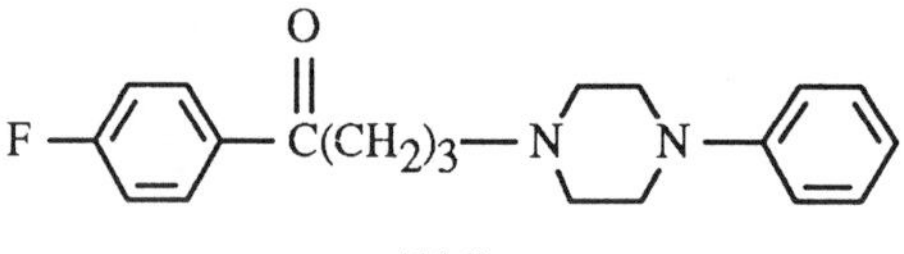

(**114**)

12.3.12.5.5 Diarylbutylamines

A group of compounds, which for convenience may be classed as butyrophenone derivatives, are the diarylbutylamines. These analogues may be considered as butyrophenones, in which the keto function is replaced by an aryl ring (**115a**). The best known example is pimozide (**115b**). The SAR for

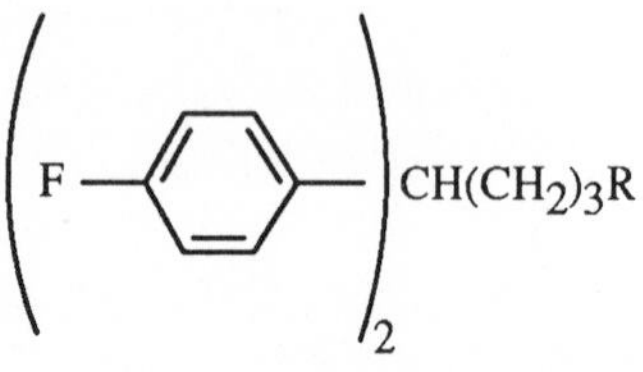

(**115a**)

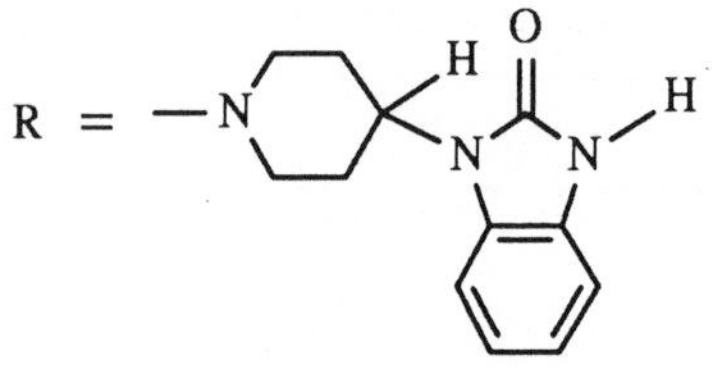

(**115b**)

this group is quite similar to that of the butyrophenones, *i.e.* high potency is associated with (i) *p*-fluoro substituents in both aryl rings; (ii) an unbranched propylene bridge; and (iii) a properly substituted piperidine ring. Other examples of this group are penfluridol (**115c**) and fluspirilene (**115d**). The characteristics of this group are their high potency and long duration of action.

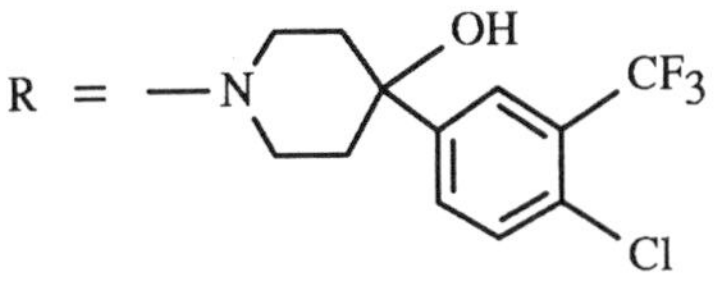

(**115c**)

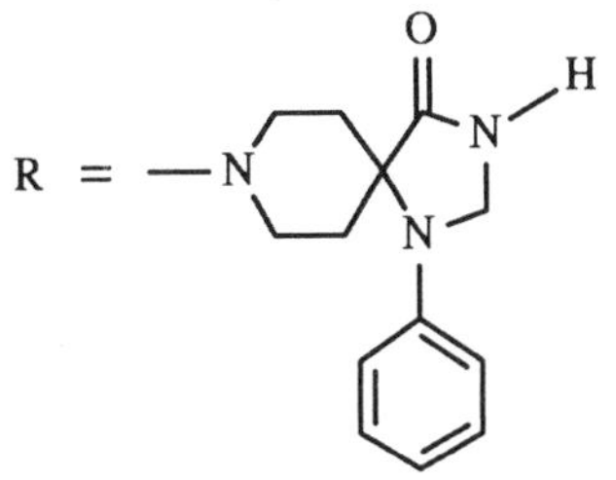

(**115d**)

12.3.12.6 Indole Analogues

The best known representative of this group of neuroleptics is oxypertine (**116**). This clinically effective antipsychotic also has mood-elevating and stimulant properties, which make it useful for treating the apathy often associated with schizophrenia.

The general formula in (**117**) shows the possible variations that have been studied. Alkyl or alkoxy groups in the indole nucleus only cause a marked effect in the head-withdrawal reflex test. Although a 2-methyl substituent enhances the activity of oxypertine in comparison with its unsubstituted congener, it has an inconsistent effect in other analogues. Maximum neuroleptic potency is associated with a two- or three-carbon side chain. Aryl substitution of the piperazine nitrogen atom is required for neuroleptic activity. A phenyl or phenyl-substituted group provides the highest activity.

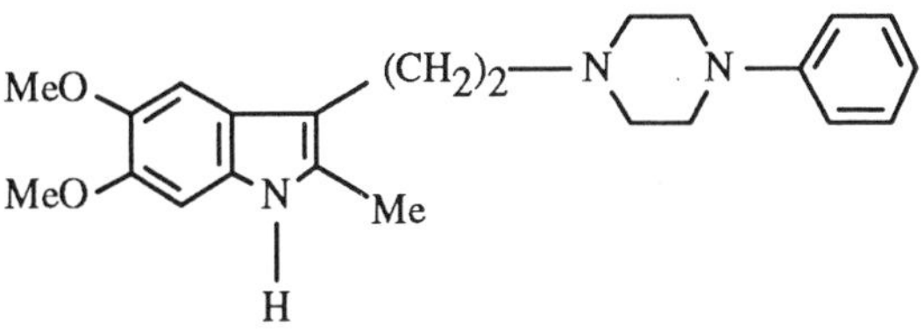

(**116**)

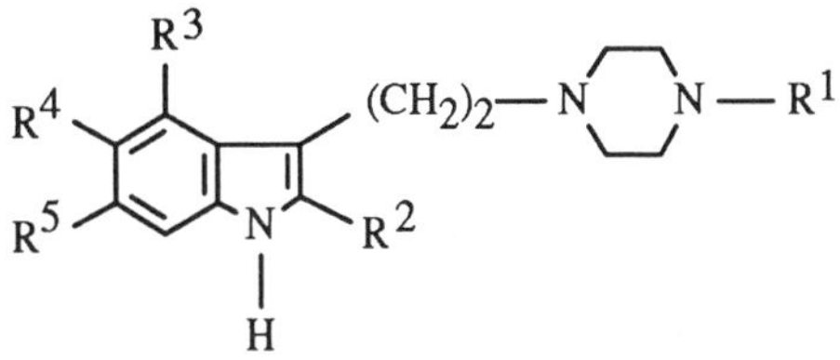

(**117**)

The other well-known indole-containing analogue having antipsychotic activity is molindone and this will be dealt with under the β-aminoketones.

12.3.12.7 β-Aminoketones

Various aromatic β-aminoketones (**118**) have been synthesized and found to possess neuroleptic activity. Of the five analogues shown in (**118**), the first two have about one-third of the activity of chlorpromazine and the others are less active. Substitution in the aromatic ring in positions 6 and 7 usually increases potency, and the 6,7-dimethyl analogue is the most potent compound of the series, being almost equiactive with chlorpromazine.[7]

Molindone (**119**) is one of the most potent compounds of this group. In blocking the emetic action of apomorphine, it is more potent than chlorpromazine. Clinically, molindone is equipotent with trifluoperazine, causing less sedation and some stimulation.

12.3.12.8 Benzamides

The procainamide derivative, metoclopramide (**120**), is an antiemetic and at high doses it produces neuroleptic effects. The first compound of this group which was shown to have antipsychotic properties was sulpiride (**121**). SAR studies[7,92] have concerned themselves with the following factors.

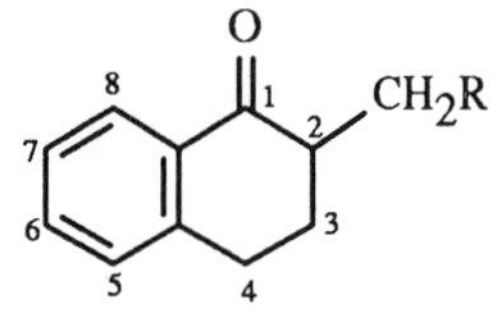

(118)

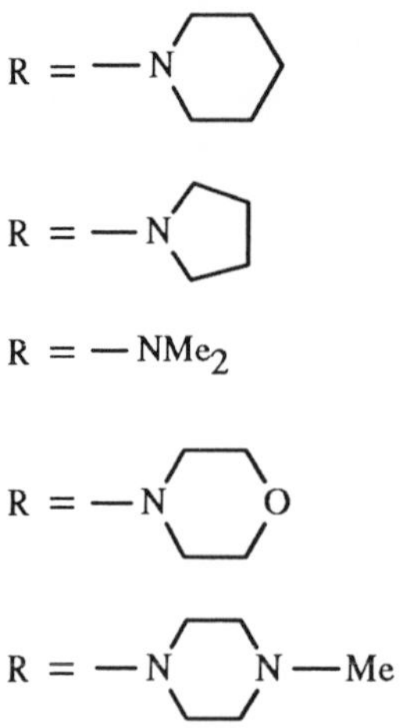

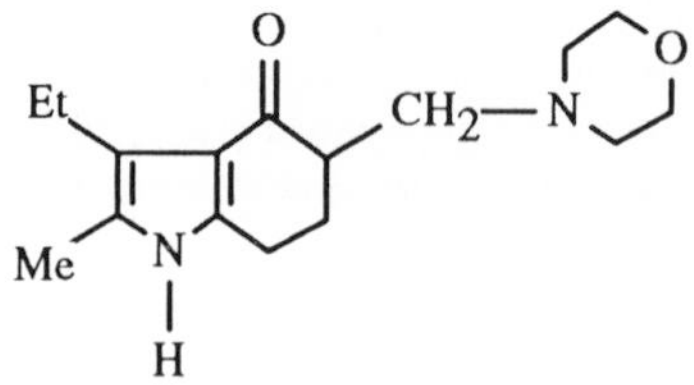

R = —N⟨piperidine⟩

R = —N⟨pyrrolidine⟩

R = —NMe₂

R = —N⟨morpholine⟩

R = —N⟨piperazine⟩N—Me

(119)

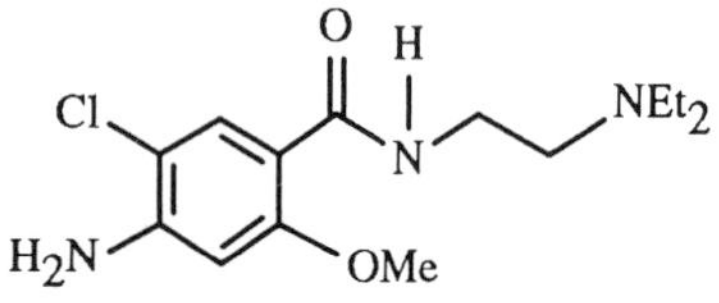

(120)

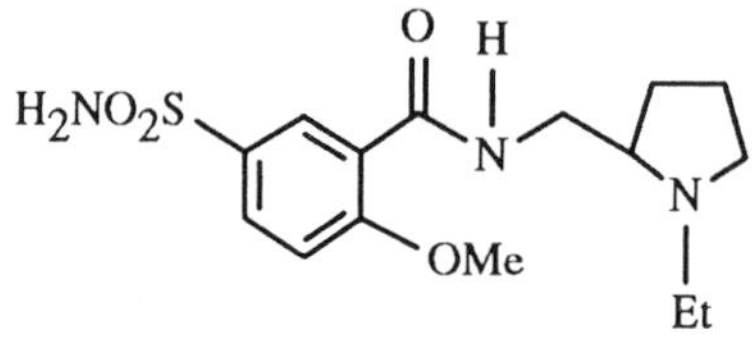

(121)

12.3.12.8.1 Chain modification

Increasing the distance between the two nitrogen atoms in the side chain by an extra carbon atom (*i.e.* three), causes a large loss in *in vitro* dopaminergic activity. A benzyl group on the basic nitrogen atom seems to provide optimal activity in inhibiting apomorphine-induced stereotypy (Table 8). Incorporation of the side chain into a five- or six-membered ring produces interesting effects. Thus, the pyrrolidine analogue is potent, whereas expansion of the ring by one carbon atom leads to a large decrease in activity if the benzamide group is attached at position 3 of the piperidine ring. In striking contrast, if the attachment occurs at position 4, the activity is restored. It has also been shown that an ethylene bridge across the 2 and 6 positions of the piperidine ring produces a large increase in the antiemetic activity. This has been interpreted as being due to a strict positional requirement on the amine nitrogen atom. It has been suggested that the *N*-ethylpyrrolidine series (*e.g.* sulpiride) and the *N*-benzylpiperidine group (*e.g.* clebopride; **122**) have a different SAR and are, in fact, two different classes of compound. Although the retroamide of sulpiride is inactive, the compound BRL 20596 (**123**) retains central antidopaminergic activity.

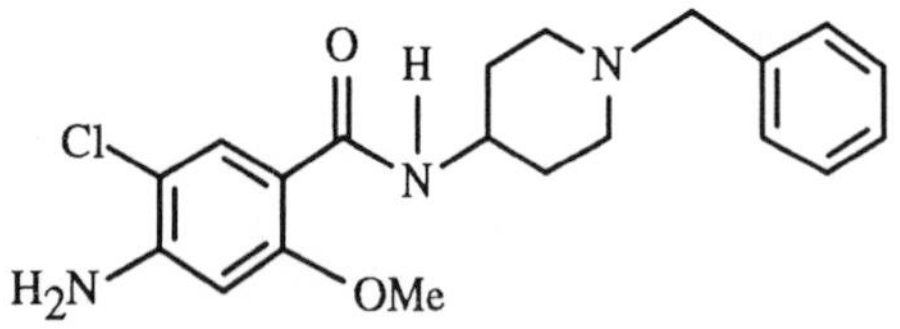

(122)

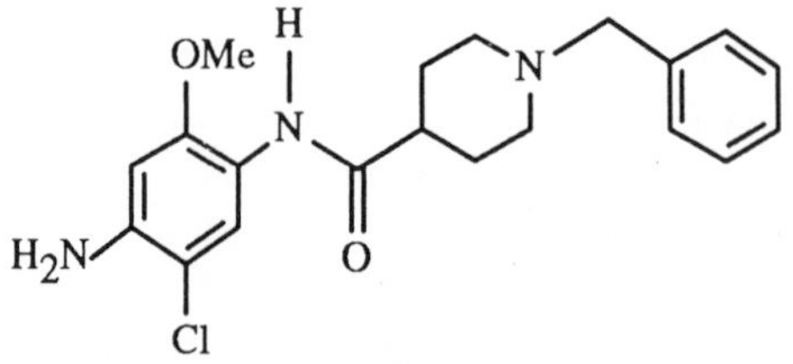

(123)

12.3.12.8.2 Aromatic ring substitution

Benzamides having no substituent in the ring except an *o*-methoxy group display only poor activity. The addition of a group, almost regardless of its nature, at position 3 or 5 produces active compounds. Thus the 5-chloro analogue of cipropride is 150 times more potent than cipropride (**124**) in inhibiting apomorphine-induced climbing in mice. The 5-hydroxyethyl derivative of sulpiride, MD781400 (**125**), is 530 times as potent as sulpiride in the latter test system. It is known that the

Table 8 Chain Modifications of Metoclopramide[92]

Compound structure	Inhibition of apomorphine-induced stereotypy (ED_{50} $\mu mol\,kg^{-1}$)		Ref.
Metoclopramide	10	s.c.	a
	7.8	i.p.	b
	20	p.o.	c
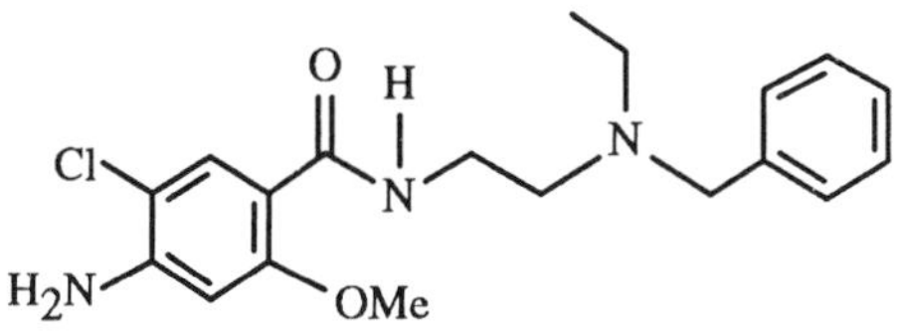 YM-(1)	1.0	s.c.	a
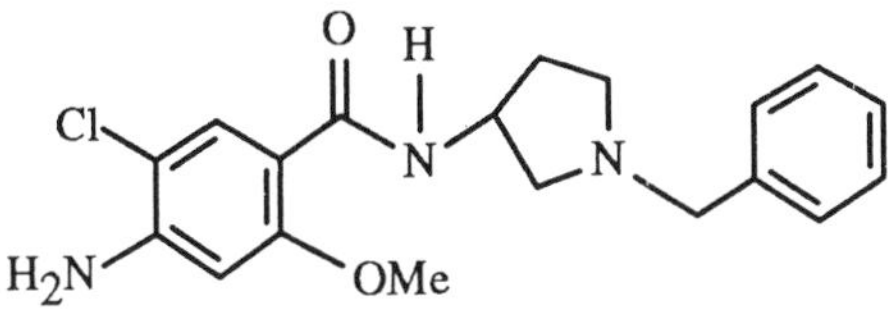 YM-(40)	0.43	s.c.	a
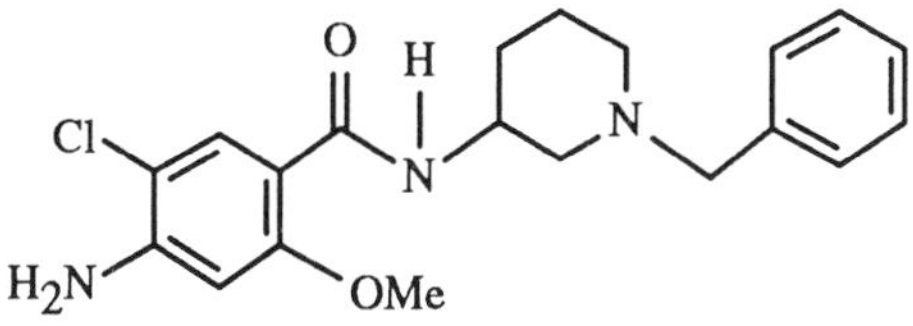 PR-(11)	>300	p.o.	c
Clebopride	0.90	i.p.	b
	5.0	p.o.	c

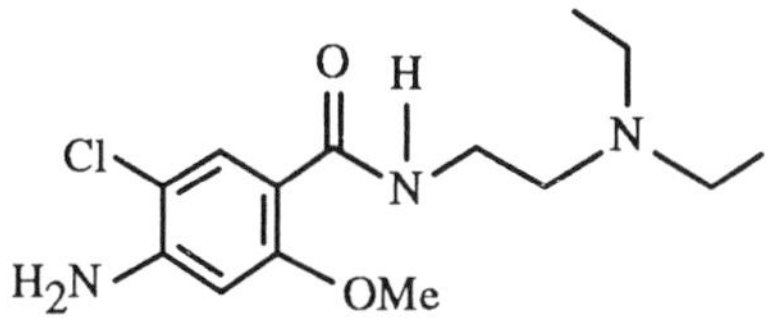

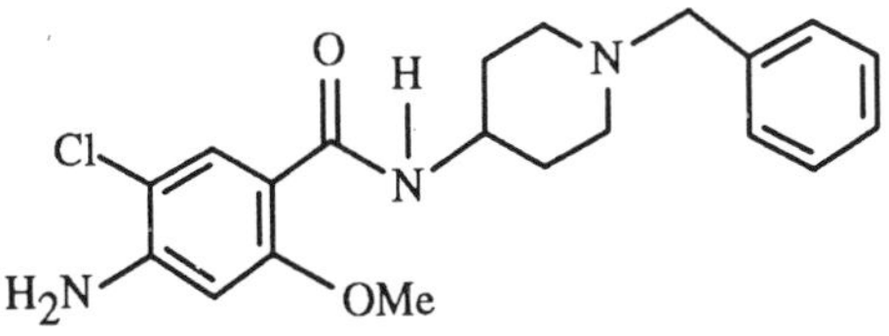

[a] Iwanani *et al.*, *J. Med. Chem.*, 1981, **24**, 1224. [b] Köhler *et al.*, *Acta Psychiatr. Scand. Suppl.*, 1984, **311**, 69. [c] Prieto *et al.*, *J. Pharm. Pharmacol.*, 1977, **29**, 147.

activity of sulpiride can be increased by replacement of the aminosulfonyl group by a more lipophilic substituent such as ethylsulphonyl, *e.g.* sultopride (**126**), which is an effective antipsychotic drug.

The most potent benzamide so far reported in the literature is YM-09151-2 (**127**). This compound is 408 and 13 times more potent than metoclopramide and haloperidol, respectively, in inhibiting apomorphine-induced stereotypy.

In order to improve the oral activity of sulpiride, Ogren and Florvall, at Astra Läkemedel,[92] introduced a second methoxy group next to the amide bond. The analogy here is the sterically hindered anilide xylocaine. This led to the synthesis of remoxipride (**128**). In antagonizing the effects of apomorphine in the rat, it is 50 times more potent than sulpiride. It also appears to be an antipsychotic agent which does not cause extrapyramidal side effects. Another analogue in this series, raclopride (**129**), has the highest separation between the blockade of hyperactivity and induction of catalepsy in the rat in this group. It is currently being evaluated as an antipsychotic.

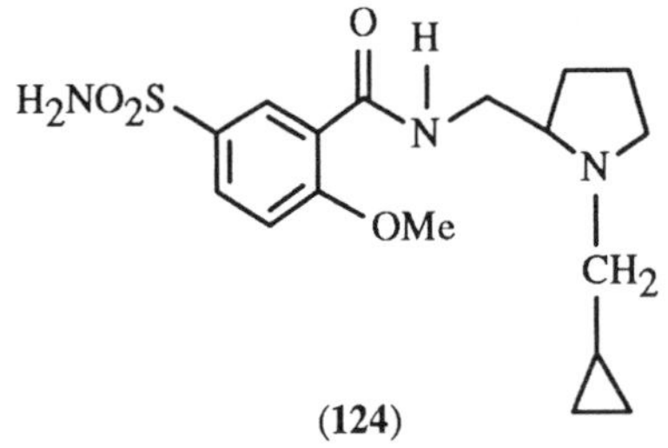

(**124**)

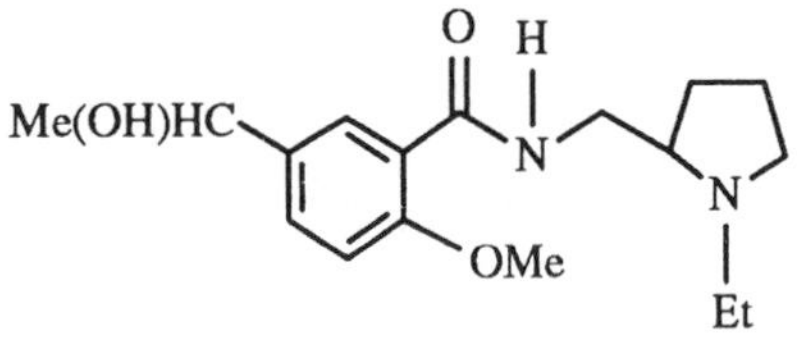

(**125**)

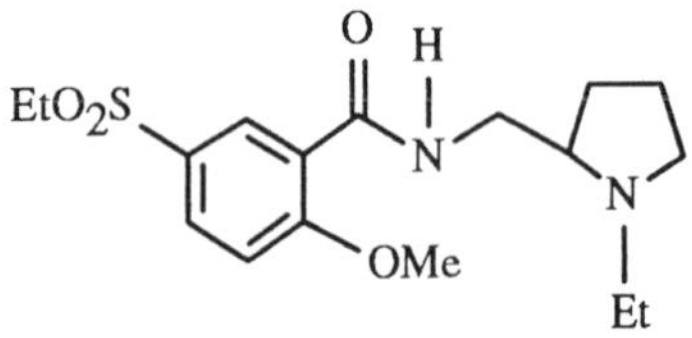

(**126**)

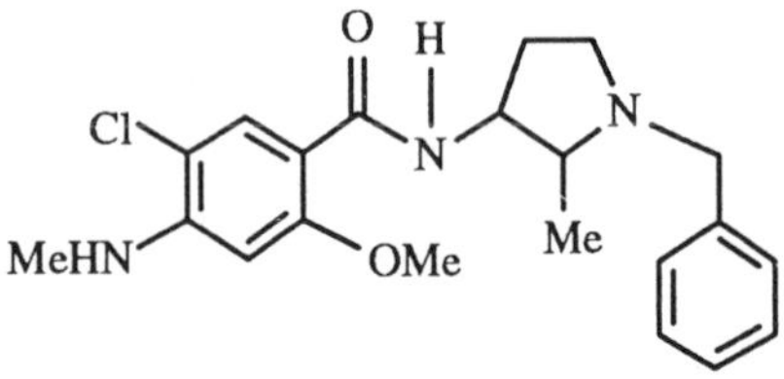

(**127**)

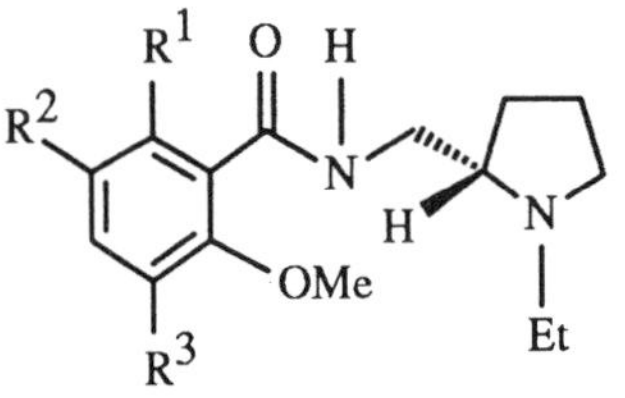

(**128**) R^1 = OMe; R^2 = Br; R^3 = H
(**129**) R^1 = OH; R^2 = Cl; R^3 = Cl

12.3.12.9   3-Benzazepines

Selective D-1 agonists that have arisen from the 3-benzazepine ring system have been dealt with in Section 12.3.11.14. It was also from this group of compounds that the first selective D-1 antagonist, SCH 23390[43] (**130**), was developed. Extensive studies by groups at SK&F[5,66] and Schering[43] in the USA have shown that the most important methods for obtaining antagonistic activity in this series are: (i) replacement of the 7-hydroxy by chloro or bromo groups; (ii) the introduction of a thiophenyl or a related group at position 9; and (iii) *O,O*- and *N*-trimethylation of SKF 38393 (**55**) to give SCH12679. As in the case of the agonists, the activity resides mainly in the (*R*) enantiomer. The differential affinity for the D-1 receptor is very high, *i.e.* 2000-fold, in comparison with the D-2 receptor.[43]

The main interest in these D-1 antagonists is based on the prediction that they should produce fewer extrapyramidal side effects in humans when being used to treat psychoses.

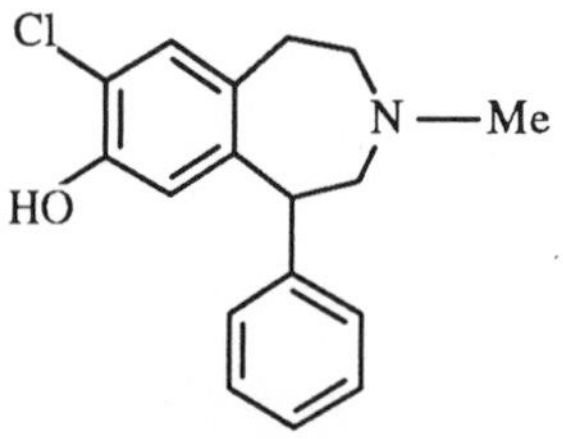

(**130**)

12.3.12.10   Reserpine and Related Compounds

Reserpine (**131**) occupies a special place in the history of psychopharmacology[7] due to its use as a major tranquilliser in the 1950s, and its influence on our understanding of basic neurochemical mechanisms occurring in the nerve ending. It is the principal alkaloid of *Rauwolfia serpentina*, and extracts of this plant have been used for a long time in traditional Indian folk medicine. Due to the discovery of the neuroleptics of the phenothiazine class, and also because of various side effects caused by reserpine, its use for the treatment of schizophrenia is now a thing of the past. However, it still remains in use as a pharmacological tool. It should also be emphasized that, although it is classified as a neuroleptic, its mode of action differs from that of other compounds in this group, *i.e.* it does not block DA receptors, it depletes neurotransmitter storage sites. For SAR details, the reader is referred to several comprehensive reviews by Kaiser and Setler.[7]

An investigation of analogues of the ipecac alkaloid, emetine, led to the discovery of the benzoquinolizine derivative, tetrabenazine (132). This compound has a similar pharmacological profile to that of reserpine; however, it is shorter acting and less potent.

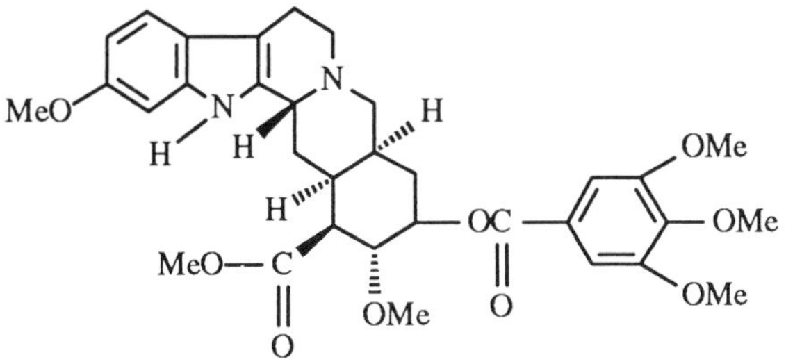

(131)

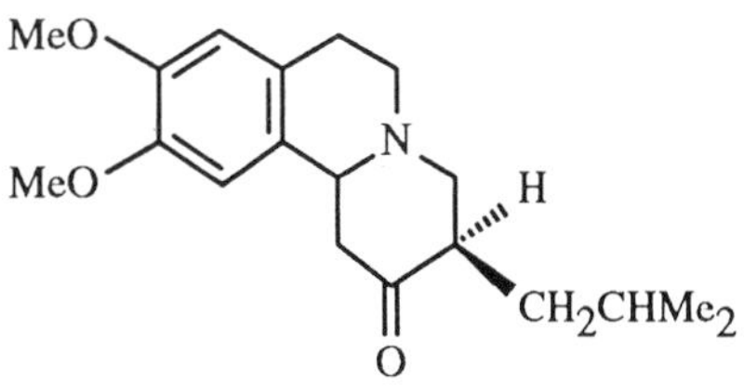

(132)

12.3.13 STEREOCHEMISTRY OF DOPAMINE AGONISTS AND ANTAGONISTS

Unlike the two other endogenous catecholamines, adrenaline and noradrenaline, dopamine does not have an asymmetric carbon atom. Nevertheless, DA receptors possess a high degree of chirality and they are able to discriminate between stereoisomers of dopaminergic agonists and antagonists.[4-6,8,93,109,110]

12.3.13.1 Agonists

The active enantiomer of apomorphine, *i.e.* the $(-)$ form, has the $(6aR)$ absolute configuration (133). This was established by chemical degradation means and confirmed by optical rotatory dispersion and X-ray crystallographic studies.

In a similar manner, the absolute configuration of $(-)$-5-hydroxy-2-(dipropylamino)tetralin (134a) has been established by degradative and X-ray analysis procedures. It has the $(2S)$ configuration. It should be remembered that the Cahn–Ingold–Prelog rules assign opposite letters to the similar absolute configurations occurring at the chiral centres in the aporphines and 2-aminotetralins. This enantiomer is more potent than its antipode in a number of dopaminergic test systems. This also applies to the 5,6-dihydroxy analogue (134b). In sharp contrast, 7-hydroxy-2-(di-*n*-propylamino)tetralin (135a) and 6,7-dihydroxy-2-(di-*n*-propylamino)tetralin (135b) exhibit the opposite stereochemical requirement; their $(2R)$-$(+)$ enantiomers are more potent than their optical antipodes.

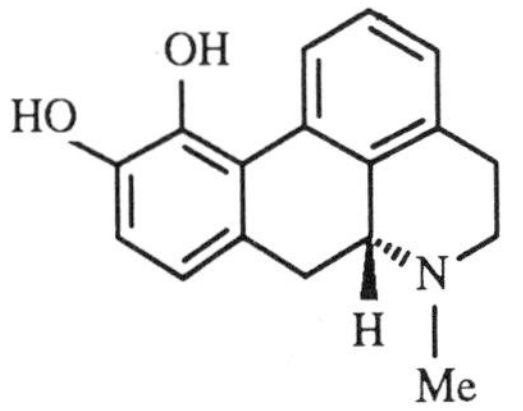

(133)

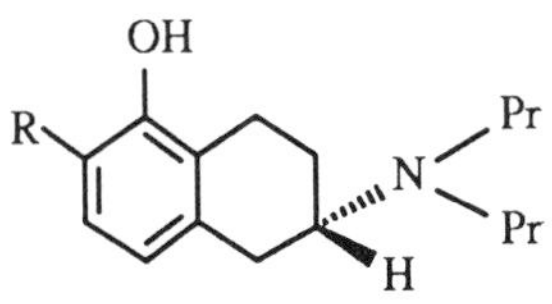

(134a) R = H
(134b) R = OH

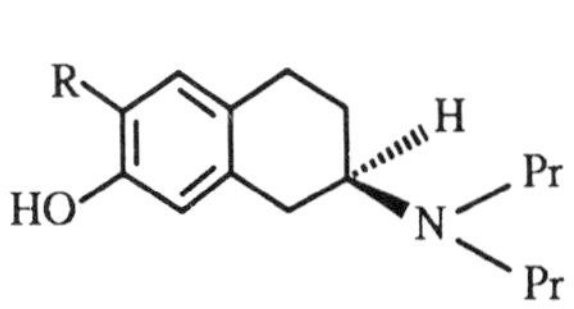

(135a) R = H
(135b) R = OH

These stereochemical differences have been elegantly rationalized in a simple manner by McDermed *et al.*[94] They suggested that the two most important binding sites in the DA receptor interact with the amino nitrogen and the hydroxyl group, which is '*meta*' to the ethylamine side

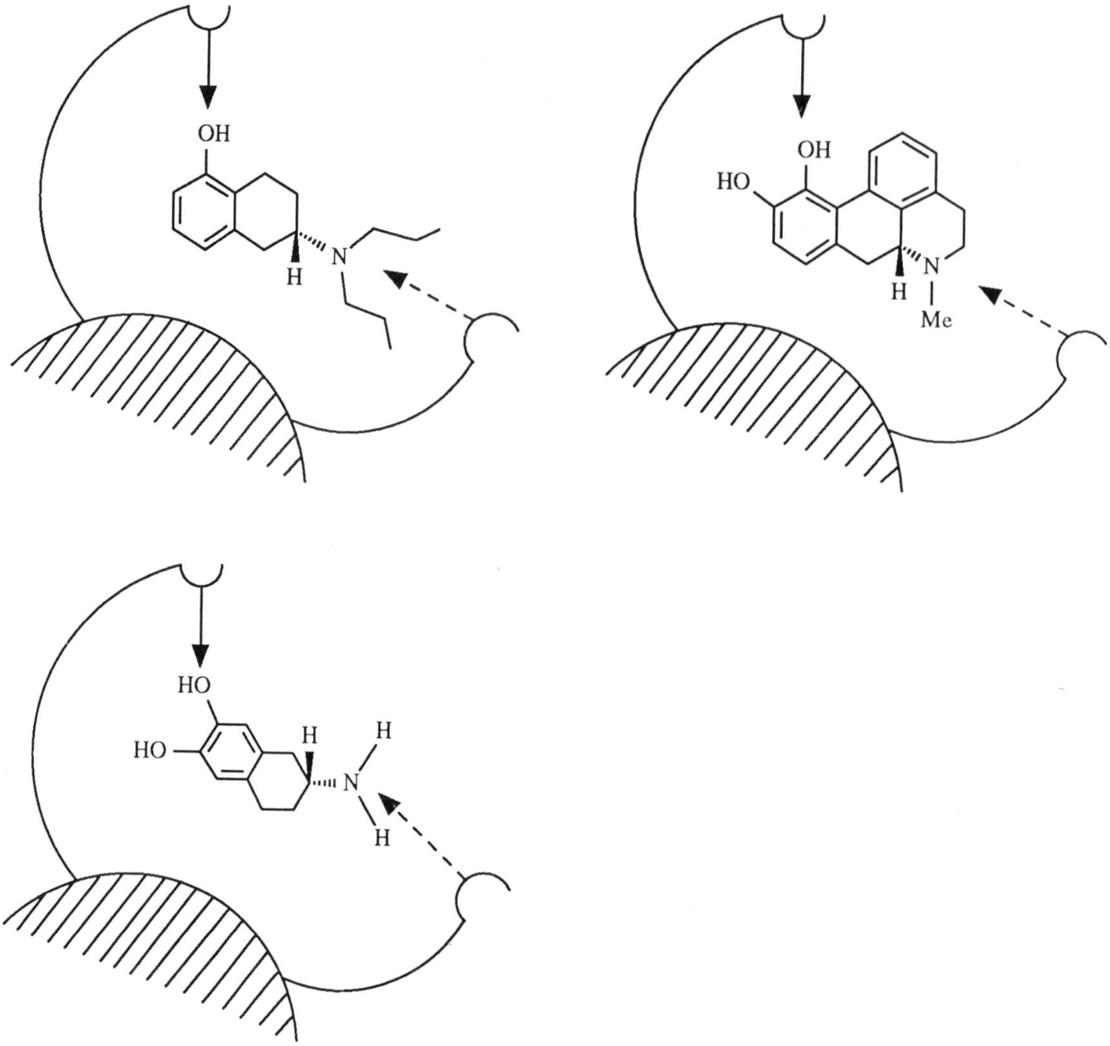

Figure 1   The binding of chiral agonists to the dopamine receptor[94]

chain. Thus, although (2S)-(−)-5-hydroxy-2-(di-*n*-propylamino)tetralin (**134a**) and (6a*S*)-(−)-apomorphine (**133**) both bind in a similar manner to the receptor (Figure 1), (2*R*)-(+)-6,7-dihydroxy-2-aminotetralin must be rotated with respect to the other two compounds in order to fit this model. Similar models have been proposed by Kaiser and Jain[5] regarding the binding of the 3-benzazepines to the DA receptor.

The absolute configuration at C-5 of the ergoline ring system (**136**) of naturally occurring derivatives is (*R*). Compounds with the opposite absolute configuration are reported to be inactive. The semisynthetic analogues, lergotrile (**37**), pergolide (**38**) and bromocriptine (**35**), also have the (*R*) configuration at C-5.

The absolute configuration of (−)-3-(3-hydroxyphenyl)-*N*-*n*-propylpiperidine (3-PPP; **137**), has been shown by X-ray crystallography to be (*S*).

In Section 12.3.11.7 it was mentioned that in the octahydrobenzo[*f*]quinoline series, the (±)-*trans* isomers were more potent than the (±)-*cis* isomers. In the case of the naphthoxazine (**30**) group of DA agonists, the absolute configuration of the (+) enantiomer of the *trans* series (*i.e.* (+)-PHNO; **138**) has been shown[77] to be *R* for C-4a. Thus the absolute configurations of (+)-PHNO and (+)-7-hydroxy-*N*,*N*-dipropyl-2-aminotetralin are comparable.

Resolution of SKF38393 (**55**) has shown that the dopaminergic activity resides almost exclusively in the (*R*) enantiomer.

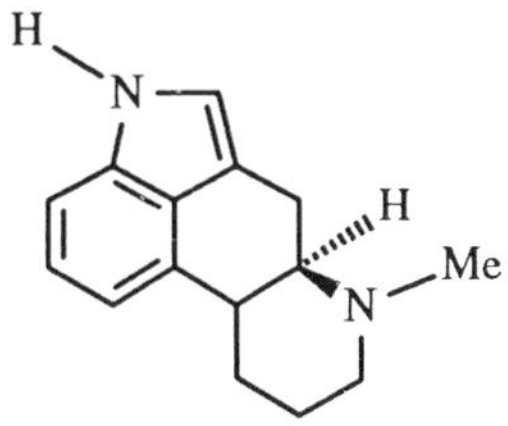

(136) 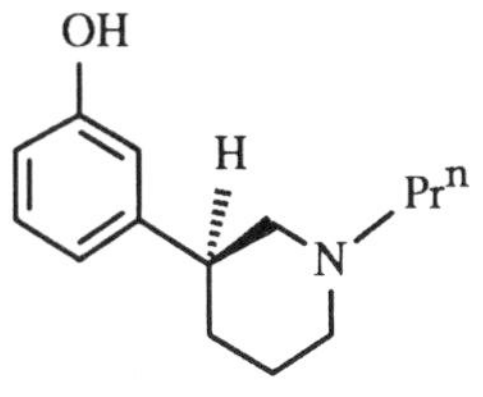   (137) 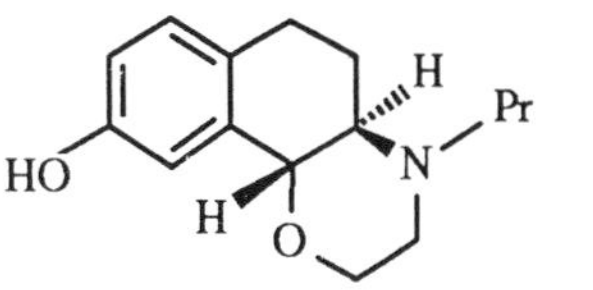   (138)

12.3.13.2 Antagonists

In the case of (+)-butaclamol (**139**) and (+)-dexclamol, it has been shown that the absolute configuration at the three asymmetric centres is (3*S*, 4a*S*, 13b*S*).[7] The neuroleptic activity of sulpiride resides in the (−) isomer, which has the (*S*) configuration (**140**). The (+) enantiomer having the (*R*) configuration is about 10–20 times less active as a neuroleptic in various tests.

Further discussions on the stereochemistry and receptor topology of these compounds can be found in the review article by de Paulis.[92] The stereochemical properties of the thioxanthene analogues have also been covered in Section 12.3.12.2.

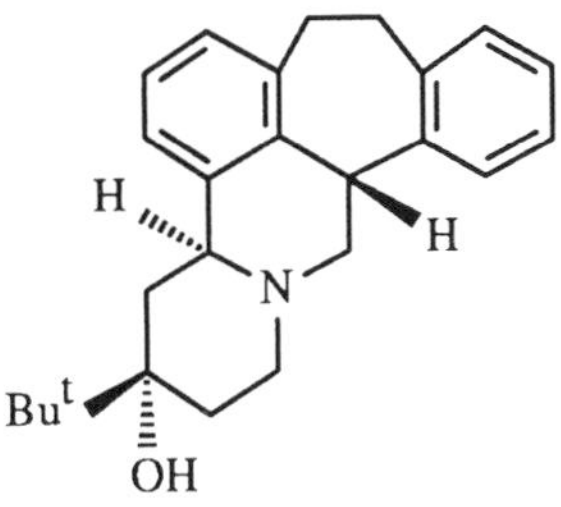

(139) 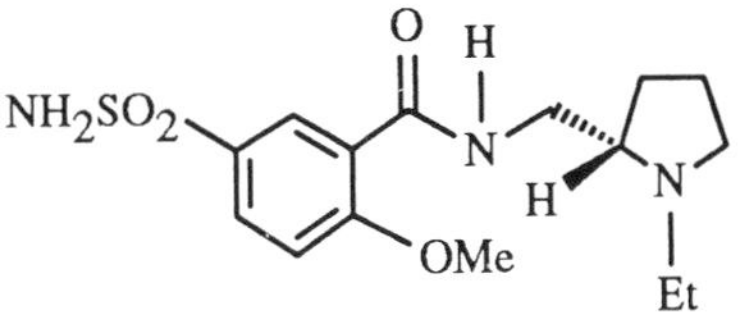   (140) 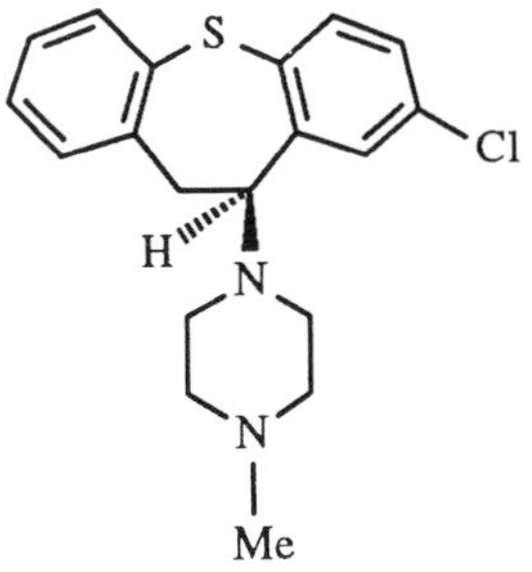   (141)

In the case of octoclothepin (**141**), almost all the neuroleptic activity resides in the (+) isomer. The absolute configuration, as determined by X-ray crystallography, is (*S*).

For further details on the stereochemistry of DA agonists and antagonists, the reader is referred to the extensive review by Smith.[93]

12.3.14 THE RECEPTOR-PREFERRED CONFORMATION OF DOPAMINE

Although it is conceivable that the exact receptor-preferred conformation of DA might be different at D-1 and D-2 receptors, it is possible to reach some general conclusions which appear to be applicable to both receptors.

The conformational analysis of the receptor-preferred conformation of DA[95a] can be divided into three levels of complexity (Figure 2): (i) DA can exist in a *trans* or two *gauche* forms (Figure 2a); (ii) there are two possible extremes for the *trans* form, *i.e.* with the catechol ring perpendicular to the —CH_2NH_2 bond (*trans*-α) or coplanar to it (*trans*-β; Figure 2b); and (iii) when the catechol ring is coplanar to the side chain (*trans*-β), there are two further possibilities depending on the orientation of the ring, *i.e.* the α and β rotamers (Figure 2c).

With regard to the possibilities under (i), some theoretical studies indicate a preference for the *trans* and some for the *gauche* form; the general conclusion is that the energy difference between these forms is only of the order of 4–8 kJ mol^{-1}. However, all the pharmacological evidence using rigid and semirigid DA analogues shows convincingly that the receptor-preferred conformation is a form of the *trans* species.

The second question of whether, at the receptor, the catechol ring is perpendicular (*trans*-α) or coplanar (*trans*-β) to the —CH_2NH_2 bond, is more difficult to answer. In the crystal, the preferred form is *trans*-α (Figure 3a). Molecular orbital studies of NMR coupling constants also indicate that the preferred form is *trans*-α. It is known, however, that the potential energy difference between these

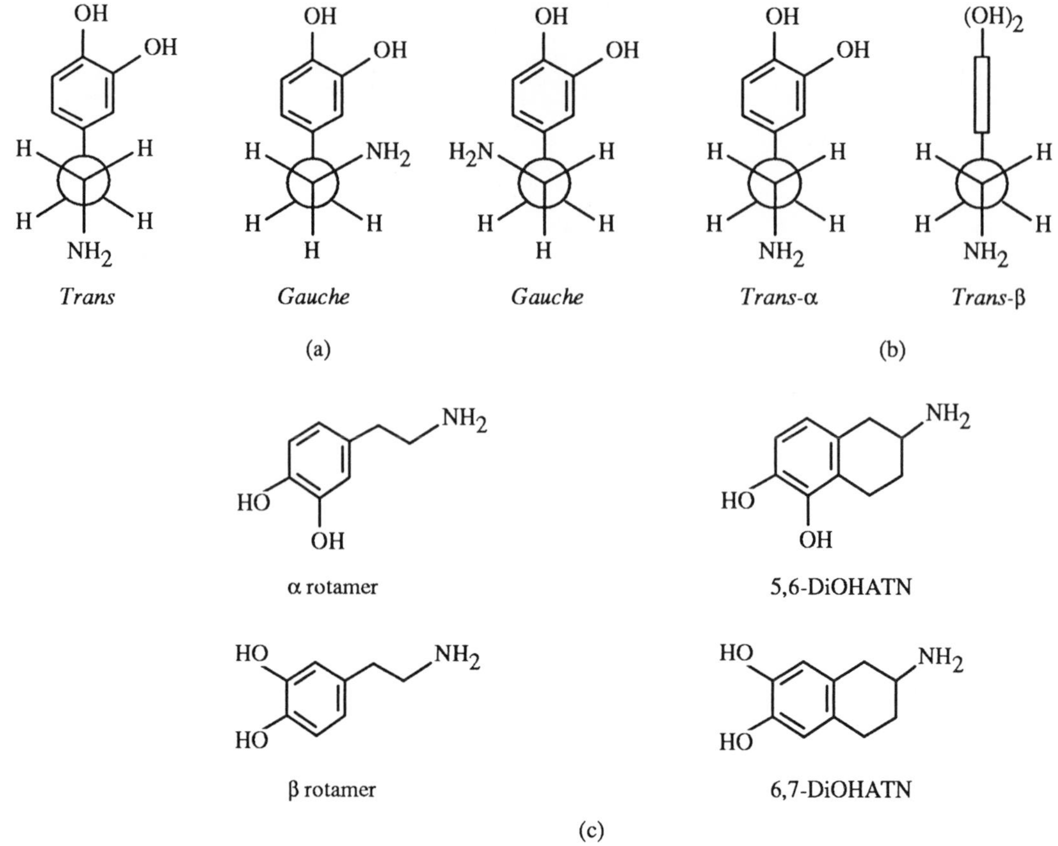

Trans   *Gauche*   *Gauche*   *Trans-α*   *Trans-β*

(a)   (b)

α rotamer   5,6-DiOHATN

β rotamer   6,7-DiOHATN

(c)

Figure 2 Conformational analysis of dopamine: (a) and (b) are Newman projections, (c) is an analysis of the extreme forms of the *trans-β* conformer and its corresponding 2-aminotetrahydronaphthalene (ATN) analogues[95a]

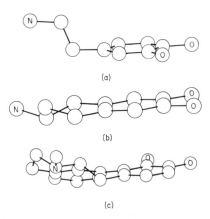

(a)

(b)

(c)

Figure 3 Solid state conformations of (a) dopamine · HCl; (b) 6,7-diOHATN · HBr; and (c) apomorphine · HCl[95a]

two forms is also quite small. The most direct evidence in favour of the hypothesis that the *trans-β* form is the active one is the fact that such pharmacologically active analogues as 6,7-di-OHATN (Figure 3b) and apomorphine (Figure 3c) are both allied to the *trans-β* rather than the *trans-α* form, *i.e.* they are fairly 'planar' molecules. Indeed, the surprising inactivity of a cyclopropane analogue of DA **(66)** on peripheral and central dopaminergic receptors has been explained by the fact that its preferred conformation may correspond more closely to the *trans-α* rather than the *trans-β* form of DA. This conclusion is also supported by the X-ray analysis of the conformation of *N,N*-dimethyl-2-phenylcyclopropylamine.

Similar problems of unfavourable steric bulk were also suggested as a possible explanation for the inactivity of certain 6-*exo*- and *endo*-(3,4-dihydroxyphenyl)-2-azabicyclo[2.2.2]octanes. Further

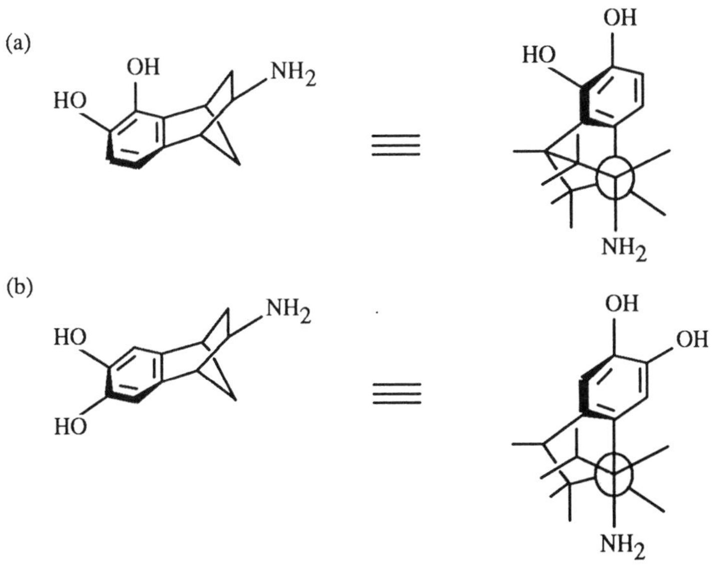

Figure 4 (a) *exo*-2-Amino-5,6-dihydroxybenzonorbornene; (b) *exo*-2-amino-6,7-dihydroxybenzonorbornene[95a]

evidence against the *trans*-α conformer being the active species was provided by the finding that various *exo*-2-aminobenzonorbornene (Figure 4a), which are rigid analogues of the *trans* form, are inactive *in vivo*.

Thus if it is accepted that the *trans* coplanar form of DA (*trans*-β) is probably the receptor site preferred conformation, the final remaining uncertainty is that of the preferred orientation of the catechol ring, *i.e.* the α or β rotamer (Figure 2c). Fortunately, a more or less direct answer can be provided to this question by studying various catechol (5,6- and 6,7-diOH) derivatives of 2-aminotetralin (ATN; Figure 2c). These semirigid analogues of the *trans*-β form of DA are known to be very potent DA receptor agonists. In various *in vitro* and *in vivo* tests, the 6,7 isomer is consistently much more active than its 5,6 positional isomer. Certain authors, however, are of the opinion that in some behavioural test systems, the 5,6 isomer is more potent than the 6,7 analogue. Such behavioural experiments are always complicated by the large number of factors affecting drug action, such as distribution, metabolism, uptake and action at multiple DA receptors. The author has recently shown that some of the *in vivo* differences between the 6,7 and 5,6 isomers are due to the fact that the former compound is readily metabolized by COMT. The consistent *in vitro* data are thus probably a much better guide to the receptor site preferred conformation of DA than are the behavioural results. The third possible catechol isomer of ATN, *i.e.* the 7,8-diOH form, has been shown to be inactive (Costall and Naylor, personal communication). In addition, it has been shown that the (+) enantiomer of 6,7-diOHATN is about 100 times more potent than the (−) form, and about four times more active than DA itself, in stimulating the DA sensitive adenylate cyclase system. Thus, with regard to its pharmacological activity, 6,7-diOHATN seems to be almost an ideal semirigid analogue of DA.

The amino group in 6,7-diOHATN can, of course, adopt an equatorial or an axial conformation. In the crystal structure, the equatorial form was found to be the preferred one. Theoretical calculations have also shown that this form is 36.4 kJ mol^{-1} more stable than the axial one. Thus, although 6,7-diOHATN is not a 'completely' rigid molecule (this is, of course, an idealized concept), its conformational mobility is sufficiently restricted to allow the suggestion that the nonbonded distance and torsion angles of the DA skeleton in it (Table 9) probably correspond closely to those of DA at its receptor. For comparison, the corresponding values found in the crystal structure of DA·HCl are shown in Table 10.

Costall *et al.*[96] have recently again presented arguments in favour of their hypothesis that the receptor-preferred conformation of DA is α rather than β. This is based on a series of rigid multiring analogues of DA that have been prepared over the years by Cannon and coworkers.[6] However, these compounds are *N*-alkylated analogues of DA, and it is known that in such analogues there is a shift of preference from the β to the α rotamer. Thus, because DA itself is a primary amine, the value of results obtained with secondary and tertiary amines is doubtful. Clearly, an active analogue of DA, such as 6,7-diOHATN, which is a primary amine and bears a very close structural resemblance

Table 9   6,7-DiOHATN·HBr Torsion Angles and Interatomic Distances. The Values are Derived From Atomic Coordinates Obtained by X-ray Analysis[95a]

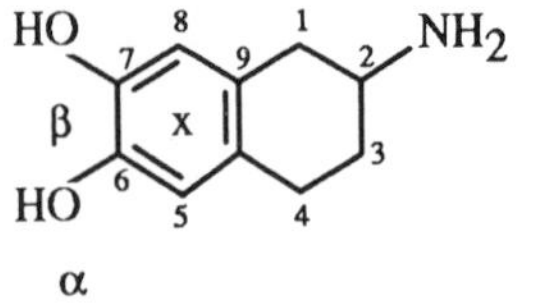

Torsion angles	(°)	Interatomic distances	(Å)
$C_8C_9C_1C_2$	165.2	N–x	5.15
$C_9C_1C_2N$	168.1	N–Oα	7.88
$C_1C_2C_3C_4$	−59.9	N–Oβ	7.32
$NC_2C_3C_4$	177.6		
$C_9C_1C_2C_3$	44.7	N above plane of benzene ring	0.001

Table 10   DA·HCl Torsion Angles and Interatomic Distances. The Values are Derived From Published Atomic Coordinates[95b]

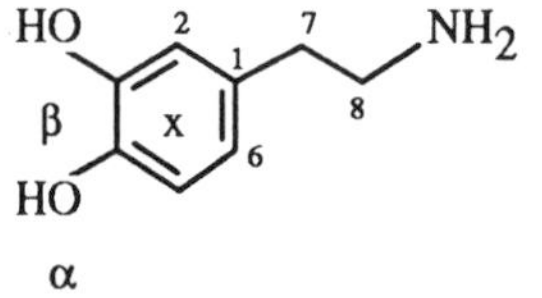

Torsion angles	(°)	Interatomic distances	(Å)
$C_6C_1C_7C_8$	−99	N–x	5.14
$C_2C_1C_7C_8$	79	N–Oα	7.83
$C_1C_7C_8N$	174	N–Oβ	6.83
		N above plane of ring	1.61

to DA, is a much better guide to its receptor-preferred conformation than *N*-alkylated and multiring compounds. In line with the general remark by Martin[97] about differences in the mode of binding by analogues, it has been suggested that *N*-alkylated analogues may interact with accessory binding sites. For the sake of clarity, however, it should be pointed out that such compounds can be useful in attempts to obtain information about the preference for *trans* and *gauche* forms and the importance of coplanarity, *i.e.* factors (i) and (ii) in the conformational analysis.

It was the intention in this section to show that in attempting to decide what the receptor-preferred conformation of a molecule is, one should ideally try to combine the information provided by various techniques, *i.e.* X-ray crystallography, conformationally restricted analogues, NMR and theoretical energy calculations.

12.3.15   TOPOGRAPHICAL MODELS OF DA RECEPTORS

An attempt will be made to deal with the various models that have been proposed for the DA receptor,[4,5,8,65] in a more or less chronological order. Sheppard and Burghardt,[98] in 1974, pointed out the importance of the distances between the *m*-hydroxy and the nitrogen atom in DA agonists, as well as the possible existence of a hydrophobic region in the receptor that could interact with (*R*)-α-methyl, 2-phenyl and various *N*-alkyl substituents. In the following year, Dandiya *et al.*[99] suggested a pre- and post-synaptic receptor model, with affinity for the 'trans–cisoid' and 'trans–transoid' DA conformers, respectively. Grol and Rollema,[100] in 1977, attempted to explain the inactivity of isoapomorphine as being due to an interaction of the aromatic A ring with a receptor boundary. A year later, Goldberg *et al.*[101] suggested that the β conformer of DA is the active one for

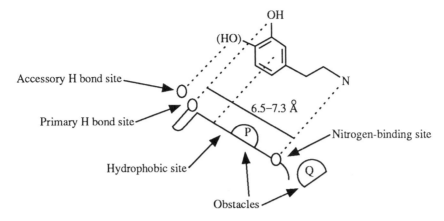

Figure 5 Topographical model for DA receptors:[65] Seeman's model (1980)

the vascular DA receptor. It was envisaged that the amino group interacts with the receptor *via* hydrogen bonding through the nitrogen lone pair or the hydrogens of the amine. Two sites were postulated for the binding of the catechol group and, in addition, for the A ring of the aporphines, a hydrophobic region. In 1979, McDermed *et al.*[94] postulated their model accounting for enantioselectivity, which was mentioned in Section 12.3.13.1.

A detailed model of D-2 receptors was postulated in 1980 by Seeman in an extensive review[21] on brain DA receptors (Figure 5). The essential features were: (i) a hydrogen-bonding group corresponding to the *m*-hydroxy group, and possibly an accessory hydrogen-bonding site corresponding to the *p*-hydroxy group in DA; (ii) high fat solubility, obtained by expansion of the carbon framework of DA analogues or introduction of *N*-alkyl substituents, which is considered to be helpful but not essential; (iii) a nitrogen atom positioned about 0.6 Å above the plane of the aromatic ring bearing the hydrogen-bonding groups; (iv) a distance of less than 7.3 Å between the *m*-hydroxy group and the nitrogen atom; and (v) avoidance of steric hindrance factors in the form of an « obstacle Q » located near the binding site for the nitrogen atom, which would account for the inactivity of octahydrobenzo[*g*]quinolines and norapomorphines with substituents on the nitrogen larger than propyl. A second region of bulk intolerance, called « obstacle P », rationalized the inactivity of octahydrobenzo[*h*]quinolines and isoapomorphine.

Seiler and Markstein[102] (1982) examined the binding of phenolic aminotetralins to the striatal D-1 receptor. Their model, which was similar to McDermed's, has two major binding sites complementary to the *m*-hydroxy and the nitrogen of the 7-OH(+)-(2*R*)- and 5-OH(−)-(2*S*)-ATN series. In the 5-OH series, but not the 7-OH series, an accessory binding site could accommodate the *N*,*N*-dipropyl substituents. According to this model, DA would interact with the receptor in the β rotameric form, and the *N*,*N*-dipropyl groups would force the α rotamer to become the preferred conformation. A year later (1983), Nichols[4] described a model similar to that of McDermed's, which included enantioselective–stereoselective nitrogen and *m*-OH sites, a steric boundary and a hydrophobic site or a region of bulk tolerance. It was suggested that the latter site was of importance for D-2 or DA$_2$ receptors.

Following their extensive studies on aporphine derivatives, Neumeyer *et al.*[8] suggested a model for the DA receptor having the following elements (Figure 6): (i) putative binding sites, M$_1$ and M$_2$, on the receptor surface, complementary to the hydroxyl groups of the *meta* and *para* positions of the DA element in the aporphines; a binding site (M$_3$) for hydroxyl groups at position 2 of the aporphines which diminishes affinity; (ii) an electronegative site, B, complementary to the nitrogen of agonist molecules; the distance between the *m*-hydroxy group and the nitrogen atom was calculated to be 6.9 ± 0.4 Å; (iii) an obstacle that inhibits the binding of aporphines with a (6a*S*) configuration; and (iv) an explanation of enantioselectivity in terms similar to those of McDermed.

The topography of the renal DA receptor (Figure 7) has been investigated by Erhardt (1983).[4] Cartesian coordinates were used to indicate the recognition sites of the receptor, which are: (i) a single *x*, *y* plane containing the amine (A) and catechol recognition sites (H$_m$ and H$_p$); the distance between A and H$_m$ or H$_p$ approximates 7 Å; (ii) a steric parameter, S$_1$, in agreement with McDermed's model; (iii) a second steric parameter, S$_2$ ('ceiling'), located approximately 2 Å above the *x*, *y* plane; and (iv) an auxiliary lipophilic-binding site, B, located opposite the steric parameter, S$_1$.

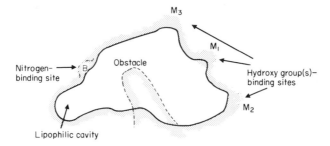

Figure 6   Topographical model for DA receptors:[65] Neumeyer's model (1983)

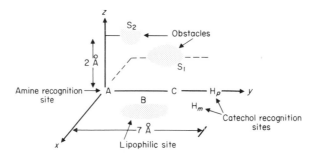

Figure 7   Topographical model for DA receptors:[65] Erhardt's model (1983)

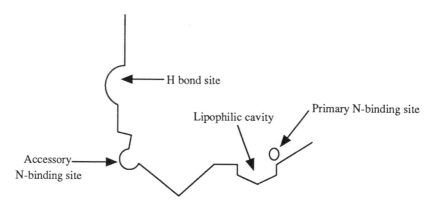

Figure 8   Topographical model for DA receptors:[65] Wikström's model (1985)

Wikström *et al.*[103] (1985) have examined the SAR of DA agonists acting on pre- and post-synaptic receptors. They suggest that these receptors have similar properties (Figure 8),[65] which are: (i) a hydrogen-bonding site which is complementary to the 5-OH group of the 2-aminotetralins, or the 7-OH group of the octahydrobenzo[*f*]quinolines; (ii) an accessory binding area which accommodates the nitrogen of the pyrrole group in the ergolines; (iii) a lipophilic cavity that can accommodate a maximum of three carbon atoms and which is located at the lower part of the receptor, *i.e.* downwards; and (iv) a lipophilic cavity that can accommodate alkyl groups larger than propyl.

In addition, it was suggested that when a propyl group, either as an *N*-alkyl substituent or as part of a piperidine ring, fits into the 'downwards' lipophilic cavity, the compound will exhibit presynaptic activity. In contrast, when an *N-n*-propyl or larger group fits into the 'upwards' lipophilic cleft, the compound will exhibit predominantly postsynaptic activity. The difference between the pre- and post-synaptic DA receptors is therefore thought to relate to the greater accessibility of the nitrogen-binding site in the presynaptic receptor.

Extensive studies by Seeman *et al.*[104] (1985) on a large number of DA agonists and antagonists, and their ability to displace the binding of [³H]spiperone to D-2 receptors has led to a refinement in the model first postulated in 1980. The main features of this tetrahedral model (Figure 9) are: (i) two

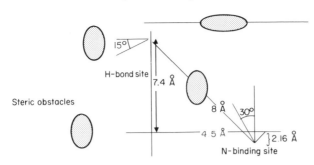

Figure 9 Topographical model for DA receptors:[65] Seeman's model (1985)

binding sites for hydrogen bonds with the *m*-OH and the nitrogen, the extremities of which are separated by 8 Å; (ii) hydrogen-bonding receptor groups which are directed between 15° and 30° orthogonal to the surface of the receptor; and (iii) a series of obstacles at 7, 10 and 1 o'clock, which account for the inactivity of certain analogues. The 'bottom' of the receptor and the 'back wall' are assumed to be hydrophobic surfaces. This model has many advantages, one of which is that it is able to explain the activity of the aminoindans.

Kaiser[4,5] has also been responsible for proposing various models of the DA receptor, beginning in 1984 and the latest of which appeared in 1986. This model consists of nine possible binding sites (Figure 10), which together account for features of both the D-1 and D-2 receptors. The essential features of this model are: (i) an electronegative amine site complementary to the side chain nitrogen of the dopaminergic pharmacophore (*i.e.* the *m*-hydroxyphenethylamine unit); (ii) a site, M, complementary to the OH *meta* to the ethylamine chain; (iii) a site, N, interacting with the aromatic nitrogen of the pyrroethylamine pharmacophore of the dopaminergic ergot-like compounds; this primary nitrogen-binding site is located 2.0 Å away from a secondary binding site, P, for the *p*-OH group; (iv) accessory binding sites are proposed for (v) the aromatic ring of the pharmacophore (II_1); (vi) the 1-phenyl substituent of 3-benzazepines (II_2); and (vii) the benzo-fused A ring of aporphines (II_3). Additional sites which are tentatively suggested are: (viii) a lipophilic cavity in the area of steric intolerance, which maximally fits a properly 'downwards'-orientated *n*-propyl group; and (ix) a site in a properly oriented 'upward' direction that may accept lipophilic groups exceeding the size of an *n*-propyl substituent. Present in both D-1 and D-2 subtypes are sites (i), (ii), (iv) and (v). Sites (iii) and (viii) are related with D-2 activity, whereas (vi) and (ix) are present in D-1 receptors. Grol *et al.*[105] (1985) postulated two binding sites, *P* and *M* (Figure 11), complementary to the *p*-OH and *m*-OH

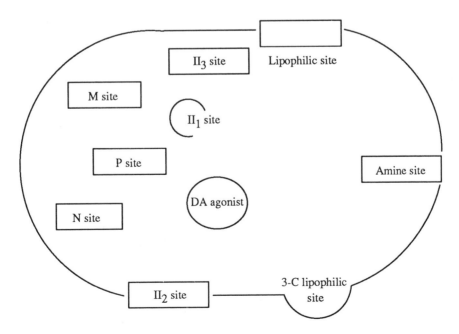

Figure 10 Topographical model for DA receptors:[65] Kaiser and Jain model (1986)

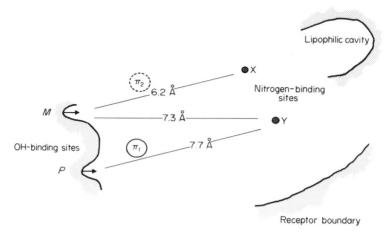

Figure 11   Topographical model for DA receptors:[65] Grol's model (1985)

groups of agonists; X and Y are putative electronegative-binding sites complementary to the nitrogen atom. These two sites are proposed to rationalize the activity of agonists in which the *m*-OH to N distance varies between 5.5 and 7.4 Å. This latter parameter accounts for the binding of α and β forms of DA analogues. π_1 is an interaction site for an aromatic ring and π_2 is an accessory site for the 1-aryl group of the 3-benzazepines.

Asselin *et al.*[80] (1986) have questioned the need to postulate two nitrogen-binding sites. They based their view on SAR studies of 3*H*-benz[*e*]indol-8-amines, and suggested that a phenolic hydroxyl group and a pyrrole ring can exert similar actions at the DA receptor, *i.e.* acting as H bond donors.

Recently, various authors have examined the stereochemical features of DA agonists from several chemical classes using NMR spectroscopy, molecular mechanics calculations (MMP2)[106-110] and molecular electrostatic potential (MEP) patterns.[111] Unfortunately, limitations of space prevent coverage of these topics in this chapter.

12.3.16   THE HISTORICAL BACKGROUND TO THE DEVELOPMENT OF CHLORPROMAZINE

The origins of the investigations which ultimately led to the development of chlorpromazine (CPZ) can be traced back to work on the structure of quinine and efforts to discover new antimalarial drugs. Full details of this process can be found in review articles by Zirkle[112] and Swazey.[113]

Quinine, a constituent of *Cinchona* bark, has been known to be active against malaria since the 1600s. This was due to the Jesuits, who obtained this knowledge from natives in Peru. In 1820, Pelletier and Caventou isolated quinine in a pure form and, by 1854, its empirical formula had been established by Strecker as being $C_{20}H_{24}N_2O_2$. Perkin, without even knowing the structure of the molecule, attempted in 1856 to 'synthesize' quinine by oxidizing alkyltoluidine, based on the following stoichiometry:

$$2C_{10}H_{13}N + 1\tfrac{1}{2}O_2 \rightarrow C_{20}H_{24}N_2O_2 + H_2O$$

Although this was quite useless as a synthesis, Perkin did discover that the oxidation of aniline produced the purple dye mauve. This led to the founding of the dye industry in the UK and then later in Germany. In connection with further research on dyes in Germany, Caro showed, in 1876, that heating dimethylaminoaniline with sulfur and oxidizing the product produced a new blue dye, methylene blue (**142**). In 1883, Bernthsen investigated the nature of this product and showed that the basic nucleus was the phenothiazine ring system. Working on the distribution of dyes in various animal organs, Ehrlich, in 1891, showed that methylene blue had antimalarial activity in humans.

As a result of many years work by various people, Rabe, 1911, was able to suggest the correct structure for quinine (**143**). This was not confirmed by total synthesis until 1944. During World War I, the Germans were cut off from their supplies of quinine and therefore set about synthesizing synthetic substitutes. Based on Ehrlich's observation that methylene blue had some activity against malaria in humans, Schulemann and coworkers prepared various analogues of this compound. As the structure of quinine was known with a reasonable degree of certainty, and due to the fact that it is essentially a heterocyclic ring system which contains a basic nitrogen atom in a second ring or 'side chain', this may have led Schulemann to prepare derivatives of methylene blue containing a basic side chain, the most active of which is shown in (144). It is of interest that this side chain also occurs in the phenothiazine derivative diethazine. Further work by Schulemann established the importance of the presence of aminoalkyl side chains in compounds having antimalarial activity.

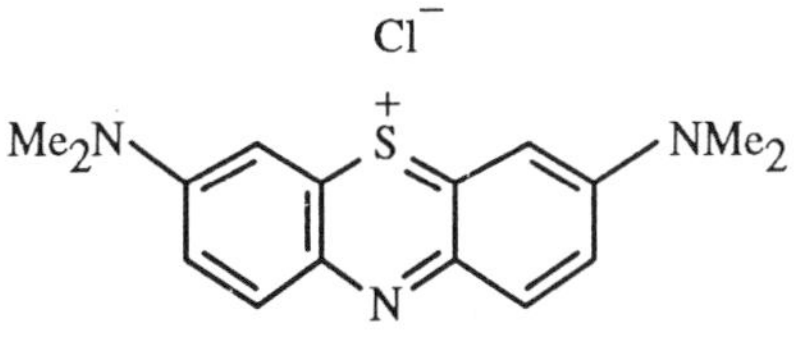

(142)

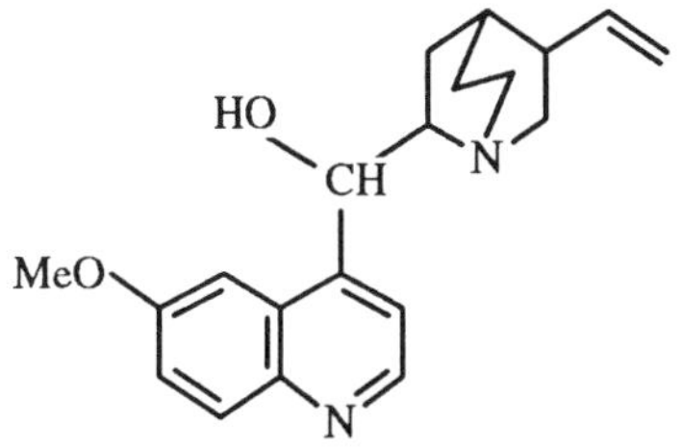

(143)

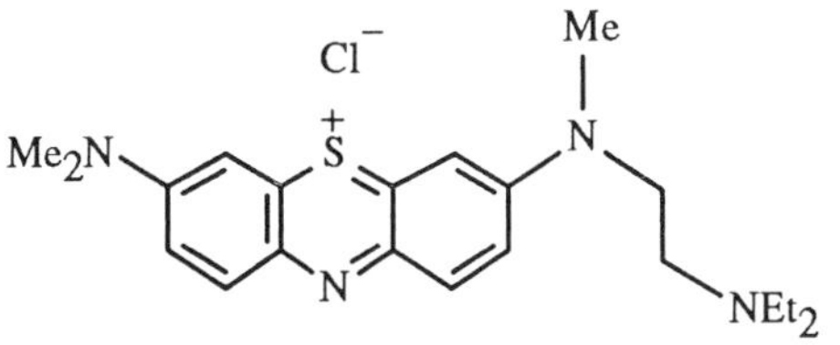

(144)

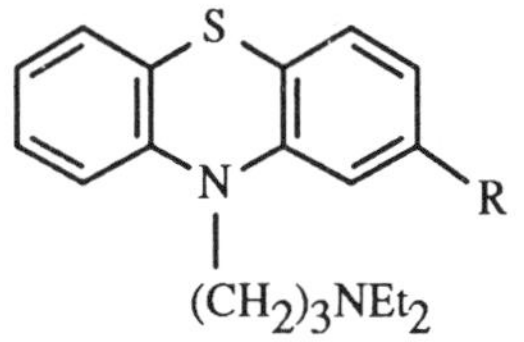

(145)

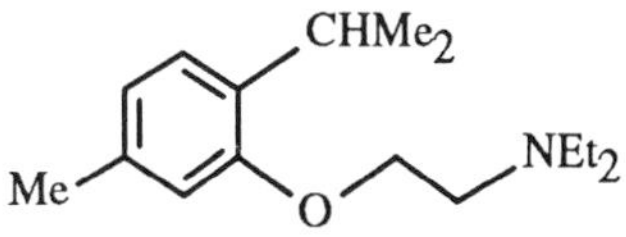

(146)

In 1944, during World War II, there was a further effort to find new antimalarials due to the Japanese cutting off the Allies' supply of quinine. In the USA, Gilman and Shirley prepared various derivatives of phenothiazine containing aminoalkyl side chains attached to the central N atom as possible antimalarials. However, these compounds were found to be essentially lacking in antimalarial activity. It is of interest that one of their derivatives (145; R = H) is very close to the compound chlorproethazine (145; R = Cl), which was shown some years later by workers at Rhône-Poulenc to be a muscle relaxant and tranquillizer.

Another aspect of the story occurred in 1933 when Fourneau at the Pasteur Institute began a search for adrenaline antagonists. As a result of screening many compounds, Fourneau found 929F (146) to be active in this respect. In fact, Fourneau had first made this compound in 1910 as part of a programme also aimed at finding new antimalarials.

As part of a study intended to find histamine antagonists, Bovet and Staubs showed in 1937, that 929F was also strikingly effective in protecting guinea pigs against the lethal effects of histamine. It was also active in blocking other histamine-induced effects.

Rhône-Poulenc was involved in synthesizing new antimalarials and they were also interested in Bovet's work at the Pasteur Institute on antihistamines. Work in this area by Rhône-Poulenc led to the development of 2339RP, which was named phenbenzamine (147). This proved to be effective in humans as an antihistamine. Due to the disruptions of World War II, workers at Rhône-Poulenc were not aware of Gilman and Shirley's negative results and Charpentier, influenced also by Ehrlich's findings with methylene blue, decided to prepare some aminoalkyl derivatives of phenothiazine similar to those prepared by Gilman and Shirley. It was also soon confirmed that they were inactive as antimalarials, but due to additional interest in antihistamines, they were also screened for this activity and certain compounds were found to be very potent. This was first shown in 1944, the same year that Gilman and Shirley reported their negative results.

Among the active compounds was 3015RP or fenethazine (148), which was found to have strong and long-lasting antihistaminic properties. On this basis, Charpentier synthesized other analogues, and one of the first seven to be tested, 3277RP or promethazine (149), surpassed even fenethazine in antihistaminic activity.

Four main properties of the antihistamines focussed Rhône-Poulenc's attention, and efforts in 1950 were made to develop other phenothiazine analogues, which had their main action on the CNS. (i) The most common side effect with the antihistamines was that they often led to sedation. (ii) In 1946, Bovet and coworkers showed that diethazine was a useful drug in treating Parkinson's disease. (iii) At the Merck Institute in the USA, Winter developed animal models for studying the CNS

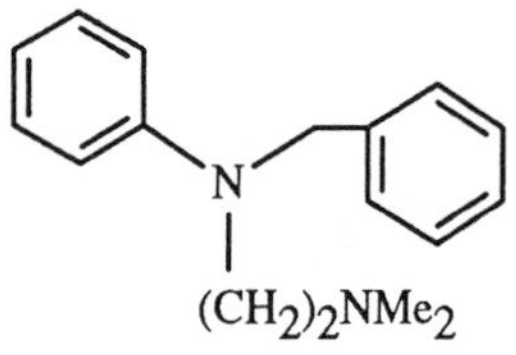

(147) 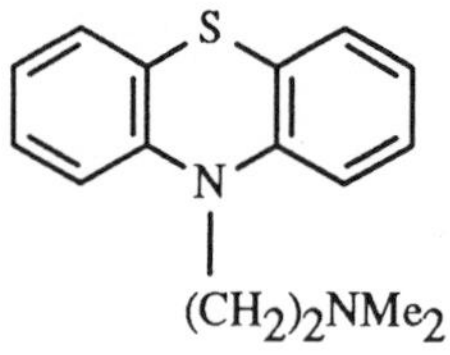 (148) 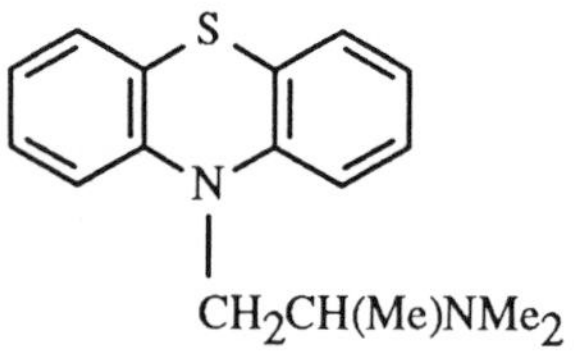 (149)

effects of the antihistamines. Two of these tests were the barbiturate sleeping time and rope-climbing ability in rats. Winter reported the results in 1948–1949. (iv) Laborit, a French surgeon, showed that some antihistamines could be used in clinical anaesthesia as potentiating agents.

Charpentier, the organic chemist, and Courvoisier, the pharmacologist, started their search for a phenothiazine derivative with more CNS activity in 1950. Courvoisier used three screening tests: (i) potentiation of general anaesthetics; (ii) potentiation of analgesics; and (iii) effects on conditioned reflex behaviour. Preliminary screening showed that 3276RP, later known as promazine (150), had the highest CNS activity among a group of compounds that Charpentier had first made in 1944. It is of interest that in their initial studies on the antihistamine activity of these compounds, 3276RP had been shown to have only weak activity and had been discarded, whilst the more potent compound promethazine (3277RP; 149) was investigated further.

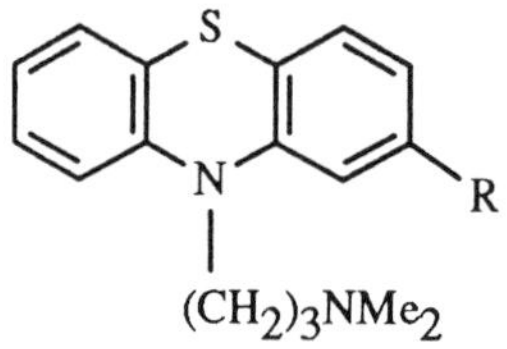

(150) R = H
(72) R = Cl

At the time promazine's CNS activity was identified, Charpentier had just synthesized 2-chlorophenothiazine. In view of the results with promazine, Charpentier decided to add the same side chain to 2-chlorophenothiazine to produce the compound 4560RP, later known as chlorpromazine (72). On December 11, 1950, it was sent to Courvoisier for pharmacological evaluation. Preliminary screening showed that it had exceptional activity, and further investigation resulted in its successful clinical use. In 1951–1952 in France it was shown to be useful as a major tranquillizer.

In conclusion, it can be seen that it is not really true to say that the development of chlorpromazine was 'an accident'. Rhône-Poulenc knew that the phenothiazine antihistamines had some CNS activity, and they simply attempted to optimize this by molecular manipulation. The importance of suitable screening tests in such work is obvious.

12.3.17 THE MODE OF ACTION OF THE NEUROLEPTICS

Currently, the most widely accepted theory of the mechanism of action of the neuroleptic drugs is that they bring about their antipsychotic effects by blockade of DA receptors in the CNS.[1,7,21,33,63,90] This, of course, is part of the so-called 'dopamine theory of schizophrenia', which has been succinctly stated as follows:[21] 'certain (but unknown) dopaminergic pathways are overactive in schizophrenia'. The evidence for this theory has been reviewed by several authors.[63,64]

Before the introduction of radioligand binding and PET scan studies, which have been able to provide direct evidence for the interaction of neuroleptics with DA receptors,[21] the evidence for DA receptor blockade was largely indirect and is summarized briefly below.

12.3.17.1 DA Turnover

As early as 1963, Carlsson and Lindqvist[114] showed that neuroleptics accelerated the turnover of catecholamines and implied that these compounds might block receptors for both NA and DA.

12.3.17.2 Neuroleptic Blockade of DA Mimetic Drugs

In 1965, it was shown by Ernst[115] that apomorphine directly stimulates DA receptors. Van Rossum[116] suggested in 1966 that as the neuroleptics were able to inhibit the effects of apomorphine and amphetamine (an indirect DA agonist), this probably occurred through blockade of DA receptors.

12.3.17.3 Neuroleptic-induced Catalepsy and Parkinsonism

Neuroleptics induce catalepsy in animals and Parkinsonian-like side effects in some patients.[1] Since it was known that Parkinson's disease was associated with a deficiency in DA levels in the brain, the above findings provided extra evidence for the involvement of DA receptors.

12.3.17.4 Blockade of the Neurophysiological Actions of DA

Iontophoresis experiments with DA have shown that it produces a prolonged IPSP, which can be inhibited by neuroleptics.[1]

12.3.17.5 Neuroleptic-induced Hyperprolactinaemia and Galactorrhoea

It is known that various DA analogues reduce the release of prolactin from pituitary cells. This effect can be blocked by various neuroleptics, which can result in hyperprolactinaemia and galactorrhoea.[1,3]

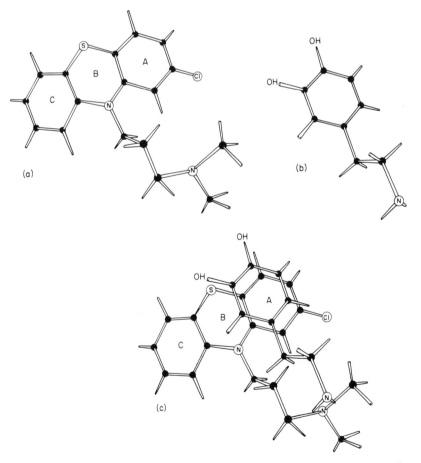

Figure 12 Molecular structures of (a) chlorpromazine and (b) dopamine as determined by X-ray crystallographic analysis. (c) Illustrates how dopamine may be superimposed on a portion of the chlorpromazine molecule. Such a model could account for the blockade of dopamine receptors by chlorpromazine[90]

12.3.17.6   Conformational Similarities Between DA and Certain Neuroleptics

In 1971, Horn and Snyder[90] pointed out certain similarities between the X-ray structures of DA and chlorpromazine, which could possibly account for the blockade of DA receptors (Figure 12). This initial suggestion was later elaborated on by other workers, *e.g.* Humber *et al.*,[117] who used butaclamol and apomorphine to reach similar conclusions.

12.3.17.7   Neuroleptic Binding *in Vivo* and Positron Emission Tomography (PET)

Using analogues of chlorpromazine, spiperone or raclopride containing either ^{11}C, ^{18}F or ^{76}Br atoms and *via* positron-emission tomography scanning, various groups have obtained the most direct *in vivo* evidence so far available for the binding of neuroleptics to DA receptors in the human brain.[118,119,140]

12.3.18   FUTURE PROSPECTS FOR THE DEVELOPMENT OF NOVEL ANTIPSYCHOTIC DRUGS

A number of recent review articles[120–122] have dealt extensively with the possibilities of finding new types of drugs to treat psychosis. These include the atypical antipsychotic agents such as fluperlapine (151) and setoperone (152), which are said to produce fewer extrapyramidal side effects, and various neuropeptides as well as miscellaneous agents.

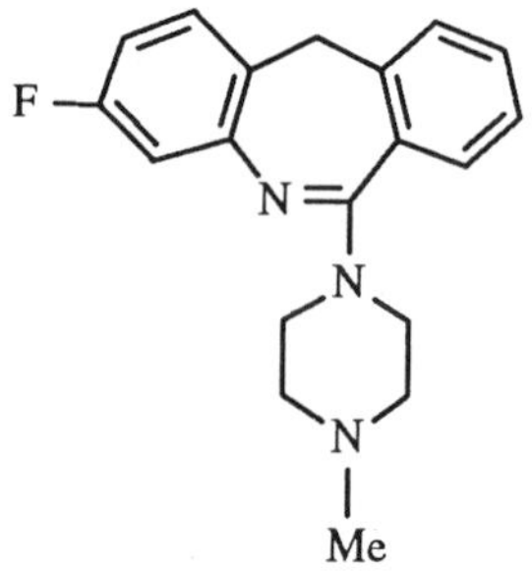

(151)

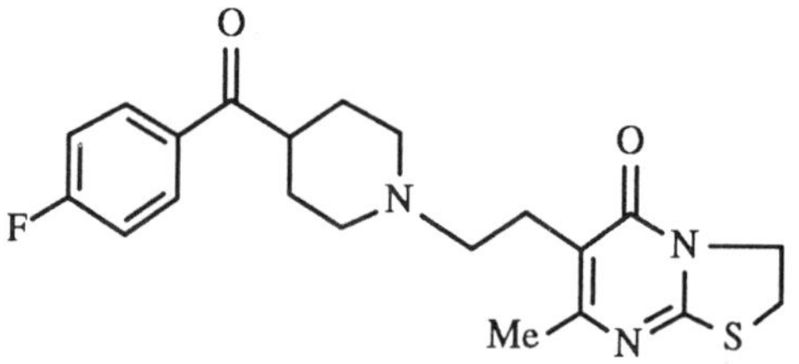

(152)

12.3.19   BIOLOGICAL PROPERTIES OF SELECTIVE DOPAMINERGIC AGONISTS AND ANTAGONISTS

12.3.19.1   Agonists

12.3.19.1.1   *Dopamine and L-DOPA (see Scheme 1)*

These were the first two compounds that were available to the earlier workers in the DA area. DA has the great disadvantage that it does not pass through the blood–brain barrier and studies with the neurotransmitter itself were largely restricted to intracranial injections to study effects on gross behaviour and iontophoretic application to investigate the neurophysiological properties of this amine. These studies have been reviewed by several authors.[1,123] DA itself is not a very 'pure' agonist as, in addition to dopaminergic actions, it produces effects on α and β receptors, depending on the dose administered.

L-DOPA was used in the early phase of interest in dopaminergic systems because it was able to pass into the brain. The report by Carlsson *et al.*[124] in 1957 that L-DOPA was able to reverse the hypokinetic action of reserpine in animals is one of the classical papers from this era. The neuropharmacological effects of L-DOPA in animals have been reviewed.[1]

In recent years, the use of the above two compounds in neurobiological research in the DA area has declined due to the development of more potent and selective agents.

12.3.19.1.2 *Apomorphine and* **N**-*propylnorapomorphine*

Apomorphine (**32**) is the DA agonist that is most widely used in dopaminergic research.[125,126] It was, in fact, the first semisynthetic DA agonist that was available to the pharmacologist. It has been shown to exert significant antiparkinsonian effects, but, due to its nephrotoxic actions, it is not in clinical use.

N-Propylnorapomorphine (NPA) is also quite often used in DA research, although much less than apomorphine. In a comparative study, it has been shown that NPA is several times more active than apomorphine in a number of test systems.[127] Both compounds are D-1/D-2 agonists.[128] The four stereoisomers of these two compounds (*i.e.* the two (*R*) and (*S*) pairs) have been tested for their stereoselectivity for D-1 and D-2 receptors *in vitro*. It was found that (*S*)-(+)-apomorphine acted as an antagonist at both these receptor types, whilst the other three isomers were agonists.[128]

12.3.19.1.3 *Bromocriptine*

Bromocriptine (**35**) predominantly stimulates D-2 receptors but it is a mixed 'agonist–antagonist' at these receptors.[129] Unlike some other DA agonists, it does not differentiate between low and high affinity binding states of the D-2 receptor. It also exhibits the properties of a mixed 'agonist–antagonist' at presynaptic DA receptors.

It is known that the antiparkinsonian activity of bromocriptine is diminished by pretreatment with the synthesis inhibitor α-MPT. This suggests that some intact nigrostriatal neurons are required in order to observe a therapeutic response. Bromocriptine also interacts with serotonin and adrenergic receptors.

12.3.19.1.4 *SKF-38393 (55)*

This compound was the first example of an agonist that was able to clearly differentiate between D-1 and D-2 receptors, being selective for the former type.[66,130] It exhibits activity in both the peripheral and central nervous systems. In the periphery, it produces dilation of the vasculature such as the renal and mesenteric beds. SKF-38393 activates the D-1 cyclase ($EC_{50} = 0.07\ \mu M$) and produces contralateral rotation in 6-OH-DA-lesioned rats. It does not produce the typical pattern of stereotypy seen with apomorphine. It does, however, induce increased grooming behaviour.

12.3.19.1.5 *LY141865*

The partial ergoline analogue, LY141865, has been shown to selectively stimulate the D-2 receptor. In addition, it is also able to discriminate between the DA_2 and the DA_1 receptors in the cardiovascular system. The fact that LY141865 and LY171555 (**45a**), the (−) enantiomer of LY141865, are able to selectively stimulate peripheral presynaptic DA receptors, *i.e.* the DA_2 type, suggests that the D-2 and the DA_2 receptors may be the same or very similar in nature.[130]

12.3.19.1.6 *N-0500, PHNO (30)*

This compound was the first representative of a new type of DA agonist—the hexahydro-naphthoxazines—and has been shown by two groups of researchers to be a very potent and selective D-2 agonist, with a low affinity for various other receptors.[77,78] Initial clinical results for the treatment of Parkinson's disease were promising.[79]

12.3.19.1.7 *N-0437 (17)*

N-0437, like N-0500, is a very potent and selective D-2 agonist with little affinity for various other receptors.[30,35] Studies with [^{3}H]-N-0437 have shown that it is very useful for autoradiographic studies on the distribution of D-2 receptors in the CNS. The compound is being evaluated in humans for its antiparkinsonian activity.

12.3.19.1.8   Lisuride (36)

This compound was used originally as a prophylactic agent to treat migraine. It stimulates pre- and post-synaptic DA receptors. It is an agonist at 5-HT receptors and it blocks NA receptors in the CNS.[131]

12.3.19.1.9   3-PPP (5)

Due to the fact that this compound was the first clear-cut example of a DA agonist with autoreceptor selectivity, more is known about its properties than any other compound of a similar type. (+)-3-PPP has many of the properties of a classical direct-acting dopaminergic agonist, *i.e.* it stimulates both DA autoreceptors and postsynaptic DA receptors. In addition, in certain test models, it appears to exhibit partial agonist activity. (−)-3-PPP produces more varied effects. Depending on the anatomical location of the DA receptors and the experimental conditions, it produces agonistic and/or antagonistic activities. The work to date has been extensively reviewed.[68]

12.3.19.2   Antagonists

12.3.19.2.1   Chlorpromazine (72)

This compound is a nonselective blocker of both D-1 and D-2 receptors.[21] It also has anticholinergic, antihistaminic and antiadrenergic properties. Clearly, it is not the experimental pharmacologist's first choice when a selective neuroleptic is required.[132]

12.3.19.2.2   Haloperidol (101)

This drug has a similar pharmacological profile to the phenothiazines, in particular those of the piperazine class. It has little anticholinergic activity and is less potent than chlorpromazine as an adrenergic antagonist.[91,132]

12.3.19.2.3   Sulpiride (121)

The main academic interest in sulpiride lies in the fact that (−)-sulpiride is a D-2 receptor antagonist,[130] which also has, according to some authors, a selectivity for presynaptic DA receptors.

12.3.19.2.4   SCH23390 (130)

As mentioned in a previous section, the main interest in SCH23390 is the fact that it is a selective D-1 antagonist.[43] Efforts to study it clinically have been hindered by bioavailability problems.

12.3.19.2.5   YM-09151-2 (127)

This compound has the distinction of being the most potent and selective D-2 antagonist currently available.[133]

12.3.19.2.6   Pimozide (115b)

This drug has a neuroleptic profile that is more akin to haloperidol than chlorpromazine. In comparison with other neuroleptics, it is slower in onset but has a longer duration of action. Its effects on the noradrenergic system are minimal. No significant changes in cardiovascular haemodynamics have been reported in animal experiments.[134]

12.3.20 PROPERTIES OF DOPAMINE AGONISTS AND ANTAGONISTS USED IN THERAPY

One of the best sources of general and detailed information on drugs used in therapy is *Martindale—The Extra Pharmacopoeia*, to which the reader is referred for further information.

12.3.20.1 Agonists

12.3.20.1.1 *L-DOPA (see Scheme 1)*

Currently, this is the most effective therapy for Parkinson's disease.[135] Unlike DA, it is able to pass through the blood–brain barrier. The oral dose begins around 300 mg–1 g, and this is then increased by steps of 100–500 mg over a period, to a maximum dose of 4–6 g per day. By combining L-DOPA with a peripheral decarboxylase inhibitor, such as benserazide or carbidopa, it is possible to lower the dose to a quarter of that mentioned above.

Side effects include intestinal disturbances, orthostatic hypotension and psychiatric problems. Extended use of the drug can lead to the so-called 'on–off' syndrome, *i.e.* alternating periods of mobility and hypokinesia.

12.3.20.1.2 *Bromocriptine mesylate (35)*

This drug was originally developed for the treatment of hyperprolactinaemia, rather than Parkinson's disease. Oral doses for the treatment of the latter disease begin at 1–25 mg once or twice a day, followed by an increase every two days of 2–5 mg per day, to a maximum dose of 20–40 mg per day. Side effects are similar to these occurring with L-DOPA.[129]

12.3.20.1.3 *Lisuride maleate (36)*

This drug has a similar area of application to that of bromocriptine. At the moment, it is still in an experimental stage regarding its application in Parkinson's disease. Doses in the range of 1.2–5 mg per day have been investigated in this disease.[135]

12.3.20.1.4 *Fenoldopam (SKF 82526) (56)*

This compound, a selective peripheral DA_1 agonist, has already been mentioned in Section 12.3.11.14. Although this drug is not routinely used in the clinic, it is the most promising agonist of the 3-benzazepine group that has so far been developed.[29] It has been shown to be free of α, β or DA_2 receptor effects at therapeutic concentrations. It reduces blood pressure by lowering peripheral vascular resistance.[141]

12.3.20.2 Antagonists

12.3.20.2.1 *Chlorpromazine·HCl (72)*

The dose range in psychiatric cases is 75 to 800 mg daily, in divided doses. As an antiemetic, 25 to 50 mg orally. The side effects that may be encountered with this drug include drowsiness, dryness of the mouth, postural hypotension, tachycardia, photosensitivity and skin rashes.

12.3.20.2.2 *Fluphenazine·HCl (75b)*

For the treatment of psychosis, up to 15 mg daily in divided doses is prescribed. For anxiety states, 1–2 mg daily is used. The side effects encountered are similar to those seen for chlorpromazine. As fluphenazine is a piperazine derivative, extrapyramidal symptoms are particularly likely to occur. Sedation and hypotension occur less frequently than with chlorpromazine.

12.3.20.2.3 Thioridazine · HCl (74a)

The normal dose range for schizophrenia is 30 to 600 mg daily, in divided doses. The toxic effects are similar to those described for chlorpromazine. Thioridazine has the advantage that it produces less sedation than chlorpromazine and extrapyramidal disorders are rare.

12.3.20.2.4 Haloperidol (101)

Doses for psychosis range from 3–9 mg daily, in divided doses (Martindale), to 1–100 mg daily according to the USP. Extrapyramidal side effects including akathisia and dystonic reactions occur frequently and are apparently dose related.

12.3.20.2.5 Pimozide (115b)

The normal dose range is 2–10 mg daily. It is effective in treating the hallucinations, delusions and inertia occurring during schizophrenic episodes, without causing drowsiness. It is apparently not effective in mania or psychomotor overactivity.

12.3.20.2.6 Sulpiride (121)

This compound is classed as an atypical neuroleptic. In comparison with conventional neuroleptics, it provokes fewer acute dyskinetic syndromes at antipsychotic doses. However, following high dose administration, extrapyramidal syndromes can be encountered. All dose levels can provoke amenorrhoea or galactorrhoea due to hyperprolactinaemia. The dose is normally 200 mg per day, and this can be increased after three days to 200 mg 3–4 times a day.

12.3.21 REFERENCES

1. A. S. Horn, J. Korf and B. H. C. Westerink (eds.), 'The Neurobiology of Dopamine', Academic Press, London, 1979.
2. I. Creese and C. M. Fraser (eds.), 'Dopamine Receptors', Liss, New York, 1987.
3. W. Winlow and R. Markstein (eds.), 'The Neurobiology of Dopamine Systems', Manchester University Press, Manchester, 1986.
4. C. Kaiser and J. W. Kebabian, *ACS Symp. Ser.*, 1983, **24**.
5. C. Kaiser and T. Jain, *Med. Res. Rev.*, 1985, **5**, 145.
6. J. G. Cannon, in 'Drug Research', ed. E. Jucker, Birkhäuser, Basel, 1985, vol. 29, p. 303.
7. C. Kaiser and P. E. Setler, in 'Burger's Medicinal Chemistry', ed. M. E. Wolff, Wiley-Interscience, New York, 1981, Part III, 4th edn., p. 859.
8. A. Carlsson and J. L. G. Nilsson (eds.), 'Dopamine Receptor Agonists', Swedish Pharmaceutical Press, Stockholm, 1983, vols. 1 and 2.
9. A. Carlsson, in 'Pre and Postsynaptic Receptors', ed. E. Usdin and W. E. Bunney, Dekker, New York, 1975, p. 49.
10. B. H. C. Westerink, *Neurochem. Int.*, 1985, **7**, 221.
11. J. J. Warsh, A. S. Chiu and D. D. Godse, in 'Analysis of Biogenic Amines', ed. G. Baker and R. Coutts, Elsevier, Amsterdam, 1982, part A, p. 203.
12. A. R. Cools and J. M. van Rossum, *Psychopharmacology (Berlin)*, 1976, **45**, 243.
13. J. C. van Oene and A. S. Horn, *J. Pharm. Pharmacol.*, 1985, **37**, 844.
14. W. Kehr, A. Carlsson, M. Lindqvist, T. Magnusson and C. Atack, *J. Pharm. Pharmacol.*, 1972, **24**, 144.
15. (a) R. H. Roth, *Commun. Psychopharmacol.*, 1979, **3**, 429; (b) R. H. Roth, in 'Dopaminergic Systems and their Regulation', ed. G. Woodruff, Macmillan, London, 1986.
16. L. R. Skirboll, A. A. Grace and B. S. Bunney, *Science (Washington, D.C.)*, 1979, **206**, 80.
17. J. W. Kebabian and D. B. Calne, *Nature (London)*, 1979, **277**, 93.
18. P. Onali, M. C. Olianas and G. L. Gessa, *Eur. J. Pharmacol.*, 1984, **99**, 127.
19. M. Pizza, F. D.'Agostini, M. Da Prada, P. F. Spano and W. E. Haefely, *Eur. J. Pharmacol.*, 1987, **136**, 263.
20. P. Seeman, M. Wong and J. Tedesco, *Soc. Neurosci. Abstr.*, 1975, **1**, 405.
21. P. Seeman, *Pharmacol. Rev.*, 1980, **32**, 229.
22. I. Creese, D. R. Sibley, M. M. Hamblin and S. E. Leff, *Annu. Rev. Neurosci.*, 1983, **6**, 43.
23. A. S. Horn, in 'Trends in Medicinal Chemistry', ed. E. Mutschler and E. Winterfeldt, VCH, Weinheim, 1987, p. 243.
24. S. Urwyler and R. Markstein, *J. Neurochem.*, 1986, **46**, 1058.
25. L. I. Goldberg, P. H. Volkman and J. D. Kohli, *Annu. Rev. Pharmacol. Toxicol.*, 1978, **18**, 57.
26. A. Hilditch and G. M. Drew, *Trends Pharmacol. Sci.*, 1985, **6**, 396.
27. I. Cavero, R. Massingham and F. Lefevre-Borg, *Life Sci.*, 1982, **31**, 939.
28. I. Cavero, R. Massingham and F. Lefevre-Borg, *Life Sci.*, 1982, **31**, 1059.
29. J. P. Hieble, *Annu. Rep. Med. Chem.*, 1987, **22**, 107.

30. J. van der Weide, J. B. de Vries, P. G. Tepper and A. S. Horn, *Eur. J. Pharmacol.*, 1987, **134**, 211.
31. M. Williams and D. C. U'Prichard, *Annu. Rep. Med. Chem.*, 1984, **19**, 283.
32. J. M. Palacios and J. K. Wamsley, in 'Handbook of Chemical Neuroanatomy', ed. A. Björklund, T. Hökfelt and M. Kuhar, Elsevier, New York, 1984, vol. 3, p. 325.
33. L. L. Iversen, *Science (Washington, D.C.)*, 1975, **188**, 1084.
34. G. Di Chiara, M. L. Porcedda, W. Fratta and G. L. Gessa, *Nature (London)*, 1977, **267**, 270.
35. J. van der Weide, J. B. de Vries, P. G. Tepper and A. S. Horn, *Eur. J. Pharmacol.*, 1986, **125**, 273.
36. P. G. Guyenet, Y. Agid, F. Javoy, J. C. Beaujouan, J. Rossier and J. Glowinski, *Brain Res.*, 1975, **84**, 227.
37. P. C. Waldmeier, *Eur. J. Pharmacol.*, 1983, **90**, 115.
38. J. F. van der Werf, J. B. Sebens, W. Vaalburg and J. Korf, *Eur. J. Pharmacol.*, 1983, **87**, 259.
39. M. G. P. Feenstra, H. Rollema, T. B. A. Mulder, B. H. C. Westerink and A. S. Horn, *Life Sci.*, 1983, **32**, 1313.
40. A. S. Horn, J. B. de Vries, D. Dijkstra and A. H. Mulder, *Eur. J. Pharmacol.*, 1982, **83**, 35.
41. J. W. Langston and I. Irwin, *Clin. Neuropharmacol.*, 1986, **9**, 485.
42. M. Nomoto, P. Jenner and C. D. Marsden, *Neurosci. Lett.*, 1985, **57**, 37.
43. A. Barnett, *Drugs of the Future*, 1986, **11**, 49.
44. J. L. Waddington, *Biochem. Pharmacol.*, 1986, **35**, 3661.
45. A. R. Braun, P. Barone and T. N. Chase, in 'Neurobiology of Central D_1-Dopamine Receptors', ed. G. R. Breese and I. Creese, Plenum Press, New York, 1986, p. 151.
46. J. R. Walters, D. A. Bergstrom, J. H. Carlson, T. N. Chase and A. R. Braun, *Science (Washington, D.C.)*, 1987, **236**, 719.
47. G. S. Robertson and H. A. Robertson, *Trends Pharmacol. Sci.*, 1987, **8**, 295.
48. M. F. Lokhandwaka and R. J. Barrett, *J. Auton. Pharmacol.*, 1982, **3**, 189.
49. J. P. Changeux, A. Devillers-Thierry and P. Chemouilli, *Science (Washington, D.C.)*, 1984, **225**, 1335.
50. H. G. Dohlman, M. G. Caron and R. J. Lefkowitz, *Biochemistry*, 1987, **26**, 2657.
51. S. E. Senogles, N. Amlaiky, A. L. Johnson and M. G. Caron, *Biochemistry*, 1986, **25**, 749.
52. J. Ramwani and R. K. Mishra, *J. Biol. Chem.*, 1986, **261**, 8894.
53. F. J. Bosker, F. J. van Bussel, A. P. G. M. Thielen, Y. L. Soei, G. T. Sieswerda, J. Dijk, P. G. Tepper, A. S. Horn and W. Möller, *Eur. J. Pharmacol.*, 1989, **13**, 319.
54. J. S. Fedan, G. K. Hogaboom and J. P. O'Donnell, *Biochem. Pharmacol.*, 1984, **33**, 1167.
55. N. Amlaiky and M. G. Caron, *J. Neurochem.*, 1986, **47**, 196.
56 P. Seeman and H. B. Niznik, *Eur. J. Pharmacol.*, 1986, **127**, 297.
57. J. Y. Lew, E. Meller and M. Goldstein, *Eur. J. Pharmacol.*, 1985, **113**, 145.
58. K. Redouane, P. Sokoloff, J. C. Schwartz, A. Hamdi, A. Mann, C. G. Wermuth, J. Roy and J. L. Morgat, *Biochem. Biophys. Res. Commun.*, 1985, **130**, 1086.
59. J. L. Neumeyer, J. H. Guan, H. B. Niznik, A. Dumbrille-Ross, P. Seeman, S. Padmanablan and D. R. Elmaleh, *J. Med. Chem.*, 1985, **28**, 405.
60. O. Gredal and M. Nielsen, *J. Neurochem.*, 1987, **48**, 364.
61. O. Gredal and M. Nielsen, *J. Neurochem.*, 1987, **48**, 370.
62. R. Duvoisin, *Pharmacol. Ther.*, 1987, **32**, 1.
63. H. Y. Meltzer, *Schizophr. Bull.*, 1980, **6**, 456.
64. T. J. Crow, E. C. Johnstone, J. F. W. Deakin and A. Longden, *Lancet*, 1976, **II**, 563.
65. H. E. Katerinopoulos and D. I. Schuster, *Drugs of the Future*, 1987, **12**, 223.
66. J. Weinstock, J. P. Hieble and J. W. Wilson, III, *Drugs of the Future*, 1985, **10**, 645.
67. U. Hacksell, L. E. Arvidsson, U. Svensson, J. L. G. Nilsson, D. Sanchez, H. Wikström, P. Lindberg, S. Hjorth and A. Carlsson, *J. Med. Chem.*, 1981, **24**, 1475.
68. D. Clark, S. Hjorth and A. Carlsson, *J. Neural Transm.*, 1985, **62**, 1, 171.
69. M. Pinder, D. A. Buxton and D. M. Green, *J. Pharm. Pharmacol.*, 1971, **23**, 995.
70. R. I. Thrift, *J. Chem. Soc. C*, 1967, 288.
71. G. N. Woodruff, A. O. Elkhawad and R. M. Pinder, *Eur. J. Pharmacol.*, 1974, **25**, 80.
72. J. G. Cannon, J. C. Kim, M. A. Aleem and J. P. Long, *J. Med. Chem.*, 1972, **15**, 348.
73. J. D. McDermed, G. M. McKenzie and A. P. Philips, *J. Med. Chem.*, 1975, **18**, 362.
74. A. S. Horn, H. Griever-Kazemier and D. Dijkstra, *J. Med. Chem.*, 1982, **25**, 993.
75. T. B. A. Mulder, C. J. Grol, D. Dijkstra and A. S. Horn, *Eur. J. Pharmacol.*, 1985, **112**, 73.
76. A. S. Horn, B. Kaptein, N. A. Vermue, J. B. de Vries and T. B. A. Mulder, *Eur. J. Med. Chem.*, 1987, **23**, 325.
77. J. H. Jones, P. S. Anderson, J. J. Baldwin, B. V. Clineschmidt, D. E. McClure, G. E. Lundell, W. C. Randall, G. Martin, M. Williams, J. M. Hirschfield, G. Smith and P. K. Lumma, *J. Med. Chem.*, 1984, **27**, 1607.
78. D. Dijkstra, B. Hazelhoff, T. B. A. Mulder, J. B. de Vries, H. Wijnberg and A. S. Horn, *Eur. J. Med. Chem.*, 1985, **20**, 247.
79. A. Jon Stoessel, E. Mak and D. B. Calne, *Lancet*, 1985, **II**, 1330.
80. A. A. Asselin, L. G. Humber, K. Voith and G. Metcalf, *J. Med. Chem.*, 1986, **29**, 654.
81. N. E. Anden, H. Nilsson, E. Ros and U. Thornström, *Acta Pharmacol. Toxicol.*, 1983, **52**, 51.
82. J. Mierau, Boehringer Ingelheim, personal communication.
83. C. S. Schneider and J. Mierau, *J. Med. Chem.*, 1987, **30**, 494.
84. J. Moragues, J. Prieto, R. G. W. Spickett, A. Vega, W. Zalazar and D. J. Roberts, *Farmaco, Ed. Sci.*, 1980, **35**, 951.
85. A. Hamada, Y. A. Chang, N. Uretsky and D. D. Miller, *J. Med. Chem.*, 1984, **27**, 675.
86. Y. A. Chang, J. Ares, K. Anderson, B. Sabol, R. A. Wallace, T. Farooqui, N. Uretsky and D. D. Miller, *J. Med. Chem.*, 1987, **30**, 214.
87. D. Dijkstra, T. B. A. Mulder, H. Rollema, P. G. Tepper, J. van der Weide and A. S. Horn, *J. Med. Chem.*, 1988, **31**, 2178.
88. M. W. Harrold, Y. A. Chang, R. A. Wallace, T. Farooqui, L. J. Wallace, N. Uretsky and D. D. Miller, *J. Med. Chem.*, 1987, **30**, 1631.
89. E. Schenker and H. Herbst, in 'Progress in Drug Research', ed. E. Jucker, Birkhauser, Basel, 1963, vol. 5, p. 269.
90. A. S. Horn and S. H. Snyder, *Proc. Natl. Acad. Sci. U.S.A.*, 1971, **68**, 2325.
91. P. A. Janssen, in 'Industrial Encyclopedia of Pharmacology and Therapeutics', ed. C. J. Cavalito, Pergamon Press, New York, 1973, vol. 1, section 5, p. 37.

92. T. de Paulis, in 'Proceedings of the VIIIth International Symposium on Medicinal Chemistry', ed. R. Dahlbom and J. L. G. Nilsson, Swedish Pharmaceutical Press, Stockholm, 1985, vol. 1, p. 405.
93. D. F. Smith (ed.), 'Handbook of Stereoisomers of Drugs in Psychopharmacology', CRC Press, Boca Raton, FL, 1984.
94. J. D. McDermed, H. S. Freeman and R. M. Erris, in 'Catecholamines: Basic and Clinical Frontiers', ed. E. Usdin, I. J. Kopin and J. Barchas, Pergamon Press, New York, 1979, vol. 1, p. 568.
95. (a) A. S. Horn and J. R. Rodgers, *J. Pharm. Pharmacol.*, 1980, **32**, 521; (b) R. Bergin and D. Carlström, *Acta Crystallogr., Sect. B*, 1968, **24**, 1506.
96. B. Costall, S. K. Lim, R. J. Naylor and J. G. Cannon, *J. Pharm. Pharmacol.*, 1982, **34**, 246.
97. Y. C. Martin, 'Quantitative Drug Design', Dekker, New York, 1978, p. 365.
98. H. Sheppard and C. R. Burghardt, *Mol. Pharmacol.*, 1974, **10**, 721.
99. P. C. Dandiya, H. L. Sharma, S. K. Patni and R. S. Gambhir, *Experientia*, 1975, **31**, 1441.
100. C. J. Grol and H. Rollema, *J. Pharm. Pharmacol.*, 1977, **29**, 153.
101. L. I. Goldberg, J. D. Kohli, A. N. Kotake and P. H. Volkman, *Fed. Proc., Fed. Am. Soc. Exp. Biol.*, 1978, **37**, 2396.
102. M. P. Seiler and R. Markstein, *Mol. Pharmacol.*, 1982, **22**, 281.
103. H. Wikström, B. Andersson, D. Sanchez, P. Lindberg, L. E. Arvidsson, A. M. Johansson, J. L. G. Nilsson, K. Svensson, S. Hjorth and A. Carlsson, *J. Med. Chem.*, 1985, **28**, 215; H. Wikstrom, *Thesis*, University of Uppsala, 1983.
104. P. Seeman, M. Watanabe, D. Grigoriadis, J. L. Tedesco, S. R. George, U. Svensson, J. L. G. Nilsson and J. L. Neumeyer, *Mol. Pharmacol.*, 1985, **28**, 391.
105. C. J. Grol, L. J. Jansen and H. Rollema, *J. Med. Chem.*, 1985, **28**, 679.
106. H. Wikström, J. H. Lii and N. L. Allinger, *J. Med. Chem.*, 1987, **30**, 1928.
107. A. M. Johansson, A. Karlen, C. J. Grol, S. Sundell, L. Kenne and U. Hacksell, *Mol. Pharmacol.*, 1986, **30**, 258.
108. A. Karlen, A. M. Johansson, L. Kenne, L. E. Arvidsson and U. Hacksell, *J. Med. Chem.*, 1986, **29**, 917.
109. M. Froimowitz, J. L. Neumeyer and R. J. Baldessarini, *J. Med. Chem.*, 1986, **29**, 1570.
110. M. Froimowitz and R. J. Baldessarini, *J. Pharm. Sci.*, 1987, **76**, 557.
111. D. Kocjan, M. Hodoscek and D. Hadzi, *J. Med. Chem.*, 1986, **29**, 1418.
112. C. L. Zirkle, in 'How Modern Medicines are Discovered', ed. F. H. Clarke, Future, New York, 1973, p. 55.
113. J. P. Swazey, 'Chlorpromazine in Psychiatry', MIT Press, Cambridge, MA, 1974.
114. A. Carlsson and M. Lindqvist, *Acta Pharmacol. Toxicol.*, 1963, **20**, 140.
115. A. M. Ernst, *Psychopharmacology (Berlin)*, 1965, **7**, 391.
116. J. M. van Rossum, *Arch. Int. Pharmacodyn. Ther.*, 1966, **160**, 492.
117. L. G. Humber, F. Bruderlein and K. Voith, *Mol. Pharmacol.*, 1975, **11**, 833.
118. J. J. Frost, *Trends Pharmacol. Sci.*, 1986, **7**, 490.
119. D. F. Wong, H. N. Wagner, Jr., L. E. Tune, R. F. Dannals, G. D. Pearlson, J. M. Links, C. A. Tamminga, E. P. Broussolle, H. T. Ravert, A. A. Wilsson, J. K. Thomas, T. J. Malat, J. A. Williams, L. A. O'Tuama, S. H. Snyder, M. J. Kuhar and A. Gjedde, *Science (Washington, D.C)*, 1986, **234**, 1558.
120. J. S. de Graaf and R. M. Pinder, in 'Handbook of Studies on Schizophrenia', ed. G. Burrows, T. Norman and G. Rubinstein, Elsevier, Amsterdam, 1986, p. 47.
121. M. L. Cornfeldt and G. M. Shutske, *Drug Dev. Res.*, 1986, **9**, 1.
122. F. J. Vinick and M. R. Kozlowski, *Annu. Rep. Med. Chem.*, 1986, **2**, 1.
123. O. Hornykiewicz, *Pharmacol. Rev.*, 1960, **18**, 925.
124. A. Carlsson, M. L. Lindqvist and T. Magnusson, *Nature (London)*, 1957, **180**, 1200.
125. T. L. Sourkes and S. Lal, *Adv. Neurochem.*, 1975, **1**, 247.
126. G. Di Chiara and G. L. Gessa, *Adv. Pharmacol. Chemother.*, 1978, **15**, 88.
127. M. K. Menon, W. G. Clark and J. L. Neumeyer, *Eur. J. Pharmacol.*, 1978, **52**, 1.
128. M. E. Goldman and J. W. Kebabian, *Mol. Pharmacol.*, 1984, **25**, 18.
129. A. N. Lieberman and M. Goldstein, *Pharmacol. Rev.*, 1985, **37**, 217.
130. J. C. Stoof and J. W. Kebabian, *Life Sci.*, 1984, **35**, 2281.
131. W. Kehr, *Eur. J. Pharmacol.*, 1977, **41**, 261.
132. C. J. E. Niemeyer and P. A. J. Janssen, *Life Sci.*, 1979, **24**, 2201.
133. H. B. Niznik, D. E. Grigoriadis, I. Pri-Bar, O. Buchman and P. Seeman, *Naunyn-Schmiedeberg's Arch. Pharmacol.*, 1985, **329**, 333.
134. P. A. J. Janssen and J. P. Tollenaere, in 'Chronicles of Drug Discovery', ed. J. S. Bindra and D. Lednicer, Wiley-Interscience, New York, 1983, vol. 2, p. 33.
135. N. P. Quinn, *Drugs*, 1984, **28**, 236.
136. B. H. C. Westerink, G. Damsma, H. Rollema, J. B. de Vries and A. S. Horn, *Life Sci.*, 1987, **41**, 1763.
137. O. E. Brodde, *Life Sci.*, 1982, **31**, 289.
138. I. R. Youde, M. J. Raxworthy, P. A. Gulliver, D. Dijkstra and A. S. Horn, *J. Pharm. Pharmacol.*, 1984, **36**, 309.
139. P. Seeman and H. C. Guan, *Mol. Pharmacol.*, 1987, **32**, 760.
140. L. Farde, F. A. Wiesel, C. Halldin and G. Sedvall, *Arch. Gen. Psychiatry*, 1988, **45**, 71.
141. R. Carey, R. Stone, J. Dubb, L. Townsend, C. Rose and D. Kaiser, *J. Clin. Invest.*, 1984, **74**, 2198.
142. J. Bunzow, H. van Tol, D. Grandy, P. Albert, J. Saľom, M. Christie, C. Machida, K. Neve and O. Civelli, *Nature (London)*, 1989, **336**, 783.
143. J. A. Temlett, P. N. Chong, W. H. Oertel, P. Jenner and C. D. Marsden, *Eur. J. Pharmacol.*, 1988, **156**, 197.
144. M. Beaulieu, Y. Itoh, P. Tepper, A. S. Horn and J. W. Kebabian, *Eur. J. Pharmacol.*, 1984, **105**, 15.

12.4
Peripheral Dopamine Receptors

FRANCIS INCE

Fisons Pharmaceutical Division, Loughborough, UK

12.4.1 INTRODUCTION

The pharmacological and physiological properties of dopamine (DA; **1**) have been extensively studied over the last 70 years. Following its synthesis in 1910, it was classed as a sympathomimetic amine, as only its adrenergic properties were recognized. Subsequently it was proposed that DA was an intermediate in the biosynthesis of adrenaline and noradrenaline from L-tyrosine and, following its identification in a variety of neuronal tissues, it was also suggested that it was a neurotransmitter in its own right. A number of the properties of DA could be rationalized if it was assumed that specific DA receptors existed; thus, prior to 1970, the peripheral actions of DA were explained in terms of the established groups of adrenergic receptors and a population of DA receptors. DA receptor systems have been subjected to increasing scrutiny, and a number of observations, initially with central, but also with peripheral DA receptors, led to the proposal that at least two subgroups of DA receptors exist. The majority of the work covered in this chapter has been directed towards the elucidation of the properties of agonists and antagonists at these peripheral DA receptor types, and has been the subject of a number of books and recent reviews.[1-8]

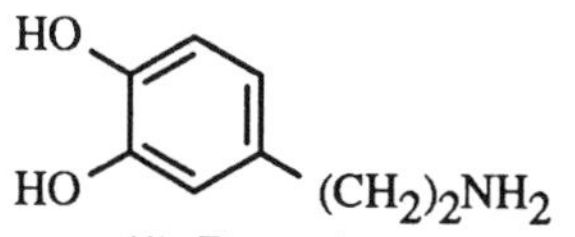

HO—
HO—(CH$_2$)$_2$NH$_2$

(1) Dopamine

By its very nature, this chapter can review, in detail, only a proportion of the total amount of work that has been generated over the years, and reference to many results of scientific value through books and reviews is a regrettable necessity. It is to be hoped that workers in the DA receptor area will not feel too aggrieved if their observations fall into this category.

12.4.2   BIOSYNTHESIS, DISTRIBUTION, SITES OF ACTION AND METABOLISM OF DOPAMINE

12.4.2.1   Biosynthesis

The biosynthesis of DA is shown in Scheme 1, and involves the sequential action of the enzymes tyrosine 3-hydroxylase and aromatic-L-amino-acid decarboxylase on L-tyrosine. Whilst most of the elucidation of this biochemical pathway has been carried out using tissue from the central nervous system, it is evident that a similar sequence of reactions occurs in peripheral tissues.

12.4.2.1.1   Tyrosine 3-hydroxylase (EC 1.14.16.2)

Tyrosine 3-hydroxylase appears to be a soluble, tetrahydropteridine dependent, iron-containing enzyme that converts L-tyrosine (**2**) into L-3,4-dihydroxyphenylalanine (L-DOPA; **3**), this being the rate-limiting step in the biosynthesis of DA.[9,10] The enzyme is subject to impulse (neuronal) flow stimulation and end product inhibition of catalytic activity, as might be expected of an intra-neuronal enzyme.

12.4.2.1.2   Aromatic-L-amino-acid decarboxylase (EC 4.1.1.28; DOPA decarboxylase)

This is a nonspecific, pyridoxyl phosphate dependent enzyme that is present in most tissues, and effects the decarboxylation of a number of aromatic L-amino acids. In the case of L-DOPA (**3**), the decarboxylation occurs in the cytoplasm, and most of the DA so formed is stored in granules within vesicles in the nerve endings, together with a number of other compounds, *e.g.* other catecholamines, chromogranins and ATP.[10,11] It is of interest to note that for L-DOPA to be effective in the treatment of Parkinson's disease it is necessary to coadminister a peripheral DOPA decarboxylase inhibitor, so that the required plasma levels of L-DOPA are maintained.[12]

12.4.2.2   Distribution

12.4.2.2.1   Endogenous DA

As might be expected for a putative neurotransmitter, DA concentrations are highest in neuronal tissue,[13] with high concentrations being found in the lungs, heart, kidney, liver and spleen.[4,8] The

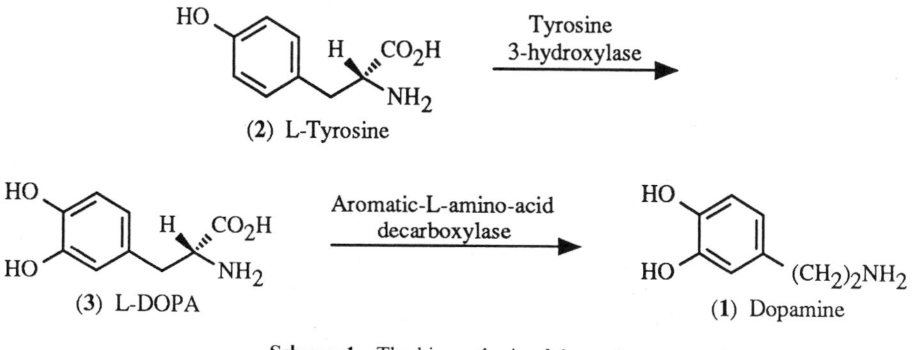

HO—
H   CO$_2$H
NH$_2$

(2) L-Tyrosine

→ Tyrosine 3-hydroxylase →

HO—
HO—
H   CO$_2$H
NH$_2$

(3) L-DOPA

→ Aromatic-L-amino-acid decarboxylase →

HO—
HO—(CH$_2$)$_2$NH$_2$

(1) Dopamine

Scheme 1   The biosynthesis of dopamine

DA is stored in granules within vesicles in the nerve endings, and is released following neuronal depolarization, or by stimulation with other chemical agents.[8] The DA so released is a substrate for the uptake processes, $Uptake_1$ or $Uptake_2$, events that generally precede metabolic deactivation. The $Uptake_1$ process found in dopaminergic nerves is a high affinity, low capacity, calcium dependent, energy-requiring process that is selective for DA;[4,14] noradrenaline is taken up by a separate $Uptake_1$ process. The $Uptake_1$ process conserves the released DA, which is returned to the neuronal vesicles. $Uptake_2$ is a low affinity, high capacity, nonselective, mainly extraneuronal process.[14,15]

12.4.2.2.2   *Exogenous DA*

At low extracellular concentrations a proportion of the DA is a substrate for the $Uptake_1$ process and is stored in neuronal vesicles unchanged. The remainder of the DA at low concentrations, and the majority at higher concentrations, is taken up by the $Uptake_2$ process.[14,15] Following removal by the $Uptake_2$ process, DA is extensively metabolized by a number of enzyme systems that will be described below (see Section 12.4.2.4).

12.4.2.3   Sites of Action

12.4.2.3.1   *Receptors*

DA interacts with a number of cell surface receptors in the central nervous system and also at certain peripheral sites.[4,8] This aspect will be discussed more extensively in later sections.

12.4.2.3.2   *Interaction with uptake processes and enzymes*

As mentioned above, DA is a substrate for the $Uptake_1$ and $Uptake_2$ processes, and it can act as an inhibitor of the $Uptake_1$ process for noradrenaline.[14] DA is also a substrate for a number of metabolic enzyme systems (see below), and it can also act as an enzyme inhibitor in certain cases.[16]

12.4.2.4   Metabolism

The enzyme systems that are important in the metabolism of DA are shown in Scheme 2.

12.4.2.4.1   *DA β-hydroxylase (EC 1.14.17.1)*

DA β-hydroxylase is a copper-containing monooxygenase that requires ascorbate as a cofactor. It is a relatively nonselective enzyme that will act on a range of arylethylamines, but its most important role is the catalysis of the stereospecific hydroxylation of DA to noradrenaline (**4**), and for this purpose it is located primarily in sympathetic nerve endings and the adrenal medulla.[17] Given that this enzyme plays a pivotal role in the intraneuronal removal of DA and the generation of noradrenaline, a number of DA β-hydroxylase inhibitors have been synthesized with the aim of examining their potential for the treatment of cardiovascular disorders.[17,18]

12.4.2.4.2   *Monoamine oxidase (EC 1.4.3.4, flavin; EC 1.4.3.6, copper)*

'Monoamine oxidase' is a rather loose description of a group of flavin or copper dependent enzymes that are partly responsible for the termination of the actions of DA and other biologically active amines.[19,20] They effect the oxidative deamination of DA, other catecholamines and a number of other substrates, mainly in the liver, but they are also present in most other tissues. In the case of DA the product of oxidation, 3,4-dihydroxyphenylacetaldehyde, is metabolized further to give 3,4-dihydroxyphenylacetic acid (DOPAC; **5**), and a number of other metabolites. The same enzymes also oxidize 3-methoxytyramine (**6**), a product of the action of COMT on DA (see below), to give homovanillic acid (HVA; **7**). DOPAC and HVA are compounds that are frequently taken to be indicators of DA turnover.

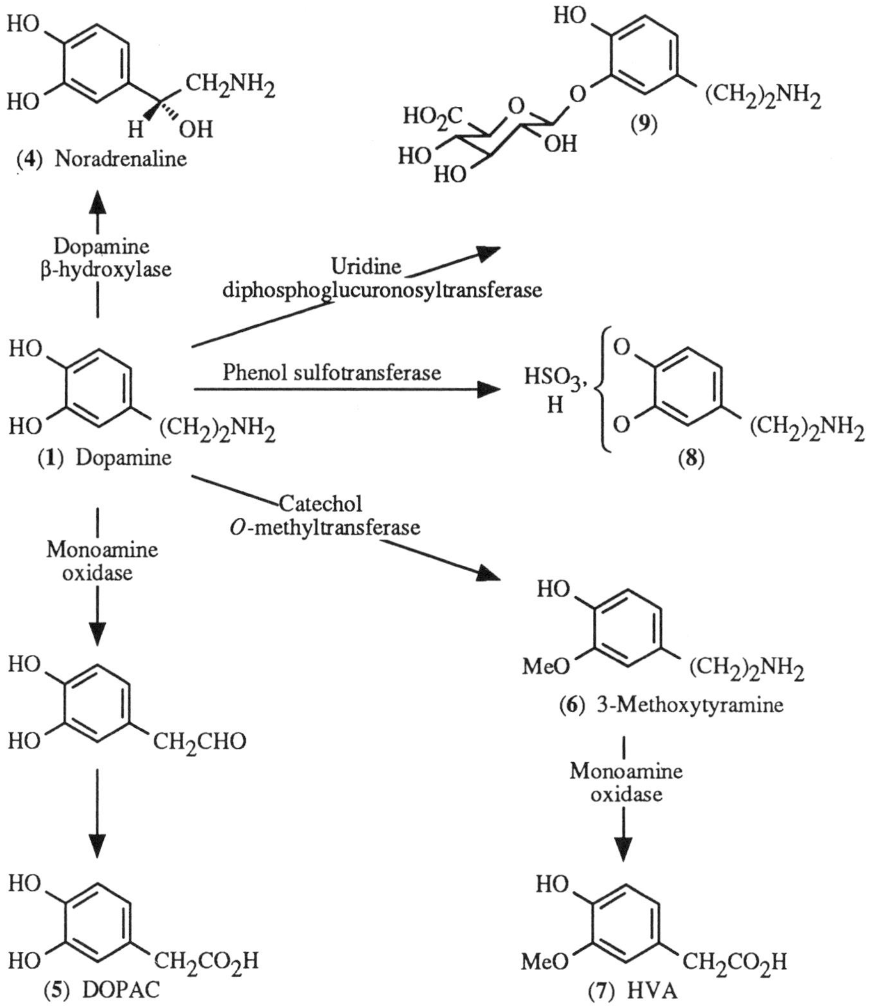

Scheme 2 The metabolism of dopamine

12.4.2.4.3 Catechol O-methyltransferase (EC 2.1.1.6; COMT)

COMT catalyzes the transfer of a methyl group from S-adenosyl-L-methionine to one of the hydroxy groups of the catechol moiety of DA or other catechol-containing compounds.[21] It is a common enzyme throughout the body, with high concentrations being found in the liver and kidney.[20,21] COMT is an extraneuronal enzyme that is involved in the metabolism of the majority of the catecholamines released from nerve terminals, and also in the destruction of catecholamines circulating in the blood stream following their removal by the Uptake$_2$ process.[20] In the case of DA the major product is 3-methoxytyramine (6), but in other cases the enzyme is less selective and both the 3- and 4-methoxyphenols are produced.[20,21]

12.4.2.4.4 Phenol sulfotransferase (EC 2.8.2.1; PST)

PST catalyzes the transfer of a sulfate group from 3'-phosphoadenosine-5'-phosphosulfate (PAPS) to one of the hydroxy groups of a catecholamine or other catechol- or phenol-containing compounds. The enzyme is found in high concentrations in the gut wall, liver and the platelets and, together with COMT, is responsible for the deactivation and elimination by conjugation of most of the catecholamines taken orally, *i.e.* either in the diet or in attempted oral administration of catecholamine-containing drugs. PST is not a particularly selective enzyme and both the 3- and 4-sulfates (8) of DA have been reported to occur in human plasma.[20,22] Following an oral dose of

DA the majority of the material is sulfated during its passage through the gut wall and is found in the plasma as the sulfate conjugates; consequently the oral bioavailability of DA is very poor. The sulfate conjugates have little biological activity and, since they do not appear to be desulfated, do not act as a reservoir of DA.[23]

12.4.2.4.5 *Uridine diphosphoglucuronosyltransferase (EC 2.4.1.17)*

This enzyme transfers a glucuronic acid group from uridine diphospho-α-D-glucuronic acid to the hydroxy group of a catechol, phenol, acid or amine to produce the β-D-glucuronide derivative (*e.g.* **9**).[20,24] The enzyme is present in high concentrations in the liver and, although the formation of glucuronide conjugates is a minor metabolic pathway in the case of DA, it does assume some considerable relevance in the metabolism and elimination of other catecholamines, some of which have actions at DA receptors.[25]

12.4.3 CHEMISTRY OF DOPAMINE

12.4.3.1 Synthesis and Properties

Since the first synthesis of DA in 1910 a number of methods have been developed for the construction of appropriately substituted 2-arylethylamines.[26] DA itself is an air sensitive compound in all its forms, with the free base and solutions of salts, and even the solid salts, being prone to oxidation, a process that is followed by a number of other cyclization and oxidation reactions. The pK_a values for DA are: pK_{a_1}, 9.06; pK_{a_2}, 10.60; pK_{a_3}; 12.05, and the $\log D\,(7.4)$ is -2.36.

12.4.3.2 Analysis of DA and its Metabolites

A variety of methods have been developed for the analysis of DA, DA-like compounds and their metabolites in biological samples.[8] One of the most sensitive and widely used methods appears to be high performance liquid chromatography linked to an electrochemical detection system.[27] This method of analysis has a sensitivity in the low picogramme range and can also be applied to a variety of DA-like compounds and, with some modifications, to a number of metabolites.[28]

12.4.4 CLASSIFICATION AND LOCALIZATION OF DOPAMINE RECEPTORS

Prior to 1970 the actions of DA were explainable with the established groups of adrenergic receptors and a single population of DA receptors, although a certain amount of evidence was being accumulated suggesting the existence of multiple DA receptors.[29] This evidence appeared first in studies on central DA receptors, but was followed by evidence for the existence of two types of peripheral DA receptor. The situation has been clarified further with the discovery of DA receptor agonists and antagonists with increasing selectivities.

The nomenclature of DA receptors is rather confusing. In this chapter peripheral DA receptors are classified using the DA_1/DA_2 nomenclature of Goldberg, whereas the D_1/D_2 classification is used for central DA receptors.

12.4.4.1 Central DA Receptors

Whilst a detailed discussion will not be undertaken here, it is worth noting the major steps in the evolution of the nomenclature of the classification of central DA receptors. A number of different approaches have been made. Thus the DAe/DAi classification was based on the excitatory or inhibitory properties of DA, and the D_1/D_2 classification was based on data derived from a variety of *in vitro* and *in vivo* experiments. With the emergence of ligand binding as an important tool for research, the D_1/D_2 system was extended to the $D_1/D_2/D_3/D_4$ classification; however further work has led to a clarification in this area, and the basic classification is currently that of D_1 and D_2 receptors that can exist both in a high and low affinity state. For a more detailed account of central DA receptors the reader is referred to Chapter 12.3.

12.4.4.2 Peripheral DA Receptors

Following a number of experiments by earlier workers, in which the peripheral properties of DA were explained in terms of activity at adrenergic receptors, Goldberg and coworkers showed that DA has specific actions on the renal vasculature in the anaesthetized dog in the presence of α and β adrenoceptor antagonists, and they suggested that these effects were mediated *via* a specific population of DA receptors.[29] It had also been noticed that DA inhibited the neuronal release of noradrenaline, and a population of DA receptors on sympathetic nerve terminals was proposed to account for these observations.[30] With the discovery of more selective agonists and antagonists these observations have been extended, and the DA_1/DA_2 system of classification of peripheral DA receptors was proposed by Goldberg.[31] This area has been the subject of a number of recent reviews.[1,4-6]

12.4.4.2.1 Localization of DA_1 and DA_2 receptors

Anatomically those DA_1 and DA_2 receptors that are involved in the pharmacological and physiological actions of DA agonists and antagonists are cell surface receptors, located on opposite sides of the neuro-effector junction, as shown in Figure 1. It remains to be seen whether a similar situation exists for the DA_2 and presumed DA_1 receptors that appear to be involved in the suppression of ganglionic neurotransmission.[5,6,32]

DA_1 receptors have been identified in a number of tissues from a variety of animal species.[33-36] Likewise DA_2 receptors have been identified in a variety of neuronal tissues from a number of animal species.[33-37]

12.4.4.2.2 Properties of DA_1 receptors

DA_1 receptors are located postjunctionally; they appear to stimulate adenylate cyclase activity[38,39] and there is mounting evidence that they are similar to central D_1 receptors.[34] Efforts to isolate and characterize DA_1 receptors have met with little success, in contrast to the equivalent studies with central D_1 receptors, where some progress has been made.[39,40] The stimulation of DA_1 receptors produces a number of important pharmacological and physiological effects,[3-6,34] *e.g.* the relaxation of renal and mesenteric arterial smooth muscle. Recently DA_1 agonists have been shown to be involved in the suppression of sympathetic ganglionic neurotransmission *via* a population of DA_1-like receptors.[32] Observations using DA_1 selective antagonists show some anomalies and it remains to be seen if different classes of DA_1 receptors are required to explain these results.[2,36]

12.4.4.2.3 Properties of DA_2 receptors

DA_2 receptors are located prejunctionally; they appear to inhibit adenylate cyclase activity[38,39] and evidence from a variety of sources indicates that they are similar to central D_2 receptors.[34]

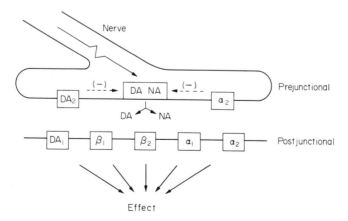

Figure 1 A sympathetic neuro-effector junction. NA, noradrenaline; DA, dopamine; α_1, α_2, β_1, β_2, adrenergic receptors; DA_1, DA_2, dopaminergic receptors; (−), negative feedback on neurotransmitter release

Attempts to isolate and characterize DA_2 receptors have met with little success, unlike the equivalent studies with central D_2 receptors, where considerable progress has been made.[39,40] In the case of DA_2 receptors, located on axonal varicosities and perhaps certain ganglion cell bodies, stimulation results in the reduction of the release of noradrenaline and possibly other neurotransmitters.[33] The stimulation of DA_2 receptors, particularly those that result in a reduction in the release of noradrenaline, produces a number of important pharmacological and physiological effects,[3-6,33,34] *e.g.* a vasodilation that is a result of the reduction in the vascular tone maintained by neurally released noradrenaline and a bradycardia following effects on the cardioaccelerator nerve.

It is of considerable therapeutic interest that a group of DA_2/D_2 receptors present in the chemoreceptor trigger zone (CTZ) of the area postrema (outside the blood–brain barrier) are involved in the mediation of the sensation of nausea and eventually the induction of emesis.[41,42] Up to now the structural requirements for the activation of the various groups of DA_2 receptors have not been separated, consequently all DA_2 (and D_2) receptor agonists eventually cause nausea and emesis when dosed orally or parenterally to conscious animals and humans.

12.4.4.3 Transduction Mechanisms and Postreceptor Events

There is considerable evidence to support the view that DA_1 receptors are positively linked to adenylate cyclase by a G_s protein and, although the evidence is less impressive, it appears that DA_2 receptors are negatively linked to adenylate cyclase by a G_i protein.[38,39] The intracellular events that follow the modulation in the production of cAMP in peripheral DA receptor dependent systems have not been studied as extensively as their central DA receptor equivalents. In the case of the latter, the regulation of protein phosphorylation would seem to be important, given that a number of intracellular proteins have been identified in DA dependent systems, some of which appear to be specific phosphatase inhibitors.[43]

12.4.5 EVALUATION OF DOPAMINE RECEPTOR ACTIVITY

12.4.5.1 DA_1 Receptor Activity

12.4.5.1.1 In vitro DA_1 receptor activity

The *in vitro* activity of agonists and antagonists at DA_1 receptors has been assessed by several different methods. Radioligand binding studies, so commonly used in the case of central D_1 receptors,[38,44] have not been widely reported; however, it appears that [^{3}H]spiroperidol binding to rabbit mesenteric or renal artery preparations shows some promise.[35] Measurement of cAMP levels has been widely used to assess D_1/DA_1 activity, given that these receptors stimulate adenylate cyclase activity.[38,39] The majority of the work in this area has been carried out using central D_1-linked adenylate cyclase systems; however some DA_1-linked systems have been reported,[35] together with those from bovine parathyroid cells,[45] and in cultured rat mesangial cells.[46]

A number of isolated tissue preparations have been examined.[33-36] Although there is a reasonable correlation between the results obtained using these preparations and *in vivo* DA_1 assays, there are some anomalies.[36] The effects of DA_1 agonists and antagonists have also been studied using a population of DA_1-like receptors that suppress neurotransmission in the stellate ganglion of the dog.[32] *In vitro* arterially perfused vascular beds have been studied, *e.g.* the mesenteric bed in the rabbit, cat and dog and the renal bed in the rat.[34] There is a reasonable correlation with results obtained using *in vivo* DA_1 assays, although there are some exceptions.

12.4.5.1.2 In vivo DA_1 receptor activity

Since the introduction of the canine renal blood flow model for the assessment of *in vivo* DA_1 receptor activity by Goldberg,[47] changes in regional blood flow have been investigated in a number of other species.[34] When using most of these preparations for the study of DA_1 agonists it is necessary that both α and β adrenoceptors and DA_2 receptors be blocked with suitable antagonists. The *in vivo* effects of DA_1 agonists and antagonists have also been studied using a population of DA_1-like receptors that suppress neurotransmission in the stellate ganglion of the dog and the rat.[32]

12.4.5.2 DA$_2$ Receptor Activity

12.4.5.2.1 In vitro DA$_2$ receptor activity

The *in vitro* activity of agonists and antagonists at DA$_2$ receptors has been studied using a number of different methods. Radioligand binding studies have been carried out, but these have used mainly central D$_2$ receptor preparations.[38,40,44] Inhibition of cAMP production has been investigated as a means of assessing DA$_2$ receptor activity.[39]

A variety of isolated tissue preparations from a number of species have been examined and this area has been the subject of a number of reviews.[33-37] Both the direct measurement of [^{3}H]noradrenaline release in response to nerve stimulation and the measurement of responses of adrenergically inervated tissues following electrical stimulation have been studied. Of particular interest are the rabbit ear artery and rectococcygeus muscle preparations.

12.4.5.2.2 In vivo DA$_2$ receptor activity

Several methods have been developed for the *in vivo* assessment of activity at DA$_2$ receptors, and a number of comprehensive reviews are available.[33-37] Of particular interest are the cat cardioaccelerator nerve and nictitating membrane preparations and effects of sympathetic nerve stimulation on regional blood flow (most commonly femoral) in the dog, cat or rabbit. Given the propensity of DA$_2$ receptor agonists to cause nausea and eventually emesis, this activity has been studied in a number of models,[42] of which the conscious dog appears to be the most extensively used.[48]

12.4.6 STRUCTURE–ACTIVITY RELATIONSHIPS OF DOPAMINE RECEPTOR AGONISTS

There have been many studies of the structure–activity relationships (SAR) of peripheral and central DA receptor agonists, and these have been the subject of a number of extensive reviews.[2,4,33,34,36,49-51] The purpose of this section is to summarize the important features of the SAR of peripheral DA$_1$ and DA$_2$ receptor agonists, with reference to data from the biological assays described in Section 12.4.5.

12.4.6.1 SAR of DA$_1$ Receptor Agonists

The potencies of a number of DA$_1$ receptor agonists are shown in Table 1. These potencies have been taken from, or in a few cases calculated from, data given in the references cited, and are quoted relative to DA = 1. As can be seen from the table, the number of different screening methods used makes direct comparison of the potency of all compounds impossible, consequently the data should be treated with some caution.

12.4.6.1.1 Arylalkylamines

Amongst the many simple analogues of DA that have been prepared it is relatively uncommon to find compounds with activity similar to, or greater than, DA. Only those compounds that retain a basic nitrogen atom possess DA$_1$ agonist activity and, apart from epinine (**10**), alkyl substituents on the nitrogen atom generally result in a reduction of activity. Exceptions to this latter generalization are to be found in a series of compounds in which the alkyl substituent contains a second nitrogen atom that may possess a second catecholamine or arylalkylamine moiety,[52] and also a group of compounds represented by Sandoz 27403 (**11**).[53] Currently the most interesting of these groups of compounds is dopexamine hydrochloride (**12**), described in more detail in Section 12.4.8.3.3.

Modifications to the ethyl portion of DA also result in compounds with lower activity,[54] although it is interesting to note that both adrenaline and noradrenaline have been reported to possess DA$_1$ receptor activity.[55] Of the many modifications that have been made to the aryl group of DA, only those compounds that retain the catechol moiety possess useful activity and a satisfactory catechol isostere has yet to be identified. There appears to be limited scope for the addition of extra

Table 1 The Potency of Dopamine Receptor Agonists

Compound	DA_1 $(DA = 1)$	DA_2 $(DA = 1)$	Biological assay (in vitro or in vivo)	Ref.
(10)	1		Canine renal blood flow	34
		2	Rabbit ear artery	33
(11)	0.25		Rabbit splenic artery	53
	1.2		Canine renal blood flow	a
		1.5	Rabbit ear artery	a
(12)	0.34		Canine renal blood flow	104
		0.17	Rabbit ear artery	104
(13b)	10		Canine renal blood flow	a
	NA		Rabbit ear artery	a
(14a)	12[b]		Adenylate cyclase	58
		2.5	Rabbit ear artery	58
(14b)		2700	Rabbit ear artery	58
(15b)	1		Canine renal blood flow	34
(15c)	0.03		Canine renal blood flow	59
		3	Rabbit ear artery	59
(16a)	NA		Canine renal blood flow	34, 60
		0.6	Rabbit ear artery	60
(16b)	1		Canine renal blood flow	34
	2		Canine renal blood flow	60
	1		Rabbit splenic artery	53
		36	Rabbit ear artery	60
		66[c]	Canine femoral blood flow	120
(17a)	1		Canine renal blood flow	34
	0.4		Canine renal blood flow	a
	5		Rabbit splenic artery	53
		13	Rabbit ear artery	104
		8	Rabbit ear artery	61
(17b)	0.25		Rabbit splenic artery	53
	0.25		Canine renal blood flow	34
		15	Rabbit ear artery	a
(18a)	0.01[b]		Canine renal blood flow	34
		6	Rabbit ear artery	33
		4[c]	Canine femoral blood flow	120
(18b)	0.02		Canine renal blood flow	34
		50[c]	Canine femoral blood flow	120
(19)	8		Canine renal blood flow	52
		6	Rabbit ear artery	52
(20a)	1		Adenylate cyclase	59
		8	Rabbit ear artery	59
(21)	0.1		Canine renal blood flow	a
		14	Rabbit ear artery	74
(22a)	0.02		Canine renal blood flow	60
		1.1	Rabbit ear artery	60
(22b)	5		Canine renal blood flow	60
		200	Rabbit ear artery	60
(23a)	1		Canine renal blood flow	a
		16	Rabbit ear artery	a
(24b)	0.01[b]		Canine renal blood flow	34
(25)	10		Canine renal blood flow	65a
		NA	Dog cardioaccelerator nerve	108
(28)		0.1	Rabbit ear artery	72
(29a)		10	Ligand binding	73
		5	Rabbit ear artery	a
(29b)		0.1	Rabbit ear artery	72
(30a)		0.6	Rabbit ear artery	72
(30b)		36	Rabbit ear artery	72
(31)	Weak		Canine renal blood flow	59
		0.3	Rabbit ear artery	59
(32)	0.05		Canine renal blood flow	62
		NA	Canine femoral blood flow	62
(33)	0.7		Adenylate cyclase	121
(34)	1		Adenylate cyclase	121
(37a)		460	Cat cardioaccelerator nerve	33
(38a)		350	Cat cardioaccelerator nerve	33
(38b)		80	Cat cardioaccelerator nerve	33
(39a)		0.3	Cat cardioaccelerator nerve	33
(40)	0.7		Canine renal blood flow	25
		0.3	Rabbit ear artery	25

Table 1 (*Continued*)

Compound	DA_1 (DA = 1)	DA_2 (DA = 1)	Biological assay (in vitro or in vivo)	Ref.
(41b)		1	Rabbit ear artery	33
		5	Cat cardioaccelerator nerve	33
(42a)		0.4	Cat cardioaccelerator nerve	33
(42b)		5	Cat cardioaccelerator nerve	33
(42c)		70	Cat cardioaccelerator nerve	33
(44)		0.5	Cat cardioaccelerator nerve	33
(47a)		1	Isolated rat kidney	122
(47b)		1	Rabbit ear artery	a
(50)		0.7	Rabbit ear artery	72
(64a)	0.03		Canine renal blood flow	34
		0.9	Rabbit ear artery	72
		1.5	Cat cardioaccelerator nerve	33
		1^c	Canine femoral blood flow	123
(64b)	0.04		Canine renal blood flow	34
		1^c	Canine femoral blood flow	123
(65)	0.004		Canine renal blood flow	a
		52	Rabbit ear artery	a

^{a} Unpublished results. ^{b} Partial agonist. ^{c} N,N-Di-n-propyldopamine = 1.

substituents; however, compounds with a fluoro, chloro or methyl substituent retain activity.[52,56] The addition of a 2-arylethyl group confers useful activity on a series of DA derivatives (**13a**) and exceptional activity on a number of dopexamine hydrochloride analogues (**13b**; *e.g.* Ar = 3-hydroxyphenyl).[57]

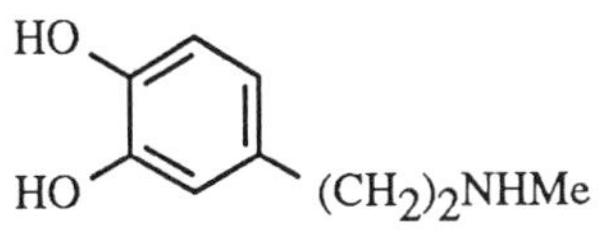

HO
HO—(CH$_2$)$_2$NHMe
(**10**) Epinine

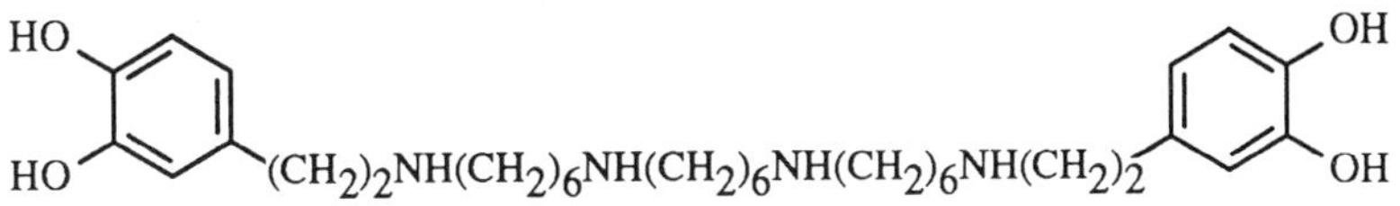

HO
HO—(CH$_2$)$_2$NH(CH$_2$)$_6$NH(CH$_2$)$_6$NH(CH$_2$)$_6$NH(CH$_2$)$_2$—OH OH
(**11**) Sandoz 27403

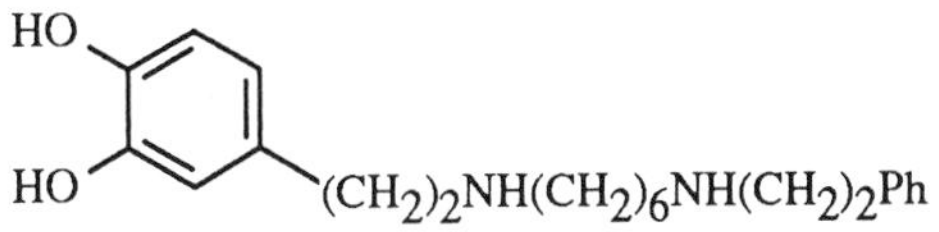

HO
HO—(CH$_2$)$_2$NH(CH$_2$)$_6$NH(CH$_2$)$_2$Ph
(**12**) Dopexamine hydrochloride

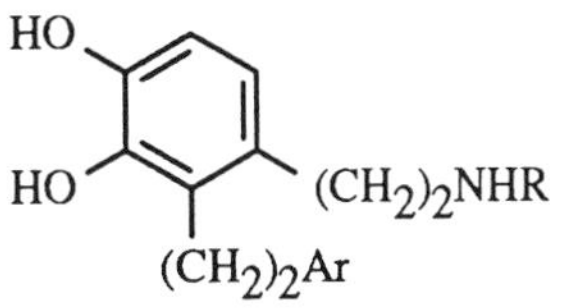

HO
HO—(CH$_2$)$_2$NHR
(CH$_2$)$_2$Ar
(**13a**) R = H
(**13b**) R = (CH$_2$)$_6$NH(CH$_2$)$_2$Ph

12.4.6.1.2 Heteroarylalkylamines

Many heteroaryl analogues of DA have been prepared in the search for an effective catechol isostere with activity at DA_1 receptors. Up to now the benzothiazolone (**14a**) is the only compound that shows an interesting level of activity, although it is also a potent DA_2 agonist.[58]

12.4.6.1.3 Aminomethyl derivatives

The conformational flexibility of the arylethylamines has been reduced by incorporating the ethyl portion into a ring with a pendant aminomethyl group. Of interest amongst this type of compound are the dihydroxytetralin (**15a**), isochroman (**15b**)[4] and a number of benzocyclobutenes (*e.g.* **15c**).[52,59]

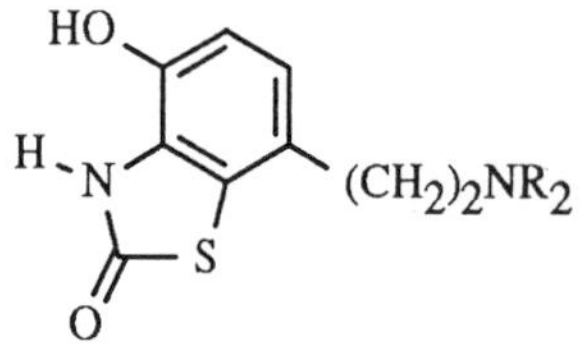

(14a) R = H

(14b) R = Pr^n

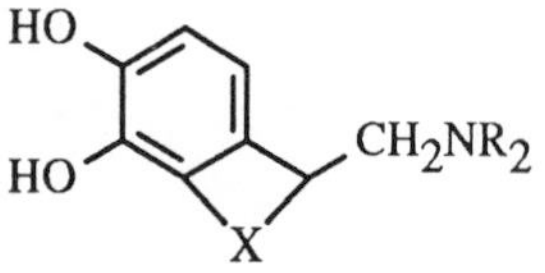

(15a) X = (CH$_2$)$_3$, R = H

(15b) X = (CH$_2$)$_2$O, R = H

(15c) X = CH$_2$, R = Pr^n

12.4.6.1.4 2-Aminotetralins and their analogues

An alternative approach that reduces the conformational flexibility of the arylethylamines has been to incorporate the ethyl moiety into a ring with an amino substituent. This area has been extensively studied,[4,6,33-36,49,51] and, in particular, the dihydroxy derivatives of 2-aminotetralin, *i.e.* 2-amino-5,6-dihydroxy-1,2,3,4-tetrahydronaphthalene (16a), commonly known as 5,6-ADTN, and its 6,7-dihydroxy isomer (17a), commonly known as 6,7-ADTN, and their derivatives deserve mention. (The nomenclature in this area is confusing with 5,6-ADTN also being named as 6-amino-5,6,7,8-tetrahydronaphthalene-1,2-diol and 6,7-ADTN being the isomeric 2,3-diol.) These compounds are of particular interest given that they are related to apomorphine (18a), one of the more important compounds in the history of DA research (see Section 12.4.6.1.8). Many substituted 2-aminotetralin analogues have been made, and in general their SAR are similar to those seen with DA analogues, although there are some notable exceptions.

In terms of changes at the nitrogen atom, the weak activity of the 5,6-ADTN (16a), when compared with its *N,N*-di-*n*-propyl derivative (16b) and the 6,7-ADTN (17a), is a curious, and as yet unexplained, observation.[34,60] Compounds with alkyl substituents on the nitrogen atom are generally more active than the equivalent DA analogue, with the *n*-propyl group being particularly favoured. In common with the DA analogues described in Section 12.4.6.1.1, compounds containing nitrogen substituents that possess a second nitrogen atom that can bear another catecholamine or arylalkylamine moiety (*e.g.* 19), are potent DA$_1$ agonists, some of which are orally active.[52]

In general, compounds that have extra substituents in the tetralin portion are less active than the equivalent unsubstituted compounds (*e.g.* 20; R^2 or R^3 = alkyl or halogen);[4,61] however, the compounds where R^2 or R^3 = F retain useful DA$_1$ activity, *e.g.* (20a). As in the DA series, a suitable catechol isostere has yet to be identified, given that only those compounds that retain the catechol moiety are active, although the 5-hydroxy compound (21) is a notable exception, being a weak DA$_1$ agonist.[4]

One of the most interesting aspects of the SAR in this area is the relationship of the configuration of the carbon atom bearing the amino group to the hydroxylation pattern in the aromatic ring. It has been found that the DA$_1$ (and DA$_2$) receptor activity resides in the (2S)-5,6-ADTNs (22) and in the (2R)-6,7-ADTNs (23).[4,50,60] These observations have had a major impact on the hypotheses dealing with models of the DA receptor, and this topic will be covered in more detail in Section 12.4.6.2.

Several analogues of the 2-aminotetralins have been investigated, but the 3-aminochromans,[62] 2-aminoindanes, 2-amino-3,4-dihydroquinazolines and the 2-aminobenzocycloheptanes[4] are all inactive or only weakly active as DA$_1$ agonists. The same is true for the octahydrobenzo-[*f*]quinolines, the octahydrobenzo[*g*]quinolines and the octahydrobenzo[*h*]isoquinolines[4] (some of these compounds are potent DA$_2$ agonists, see Section 12.4.6.3.7).

12.4.6.1.5 4-Aryl-1,2,3,4-tetrahydroisoquinolines

Nomifensine (24a) is an antidepressant agent with weak *in vivo* activity at DA receptors.[63] A number of nomifensine analogues have been prepared[63,64] and the most active as a DA$_1$ receptor agonist would appear to be the (4R)-3',4'-dihydroxy derivative (24b). It has been suggested that this compound is an active metabolite of nomifensine, and it is interesting to note that the configuration of the carbon atom bearing the aryl substituent is important for activity.[64]

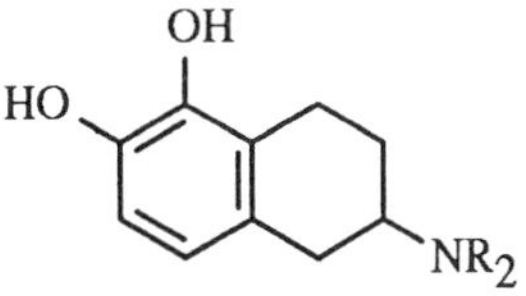

OH

HO

5,6-ADTN
(16a) R = H
(16b) R = Pr^n

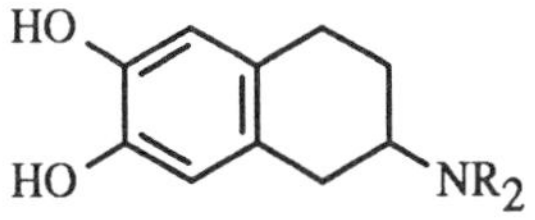

HO
HO

6,7-ADTN
(17a) R = H
(17b) R = Pr^n
(17c) R = $(CH_2)_2Cl$

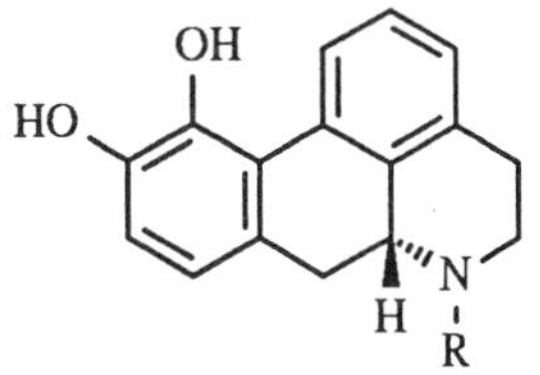

OH
HO

(18a) R = Me; Apomorphine
(18b) R = Pr^n
(18c) R = $(CH_2)_2Cl$

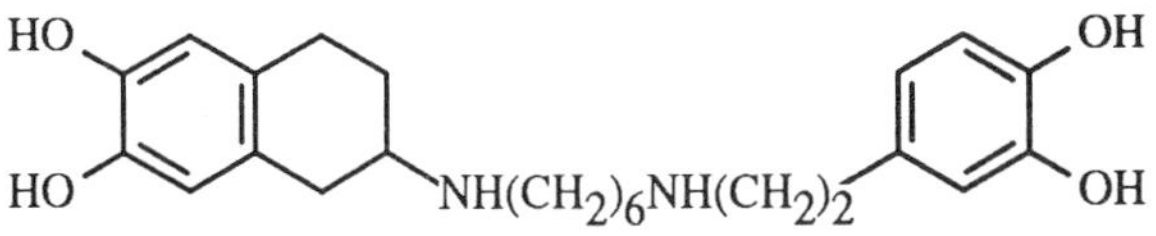

HO
HO
$NH(CH_2)_6NH(CH_2)_2$

OH
OH

(19)

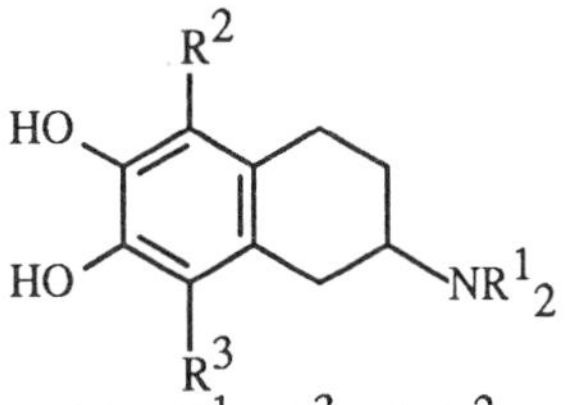

R^2
HO
HO
NR^1_2
R^3

(20a) $R^1 = R^3 = H$, $R^2 = F$

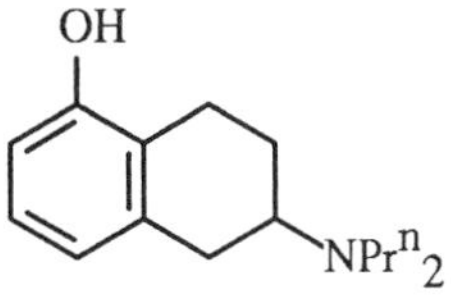

OH

NPr^n_2

(21)

OH
HO

H
NR_2

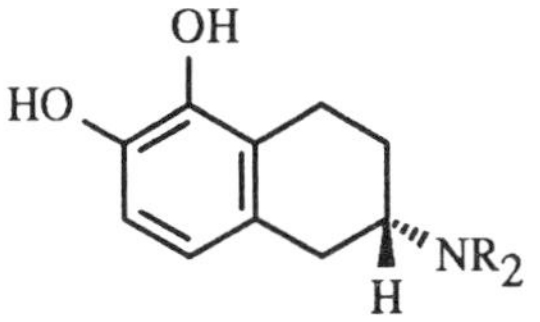

(2S)-5,6-ADTN
(22a) R = H
(22b) R = Pr^n

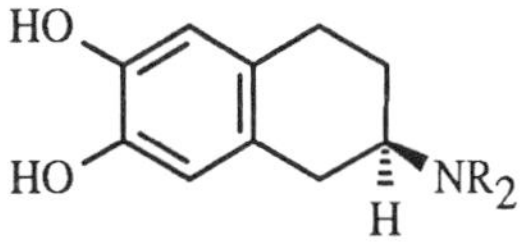

HO
HO

H
NR_2

(2R)-6,7-ADTN
(23a) R = H
(23b) R = Pr^n

12.4.6.1.6 2,3,4,5-Tetrahydro-1H-3-benzazepines

One of the most significant advances in the progress of the understanding of the DA_1 receptor has been the discovery of a group of potent and selective agonists (and antagonists, see Section 12.4.7.1.4) that are 3-benzazepine derivatives. The most interesting of these compounds, fenoldopam (**25**), is described in more detail in Section 12.4.8.3.4.

The SAR in this area has been the subject of a number of reviews[2,4,25] and other reports,[65,66] and only the important points are mentioned below. Potent DA_1 receptor activity is most usually associated with the secondary amines, although compounds possessing the N-allyl substituent retain useful activity, but DA_2 agonist activity is generally increased.[66] The most active compounds in this area possess a (1R)-aryl substituent bearing a hydroxy group. As in the cases of the 2-aminotetralins and the 2-arylethylamines, the catechol is essential for good DA_1 activity, and there is some scope for the introduction of extra substituents, particularly fluorine and chlorine, in the 6-position. The active compounds in this area have been important in providing extra information with respect to the possible location and nature of the interactive groups at the DA_1 receptor and have led to further models of the DA_1 receptor (see Section 12.4.6.2).

12.4.6.1.7 Ergot alkaloids, derivatives and part structures

Whilst the ergot alkaloids and their derivatives are well known as DA receptor agonists, very few have any DA_1 receptor activity,[4,34] although the benzothiazolone (**14a**) might be considered to be related to the indolone analogues as part structures of the ergolines (see Section 12.3.6.1.2).

12.4.6.1.8 Aporphines, derivatives and part structures

Apomorphine (**18a**) is probably the most widely studied DA receptor agonist. Despite its popularity, it is a rather weak partial agonist at peripheral DA_1 receptors[4,34] (however it is a potent

DA_2 receptor agonist, see Section 12.4.6.3.10). Most of the simple derivatives and partial structures of apomorphine are either inactive or weak DA_1 receptor agonists, the 2-aminotetralins (**16**; R = alkyl) being the most notable exceptions (see Section 12.4.6.1.4). It is interesting to note that isoapomorphine (**26**) is inactive as a DA receptor agonist, an observation that has had a considerable influence on the evolution of models of the DA receptor.[4,50−52]

12.4.6.1.9   Prodrugs of DA_1 receptor agonists

It will have become apparent from the descriptions of the SAR given in the previous sections that the catechol moiety is essential for good DA_1 receptor activity. It is also the case that the efficiency of the enzyme systems mentioned in Section 12.4.2.4 result in the majority of catechol-containing compounds being poorly absorbed and/or of short duration of action. One solution to the problem of poor oral bioavailability and, less predictably, to the problem of short duration of action, has been to prepare prodrugs of the active compound and allow the appropriate enzymes (usually in the plasma) to effect the desired chemical transformation.[67]

A number of DA_1 receptor agonists have been modified in this way to produce prodrugs. The most well known is probably L-DOPA (**3**), where the action of aromatic-L-amino-acid decarboxylase produces DA.[12] Another common approach has been to prepare a suitable diester derivative of the catechol; compounds such as ibopamine (**27a**), designed as a prodrug of epinine (**10**),[68] and esters of various DA and L-DOPA derivatives[69,70] are amongst the most well studied. The presence of high concentrations of the enzyme γ-glutamyltransferase in the kidney has prompted the preparation of a number of γ-glutamylamides of DA and L-DOPA and some of their diester derivatives (*e.g.* **27b**), as renal selective double prodrugs.[69] As was mentioned in Section 12.4.6.1.5, it is thought that the DA_1 receptor activity of some nomifensine analogues could be the result of hydroxylation of the 4-aryl substituent, a process that can produce the active 3′,4′-dihydroxy derivative.[64] Consequently nomifensine may be a prodrug.

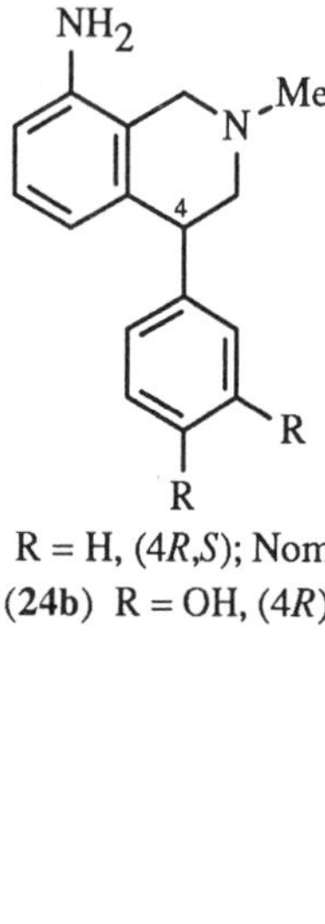

(**24a**) R = H, (4*R*,*S*); Nomifensine
(**24b**) R = OH, (4*R*)

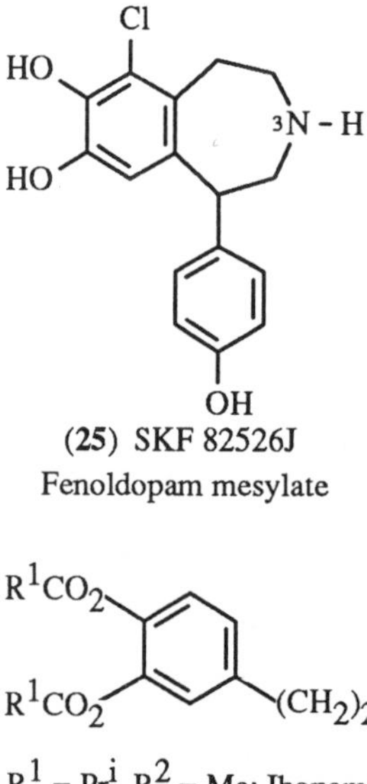

(**25**) SKF 82526J
Fenoldopam mesylate

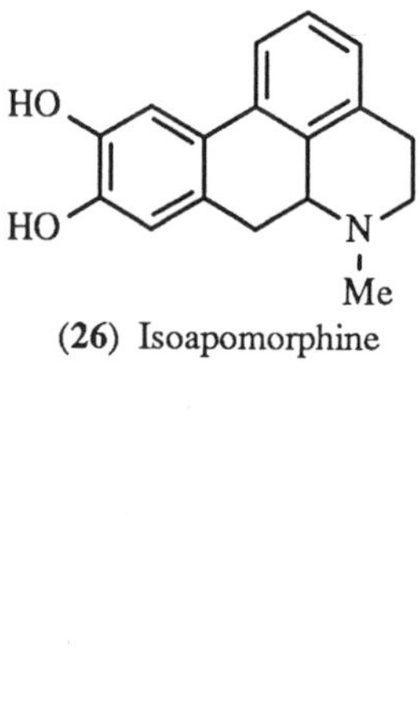

(**26**) Isoapomorphine

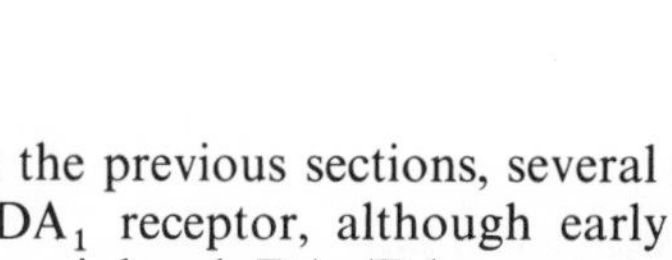

(**27a**) $R^1 = Pr^i$, R^2 = Me; Ibopamine
(**27b**) R^1 = Me, R^2 = $CO(CH_2)_2CH(NH_2)CO_2H$

12.4.6.2   DA$_1$ Receptor Models

Based on the SAR data described in the previous sections, several attempts have been made to produce a convincing model of the DA_1 receptor, although early work in this area did not necessarily discriminate between the peripheral DA_1/DA_2 receptors and their central D_1/D_2 counterparts. More recently, approaches to conceptual models of the DA_1 receptor have been described and the topic has been the subject of several reviews.[4,50−52] The major points of interest are the effect on agonist binding or potency of: (i) the nature of the catechol binding site, (ii) the conformation adopted by DA and other flexible DA agonists at the active site of the receptor, (iii) the preferential binding of one enantiomer of a racemate, (iv) the possibility for the interaction of any substituents with more remote binding sites, (v) the exclusion of steric bulk from certain regions, and (vi) the charge distribution between the catechol and amine moieties.

In the published models, a number of these features are presumed to be common to both the DA_1 and DA_2 receptors. Whilst this may be the case, there are significant differences in the SAR of DA_1 and DA_2 agonists that need to be accommodated in any model of the DA_1 receptor. Given that the catechol is a prerequisite for good DA_1 agonist activity, the nature of the catechol binding site is of utmost importance, and must differ in some way from the equivalent region of the DA_2 receptor. Secondary amines appear to be particularly common as DA_1 agonists; consequently the binding site for the amino group must reflect this preference. At the DA_1 receptor there are at least two more remote binding sites that can be occupied by substituents possessed by potent DA_1 agonists. Dopexamine hydrochloride (**12**) and fenoldopam (**25**) typify the classes of compounds that have helped to define these accessory binding sites.

Of the various conceptual models of the DA receptor, only two have attempted to define the important aspects of the DA_1 receptor. The model of Kaiser[4,50] makes particular use of the compounds related to fenoldopam. In this approach one of the more interesting aspects concerns the conformation adopted by the (1*R*)-aryl substituent with respect to the hydroxy group of the catechol that interacts with the receptor. The pseudo-axial/7-hydroxy conformation is favoured over the pseudo-equatorial/8-hydroxy alternative (Figure 2), although there is little difference in the local energy minima of the two conformations and the pseudo-equatorial conformation is present in (*R*)-fenoldopam hydrobromide in the solid state.[25]

An alternative conceptual model of the DA_1 receptor makes particular use of compounds related to dopexamine hydrochloride (**12**).[52] This approach involved the generation of a composite volume of a number of DA_1 agonists, *e.g.* the 2-aminotetralin derivative (**22b**), (*R*)-fenoldopam (**25**) in the pseudo-equatorial conformation, and dopexamine hydrochloride (**12**) in a relatively extended conformation of the DA nitrogen substituent (Figure 3). Given the extremely flexible nature of the nitrogen substituent in the latter compound, its position with respect to the catecholamine binding sites is uncertain, but it has been shown that the length of chain between nitrogens, the second nitrogen atom and the distal aryl group are all important for good DA_1 agonist activity.[52] This model was used to design some new dopexamine hydrochloride analogues, and resulted in the synthesis of a series of very potent DA_1 agonists, *e.g.* (**13b**).[57]

These hypothetical models have limited usefulness, and, until the DA_1 receptor is isolated, purified, analyzed and eventually reconstituted in a functional setting, it is unlikely that any major advances will be made.

12.4.6.3 SAR of DA_2 Receptor Agonists

The potencies of a number of DA_2 receptor agonists are shown in Table 1. These potencies have been taken from, or in a few cases calculated from, the data given in references cited and are quoted

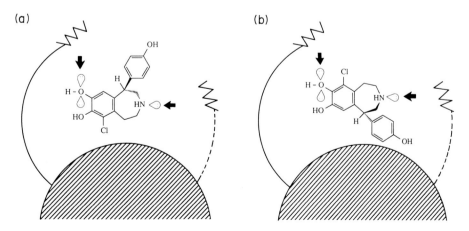

Figure 2 The interaction of fenoldopam with a model of the DA_1 receptor: (a) *via* 8-hydroxy binding; (b) *via* 7-hydroxy binding (reproduced from ref. 4 by permission of John Wiley & Sons)

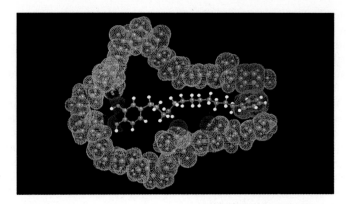

Figure 3 The interaction of dopexamine hydrochloride with a model of the DA_1 receptor

relative to DA = 1. As can be seen from the table, the number of different screening methods used makes direct comparison of the potency of all compounds impossible, consequently the data should be treated with some caution.

12.4.6.3.1   Arylalkylamines

It is reasonably common to find simple analogues of DA that are as potent, or more potent, than the parent compound. Although a basic nitrogen atom is required for good DA_2 agonist activity, a few analogues of DA containing a sulfur or selenium atom have some weak activity.[71] Alkyl groups can be added to the nitrogen atom and, in general, primary and secondary amines are less active than the corresponding tertiary amines. In the latter case it has been found that one of the nitrogen substituents should not be larger that *n*-propyl, while the other can be varied quite widely, with *n*-propyl and 2-arylethyl being particularly common.[2,4,6,49,51,52] Alterations and substituents in the ethyl moiety result in compounds that are markedly less active. Numerous changes have been made to the catechol-containing aryl group and, in contrast to the case with DA_1 receptor agonist activity, DA_2 receptor agonist activity is retained in many of the compounds.[4,51,52,56]

Of particular importance are the observations that the catechol can be replaced by arrays of functional groups that act as catechol isosteres. Indeed *m*-tyramine analogues (*e.g.* **28**), possessing a single hydroxy group, retain useful DA_2 agonist activity.[4,51,72] Among the isosteres the sulfonamide (**29a**) and the formanilide (**29b**) are of some interest.[52,72,73] This has given rise to a number of relatively simple DA analogues that are orally active DA_2 receptor agonists; however, the problem of emesis with this group of compounds remains to be solved.

$$HO-\text{—}(CH_2)_2NPr^n_2$$

(28)

$$R^1HN-\text{—}(CH_2)_2NPr^n_2$$

(29a) $R^1 = SO_2Me$
(29b) $R^1 = CHO$

12.4.6.3.2   Heteroarylethylamines

Many different heteroaryl analogues of DA have been prepared,[2,4,49,58,72,73] both in the search for new catechol isosteres and also as part structures of the ergot alkaloids. As a result of the latter, the indole nucleus has figured prominently in these studies, and some of the compounds derived from the oxindole moiety are among the most active DA_2 agonists that have been reported, *e.g.* the oxindole (**30b**) and particularly the benzothiazolone (**14b**).[58,72]

12.4.6.3.3   Aminomethyl derivatives

For the reasons mentioned in Section 12.4.6.1.3, a number of compounds of this class have been studied and are generally more potent at DA_2 receptors than at DA_1 receptors. Of interest are the dihydroxy derivatives of the tetralin (**15a**), the isochroman (**15b**)[4] and the benzocyclobutenes (**15c** and **31**).[52,59]

12.4.6.3.4 2-Aminotetralins and their derivatives

For the reasons mentioned in Section 12.4.6.1.4, many compounds of this type have been studied. In general, the SAR is the expected combination of that which has already been described.[4,6,33,49–51,61] Tertiary amines are usually more potent DA_2 agonists than the corresponding primary and secondary amines and, provided that one substituent is no larger than *n*-propyl, some variation is possible with the other substituent.[2,4,49–51] Compounds that retain the catechol group are particularly active. It has, however, been found that there is considerable scope for modification of the catechol, with several monohydroxy compounds being active,[2,4,49–51,61,74] and a number of catechol isosteres having been investigated.[75,76] It is interesting to note that the 3-aminochroman (**32**) is inactive as a DA_2 agonist.[62]

In common with the case of DA_1 receptor activity, the relationship of the configuration of the carbon bearing the amino substituent to the hydroxylation pattern in the aromatic ring is crucial.[4,50] The (2S)-5,6-ADTNs (**22**) and (2S)-5-AHTNs (**33**) and the (2R)-6,7-ADTNs (**23**) and (2R)-7-AHTNs (**34**) are the most active compounds, with the (2S)-5,6-ADTN derivative (**22b**) one of the most potent DA_2 agonists yet described.[60,74]

The addition of an *N*-2-chloroethyl substituent to 6,7-ADTN has produced derivatives that are irreversible agonists (*e.g.* **17c**) or antagonists at D_2 receptors.[77] The latter type of compound could be useful in the analysis of DA receptor responses (see Section 12.4.7.2.5).

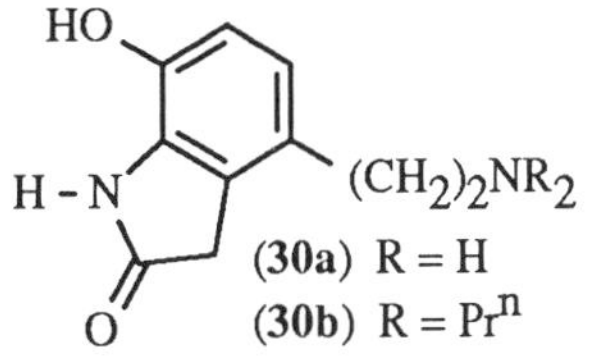

(**30a**) R = H
(**30b**) R = Pr^n

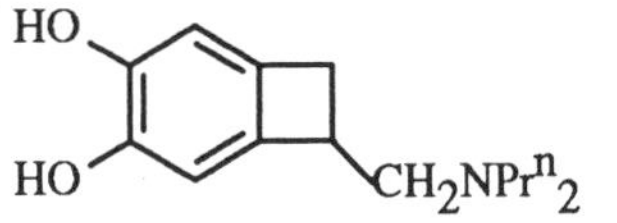

(**31**)

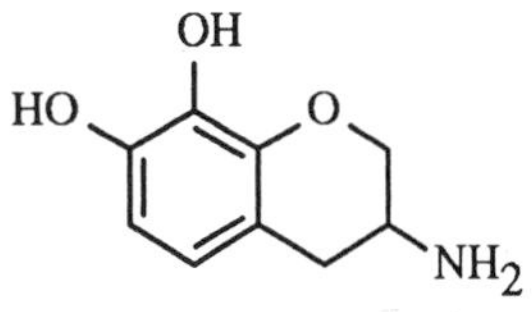

(**32**)

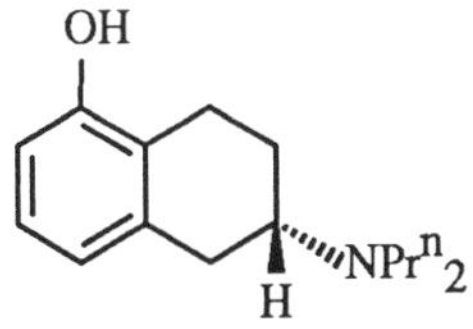

(**33**) (2S)-5-AHTN

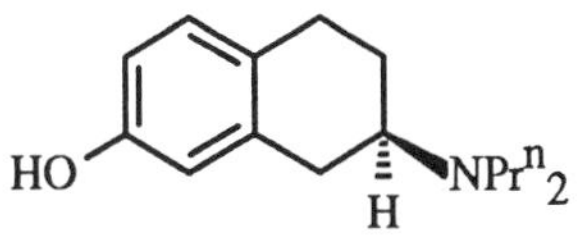

(**34**) (2R)-7-AHTN

12.4.6.3.5 2-(Arylmethyl)piperidines and 3-arylpiperidines

An alternative approach to the problem of reducing the conformational flexibility of the arylethylamines has been to incorporate the nitrogen atom into a ring. Of the possibilities that have been studied in some detail, the 3-arylpiperidines (**35**) are more interesting than the 2-(arylmethyl)-piperidines (**36**).[4,49–51] The former compounds, of which 3-PPP (**35**; R^1 = 3-OH, R^2 = Pr^n) is the most widely studied, are of particular interest from the point of view of their actions at central DA autoreceptors, a topic that is covered in Chapter 12.3.

12.4.6.3.6 4-Aryl-1,2,3,4-tetrahydroisoquinolines

Although analogues of nomifensine are better known for their DA_1 receptor activity, radioligand binding studies indicate that they interact with DA_2 receptors.[64]

12.4.6.3.7 Octahydrobenzoquinoline and isoquinoline derivatives

The mono- and di-hydroxylated octahydrobenzo[*g*]quinolines (**37**), octahydrobenzo[*f*]quinolines (**38**) and the octahydrobenz[*h*]isoquinolines (**39**) and a number of their analogues have been studied, both as tricyclic analogues of the 2-aminotetralins or as part structures of apomorphine.[4,44,49-51,78] Many of these compounds are quite potent DA_2 receptor agonists and the SAR are similar to those seen with the previously described series. The presence of an additional ring fusion introduces the possibility of *cis–trans* isomers. Where they have been studied, the compounds in the benzo[*g*]quinoline (37) and benzo[*f*]quinoline (38) series that contain the *trans* ring fusion are more active than the *cis* isomers; however, in the benz[*h*]isoquinolines (39), the *cis* compounds are marginally more active than their *trans* isomers. A number of heterocyclic analogues of this series of compounds have also been prepared, and some are potent DA_2/D_2 agonists.[79]

12.4.6.3.8   *2,3,4,5-Tetrahydro-1H-3-benzazepines*

Compounds of this type are best known for their DA_1 agonist activity, but many possess significant DA_2 agonist activity.[2,4,25,65,66] These compounds are usually tertiary amines, with the *N*-allyl substituent being particularly common. One of the more extensively studied compounds is the *N*-allyl derivative of fenoldopam (40; SKF 85174J).[25,80]

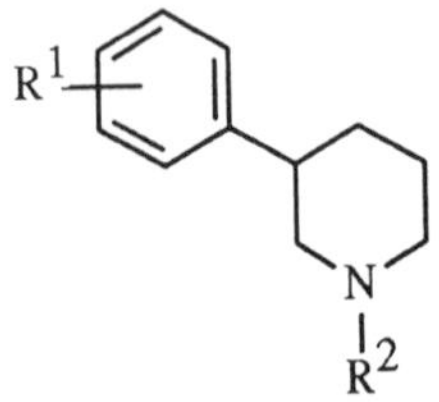

(35) R^1 = 3-OH, R^2 = Pr^n; 3-PPP 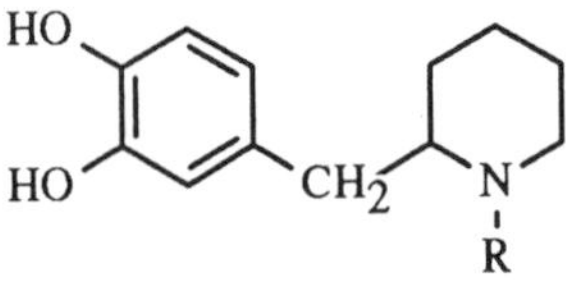   (36) 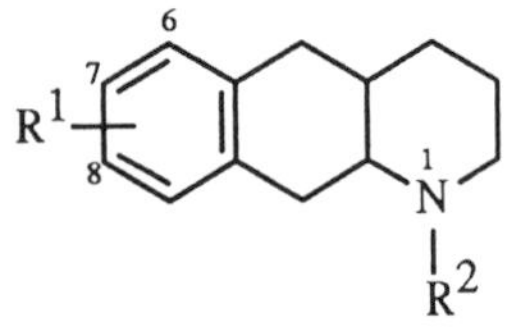   (37a) R^1 = 6,7-$(OH)_2$, R^2 = Et; *trans*

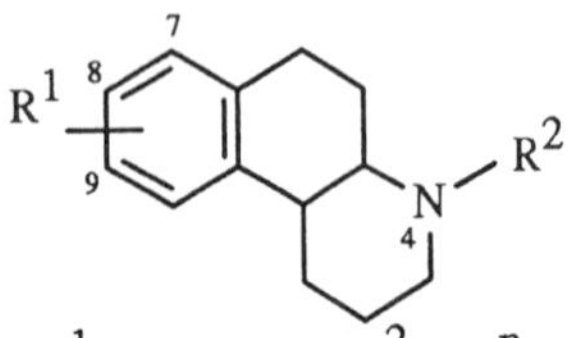

(38a) R^1 = 7,8-$(OH)_2$, R^2 = Pr^n; *trans*
(38b) R^1 = 8,9-$(OH)_2$, R^2 = Pr^n; *trans*   (39a) R^1 = 8,9-$(OH)_2$, R^2 = H; *cis* 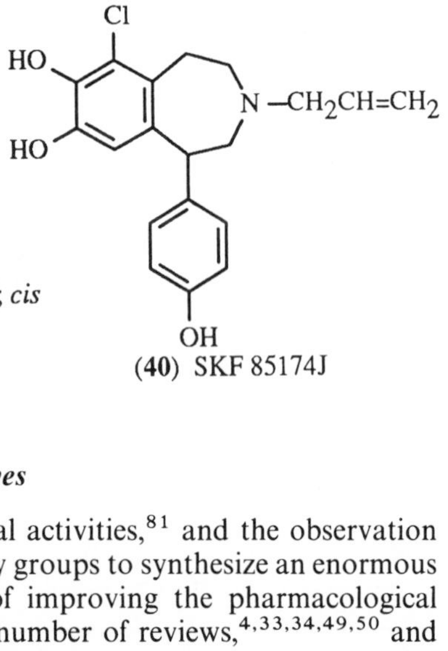   (40) SKF 85174J

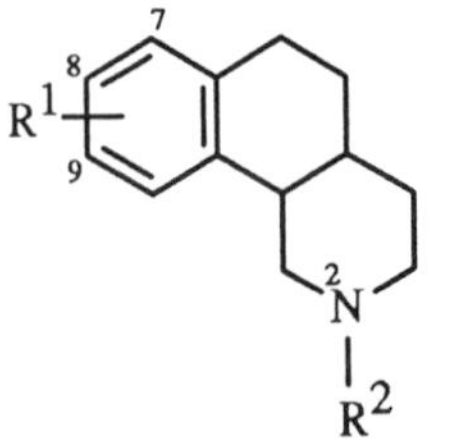

12.4.6.3.9   *Ergot alkaloids, partial structures and their derivatives*

The ergot alkaloids exhibit a broad range of pharmacological activities,[81] and the observation that some are DA_2 (or D_2) receptor agonists has stimulated many groups to synthesize an enormous number of partial structures and derivatives, with the aim of improving the pharmacological selectivity. The progress in this area has been the subject of a number of reviews,[4,33,34,49,50] and consequently only the important aspects will be covered here, with the properties of a number of the more extensively studied compounds being summarized in Section 12.4.8.3.6.

Given the complex structure of the naturally occurring ergot alkaloids, *e.g.* α-ergocryptine (41a), there is some considerable scope for the synthesis of novel analogues. A small alkyl substituent, preferably no larger than *n*-propyl, on the nitrogen atom at position 6 affords compounds that are potent DA_2 agonists. Numerous modifications have been made to the 8β 'peptide' substituent, although bromocriptine (41b), one of the more extensively studied compounds, retains this substituent intact. Other derivatives at the 8 position are also important, *e.g.* β-cyanomethyl (42a; lergotrile), β-methylthiomethyl (42b; pergolide), α-ureido (42c; lisuride), and α-sulfonylureido (42d) analogues. The 9,10 double bond is not essential for DA_2 activity, provided that a 5,10 *trans* ring junction is present in the reduced compounds. A group of 9-oxaergolines (43) have been synthesized, and have been shown to be potent DA_2/D_2 receptor agonists.[4] The indole moiety of the ergolines has been modified, but apart from simple changes, *e.g.* halogen substitution as in bromocriptine (41b) and lergotrile (42a), little has been achieved.[4]

Many partial structures of the ergolines have been prepared, both with the hope of finding new selective DA_2 agonists, and also with the aim of determining the pharmacophore responsible for DA_2 receptor activity. 4-Substituted indoles (*e.g.* **44**) have figured prominently in this work, as have a number of bicyclic and tricyclic analogues containing the pyrrole, pyrazole and pyrimidine moieties (*e.g.* **45, 46, 47**),[2,4,49,50,82] although the majority of the data are related to activity at D_2 receptors. Amongst the latter group, quinpirole (**47b**) is of some importance and is covered in more detail in Section 12.4.8.3.8. The 4,7-phenanthroline derivative (**48**) is the most potent of a group of simplified ergoline analogues.[83] The oxindoles (**30**) and benzothiazolones (**14**) are very potent DA_2 agonists that might also be considered to be derived from the ergot alkaloids.[2,58]

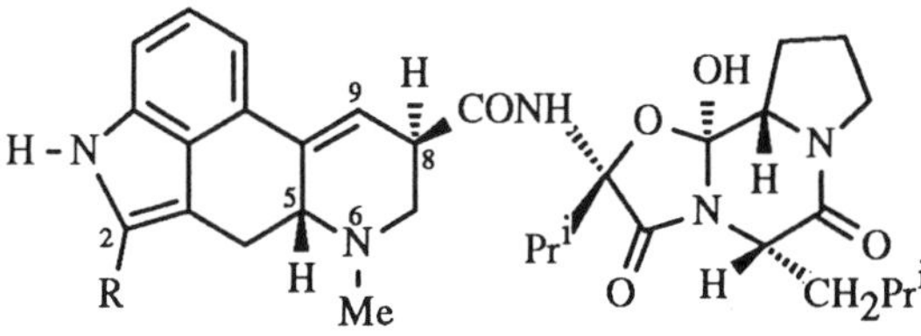

(**41a**) R = H; α-Ergocryptine
(**41b**) R = Br; Bromocriptine

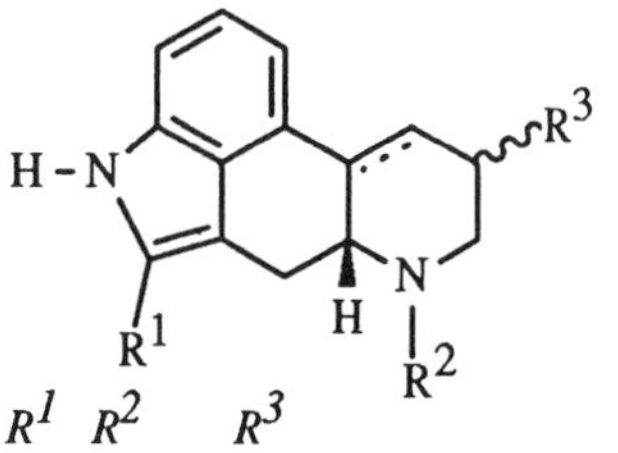

	R^1	R^2	R^3	
(**42a**)	Cl	Me	β-CH$_2$CN;	Lergotrile
(**42b**)	H	Pr^n	β-CH$_2$SMe;	Pergolide
(**42c**)	H	Me	α-NHCONEt$_2$;	Lisuride
(**42d**)	H	Me	α-NHSO$_2$NEt$_2$	

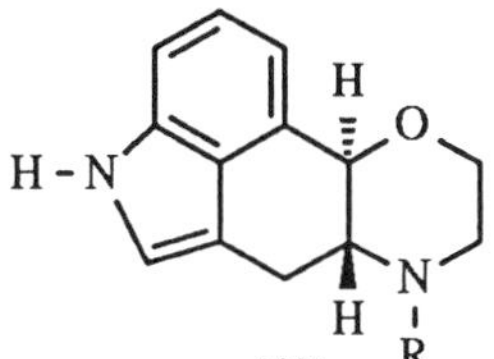

(**43**)

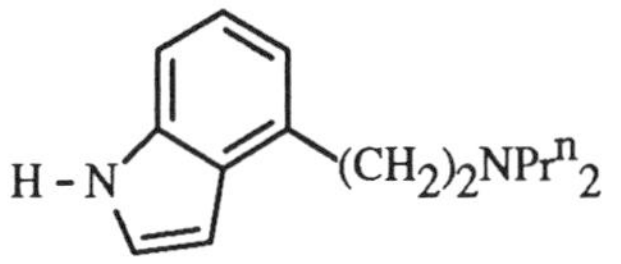

(**44**)

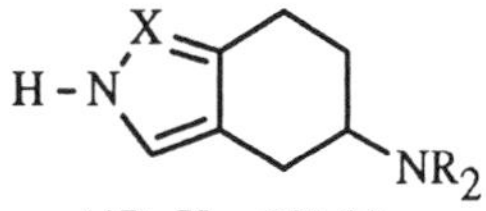

(**45**) X = CH, N

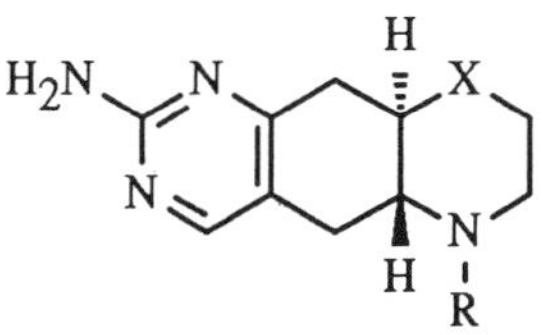

(**46**) X = CH$_2$, O

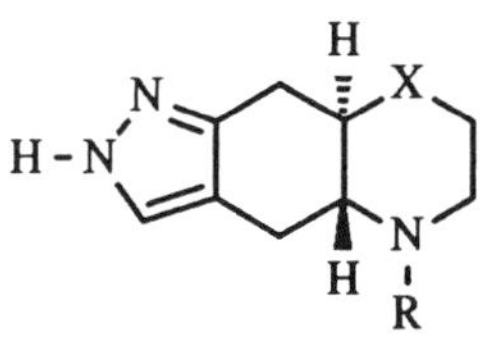

(**47**) X = CH$_2$, O
(**47a**) R = Pr^n (*RR, SS*), X = CH$_2$; LY 141865
(**47b**) R = Pr^n (*RR*), X = CH$_2$; Quinpirole, LY 171555

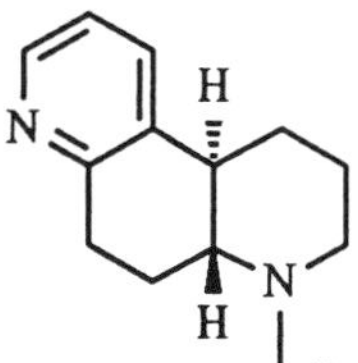

(**48**) Pr^n

In all the cases where the chirality has been determined, it is the enantiomer with the (5*R*) configuration (or its equivalent in the partial structures) that has been found to be the most active. This has been a point of some interest, in particular with respect to the chirality of the carbon atom bearing the amino group in the catechol-containing DA_2 agonists, and has had a considerable influence on the hypotheses dealing with the ergoline pharmacophore.[4,49,50,84]

12.4.6.3.10 *Aporphine alkaloids, partial structures and derivatives*

Apomorphine (**18a**) is one of the more extensively studied DA_2 receptor agonists, and it has been the basis for much of the work in the DA receptor area.[4,6,33,34,44,49−51,85] Several aspects of partial structures and derivatives of apomorphine have, necessarily, been covered in previous sections and will not be reiterated here. The SAR of the aporphines are generally similar to those of the other structural types. Those analogues that possess a small alkyl group, ideally no larger than *n*-propyl, as a substituent on the nitrogen atom are potent DA_2 agonists. A variety of mono- and poly-hydroxy compounds have been prepared, some of which retain useful activity.[51] Several secoapomorphine analogues have been prepared, but they have little DA_2 activity.[4,49,51] The preparation of *N*-2-chloroethylnorapomorphine (**18c**) resulted in a compound that is an irreversible antagonist of DA_2 receptors.[86]

Studies have shown that the two enantiomers of apomorphine and *N*-propylnorapomorphine (**18b**) possess different activities at DA receptors. Thus the (6a*R*) enantiomers are DA agonists, whereas the (6a*S*) enantiomers appear to be DA antagonists.[87] Interestingly the racemic isoapomorphine (**26**) is inactive,[4,49] an observation that has had a marked influence on the evolution of conceptual models of the DA receptor.[4,49-51]

12.4.6.3.11 Prodrugs of DA₂ receptor agonists

Prodrugs of a number of DA agonists were described in Section 12.4.6.1.9. Several of these are derived from mixed DA$_1$/DA$_2$ agonists, *e.g.* DA, epinine (**10**) and 5,6-ADTN (**16**), and the details will not be reiterated here. It has been suggested that the activity seen with the 6-methyl-5-AHTN (**49**) could be the result of metabolic activation of the methyl group,[88] a process that would presumably produce a catechol isostere. The oxindole (**50**) is a DA$_2$ agonist that has been studied quite extensively,[2] and it has been shown that it is a prodrug of the hydroxy derivative (**30b**),[89] a feature that could result in enhanced central/peripheral selectivity.

12.4.6.3.12 Miscellaneous compounds

Although many compounds with structures that are not obviously related to DA have been reported to possess DA receptor activity,[4,49,50] most of the work has involved central DA receptors, and very few compounds have actions that can be said to be typical of peripheral DA receptor agonists. The 2-imidazoline (**51**) has some action on DA receptors in the coronary vasculature, but other actions of this compound are typical of an α adrenoceptor agonist.[4]

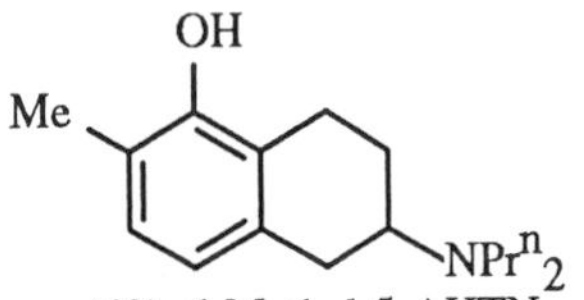

(**49**) 6-Methyl-5-AHTN 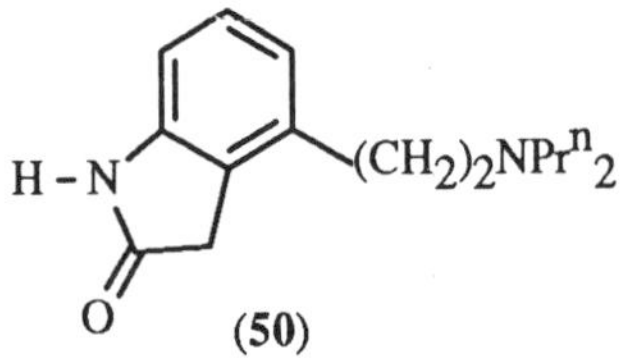   (**50**) 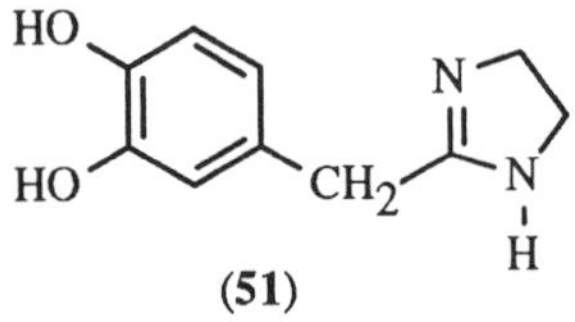   (**51**)

12.4.6.4 DA₂ Receptor Models

Given the apparent similarity between the DA$_2$ and D$_2$ receptors, few, if any, of the receptor models have attempted to distinguish between the peripheral and central sites of action. Thus the DA receptor models of Seeman, Neumeyer, Wikstrom, Erhardt and Grol (see Chapter 12.3) could all be considered to be representations of the DA$_2$ (D$_2$) receptor.[4,50,51,84]

Whilst some aspects of the SAR of the DA$_2$ receptor are similar to those described for the DA$_1$ receptor, the single most obvious difference between the two receptor types is the ability of DA$_2$ receptors to be activated by compounds that do not necessarily possess a catechol. This feature of the SAR is presumably a consequence of some, as yet undefined, difference in the catechol binding region of the two receptors. There are also differences in the region of the receptors that is responsible for the binding of the amino group, since many tertiary amines are potent DA$_2$ agonists, provided that one substituent is not larger than *n*-propyl. The activity of compounds related to the ergot alkaloids needs to be considered, both from the point of view of the indole acting as a catechol isostere, and also the ability of the DA$_2$ receptor to be activated by compounds with both large (bromocriptine; **41b**) and small (pergolide; **42b**) substituents in the ergoline 8-position.

Having noted the above differences, there is no convincing model of the DA$_2$ receptor, apart from the DA$_2$/D$_2$ models mentioned above, and these hypothetical models have limited usefulness. Fortunately structural work in the DA$_2$ receptor area is more advanced than that related to the DA$_1$ receptor, and it is to be hoped that it will not be too long before the DA$_2$ receptor is isolated, purified, analyzed and eventually reconstituted in a functional setting. Until then it is unlikely that any major advances will be made.

12.4.7 STRUCTURE–ACTIVITY RELATIONSHIPS OF DOPAMINE RECEPTOR ANTAGONISTS

Since the recognition that chlorpromazine (**52**), and other psychopharmacologically similar compounds, exert some of their actions by the antagonism of the effects of endogenous DA, the field of DA receptor antagonists has been one of intense study. The majority of this work has been aimed at the unravelling of the intricacies of central D_1 and D_2 receptors, and the SAR in this area are covered in some detail in Chapter 12.3. Many of the compounds prepared during the course of this work are also DA_1 and/or DA_2 antagonists, and these have led, in turn, to compounds that are selective for peripheral, rather than central, DA receptors, and also for either DA_1 or DA_2 receptors.[4,5,25,33–36,44,90] Apart from the actions of DA_2 antagonists as antiemetics,[42] there are only a few therapeutic applications for these selective peripheral DA antagonists.[91] A number are extremely useful pharmacological tools, but in most cases the SAR at DA_1 and DA_2 receptors are rather limited.

12.4.7.1 DA₁ Receptor Antagonists

The activities of a number of DA_1 receptor antagonists are shown in Table 2. These activities have been taken from, or in a few cases calculated from, data given in references cited. As can be seen from the table, the number of different screening methods used makes direct comparison of the activities of all compounds impossible; consequently the data should be treated with some caution.

12.4.7.1.1 *Tricyclic antidepressants*

Compounds such as fluphenazine (**53**), *cis*-α-flupenthixol (**54**) and a number of other tricyclic antidepressants have been used as DA_1 antagonists.[36] They are, however, either nonselective DA_1/DA_2 or selective DA_2 antagonists and have been superseded by better compounds.

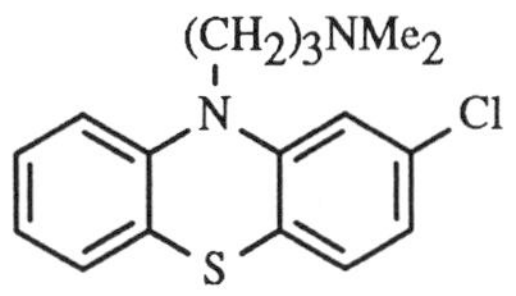

(52) Chlorpromazine

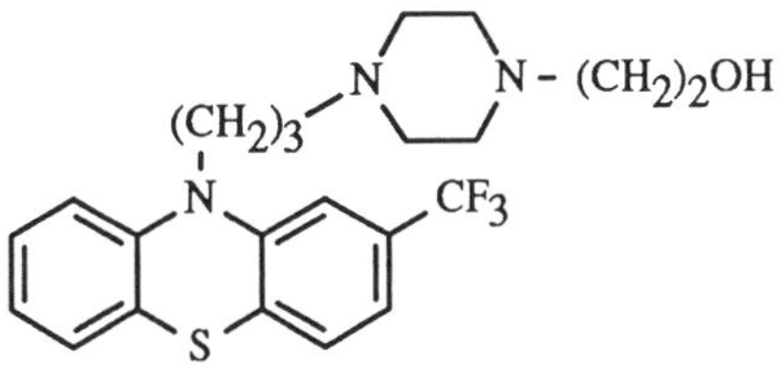

(53) Fluphenazine

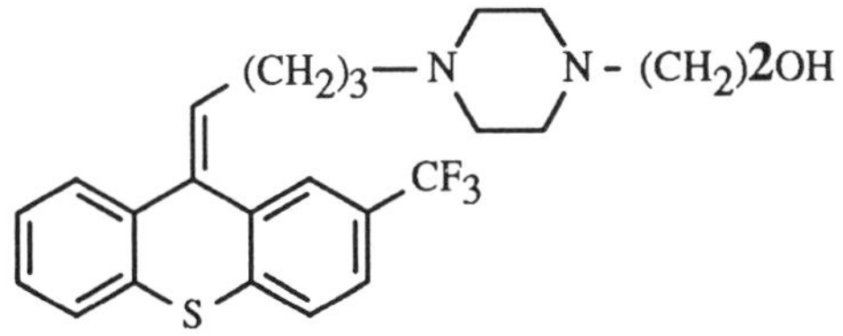

(54) *cis*-α-Flupenthixol

12.4.7.1.2 *Aporphines*

A number of aporphine alkaloids and their derivatives have been shown to be DA antagonists, and bulbocapnine (**55**) is the most commonly used DA_1 antagonist in this group of compounds.[92] All retain a basic nitrogen atom and it is interesting to note that the configuration at position 6a is (*S*), the opposite of that found in apomorphine (**18a**), a weak DA_1 agonist.[34] Where the enantiomeric pairs are available it appears that this stereochemical difference is a feature of the SAR of the aporphines with respect to agonists and antagonists.[87] Although the SARs of the aporphines as DA agonists have been studied extensively, much remains to be done in the field of DA antagonists.

Table 2 The Potency of Dopamine Receptor Antagonists

Compound	DA_1	DA_2	Biological assay (in vitro or in vivo)	Ref.
(52)		0.5	Dog emesis[a]	91
(53)	2.5		Canine mesentery[b]	36
	0.8		Rabbit splenic artery[b]	36
		0.03	Cat heart[c]	36
		> 10	Rabbit rectococcygeus muscle[b]	36
(54)	0.2		Canine mesentery[b]	36
	0.07		Rabbit splenic artery[b]	36
		0.03	Car heart[c]	36
		> 10	Rabbit rectococcygeus muscle[b]	36
(55)	0.6[d]		Rabbit splenic artery[b]	53
(56)	3.8		Canine mesentery[b]	36
	> 100		Rabbit splenic artery[b]	36
	16		Isolated rat kidney[b]	93
		0.06	Cat heart[c]	36
		0.02	Rabbit rectococcygeus muscle[b]	36
		0.02	Rabbit ear artery[b]	94a
(56a)	0.046		Canine renal blood flow[e]	94b
		0.0004	Canine renal artery[f]	94b
		0.009	Rabbit ear artery[b]	94a
(56b)	0.046		Canine renal blood flow[e]	94b
		> 0.046	Canine renal artery[f]	94b
		1	Rabbit ear artery[b]	94a
(57a)	0.008		Canine mesentery[b]	36
	0.00002		Rabbit splenic artery[b]	36
		> 10	Cat heart[c]	36
		> 1	Rabbit rectococcygeus muscle[b]	36
(57b)	0.0006		Rabbit splenic artery[g]	25
		2	Rabbit ear artery[g]	25
(58)	> 2.7		Canine mesentery[b]	36
	0.7		Rabbit splenic artery[b]	36
		0.03	Cat heart[c]	36
		0.004	Rabbit rectococcygeus muscle[b]	36
		0.015	Dog emesis[a]	91
		1.4	Rabbit ear artery[g]	96
(59)	1.9		Rabbit splenic artery[b]	53
		0.2	Rabbit ear artery[g]	96
(60)	0.002		Isolated rat kidney[b]	93
		0.36	Rabbit ear artery[g]	96
(61)		0.16	Dog emesis[a]	91
		0.36	Dog emesis[a]	98
(62)		0.011	Dog emesis[a]	91
		0.57	Rabbit ear artery[g]	96
(63)	> 23.6		Canine mesentery[b]	36
	> 100		Rabbit splenic artery[b]	36
	> 5000		Canine renal blood flow[b]	100b
		0.005	Cat heart[c]	36
		0.01	Rabbit rectococcygeus muscle[b]	36
		0.007	Dog emesis[a]	91
		0.08	Dog emesis[a]	98
		3	Canine femoral blood flow[b]	100b

[a] ED_{50} (mg kg^{-1}), s.c. [b] Dose (µmol kg^{-1}) or concentration (µM) that produces a two-fold shift to the right in the dose response curve to DA. [c] Dose (µmol kg^{-1}) required to reduce the response to DA by 50%. [d] Slope of Schild plot $\neq$ 1. [e] Dose (µmol kg^{-1} min^{-1}, i.a.) that produces the maximum antagonism of the effect of DA on renal blood flow. [f] Dose (µmol kg^{-1} min^{-1}, i.a.) that produces the maximum antagonism of the effect of DA on the reduction in renal blood flow induced by electrical nerve stimulation. [g] K_B (nM).

12.4.7.1.3 N-*Aminoalkylbenzamides*

The SAR of the benzamides at peripheral DA receptors have not been studied in great detail. Some have useful DA_1 antagonist activity, but as a group they are generally selective DA_2 antagonists. Sulpiride (56) is one of the more extensively studied benzamides,[93] and it has been found that its two enantiomers have different selectivities as DA antagonists. (*S*)-Sulpiride (56a) is a selective DA_2 antagonist, whereas (*R*)-sulpiride (**56b**) appears to be a nonselective DA_1/DA_2 antagonist, all depending on the tissue being studied.[94] It remains to be seen if this aspect of the SAR is a common feature of sulpiride analogues.

12.4.7.1.4 *2,3,4,5-Tetrahydro-1H-3-benzazepines*

The description of the potent, selective DA_1 receptor antagonist activity of a group of benzazepine derivatives has revolutionized the analysis of DA receptor-mediated effects. Compounds of this type, *e.g.* SCH 23390 (**57a**) and SKF 83566 (**57b**), have made the classification of DA_1 receptor populations relatively simple, and have made it much easier to analyze the responses to mixed DA_1/DA_2 agonists.[4,25,34,90] Although these benzazepines show a marked selectivity for DA_1 receptors, they have been shown to have actions at other receptors, *e.g.* as $5\text{-}HT_1$ antagonists.[95]

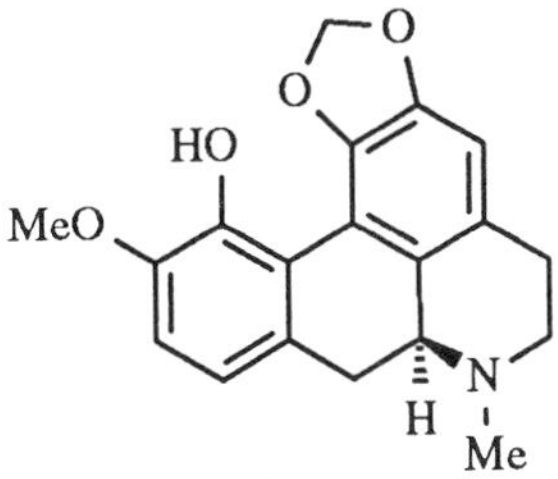

(**55**) Bulbocapnine

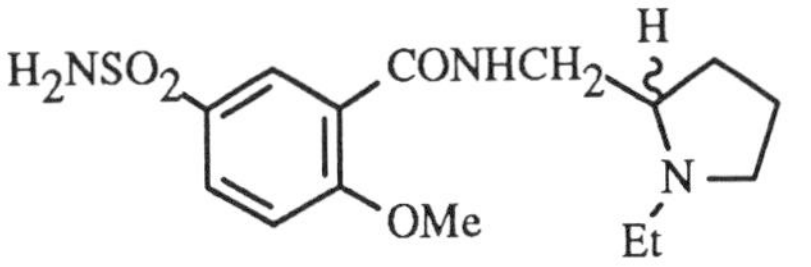

(**56a**) (*S*)-Sulpiride; ◀ H

(**56b**) (*R*)-Sulpiride; ⠤ H

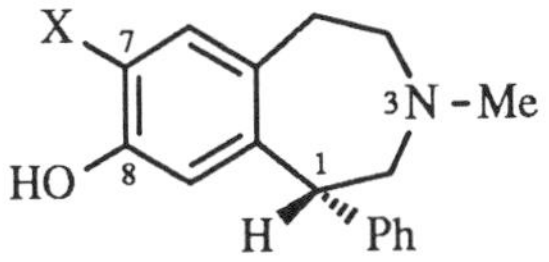

(**57a**) X = Cl; SCH 23390
(**57b**) X = Br; SKF 83566

The SAR of these derivatives have been reviewed[25,90] and only the important aspects will be repeated here. The most effective antagonists possess a tertiary amine (usually the *N*-methyl derivative), an 8-hydroxy group and a small 7 substituent (most commonly chlorine or bromine). They also contain a 1-aryl substituent, usually a phenyl group, with the most active enantiomer having the (1*R*) configuration. This is the same configuration found in the most potent enantiomer of the DA_1 agonists that are also benzazepines, *e.g.* fenoldopam (**25**).

12.4.7.2 DA_2 Receptor Antagonists

The activities of a number of DA_2 receptor antagonists are shown in Table 2. These activities have been taken from, or in a few cases calculated from, data given in references cited. As can be seen from the table, the number of different screening methods used makes direct comparison of the activity of all compounds impossible; consequently the data should be treated with some caution.

12.4.7.2.1 *Butyrophenones*

Butyrophenones, such as haloperidol (**58**), have been used as DA_2 antagonists,[5,33,36,91,96] and spiroperidol (spiperone; **59**) has been used, particularly in radiolabelled form, for D_2/DA_2 radioligand binding studies.[35,44] Despite the fact that such compounds are commonly used in studies of DA_2 receptors, the SAR of the butyrophenones at DA_1/DA_2 receptors have not been extensively studied. Many aspects of the SAR of the butyrophenones at D_2 receptors have been reported and this topic is covered in some detail in Chapter 12.3.

12.4.7.2.2 *Polycyclic antidepressants and antipsychotics*

Despite the fact that most of the SAR with this structurally somewhat diverse group of compounds have been generated using systems based on D_2 receptors, a number of compounds have, at various times, been used as DA_2 antagonists. Of particular note in this context are fluphenazine (53), *cis*-α-flupenthixol (54) and (+)-butaclamol (60).[5,33,36,44]

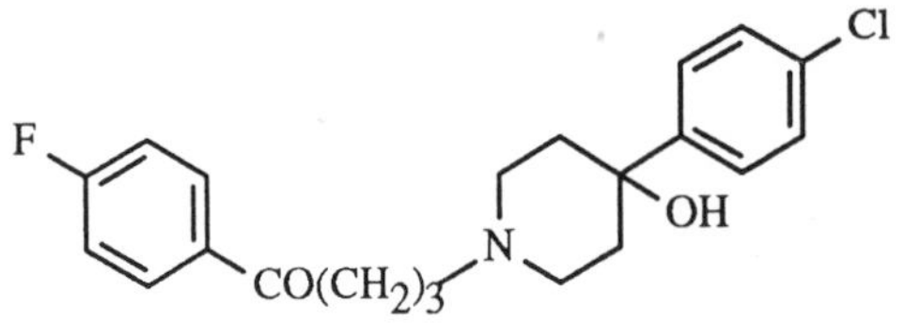

(58) Haloperidol

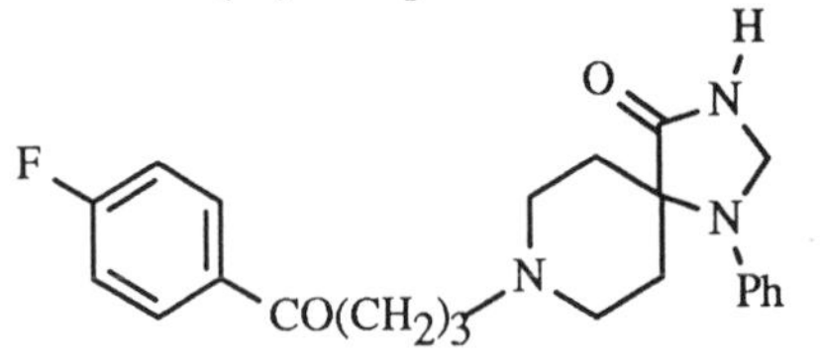

(59) Spiperone

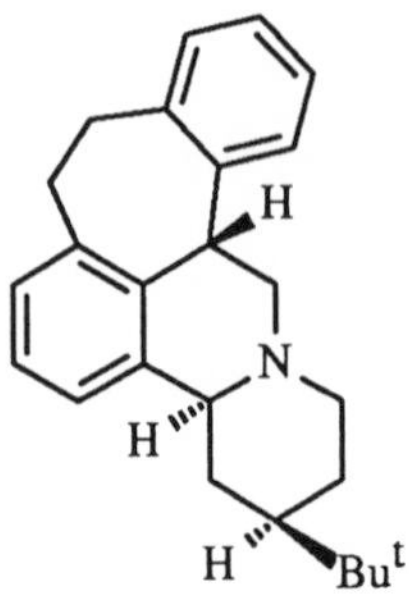

(60) (+)-Butaclamol

12.4.7.2.3   N-Aminoalkylbenzamides

Metoclopramide (61)[97] and sulpiride (56)[93] are among the most frequently used DA_2 antagonists but, in common with the other areas described in this section, the majority of the SAR reported have been carried out using D_2 receptors. These aspects are covered in Chapter 12.3 and will not be reiterated here. As mentioned in Section 12.4.7.1.3, the two enantiomers of sulpiride have different selectivities, with (S)-sulpiride (56b) being the more active as a DA_2 antagonist.[94]

A number of benzamides have been used as antiemetics, and it is thought that they block a population of D_2/DA_2 receptors in the chemoreceptor trigger zone (CTZ) of the area postrema. It is interesting to note that the properties of some metoclopramide analogues, which are not D_2/DA_2 antagonists, have been described.[98] However, a number of these compounds have been found to block the emesis induced by *cis*-platin.[98]

12.4.7.2.4   N-Alkylpiperidines

Compounds such as pimozide (62) have been used as DA_2 antagonists in the past,[5] but the compound of most interest in this group is domperidone (63).[99] Domperidone is a very selective DA_2 antagonist but, unlike the majority of its predecessors, it does not penetrate the blood–brain barrier, and consequently it has been extremely useful in the analysis of the peripheral actions of DA_2/D_2 agonists.[100] Domperidone emerged from a group of compounds that were being investigated for their potential to modify the effects of D_2 receptors and, as might be expected, the SAR at DA_2 receptors are very limited.

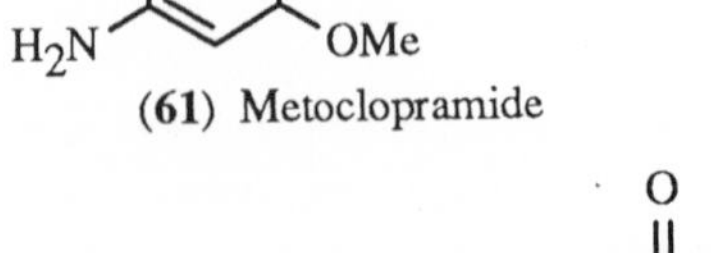

(61) Metoclopramide

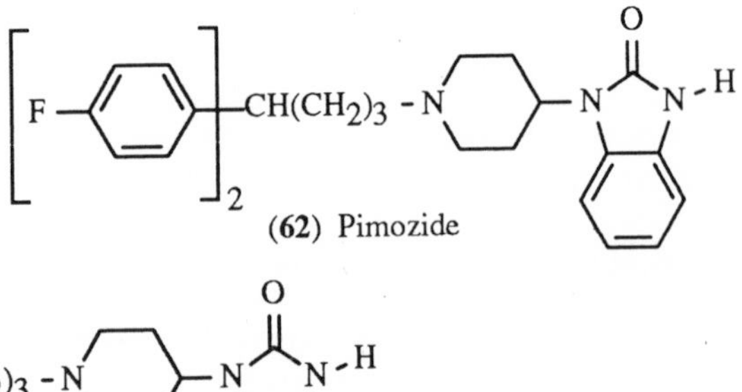

(62) Pimozide

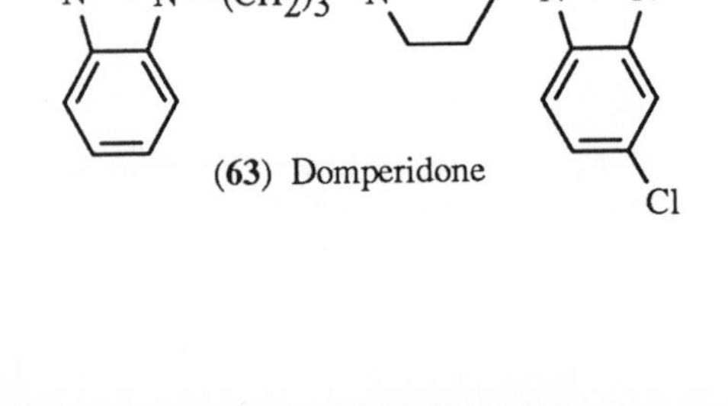

(63) Domperidone

12.4.7.2.5 *Irreversible antagonists*

It has been found that the use of an irreversible antagonist can help in the analysis of receptor responses by reducing receptor reserve, or by producing a long-lasting antagonism of receptors that would otherwise interfere with those being studied. A number of chemical modifications to agonists or competitive antagonists have given rise to irreversible antagonists. The replacement of an *N*-alkyl group with an *N*-2-chloroethyl group affords a mustard derivative that is presumed to alkylate a nucleophile at the active site of the receptor. Alternatively a photolabile group has been incorporated into the antagonist and, upon irradiation, the photoproduct, *e.g.* a nitrene in the case of an azido-substituted antagonist, reacts with a component of the active site of the receptor. Both of these approaches have been extended to D_2/DA_2 receptor analysis, *e.g.* to the *N*-2-chloroethyl derivative of norapomorphine (**18c**),[86] to similar derivatives of 6,7-ADTN,[77] and to the azido derivative of a number of DA antagonists.[40a]

12.4.8 BIOLOGICAL PROPERTIES OF SELECTED DOPAMINE AGONISTS AND ANTAGONISTS IN ANIMALS AND HUMANS

12.4.8.1 DA_1 Receptor Agonists

The activation of postjunctional DA_1 receptors on blood vessels results in vasodilation, activation of those on renal tubules results in diuresis and natriuresis, and activation of those in the adrenal cortex results in the inhibition of aldosterone release. Given these observations, DA_1 receptor agonists have been investigated for use in the treatment of diseases such as hypertension, acute and chronic heart and renal failure, and they could have some application in the treatment of angina pectoris.[2-6,47] Many advances have been made and a number of parenteral preparations are being used, particularly for acute conditions, but a satisfactory, orally effective DA_1 agonist has not been developed.

12.4.8.2 DA_2 Receptor Agonists

The activation of prejunctional DA_2 receptors on sympathetic nerve endings effects a reduction in the release of noradrenaline. For the nerves on blood vessels this gives rise to a vasodilation (a reduction in the neurogenic vasoconstriction) and for the nerves involved in control of heart rate this results in a bradycardia. A considerable amount of effort has been directed towards using the former effect as a basis for producing peripheral vasodilators for the treatment of hypertension, with the latter effect reducing the expected reflex tachycardia.[2-6,33,47] Unfortunately, with the compounds currently available, it has proved to be impossible to separate the actions of agonists at peripheral DA_2 receptors from their actions at the DA_2/D_2 receptors in the CTZ that, when stimulated, produce nausea and emesis.

12.4.8.3 Biological Properties of DA Receptor Agonists

12.4.8.3.1 *Dopamine (1)*

DA is a mixed DA_1/DA_2 agonist, but it is also an agonist at β_1, α_1 and α_2 adrenoceptors, with a modest separation of these pharmacological effects at the therapeutic doses.[6,47,52,101,102] Such a multifactorial pharmacology produces a complex haemodynamic response during an intravenous infusion of DA (DA has very poor oral bioavailability and is not administered by that route). In humans at $< 3\,\mu g\,kg^{-1}\,min^{-1}$ DA_1 and DA_2 effects result in vasodilation; at about $3-6\,\mu g\,kg^{-1}\,min^{-1}$ this is accompanied by diuresis and natriuresis and there may be some evidence of nausea and possibly emesis; at about $5-10\,\mu g\,kg^{-1}\,min^{-1}$ the inotropic effect and possibly an arrythmogenic effect that appears to be related to the β_1 adrenoceptor stimulation is present; at $> 10\,\mu g\,kg^{-1}\,min^{-1}$ the vasoconstriction caused by α_1/α_2 adrenoceptor stimulation is evident,[101] and can appear at lower doses.

Thus in acute heart failure, and other conditions that result in or from a low cardiac output, infusion rates of $1-10\,\mu g\,kg^{-1}\,min^{-1}$ are used, the therapeutic effect being derived from the afterload-reducing action of DA_1 (and DA_2) receptor stimulation, and also from the direct inotropic effect of β_1 adrenoceptor stimulation. In other low cardiac output states, such as shock, the high infusion rates are also used to take advantage of the α-mediated peripheral vasoconstriction that reduces the blood flow to nonessential organs.[101]

The major limitations of the use of DA are: (i) the lack of oral activity, (ii) the short duration of action, (iii) the nausea and emesis that result from the stimulation of DA_2 receptors in the CTZ, (iv) the arrhythmias that appear to accompany β_1 adrenoceptor stimulation, and (v) the α-adrenoceptor-mediated vasoconstrictor activity.

12.4.8.3.2 L-DOPA (3)

The most common treatment for Parkinson's disease is the oral administration of a combination of L-DOPA with a peripheral DOPA decarboxylase inhibitor. This combination maximizes the amount of L-DOPA that is taken up into the CNS, where it acts as a prodrug for DA which is produced by decarboxylation.[12] In the absence of the peripheral decarboxylase inhibitor L-DOPA is converted into DA which gives rise to significant peripheral physiological effects.[102,103]

A dose of 1–1.5 g of L-DOPA appears to be equivalent to an infusion rate of 2–4 μg kg^{-1} min^{-1} of DA.[102] Doses of 1–8 g d^{-1}, usually in divided doses, have been used in the treatment of hypertension and chronic heart failure by taking advantage of the DA_1- (and DA_2-) mediated vasodilation.[102,103]

The occurrence of nausea and emesis, a result of DA_2-mediated effects, has limited the use of L-DOPA,[102] although there is a rapid tachyphylaxis to these effects. The postural hypotension sometimes seen may also be related to DA_2 receptor stimulation.[102]

12.4.8.3.3 Dopexamine hydrochloride, Dopacard (FPL 60278AR; 12)

Dopexamine hydrochloride was discovered during attempts to simplify the complex pharmacology observed with DA.[52] In animal studies it has been shown to be a selective DA_1 receptor and β_2 adrenoceptor agonist with some DA_2 receptor agonist activity but very little β_1 and no α adrenoceptor stimulant activity.[104] It is also a potent inhibitor of the Uptake$_1$ process for noradrenaline.[105] Like DA, dopexamine hydrochloride has a very poor bioavailability and is administered by intravenous infusion.

In humans dopexamine hydrochloride is being used for the treatment of acute heart failure, cardiovascular crises in chronic heart failure and other conditions that result in or from a low cardiac output.[52,106] It also shows promise as a means of cardiac support following coronary by-pass surgery,[106] and is being investigated in the treatment of sepsis. Intravenous infusions of 0.5–10 μg kg^{-1} min^{-1} have been used, the most common dose being 0.5–6 μg kg^{-1} min^{-1}.

Few side effects have been reported. A tachycardia is noticeable at doses that are above the commonly used therapeutic doses; there is some evidence for a modest tachyphylaxis, but little evidence for any nausea or emesis.

12.4.8.3.4 Fenoldopam mesylate (SKF 82526J; 25)

Fenoldopam is a selective DA_1 agonist (with some α_2 adrenoceptor antagonist activity). Its discovery and development have been the subject of a number of comprehensive reviews.[4,25,102,107,108] It is one of the more important compounds to have emerged in recent years both from the point of view of the understanding of DA_1 receptor effects and the potential of such a compound in the treatment of cardiovascular diseases. In humans doses of 25–100 mg orally have been shown to produce an antihypertensive effect, but unfortunately this was of short duration, as fenoldopam is subject to a large first pass effect.[102,107,108] Beneficial effects have been seen with oral doses of 50–200 mg in studies of chronic heart failure patients; no tolerance was seen after multiple dosing and it remains to be seen if fenoldopam becomes established in this therapeutic area.[108] Fenoldopam, in doses of 0.025–0.5 μg kg^{-1} min^{-1}, shows some promise as an intravenous therapy for acute conditions, *e.g.* in hypertensive crises[109] and in heart failure.[110]

There are some side effects that have been noted. As might be expected a mild tachycardia and a low incidence of headache and flushing at higher doses have been reported,[102] but of most concern is the increase in renin secretion.[107,108] It is assumed that this latter effect is the result of stimulation of DA_1 receptors on the juxtaglomerular cells.

12.4.8.3.5 *Ibopamine (SB 7505; 27a)*

Ibopamine is a prodrug of epinine and has been extensively studied in both animals and humans.[68] The presence of the ester groups protects the catechol from metabolism in the gut wall and the liver. This modification has converted the short acting, orally inactive, epinine into an orally active, much longer acting analogue that releases free epinine by the action of plasma esterase activity. Having said this, doses of 50–300 mg (equivalent to an infusion of about 4 μg kg^{-1} min^{-1} of DA or epinine) are still required to produce a significant effect in chronic heart failure patients. It remains to be seen if ibopamine becomes established in the therapy of chronic heart failure.

12.4.8.3.6 N,N-*Dialkyl-DA derivatives*

N,N-Di-n-propyl-DA (**64a**)[102,111] and N-n-butyl-N-n-propyl-DA (**64b**)[102,112] have been studied quite extensively, in particular with respect to their effects on haemodynamic parameters following intravenous infusion. The latter compound has been administered to humans in doses of up to 20 μg kg^{-1} min^{-1} and produced effects that were characteristic of a mixed DA$_1$/DA$_2$ agonist, but at doses of 40 μg kg^{-1} min^{-1} emesis occurred.[102]

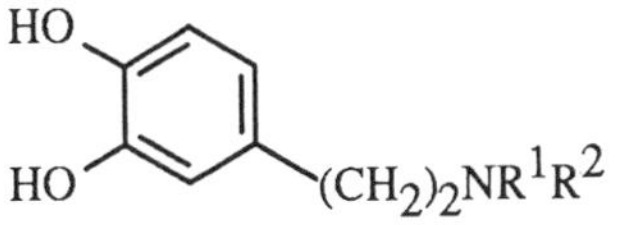

HO,

HO $(CH_2)_2NR^1R^2$

(**64a**) $R^1 = R^2 = Pr^n$
(**64b**) $R^1 = Pr^n, R^2 = Bu^n$

12.4.8.3.7 *Ergolines*

Given the propensity for DA$_2$ agonists to cause nausea and emesis, it has not been possible to use the ergolines, such as bromocriptine (**41b**), lergotrile (**42a**), pergolide (**42b**) and lisuride (**42c**), in humans as a treatment for cardiovascular diseases,[5,6,107,113] although bromocriptine and pergolide are used to treat hyperprolactinaemia.[5,6,114] Some of the more recent ergolines that have been investigated as antihypertensive agents appear to be less prone to cause nausea and emesis, *e.g.* Hydergine.[102]

In animals many of the ergolines[5,6,111,115] and the 9-oxaergolines (**43**)[116] are quite effective antihypertensive agents; however, the majority cause nausea and emesis as a result of the DA$_2$ agonist activity and most compounds are agonists and/or antagonists at other receptor types; a feature that results in some interspecies differences in activity.[5,6]

12.4.8.3.8 *LY 141865 (47a) and quinpirole (LY 171555; 47b)*

Studies in humans using quinpirole (0.1–14 mg d^{-1}) have shown that there is no reduction in the blood pressure of normotensive or hypotensive individuals, with a slight increase in blood pressure in some cases.[2,107] These observations differ from those seen in most animal models, where both quinpirole and LY 141865 are capable of reducing both blood pressure and heart rate.[2,107,117] In conscious rats quinpirole causes an increase in blood pressure, thought to be the result of the stimulation of central D$_2$ receptors, an observation that has been correlated with the equivalent effect seen in humans. As might have been expected, LY 141865 is an emetic in dogs.

12.4.8.3.9 *2-Aminotetralins*

Although a number of 2-aminotetralins have been extensively studied in animals,[4,6,33–36,49–51] very few members of this group of compounds have found any therapeutic applications. It appears that only those compounds that do not contain a catechol moiety show any promise, and the most notable of these are the monohydroxy derivatives, *e.g.* N-0437 (**65**). This compound is a potent DA$_2$/D$_2$ agonist that has been claimed to lower intraocular pressure, and is also being evaluated in the treatment of Parkinson's disease.[118]

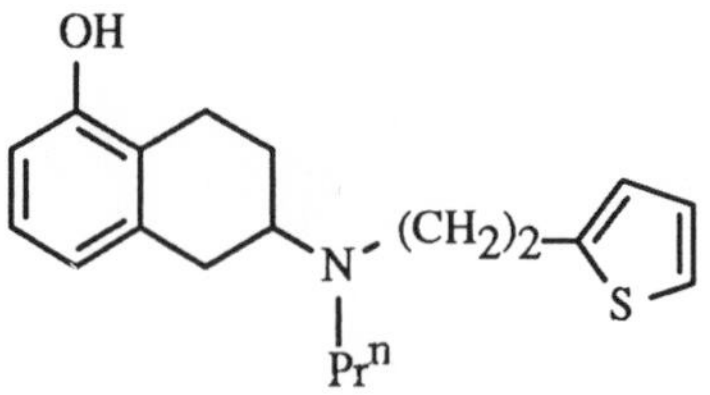

(65) N-0437

12.4.8.3.10   Apomorphine (18a) and other aporphine analogues

Apomorphine is one of the most extensively studied of the DA receptor agonists and, together with its *N-n*-propyl derivative (**18b**), is a selective DA_2 agonist.[4,6,34,83] Apomorphine has been used as an emetic in humans (0.1 mg kg^{-1}, subcutaneously).[119]

12.4.8.4   DA Receptor Antagonists

Despite the extensive use of DA receptor antagonists in the treatment of abnormalities of the CNS, there are very few therapeutic applications for this group of compounds in peripheral diseases. DA_2/D_2 antagonists are used as antiemetics, a result of their ability to block a population of DA_2/D_2 receptors in the CTZ of the area postrema,[42] and they also have some actions on the gastrointestinal system.[91,97,99]

The importance of DA receptor antagonists in the study of DA receptors in animals cannot be overemphasized. They have played a pivotal role in the classification of differing receptor types, and also in the distinction between the central and peripheral actions of DA receptor agonists.[4,5,34,36,90,100]

12.4.8.5   Biological Properties of DA Receptor Antagonists

12.4.8.5.1   SCH 23390 (57a) and other 3-benzazepines

SCH 23390 is one of the most useful and selective DA_1 receptor antagonists that has been described.[25,90] It is a member of a family of compounds, *e.g.* SKF 83566 (**57b**), that share this property and they have been extensively used in the classification of the different DA receptor types.[4,25,34,36,90]

12.4.8.5.2   Bulbocapnine (55) and other aporphines

A number of aporphines are also DA antagonists[86] and of these the most commonly used is bulbocapnine,[92] a compound that is a selective DA_1 antagonist. *N*-2-Chloroethylnorapomorphine (**18c**) has been shown to be an irreversible antagonist of DA_2 receptors,[87] a property that is useful in the analysis of DA receptor responses.

12.4.8.5.3   Domperidone (63)

Domperidone is one of the most selective DA_2 antagonists and it does not appear to penetrate the blood–brain barrier. As a consequence of this combination of properties it has been particularly useful in the analysis of peripheral *versus* central DA_2 receptor effects.[34,36,100] Given the ability of domperidone to block the DA_2 receptors in the CTZ, it has antiemetic properties in humans (30–60 mg d^{-1}).[99]

12.4.8.5.4   Sulpiride (56) and other benzamides

An interesting aspect of the action of sulpiride emerged when it was found that the two enantiomers have different properties with respect to the antagonism of DA receptors. Thus

(R)-sulpiride (**56b**) is a nonselective DA_1/DA_2 receptor antagonist, whereas (S)-sulpiride (**56b**) and several other benzamides, *e.g.* metoclopramide (**61**), are selective DA_2 receptor antagonists.[94] A number of the benzamides have also been assessed as antiemetics, with metoclopramide being used for this purpose in humans (0.5 mg kg^{-1} d^{-1}).[97]

12.4.8.5.5 Haloperidol (58) and other butyrophenones

Haloperidol is a selective DA_2 receptor antagonist, but the DA_2/DA_1 separation is dependent upon the animal model being used. Thus in the anaesthetized dog the DA_1/DA_2 separation is modest (< 2), whereas in the anaesthetized cat the separation is much larger.[35,44]

A large number of butyrophenones have been used in radioligand binding studies, with radiolabelled analogues being particularly common, usually ^{3}H, but also ^{14}C (^{11}C or ^{13}C have also been prepared).[35,44] [^{3}H]Spiperone (**59**) is probably the most widely used, although many others have been prepared and investigated.

ACKNOWLEDGEMENTS

The author would like to express his thanks to George Smith for his permission to quote the unpublished results shown in Table 1, and to various colleagues, past and present, who have contributed in many ways to the Fisons Dopamine Projects; particularly to John Dixon, George Smith and Brian Springthorpe for hours of thought-provoking discussion and also for critically reading this chapter and making many useful suggestions for its improvement.

12.4.9 REFERENCES

1. I. Creese and C. M. Fraser (eds.), 'Receptor Biochemistry and Methodology', Liss, New York, 1987, vol. 8.
2. J. P. Hieble, *Annu. Rep. Med. Chem.*, 1987, **22**, 107.
3. R. Felder and R. M. Carey, in 'Brain Peptides and Catecholamines in Cardiovascular Regulation', ed. J. P. Buckley and C. M. Ferrario, Raven Press, New York, 1987, p. 79.
4. C. Kaiser and T. Jain, *Med. Res. Rev.*, 1985, **5**, 145.
5. I. Cavero, R. Massingham and F. Lefevre-Borg, *Life Sci.*, 1982, **31**, 939, 1059.
6. M. F. Lokhandwala and R. J. Barrett, *J. Auton. Pharmacol.*, 1982, **3**, 189.
7. J.-L. Imbs and J. Schwartz (eds.), *Adv. Pharmacol. Ther., Proc. Int. Congr. Pharmacol., 7th, 1978*, 1979.
8. A. S. Horn, J. Korf and B. H. C. Westerink (eds.), 'The Neurobiology of Dopamine', Academic Press, London, 1979.
9. R. Roth, in ref. 8, p. 101.
10. R. J. Walker, in 'The Neurobiology of Dopamine Systems', ed. W. Winlow and R. Markstein, Manchester University Press, Manchester, 1986, p. 3.
11. T. L. Sourkes, in ref. 8, p. 123.
12. N. P. Quinn, *Drugs*, 1984, **28**, 236.
13. Z. Lackovic and M. Relja, *Fed. Proc., Fed. Am. Soc. Exp. Biol.*, 1983, **42**, 3000.
14. L. L. Iversen, in 'Handbook of Psychopharmacology', ed. L. L. Iversen, S. D. Iversen and S. H. Snyder, Plenum Press, New York, 1975, vol. 3, p. 381.
15. G. Hellman, G. Hertting and B. Peskar, *Br. J. Pharmacol.*, 1971, **41**, 256.
16. S. E. Purdy, J. A. Blair and P. A. Barford, *Biochem. J.*, 1981, **195**, 769; L. Hiripi and G. B. Stefano, *Life Sci.*, 1980, **27**, 1205.
17. L. I. Kruse, C. Kaiser, W. E. DeWolf, Jr., J. S. Frazee, R. W. Erickson, M. Ezekiel, E. O. Ohlstein, R. R. Ruffolo, Jr. and B. A. Berkowitz, *J. Med. Chem.*, 1986, **29**, 887 and refs. therein.
18. L. I. Kruse, C. Kaiser, W. E. DeWolf, Jr., J. S. Frazee, E. Garvey, E. L. Hilbert, W. A. Faulkner, K. E. Flaim, J. L. Sawyer and B. A. Berkowitz, *J. Med. Chem.*, 1986, **29**, 2465.
19. K. Tipton, in ref. 8, p. 145.
20. I. J. Kopin, *Pharmacol. Rev.*, 1985, **37**, 333.
21. H. C. Guldberg, in ref. 8, p. 133; B. H. C. Westerink, *Neurochem. Int.*, 1985, **7**, 221.
22. R. M. Weinshilboum, *Fed. Proc., Fed. Am. Soc. Exp. Biol.*, 1986, **45**, 2220, 2223.
23. K. Murata, K. Noda, K. Kohno and M. Samejima, *J. Pharm. Sci.*, 1988, **77**, 565; T. Bradley, P. Hjemdhal, G. F. Dibona, B. A. Osikowska, P. S. Sever and L. I. Goldberg, *Acta Physiol. Scand.*, 1985, **125**, 739.
24. L. K. Low and N. Castagnoli, in 'Burger's Medicinal Chemistry', ed. M. E. Wolff, 4th edn., Wiley, New York, 1980, part 1, p. 182.
25. J. Weinstock, J. P. Hieble and J. W. Wilson, III, *Drugs of the Future*, 1985, **10**, 645.
26. C. J. Grol, in ref. 8, p. 7.
27. J. J. Warsh, A. S. Chiu and D. D. Godse, in 'Analysis of Biogenic Amines', ed. G. Baker and R. Coutts, Elsevier, Amsterdam, 1982, part A, p. 203.
28. J. E. Swagzdis, R. Gifford and B. A. Mico, *J. Chromatogr.*, 1985, **345**, 203; M. A. Elchisak, *Fed. Proc., Fed. Am. Soc. Exp. Biol.*, 1986, **45**, 2241.
29. L. I. Goldberg, in ref. 7, p. 1.

30. M. A. Enero and S. Z. Langer, *Naunyn-Schmiedeberg's Arch. Pharmacol.*, 1975, **289**, 179.
31. L. I. Goldberg and J. D. Kohli, *Commun. Psychopharmacol.*, 1979, **3**, 447.
32. M. H. Sabouni, K. A. Alkadhi and M. F. Lokhandwala, *J. Pharmacol. Exp. Ther.*, 1986, **236**, 65
33. J. L. Willems, W. A. Buylaert, R. A. Lefebvre and M. G. Bogaert, *Pharmacol. Rev.*, 1985, **37**, 165.
34. J. D. Kohli and L. I. Goldberg, in ref. 1, p. 97; L. I. Goldberg, J. D. Kohli and D. Glock, in 'Dopaminergic Systems and Their Regulation'; IUPHAR Satellite Symposium, ed. G. N. Woodruff, J. A. Poat and P. J. Roberts, Macmillan, London, 1986, p. 195.
35. O.-E. Brodde, *Life Sci.*, 1982, **31**, 289.
36. A. Hilditch and G. M. Drew, *Trends Pharmacol. Sci.*, 1985, 396.
37. S. Z. Langer and M. L. Dubocovich, in ref. 7, p. 233.
38. E. J. Hess and I. Creese, in ref. 1, p. 1.
39. E. Kelly and S. R. Nahorski, *Rev. Neurosci.*, 1986, **1**, 35.
40. (a) H. B. Niznik, *Mol. Cell. Endocrinol.*, 1987, **54**, 1; (b) P. G. Strange, in ref. 1, p. 29.
41. E. Stefanini and Y. Clement-Cornier, in 'Apomorphine and other Dopaminometics', ed. G. U. Corsini and G. L. Gessa, Raven Press, New York, 1981, vol. 1, p. 297.
42. J. H. Barnes, *Mol. Aspects Med.*, 1984, **7**, 399.
43. H. C. Hemmings, Jr., I. Walaas, C. C. Ouimet and P. Greengard, in ref. 1, p, 115.
44. P. Seeman, *Pharmacol. Rev.*, 1980, **32**, 229.
45. E. M. Brown, M. F. Attie, S. Reen, D. G. Gardner, J. Kebabian and G. D. Aurbach, *Mol. Pharmacol.*, 1980, **18**, 335.
46. P. J. Shultz, J. R. Sedor and H. E. Abboud, *Am. J. Physiol.*, 1987, **253**, H358.
47. L. I. Goldberg, *Pharmacol. Rev.*, 1972, **24**, 1.
48. G. M. Drew, A. J. Gower, A. Hilditch and A. S. Marriott, *Br. J. Pharmacol.*, 1982, **75**, 146P.
49. J. G. Cannon, *Annu. Rev. Pharmacol. Toxicol.*, 1983, **23**, 103.
50. C. Kaiser, in 'New Methods of Drug Research', ed. A. Makriyannis, Prous, Barcelona, Spain, 1987, vol. 1, p. 129.
51. H. E. Katerinopoulos and D. I. Schuster, *Drugs of the Future*, 1987, **12**, 223.
52. R. A. Brown, R. C. Brown, J. C. Hall, J. Dixon, J. B. Farmer, R. A. Foulds, F. Ince, S. E. O'Connor, W. T. Simpson, G. W. Smith, B. Springthorpe and A. C. Tinker, *Spec. Publ. R. Soc. Chem.*, 1986, **55**, 169.
53. A. Hilditch and G. M. Drew, *Eur. J. Pharmacol.*, 1981, **72**, 287.
54. R. M. Riggs, A. T. McKenzie, S. R. Byrn, D. E. Nicols, M. M. Foreman and L. L. Truex, *J. Med. Chem.*, 1987, **30**, 1914.
55. R. J. Crooks and G. R. Martin, *Br. J. Pharmacol.*, 1979, **67**, 474P.
56. J. R. McCarthy, J. McCowan, M. B. Zimmerman, M. A. Wenger and L. W. Emmert, *J. Med. Chem.*, 1986, **29**, 1586.
57. J. Dixon, F. Ince and B. Springthorpe (Fisons PLC), *Eur. Pat.* 223 598 (1987) (*Chem. Abstr.*, 1988, **108**, 55 643r).
58. J. Weinstock, D. E. Gaitanopoulos, O. D. Stringer, R. G. Franz, J. P. Hieble, L. B. Kinter, W. A. Mann, K. E. Flaim and G. Gessner, *J. Med. Chem.*, 1987, **30**, 1166.
59. K. Brown, R. C. Brown, J. Dixon, A. C. Tinker, R. A. Brown, S. E. O'Connor and G. W. Smith, *Med. Chem., Proc. Int. Symp., 8th, 1984*, 1985, 454.
60. F. Ince, B. Springthorpe, R. A. Brown, J. C. Hall, S. E. O'Connor and G. W. Smith, *Med. Chem., Proc. Int. Symp., 8th, 1984*, 1985, 442.
61. J. Weinstock, D. E. Gaitanopoulos, H.-J. Oh, F. R. Pfeiffer, C. B. Karash, J. W. Venslavsky, H. M. Sarau, K. E. Flaim, J. P. Hieble and C. Kaiser, *J. Med. Chem.*, 1986, **29**, 1615.
62. A. S. Horn, B. Kaptein, T. B. A. Mulder, J. B. de Vries and H. Wynberg, *J. Med. Chem.*, 1984, **27**, 1340.
63. R. M. Riggs, D. E. Nichols, M. M. Foreman, L. E. Truex, D. Glock and J. D. Kohli, *J. Med. Chem.*, 1987, **30**, 1454.
64. P. A. Dandridge, C. Kaiser, M. Brenner, D. Gaitanopoulos, L. D. Davis, R. L. Webb, J. A. Foley and H. M. Sarau, *J. Med. Chem.*, 1984, **27**, 28.
65. (a) J. Weinstock, D. L. Ladd, J. W. Wilson, C. K. Brush, N. C. F. Yim, G. Gallagher, Jr., M. E. McCarthy, J. Silvestri, H. M. Sarau, K. E. Flaim, D. M. Ackerman, P. E. Setler, A. J. Tobia and R. A. Hahn, *J. Med. Chem.*, 1986, **29**, 2315; (b) J. Weinstock, H.-J. Oh, C. W. DeBrosse, D. E. Eggleston, M. Wise, K. E. Flaim, G. W. Gessner, J. L. Sawyer and C. Kaiser, *J. Med. Chem.*, 1987, **30**, 1303.
66. S. T. Ross, R. G. Franz, G. Gallagher, Jr., M. Brenner, J. W. Wilson, R. M. DeMarinis, J. P. Hieble and H. M. Sarau, *J. Med. Chem.*, 1987, **30**, 35.
67. N. Bodor and J. J. Kaminski, *Annu. Rep. Med. Chem.*, 1987, **22**, 303.
68. O. Visioli (ed.), *Arzneim.-Forsch.*, 1986, **36**, 285.
69. T. M. Dolak and L. I. Goldberg, *Annu. Rep. Med. Chem.*, 1981, **16**, 103.
70. A. Garzon-Aburbeh, J. H. Poupaert, M. Claesen and P. Dumont, *J. Med. Chem.*, 1986, **29**, 687; D. R. Cooper, C. Marrel, H. Van de Waterbeemd, B. Testa, P. Jenner and C. D. Marsden, *J. Pharm. Pharmacol.*, 1987, **39**, 809.
71. Y.-A. Chang, J. Ares, K. Anderson, B. Sabol, R. A. Wallace, T. Farooqui, N. Uretsky and D. D. Miller, *J. Med. Chem.*, 1987, **30**, 214.
72. G. Gallagher, Jr., P. G. Lavanchy, J. W. Wilson, J. P. Hieble and R. M. DeMarinis, *J. Med. Chem.*, 1985, **28**, 1533; R. M. DeMarinis, G. Gallagher, Jr., R. F. Hall, R. G. Franz, C. Webster, W. F. Huffman, M. S. Schwartz, C. Kaiser, S. T. Ross, J. W. Wilson and J. P. Heible, *J. Med. Chem.*, 1986, **29**, 939.
73. R. D. Clark, J. M. Caroon, N. E. Isaac, D. L. McClelland, A. D. Michel, T. A. Petty, R. P. Rosenkrantz and L. D. Waterbury, *J. Pharm. Sci.*, 1987, **76**, 411.
74. R. A. Brown, Y. Crimp and S. E. O'Connor, *Br. J. Pharmacol.*, 1982, **77**, 536P.
75. N. R. A. Beeley, G. Cremer, A. Dorlhene and J.-P. Meingan, *Med. Chem., Abstr. Int. Symp., 9th, 1986*, 1986, 299; N. R. A. Beeley, G. Cremer, M. Dimsdale and J. Manoury (Synthelabo S. A.), *Eur. Pat. Appl.*, EP 74 903 (1983) (*Chem. Abstr.*, 1983, **99**, 53 413n).
76. D. E. Nichols, J. M. Cassady, P. E. Persons, J. A. Clemens and E. B. Smalstig, *J. Med. Chem.*, 1989, **32**, 2128.
77. A. W. Hall, R. J. K. Taylor, S. H. Simmonds and P. G. Strange, *J. Med. Chem.*, 1987, **30**, 1879.
78. R. Nordmann and A. Widmer, *J. Med. Chem.*, 1985, **28**, 1540.
79. J. H. Jones, P. S. Anderson, J. J. Baldwin, B. V. Clineschmidt, D. E. McClure, G. F. Lundell, W. C. Randall, G. E. Martin, M. Williams, J. M. Hirschfield, G. Smith and P. K. Lumma, *J. Med. Chem.*, 1984, **27**, 1607; D. Dykstra, B. Hazelhoff, T. B. A. Mulder, J. B. de Vries, H. Wynberg and A. S. Horn, *Eur. J. Med. Chem.—Chim. Ther.*, 1985, **20**, 247.
80. A. L. Blumberg, J. W. Wilson and J. P. Hieble, *J. Cardiovasc. Pharmacol.*, 1985, **7**, 723.

81. M. Goldstein, D. B. Calne, A. Lieberman and M. O. Thorner, 'Ergot Compounds and Brain Function', Raven Press, New York, 1980; B. Berde and H. O. Schild, 'Handbook of Experimental Pharmacology', Springer-Verlag, New York, 1978, vol. 49.

82. R. C. Booher, E. C. Kornfeld, E. B. Smalstig and J. A. Clemens, *J. Med. Chem.*, 1987, **30**, 580.

83. F. Claudi, G. Cristalli, S. Martelli, V. Perlini, M. Massi and F. Venturi, *J. Med. Chem.*, 1986, **29**, 1061.

84. J. Kidric, D. Kocjan and D. Hadzi, *Experientia*, 1986, **42**, 327; D. Kocjan, M. Hodoscek and D. Hadzi, *J. Med. Chem.*, 1986, **29**, 1418; H. Wikstrom, J.-H. Lii and N. L. Allinger, *J. Med. Chem.*, 1987, **30**, 1928.

85. S. Lal, *Prog. Neuro-Psychopharmacol. Biol. Psychiatry*, 1988, **12**, 117; G. L. Gessa and G. U. Corsini (eds.), 'Apomorphine and Other Dopaminomimetics', Raven Press, New York, 1981, vols. 1 and 2.

86. J. L. Neumeyer, S.-J. Law, R. J. Baldessarini and N. S. Kula, *J. Med. Chem.*, 1980, **23**, 594.

87. M. Froimowitz, J. L. Neumeyer and R. J. Baldessarini, *J. Med. Chem.*, 1986, **29**, 1570.

88. J. G. Cannon, D. C. Furlano, R. G. Dushin, Y. Chang, S. R. Baird, L. N. Soliman, J. R. Flynn, J. P. Long and R. K. Bhatnagar, *J. Med. Chem.*, 1986, **29**, 2016.

89. B. A. Mico, J. E. Swagzdis, D. A. Federowicz and K. Straub, *J. Pharm. Sci.*, 1986, **75**, 929.

90. A. Barnett, *Drugs of the Future*, 1986, **11**, 49.

91. J. L. Neumeyer and S. Szabo, *Eur. J. Pharmacol.*, 1983, **88**, 273; H. Kilbinger and T. R. Weihrauch, *Pharmacology*, 1982, **25**, 61; C. J. E. Niemegeers, *Psychopharmacology*, 1982, **78**, 210.

92. J. D. Kohli, D. Glock and L. I. Goldberg, *J. Pharm. Pharmacol.*, 1986, **38**, 401.

93. S. E. O'Connor and R. A. Brown, *Gen. Pharmacol.*, 1982, **13**, 185.

94. (a) R. A. Brown and S. E. O'Connor, *Br. J. Pharmacol.*, 1981, **73**, 189P; (b) A. S. Bass and N. W. Robie, *J. Pharmacol. Exp. Ther.*, 1984, **229**, 67.

95. T. Skarsfeldt and J. J. Larsen, *Eur. J. Pharmacol.*, 1988, **148**, 389.

96. O. S. Steinsland and J. P. Hieble, *Science (Washington, D.C.)*, 1978, **199**, 443.

97. R. Albibi and R. W. McCallum, *Ann. Int. Med.*, 1983, **98**, 86; R. A. Harrington, C. W. Hamilton, R. N. Brogden, J. A. Linkewich and J. A. Romankiewicz, *Drugs*, 1983, **25**, 451.

98. (a) M. S. Hadley, F. D. King, B. McRitchie, D. H. Turner and E. A. Watts, *J. Med. Chem.*, 1985, **28**, 1843; (b) I. Monkovic, D. Willner, M. A. Adam, M. Brown, R. R. Crenshaw, C. E. Fuller, P. F. Juby, G. M. Luke, J. A. Matiskella and T. A. Montzka, *J. Med. Chem.*, 1988, **31**, 1548.

99. R. N. Brogden, A. A. Carmine, R. C. Heel, T. M. Speight and G. S. Avery, *Drugs*, 1982, **24**, 360.

100. (a) J. L. Willems, M. G. Bogaert and W. Buylaert, *Jpn. J. Pharmacol.*, 1981, **31**, 131; (b) J. D. Kohli, D. Glock and L. I. Goldberg, *Eur. J. Pharmacol.*, 1983, **89**, 137.

101. M. R. Lee, *Clin. Sci.*, 1982, **62**, 439; J. R. Plachetka, in 'Cardiovascular Drugs and the Management of Heart Disease', ed. G. W. Ewy and R. Bressler, Raven Press, New York, 1982, p. 69.

102. L. I. Goldberg and M. B. Murphy, *Clin. Exp.—Theory Pract.*, 1987, **A9**, 1023.

103. S. I. Rajfer, A. H. Anton, J. D. Rossen and L. I. Goldberg, *N. Engl. J. Med.*, 1984, **310**, 1357; S. I. Rajfer, J. D. Rossen, J. W. Nemanich, F. L. Douglas, F. Davis and J. Osinski, *J. Am. Coll. Cardiol.*, 1987, **10**, 1286.

104. R. A. Brown, J. Dixon, J. B. Farmer, J. C. Hall, R. G. Humphries, F. Ince, S. E. O'Connor, W. T. Simpson and G. W. Smith, *Br. J. Pharmacol.*, 1985, **85**, 599; G. W. Smith, J. C. Hall, J. B. Farmer and W. T. Simpson, *J. Pharm. Pharmacol.*, 1987, **39**, 636.

105. P. D. Mitchell, G. W. Smith, E. Wells and P. A. West, *Br. J. Pharmacol.*, 1987, **92**, 265; A. S. Bass, J. D. Kohli, N. Lubbers and L. I. Goldberg, *J. Pharmacol. Exp. Ther.*, 1987, **242**, 940; A. S. Bass, J. D. Kohli, N. Lubbers and L. I. Goldberg, *Fed. Proc., Fed. Am. Soc. Exp. Biol.*, 1987, **46**, 1145.

106. P. G. Hugenholz (ed.), *Am. J. Cardiol.*, 1988, **62**, suppl. C.

107. R. A. Hahn, *Drug Dev. Res.*, 1984, **4**, 285.

108. M. F. Lokhandwala, *Drug Dev. Res.*, 1987, **10**, 123.

109. R. R. Weber, C. E. McCoy, J. A. Ziemniak, E. D. Frederickson, L. I. Goldberg and M. B. Murphy, *Br. J. Clin. Pharmacol.*, 1988, **25**, 17.

110. J. B. Young, C. A. Leon, C. M. Pratt, C. Kingry, A. A. Taylor and R. Roberts, *Am. Heart J.*, 1988, **115**, 378.

111. J. G. Cannon, *Drugs of the Future*, 1982, **7**, 469.

112. J. Z. Ginos, *Drugs of the Future*, 1986, **11**, 191.

113. T. T. Yen, N. B. Stamm and J. A. Clemens, *Life Sci.*, 1979, **25**, 209.

114. L. Lemberger, R. Crabtree and J. T. Callaghan, *Clin. Pharmacol. Ther.*, 1980, **27**, 642.

115. A. Temperilli, D. Ruggieri and P. Salvati, *Eur. J. Med. Chem.*, 1988, **23**, 77; E. Fluckiger, U. Briner, B. Clark, A. Closse, A. Enz, P. Gull, A. Hofmann, R. Markstein, L. Tolscvai and H. R. Wagner, *Experientia*, 1988, **44**, 431.

116. R. T. Owen, *Drugs of the Future*, 1983, **8**, 849.

117. R. Mannhold, *Drugs of the Future*, 1987, **12**, 558; Y. Igarashi, Y. F. Chen, J. M. Wyss, M. D. Lindheimer and S. Oparil, *Pharmacology*, 1987, **35**, 194.

118. A. S. Horn (Nelson Research and Development Co.), *U.S. Pat.* 4657925 (1987) (*Chem Abstr.*, 1987, **107**, 70818z); A. S. Horn, *Drugs of the Future*, 1987, **12**, 220.

119. 'Martindale, The Extra Pharmacopoeia', 28th edn., ed. J. E. F. Reynolds, Pharmaceutical Press, London, 1982, p. 891.

120. W. A. Buylaert, J. L. Willems and M. G. Bogaert, *J. Pharm. Pharmacol.*, 1978, **30**, 113.

121. M. P. Seiler and R. Markstein, *Mol. Pharmacol.*, 1982, **22**, 281.

122. M. F. Lokhandwala and M. L. Steenberg, *J. Pharmacol. Exp. Ther.*, 1984, **228**, 161.

123. J. D. Kohli, A. B. Weder, L. I. Goldberg and J. Z. Ginos, *J. Pharmacol. Exp. Ther.*, 1980. **213**, 370.

12.5

Histamine Receptors

DAVID G. COOPER and RODNEY C. YOUNG

Smith Kline & French Research Ltd, Welwyn, UK

GRAHAM J. DURANT

University of Toledo, OH, USA

and

C. ROBIN GANELLIN

University College, London, UK

12.5.1   INTRODUCTION

Histamine, 2-(imidazol-4-yl)ethylamine[1] (Figure 1), is a chemical messenger involved in various complex biological actions and it is widely distributed in the plant and animal kingdoms.[2] In mammals, including man, it occurs mainly in an inactive bound form in most body tissues. When released, it interacts with specific macromolecular receptors on the cell surface or within a target cell to elicit change in many different bodily functions.

Histamine was first reported in 1907 by Windaus and Vogt,[3] who synthesized the compound because of its chemical resemblance to the naturally occurring alkaloid pilocarpine and to the amino acid histidine; these authors had no inkling of its physiological activity and, indeed, it was not known at that time that histamine occurred in living organisms. Subsequently, in 1910, histamine was shown to be produced from histidine by bacterial decarboxylation,[4] to occur in ergot extracts, and to cause powerful pharmacological effects. In their classic papers Dale and Laidlaw showed[5,6] that histamine was a potent stimulant of smooth muscle contraction and that it caused pronounced vascular reactions which closely resembled the effects seen after anaphylactic shock.

These classic investigations laid the foundation for the intensive study that was to follow. Histamine was later found to be a constituent of many tissues and came to be regarded as a substance liberated in response to injurious stimuli. Although histamine had been shown by Popielski[7] in 1920 to stimulate secretion of gastric acid, attention was directed toward a pathological role for histamine rather than a physiological function.

12.5.2   ACTIONS OF HISTAMINE

Free histamine produces many powerful and varied biological actions and appears to act on specific receptors in the membranes of cell surfaces. For introductory discussions on the general

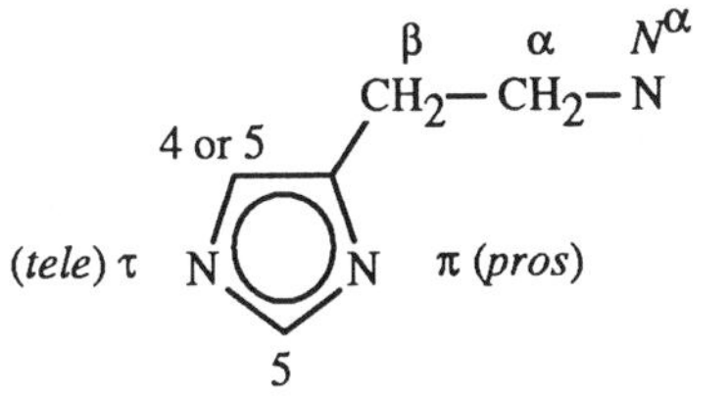

Figure 1 Histamine numbering according to Black and Ganellin.[1] Because the imidazole ring in histamine and histidine is tautomeric, much confusion has arisen from the lack of uniformity in selecting the particular nitrogen atom from which to begin numbering. Thus, systematic numbering by chemists assigns 3 to the ring nitrogen adjacent to side chain (which is then in the 4 position), whereas biochemists assign the number 1. To avoid this ambiguity the IUPAC–IUB Commission on Biochemical Nomenclature introduced the system that the imidazole N nearer to the side chain is designated *tele* (symbol π). The carbon atom between the two imidazole nitrogens is position 2 and other free carbon atom position is assigned 4, or 5 (or occasionally designated 4(5)-), depending on whether one of the imidazole nitrogen carries a substituent (see ref.1)

pharmacology and actions of histamine the reader is directed to standard reference works on pharmacology.[8-10] More research orientated texts are to be found in symposia proceedings[11-17] and special monographs.[18-24,487] Receptors for histamine have not yet been isolated or identified by physical or chemical means (but see Section 12.5.5.8), but their presence is inferred pharmacologically by the use of synthetic agonists and antagonists. Three types of pharmacological receptor have been described and are designated as H_1, H_2 and H_3.

Histamine acting *via* H_1 receptors stimulates many smooth muscles to contract such as those in the gut, the uterus and the bronchi. Contraction of the bronchi leads to restriction of the passage of air into and out of the lungs as in asthma. In some smooth muscle, however, it causes relaxation, notably that of fine blood vessels, which leads to vasodilation and may produce a pronounced fall in blood pressure. In addition, histamine increases the permeability of the walls of the capillaries so that more of the constituents of the plasma can escape into the tissue spaces, leading to an increase in the flow of lymph and its protein content, and formation of oedema. These effects are manifest in the well-known redness and wheal associated with histamine release (the so-called 'triple response' first described by Lewis[25]), as may occur after a scratch from a blunt instrument or nettle sting. There are striking differences, however, in the response of different animal species to histamine. For example, the rat is relatively resistant, whereas the guinea pig and man are very sensitive.

From these actions it appears that histamine has a physiological role as part of the body's defences against a hostile environment. Histamine is found in the body's surfaces: in the skin, in the respiratory membrane and adjacent tissue, and in the lining of the alimentary canal. Histamine may be released when the body is subjected to various kinds of maltreatment, such as mechanical damage, burning, infection or some drugs.

Histamine assists the body in removing the products of cell damage during inflammation. In man, the most common circumstance in which histamine is liberated is as a result of the antibodies produced against foreign proteins. Under extreme circumstances, however, the effects of histamine become pathological, leading to exaggerated responses with distressing results, as may occur in some allergic conditions.

Histamine has a physiological function in regulating the secretion of acid in the stomach where, acting on the H_2 receptor, it stimulates the parietal cells to produce hydrochloric acid. This is probably protective since the acid controls the local bacterial population. A pathological situation can arise, however, as in the formation of gastric or duodenal ulcers.

Histamine also has other actions where the role is much less understood. It can stimulate the heart to beat faster or to increase its force of contraction. It is able to modify the responsiveness of various types of lymphocyte in the blood during the course of immunological reactions, and may also affect the movements of specialized cells in the blood.

Histamine storage sites and receptors are present in the brain, and the biochemical enzymes required for producing and disposing of histamine are also present; it is probable that histamine has a neurotransmitter role acting through histaminergic neurones but its function is unclear, although it seems that it may be involved in maintaining alertness.

The histamine H_3 receptor is relatively unexplored. It can apparently regulate histamine synthesis and release in the brain and may therefore act as an autoreceptor involved in transmission of neuronal signals, but the consequence is still a matter for speculation.

12.5.3 BIOSYNTHESIS AND METABOLISM OF HISTAMINE

Histamine is formed from the amino acid L-histidine by decarboxylation (Figure 2). Two enzymes can catalyze the reaction: the highly specific and active L-histidine decarboxylase and the less specific

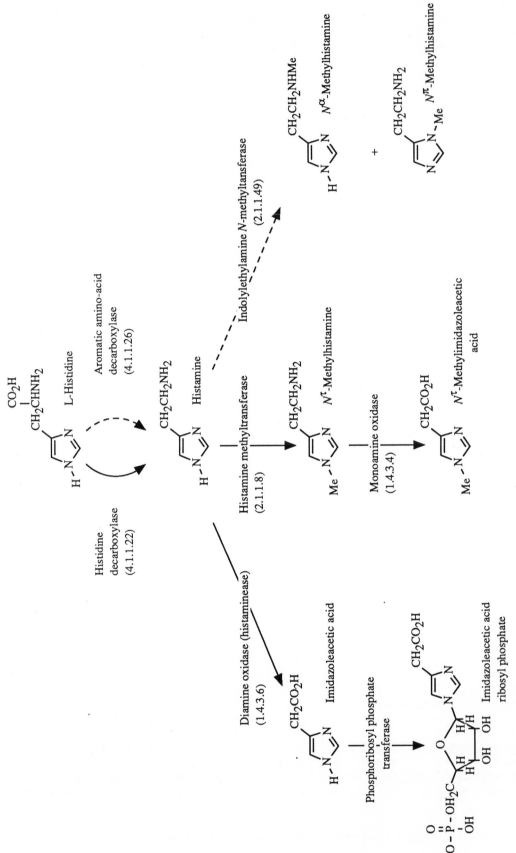

Figure 2 Pathways in the biosynthesis and metabolism of histamine. The systematic EC classifications of some of the enzymes are given in parentheses

aromatic amino acid decarboxylase. The latter is identical with DOPA decarboxylase and is considerably more active with DOPA as a substrate than with histidine. Both enzymes use pyridoxal phosphate as a coenzyme.

The mechanism of decarboxylation probably involves formation of a Schiff's base between histidine anion and pyridoxal phosphate, followed by interaction with a nonprotonated amino group of the apoenzyme to facilitate elimination of the CO_2.

Released histamine does not last long in the body since it is rapidly inactivated and disappears from the blood stream within minutes. Its inactivation occurs mainly by one of two mechanisms (Figure 2). It may be methylated in the imidazole ring by the enzyme histamine-N-methyltransferase, which uses S-adenosylmethionine as a methyl donor; the product has virtually no pharmacological activity and is rapidly deaminated by monoamine oxidase through to the corresponding methyl-imidazoleacetic acid. The other route of metabolism is by the enzyme histaminase, also known as diamine oxidase because it also acts on other diamines such as cadaverine and putrescine. Diamine oxidase deaminates the side chain *via* a complex involving pyridoxal as coenzyme, which is then oxidized to imidazoleacetic acid. The latter is then largely conjugated with ribose and excreted in the urine as a ribosyl phosphate. The relative importance of the two metabolism pathways varies between species, *e.g.* the deamination of histamine and conversion into ribosylimidazolacetic acid is the major pathway in the rat and a minor one in man. However, during the course of human pregnancy, diamine oxidase in the plasma increased 1000-fold. In the guinea pig, both routes appear to be important.

Other minor metabolites of histamine have been described. N^{α}-Acetylhistamine may be formed by bacteria in the gut and excreted in the urine. Trace amounts of side chain N^{α}-mono- and N^{α},N^{α}-di-methylhistamines are also found in the urine and appear to be formed during gastric acid secretion. They may be produced by the enzyme indolylethylamine-N-methyltransferase.[26] The latter has also been shown to give N^{π}-methylhistamine (*in vitro*).

Some drugs are known (Table 1) which will affect histamine formation or inactivation, but so far these actions have not been put to general therapeutic use although they are of value in the laboratory for experimental studies. Thus brocresine (5) and other benzyloxyamines (originally characterized as monoamine oxidase inhibitors) inhibit histidine decarboxylase, although they are nonspecific in their action because they combine with the pyridoxal coenzyme. More specific are α-methylhistidine (2) and N^{α}-aminohistidine (1) (also named incorrectly as α-hydrazinohistidine)

Table 1 Some Inhibitors of the Enzymes Involved in Histamine Synthesis and Metabolism

Compound	In vitro potency $K_i(M)$	Ref.
Histidine decarboxylase (EC 4.1.1.22)		
(1) N^{α}-Amino-L-histidine[a]	7×10^{-5}	27
(2) α-Methyl-L-histidine	4.8×10^{-4}	28
(3) α-Fluoromethyl-L-histidine	3.2×10^{-5}	29
(4) McN-A-1293[b]	1.7×10^{-5}	30
(5) Brocresine (NSD 1055)[c]	1.5×10^{-7}	30, 31
(6) Imidazol-4-ylmethoxyamine	2×10^{-7}	32
Imidazole-N-methyltransferase (EC 2.1.1.8)		
(7) Homodimaprit (SK&F 91488)[d]	1×10^{-6}	33, 34
(8) Chloroquine	$>1 \times 10^{-5}$	35
(9) Amodiaquine	1×10^{-8}	33
(10) Metoprine	1×10^{-7}	35
(11) TMQ[e]	7×10^{-9}	36
(12) Impromidine	5×10^{-7}	37
Diamine oxidase (*histaminase*) (EC 1.4.3.6)		
(13) Aminoguanidine	5×10^{-8}	38
(6) Imidazol-4-ylmethoxyamine	9×10^{-9}	39
(12) Impromidine	7×10^{-9}	37
Imidazoleacetate phosphoribosylphosphate transferase		
Sodium salicylate	2×10^{-4}	40, 41

[a] Also erroneously named α-hydrazinohistidine. [b] 4-(Imidazol-4-yl)-3-aminobutan-2-one. [c] 4-Bromo-3-hydroxybenzyloxyamine. [d] See also Table 12. [e] 2,4-Diamino-5-methyl-6-[(3,4,5-trimethoxyanilino)-methyl]quinazoline.

and the most potent and most useful of the inhibitors, α-fluoromethylhistidine (3). Indeed, the latter has proved to be an extremely valuable pharmacological tool for animal studies *in vivo* and has especially been used to study brain histamine levels; it has also been used for treatment of patients with mastocytosis.

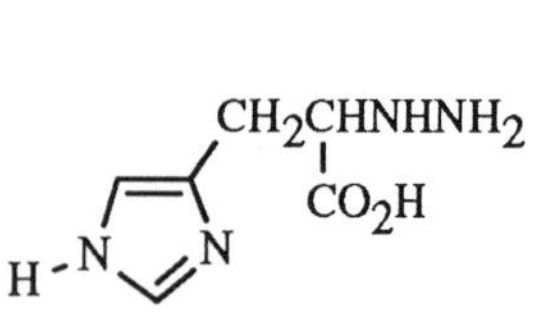

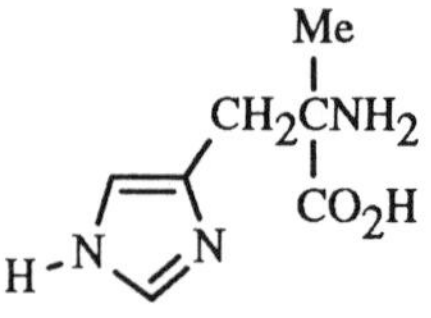

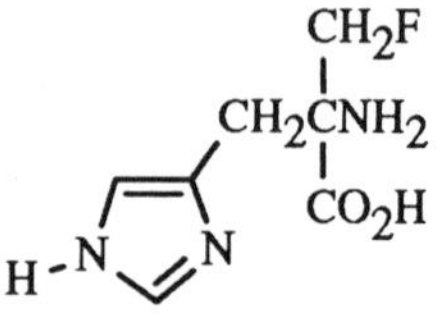

The antimalarial drugs chloroquine (8) and amodiaquine (9), and the folate antagonists metoprine (10) and TMQ (11), inhibit the inactivating enzyme imidazole-*N*-methyltransferase; the compound SK&F 91488, homodimaprit (7), has also been used successfully in animal experiments as an inhibitor of histamine-*N*-methyltransferase *in vivo*. Aminoguanidine (13), imidazolylmethoxyamine (6), and impromidine (12) inhibit diamine oxidase (histaminase).

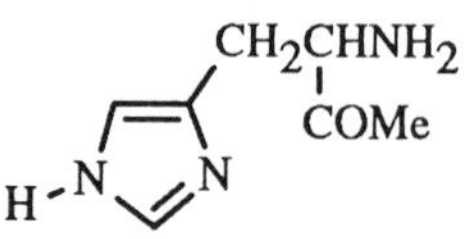

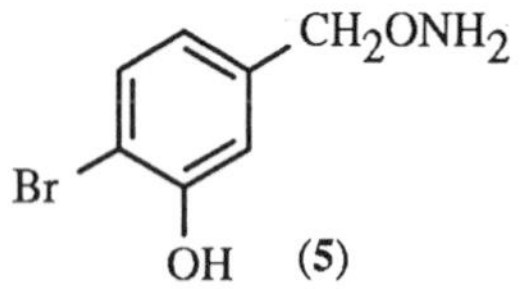

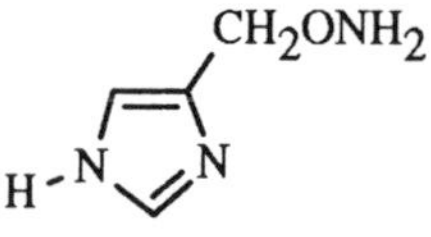

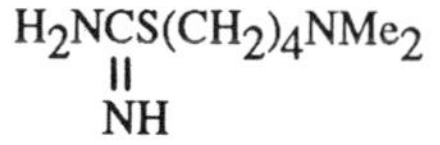

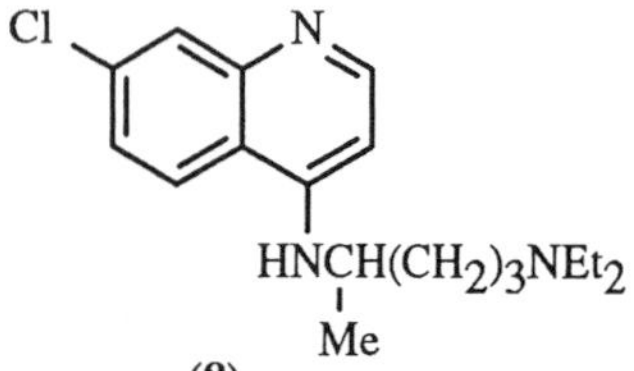

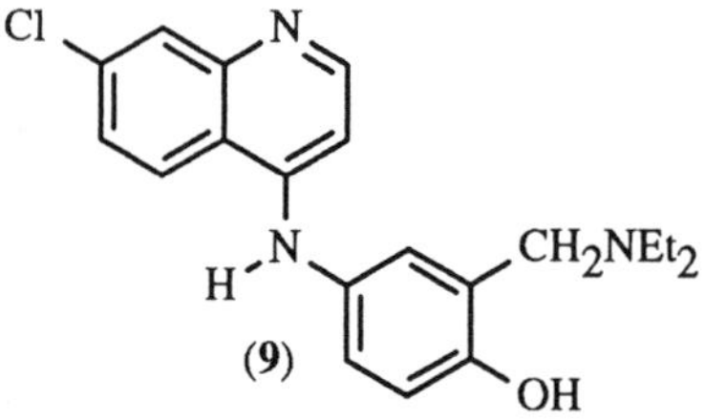

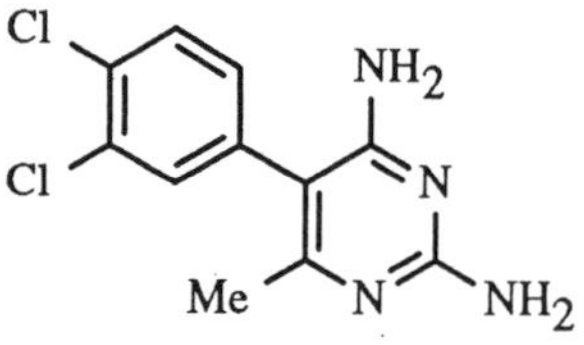

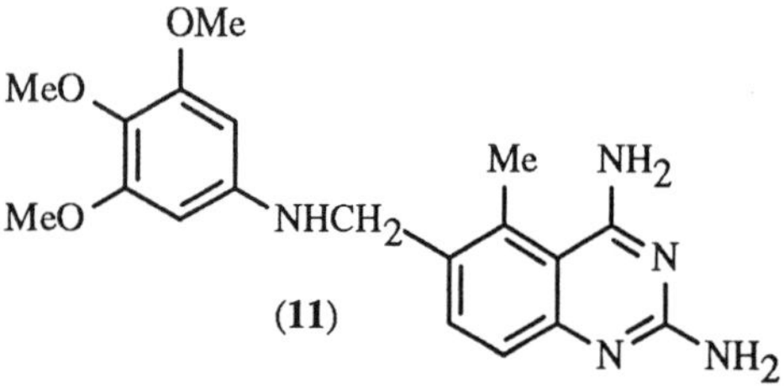

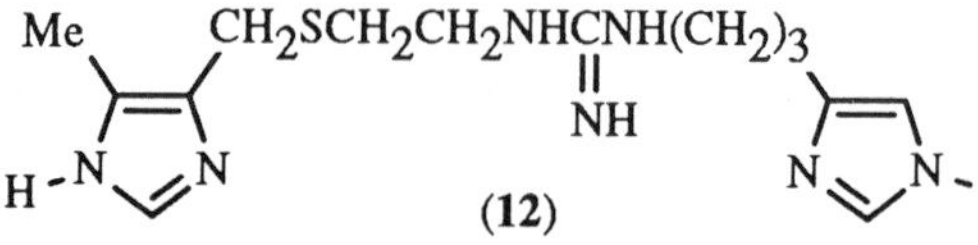

Histamine may also be removed from circulation by rapid absorption into some tissues (*e.g.* heart and aorta) but no specific uptake process has yet been identified. This contrasts with other amine transmitters such as acetylcholine and noradrenaline, which have uptake systems; these other biogenic amines are conserved because their production requires multistage biosynthetic pathways.

12.5.4 HISTAMINE STORAGE AND RELEASE

The chief sites of histamine location in the body are the mast cell and its circulating counterpart in the blood, the basophil. In some species other blood-borne cells may also be involved, *e.g.* platelets in the rabbit and pig. These cells synthesize histamine and then store it and if the histamine is released from these stores it is slowly resynthesized. There are, however, organs in which the histamine-containing cells have not yet been identified. Some tissues also have a high capacity for synthesizing histamine without storing it, and cells in regenerating or rapidly growing tissues produce large amounts of histamine, which is continuously released.

The existence of the tissue mast cell and blood basophil was recognized by Paul Ehrlich in 1877 and 1879 respectively, but it was not until 1953 that Riley and West first suggested[42] that the mast cell was a repository for histamine. There is approximately 10 pg of histamine stored in a mast cell and about 1–1.2 pg in the basophil.[22]

Histamine is released explosively from the mast cell and basophil by an energy dependent mechanism in response to various small stimuli, *e.g.* trauma, toxins, dextran, basic compounds and in some immunological reactions.

Many basic drugs containing amine, diamine, diamidine or guanidine groups are histamine releasers, *e.g.* morphine, tubocurarine, stilbamidine, guanethidine.[43] The synthetic polymeric polyamine, compound 48/80 **(14)** (formed by the acid-catalyzed condensation of *p*-methox-*N*-methylphenylethylamine with formaldehyde, see ref. 44 for characterization), is a potent histamine releaser which is widely used in experimental laboratory studies. Its effect is blocked by anoxia and some metabolic inhibitors. The toxin peptide 401 is a mast cell degranulating peptide from bee venom,[45] which is a basic molecule composed of 22 amino acid residues and strongly resembles compound 48/80 in its specificity and mode of action. Mast cells are heterogeneous and respond differently to histamine-releasing agents depending on species and tissue location.[46]

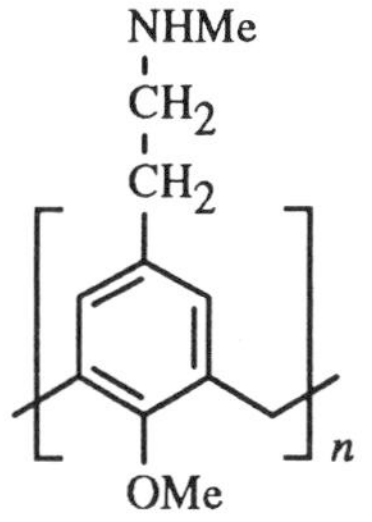

NHMe

CH$_2$

CH$_2$

OMe

(14) Compound 48/80

Mast cells and basophils bear specific receptors on their surface for the immunoglobulin IgE, which binds IgE antibody molecules with high affinity, as occurs in immediate hypersensitivity reactions. Attachment of antigen to more than one cell-bound IgE antibody (multivalent binding) triggers off a sequence of biochemical events. Thus, bridging of IgE receptors on rat mast cells induces phospholipid methylation, a rise in intracellular cAMP and activation of protein kinase, mobilization of intracellular Ca^{2+} ions and an increase in Ca^{2+} flux.[47] These responses are accompanied by rapid extrusion of granules from the mast cell. The granules then dissociate to release histamine and other mediators such as heparin and leukotrienes into the surrounding tissue and blood stream.

12.5.5 HISTAMINE RECEPTORS

The early studies on histamine indicated a similarity in some of its effects with the symptoms which appeared during inflammation and with symptoms characteristic of shock produced by trauma or allergic reactions. It became widely assumed that histamine was a principal mediator of inflammation and shock and this stimulated a search by Bovet in Paris for substances capable of counteracting these apparent injurious effects. Initial findings were published in 1937 and led to the development of the antihistamine drugs in the 1940s and to their introduction for the treatment of allergic conditions such as urticaria and hay fever (see Section 12.5.12.1).

12.5.5.1 Background to the Concept of Histamine Receptors

Pharmacologically, the antihistamines were found to be effective antagonists of the action of histamine in stimulating contractions of smooth muscle, notably from the bronchi, gut and uterus. They were also shown to antagonize many of the actions of histamine on the vascular system, although they were not able to abolish completely the blood-pressure-lowering effect. Quantitative pharmacological studies on blood pressure and on isolated smooth muscle suggested that the mode of antagonism was competitive and, in 1947, Schild introduced pA_x values to characterize the antagonism.[48] Two typical compounds, mepyramine **(15**; Neoantergan) and diphenhydramine **(16**;

Benadryl) were shown to be specific in antagonizing histamine-stimulated contractions of the isolated ileum of the guinea pig, relative to other stimulants; they were effective at low concentrations and the antagonism they produced was surmountable; the dose–response relationships were consistent with the notion that these compounds were competing with histamine for occupation of its receptors.

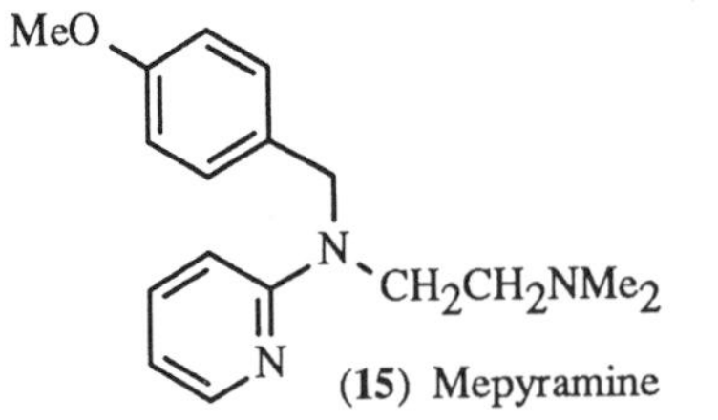

MeO

N–CH₂CH₂NMe₂

(15) Mepyramine

OCH₂CH₂NMe₂

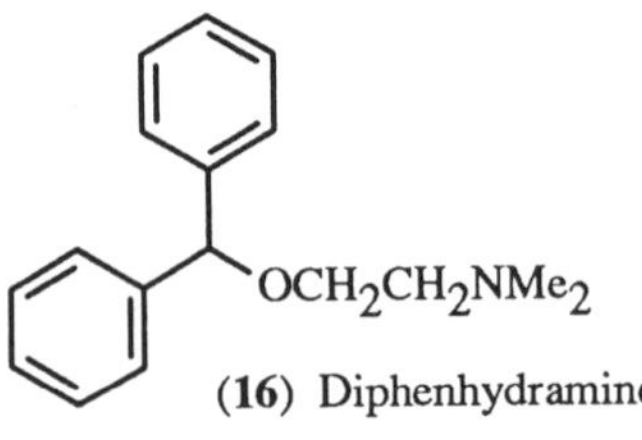

(16) Diphenhydramine

These competitive antagonists were used to establish the criteria for comparing receptors in different tissues and species; for example, mepyramine gave similar pA_2 values when tested against histamine on the perfused lung of the guinea pig, on the isolated ileum and trachea of the guinea pig, and on human bronchi; the results indicated a homogeneity for the histamine receptors in these tissues. The antagonists were also used to identify agonists which acted on the same receptors; thus, the activities of histamine and 2-(2-pyridyl)ethylamine (Table 15) on the guinea pig ileum were found to vary in the ratio of approximately 1:30, but they gave the same pA_2 values with mepyramine or diphenhydramine; this is the expected result if the agonists are acting on the same receptors and the antagonism is competitive.[49]

12.5.5.2 Definition of Histamine H₁ Receptors

Several other actions of histamine had been noted which could not be specifically antagonized by mepyramine and related drugs: for example, stimulations of gastric acid secretion, stimulation of isolated atria, inhibition of rat uterus and the vasodilator effects of large doses of histamine. Such observations led to occasional suggestions for the existence of more than one type of histamine receptor but proof was lacking. Thus Folkow and coworkers reported[50] in 1948 that the antihistamine Benadryl (diphenhydramine) did not fully block the vasodilator effects of large doses of histamine in the cat, and suggested that 'there are two types of receptors sensitive to histamine, only one of which can be blocked by Benadryl and related compounds'. Such considerations led Ash and Schild to propose[51] in 1966 that the actions of histamine blocked by the antihistamine drugs characterized one type of histamine receptor, which they called the H₁ receptor. They suggested that other actions of histamine, not specifically antagonized, were probably mediated by other histamine receptors but the characterization of these receptors awaited the discovery of specific antagonists.

There is no formal further subclassification of H₁ receptors, but substantial differences have been noted for the affinities of various antihistamines (H₁ receptor antagonists) in inhibiting the binding of radiolabelled ligands to brain tissue from different animal species.

12.5.5.3 Definition of Histamine H₂ Receptors

Some pointers to the differentiation of histamine receptors had been obtained by considering the relative activities of agonists on different tissue systems. For example, Grossman and coworkers[52] compared the histamine-like activities of some 60 compounds chemically related to histamine, and noted the apparent lack of uniform correlation between activity on gastric secretion in the dog and cat and activities on guinea pig intestinal strip or cat blood pressure. A more extensive list was later compiled by Jones;[53] he, too, pointed out that certain compounds were relatively selective, mimicking histamine in only some pharmacologic actions. Ash and Schild made quantitative estimates of the relative activities of different histamine cogeners, on the isolated guinea pig iluem, on the isolated rat uterus, and *in vivo* as stimulants of rat gastric acid secretion; they obtained a correlation in activity ratios which suggested that a common receptor mechanism might be involved in rat gastric acid secretion and rat uterus inhibition.

Further indications of two receptor populations were provided from quantitative studies of methylhistamines (Table 9). Black and coworkers[54] estimated activities relative to histamine on guinea pig ileum (H_1) and guinea pig atrium (non-H_1), *i.e.* two *in vitro* systems taken from the same animal species. They found that the two assays gave indistinguishable estimates of the relative activities of N^α-methylhistamine, N^α,N^α-dimethylhistamine, α-methylhistamine, and β-methylhistamine (see Figure 1 for numbering). 4-Methylhistamine, however, was much more active on the atrium (43% of histamine) than on the ileum (0.23%). Conversely, 2-methylhistamine was significantly less active (4.4%) on the atrium than on the ileum (16.5%). Similar results were obtained using rat tissues, *viz*: gastric motility *in vivo* (H_1), gastric acid secretion *in vivo* (non-H_1), and uterine muscle *in vitro* (non-H_1). These results, analyzed statistically, were in keeping with the notion of there being a homogeneous population of histamine receptors in these three non-H_1 systems. However, in order to classify these receptors, it was necessary to use a specific antagonist. Work to produce such a compound had started in 1964 at Smith Kline and French Laboratories, England and, in 1972, Black and coworkers were able to announce[54] the discovery of burimamide, *N*-methyl-*N'*-[4-(imidazol-4-yl)butyl]thiourea (**17**), a specific competitive antagonist of histamine on these non-H_1 tissue systems, thereby defining histamine H_2 receptors. Subsequently, many more potent antagonists were discovered (see Section 12.5.13).

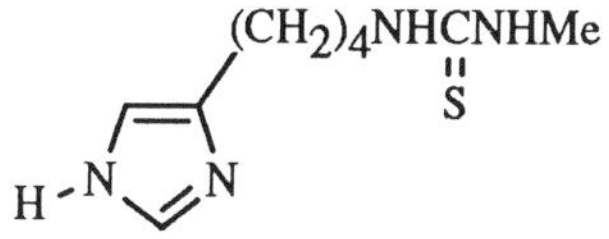

(**17**) Burimamide

A considerable research effort in many laboratories using selective histamine-like agonists and the specific histamine antagonists has subsequently characterized actions of histamine in terms of H_1 and H_2 receptor types for many tissue systems and animal species. The distribution of these receptor types in different tissue systems is discussed fully in references summarized in Section 12.5.5.9. A few actions of histamine have subsequently been described which are apparently not blocked by H_1 and H_2 receptor antagonists, either singly or in combination, and inevitably this sharpens the quest for further receptor subclasses.

So far, there is no division of H_2 receptors into further subclasses. There have been some reports of differences between activities of antagonists in inhibiting histamine-stimulated acid secretion and antagonism of histamine on the atrium, but this has been accounted for[55] by a pharmacokinetic effect whereby lipophilic antagonists are lost through the gastric mucosal membrane into the gastric acid secretion, so that they appear to be less active.

12.5.5.4 Definition of Histamine H_3 Receptors

The first serious suggestion for an H_3 receptor was made in 1983 by Arrang, Garbarg and Schwartz,[56] when it was demonstrated that histamine could inhibit its own release from cerebral neurones in rat cortex and that this effect was competitively inhibited by burimamide at nanomolar concentrations (which is far below the concentration required for H_2 receptor antagonism) but that more potent H_2 receptor histamine antagonists were much less active; H_1 receptor antihistamines were also ineffective. The suggestion was confirmed[57] in 1987 by the discovery that α-methylhistamine is a potent and highly selective agonist and that thioperamide (**18**) is a very specific competitive antagonist that does not act at H_1 or H_2 receptors. It appears that these H_3 receptors are presynaptic autoreceptors and that they not only control histamine release but also histamine synthesis.

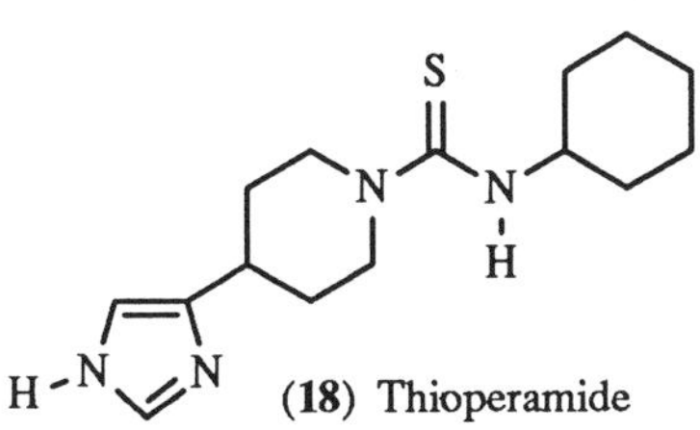

(**18**) Thioperamide

The presence of H_3 receptors in peripheral tissues has also been reported and here too they appear to be involved with the nervous system. Thus, histamine depresses sympathetic neurotransmission in the guinea pig mesenteric artery by interacting with H_3 receptors on the perivascular nerve terminals;[58] this important observation suggests that histamine may control the release of other neurotransmitters.[59] Inhibitory histamine H_3 receptors also exist in the guinea pig ileum where their role appears to be to modify the magnitude of histamine contraction rather than affecting histamine release.[60] Particularly intriguing is the discovery of H_3 receptors in the lung;[57] this raises the question of whether they control histamine release in anaphylaxis and whether they may be manipulated to provide therapy in asthma. Indeed it has been suggested that H_3 receptors may have a modulating role on excitatory neurotransmission in airways.

12.5.5.5 Bioassay of Compounds at Histamine Receptors

A wide variety of functional assays at histamine receptors has been used and many of them are briefly mentioned below.

12.5.5.5.1 *H_1 receptor systems*

(i) The pharmacology of histamine receptors owes a great deal to the guinea pig, the latter being exquisitely sensitive to histamine. The first antihistamines (H_1 receptor antagonists) were found because they protected unanaesthetized guinea pigs against the lethal bronchoconstriction caused by inhaling histamine administered as an aerosol from a nebulizer.[61]

(ii) Antagonism of histamine bronchoconstriction in the anaesthetized guinea pig or cat, using the method of Konzett and Roessler (1940) with various modifications has been extensively used.[62] In general, lung volume changes can be recorded and the antihistamines tested by intravenous injection at various dose levels for effectiveness in antagonizing the bronchoconstriction induced by intravenously administered histamine.

(iii) Histamine vasodepressor responses induced in anaesthetized dogs have long been employed to assess antihistamine potency. The depressor responses recorded before and after intravenous injection of histamine in doses of 0.5–1.0 μg kg^{-1} are compared. There is a complication, however, in that the depressor response is also mediated by H_2 receptors and to avoid this problem a more modern procedure uses a selective H_1 receptor agonist, such as 2-(2-pyridyl)ethylamine (Table 15) in place of histamine.[63]

(iv) Various procedures have been described to test the antagonism by antihistamine drugs (H_1 receptor antagonists) of the increased vascular permeability induced by histamine when injected intradermally in guinea pigs or rabbits. The effect is readily visualized by the use of systemic injection of dyes such as trypan blue or Pontamine sky blue which can be shown to concentrate in the localized histamine-injected areas.

(v) Many other approaches have been described which depend on some aspect of experimentally induced anaphylaxis caused by an antigen–antibody reaction and consequent histamine release (see ref. 64). They are, however, less direct.

The methods generally employed for the clinical evaluation of the H_1 receptor antihistamine drugs in humans basically involve qualitative and quantitative assessments of their effectiveness as antiallergic and antianaphylactic agents,[64] as follows.

(vi) Assessment of the degree of antagonism of locally histamine-induced flare and wheal responses following intracutaneous injection of histamine.

(vii) Intradermal tests using serial dilutions of various allergens, *e.g.* extracts of ragweed pollen or timothy grass. Control responses are recorded in a sufficiently large number of patients and the surface area of the local skin reactions measured and compared. The antihistamine drug is then given orally and, in general, after an interval of 45 min patients are retested with the same allergens on comparable skin sites of their opposite arms.

(viii) Antagonism of passively sensitized skin reactions produced by intradermal injections of serial dilutions of serum containing a high titre of cottonseed reagins, followed in 24 h by intradermal injections of a constant amount of cottonseed extract at each site.

(ix) Antagonism of the cardiovascular responses to rapid intravenous injections of betahistine (Table 15) provided a convenient method for direct quantitative measurement of H_1 receptor blockade in man.[65]

(x) The time-honoured system for studying the actions of histamine and its antagonists utilizes the isolated guinea pig ileum, in a suitable medium such as Tyrode's solution gassed with 95% O_2/5% CO_2 and maintained at a constant temperature, usually between 30 and 37 °C. The force of contraction to doses of histamine before and after treatment with an antagonist is then compared.

The period for equilibration of the antagonist before rechallenge with histamine can be critical as some antihistamines are slow to reach their maximal effects. Likewise it is important to use suitable criteria to determine reversibility, specificity and evidence for competition.

The great advantage of using an isolated contractile tissue is that it can be used to assay agonists both with respect to intrinsic activity and to affinity. It is extremely important, however, to check for specificity and there are a number of important criteria which have to be observed[66] which include:

(a) For a histamine-like agonist, the dose–response curve should be parallel to histamine and reach the same maximum.

(b) Each agonist should act directly on the histamine receptor and not indirectly by the release of tissue histamine stores.

(c) The possibility that agonists are producing responses by an action on receptors other than histamine receptors should be excluded whenever possible. The specificity of action of agonists on histamine receptors should be examined in several ways, including studies of various competitive antagonists and measurement of pA_2 values using antihistamine compounds and antagonists at other types of receptor.

(d) All processes, other than passive diffusion, which effectively reduce the concentration of agonists in the region of the receptor should be eliminated. Histamine may be lost from the aqueous medium by being taken up into some tissues or by metabolic action of enzymes. Under such circumstances histamine and some analogues will appear less potent at the histamine receptor than they actually are.

(e) For each agonist the concentration in the bathing medium should be known and maintained long enough to reach the maximum response to the concentration used.

(f) The experiment should be so designed that changes in sensitivity of the preparation to agonists can be detected and taken into account in the calculation of potencies.

(g) The drug should be examined for agonist and antagonist activity at the histamine receptor. This is especially important when defining the action of a partial agonist.

The isolated guinea pig ileum is the most widely used tissue for assaying H_1 receptor agonists but other smooth muscle preparations have occasionally been used, *e.g.* guinea pig trachea, guinea pig perfused lung, guinea pig and cat uterus, human bronchial muscle, some vascular smooth muscle tissues.

Biochemical markers (see also Section 12.5.5.9), which depend on the receptor–stimulus–response coupling or end product, have also been used and may offer convenience for rapid screening, *e.g.*

(xi) histamine-induced glycogenolysis in mouse brain slices;[67]

(xii) histamine-induced elevation of cGMP (cyclic guanosine 3′,5′-monophosphate) levels in intact mouse neuroblastoma cells;[68]

(xiii) an H_1-receptor-mediated potentiation of the H_2-receptor-mediated stimulation of cAMP (cyclic adenosine 3′,5′-monophosphate) in slices of guinea pig hippocampus.[69]

12.5.5.5.2 *H_2 receptor systems*

Undoubtedly, the most important therapeutic use for the H_2 receptor histamine antagonists is in the control of gastric hyperacidity, leading to the healing of both gastric and duodenal ulcers. Various *in vivo* animal preparations have been described, *e.g.* the lumen perfused stomach of the anaesthetized rat or cat; the conscious rat or dog fitted with a Heidenhain pouch or gastric fistula.

A convenient preparation for assaying new compounds (either agonists or antagonists) *in vivo* is the lumen perfused stomach of the anaesthetized rat described by Parsons.[70] This is a modification of the Ghosh and Schild method.[71] The stomach of the starved, atropinized, anaesthetized rat is perfused with glucose solution *via* cannulae placed in the oesophagus and in the pyloric antrum. The perfusate is collected *via* a funnel and passed over a micro flow-type glass electrode system which continuously measures changes in pH. Antagonists can be tested by rapid intravenous injection against a slow intravenous infusion of histamine (or dimaprit, Table 15), which causes a near maximal stimulation of acid secretion.[72] Agonists can be tested by rapid intravenous injection and the acid output compared and matched with that produced by a similarly given dose of histamine.

It is important to realize that a compound which blocks histamine-stimulated gastric acid secretion, even if the blockade is surmountable, is not necessarily an antagonist at H_2 receptors because acid secretion is a very complex process and there are many ways in which it can be inhibited. It is essential, therefore, to correlate activity with *in vitro* assays.

There are two *in vitro* assays which were used for the first characterization of H_2 receptors: the histamine-stimulated increase in the rate of beating of the isolated right atrium of the guinea pig and the histamine-induced relaxation of a contracted (by electrical or carbachol stimulation) piece of uterine muscle from the rat.[72] The atrial preparation is much easier to control; a triangular piece of the right atrium may be used which contains the sino-atrial node so that it continues to beat spontaneously and the rate is monitored *via* a force transducer attached to the muscle. Other preparations in use include the inotropic action of histamine on ventricular muscle[73] from the guinea pig or cat and the lipolytic effect on fat cells from the dog.[74]

In vitro assays for acid secretion have been more difficult to establish, but isolated stomach preparations have been successfully used, for example from the dog, rat and mouse.

It is also possible to work with isolated parietal cells using cAMP accumulation as a marker of response or taking aminopyrine (19) concentration as an index. Aminopyrine is a weak base (pK_a 5.0) which is largely unionized at cytoplasmic pH and freely diffuses across plasma membranes. Once it has entered an acidic compartment in the stimulated parietal cell it becomes protonated and is locked in by the surrounding plasma membranes. It is measured as the ^{14}C isotope.[75] Using fluorescent microscopy, another weak base, acridine orange, has been used as a marker.[76]

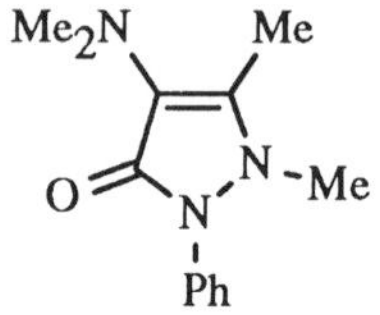

(19) Aminopyrine

H_2 receptor activation is associated with the accumulation of cAMP, due to activation of adenylate cyclase, in other tissues too,[77] for example in heart muscle (ventricle), vascular smooth muscle, plasma basophils,[78] T-lymphocytes, and brain (see Section 12.5.5.9).

12.5.5.5.3 *H_3 receptor systems*

In the assay described[56,57] in the original papers characterizing H_3 receptors, rat cerebral cortex slices are incubated with [^{3}H]histidine, which leads to endogenous synthesis of [^{3}H]histamine within the histaminergic neurones. The preparation is washed well and then exposed to K^+, which evokes an increase in histamine efflux. The presence of additional unlabelled histamine (or other agonist) in the bathing medium depresses the evoked release of histamine (measured as [^{3}H]histamine) without affecting basal efflux. Antagonists block the depressive action of histamine. A superfusion technique using electrically evoked release has also been established.[79]

12.5.5.6 **Distribution of Histamine Receptors**

Histamine has been shown to have many powerful and diverse biological actions; some actions on tissues appear to be direct but other actions may involve other chemical regulators such as adrenaline or acetylcholine. The pattern of biological response is diverse; some tissues are stimulated, others are inhibited. Some responses are rapid (within seconds), other responses may take many minutes to develop. Such a complexity makes it difficult to analyze the actions of histamine or to see a consistent pattern.

The discovery of competitive antagonists and the classification into receptor subtypes brings a much greater semblance of order to histamine pharmacology. Such a systematization does not provide the mechanisms of action but it does help to pinpoint the sites of action.

It is not the purpose of this section to provide a comprehensive review of histamine receptor location with respect to different tissues and functions but to at least expose sufficient of the subject as to point the reader in the appropriate direction if additional information is required (see Table 2).

The action of histamine in stimulating contraction of smooth muscle has already been mentioned in connection with the definition of H_1 receptors (Section 12.5.5). These actions, mediated by H_1 receptors, occur in the smooth muscle of various parts of the gastrointestinal tract, lungs and genitourinary systems. There have also been various reports of inhibitory (relaxant) actions of histamine which are apparently mediated by H_2 receptors, *e.g.* in the lower oesophageal sphincter of

Table 2 Some Examples of Histamine Actions Mediated *via* H_1 and H_2 Receptors[22,80-82]

Tissue	Species	Receptor	Effect
Smooth muscle (nonvascular)			
Gut: ileum	Guinea pig	H_1	Contracts
fundus	Rat	H_1	Contracts
		H_2	Relaxes
Gall bladder	Guinea pig	H_1	Contracts
		H_2	Relaxes
Lung: bronchus	Guinea pig, human	H_1	Contracts
		H_2	Relaxes
trachea	Cat	H_1/H_2	Relaxes
Uterus	Guinea pig	H_1	Contracts
	Rat	H_2	Relaxes
Vas deferens	Mouse	H_2	Relaxes
Urinary bladder	Guinea pig, human	H_1	Contracts
Vascular			
Peripheral resistance vessels	Cat, guinea pig	H_1	Dilates (rapid)
		H_2	Dilates (slow)
	Rabbit	H_1	Constricts
		H_2	Dilates
Pulmonary vessels	Guinea pig	H_1	Constricts
		H_2	Dilates
Vascular permeability	Cat, guinea pig	H_1	Increase
Cardiac			
Atrium (right)	Guinea pig	H_2	Increases rate (chronotropic)
Atrium (left)	Guinea pig	H_1	Increases force (inotropy)
Ventricle	Guinea pig	H_2	Increases force (inotropy)
Gastric mucosa	Rat, cat, dog, pig, mouse, human	H_2	Acid secretion
Immunological			
T lymphocytes	Human	H_2	Inhibits histamine release
	Human	H_2	Inhibits T lymphocyte cytolysis
	Human	H_2	Suppress response to mitogens
Neutrophil	Human	H_2	Inhibits lysosomal enzyme release
Eosinophil	Human	H_2	Inhibits chemotactic response
Central nervous system	Rat	H_1	Wakefulness (arousal)
	Mouse	H_1	Glycogenolysis (increased energy metabolism)
	Goat	H_1	Antidiuresis
	Rat, goat	H_1	Vasopressin release
Chromaffin tissue	Cat, rat	H_1	Releases catecholamines

the opossum, bovine stomach, chicken ileum, guinea pig gall bladder, trachea and bronchus of various species including man, mouse vas deferens and rat uterus. The distribution of receptors is species dependent and in many cases both receptor types appear to be present and causing opposing effects but this is not a general rule. This raises interesting questions about possible function and requires careful study with respect to both drug concentration and time dependency. In some circumstances, *e.g.* cat bronchus and horse trachea, there may be actions of histamine not mediated by either H_1 or H_2 receptors.

Histamine also affects the tone of vascular smooth muscle. Thus, dilation of peripheral resistance vessels leads to the profound fall in blood pressure observed in most species after the injection of histamine. Both H_1 and H_2 antagonists have to be administered together to fully block the hypotensive effect. These vascular receptor responses may also appear to vary with time; *e.g.* in cat and dog mesentery, H_1 receptor responses occur rapidly but are poorly sustained, whereas H_2 receptor responses are slower in onset but well sustained. In the human, too, both types of receptors mediate histamine-induced hypotension. Thus, vasodilator responses have been analyzed for blood flow in the human forearm and both antagonists were required to fully block the effect; it would appear that, therapeutically, to counteract vascular shock produced by histamine release it is important to coadminister an H_1 receptor antihistamine and an H_2 receptor antagonist. Not all species are similar, however; for example the rabbit differs in showing a biphasic response; there is an

H_1-receptor-mediated vasoconstriction and a rise in blood pressure, followed by the H_2-receptor-mediated vasodilatation and profound hypotension.

In the pulmonary circulation of most species the responses due to H_1 and H_2 receptors oppose one another, H_1 receptors being associated with vasoconstriction, H_2 receptors with vasodilatation. Thus, mechanistic studies of vascular histamine responses are complicated by differences between species, vascular beds and temporally.

Histamine also increases vascular permeability, leading to extravasation of albumin and oedema formation *via* an action involving H_1 receptors. It appears that histamine may be a regulator of transport across vascular membranes and have a vital role in the processes leading to tissue repair after injury. Whether histamine also has a nonpathological vascular role is unknown but it has been speculated that histamine may be involved in the local control of tissue homeostasis. The idea that endogenous histamine might provide the 'fine adjustment of the circulation to local metabolic needs' was first raised by Dale in 1919 and subsequently extended by Schayer in 1965.

Histamine has various actions on the heart but the effects are species dependent; in the guinea pig it increases the atrial rate (chronotropy), atrial and ventricular force (inotropy), slows atrio-ventricular conduction, and affects automaticity. The human heart appears to be similar to the guinea pig and there is a strong possibility that anaphylactic release of cardiac histamine could cause marked arrhythmias.

In addition to vascular actions of histamine which may occur during the inflammatory process, it appears that histamine has an immunoregulatory role. This is one of the fascinating developments which has occurred subsequent to the discovery of H_2 receptor antagonists; for example, histamine has been shown to inhibit its own release, inhibit T-lymphocyte-mediated cytolysis (indeed, T lymphocytes may develop H_2 receptors as they mature), inhibit enzyme release from leukocytes, inhibit production of migration inhibitory factor, modulate eosinophil migration, and suppress human lymphocyte responses to mitogens.

Evidence has accumulated to suggest that histamine may have a regulatory role in the brain as a central neurotransmitter, but direct evidence of function is lacking. Histamine is present in the brain; its distribution is uneven and histamine sensitive neurones have been demonstrated using microelectrophoretic measurements; indeed histamine is stored in synaptic vesicles. Various investigations have indicated the presence of H_1, H_2 and H_3 receptors, and it seems likely that histamine affects states of wakefulness and some neuroendocrine processes.

12.5.5.7   Histamine Receptors Studied with Radioligands and Photoaffinity Labels

Binding techniques which have been so fruitful in investigating the properties of various receptors have also been applied to histamine receptors. The various radioligands which have been described are collected in Table 3.

The first radioligand to be synthesized for H_1 receptors was [³H]mepyramine (20) and its use was demonstrated with homogenates of smooth muscle of the guinea pig ileum.[83] In this preparation there is very good agreement between the affinity constants determined for a range of ligands from the inhibition of [³H]mepyramine binding and the values derived from competitive antagonism of the contractile response to histamine. This ligand has been of especial use in exploring H_1 receptor binding in membrane preparations of brain tissue; it has high selectivity for the H_1 receptor and

Table 3   Radiolabelled Ligands for Detecting Histamine Receptors

Receptor ligand		K_D (nM)	Tissue[a]	Ref.
H_1	[³H]Mepyramine (20)	1.7	Brain	83
H_1	(21) [³H]Doxepin	0.26	Brain	84
H_1	(22) [³H]Mianserin	2.4	Cerebellum	85
H_1	(23) (+)-[³H]QMDP[b]	0.9	Cerebellum	86
H_1	(24) [¹²⁵I]Iodobolpyramine	0.15	Cerebellum	87
H_1	(25) [¹²⁵I]Iodoazidophenpyramine	0.012	Cerebellum	88
H_1	(26; R = NH₂) [¹²⁵I]-8-Iodo-7-aminoketanserin	3.4[c]	Cerebellum	89
H_2	(27) [³H]Tiotidine	17	Cerebral cortex	90
H_2	(28; R = NH₂) [¹²⁵I]Iodoaminopotentidine	0.4	Striatum	91
H_2	(29; R = H) [³H]Histamine	3.8	Rat cerebral cortex	92
H_3	(29; R = Me) (R)-[³H]-α-Methylhistamine	0.5	Rat cerebral cortex	57

[a] Guinea pig, unless stated. [b] Quaternary ammonium derivative of methyldiphenhydramine. [c] K_i value.

shows high specificity in binding. It has also been used to study H_1 receptor location in tissue sections for autoradiography and in the brain of living animals. Two other tritium-labelled ligands which have been used are [³H]doxepin (**21**) and [³H]mianserin (**22**). They have higher affinity for the H_1 receptor but are much less selective since they are also potent antidepressants; doxepin has a high affinity for a number of receptor systems[84] and mianserin has high affinity for the 5-HT$_2$ receptor.[85]

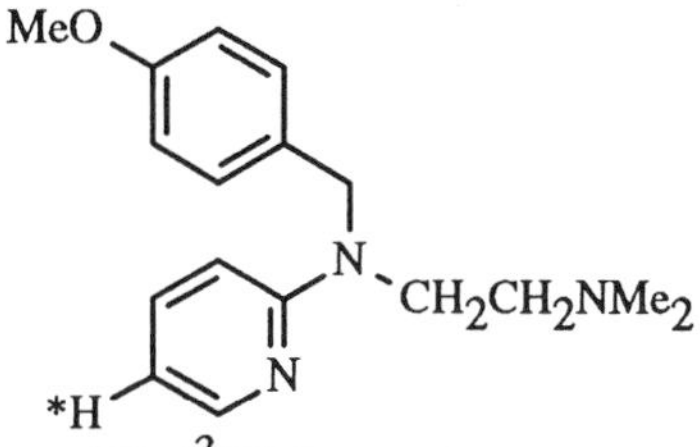

(20) [³H]Mepyramine

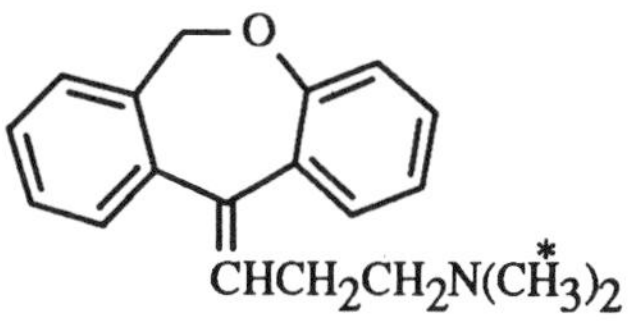

(21) [³H]Doxepin

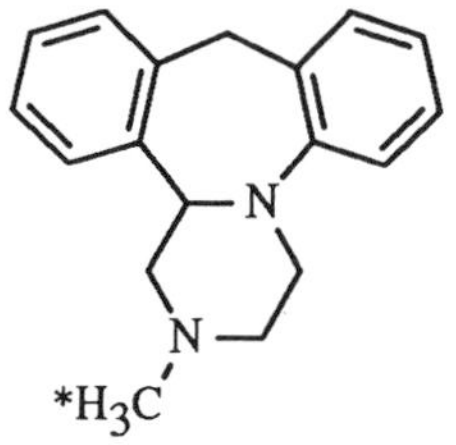

(22) [³H]Mianserin

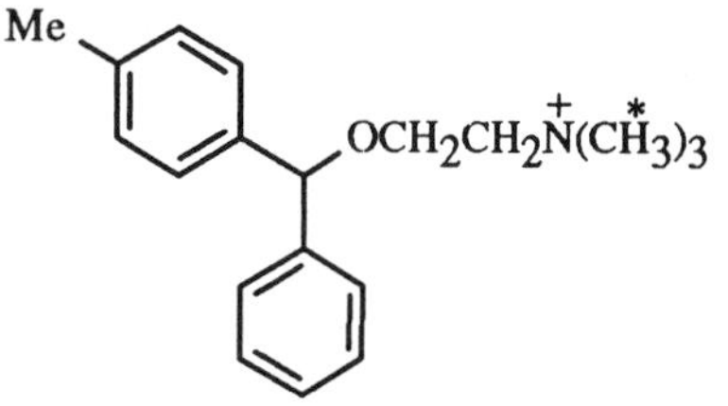

(23) (+)-[³H]QMDP

A quaternary ligand, [³H]N,4-dimethyldiphenhydramine ([³H]QMDP; 23) has been identified as a tool for kinetic studies. This compound is chiral and the (+) isomer is the more active enantiomer.[86]

High affinity ¹²⁵I-labelled ligands offer considerable technical advantages over corresponding ³H ligands since they can be obtained with 50–100 times higher specific radioactivity and thereby provide increased sensitivity for receptor assays.

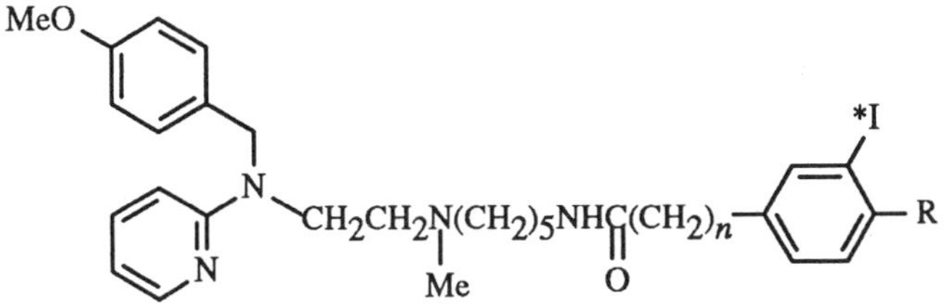

(24) [¹²⁵I]Iodobolpyramine; n = 2, R = OH
(25) [¹²⁵I]Iodoazidophenpyramine; n = 1, R = N$_3$

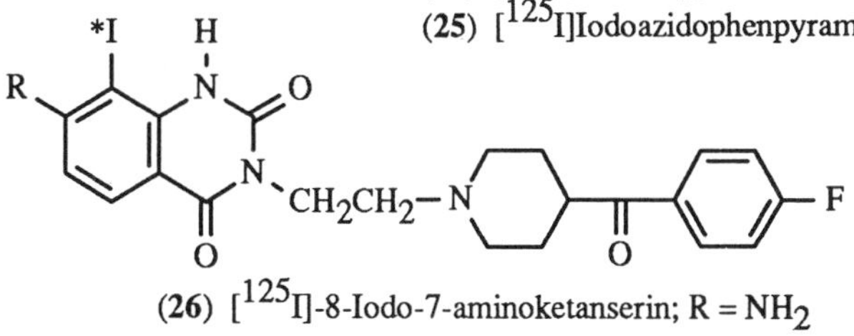

(26) [¹²⁵I]-8-Iodo-7-aminoketanserin; R = NH$_2$

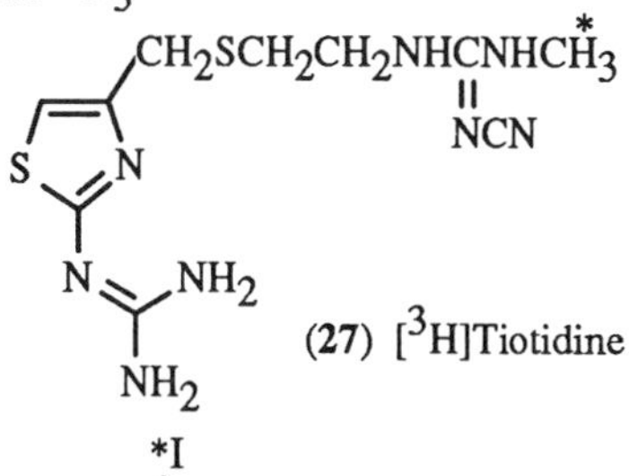

(27) [³H]Tiotidine

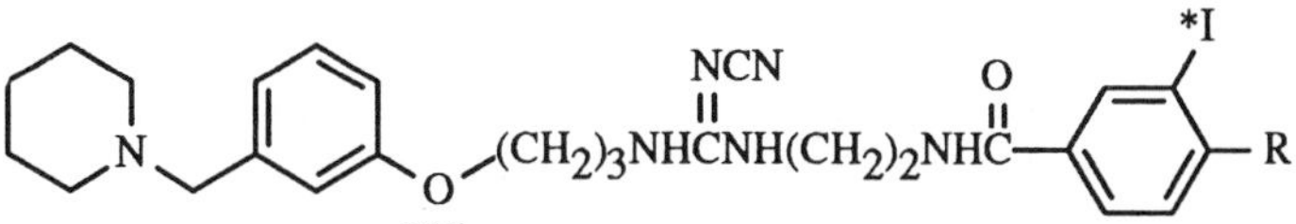

(28) [¹²⁵I]Iodoaminopotentidine; R = NH$_2$

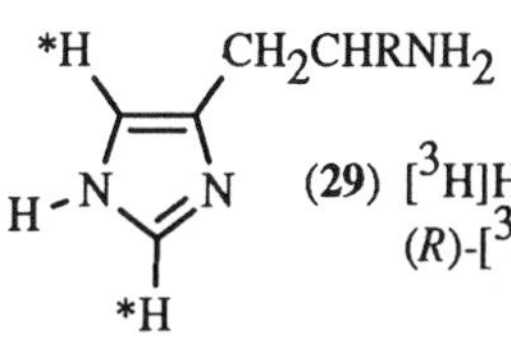

(29) [³H]Histamine; R = H
(R)-[³H]α-Methylhistamine; R = Me

Direct iodination of mepyramine (into the 5-position of the pyridine ring) or of the hydroxy analogue gave iodo compounds (**30** and **31**) with reduced affinities relative to mepyramine. Likewise, iodination of a hydroxybenzyl analogue of temelastine also gave a diiodo product (**32**) having reduced affinity.[87] These results are in keeping with previous structure–activity analysis of H_1 antihistamines which showed that affinity is very sensitive to substituent effects in the aromatic rings (see Section 12.5.12.4).

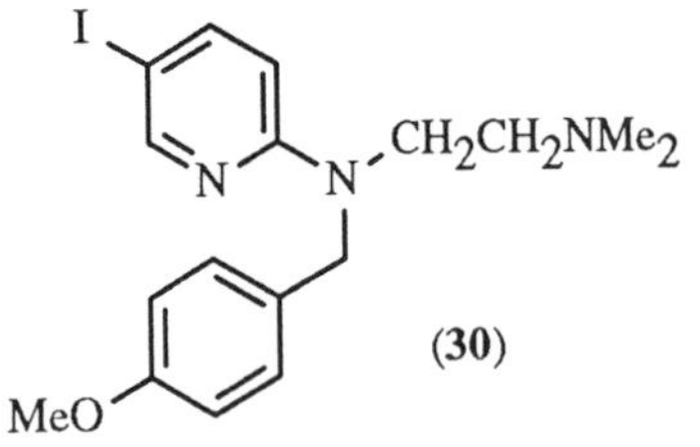

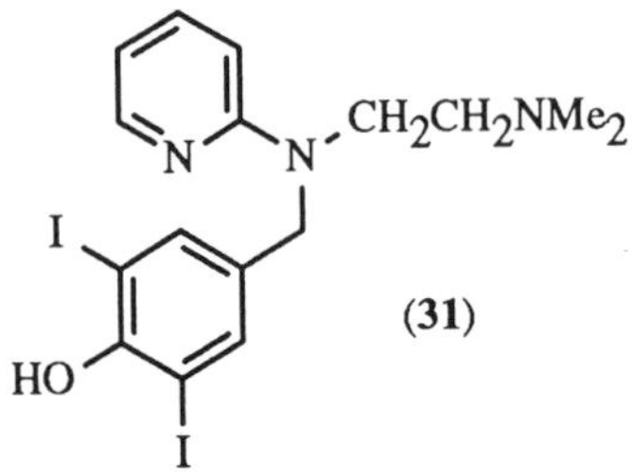

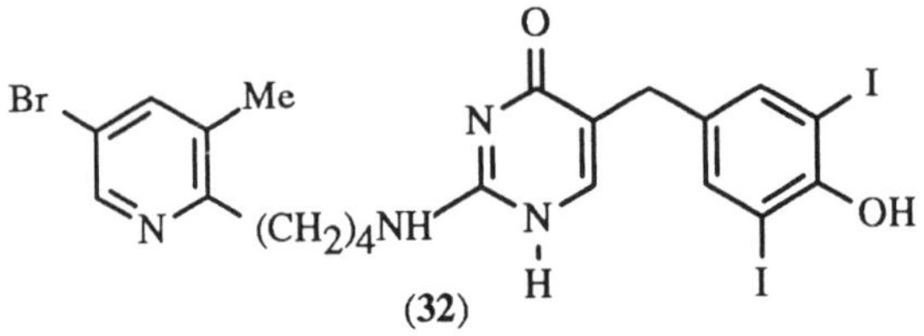

An alternative strategy of incorporating the label into a group attached to an atom chain, at a position in the drug structure which does not interfere with drug–receptor interaction, led to the synthesis of a series of aminoalkyl derivatives of mepyramine (**33**; $n = 2$–7, R = H). Iodination using the Bolton–Hunter procedure followed by binding assays afforded [^{125}I]iodobolpyramine[93] as the compound with the optimum chain length ($n = 5$) for the highest affinity ($K_i = 0.11$ nM); [^{125}I]iodobolpyramine (**24**) has high affinity and good pharmacological specificity for H_1 receptors, and has been used to reveal H_1 receptor distribution in the guinea pig brain.[93] The diiodo derivative (**33**; $n = 5$, R = I) has even greater affinity ($K_i = 0.013$ nM) but has not been used for labelling studies.

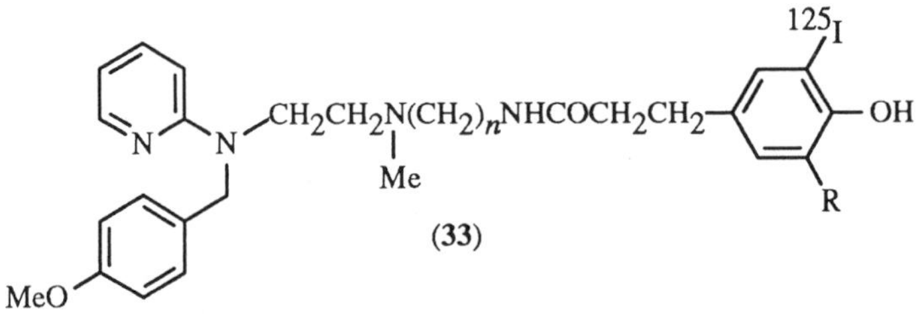

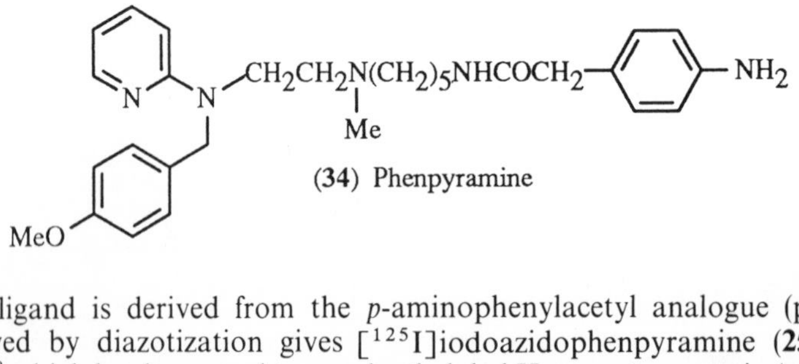

Another iodo ligand is derived from the *p*-aminophenylacetyl analogue (phenpyramine; **34**). Iodination followed by diazotization gives [^{125}I]iodoazidophenpyramine (**25**), a photoaffinity iodinated ligand[88] which has been used to covalently label H_1 receptor protein (see Section 12.5.5.8).

A photoaffinity analogue of histamine, N^α-(4-azido-2-nitrophenyl)histamine (**35**), has been described which on photolysis binds irreversibly to block the function of H_1 receptors in some tissue systems, *e.g.* in guinea pig vas deferens and aorta but not in canine trachealis.[94] High concentrations (10^{-5} M) are required, however, and the specificity of the compound for H_1 receptors is doubtful, *e.g.* in the guinea pig ileum it blocks muscarinic receptor function in the same concentration range as for H_1 receptor function. As a nonphotolyzed ligand it has K_B values in the 10^{-5} M range.

(35)

(36) 7-Azidoketanserin

A much more potent H_1 receptor photoaffinity ligand is 7-azidoketanserin (36) (as a reversible, nonphotolyzed ligand it has an $IC_{50} = 1.2$ nM, but it also binds to serotonin receptors.[95] Photolabelling of H_1 receptors occurs within an $IC_{50} = 12$ nM, and at serotonin (5-HT$_2$) receptors the $IC_{50} = 5.6$ nM). The isomeric 6-azidoketanserin is more selective for H_1 receptors (nonphotolyzed) but is apparently less specific on photolysis. Although both azides show similar reversible (*i.e.* nonphotolyzed) binding characteristics, there are important differences in their photolabelling properties. The 7-azido isomer reportedly shows irreversible binding by a true photoaffinity mechanism, whereas 6-azidoketanserin does not; thus photolysis in the presence of a scavenger, *p*-aminobenzoic acid, dramatically reduces the photolabelling of H_1 receptors by 6-azidoketanserin but not by the 7-azido isomer. An iodinated version, [^{125}I]8-iodo-7-azidoketanserin (26; R = N$_3$) has also been developed as a photoaffinity label (see Section 12.5.5.8 below).[96]

Attempts to obtain good radiochemical ligands for H_2 receptors have been much less successful; early reports that [^{3}H]cimetidine labelled H_2 receptors were later shown to be erroneous. [^{3}H]Cimetidine appears to bind to a site which recognizes the imidazole substructure and this obscures binding to the H_2 receptor.[97-99] Specific labelling of H_2 receptors with [^{3}H]ranitidine[98] or [^{3}H]impromidine was also unsuccessful. Some success has been obtained using [^{3}H]tiotidine (27); this too, in the early days, gave spurious results but subsequent studies with purer preparations of the ligand are consistent with H_2 receptor binding. Specific binding with [^{3}H]tiotidine is relatively low in comparison with the nonspecific binding, however, and the ligand is difficult to work with, but the inhibition constants for a range of other H_2 receptor antagonists are well correlated with pharmacological assays.[90,100] A high affinity iodoligand, [^{125}I]iodoaminopotentidine (28; R = NH$_2$) has subsequently been devised and used with dramatic effect to reveal H_2 receptor distribution in the guinea pig brain.[91] Diazotization afforded the corresponding photoaffinity iodinated ligand [^{125}I]iodoazidopotentidine (28; R = N$_3$).

Attempts to use [^{3}H]histamine (29; R = H) in binding studies have also been fraught with difficulties because of an apparent heterogeneity in the binding sites. However, when considerable precautions are taken, it appears possible to identify an H_2 receptor binding site in rat brain.[92] However, the behaviour of agonists and antagonists as inhibitors of [^{3}H]histamine binding in this tissue appears to be very complex.

H_3 histamine receptors have been labelled using [^{3}H](R)-α-methylhistamine (29; R = Me) in rat brain and guinea pig lung.[57]

12.5.5.8 Isolation of Histamine Receptors

Histamine receptors have not so far been identified by chemical means but there have been attempts to isolate and purify the H_1 receptor protein from membrane fractions of various tissues. Early studies using cat smooth muscle were unsuccessful,[101] but the H_1 receptor protein from guinea pig or rat cerebellar membranes has been solubilized using digitonin as detergent. A fourfold purification of the solubilized receptor has been achieved by affinity chromatography on a wheat germ agglutinin column, suggesting that the H_1 receptor is a glycoprotein.[102]

Target size inactivation analysis of lyophilized membranes from bovine and human cerebral cortex gives a molecular mass of 160 000 Da.[103] A higher value of 430 000 Da, obtained from sedimentation analysis of a preparation from guinea pig brain, is probably due to the existence of large amounts of digitonin detergent bound to the receptor protein.[104]

Photoaffinity labelling of guinea pig cerebellar membranes by [^{125}I]iodoazidophenpyramine (see Section 12.5.5.7; Table 3; 25), followed by sodium dodecyl sulfate polyacrylamide gel electrophoresis of the proteins indicates that at least part of the ligand-binding domain of the H_1 receptor resides within a protein subunit of apparent molecular mass 57 000 Da.[88] Interestingly, with cardiac (atrial) membranes this ligand labelled a subunit of 68 000 Da, possibly indicating a receptor isoform.[105]

Another photoaffinity label, $[^{125}I]$8-iodo-7-azidoketanserin (**26**; R = N_3), (which, however, is less specific since it also labels serotonin receptors) gave two labelled peptides from guinea pig cerebellum, having molecular masses of 58 000 and 63 000 Da.[96]

Claims to have separated H_1 and H_2 membrane receptors from calf thymocytes can be discounted for lack of adequate pharmacological characterization.[106]

12.5.5.9 Biochemical Consequences of Histamine Receptor Stimulation

The differentiation between subclasses of histamine receptors has been made by the use of selective agonists and antagonists in classical pharmacological experiments. The distinction is supported by biochemical studies which indicate that the cellular reactions influenced by H_1, H_2 and H_3 receptor mechanisms are fundamentally very different (see Figure 3).

Histamine, like many other hormones and neurotransmitters acts on receptors at the surface of their target cells to induce formation of an intracellular mediator or message. Where this leads to activation of a contractile or secretory event, the ultimate message is a change in the concentration of free Ca^{2+} in the cytoplasm. This is true for most of the responses elicited by either H_1 or H_2 receptors, but the immediate biochemical responses induced by these two receptors are quite distinct.

For the H_1 receptor, the primary mechanism of action appears to be an increased breakdown of phosphatidylinositol (PI). The general scheme is that combination of agonist with its receptor activates a phosphodiesterase, which catalyzes the breakdown of phosphatidylinositol 4,5-diphosphate to give *myo*-inositol 1,4,5-triphosphate and 1,2-diacylglycerol. These two products act as second messengers; inositol 1,4,5-triphosphate has been shown to induce the release of Ca^{2+}, and diacylglycerol to activate protein kinase C.[107]

Calcium has a multitude of effects within cells. In the case of smooth muscle cell it has a direct interaction with the contractile apparatus and the regulatory protein calmodulin. Other biochemical responses that can be influenced *via* Ca^{2+} and have been shown to involve H_1 receptors are the formation of cGMP (in cultured mouse neuroblastoma cells and bovine superior cervical ganglia) and glycogenolysis (in mouse brain).

Such effects offer circumstantial evidence to link increases in intracellular Ca^{2+} concentration to the functioning of many H_1-receptor-mediated responses; so far, however, changes in Ca^{2+} concentration have not been directly observed, even when monitored in neuroblastoma cells with the luminescent protein aequorin.[108]

There is a considerable literature indicating that H_2 receptors are invariably coupled to activation of adenylate cyclase, leading to elevation of intracellular cAMP levels. The major physiological

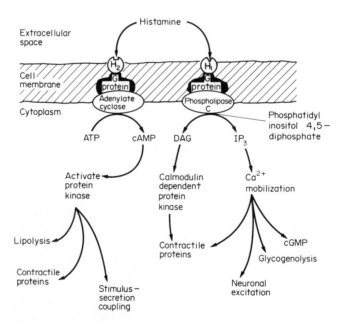

Figure 3 Intracellular messengers mediating some of the actions of histamine.

effects of H_2 receptor action, such as changes in muscle contractility and stimulation of secretory responses, require alterations in intracellular Ca^{2+} concentration. Increases in levels of cAMP after H_2 receptor stimulation have been shown for such diverse situations as in the secretion of acid from gastric glands, inotropic action in ventricular muscle, lipolysis in fat cells, cytolytic activity of T-lymphocytes, lysosomal enzyme release from neutrophils and inhibition of histamine release from basophils.[77,109] Increases in cAMP levels also result from histamine stimulation in brain tissue and are probably concerned with potentiation of certain excitatory signals.

12.5.6 CHEMICAL CONSTITUTION OF HISTAMINE

12.5.6.1 Dynamic Structures

Histamine comprises an imidazole ring and an amino group connected by a short chain of two carbon atoms (Figure 1). The amino and imidazole groups are both basic, and are protonated in acidic solution. The imidazole ring is a planar aromatic system with six π-electrons; it is a cyclic amidine, incorporating two types of nitrogen atom, which is tautomeric and exists in neutral solution as two different tautomers. The single bonds in the carbon atom chain permit rotation, giving rise to different conformations of the molecule.

Due to the above properties, histamine in solution is a mixture of many species undergoing rapid interconversion, *viz.* ionic forms, tautomers, and conformers. As indicated in Figure 4, these species differ in electronic charge, position of hydrogen atoms, and overall shape, and, since these chemical properties are fundamental in determining interactions between molecules, they have a special importance when considering relationships between chemical structure and biological activity. Which of the species are of biological importance is not self evident and, since they are in equilibria, the very process of interconversion between species may have a biological significance. Thus, histamine is a dynamic molecule and a much more complex chemical than is suggested by the simple structural formula of Figure 1.

12.5.6.2 Histamine Protonation and Tautomerism

Histamine has two basic centres, and titration of histamine dication in aqueous solution gives three stoichiometric pK_a values. The first stoichiometric ionization constant ($pK_{a1} = 5.80$ at 37 °C) corresponds to dissociation from the ring NH^+ to give the monocation (Figure 5), and the second ionization constant ($pK_{a2} = 9.40$ at 37 °C) corresponds to dissociation at the side chain $-NH_3^+$ group to give the uncharged molecule (Table 4). In strong alkali, the ring again ionizes at the ring NH ($pK_{a3} = 14$) to give an anion. At physiological pH (7.4) the main form is the monocation (see Figure 6); however, the pH may be considerably lower in the vicinity of some membranes, and below pH 5.8 the dication will predominate. Values for the relative populations at 37 °C in water at pH 7.4 and 5.4 are given in Table 4.

Since the imidazole ring possesses two nitrogen sites for possible proton attachment, the monocation and uncharged forms of histamine can each exist in two tautomeric forms of the imidazole ring, *viz.* with the proton on the N adjacent (N^π—H tautomer)* or N distal (N^τ—H tautomer)* to the side chain. Experimental data on tautomeric behaviour come from pK_a measurements, nuclear magnetic resonance spectroscopy (NMR), X-ray crystallography and theoretical calculations (Table 5).

In aqueous solution, pK_a comparison of N-methyl- or N-benzyl-histamines suggests that about 80% of histamine monocation is in the N^τ—H tautomer and 20% in the N^π—H tautomer.[112] Similar results using the Hammett equation indicate that tautomer preference is determined by the electron-withdrawing effect of the side chain,[113] and additional corroborative evidence comes from ^{13}C NMR spectroscopy.[114] Histamine base (*i.e.* the uncharged neutral form) in water has also been shown by ^{13}C NMR to resemble the monocation in its preference for the N^τ—H tautomer.[115]

These results from aqueous solutions are in contrast to crystal structure determinations where histamine monocation is found to crystallize (as the bromide salt) in the N^τ—H tautomeric form[116,119] but histamine base crystallizes as the N^τ—H tautomer.[120] However, both tautomers of histamine base have been shown to coexist in a crystalline complex with copper and carbon

---

* This nomenclature[1] is based on that recommended for histidine by the IUPAC–IUB Commission on Biochemical Nomenclature 1972; it is preferred to the alternative use of N^1—H and N^3—H, which is ambiguous and can be very confusing.

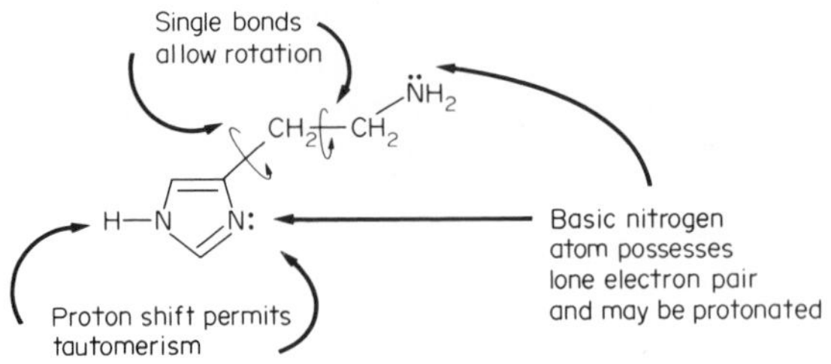

Form	Effect	Cause
Ion	Differ in position of H and charge	Basic nitrogen atoms
Tautomer	Differ in position of H and lone electron pair	Imidazole ring has N: and NH
Conformer	Differ in shape	Single bonds in side chain give flexibility

Figure 4 Diagram showing why histamine exists in different chemical forms or species

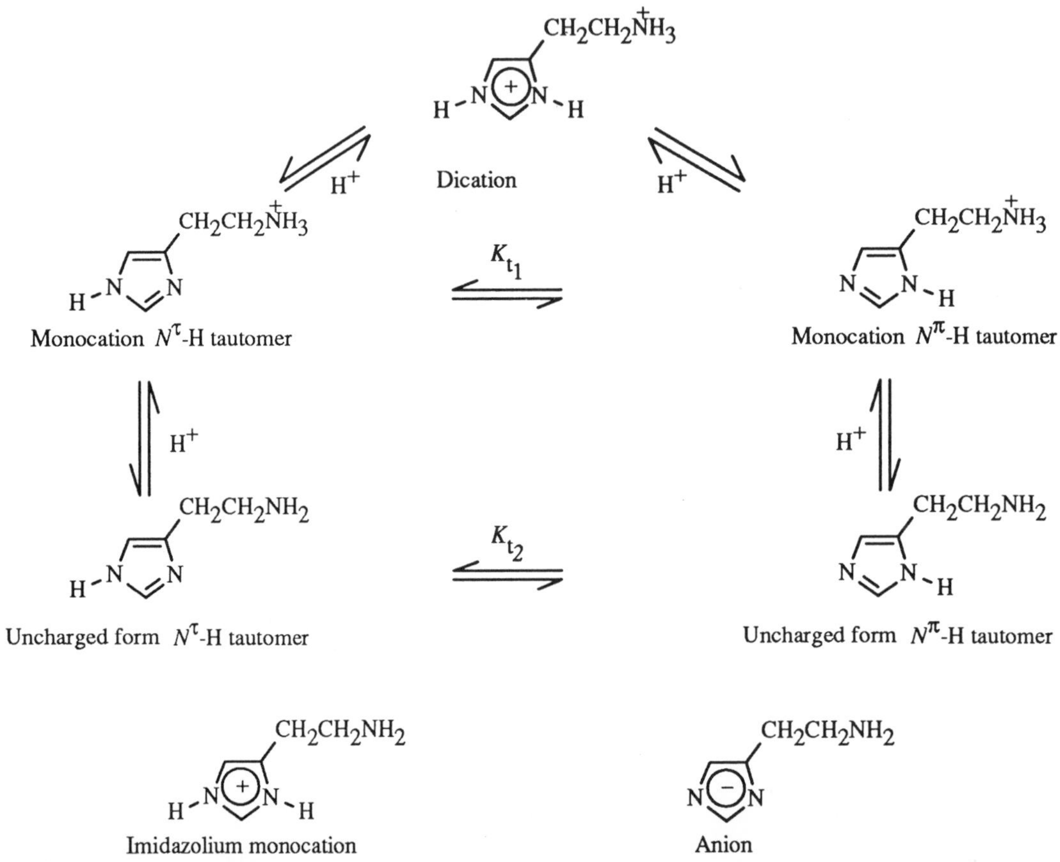

Figure 5 Ionic and tautomeric equilibria between histamine species. Side-chain deprotonation of the dication furnishes the imidazolium monocation and this must also be present in solution, but at very low concentration. At very high pH (> 12) significant amounts of the anion would also form

monoxide; one molecule of histamine is chelated (N^{τ}—H form) and a second molecule bridges between two Cu atoms (N^{π}—H form).[121] Here the tautomeric state is clearly determined by the nature of the coordination to the metal cation (see also Section 12.5.6.4).

Crystal structures represent a 'frozen' situation, however, and give no indication of the relative stability of the various forms under equilibrating conditions. Nevertheless, molecular orbital calculations on the isolated molecule indicated that the N^{τ}—H tautomer is preferred for the monocation, but that the N^{π}—H tautomer is preferred for the neutral form, in agreement with the solid state findings.[117,118,122] The predictions from theoretical methods do have to be treated with caution, however, since the results are very sensitive to the geometries used to represent the histamine molecule. In imidazoles, the internal bond angles change on tautomerism.[117] Later calculations, however, have included geometry optimization so that the results should be more reliable.[122,123]

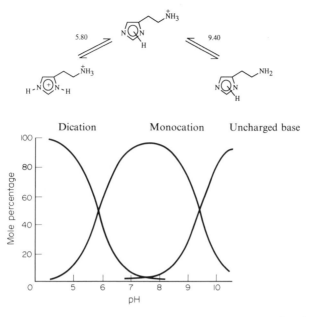

Figure 6 Species composition of histamine at 37 °C in water as a function of pH, using the values $pK_{a_1} = 5.80$ and $pK_{a_2} = 9.40$

Table 4 Histamine pK_a Values at Different Temperatures,[110] and Population of Histamine Species (expressed as mole percentage) in Aqueous Solution[a] at 37 °C and pH 7.4 and 5.4

Temperature (°C)	Apparent pK_a values (corrected to zero ionic strength)	
	pK_{a1} (imidazolium)	pK_{a2} (ammonium)
15	6.23	10.03
20	6.14	9.93
25	6.04	9.75
30	5.94	9.61
35	5.84	9.47

Species (see Figures 5 and 6)	Mole percentage of species	
	At pH 7.4	At pH 5.4
Dication	2.4	71.5
Monocations	96.6	28.5
Uncharged forms (base)	1	3×10^{-3} [b]
Anion	2.5×10^{-7} [b]	1×10^{-11} [b]

[a] Derived from pK_a values at 37 °C from ref. 110: $pK_{a1} = 5.80$; $pK_{a2} = 9.40$; $pK_{a3} = 14$.
[b] These values replace those originally published by Durant et al.,[111] in which an error was made in the calculations.

Tautomer stability may be markedly affected by solvent, and the above results may indicate that water has a profound effect on tautomer preference for histamine. This finding is of importance for structure–activity investigations since histamine receptors may be in a nonaqueous milieu, and the suggestion has been made that tautomerism may be involved machanistically in the H_2 receptor action of histamine.[111,113,118,122,207]

12.5.6.3 Histamine Conformation

Histamine is a flexible molecule and rotation about the single bonds in the side chain alters the overall shape. It can be described by the orientation of the imidazole ring (angle θ_1 shown in Figure 7) and by the conformation of the side chain (angle θ_2). Information on the conformational properties of histamine comes mainly from NMR spectroscopy (in solution), X-ray crystallography

Table 5 Histamine Tautomer Preference by Different Procedures

Procedure (medium)	Monocation (% N^τ—H)	Ref.	Base (% N^π—H)	Ref.
pK_a methods (H$_2$O, 25 °C)				
direct comparison	80	112		
by Hammett equation	80	113		
^{13}C NMR (H$_2$O, 30–32 °C)				
chemical shift	80	114		
^{13}C,H coupling	>90	115	<10	115
Crystal (lattice)	100	116	100	120
	100	119	33	121
Molecular orbital calculation (isolated molecule)				
depends on geometry (25 °C)	>99.99	117	75	117
	>99.99	118	>99.99	118
		122	85, 95	122

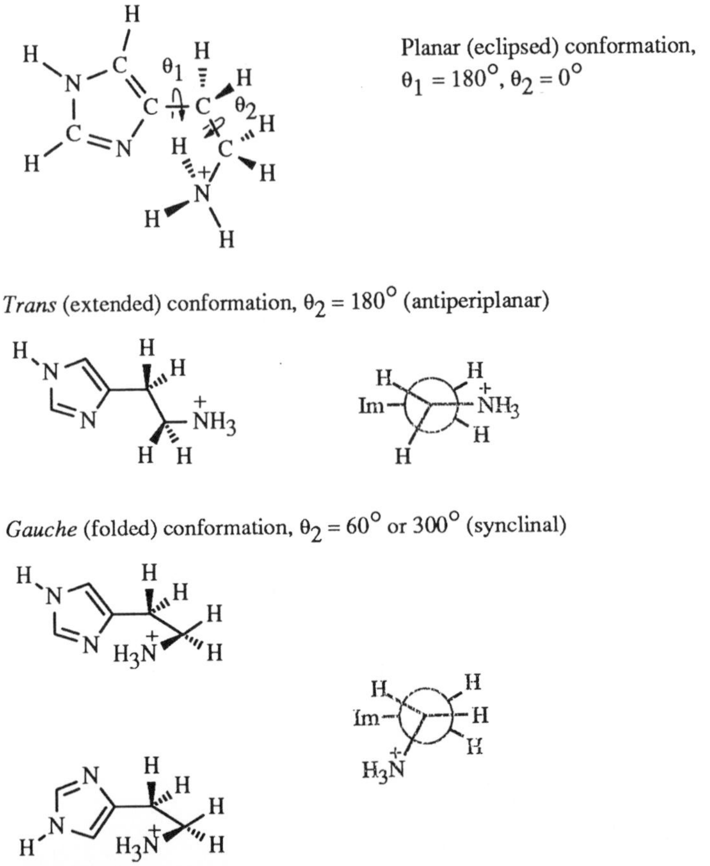

Planar (eclipsed) conformation, $\theta_1 = 180°$, $\theta_2 = 0°$

Trans (extended) conformation, $\theta_2 = 180°$ (antiperiplanar)

Gauche (folded) conformation, $\theta_2 = 60°$ or $300°$ (synclinal)

Figure 7 Histamine monocation (N^τ-H tautomer) showing torsion angles (θ) and *trans* and *gauche* conformations; θ_1 measures the rotation of the imidazole ring, while θ_2 measures the rotation within the side chain

(on the solid) and theoretical calculation (isolated molecules) (Table 6). As with other disubstituted ethanes, the most stable conformers of histamine are those in which the hydrogen atoms in the side chain have a staggered arrangement, *viz. trans* (fully extended chain, $\theta_2 = 180°$) and *gauche* (folded chain, $\theta_2 = 60°$ or $360°$).

In aqueous solution, NMR studies indicate that histamine is a mixture of approximately equal amounts of *trans* and *gauche* conformers, but the studies do not indicate the imidazole orientation (θ_1).[124,125] Crystal structures (Table 6), have so far yielded only the *trans* conformation for all species of histamine (*i.e.* dication, monocation and uncharged forms) but they indicate that various

Table 6 Stable Conformations of Histamine by Different Procedures (θ_1 and θ_2 as defined in Figure 7)

	Dication	Monocation	Base	Ref.
Side chain conformers (T, $\theta_2 = 180°$; G, $\theta_2 = 60°$)				
In solution				
NMR in D_2O	T + G	T + G		124, 125
IR or NMR in $CHCl_3$			T + G	126
In crystals	T	T	T, G[a]	116, 119, 120
Molecular orbital calculation				
EHT method	T + G	T + G		124, 127
CNDO/2, INDO, PCILO	T	G	G	122, 124, 128–130
with F^- counterion	T + G	G		131
Imidazole orientation[b] (θ_2, approximately 180°; θ_1, rounded to the nearest degree)				
In crystals	4°, 7°, 9°	90°	66°	116, 119, 120
	27°, 30°, 83°[c]			132–136

The abbreviations used are: EHT extended Hückel theory; INDO intermediate neglect of differential overlap; PCILO perturbative configuration interaction using localized orbitals; CNDO complete neglect of differential overlap; NMR nuclear magnetic resonance spectroscopy; IR infrared spectroscopy; T *trans* conformation, $\theta_2 = 180°$, antiperiplanar; G *gauche* conformation, $\theta_2 = 60°$, or 300°, synclinal.

[a] In metal complexes, chelated forms of histamine may have a *gauche* or nearly planar (synperiplanar) conformation in which hydrogen atoms are eclipsed. [b] θ_1 represents the dihedral angle between the two planes formed respectively by the imidazole ring and the —C—C—N side chain. [c] Sulfate (4°, 9°), tetrachlorocobaltate (7°), dichloride (27°), dibromide (30°), diphosphate monohydrate (83°), $CaCl_2$ complex.

imidazole orientations are attained, ranging from almost fully planar ($\theta_1 = 0°$) to completely out of plane ($\theta_1 = 90°$).

Molecular orbital calculations on the isolated molecule give various predictions for histamine conformation, depending on the method used (see Table 6); the EHT (extended Hückel theory) method agrees well with the experimental findings of NMR, in predicting a mixture of *trans* and *gauche* conformers.[124,127] The molecular orbital calculations also show that there are substantial energy barriers to interconversion between *trans* and *gauche* formations but that rotation of the imidazole ring is much less restricted. These predictions are in keeping with the observations from crystallography, *viz.* a single value for θ_2 but a multiplicity of values for θ_1.

The foregoing studies all relate to 'free' histamine. The situation may be quite different with 'bound' histamine, *e.g.* at a receptor or to an active site in an enzyme. Histamine chelates to metal ions, and in this form the molecule may be folded (*gauche* conformation) or fully planar ('eclipsed' conformation). Crystal structures of (histamine)$_2$Cu^{II}, (histamine)$_2$Ni^{II} and (histamine)$_3$Ni^{II} show chelation in which histamine is almost fully planar,[133,137,138] but a complex of histamine with copper and carbon monoxide [(histamine)$_3$Cu$_2^I$(CO)$_2$]$^{2+}$, [BPh$_4$]$^{2-}$ shows both *gauche* and *trans* conformations for histamine in the same crystal.[139]

12.5.6.4 Histamine as a Receptor Ligand

It is conceivable that when histamine interacts with its receptors, it functions in the chemical sense as a ligand binding to a specific molecular site and it is pertinent to mention briefly some of the properties which may have importance for ligand–receptor interaction.

Histamine is a very polar hydrophilic molecule; the partition coefficient for histamine free base between 1-octanol and water buffer at pH 11.8 is low ($P = 0.2$), *i.e.* over 80% remains in the aqueous solution. Histamine has a strong capacity for hydrogen bonding, in which the ammonium and imidazolium cations act as hydrogen donors and the uncharged ring (in the monocation or free base) acts both as hydrogen donor and acceptor.

Electronic charge distributions within the histamine molecule have been calculated by several research groups.[118,127–130,141] The individual calculations differ in the numerical values predicted but they indicate that all the nitrogen atoms are negatively charged, that there is little net charge on the carbon atoms, and that the positive charge is distributed widely over all the hydrogen atoms in the molecule, although tending to be concentrated on the N—H hydrogens. A different approach considers the electron density with respect to the covalent radii of atoms and also suggests that the positive charge in the monocation is dispersed over the whole molecule.[215] Perhaps a more helpful way of visualizing the influence of charge distribution is by the use of molecular electrostatic energy maps, which indicate energy contours around the histamine cation for interaction with a point negative charge or for deprotonation.[118,207]

Most work on histamine as a ligand has been concerned with metal complexes, either in solution (formation constants) or in the solid state. Histamine forms stable complexes with the divalent transition metal cations Cu, Ni, Co, Zn and Cd, and the measured stability constants (Table 7) are in the standard order Zn < Cu > Ni > Co. Crystal structure determinations have established the geometry for coordination between histamine and Cu^{II} or Ni^{II} (see above) and confirm that histamine base chelates to the metal cation *via* the side chain $-NH_2$ and the ring $-N^\pi$ nitrogen atoms, forming a six-membered ring. The imidazole N atom appears to coordinate first and, indeed, a detailed kinetic analysis of the reaction between Ni^{2+} with histamine indicates a biphasic kinetic behaviour due to parallel complexing of the individual tautomers of histamine base.[149] Complexation at N^π leads to a stable chelate, but the N^τ complex is a dead end because chelation cannot occur; it has to dissociate in a slower step before it can convert to the chelated product. The analysis is supported by comparison with N^τ-methylhistamine. This is an extremely interesting observation which provides a chemical precedent for the argument that histamine presenting itself at the receptor in an inappropriate tautomeric form would have to dissociate, tautomerize, and then recombine in order to be effective. It is of interest that analogous reasoning was used in the design of the H_2 antagonist metiamide.[150]

The above complexes may contain more than one molecule of histamine per atom; in solution, 1:1, 2:1 and, in the case of Ni, Co and Zn, 3:1 complexes are formed. The values of the successive formation constants given in Table 7 indicate that chelation of the first molecule of histamine to metal cation has higher stability than chelation of the second and third molecules. In contrast, histamine monocation forms a crystalline complex with Ca which is not chelated; the N^π nitrogen coordinates to the metal but the N^α nitrogen remains free (but protonated). This is in keeping with binding studies of alkaline earth divalent cations Mg, Ca, Sr and Ba, where histamine forms only weak 1:1 complexes.

Much past interest has centred on the binding of histamine in mast cells, and the nature of the complex presumed to form with heparin.[151,152] The possibility of a ternary histamine–zinc–heparin complex has also been explored but the role of zinc has since been questioned. The state of the histamine molecule (*e.g.* conformation or protonation) in this complex is still not known, but NMR spectroscopy studies suggest that histamine in mast cells is relatively labile, with rapid exchange occurring between bound histamine and pools of free histamine in water compartments confined in the granule matrix.[422]

12.5.7 AGONISTS AT HISTAMINE RECEPTORS

12.5.7.1 General Structure–Activity Studies

The early studies of histamine analogues investigated various imidazole derivatives and related heterocyclic compounds. Structure–activity aspects have been reviewed in detail by Barlow,[10] Jones,[53] Paton[66] and Ganellin.[155] In general, close congeners are less active; exceptions are certain methyl derivatives (see below). Shortening or lengthening of the side chain, or replacement of the amino group by an uncharged group greatly reduces, or abolishes, histamine-like activity.

Replacing the imidazole ring of histamine by other heterocycles reduces histamine-like activity (Table 8) and some very interesting observations have been made. Walter *et al.* (1941) originally

Table 7 Stability Constants of Histamine Metal Complexes in Aqueous Solution at 37 °C

	Cu^{2+}	Ni^{2+}	Zn^{2+}	Co^{2+}	Cd^{2+}	Ca^{2+}	Sr^{2+}	Ba^{2+}	Mg^{2+}
Ref.	142, 145	143, 145	144, 145	144, 145	145, 146	147	147	147	147
$\log K_1^a$	9.28	6.60	5.03	4.89	4.54^b	3.07	2.96	2.87	2.50
$\log K_2$	6.30	4.84	4.78	3.54	3.25				
$\log K_3$		2.93^c	2.28	2.03^d					
$\log \beta_2^e$	15.58	11.44	9.81	8.43	7.79				

^{a} $\log K_1$ refers to the first formation constant, with stoichiometry histamine:metal cation = 1:1; $\log K_2$ and $\log K_3$ are respectively the successive second and third formation constants with 2:1 and 3:1 stoichiometry. ^{b} At 40 °C. ^{c} Formation equilibrium constant[149] for the monodentate complex to the N^τ nitrogen atom of histamine, $\log K = 2.88$ at 25 °C. ^{d} At 25 °C.[148] ^{e} $\log \beta_2 = \log K_1 K_2$.

Table 8 H$_1$ Receptor Agonist Activities of Aminoethylheterocyclic Compounds (R = —CH$_2$CH$_2$NH$_2$) Determined *in vitro* on Guinea Pig Ileum. The Potencies are Expressed as the Ratio, Molar Concentration of Histamine/Molar Concentration of Compound Necessary to Produce Equal Effects, Relative to Histamine = 100 (NA = not active)

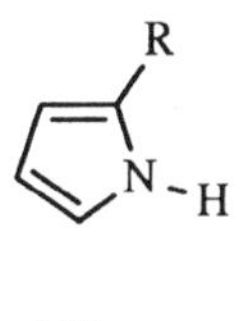

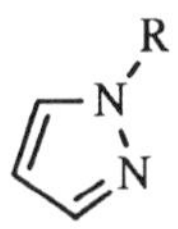

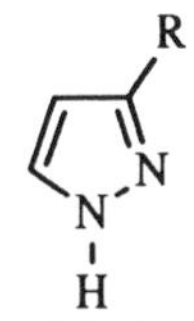

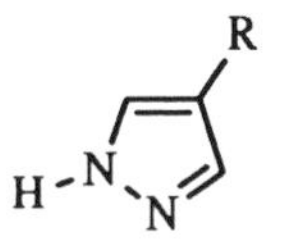

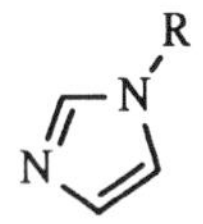

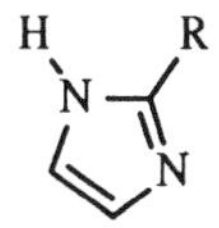

NA	0.2	0.1, 1	0.1[a]	NA	0.1
Ref. 157	53	111, 158, 53	53, 158	53	159
100	1.2	NA	13, 73, 10	NA	0.5
Ref.	159	53	111, 53, 160	53	161
2	30, 26	0.01	9, 6, 5	NA	<0.001
Ref. 53	157, 111	111	157, 111, 158	162	111
5	0.1	0.2	NA	0.1[a]	
Ref. 157	157	157	157	158	

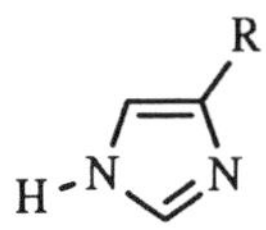

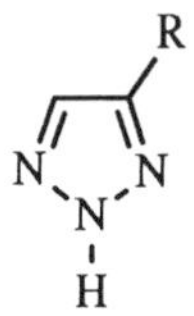

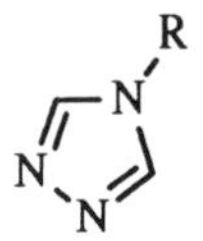

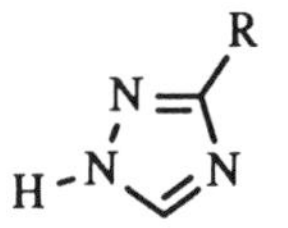

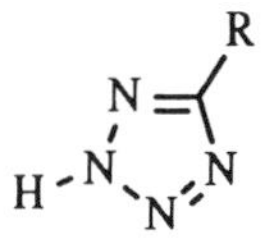

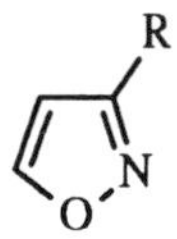

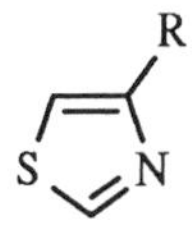

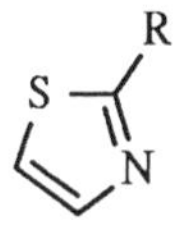

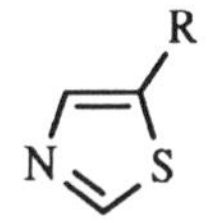

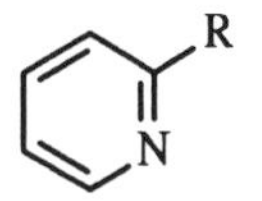

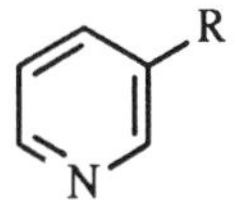

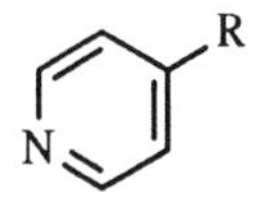

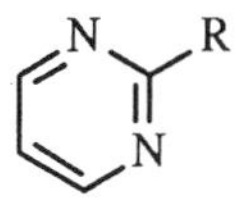

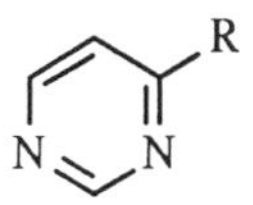

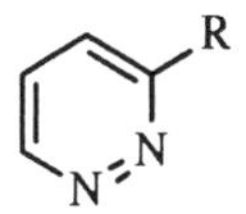

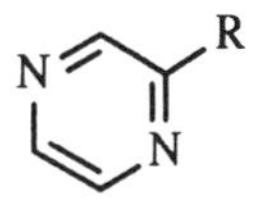

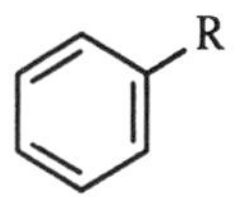

[a] Only achieves 40–45% of histamine's maximal response.

described[156] the finding that 2-pyridylethylamine was a histamine-like stimulant of guinea pig smooth muscle contraction, whereas the isomer 4-pyridylethylamine was not active.

Subsequently, many other heterocyclic analogues were reported on and have been summarized in the above-mentioned reviews.

Some compounds exhibit receptor selectivity as agonists and are valuable tools for studying histamine pharmacology (see Section 12.5.10; Table 15). For example, 2-pyridylethylamine and 2-thiazolylethylamine are relatively selective H$_1$ receptor agonists,[111] and N^α-methyl-2-pyridylethylamine (betahistine) has been used clinically as a peripheral vasodilator (see below, Section 12.5.7.2). 3-Pyrazolylethylamine has modest selectivity as an H$_2$ receptor agonist; as a stimulant of acid secretion[163] it was introduced for clinical use as a diagnostic agent (betazole; Histalog^R).[164,165]

12.5.7.2 Methyl Substituents in Histamine

All the possible monomethyl-substituted histamines have been synthesized[166] and most have been assayed quantitatively for agonist activities at all three histamine receptors. These compounds comprise a very interesting chemically homogeneous series for structure–activity studies. None of the compounds is more potent than histamine *in vitro*, at H$_1$ or H$_2$ receptors (Table 9), although methylation at the side chain amino nitrogen (N^α position) causes only a relatively small reduction in potency (N^α-methyl- and N^α, N^α-dimethyl-histamine are reported to be two to three times more potent than is histamine as stimulants of gastric acid secretion *in vivo* in the dog,[53] but this is

Table 9 Histamine Receptor Agonist activities (H_1, H_2 and H_3) of Methylhistamines Relative to Histamine = 100

	H_1 in vitro guinea pig ileum	in vitro guinea pig atrium	H_2 in vitro rat uterus	in vivo rat gastric acid	H_3 in vitro rat cortex
Monosubstituted					
π	< 0.01[a] NA[e]	< 0.1[b,c]	0.06[b,d]	< 0.2[a]	< 4[aa]
2	16.5[f] 16[g], 14[h], 30[e]	4.4[f] 4.4[h]	2.1[f]	2.0[f]	< 0.08[aa]
τ	0.42[i] 0.45[j], 0.6[e]	< 0.1[i] < 0.1[j]	0.2[b]	< 0.01[a]	< 4[aa]
4	0.23[f] 0.9[k], 1[l]	43[f] 71[k]	25.3[f] 31[m]	39[f] 40[l]	< 0.008[aa]
β ($\pm$)	0.83[i]	0.89[i]	0.42	0.4[a]	300[ab]
α ($\pm$)	0.36[i]	0.74[i]	0.20[b]	0.8[a]	
$(+)$-(S)	0.49[x]	1.7[x]			13[ac]
$(-)$-(R)	0.49[x]	1.0[x]			1550[ac]
N^α	72[i] 81[k] 85[s]	74[i] 185[k]	34[b] 170[m,n] 58[p]	74[a] 51[p] 60[u]	270[aa]
Disubstituted					
2,4	0.3[w]	3.8[w]			
τ,N^α	0.7[j]	< 0.1[j]			
4,N^α	0.16[a] 0.2[q], 1.3[k]	36[b] 95[k]	10[m] 25[q]	8.2[a] 25[q]	
4,α($\pm$)	0.08[b] 0.05[r]	5.8[b]	0.94[b] 1[m], 2–10[r]	5–10[r]	
$(+)$-(S)	0.26[z]	8.7[z]			
$(-)$-(R)	0.33[z]	4.8[z]			
β,β	< 0.001[a]			NA[a]	120[ab]
α,α					300[ab]
$\alpha,N^\alpha(+)$-(R)	0.69[y]	0.42[y]			4.1[ad]
$(-)$-(S)	0.71[y]	0.98[y]			0.13[ad]
N^α,N^α	44[i,s]	51[i]	24[b]	19[a], 60[u]	170[aa]
Trisubstituted					
2,N^α,N^α	16.8[a]			1.4[a]	
τ,N^α,N^α	0.14[j]	NA[j]			
4,N^α,N^α	0.1[a]	13.5[b]		3.0[a]	
$N^\alpha,N^\alpha,N^\alpha$	1[s,t]			Weak[v]	

NA No agonist activity detected. [a] Ref.166. [b] Ref. 159. [c] 20% max. [d] 70% max. [e] Ref. 157. [f] Ref. 54. [g] Ref. 167. [h] Ref. 168. [i] Ref. 124. [j] Ref. 169. [k] Ref. 170. [l] Ref. 171. [m] Ref. 172. [n] pD_2 4.91 $\pm$ 0.30, not significantly different from histamine (4.68 $\pm$ 0.27). [p] Ref. 51. [q] Ref. 173. [r] Ref. 174. [s] Ref. 175. [t] Probably an overestimate, since this substance also possesses nicotinic actions. [u] Ref. 176. [v] Ref. 111. [w] Ref. 177; 40% max (H_1); 80% max (H_2). [x] Ref. 178. [y] Ref. 179. [z] Ref. 180. [aa] Ref. 56. [ab] Ref. 181. [ac] Ref. 57. [ad] Ref. 182.

probably due to greater metabolic stability relative to histamine). Methylation at the side chain carbon atoms (α or β positions) has a marked effect and such compounds have only weak activity at H_1 or H_2 receptors (see Figure 1 for numbering).

At H_3 receptors, however, N^α, α- and β-methylhistamines are potent agonists. Introduction of methyl at the side chain carbon atoms introduces a chiral centre; resolution of the optical isomers, assignment of absolute configuration, and determination of histamine-like agonist potencies has been reported for α-methylhistamine and α, N^α-dimethylhistamine.[178,179] No difference was found in activity for the enantiomers at the H_1 receptor (guinea pig ileum); a small difference was found at H_2 receptors (guinea pig atrium) (activity ratio of isomers $(+)$:$(-)$ 1.7 and 2.3 respectively) but this may not be truly significant (see also Table 17). However, a marked stereochemical dependence exists for α-methylhistamine at H_3 receptors, activity residing almost entirely with the (R)-$(-)$ entantiomer[57] (*i.e.* the reverse of the chiral discrimination apparent at H_2 receptors). Surprisingly, although N^α- and α-methylhistamines are potent H_3 agonists, the combination of substituents, *i.e.* N^α,α-dimethylhistamine, has only weak activity; N-methylation apparently causes at least a 100-fold drop in potency.[182]

Methylation in the imidazole ring at positions 2 or 4 (5) imparts relative selectivity at H_1 or H_2 receptors.[54] Thus 2-methylhistamine had approximately 20% of the potency of histamine as an H_1 receptor agonist determined *in vitro* on the guinea pig ileum, but only 2–4% of the potency as an H_2 receptor agonist (*in vitro* on the rat uterus, or guinea pig atrium or *in vivo* as a stimulant of gastric acid secretion in the anaesthetized rat). Conversely, 4-methylhistamine (some authors refer to this compound as 5-methylhistamine) showed approximately 40% of the potency of histamine as an H_2 receptor agonist, but only 0.2% potency as an H_1 receptor agonist. These compounds have become valuable tools for elucidating histamine pharmacology (*cf.* Section 12.5.10, Table 15); they are not active at H_3 receptors.

N^τ-Methylhistamine is one of the main natural metabolites of histamine, being the product of methylation by histamine-N-methyltransferase (EC 2.1.1.8, Figure 2); N^τ-methylhistamine and its isomer N^π-methylhistamine are not active at any of the receptors.

Although α-methylhistamine is only weakly active as an H_2 receptor agonist, α-methylation of 4-methylhistamine appears to cause less of a reduction in H_2 receptor potency; thus 4,α-dimethylhistamine (Table 9) is reported[174] to have 5–10% of the potency of histamine as a stimulant of rat gastric acid secretion and found to have approximately 6% of the potency of histamine as a stimulant on the guinea pig atrium,[159,180] although it has only 1% of the activity of histamine on the rat uterus preparation. This is most unusual because it appears that relative to α-methylhistamine, the introduction of a second methyl group (at the 4-position) has resulted in a marked (five- to ten-fold) increase in H_2 receptor agonist potency.

N^α-Methyl-2-pyridylethylamine is a selective H_1 receptor agonist of similar potency to 2-pyridylethylamine itself, measured on the isolated guinea pig ileum,[183] but it appears to be only a partial agonist at cerebral H_1 receptors[184] and it may also be a stimulant of some H_2 receptor systems.[223] It is not an agonist at H_3 autoreceptors but acts as a moderate antagonist. It has been used clinically as a peripheral vasodilator for treatment of Meniere's disease under the generic name betahistine (Serc).[185,186] A second N-methyl substituent also appears to be well tolerated at the receptor, and N^α, N^α-dimethyl-2-pyridylethylamine is reported to be equally potent.[158]

12.5.7.3 Higher Alkyl and Aryl Substituents

Histamine derivatives containing higher alkyl substituents have been tested and, in general, the larger substituents cause a reduction in potency (Table 10).

At H_1 receptors, 2-ethylhistamine was less active than 2-methylhistamine as an agonist, 2-propyl-, 2-isopropyl- and 2-butyl-histamines were weakly active.[167] Some 2-arylhistamines are agonists[190] even though the aryl group is a relatively bulky substituent, *e.g.* 2-phenyl-,2-(3-pyridyl)- and 2-(4-pyridyl)-histamines.[167,168] However, *para*-substituted compounds may be only weak partial agonists.[168] These results suggest that the aryl groups reduce efficacy of the agonists (relative to histamine) but increase the affinity for H_1 receptors, and the measured potency is the net balance between these effects. Substituent planarity may be important, since ethyl and phenyl substituents appear to be accommodated, but *n*-propyl- and isopropyl are not. Side chain N-alkylhistamines have been variously studied;[188,189] agonist activity falls in the series Me > Et > Pr^n $\approx$ CH_2Ph. Although N^α,N^α-diethylhistamine has weak agonist activity, the pyrrolidino and piperidino analogues are weak antagonists (Table 10).[169]

At H_2 receptors 4-ethylhistamine was slightly less active than 4-methylhistamine as an agonist, 4-propylhistamine was a partial agonist and 4-butylhistamine was inactive.[170] In the cat, 4-ethylhistamine resembled 4-methylhistamine as a stimulant of gastric acid secretion, but 4-isopropylhistamine was inactive.[187]

N^τ-Ethyl and N^τ,N^τ-djethyl derivatives of 4-methylhistamine have some activity as H_2 receptor agonists but the homologues N^τ-isopropyl and N^τ-*t*-butyl are not active.[176]

12.5.7.4 Polar Substituents

There have been very few studies of polar substituted histamines or congeners. Electron-withdrawing groups (*e.g.* Cl, Br, NO_2) in the 4-position of histamine reduce agonist activity and have been studied with respect to possible effects on imidazole tautomerism;[111,113] 2- and 4-fluorohistamines, 2-trifluoromethylhistamine, 2-cyanohistamine and 2-carboxyhistamine have been synthesized[191–193] but their activities at histamine receptors have not been reported. 2-Aminohistamine[194] is a relatively selective H_2 receptor agonist (*ca.* 30% of the H_2 receptor potency of

Table 10 Histamine Receptor Activities (H_1 and H_2) of Alkyl (Higher than Methyl) and Aryl Histamines, Relative to Histamine = 100

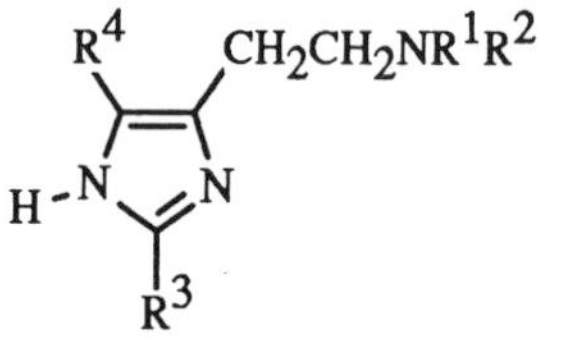

Substituents R¹	R²	R³	R⁴	H_1 in vitro guinea pig ileum	H_2 in vitro guinea pig atrium	H_2 in vivo gastric acid (rat)
H	H	Et	H	5[a], 6.9[a]	1.4[u]	
H	H	Pr^n	H	0.6[a], 0.3[b,c]		
H	H	Pr^i	H	c[a], 0.6[b,c]		
H	H	Bu^n	H	0.5[a]		
H	H	Ph	H	13[a], 19.1[b,d]		
H	H	PhCH$_2$	H	2.5[a], 0.8[b]		
H	H	2-Pyridyl	H	0.9[b]		
H	H	3-Pyridyl	H	13[a], 11.0[b]		
H	H	4-Pyridyl	H	9.1[b]		
H	H	p-MeC$_6$H$_4$	H	0.4[a,d]		
H	H	p-ClC$_6$H$_4$CH$_2$	H	3.6[a,d]		
H	H	PhCH$_2$CH$_2$	H	3.6[a,e]		
H	H	H	Et	4.5[f]	53[f]	g, h
Me	H	H	Et	2.0[f]	33[f]	
H	H	H	Pr^n	0.9[d,f]	7[f,i]	
Me	H	H	Pr^n	0.5[f,j]	6[d,f]	
H	H	H	Pr^i			NA[g,k]
H	H	H	Bu^n	NA[f,k]	NA[f,k]	
H	H	H	C$_6$H$_{11}$	NA[u]	NA[u]	
H	H	H	Ph	NA[u]	NA[u]	
Me	H	H	Ph	NA[u]	NA[u]	
Et	H	H	H	7[r,s,t]	21[r]	
Pr^n	H	H	H	0.2[r,s,t]	NA[r]	
Et	Me	H	H	5.5[r]	29.5[r]	
Pr^n	Me	H	H	0.2[r,j]	NA[r]	
C$_6$H$_{11}$	H	H	H	0.6[r,j]	NA[r]	
CH$_2$Ph	H	H	H	10[l]		11[m]
Et	Et	H	H	1[l,s], 10[n]		3[m]
Et	H	H	Me			p, q
Et	Et	H	Me			p, q
Pr^i	H	H	Me			NA[k,p]
Bu^t	H	H	Me			NA[k,p]

[a] Ref. 167. [b] Ref. 168. [c] Only achieved 30% of histamine's maximal response. [d] Only achieved 40% histamine's maximal response. [e] Only achieved 88% of histamines maximal response. [f] Ref. 170. [g] In the anaesthetized cat, ref 187. [h] Equiactive with 4-methylhistamine (R^4 = Me, $R^1 = R^2 = R^3$ = H). [i] Only achieved 50% of histamine's maximal response. [j] Only achieved 20% of histamine's maximal response. [k] NA = no agonist activity detected. [l] Ref. 51. [m] In the anaesthetized rat, ref. 51. [n] Ref. 169. [p] In the anaesthetized rat, ref. 176. [q] 5% of the potency of 4-methylhistamine (R^4 = Me, $R^1 = R^2 = R^3$ = H). [r] Ref. 177. [s] Less quantitative data have been reported in ref. 188. [t] Less quantitative data have been reported in ref. 189 [u] Ref. 180.

histamine, but only 1% at H_1 receptors);[195] surprisingly, introduction of a 4-methyl group makes the compound almost inactive.

Similarly, a 5-amino substituent in 1,2,4-triazol-3-ylethylamine[196] markedly reduces H_1 receptor agonist activity and renders the compound relatively selective as an H_2 receptor agonist.[160]

12.5.8 THE ACTIVE FORM OF HISTAMINE AT H_1 AND H_2 RECEPTORS

Since various species of histamine exist, each should be considered for possible biological significance. Some indication of their likely importance comes from structure–activity considerations of analogues (congeners). Furthermore, the existence of three receptor populations for histamine raises the interesting question of whether the chemical mechanism of histamine–receptor interaction differs between the three types of receptor.

12.5.8.1 Evidence for the Monocation

It was pointed out in Section 12.5.6.2 that histamine exists in various ionic forms. The graphical plot of the species population as a function of pH (Figure 6) shows that the curve for the monocation achieves a maximum in the pH range 7–8; since this is also the physiological range for pH neutrality, it suggests, but does not prove, that the physiologically important species is the monocation.

Below pH 5.8, at values which are still physiological, histamine dication predominates; however, indications that the dication is probably not an active form come from comparing active histamine analogues which have a low pK_a such that their dication population is extremely small. Examples are 3-(1,2,4-triazolyl)ethylamine, 2-thiazolylethylamine and 4-chlorohistamine, shown in Table 11. These compounds have very low dication populations even at pH 5.4 (*e.g.* 3-(1,2,4-triazolyl)ethylamine has only 0.01% of molecules as the dication at pH 5.4) and yet they have at least 10% of the potency of histamine at either H_1 or H_2 receptors.

There is less evidence as to whether the uncharged (free base) form is active. All compounds so far known to be active are strongly basic amines (see ref. 53) which exist mainly in cationic forms at physiological pH. The tertiary amine N^α, N^α-dimethylhistamine is active at H_1 and H_2 receptors but the quaternary ammonium derivative $N^\alpha,N^\alpha,N^\alpha$-trimethylhistamine is extremely weak (Table 9). Therefore, a proton on the N^α-ammonium group appears to be of importance for agonist activity at both H_1 and H_2 receptors.[111] If the main function of the proton were hydrogen bonding, then activity would appear to reside exclusively with the monocation. That this is not the only criterion, however, is suggested by comparing the N^α-acetyl and N^α-guanyl derivatives, both of which can provide a proton for hydrogen bonding, and yet are respectively inactive or relatively weak.[155]

Another possible function of the proton is that it dissociates, generating the uncharged form, possibly as a transient species (Figure 5). The uncharged form might be required for access (*e.g.* penetration of membranes) or be involved in assisting imidazole-mediated proton transfer at the receptor site.[118,122] In the latter situation, the uncharged N^α atom might act as a lone pair electron donor.

Another approach to determine the active species has been to examine the influence of pH on agonist activity. Some studies[197–199] have been conducted with histamine on the isolated guinea pig ileum in the pH range 6.6–8.3 and the observed changes in response have been attributed to ionization of a group having a pK_a of 6.8–7.0. Since this pK_a does not correspond to those of histamine, it was argued that ionization must be due to the receptor. This may not be a valid argument, however, since pK_a values alter under nonaqueous conditions, *e.g.* in membranes.

Table 11 Histamine Congeners with Weakly Basic Rings

Compound name	Structure	Ring pK_a[b]	Mole percentage of dication[b] pH 7.4	pH 5.4	Receptor Activity[a] H_1 ileum	H_2 atrium
Histamine	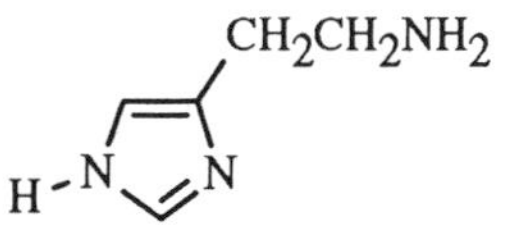	5.8	2.5	71.5	100	100
2-Thiazolylethylamine	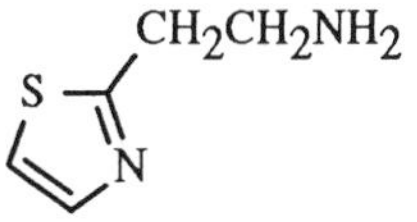	≈ 1.5	10^{-4}	10^{-2}	26	
4-Chlorohistamine	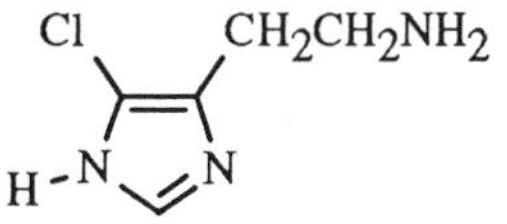	3.1	5×10^{-3}	0.5		11
1,2,4-Triazol-3-ylethylamine	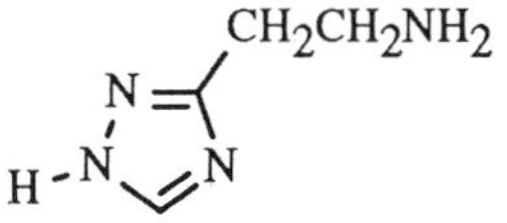	1.4	10^{-4}	10^{-2}	12.7	6.8

[a] Agonist activities determined *in vitro* on guinea pig tissues. Potencies are expressed (relative to histamine = 100) as the ratio, molar concentration of histamine/molar concentration of compound necessary to produce equal effects.[155] [b] Determined at 37 °C.

Another problem is that a change in pH may affect tissue response so that it becomes difficult to attribute observed response changes necessarily to changes in drug ionization, *e.g.* see other discussions regarding related studies on cardiovascular tissues.[200-202] Further studies on guinea pig gall bladder, which contains both H_1 and H_2 receptors, with agonists having different pK_a properties, *e.g.* 2-pyridylethylamine and dimaprit (see Section 12.5.10) suggest[203] that pH changes affect receptor responses rather than reflecting changes in the ionic species of histamine (see also Section 12.5.9.1).

12.5.8.2   Evidence for an Active Tautomer at H_1 Receptors

Many years ago Niemann and Hays (1942) concluded[162] that the active form of histamine was the monocationic tautomer, which could form an intramolecular hydrogen bond (now referred to as the N^τ—H tautomer, Figure 1). This conclusion followed from the finding that 2-pyridylethylamine was a histamine-like stimulant of guinea pig smooth muscle contraction, whereas 4-pyridylethylamine was not active (Table 8);[156,204] 3-pyridylethylamine was also not active, indicating that the other tautomer (*i.e.* N^π—H) of histamine must also be devoid of activity.

Similar comparisons may be made between 2-thiazolylethylamine and 5-thiazolylethylamine,[111] and between histamine and *N*-aminoethylimidazole (Table 8). It is necessary to be cautious, however, in arguing from inactive compounds, *e.g.* many of the inactive structures indicated in Table 8 would correspond to either one of the histamine tautomers. The active compounds clearly indicate, however, that the N^τ—H tautomer of histamine is very likely to be an active form at H_1 receptors.

Although histamine is tautomeric, it is probable that imidazole tautomerism is not functionally involved in H_1 receptor stimulation since 2-pyridylethylamine and 2-thiazolylethylamine cannot tautomerize and are effective H_1 receptor agonists.

12.5.8.3   Evidence for Involvement of Tautomerism at H_2 Receptors

Although the above nontautomeric heterocyclic ethylamines are active as H_1 receptor agonists, they are only weakly active at H_2 receptors and it appears that effective H_2 receptor agonists so far known are compounds which can undergo a 1,3-prototropic tautomerism.[111] Another indication that tautomerism may be important for H_2 receptor agonist activity comes from a comparison of the activities of 4-substituted histamine derivatives. Electron-withdrawing substituents in the 4-position of the imidazole ring change the relative tautomer concentrations and the reductions in the N^τ—H tautomer populations approximately parallel the changes in H_2 receptor activities.[111,113] This is not conclusive evidence because the 4-substituent in histamine exerts other 'effects', *e.g.* steric, polar, hydrophobic, which may also markedly affect agonist activity.[205]

The above results permit speculation that the N^τ—H tautomer is the biologically active form of histamine at H_2 receptors and that it is also possible that the free energy difference between the two tautomers must be small for effective biological activity. One may distinguish between two cases: either the N^τ—H tautomer is involved statically in bidentate acceptor–donor hydrogen bonding or tautomerism (or proton transfer) is involved dynamically and histamine acts as a proton transfer agent.[113] In the latter situation (Figure 8) one can envisage the imidazole ring catalyzing the transfer of a proton from site A to site B at the receptor, and perhaps a catalytic mechanism of some kind may be involved in the events leading to an effective H_2 receptor response.[111] Such a proton transfer mechanism is analogous to the function of imidazole in the histidyl residues of certain enzymes, *e.g.* in the proton relay at the catalytic site of chymotrypsin.[206]

A mechanism involving tautomerism finds support on theoretical grounds. Using molecular orbital calculations *ab initio* Weinstein and coworkers[118,207] found that electron charge distribution in the imidazole ring of histamine was different for the monocation in comparison with the base (see discussion in Section 12.5.6.2) to the extent that the tautomer preference was reversed. Similar changes occurred after simulating an interaction between the cationic side chain of histamine monocation with a negatively charged group, *e.g.* OH^-. In both cases there was a shift in the dominant tautomeric form caused by a change in the reactivity of the ring nitrogen atoms, as demonstrated by the molecular electrostatic potentials and total molecular energies. Weinstein and coworkers proposed that a similar interaction would occur at the receptor and they envisage (Figure 8) that histamine interacts with an anionic receptor site (I) through its cationic side chain (*i.e.* the protonated amino group) and at two other sites (II) and (III) through the ring N^τ—H and N^π atoms.

They suggest that neutralization of the cationic charge by the receptor acts as an essential 'triggering mechanism' to induce the tautomeric change needed to transfer a proton from site III to site II in stimulating H_2 receptors. The dynamic aspect of the proton transfer between sites II and III is analogous to that suggested above.

There is still some doubt, however, about whether tautomerism is necessarily involved in the action of histamine since 2-thiazolylethylamine is nontautomeric but possesses approximately 2% of the potency of histamine as a stimulant of the guinea pig atrium *in vitro* (see Table 15) and 2–7% potency in stimulating formation of cyclic AMP,[208,210] although it is much less effective as a stimulant of other H_2 receptor systems.

The highly selective H_2 receptor agonist dimaprit, [*S*-(3-*N*,*N*-dimethylaminopropyl)isothiourea], provides additional evidence (see Section 12.5.9.1). Inspection of the formula (Figure 12) suggests that the —$NHMe_2^+$ group corresponds to the —$NHMe_2^+$ group of N^α,N^α-dimethylhistamine and that the isothiourea group of dimaprit may simulate the imidazole ring. Isothioureas resemble imidazoles in being amidines, which in the uncharged form have N—H and N (lone pair of electrons) and undergo 1,3-prototropic tautomerism. Tautomerism of dimaprit is depicted in Figure 12 and a comparison made with N^α,N^α-dimethylhistamine showing a possible similarity in function as proton transfer agents; alternatively dimaprit may be involved statically in bidentate hydrogen bonding, resembling the N^τ—H tautomer of histamine.

The highly potent H_2 receptor agonist impromidine (**40**; Table 13) also possesses a tautomeric imidazolylpropyl side chain which is believed to be an essential molecular component of the

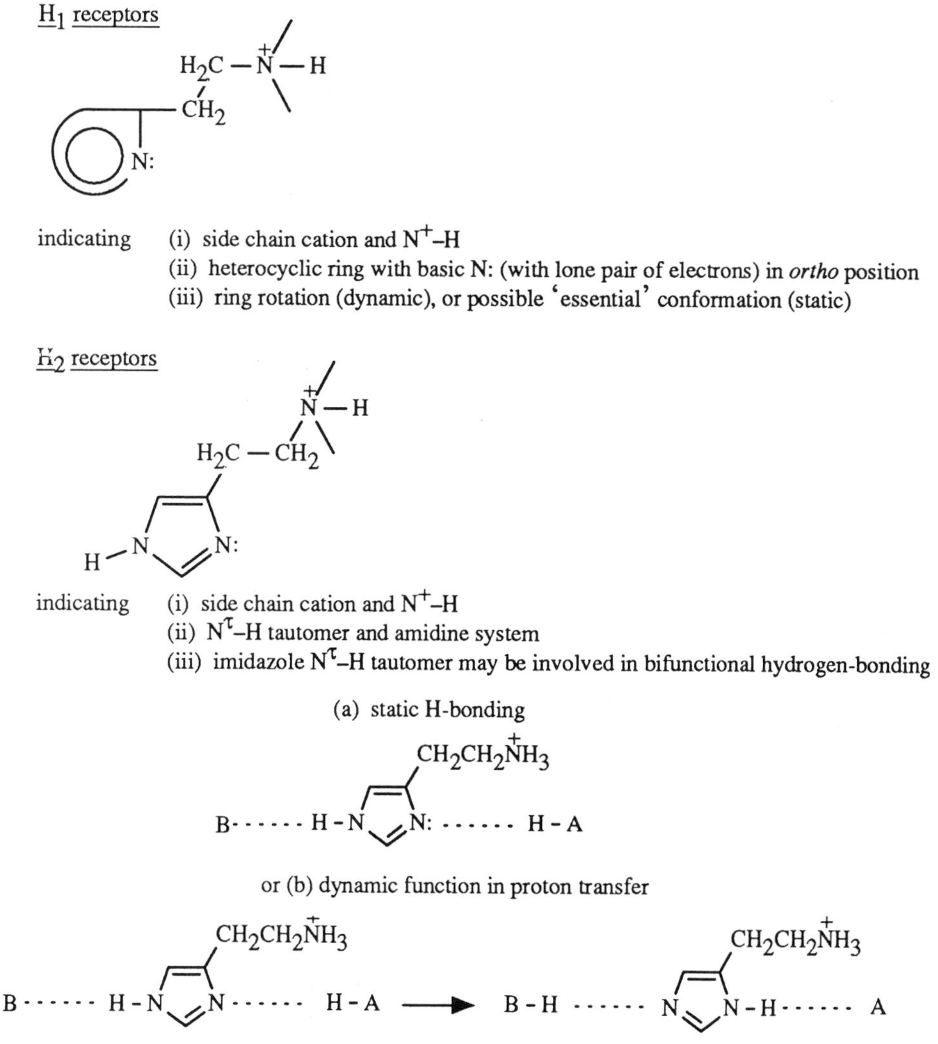

H₁ receptors

indicating   (i) side chain cation and N^+–H
                (ii) heterocyclic ring with basic N: (with lone pair of electrons) in *ortho* position
                (iii) ring rotation (dynamic), or possible 'essential' conformation (static)

H₂ receptors

indicating   (i) side chain cation and N^+–H
                (ii) N^τ–H tautomer and amidine system
                (iii) imidazole N^τ–H tautomer may be involved in bifunctional hydrogen-bonding

(a) static H-bonding

or (b) dynamic function in proton transfer

Figure 8 Functional chemical requirements of histamine as an agonist at H_1 and H_2 receptors

or (c) interaction of histamine monocation (N^τ–H tautomer) with
three sites at the H_2 receptor, proposed by Weinstein *et al.*
showing initial and modified binding states. Reproduced with
permission of authors and publisher

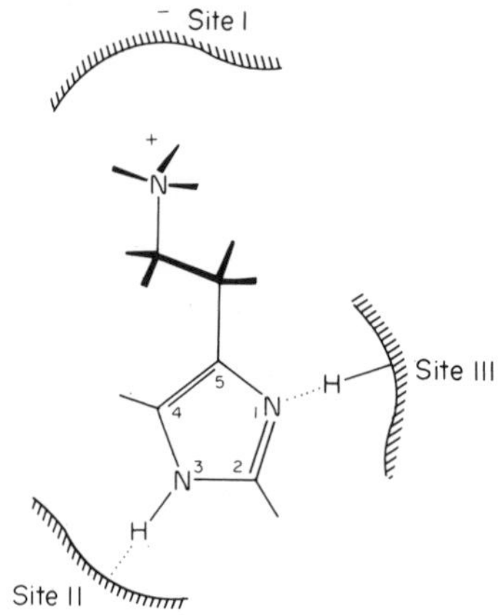

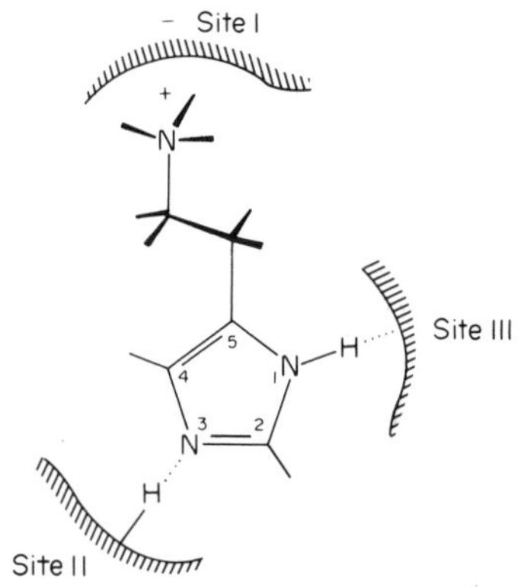

Figure 8   *(Contd.)*

molecule for agonist efficacy (see Section 12.5.9.4). Structure–activity investigations have shown that corresponding nontautomeric analogues are not agonists, suggesting that here, too, H_2 receptor agonist activity is associated with a tautomeric group.

12.5.8.4   Evidence for An Active Conformation

Kier (1968) first proposed[127] that the dual activity of histamine (at H_1 and non-H_1 receptors) is a consequence of the ability of its monocation to adopt two distinct and preferred conformations, *viz. trans* and *gauche* conformers (see Section 12.5.6.3), and he assigned H_1 receptor activity to the *trans* rotamer (based on an arbitrary comparison with the structure of the H_1 receptor antagonist, triprolidine) and provisionally associated H_2 activity with the *gauche* rotamer. There is no reason *a priori* why drug conformation should be the decisive factor that distinguishes the respective receptor actions of histamine and, so far, there is insufficient corroborative experimental evidence for this proposal. The suggestion is interesting but highly speculative. It has, however, prompted many further conformational studies of histamine and analogues.

A series of methyl-substituted histamines was studied with respect to conformational properties and receptor selectivities[211] and it was suggested that the dramatic receptor selectivity of 4-methyl-histamine (which has 40% of the potency of histamine as an H_2 receptor stimulant but only 0.2% at H_1 receptors) could be accounted for in the difference between its conformational properties and those of histamine; this permitted the definition[212,213] of an 'H_1-essential' conformation, *i.e.* a conformation essential to drug activity which has to be adopted by histamine at some stage during interaction at the H_1 receptor site. This is the fully extended *trans* conformation, where $\theta_1 = 0°$ and $\theta_2 = 180°$, in which the carbon and nitrogen atoms are coplanar with the ring (illustrated in Figure 9), and there is a maximum separation (interatomic distance of 5.1 Å) between the charged ammonium group and the ring N^π nitrogen atom. Furthermore, in this conformation any effect from the side chain in obscuring the lone electron pair at N^π is minimal. This would be a very satisfactory situation if the nitrogen atom were involved in donating its electron pair during productive drug–receptor interaction.

The described 'H_1-essential' conformation is not a minimum energy form, but is calculated to have an energy about 3 kcal mol^{-1} (1 cal = 4.18 J) above the minimum (although the value may be an overestimate).[214] This leads one to speculate that histamine may be required to undergo a conformational change during H_1 receptor stimulation. One can envisage that a histamine molecule would arrive in the neighbourhood of the site of action in one of its most probable (minimum energy) conformations and that it might then either interact with the receptor and undergo a change which involves the 'H_1-essential' conformation or, under a perturbing influence of the receptor, it might adopt the 'H_1-essential' conformation prior to forming a drug–receptor complex. The described conformation may be only one of several forms involved during receptor stimulation or, indeed, it may be involved in only a transient manner while the agonist undergoes a required conformational change, *i.e.* a dynamic effect. Thus, rotation of the imidazole ring may also be involved in the action of histamine at H_1 receptors.

This proposed 'essential' conformation is in accord with Kier's suggestion of a *trans* conformation for histamine at H_1 receptors but it goes much further in that it identifies orientation (or rotation) of the imidazole ring as being critical. It is of interest that no rigid analogue of histamine (in which ring rotation is not possible) has been found to have more than approximately 0.5% of the agonist activity of histamine (see Figure 10). This is in contrast with the situation for muscarinic, β-adrenergic, dopaminergic and serotonergic receptors, where active rigid congeners have been discovered.

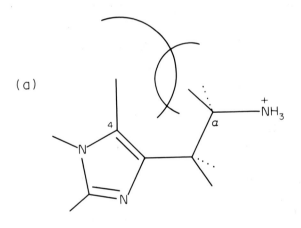

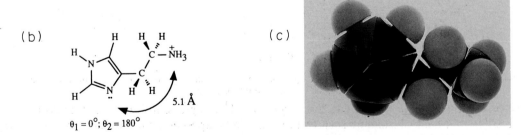

Figure 9 Showing (a) steric interaction between the C_4-methyl and α-methylene groups in 4-methylhistamine in the coplanar ($\theta_1 = 0°$), *trans* ($\theta_2 = 180°$) conformation; intersecting arcs represent the overlap of van der Waals zones. (b) Proposed H_1 receptor 'essential' conformation of histamine. (c) CPK molecular model of histamine monocation in the proposed H_1 receptor 'essential' conformation. The model illustrates the close approach between the hydrogen atoms of the side chain α-CH$_2$ and the ring 4-position

(a) Monocyclic structures (ref. 227)

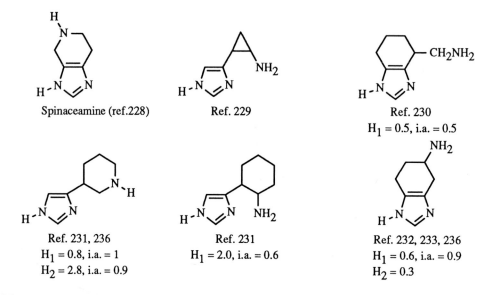

cis $H_1 < 0.1$, $H_2 = 0.7$
trans $H_1 < 0.1$, $H_2 = 0.4$

$H_1 < 0.1$, $H_2 = 0.2$

(b) Two-ring structures

Spinaceamine (ref. 228)

Ref. 229

Ref. 230
$H_1 = 0.5$, i.a. = 0.5

Ref. 231, 236
$H_1 = 0.8$, i.a. = 1
$H_2 = 2.8$, i.a. = 0.9

Ref. 231
$H_1 = 2.0$, i.a. = 0.6

Ref. 232, 233, 236
$H_1 = 0.6$, i.a. = 0.9
$H_2 = 0.3$

(c) Tricyclic structures (refs. 230, 234–236)

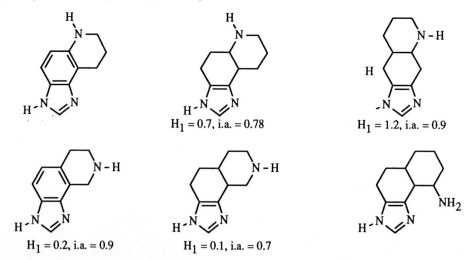

$H_1 = 0.7$, i.a. = 0.78

$H_1 = 1.2$, i.a. = 0.9

$H_1 = 0.2$, i.a. = 0.9

$H_1 = 0.1$, i.a. = 0.7

Figure 10 Some examples of conformationally rigid or semi-rigid analogues of histamine (potencies relative to histamine = 100; i.a. = intrinsic activity

Since 4-methylhistamine is an effective agonist at H_2 receptors, it follows that conformations inaccessible to 4-methylhistamine such as those where θ_1 approaches 0°, are not involved in H_2 receptor interactions.

12.5.8.5 Chemical Function of Agonists at Histamine Receptors

The chemical functional requirements for histamine activity revealed by the foregoing structure–activity analysis are summarized in Figure 8. The active form of histamine at H_1 and H_2

receptors is likely to be the N^{τ}—H tautomer of the monocation, which is also the most prevalent species in water at around neutrality, and a side chain NH appears to be needed. However, different chemical properties of histamine may be associated with interactions at these two receptor types. At the H_1 receptor, imidazole tautomerism is not a functional requirement, but the presence of the nitrogen atom *ortho* to the ammonium–ethyl group appears to have special significance. The ring may also need to achieve coplanarity with the side chain, or be involved dynamically and rotate without hindrance. At the H_2 receptor, the tautomeric property of the imidazole ring of histamine appears to be of importance and histamine might act statically, in bifunctional hydrogen bonding, or act dynamically, as a proton transfer agent.

At the H_3 receptor, there appears to be a critical requirement to have an unsubstituted imidazole ring, but few non-imidazole analogues have been reported on.

12.5.9 AMIDINES AS H_2 RECEPTOR AGONISTS

The compounds so far discussed have a close structural similarity to histamine, being hetero-arylethylamine derivatives. There are other compounds, having a less obvious chemical resemblance, which have been claimed to act at H_2 receptors. They are all tautomeric amidine derivatives and to this extent they share a common feature with histamine (the imidazole ring of histamine is a tautomeric amidine); this may, however, be coincidental and does not necessarily imply a common mechanism of action. Specific compounds of interest are dimaprit (an isothiourea derivative), clonidine and tolazoline (imidazoline derivative), impromidine and other imidazolylalkylguanidines and isothioureas.

12.5.9.1 Dimaprit, a Highly Selective H_2 Receptor Agonist

Dimaprit is *S*-[3-(*N*,*N*-dimethylamino)propyl]isothiourea (Table 12) and the name is derived thus: DI-Methyl-Amino-PRopyl-Iso-Thiourea. It is normally available as the dihydrochloride salt. The activity of dimaprit as a highly selective H_2 receptor agonist was discovered at Smith Kline & French Laboratories during studies of isothiourea derivatives as partial agonists and potential H_2 receptor histamine antagonists.[72] Dimaprit has been shown *in vitro* to have approximately 17.5% of the potency of histamine on the rat uterus and 71% on the guinea pig right atrium, achieving similar maximal responses; it had less than 0.0001% of the activity of histamine on the guinea pig isolated ileum. The separation in activity between H_2 and H_1 receptor stimulation is thus greater than 100 000:1, and dimaprit has become an extremely valuable tool for probing the actions of histamine.

Dimaprit, like histamine, appears to have very specific structural requirements for activity; structure–activity relationships have been described in refs. 216–222. The simple analogues in Table 12 are only weakly active or inactive, and there is a strong parallel between the structure–activity relationships among congeners of dimaprit and histamine which suggests a similar mode of action at the H_2 receptor.[216,220] From the medicinal chemist's viewpoint it is of interest to compare the chemical properties of dimaprit and histamine and seek the similarities which may define action at H_2 receptors. Like histamine, dimaprit has two basic groups connected by a short $(CH_2)_x$ chain. In water, at physiological pH, it is a mixture of four differently ionized species, shown in Figure 11, *viz.* a dication, two monocations and the uncharged form. The pK_a values determined at 40 °C by potentiometric titration (8.23 and 9.23) indicate that at pH 7.4, the main form of dimaprit is the dication (I) and that only 0.2% of the molecules will be in the uncharged form (IV), the remainder (12%) being present as monocation. From NMR spectroscopy it has been shown that the relative concentrations of the two species II and III in aqueous solution $K_t = (III)/(II)$ is approximately 1.4, indicating that at pH 7.4 about 5% of molecules will be present as monocation (II) and about 7% as monocation (III).

The isothiourea group in dimaprit is a planar six π-electron system incorporating an amidine moiety which, in its uncharged form, has two types of nitrogen atom, *viz.* the single-bonded —NH_2 and the double-bonded =NH, which has a lone pair of electrons: it can therefore undergo a 1,3-prototropic tautomerism to transfer a proton from —NH_2 to =NH. Thus in the monocation (II), the —$NHMe_2^+$ group corresponds to the —NH^+ of histamine (or, more correctly, to the —$NHMe_2^+$ group of N^α,N^α-dimethylhistamine) and the isothiourea group simulates the functional nature of the imidazole ring of histamine, as shown in Figure 12.

It seems likely therefore that the monocation (II) is the receptor active form of dimaprit even though it is a minor species at pH 7.4. A study of activity changes on the guinea pig isolated atrium at different pH values is consistent with this view.[222] Again, as for histamine, the quaternary

Table 12 H_2 Receptor Agonist Activities of Structural Analogues of Dimaprit
Relative to Histamine = 100

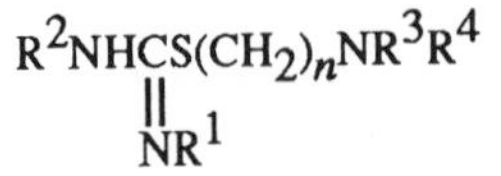

$$R^2NHCS(CH_2)_nNR^3R^4$$
$$\overset{\|}{NR^1}$$

R^1	R^2	NR^3R^4	n	*In vivo* rat gastric acid	*In vitro* guinea pig atrium
H[a]	H	NMe_2	3	19.5	71
H[b]	H	NMe_2	2	0.1	1[c]
H[d]	H	NMe_2	4	0.2	NA[e]
H	H	NMe_2	5		NA[e]
Me[f]	H	NMe_2	3	< 0.2	< 0.005
Me	Me	NMe_2	3		0.02[g]
H	H	$N(CH_2)_5$	3		NA[e]
H	H	NH_2	2		Unstable[g]
H	H	NH_2	3		Unstable[h]
H	H	NHMe	3		Unstable[g]
H	H	NMe_3^+	3		< 0.02[i]
H	H	NH_2	4		Weak[g]
Ac	H	NMe_2	3		< 0.02[i]
Ph	H	NMe_2	3		< 0.02[i]
NO_2	H	NMe_2	3		< 0.02[i]
CN	Me	NMe_2	3		< 0.02[i]

[a] Dimaprit, ref. 216. [b] SK&F 91487, nordimaprit, ref. 216. [c] Only achieves 60% of histamine's maximal response. [d] SK&F 91488, homodimaprit, negligible activity; ref. 216. [e] Negligible activity *in vitro* on guinea pig papillary muscle, ref. 217, also 218. [f] SK&F 92054 ref. 219. [g] Ref. 220. [h] Ref. 221. [i] Ref. 222.

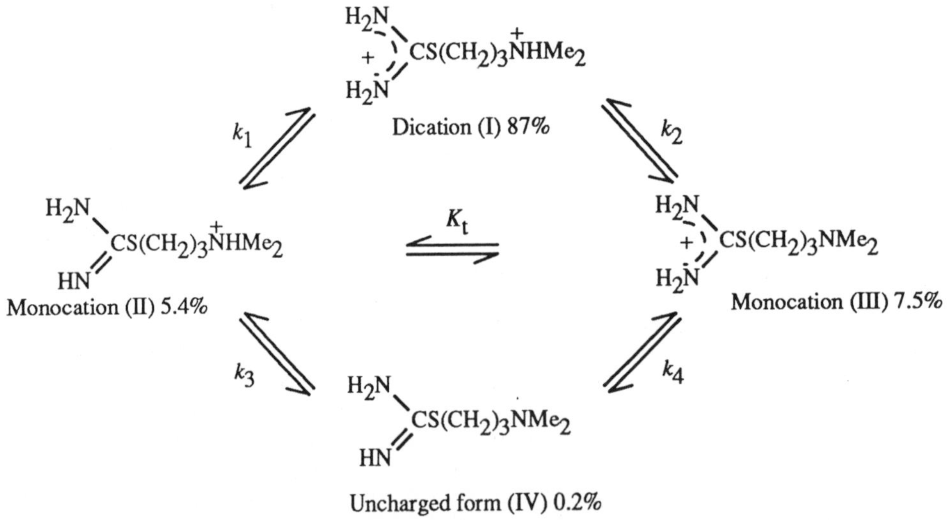

Figure 11 Ionic and tautomeric equilibria for dimaprit and relative populations (mol %) of species in aqueous solutions at 40 °C and pH 7.4 (Durant *et al*). The apparent stoichiometric pK_a values measured by potentiometric titration in water at 40 °C are pK_{a_1} 8.23 and pK_{a_2} 9.23; where $K_{a_1} = k_1 + k_2$; $K_{a_2} = k_3 + k_4$. The relative concentrations of the two monocations, K_t, was measured by observing the NMR spectra at different pH values; $K_t = (III)/(II) = (k_2/k_1) - 1.4$

ammonium derivative is not active,[222] suggesting that the monocation requires an NH group. The primary amine analogue of dimaprit would be of especial interest for comparison but, unfortunately, it is unstable and rapidly cyclizes in solution.[221]

The stereochemical resemblance between histamine and dimaprit is less clear. There are differences in the geometries of the isothiourea group and imidazole ring and in the extended conformations there is a much greater distance between the amidine and ammonium groups in dimaprit than in histamine. However, dimaprit has a flexible chain which may fold to orientate the functional groups into relative positions that resemble those of the groups in histamine. Indeed, dimaprit must

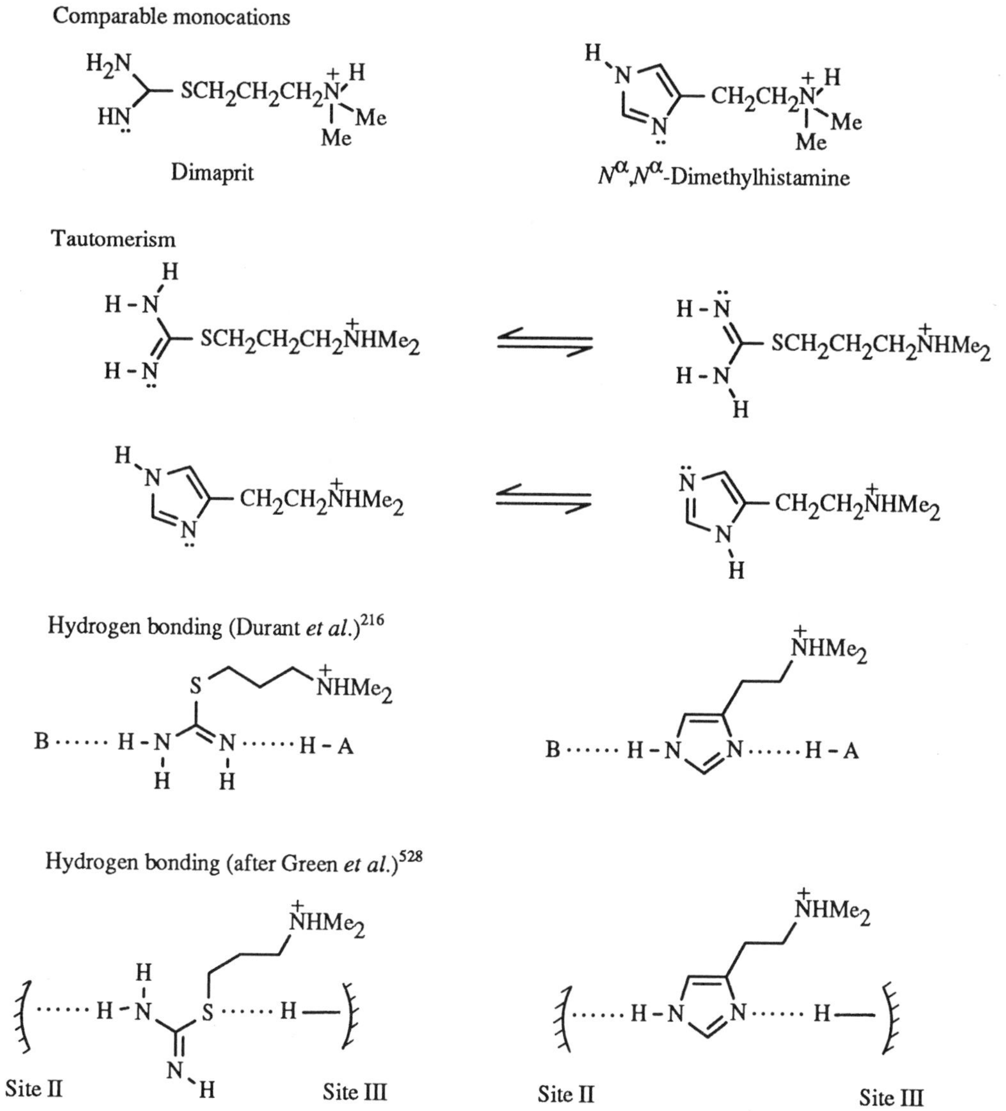

Comparable monocations

Dimaprit

N^α,N^α-Dimethylhistamine

Tautomerism

Hydrogen bonding (Durant *et al.*)[216]

Hydrogen bonding (after Green *et al.*)[528]

Site II   Site III   Site II   Site III

Figure 12 Comparison between dimaprit and N^α,N^α-dimethylhistamine. The isothiourea group in dimaprit may function like imidazole in histamine. Both can form monocations having side chain $^+$NH. Isothiourea and imidazole have N—H and N:, are planar, have 6 π-electrons and are tautomeric amidines (*cf.* Figure 8)

match a receptor active conformation of histamine and, since the lower and higher chain homologues are not active (Table 12), it should be possible to define the likely active conformations; so far, these have not been indicated clearly enough by calculations of conformational energies.[224,225]

An alternative possibility is that dimaprit does not tautomerize but simulates H bonding of the N^τ—H tautomer of histamine *via* the NH and S atoms; in this circumstance the other $=$N— group would correspond to a substituent in the imidazole 2-position of histamine (Figure 12).

Whatever may be the details of the drug–receptor interaction in molecular terms, it appears that dimaprit represents a very interesting, novel and possibly unique example of bioisosterism between isothiourea and imidazole. This bioisosterism does not appear to extend to other examples. Replacing the imidazole group in such structures as imidazolylalkylguanidine or imidazolyl-alkylisothiourea, which are partial agonists at H$_2$ receptors, leads to bisisothiouronium alkanes or isothiouronium alkylguanidines which are also weak partial agonists, but where the relative quantitative changes in activity are not the same for the different series.[226] Such comparisons depend upon the ability of the whole molecule to bind at the receptor. In the examples reported, the binding is clearly not very efficient since the compounds are not very active.

12.5.9.2 Clonidine

Clonidine [2-(2,6-dichlorophenylamino)-2-imidazoline] (37) is a potent antihypertensive (Catapres) whose action is thought to be *via* stimulation of central α-adrenergic receptors but in some tissue systems clonidine behaves as if it were a weakly active H_2 receptor agonist (see discussion in ref. 155). Structure–activity relationships among clonidine analogues have been explored and suggest a separation between activities;[237,238] thus for a series of substituted 2-anilinoimidazolines, derivatives with 2,6-substitution in the phenyl ring were found to mimic histamine in stimulating isolated guinea pig atria or gastric acid secretion in the anaesthetized rat, whereas derivatives with 2,3-, 2,4-, or 2,5-substitution were weakly active or inactive. All these compounds, however, are reported to be active in producing hypotension and bradycardia.[239]

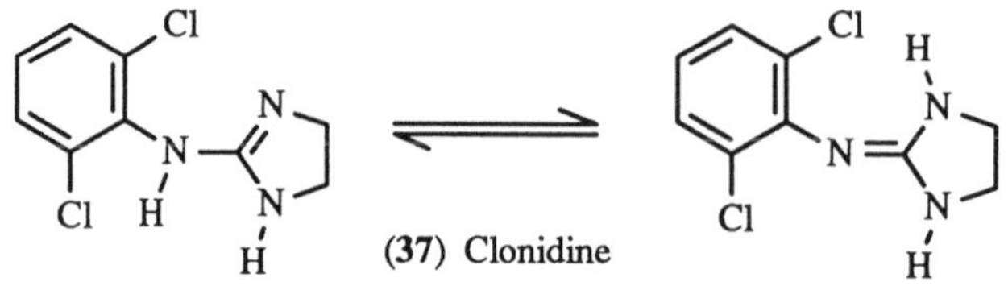

Amino—imidazoline tautomer   (37) Clonidine   Imino—imidazolidine tautomer

Clonidine is not an amine and the structure of its cation is not closely related to histamine monocation; the pK_a of the aminoimidazoline system of clonidine (reported 8.05 for 1:1 aqueous ethanol)[240] indicates that at pH 7.4 about 20% of clonidine molecules would be unprotonated and, in principle, able to participate in tautomerism. However, pK_a studies of *N*-methyl analogues indicate[241] that the tautomeric equilibrium constant $K_t \approx 1000$; thus, clonidine base exists largely in one tautomeric form (iminoimidazolidine; 37) with the double bond exocyclic and would not readily participate in proton transfer. It is not known whether the base or cation is the biologically active form for mimicking histamine.

12.5.9.3 Tolazoline

Tolazoline (2-benzyl-2-imidazoline; 38) is an α-adrenergic blocking agent and peripheral vasodilator which has been used (Priscol) to treat peripheral vascular disease. Tolazoline acts as a weak partial agonist at H_2 receptors. On the guinea pig isolated right atrium tolazoline has 3–4% of the agonist activity of histamine but gives a submaximal response.[242,243,248] However, unlike histamine, tolazoline does not inhibit stimulated contractions of the rat uterus. The action of tolazoline at H_2 receptors is thus complex; as a further complication, tolazoline may release histamine[244] but it appears unlikely that its histamine-like actions are necessarily due to histamine release, and tolazoline is much less active (or inactive) at histamine H_1 receptors.[245]

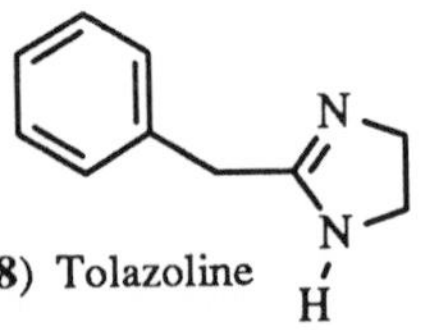

(38) Tolazoline

Chemically, tolazoline has only a partial resemblance to histamine and, as with clonidine, it is difficult to envisage how these substances mimic histamine to stimulate H_2 receptors. Tolazoline is not an amine although it is strongly basic[246] ($pK_a = 10.37$); in its neutral base form tolazoline is tautomeric and through symmetry has two identical tautomers but, at pH 7.4, tolazoline would exist almost entirely as the cation. Tautomerism may be important to its action at H_2 receptors since the *N*-methyl derivative, which cannot tautomerize, is not active as a stimulant,[155] either of gastric acid secretion or of the atrium, but there may be other reasons why the *N*-methyl derivative is not active, *e.g.* steric.

Tolazoline and clonidine have a formal chemical resemblance since both are imidazolines; however, clonidine base exists mainly in the iminoimidazolidine form, which is quite distinct from the imidazoline form of tolazoline base. The 2,6-dichloro analogue of tolazoline is reported to be more potent than tolazoline and equal to clonidine when tested as an agonist on electrically driven guinea pig ventricular strips.[247] A few analogues of tolazoline have been tested; in particular, ($\pm$)-tetrahydrozoline and α-methyltolazoline have been shown to act like tolazoline as partial stimulants in H_2 receptor systems.[245,248,249] It appears that the activity of tetrahydrozoline mainly resides in its (+) isomer.[245]

12.5.9.4 Impromidine, a Selective and Potent H_2 Receptor Agonist

Impromidine, N-[3-(imidazol-4-yl)propyl]-N'-{2-[(5-methylimidazol-4-yl)methylthio]ethyl}-guanidine (SK&F 92676), is a highly potent and specific H_2 receptor agonist (Table 13; **40**). Impromidine was the first compound shown to be more potent than histamine on *in vitro* tissue preparations; on the spontaneously beating isolated guinea pig right atrium impromidine was found to be 48 times more potent than histamine as a stimulant achieving the same maximal response. Impromidine is not as active on the rat uterus preparation (although it still has nine times the potency of histamine) and it behaves as a partial agonist, achieving only 80% of histamine's maximal response. Impromidine has also been found to be a partial agonist *in vitro* on histamine sensitive adenylate cyclase, although it is much more potent than is histamine.

Impromidine is a powerful stimulant of gastric acid, having 17–27 times the potency of histamine in rat, cat and dog preparations when given intravenously;[250] impromidine is also active in man.[251] Impromidine is not an agonist at H_1 or H_3 receptors; it is, however, weakly active as an H_1 receptor antagonist and a potent H_3 receptor antagonist.[56] It is also a potent inhibitor of the enzyme imidazole-N-methyl transferase (Table 1).[37]

Table 13 Impromidine and Analogues Containing the 2(5-Methylimidazol-4-ylmethylthio)ethyl Group and Activities at the H_2 Receptor Determined *in vitro* on the Guinea Pig Right Atrium (Relative to Histamine = 1)

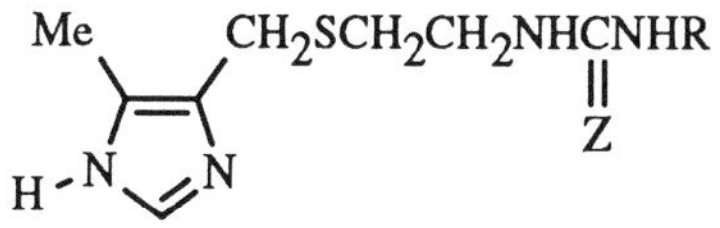

Compound	R^a	Z	Agonist[b] Potency	Agonist[b] i.a.	Antagonist[c] pA_2	Antagonist[c] Ref.
(39)	Me (SK&F 92408)	NH			4.8	250
(40)[d]	Im^1(CH$_2$)$_3$—	NH	48	1		250
(41)	Im^1(CH$_2$)$_2$—	NH	1.9	1		252
(42)	Im^1(CH$_2$)$_4$—	NH	0.83	0.2	5.94	252
(43)	Im^2(CH$_2$)$_3$—	NH	0.007	0.1	5.80	252
(44)	Th(CH$_2$)$_3$—	NH			6.50	252
(45)	Im^1(CH$_2$)$_3$—	NCN			6.24	252
(46)	Im^1(CH$_2$)$_3$—	NMe	0.06	0.9		252
(47)	Im^1(CH$_2$)$_3$—	SMe	0.01	0.2	4.75	252
(48a)	Im^1(CH$_2$)$_3$—	S			5.92	252
(48b)	Im^1(CH$_2$)$_3$—	O			5.2	252
(49)	Im^1(CH$_2$)$_3$NHCNH(CH$_2$)$_8$— $\parallel$ NH	NH	22	0.4	8.0	253
(50a)[e]	Im^{1}CH$_2$CH— (−)-(R) $\mid$ Me	NH	7.4			254, 389
(50b)	Im^{1}CH$_2$CH— (+)-(S) $\mid$ Me	NH			5.63	254, 389
(51)	H $\mid$ Im^{1}C=CCH$_2$— *trans* $\mid$ H	NH	3.9	1		255

[a] Im^1 = 4(5)-imidazolyl, Im^2 = N^τ-methylimidazol-4-yl, Th = thiazol-2-yl. [b] Agonist potency relative to histamine = 1, i.a. = intrinsic activity (*i.e.* percentage of histamine's maximal response). [c] Antagonism of histamine-stimulated chronotropy. [d] Impromidine (SK&F 92676). [e] Sopromidine.

A feature of the pharmacology of impromidine is its high potency compared to histamine, which appears to be due to an increased affinity for H_2 receptors rather than to an increase in efficacy (using Stephenson's nomenclature). This is obvious for the uterus preparation where impromidine is not a full agonist and yet is more potent than histamine; it would seem that in comparison with histamine many more receptors have to be occupied by impromidine in order to achieve a response.

The chemical structure poses interesting questions in relation to pharmacological activity. Impromidine is a guanidine derivative having two different imidazolylalkyl substituents and it is instructive to compare it with analogous guanidines, *viz.* the partial structures SK&F 91486 (**52**) and SK&F 92408 (**39**) (Tables 13 and 14). The guanidine SK&F 91486 is a weak partial agonist at H_2 receptors and must have a low efficacy relative to histamine.[261] SK&F 92408 is the guanidine analogue of cimetidine; it is not a partial agonist but a weak H_2 receptor antagonist of histamine, and on the isolated guinea pig atrium it had a pA_2 of 4.8, which is about 1/20 of the activity of cimetidine.[262] SK&F 92408 shows no stimulation and therefore has no efficacy at H_2 receptors, but

Table 14 Impromidine Analogues Containing the 3-(Imidazol-4-yl)propyl Group and Activities at the H_2 Receptor Determined *in vitro* on the Guinea Pig Right Atrium (Agonist Potency Relative to Histamine = 1)

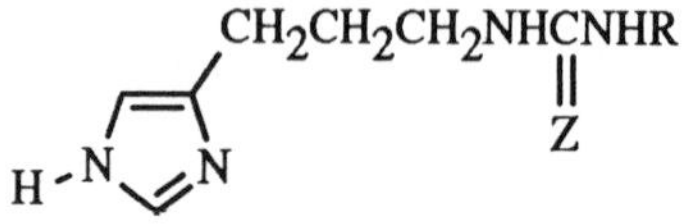

Compound	R^a	Z	Agonist[b] Potency	Agonist[b] i.a.	Antagonist[c] pA_2	Ref.
(**52**)	H (SK&F 91486)	NH	0.04	0.3	4.65	250
(**53**)	Im^1(CH$_2$)$_3$—	NH	4.8	1.0		252
(**54**)	Im^1(CH$_2$)$_4$—	NH	12	0.9		252
(**55**)	ThCH$_2$SCH$_2$CH$_2$—	NH	24	0.9		252
(**56**)	Th(CH$_2$)$_3$—	NH	27	0.9		252
(**57**)	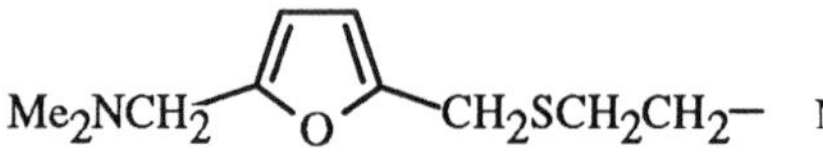 Me$_2$NCH$_2$—O—CH$_2$SCH$_2$CH$_2$—	NH	40	0.9		256
(**58a**)	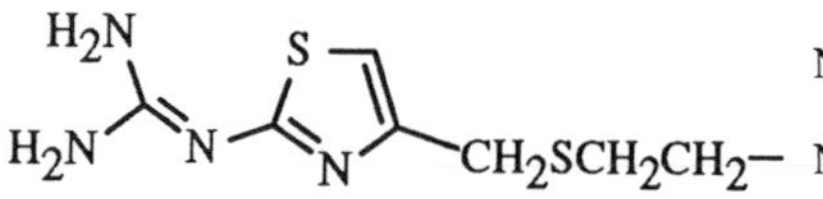 H$_2$N—, H$_2$N—, S, N —CH$_2$SCH$_2$CH$_2$—	NH	50^d	1.0		256
(**58b**)		NCN	0		7.8	256
(**59**)	Im^{3}CH$_2$SCH$_2$CH— (R)	NH	96	1.0		257
	Me (S)	NH	13	0.94		257
(**60**)	Im^{3}CH$_2$SCH$_2$CH— (R)	NH	15	1.0		257
	Et (S)	NH	4.8	0.85		257
(**61**)	Im^{3}CH$_2$SCHCH$_2$—(R)	NH	17	1.0		257
	Me (S)	NH	3.8	1.0		257
(**62a**)	PhCH$_2$SCH$_2$CH$_2$—	NH	13	1.0		258
(**62b**)	PyCH$_2$SCH$_2$CH$_2$—	NH	20	0.9		256
(**63**)	Im^1(CH$_2$)$_3$NHCNH(CH$_2$)$_8$— ‖ NH	NH	33	0.6	7.7	253
(**64**)	Ph$_2$CHSCH$_2$CH$_2$—	NH	40	1.0	e	259
(**65**)^g	PyCHCH$_2$CH$_2$— (with 4-F-phenyl) 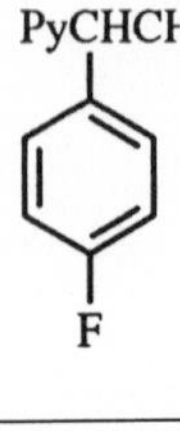	NH	~ 100	1.0	f	260

^{a} Im^1 = 4(5)-imidazolyl; Th = thiazol-2-yl; Im^3 = 5-methylimidazol-4-yl; Py = pyridin-2-yl. ^{b} Agonist potency relative to histamine = 1, i.a. = intrinsic activity (relative to histamine's maximal response = 1). ^{c} Antagonism of histamine-stimulated chronotropy. ^{d} pD_2 = 7.9; compare impromidine pD_2 = 7.8, histamine pD_2 = 6.1. ^{e} H_1 antagonist pA_2 = 6.3. ^{f} H_1 antagonist pA_2 = 7.7. ^{g} Arpromidine.

it obviously has some affinity. Yet, for imidazolylpropylguanidine (SK&F 91486), the addition of a group associated only with affinity (*i.e.* binding ability) in antagonist structures, provides a remarkable 1000-fold increase in stimulant activity. Not only has affinity increased but so has efficacy, although the efficacy of impromidine must be less than that of histamine since it is only a partial agonist on the isolated rat uterus. This means that relative to histamine the high potency is due to increased affinity for H_2 receptors. Thus it appears that the imidazolylpropylguanidine group confers efficacy and must resemble histamine at the receptor even though the side chain is longer (it has three —CH_2 groups, whereas histamine has two), and the other side chain appears only to confer affinity.

In terms of its physicochemical properties impromidine is very complex. It is an extremely polar molecule and is very basic; the guanidine group pK_a > 11) will be protonated throughout the physiological range. The imidazole rings have pK_a values around 7 and will exist under physiological conditions as mixtures of protonated forms and neutral tautomers.[252] In fact there are nine different possible cationic forms in equilibrium (including respective neutral imidazole tautomers). There is also considerable conformational flexibility in the side chains and it is difficult to predict the most likely overall shapes of the molecule.

Structure–activity studies among impromidine congeners suggest that the imidazole rings have different functions. Replacement of the 5-methylimidazol-4-yl ring by a 2-thiazolyl group in the HetCH$_2$SCH$_2$CH$_2$— chain still provides a potent agonist (**55**), but replacement of the imidazolyl-propyl group by 2-thiazolylpropyl gives a pure antagonist (**44**). These results are in accord with the idea that the HetCH$_2$SCH$_2$CH$_2$— chain confers affinity but that the imidazolylpropyl group is required for efficacy. It also appears that the tautomeric property of the latter group is an essential feature for agonist activity (*cf.* **43**). Clearly, however, tautomerism in the HetCH$_2$SCH$_2$CH$_2$— group is not essential for affinity (**55–58** and **62–65**).[253]

Agonist activity is also very sensitive to the length of the imidazolyl alkyl chain (**41, 42, 46, 53** and **54**) and to the presence of other substituents on the guanidine group (**46**). Replacing the guanidine group by nonbasic cyanoguanidine (**45** and **58b**), thiourea (**48a**), or urea groups (**48b**; Table 13) affords antagonists. Replacing the guanidine by isothiourea (wherein the chain N is replaced by S) may give an agonist (**66**) or antagonist (**67**), depending upon which chain carries the sulfur atom.[252] Bisguanidines separated by an alkylene chain (optimally eight CH$_2$ groups) also give potent partial agonists (**49** and **63**).[253]

Me ⟍ CH$_2$SCH$_2$CH$_2$XCY(CH$_2$)$_3$ ⟍

(**66**) X = S, Y = NH; H_2 agonist, 6.9 x histamine, i.a. = 0.8
(**67**) X = NH, Y = S; H_2 antagonist, pA_2 = 5.5

Other groups associated with H_2 receptor antagonist structures have been used to replace the 5-methylimidazol-4-yl ring and afford potent agonists,[256] *e.g.* dimethylaminomethylfuranyl (**57**) and guanidinothiazole (**58a**; Table 14).

A remarkable finding has come from the study of chiral analogues of impromidine. Replacement of the homohistamine group of impromidine by an α-methylhistamine group (*i.e.* an isomer in which the side chain is branched) gives two enantiomers which are found to differ markedly in their biological activities.[389] The (*R*)-(−) enantiomer, sopromidine[445] (**50a**), is a strong H_2 receptor agonist (7.4 times the potency of histamine on the atrium), whereas the (*S*)-(+) enantiomer (**50b**) has no efficacy but is an antagonist.[254] Thus, although histamine is not chiral, the H_2 receptor clearly is.

Branching of the chain has also been examined for the 5-methylimidazol-4-ylmethylthioethyl group.[257] With these compounds (**59–61**; Table 14), both enantiomers are agonists but the enantiomeric activity ratios are modest (3–7). One of these compounds (**59**; *R*) is nearly 100 times as potent as histamine.

Hybrid structures of impromidine and dimaprit have also been investigated, leading to bis-isothiouronium alkylguanidines (**68**), which are H_2 receptor agonists with potencies in the range 10 –250% of that of histamine.[263] Formally, these compounds are analogues of impromidine (*e.g.* **53** and **54**) in which the imidazole rings have been replaced by isothiourea groups. The most potent is compound (**68**), where *n* = 3, *m* = 4.

Pharmacological hybrids related to impromidine have also been described which combine H_1 antagonists with H_2 agonist properties.[259,260] However, although they include some very potent H_2

$$H_2NCS(CH_2)_nNHCNH(CH_2)_mSCNH_2$$

(68) n and $m = 3-5$

agonists (*e.g.* **64, 65**; Table 14), the level of H_1 antagonism is relatively weak (pA_2 determined *in vitro* on the guinea pig ileum in the range 5.5–7.5). Compound (**65**) (arpromidine) is approximately 100 times as potent as histamine.[260]

12.5.10 SELECTIVE AGONISTS AND CHEMICAL CONTROL SUBSTANCES FOR PHARMACOLOGICAL CHARACTERIZATION OF HISTAMINE RECEPTORS

The respective classes of histamine antagonists (see Sections 12.5.12 and 12.5.13 below) provide valuable tools for pharmacological receptor classification of histamine actions but it is often helpful to complement studies by using selective agonists that mimic the action of histamine. Such compounds have been discussed above but it is convenient to group together the most available and widely used examples. Relatively selective compounds are listed in Table 15 with an indication of their potencies determined relative to histamine.

There are no potent selective H_1 receptor agonists; relatively selective compounds are 2-methyl-histamine, 2-(2-pyridyl)ethylamine, betahistine (N^α-methyl-2-pyridylethylamine) and 2-(2-thia-zolyl)ethylamine but they are all less active than histamine. The heterocyclic analogues retain the ring nitrogen atom adjacent to the side chain, as in histamine, but do not possess the tautomeric NH. Betahistine is available for human investigation, having been introduced clinically [Serc, Duphar (Holland) and Unimed Inc. (US)]. There is a good separation between H_1 and H_2 receptor activities of the heterocyclic analogues but there is some residual H_2 receptor activity, which is especially evident on the guinea pig atrium preparation. However, 2-pyridylethylamine and betahistine are only partial agonists on the guinea pig atrium (compared with histamine, they do not achieve greater than 40–50% of the maximal response) so that these compounds, although being less active than 2-methylhistamine, are effectively more selective (see also Section 12.5.7.2). Betahistine is also a weak H_3 receptor antagonist so that under some circumstances it could potentiate the actions of endogenous histamine.

Relatively selective H_2 receptor agonists shown in Table 15 are 4-methylhistamine, betazole, dimaprit and impromidine. Betazole, which is the pyrazole analogue of histamine, is a very weak agonist but it shows some selectivity towards H_2 receptors and has been widely available clinically (Histalog from Eli Lilly) since the 1950s as a diagnostic agent for investigating gastric acid secretory capacity, especially in North America. Betazole is much less active and not as selective as 4-methyl-histamine. Of particular interest are the other two agonists, *viz.* dimaprit, which is extremely selective, and impromidine which is selective, very potent, and is also available for study in humans; these have already been discussed in detail (Sections 12.5.9.1 and 12.5.9.4). Impromidine is, however, a potent antagonist at H_3 receptors so that it may potentiate the actions of endogenous histamine. This must be borne in mind when interpreting its pharmacology.

A very selective H_3 receptor agonist is (*R*)-α-methylhistamine.

Although the aforementioned agonists have a high degree of specificity for histamine receptors, they do possess other pharmacological properties and one should exercise caution in their use. Drugs may cause effects other than the intended action at receptors and it cannot follow that all observed pharmacological effects of even a highly specific agent such as dimaprit are due to histamine receptor activation. In this sense it may be helpful to use chemical control substances which match many of the chemical properties of the active drugs but which lack the specific structural properties needed for effective receptor activation. Some convenient examples of chemical control compounds are listed in Table 16. Tele-methylhistamine, which has some residual activity but is inactive at H_2 receptors, can be used for comparison with histamine itself or with 2- or 4-methylhistamines. 4-Pyridylethylamine, which has no H_1 receptor activity, may be used for comparison with 2-pyridylethylamine as an H_1 agonist. *N*-Methyldimaprit, SK&F 92054, serves as a control for dimaprit when used as an H_2 receptor agonist;[219] it has replaced a previously described compound (nordimaprit, SK&F 91487) which was still a weak partial agonist on the atrium. A suitable control for impromidine is *N*-methylimpromidine (**46**)[252] or the (*R*) and (*S*) enantiomers of sopromidine.[254]

Table 15 Relatively Selective H_1, H_2 and H_3 Receptor Agonists in General Use[a] (activities[a] relative to histamine = 100, with 95% fiducial limits in parentheses)

Name	Structure	H_1		H_2		H_3
		Guinea pig ileum	Guinea pig atrium	Gastric acid, rat	Rat uterus	Cerebral cortex, rat
Histamine		100	100	100	100	100
H_1 receptor agonists						
2-Methylhistamine	$CH_2CH_2NH_2$ structure	16.5 (15.1–18.1)	4.4 (4.1–4.8)	2.0	2.1 (1.5–3.4)	< 0.08
2-(2-Pyridyl)ethylamine	$CH_2CH_2NH_2$ structure	5.6 (5.0–6.3)	[2.5] 50% max.	≈0.2	< 0.05 20% max.	
Betahistine[b]	CH_2CH_2NHMe structure	8.0 (7.2–8.8)	[1.5] 40% max.	≈0.2		Antagonist $K_1 = 6.9\ \mu M$
2-(2-Thiazolyl)ethylamine	$CH_2CH_2NH_2$ structure	26 (20–32)	2.2 (2.0–2.5)	≈0.3	0.34 50% max.	< 0.008
H_2 receptor agonists						
4(5)-Methylhistamine	$CH_2CH_2NH_2$ structure	0.23 (0.20–0.27)	43 (40–46)	39	25 (19–37)	< 0.008
Betazole[c]	$CH_2CH_2NH_2$ structure	0.12 (0.10–0.14)	2.1 (1.4–2.8)	≈0.5	0.11 (0.08–0.15)	

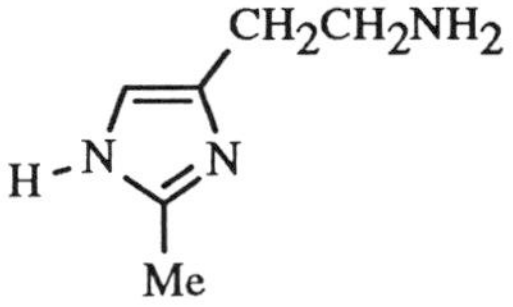

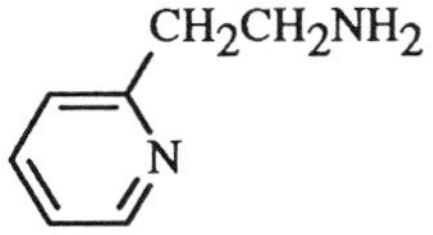

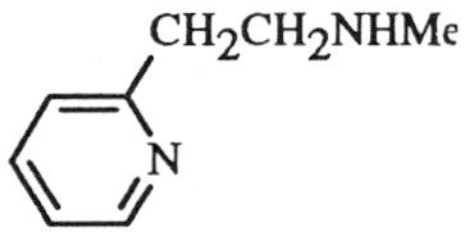

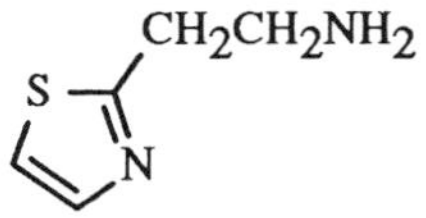

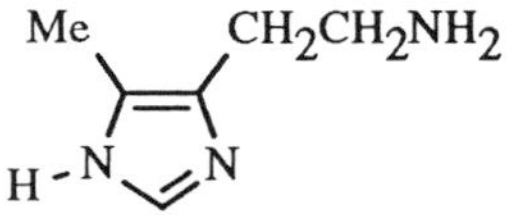

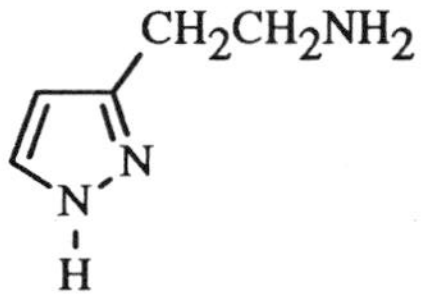

Table 15 (*Contd.*)

Name	Structure	H_1		H_2		H_3
		Guinea pig ileum	*Guinea pig atrium*	*Gastric acid, rat*	*Rat uterus*	*Cerebral cortex, rat*
Dimaprit	$H_2NCSCH_2CH_2CH_2NMe_2$ $\parallel$ NH	$< 10^{-4}$	71 (61–81)	20	17 (14–21)	< 0.008
Impromidine	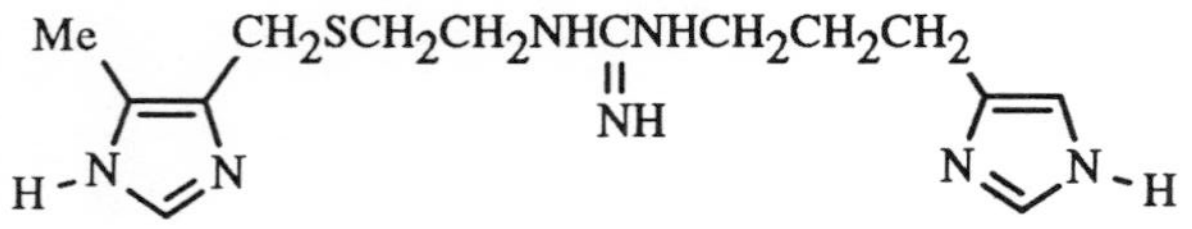 (see structure)	$< 10^{-3}$ Antagonist $K_B = 3.4\ \mu M$	4810 (3760–6010)	1680	930 80% max. (570–1520)	< 0.03 Antagonist $K_B = 0.065\ M$
H_3 receptor agonists						
(*R*)-α-Methylhistamine	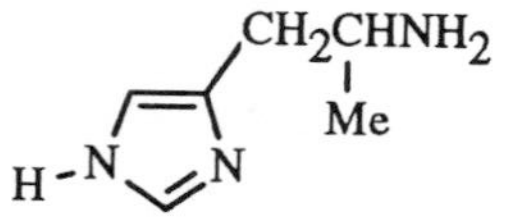 (see structure)	0.49	1.0			1550

Impromidine structure:

Me — (imidazole ring, H–N···N) — $CH_2SCH_2CH_2NHCNHCH_2CH_2CH_2$
$\parallel$
NH
(attached to imidazole ring with N–H)

(*R*)-α-Methylhistamine structure:

CH_2CHNH_2
$|$
Me
(attached to imidazole ring, H–N···N)

[a] H_1 and H_2 receptor activities (relative to histamine = 100; with 95% fiducial limits in parenthesis) determined by R.C. Blakemore and M.E. Parsons (Smith Kline and French Research Ltd) on the following tissues: (i) ileum, tested for stimulating contraction of the isolated guinea pig ileum in the presence of atropine; (ii) atrium, tested for stimulation of rate in the spontaneously beating isolated guinea pig right atrium in the presence of propranolol; (iii) gastric acid, tested by rapid intravenous injection for stimulation of gastric acid secretion in the atropinized and vagotomized anaesthetized rat; and (iv) uterus, tested for inhibition of electrically evoked contractions of the isolated rat uterus in the presence of propranolol. H_3 receptor activities from refs. 56 and 57 determined from inhibition of potassium-evoked [^{3}H]histamine release on slices of rat cerebral cortex. [b] Betahistine; Serc, Duphar (Holland) and Unimed Inc. (U.S.). [c] Betazole; Histalog, Eli Lilly Co.

Table 16 Compounds for Use as Chemical Controls (Activities[a] Relative to Histamine = 100) in Comparison with Selective Histamine Receptor Agonists

H_1/H_2	Active agent	Control	H_1 Guinea pig ileum	Guinea pig atrium	H_2 Rat gastric acid
H₁ H₂	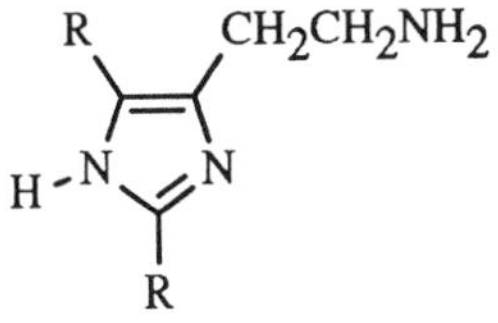 Histamine 2-Methylhistamine 4-Methylhistamine	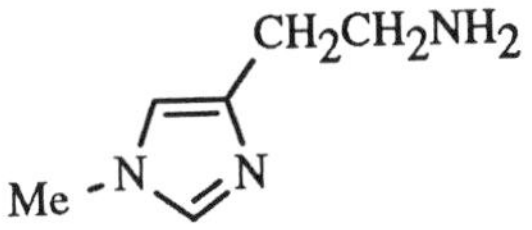 *Tele*-methylhistamine	0.42	< 0.1	< 0.01
H₁	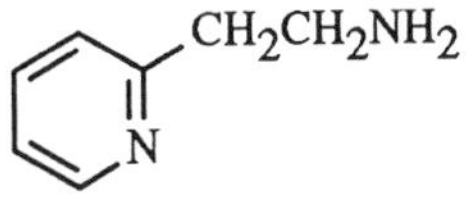 2-(2-Pyridyl)ethylamine	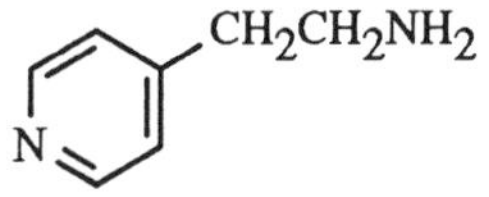 2-(4-Pyridyl)ethylamine	< 0.001	< 0.01	≈0.4
H₂	$H_2NCS(CH_2)_3NMe_2$ $\overset{\parallel}{NH}$ Dimaprit	$H_2NCS(CH_2)_3NMe_2$ $\overset{\parallel}{MeN}$ *N*-Methyldimaprit	< 0.005	< 0.005	< 0.2

[a] Determined by R.C. Blakemore and M.E. Parsons, see Table 15 for further details.

Many other control substances may be devised, but most of the compounds mentioned have the merit of being available synthetically. The use of such controls should be considered whenever the analysis of histamine-mediated effects appear to be complex. If, in a particular test system, both the active agent and the chemical control are found to be similarly active, one must seriously question whether the effect arises from direct interaction with histamine receptors.

12.5.11 CHIRALITY AT HISTAMINE RECEPTORS

Although histamine is an achiral molecule, there is now excellent evidence for chiral discrimination by all three types (H₁, H₂, and H₃) of histamine receptor.

The first study of a chiral agonist was that of Chapman and Williams (1953),[266] who described the synthesis of 2-(2-aminopropyl)pyridine and its resolution into (+) and (−) isomers. Although 2-pyridylethylamine (Table 15) is a selective H₁ receptor agonist, the α-methyl derivative (**69**; Table 17) has less than 1% of the activity of histamine but showed some stereoselectivity, the (+) isomer consistently being approximately three times as active as the (−) isomer.[267]

An extensive study of chiral histamine analogues has been described by Schunack and coworkers.[236,262] Various analogues (**71–75**) of α-methylhistamine (**70**) were synthesized and resolved into enantiomers (Table 17). None showed stereoselectivity at the H₁ receptor. At the H₂ receptor, however, those enantiomers having an absolute configuration corresponding to D-histidine, *i.e.* an (R) configuration, possessed greater activity, with ratios varying between 1.7 and 7 (see also Section 12.5.7.2). Similarly, for β-methylhistamine (**76**) there is not stereoselectivity indicated at the H₁ receptor, but for the H₂ receptor there is an apparent activity ratio of (−):(+) = 7.3:1.

At the H₃ receptor, however, α-methylhistamines are potent agonists which show pronounced stereoselectivity. The stereoselective discrimination is in the opposite sense to that demonstrated at the H₂ receptor. For α-methylhistamine,[57] the activity ratio is (R):(S) = 120.

Although the H₁ receptor shows no stereoselective discrimination towards agonists, there are well-known examples of antagonists which are stereoselective, *e.g.* chlorpheniramine, neobenodine, carbinoxamine, dimethindene and clemastine (see Section 12.5.12.4 and Table 18).

Table 17 Activities (Relative to Histamine = 100) and Activity Ratios of Enantiomeric Agonists at H_1, H_2 and H_3 Receptors

Compound[a]		H_1 Guinea pig ileum	H_2 Guinea pig atrium	H_3 Rat cortex	Ref.
(69)	PyCH$_2$CHNH$_2$ | Me	(+) (−) (+):(−) 0.12 3			267
(70)	Im^{1}CH$_2$CHNH$_2$ | Me	(+)-(S) 0.49 (−)-(R) 0.49 (S):(R) 1	1.74 1.02 1.7	13 1550 0.0084	57, 178
(71)	Im^{1}CH$_2$CHNHMe | Me	(−)-(S) 0.71 (+)-(R) 0.69 (S):(R) 1	0.98 0.42 2.3	0.13 4.1 0.032	179, 182
(72)	Im^{2}CH$_2$CHNH$_2$ | Me	(+)-(S) 0.26 (−)-(R) 0.33 (S):(R) 1	8.71 4.78 1.8		180
(73)	Im^{1}CH$_2$CHNH$_2$ | CH$_2$Cl	(−)-(R) 0.32 (+)-(S) 0.30 (R):(S) 1	42.7 17.4 2.5		268
(74)	Im^{1}CH$_2$CHNHMe | CH$_2$Cl	(−)-(R) 0.30 (+)-(S) 0.29 (R):(S) 1	51.3 7.1 7.2	0.006 1.1 0.0055	268, 182
(75)	(structure)	(−)-(S) 0.29 (+)-(R) 0.29 (S):(R) 1	2.09 0.30 7		269
(76)	Im^{1}CHCH$_2$NH$_2$ | Me	(−) (+) (−):(+) 1	7.3		236, 262

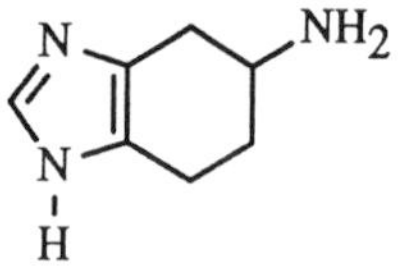

[a] Py = pyridin-2-yl   Im^1 = imidazol-4-yl   Im^2 = 5-methylimidazol-4-yl.

At the H_2 receptor, the enantiomers of sopromidine show remarkable selectivity;[254,262] the (R)-(−) enantiomer is a potent agonist, whereas the (S)-(+) enantiomer is an antagonist (Section 12.5.9.4; **50**, **51**; Table 13). Other methyl derivatives of impromidine are H_2 agonists, (R):(S) ratios of approximately 3–7 (**59**–**61**; Table 14), and one of them (**59**, (R) enantiomer) is an extremely potent agonist, being nearly 100 times that of histamine.[257] There is also a report[245] that the (+) isomer of tetrahydrozoline is an H_2 receptor agonist (see Section 12.5.9.3).

12.5.12 ANTAGONISTS AT HISTAMINE H_1 RECEPTORS

12.5.12.1 Introduction

It is now more than 50 years since the discovery of the first H_1 receptor histamine antagonists ('antihistamines'). Many different structural classes of compounds are now known to show high antagonist potency at this receptor. The subject has been extensively reviewed and includes some detailed accounts of structure–activity relationships.[10,155,270–280]

The first H_1 receptor antagonists, the original antihistamines, were discovered by Bovet and collaborators[61] in 1937. These authors reported that 2-(N-piperidinomethyl)-1,4-benzodioxan (piperoxan; Figure 13) and related aryl ethers protected guinea pigs against lethal doses of histamine. Results from early studies[281] with these and analogous derivatives of ethylenediamine suggested a clinical potential for treating allergic and inflammatory disorders. Intense research activity ensued, aimed at discovering clinically effective antihistaminic agents. It was soon apparent that activity could be increased markedly with the introduction of a second aromatic or heterocyclic ring into the structures and, of the thousands of analogues that were synthesized and evaluated, some notable compounds were subsequently introduced into therapy. These included mepyramine, diphenhydramine, chlorpheniramine, triprolidine and the phenothiazine derivative promethazine (Figure 13). A fuller discussion of these classical studies is included in the reviews. Pharmacological studies showed that, in addition to protecting guinea pigs against histamine-induced bronchospasm, these compounds also antagonized histamine-induced contraction of various other smooth muscles and lessened the symptoms of anaphylactic shock.

The pharmacological receptors involved in these mepyramine and diphenhydramine sensitive responses were subsequently defined[51] as histamine H_1 receptors (see Section 12.5.5).

For many years, the more active histamine H_1 receptor antagonists have been represented by a general formula comprising two aromatic groups linked by a short chain of atoms to a tertiary amino group as shown in Figure 14, which encompasses the following features:
Ar^1 is aryl or heteroaryl which may be further substituted; Ar^2 is a second aryl ring or an arylmethyl group. The two aryl groups Ar^1 and Ar^2 may be bridged to form tricyclic derivatives; X is an sp^2- or sp^3-hybridized carbon, a nitrogen or an sp^3 carbon with an oxygen (ether) link connecting the side chain to the aromatic rings; C—C represents a short chain of carbon atoms which may be saturated, unsaturated, branched, or form part of a ring system; NR^1R^2 is generally a tertiary amino group which may be part of a ring system. The most common groups are dimethylamino and pyrrolidino.

These structures do not have a close chemical resemblance to histamine except that they do appear to share the feature of an ammonium alkyl chain. It is presumed that they bind to the same anionic site at the receptor as does histamine, but that the aromatic rings bind to a nearby accessory region.

Similar general structures have been published in many reviews to indicate the salient features of most histamine H_1 receptor antagonists. However, there are now many compounds (Figure 15) which show high potency yet do not fit this general structure. Examples include the hypertensive agent indoramine (77) and the related compound (78), both of which are potent H_1 receptor antagonists yet lack a benzhydryl type of aromatic ring system.[282] More recent compounds include the isocytosine derivative temelastine[283,284] (79) and the cyclic thioamide,[285,388,536] AHR-11325 (81; rocastine). Astemizole (Figure 17) is a member of a series of potent selective H_1 receptor antagonists containing the benzimidazole ring system, but it does incorporate features of the general structure.[286]

Many attempts have been made to correlate histamine H_1 antagonist activity with the physical properties of compounds and this work has been extensively reviewed. The physical properties that have been used include ionization constants, solubility, surface properties, spectral data (UV, IR,

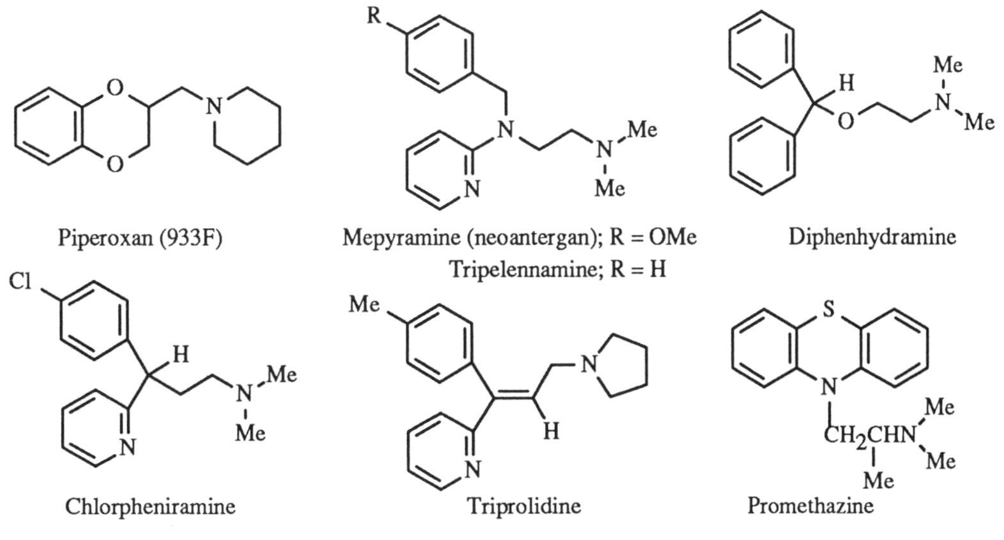

Figure 13 Structures of some early antihistamines (H_1 antagonists)

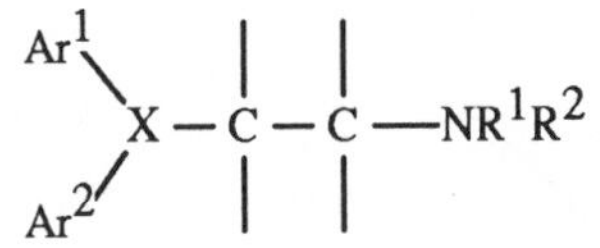

Figure 14   General structure of H_1 receptor histamine antagonists ('antihistamines')

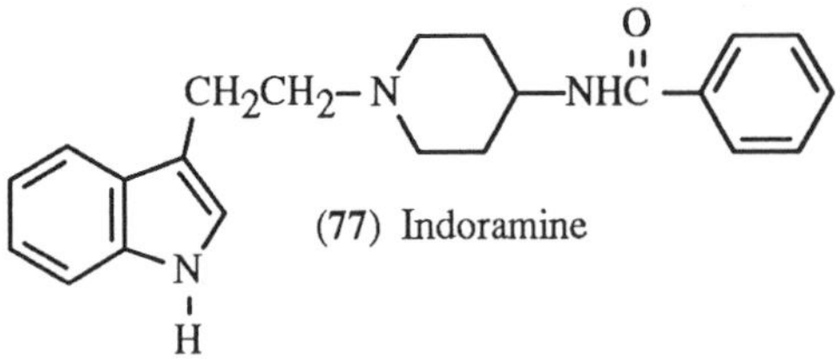

Figure 15 H_1 receptor antagonists which are outside the scope of the general antihistamine structure shown in Figure 14

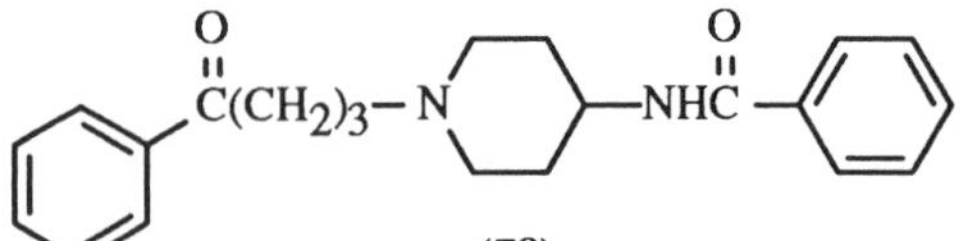

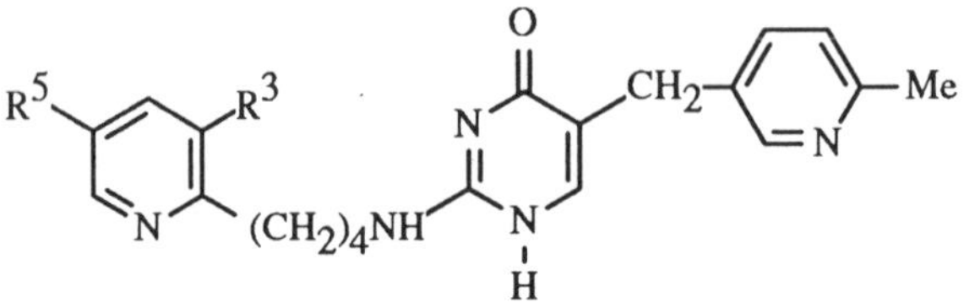

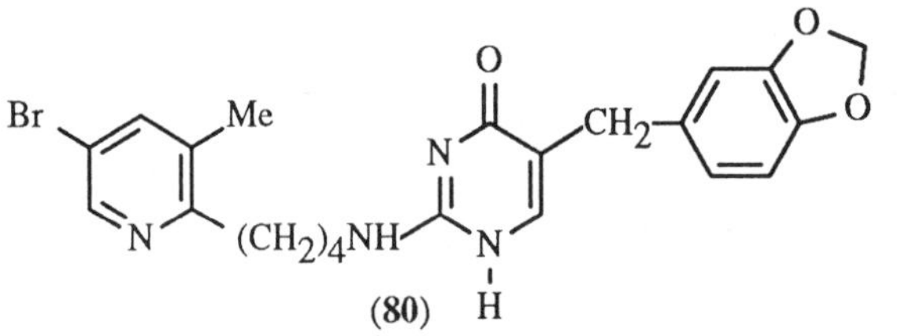

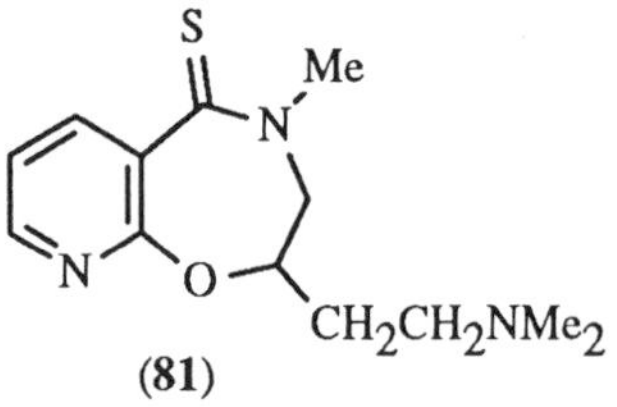

NMR), bond stabilities, charge localization, dipole moment, lipophilicity and 'Hansch' parameters. Many of the structure–activity relationships described in the literature apply only within the series of compounds being studied and may not have a general applicability.

The properties that appear most commonly to describe high potency are the basicity of the side chain, the lipophilicity of the aryl rings and their spatial arrangement.

12.5.12.2   Side Chain Basicity

The majority of potent antihistamines are tertiary amines which have pK_a values sufficiently high for them to exist at physiological pH in the protonated ammonium cation form. In general quaternary ammonium salts are less effective, although there are examples which are potent antihistamines, *e.g.* diphenydramine methoidide,[287,288] pirdonium bromide[276] (Aprobit)[289] and thiazinamium sulfate;[290] the high level of anticholinergic activity in these compounds, however, makes them clinically unacceptable.

Many attempts have been made to correlate the basicity of antihistamines with activity. Marshall[291] related pK_a and pA_2 values in antihistamines belonging to different structural groups and optimal activity was found with analogues having a pK_a of about 8.6. However it appears that in several classes of antihistamines containing a tertiary amino group, such as the ethylenediamines, ethanolamines and propylamines, some of the more potent compounds have pK_a values above 9.0. One well known 'non-ammonium' compound is antazoline, which is an imidazoline derivative.[292] The imidazoline group is strongly basic ($pK_a = 10.1$) and differs stereochemically in being planar, whereas the ammonium group is tetrahedral.

Some more recently discovered antihistamines are not basic, however, and must act in non-charged forms, *e.g.* loratidine[293] (Figure 17) and temelastine (Figure 15).[283] The latter has pK_a values of 2.6, 3.7 and 5.9; a less basic analogue (**80**; Figure 15) lacking the pK_a at 5.9 due to the methylpyridine ring is also very active ($pA_2 = 9.15$); temelastine is discussed further, below.

12.5.12.3 Lipophilicity

Antihistamine drugs are generally lipophilic molecules and have high lipid–water partition coefficients, P, but they span a wide range of lipophilicities. The measurement of partition coefficients is complicated by the high basicities (pK_a) of antihistamine drugs since, at pH 7.4, the compounds exist mainly as protonated cationic forms which are much less lipophilic than the free bases. The empirically determined partition coefficient for any compound is thus dependent on its pK_a and the pH of the aqueous phase. In considering lipophilicity for structure–activity relationships, it is important therefore to compare like with like, either by correcting for the presence of individual species or by using the P values for only one of the species, *e.g.* the free base. It is possible to predict octanol–water partition ratios using empirical rules suggested by Rekker[299] and the 'hydrophobic fragmental constants' (f values) defined by Nys and Rekker.[294,295]

Application of the Hansch approach of multiparameter correlation analysis (QSAR) to a series of ring-substituted diphenhydramine and diarylaminoalkene derivatives indicates that activity does not correlate simply with molecular lipophilicity.[278,296–298] The analyses generally emphasize the importance of steric effects of substituents and have also drawn attention to the possible role of hydrophobic effects, since for a given structural type activity correlates with the lipophilicity of only one of the aryl rings, *i.e.* the two aromatic rings appear to act differently, and it is probable that only one ring contributes *via* hydrophobic bonding.[278]

12.5.12.4 Stereochemistry

The fine detail of chemical structure in the various chemical classes of antagonists may profoundly affect antihistaminic activity, and some structures are particularly sensitive to substituent effects and stereochemistry. Thus the *p*-chloro-substituted compounds chlorpheniramine and chlorcyclizine are each at least 10 times more potent *in vitro* than their unsubstituted analogues. *Ortho* substitution in an aryl group, or *para* substituents in both of the aryl groups, may lead to a reduction in activity as has been demonstrated with diphenhydramine[300] and mepyramine[87] derivatives. Triprolidine, which has pyridyl and pyrrolidino groups in a *trans* configuration about the double bond, is reported to be 1000 times more potent (on the guinea pig ileum *in vitro*) than the *cis* isomer (Table 18).[301] Likewise, pyrrobutamine is many times more potent than its geometrical isomer.[301]

Some chiral antihistamine drugs show pronounced stereoselective activity (Table 18). The (+) forms of chlorpheniramine and neobenodine are each much more potent than their (−) enantiomers. (+)-Chlorpheniramine has also been shown to be some 200 times more effective than its enantiomer *in vivo* in protecting guinea pigs against histamine.[305] Similarly, 100-fold differences have been seen in competitive binding studies to brain homogenates.[83,304] The absolute configuration of (+)-chlorpheniramine has been established[306] as (S) and the crystal structure of the maleate has been determined.[307] Analogously, activity has been shown to reside with the (+) isomers of pheniramine and brompheniramine[308] and they too have the (S) configuration.[306] The active chiral diphenhydramine derivatives (*e.g.* neobenodine and clemastine) have the (R) configuration.[278,312] The change is only apparent, however, since the designation depends on the order of substituent priority as determined by the Cahn–Prelog rules. The active isomers of the pheniramines correspond stereochemically to the active isomers of the diphenhydramines. This can be clearly seen for carbinoxamine, which is a pyridine analogue of a diphenhydramine and has an (S) configuration for the active isomer.[309]

The above results showing that drug activity is very sensitive to the precise stereochemistry clearly indicate that specific molecular interactions must occur between drug and receptor. It does not follow, however, that all steric effects are intermolecular. One must always consider the possibility that intramolecular interactions can alter drug chemistry; see, for example, the structure–activity analysis of temelastine analogues in Section 12.5.12.7.

Not all chiral antihistamine drugs show stereoselective antagonist activity and it appears that an asymmetric centre close to the side chain nitrogen, as in promethazine,[313] isothipendyl[308] and clemastine,[278] is of minor importance for stereoselectivity. An unusual case is levocabastine, where stereoselective antihistamine activity *in vivo* is time dependent, suggesting that metabolic deactivation of the dextro enantiomer is more rapid. Thus, in guinea pigs the (−):(+) potency ratio is 4 after 1 h, but 90 after 24 h.[314] For further discussion of stereochemical effects the reader should consult refs. 277 and 278.

Stereoisomeric pairs of compounds, such as those indicated in Table 18, are useful tools for studying the pharmacology of histamine H_1 receptors, since the less active isomer serves as

Table 18　Some Stereoisomeric Pairs of H_1 receptor Histamine Antagonists showing Difference in Activity Determined *in vitro* on the Guinea Pig Ileum or other Assay as Indicated

Structure[e]	Name	Isomer	Activities pA$_2^*$	Other	Ref.
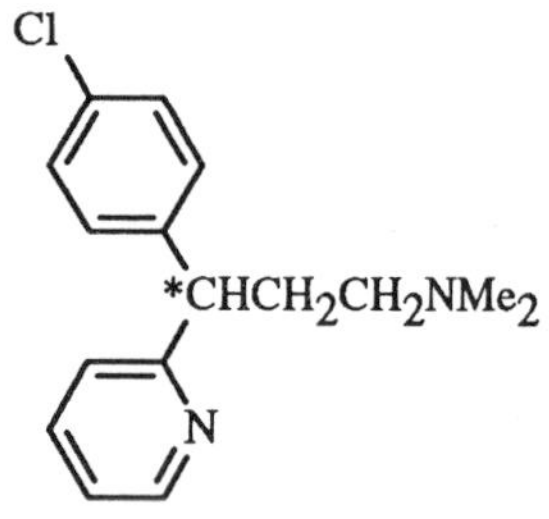 Cl ... *CHCH$_2$CH$_2$NMe$_2$ (pyridine)	Chlorpheniramine	(+)-(S)	9.30	9.10[b]	302
		(−)-(R)	7.84	6.70[b]	83
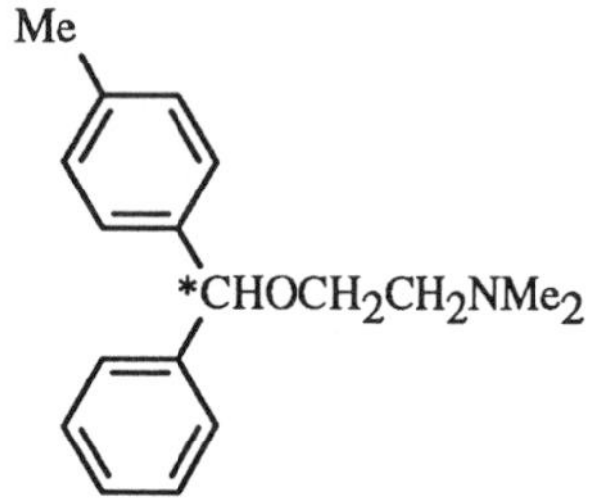 Me ... *CHOCH$_2$CH$_2$NMe$_2$ (phenyl)	Neobenodine	(+)-(R)	8.76		288
		(−)-(S)	6.87		303
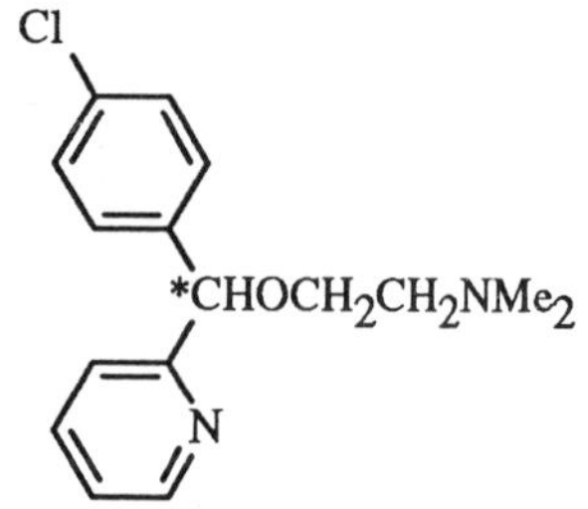 Cl ... *CHOCH$_2$CH$_2$NMe$_2$ (pyridine)	Carbinoxamine	(−)-(S)		6.4 nM[c]	309
		(+)-(R)		185 nM[c]	310
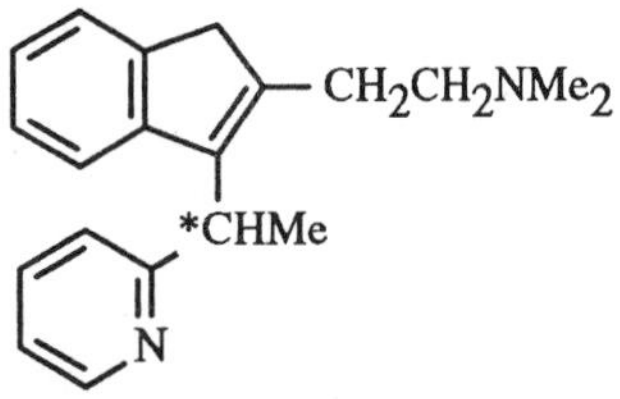 (indene) CH$_2$CH$_2$NMe$_2$ *CHMe (pyridine)	Dimethindene	(−)	9.1	9.4[d]	311
		(+)	7.8	6.3[d]	311
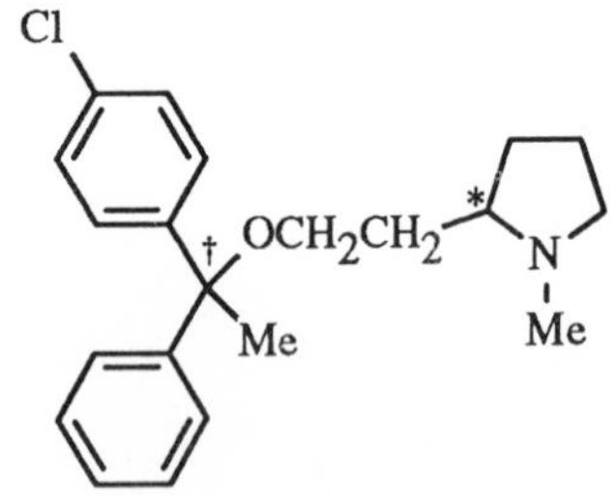 Cl ... OCH$_2$CH$_2$ — N(Me) pyrrolidine, Me, phenyl	Clemastine	(†R,*S)	9.45		312
		(†S,*S)	7.99		278
		(†R,*R)	9.40		
	compare also (R*) isomers:	(†S,*R)	8.57		
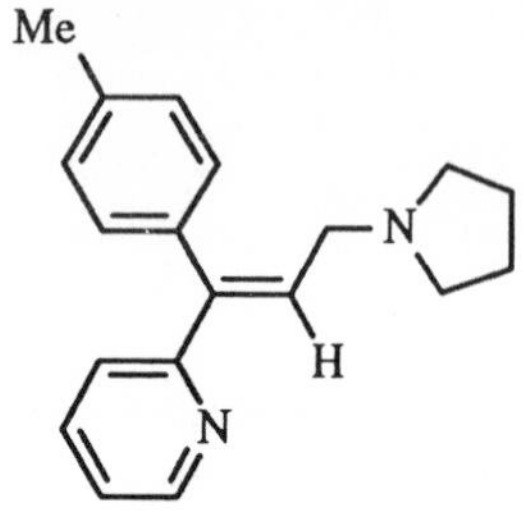 Me ... (phenyl)=CH—N pyrrolidine, (pyridine) H	Triprolidine	Trans	9.94		301

Table 18 (*Contd.*)

Structure[e]	Name	Isomer	Activities		Ref.
			pA_2^a	Other	
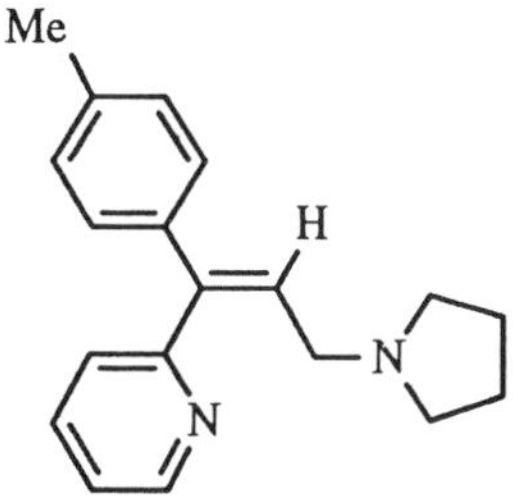	*Cis* isomer of triprolidine	*Cis*	6.88		301

[a] Antagonism of histamine-induced contraction of the guinea pig ileum *in vitro*. [b] Inhibition of [^{3}H]mepyramine binding to guinea pig cerebellum *in vitro*. [c] ED$_{50}$ determined *in vitro* on the guinea pig ileum. [d] On the guinea pig electrically driven left atrium *in vitro*. [e] * and † denote chiral centres for optical isomers.

a chemical control (*cf.* discussion of chemical control substances in Section 12.5.10). This is particularly valuable with antihistamine drugs since they may also interact with membranes, and other receptors, and their selectivity towards histamine receptors may not always be adequately separated from other such effects.

Although activity appears to be stereodependent, it has been difficult to discern what are the precise stereochemical requirements for antihistamine structures. Part of the problem lies in the conformational flexibility of the antihistamines; various conformations are usually possible for the side chain and various orientations may be taken by the aromatic rings. Kier[127] compared triprolidine with histamine and noted that in the *trans* conformer of histamine, the distance of 4.6 Å between the imidazole *pros* nitrogen and side chain nitrogen atoms, could be matched by a similar distance in triprolidine between the pyridine and side chain nitrogen atoms. One cannot infer, however, that this indicates the active conformation for triprolidine since it assumes that the nitrogen atoms of the agonist and antagonist molecules are involved in similar binding to the same receptor site. Subsequently it was shown[315] that the phenyl analogue of triprolidine is equiactive as an antagonist, *i.e.* the pyridyl nitrogen is not an essential requirement. Thus, the direct comparison of internitrogen distances does not provide a sufficiently sound basis. A simpler description was offered by Witiak,[316] who suggested that the most active antihistamines have an intramolecular distance of 5–6 Å between the side chain ammonium nitrogen and the centre of one of the aromatic rings, but this is probably not exclusive.[296] A useful basis for comparison is offered by mianserin (**22**; Table 3), which is a rigid tricyclic analogue of mepyramine and has almost identical affinity as an H$_1$ receptor antagonist.

Consideration of likely active conformations have prompted studies of antihistamine stereochemistry in the solid state by crystal structure determination,[307,317–323] in solution by NMR spectroscopy[324–326] or circular dichroism,[326,327] and by theoretical quantum mechanical calculation.[328] The crystal structure studies have shown molecules being generally in extended (*trans*) conformations and several authors have attributed activity to the extended conformations; such suggestions are very speculative. The studies in solution indicate coexistence of folded and extended conformers for several antihistamines; the relative population may also depend on the solvent, *e.g.* pheniramine was found to be predominantly in an extended form in water but the ratio was shifted towards the folded form in chloroform, probably through formation of an intramolecular H bond in the monocation.[326] Some conformationally restricted (semirigid) analogues have been studied in which it is not possible to achieve the equivalent of a fully extended *trans* side chain conformation and it appears that such compounds retain activity as antihistamines (*cf.* mianserin; **22**; Table 3.) Another approach taken has been to measure the dipole moments of antihistamines in solution and then to use a vector analysis to identify the various conformer populations.[330]

12.5.12.5 Structures Combining H$_1$ Receptor Antagonist Activity With Other Properties

In recent years, many other compounds of diverse chemical structures have been found to be potent histamine H$_1$ receptor antagonists. Examples include the tricyclic antidepressant drugs such as mianserin and doxepin (Figure 16), cyproheptadine and azatidine, which , in addition to their other activities, have extremely high affinity for histamine H_1 receptors. The blockade of H_1 receptors does not appear to be an important factor for antidepressant activity, but could contribute to sedative actions and possible peripheral side effects.[331]

A potent histamine H_1 receptor antagonist is levocabastine (Figure 16), which is the optical isomer of a derivative of 4-phenylcyclohexylamine of known stereochemistry. Levocabastine is reported[314,332] to be selective and more potent than previously reported H_1 receptor antagonists, including azatidine, cyproheptadine and ketotifen, and to be effective in clinical studies in patients suffering from allergic conjunctivitis.

Generally, in attempting to identify histamine H_1 receptor antagonists with potentially greater clinical efficacy than earlier compounds, two approaches have been adopted. In one approach, attempts have been made to identify compounds combining H_1 receptor antagonism with additional and potentially beneficial properties. The second approach has been to seek antihistamines which do not easily penetrate the CNS (central nervous system) in the hope of limiting 'side effects' such as sedation.

It has long been recognized that conventional antihistamines frequently exhibited other activities such as anticholinergic or antiemetic activity. Additional actions such as bradykinin, serotonin or leukotriene antagonism that have been noted with some more recent compounds (*e.g.* azatidine[357]) have been considered to be potentially beneficial. Blockade of additional mediators of the allergic response could potentially broaden therapeutic utility of H_1 receptor antagonists into more severe allergic conditions, although evidence for this is limited. An additional property claimed for some H_1 receptor antagonists (including azelastine,[333] oxatomide[334] and ketotifen[335]; Figure 16) is their ability to inhibit anaphylactic release of histamine. This effect has been described as mast cell stabilizing activity and attempts have been made to design compounds with this dual action by combining the structural features of chromolyn-like and antihistaminic components.[336]

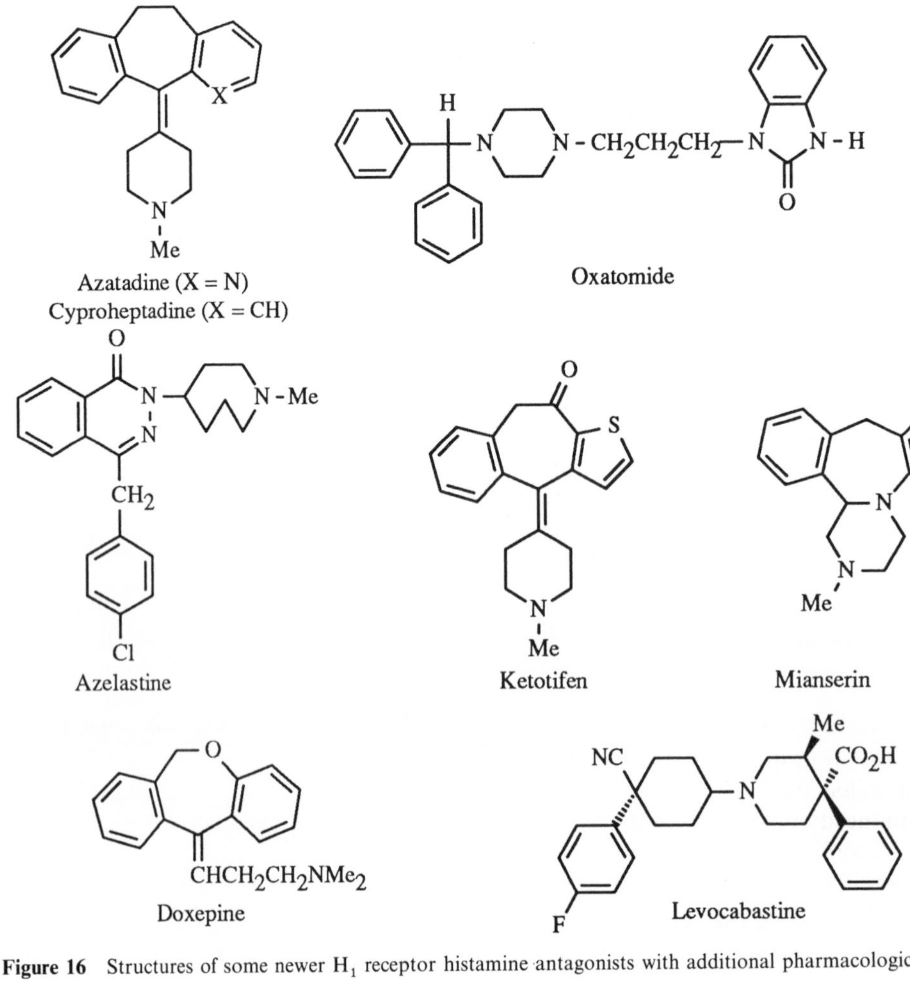

Figure 16 Structures of some newer H_1 receptor histamine antagonists with additional pharmacological actions

The mechanism of this action of many antihistamines in inhibiting allergic release of histamine from the mast cells is not well understood. However recent evidence has demonstrated that the lipid mediator, platelet activating factor (PAF, 1-*O*-alkyl-2-acetyl-*sn*-glyceryl-3-phosphorylcholine) induces sustained inflammatory activity and bronchial hyperreactivity and this has focused attention upon PAF involvement in asthma. In fact, of all the mediators so far described, PAF appears to mimic pathology of asthma most clearly.[337] The capacity of ketotifen to inhibit responses to PAF is reported to be comparable with its capacity to effect H_1 antagonism *in vivo*. Other H_1 receptor antagonists were reported to be inactive against PAF-induced bronchospasm.[338] The proposed mechanism accords with clinical experience with chronically administered ketotifen, which is reportedly comparable with chromoglycate and theophylline in the therapy of bronchial asthma.[338] An analogue of loratidine (Figure 17) in which COMe replaces CO_2Et (Sch 37370) is also reported to be a potent dual PAF and histamine antagonist.[378] L630435 is a quaternary derivative of the H_1 receptor antagonist, mequitazine, which is reported to be a powerful inhibitor of PAF-induced platelet aggregation and bronchoconstriction.[339]

12.5.12.6 Nonsedative H_1 Receptor Antagonists

One of the main factors for the resurgence of interest in histamine H_1 receptor antagonists in the 1980s has been the discovery and development of antihistamines relatively free of sedative side effects.[376] The major side effect of the classical antihistamine is sedation, although many also possess anticholinergic and other activities, such as interacting with dopaminergic pathways.[374,377] It has been claimed that sedation results directly from occupation of cerebral H_1 receptors,[340] although the evidence is not conclusive (see, for example, ref. 375). However some corroborative evidence comes from a double-blind study of the effects of the enantiomers of chlorpheniramine and dimethindene on alertness and performance in six healthy human volunteers.[341] It was found that only those enantiomers active as H_1 receptor antagonists (*i.e.* (+)-chlorpheniramine and (−)-dimethindene, see Table 18) caused drowsiness and impaired performance. See ref. 342 for a discussion of the structural features of the conventional antihistamines which may otherwise be associated with sedative side effects.

Mequitazine (Figure 17) is a potent H_1 receptor antagonist derived from a phenothiazine ring system and containing a quinuclidinyl side chain. It has been reported that central effects occur only at high doses of mequitazine and this was originally attributed to its affinity for peripheral receptors being greater than for central H_1 receptors.[343] It now appears more likely that the reduced sedative effects with mequitazine are associated with its difficulty in crossing the blood–brain barrier.[344] The conformations of some quinuclidinyl-substituted compounds were studied using molecular orbital calculations and the conclusion was reached that ease of penetration of the blood–brain barrier was related to drug conformation with the added proposition that the sedative action requires a specific stereochemical interaction with central histamine H_1 receptors.[345]

Terfenadine (Figure 17) is a selective H_1 receptor antagonist with weak anticholinergic activity and minimal activity at α or β adrenoceptors or histamine H_2 receptors. Terfenadine was derived from a CNS programme aimed at designing dopamine receptor antagonists, chemically related to haloperidol and azacyclonol;[346] the compounds showed only weak activity as CNS depressants, however, but led to terfenadine as a peripherally acting H_1 receptor histamine antagonist. Sedative side effects observed in animal or widespread clinical studies have been minimal.[347]

The *in vitro* concentrations of terfenadine inhibiting the binding of [³H]mepyramine by 50% (IC_{50}) were 0.2 and 0.3 μmol respectively for ileal and brain receptors. Under these *in vitro* conditions, terfenadine therefore does not preferentially block peripheral histamine H_1 receptors. *In vivo* binding of [³H]mepyramine to mouse cerebral cortex is not significantly modified by treatment with terfenadine (or mequitazine) compared with other antihistamines (promethazine, mepyramine, cyproheptadine, triprolidine, (+)-chlorpheniramine and diphenhydramine) when compared at 'therapeutic' doses. These results suggest that terfenadine differs from conventional antihistamines in not readily penetrating the blood–brain barrier.[347]

Terfenadine has moderate activity *in vivo* in animal models of antihistaminic activity, including histamine-induced bronchoconstriction and histamine-induced lethality in guinea pigs (ED_{50} 0.1 to 0.34 mg kg^{-1}, p.o.). Terfenadine is extensively metabolized and a metabolite (or metabolites) may contribute to activity *in vivo*. Pharmacodynamic properties of terfenadine and therapeutic efficacy have been reviewed.[347] Clinical studies have shown terfenadine to be comparable to other antihistaminics in its efficacy, and the incidence of sedation due to terfenadine was comparable with that of placebo and significantly less than with conventional antihistamines. The marked improvement in

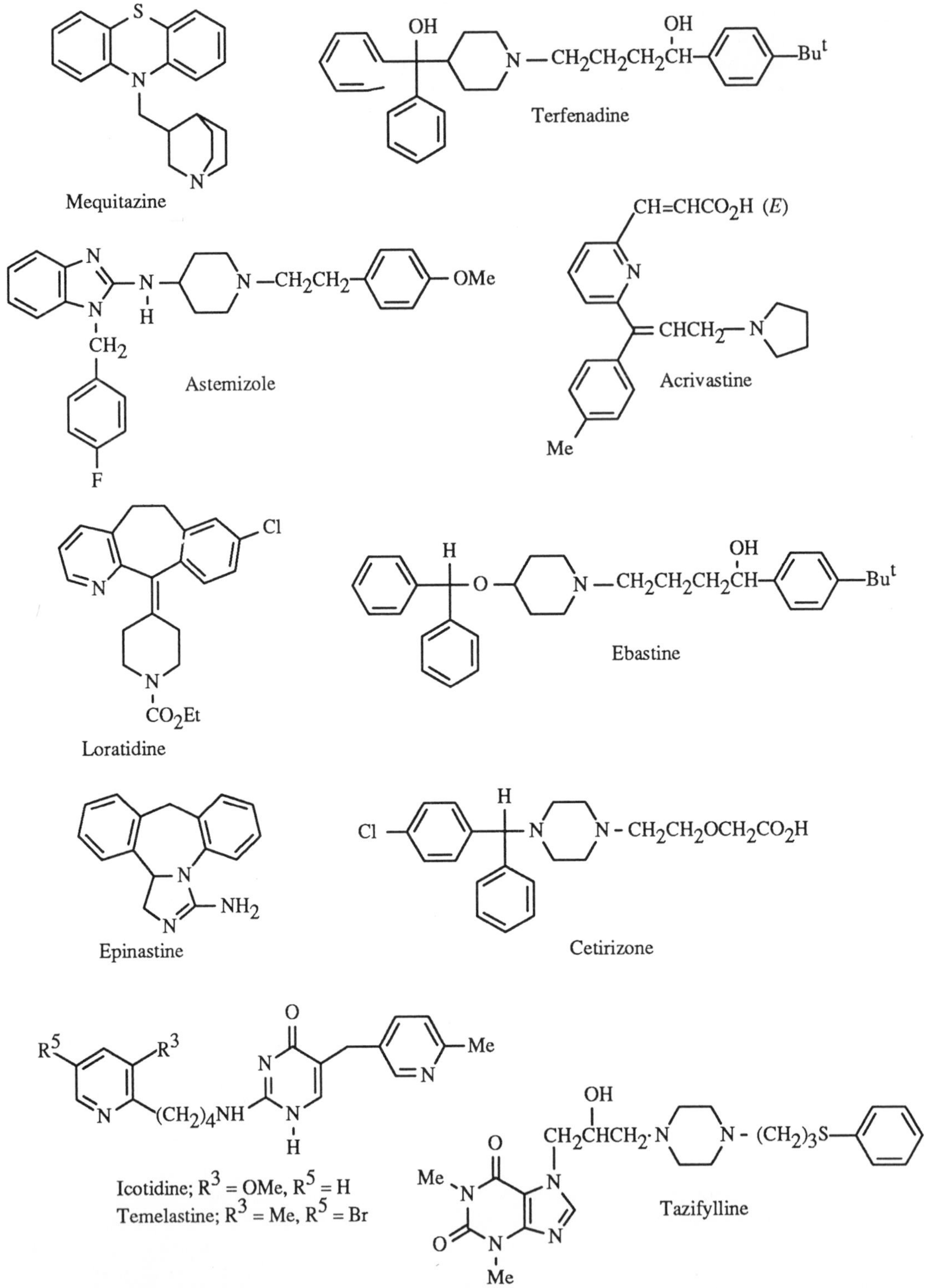

Figure 17 Structures of some newer H_1 receptor histamine antagonists with a reportedly low incidence of sedative side effects

side effect profile of terfenadine over conventional antihistamines led to its widespread clinical usage (therapeutic dose 60 mg) in the treatment of perennial rhinitis and histamine-mediated skin disorders. A structurally related product, ebastine (LAS W-090; Figure 17), has also been claimed to have a low liability to produce sedative effects.[348]

Astemizole (Figure 17) is another H_1 receptor antagonist that has been introduced into clinical practice as a 'nonsedating' antihistamine. The chemical development[286] and pharmacological and clinical profile of astemizole have been reviewed.[349-351] Astemizole is a potent and relatively selective H_1 receptor antagonist with a slow onset and long duration of action that is reportedly free of central and sedative effect.[359] Astemizole is extensively metabolized and metabolites are likely to contribute to its *in vivo* antihistaminic activity and its extended duration of pharmacological action. The usual clinical trials have confirmed its effectiveness in the therapy of allergic rhinitis and related conditions.[351,353]

The selectivity of astemizole was demonstrated in a series of tests in rats at doses up to 200 times the antihistaminic dose and in tests measuring central activities up to 1600 times.[350] There appears to be no significant difference in the *in vitro* affinity of astemizole for histamine H_1 receptors in guinea pig lung ($K_i = 3.0$ nM) and on cerebral cortex ($K_i = 4.4$ nM) as measured by displacement of [^{3}H]mepyramine binding from membranes of these tissues.[293] In *ex vivo* binding studies there was a large dissociation between histamine H_1 receptor occupancy in the lung (> 80% for two days) and the cerebellum (< 20%) with astemizole, compared with a parallel occupancy with mepyramine.[350] It appears likely therefore that the reduced level of central activity with astemizole is related to its poor penetration of the blood–brain barrier.

Loratadine (SCH 29851; Figure 17) is a 'nonsedating' antihistamine that was developed from the tricyclic antihistaminic agent azatadine (Figure 16) by converting the basic piperidino tertiary nitrogen function into a neutral carbamate derivative and introducing a chlorine substituent into the benzene ring.[354] Loratidine is reported to be comparable in antihistaminic potency to terfenadine and to lack CNS effects.[293,485] Results from *in vitro* ligand binding studies indicate that loratadine differs from the 'non sedating' antihistamines, terfenadine, astemizole and mequitazine in causing significantly reduced inhibition of [^{3}H]mepyramine binding to membranes from guinea pig brain ($K_i = 118$ nM) compared with lung ($K_i = 35$ nM).[293] It is therefore suggested that loratidine is somewhat selective for peripheral compared with central histamine receptors. Initial human studies have been published.[535]

Acrivastine (BW 825C; Figure 17) is derived from the classical antihistamine triprolidine (Figure 13) by introducing an acrylic acid residue into the 2-position of the pyridine ring. The effect of this substitution is reported[486] to reduce the sedative side effects typically associated with triprolidine but with no reduction in antihistaminic potency. This is likely to be due to low penetration of the blood–brain barrier, presumably through formation of the zwitterion, and distribution studies with acrivastine in guinea pigs and rats yielded brain:plasma ratios in the range 0.02–0.05 after i.v. administration. A study in human subjects concluded that acrivastine, at doses causing more peripheral H_1 receptor antagonism than triprolidine, has considerably reduced CNS activity.[358]

Temelastine (SK&F 93944; Figure 17) is a highly selective histamine H_1 receptor antagonist that was designed[352] by modifying and optimizing the pyridine ring substituents in the combined H_1/H_2 receptor antagonist icotidine (Figure 17). Pharmacological studies with temelastine have been summarized;[284] comparable or improved activity relative to mepyramine was demonstrated in a range of assays for H_1 receptor antagonism *in vitro* and *in vivo* by i.v. and oral administration. Studies on the penetration of [^{14}C]temelastine, labelled either in the isocytosine ring or in the butyl chain, showed that brain concentrations were minimal when compared with steady state blood concentrations.[284] In contrast, brain concentrations of [^{3}H]mepyramine exceeded blood concentrations by a factor of approximately 3. The potency ($K_i = 32.5$ nM) with which temelastine inhibits [^{3}H]mepyramine binding to mouse brain H_1 receptors *in vitro* is low compared with the K_B value of 0.28 nM measured against histamine stimulation of H_1 receptors in guinea pig ileum. *In vivo* binding studies to mouse cortex H_1 receptors also demonstrated that temelastine has relatively low ability to penetrate the blood–brain barrier compared with mepyramine or promethazine.[529] Behavioural tests in mice suggested that temelastine had no detectable effect on CNS function except when extremely high doses were used.[529] Preliminary reports on the safety and efficacy of temelastine in patients with hay fever have been published.[530]

Other H_1 receptor antagonists that are reported to have reduced sedative side effects include the theophylline derivative tazifylline,[355] epinastine[356] (WAL 801), which is a guanidine analogue of mianserin, and cetirizine,[360] a human metabolite of hydroxyzine (Figure 17).

12.5.12.7 Structure–Activity Studies Related to Temelastine

There have been few structure–activity rationalizations relating to the newer 'nonsedating' antihistamines. A particularly interesting example is temelastine (Figure 17).

The pyridylbutylisocytosine (2-aminopyrimidin-4-one) derivative icotidine (SK&F 93319) was developed as a histamine antagonist which combined approximately equal affinities for both H_1 and

H_2 receptors.[361-363] Studies which showed that icotidine did not cross the blood–brain barrier provided a lead to design a selective and non-CNS-penetrating histamine H_1 receptor antagonist which should thereby avoid unwanted side effects. The structure–activity studies leading from icotidine to temelastine were an extension of those leading from the H_2 antagonist oxmetidine[364] (see Section 12.5.13.3) to give icotidine. Many of the observations made regarding structure–activity relationships in the optimization of icotidine were used to optimize H_1 receptor activity and

Table 19 Chemical Structures Indicating some of the Steps Taken for the Discovery of Temelastine (SK&F 93944)

Structure		pA_2^a	
		H_1	H_2
Cimetidine		< 4	6.1
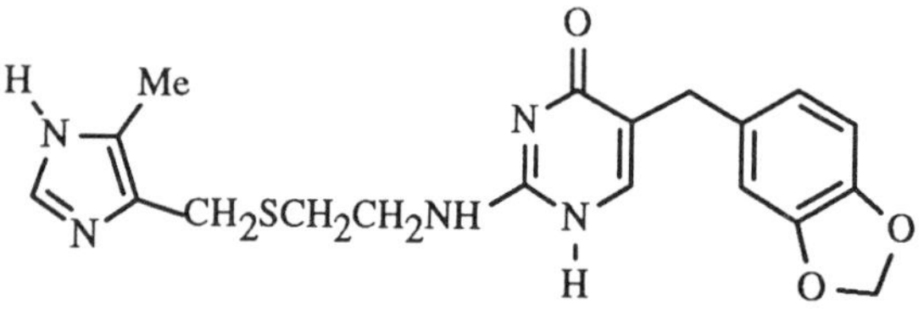	Oxmetidine (SK&F 92994), H_2 antagonist, also possesses weak H_1 antagonist activity	5.4	*ca.* 6.9
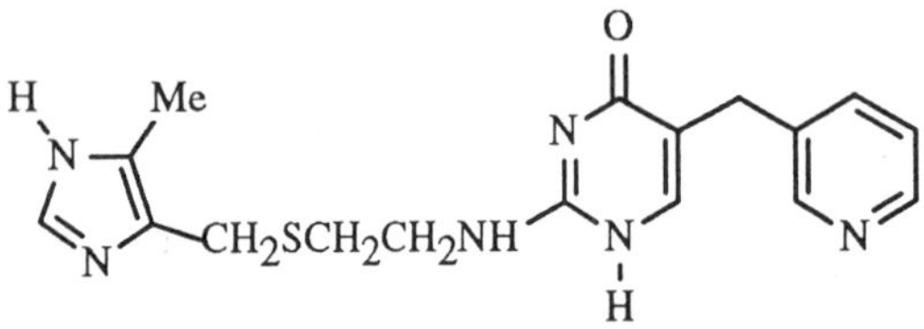	3-Picolinyl in place of methylenedioxybenzyl in the isocytosine 5-position *e.g.* SK&F 92018	5.2	7.0
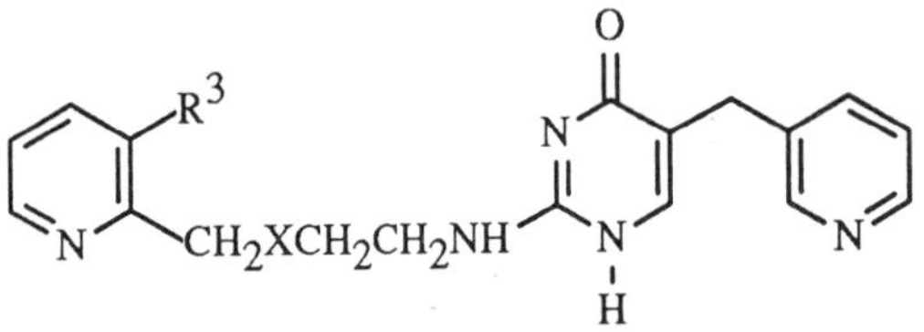	Substituted pyridine in place of imidazole enhances H_1, *e.g.* R^3 = Br	7.0	6.9
	—CH$_2$— in place of —S— enhances H_1, *e.g.*, R^3 = Br	8.7	*ca.* 6.5
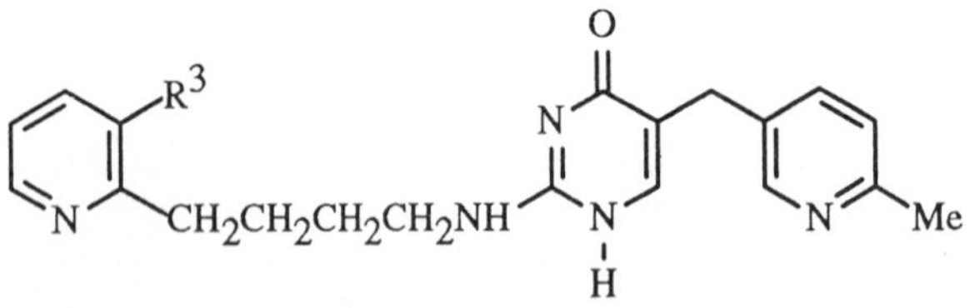	6-Methyl-3-picolinyl in the isocytosine ring; H_1 and H_2 antagonist potencies (*in vitro*) in balance when R = OMe, *i.e.* icotidine (SK&F 93319)	7.8	7.5
	Larger substituents increase H_1 and reduce H_2 antagonist potencies, *e.g.* R^3 = Me	8.7	7.0
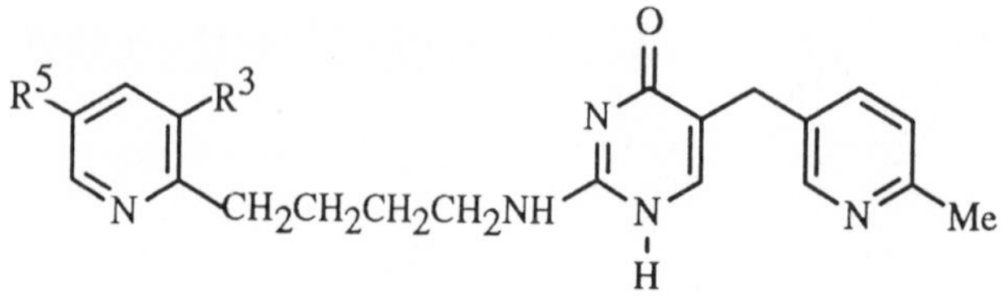	R^5 substituent increases H_1 and reduces H_2 antagonist potencies. Temelastine has R^3 = Me, R^5 = Br	9.55	*ca.* 5.9

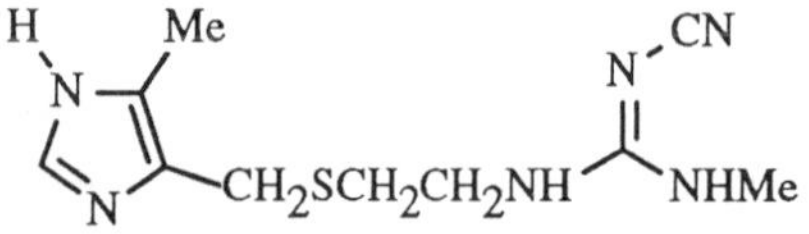

[a] Antagonist activities *in vitro* against histamine-stimulated contraction of the guinea pig ileum (H_1) or chronotropy of the guinea pig right atrium (H_2); $pA_2 = -\log K_B$.

minimize activity at the H_2 receptor to give temelastine. It is therefore worth considering the design of both compounds. Some of the steps taken for the discovery of icotidine and temelastine are shown in Table 19.

The work stemmed from the observation that H_2 receptor histamine antagonists possessing a 5-substituted isocytosine moiety also had some (albeit weak) H_1 antagonist activity. For example, the H_2 antagonist oxmetidine (SK&F 92994)[364] and the corresponding picolinyl analogue (SK&F 93018; Table 19) had pA_2 values 5.2–5.4 as H_1 antagonists on the isolated guinea pig ileum. Oxmetidine, like cimetidine, is an imidazole derivative and it was demonstrated that replacement of the imidazole ring by a pyridine ring retained H_2 antagonist activity and enhanced H_1 antagonist activity. Additionally, it was shown that replacing the sulfide linkage (—S—) in the linking chain by a methylene linkage (—CH_2—) further enhanced H_1 antagonist activity.

In the above structures it was found that activity was sensitive to the substituent in the pyridine ring at the position adjacent to the side chain. Various electronic, lipophilic and steric parameters for the substituents were examined to correlate structure with activity and it appeared that activity was relatable to substituent size. Figure 18 shows linear correlations of H_1 receptor antagonist activity (determined *in vitro* on the guinea pig ileum) for two series of substituted pyridines, where X = S and X = CH_2 respectively, using a steric parameter for the substituents. This particular parameter represents the minimum van der Waals' radius of the substituent in the plane of the pyridine ring measured towards the CH_2 of the chain at the pyridine 2-position and was obtained from the tables published by Verloop *et al.*[365] There is a consistent increase in potency of at least one pA_2 unit between the two series for any given substituent.

Figure 19 shows a correlation for the closely related series X = CH_2, in which a 6-methyl group is present in the isocytosine 5-picolinyl substituent, using the same steric parameters for an extended range of substituents. Both H_1 (ileum) and H_2 (atrium) antagonist potencies are plotted and it can be seen that in this series, for each compound, H_1 potency is greater than H_2, and the two activities appear to have different optima with respect to substituent size. The two activities are almost in balance when R = OMe, *viz.* for icotidine (SK&F 93319).

Icotidine has an octanol:water partition coefficient of 435:1, which is much higher than is usual for H_2 receptor antagonists (*e.g.* cimetidine partition coefficient = 2.5) but is less than that of most H_1 receptor antihistamines.

Icotidine, although lipophilic, was shown (by whole-body autoradiography using labelled compounds) not to penetrate the CNS. This observation led to an opportunity to develop rationally

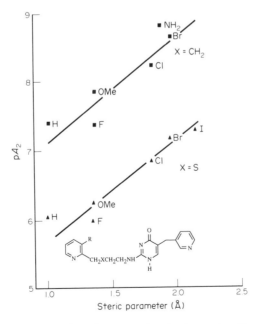

Figure 18 Correlation between H_1 receptor histamine antagonism (*in vitro* against histamine-induced contractions of the guinea pig ileum, represented as the pA_2 value on the ordinate axis) for two series of substituted pyridine derivatives, X = CH_2(■), X = S (▲), and a steric parameter (Verloop *et al.*)[365] for the respective substituents (abscissa, Å). Antagonists were introduced into contact with the tissue for 8 min prior to histamine assay, except for compounds X = CH_2, R = F; X = S, R = F, OMe, Br, which had only 2 min contact

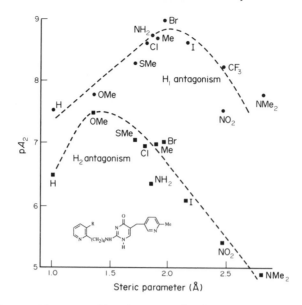

Figure 19 Relationship between H_1 receptor histamine antagonism (upper curve, *in vitro* against histamine-induced contractions of the guinea pig ileum) and H_2 receptor histamine antagonism (lower curve, *in vitro* against histamine stimulation of the rate of beating of the guinea pig right atrium), represented as the pA_2 values on the ordinate axis, and a steric parameter (Verloop *et al.*) for the respective substituents (abscissa, Å) in substituted pyridylbutylisocytosines. Icotidine (SK&F 93319) has R = OMe. H_1 antagonism was assayed after 8 min contact between the tissue and the antagonist; H_2 antagonism was assayed after 60 min contact, except for the compounds R = H and Cl, which had 8 min

a selective non-CNS-penetrating H_1 antagonist providing that the activity ratio could be modified to make it sufficiently H_1 receptor selective.

Examination of the plot shown in Figure 19 reveals a possible approach. Relative to icotidine (R = OMe), H_2 antagonist activity falls with increasing size of the steric parameter, while H_1 antagonist activity continues to rise. Maximum H_1 antagonist activity together with the greatest separation from H_2 antagonism occurs in the region of bromo, methyl and amino substituents. This modification results in a separation between H_1 and H_2 antagonist activities of approximately two orders of magnitude. Additional structural modifications were made to increase the separation still further and it was found that H_1 antagonist activity could be raised and H_2 antagonist activity reduced by a suitable R^5 substituent in the 5-position of the pyridine ring.

Quantitative structure–activity studies were carried out in a series of 3,5-disubstituted pyridyl-butylisocytosines (**79**; Figure 15). Equation (1) shows the relationship between the H_1 antagonist activity assayed *in vivo* in the anaesthetized guinea pig for protection against histamine-induced bronchoconstriction, expressed as $\log 1/C$ where C is the dose in $\mu mol\,kg^{-1}$ that produces a (dose ratio -1) = 10 against histamine. The equation is expressed in terms of the steric parameter of the 3-substituent, derived from Verloop and representing the minimum van der Waals' radius in the direction of the side chain methylene, and in terms of the electronic parameters of the 3- and 5-substituents represented by σ_m; the substituents are selected from H, Me, OMe, NH_2, F, Cl, Br, I.

$$\log 1/C \;=\; 5.56 \;+\; 1.70\,B \;+\; 0.80\,(\sigma_m 5 - \sigma_m 3)$$
$$n \;=\; 22, \quad r \;=\; 0.95, \quad s \;=\; 0.22 \tag{1}$$

From the *in vivo* study the conclusions were as follows. Optimum potency at the H_1 receptor is obtained when the R^3 substituent extends about 2 Å in the direction of the side chain and the group is electron donating, and where the R^5 group is electron withdrawing. Unlike many previous QSAR studies of histamine H_1 receptor antagonists, this correlation contains no significant contributions from lipophilicity parameters. For temelastine, R^3 is methyl, which is electron donating with a near optimum steric parameter 1.9 Å, while R^5 is bromo, which is electron withdrawing; the *in vivo* dose for a (dose ratio -1) = 10 is 0.03 $\mu mol\,kg^{-1}$, and for a (dose ratio -1) = 2 it is 0.005 $\mu mol\,kg^{-1}$ (0.002 $mg\,kg^{-1}$). Potency *in vitro* ($pA_2 = 9.55$; Table 19) has been increased by over 10 000-fold relative to the initial lead compound, oxmetidine.

Why is it that icotidine and temelastine hardly enter the brain although they have octanol/water partition coefficients greater than 100:1 (435 and 3900 respectively)? As discussed in Section 12.5.13.12, it appears that high octanol/water partition *per se* is not a sufficient condition to ensure brain penetration and it is likely that the pronounced hydrogen-bonding ability of the isocytosine structure is a very important factor in keeping these compounds out of highly lipophilic tissue regions. This feature certainly would not account for the low penetration of a compound like terfenadine (although its penetration is still considerably higher than for temelastine) and it is likely that protein binding has an important role in helping to maintain compounds such as terfenadine in peripheral tissues.

Computergraphic modelling studies of the above compounds indicate that the R^3 substituent restricts rotation τ_1 of the pyridine ring and that larger groups (*i.e.* Br, Me, NH_2) favour the conformation where the first two carbon atoms of the chain lie in the plane of the pyridine ring (Figure 20) and are *syn* to the pyridine nitrogen. In addition, if rotation about τ_2 is also restricted, a *trans* arrangement of the first three bonds of the chain is achieved.

Two approaches were taken to design compounds favouring this conformation, namely, the bicyclic tetrahydroquinoline structure (**83**) and the aminopyridine structures (**84**).

In the tetrahydroquinoline the first carbon atom of the chain and the pyridine 3-substituent are incorporated into the second ring, which freezes out rotation and limits the torsion angle τ to certain known positions. Compound (**83**; $pA_2 = 8.92$) has two to three times the potency of compound (**82**; $pA_2 = 8.68$), both *in vitro* and *in vivo* as an H_1 receptor histamine antagonist, confirming the postulate that a conformation near the *trans* ($\tau = 180°$) conformation is important for potency at the histamine H_1 receptor.

In the aminopyridines (**84**), amino replaces the first methylene of the chain and by being planar (sp^2 nitrogen) restricts rotation to favour the predicted active conformation and affords potent compounds,[140] *e.g.* (**84**), $R^3 = Me$, $R^5 = Cl$, $pA_2 = 8.80$; as for temelastine, this last compound has negligible ability to penetrate the CNS. Interestingly, in this series, activity appears to correlate with the lipophilicity of substituent R^3, presumably because in these compounds the substituent is not required for restricting rotation.

12.5.12.8 Speculative Molecular Models of H_1 Receptors

The H_1 receptor antihistamines have been characterized pharmacologically as competitive antagonists of histamine but, as pointed out by Ariens,[366] this is a functional antagonism and it does not prove that they act at precisely the same molecular locus as histamine. That is to say, although histamine and the antihistamines appear to compete for the same receptors, they do not have to interact with precisely the same set of atoms at the receptor site. This makes it difficult to draw inferences about the molecular nature of the receptor through analysis of the chemistry of antihistamines.

Comparison of the structures of the 'classical' antihistamines with that of histamine indicate, as common features, a charged ammonium group (the 'side chain') and a flat aromatic ring. However, as discussed in the previous sections, one cannot presume that the rings of the agonist and antagonists necessarily interact with the same molecular site at the receptor. Furthermore, we now know that it is not necessary to have a formally cationic molecule (*cf.* temelastine analogue **80**, Figure 15, and loratidine, Figure 17) and many other structural types of compounds have been shown to be potent H_1 receptor antagonists.

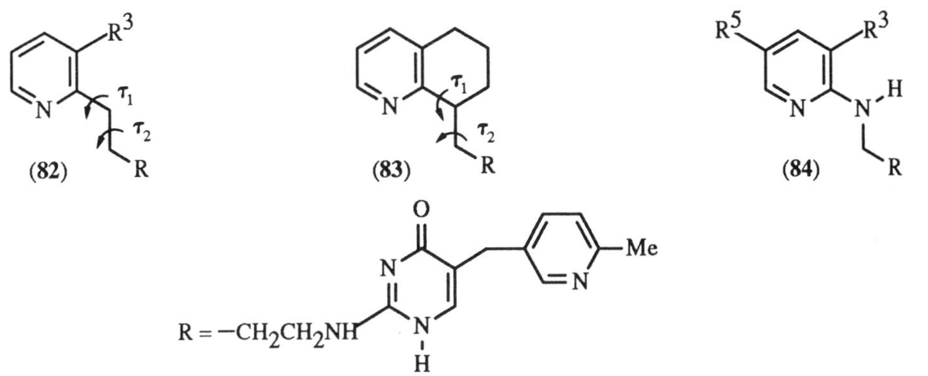

Figure 20 Conformationally restricted analogues (**83**) and (**84**) of pyridylbutylisocytosines (**82**), active as H_1 receptor histamine antagonists, indicate that coplanarity of the pyridine ring and methylene chain is important for activity

It seems very likely that different structures may have different modes of binding to accessory regions of the receptor active site. The unanswered question is still: what are the complementary groups on the receptor? Ariens and coworkers proposed[366] that agonists such as histamine, being highly polar, react with receptors at sites which are rich in polar groups, *i.e.* in a strongly hydrophilic region. In the vicinity, however, there may be a less specific lipoid region which would serve as a complementary area to the hydrophobic rings found in the antihistamines. Ariens envisaged that the ammonium side chain and the flat rings then provide additional binding to these accessory lipoid areas (see also refs. 10 and 367).

Previously, H_1 and H_2 receptors have been differentiated by the use of chemically very distinct classes of specific antagonists. H_1 antihistamines were seen to be lipophilic and to exist predominantly in the cationic form at physiological pH. H_2 antagonists are uncharged and very polar hydrogen-bonding structures (see Section 12.5.13.2). These differences suggested that the binding sites for H_1 and H_2 receptors must have different chemical properties.

The isocytosine compounds (Section 12.5.12.7), however, exemplify a new structural type of antagonist at H_1 receptors which represents an important departure from the conventional view of antihistamines. Since very similar isocytosine structures are potent antagonists at H_1 or H_2 receptors, it is clear that the receptors must have some pronounced chemical features in common.

The results with compound (83) also show, however, that the receptors are clearly differentiated by stereochemical requirements. At the H_2 receptor, compound (83) has negligible activity (pA_2 on the atrium < 4.3), whereas compound (82) has a pA_2 (atrium) $= 7.0$. Thus the conformational properties of the drug molecules needed for binding to the H_1 and H_2 receptors are different. Any further advance to our knowledge of receptor chemistry will have to wait for these receptors to be isolated and sequenced.

12.5.12.9 Clinical Utility of Histamine H_1 Receptor Antagonists

The clinical indications and therapeutic efficacy of conventional antihistaminic agents and comparative clinical data on terfenadine and astemizole have been reviewed.[368,369] The clinical pharmacokinetics of H_1 receptor antagonists has also been reviewed.[370] The most widespread usage of H_1 receptor antagonists is in seasonal and perennial rhinitis, frequently in combination with the nasal decongestant, pseudoephedrine. H_1 receptor antagonists are also widely used in dermatological disorders, in particular urticaria and pruritus.

The major advantage of the new 'nonsedative' H_1 receptor antagonists is in allergic rhinitis and in this indication terfenadine and astemizole, in prescribed doses, are reported to be as effective as chlorpheniramine and clemastine and without the sedative liability of the latter compounds.[368] Both terfenadine and astemizole may also be preferential to other H_1 receptor antagonists in urticaria or pruritus, providing that the pruritus does not have a central component. It has been stated[369] that an ideal H_1 receptor antagonist would have the characteristics of high potency, freedom from adverse effects, rapid onset of clinical benefits and a long but not inordinately long duration of action. Terfenadine has relatively low potency and astemizole has some undesirable features with regard to its pharmacokinetic characteristics, so that these two compounds are not ideal.

Whether astemizole, terfenadine or any of the newer H_1 receptor antagonists will broaden the clinical spectrum of use for H_1 receptor antagonists remains to be established. It has long been known that conventional antihistamines are relatively ineffective in the treatment of chronic asthma. Since anticholinergic activity and central side effects generally limit the dose of antihistaminic drug that can be used, the advent of highly selective H_1 receptor antagonists has provided tools to reinvestigate the role of histamine in the pathogenesis of asthma. Pretreatment of asthmatic patients with astemizole (at a dose sufficient to inhibit the skin weal reaction to $10\ \mu g\,mL^{-1}$ of histamine) considerably attenuates the early phase of the immediate asthmatic reaction in allergen provocation; thereafter the effect diminishes, however.[371,372] The later bronchoconstrictor response relates more to the release of other spasmogenic autocoids, including leukotriene LTC_4. Leukotriene receptor antagonists and inhibitors of leukotriene biosynthesis have been discovered and several compounds have been taken into development.[373] Combined blockade of mediators of early and late phases of allergic bronchoconstrictor response is therefore a future prospect in the therapy of bronchial asthma. The concept of platelet activating factor (PAF) involvement in asthma pathogenesis provides an alternative rationale for new drug design and development, and the evidence[338] for the clinical benefit from the use of H_1 receptor antagonists in chronic asthma holds promise for the future.

12.5.13 ANTAGONISTS AT HISTAMINE H$_2$ RECEPTORS

12.5.13.1 The Discovery of H$_2$ Antagonists

The discovery and development of cimetidine, the first clinically useful H$_2$ receptor histamine antagonist, has become one of the classic examples of drug design in medicinal chemistry. The first compound to be described as an H$_2$ receptor histamine antagonist, however, was burimamide (**86a**; Table 20) by Black and coworkers[54] in 1972. Its discovery was the culmination of a research programme initiated in 1964 at Smith Kline & French Laboratories, UK. Some of the early structure–activity studies, starting from histamine and leading *via* N^α-guanylhistamine through to burimamide have been summarized in various articles.[379–381] Concurrently, other researchers had sought antagonists using the early H$_1$ antihistamine 929F as a starting point; they obtained an antisecretory agent but not an H$_2$ receptor antagonist.[382]

The inability of the H$_1$ receptor antihistamine drugs to inhibit histamine-stimulated gastric acid secretion had been known for many years[383] but there had been few published reports of concerted efforts to discover a specific antagonist to this action of histamine. Robertson and Grossman[384] screened compounds in a search for inhibitors of gastric acid secretion, and Grossman and coworkers reported[52] on an extensive study of compounds, chemically related to histamine, which were examined for their action on acid secretion and also tested as possible inhibitors of histamine stimulation. Other researchers[51,385,158] also examined close analogues of histamine for possible antagonism of histamine-stimulated acid secretion. None of these studies established a histamine antagonist.

The approach taken at SK&F was also to use histamine as a chemical starting point, and seek a molecule that would have sufficient chemical resemblance to histamine in order to be 'recognized' at the receptor, but bind more strongly than histamine. In the first four years some 200 close structural analogues of histamine were synthesized and tested before a weakly active 'lead' was uncovered. This was the simple guanidine derivative of histamine,[386] *viz.* N^α-guanylhistamine (**85**; X = NH) and its isothiourea isostere (**85**; X = S). It was then found that potency could be enhanced by lengthening the side chain and a series of amidines was synthesized. These lacked specificity, however, since they were partial agonists. Attempts to remove the agonist component led to replacement of the strongly basic amidine group by nonbasic groups which, though polar, would not be charged, *e.g.* thiourea, and further lengthening of the side chain resulted in a marked increase in activity and provided the compound burimamide (**86a**; Table 20). The latter was shown to be a specific competitive antagonist of histamine at non-H$_1$ receptors, and thereby permitted the definition of histamine H$_2$ receptors.[54]

Burimamide was the first H$_2$ receptor antagonist to be examined in man but it was not considered sufficiently potent for therapeutic use. In an attempt to achieve a further increase in antagonist potency, attention was focused on the imidazole ring of burimamide, and the burimamide structure was modified so as to increase the equilibrium concentration of imidazole species considered most likely to be active. Replacing a methylene group (—CH$_2$—) with an isosteric sulfide (—S—) link in the side chain and substituting a methyl group in the ring furnished the more active compound metiamide (**86e**; Table 20).[150]

Metiamide was examined clinically but had to be abandoned when several cases of granulocytopenia were uncovered during trials. The possibility that this was associated with the presence of a thiourea group in metiamide led to the investigation of non-thiourea analogues. Returning to the guanidine derivatives, an alternative way was sought to reduce guanidine basicity. The basicity of guanidines is very susceptible to substituent effects and can be markedly reduced by substituting powerful electron-withdrawing groups at the nitrogen atoms. This approach was successful and the corresponding cyanoguanidine was synthesized and found to be a potent antagonist, comparable with metiamide, and was selected for development.[262] This compound is cimetidine (SK&F 92334; **86j**; Table 20) and contains the cyanoimino group (=N—CN) in place of the thione (=S) sulfur atom.[387]

Cimetidine was first marketed at the end of 1976 in the UK under the trademark Tagamet. It has since been introduced throughout the world and used extensively for the treatment of conditions

Table 20 Structures and H_2 Receptor Histamine Antagonist Activities of Burimamide, Metiamide, Cimetidine and some Isosteres[155,262]

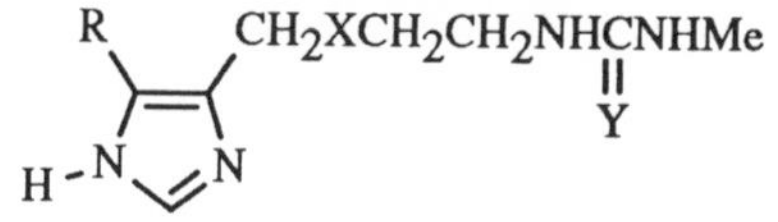

$$R \underset{H-N \diagdown N}{\overset{}{\diagup}} CH_2XCH_2CH_2NHCNHMe \overset{\|}{Y}$$

	Compound	R	X	Y	K_B^a (μM)	ID_{50}^b (μmol kg^{-1})
(86a)	Burimamide	H	CH_2	S	7.8	6.1
(86b)		H	O	S	28	23
(86c)		H	S	S	3.2	5.3
(86d)		Me	CH_2	S	8.9	24
(86e)	Metiamide	Me	S	S	0.92	1.6
(86f)		Me	S	O	22	27
(86g)		Me	S	NH_2^+	16	12
(86h)		Me	S	$NCONH_2$	7.1	7.7
(86i)		Me	S	$NCOCH=$	7.4	8.4
(86j)	Cimetidine	Me	S	NCN	0.79	1.4
(86k)		Me	S	NNO_2	1.4	2.1
(86l)	SK&F 92456	Me	S	$CHNO_2$	1.4	1.0

^{a} Inhibition of histamine stimulation of the rate of beating of the guinea pig isolated right atrium. ^{b} Inhibition of near maximal histamine-stimulated gastric acid in the perfused stomach of the anaesthetized rat.

associated with gastric hyperacidity. Its use resulted in a therapeutic revolution for the medical management of duodenal ulcer disease. For several years it was the biggest selling single prescription product (by US dollar world-volume of sales).

Five years after the introduction of cimetidine, a second H_2 antagonist was marketed (in 1981). This was ranitidine (Zantac), a non-imidazole compound discovered at Glaxo Laboratories (see below). It too enjoyed widespread use and eventually (1988) became the biggest selling prescription product, displacing cimetidine to second place.

It was not until 1985/87 that other H_2 antagonists were marketed. These are famotidine, nizatidine and roxatidine (see below).

12.5.13.2 General Structural Types of H_2 Antagonists

The highly successful development of cimetidine as an H_2 receptor histamine antagonist stimulated a search for other more potent examples from this pharmacological class of agent, and many other compounds have since been described. Early structure–activity studies of cimetidine and analogues drew attention to the apparent special significance of the following structural features of which cimetidine was a representative example (*e.g.* see ref. 265): (i) an imidazole ring or similar nitrogen heterocycle; (ii) a flexible chain, especially —$CH_2SCH_2CH_2$—; and (iii) a planar π-electron group which is very 'polar' and has potential for strong H bonding (both as acceptor and donor), and contains the system —NH—C—NH—.

Subsequent investigations in many laboratories have provided examples of other structural features and expanded considerably the scope for active structures. Indeed, there is now a considerable diversity in the chemistry of active H_2 receptor histamine antagonists. It is convenient to divide compounds into two main structural classes, *viz*: (1) compounds containing a flexible connecting chain; and (2) diaryl structures.

Compounds with structures containing a flexible connecting chain are represented by the general formula in Figure 21, *i.e.* comprising an 'aromatic ring', a 'flexible chain' and a 'polar hydrogen-bonding group'. The compounds are grouped conveniently into four main types according to the archetypal member of the group, namely: cimetidine (imidazolylalkyl compounds and analogues), tiotidine (guanidinothiazoles), ranitidine (dimethylaminomethylfurans and analogues) and lamtidine (piperidinomethylphenoxypropyl derivatives). These are shown, with some examples,

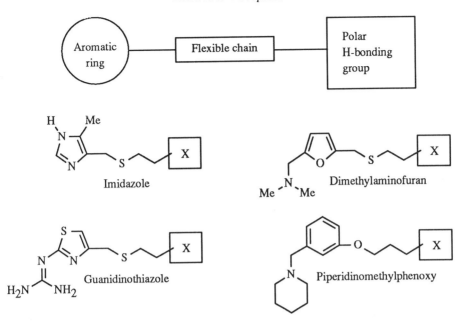

Figure 21 General formula of H_2 receptor histamine antagonists containing a flexible connecting chain; there are four main types of structure according to the archetypal drug and the aromatic ring

respectively in Tables 21, 23, 24, 27–29 and 33–37 and are discussed in the respective Sections 12.5.13.3–12.5.13.8.

Compounds exemplifying diaryl structures are mifentidine and zaltidine, and these are discussed in Section 12.5.13.10 (Table 30).

12.5.13.3 Structure–Activity Relationships for the Polar Hydrogen-bonding Group in Cimetidine Analogues

The similar behaviour of cimetidine and metiamide as H_2 receptor histamine antagonists, and the close similarity in physicochemical characteristics of thiourea and cyanoguanidine (Table 21), permit the description of the thiourea and cyanoguanidine groups in the present context as bioisosteres.[262] The equi-effectiveness of cyanoguanidine and thiourea groups in H_2 receptor antagonists was also demonstrated by the close parallelism for a series of imidazole derivatives in which the thioureas and corresponding cyanoguanidine antagonists were compared.[262] The extent of chemical isosterism is strikingly illustrated by the almost identical molecular arrangements found in crystal structures of metiamide and cimetidine.

Many other potential thiourea replacement groups have been examined. In structure–activity analyses of the H_2 receptor histamine antagonists, physicochemical properties such as acidity, hydrophilicity, dipole moment and geometry have been emphasized. Thiourea, urea, guanidine, cyanoguanidine, nitroguanidine and cyclic acylguanidines comprise the variable structural units of a small homogeneous group of compounds ($Y = S$, O, NH_2^+, $N—CN$, $N—NO_2$ and $N—CO$) which provide the basis for analysis of physicochemical properties in relation to biological activity.[262,381,388] In Table 21 are listed some properties of these moieties.

All these molecules are planar π-electron systems with similar geometries, *e.g.* equal $C—N$ bond distances and bond angles. They are also weakly amphoteric, *i.e.* both weakly acidic and weakly basic with similar pK_a values so that at pH 7.4 they are un-ionized. These molecules are all polar and hydrophilic, with high dipole moments (μ), and low octanol–water partition coefficients (P). However, the partition coefficient of urea is even lower than that of thiourea, cyanoguanidine or nitroguanidine, and it is also much more water soluble. Thus, it appears that urea is considerably more hydrophilic than either thiourea or cyanoguanidine and this may account for the weaker activity of urea structures as antagonists.

In addition to the example of urea just discussed, early structure–activity studies had suggested that among the hydrophilic structures, potency as H_2 receptor antagonists appeared to be inversely related to hydrophilicity. Later, a correlation was found between antagonist activity and the

Table 21 Comparison of some Physicochemical Properties of Thiourea, Cyanoguanidine, Nitroguanidine, 1,1-Diamino-2-nitroethene and Isocytosine

	R	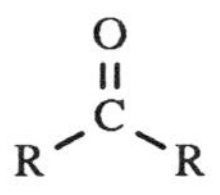 Urea $R{-}N{-}C({=}O){-}N{-}R$	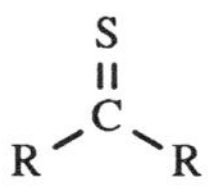 Thiourea $R{-}N{-}C({=}S){-}N{-}R$	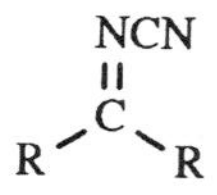 Cyanoguanidine $R{-}N{-}C({=}NCN){-}N{-}R$	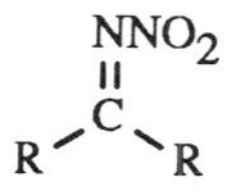 Nitroguanidine $R{-}N{-}C({=}NNO_2){-}N{-}R$	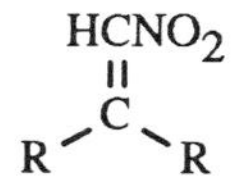 Diaminonitroethene $R{-}N{-}C({=}CHNO_2){-}N{-}R$	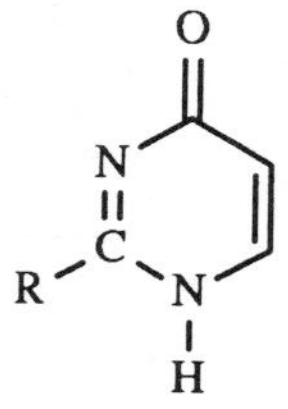 Isocytosine
Proton dissociation (weakly amphoteric)							
pK_a (acid) proton lost (at 25 °C)	NH$_2$	13.7[a]	15[g]	14[i]	12.2[n]	14[d]	9.6[s]
	NHMe						
pK_a (base) proton gained (at 25 °C)	NH$_2$	−0.15[b]	−1.2[h]	−0.4[j]	−0.93[o]	2.7[d]	4.0[s]
	NHMe		−1.3[h]				
Polarity							
Dipole moment, μ (Debye)	NH$_2$	4.56[c]	4.89[c]	8.16[k]	6.95[p]	7.64[q]	
	NMe$_2$	3.50[t,u]	4.65[t]				
Partition (octanol:H$_2$O log P (at 37 °C)	NH$_2$	−1.66[d]	−1.05[d]	−1.15[d]	−0.89[d]	−1.28[d]	−0.97[d]
	NMe$_2$			−0.4[d]			
	NHMe	−0.96[d]	−0.24[d]		−0.71[d]		
Solubility (H$_2$O) S_i (at 25 °C)	NH$_2$	20 M[e]	2.2 M[e]	0.5 M[e]			
Geometry (planar)							
Restricted C—N bond							
Rotation ΔG (kcal mol^{-1}; 1 kcal = 4.18 kJ)	NHMe	~7.5[f]	11.8[f]	12.4[l]	10.9[m]	11.8[q], <10[q,r]	
	NMe$_2$			9.2[m]		10.7(C=C)[q,r]	

[a] Ref. 402. [b] Ref. 403. [c] Dioxane, ref. 404. [d] Ref. 405. [e] Ref. 406. [f] Ref. 407. [g] Ref. 408. [h] Ref. 409. [i] Ref. 410. [j] Ref. 411. [k] Ref. 412. [l] McCarty and Wieland;[414] although the authors ascribe the barrier to that of C = N inversion, it is more probably due to C—N rotation. [m] Ref. 415. [n] Ref. 416. [o] Ref. 417. [p] Ref. 418. [q] Rotational barriers refer to respectively, C—N (11.8), C—N' (< 10), and C=C (10.7). [r] Ref. 419. [s] Ref. 420; in benzene. [u] Ref. 421; in dioxane.

octanol–water partition of the variable structural unit (HY) for a series of 10 closely related structures (Figure 22) containing the (5-methylimidazol-4-yl)methylthioethyl group attached to a 1,3-amidine NH system, formally uncharged at pH 7.4. In this correlation a 10-fold increase in P brought about a 100-fold increase in antagonist potency, according to equation (2), where K_B is the apparent dissociation constant for the drug-receptor complex determined *in vitro* against histamine-stimulated increase in the rate of beating of the guinea pig right atrium, and P is the incremental octanol–water partition coefficient for the group HY.

$$- \log K_B = 2.0 \log P + 7.4 \qquad (2)$$

From equation (2) it was argued that isosteric replacement of $N—NO_2$ in nitroguanidine, by $CH—NO_2$, should reduce H-bonding ability and therefore reduce the degree of aqueous solvation (*i.e.* render the molecule less hydrophilic), and hence increase potency. The 1,1-diamino-2-nitroethene group (in **86**; $Y = CHNO_2$, $R = Me$) was selected after consideration of pK_a values and proton equilibria.[388] This led to the first introduction of a diaminonitroethene group into a drug structure. In the event, it was shown that the diaminonitroethene (SK&F 92456; **86l**) was not more potent than cimetidine, but approximately equi-active (Table 20). Studies by octanol–water partition indicated that the chemical reasoning was oversimplified and that the diaminonitroethene group was in fact more hydrophilic than nitroguanidine (Table 21).

The diaminonitroethene (**86l**; Table 20) was anomalous, however, in being approximately 30 times more active than predicted by equation (2), indicating that some property other than that represented by the lipophilicity parameter was making a marked contribution to activity. Since the various groups in these structures are all highly polar, this led to an investigation of the group dipole moments.[390,394]

The dipole moments of various model compounds were measured[391,392] but no correlation was obtained with biological activity. It appeared likely, however, that dipole orientation might be of importance and CNDO/2 and MNDO molecular orbital calculations were carried out to provide estimates of both dipole moment and orientation (Table 22).[393] The result was a very significant correlation between dipole orientation, octanol/water partition (P) and activity (K_B; equation 3) for 13 compounds which extended over three orders of magnitude (Figure 23). It has been speculated therefore that for the cyanoguanidine and related polar groups the strength of their hydrogen-bonding interaction with the receptor is determined by the dipole's ability to align with the receptor.[394] In equation (3) the angle θ is defined as the difference between the orientation (ψ) of the dipole with respect to the terminal C—N bond in the side chain (Figure 24) and a proposed optimum angle of $30°$ (*i.e.* $\theta = 30 - \psi$), K_B and P are defined as for equation (2).

$$- \log K_B = 9.12 \cos \theta + 0.60 \log P - 2.71$$
$$n = 13, \quad r = 0.91, \quad s = 0.41 \qquad (3)$$

The most active compound in the series is the nitropyrrole derivative (**87f**) whose dipole is orientated close to the optimum of $30°$, and it is also the least hydrophilic antagonist. In addition, the structurally different squaramide (**87m**) is well accommodated.

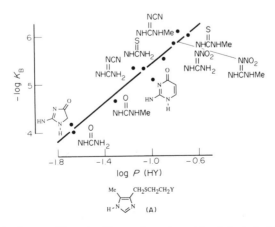

Figure 22 Apparent correlation between histamine H_2 receptor antagonist activity (pA_2 determined *in vitro* on guinea pig atrium) and octanol–water partition coefficient (log P) for the group HY in a limited series of imidazole-derived antagonists of structure (A). The least squares regression for the filled circles (●) has the equation (2): $- \log K_B = 2.0 \log P + 7.4$

Table 22　Physical Properties and H_2 Receptor Antagonist Activities of a Set of Cimetidine Analogues for a Correlation Study of Lipophilicity, Dipole Moments and Dipole Orientation[393-395]

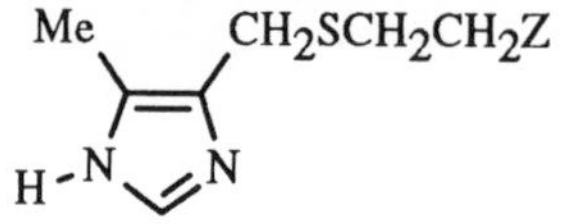

$$\text{Me} \qquad CH_2SCH_2CH_2Z$$

Compound	Z	Atrium $-\log K_B$	log P	$\psi°$	Cos θ (CNDO/2)	μ_x
(87a)	NCN ‖ NHCNHMe	6.10	0.40	13	0.96	4.56
(87b)	S ‖ NHCNHMe	6.04	0.55	0	0.87	3.42
(87c)	NNO_2 ‖ NHCNHMe	5.84	0.13	13	0.96	5.46
(87d)	$CHNO_2$ ‖ NHCNHMe	5.85	− 0.40	33	1.00	6.69
(87e)	O ‖ NHCNHMe	4.69	− 0.06	0	0.87	2.06
(87f)	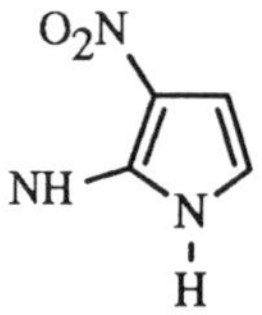 O_2N-nitropyrrole ring, NH	7.31	1.04	27	1.00	5.24
(87g)	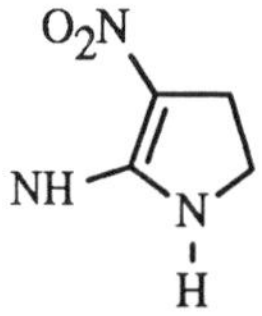 O_2N-nitrodihydropyrrole ring, NH	6.31	− 0.87	28	1.00	6.26
(87h)	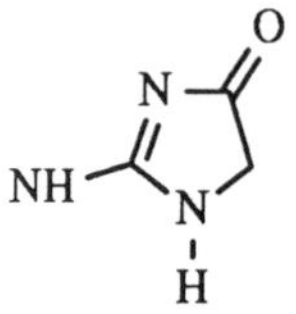 imidazolinone ring, NH	4.21	− 0.5	− 6	0.81	2.71
(87i)	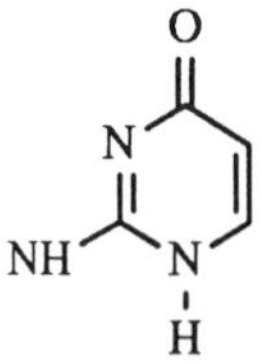 pyrimidinone ring, NH	5.13	0.02	2	0.88	4.89
(87j)	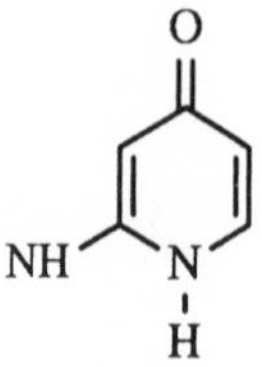 pyridinone ring, NH	4.80	0.8	− 5	0.82	2.59
(87k)	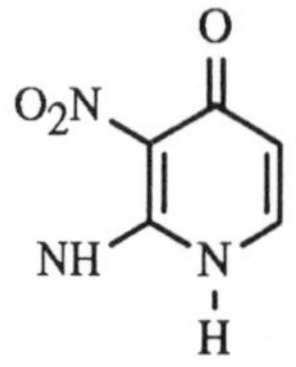 O_2N-nitropyridinone ring, NH	6.44	− 0.2	17	0.97	7.03

Table 22 *(Contd.)*

Compound	Z	Atrium $-\log K_B$	log P	$\psi°$	Cos θ (CNDO/2)	μ_x
(87l)		4.57	− 0.74	0	0.87	4.37
(87m)		4.23	− 0.08	− 15	0.71	0.78
(87n)		< 4.5	− 0.4	− 143		− 5.75
(87o)		< 4.0	0.79	− 82		− 3.86

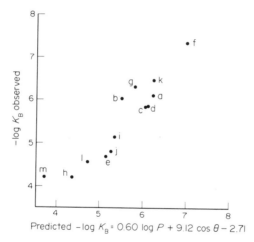

Figure 23 Comparison of observed (vertical axis) and predicted (horizontal axis; by equation 3) H_2 receptor histamine antagonist activities (− log K_B) for the series of antagonists (structures **87a–87o** in Table 22). Compounds **(87n)** and **(87o)** are too weakly active to be included on the plot

Another study[395] of the same set of compounds using MNDO optimized structures found a correlation with the dipole moment component μ_x directed along the N—H bond of the nitrogen atom bearing the (5-methylimidazol-4-yl)methylthioethyl chain, as given in equation (4). However, this correlation has involved a correlation to eight of the structures for the energy required to convert them into planar forms.

$$-\log K_B \;=\; 0.50\,\mu_x \;+\; 1.52\log P \;+\; 3.92$$

$$n \;=\; 13, \quad r \;=\; 0.89, \quad s \;=\; 0.65, \quad F \;=\; 18.8 \tag{4}$$

Interest in the dipolar property of these compounds promoted an investigation of analogues of cimetidine having zwitterionic groups (Table 23) as replacements for cyanoguanidine, for instance the amidinosulfonic acid **(88a)** and the 2-amino-3-hydroxypyridine **(88b)**, both of which are approximately equipotent with cimetidine in the guinea pig atrium.[396] Here, dipole orientation alone was

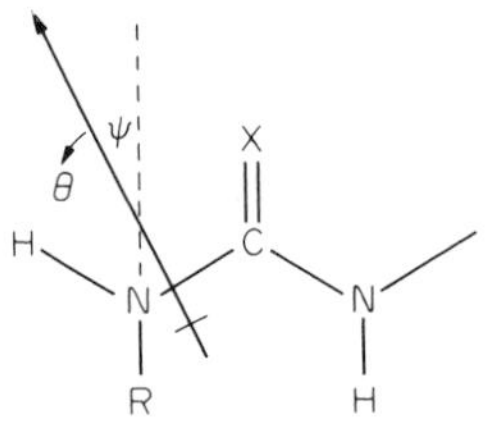

Figure 24 Definition of the orientation parameter, θ, *viz.*, the deviation from the optimal angle ψ of the dipole orientation with respect to the side chain N–R bond. The optimum for ψ was found to be 30°, and the ideal orientation would have $\theta = 0°$

found to be highly correlated with antagonist activity, corrected for ionization at pH 7.4, amongst those compounds having rigid dipoles, and again the optimum value of ψ was found to be 30° (equation 5).

$$-\log K_{B(corr.)} = 3.73 \cos\theta + 2.35 \qquad (5)$$

The importance of dipole orientation in both series has been interpreted in terms of an orientational factor whereby the dipole of the cyanoguanidine or replacement group is assisting in the establishment of hydrogen-bonded interactions of that group with the receptor.[394] It has been proposed that if the hydrogen-bonding contribution to receptor binding is given by equation (6), within these series of analogues the hydrogen-bonding potential might be similarly high and that most of the variance might be due to the orientational term, cos θ.

$$-\log K_B \alpha \, \Delta G_{H-bonding} \, \cos\theta \qquad (6)$$

The value of such a correlation study is that it may provide a model for considering the mode of action of antagonists, and for suggesting alternative structures for synthesis and testing. The active H_2 receptor histamine antagonists are all very polar molecules containing groups which may enter into strong hydrogen-bonding interactions. Charge delocalization within the polar group results in a dipole moment and also acidifies the NH functionalities, enhancing hydrogen-bonding ability, and it seems very likely that binding between antagonist molecules and the H_2 receptor involves powerful hydrogen bonding.

Within the limitations imposed by the selection of a series of compounds where close structural homogeneity is maintained, it appears from the initial correlation (equation 2) that activity depends on lipophilicity or is inversely related to hydrophilicity. Since these compounds were evaluated *in vitro*, partition is unlikely to represent an overall distribution property, although it could reflect access to the receptor. It is thought to be more probable, however, that partition represents a property or process concerned with receptor interaction, for example involving desolvation, *i.e.* a hydrophobic effect. That is, these very polar molecules would be strongly solvated by hydrogen bonding to surrounding water molecules and would have to dissociate themselves from the surrounding water-solvent shell in order to participate in hydrogen-bonding interactions with the receptor. A reduced hydrophilicity should reflect a greater readiness to desolvate from the water solvent.

In addition to lipophilicity (log P), differences in activity as H_2 receptor histamine antagonists are accounted for by dipole orientation with respect to the side chain. It seems probable, therefore, that the amidine-type moiety in this series of compounds has an orientational function rather than being involved in direct dipole–dipole or dipole–charge interactions at the receptor.

Since the orientation cos θ term in the equations (3) and (5) was defined by reference to the R—N bond (Figure 24), it can also be considered to relate to the N—H bond of the same nitrogen atom, suggesting a role for the R—NH group in hydrogen bonding to the H_2 receptor. Likewise, equation (4) relates μ_x to the same N—H bond.

Thus one may envisage that drug molecules in aqueous solution are in a water-solvent shell and have to undergo desolvation and align themselves through electrostatic interaction at a polar receptor. They then undergo hydrogen-bonding and dipolar interactions with the receptor, which presumably therefore take place in a nonaqueous environment.

Unlike cyanoguanidine, aminoheterocyclic groups such as 2-aminopyrimidin-4-one (isocytosine) and 2-amino-3-nitropyrrole offer the possibility for further substitution. This has been exploited to advantage in the former example, where substitution at the ring 5-position with lipophilic substituents led to large increases in H_2-antagonist activity,[397,398] *e.g.* in (**88d**) and oxmetidine

Table 23 H$_2$ Receptor Antagonist Activities of some Cimetidine Analogues determined *in vitro* on the Guinea pig Right Atrium

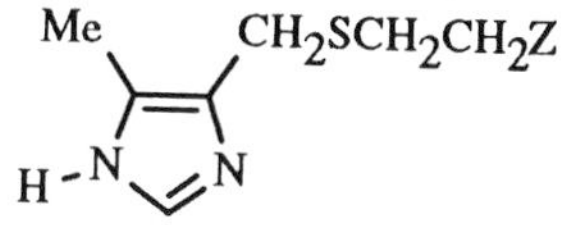

Compound	Z		Antagonist K_B (μM)	Ref.
(88a)	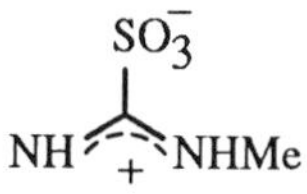		1.3	396
(88b)	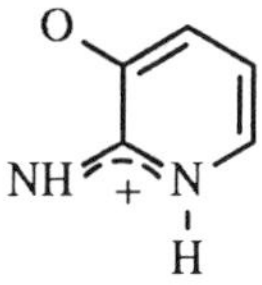		1.3	396
(88c) (88d) (88e)	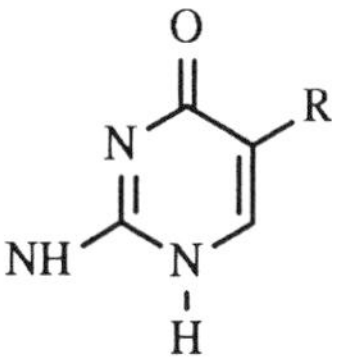	R = H R = CH$_2$Ph R = CH$_2$—	7.4 0.5 0.2	397 397 283
(88f) (88g)		R = H R = CH$_2$Ph	0.049 0.31	394
(88h)	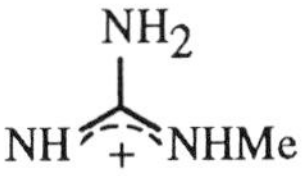		16	252
(88i)	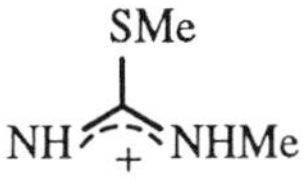		100	252

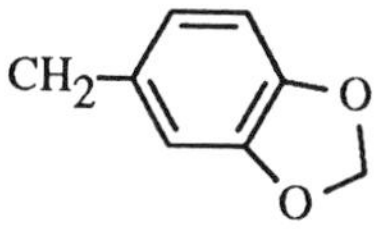

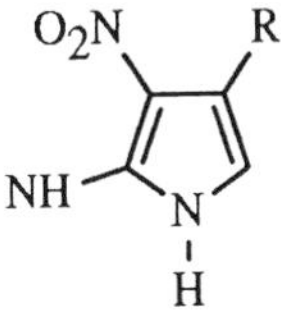

(**88e**; Table 23).[283] In these examples, the lipophilicities of the benzyl and methylenedioxybenzyl substituents appear to be optimal for activity.[398] Thus activity for 11 5-substituted compounds was correlated with a lipophilicity parameter R_m according to equation (7), where R_m is determined by thin layer chromatography. Analogues of similar or greater potency, however, have also been described having more polar substituents, and these findings have been rationalized in terms of an alternative model based on interaction of the 5-substituent with a putative arginine residue in the receptor.[399] Calculated energies of interaction (E) were correlated for 17 5-substituted compounds according to equation (8). Of particular value, substituents such as 3-picolinyl, (6-methyl-pyridin-3-yl)methyl and 4-methylpyridin-2-one were investigated in the cimetidine series and then applied to non-imidazole structures (see Section 12.5.13.7 and Table 19).

$$-\log K_B = 2.31\,R_m - 0.41\,(R_m)^2 + 3.81$$
$$n = 11, \quad r = 0.96, \quad s = 0.23, \quad F = 51.6 \tag{7}$$

$$-\log K_B = 0.55\,E + 4.81 \tag{8}$$
$$n = 17, \quad r = 0.94, \quad F = 116.7$$

Analogous substitution in the pyrrole ring 4-position of (88f; Table 23), however, failed to match the activity enhancements seen with the pyrimidinones and it appears, on the basis of spectroscopic evidence, that undesirable steric interactions take place between the 4-substituent and the nitro group.

In general it has been found that replacement of the cyanoguanidine group in cimetidine by basic groups such as isothiourea or guanidine give only weak antagonists,[252] *e.g.* (88h) and (88i; Table 23). However, introducing a second imidazolylalkyl group (89; Table 24) increases potency approximately 8–80-fold.[252] When the second group is imidazolylpropyl, however, a potent agonist results[250] *i.e.* impromidine (see Section 12.5.9.4). By contrast, analogous disubstitution of neutral groups such as thiourea or cyanoguanidine provides only a modest increase in antagonist potency.[400,401]

Large additional increases in potency can be achieved by linking two molecules of (88h) *via* a polymethylene chain giving (90), in which $n = 8$ appears to be an optimum alkane chain length for potency ($K_B = 8.5$ nM). By comparing the receptor affinities of partial structures it has been deduced that both of the imidazole rings and both of the guanidine groups are involved in specific interactions with the receptor.[253]

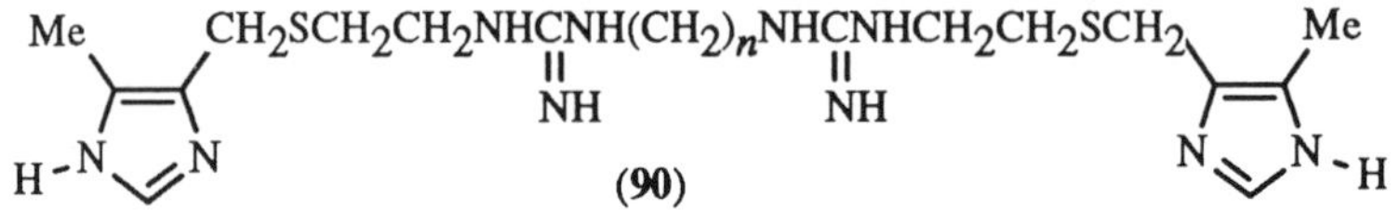

$$Me \diagdown \underset{H-N\diagup N}{\diagup} CH_2SCH_2CH_2NHCNH(CH_2)_nNHCNHCH_2CH_2SCH_2 \underset{N\diagdown N-H}{\diagup} Me$$
$$\overset{\|}{NH} \qquad \overset{\|}{NH}$$

(90)

12.5.13.4 Conformational Studies with Cimetidine and Analogues

Although differences in polarity and partition may account for the quantitative differences in antagonist potencies of cimetidine analogues, another important factor may be the difference in conformational behaviour of the 'polar hydrogen-bonding group'.

Thioureas, cyanoguanidines and isocytosines differ in the conformational preferences shown by N substituents (Figure 25). Of the four possible planar forms of N,N'-disubstituted thioureas and N,N'-disubstituted-N''-cyanoguanidines, only three conformations of thiourea structures such as metiamide (namely Z,Z, Z,E and E,Z) and two conformations of cyanoguanidine structures such as cimetidine (namely Z,E and E,Z) have been observed[381] by low temperature NMR spectroscopy in CD_3OD. The E,E form in both structures and the Z,Z form in cyanoguanidines are presumably disfavoured by steric interactions between the substituents. N-Substituted isocytosine can assume only the two planar forms corresponding to Z,Z and E,Z configurations. The E,Z conformation is unique in being the only conformation common to all these structures and, if it is assumed that a specific conformation of this group is associated with pharmacological activity in H_2 receptor antagonists, the E,Z conformation is the likely candidate. Furthermore, it is the preferred conformation for the very active aminonitroheterocycles, such as the aminonitropyrrole (87f).

Table 24 Bis-substituted Analogues of Cimetidine as H_2
Receptor Antagonists Determined *in vitro* on the Guinea
Pig Right Atrium[400,401]

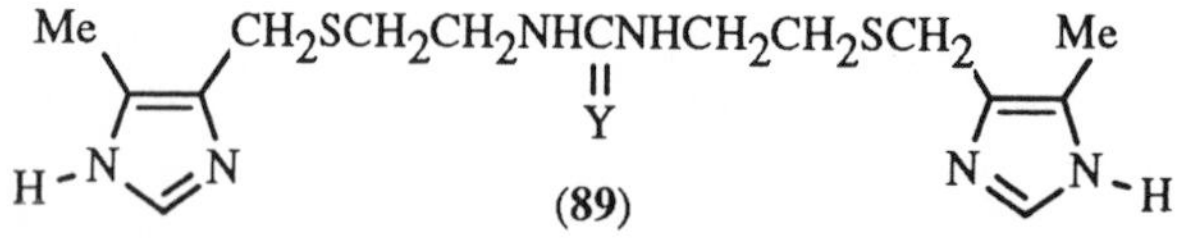

$$Me \diagdown \underset{H-N\diagup N}{\diagup} CH_2SCH_2CH_2NHCNHCH_2CH_2SCH_2 \underset{N\diagdown N-H}{\diagup} Me$$
$$\overset{\|}{Y}$$

(89)

Y	Antagonist K_B (μM)	
	(86)[a]	(89)
SMe$^+$	100	13.5
NH$_2^+$	16	0.21
O	22	2.7
S	0.92	0.68
NCN	0.79	0.22
CHNO$_2$	1.4	0.31

[a] For structure (86), see Table 20.

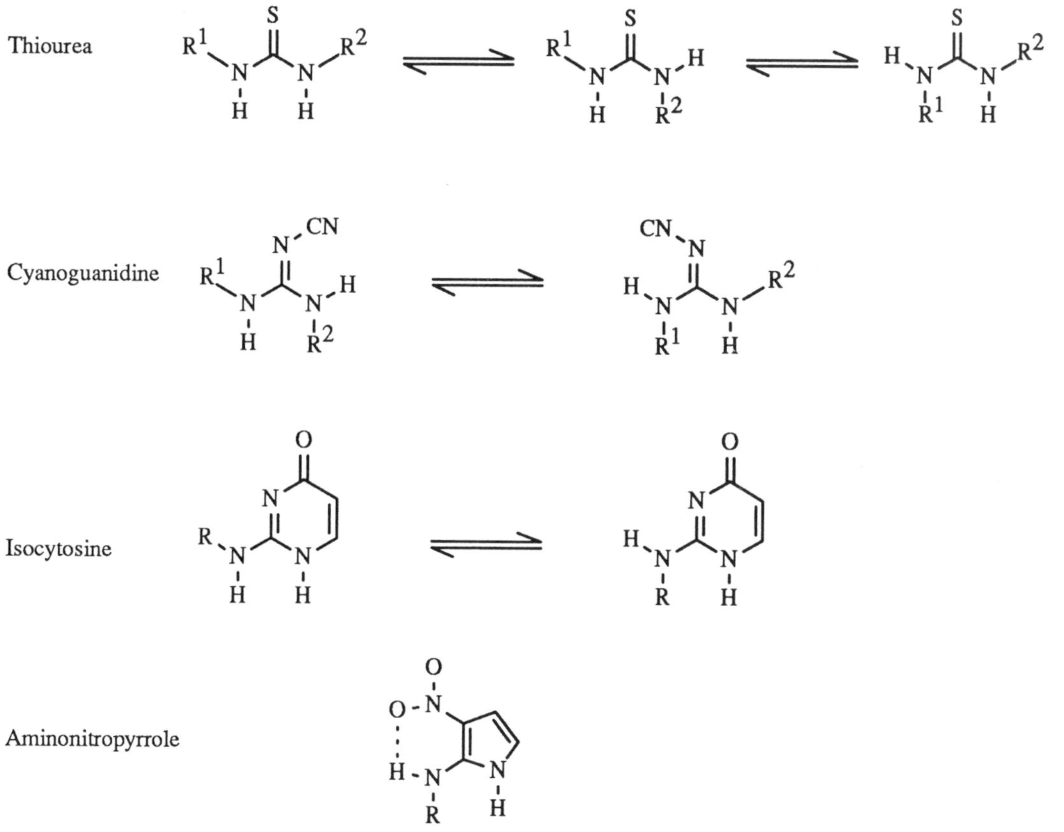

Figure 25 Planar conformations of N,N^1-disubstituted thioureas and N''-cyanoguanidines, N-substituted isocytosines and aminonitropyrroles

The importance of chain length in the antagonists raises the question of whether certain conformations may be associated with antagonist activity. The overall molecular conformation of the antagonist molecules is determined by the alkane side chain. Studies of metiamide and cimetidine in deuteromethanol solution by NMR spectroscopy indicate that the ethane grouping (—CH_2CH_2—) in the side chain is probably a statistical mixture of *gauche* and *trans* forms.[381] IR spectroscopic studies of solutions in bromoform indicate that mixtures of inter- and intramolecularly hydrogen-bonded species are formed.[423]

The structures of some antagonists have been studied by crystallography. In burimamide the molecules are linked together by a complex network of hydrogen bonds between the imidazole rings (NH$\cdots$N), and between the thiourea residues (NH$\cdots$S), but there are no thiourea–imidazole contacts and the alkyl chain is extended and approximately planar.[424] The crystal structures of metiamide and thiaburimamide differ from that of burimamide; the molecules are folded and there is an intramolecular NH$\cdots$N hydrogen bond from a thiourea NH to the imidazole N^π atom, forming a 10-membered ring in which the —CH_2CH_2— bond has the *trans* conformation.[425]

The molecular conformation of cimetidine is very similar to that adopted by metiamide and thiaburimamide, and a 10-membered ring is formed by an intramolecular NH$\cdots$N hydrogen bond from a cyanoguanidine NH to the imidazole N^π atom.[426] Indeed, the crystal structure is notable for its close similarity to that of metiamide. The cyanoguanidine groups are in an E,Z configuration and the lone electron pair on the imino nitrogen functions in the structure to form a N—H$\cdots$N hydrogen bond between pairs of cyanoguanidine groups, thus giving rise to a 12-membered ring system which closely resembles the eight-membered rings formed between pairs of thiourea groups in metiamide.[427]

An interesting relationship between the crystal structure and crystal stability has been demonstrated for these compounds, stability being correlated with increasing melting point and reduced aqueous solubility (Table 25).[425]

The above cimetidine structure is of crystals obtained from cyanomethane, but from aqueous solution it is possible to obtain a monohydrate.[428,429] In contrast to the anhydrous form there is no

Table 25 Physicochemical Properties of Burimamide, Metiamide, Cimetidine and some Isosteres. Arranged in Order of Increasing Melting Point and Decreasing Aqueous Solubility[425]

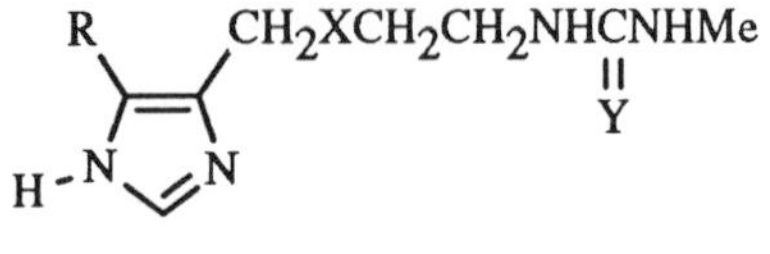

$$R \quad CH_2XCH_2CH_2NHCNHMe$$
$$\underset{H-N\diagdown N}{\diagup} \quad \quad \overset{||}{Y}$$

Compound	R	X	Y	M.p.[a] (°C)	Imidazole[b] pK_a (37°C)	log P^c (37°C)	Aqueous solubility[c] at 37°C (g L^{-1})	(M)
Thiaburimamide	H	S	S	98–99	6.47	0.15	70.4	0.306
Methylburimamide	Me	CH$_2$	S	110–112	8.08	0.98	25.4	0.112
Nitroguanidine isostere	Me	S	NNO$_2$	112–114	7.09[d]	0.18		
Burimamide	H	CH$_2$	S	128–129	7.51	0.4	14.7	0.069
Cimetidine	Me	S	NCN	141–143	7.09	0.4	11.4	0.045
Metiamide	Me	S	S	152–154	7.09	0.5	3.2	0.013
Urea isostere	Me	S	O	158–159	7.09[d]	−0.06		
Oxaburimamide	H	O	S		6.2[e]	−0.30		

[a] Ref. 262. [b] pK_a determined potentiometrically by M.J. Graham. [c] Log$P$ ($C_{octanol}/C_{H_2O}$) and aqueous solubility determined by R.C. Mitchell; see ref. 425. [d] Ring pK_a not measured; assigned by analogy with metiamide and cimetidine. [e] Ring pK_a not measured; assigned by analogy with 4-methoxymethylimidazole (determined by M. J. Graham).

intramolecular hydrogen bond in cimetidine hydrate but the molecule is still folded; hydrogen bonding to a water molecule links the imidazole and cyanoguanidine ends of the molecule, and the conformations about all the bonds in the side chain are *gauche*.

Replacement of CH$_2$ by S in burimamide was made initially as an 'isosteric' substitution which would modify the electronic properties of the side chain; however, it was pointed out that the replacement may slightly lengthen the chain and increase conformational flexibility.[150] The crystal structures and IR studies provide evidence for the formation of a cyclic intramolecularly hydrogen-bonded conformation in these compounds with a sulfide side chain. It is interesting that a 10-membered ring should form and one must consider that this may contribute to the greater activity of these molecules. It is not known whether the molecule has to achieve this configuration in order to be biologically active, or whether the sulfide link simply functions to increase molecular flexibility in a way that is biologically advantageous. Thus, in addition to the electronic effects, it is likely that conformational effects of the sulfide linkage also contribute to the activity of these compounds as histamine antagonists. It is remarkable how many potent non-imidazole H$_2$ antagonists identified for potential clinical development retain the sulfide link.

Attempts to improve the H$_2$ antagonist activities of metiamide and cimetidine by structurally modifying the flexible chains have been unsuccessful. Chain branching[430,431,444] at any of the carbon atoms as well as replacement of the sulfide sulfur atom by other heteroatom linkages[435,436] all led to considerable losses of activity. Incorporation of a ring structure between imidazole and the thiourea or cyanoguanidine groups using tropane,[434] or a phenylene system[432] (see Section 12.5.13.11 and Table 31), or tetrahydrobenzimidazole[433] was similarly unsuccessful, resulting, at best, in very weakly active compounds.

12.5.13.5 Heterocyclic Analogues of Cimetidine

The effectiveness of analogues of cimetidine as H$_2$ antagonists is very sensitive to the nature of the substituents in the imidazole ring. As described elsewhere,[150] manipulation of the burimamide structure led to analogues of both higher and lower H$_2$ antagonist activity, and a comparison of their ionic and tautomeric properties prompted the suggestion that the neutral N$^\tau$—H form of the imidazole ring, which corresponds to the preferred form of imidazole in histamine under the same conditions (see Section 12.5.6.2), is required for effective interaction with the H$_2$ receptor. The predominating imidazole species of cimetidine or metiamide in aqueous solution at pH 7.4 is the N$^\tau$—H form, which accounts for about 54% of all imidazole species.

Although substituent effects on activity are primarily electronic, the size of the R group in the imidazole 4(5)-position is also important, *e.g.* the 4(5)-chloro analogue of metiamide is equipotent with metiamide.[437] Methylthio was predicted[438] to give a good compromise between steric and electronic effects and the cyanoguanidine analogue of this compound was subsequently reported[439] to be approximately four times more active than cimetidine *in vitro*.

The imidazole ring in metiamide and its analogues is not an essential requirement for H_2 antagonist activity and can be successfully replaced by other heterocycles (Table 26). Reasonable levels of activity can be maintained provided that a pyridine-type nitrogen is retained in the position adjacent to the methylthioethyl side chain,[438] for example by replacing imidazole by pyridine, thiazole or isothiazole.[97,155,400] An exception to this generalization, however, is the oxazole derivative CRC 1970 (Table 26), in which the side chain is attached to the ring 5-position, adjacent to oxygen, and it is claimed that its activity is comparable with cimetidine.[440] Retention of only the imidazole ring NH function in cimetidine and metiamide by replacing imidazole by 2- or 3-substituted indoles, however, led to only weak antagonists.[441]

Pyridine has proved to be an especially useful replacement for imidazole in allowing possibilities for subsequent ring substitution. In the 2-pyridyl analogue of cimetidine, small substituents at the pyridyl 3-position were found to be well tolerated, and even enhanced activity, while large groups

Table 26 Some Heterocyclic Analogues of Cimetidine as H_2 Receptor Antagonists[400,440,441]

$$Het-CH_2SCH_2CH_2NHCNHMe$$
$$\overset{\|}{Y}$$

Het	Y	Guinea pig atrium in vitro K_B (μM)	Rat gastric secretion in vivo ID_{50} ($\mu mol\,kg^{-1}$)
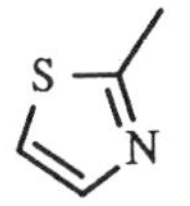	S	1.0	1.3
	NCN	0.71	2.6
	$CHNO_2$	1.1	0.8
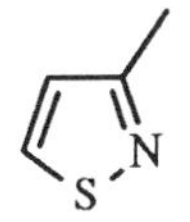	S	2.3	3.0
	NCN	0.71	1.6
	$CHNO_2$	0.62	0.6
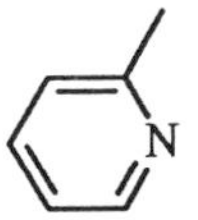	S	1.9	13
	NCN	0.93	9
	$CHNO_2$	2.2	3.1
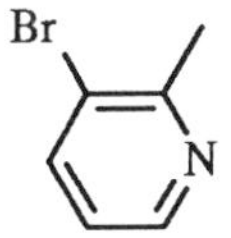	S	1.2	2.3
	NCN	0.22	2.4
	$CHNO_2$	0.85	1.4
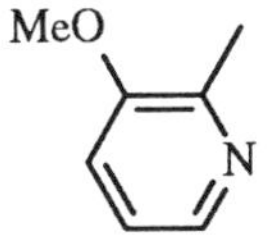	NCN	0.21	
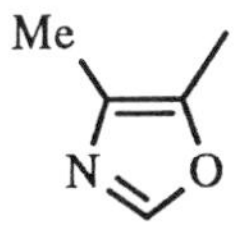	NCN^a	0.55	
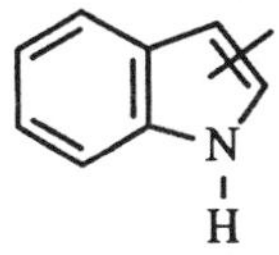	NCN^b	'Weak'	

[a] CRC 1970. [b] Side chain attached at indole 2- or 3-position.

reduced activity. As in the imidazole analogues, there appeared to be an optimum size for substituents at the pyridine 3-position which might be explained in terms of stabilization of a particular side chain conformation for effective interaction with the H_2 receptor. Analogues which contain a substituted 2-aminopyrimidin-4-one (isocytosine) moiety in place of cyanoguanidine are of particular interest in providing[363] some very potent antagonists of histamine at not only the H_2 but also the H_1 receptors (see Section 12.5.12.7), *e.g.* icotidine and Figure 19.

12.5.13.6   Tiotidine and Related Compounds

Tiotidine (**92a**; ICI 125211; Table 27) is the direct analogue of cimetidine in which the methyl-imidazole ring is replaced by a guanidinothiazole group of similar basicity.[442] This compound is considerably more potent than cimetidine by a factor of about 20–30-fold *in vitro* in the guinea pig right atrium.[443] Because of its unprecedented *in vitro* activity, tiotidine was the first H_2 antagonist to be useful in radioligand binding studies[90] (Section 12.5.5.7; Table 3).

The guanidinothiazole moiety appears to account for much of the H_2 receptor affinity of the tiotidine molecule, as demonstrated[443] by the activity of the derivative ICI 17148 (Table 27), which has $K_B = 3.6$ μM. Numerous guanidinothiazole derivatives have subsequently been prepared, many of which exhibit moderate to high H_2 antagonist activities (examples in Table 27).

Structure–activity relationships amongst these derivatives differ somewhat from those observed in analogues of cimetidine. For example, methylation at the thiazole 5-position (**93**; Table 27), in

Table 27   Tiotidine and Related Guanidinothiazoles as H_2 Receptor Antagonists Determined *in vitro* on the Guinea Pig Right Atrium

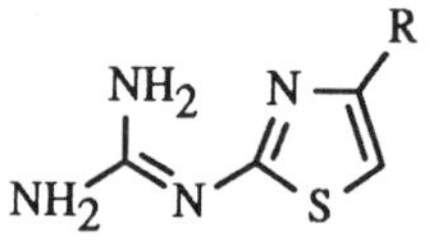

Compound		R	K_B (μM)	*Ref.*
(**92a**)	Tiotidine[a]	$CH_2SCH_2CH_2NHCNHMe$ $\parallel$ NCN	0.018	442
(**92b**)	ICI 17148	Me	3.6	443
(**92c**)	Famotidine[b]	$CH_2SCH_2CH_2CNH_2$ $\parallel$ NSO_2NH_2	0.017	446
(**92d**)	BL 6341A	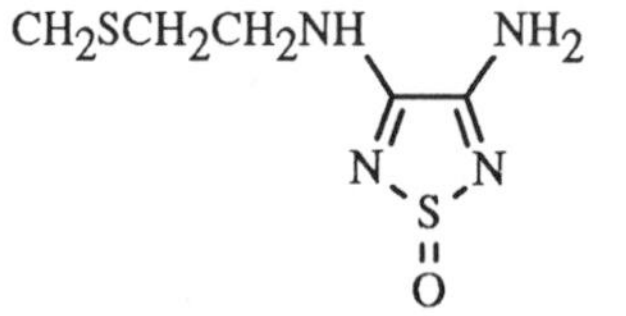	0.027 0.007	447 448
(**93**)			0.10	443
(**94**)[c]				449 465

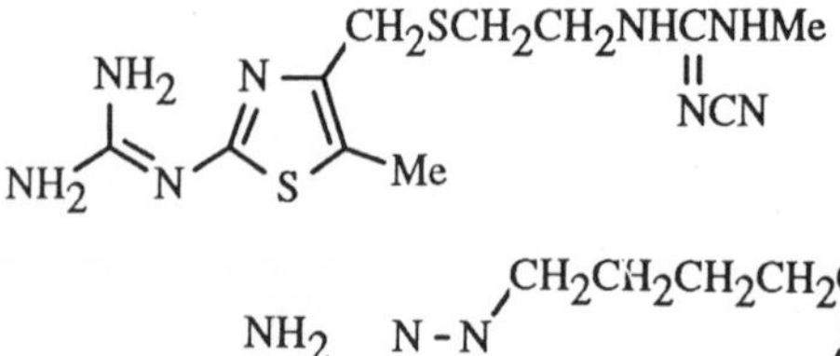

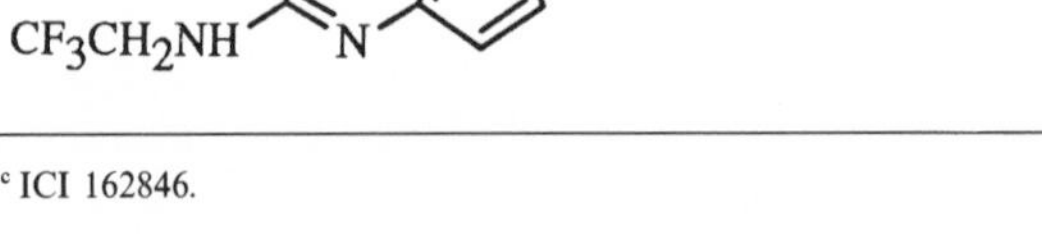

[a] ICI 125211. [b] YM 11170. [c] ICI 162846.

contrast with that at the corresponding imidazole 5(4)-position, led to a reduction in antagonist activity,[443] suggesting that the spatial disposition of the two rings differ at the receptor. Extensive patent coverage suggests that the thiazole ring in tiotidine and related compounds can be replaced by a variety of alternative heterocycles, including pyridine and pyrazole, in which a pyridine-type nitrogen is positioned *ortho* to both points of substitution (*e.g.* **94**).

The scope for replacement of the cyanoguanidine group in tiotidine is wide by comparison with cimetidine. The most successful replacements are essentially planar groups with the potential for participating in dipolar and hydrogen-bonding interactions with the receptor,[443] and include aminoheterocycles through to simple amides and basic amidine moieties (examples in Tables 27 and 36). There is also a degree of tolerance to modification of the flexible 4-membered chain not found in cimetidine. For example, the 1,3-phenylene analogue (**108a**; Table 30) of tiotidine is reported to be very active.[443]

Physicochemical studies have shown[466] that the guanidinothiazole moiety exists predominantly in the tautomer shown in structure (**95**) and that there is evidence for the formation of an intramolecular hydrogen bond between the ring nitrogen and a guanidine NH, which, it has been suggested,[443] might be present in aqueous solution. This hydrogen-bonded species has been considered to be relevant to the biological activity of its derivatives.

(**95**)

12.5.13.7 Ranitidine and Related Compounds

The discovery of ranitidine demonstrated that a nitrogen heterocycle was not a necessary structural feature for an H_2 receptor antagonist, but that the nitrogen functionality could be exocyclic. In ranitidine (**96a**; Table 28) the methylimidazole ring of cimetidine is replaced by the dimethylaminomethyl-substituted furan ring, while the cyanoguanidine is replaced by the 1,1-di-amino-2-nitroethene group found in the cimetidine analogue SK&F 92456 (Table 21). Ranitidine is some 4–10 times more potent than cimetidine.[450]

Structure–activity patterns amongst ranitidine analogues again appear to differ from those in the cimetidine series.[451,461] For instance, the thiourea (**96b**) and cyanoguanidine (**96c**) analogues of ranitidine are reported to be less active than metiamide or cimetidine in inhibiting histamine-stimulated gastric acid secretion in the rat.[451] Moreover, substitution of a methyl group at the furan ring 3-position (**97a**) in ranitidine appears to substantially reduce activity[451] in contrast to its beneficial effect in the analogous 4(5)-position of imidazole in cimetidine analogues, although the isomeric 4-methyl derivative (**97b**) of ranitidine was active (Table 28). These findings, together with the observation[455] that introducing a dimethylaminomethyl group at the imidazole 2-position of cimetidine results in a loss of activity, suggest[400] that the furan and imidazole rings are not behaving as simple isosteres, in which O replaces N. The dimethylamino group in ranitidine with a pK_a of 8.44 at 25 °C is a stronger base than the imidazole ring in the cimetidine but the similar H_2 antagonist activity of the less basic trifluoroethylamino analogue (**98**) of ranitidine suggests that these compounds probably act in their neutral forms.

As with tiotidine, extensive efforts have been made to exploit the structural novelty of ranitidine as a lead in the quest for potent, new antagonists. Thus, for example, replacement of the furan ring of ranitidine by thiazole led to nizatidine (**99**), which is reported[452] to be some 5–18 times as potent as cimetidine.

A combination of the furanyl system of ranitidine with the 5-substituted aminopyrimidinone moiety utilized in icotidine (Table 19) resulted[453,454] in the very potent H_2 antagonists, lupitidine (**100a**) and donetidine (**100b**). Lupitidine has a K_B value of 17 nM after 60 min equilibration, in the histamine-stimulated guinea pig right atrium, and an extended duration for its antisecretory effect in the dog and man compared with ranitidine.

Use of the diamino-1,2,5-thiadiazole system (**101**) as a replacement for the diaminonitroethene in ranitidine also increases potency. The discovery of the value of this replacement was made almost simultaneously by chemists at Merck Sharpe and Dohme and Bristol Laboratories.[447,448]

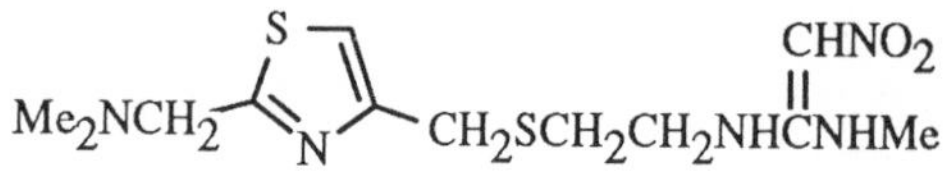

Me$_2$NCH$_2$—[thiazole, S, N]—CH$_2$SCH$_2$CH$_2$NHCNHMe (with CHNO$_2$ group)

(99) Nizatidine

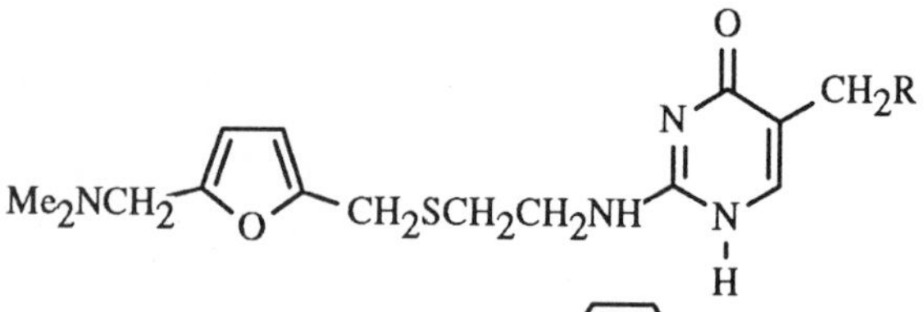

Me$_2$NCH$_2$—[furan, O]—CH$_2$SCH$_2$CH$_2$NH—[pyrimidinone ring with CH$_2$R, N, N—H, O]

(100a) Lupitidine; R = —[pyridine, N]—Me

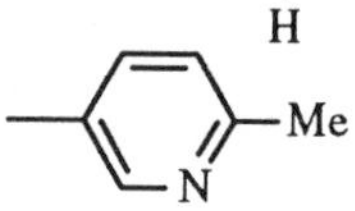

(100b) Donetidine; R = —[pyridinone, N—H, O]

Me$_2$NCH$_2$—[furan, O]—CH$_2$SCH$_2$CH$_2$NH—[thiadiazole ring, N—S(=O)—N, NH$_2$]

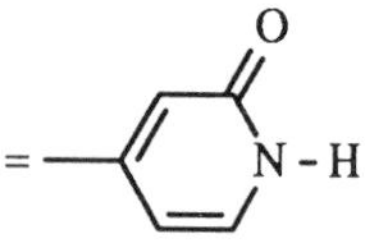

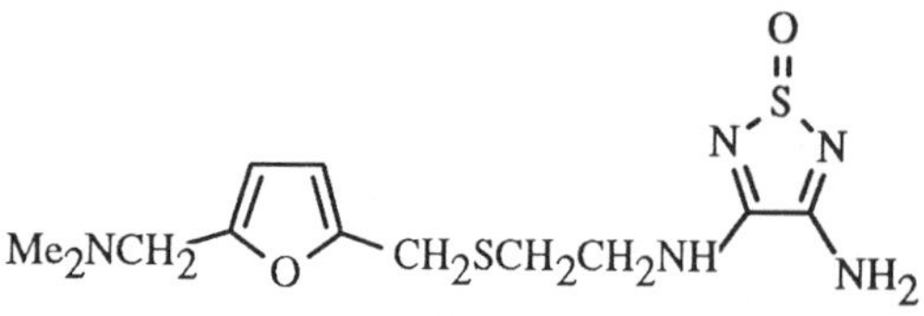

(101)

12.5.13.8 Lamtidine and Related Aminomethylphenoxy Derivatives

Further evolution of the ranitidine structure led to placing the furanyl oxygen into an exocyclic situation as in phenoxy, and to replacing dimethylamino by piperidino. The particular combination, piperidinomethylphenoxypropyl has provided some very potent antagonists (Table 29).

Lamtidine (**102a**) and loxtidine (**102b**) are two of the original examples which are not only significantly more potent than ranitidine, but also display extended antisecretory effects in the dog.[456,457] In addition, lamtidine has been shown to produce insurmountable antagonism of histamine-induced chronotropy in the guinea pig atrium.[456] The duration of antisecretory activity of these compounds appears to be remarkably sensitive to structural modification of the piperidino group.[457,458,462] For example, the dimethylamino analogue of lamtidine has a similar potency and time course to ranitidine.

The scope for structural modification to or replacement of the aminotriazole terminal group in these antagonists, like that in tiotidine, is apparently very wide.[462] Again, the most effective groups are planar, hydrogen-bonding moieties, which possess at least one NH function, and include amides and aminoheterocycles. One example of particular interest is zolantidine (**103a**), a potent H$_2$ antagonist which, unlike the previously described H$_2$ antagonists, can cross the blood–brain barrier

Table 28 Ranitidine and some Analogues as H$_2$ Receptor Antagonists Determined *in vivo* as Inhibitors of Histamine-stimulated Gastric Acid Secretion in the Anaesthetized Rat[451]

Compound	ID_{50} (mg kg^{-1})
Me$_2$NCH$_2$—[furan, O]—CH$_2$SCH$_2$CH$_2$NHCNHMe (with Y group)	
(**96a**) Ranitidine[a]; Y = CHNO$_2$	0.18
(**96b**) Y = S	2.32
(**96c**) Y = NCN	1.39
R^4, R^3 — Me$_2$NCH$_2$—[furan, O]—CH$_2$SCH$_2$CH$_2$NHCNHMe (with CHNO$_2$)	
(**97a**) R^3 = Me, R^4 = H	> 10
(**97b**) R^3 = H, R^4 = Me	0.25
(**98**) CF$_3$CH$_2$NHCH$_2$—[furan, O]—CH$_2$SCH$_2$CH$_2$NHCNHMe (with CHNO$_2$)	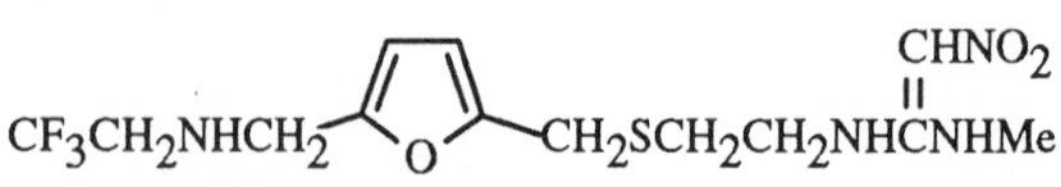 0.30

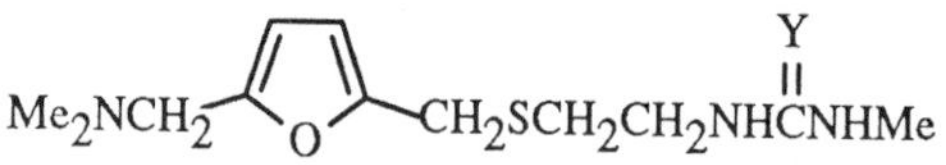

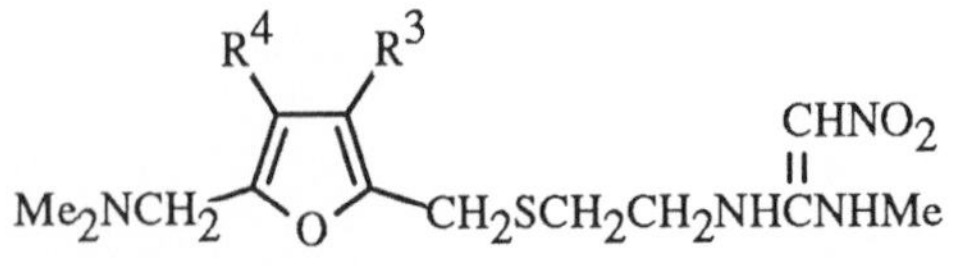

[a] AH 19065.

Table 29 3-(Piperidinomethyl)phenoxypropyl Derivatives as H_2 Receptor Antagonists Determined *in vitro* on the Guinea Pig Right Atrium

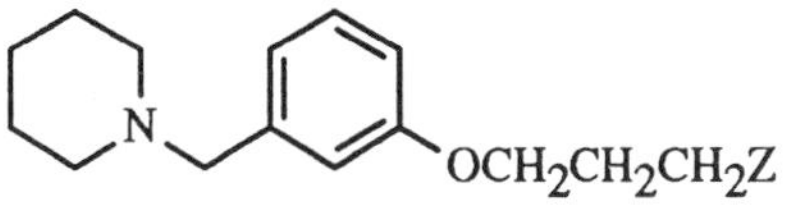

OCH$_2$CH$_2$CH$_2$Z

Compound		Z		K_B (μM)	Ref.
(102a)	Lamtidine[a]	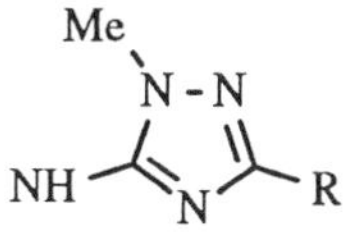	R = NH$_2$	0.07	456
(102b)	Loxtidine[b]		R = CH$_2$OH	n.c.[e]	457
(103a)	Zolantidine[c]	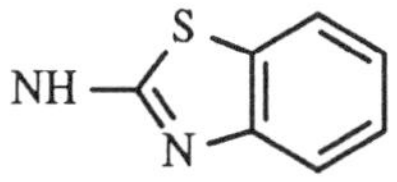		0.035	459
(103b)	Roxatidine[d]	NHCOCH$_2$OCOMe		0.11	463
(103c)	BMY 25368	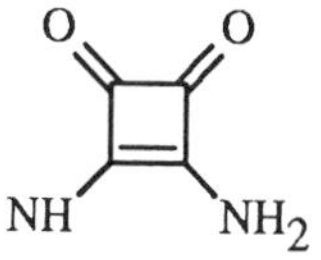		0.013	460
(103d)	BMY 25260	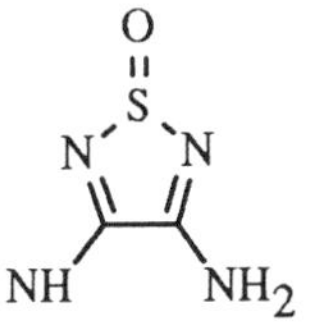		0.04	447
	L643661			0.02	448

[a] AH 22216. [b] AH 23844. [c] SK&F 95282. [d] TZU 0460, Roxatidine acetate, Pifatidine, Aceroxatidine, Hoe-760. [e] N.c. = non competitive.

(see Section 12.5.13.11).[459] Some other examples which have been selected for development as potential therapeutic agents (Tables 29 and 35) are roxatidine (**103b**), BMY 25368 (**103c**) and BMY 25260 (L 643661; **103d**). The latter acts as an apparent irreversible antagonist[464] but here too, structural modification to the piperidino group markedly changes the duration of action.[460]

12.5.13.9 Nonheterocycles in Place of Imidazole

Effective replacements for imidazole in cimetidine and related compounds are not limited to groups which incorporate aromatic rings. Comparison of the selective H_2 receptor agonist dimaprit with histamine suggests that the isothioureidomethyl moiety may be functionally equivalent to imidazole, and when introduced as a replacement for imidazole in burimamide resulted in a weak antagonist.[467] The homologue was more active ($K_B = 7$ μM; **104**; $n = 6$). In an extension to this approach a much more potent antagonist (**105**), which contains an isoureido group, was prepared[467] ($K_B = 0.063$ μM). These results emphasize the symmetrical element in H_2 receptor antagonist

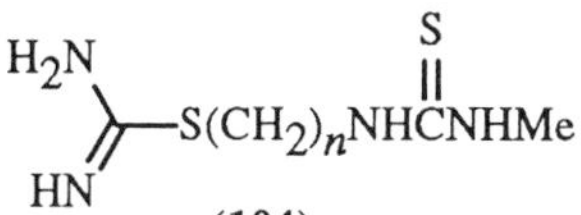

(104)

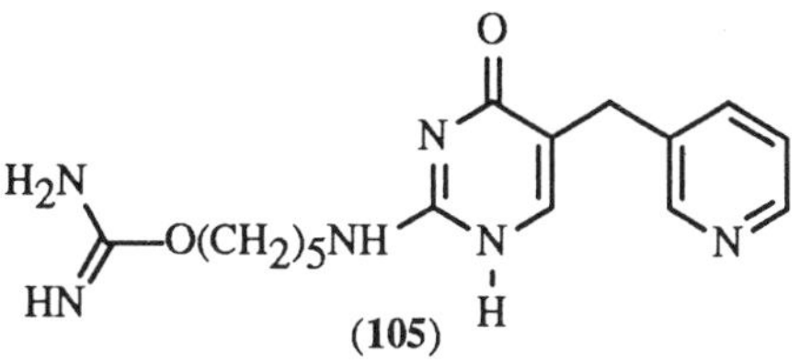

(105)

structures in that cimetidine has an amidine function at each end of the molecule present as partial structures of the imidazole ring and cyanoguanidine moieties. Bisisothiouroniumalkylguanidines (**68**) have also been examined[263] as nonheterocyclic analogues of impromidine (Section 12.5.9.4).

12.5.13.10 Diaryl Structures

Not all H_2 receptor antagonists can be considered as descendants of the first clinically effective compound, metiamide. In an original approach, Lipinski and coworkers took histamine as their starting point and introduced replacements for the imidazole ring and terminal amino group based on their bioequivalence in other drug series.[468] Thus, replacement of the amino group by a 4-substituted imidazole to give a symmetrical bisimidazolylalkane, followed by replacement of one imidazole ring by an aminotriazole moiety, led to the novel compounds (**106**; Table 30) of which (**106c**) is a slightly more potent H_2 antagonist ($K_B = 0.24$ μM) than cimetidine.

Although these compounds bear little structural resemblance to cimetidine, they are reported to share similar physicochemical properties to the extent that both molecules will be predominantly uncharged at pH 7.4 and their octanol/water distribution coefficients are similar. No definite conclusion could be made about whether (**106c**) and cimetidine share common receptor binding sites, although on comparing internitrogen distances, it was suggested that (**106c**) might bind to sites in the receptor which recognize one of the *trans* conformations of histamine. This approach was developed further and the minimum structural features defined for this type of antagonist.[469] An

Table 30 Diaryl Structures as H_2 Receptor Antagonists Determined *in vitro* on the Guinea Pig Right Atrium

Compound			K_B (μM)	Ref.
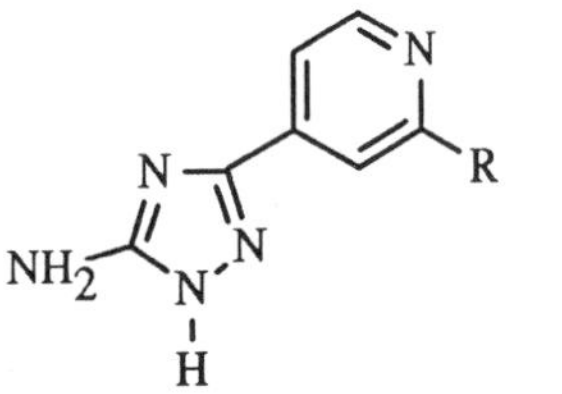	(**106a**)	R = H	42	468
	(**106b**)	R = NH$_2$	2.2	
	(**106c**)	R = NHEt	0.24	
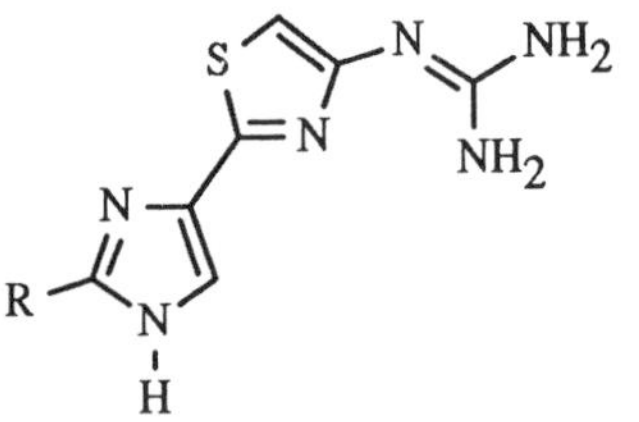	(**107a**)	R = H	0.10	470
	(**107b**)[a]	R = Me[a]	0.018	
	(**107c**)	R = NH$_2$	0.013	
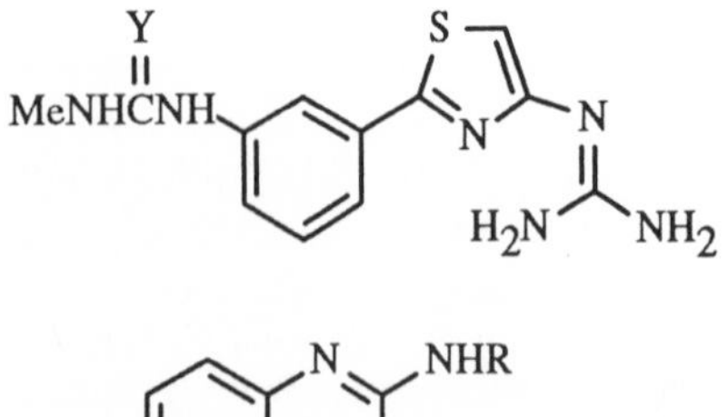	(**108a**)	Y = NCN	0.002 / 0.014	443 / 446
	(**108b**)	Y = S	0.008	443
	(**108c**)	Y = CHNO$_2$	0.001	443
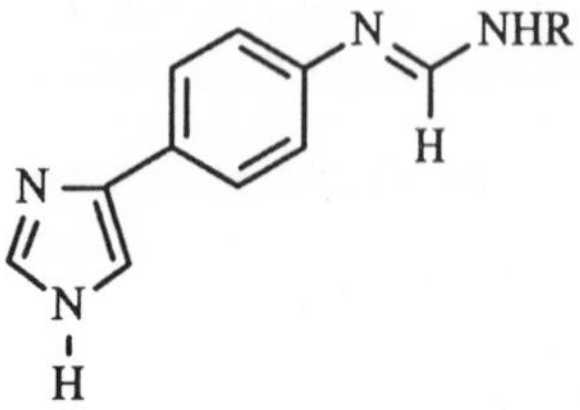	(**109a**)	R = H	30	471
	(**109b**)	R = Me	1.2	
	(**109c**)	R = Et	0.019	
	(**109d**)	R = Pr^n	0.032	
	(**109e**)[b]	R = Pr^i	0.024	
	(**109f**)	R = Bu^t	0.017	

[a] Zaltidine, CP 57,361-1. [b] Mifentidine, DA 4577.

attempt to correlate receptor affinities with a lipophilicity parameter for a series in which R = NH-alkyl or NH(CH$_2$)$_n$-aryl in (**106**) was unsuccessful.

In progressing to (**106**) *via* the symmetrical bisimidazole structures, ambiguity had been introduced, making any direct comparison with histamine uncertain. On subsequent replacement of the aminopyridine group in (**106**) by the 5-[(dimethylamino)methyl]furan or guanidinothiazole moieties found in ranitidine and tiotidine, encouraging levels of H$_2$ antagonist activity were obtained, suggesting that the pyridine fragment was acting as a histamine imidazole replacement. Further replacement of the aminotriazole group by a substituted imidazole ring afforded[470] a potent antagonist, zaltidine (**107b**; Table 30). This structure should also be considered in comparison with the *m*-phenylene analogues (**108**) of tiotidine and with mifentidine (**109e**).

In their approach, Donetti and coworkers[471] began with the weak H$_2$-receptor partial agonist, N^{α}-guanylhistamine (**85**; X = NH) in the search for novel H$_2$ antagonists. It was reasoned that a greater separation between the agonist and antagonist properties of this compound might be achieved by introducing a degree of rigidity into the molecule, and a phenyl ring, which might also offer increased receptor binding, was chosen for that purpose. This identified an area for chemical exploration, namely, 4(5)-phenylimidazoles (**110**) substituted in the phenyl moiety by guanidine or amidine groups.[477]

(**110**)

$$R^1 = -N{=}\overset{NH_2}{\underset{}{C}}NHR^2, \quad -N{=}\overset{NHR^2}{\underset{}{C}}H, \quad -\overset{NH}{\underset{}{C}}NHR^2$$

$$R^2 = H \text{ or } Me$$

The resulting compounds varied widely in their H$_2$ antagonist properties. Significant antagonist activity was found only among the *meta*-substituted guanidine and benzamidine derivatives, and in the *para*-substituted formamidine compounds. Moreover, the latter (**109**; Table 30) were very sensitive to the size of the terminal alkyl moiety, R, with K_B values ranging from 30 μM for R = H to 17 nM for R = Bu^t. Mifentidine (R = Pr^i) was reported[471] to be 20–50 times as potent as cimetidine *in vivo* and *in vitro*, which is comparable with tiotidine. This compound was considered initially to be acting in its positively charged form (protonated in the amidine group) because of its pK_a of 8.88 and also due to inactivity of some weakly basic analogues, and that such a species might bind to an anionic site in the H$_2$ receptor through electrostatic and hydrogen-bonded interactions.[472] However, the K_B values of mifentidine compared at different pH values indicated that the biologically active species as probably the uncharged form,[473] and this view was later supported by studies on *N*-fluoroethyl-substituted derivatives.[476]

By comparing the effects of bioisosteric replacements for imidazole in mifentidine, it was inferred that the imidazole moiety plays a different role in binding to the H$_2$ receptor from that in cimetidine.[474] Further structural modification of these compounds by replacement of the imidazole ring by a *meta*-substituted guanidinothiazole moiety, and replacement of the terminal isopropyl group whose activity at best only approached that of mifentidine.[474, 475]

Other diaryl derivatives have been studied as conformationally restricted analogues of cimetidine and ranitidine and these are discussed in the next section.

12.5.13.11 Comparisons Between Different Structural Types of H$_2$ Antagonist

While H$_2$ receptor histamine antagonists have become the subject of numerous structure–activity studies, comparisons have largely been made within, rather than between, the different known structural types. Superficially, ranitidine, tiotidine and cimetidine can be considered to be structurally analogous to the extent that they all consist of a moderately basic group attached to a polar, potentially hydrogen-bonding group by a flexible four-atom chain.[438,446] The possibility that the polar group might engage in hydrogen-bonding interactions with the H$_2$ receptor has already been discussed for cimetidine and tiotidine analogues, and it is probable that these groups bind to the same site. Whether the basic moieties in these three compounds function in a similar manner and interact with a common site in the receptor is more open to speculation.

Although the unprotonated form has been assumed to be the biologically active species in each case, the high degree of flexibility of the linking chain makes any analysis of the juxtaposition of binding sites for the two groups in these compounds extremely difficult. Clues as to the spatial disposition of the binding sites for tiotidine analogues are found in conformationally restricted analogues such as (108a) and (111)–(113) (Table 31) in which the thiourea or cyanoguanidine groups have an 'anti' relationship.[443]

Replacement of the flexible four-atom chain in cimetidine and ranitidine by a *m*-phenylene unit to give (114) and (115) leads to abolition of H_2 antagonist activity,[432,443] although the closely related analogues (116) and (117) exhibit activities similar to cimetidine *in vitro* (but these latter contain higher affinity 'hydrogen-bonding groups').[432,459]

These results appear to support the notion of a common binding site for the basic moieties in cimetidine, ranitidine and tiotidine, but suggest that the ability of these compounds to act as ligands is highly dependent upon molecular geometry, as would be expected. A correlation study, based on interaction energies calculated using a monopole bond polarizability method, suggests that a glutamate anion in the receptor is a potential binding site for the basic aryl groups.[478]

Another difference between these three antagonist types is the scope for structural modification in the 'polar hydrogen-bonding group'. Whilst amongst analogues of cimetidine there appears to be a fairly narrow range of structures for polar groups and linking chains for effective antagonist activity, the corresponding range is somewhat broader for ranitidine analogues and broader still for tiotidine analogues. Clearly, there is some degree of cooperativity operating between the two terminal groups in these compounds.

12.5.13.12 Brain-penetrating H_2 Antagonists

A large body of evidence exists to support the proposal that histamine has a physiological function in brain.[69,479] For many years the investigation of a possible role for central histamine H_2

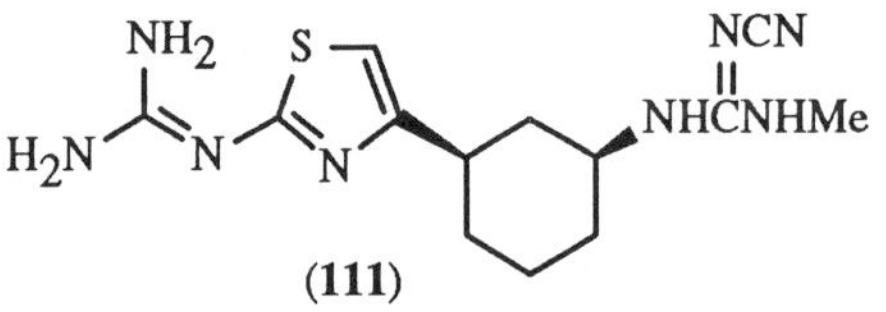

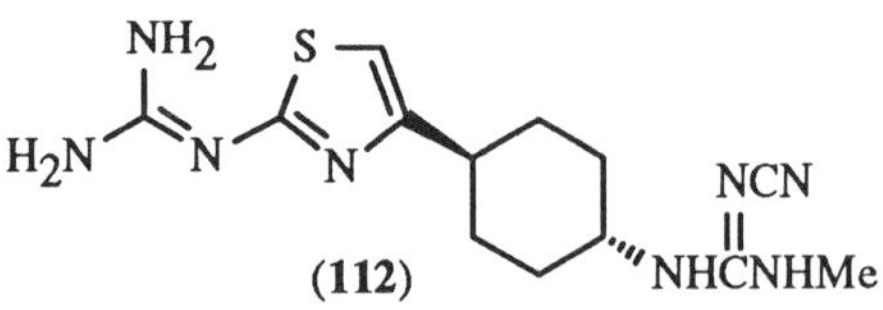

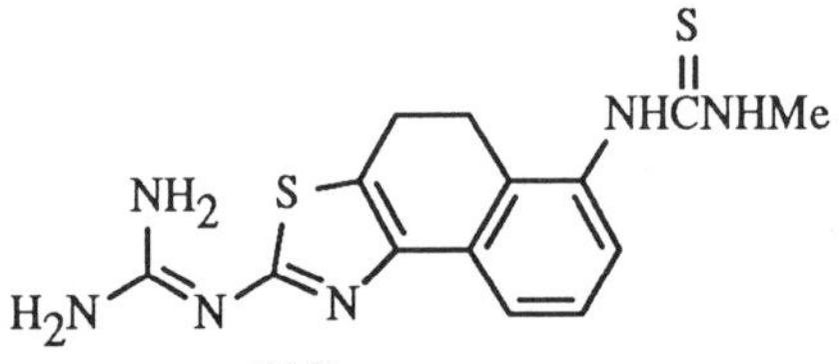

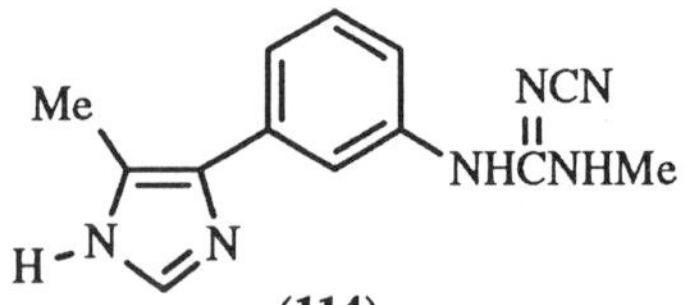

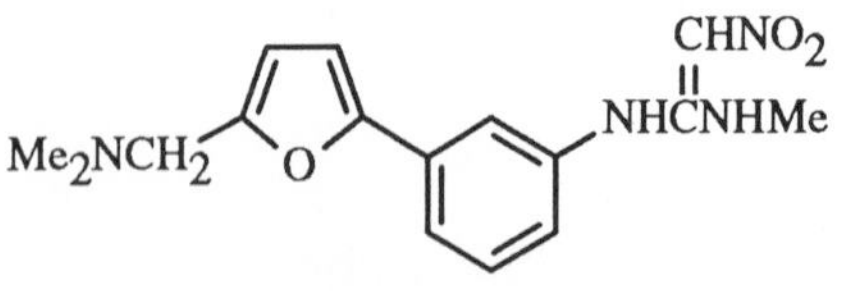

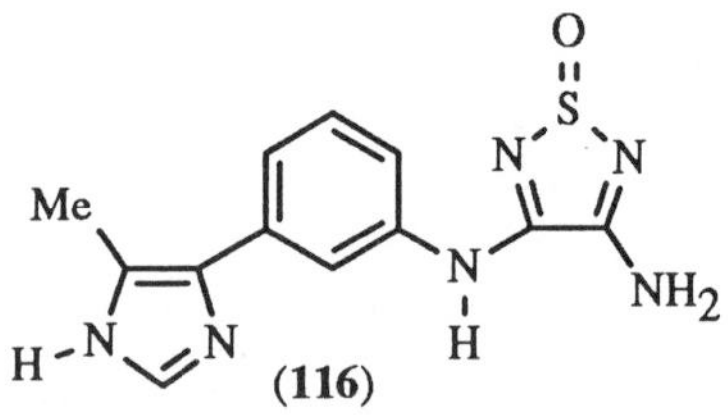

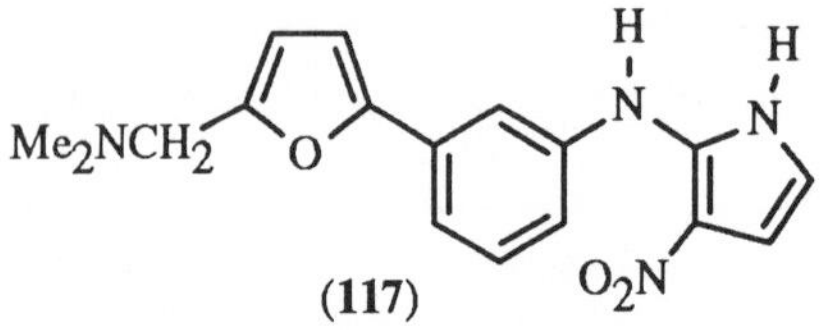

Table 31 Some Conformationally Restricted Analogues of Tiotidine, Cimetidine and Ranitidine, Investigated as H_2 Receptor Antagonists

receptors had been limited by the lack of an antagonist possessing the required combination of potency, selectivity and ability to cross the blood–brain barrier in sufficiently high concentrations. In attempting to overcome this problem, Young *et al.* designed new H_2 antagonists, using physicochemical properties as a guide to promote their passive diffusion into the brain.[459]

The rate and extent of entry of a compound into the brain are generally considered to be determined primarily by partition coefficient, ionization constant(s), and molecular size but no single partition solvent system has emerged as a universally applicable model for brain penetration, although the octanol/water system has received particular attention, and Hansch and coworkers have suggested[480,481] that a partition coefficient in this system of about 100 is optimal for entry into the CNS. Comparisons between known H_2 antagonists, however, suggest that there is no such simple relationship between their brain penetration and octanol/water partition coefficients.[459]

In seeking a physicochemical model to serve as a guide for increasing the partitioning of H_2 antagonists across the blood–brain barrier, Young *et al.* compared[459] the equilibrium brain/blood concentration ratios of a set of six radiolabelled compounds measured in anaesthetized rats, with their physicochemical properties (Figure 26). Three of these compounds were H_2 receptor antagonists having high octanol–water partition coefficients (*P*) greater than 100 (icotidine, lupitidine and **118**), and three were compounds known to readily enter the brain (clonidine, mepyramine and imipramine).

Regression analysis of the data revealed no significant relationship between brain penetration and the logarithm of the partition coefficients for the neutral forms of the compounds, measured in the octanol/water, chloroform/water or cyclohexane/water systems, or with molecular weight. However, a highly significant correlation was obtained with the $\Delta \log P$ term (equation 9) which accounts for some 93% of the variance in the brain penetration data and extends over four orders of magnitude. The $\Delta \log P$ parameter for a compound is an additive–constitutive term, defined (equation 10) as the difference between its octanol/water and cyclohexane/water $\log P$ values, and is related to the hydrogen-bonding ability of a compound as shown in (equation 11), where I_H denotes the additive increment to hydrogen bonding from molecular fragments, defined by Seiler,[482] and *b* is a constant.

$$\log(C_{\text{brain}}/C_{\text{blood}}) = -0.60\Delta\log P + 1.23 \qquad (9)$$

$$\Delta\log P = \log P_{\text{oct}} - \log P_{\text{cyh}} \qquad (10)$$

$$\Delta\log P = \Sigma I_H - b \qquad (11)$$

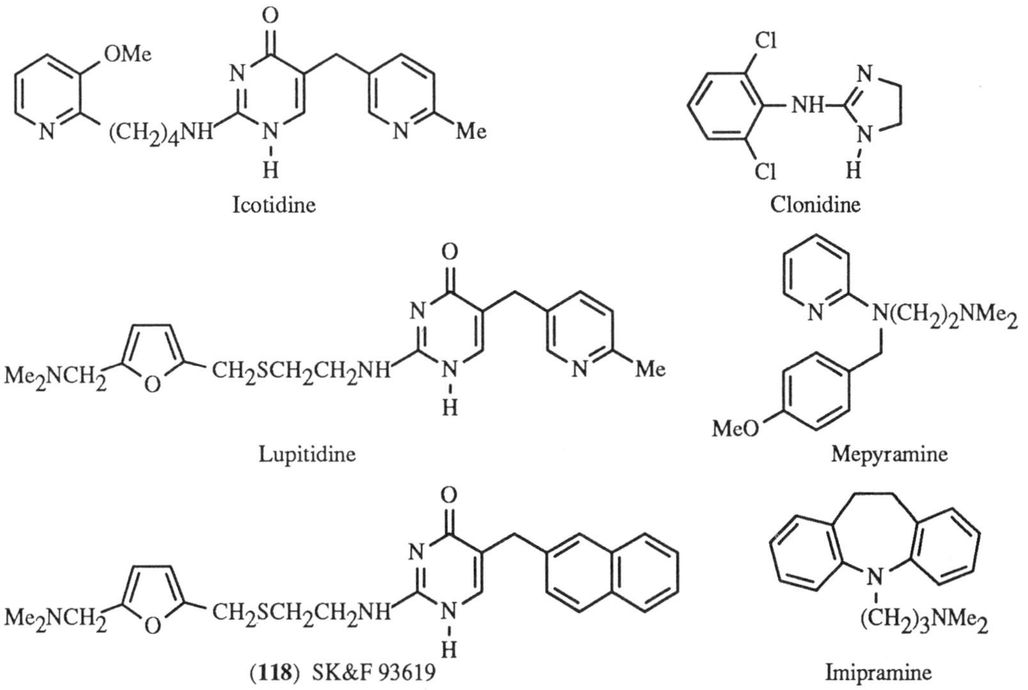

Icotidine

Clonidine

Lupitidine

Mepyramine

(118) SK&F 93619

Imipramine

Figure 26 Six compounds initially studied for brain penetration by measuring the equilibrium brain/blood concentration ratios of radiolabelled drug in the anaesthetized rat

Thus, equation (9) suggests that brain penetration might be increased by decreasing the overall hydrogen-bonding ability of a compound. Using this model as a guide, the scope was explored for reducing the effective hydrogen-bonding abilities of different structural types of H_2 antagonists by encouraging intramolecular hydrogen bonding, sterically hindering hydrogen-bonding groups and by removing polar groups not considered essential for antagonists activity.[459]

The archetypal drugs, cimetidine, tiotidine and ranitidine, are all very hydrophilic compounds which do not readily cross the blood–brain barrier (Table 32). For cimetidine, it is possible to replace

Table 32　Brain Penetration Data and Activities of some H_2 Receptor Antagonists Studied for the Design of Zolantidine[459]

Compound		$\dfrac{C_{brain}}{C_{blood}}$	$\Delta \log P$	Atrium K_B (µM)
Cimetidine		0.038		0.79
Tiotidine		0.152		0.018
Ranitidine		0.059		0.089
(119)	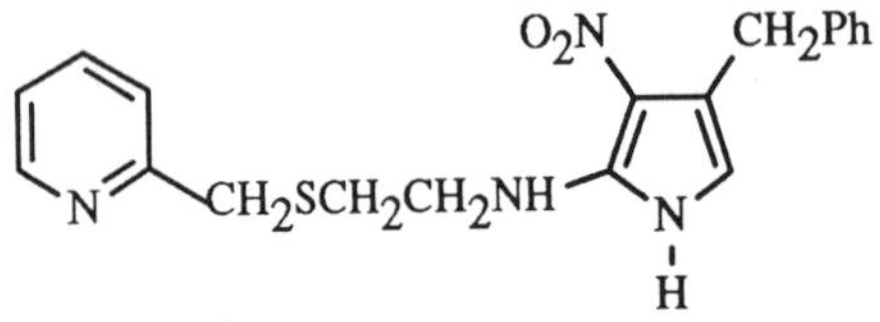	0.75		0.11
(120) 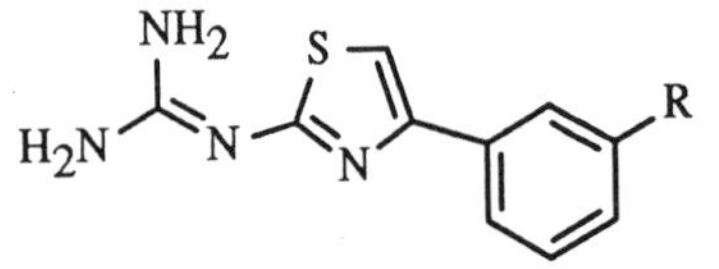	$R = NHCNHMe$ (NCN)	0.29	4.26	0.015
(121)	$R = H$	0.510	3.92	1.17
(122)	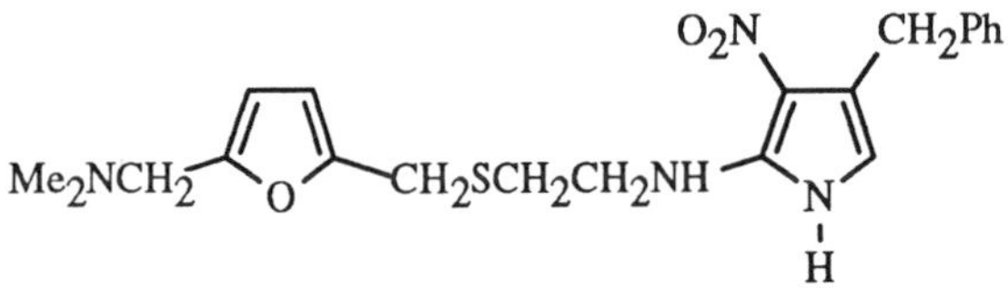	0.184	2.54	0.45
(123)	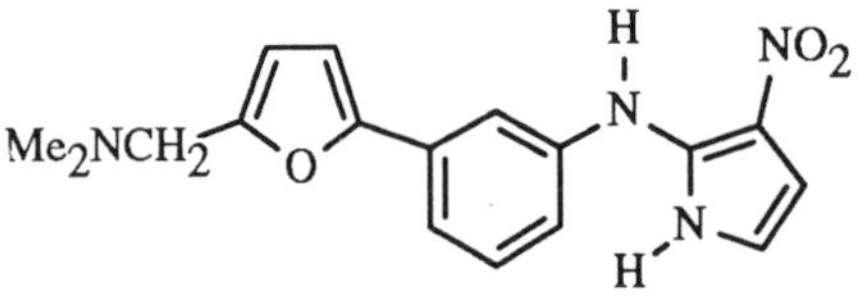	0.545	2.88	0.95
(124)	$R = NHCOMe$	0.346	1.93	0.016
(125)	$R = NHSO_2Me$			21.4
(126)	$R = OH$	0.947	1.47	0.19
(127)	$R = NHPh$			2.00
(128)	$R = NH$ 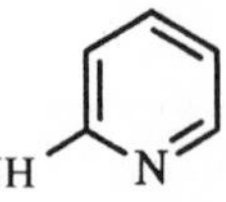 (2-pyridyl)	4.85	1.06	0.81
(129)[a]	$R = NH$ 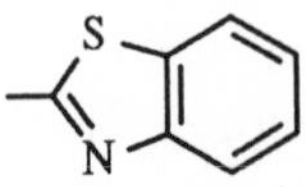 (benzothiazol-2-yl)	1.38	1.69	0.035

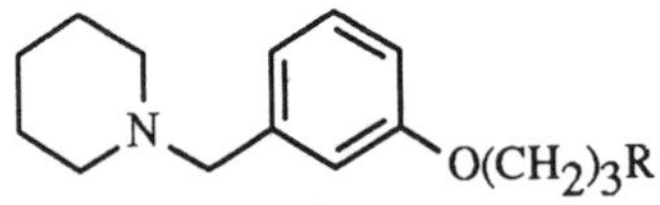

[a] Zolantidine.

the imidazole and cyanoguanidine moieties by less polar groups to give antagonists of superior H_2 antagonist activity. The 2-amino-3-nitropyrrole group was found to be a useful replacement for cyanoguanidine in this context as it is much less hydrophilic, partly due to the ability of the amino and nitro groups to form an intramolecular hydrogen bond, and because it makes a much larger contribution to receptor affinity. While significant reductions in polarity and corresponding improvements in brain penetration were achieved, the best combination of brain penetration and antagonist activity was found in (119), which had a steady state brain/blood ratio of 0.75, and K_B of 0.11 μM, but this was considered to be inadequate in a compound for studying the central effects of histamine.

Likewise, structural modifications to tiotidine or ranitidine that reduced hydrogen-bonding ability led to substantial improvements in brain penetration (*e.g.* compounds 120–123 in Table 32) but still these compounds did not have the desired combination of brain penetrability and antagonist potency.

The development of antagonists with a piperidinomethyl–phenoxypropyl system (*e.g.* lamitidine 102a and roxatidine 103b) offers considerable advantages over the ranitidine type of structure in being both relatively nonpolar and in tolerating a wide variety of terminal polar groups. The acetamide derivative (124; Table 32), which is reported[483] to be a very effective inhibitor of gastric acid secretion, has a relatively low polarity ($\Delta \log P$ value of only 1.93) and shows a significant level of brain penetration. The most polar group in (124) is the amide moiety, which has a hydrogen-bonding contribution (I_H) of 2.56.

A minimum structural requirement for H_2 antagonist activity in compounds of this type appears to be a hydrogen-bond donor group, and in attempting to increase brain penetration, the overall hydrogen-bonding ability of analogues of (124) was further decreased by introducing replacements for the amide function having lower I_H values. Three such groups are the sulfonamide, aliphatic hydroxyl and aromatic amino groups, reported by Seiler[482] to have I_H values of 1.93, 1.82 and 0.61, respectively, and introduction of these in place of the carboxamide group in (124) led to compounds (125) to (128) (Table 32).

Unlike (124), the sulfonamide analogue (125) is virtually devoid of H_2 antagonist activity, while the carbinol (126) and the aminopyridine derivative (128) are moderately effective antagonists, which cross the blood–brain barrier in relatively high concentrations, to give brain/blood ratios of 0.95 and 4.9 respectively. Investigation of further examples of aromatic amino moieties led to the discovery of compounds possessing good combinations of receptor affinity and brain penetration, notably the 2-aminobenzothiazole derivative (129), whose affinity is similar to that of tiotidine, and brain-penetrating ability is similar to that of clonidine. This compound, zolantidine, is a very specific, reversible and competitive H_2 receptor histamine antagonist and has been identified for use in studies of histaminergic mechanisms in brain.[484]

Zolantidine is active as an H_2 antagonist *in vivo* but shows hardly any activity against histamine-stimulated acid secretion. This is believed to be due to a pharmacokinetic effect whereby it has been shown that very lipophilic H_2 antagonists (zolantidine has $P = 600\,000$ for octanol–water partition) show considerably reduced activity as inhibitors of acid secretion relative to activity on the atrium, due to their ready penetration of cell membranes and subsequent loss of antagonist through the gastric mucosal membrane into the gastric acid secretion.[55]

The novel physicochemical model which guided the synthesis of novel H_2 antagonists throughout this study represents an important development in the rational design of brain-penetrating compounds. Its validity, reassessed at the end of the study when the brain penetration data for 20 compounds had been gathered, confirmed that a highly significant relationship still applied (equation 12 and Figure 27).

$$\log(C_{brain}/C_{blood}) = -0.48 \, \Delta \log P + 0.89$$
$$n = 20, \quad r = 0.83, \quad s = 0.44, \quad F = 40.2 \tag{12}$$

In view of the structural variation encompassed by the above 20 compounds, it was suggested that the $\Delta \log P$ parameter might find more general utility in the design of other types of drugs where brain penetration is to be increased.[459] Furthermore, it should be applicable in the converse sense, to restrict the entry of compounds into the brain *e.g.* see structure–activity study relating to the discovery of the non-CNS-penetrating H_1 antagonist temelastine (Section 12.5.12.7).

12.5.13.13 H₂ Antagonists Investigated in Human Studies

Since the early 1970s many histamine H_2 receptor antagonists have been investigated as gastric antisecretory agents in man. Early results with burimamide, which supported the therapeutic

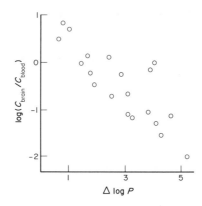

Figure 27 Relationship between brain penetration (steady state brain/blood concentration ratio) and $\Delta \log P$ $(\log P_{oct} - \log P_{cyh})$ for 20 structurally diverse compounds

strategy of H_2 receptor blockade, also highlighted the lack of potency of this compound. Several analogues with increased potency were subsequently selected as potential development candidates, and these are listed in Table 33 with gastric antisecretory and *in vitro* antagonist data from animal studies.

Metiamide, which was shown to be clinically effective in inhibiting gastric acid secretion, was later suspended from clinical trials following the detection of a low incidence of granulocytopenia.[508] Its successor, cimetidine, which incorporates the cyanoguanidine group as a replacement for the putatively toxic thiourea moiety, does not exhibit this side effect, and was subsequently launched in the UK in 1976 under the name Tagamet. Cimetidine is now firmly established in the treatment of peptic ulceration by both oral and parenteral routes and is also prescribed in Zollinger–Ellison syndrome and reflux oesophagitis, giving symptomatic relief and significantly promoting healing.

The close structural analogue, etintidine, was found to be twice as potent as cimetidine *in vitro* and twice as potent in gastric fistula dogs after intravenous injection.[490] Because of a lack of therapeutic advantage over cimetidine in clinical trials, however, the development of etintidine was suspended.

Oxmetidine, which incorporates a 5-substituted aminopyrimidinone moiety as a replacement for the cyanoguanidine group of cimetidine, is a more potent H_2 antagonist, but its effect is similar in duration.[283] As an inhibitor of histamine-stimulated gastric acid secretion *in vivo*, its potency relative to cimetidine varied between about two-fold in the dog p.o. to about 15-fold in the rat i.v. Oxmetidine inhibits gastric acidity in man (400 mg b.i.d.) and is efficacious in the treatment of duodenal ulcer at the same dose.[517] This compound was withdrawn in the latter stages of clinical assessment due to infrequent liver-related side effects.[509–511]

Icotidine, which is structurally related to oxmetidine, is a moderately potent H_1 receptor antagonist as well as being effective in blocking the H_2 receptor-mediated actions of histamine *in vivo* and *in vitro*.[361]

Ranitidine (Table 34) represents a structurally novel type of H_2 antagonist.[450] It was claimed to be some four to five times as potent as cimetidine in inhibiting histamine-stimulated gastric acid secretion in man, and at a dose of 150 mg b.i.d., it was clinically effective in healing gastric and duodenal ulcers over a four to six week period.[518] This compound was the second H_2 antagonist to become commercially available, and was first marketed by the Glaxo company in 1981 under the name Zantac.

Various analogues of ranitidine have subsequently been synthesized and taken into development, some of which differ only marginally in structure and have very similar pharmacological properties. Replacement of the furan ring in ranitidine by thiazole furnished the compound nizatidine, which was reported[452] to be some 5–18 times as potent as cimetidine, and was launched onto the market in the UK in 1987 as Axid by the Lilly Corporation as a once-daily antisecretory agent.[524]

More radical structural modification of ranitidine has led to some compounds which display markedly different profiles of activity. For example, combining the structural features of ranitidine and icotidine resulted in lupitidine,[453] a very potent H_2 antagonist which showed an extended duration of antisecretory activity, compared with previously known H_2 antagonists, including ranitidine and cimetidine. It was also found to be a highly effective inhibitor of nocturnal gastric secretion in humans at 0.6 and 0.9 mg kg^{-1} and 40 mg doses.[519] Clinical trials with lupitidine were suspended, however, when gastric mucosal changes in the forestomachs of rats were noticed at the high chronic dose of 1 g kg^{-1} d^{-1}.[512] The close analogue, donetidine,[454] which was under develop-

Table 33 Activities of H$_2$ Antagonists Related to Burimamide Which Have Been Taken to Human Study[a]

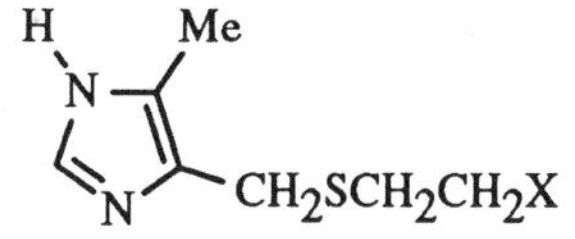

Name	X	Guinea pig atrium K_B (μM)	Inhibition of gastric acid secretion				
			ID_{50} (μmol kg^{-1})	Route	Species	Preparation	Ref.
Metiamide SK&F 92058	S ‖ NHCNHMe	0.92	1.6	iv	Rat	GS	488
			3.1	iv	Dog	HP	488
			16	po	Dog	HP	488
Cimetidine, SK&F 92334	NCN ‖ NHCNHMe	0.79	1.37	iv	Rat	GS	387
			77	iv	Rat	pl	489
			58	po	Rat	pl	489
			1.70	iv	Dog	HP	387
			10[a]	po	Dog	HP	387
Etintidine, BL 5641 A	NCN ‖ NHCNHCH$_2$C $\equiv$ CH	0.25	3.9	ip	Rat	gf	490
			0.97	iv	Dog	gf	491
			1.3	po	Dog	HP	491
SK&F 92456	CHNO$_2$ ‖ NHCNHMe	1.4	1.0	iv	Rat	GS	388
Oxmetidine, SK&F 92994	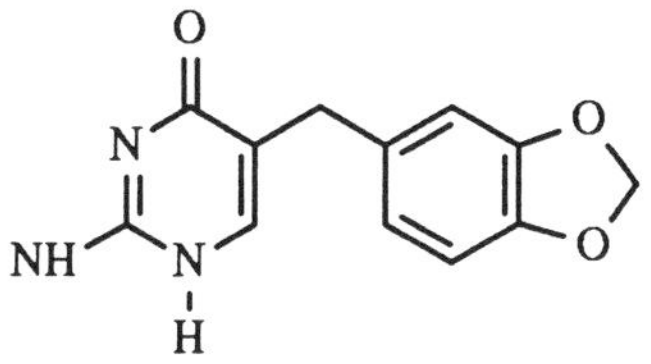	0.2[d] (DR = 2)	0.092	iv	Rat	GS	283
			0.5[b]	iv	Dog	HP	283
			5	po	Dog	HP	283
Icotidine, SK&F 93319	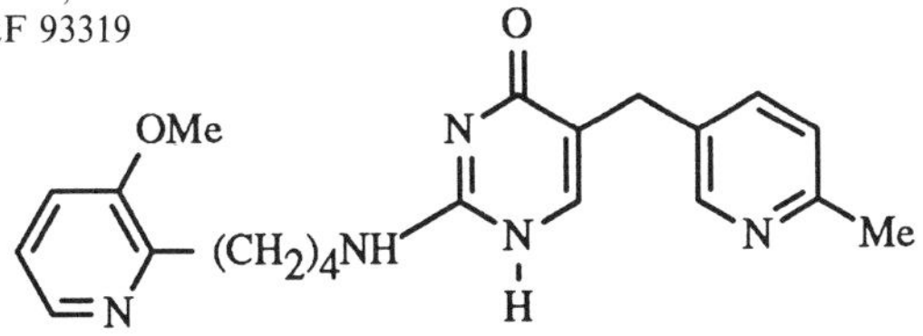	0.032	0.21	iv	Rat	GS	361
			0.5[c]	iv	Dog	HP	361
			2.5[a]	po	Dog	HP	361

[a] Footnotes and abbreviations after Table 37.

ment for parenteral use in the treatment of stress-related gastric mucosal and upper gastrointestinal damage, was also suspended during clinical trials.[520]

The diaminothiadiazole oxide derivative[447] BMY 25271 and its close analogue[493,494] Wy 45727 are potent but short-acting H$_2$ antagonists, which exhibit some 30–50 times the antisecretory activity of cimetidine after oral dosing.

The amide derivative ramixotidine[495,496] is less potent than cimetidine and ranitidine, but has a longer duration of action. Clinical development of this compound was suspended in 1987.

The discovery of the very potent H$_2$ antagonists lamtidine[456] and loxtidine[457] (Table 35) by the Glaxo company was a significant breakthrough in the quest for more potent and longer-acting antagonists, and introduced the piperidinylmethylphenoxypropyl moiety as a replacement for the related ranitidine side chain. As inhibitors of histamine-stimulated gastric acid secretion in the dog, these compounds are reported to be 5–10 times as potent as ranitidine. Both compounds exhibit an extended duration of antisecretory activity, and that of lamtidine is particularly marked. While the effect of ranitidine lasted for about 8 h in the dog after oral administration, lamtidine was still active after 24 h. The time course of pharmacological action amongst compounds with side chains

Table 34   Activities of H_2 Antagonists Derived from Ranitidine Which Have Been Taken to Human Study[a]

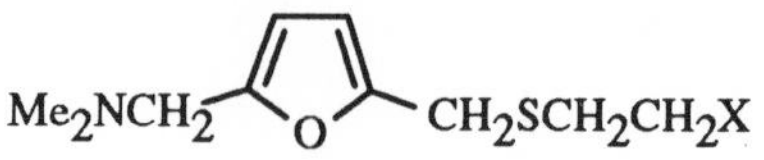

$$Me_2NCH_2 \diagdown O \diagdown CH_2SCH_2CH_2X$$

Name	X	Guinea pig atrium K_B (µM)	Inhibition of gastric acid secretion				
			ID_{50} (µmol kg^{-1})	Route	Species	Preparation	Ref.
Ranitidine, AH 19065	CHNO₂ ‖ NHCNHMe	0.063	0.37	iv	Rat	GS	450
			0.20	iv	Dog	HP	492
			0.66	po	Dog	HP	450
Lupitidine, SK&F 93479		0.016	0.14	iv	Rat	GS	453
			0.25[a]	iv	Dog	HP	453
			0.625[a]	po	Dog	HP	453
Donetidine, SK&F 93574	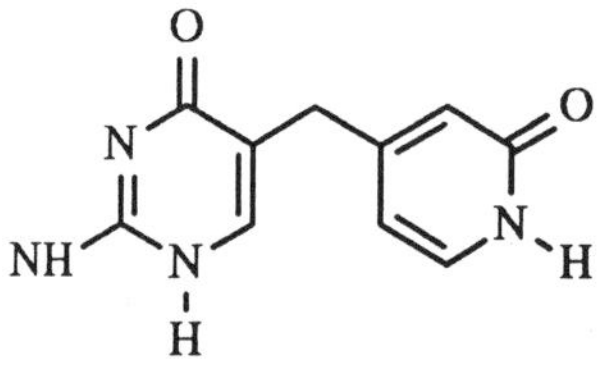	0.027	0.006	iv	Rat	GS	454
BMY 25271		0.026	0.041	iv	Rat	pl	447
		0.006	0.018	iv	Dog	HP	448
							460
Wy 45727		0.006	1.5	iv	Rat	pl	493
			0.5	iv	Dog	ip	493
			0.6	po	Dog	ip	494
Ramixotidine, CM 57755		4.0	2.6	iv	Rat	GS	495
			4.6	iv	Dog	gf	496
		Rat uterus K_B					
Nizatidine, LY 139037		0.08	1.48	iv	Rat	pl	452
			0.081	iv	Dog		452
			0.18	po	Dog		452

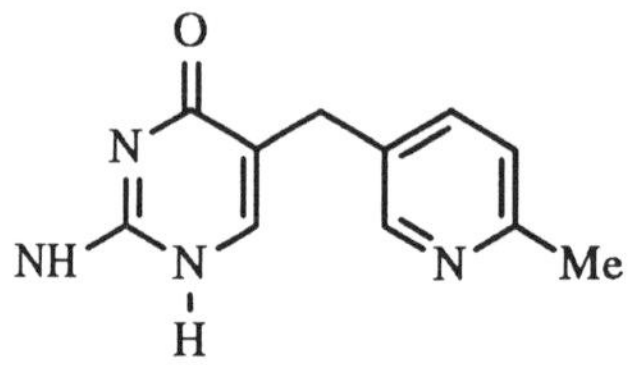

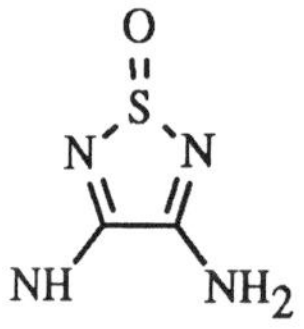

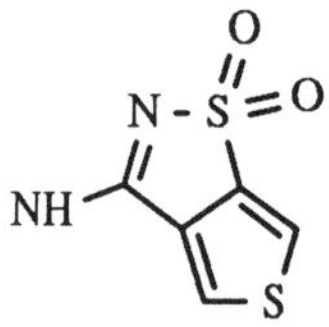

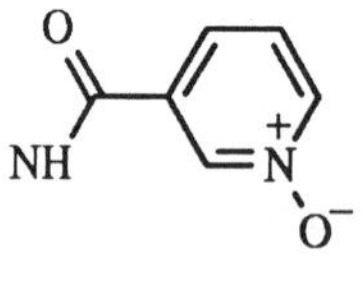

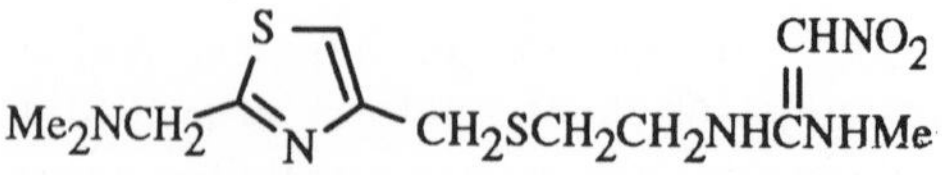

[a] Footnotes and abbreviations after Table 37.

containing arylmethylamino groups has been found to vary according to the nature of the amino substituent. For example, replacing the piperidinyl group in lamitidine by dimethylamino gave a compound with a similar potency and time course to ranitidine. The development of both lamitidine and loxtidine was subsequently suspended because of the induction of gastric carcinoid

Table 35 Activities of H$_2$ Antagonists Derived from Lamitidine Which Have Been Taken to Human Study[a]

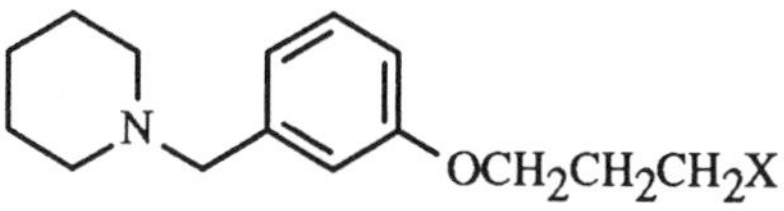

Name	X	Guinea pig atrium K_B (μM)	Inhibition of gastric acid secretion				
			ID_{50} (μmol kg^{-1})	Route	Species	Preparation	Ref.
Lamitidine, AH 22216	(triazole, Me/NH/NH$_2$)	0.07 (DR = 2)	0.049	iv	Rat	GS	456
			0.055	iv	Dog	HP	496
			0.084	po	Dog	HP	456
Loxtidine, AH 23844	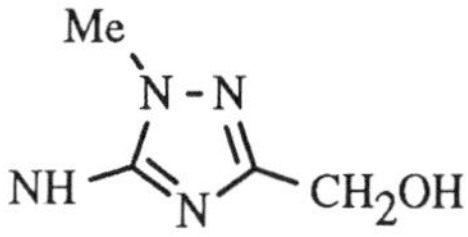 (triazole, Me/NH/CH$_2$OH)	NC[e]	0.039	iv	Dog	HP	457
			0.075	po	Dog	HP	457
Sufotidine	(triazole, Me/NH/CH$_2$SO$_2$Me)	0.20	0.45	iv	Rat	GS	531
			0.33	iv	Dog	HP	531
			0.81	po	Dog	HP	531
TAS (Wakamoto)	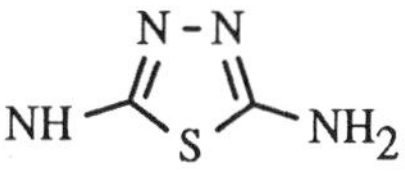 (thiadiazole, NH/NH$_2$)	0.054	3.2	id	Rat	pl	498
BMY 25260, L 643441	(thiadiazole S-oxide, NH/NH$_2$)	0.04 0.02					447 448
			0.036	iv	Dog	gf	448
			0.88	po	Dog	gf	464
BMY 25368, SK&F 94482	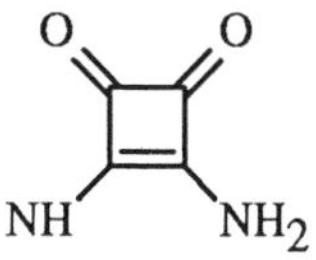 (cyclobutenedione, NH/NH$_2$)	0.013	0.023	iv	Dog	HP	460
Wy 45086	(benzisothiazole dioxide, NH)	0.008	2.4		Rat	pl	499
			2.4		Dog	pp	499
Wy 45662	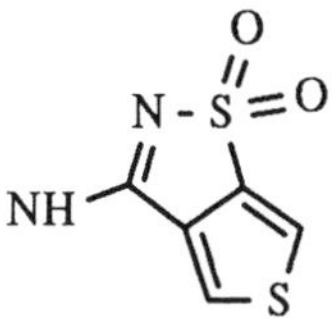 (thienoisothiazole dioxide, NH)	NC	0.7	id	Rat	pl	500, 501
Roxatidine, TZU 0460, Hoe 760	NHCCH$_2$OCMe (O, O)	0.27	1.1	iv	Rat	GS	497
			0.75	iv	Dog	HP	497
			0.91	po	Dog	HP	497

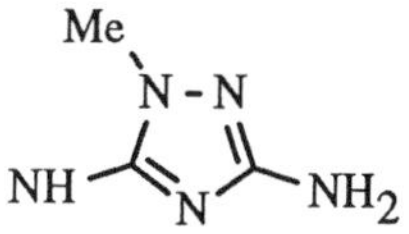

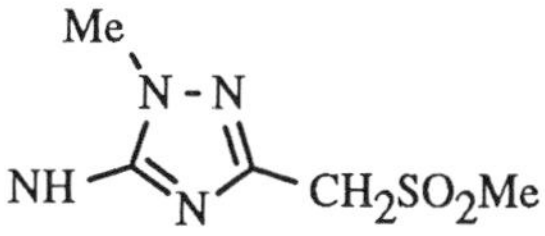

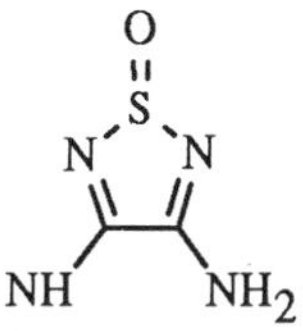

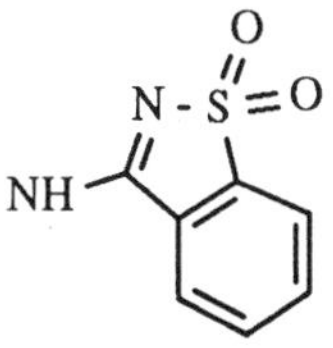

[a] Footnotes and abbreviations after Table 37.

tumours in the rat after prolonged high dose treatment.[513] However this is believed to be due to the physiological consequence of prolonged persistent achlorhydria.[514] A methanesulfonyl analogue, sufotidine, which also has a long half-life in animals, was taken into development instead.[531]

Analogues of lamtidine bearing alternative dipolar groups, which have been investigated for potential drug use are shown in Table 35. Of particular note are BMY 25368 (SK&F 94482) and L 643441 (BMY 25260), which are very potent antagonists and exhibit prolonged antisecretory activity.[460,448,537] Thirteen hours after an oral dose of BMY 25368 in the Heidenhain pouch dog, its antisecretory effect was still demonstrable. *In vitro* both BMY 25368 and L 643441 produced 'insurmountable' antagonism in the guinea pig atrium against dimaprit stimulation and were found to be difficult to remove from the tissue by washing.[464] In both compounds, the tightness of binding to H_2 receptors in the atrium correlated reasonably well with the duration of their antisecretory activity in dogs. As in the diaminotriazole series, the structure of the amino substituent could profoundly affect the time course of antisecretory activity of both the diaminothiadiazole 1-oxide and diaminocyclobutenedione derivatives in the piperidinylmethylphenoxypropyl series of compounds. In each case, piperidine was found to be optimal, while larger and smaller cyclic amines and dimethylamine resulted in diminished duration of action.

The reduced form of L 643441, BMY 25405, displays similar properties[460] and there is also an isomeric form, TAS.[498] Less potent analogues of lamitidine are roxatidine,[479] Wy 45086 and Wy 45662 (refs. 499–501). Roxatidine, which was developed by the Teikoku Hormone Corporation, is marketed for the treatment of gastric and duodenal ulcers, Zollinger–Ellison syndrome and reflux oesophagitis as Altat, and is a relatively short-acting compound.[523]

Another novel type of H_2 antagonist which has become a prototype for further modification is tiotidine.[442] This compound is more potent than cimetidine, especially *in vitro*, and is approximately

Table 36 Activities of H_2 Antagonists Derived from Tiotidine Which Have Been Taken to Human Study[a]

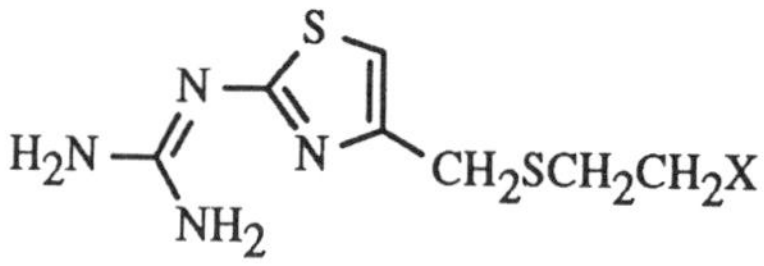

Name	X	Guinea pig atrium K_B (μM)	Inhibition of gastric acid secretion				
			ID_{50} ($\mu mol\,kg^{-1}$)	Route	Species	Preparation	Ref.
Tiotidine, ICI 125211	NCN ‖ NHCNHMe	0.015	0.2[a] 0.69	iv po	Dog Dog	gf HP	442 490
BL 6341 A	(structure)	0.027	0.075 0.040 0.35	iv iv po	Rat Dog Dog	pl HP HP	502 447 460 502
Famotidine, YM 11170	NSO_2NH_2 ‖ CNH_2^-	0.017[f]	1.3 1.3 2.6 0.011 0.031	iv po id iv po	Rat Rat rat Dog Dog	pl pl pl HP HP	489 489 489 503 503
Tuvatidine, HUK 978	(structure)	Binding[g] 0.02	0.28 1.8 0.065 0.4	iv po iv po	Rat Rat Dog Dog	GS gf HP HP	504 504 504 504

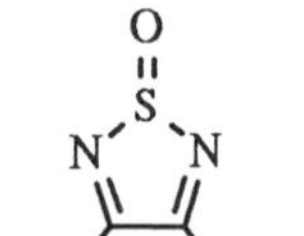

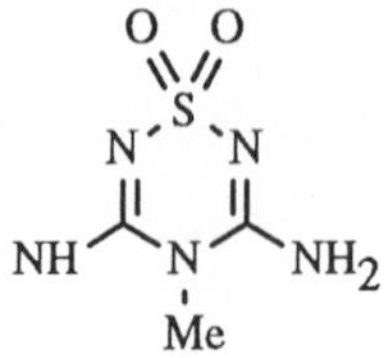

[a] Footnotes and abbreviations after Table 37.

eight times as potent in man,[521,522] with a relatively slow onset and prolonged duration of action (Table 36). After chronic high dosing in rats, however, stomach lesions were discovered, and clinical trials had to be suspended.[515]

Three analogues of tiotidine are BL 6341A, famotidine,[489,502] and tuvatidine.[504] The former compound, which contains the same thiadiazole oxide group as the previously described compounds BMY 25271 and L 643441, has a relatively long time-course of antisecretory activity (over 12 h in man), and in the Heidenhain pouch dog is about 10–100 times more potent than cimetidine in various animal models.[460] Famotidine was reported to be 40–400 times as potent as cimetidine in inhibiting acid secretion in the dog.[503] It was launched by the Yamanouchi Company in Japan in 1985 as Gaster as a once-daily H_2 antagonist, prescribed for treating duodenal and gastric ulceration and Zollinger–Ellison syndrome. A dose of 40 mg of famotidine nocte healed ulcers in 81/87 patients after eight weeks.[525] Like L 643441 and BMY 25368, famotidine has been claimed to bind tightly to H_2 receptors in isolated guinea pig atria to give a degree of antagonism which was not surmountable by increasing the concentration of dimaprit.

The guanidinopyrazole derivative, ICI 162846 (Table 27), is one of a series of potent, novel tiotidine analogues patented by ICI. In phase I trials this compound blocked basal and stimulated gastric acid secretion at low oral doses for at least 4 h.[465]

Table 37 Activities of Diaryl H_2 Antagonists Which Have Been Taken to Human Study

Name	X	Guinea pig atrium K_B (μM)	Inhibition of gastric acid secretion				
			ID_{50} (μmol kg^{-1})	Route	Species	Preparation	Ref.
Mifentidine, DA 4577	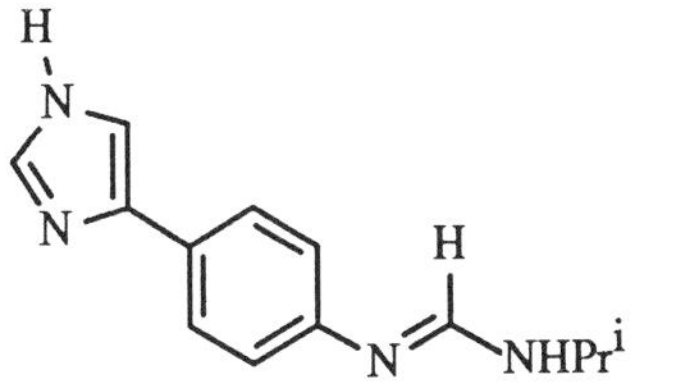	0.024	0.063	iv	Rat	GS	471
			0.08	iv	Dog	HP	471
			0.23	po	Dog	HP	471
DA 4643	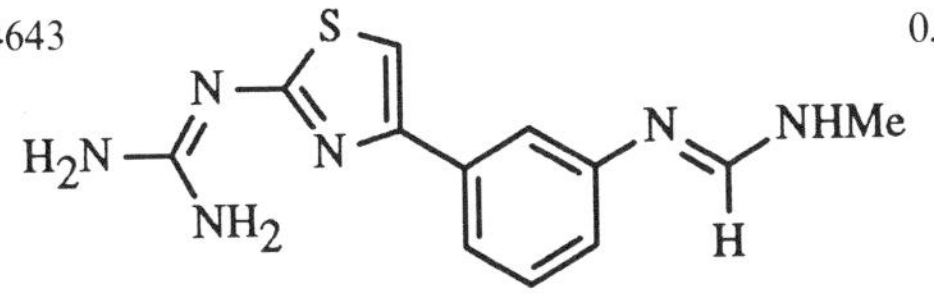	0.017	0.073	iv	Rat	GS	506
			0.11	iv	Dog	HP	507
Zaltidine, CP 57361	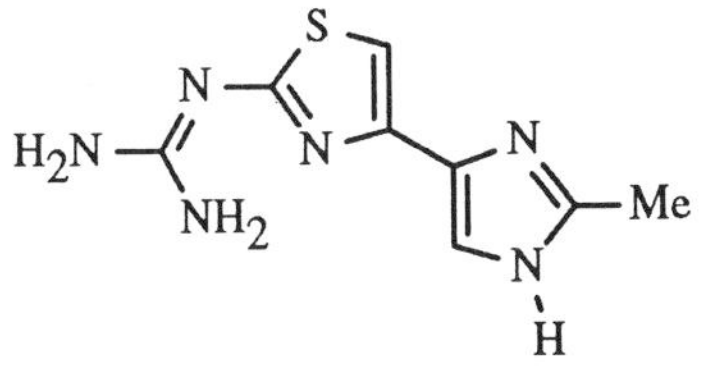	0.013	0.011	iv	Dog	HP	505

The K_B value is that published in the given reference, for the antagonism of the histamine- or dimaprit-stimulated increase in rate for the spontaneously beating guinea pig right atrium *in vitro*. It represents the apparent dissociation constant for the antagonist–receptor interaction, and is the concentration of antagonist that requires a doubling dose of agonist (histamine or dimaprit) to match the agonist response obtained in the absence of antagonist.

The ID_{50} represents the dose in μmol kg^{-1} to inhibit by 50% a near maximal level of histamine-stimulated gastric acid secretion, by the route shown, in rat or dog, as published in the given reference. Various preparations have been used and the results between preparations are not strictly comparable; in particular, the pylorus-ligated (pl) rat is not very sensitive to H_2 receptor antagonists, since the assay is for basal secretion of acid (*i.e.* not specifically stimulated by histamine).

GS = the modified Ghosh–Schild preparation of the perfused lumen of the anaesthetized and atropinized rat,
HP = Heidenhain Pouch conscious dog,
gf = gastric fistula conscious rat or dog,
pl = pylorus ligated anaesthetized rat,
pp = Pavlov Pouch dog,
ip = innervated gastric pouch.

[a] 70% inhibition. [b] 60% inhibition. [c] 40% inhibition. [d] K_B not available, but comparison at DR = 2 indicates that is has approximately 16 times the potency of cimetidine. [e] Noncompetitive inhibition. [f] Ref. 446. [g] Inhibition of [^{3}H]tiotidine binding to membranes from guinea pig cerebral cortex.

Another diaryl analogue, more potent and longer acting than cimetidine or ranitidine, is zaltidine which, in humans, had an ID_{50} of 40 mg and gave significant suppression of acid secretion after 24 h.[527]

The structurally novel diaryl H_2 antagonist, mifentidine[471] (Table 37), is a relatively short-acting antisecretory agent of greater potency than ranitidine in animal studies and has been studied clinically.[526] A follow-up to this compound is the guanidinothiazole analogue[506,507] DA 4643, which is claimed to be a potent H_2 antagonist. Another diaryl analogue, more potent and longer acting than cimetidine or ranitidine, is zaltidine which, in humans, had an ID_{50} of 40 mg and gave significant suppression of acid secretion after 24 h.[527]

12.5.14 ANTAGONISTS AT HISTAMINE H_3 RECEPTORS

As indicated in Section 12.5.5.4 H_3 receptor histamine antagonist activity was discovered among a group of H_2 receptor antagonists.[56] Burimamide (**86a**) was the most potent, whereas metiamide and cimetidine were much less active (Table 38). Ranitidine (**96a**; Table 28) and tiotidine (**92a**; Table 27) were not active. It was also found that the potent H_2 agonist impromidine (**40**) was a very potent H_3 receptor antagonist. The partial structure SK&F 91486 (**52**) was also as active as impromidine as an H_3 antagonist. These results can be summerized in the formula (**130**), *i.e.* the most potent compounds are unsubstituted imidazoles and have $n = 3$–4, R = H or Me, Z = S or NH.

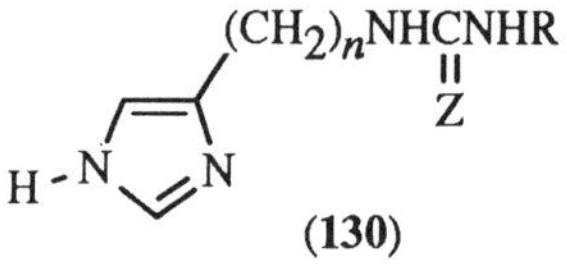

(**130**)

The need for an imidazole ring is not absolute since betahistine[184] (a pyridine derivative, Table 15) and phencyclidine[532] (a phenyl compound) are also reported to have some activity, although they are relatively weak.

Table 38 Some Compounds Reported to be H_3 Receptor Histamine Antagonists Determined *in vitro* against Histamine Inhibition of Potassium Evoked [^{3}H]Histamine Release on Rat Brain Cortex Slices

	Compound	K_B or K_i (nM)	*Ref.*
(**86a**)	Burimamide[a]	70[b]	56
(**86e**)	Metiamide[a]	2500[b]	56
(**86j**)	Cimetidine[a]	33 000[b]	56
(**40**)	Impromidine[c]	65[b]	56
(**52**)	SK&F 91486[b]	88[b]	56
	Betahistine[e]	6900[f]	184
	Phencyclidine	25 000[f]	532
(**18**)	Thioperamide	2.1[f]	57
(**131**)[g]	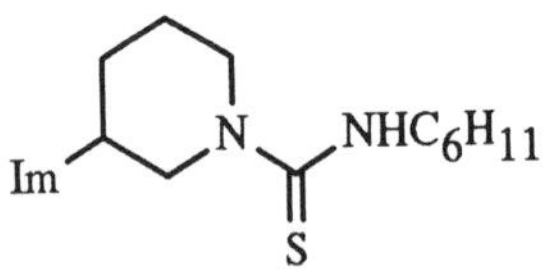	40[f]	533
(**132**)[g]	ImCH$_2$CH$_2$NHCO(CH$_2$)$_m$R $m = 3$, R = Ph $m = 3$, R = C$_6$H$_{11}$	80[f] 50[f]	534 534
(**133**)[g]	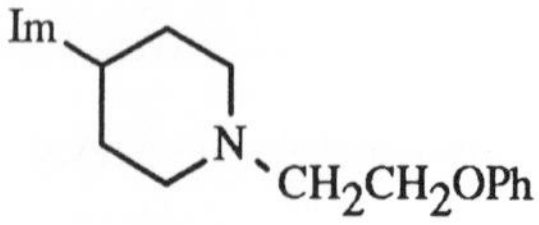	67[f]	533
(**134**)[g]	ImCH$_2$CH$_2$NH(CH$_2$)$_m$Ph $m = 2$ or 3	600[f]	534

[a] Structure in Table 20. [b] K_B value. [c] Structure in Table 13. [d] Structure in Table 14. [e] Structure in Table 15. [f] K_i value. [g] Im = 4(5)imidazolyl.

The highly selective and potent H_3 antagonist, thioperamide (18), first reported by Arrang *et al.*[573] can be considered to be a burimamide analogue in which the side chain has been cyclized into a piperidine ring, and a cyclohexyl group substituted on the terminal thioureido N atom ($R = C_6H_{11}$) in place of methyl. The position of imidazole substitution in the piperidine ring appears to be important since the 3-isomer (131) of thioperamide is reported to be about 20 times less active.[533]

The urea analogue of thioperamide is reported to be about eight times less potent.[533] Amide derivatives of histamine have also been reported[534] to be H_3 receptor antagonists, *e.g.* (132). There is apparently no absolute requirement to have an amidic type of functionality, however, since a phenoxyethylpiperidine analogue (133) of thioperamide was also reported[533] to have activity, as had N^α-phenylethyl- and N^α-phenylpropyl-histamines[534] (134); however, it appears likely that amines are generally less active than amides.

It is clear that there is much to be explored in examining structure–activity relationships for H_3 receptor antagonists, although it remains to be seen whether a drug will become established for a therapeutic application.

12.5.15 REFERENCES

1. J. W. Black and C. R. Ganellin, *Experientia*, 1974, **30**, 111.
2. O. B. Reite, *Physiol. Rev.*, 1972, **52**, 778.
3. A. Windaus and W. Vogt, *Ber. Dtsch. Chem. Ges.*, 1907, **40**, 3691.
4. D. Ackermann, *Z. Physiol. Chem.*, 1910, **65**, 504.
5. H. H. Dale and P. P. Laidlaw, *J. Physiol.*, 1910, **41**, 318.
6. H. H. Dale and P. P. Laidlaw, *J. Physiol.*, 1911, **43**, 182.
7. L. Popielski, *Pfluegers Arch. Gesamte Physiol. Menschen Tiere*, 1920, **178**, 214.
8. W. C. Bowman and M. J. Rand, in 'Textbook of Pharmacology', 2nd edn., Blackwell, Oxford, 1980, p. 12.1.
9. A. Goodman Gilman, L. S. Goodman, T. W. Roll and F. Muriol, (eds.), in 'Goodman and Gilman's The Pharmacological Basis of Therapeutics', 7th edn., Macmillan, New York, 1985, p. 605.
10. R. B. Barlow, in 'Introduction to Chemical Pharmacology', 2nd edn., Methuen, London, 1964, p. 344.
11. *Ann. N.Y. Acad. Sci.*, 1950, **50**, Art. 9, 1015.
12. G. E. Wolstenholme and C. M. O'Connor, (eds.), 'Histamine', Churchill, London, 1956.
13. *Fed. Proc., Fed. Am. Soc. Exp. Biol.*, 1964, **23**, 1095; 1965, **24**, 1311; 1967, **26**, 211.
14. C. Maslinski, (ed.), 'Histamine', Proceedings of Satellite Symposium', Academic Press, New York, 1973.
15. T. O. Yellin (ed.), 'Histamine Receptors', Proceedings of the A. N. Richards Symposium, Philadelphia, SP-New York, 1979.
16. B. Uvnäs and K. Tasaka, (eds.), *Adv. Biosci.*, 1982, **33**.
17. C. R. Ganellin and J.-C. Schwartz, (eds.), *Adv. Biosci.*, 1985, **51**.
18. M. Rocha e Silva, (ed.), *Handb. Exp. Pharmakol.*, 1966, **18/1**.
19. M. Rocha e Silva, (ed.), *Handb. Exp. Pharmakol.*, 1978, **18/2**.
20. G. Kahlson and E. Rosengren, 'Biogenesis and Physiology of Histamine', Physiological Society, Arnold, London, 1971, Monograph 21.
21. M. Schachter, (ed.), 'Histamine and Antihistamines', *Int. Encycl. Pharmacol. Therap.*, 1973, Section 74.
22. M. A. Beaven, 'Histamine: Its Role in Physiological and Pathological Processes', Monographs in Allergy, Karger, Basel, 1978, vol. 13.
23. C. R. Ganellin and G. J. Durant, in 'Burger's Medicinal Chemistry', ed. M. E. Wolff, 4th edn., Wiley-Interscience, New York, 1981, vol. 3, p. 487.
24. C. R. Ganellin and M. E. Parsons, (eds.), 'Pharmacology of Histamine Receptors', Wright, Bristol, 1982.
25. W. C. Bowman and M. J. Rand, 'Textbook of Pharmacology', 2nd edn., Blackwell, Oxford, 1980, p. 12.7.
26. K. S. Herman, R. R. Bowsher and D. P. Henry, *J. Biol. Chem.*, 1985, **260**, 12 336.
27. R. J. Levine and W. W. Noll, *Ann. N.Y. Acad. Sci.*, 1969, **166**, 246.
28. F.-J. Leinweber and G. A. Braun, *Mol. Pharmacol.*, 1970, **6**, 146.
29. J. Kollonitsch, A. A. Patchett, S. Marburg, A. L. Maycock, L. M. Perkins, G. A. Doldouras, D. E. Duggan and S. D. Aster, *Nature (London)*, 1978, **274**, 906.
30. R. J. Taylor, *Biochem. Pharmacol.*, 1978, **27**, 2653.
31. K. H. Mole and D. M. Shepherd, *J. Pharm. Pharmacol.*, 1973, **25**, 609.
32. K. H. Mole and D. M. Shepherd, *Arch. Int. Pharmacodyn. Ther.*, 1972, **195**, 109.
33. M. A. Beaven and R. E. Schaff, *Biochem. Pharmacol.*, 1979, **28**, 183.
34. M. A. Beaven and R. E. Schaff, *Agents Actions*, 1979, **9**, 455.
35. D. S. Duch, S. Bowers and C. A. Nichol, *Biochem. Pharmacol.*, 1978, **27**, 1507.
36. D. S. Duch, M. P. Edelstein and C. A. Nicholl, *Mol. Pharmacol.*, 1980, **18**, 100.
37. M. A. Beaven and N. B. Roderick, *Biochem. Pharmacol.*, 1980, **29**, 2897.
38. M. A. Beaven and R. E. Shaff, *Biochem. Pharmacol.*, 1975, **24**, 979.
39. T. Bieganski, C. R. Ganellin, J. Kusche and C. Maslinski, *Eur. J. Med. Chem.*, 1985, **20**, 433.
40. M. A. Beaven, Z. Horakova and H. R. Keiser, *Experientia*, 1976, **32**, 1180.
41. J. Moss, M. C. de Mello, M. Vaughan and M. A. Beaven, *J. Clin. Invest.*, 1976, **58**, 137.
42. J. F. Riley and G. B. West, *J. Physiol. (London)*, 1953, **120**, 528.
43. F. C. MacIntosh and W. D. M. Paton, *J. Physiol. (London)*, 1949, **109**, 190.
44. G. W. Reed and J. F. Lenney, *J. Med. Chem.*, 1972, **15**, 320.

45. H. Breithaupt and E. Habermann, *Naunyn-Schmiedeberg's Arch. Pharmacol.*, 1968, **261**, 252.
46. F. L. Pearce, *Pharmacology*, 1986, **32**, 61.
47. T. Ishizaka, in ref. 17, p. 401.
48. H. O. Schild, *Br. J. Pharmacol.*, 1947, **2**, 189.
49. O. Arunlakshana and H. O. Schild, *Br. J. Pharmacol.*, 1959, **14**, 48.
50. B. Folkow, K. Haeger and G. Kahlson, *Acta Physiol. Scand.*, 1948, **15**, 264.
51. A. S. F. Ash and H. O. Schild, *Br. J. Pharmacol. Chemother.*, 1966, **27**, 427.
52. M. I. Grossman, C. Robertson and C. E. Rosiere, *J. Pharmacol. Exp. Ther.*, 1952, **104**, 277.
53. R. G. Jones, in ref. 18, p. 1.
54. J. W. Black, W. A. M. Duncan, G. J. Durant, C. R. Ganellin and M. E. Parsons, *Nature (London)*, 1972, **236**, 385.
55. N. J. Shankley, J. W. Black, C. R. Ganellin and R. C. Mitchell, *Br. J. Pharmacol.*, 1988, **94**, 264.
56. J. M. Arrang, M. Garbarg and J.-C. Schwartz, *Nature (London)*, 1983, **302**, 832.
57. J. M. Arrang, M. Garbarg, J. C. Lancelot, J. M. Lecomte, H. Pollard, M. Robba, W. Schunack and J.-C. Schwartz, *Nature (London)*, 1987, **327**, 117.
58. S. Ishikawa and N. Sperelakis, *Nature (London)*, 1987, **327**, 158.
59. K. Tamura, J. M. Palmer and J. D. Wood, *Neuroscience*, 1988, **25**, 171.
60. J. P. Trzeciakowski, *J. Pharmacol. Exp. Ther.*, 1987, **243**, 874.
61. D. Bovet and A.-M. Staub, *C. R. Seances Soc. Biol. Ses. Fil.*, 1937, **124**, 547.
62. H. Konzett and R. Roessler, *Naunyn-Schmiedeberg's Arch. Exp. Pathol. Pharmakol.*, 1940, **195**, 71.
63. A. Wright, P. Raval, R. J. Eden and D. A. A. Owen, *J. Pharmacol. Methods*, 1987, **18**, 123.
64. K. I. Melville, in ref. 21, p. 127.
65. M. Boyce, *Br. J. Clin. Pharmacol.*, 1984, **18**, 227P.
66. D. M. Paton, in ref. 21, p. 3.
67. T. T. Quach, A. M. Duchemin, C. Rose and J.-C. Schwartz, *Mol. Pharmacol.*, 1980, **17**, 301.
68. E. Richelson, *Science (Washington, D.C.)*, 1978, **210**, 69.
69. J.-C. Schwartz, G. Barbin, A. M. Duchemin, M. Garbarg, C. Llorens, H. Pollard, T. T. Quach and C. Rose, in ref. 24, p. 351.
70. M. E. Parsons, Ph.D. Thesis, University of London, 1969.
71. M. N. Ghosh and H. O. Schild, *Br. J. Pharmacol.*, 1958, **13**, 54.
72. M. E. Parsons, D. A. A. Owen, C. R. Ganellin and G. J. Durant, *Agents Actions*, 1977, **7**, 31.
73. S. C. Verma and J. H. McNeill, *J. Pharmacol. Exp. Ther.*, 1977, **200**, 352.
74. V. R. Grund, N. D. Goldberg and D. B. Hunninghake, *J. Pharmacol. Exp. Ther.*, 1975, **195**, 176.
75. A. H. Soll, in ref. 17, p. 253.
76. T. Berglindh, D. R. Dibona, S. Ito and G. Sachs, *Am. J. Physiol.*, 1980, **238**, G165.
77. C. L. Johnson, in ref. 24, p. 146.
78. M. Plaut and L. M. Lichtenstein, in ref. 24, p. 392.
79. J. F. Van der Werf, A. Bast, G. J. Bijloo, A. Van der Vliet and H. Timmerman, *Eur. J. Pharmacol.*, 1987, **138**, 199.
80. N. Chand and P. Eyre, *Agents Actions*, 1975, **5**, 277.
81. G. Bertaccini and G. Coruzzi, *Pharmacology*, 1981, **23**, 1.
82. G. Bertaccini and G. Coruzzi, in 'Receptors and the Upper G. I. Tract', ed. B. I. Hirschowitz and J. G. Spenney, ATC, 1983, p. 201.
83. S. J. Hill, P. C. Emson and J. M. Young, *J. Neurochem.*, 1978, **31**, 997.
84. V. T. Tran, R. Lebovitz, L. Toll and S. H. Snyder, *Eur. J. Pharmacol.*, 1981, **70**, 501.
85. S. J. Peroutka and S. H. Snyder, *J. Pharmacol. Exp. Ther.*, 1981, **216**, 142.
86. J. M. Treherne and J. M. Young, *Br. J. Pharmacol.*, 1988, **94**, 797.
87. R. C. Blakemore, C. R. Ganellin, M. Garbarg, C. Gros, R. J. Ife, M. Körner, M. Ruat, J.-C. Schwartz, W. Tertiuk and C. J. Theobald, *Eur. J. Med. Chem.*, 1987, **22**, 91.
88. M. Ruat, M. Körner, M. Garbarg, C. Gros, J.-C. Schwartz, W. Tertiuk and C. R. Ganellin, *Proc. Natl. Acad. Sci. USA*, 1988, **85**, 2743.
89. A. Schotte and J. E. Leysen, *Eur. J. Pharmacol.*, 1988, **145**, 213.
90. G. A. Gajtkowski, D. B. Norris, T. J. Rising and T. P. Wood, *Nature (London)*, 1983, **304**, 65.
91. M. Ruat, W. Schunack and J.-C. Schwartz, personal communication.
92. G. H. Steinberg, J. G. Eppel, M. Kandel, S. I. Kandel and J. W. Wells, *Biochemistry*, 1985, **24**, 6095, 6107, 6115.
93. (a) M. Körner, M. L. Bouthenet, C. R. Ganellin, M. Garbarg, C. Gros, R. J. Ife, N. Sales and J.-C. Schwartz, *Eur. J. Pharmacol.*, 1986, **120**, 151; (b) M. L. Bouthenet, M. Ruat, N. Sales, M. Garbarg and J.-C. Schwartz, *Neuroscience*, 1988, **26**. 553.
94. G. K. Hogaboom, K. S. Ice, D. L. Horstmeyer, J. P. O'Donnel and J. S. Fedan, in ref. 17, p. 13.
95. W. Wouters, J. Van Dun, J. E. Leysen and P. M. Laduron, *FEBS Lett.*, 1985, **182**, 291; *J. Biol. Chem.*, 1985, **260**, 8423.
96. A. Doble, J. Ménager, O. Ferris and P. M. Laduron, *Br. J. Pharmacol.*, 1989, **96**, 317P.
97. I. R. Smith, M. T. Cleverley, C. R. Ganellin and K. M. Metters, *Agents Actions*, 1980, **10**, 422.
98. D. Bristow, J. R. Hare, J. R. Hearn and L. E. Martin, *Br. J. Pharmacol.*, 1981, **72**, 547P.
99. T. J. Rising, D. B. Norris, S. E. Warrander and T. P. Wood, *Life Sci.*, 1980, **27**, 199.
100. T. J. Rising and D. B. Norris, in ref. 17, p. 61.
101. M. K. Uchida, *Gen. Pharmacol.*, 1978, **9**, 145.
102. M. Garbarg, E. Yeramian, M. Korner and J.-C. Schwartz, in ref. 17, p. 19.
103. T. Kuno, N. Kubo and C. Tanaka, *Biochem. Biophys. Res. Commun.*, 1985, **129**, 639.
104. L. Toll and S. H. Snyder, *J. Biol. Chem.*, 1982, **257**, 13 593.
105. M. Ruat, M. L. Bouthenet, J.-C. Schwartz and C. R. Ganellin, 1989, in press.
106. M. Osband and R. McCaffrey, *J. Biol. Chem.*, 1979, **254**, 9970.
107. H. Carswell, P. R. Daum and J. M. Young, in ref. 17, p. 27.
108. E. Richelson, in ref. 17, p. 237.
109. C. L. Johnson, in 'The Chemical Regulation of Biological Mechanisms', ed. A. M. Creighton and S. Turner, Royal Society of Chemistry, London, 1982, p. 16.

110. T. B. Paiva, M. Tominaga and A. C. M. Paiva, *J. Med. Chem.*, 1970, **13**, 689.
111. G. J. Durant, C. R. Ganellin and M. E. Parsons, *J. Med. Chem.*, 1975, **18**, 905.
112. C. R. Ganellin, *J. Pharm. Pharmacol.*, 1973, **25**, 787.
113. C. R. Ganellin, in 'Molecular and Quantum Pharmacology', ed. E. D. Bergmann and B. Pullman, Reidel, Dordrecht, 1974, p. 43.
114. W. F. Reynolds and C. W. Tzeng, *Can. J. Biochem.*, 1977, **55**, 576.
115. R. E. Wasylishen and G. Tomlinson, *Can. J. Biochem.*, 1977, **55**, 579.
116. K. Prout, S. R. Critchley and C. R. Ganellin, *Acta Crystallogr., Sect. B*, 1974, **30**, 2884.
117. W. G. Richards, J. Wallis and C. R. Ganellin, *Eur. J. Med. Chem.*, 1979, **14**, 9.
118. H. Weinstein, D. Chou, C. L. Johnson, S. Kang and J. P. Green, *Mol. Pharmacol.*, 1976, **12**, 738.
119. L. B. Cole and E. M. Holt, *J. Chem. Soc., Perkin Trans. 1*, 1986, 151.
120. J. J. Bonnet and J. A. Ibers, *J. Am. Chem. Soc.*, 1973, **95**, 4829.
121. M. Pasquali, G. Marini, C. Floriani, A. Gaetani-Manfredotti and C. Guastini, *Inorg. Chem.*, 1980, **19**, 2525.
122. S. Topiol, H. Weinstein and R. Osman, *J. Med. Chem.*, 1984, **27**, 1531.
123. P. Reggio, S. Topiol and H. Weinstein, *J. Med. Chem.*, 1986, **29**, 2412.
124. C. R. Ganellin, E. S. Pepper, G. N. J. Port and W. G. Richards, *J. Med. Chem.*, 1973, **16**, 610.
125. N. S. Ham, A. F. Casy and R. R. Ison, *J. Med. Chem.*, 1973, **16**, 470.
126. S. R. Byrn, C. W. Graber and S. L. Midland, *J. Org. Chem.*, 1976, **41**, 2283.
127. L. B. Kier, *J. Med. Chem.*, 1968, **11**, 441.
128. B. Pullman and J. Port, *Mol. Pharmacol.*, 1974, **10**, 360.
129. J. P. Green, S. Kang and S. Margolis, *Mem. Soc. Endocrinol.*, 1971, **19**, 727.
130. J.-L. Coubeils, P. Corrière and B. Pullman, *C. R. Hebd. Seances Acad. Sci., Ser. D*, 1971, **272**, 1813.
131. R. J. Abraham and D. Birch, *Mol. Pharmacol.*, 1975, **11**, 663.
132. T. Yamane, T. Ashida and M. Kakudo, *Acta Crystallogr., Sect.B*, 1973, **29**, 2884.
133. J. J. Bonnet and Y. Jeannin, *Acta Crystallogr., Sect. B*, 1972, **28**, 1079.
134. J. J. Bonnet, Y. Jeannin and M. Laaouini, *Bull. Soc. Fr. Mineral. Cristallogr.*, 1975, **98**, 208.
135. D. F. Decou, Dissertation No. 64-9987, Univ. Microfilms Inc., Ann Arbor, Michigan, 1964.
136. M. V. Veidis, G. J. Palenik, R. Schaffrin and J. Trotter, *J. Chem. Soc. A*, 1969, 2659.
137. J. J. Bonnet and Y. Jeannin, *Acta Crystallogr., Sect. B*, 1970, **26**, 318.
138. J. J. Bonnet and Y. Jeannin, *Bull. Soc. Fr. Mineral. Cristallogr.*, 1970, **93**, 287.
139. M. Pasquali, C. Floriani, A. Gaetani-Manfredotti and C. Guastini, *J. Chem. Soc., Chem. Commun.*, 1979, 197.
140. R. J. Ife, K. W. Catchpole, G. J. Durant, C. R. Ganellin, C. A. Harvey, M. L. Meeson, D. A. A. Owen, M. E. Parsons, B. P. Slingsby and C. J. Theobald, *Eur. J. Med. Chem.*, 1989, **24**, 249.
141. G. Simons and E. R. Talaty, *J. Am. Chem. Soc.*, 1977, **99**, 2407.
142. D. D. Perrin, I. G. Sayce and V. S. Sharma, *J. Chem. Soc. A*, 1967, 1755.
143. D. D. Perrin and V. S. Sharma, *J. Chem. Soc. A*, 1968, 446.
144. D. D. Perrin and V. S. Sharma, *J. Chem. Soc. A*, 1969, 2060.
145. A. Kayali and G. Berthon, *J. Chim. Phys. Phys.–Chim. Biol.*, 1980, **77**, 333.
146. W. C. Nicholas and W. C. Fernelius, *J. Phys. Chem.*, 1951, **65**, 1047.
147. P. A. Kramer, J. R. Hazlett and D. O. Kildsig, *J. Pharm. Sci.*, 1977, **66**, 542.
148. B. L. Mickel and A. C. Andrews, *J. Am. Chem. Soc.*, 1955, **77**, 5291.
149. P. Dasgupta and R. B. Jordan, *Inorg. Chem.*, 1985, **24**, 2721.
150. J. W. Black, G. J. Durant, J. C. Emmett and C. R. Ganellin, *Nature (London)*, 1974, **248**, 65.
151. J. P. Green, in 'Mechanism of Release of Biogenic Amines', Pergamon, London, 1966, p. 125.
152. J. P. Green, *Fed. Proc., Fed. Am. Soc. Exp. Biol.*, 1967, **26**, 211.
153. L. Kerp, *Int. Arch. Allergy Appl. Immunol.*, 1963, **22**, 112.
154. B. Uvnäs, C. H. Åborg and U. Bergquist, *Acta Physiol. Scand.*, 1975, **93**, 401.
155. C. R. Ganellin, in ref. 24, p. 10.
156. L. A. Walter, W. H. Hunt and R. J. Fosbinder, *J. Am. Chem. Soc.*, 1941, **63**, 2771.
157. H. M. Lee and R. G. Jones, *J. Pharmacol. Exp. Ther.*, 1949, **95**, 71.
158. F. G. Van den Brink, in 'Histamine and Antihistamines. Molecular Pharmacology, Structure–Activity Relations, Gastric Acid Secretion', Drukkerij Gebr. Janssen N. V., Nijmegen, 1969, p. 179.
159. R. C. Blakemore and M. E. Parsons, Smith Kline and French Research Ltd.
160. L. L. Grechishkin, L. K. Gavrovskaya and V. L. Goldfarb, *Pharmacology*, 1977, **15**, 512.
161. W. Schunack, *Arch. Pharm. (Weinheim, Ger.)*, 1975, **308**, 75.
162. C. Niemann and J. T. Hays, *J. Am. Chem. Soc.*, 1942, **64**, 2288.
163. C. E. Rosiere and M. I. Grossman, *Science (Washington, D.C.)*, 1951, **113**, 651.
164. C. B. Clayman, J. B. Kirsner and H. Ford, *JAMA, J. Am. Med. Assoc.*, 1961, **175**, 908.
165. R. I. Breuer and J. B. Kirsner, *Ann. N.Y. Acad. Sci.*, 1967, **140**, 882.
166. G. J. Durant, J. C. Emmett, C. R. Ganellin, A. M. Roe and R. A. Slater, *J. Med. Chem.*, 1976, **19**, 923.
167. P. Dziuron and W. Schunack, *Eur. J. Med. Chem.*, 1975, **10**, 129.
168. M. Hepp, P. Dziuron and W. Schunack, *Arch. Pharm. (Weinheim, Ger.)*, 1979, **312**, 637.
169. W. Schunack, *Arch. Pharm. (Weinheim, Ger.)*, 1978, **311**, 552.
170. H.-G. Lennartz, M. Hepp and W. Schunack, *Eur. J. Med. Chem.*, 1978, **13**, 229.
171. G. Bertaccini, M. Impicciatore, T. Vitali and V. Plazzi, *Farmaco, Ed. Sci.*, 1972, **27**, 680.
172. G. Bertaccini, E. Molina, T. Vitali and L. Zappia, *Br. J. Pharmacol.*, 1979, **66**, 13.
173. G. Bertaccini, M. Impicciatore and T. Vitali, *Farmaco, Ed. Sci.*, 1976, **31**, 934.
174. M. Impicciatore, G. Bertaccini, M. Chiavarini, T. Vitali and F. Bordi, *Farmaco, Ed. Sci.*, 1978, **33**, 696.
175. G. Bertaccini and T. Vitali, *J. Pharm. Pharmacol.*, 1964, **16**, 441.
176. T. Vitali, V. Plazzi, F. Bordi, G. Bertaccini and M. Impicciatore, *Farmaco, Ed. Sci.*, 1979, **34**, 41.
177. M. Hepp and W. Schunack, *Arch. Pharm. (Weinheim, Ger.)*, 1980, **313**, 756.
178. G. Gerhard and W. Schunack, *Arch. Pharm. (Weinheim, Ger.)*, 1980, **313**, 709.
179. G. Gerhard and W. Schunack, *Arch. Pharm. (Weinheim, Ger.)*, 1980, **313**, 780.

180. W. Schunack, A. Buschauer, S. Büyüktimkin, P. Dziuron, S. Elz, G. Gerhard, E. Lebenstedt, H.-G. Lennartz, S. Schwarz, M. Spitzhoff and R. Steffens, in 'Proceedings 8th International Symposium on Medicinal Chemistry', ed. R. Dahlbohm and J. L. Nilsson, Swedish Pharmaceutical Press, Stockholm, 1985, vol. 2, p. 169.
181. J. M. Arrang, M. Garbarg, W. Schunack, J. C. Schwartz and R. O. Lipp, *Eur. Pat.* 214 058 (1987).
182. J. M. Arrang, J.-C. Schwartz and W. Schunack, *Eur. J. Pharmacol.*, 1985, **117**, 109.
183. E. J. Ariens and A. M. Simonis, *Arch. Int. Pharmacodyn. Ther.*, 1960, **127**, 479.
184. J. M. Arrang, M. Garbarg, T. T. Quach, M. D. Trung Tuong, E. Yeramian and J.-C. Schwartz, *Eur. J. Pharmacol.*, 1985, **111**, 73.
185. J. H. Seipel and J. E. Floam, *J. Clin. Pharmacol.*, 1975, **15**, 144.
186. T. J. Wilmot and G. N. Menon, *J. Laryngol. Otol.*, 1976, **90**, 833.
187. M. Impicciatore, M. Chiaverini, R. Razzetti and T. Vitali, *Eur. J. Pharmacol.*, 1979, **57**, 79.
188. B. N. Craver, W. Barrett, A. Cameron and E. Herrold, *Arch. Int. Pharmacodyn. Ther.*, 1951, **87**, 33.
189. C. F. Heubner, R. A. Turner and C. R. Scholz, *J. Am. Chem. Soc.*, 1949, **71**, 3942.
190. C. F. Heubner, *J. Am. Chem. Soc.*, 1951, **73**, 4667.
191. K. L. Kirk and L. A. Cohen, *J. Am. Chem. Soc.*, 1973, **95**, 4619.
192. H. Kimoto, K. L. Kirk and L. A. Cohen, *J. Org. Chem.*, 1978, **43**, 3403.
193. H. Kimoto and L. A. Cohen, *J. Org. Chem.*, 1980, **45**, 3831.
194. W. Nagai, K. L. Kirk and L. A. Cohen, *J. Org. Chem.*, 1973, **38**, 1971.
195. M. Impicciatore, G. Morini, M. Chiavarini, P. V. Plazzi, F. Bordi and F. Vitali, *Agents Actions*, 1986, **18**, 134.
196. K. Biemann and H. Bretschneider, *Monatsh. Chem.*, 1958, **89**, 603.
197. M. Rocha e Silva, *Arch. Int. Pharmacodyn. Ther.*, 1960, **128**, 355.
198. E. J. Ariens and A. M. Simonis, *Arch. Int. Pharmacodyn. Ther.*, 1963, 141, 309.
199. A. Gero and M. T. Daniele, *Arch. Int. Pharmacodyn. Ther.*, 1970, **183**, 315.
200. M. J. Hughes and I. A. Coret, *Can. J. Physiol. Pharmacol.*, 1976, **54**, 118.
201. R. C. Dage and H. F. Hardman, *Eur. J. Pharmacol.*, 1970, **11**, 13.
202. J. M. Hand and C. K. Buckner, *Eur. J. Pharmacol.*, 1981, **70**, 225.
203. W. W. La Morte, S. J. Hingston and W. E. Wise, *J. Pharmacol. Exp. Ther.*, 1981, **217**, 638.
204. W. H. Hunt and R. J. Fosbinder, *J. Pharmacol Exp. Ther.*, 1942, **75**, 299.
205. F. J. Luque, F. Sanz, F. Illas, R. Pouplana and Y. G. Smeyers, *Eur. J. Med. Chem.,*, 1988, **23**, 7.
206. D. M. Blow, *Acc. Chem. Res.*, 1976, **9**, 145.
207. H. Weinstein, A. P. Mazurek, R. Osman and S. Topiol, *Mol. Pharmacol.*, 1986, **29**, 28.
208. C. L. Johnson, H. Weinstein and J. P. Green, *Biochim. Biophys. Acta.*, 1979, **587**, 155.
209. J. M. Palacios, M. Garbarg, G. Barbin and J.-C. Schwartz, *Mol. Pharmacol.*, 1978, **14**, 971.
210. P. D. Kanof and P. Greengard, *Mol. Pharmacol.*, 1979, **15**, 445.
211. C. R. Ganellin, G. N. J. Port and W. G. Richards, *J. Med. Chem.*, 1973, **16**, 616.
212. C. R. Ganellin, *J. Med. Chem.*, 1973, **16**, 620.
213. L. Farnell, W. G. Richards and C. R. Ganellin, *J. Med. Chem.*, 1975, **18**, 662.
214. W. G. Richards, J. Hammond and D. G. Aschmann, *J. Theor. Biol.*, 1975, **51**, 237.
215. W. G. Richards and J. Wallis, *J. Med. Chem.*, 1976, **19**, 1250.
216. G. J. Durant, C. R. Ganellin and M. E. Parsons, *Agents Actions*, 1977, **7**, 39.
217. G. Bertaccini, G. Coruzzi and T. Vitali, *Pharmacol. Res. Commun.*, 1978, **10**, 747.
218. G. Coruzzi, V. Plazzi and G. Bertaccini, *Boll. Soc. Ital. Biol. Sper.*, 1978, **54**, 910.
219. R. C. Blakemore, C. R. Ganellin, B. K. Leigh, M. E. Parsons, C. A. Price, I. R. Smith and W. Tertiuk, *Agents Actions*, 1986, **19**, 18.
220. G. J. Sterk, H. Van der Goot and H. Timmerman, *Acrh. Pharm. (Weinheim, Ger.)*, 1986, **319**, 624.
221. G. J. Sterk, H. Van der Goot and H. Timmerman, *Eur. J. Med. Chem.*, 1984, **19**, 93.
222. G. J. Sterk, H. Van der Goot and H. Timmerman, *Eur. J. Med. Chem.*, 1984, **19**, 545.
223. P. R. Gater, S. E. Webber, G. P. H. Gui, C. C. Jordan, N. A. Hayes, J. J. Ashford and J. C. Foreman, *Agents Actions*, 1986, **18**, 342.
224. G. M. Cuiffo, L. S. Mayorga, M. R. Estrada, R. R. Ibanez, M. B. Santillan and E. A. Jauregui, *J. Mol. Struct.*, 1983, **92**, 63.
225. Y. G. Smeyers, F. J. Romero-Sanchez and A. Hernandez-Laguna, *J. Mol. Struct.*, 1985, **123**, 431.
226. G. J. Sterk, H. Van der Goot and H. Timmerman, *Arch. Pharm. (Weinheim, Ger.)*, 1986, **319**, 1057.
227. J. W. Banning, R. K. Griffith and R. A. Dipietro, *Agents Actions*, 1985, **17**, 138.
228. H. H. Dale and H. W. Dudley, *J. Pharmacol. Exp. Ther.*, 1921, **18**, 103.
229. A. Burger, M. Bernabé and P. W. Collins, *J. Med. Chem.*, 1970, **13**, 33.
230. E. Lebenstedt and W. Schunack, *Arch. Pharm. (Weinheim, Ger.)*, 1977, **310**, 455.
231. W. Schunack, *Arch. Pharm. (Weinheim, Ger.)*, 1973, **306**, 934.
232. W. Schunack, *Agents Actions*, 1974, **4**, 195.
233. S. Schwarz and W. Schunack, *Arch. Pharm. (Weinheim, Ger.)*, 1979, **312**, 933.
234. E. Lebenstedt and W. Schunack, *Arch. Pharm. (Weinheim, Ger.)*, 1974, **307**, 894.
235. E. Lebenstedt and W. Schunack, *Arch. Pharm. (Weinheim, Ger.)*, 1975, **308**, 413.
236. W. Schunack, A. Buschauer, S. Büyüktimkin, P. Dziuron, S. Elz, G. Gerhard, E. Lebenstedt, H. G. Lennartz, S. Schwarz, M. Spitzhoff and R. Steffens, in 'Proceedings 8th International Symposium on Medicinal Chemistry', ed. R. Dahlbom and J. L. Nilsson, Swedish Pharmaceutical Press, Stockholm, 1985, vol. 2, p. 169.
237. I. C. Medgett and M. W. McCulloch, *Proc. Aust. Physiol. Pharmacol. Soc.*, 1978, **9**, 167P.
238. I. C. Medgett and M. W. McCulloch, *Arch. Int. Pharmacodyn. Ther.*, 1979, **240**, 158.
239. P. B. M. W. M. Timmermans and P. A. Van Zwieten, *Arch. Int. Pharmacodyn. Ther.*, 1977, **228**, 237.
240. B. Ruot, G. Leclerc. C. G. Wermuth, F. Miesch and J. Schwartz, *J. Med. Chem.*, 1976, **19**, 1049.
241. K. H. Pook, H. Stähle and H. Daniel, *Chem. Ber.*, 1974, **107**, 2644.
242. S. C. Verma and J. H. McNeill, *Agents Actions*, 1977, **7**, 191.
243. T. O. Yellin, J. W. Sperow and S. H. Buck, *Nature (London)*, 1975, **253**, 561.
244. K. E. Light and M. J. Hughes, *Agents Actions.* 1979, **9**, 141.

245. T. O. Yellin, S. H. Buck and E. M. Johnson, in ref. 15, p. 79.
246. J. Elguero, E. Gonzalez, J.-L. Imbach and R. Jacquier, *Bull. Soc. Chim. Fr.*, 1969, 4075.
247. P. E. Kearney, E. Malta and C. Raper, *Clin. Exp. Pharmacol. Physiol.*, 1979, **6**, 218.
248. J. Sanders, D. D. Miller and P. N. Pantil, *J. Pharmacol. Exp. Ther.*, 1975, **195**, 362.
249. T. O. Yellin, M. S. Katchen, S. R. Lavenhar and E. G. Nelson, *Acta. Physiol., Scand. Suppl.*, 1978, 219.
250. G. J. Durant, W. A. M. Duncan, C. R. Ganellin, M. E. Parsons, R. C. Blakemore and A. C. Rasmussen, *Nature (London)*, 1978, **276**, 403.
251. R. H. Hunt, J. G. Mills, J. Beresford, J. A. Billings, W. L. Burland and G. J. Milton-Thompson, *Gastroenterology*, 1980, **78**, 505.
252. G. J. Durant, C. R. Ganellin, D. W. Hills, P. D. Miles, M. E. Parsons, E. S. Pepper and G. R. White, *J. Med. Chem.*, 1985, **28**, 1414.
253. G. J. Durant, *Chem. Soc. Rev.*, 1985, **4**, 375.
254. W. Schunack and G. Gerhard, *Naunyn-Schmiedeberg's Arch. Pharmacol.*, 1982, **319**, R56.
255. C. Sellier, A. Buschauer, S. Elz and W. Schunack, *10th Int. Med. Chem. Symp., Budapest*, 1988, Poster.
256. G. J. Sterk, H. Van der Goot and H. Timmerman, *Eur. J. Med. Chem.*, 1987, **22**, 427.
257. S. Elz and W. Schunack, *Arzneim.-Forsch.*, 1988, **38**, 327.
258. G. J. Sterk, H. Van der Goot and H. Timmerman, *Eur. J. Med. Chem.*, 1986, **21**, 305.
259. G. J. Sterk, J. Koper, H. Van der Goot and H. Timmerman, *Eur. J. Med. Chem.*, 1987, **22**, 491.
260. A. Buschauer, *Eur. J. Med. Chem.*, 1988, **23**, 1; *J. Med. Chem.*, 1989, **32**, 1963.
261. M. E. Parsons, R. C. Blakemore, G. J. Durant, C. R. Ganellin and A. C. Rasmussen, *Agents Actions*, 1975, **5**, 464.
262. G. J. Durant, J. C. Emmett, C. R. Ganellin, P. D. Miles, H. D. Prain, M. E. Parsons and G. R. White, *J. Med. Chem.*, 1977, **20**, 901.
263. G. J. Sterk, Ph.D. Thesis, Vrije Universiteit, Amsterdam, 1987, p. 114.
264. J.-M Arrang and J.-C. Schwartz, personal communication.
265. R. Ganellin, *J. Med. Chem.*, 1981, **24**, 913.
266. N. B. Chapman and J. F. A. Williams, *J. Chem. Soc.*, 1953, 2797.
267. J. D. P. Graham and R. S. Tonks, *Arch. Int. Pharmacodyn. Ther.*, 1956, **106**, 457.
268. G. Gerhard and W. Schunack, *Arch. Pharm. (Weinheim, Ger.)*, 1981, **314**, 1040.
269. S. Schwarz and W. Schunack, *Arch. Pharm. (Weinheim, Ger.)*, 1979, **312**, 933.
270. D. Bovet, *Ann. N.Y. Acad. Sci.*, 1950, **50**, 1089.
271. B. N. Halpern, *Arch. Int. Pharmacodyn. Ther.*, 1942, **68**, 339.
272. C. P. Huttrer, *Enzymologia*, 1948, **12**, 277.
273. F. Leonard and C. P. Huttrer, in 'Histamine Antagonists. Review No. 3' Chemical–Biological Coordination Center, National Research Council, Washington, DC, 1950.
274. B. Idson, *Chem. Rev.*, 1950, **47**, 307.
275. M. Protiva, in 'Chemie Antihistaminovych Látek Histaminove Skupiny', Praha: Ceskoslovenske Akademie Ved, 1955.
276. A. F. Harms, W. Hespe, W. Th. Nauta, R. F. Rekker, H. Timmerman and J. DeVries, in 'Drug Design', ed. E. J. Ariens, Academic Press, New York, 1975, vol VI, p. 2.
277. A. F. Casy, in ref. 19, p. 175.
278. W. Th. Nauta and R. F. Rekker, in ref. 18, p. 215.
279. D. T. Witiak and R. C. Cavestri, in 'Burger's Medicinal Chemistry', ed. M. E. Wolff, 4th edn., Wiley-Interscience, New York, 1981, vol. 3, p. 553.
280. G. J. Durant, C. R. Ganellin, R. Griffiths, C. A. Harvey, D. A. A. Owen and G. S. Sach, in ref. 17, p. 3.
281. D. Bovet, *Science (Washington, D.C.)*, 1959, **129**, 1255.
282. J. L. Archibald, P. Fairbrother and J. L. Jackson, *J. Med. Chem.*, 1974, **17**, 739.
283. R. C. Blakemore, T. H. Brown, G. J. Durant, J. C. Emmett, C. R. Ganellin, M. E. Parsons and A. C. Rasmussen, *Br. J. Pharmacol.*, 1980, **70**, 105P.
284. E. A. Brown, R. Griffiths, C. A. Harvey and D. A. A. Owen, *Br. J. Pharmacol.*, 1986, **87**, 569.
285. C. A. Leonard, C. B. Jackson, D. J. Stephens, A. G. Proakis and R. S. Alphin, *Pharmacologist*, 1984, **26**, 221 (Abstr. 486–489).
286. F. Janssens, J. Torremans, M. Janssen, R. A. Stokbroekx, M. Luyckx and P. A. J. Janssen, *J. Med. Chem.*, 1985, **28**, 1925, 1934, 1943.
287. E. R. Loew, R. MacMillan and M. E. Kaiser, *J. Pharmacol. Exp. Ther.*, 1946, **86**, 229.
288. R. F. Rekker, H. Timmerman, A. F. Harms and W. Th. Nauta, *Chim. Ther.*, 1972, **7**, 279.
289. W. Albanus, E. Hansson and C. G. Schmiterlöw, *Acta Pharmacol. Toxicol.* 1961, **18**, 105.
290. H. Friebell, H. Flick and C. Reichle, *Arzneim.-Forsch.*, 1954, **4**, 171.
291. P. B. Marshall, *Br. J. Pharmacol.*, 1955, **10**, 270.
292. R. Meier, *Ann. N.Y. Acad. Sci.*, 1950, **50**, 1161.
293. H. Ahn and A. Barnett, *Eur. J. Pharmacol.*, 1986, **127**, 153.
294. G. G. Nys and R. F. Rekker, *Chim. Ther.*, 1973, **8**, 521.
295. G. G. Nys and R. F. Rekker, *Eur. J. Med. Chem.*, 1974, **9**, 361.
296. R. F. Rekker, W. Th. Nauta, T. Bultsma and C. G. Waringa, *Eur. J. Med. Chem.*, 1975, **10**, 557.
297. C. G. Waringa, R. F. Rekker and W. Th. Nauta, *Eur. J. Med. Chem*, 1975, **10**, 349.
298. E. Kutter and C. Hansch, *J. Med. Chem.*, 1969, **12**, 647.
299. B. Testa and L. Murset-Rossetti, *Helv. Chim. Acta*, 1978, **61**, 2530.
300. R. F. Rekker, H. Timmerman, A. F. Harms and W. Th. Nauta, *Arzneim.-Forsch.*, 1971, **21**, 688.
301. R. R. Ison, F. M. Franks and K. S. Soh, *J. Pharm. Pharmacol.*, 1973, **25**, 887.
302. F. G. Van den Brink and E. J. Lien, *Eur. J. Pharmacol.*, 1977, **44**, 251.
303. M. J. Jarrousse and M. T. Regnier, *Ann. Pharm. Fr.*, 1951, **9**, 321.
304. R. S. L. Chang, V. T. Tran and S. H. Snyder, *J. Neurochem.*, 1979, **32**, 1653.
305. F. E. Roth and W. M. Govier, *J. Pharmacol. Exp. Ther.*, 1958, **124**, 347.
306. A Shafi'ee and G. Hite, *J. Med. Chem.*, 1969, **12**, 266.
307. M. N. G. James and G. J. B. Williams, *Can. J. Chem.*, 1974, **52**, 1872.

308. F. E. Roth, *Chemotherapia*, 1961, **3**, 120.
309. V. Barough, H. Dall, D. Patel and G. Hite, *J. Med. Chem.*, 1971, **14**, 834.
310. A. P. Roszkowski and W. M. Govier, *Pharmacologist*, 1959, **1**, 60.
311. U. Borchard, D. Hafner and R. Heise, in *Naunyn-Schmiedeberg's Arch. Pharmacol.*, 1985, **330** (suppl.), Abstr. 42, R. 9.
312. A. Ebnother and H. P. Weber, *Helv. Chim. Acta*, 1976, **58**, 2462.
313. L. Toldy, L. Vargha, I. Toth and J. Borsy, *Acta Chim. Acad. Sci. Hung.*, 1959, **19**, 273.
314. R. A. Stokbroekx, M. G. M. Luyckx, J. L. M. Williams, M. Janssen, J. O. M. M. Bracke, R. L. P. Joosen and J. P. van Wauwe, *Drug Dev. Res.*, 1968, **8**, 87.
315. R. R. Ison and A. F. Casy, *J. Pharm. Pharmacol.*, 1971, **23**, 848.
316. D. T. Witiak, in 'Medicinal Chemistry', ed. A. Burger, 3rd edn., Wiley-Interscience, New York, 1970, p. 1643.
317. C. Escobar, P. Marsau and J. Clastre, *C. R. Hebd. Seances Acad. Sci., Ser. C*, 1968, **267**, 1399.
318. M. N. G. James and G. J. B. Williams, *J. Med. Chem.*, 1971, **14**, 670.
319. M. N. G. James and G. J. B. Williams, *Can. J. Chem.*, 1974, **52**, 1880.
320. G. R. Clark and G. J. Palenik, *J. Am. Chem. Soc.*, 1972, **94**, 4005.
321. P. Marsau and B. Busetta, *Acta Crystallogr., Sect. B*, 1973, **29**, 986.
322. P. Marsau and Y. Cam, *Acta Crystallogr., Sect. B*, 1973, **29**, 980.
323. G. Precigoux, Y. Barrans, B. Busetta and P. Marsau, *Acta Crystallogr., Sect. B*, 1975, **31**, 1497.
324. N. S. Ham, *J. Pharm. Sci.*, 1971, **60**, 1764.
325. N. S. Ham, *J. Pharm. Sci.*, 1976, **65**, 612.
326. B. Testa, *Jerusalem Symp. Quantum Chem. Biochem.*, 1974, **7**, 241.
327. N. Berova, St. Bojadziev and G. Snatzke, *Proc. Int. Conf. Circular Dichroism*, 1985, **6**, 303.
328. B. Pullman, P. Courriere and H. Berthod, *Mol. Pharmacol.*, 1975, **11**, 268.
329. P. E. Hanna and A. E. Ahmed, *J. Med. Chem.*, 1973, **16**, 963.
330. J. Barbe, A. Blanc and J. Hurwic, *C. R. Hebd. Seances Acad. Sci., Ser. C*, 1974, **278**, 211.
331. H. Hall and S. Ogren, *Life Sci.*, 1984, **34**, 597.
332. F. Awouters, J. Vermeire, F. Smeyers, P. Vermote, R. Van Beek and C. J. E. Niemegeers, *Drug Dev. Res.*, 1986, **8**, 95.
333. H. Zechel, N. Brock, D. Lenke and U. Achterrath-Tuckermann, *Arzneim.-Forsch.*, 1981, **31**, 1184.
334. M. B. Emanuel and G. D. W. Towse, *Drugs of Today*, 1980, **16**, 219.
335. U. Martin and D. Romer, *Arzneim.-Forsch.*, 1978, **28**, 1.
336. D. R. Buckle, C. J. M. Rockell, H. Smith and B. A. Spicer, *J. Med. Chem.*, 1986, **29**, 2262.
337. P. J. Barnes and K. Fon Chung, *Trends Pharmacol. Sci.*, 1987, **8**, 285.
338. J. Morley, C. P. Page, L. Muzzoni and S. Sanjar, *Ann. Allergy*, 1986, **56**, 335.
339. M. Criscuoli, S. Subissi, L. Daffonchio and C. Omini, *Agents Actions*, 1986, **19**, 246.
340. In ref. 24, p. 381; see also C. Rose, T. T. Quach, C. Llorens and J.-C. Schwartz, *Arzneim.-Forsch.*, 1982, **32(ii)**, 1171.
341. A. N. Nicholson, P. A. Pascoe, C. Turner, C. R. Ganellin, A. F. Casy and A. D. Mercer, *Br. J. Clin. Pharmacol.*, 1989.
342. E. J. Lien, in 'SAR: Side Effects and Drug Design', Marcel Dekker, New York, 1987, p. 184.
343. A Uzan, G. Le Fur and C. Malgouris, *J. Pharm. Pharmacol.*, 1979, **31**, 701.
344. T. T. Quach, A. M. Duchemin, C. Rose and J.-C. Schwartz, *Eur. J. Pharmacol.*, 1979, **60**, 391.
345. J. Barker, P. R. Andrews, E. J. Lloyd, P. Brouant, J.-C. Soyfer, J.-P. Galy and A.-M. Galy, *Eur. J. Med. Chem.*, 1983, **18**, 531.
346. A. A. Carr and D. R. Meyer, *Arzneim.-Forsch*, 1982, **32**, 1157.
347. E. M. Sorkin and R. C. Heel, *Drugs*, 1985, **29**, 34.
348. J. Vincent, D. J. Sumner and J. L. Reid, *Br. J. Clin. Pharmacol.*, 1988, **26**, 503.
349. F. Janssens, M. A. C. Janssen, F. Awouters, C. J. E. Niemegeers and G. V. Bussche, *Drug Dev. Res.*, 1986, **8**, 27.
350. C. J. E. Niemegeers, F. Awouters and P. A. J. Janssen, *Agents Actions*, 1986, **18**, 141.
351. N. Rombaut and G. Vanden Bussche, *Z. Hautkr.*, 1985, **60** (suppl.), 29.
352. D. G. Cooper, G. J. Durant, C. R. Ganellin, C. A. Harvey, M. L. Meeson, D. A. A. Owen, G. S. Sach and M. A. Wilczynska, in 'Proceedings 8th International Symposium on Medicinal Chemistry', ed. R. Dahlbom and J. L. G. Nilsson, Swedish Pharmaceutical Press, Stockholm, 1985, vol. 2, p. 198.
353. A. N. Nichloson, *Trends Pharmacol. Sci.*, 1987, **8**, 247.
354. A Barnett, L. C. Iorio, W. Kreutner, S. Tozzi, H. S. Ahn and A. Gulbenkian, *Agents Actions*, 1984, **14**, 590.
355. A. Poizot, D. Dumez, P. Ferrandon, C. Le Fournier, A. Michel and J. M. Armstrong, *Arzneim.-Forsch*, 1986, **36**, 695.
356. A. Fügner, W. D. Bechtel, F. J. Kuhn and J. Mierau, *Arzneim.-Forsch.*, 1988, **38** (ii), 1446.
357. S. Tozzi, F. E. Roth and I. L. A. Tabachnick, *Agents Actions*, 1974, **4**, 264.
358. A. F. Cohen, M. Hamilton, R. Philipson and A. W. Peck, *Clin. Pharmacol. Ther.*, 1985, **38**, 381.
359. J. Van Wauwe, F. Awouters, C. J. E. Niemegeers, F. Janssens, J. M. Van Nueten and P. A. J. Janssen, *Arch. Int. Pharmacodyn. Ther.*, 1981, **251**, 39.
360. J. C. Pechadre, D. Vernay, F. F. Trolese, M. Bloom, P. Dupont and J. P. Rihoux, *Eur. J. Clin. Pharmacol.*, 1988, **35**, 255.
361. R. C. Blakemore, T. H. Brown, D. G. Cooper, G. J. Durant, C. R. Ganellin, R. J. Ife, M. E. Parsons, A. C. Rasmussen and G. S. Sach, *Br. J. Pharmacol.*, 1983, **80**, 437P.
362. C. A. Harvey and D. A. A. Owen, *Br. J. Pharmacol.*, 1983, **80**, 438P; 1984, **83**, 427.
363. C. R. Ganellin, R. C. Blakemore, T. H. Brown, D. G. Cooper, G. J. Durant, C. A. Harvey, R. J. Ife, D. A. A. Owen, M. E. Parsons, A. C. Rasmussen and G. S. Sach, *N. Engl. Soc. Allergy Proc.*, 1986, **7**, 126.
364. R. C. Blakemore, T. H. Brown, G. J. Durant, J. C. Emmett, C. R. Ganellin, M. E. Parsons and A. C. Rasmussen, *Br. J. Pharmacol.*, 1980, **70**, 105P.
365. A. Verloop, W. Hoogenstraaten and J. Tipker, in 'Drug Design', ed. E. J. Ariens, Academic Press, New York, 1976, vol. 7, p. 165.
366. E. J. Ariens, A. M. Simonis and J. M. van Rossum, *Mol. Pharmacol.*, 1964, **1**, 212, 225.
367. W. Th. Nauta, R. F. Rekker and A. F. Harms, *Proc. Int. Pharmacol. Meet.*, 3rd, 1966, **7**, 305.
368. V. Popa, *Clin. Chest Med.* 1986, **7**, 367.
369. M. A. Drouin, *Ann. Allergy*, 1985, **55**, 747.
370. D. M. Paton and D. R. Webster, *Clin. Pharmacokinet.*, 1985, **10**, 477.
371. S. T. Holgate, *Agents Actions*, 1986, **18**, 281.

372. P. H. Howarth and S. T. Holgate, *J. Allergy Clin. Immunol.*, 1985, **75**, (suppl), 166.
373. J. G. Gleason, C. D. Perchonock and T. J. Torphy, *Annu. Rep. Med. Chem.*, 1986, **21**. 73.
374. J. Bergman and R. D. Spealman, *J. Pharmacol. Exp. Ther.*, 1988, **245**, 471.
375. A. W. Peck, A. S. E. Fowle and C. Bye, *Eur. J. Clin. Pharmacol.*, 1975, **8**, 455.
376. M. L. Brandon, *Drugs*, 1985, **30**, 377.
377. A. N. Nicholson, *Aviat. Space Environ. Med.*, 1985, **56**, 293.
378. J. J. Piwinski, J. K. Wong, M. J. Green, A. K. Ganguly, M. Motasim Billah and R. E. West, in '198th ACS Meeting', Miami, Sept. 1989, Abstr. Medi 88.
379. C. R. Ganellin, G. J. Durant and J. C. Emmett, *Fed. Proc., Fed. Am. Soc. Exp. Biol.*, 1976, **35**, 1924.
380. C. R. Ganellin, *J. Appl. Chem. Biotechnol.*, 1978, **28**, 183.
381. C. R. Ganellin, in ref. 19, p. 251.
382. P. E. Cross, R. P. Dickinson, J. E. G. Kemp, P. R. Leeming and L. G. Pullman, *J. Med. Chem.*, 1977, **20**, 1317.
383. E. R. Loew, M. E. Kaiser and V. Moore, *J. Pharmacol. Exp. Ther.*, 1945, **83**, 120.
384. C. Robertson and M. I. Grossman, *Arch. Int. Pharmacodyn. Ther.*, 1952, **91**, 1.
385. T. M. Lin, R. S. Alphin, F. G. Henderson, D. N. Benslay and K. K. Chen, *Ann. N.Y. Acad. Sci.*, 1962, **99**, 30.
386. G. J. Durant, M. E. Parsons and J. W. Black, *J. Med. Chem.*, 1975, **18**, 830.
387. R. W. Brimblecombe, W. A. M. Duncan, G. J. Durant, J. C. Emmett, C. R. Ganellin and M. E. Parsons, *J. Int. Med. Res.*, 1975, **3**, 86.
388. *Drugs of the Future*, 1987, **12**, 929.
389. W. Schunack, S. Schwarz, G. Gerhard, S. Büyüktimkin and S. Elz, in ref. 17, p. 39.
390. C. R. Ganellin and R. C. Young, in 'Neuropharmacology and Pesticide Action', ed. M. G. Ford, P. N. R. Usherwood, R. C. Reay and G. G. Lunt, Ellis Horwood, Chichester, 1986, chap. 5.
391. R. C. Young, C. R. Ganellin, M. J. Graham and E. H. Grant, *Tetrahedron*, 1982, 38, 1493.
392. R. C. Young, C. R. Ganellin, M. J. Graham and M. L. Roantree, *Tetrahedron Lett.*, 1985, **26**, 1897.
393. R. C. Young, *J. Pharm. Pharmacol.*, 1987, **39**, 861.
394. R. C. Young, G. J. Durant, J. C. Emmett, C. R. Ganellin, M. J. Graham, R. C. Mitchell, H. D. Prain and M. L. Roantree, *J. Med. Chem.*, 1986, **29**, 44.
395. G. M. Donné-Op den Kelder, E. E. J. Haaksma and H. Timmerman, *Quant. Struct.-Act. Relat.*, 1988, **7**, 7.
396. R. C. Young, C. R. Ganellin, M. J. Graham, R. C. Mitchell, M. L. Roantree and Z. Tashma, *J. Med. Chem.*, 1987, **30**, 1150.
397. T. H. Brown, R. C. Blakemore, G. J. Durant, J. C. Emmett, C. R. Ganellin, M. E. Parsons, D. A. Rawlings and T. F. Walker, *Eur. J. Med. Chem.*, 1988, **23**, 53.
398. J.-P. Spengler, K. Wegner and W. Schunack, *Agents Actions*, 1984, **14**, 566.
399. H.-D. Holtje, P. Batanowski, J.-P. Spengler and W. Schunack, *Arch. Pharm. (Weinheim, Ger.)*, 1985, **318**, 542.
400. C. R. Ganellin, G. J. Durant, J. C. Emmett, D. W. Hills, R. J. Ife, P. D. Miles and M. E. Parsons, in 'Proceedings 8th International Symposium on Medicinal Chemistry', ed. R. Dahlbom and J. L. G. Nilsson, Swedish Pharmaceutical Press, Stockholm, 1985, vol. 2, p. 153.
401. A. Borchers, H. Engler, I. Szelenyi and W. Schunack, *Arzneim.-Forsch.*, 1982, **32** (ii), 1509.
402. G. Charlot and B. Tremillon, in 'Les Reactions Chimiques dans les Solvents et les Sels Fondus', Gautier-Villars, Paris, 1963, p. 90.
403. D. W. Farlow and R. B. Moodie, *J. Chem. Soc. B*, 1971, 407.
404. W. D. Kumler and G. M. Fohlen, *J. Am. Chem. Soc.*, 1942, **64**, 1944.
405. W. D. Kumler and P. T. Sah, *J. Org. Chem.*, 1953, **18**, 669.
406. R. C. Mitchell, unpublished data; Smith Kline and French Research Ltd.
407. H. Stephen and T. Stephen, in 'Solubilities of Inorganic and Organic Compounds', Pergamon, Oxford, 1963, vol. 1.
408. M. L. Filleux-Blanchard and A. Durand, *Org. Magn. Reson.*, 1971, **3**, 187.
409. M. Herlem, *Bull. Soc. Chim. Fr.*, 1965, 3329.
410. M. J. Janssen, *Recl. Trav. Chim. Pays-Bas*, 1962, **81**, 650.
411. N. Kameyama, *Kogyo Kagaku Zasshi*, 1921, **24**, 98; *Chem. Abstr.*, 1922, **16**, 2247.
412. R. C. Hirt, R. G. Schmitt, H. L. Strauss and J. G. Koren, *J. Chem. Eng. Data*, 1961, **6**, 610.
413. W. C. Schneider, *J. Am. Chem. Soc.*, 1950, **72**, 761.
414. C. G. McCarty and D. M. Wieland, *Tetrahedron Lett.*, 1969, 1787.
415. H. Kessler and D. Liebfritz, *Tetrahedron*, 1970, **26**, 1805.
416. J. E. DeVries and E. St. Clair Grantz, *J. Am. Chem. Soc.*, 1954, **76**, 1008.
417. T. G. Bonner and J. C. Lockhardt, *J. Chem. Soc.*, 1958, 3858.
418. G. Isaksson and J. Sandström, *Acta. Chem. Scand.*, 1973, **27**, 1183.
419. D. J. Brown and T. Teitei, *Aust. J. Chem.*, 1965, **18**, 559.
420. H. Lumbroso and D. M. Bertin, *Bull. Soc. Chim. Fr.*, 1970, 1728.
421. C. I. Béguin and T. Gäumann, *Helv. Chim. Acta.*, 1958, **49**, 1971.
422. D. L. Rabenstein, R. Ludowyke and D. Lagunoff, *Biochemistry*, 1987, **26**, 6923.
423. R. C. Mitchell, *J. Chem. Soc., Perkin Trans. 2*, 1980, 915.
424. B. Kamenar, K. Prout and C. R. Ganellin, *J. Chem. Soc., Perkin Trans. 2*, 1973, 1734.
425. K. Prout, S. R. Critchley, C. R. Ganellin and R. C. Mitchell, *J. Chem. Soc., Perkin Trans. 2*, 1977, 68.
426. E. Hädicke, F. Frickel and A. Franke, *Chem. Ber.*, 1978, **111**, 3222.
427. K. Prout and C. R. Ganellin, in 'Structural Studies on Molecules of Biological Interest', ed. G. Dodson, J. P. Glusker and D. Sayre, Clarendon Press, Oxford, 1981, p. 176.
428. P. E. Glover, D. Phil. Thesis, University of Oxford, 1979.
429. B. Kojic-Prodic, Z. Ruzic-Toros, N. Bresciani-Pahor and L. Randaccio, *Acta. Crystallogr., Sect. B*, 1980, **36**, 1223.
430. K. Wegner, E. Fritschi and W. Schunack, *Arch. Pharm. (Weinheim, Ger.)*, 1978, **311**, 98.
431. A. Borchers, N. Büyüktimkin and W. Schunack, *Sci. Pharm.*, 1983, **51**, 3.
432. J. M. Hoffman, A. M. Pietruszkiewicz, C. N. Habecker, B. T. Phillips, W. A. Bolhofer, E. J. Cragoe, M. L. Torchiana, W. C. Lumma and J. J. Baldwin, *J. Med. Chem.*, 1983, **26**, 140.
433. E. P. Krebs, *Helv. Chim. Acta.*, 1979, **62**, 507.

434. J. R. Bagley and T. N. Riley, *J. Heterocycl. Chem.*, 1982, **19**, 485.
435. J. Herke and W. Schunack, *Arch. Pharm. (Weinheim, Ger.)*, 1979, **312**, 35.
436. J. Herke and W. Schunack, *Arch. Pharm. (Weinheim, Ger.)*, 1982, **315**, 641.
437. G. J. Durant, T. H. Brown, J. C. Emmett, C. R. Ganellin, H. D, Prain and R. C. Young, *Spec. Publ. Chem. Soc.*, 1982, **42**, 27.
438. T. H. Brown and R. C. Young, *Drugs of the Future*, 1985, **10**, 51.
439. W. Liebenow, H. Engler and K. Mannhardt, *Br. Pat.* 2 094 300, (1982).
440. G. Comisso, R. Toso, G. Gratton, F. Kajfez and V. Sunjic, *Acta Pharm. Jugosl.*, 1979, **29**, 125.
441. H. Tecle, L. Robichaud and C. F. Schwender, *J. Med. Chem.*, 1981, **24**, 1095.
442. T. O. Yellin, S. H. Buck, D. J. Gilman, D. F. Jones and J. M. Wardleworth, *Life Sci.*, 1979, **25**, 2001.
443. D. J. Gilman, D. F. Jones, K. Oldham, J. M. Wardleworth, *Spec. Publ. Chem. Soc.*, 1982, **42**, 58.
444. S. Elz and W. Schunack, *Arzneim.-Forsch.*, 1988, **38**, (1), 7.
445. S. Elz, G. Gerhard and W. Schunack, *Eur. J. Med. Chem.*, 1989, **24**, 259.
446. C. R. Ganellin, in ref. 17, p. 47.
447. A. A. Algieri, G. M. Luke, R. T. Standridge, M. Brown, R. A. Partylea and R. R. Crenshaw, *J. Med. Chem.*, 1982, **25**, 210.
448. W. C. Lumma, P. S. Anderson, J. J. Baldwin, W. A. Bolhofer, C. N. Habecker, J. M. Hirshfield, A. M. Pietruszkiewicz, W. C. Randall, M. W. Torchiana, S. F. Britcher, B. V. Clineschmidt, G. H. Denny, R. Hirschmann, J. M. Hoffman, B. T. Phillips and K. B. Streeter, *J. Med. Chem.*, 1982, **25**, 207.
449. T. O. Yellin and D. J. Gilman, *Eur. Pat.*, 0 060 090, (1982).
450. J. Bradshaw, R. T. Brittain, J. W. Clitherow, M. J. Daly, D. Jack, B. J. Price and R. Stables, *Br. J. Pharmacol.*, 1979, **66**, 464P.
451. J. Bradshaw, M. E. Butcher, J. W. Clitherow, M. D. Dowle, R. Hayes, D. B. Judd, J. M. McKinnon and B. J. Price, *Spec. Publ. Chem. Soc.*, 1982, **42**, 45.
452. T. M. Lin, D. C. Evans, M. W. Warrick, R. P. Pioch and R. R. Ruffolo, *Gastroenterology*, 1983, **84**, 1231.
453. R. C. Blakemore, T. H. Brown, G. J. Durant, C. R. Ganellin, M. E. Parsons, A. C. Rasmussen and D. A. Rawlings, *Br. J. Pharmacol.*, 1981, **74**, 200P.
454. R. C. Blakemore, T. H. Brown, R. J. Chenery, G. J. Durant, C. R. Ganellin, M. E. Parsons, A. C. Rasmussen and D. A. Rawlings, *Br. J. Pharmacol.*, 1985, **86**, 570P.
455. A. Buschauer, K. Wegner and W. Schunack, *Eur. J. Med. Chem.*, 1982, **17**, 505.
456. R. T. Brittain, M. J. Daly, J. M. Humphray and R. Stables, *Br. J. Pharmacol.*, 1982, **76**, 195P.
457. R. T. Brittain and D. Jack, *J. Clin. Gastroenterol.*, 1983, **5**, (suppl. 1), 71.
458. R. Stables, M. J. Daly and J. M. Humphray, *Agents Actions*, 1983, **13**, 166.
459. R. C. Young, R. C. Mitchell, T. H. Brown, C. R. Ganellin, R. Griffiths, M. Jones, K. K. Rana, D. Saunders, I. R. Smith, N. E. Sore and T. J. Wilks, *J. Med. Chem.*, 1988, **31**, 656.
460. J. P. Buyniski, R. L. Cavanagh, A. W. Pircio, A. A. Algieri and R. R. Crenshaw, in 'Highlights in Receptor Chemistry', ed. C. Melchiorre and M. Giannella, Elsevier, Amsterdam, 1984, p. 195.
461. M. J. Daly and B. J. Price, in 'Progress in Medicinal Chemistry', ed. G. P. Ellis and G. B. West, Elsevier, Amsterdam, 1983, vol. 20, p. 337.
462. D. E. Bays and B. J. Price, in 'Proceedings 8th International Symposium on Medicinal Chemistry', ed. R. Dahlbom and J. L. G. Nilsson, Swedish Pharmaceutical Press, Stockholm, 1985, vol. 2, p. 183.
463. M. Tarutani, H. Sakuma, K. Shiratsuchi and M. Mieda, *Arzneim.-Forsch.*, 1985, **359** (1), 703.
464. M. L. Torchiana, R. G. Pendleton, P. G. Cook, C. A. Hanson and B. V. Clineschmidt, *J. Pharmacol. Exp. Ther.*, 1983, **224**, 514.
465. J. A. Wilson, D. A. Johnston, J. Penston and K. G. Wormsley, *Br. J. Clin. Pharmacol.*, 1986, **21**, 685.
466. R. G. Button, J. P. Cairns and P. J. Taylor, *J. Chem. Soc., Perkin Trans. 2*, 1985, 1555.
467. R. J. Ife, Smith Kline and French Research Ltd., unpublished studies.
468. C. A. Lipinski, *J. Med. Chem.*, 1983, **26**, 1.
469. C. A. Lipinski, J. L. LaMattina and L. A. Hohnke, *J. Med. Chem.*, 1985, **28**, 1628.
470. C. A. Lipinski, J. L. LaMattina and P. J. Oates, *J. Med. Chem.*, 1986, **29**, 2154.
471. A. Donetti, E. Cereda, E. Bellora, A. Gallazzi, C. Bazzano, P. Vanoni, P. Del Soldato, R. Micheletti, F. Pagani and A. Giachetti, *J. Med. Chem.*, 1984, **27**, 380.
472. C. Bazzano, P. C. Vanoni, M. Mondoni, A. Gallazzi, E. Cereda and A. Donetti, *Eur. J. Med. Chem.*, 1986, **21**, 27.
473. E. E. J. Haaksma, B. Rademaker, K. Kramer, J. Ch. Eriks, A. Bast and H. Timmerman, *J. Med. Chem.*, 1987, **30**, 208.
474. G. Bietti, E. Cereda, A. Giachetti, R. Micheletti, A. Bast, H. Timmerman and A. Donetti, *Eur. J. Med. Chem.*, 1988, **23**, 267.
475. G. Bietti, E. Cereda, A. Donetti, P. Del Soldato, A. Giachetti and R. Micheletti, *Eur. Pat.*, 89 730, (1983).
476. A. Donetti, E. Cereda, A. Ezhaya and R. Micheletti, *J. Med. Chem.*, 1989, **32**, 957.
477. C. Scarpignato, A. Donetti, A. Giachetti and S. Daniotti, *Drugs of the Future*, 1987, **12** (suppl. 1), 5.
478. M. Tintelnot, *Arch. Pharm. (Weinheim, Ger.)*,, 1987, **320**, 275.
479. J.-C. Schwartz, J. J. Arrang, M. Garbarg and M. Korner, *J. Exp. Biol.*, 1986, **124**, 203.
480. W. R. Glave and C. Hansch, *J. Pharm. Sci.*, 1972, **61**, 589.
481. C. Hansch, J. P. Björkroth and A. Leo, *J. Pharm. Sci.*, 1987, **76**, 663.
482. P. Seiler, *Eur. J. Med. Chem.*, 1974, **9**, 473.
483. T. Shibata, 104th Annual Meeting Japanese Pharmaceutical Association (Sendai), 1984.
484. C. R. Calcutt, C. R. Ganellin, R. Griffiths, B. K. Leigh, J. P. Maguire, R. C. Mitchell, M. E. Mylek, M. E. Parsons, I. R. Smith and R. C. Young, *Br. J. Pharmacol.*, 1988, **93**, 69.
485. F. J. Villani, C. V. Magatti, D. B. Vashi, J. Wong and T. L. Popper, *Arzneim.-Forsch.*, 1986, **36**, 1311.
486. H. J. Leighton, R. F. Batz and J. W. A. Findlay, *Pharmacologist*, 1983, **25**, 163.
487. A. Buschauer, W. Schunack, J. M. Arrang, M. Garbarg, J.-C. Schwartz and J. M. Young, in 'Receptor Pharmacology and Function', ed. M. Williams, R. A. Glennon and P. B. M. W. M. Timmermans, Dekker, New York, 1989, p. 293.
488. J. W. Black, W. A. M. Duncan, J. C. Emmett, C. R. Ganellin, T. Hesselbo, M. E. Parsons and J. H. Wyllie, *Agents Actions*, 1973, **3**, 133.
489. M. Takeda, T. Takagi, Y. Yashima and H. Maeno, *Arzneim.-Forsch.*, 1982, **32** (ii), 734.

490. R. L. Cavanagh, J. J. Usakewicz and J. P. Buyniski, *J. Pharmacol. Exp. Ther.*, 1983, **224**, 171.
491. R. L. Cavanagh, J. J. Usakewicz and J. P. Buyniski, 64th Ann. Meeting Fed. Am. Soc. Exp. Biol., Anaheim, California, 1980.
492. R. T. Brittain and M. J. Daly, *Scand. J. Gastroenterol.*, 1981, **16**, (suppl. 69), 1.
493. S. T. Nielsen, *J. Pharmacol. Exp. Ther.*, 1987, **242**, 607.
494. A. A. Santilli, A. C. Scotese, R. L. Morris, S. T. Nielsen and D. P. Strike, *Eur. J. Med. Chem.*, 1989, **24**, 87.
495. A. Lavezzo, L. Manzoni, G. Aureggi, D. Nisato, A. Bianchetti and P. Carminati, *Int. J. Tissue. React.*, 1984, **6**, 155.
496. J. M. Humphray, M. J. Daly and R. Stables, *Gut*, 1982, **23**, A899, Abstr. T. 36.
497. M. Tarutani, H. Sakuma, K. Shiratsuchi and M. Mieda, *Arzneim.-Forsch*, 1985, **35**, 703.
498. M. Tsuritani, H. Matsukawa, H. Aoki and M. Seya, 57th Annual Meeting of Japanese Pharmacological Society, Kyoto, 1984, Abstr. 0-92.
499. S. T. Nielsen, P. Dove, G. Palumbo, A. Sandor, C. Buonato, G. Schiehser, A. Santilli and D. Strike, *Fed. Proc., Fed. Am. Soc. Exp. Biol.*, 1984, **43**, 1074, Abstr. 4617.
500. A. A. Santilli, A. C. Scotese, R. L. Morris, G. A. Schiehser, D. M. Teller, S. T. Nielsen and D. P. Strike, *J. Med. Chem.*, 1988, **31**, 1479.
501. S. T. Nielsen, *Agents Actions*, 1986, **19**, 158.
502. R. L. Cavanagh, J. J. Usakewicz and J. P. Buyniski, *Fed. Proc., Fed. Am. Soc. Exp. Biol.*, 1981, **40**, 693, Abstr. 2652.
503. T. Takagi, M. Takeda and H. Maeno, *Arch. Int. Pharmacodyn. Ther.*, 1982, **256**, 49.
504. J. D. Coombes, D. B. Norris, T. J. Rising, B. C. Ross and A. Steward, *Life Sci.*, 1985, **37**, 1711, 1719.
505. P. J. Oates, C. A. Lipinski, G. M. Frame, J. L. La Mattina and M. G. Page, *Gastroenterology*, 1985, **88**, 1520.
506. A. Donetti, G. Trummlitz, G. Bietti, E. Cereda, C. Bazzano and H. U. Wagner, *Arzneim.-Forsch.*, 1985, **35** (1), 306.
507. G. Bietti, A. Donetti and A. Giachetti, *Drugs of the Future*, 1985, **10**, 551.
508. J. A. H. Forrest, D. J. C. Shearman, R. Spence and L. R. Celestin, *Lancet*, 1975, **1**, 392.
509. H. J. Zimmerman, L. Jacob, H. Bassan, J. Gillespie, L. Lukacs and C. O. Abernathy, *Proc. Soc. Exp. Biol. Med.*, 1986, **182**, 511.
510. G. F. Rush, D. Alberts, S. Lupo, L. A. Yodis, T. H. Brown and G. J. Durant, *J. Pharmacol. Exp. Ther.*, 1988, **244**, 113.
511. R. A. Wilson, T. Hall, and J. Hart, *J. Appl. Toxicol.*, 1988, **8**, 223.
512. G. R. Betton and G. K. Salmon, *Scand. J. Gastroenterol.*, 1984, **19** (suppl. 101), 103.
513. K. Wormsley, *Gut*, 1984, **25**, 1416.
514. R. T. Brittain, D. Jack, J. J. Reeves and R. Stables, *Br. J. Pharmacol.*, 1985, **85**, 843.
515. C. S. Streett, R. E. Cimprich and J. L. Robertson, *Scand. J. Gastroenterol.*, 1984, 19 (suppl. 101), 109.
516. P. J. Barnes and M. Ichinose, *Trends Pharmacol. Sci.*, 1989, **10**, 264.
517. J. G. Mills, P. G. Brunet and R. Griffiths, *Gut*, 1982, **23**, 157.
518. J. B. Zeldis, L. S. Friedman and K. J. Isselbacher, *New Engl. J. Med.*, 1983, **309**, 1368.
519. H. G. Dammann, P. Muller and B. Simon, *Lancet*, 1982, **1**, 224.
520. W. L. Burland, J. G. Mills and L. J. Richardson, *Acta Pharmacol. Toxicol.*, 1986, **59** (suppl. 5), 319, Abstr. 1626.
521. J. E. Valenzuela, R. B. Strecker and A. P. Douglas, *Dig. Dis. Sci.*, 1981, **26**, 433.
522. C. T. Richardson, M. Feldman, C. Brater and J. Welborn, *Gastroenterology*, 1981, **80**, 301.
523. T. Takabatake, H. Ohta, Y. Yamamoto, Y. Ishida, H. Hara, S. Nakamura, Y. Ushiogi, S. Satoh and N. Hattori, *Eur. J. Clin. Pharmacol.*, 1986, **30**, 709.
524. R. Vargas, J. R. Ryan, F. G. McMahon and G. Regel, *J. Clin. Pharmacol.*, 1985, **25**, 455.
525. J. L. Smith, *Digestion*, 1985, **32** (suppl. 1), 15.
526. G. Bianchi Porro, M. Lazzaroni, B. P. Imbimbo, O. Sangaletti, C. Ghirdosi and S. Daniotti, *Eur. J. Clin. Pharmacol.*, 1987, **32**, 555.
527. G. Laferla, N. Buchanan, J. Hearns, G. P. Crean, K. E. L. McColl and A. T. Clucas, *Br. J. Clin. Pharmacol.*, 1986, **22**, 395.
528. J. P. Green, C. L. Johnson and H. Weinstein, in 'Psychopharmacology: a Generation of Progress', ed. M. A. Lipton, A. Di Mascio and K. F. Killam, Raven Press, New York, 1978, p. 319.
529. C. R. Calcutt, C. R. Ganellin, B. Jackson, B. K. Leigh, D. A. A. Owen and I. R. Smith, *Eur. J. Pharmacol.*, 1987, **133**, 65.
530. M. K. McCall, N. Nair, S. Wong, R. G. Townley, D. Lang and S. J. Weiss, *J. Allergy Clin. Immunol.*, 1985, **75**, 168.
531. J. M. Humphray, D. E. Bays, R. T. Brittain, J. J. Reeves and R. Stables, *Br. J. Pharmacol.*, 1988, **95**, 749P.
532. J. M. Arrang, N. Defontaine and J.-C. Schwartz, *Eur. J. Pharmacol.*, 1988, **157**, 31.
533. J. M. Arrang, M. Garbarg, J. C. M. Lancelot, J. M. Lecomte, M. F. Robba and J.-C. Schwartz, *Eur. Pat.*, 0 197 840, (1986).
534. R. Lipp, W. Schunack, J. M. Arrang, M. Garbarg and J.-C. Schwartz, '10th International Symposium on Medicinal Chemistry', Budapest, 1988, Poster presentation, Abstr. p. 119.
535. I. J. Roman, N. Kassem, R. P. Gural and J. Herron, *Ann. Allergy*, 1986, **57**, 253.
536. A. D. Cale, T. W. Gero, K. R. Walker, Y. S. Lo, W. J. Welstead, L. W. Jaques, A. F. Johnson, C. A. Leonard, J. C. Nolan and D. N. Johnson, *J. Med. Chem.*, 1989, **32**, 2178.
537. S. G. Chiverton, D. W. Burget and R. H. Hunt, *Gut*, 1989, **30**, 594.

12.6

Cholinergic Receptors

JÜRGEN WESS, THOMAS BUHL, GÜNTER LAMBRECHT AND
ERNST MUTSCHLER

University of Frankfurt/Main, FRG

12.6.1 CHOLINERGIC RECEPTORS: DEFINITION

Acetylcholine (ACh; **3**; equation 1) is one of the major neurotransmitters in both the central and the peripheral nervous systems. In addition to its role as the transmitter in all postganglionic parasympathetic nerves, it has transmitter function in all preganglionic fibers of peripheral autonomic ganglia, motor nerves to skeletal muscle and certain synapses within the CNS. As with other neurotransmitters or hormones, the physiological effects of ACh are mediated by specialized cell surface receptors, known as cholinergic receptors or cholinoceptors, which upon binding of ACh initiate a series of biochemical and/or electrophysiological events that eventually lead to the final cellular response.

$$\underset{\textbf{(1)}}{Me_3\overset{+}{N}CH_2CH_2OH} + \underset{\textbf{(2)}}{CoAS\overset{O}{\overset{\|}{C}}Me} \xrightarrow[\text{(ChAT)}]{\substack{\text{choline}\\ \text{acetyltransferase}}} \underset{\textbf{(3) ACh}}{Me_3\overset{+}{N}CH_2CH_2O\overset{O}{\overset{\|}{C}}Me} + CoASH \qquad (1)$$

12.6.2 ACETYLCHOLINE: SYNTHESIS, STORAGE, RELEASE AND ENZYMATIC CLEAVAGE

ACh (**3**) is synthesized in the cytoplasm of cholinergic nerve terminals from choline (**1**) and acetyl CoA (**2**) through the catalytic action of the enzyme choline acetyltransferase (ChAT; $M \approx 68\,000$; equation 1).[1] The synthesis of acetyl CoA takes place in the mitochondria, which are present in large numbers in the axonal terminal. Choline, on the other hand, is mainly provided by transport into the nerve endings from the extracellular fluid by two kinetically distinct uptake mechanisms: (i) a saturable, sodium dependent, high affinity process; and (ii) a high capacity, low affinity process.[2] It is believed that the high affinity transport system, which can be specifically blocked by hemicholinium, is crucial for the delivery of choline into the axon terminals.

Most of the ACh synthesized in the cytoplasm is sequestered in synaptic vesicles (mean diameter 20–40 nm). There is evidence that the uptake of ACh into these storage organelles involves the action of a proton-translocating ATPase.[3,4] Estimates of the ACh content of the synaptic vesicles range from 1000 to over 50 000 molecules per vesicle.[1] Besides ACh, the vesicles may also contain ATP,[3] proteoglycan[3] or peptide hormones such as vasoactive intestinal polypeptide (VIP),[5,6] which probably act as cotransmitters. When an action potential arrives at the cholinergic nerve terminal, ACh is released by fusion with the presynaptic membrane of nearby ACh-containing vesicles.[4] This process is critically dependent on the influx of Ca^{2+} ions into the nerve ending, which is in turn triggered by the action potential.[7] In agreement with the proposed vesicular mechanism of ACh liberation, electrophysiological experiments have demonstrated that ACh is in fact released in the form of discrete quanta.[1] The vesicular release of ACh can be specifically inhibited by botulinum toxin (a mixture of several individual toxins produced by *Clostridium botulinum*),[8] which is the cause of botulism, a serious neuroparalytic condition. However, recent investigations have revealed alternative modes of ACh release (*e.g.* release from cytoplasmic pools) which can no longer be explained by the classical vesicular hypothesis alone.[3]

ACh released into the synaptic cleft may bind to and activate specific cholinergic receptors located in the pre- and/or post-synaptic membrane. However, consistent with its role as a neurotransmitter, ACh present in the synaptic cleft is rapidly inactivated, mainly due to hydrolytic cleavage through the catalytic action of the enzyme acetylcholinesterase (AChE; also called specific or true AChE). Neither of the hydrolysis products, acetic acid and choline, displays significant cholinergic activity. Although AChE (for entire amino acid sequence, see ref. 9) is usually enriched in the membranes of cholinergic synapses, it is also found on noncholinergic neurons or cells not supplied with cholinergic nerves (*e.g.* erythrocytes). AChE, which exists in several different molecular forms,[10] is one of the most efficient enzymes known and has the capacity to hydrolyze 3×10^5 ACh molecules per enzyme molecule per minute.[1] Another ACh-hydrolyzing enzyme, structurally closely related to AChE, is butyrylcholinesterase (BuChE; also known as serum-ChE, pseudo-ChE or nonspecific ChE).[11] BuChE can be distinguished from AChE on the basis of substrate selectivity.[1] AChE, for example, hydrolyzes ACh at a greater velocity than choline esters with acyl groups larger than acetate, while BuChE displays a clear preference for butyrylcholine as a substrate. Although BuChE is present in the plasma, liver, glia and a variety of other tissues, no clearly defined functional role has so far been identified for this enzyme.

12.6.3 SUBCLASSIFICATION OF CHOLINERGIC RECEPTORS INTO NICOTINIC AND MUSCARINIC RECEPTORS

In 1914 Sir Henry Dale[12] introduced the terms 'nicotinic' and 'muscarinic' to describe the different physiological effects of ACh that were mimicked by the alkaloids nicotine (from tobacco, *Nicotiana tabacum*) and muscarine (isolated from the toadstool *Amanita muscaria*), respectively. Later studies showed that Dale's classical experiments were consistent with the concept that ACh acted through two major receptor subtypes, which are now referred to as nicotinic and muscarinic ACh receptors. Nicotinic receptors can be selectively stimulated by agents such as nicotine, 1,1-dimethyl-4-phenylpiperazinium (DMPP) or phenyltrimethylammonium (PTMA) and are highly sensitive to blockade by compounds such as (+)-tubocurarine, hexamethonium or decamethonium. Muscarinic receptors, on the other hand, are selectively activated by agonists such as muscarine, methacholine, arecoline or pilocarpine and are blocked by antagonists such as atropine, scopolamine or 3-quinuclidinylbenzilate (QNB). However, nicotinic and muscarinic receptors do not only differ in their affinities for agonists and antagonists, but also in many other fundamental respects such as location, function, molecular architecture and receptor–effector coupling mechanisms (see below).

12.6.4 NICOTINIC RECEPTORS

The nicotinic ACh receptor (nAChR) is by far the best-characterized neurotransmitter receptor and has proved to be an ideal model for the study of the structure and function of membrane receptors in general. Furthermore, the study of the nAChR is also of great importance with regard to human pathology, since it is known that a neuromuscular disease, myasthenia gravis, results from the loss of functional skeletal muscle nAChRs due to an autoimmune reaction.[13] In the following chapters, current knowledge about the location, structure, function and heterogeneity of nAChRs is briefly outlined. For other important aspects of the nAChR concerning, for example, receptor synthesis[14, 15] or regulation of receptor number,[16, 17] the reader is referred to several excellent reviews.

12.6.4.1 Assay Methods for Nicotinic Receptors

The nAChR has been extensively studied by electrophysiological, pharmacological, biochemical, immunological and, more recently, molecular biological approaches, principally due to two main reasons. The first is the rich source of nAChRs present in the electric organs in several species of fish, such as *Torpedo marmorata* and *Torpedo californica* (marine elasmobranch fish), or the electric eel, *Electrophorus electricus* (a freshwater teleost). The concentration of nAChRs in *Torpedo* electric organ, for example, is about 2500 times higher than that found in adult skeletal muscle.[18] As the cells (electrocytes or electroplaques) constituting the electric organs embryologically derive from skeletal muscle cells, it is not surprising that their nAChRs are structurally and functionally closely related to those of the neuromuscular junction in higher mammals (*cf.* Section 12.6.4.6). The second factor that has critically contributed to the early characterization of the nAChR has been the availability of certain α-neurotoxins, *e.g.* α-bungarotoxin (α-BTX) and α-cobratoxin, isolated from the venoms of various elapid and hydrophid snakes.[19] These small polypeptides ($M = 7000$–8000) specifically bind to nAChRs by forming noncovalent but extremely tight complexes (K_D values 10^{-8}–10^{-12} M).[19]

The snake α-toxins, in addition to other nicotinic ligands such as (+)-tubocurarine or decamethonium, have provided the means for assaying receptor binding and for affinity purification of the nAChR (*cf.* Section 12.6.4.5). Moreover, nAChRs have also been identified by the use of specific affinity reagents such as 4-(*N*-maleimido)benzyltrimethylammonium (MBTA; 4) or bromoacetylcholine (5), which, under reducing conditions, covalently bind to the receptor protein.[20] More recently, the identification of peripheral as well as central putative nAChR sites has also been achieved by the use of tritiated nicotinic agonists such as [^{3}H]nicotine or [^{3}H]ACh (see below).[21]

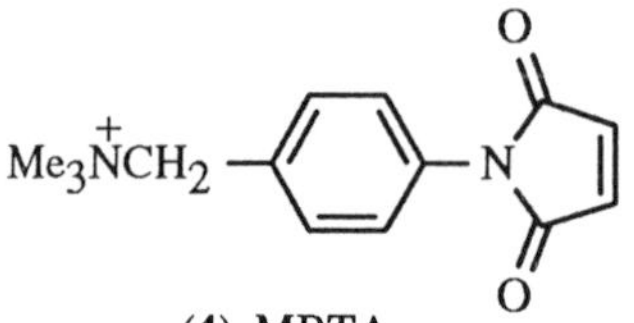

$Me_3\overset{+}{N}CH_2$ ———⟨benzene ring⟩——— N (maleimide ring with two O) $Me_3\overset{+}{N}CH_2CH_2O\overset{O}{\overset{\|}{C}}CH_2Br$

(4) MBTA 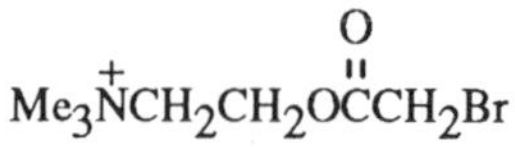   **(5) Bromoacetylcholine**

The functional consequences of stimulating or blocking skeletal muscle nAChRs can be studied in a variety of different *in vivo* (*e.g.* tibialis anterior muscle of the cat) and *in vitro* preparations (*e.g.* frog rectus abdominis muscle or rat phrenic nerve–diaphragm preparation) by recording muscle contraction reponses.[22] Likewise, the electrophysiological events following the activation of both skeletal muscle and neuronal nAChRs can be investigated by various different experimental approaches.[17, 23, 24, 28] The advent of patch clamp technology has allowed a uniquely detailed view of nAChR function in the form of single-channel recordings.[25]

Other developments which have greatly advanced the study of nAChRs have been the availability of antibodies raised against many antigenic sites of the receptor,[26] as well as the recent application of recombinant DNA technology,[27] which has provided exciting new insights into nAChR structure and function (*cf.* Sections 12.6.4.6 and 12.6.4.7).

12.6.4.2 Location and Function of Nicotinic Receptors

12.6.4.2.1 Peripheral nicotinic receptors

The major function of peripheral nAChRs is to mediate the excitatory actions of ACh released at the neuromuscular junction[28] and in autonomic ganglia.[29] Stimulation of nAChRs located on the motor endplates of skeletal muscle leads to a localized postjunctional endplate potential (EPP), which then triggers the muscle action potential that finally leads to contraction. Activation of postjunctional nAChRs on autonomic ganglion cells gives rise to the fast excitatory postsynaptic potential (fast EPSP), which, when attaining a critical amplitude, generates an action potential in the postganglionic neuron. In the adrenal medulla, which is embryologically and anatomically homologous to a sympathetic ganglion, stimulation of nAChRs results in the release of epinephrine (adrenaline).

In addition to their well-known localization on the postjunctional membranes of autonomic ganglia and the neuromuscular junction, excitatory nAChRs have also been identified on a large number of sensory nerve endings.[30] Moreover, it is well established that preganglionic nerve endings[29] as well as sympathetic,[31] parasympathetic (*e.g.* in the heart)[32] and motor nerve terminals[33, 34] possess cholinoceptive sites which can be activated by nicotinic drugs. Usually, stimulation of these presynaptic nAChR sites leads to an increase in neurotransmitter release due to depolarization of the axon terminal.[32-34] However, under certain experimental conditions, decreases in transmitter output have also been reported.[29]

12.6.4.2.2 Central nicotinic receptors

Nicotine produces a large variety of centrally induced physiological and behavioral effects, including alterations in respiration, heart rate and blood pressure, as well as antinociception, suppression of appetite and increase in spontaneous activity.[30, 35] Most of these effects are thought to result from interaction of the alkaloid with specific central nAChRs. However, to date, electrophysiological studies have convincingly demonstrated the existence of postsynaptic nAChRs in only a few subcortical neurons. These include, for example, neurons in the thalamic medial habenular nucleus[36] and the interpeduncular nucleus,[37] as well as the most thoroughly investigated spinal Renshaw cells.[38] In addition, biochemical studies have shown that central nAChRs may also be present on cholinergic[39, 41, 42] and noncholinergic (*e.g.* dopaminergic or serotoninergic)[40-42] nerve terminals. The functional role of these presynaptic nAChRs appears to be the facilitation of neurotransmitter release.[40-42]

Consistent with the broad range of effects produced by nicotinic drugs, high affinity binding of various radiolabeled nicotinic ligands has been demonstrated in several regions of the central nervous system (CNS).[43-48] The distribution of the nicotinic binding sites thus identified is clearly different from that found for the binding of muscarinic ligands.[46] In human brain, for example, $(-)$-[^{3}H]nicotine binding is highest in the nucleus basalis of Meynert and thalamus and lowest in the cerebral cortex and caudate nucleus.[43]

12.6.4.3 Electrophysiological Consequences of Nicotinic Receptor Activation

All types of nAChRs so far examined produce the same type of electrophysiological response, a rapid increase in membrane permeability to small cations, resulting in membrane depolarization. The ion channel involved in this process is an integral part of the nAChR complex (*cf.* Section 12.6.4.6) and binding of ACh leads to its opening by producing a change in the receptor conformation.[49-56] Therefore, the nAChR represents the prototype of a neurotransmitter-gated ion channel. The activated channel allows the rather nonselective permeation of cations less than ~ 0.65 nm in diameter (Na^+, K^+, Ca^{2+}), but it does not conduct anions.[49-56] This translocation of cations is a purely passive phenomenon, driven by the electrochemical gradients across the membrane. It results in a net influx of positive charges (mainly carried by Na^+), which is responsible for membrane depolarization. Channel opening is an extremely rapid event occurring in < 300 μs after ACh release.[56] As the Hill coefficient of nAChR-mediated electrophysiological responses is usually greater than 1 and less than 2, it is suggested that the binding of two (or more) ACh molecules is required for channel opening.[49-57] The nAChR at the neuromuscular junction, for example, which is the electrophysiologically most thoroughly investigated type of nAChR, displays a channel lifetime of about 1–10 ms, depending on the location of the receptor in the membrane (junctional or extrajunctional) and the developmental stage of the synapse.[16, 17, 28] Channel conductance values amount to about 20–50 pS,[16, 17, 28, 55] corresponding with the permeation of about 10^4 cations during each individual channel opening. Interestingly, single-channel current measurements have revealed that each individual channel 'opening' is interrupted by one or more very brief closings in the μs time range (flickering or 'Nachschlag' phenomenon).[58, 59]

High agonist concentrations rapidly lead to nAChR desensitization, accompanied by channel closing.[49-57] Recent evidence suggests that receptor phosphorylation by a cAMP-dependent protein kinase is critically involved in this process.[60-62] Desensitization occurs in two steps, fast and slow, the affinity of agonists for the receptor increasing by two orders of magnitude in each step.[51, 55, 57] Based on this observation, four general functional states of the receptor can be distinguished: a resting state (channel closed, relatively low affinity for agonists), an activated state (channel open, affinity for agonists unknown) and two desensitized states (channel closed, high affinity for agonists).[51, 55, 57]

12.6.4.4 Nicotinic Receptor Subtypes

It is generally accepted that nAChRs of skeletal muscle and autonomic ganglia are not identical. This concept is mainly based on the availability of selective stimulating and blocking agents. 1,1-Dimethyl-4-phenylpiperazinium (DMPP; **6**) and phenyltrimethylammonium (PTMA; **7**), for example, selectively activate nAChRs involved in ganglionic and neuromuscular transmission, respectively (Table 1).[1] On the other hand, agents such as hexamethonium (C_6; **8**) or mecamylamine (**10**) are rather selective blockers of ganglionic nAChRs, whereas decamethonium (C_{10}; **9**) or α-bungarotoxin (α-BTX) selectively antagonize the nicotinic actions of ACh at the neuromuscular junction (Table 1).[1]

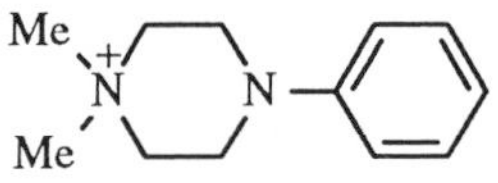

(6) DMPP 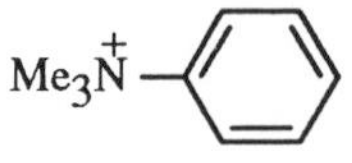   (7) PTMA   (8) Hexamethonium; $n = 6$ (10) Mecamylamine
                                    (9) Decamethonium; $n = 10$

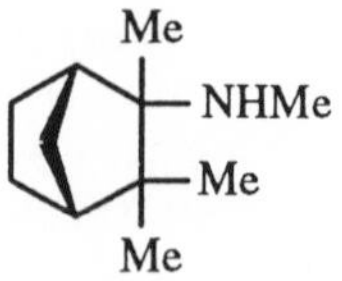

Table 1   Nicotinic Receptor Subtypes

	Nicotinic receptor, 'ganglionic type'	*Nicotinic receptor, 'muscular type'*
Location	Autonomic ganglia, CNS	Skeletal muscle, fish electric organ
Selective agonists	DMPP (6)	PTMA (7)
Selective antagonists	Hexamethonium (8)	Decamethonium (9)
	Mecamylamine (10)	α-Bungarotoxin
Proposed nomenclature	N_G (ref. 1)	N_M (ref. 1)
	N_n (ref. 18)	N_m (ref. 18)

As far as central nAChRs are concerned, current evidence suggests that the mammalian brain mainly contains nAChRs of the ganglionic (C_6 and mecamylamine-sensitive) type (Table 1).[21,45,63] Although several studies indicate that neuronal 'C_6-type' nAChRs can be selectively labeled by nanomolar levels of [³H]nicotine or [³H]ACh (in the presence of atropine),[21,45] exceptions from this rule have been reported.[64] In addition, high-affinity binding of [¹²⁵I]-α-BTX has also been demonstrated in many CNS regions,[45,47,65] although the brain areas mapped by α-BTX are to a large extent different from those labeled by [³H]nicotine or [³H]ACh.[45,47] Based on this latter finding as well as on additional functional experiments, it appears that most central α-BTX binding sites do not represent functional nAChRs.[21,63] However, there is clear evidence that α-BTX is not generally inactive as a central nicotinic antagonist, and that [¹²⁵I]-α-BTX may in fact label functional nAChRs in at least some brain areas, such as the optic tectum.[18,21,65] Consequently, it has been concluded that there may be two types of neuronal nAChRs differing in their sensitivity to α-BTX.[18]

Further evidence for the existence of nAChR subtypes is derived from recent structural studies of neuronal nAChRs using conventional biochemical methods as well as recombinant DNA technology. These new findings will be described in some detail in Section 12.6.4.7.

12.6.4.5   Isolation and Purification of Nicotinic Receptors

Nicotinic receptors have been purified first from the electric organs of several fish species (*cf.* Section 12.6.4.1), but subsequently also from skeletal muscle and neuronal tissue. Although a large variety of different purification techniques have been reported,[20,53,66] these procedures can be summarized briefly as follows. After homogenization of the receptor-containing tissue, which is usually carried out in the presence of protease inhibitors, nAChRs can be conveniently solubilized from crude membrane fractions by nonionic detergents, such as Triton X-100 or Tween 80, or bile salts. The most commonly used method for the purification of the solubilized receptor is adsorption to affinity gels consisting of an α-neurotoxin (*e.g.* α-BTX or α-cobratoxin) or a quaternary nicotinic ligand of low molecular weight coupled to an agarose bed. More recently, the purification of brain nAChRs by monoclonal antibody affinity chromatography has also been reported.[67,68] After binding to the affinity column, receptors can be specifically eluted with a solution of nicotinic agonists or antagonists. In the case of skeletal muscle nAChRs, which are present in only relatively small amounts in crude membrane extracts, lectin chromatography on concanavalin A–agarose is frequently applied in addition to α-neurotoxin affinity chromatography. Receptor preparations obtained by affinity chromatography can be further purified by sucrose density gradient centrifugation and/or ion exchange chromatography on DEAE–cellulose, DEAE–agarose or hydroxyapatite. Alternatively, starting from a crude detergent extract of pure, nAChR-rich membranes from *Torpedo marmorata*, sucrose density gradient centrifugation alone is sufficient to give a rather pure receptor preparation.[66]

Identification of the purified receptor protein is primarily based on its affinity for nicotinic ligands including α-neurotoxins and on immunological and morphological criteria (*cf.* Section 12.6.4.6). In addition, reconstitution experiments have shown that purified nAChRs can be reintegrated in a functional form into artificial vesicles or planar lipid membranes.[69]

12.6.4.6 Structure of the Nicotinic Receptor and Functional Implications

The nAChR isolated from *Torpedo* electric organ is composed of four different subunits, α, β, γ and δ, forming a pentamer in an $\alpha_2\beta\gamma\delta$ stoichiometry.[49-56,70] A large body of evidence suggests that this arrangement is generally conserved in nAChRs found in other electric fish and also in mammalian skeletal muscle, although the molecular weights of the single subunits may vary to a certain extent and slight modifications of the prototypic $\alpha_2\beta\gamma\delta$ structure may occur (see below).[18,49-56,71] However, in the case of neuronal nAChRs, wider structural variations have to be considered (see Section 12.6.4.7).

Estimates of the molecular weight of the pentameric receptor complex range from 250 000 to 300 000, depending on the tissue investigated and the technique used (*e.g.* sodium dodecyl sulfate–polyacrylamide gel electrophoresis (SDS–PAGE), gel filtration, radiation inactivation, *etc.*).[49-56] On SDS–polyacrylamide gels, for example, the different subunits of the *Torpedo californica* nAChR migrate with apparent molecular masses M of about 40 000 (α), 50 000 (β), 60 000 (γ) and 65 000 (δ).[20,24,50] All four subunits of the nAChR are glycosylated (estimated M of the carbohydrate moiety of the total receptor complex ≈ 20 000)[52] and phosphorylated, although to different extents.[16,55,56] Moreover, fatty acids appear to be linked to the α and β subunits.[72] Usually, the nAChR is closely associated with a group of cytoplasmic proteins, generally referred to as 43 000 Da or ν proteins. Several lines of evidence indicate that these proteins may be involved in anchoring the receptor to the cytoskeleton.[24,56] In addition, dimeric forms of the nAChR complex have been found in *Torpedo* electrocytes.[52] Such dimers, however, do not occur in *Electrophorus* and in vertebrates.[56]

The three-dimensional structure of the nAChR has been analyzed by a number of methods including neutron scattering, X-ray diffraction and electron microscopic techniques.[56] However, the most detailed picture of the quaternary structure of the receptor complex has so far been obtained by three-dimensional electron image analysis of tubular crystals grown from receptor-rich membrane vesicles of *Torpedo marmorata*.[73] Application of this technique strongly suggests that the nAChR complex is cylindrically shaped, and that it has a length of about 14 nm and a mean diameter ≈ 6.5 nm. The five rod-shaped subunits, which lie approximately perpendicular to the membrane plane, extend beyond the membrane about 3.5–4.5 nm on the cytoplasmic side, compared with ∼7 nm on the synaptic side. They are symmetrically arranged around a water-filled central opening, the presumed ion channel, which consists of a wide portion (diameter 2.5–3 nm) at the synaptic end and a narrow unresolved portion at the cytoplasmic end. Although the precise arrangement of the individual subunits in the membrane has not been unequivocally established, it is widely accepted that the two α chains are separated by one other subunit (Figure 1).[52,74]

Studies of the structure and function of the nAChR have been revolutionized by the recent availability of recombinant DNA technology.[27] By cloning and sequencing the complementary or genomic DNAs, the primary structures of all four subunits of *Torpedo californica* electroplax and calf muscle nAChR, as well as those of several individual nAChR subunits derived from various other sources including human muscle, have been elucidated.[27,54,75,76] The primary sequences of the *Torpedo* nAChR subunits, for example, suggest true molecular weights of 50 100 (α), 53 700 (β), 56 300 (γ) and 57 600 (δ), yielding an M of 268 000 for the protein portion of the total receptor complex.[75] In some cases, the relative molecular masses of the individual subunits calculated from the amino acid sequences are considerably different from the values determined by SDS–PAGE.[27,54,75,76] However, these discrepancies may be due to various posttranslational modifications of the receptor proteins (see above).

Marked amino acid sequence homology is observed among the four subunits of the nAChR (average homology ≈ 40%),[75,76] suggesting that the individual genes encoding them descended from a single common ancestor by gene duplication. While it appears that the α subunits are most highly conserved among different species, γ and δ form the most homologous pair within a species.[27,54,75,76]

The hydrophobicity profiles of the sequenced nAChR subunits suggest that each subunit has four hydrophobic transmembranous domains, connected by small hydrophilic loops.[27,52,54,75,76] Fourier transform analysis suggests that these membrane-spanning segments are almost certainly α-helically arranged, whereas most of the extramembranous regions are probably composed of

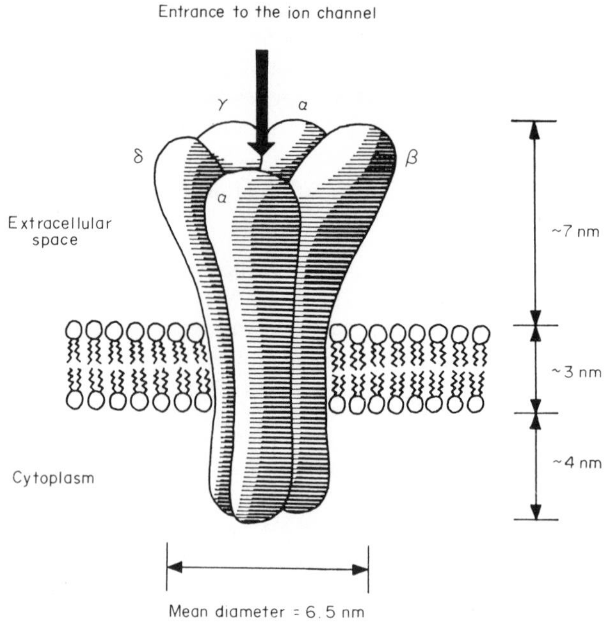

Entrance to the ion channel

Figure 1   Model of the nicotinic receptor[55]

β-sheets and random coils.[54,56,77] In addition, both Fourier analysis[77] and transfer energy calculations[78] predict that each subunit contains a fifth, amphipathic membrane-spanning helix. Because the NH_2 terminus of each subunit is thought to be located on the extracellular surface of the membrane, this latter assumption places the CO_2H terminus on the cytoplasmic side, which is in agreement with recent immunochemical studies.[79,80] It has therefore been suggested that the simplest channel model is one in which the amphipathic segment of each subunit contributes its hydrophilic face to the wall of the ion channel.[54,56,77,78] However, alternative channel models have also been proposed.[75,81]

It has been shown recently that microinjection into *Xenopus* oocytes of mRNA encoding the nAChR leads to successful translation, processing, assembly and insertion of functional nAChRs into the plasma membrane.[27,82] Expression studies in which *Xenopus* oocytes were injected with various combinations of only three of the four nAChR subunit-specific mRNAs showed that all four subunits are required for normal receptor function.[82] Moreover, in order to study the role of the individual subunits in ion transport and gating of the nAChR, hybrid receptors composed of receptor subunits from *Torpedo californica* and calf have been produced in *Xenopus* oocytes by the use of cloned cDNA.[83,84] Single-channel current measurements of the expressed hybrid receptors suggest that channel closing as well as the rate of ion transport through the open channel is determined by the δ subunit, and that the α subunit may be involved in channel opening and/or agonist dissociation.[83,84]

Interestingly, cDNA cloning studies have recently revealed the existence of a novel nAChR subunit in calf muscle, termed ε, which shows high sequence homology with the γ subunit.[85] Electrophysiological evidence suggests that replacement of the γ chain by the ε subunit is responsible for the alterations in conductance and gating properties of the receptor ion channel observed during bovine muscle development.[86]

12.6.4.7   Structural Pecularities of Neuronal Nicotinic Receptors

In contrast to nAChRs of electrocytes and skeletal muscle, until recently, little was known about the structure of neuronal nAChRs, primarily due to the lack of suitable probes (*cf.* Section 12.6.4.2.2) and the small amounts of nAChRs present in neuronal tissues. However, more recently, Whiting and Lindstrom have purified a putative neuronal nAChR by monoclonal antibody affinity chromatography from both chicken[67] and rat brain.[68] Several lines of evidence suggest that the immunopurified material, which binds nicotine with high affinity but does not bind α-BTX,[87] in fact represents functional nAChRs.[67,68,87] The isolated brain nAChRs, although similar in size to those found in

Torpedo electric organ and mammalian skeletal muscle, are composed of only two different subunits consistent with an $\alpha_2\beta_2$ or $\alpha_3\beta_2$ stoichiometry.[67,68] On the other hand, Conti-Tronconi *et al.* have recently isolated another putative brain nAChR from chicken optic lobe, which, in contrast to the proteins purified by Whiting and Lindstrom, strongly binds α-BTX.[18,88] Although the precise subunit composition of this receptor preparation could not be conclusively stated, significant differences in molecular size and bromoacetylcholine affinity-labeling patterns (*cf.* Section 12.6.4.1) were found between the chicken optic lobe nAChR and that present in chicken skeletal muscle.[18,88] Moreover, cDNA cloning studies have shown that the amino acid sequence of one of the isolated brain nAChR subunits differs considerably from that of each of the four subunits of chicken muscle nAChR (average amino acid homology $\approx 40\%$).[18] In addition, Boulter *et al.* have recently cloned a cDNA derived from a rat pheochromocytoma cell line, PC 12, coding for the α subunit of a putative 'ganglion-type' nAChR.[89] Although extensive amino acid sequence homology with the α subunit of mouse muscle nAChR has been reported,[89] it is conceivable that certain less well conserved regions of the α chain may contribute to the pharmacological differences observed between neuronal (ganglionic) and skeletal muscle nAChRs (*cf.* Section 12.6.4.4).[18]

12.6.4.8 Ligand Binding Sites of the Nicotinic Receptor

A majority of studies indicate that the nAChR contains two high affinity binding sites for ACh, one on each of the α subunits, occupation of which leads to channel opening.[49−56] As already mentioned in Section 12.6.4.1, the ACh binding sites of the nAChR can be selectively labeled by the use of specific affinity reagents such as 4-(*N*-maleimido)benzyltri[³H]methylammonium ([³H]MBTA; **4**).[20,90] Sequencing of the [³H]MBTA-labeled protein fragment has revealed that ACh binding occurs in the region of Cys 192–Cys 193,[90] which is unique to the α subunit. This finding is in agreement with a recent study of the localization of the functional region of the α subunit by site-directed mutagenesis.[91] According to current nAChR models, the ACh binding sites are therefore located close to the membrane on the extracellular portion of the nAChR.

Ligand-binding studies indicate that agents such as (+)-tubocurarine and the snake α-toxins, which have been classed as competitive antagonists of the nAChR on the basis of functional findings, in fact directly interact with the two ACh-binding sites on the receptor complex.[49−57] In keeping with this view, it has been demonstrated that short synthetic fragments of the α chain of *Torpedo*, comprising residues 185–196[92] and residues 173–204,[93] respectively (both fragments contain Cys 192–Cys 193[90]), bind to both α-BTX and (+)-tubocurarine. However, the molecular size of α-BTX (and other α-neurotoxins) and its high binding affinity to the nAChR suggest that the area of α-BTX contact with the receptor protein is much more extensive than that of ACh. Interestingly, the α subunit, most probably the region comprising residues 6–85,[94] also carries the main immunogenic region (MIR), against which most experimentally induced antibodies to native nAChRs and antibodies of myasthenic patients are directed.[26]

A vast range of compounds, including local anesthetics (*e.g.* lidocaine, procaine, tetracaine), histrionicotoxin (a frog-skin alkaloid toxin), phencyclidine, chlorpromazine, meproadifen, triphenylmethylphosphonium or aliphatic alcohols, block or modulate the nAChR-induced increase in cation permeability, but do not bind to the ACh sites.[49−57] Although it appears that these structurally diverse compounds do not interact with identical sites on the nAChR and may have differential mechanisms of action, they are generally referred to as noncompetitive blockers or noncompetitive inhibitors (NCIs).[49−57] It has been shown that NCIs bind to a variety of different sites on the nAChR, some of which are allosterically coupled to the ACh binding sites.[49−57] Several studies suggest that NCIs may act by blockade of open channels and/or by stabilization of the nAChR in the desensitized state.[19−57] However, at present considerable controversy exists about the number and location of the pharmacologically relevant binding sites of NCIs as well as their precise mechanism of action.

12.6.5 MUSCARINIC RECEPTORS

Muscarinic ACh receptors (mAChRs) have become the object of intense research by an ever increasing number of investigators during the last decade, mainly due to two reasons. First, it has been found that there are several pharmacologically distinguishable subpopulations of mAChRs both in the CNS and in the periphery (*cf.* Section 12.6.5.5), which may represent potential targets for new, therapeutically useful drugs. Second, as forebrain mAChRs have been shown to play a key role in the mechanisms underlying memory and learning[95] and impaired central cholinergic neuro-transmission is usually found in patients with Alzheimer's disease,[95-98] considerable effort has also been devoted to the study of central muscarinic mechanisms.

The following sections provide a survey of the most important aspects of the distribution, functions, effector coupling mechanisms and structural features of the mAChR. As the study of mAChR subtypes represents a particularly rapidly expanding field of research, this subject is dealt with in some more detail in Section 12.6.5.5.

12.6.5.1   Assay Methods for Muscarinic Receptors

In conjunction with the measurement of pharmacological, electrophysiological and biochemical responses (see below), the use of radioligands with high affinity and selectivity for the mAChR has allowed the identification and quantification of mAChRs in a large number of different cells and tissues. In 1965 Paton and Rang demonstrated the specific labeling by tritiated atropine of mAChRs in guinea pig ileum.[99] Since then, several tritiated muscarinic antagonists labeled to high specific activities have been used to identify and characterize mAChRs. These include reversible ligands such as 3-quinuclidinylbenzilate (QNB),[100] dexetimide [(+)-benzetimide],[101] N-methylscopolamine (NMS)[102] or N-methylatropine,[102] as well as irreversible ligands such as propylbenzilylcholine mustard (PrBCM)[103] (for chemical structures, see Sections 12.6.7.2.2 and 12.6.8.4). The finding that the affinity constants of muscarinic antagonists obtained in binding studies usually correlate well with their antimuscarinic potencies determined in functional assays strongly suggests that the identified binding sites in fact represent functional mAChRs.[100,102] The binding of agonists to mAChRs is most commonly determined by competition of unlabeled agonists with tritiated antagonists, although radiolabeled agonists such as [^{3}H]oxotremorine-M[104] or [^{3}H]-*cis*-methyldioxolane[105] (for chemical structures, see Section 12.6.7.2.1) can be used to directly label a subpopulation of receptor binding sites with relatively high affinity for agonists (*cf.* Section 12.6.5.5.6).

Due to the fact that all parasympathomimetic actions of ACh (Table 2) are mediated by mAChRs (*cf.* Section 12.6.5.2.1), countless *in vitro* and *in vivo* assay methods for the measurement of the physiological events following mAChR activation have been reported.[22] Some commonly used *in vitro* preparations include, for example, guinea pig or rat smooth muscle strips (*e.g.* ileum, jejunum, bladder or trachea), guinea pig atria or rabbit vascular tissue (*e.g.* aorta, ear artery). On the other hand, *in vivo* methods for the estimation of muscarinic activity are based, for example, on the mAChR-induced decrease in arterial blood pressure, increased tone of smooth muscle organs (*e.g.* urinary bladder) or stimulation of glandular secretion (*e.g.* saliva production).

Furthermore, the large variety of electrophysiological responses mediated by mAChRs can be studied by different experimental approaches, including modern voltage clamp and patch clamp

Table 2   Muscarinic Receptor-mediated Responses of Effector Organs Evoked by Parasympathetic Discharge or Muscarinic Agonists

Effector organ	*Response*
Heart	
Sinoatrial node	Decrease in heart rate
Atrial myocardium	Decrease in contractility and duration of the action potential
Atrioventricular node	Decrease in conduction velocity
Smooth muscle	
Eye (sphincter muscle of the iris and ciliary muscle)	Contraction (miosis and cycloplegia)
Respiratory tract	Contraction (bronchoconstriction)
Gastrointestinal tract	Contraction (increase in tone and motility); relaxation of the sphincters (usually)
Gall bladder and bile ducts	Contraction
Urinary bladder	Contraction (detrusor); relaxation (trigone and sphincter)
Arterioles	Relaxation (vasodilation; physiological significance in most cases unclear)
Glands	
Lacrimal, salivary, nasopharyngeal, bronchial, gastro-intestinal and pancreatic glands	Secretion
Sweat glands	Secretion (cholinergic sympathetic innervation)

technology (*cf.* Section 12.6.5.4). Likewise, the different biochemical events following mAChR stimulation can be measured in considerable detail due to the development of highly sensitive assay methods (*cf.* Section 12.6.5.3). Finally, the most recent application of the powerful methods of recombinant DNA technology has revealed crucial new aspects concerning the structure, location and function of mAChRs (*cf.* Section 12.6.5.7).[106]

12.6.5.2 Location and Function of Muscarinic Receptors

12.6.5.2.1 Peripheral muscarinic receptors

Muscarinic receptors (mAChRs) are widely distributed throughout the whole body. It is well documented that this type of receptor mediates the actions of ACh at peripheral effector tissues, which are innervated by postganglionic parasympathetic nerves and a few ACh-liberating, postganglionic sympathetic fibers, such as those to the sweat glands and the sympathetic vasodilator fibers (Table 2).[1] In general, these receptors are primarily involved in processes concerned with the conservation of energy and maintenance of organ function during periods of minimal activity. Interestingly, with the availability of increasingly sensitive techniques, mAChRs have also been detected in tissues in which the majority of receptors are obviously not supplied with cholinergic nerves (*e.g.* certain blood vessels, heart ventricles)[1] and in various other cells and cell systems such as lymphocytes, erythrocytes, oocytes or retina.[107] However, our knowledge about the physiological role of these receptors is still sparse.

In addition to their location on effector cells, mAChRs are also present on peripheral neurons. There is, for example, clear evidence that postsynaptic ganglionic mAChRs are involved in the modulation of the primary nicotinic pathway of ganglionic neurotransmission (*cf.* Section 12.6.4.2.1) by mediating the inhibitory postsynaptic potential (IPSP) and the slow excitatory postsynaptic potential (slow EPSP).[108] While the slow EPSP is thought to be generated by activation of mAChRs located directly on the soma of the ganglion cells, the mAChRs involved in the production of the IPSP appear to be present on catecholamine-containing small intensely fluorescent cells (SIF cells), which are scattered throughout ganglia.[108] In addition, evidence has been presented that mAChRs may also be located presynaptically on parasympathetic (autoreceptors)[109] or sympathetic nerve terminals (heteroreceptors).[31,110,111] The presynaptic autoreceptors are thought to be involved in an autoinhibitory feedback mechanism limiting ACh output during nerve stimulation.[109] Analogously, activation of muscarinic heteroreceptors on noradrenergic nerve terminals (*e.g.* in the heart[110] or certain blood vessels[111]) has been shown to decrease norepinephrine (noradrenaline) release during nerve activity. Moreover, it appears that presynaptic mAChRs mediating inhibition of ACh release may also be present on the terminals of preganglionic autonomic nerves and motor neurons.[109]

12.6.5.2.2 Central muscarinic receptors

The mammalian CNS is rich in cholinergic receptors, most of which appear to be of the muscarinic type.[112] Depending on the CNS region or cell type examined, activation of mAChRs may result in both excitation or inhibition of neurons (*cf.* Section 12.6.5.4).[112] Besides their preferential location on the soma and dendrites of central neurons, mAChRs are also present on both cholinergic and noncholinergic nerve endings.[41,113] As in the peripheral nervous system, stimulation of central muscarinic autoreceptors brings about an inhibition of ACh release, as, for example, shown in cerebral cortex, hippocampus or striatum.[41,109,113] However, depending on the brain region and the neurotransmitter involved, activation of central presynaptic heteroreceptors may lead to both inhibition or facilitation (*e.g.* at dopaminergic nerve terminals) of neurotransmitter release.[41,113]

More recently, immunocytochemical studies using monoclonal antibodies against ChAT, the ACh-synthesizing enzyme, in addition to histochemical staining methods for AChE, have identified numerous CNS sites where cholinergic (muscarinic or nicotinic) neurotransmission occurs.[114,115] Moreover, the application of new techniques such as light microscopic autoradiography has provided a detailed atlas of the quantitative distribution of mAChR sites in the mammalian CNS.[116–119] Usually, high densities of mAChRs (binding sites) are found in various forebrain areas, such as cerebral cortex, striatum or hippocampal formation, as well as in several nuclei and areas of the brainstem.[116–119] The functional importance of these receptor sites is evidenced by the finding that centrally administered muscarinic agonists and antagonists produce a large variety of physiological and behavioral responses. There is, for example, clear evidence that central mAChRs modulate many vegetative, sensory and motor functions.[115,119-121] Moreover, it appears that muscarinic mechanisms are involved in arousal, attention, rapid eye movement (REM) sleep, emotional responses, affective disorders including depression and the modulation of stress.[119-125] Finally, there is general agreement that mAChRs participate in the regulation of higher brain functions such as learning and memory.[95] Substantial evidence in support of this view is derived from the fact that the gradual loss of intellectual functions observed in Alzheimer's disease is consistently accompanied by a marked decrease in presynaptic cholinergic markers (*e.g.* ACh concentration, ChAT activity) in several forebrain areas.[95-98]

12.6.5.3 Biochemical Responses to Muscarinic Receptor Activation

Physiological muscarinic responses, in contrast to nicotinic ones, are slow in onset (lag period after ACh application 50–200 ms) and last much longer than nicotinic effects.[126] This finding already suggests that the mAChR does not represent a ligand-gated ion channel as the nAChR, but that second messenger systems may be interposed between mAChR activation and the final cellular response. In fact, countless studies have demonstrated that mAChRs mediate a variety of biochemical responses, including the breakdown of certain membrane phospholipids, inhibition of adenylate cyclase, activation of guanylate cyclase and stimulation of prostaglandin synthesis.[127-129] There is now general agreement that no single biochemical change mediates all physiological muscarinic effects, but that, depending on the tissue investigated, each of these different biochemical events may contribute to the final tissue response.

12.6.5.3.1 *Breakdown of phosphatidylinositides*

A possibly ubiquitous metabolic event following mAChR activation, which is found in virtually every tissue and cell type examined, is the breakdown of membrane-bound phosphatidylinositides by activation of phospholipase C.[130-132] Recent knowledge indicates that phosphatidylinositol 4,5-diphosphate is the key substrate in this reaction and that the products of its hydrolysis, diacylglycerol (DAG) and inositol 1,4,5-triphosphate (IP$_3$), may serve as second messengers to activate two separate but parallel biochemical pathways.[133-135] DAG is believed to act within the plane of the membrane through activation of protein kinase C, resulting in the phosphorylation of specific cellular proteins, which then contribute to the final physiological response.[136] On the other hand, the main function of IP$_3$ appears to be the mobilization of calcium from intracellular stores, particularly the endoplasmatic reticulum.[134] This biochemical event is probably involved in a variety of physiological muscarinic actions, such as various secretory responses or smooth muscle contraction.[137] Moreover, it has been shown in dog thyroid[138] and human astrocytoma cells,[139] that increased intracellular calcium levels following mAChR activation may also stimulate a calmodulin-sensitive phosphodiesterase, leading to decreased cAMP levels (*cf.* Section 12.6.5.3.2). In keeping with the role of IP$_3$ as a second messenger, Oron *et al.*[140] have recently demonstrated that intracellularly injected IP$_3$ mimics the muscarinic depolarizing chloride current in *Xenopus* oocytes, suggesting that IP$_3$ may also be involved in the depolarizing actions of muscarinic agonists in nervous tissues (see below).

Recently, the question of how mAChRs are coupled to the activation of phospholipase C has focussed considerable interest. Several studies indicate that, by analogy with the adenylate cyclase system (*cf.* Section 12.6.5.3.2), mAChR-induced stimulation of phospholipase C is also mediated by a GTP-binding regulatory protein.[141] However, it appears that the GTP-binding protein(s) involved in this reaction is (are) different from those regulating adenylate cyclase activity (see Section 12.6.5.3.2).[142-145]

12.6.5.3.2 *Inhibition of adenylate cyclase*

In the heart and various other tissues, the stimulation of mAChRs also results in an inhibition of adenylate cyclase activity.[107,146,147] It is believed that a GTP-binding regulatory protein, termed G$_i$, consisting of three different subunits (α, β and γ),[148] is involved in the inhibitory coupling of mAChRs to adenylate cyclase. Major evidence for this view has been derived from studies using pertussis toxin (an exotoxin produced by *Bordetella pertussis*; also referred to as islet-activating protein, IAP), which blocks the transfer of inhibitory information from receptors to adenylate cyclase through the ADP-ribosylation of the α subunit of G_i.[149] Thus, it has been shown by several investigators that mAChRs may lose their ability to interact with adenylate cyclase after pretreatment of intact cells or membranes with pertussis toxin.[150-153] Recently, evidence has been presented that the functional properties of G_i may be shared by another GTP-binding protein, G_o, which is structurally closely related to G_i.[154-156] Consistent with the role of G_i (or G_o) in coupling mAChRs to adenylate cyclase, it has been demonstrated that inhibition of adenylate cyclase by muscarinic agonists requires the presence of GTP.[157,158]

The physiological consequences resulting from the reduction of adenylate cyclase activity can be studied best when the activity of the enzyme has been increased by the action of stimulating neurotransmitters or other activating agents. For instance, it has been demonstrated in canine tracheal smooth muscle that the inhibitory effect of mAChR stimulation on the relaxant response to isoproterenol, prostaglandin E_2 or forskolin is paralleled by a decrease in intracellular cAMP levels and a reduction in cAMP-dependent protein kinase activity.[159] Moreover, it appears that at least some of the inhibitory muscarinic effects on myocardial contractility are mediated by inhibition of adenylate cyclase, particularly when cAMP levels have been raised through β-adrenoceptor activation.[152,160,161] However, muscarinic stimulation may also produce negative inotropic effects under conditions when cAMP levels remain unaltered, suggesting that mAChRs may regulate cardiac contractility by cAMP-independent mechanisms as well.[152,160,161]

12.6.5.3.3 *Increase in cGMP levels*

Increases in cGMP levels following mAChR stimulation have been observed in various peripheral and central tissues.[162,163] It is believed that an indirect coupling occurs between the membrane-bound mAChR and a cytosolic guanylate cyclase.[162] As the cGMP response usually requires the presence of extracellular Ca^{2+}, it has been proposed that Ca^{2+} entering the cell during muscarinic stimulation may play a crucial role in the activation of guanylate cyclase. In addition, it has also been suggested that a transient hydroperoxide metabolite of arachidonic acid, formed by a receptor-stimulated, Ca^{2+}-dependent pathway, may be involved in mediating the stimulation of cGMP synthesis.[163] By analogy with the cAMP system, it has been hypothesized that cGMP may activate a cGMP-dependent protein kinase, resulting in the phosphorylation of specific cellular proteins which then, by a yet unknown mechanism, may contribute to the final physiological response.[162,163]

The physiological relevance of the cGMP response has been confirmed by the observation that cGMP or certain cGMP derivatives can mimic several muscarinic actions in both neuronal[162-166] and nonneuronal cells.[167-169] In the heart, for instance, it appears that some of the muscarinic effects of ACh, such as inhibition of Ca^{2+} influx in atrial myocardium, may be mediated by cGMP, while many others are not.[160,161] Although various studies suggest that a reciprocal relationship may exist between the accumulation of cGMP (or the ratio cGMP/cAMP) and myocardial contractility, present evidence is insufficient to either accept or reject this hypothesis.[160,161]

Furthermore, increasing evidence suggests that cGMP may play a crucial role in mAChR-mediated vasodilation.[170,171] Several investigators have shown that muscarinic stimulation of arterial blood vessels, provided the endothelial cell layer is intact, may cause the release of a so-called endothelium-derived relaxing factor[172,173] (EDRF, most probably identical with NO[174]), which is thought to mediate the activation of guanylate cyclase. Increased cGMP levels may then lead to vascular relaxation through cGMP-dependent dephosphorylation of myosin light chain.[170,171]

12.6.5.4 Membrane Conductance Changes Following Muscarinic Receptor Activation

In the last decade a large variety of different membrane conductance changes following mAChR activation have been uncovered, greatly aided by the availability of new techniques, such as voltage clamp and patch clamp technology.[126,147,175] The slow onset of these responses suggests that intracellular or intramembrane second messengers or intermediates (*cf.* Section 12.6.5.3) may be interposed between mAChR activation·and effects on membrane ion conductance. However, in only a few cases, a clear relationship between changing levels of certain second messengers and the inhibition or activation of single types of ion channels has been established so far (see below). In the following, four of the most common membrane conductance changes induced by the stimulation of mAChRs are briefly discussed.

12.6.5.4.1 Increase in K^+ conductance

Muscarinic agonists produce an increase in membrane K^+ conductance in heart, glands, autonomic ganglia and central neurons.[175] However, the properties of the affected K^+ conductance with respect, for example, to voltage or Ca^{2+} dependence may vary from tissue to tissue.[175] In neurons, the activation of K^+ currents leads to hyperpolarization, resulting in a reduced responsiveness of the cell to excitatory stimuli and/or an inhibition of spontaneous activity.[176-179] In the heart, the mAChR-controlled increase in K^+ conductance causes a shortening of the action potential duration and hyperpolarization in atrial myocardial cells, as well as a decrease in beating frequency by reducing the rate of spontaneous diastolic depolarization in the sinoatrial node.[160] Evidence has been presented that these cardiac effects may be due to direct interaction of mAChRs with atrial K^+ channels through a GTP-binding protein, not involving the actions of any of the known second messengers.[180-183] In agreement with this view, it has been demonstrated in embryonic chick atrial cells that muscarinic regulation of cardiac K^+ channels requires the presence of intracellular GTP and is blocked by pretreatment with pertussis toxin, suggesting the involvement of G_i and/or G_o.[180] Furthermore, mammalian atrial K^+ channels have been shown to be directly activated by a G protein isolated from human erythrocytes (most probably identical with G_i).[182] Surprisingly, it appears that this response, as shown by recent single-channel current measurements in chick embryonic atrial cells, is mediated by the $\beta\gamma$, and not, as originally believed, by the α subunit of the G protein.[183]

12.6.5.4.2 Decrease in K^+ conductance

In a variety of neuronal cells however, muscarinic stimulation may also lead to a suppression of K^+ currents whose normal functions are to stabilize the neuron and to limit the output firing frequency.[175,184] Depending on the tissue investigated, it appears that at least three different types of K^+ currents may be involved in this response.[175] First, mAChR activation may lead to an inhibition of a resting K^+ conductance resulting in neuronal depolarization, as shown, for example, in guinea pig myenteric neurons.[185] Second, muscarinic inhibition of a Ca^{2+}-activated K^+ current may shorten postspike hyperpolarization (e.g. in sympathetic ganglion or hippocampal pyramidal cells), resulting in a facilitation of repetitive firing in response to other excitatory synaptic inputs.[175] Finally, muscarinic stimulation may also block Ca^{2+}-independent, voltage-operated K^+ channels (M-current), which are functional in sympathetic ganglion cells[186,187] and hippocampal[188] or cortical neurons.[189] Muscarinic suppression of the M-current leads to slow synaptic depolarization (e.g. resulting in the ganglionic slow EPSP; cf. Section 12.6.5.2.1) and continued firing of the cell in response to excitatory stimuli.[184]

12.6.5.4.3 Increase in cation conductance

Moreover, mAChRs on mammalian smooth muscle[190] and some gland cells[191,192] may mediate a nonselective increase in membrane permeability to cations, resulting in a net inward current which depolarizes the cell. These findings suggest that membrane depolarization may be an intermediate step in both contraction of smooth muscle and secretion of various gland cells. Similar membrane conductance changes leading to neuronal depolarization and increased cellular firing rate have been demonstrated in neurons of the rat locus coeruleus.[175]

12.6.5.4.4 Decrease in Ca^{2+} conductance

Finally, in heart muscle cells, mAChRs may also mediate a decrease in Ca^{2+} conductance, which, in addition to the increase in K^+ permeability (cf. Section 12.6.5.4.1), may contribute to the negative inotropic effects observed upon muscarinic stimulation.[160,193] When cardiac Ca^{2+} channels have been activated by β-adrenergic agonists, inhibition of Ca^{2+} entry into the cells by muscarinic agonists can be most clearly demonstrated.[181,194] Furthermore, a mAChR-mediated decrease in membrane permeability to Ca^{2+} ions has also been demonstrated in various neuronal cells.[175] It has been hypothesized that this electrophysiological response, beside an increase in K^+ conductance, may play a major role in presynaptic muscarinic inhibition of neurotransmitter release.[175]

12.6.5.5 Muscarinic Receptor Subtypes

The plethora of physiological (Table 2), biochemical and electrophysiological responses evoked by the stimulation of mAChRs has led to the question of whether more than one type of mAChR exists. In the last decade, considerable effort has been devoted to answering this question, and there is now clear evidence from functional tests, radioligand binding studies as well as recent receptor cloning experiments that there are several mAChR subtypes.

12.6.5.5.1 *The M_1/M_2 concept*

In 1961, Roszkowski[195] reported on the unusual pharmacological properties of a quaternary muscarinic agonist, McN-A-343 (4-[N-(3-chlorophenyl)carbamoyloxy]-2-butynyltrimethylammonium chloride; **11**). This agent, when given intravenously to dogs, produced a prominent atropine-sensitive pressor effect,[195] which is in contrast with the behavior of classical muscarinic agonists, injection of which usually results in a decrease in blood pressure. Moreover, McN-A-343 showed little activity at mAChRs in peripheral effector organs such as gastrointestinal smooth muscle or atrial myocardium.[195] In a careful analysis, Roszkowski arrived at the conclusion that McN-A-343 is a selective stimulant of excitatory mAChRs in sympathetic ganglia.[195] This assumption has later been confirmed by several other investigators.[108]

Moreover, based on the observation that McN-A-343 preferentially stimulates a subpopulation of muscarine-sensitive neurons of the snake brain (*Helix aspersa*), Woodruff and Walker proposed that mAChRs sensitive to McN-A-343 should be denoted as M_1, and those unaffected by this agent as M_2.[196] This concept has later been adopted by Goyal and Rattan in order to describe the unusual muscarinic actions of McN-A-343 seen in the lower esophageal sphincter (LES) of the opossum.[197] In this preparation, classical muscarinic agonists, such as bethanechol, cause an increase in LES pressure through direct interaction with mAChRs on the sphincter smooth muscle (M_2 receptors).[197] In contrast, following a transient increase, McN-A-343 induces a long-lasting fall in LES pressure which appears to be due to selective activation of certain neuronal mAChRs in intramural ganglia (M_1 receptors) whose stimulation results in the release of a yet unidentified inhibitory neurotransmitter.[197]

However, the drug that has provided the major impetus in focussing research into mAChR subtypes was the antimuscarinic agent pirenzepine (**12**), which is used clinically in the treatment of peptic ulcer disease (*cf.* Section 12.6.8.4).[198] The first indication of the discriminative properties of pirenzepine was provided by radioligand binding studies, carried out by Hammer *et al.* in 1980.[199] In contrast to conventional muscarinic antagonists such as atropine or N-methylscopolamine which bind to a uniform population of receptor sites in both CNS and peripheral effector organs,[102,199,200] pirenzepine displayed a novel binding profile. In competition experiments against [^{3}H]NMS and [^{3}H]propylbenzilylcholine, pirenzepine showed considerably higher affinity for mAChRs present in various neuronal tissues (*e.g.* cerebral cortex, hippocampus or sympathetic ganglia) than to those located on peripheral effector organs (*e.g.* heart, glands or intestinal smooth muscle) and certain CNS areas (*e.g.* medulla pons).[199,201] Furthermore, in several tissues such as cerebral cortex or sympathetic ganglia, pirenzepine produced unusual flat binding curves (Hill coefficients significantly less than 1), indicating that mAChRs might be heterogeneous within a given tissue, too.[199,201] In fact, the complex binding behavior of pirenzepine can best be explained in terms of the presence of a high affinity receptor population (K_D 10–20 nM) and of a receptor species with low affinity for pirenzepine (K_D 200–800 nM).[202] Following the initial competition binding studies, the existence and discrete tissue distribution of two mAChR subpopulations differing in their affinities for pirenzepine have been confirmed by direct binding using [^{3}H]pirenzepine as a radioligand and various functional studies (see below).

Based on the observation that pirenzepine, similar to the agonist McN-A-343, shows selectivity for certain neuronal mAChRs, it has been hypothesized by Hammer and Giachetti that both agents might recognize a common receptor subtype.[201] In fact, it has been demonstrated that certain functional responses to McN-A-343, such as the McN-A-343-induced pressor effect in the pithed rat, can be totally blocked by low doses of pirenzepine which have little effect on mAChRs in peripheral effector tissues.[201,203] Moreover, experiments carried out in the opossum LES have shown that pirenzepine is highly effective in blocking the McN-A-343-evoked sphincter relaxation, while not affecting the bethanechol-induced sphincter muscle contraction.[204] Thus, based on the terminology originally introduced by Woodruff and Walker,[196] mAChRs which show high affinity for pirenzepine and which are readily activated by McN-A-343 have been termed M_1, while those displaying relatively low affinity towards pirenzepine and being much less sensitive to McN-A-343 have been designated M_2.[201,202]

However, recent studies have revealed additional complexities inherent in this classification scheme.[205,206] In contrast to previous findings (see above), it has been shown that McN-A-343 displays little, if any, agonistic activity at various neuronal mAChRs to which pirenzepine binds with high affinity.[207,239,242] On the other hand, McN-A-343 may also act as a full agonist at certain peripheral mAChRs which show low affinity for pirenzepine (*e.g.* mAChRs in the guinea pig taenia caeci).[206] Due to these findings, the concept of classifying mAChRs into M_1 and M_2 subtypes is currently primarily based on the discriminative properties of pirenzepine. In addition, there is evidence that other drugs such as telenzepine (13)[208,286] exhibit a selectivity profile similar to that shown by pirenzepine.

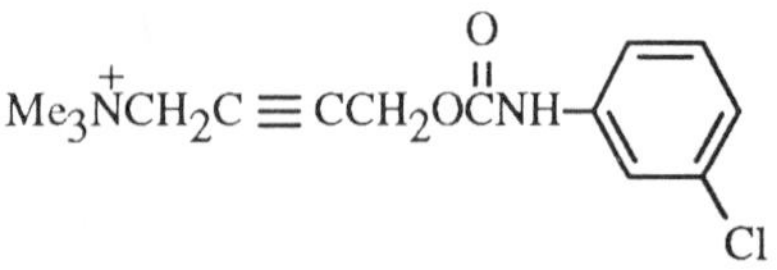

(11) McN-A-343 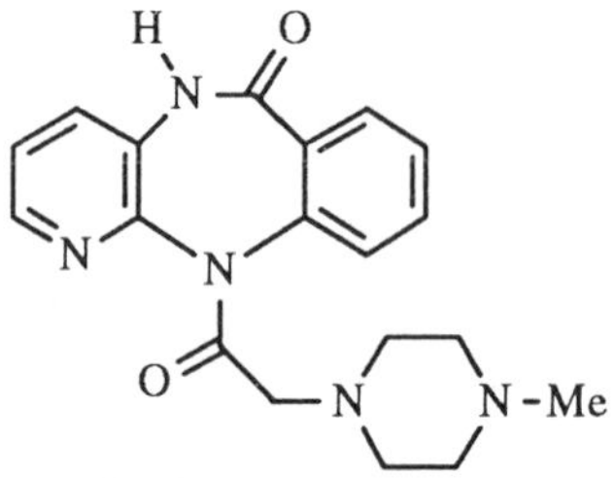   (12) Pirenzepine 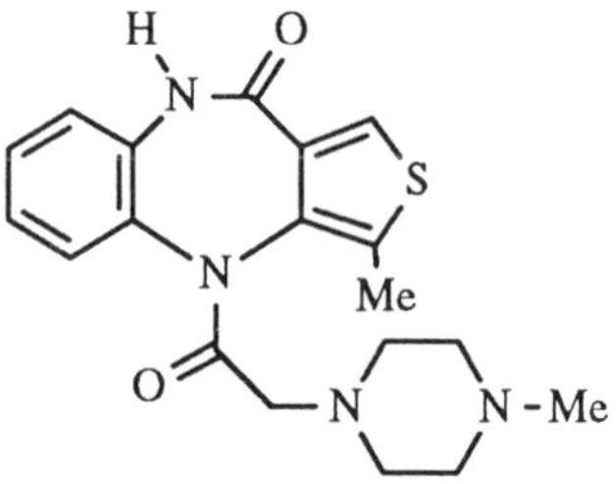   (13) Telenzepine

Until recently, little was known as to whether the existence of pharmacologically distinguishable M_1 and M_2 receptor subtypes reflects variations in the amino acid sequence of the receptor proteins or whether it is due, for example, to differential posttranslational modifications or environmental differences. However, most recent receptor cloning studies indicate that primary structure differences form the molecular basis of the observed mAChR heterogeneity (*cf.* Section 12.6.5.7).[106]

12.6.5.5.2   *M_1 receptors: location and function*

Competition binding experiments[119,199,209-211] as well as direct binding studies[212-219] carried out in the CNS have demonstrated that M_1 sites (high-affinity pirenzepine binding sites) are mainly present in forebrain areas, such as cerebral cortex, limbic system (*e.g.* amygdala, hippocampus) or basal ganglia (*e.g.* striatum), suggesting that M_1 receptors may primarily be involved in higher brain functions such as learning and memory, as well as locomotor and behavioral effects.[119,218] As M_1 sites are mainly found in cholinergic projection areas, it is assumed that M_1 receptors (binding sites) may be predominantly located postsynaptically.[119,210,218,219]

In agreement with radioligand binding studies, functional mAChRs with high affinity for pirenzepine (pA_2 8.0–8.5) have been identified in both electrophysiological and biochemical studies in several forebrain areas. It has been shown, for instance, that postsynaptic mAChRs mediating an increase in firing rate in rat hippocampal pyramidal cells can be readily blocked by low doses of pirenzepine (pA_2 8.2).[245,465] Similarly, muscarinic excitation of cortical pyramidal neurons proved to be highly sensitive to blockade by pirenzepine.[220] Although central M_1 receptors are thought to be primarily located postsynaptically (see above), there are indications that they may also be found presynaptically.[221-223] Marchi *et al.*, for example, have demonstrated that muscarinic heteroreceptors potentiating dopamine release in rat striatal nerve endings exhibit a considerably higher affinity for pirenzepine than muscarinic autoreceptors in hippocampus or cerebral cortex.[222,223]

Besides their preferential location in the CNS, muscarinic M_1 receptors are also present in peripheral autonomic ganglia. Binding studies, for instance, have clearly demonstrated the existence of high affinity pirenzepine binding sites in the intramural enteric nervous system.[224,225] Consistent with this finding, functional studies have revealed that the mAChR-mediated depolarization of submucous plexus neurons in the guinea pig small intestine is readily blocked by pirenzepine (pA_2 8.4).[226] Likewise, Kilbinger and Nafziger,[227] studying neurotransmitter release in the guinea pig longitudinal muscle–myenteric plexus preparation, have demonstrated the existence of excitatory M_1 receptors on myenteric ganglion cells mediating spontaneous ACh outflow (pA_2 pirenzepine 8.5). Based on these findings, it has been hypothesized that the selectivity of pirenzepine in inhibiting vagally induced gastric acid secretion (*cf.* Section 12.6.8.4) may be due to the preferential blockade of M_1 receptors in intramural ganglia of the stomach wall.[228,229] However, this view has been questioned by Black and Shankley who claim that the selective secreto-inhibitory effect of pirenzepine may solely be explained by its pharmacokinetic behavior.[230,231] Sympathetic ganglia also appear to be rich in M_1 receptors (*cf.* Section 12.6.5.5.1).[201, 232–235] In the rat isolated superior cervical ganglion, for example, pirenzepine is a highly effective blocker of the muscarine-induced slow EPSP ($pA_2 > 8$).[234,235,243,245]

Several attempts have been made to correlate the activation of M_1 receptors with certain electrophysiological or biochemical responses. Based on a careful analysis of literature data as well as electrophysiological measurements, North[175] proposed that both central and peripheral M_1 receptors may be linked to a certain type of K^+ channel (*cf.* Section 12.6.5.4.2). It is thought that M_1 receptor activation mediates the closure of these K^+ channels, resulting in an increase in neuronal excitability.[175]

From a biochemical point of view, it has been claimed that M_1 receptors may be specifically coupled to the breakdown of membrane-bound phosphoinositides (PI response).[236] In fact, initial studies carried out in various brain preparations revealed that the mAChR-mediated PI breakdown is blocked by pirenzepine with high affinity.[207,237] However, subsequent studies have shown that PI turnover may also be coupled to M_2 receptors in both central[238,239] and peripheral tissues.[240,241] In addition, it has been demonstrated that M_1 receptor activation may stimulate guanylate cyclase activity.[242] These findings suggest that the M_1 receptor is not specifically coupled in an obligatory fashion to a distinct biochemical response.

12.6.5.5.3 M_1 receptor heterogeneity

Most recently, Lambrecht *et al.* demonstrated in electrophysiological studies that M_1 receptors, in contrast to previous concepts, do not form a homogeneous population but may be further subclassified by the use of selective antagonists.[243–245,247,465] The most promising tools in this respect appear to be hexahydrodifenidol (**14**) and hexocyclium (**15**; Table 3).[244,245,247,465] These antimuscarinic agents, in contrast to conventional muscarinic antagonists such as atropine, display a considerably higher affinity (159- and 63-fold, respectively) for M_1 receptors mediating depolarization of rat isolated superior cervical ganglia than for those present in rat hippocampal pyramidal cells mediating increase in spike rate. Based on these findings, Mutschler, Lambrecht and coworkers[243–245,247,465] proposed that M_1 receptors should be further subclassified into at least two subtypes, one showing high affinity for pirenzepine but low affinity for hexahydrodifenidol and hexocyclium (provisionally termed $M_{1\alpha}$), and the other one having high affinity for pirenzepine as well as hexahydrodifenidol and hexocyclium (provisionally termed $M_{1\beta}$).

In agreement with this suggestion, recent receptor cloning studies have revealed that M_1 receptors in rat brain may consist of a mixture of various receptor proteins differing in their amino acid sequences (*cf.* Section 12.6.5.7).[246]

Table 3 Antimuscarinic Potencies (pA_2 Values) of Hexahydrodifenidol (**14**) and Hexocyclium (**15**) at Ganglionic and Hippocampal M_1 Receptors as Compared to Atropine (**179**) and Pirenzepine (**12**)[244, 245, 247, 465]

	pA_2 values at M_1 receptors		K_D Ratio
	Superior cervical ganglion (rat)	*Hippocampal slices (rat)*	*Hippocampus/ ganglion*
(**179**) Atropine	9.1	8.6	3.2
(**12**) Pirenzepine	8.3	8.2	1.3
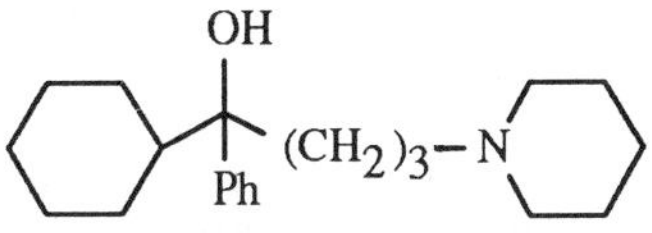 (**14**) Hexahydrodifenidol	7.9	5.7	159
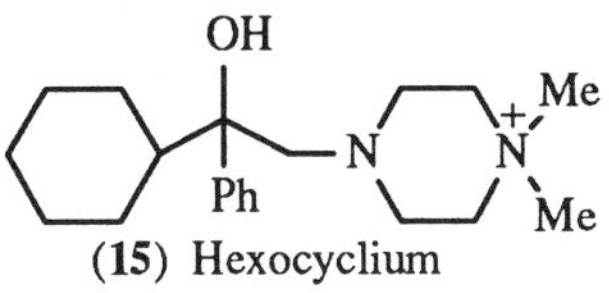 (**15**) Hexocyclium	8.8	7.0	63

(**14**) Hexahydrodifenidol

(**15**) Hexocyclium

12.6.5.5.4 *M*$_2$ *receptors: location and function*

A large number of binding studies carried out in the CNS have shown that M$_2$ sites (low affinity pirenzepine binding sites) predominate in the brainstem, cerebellum and parts of the thalamus and hypothalamus,[119,209-211,213-215,217,218] indicating that central M$_2$ receptors may be primarily involved in the regulation of vegetative, sensory and motor functions.[218] In contrast to M$_1$ receptors, which are mainly found in cholinergic projection areas, it appears that M$_2$ receptors are also enriched in brain regions which contain cholinergic cell bodies and are known as the origin of cholinergic tracts.[210,218,219] In keeping with the radioligand binding data, electrophysiological studies have demonstrated the existence of M$_2$ receptors in certain brainstem nuclei, such as nucleus parabrachialis[177] and locus coeruleus.[248] Upon stimulation, these receptors either induce neuronal hyperpolarization (nucleus parabrachialis)[177] or depolarization (locus coeruleus)[248] (*cf.* Section 12.6.5.4). Moreover, M$_2$ receptors mediating neuronal hyperpolarization have also been identified in the ventricular nucleus of the thalamus.[220] In cerebral cortex, M$_2$ receptors have been shown to mediate the excitation of GABA-ergic interneurons[220] and the slow muscarinic depolarization of single olfactory neurons.[249] Similar to peripheral autoreceptors (see below), inhibitory presynaptic mAChRs on hippocampal and cortical cholinergic nerve endings also appear to be of the M$_2$ type.[222,223,250,251]

However, the major function of M$_2$ receptors is the mediation of the muscarinic actions of ACh on peripheral effector organs. Consistent with radioligand binding data, numerous functional studies have shown that postsynaptic mAChRs in peripheral effector tissues, such as heart, glands or smooth muscle, exhibit low affinity for pirenzepine (pA$_2$ 6.5–7.0) and thus have to be classed as M$_2$ receptors.[205,252] The same holds true for prejunctional mAChRs on both sympathetic (hetero-receptors)[253-255] and parasympathetic nerve terminals (autoreceptors).[256,257] Likewise, the inhibitory presynaptic mAChRs present on cholinergic, adrenergic and peptide-containing nerve endings in the guinea pig submucous plexus also appear to be of the M$_2$ subtype.[258] Moreover, it has been shown in isolated sympathetic ganglia that M$_2$ receptors may mediate the ganglionic IPSP (*cf.* Section 12.6.5.2.1).[235] Interestingly, the ganglionic M$_2$ receptors involved in this response can be selectively blocked by gallamine.[235]

Electrophysiological studies have revealed that activation of M$_2$ receptors may lead to a variety of membrane conductance changes, such as increase in K$^+$ conductance (*e.g.* in the heart or central neurons), increase in cation conductance (*e.g.* in smooth muscle or central neurons) or decrease in Ca^{2+} conductance (*e.g.* in the heart).[175] In addition, recent electrophysiological experiments have demonstrated that cortical M$_2$ receptors may also be coupled to M-current suppression (*cf.* Section 12.6.5.4.2).[249]

Several biochemical studies suggest that M$_2$ receptors may be coupled to different metabolic events, such as inhibition of cAMP formation[207] or stimulation of PI breakdown.[240,241]

12.6.5.5.5 *M*$_2$ *receptor heterogeneity*

There is now convincing evidence, derived from both radioligand binding and functional studies, that muscarinic M$_2$ receptors are composed of at least two different receptor subpopulations. The majority of studies which have contributed to this concept have been carried out on peripheral M$_2$ receptors utilizing the discriminatory properties of selective antagonists.

In 1976 Barlow and coworkers proposed that atrial and ileal M$_2$ receptors may be different.[259] This suggestion was based on the observation that certain antagonists, such as 4-diphenylacetoxy-*N*-methylpiperidine methiodide (4-DAMP; **16**), exhibit an approximately ten-fold higher affinity for mAChRs causing ileal contraction than for those mediating negative chronotropic and inotropic responses in atria (Table 4).[259-261] A similar conclusion has been drawn by Mutschler and coworkers based on functional *in vitro* studies of certain derivatives of the antimuscarinic drugs procyclidine and difenidol and their silicon analogs.[243-245,262] Some of these agents, such as hexahydrosiladifenidol (HHSiD; **17**),[263,264] display an up to 30-fold higher affinity for smooth muscle than for cardiac M$_2$ receptors. However, HHSiD[266,267,285] (and related compounds) and 4-DAMP[234,258,265-267,286] do not only exhibit high affinity for smooth muscle M$_2$ receptors, but also for glandular M$_2$ and neuronal M$_1$ receptors as well, as shown in both functional and radioligand binding studies (Table 4).

Although HHSiD (and derivatives) and 4-DAMP clearly discriminate between cardiac and smooth muscle M$_2$ receptors in functional assays, this behavior is usually not seen in binding studies.[267] The same phenomenon is also observed in the case of the so-called cardioselective

Table 4 Functional Profiles (pA$_2$ Values) of the Antimuscarinic Agents 4-Diphenylacetoxy-*N*-methylpiperidine Methiodide (4-DAMP; **16**) and Hexahydrosiladifenidol (HHSiD; **17**) at Muscarinic Receptor Subtypes

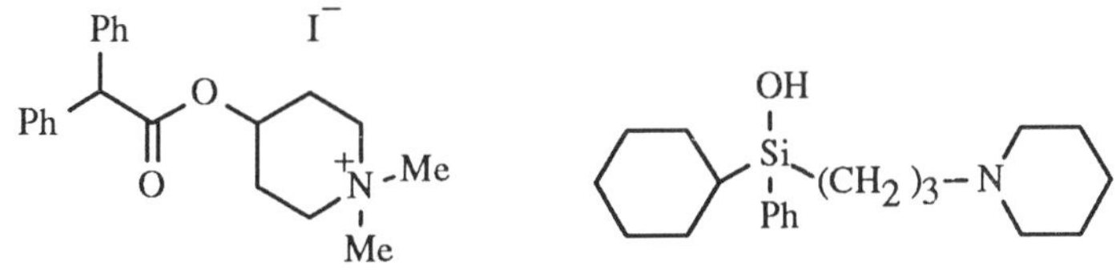

(**16**) 4-DAMP   (**17**) HHSiD

Preparation	pA$_2$ Values	
	4-DAMP	*HHSiD*
M$_1$ receptors		
Superior cervical ganglion of the rat	8.6 (ref. 234)	7.3 (refs. 243–245)
M$_2$ receptors		
Smooth muscle organs (*e.g.* guinea pig or rat ileum, trachea, urinary bladder)	8.4–9.0 (refs. 205, 259–261)	7.4–8.2 (refs. 244, 245, 263, 264)
Heart		
(*e.g.* guinea pig or rat atria; rate and force of contraction)	7.5–8.0 (refs. 205, 259–261)	6.3–6.8 (refs. 244, 245, 263, 264)

antimuscarinic agents (see below).[267,268] It has therefore been suggested that only a minor subpopulation of the M$_2$ sites in smooth muscle organs represents functional mAChRs, while the majority of smooth muscle muscarinic binding sites, which show a binding profile similar to that of cardiac M$_2$ receptors, is obviously not coupled to muscle contraction.[269]

In contrast to HHSiD or 4-DAMP, certain neuromuscular blocking drugs, such as gallamine, alcuronium or pancuronium, preferentially inhibit muscarinic responses in the heart.[270–273] However, compounds of this type appear to be of limited value in mAChR subclassification, as a majority of studies indicate that these agents interact with the mAChR in a noncompetitive fashion, at least at higher concentrations.[271,272,274] In contrast, competitively acting muscarinic antagonists endowed with cardioselectivity, such as the pirenzepine derivative AF-DX 116 (**18**)[275–277] or himbacine (**19**),[278] are also available. In functional tests, AF-DX 116, similar to himbacine, exhibits an approximately tenfold higher affinity for M$_2$ receptors in the heart than for those in smooth muscles (Table 5).[276,277] In keeping with these findings, radioligand binding studies have shown that AF-DX 116 displays high affinity to M$_2$ receptors in the heart ($K_D = 115$ nM), intermediate affinity to central M$_1$ receptors ($K_D = 760$ nM) and low affinity to M$_2$ receptors in exocrine glands ($K_D = 3200$ nM).[275] A selectivity pattern qualitatively similar to that found for AF-DX 116 has also been reported for a series of polymethylene tetraamines,[279–283] among which methoctramine (**20**)[281,283] represents the most cardioselective antimuscarinic agent known today. Thus, methoctramine shows an about 50- to 100-fold higher affinity for cardiac than for glandular and smooth muscle M$_2$ receptors (Table 5).[281,283]

In conclusion, the data described above are consistent with the view that peripheral M$_2$ receptors can be further subdivided into an M$_2$ 'cardiac' and an M$_2$ 'glandular/smooth muscle' type (Table 6).[243–245,284–286] Furthermore, it appears that the same M$_2$ receptor subtypes are also present in varying proportions in different CNS regions.[287,288] Although the concept of M$_2$ receptor heterogeneity mainly relies on the affinity differences of selective antagonists, muscarinic agonists being able to discriminate between the proposed M$_2$ receptor subtypes have also been developed.[244,245,262]

12.6.5.5.6 *Heterogeneity of agonist binding*

Whereas conventional muscarinic antagonists appear to bind to a uniform population of receptor sites, agonist binding to mAChRs in most tissues shows a clear deviation from the law of mass action with Hill coefficients significantly less than unity, indicating that binding cannot be adequately described by the interaction of muscarinic agonists with a single class of binding sites.[104,107,147,284,289,290] Data obtained from competition binding experiments can best be explained by the presence of a low (L) and a high affinity binding site (H) for muscarinic agonists, as

Table 5 Antimuscarinic Potencies (pA$_2$ Values) of AF-DX 116 (**18**), Himbacine (**19**) and Methoctramine (**20**) at M$_2$ Receptors

| | *pA$_2$ Values at M$_2$ receptors* | |
	Smooth muscle organs[a]	*Heart*[b]
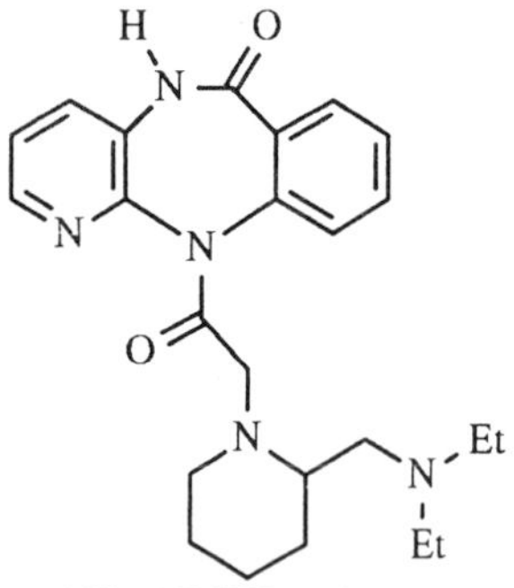 (**18**) AF-DX 116	6.3–6.4 (refs. 276, 277)	7.1–7.5 (refs. 276, 277)
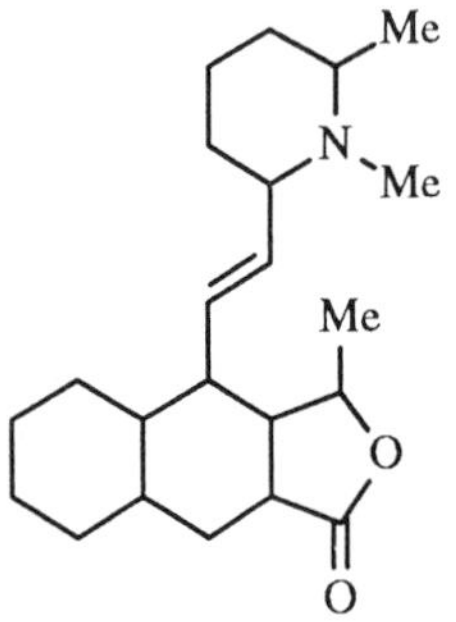 (**19**) Himbacine	7.1–7.3 (ref. 278)	8.2 (ref. 278)
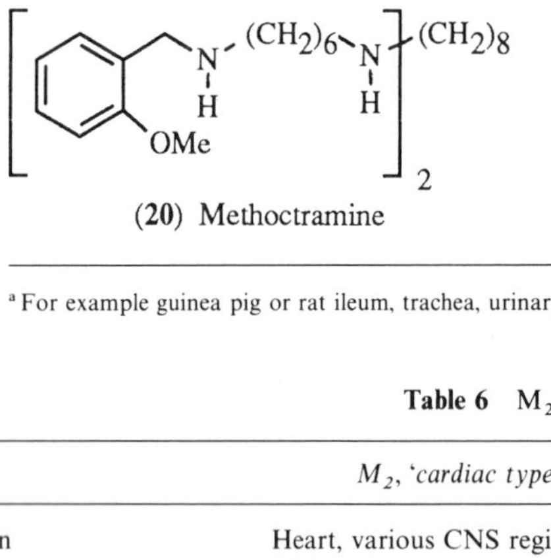 (**20**) Methoctramine	5.8–6.2 (ref. 281)	7.7–7.9 (ref. 281)

[a] For example guinea pig or rat ileum, trachea, urinary bladder. [b] Guinea pig atria.

Table 6 M$_2$ Receptor Subtypes

	M$_2$, 'cardiac type'	*M$_2$, 'Smooth muscle/glandular type'*
Location	Heart, various CNS regions	Smooth muscle, exocrine glands, various CNS regions
Selective antagonists	AF-DX 116 (**18**)	Hexahydro-sila-difenidol (HHSiD; **17**)
	Himbacine (**19**)	4-DAMP (**16**)
	Methoctramine (**20**)	
Proposed nomenclature	M$_{2a}$[a]	M$_{2\beta}$[a]
	M$_{2A}$[b]	M$_{2B}$[b]
	M$_2$[c]	M$_3$[c]

[a] Refs. 243, 247. [b] Ref. 205. [c] Ref. 286.

originally proposed by Birdsall and coworkers.[104,291,292] In addition, direct binding studies of ^{3}H-labeled agonists carried out to selectively label the high affinity sites revealed the presence of a minor population of superhigh (SH) affinity sites.[104,292] With very few exceptions, such as rat nasal mucosa where agonist binding to a homogeneous population of low affinity sites has been reported,[293,294] heterogeneity of agonist binding is found in virtually every tissue and cell type examined.[104,107,147,284,289,294]

Birdsall and coworkers have demonstrated that the ratios of affinities of muscarinic agonists to the H and L site (or SH and L site) is critically dependent on the efficacy of the agonist, being large for efficacious agonists and much smaller for partial agonists.[104,291,292] However, the absolute affinity values for the different binding sites as well as the proportions of SH, H and L sites may vary from tissue to tissue.[147,292] In addition, several investigators have shown that conversion between high and low agonist affinity states can be induced by divalent cations (*e.g.* Mg^{2+}), sulfhydryl reagents (*e.g.* NEM) or guanine nucleotides (*e.g.* GTP).[107,147,284,289,290] For example, addition of guanine nucleotides leads to a conversion of SH and H sites to L sites or 'L-like' sites.[107,147,284,289] However, the extent of this effect strongly depends on the tissue involved.

Considerable evidence suggests that the existence of the various affinity states for muscarinic agonists as well as their possible interconversion (see above) is due to the coupling of mAChRs to GTP-binding proteins (G proteins).[295,296] It is assumed that the high affinity (H) state represents an agonist–receptor–G protein ternary complex and that GTP destabilizes this complex by binding to the G protein, yielding a low affinity, binary agonist–receptor complex.[295,296] In agreement with this view, receptor reconstitution experiments have shown that isolated mAChRs in the absence of G proteins exhibit low affinity for agonists, whereas addition of G proteins (G_i or G_o; *cf.* Section 12.6.5.3.2), provided guanine nucleotides are absent, leads to the appearance of high affinity binding for muscarinic agonists.[154,297] It thus appears that L, H and SH sites do not represent distinct receptor subtypes, but may rather be considered as different conformational states of the mAChR induced by the coupling to adjacent membrane proteins. However, selective alkylation of either high or low affinity sites has been demonstrated in cerebral cortex[104,298] and heart,[299] suggesting that the different agonist affinity states may not generally be freely interconvertible.

Attempts have been made to correlate biochemical and physiological muscarinic effects with the occupancy of the different agonist affinity sites. The majority of such studies has shown that agonist binding to the low affinity site is responsible for most functional muscarinic responses.[147]

In contrast, there is obviously no clear relationship between the different agonist affinity states and M_1 and M_2 receptor subtypes as identified by pirenzepine.[300] However, it appears that at least in some parts of the CNS (*e.g.* cerebellum or cerebral cortex), there is an inverse relationship between the number of M_1 sites as detected by [³H]pirenzepine and the number of high affinity agonist binding sites.[210,211,301-303]

12.6.5.6 Isolation and Purification of Muscarinic Receptors

Muscarinic receptors, which have been covalently labeled with [³H]propylbenzilylcholine mustard[304-306] (*cf.* Section 12.6.5.1) or certain photoaffinity analogs of tritiated muscarinic antagonists,[307,308] can be solubilized by sodium dodecyl sulfate (SDS, denaturing conditions), which has enabled the size of the mAChR to be determined by SDS–PAGE. A majority of such studies, carried out in a variety of different tissues and species, have identified a single labeled polypeptide of an apparent molecular mass M of about 70 000–80 000.[304-307] However, in some studies, considerable tissue-dependent differences in molecular size of the labeled proteins have also been observed.[309,310] These variations may, for example, arise from tissue-specific posttranslational modifications (*e.g.* different extents of glycosylation)[310] and/or differences in the primary structure of the mAChRs involved (see below).

In contrast to the nAChR, progress in purifying mAChRs has long been hampered by difficulties in solubilizing the receptor in its active form and by the lack of receptor-rich tissues and specific, high-affinity ligands. However, most of these obstacles have been removed by the availability of novel, high affinity muscarinic antagonists (see Section 12.6.5.1) and the use of modern solubilization and purification techniques.

In the last decade, mAChRs have been successfully solubilized in their active forms by the use of several mild detergent systems, such as digitonin, digitonin–cholate, cholate–salt solutions, Lubrol PX, lysolecithin or CHAPS (3-[(3-cholamidopropyl)dimethylammonio]-1-propanesulfonate).[147,290,311] The solubilized receptor preparations thus obtained can be further purified by conventional biochemical methods. Although all purification procedures reported for mAChRs so far include affinity chromatography as the main step, other techniques, such as lectin chromatography[312-314] (consistent with the glycoprotein nature of the mAChR; see below), have been additionally applied (see below).

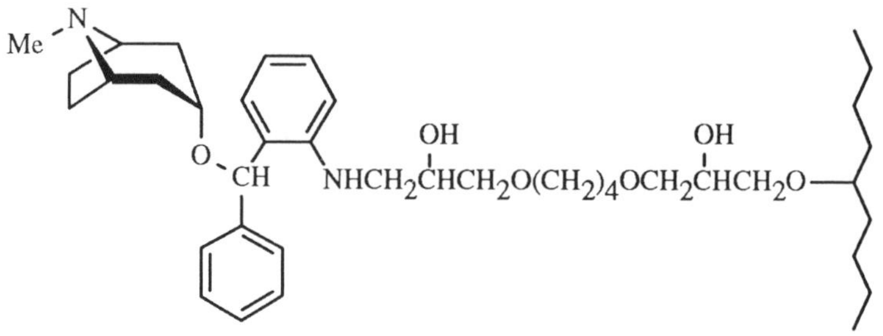

Figure 2 Chemical structure of ABT–agarose[317]

André *et al.* first reported on the purification of digitonin-solubilized mAChRs from calf forebrain using a dexetimide-containing affinity gel.[315] However, the purified material did not show appropriate ligand-binding activity.[315] In contrast, a purified preparation of digitonin/cholate-solubilized mAChRs from porcine cerebrum showed essentially the same specificity for muscarinic ligands as unpurified receptors.[316] In this case, purification to apparent homogeneity was achieved by affinity chromatography using an ABT (3-[2′-aminobenzhydryloxy]tropane)–agarose gel (Figure 2),[317] followed by gel permeation HPLC. On SDS–PA gels, the purified cerebral mAChR migrates with an apparent M of $\approx 70\,000$.[316] Similarly, mAChRs from porcine atria have been purified $100\,000$-fold to homogeneity by solubilization in digitonin/cholate and sequential lectin, ion-exchange and ABT–agarose affinity chromatography.[318] Beside a smaller polypeptide which did not bind ligands, the purified material contained one single major protein which showed specificity for muscarinic ligands and displayed an apparent M of $78\,000$ (determined on SDS–PAGE).[318] More detailed studies of the physical properties of the purified cardiac mAChR, using D_2O/H_2O sucrose gradient sedimentation and gel filtration techniques, gave a somewhat lower M of $68\,000–71\,000$,[319] which is in close agreement with the value reported above for the purified brain mAChR. Composition studies suggest the presence of about 26% carbohydrate in the cardiac mAChR yielding an estimated M of $50\,000–53\,000$ for its protein portion,[319] which is in good agreement with recent receptor cloning studies (see Section 12.6.5.7).

12.6.5.7 Primary Structure of Muscarinic Receptors

In the last few years the primary structure of various mAChR proteins derived from both peripheral and central tissues has been deduced by the powerful methods of recombinant DNA technology.[106] Numa and coworkers[320] first reported on the cloning of a porcine brain mAChR cDNA, sequence analysis of which has revealed that the encoded cerebral receptor protein consists of 460 amino acid residues with a calculated M of $51\,416$. Expression of the cloned cDNA in *Xenopus* oocytes produced functional mAChR, thus verifying the identity of the receptor protein.[320,324] Both the tissue location of the mRNA hybridizing with the cloned cerebral mAChR cDNA and the fact that pirenzepine and AF-DX 116 bind to the expressed receptors with high and low affinity, respectively, suggest that the encoded protein represents a mAChR of the M_1 subtype.[320,324]

Furthermore, the cloning and sequence analysis of a porcine heart mAChR cDNA have shown that the encoded cardiac receptor protein consists of 466 amino acid residues and has a calculated M of $51\,670$,[321,322] which is virtually identical to the value found for the cerebral M_1 receptor. The preferential location of the mRNA hybridizing with the cloned cDNA in the heart and medulla-pons suggests that the isolated cDNA encodes a muscarinic M_2 receptor.[321] This assumption is further corroborated by the finding that expression of the cardiac mAChR cDNA in a Chinese hamster ovary cell line and in *Xenopus* oocytes leads to the binding of muscarinic antagonists in these cells with affinities characteristic of the cardiac M_2 receptor subtype.[322,324]

Both the cerebral M_1 and the cardiac M_2 receptor exhibit extensive sequence homology with other receptors known to be coupled to G proteins, such as the β-adrenergic receptor or rhodopsin.[106,322,323] Based on this similarity, hydropathy data predict a structure of seven hydrophobic membrane-spanning regions, a large cytoplasmic loop, as well as the presence of potential *N*-glycosylation sites in the amino-terminal (presumptively extracellular) and potential phosphorylation sites in the carboxy-terminal region (presumptively intracellular), respectively (Figure 3).[106,322,323] By analogy with the retinal binding site of the opsins, it has also been

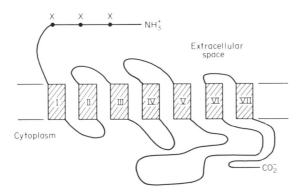

Figure 3 Model of the muscarinic receptor as predicted by hydropathy data and by analogy with rhodopsin and the β-adrenergic receptor. The arrangement of the cytoplasmic and the extracellular regions is arbitrary. I–VII are putative transmembrane segments. X denotes potential *N*-glycosylation sites

suggested that the ligand binding site on the mAChR may lie in a pocket formed by the transmembrane segments.[106,323]

Although the porcine M_1 and M_2 receptors are structurally closely related, they share only 38% of their amino acid residues, with extensive local identities found in the transmembrane domains (50–91%) and the small connecting loop regions (44–67%).[322] The most striking difference between both receptors, however, is the complete absence of sequence analogy in their large cytoplasmic loops consisting of 156 (M_1) and 180 amino acids (M_2), respectively, joining the fifth and the sixth transmembrane segment.[322] These findings therefore suggest that muscarinic M_1 and M_2 receptors represent clearly distinct gene products and that primary structure differences may form the molecular basis of pharmacologically identified M_1 and M_2 receptor subtypes (see Section 12.6.5.5).

In addition, receptor cloning studies have recently shown that cerebral M_1 receptors may not consist of a homogeneous receptor species.[246] Using a rat cerebral cortex cDNA library, Bonner *et al.* have isolated three different cDNAs encoding different mAChRs.[246] Expression studies of the cDNA clones in mouse fibroblast or monkey COS-7 cells have revealed that the three mAChRs expressed exhibit high binding affinity for pirenzepine and thus, despite considerable variations in their primary structures, may all be classed as M_1 receptors.[246] Beside differences in the total number of amino acid residues (458, 478 and 589, respectively), the three M_1 receptor proteins primarily differ in their large cytoplasmic loops connecting the fifth and the sixth transmembrane segment. This region is variable in size, comprising 157 to 203 amino acid residues, and shows little similarity among the three M_1 receptor species. It has thus been speculated that the observed variety of M_1 receptor genes may reflect specialization of different forms of the receptor for different coupling mechanisms.[246]

12.6.6 ACETYLCHOLINE: MOLECULAR PROPERTIES

The molecular properties of ACh have been the subject of extensive studies, mainly during the last two decades. By gaining an increased knowledge of the conformational and electronic properties of ACh, it was hoped to reach a better understanding of the interactions between ACh and its receptor sites. Knowledge of the pharmacophoric pattern ('active conformation') of ACh at different receptor subtypes, and postulating specific interaction sites on the receptor for attachment of the drug then leads to a 'receptor map'. Both pattern and map may subsequently be used to design novel agonists which selectively mimic the actions of ACh at its different receptor subtypes.

One approach to the study of its conformational selectivity has been the determination of the preferred conformation of the ACh molecule in the crystal, in solution and of the isolated molecule *in vacuo*. A large number of crystallographic, spectroscopic and theoretical studies have been performed,[325–331,342] but none of the techniques employed is free from objection. The studied environment (crystal, solution or vacuum) neglects possible conformational changes that can occur in the ACh molecule by interactions with the receptor. Attempts to overcome this difficulty resulted in the development and conformation–activity studies of rigid or semirigid analogs of ACh in which the possibilities of conformational variations are eliminated or greatly reduced (*cf.* Section 12.6.7).[332–334]

12.6.6.1   Conformational Properties of Acetylcholine

ACh is a flexible molecule, and a given conformation can be described by the values of four torsion angles (indicated as τ_0–τ_3 in Figure 4). Because ACh contains eight single bonds, additional torsion angles may be calculated, but their approximate values can be deduced from the values of τ_0–τ_3 and the facts that the ester group is planar and that the shape of the quaternary ammonium group is roughly that of a tetrahedron.

From a consideration of known structures of related substances, two of the torsion angles are well established.[325] In all these structures, C(5)—C(4)—N—C(3) (τ_3) forms an antiplanar extended chain with τ_3 being close to 180°, which can be expected due to van der Waals' packing and steric hindrance of the methyl groups. From studies on esters and dipeptides[325, 335] one may fix the C-7 methyl group with a C—H bond eclipsing the C(6)=O(2) double bond. Moreover, because of the partial double bond character of the C(6)—O(1) bond, the acetoxy group is planar and the torsion angle τ_0 is very close to 180°. The conformation of ACh is therefore a two torsion angle problem (τ_1 and τ_2). The value of τ_2 is of most interest, because it defines the relative dispositions of the acetoxy group and quaternary head, functions both vital to the pharmacological properties of ACh.[328, 331]

12.6.6.1.1   Crystallographic studies

X-ray crystal structure studies were the first to provide information about the values of τ_1 and τ_2. They were obtained for a series of different salts, and are listed in Table 7.[325] The torsion angles of the ACh ion, in particular τ_1, differ somewhat in the different crystals. ACh is *trans–gauche* (antiplanar–synclinal) in the crystals of its chloride, perchlorate, tetraphenylborate, hydrogen ($\pm$)-tartrate, ($\pm$)-tartrate and β-resorcylate, but *gauche–gauche* (synclinal–synclinal) in the crystal of its bromide and iodide (Figure 5). This shows that the conformation of ACh is labile and influenced by its environment.

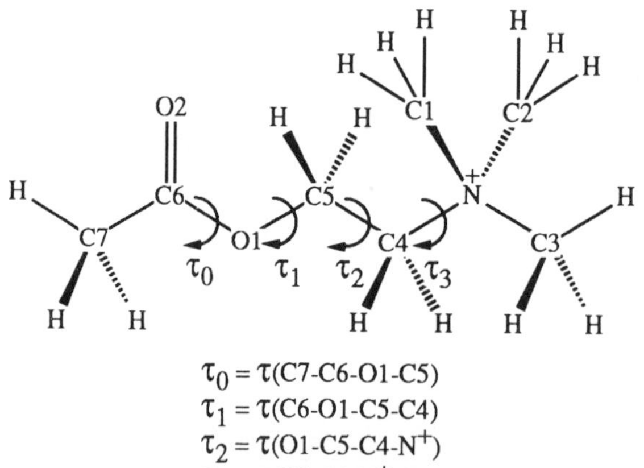

$$\tau_0 = \tau(\text{C7-C6-O1-C5})$$
$$\tau_1 = \tau(\text{C6-O1-C5-C4})$$
$$\tau_2 = \tau(\text{O1-C5-C4-N}^+)$$
$$\tau_3 = \tau(\text{C5-C4-N}^+\text{-C3})$$

Figure 4   Structural diagram of acetylcholine, showing atom and torsion angle labels

Table 7   Torsion Angles (°) τ_1 and τ_2 in the Acetylcholine Ion of Different Salts

	$\tau_1 = C(6)—O(1)—C(5)—C(4)$	$\tau_2 = O(1)—C(5)—C(4)—N$
Chloride	−165	85
Perchlorate	180	74
Tetraphenylborate	155	67
Hydrogen ($\pm$)-tartrate	163	78
($\pm$)-Tartrate	172	85
β-Resorcylate	161	80
Bromide	79	78
Iodide	83	89

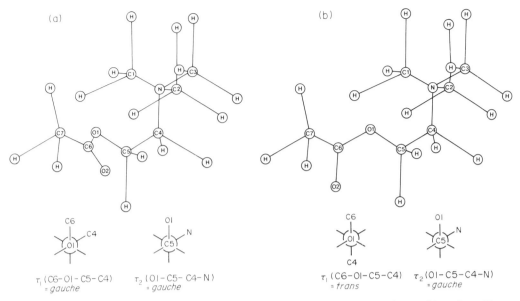

Figure 5 The structure of acetylcholine in crystalline acetylcholine bromide (a: *gauche–gauche*) and perchlorate (b: *trans–gauche*)

12.6.6.1.2 Theoretical studies

A large number of theoretical computations have been carried out to determine the conformational possibilities and preferences of ACh, both by empirical and quantum mechanical methods.[325,326,329,335] All of the different MO techniques have been used: EHT (extended Hückel theory), CNDO (complete neglect of differential overlap) and modifications of this method, *e.g.* CNDO/2, INDO (intermediate neglect of differential overlap), PCILO (perturbative configuration interaction using localized orbitals) and finally 'ab initio' methods using basis sets of various sizes.

Although a complete agreement between the results of the many kinds of calculations was not found, the data published by Pullman *et al.*[335–337] give a realistic picture of the conformational properties of the isolated ACh molecule. Using the PCILO method, a conformational energy map of ACh (isoenergy curves as a function of τ_1 and τ_2) was constructed. There was a global minimum situated at $\tau_1 = 180°$ and $\tau_2 = 60°$, which, together with the adopted values of $\tau_0 = \tau_3 = 180°$, corresponds to a *gauche* conformation of the O-1 and N atoms and a *trans* arrangement of the remaining atoms of the backbone. This conformation is very close to the one present in the crystals of several ACh salts (Table 7 and Figure 5). A local minimum situated about 4 kJ mol^{-1} above the global one was found at $\tau_1 = 120°$ and $\tau_2 = -80°$. Around both minima, and in particular around the global one, there were large plateaus of low energy. The minima are therefore associated with a considerable flexibility, especially regarding the variation of τ_1. The *trans–trans* conformation ($\tau_1 = \tau_2 = 180°$) strongly implied in the discussion concerning the active conformation of ACh at muscarinic receptors (*cf.* Section 12.6.7)[328,332–334] is 12–17 kJ mol^{-1} less stable than the *trans–gauche* one.

In order to obtain estimates of the energy needed to cause a change to less stable conformers of ACh from the most stable one, and finally to know which conformers are impossible or 'forbidden', a series of calculations have been performed by use of the MM2-program (an empirical force field approach).[325]

12.6.6.1.3 Spectroscopic studies

The use of spectroscopy in conformational studies has an advantage over X-ray diffraction and theoretical calculations in that it provides information about ACh in the solute condition. Hence conformations may be established for conditions that are close to physiological. Although the simultaneous application of Raman and IR techniques gives detailed information on the solid state and aqueous solution conformation of ACh,[325,342] the spectroscopic studies rely primarily on NMR techniques (^{1}H, ^{13}C, ^{14}N).[325,338–341] As a general conclusion of these studies, the conformations found in solution are very nearly the same as those found in crystals and as those which are low energy conformers of the isolated molecule. When more than one conformation is observed in the crystalline state, populations of different rotamers are often found in solution.

For example, the *trans–gauche* conformation with respect to τ_1 and τ_2, characteristic of the ACh chloride crystal and corresponding to the global energy minimum on the '*ab initio*' conformational energy map, is essentially preserved in water. Lichtenberg *et al.*[338] reported the presence of 91% of this *trans–gauche* form at room temperature, and a significant population of the *gauche–gauche* rotamer with τ_1 equal to 65–69°. The free energy difference between the two rotamers does not exceed 4 kJ mol^{-1}. Furthermore, the conformation of ACh in solution seems to be independent of the counterions, chloride or bromide.[339]

12.6.6.2   Electronic Properties of Acetylcholine

Charge distribution and molecular electrostatic potential fields are of central importance in understanding drug–receptor interactions, particularly if drug–receptor interactions are largely electrostatic in nature.[343, 344]

The electronic properties of ACh have been investigated by different quantum mechanical methods, *e.g.* PCILO,[335] INDO[345] and CNDO/2.[346] Although there are some differences in the results obtained with the different techniques, and the electronic charge distributions of ACh depend on the conformation,[345] the following general conclusions can be drawn.[335,345,346] (i) The N$^+$ atom is nearly neutral. The formal positive charge associated with the quaternary nitrogen in the principal valence structure is distributed among the adjacent methyl and methylene groups. Thus the three methyl groups form a large ball of spread-out positive charge. (ii) The ester oxygen and the carbonyl oxygen of ACh both carry very similar net negative charges, whereas the carbonyl carbon atom possesses an appreciable excess of positive charge. (iii) The net atomic charges of all the atoms in the acylmethyl group sum to a small positive charge.

These electronic properties of ACh help to envision mechanisms for the interaction with cholinergic receptors (*cf.* Section 12.6.7). The positively charged cationic center may interact with an anionic site on the receptor surface, and the acylmethyl group is likely to bind to the receptor through van der Waals' or weak hydrogen bonds. Charge values on the carbonyl C=O group and the ester oxygen support electrostatic interactions on an ester site of the receptor through the strongly dipolar character of the acetoxy group.

12.6.7   STRUCTURE–ACTIVITY RELATIONSHIPS OF CHOLINERGIC AGONISTS AND ANTAGONISTS

12.6.7.1   Drugs Acting Preferentially at Nicotinic Receptors

12.6.7.1.1   Agonists

There is general agreement that the structural requirements for nicotinic activity are not as stringent as those for muscarinic activity (*cf.* Section 12.6.7.2.1).[328,347–349] A protonated or quaternary nitrogen, or an equivalent group, such as sulfonium or arsonium, is responsible for the primary interaction of agonists with an anionic center of the nAChR. A partial negative charge at some distance from the onium group seems to be essential for potent nicotinic agonists. It should be situated at a position corresponding to that of the carbonyl oxygen atom of ACh, thus interacting with a secondary binding site of the receptor separated from the primary, anionic binding site by a distance of about 0.5 nm.[347] Although the stereochemistry of nicotinic agonists often has only a minor influence on activity, there are several exceptions,[350,351] suggesting that a third moiety found in that part of the molecule which links the cationic head and the negatively charged atom is involved in drug–receptor interaction. This moiety makes the molecule inactive if it is in the wrong position relative to the cationic head and the negatively charged group.[352] Large differences in nicotine (**57**) enantioselectivity can be rationalized by the existence of high and low affinity nicotine binding sites differentially contributing to different nicotinic responses.[353–355] High affinity binding sites show substantial stereoselectivity towards (−)-nicotine, whereas low affinity binding sites display similar affinities for (+)- and (−)-nicotine.

In acyclic analogs of ACh, an onium function is essential for nicotinic activity.[328] Besides quaternary ammonium compounds, dimethylsulfonium, trimethylphosphonium and trimethyl-arsonium compounds are active too, but usually weaker than the corresponding trimethyl-

Table 8 The Effect of α- and β-Methyl Substitution in ACh

$$MeCOCHR^2CHR^1\overset{+}{N}Me_3$$

Compound	R^1	R^2	Configuration	EPMR mAChR, guinea pig ileum[a,b]	EPMR nAChR, frog rectus[a,b]
(3) ACh	H	H	—	1	1
(21)	Me	H	(R/S)	49	2
(22)	H	Me	(R/S)	1.6	180

[a] EPMR = equipotent molar ratio. [b] Ref. 328.

ammonium analogs.[356] Replacement of methyl by ethyl groups in the quaternary center of ACh brings about a considerable loss of activity; the triethylammonium analog of ACh is only 1/5000 as active as ACh itself.[356] In cyclic analogs, a protonated tertiary or secondary amino group can substitute for the quaternary ammonium function of ACh.[347]

β-Methyl substitution in the choline moiety of ACh (3) reduces nicotinic activity (22), whereas in acetyl-α-methylcholine (21) high potency is preserved. The low degree of enantioselectivity of (21) and its potency similar to that of ACh do not speak for an additional interaction of the α-methyl group with the nAChR (Table 8).[356]

In choline esters with aliphatic carboxylic acids (23), nicotinic activity is preserved upon prolongation of the alkyl chain of the acid. Esters with longer alkyl chains are usually more potent at ganglionic compared to neuromuscular nAChRs.[328] Within a series of imidazolyl esters of choline (24–26) large potency differences at ganglionic and neuromuscular nAChRs suggest different steric requirements for the interaction of aromatic groups with both nAChR types (Table 9).[328] Nicotinic potency in a series of substituted benzoyl esters (27–33) depends on the Hammett substituent constant.[347,356] Nicotinic activity decreases with increasing electron-withdrawing capacity of the substituent. Loss of nicotinic activity is possibly related to a reduction of the partial negative charge on the carbonyl oxygen atom (Table 10).[357]

$$Me(CH_2)_n\overset{O}{\overset{\|}{C}}OCH_2CH_2\overset{+}{N}Me_3$$

(23)

Table 9 Potency of Imidazolyl Esters[356]

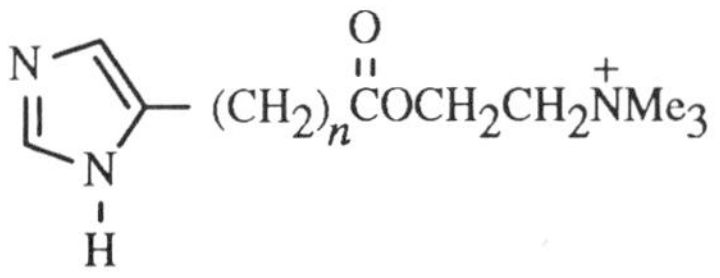

Compound	n	EPMR, ACh = 1, frog rectus	EPMR, ACh = 1, ganglia
(24)	0	1000	1.2
(25)	1	25	2.0
(26)	2	1.4	0.12

Table 10 Potency of Substituted Benzoyl Esters[356]

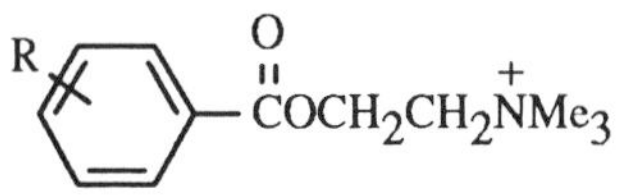

Compound	R	EPMR, ACh = 1, ganglia	Compound	R	EPMR, ACh = 1, ganglia
(27)	3-NO$_2$	10.0	(31)	4-Me	2.5
(28)	3-Cl	3.3	(32)	H	0.9
(29)	4-Cl	2.2	(33)	4-OMe	0.5
(30)	4-F	1.7			

Acetylthiocholine (**34**) and acetylselenocholine (**35**) are potent nicotinic stimulants with little activity at mAChRs.[358] Acetylthiocholine is five times more potent than ACh at ganglionic nAChRs, but 20–30 times less active at neuromuscular nAChRs.[356] Interestingly, its hydrolysis product, cholinethiol, is as potent at neuromuscular nAChRs as acetylthiocholine itself.[358]

The ethyl (**36**), propyl (**37**) and butyl ethers (**38**) of choline are almost equipotent to ACh at ganglionic nAChRs[356] and choline vinyl ether (**39**) is even more potent than ACh.[331] In choline ethyl and choline vinyl ether, α- and β-methyl substitution in the choline moiety has similar effects on nicotinic potencies as described above for ACh.[331]

$$\underset{\text{(34) } X = S \atop \text{(35) } X = Se}{\overset{\overset{\displaystyle O}{\overset{\displaystyle \|}{}}}{\text{Me}\overset{}{\text{C}}\text{XCH}_2\text{CH}_2\overset{+}{\text{N}}\text{Me}_3}} \qquad\qquad \underset{\begin{array}{l}\text{(36) } R = Et\\ \text{(37) } R = Pr^n\\ \text{(38) } R = Bu^n\\ \text{(39) } R = CH_2{=}CH\end{array}}{\text{ROCH}_2\text{CH}_2\overset{+}{\text{N}}\text{Me}_3}$$

Several aromatic choline ethers (**40**–**47**) are also highly potent nicotinic stimulants. Nicotinic activity increases with increasing electron-withdrawing capacity of the substituent(s) at the aromatic ring, suggesting that reduction of electron density on the ether oxygen favors the interaction with nAChRs.[359] Thus, the effects of electron-withdrawing substituents on nicotinic activity in benzoylcholine esters (**27**–**33**) and phenylcholine ethers (**40**–**47**) are completely opposed (Table 11).

Ketones related to ACh are generally more potent at neuromuscular nAChRs than at ganglionic nAChRs and mAChRs. The position of the carbonyl moiety is decisive for nicotinic activity; most potent is the ketone (**48**). The derivatives (**49**) and (**50**) are also nearly equipotent to ACh.[348,349,356] Analogs with only one methylene group between carbonyl and quaternary ammonium group (**51**) or those with branched chains (**52**) are less potent (Table 12).

In the series of *n*-alkyltrimethylammonium compounds, *n*-pentyltrimethylammonium (**53**; $n = 4$) displays highest activity at ganglionic and at neuromuscular nAChRs, being six times more potent and 25 times less potent than ACh, respectively. This gives evidence for an interaction of the alkyl chain with a nonpolar region of similarly limited size near the anionic center of both ganglionic and neuromuscular nAChRs.[356] Among arylalkyltrimethylammonium derivatives (**54**–**56**), activity at neuromuscular nAChRs increases with the length of the alkyl chain and is optimum at $n = 3$; further

Table 11 Potency of Aromatic Choline Ethers[356]

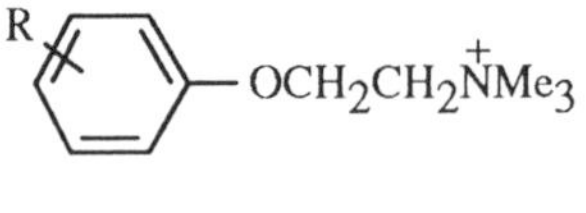

$$\text{R}\overbracket{}\!\!\!\!\!\!\!\!\!\!\!\!\!\!\!\!\text{—OCH}_2\text{CH}_2\overset{+}{\text{N}}\text{Me}_3$$

Compound	R	EPMR, ACh = 1, blood pressure	Compound	R	EPMR, ACh = 1, blood pressure
(**40**)	3,5-Br$_2$	0.0045	(**44**)	3-Me	0.089
(**41**)	3-Br	0.0046	(**45**)	4-Cl	0.12
(**42**)	3-Cl	0.0062	(**46**)	3,5-Me$_2$	0.23
(**43**)	H	0.012	(**47**)	4-Me	2.6

Table 12 Potency of Ketones Related to ACh[348,349]

$$\overset{\overset{\displaystyle O}{\overset{\displaystyle \|}{}}}{\text{RCX}\overset{+}{\text{N}}\text{Me}_3}$$

Compound	R	X	EPMR, ACh = 1, frog rectus
(**48**)	Me	CH$_2$CH$_2$	0.7
(**49**)	Me	CH$_2$CH$_2$CH$_2$	1.1
(**50**)	Et	CH$_2$CH$_2$	1.3
(**51**)	Pr^n	CH$_2$	153
(**52**)	Et	CHMeCH$_2$	700

Table 13 The Effect of Alkyl Chain Length on Nicotinic Activity[328]

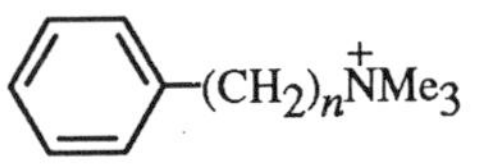

$$\langle\!\!\!\!\!\!\bigcirc\!\!\!\!\!\!\rangle\text{---}(CH_2)_n\overset{+}{N}Me_3$$

Compound	n	EPMR, ACh = 1, frog rectus
(54)	1	9.3
(55)	2	1.1
(56)	3	0.38

elongation of the alkyl chain leads to antagonists.[328,348,349] It is therefore concluded that a moiety with high electron density in a distance of three or four single bonds from the cationic center is a basic requirement for potent nicotinic stimulants (Table 13).[360] The generally lower potencies of phenoxytrimethylammonium compounds compared to the corresponding phenyltrimethylammonium analogs at neuromuscular nAChRs suggest that in these compounds the ether oxygen does not enhance the interaction with the receptor.[361]

Among cyclic nicotinic agonists, nicotine (57) is the most thoroughly studied agent. Based on MO calculations, two identically preferred conformations for nicotine are postulated. In both conformations, the pyridyl ring is perpendicular to the pyrrolidine ring, and in one conformation, the distance between the positively charged pyrrolidyl nitrogen (pK_a nicotine = 8.5) and the pyridyl nitrogen bearing a partial negative charge is similar to that between the positively and negatively charged centers in ACh.[347] Likewise, SAR within a series of cyclic amidines closely related to nicotine also suggest a two-site interaction of these agents with nAChRs.[347] Similar to 2-, 3- and 4-substituted pyridyl-N-methylpyrrolidines (58), among which nicotine (57) is most potent, 3-substitution of the pyridine ring in a series of pyridyl-N-methylpiperidine analogs (59) results in higher potencies than 2- or 4-substitution.[347]

Me(CH$_2$)$_n\overset{+}{N}$Me$_3$

(53)   (57) Nicotine 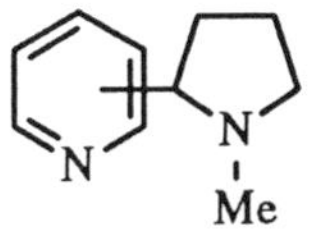   (58) 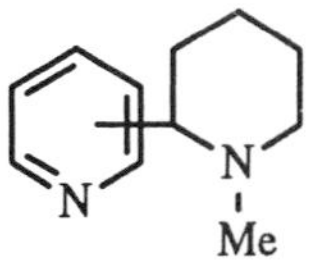   (59)

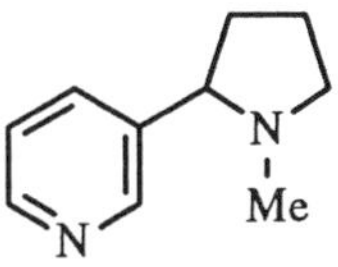

Among pentatomic cyclic ACh analogs related to muscarine (60), several potent agonists at nAChRs can be found.[362] The ketone muscarone (61), an analog of the highly selective muscarinic stimulant muscarine, is more potent than ACh at nAChRs in frog rectus abdominis, with only minor enantioselectivity.[328] One of its diastereomers, DL-allomuscarone, is even more potent at nAChRs than muscarone itself.[356] The oxathiolane analog (62) is also a potent nicotinic stimulant. It is more potent than its sulfone (63), and the corresponding sulfoxide (64) is an even weaker agonist at nAChRs than (63), indicating that an increasing polarity in the 3-position in the oxathiolane ring system is unfavorable for the interaction with nAChRs. Similar to muscarone (61), the cyclopentanone analog (65) is a potent nicotinic agonist, whereas the corresponding alcohol (66) is much weaker.[363] Several other nonpolar muscarine analogs lacking the C-5 methyl group (e.g. 67) are selective nicotinic stimulants with negligible muscarinic activity, suggesting that the C-5 methyl group is not essential for nicotinic activity (Table 14).[362]

Besides nicotine and muscarone analogs, there are only a few semirigid nicotinic agonists, and their SAR are far from being clear. One of the most potent semirigid agonists is anatoxin-a (68), a bicyclic secondary amine. Its outstanding potency might be related to a stronger coulombic interaction with nAChRs of the protonated secondary amino group compared to the bulkier quaternary ammonium moiety of classical nicotinic agonists.[364] This theory is supported by the fact that successive N-methylation of the bicyclic compound (−)-cytisine (69), which is a secondary amine, leads to stepwise decreases in nicotinic potency.[365] The quaternary agents arecolone methiodide (70) and isoarecolone methiodide (71) are also very potent semirigid agonists at nAChRs.[344,351,366] Isoarecolone methiodide (71) might serve as a template molecule for agonists of

Table 14 Nicotinic Activity of Muscarine Analogs[362]

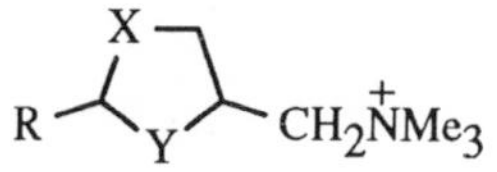

Compound	R	X	Y	EPMR, ACh = 1, frog rectus	Compound	R	X	Y	EPMR, ACh = 1, frog rectus
(60) Muscarine	Me	CHOH	O	> 50	(64)	Me	SO	O	13.6
(61) Muscarone	Me	CO	O	0.5	(65)	Me	CO	CH$_2$	2.8
(62)	Me	S	O	1.25	(66)	Me	CHOH	CH$_2$	75
(63)	Me	SO$_2$	O	4	(67)	H	CH$_2$	CH$_2$	5

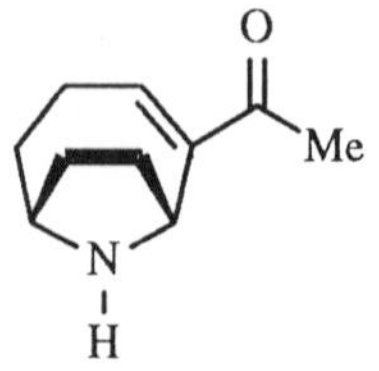

(68) Anatoxin-a 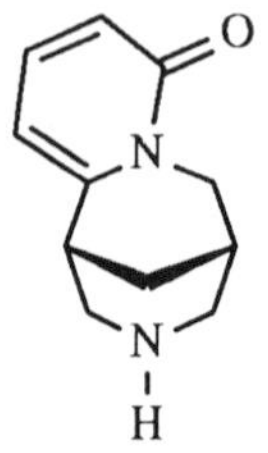   (69) (−)-Cytisine 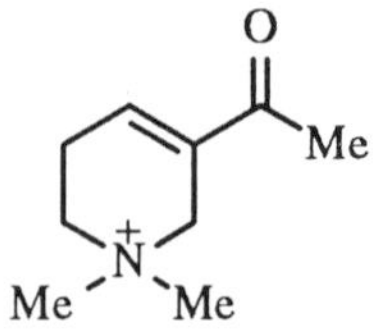   (70) 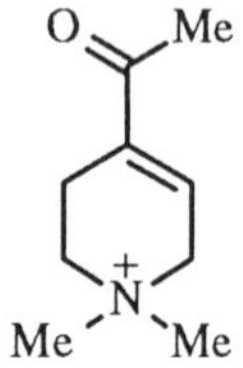   (71)

high nicotinic potency, as small deviations from the optimum sterical arrangement of its quaternary nitrogen and the carbonyl group diminish potency greatly.[344,366]

12.6.7.1.2 Antagonists

Nicotinic receptors in autonomic ganglia and those at the neuromuscular junction make different structural demands on their respective antagonists. Thus, SAR at each type of receptor will be treated separately in the following discussion. As ganglion-blocking agents had nearly completely disappeared from clinical practice more than 20 years ago, chemical and pharmacological studies of these agents have not been undertaken recently. SAR for these compounds have been extensively reviewed elsewhere[328,356,367-369] and will be only briefly summarized here.

(i) Ganglion-blocking agents

Replacement of methyl groups by ethyl groups in the ganglionic stimulant tetramethylammonium (72) leads to the ganglionic blocking agent tetraethylammonium (TEA; 73). Introduction of α-methyl groups in two of the ethyl moieties (74) increases ganglion-blocking potency about tenfold, whereas prolongation or further branching of the alkyl groups both decrease activity. In many ganglion-blocking agents (e.g. 75, 76), the diethyldiisopropylammonium (74) moiety can be identified as a common structural element (Table 15).[368]

In diquaternary polymethylenebistrialkylammonium compounds (8, 9, 77–79), the length of the polymethylene chain determines ganglion-blocking potency. Peak activity is obtained with five or six methylene groups (8, 77). In these compounds, the interquaternary distance amounts to 0.6–0.8 nm. The decamethylene derivative (9) is less potent at ganglionic nAChRs, but an efficient depolarizing neuromuscular blocker. A second peak of ganglion-blocking activity is found in compounds having 15 to 18 methylene groups (e.g. 78).[370] For unsymmetrical diquaternary compounds with one of the quaternary nitrogens incorporated into a ring system, interquaternary distances seem to be less important, as highly potent agents can be found with two to six methylene groups connecting the two nitrogen atoms. Several sulfonium and phosphonium derivatives have ganglion-blocking properties too, though they are usually weaker than the corresponding quaternary ammonium derivatives. Interestingly, replacement of only one ammonium group in tetramethylenebistrialkylammonium derivatives by a dialkylsulfonium group gives compounds (e.g. 80) with potencies higher than that of hexamethonium (Table 16).[371]

Table 15 Ganglion-blocking Agents

$$\overset{+}{N}R^1R^2R^3R^4$$

Compound	R^1	R^2	R^3	R^4	EPMR, ganglion-blocking activity[368]	Compound	EPMR, ganglion-blocking activity[368, 369]
(72)	Me	Me	Me	Me	Ganglion stimulant	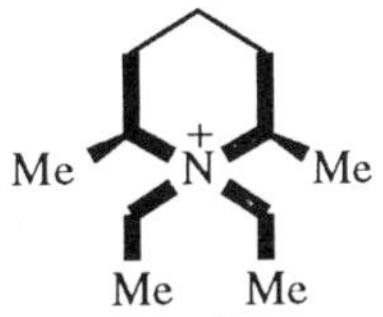 (75)	~0.1
(73) TEA	Et	Et	Et	Et	1.0	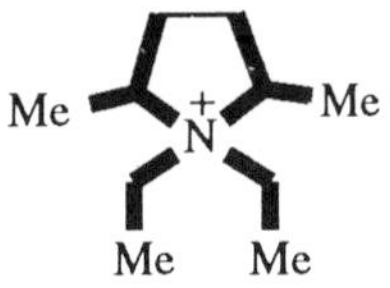 (76)	0.16
(74)	Et	Et	Pr^i	Pr^i	0.08	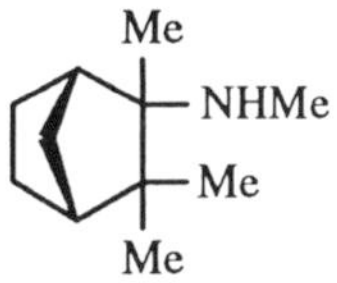 (10) Mecamylamine	0.4

Table 16 Ganglion-blocking Agents[356, 368]

$$Me_3\overset{+}{N}(CH_2)_n\overset{+}{N}Me_3 \qquad Et_2\overset{+}{S}(CH_2)_4\overset{+}{N}Me_3$$
$$(80)$$

Compound	n	EPMR, ganglion-blocking activity	Compound	n	EPMR, ganglion-blocking activity
(77)	5	1.25	(78)	16	0.26
(8) Hexamethonium	6	1.0	(79)	21	2.9
(9) Decamethonium	10	2.2	(80)		0.3[371]

Mecamylamine (10) was one of the first ganglionic blocking agents lacking a quaternary center. The most characteristic structural feature of mecamylamine and of other highly active non-quaternary ganglion blockers is a secondary or tertiary amino group with a large number of methyl groups attached to the carbon atoms adjacent to the nitrogen atom. It thus appears that a certain degree of steric hindrance of the nitrogen atom by methyl groups in its close vicinity is a prerequisite for ganglion-blocking activity in secondary and tertiary amines; primary amines are usually ganglionic stimulants. Activity of these agents is moreover dependent on the nature of the N substituents: secondary amines with two alkyl substituents larger than ethyl or isopropyl and tertiary amines with three residues larger than methyl or ethyl usually display lower activity (Table 15).[369]

(ii) Neuromuscular blocking agents

Neuromuscular blocking agents have to meet structural demands different from those of ganglion-blocking compounds[328,356] (*e.g.* in polymethylenediquaternary ammonium compounds (8, 9, 77–79), see above), although many similarities between both recognition sites are obvious.[356] For further subclassification of neuromuscular blocking agents into depolarizing and stabilizing (*i.e.* competitive, antidepolarizing) ones, Bovet's distinction by apparent morphological characteristics has proved to be very useful.[372] Molecules long and slender in shape (leptocurares), usually bearing small quaternary head groups (trimethylammonium) linked by chains which are unbranched, particularly in close vicinity to the onium groups, produce depolarizing blockade of neuromuscular transmission. In contrast, incorporation of quaternary ammonium functions into relatively bulky, rigid molecules (pachycurares) leads to stabilizing neuromuscular blockers. This can be explained by a pit or cleft on the receptor surface limiting access to the anionic binding site of the nAChR. A close approach of the cationic head of the agent to the anionic receptor site which is situated at the bottom of the cleft, seems to be essential for the induction of changes in the receptor conformation which ultimately result in membrane depolarization. Bulky molecules which cannot enter the cleft do not induce such conformational changes and therefore do not cause membrane depolarization, but they deny access of agonists to the receptor and therefore act as competitive inhibitors.

The presence of (a) cationic group(s) seems to be a necessary structural requirement for neuromuscular blocking agents. Besides quaternary ammonium salts, other cationic compounds, including sulfonium, phosphonium, arsonium and stibonium salts, exhibit neuromuscular blocking properties.[373] Several nonquaternary amines which are largely protonated at physiological pH, *e.g.* nicotine (**57**), quinine (**81**), and erythroidine (**82**) derivatives, block nAChRs at the neuromuscular junction, but often quaternization results in higher potencies. The quaternary moiety seems to ensure that the cationic charge is maintained in a minimally hydrated environment which favors electrostatic or coulombic association between cationic center(s) of the drug and anionic groups at the receptor site.[374] β-Erythroidine (**82**) and dihydro-β-erythroidine (**83**) are among the few exceptions to this rule as quaternization of the nitrogen abolishes their neuromuscular blocking activity.[374]

Neuromuscular blocking potency in simple onium compounds is determined by charge density on the onium center(s). In the series of N^+, S^+, P^+ and As^+ analogs, decrease of charge density on the onium ion is paralleled by reduced antagonistic potency at neuromuscular nAChRs. In addition to charge density, hydrophobic interactions, van der Waals bonding and charge transfer complexing are important factors determining the potency of simple onium compounds.[373]

Replacement of methyl groups by ethyl groups in the dionium depolarizing agents suxamethonium (**85**) and decamethonium (**9**) leads to the less potent suxaethonium (**86**) and decaethonium (**84**). Moreover, in decaethonium (**84**) the type of action is altered from depolarizing to stabilizing. Similarly, replacement of one or more methyl groups in each onium center of decamethonium by very large alkyl groups, such as *n*-heptyl, *n*-decyl or by an adamantyl moiety, yields stabilizing neuromuscular blockers, and markedly reduces potency.[373, 375]

The nature of the structural modifications of the chain connecting the cationic head groups of decamethonium or suxamethonium determines the mechanism of action of resulting analogs. The (*S*,*S*) and (*R*,*R*) isomers of succinyldi(α-methylcholine) (**87**), for example, are depolarizing blockers, whereas (*S*,*S*)- and (*R*,*R*)-succinyl-β-methylcholine (**88**) act competitively. Similar to the latter, succinyldi(β-phenylcholine) (**89**) is a stabilizing neuromuscular blocker, but the monophenyl analog still acts like decamethonium.[373]

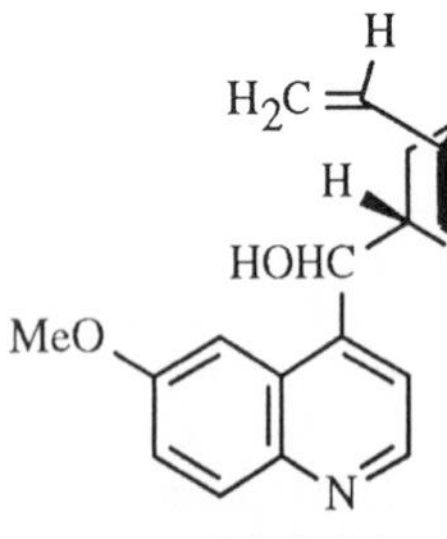

(81) Quinine 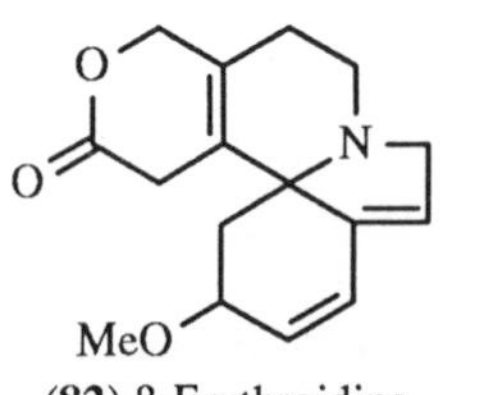   (82) β-Erythroidine 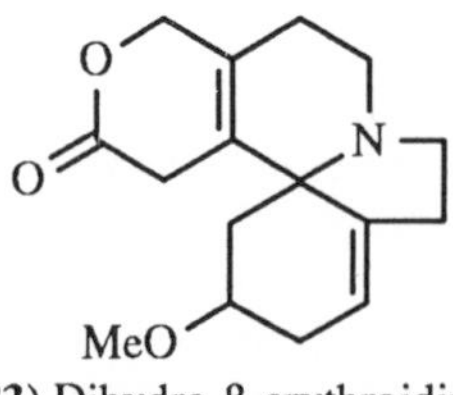   (83) Dihydro-β-erythroidine

$$R_3 \overset{+}{N}(CH_2)_{10}\overset{+}{N}R_3$$

(9) R = Me, decamethonium
(84) R = Et

$$R^1_3\overset{+}{N}CHR^2CHR^3O\overset{O}{\overset{\|}{C}}(CH_2)_2\overset{O}{\overset{\|}{C}}OCHR^3CHR^2\overset{+}{N}R^1_3$$

(85) R^1 = Me, R^2 = H, R^3 = H, suxamethonium
(86) R^1 = Et, R^2 = H, R^3 = H
(87) R^1 = Me, R^2 = Me, R^3 = H
(88) R^1 = Me, R^2 = H, R^3 = Me
(89) R^1 = Me, R^2 = H, R^3 = Ph

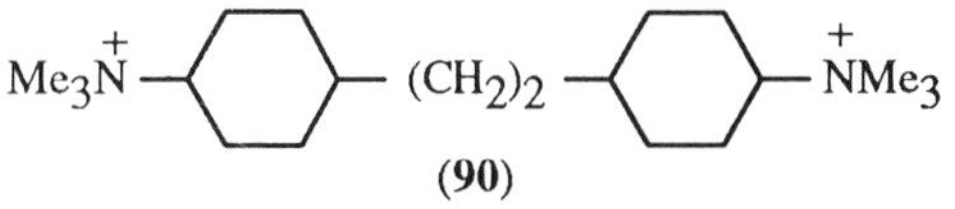

(90)

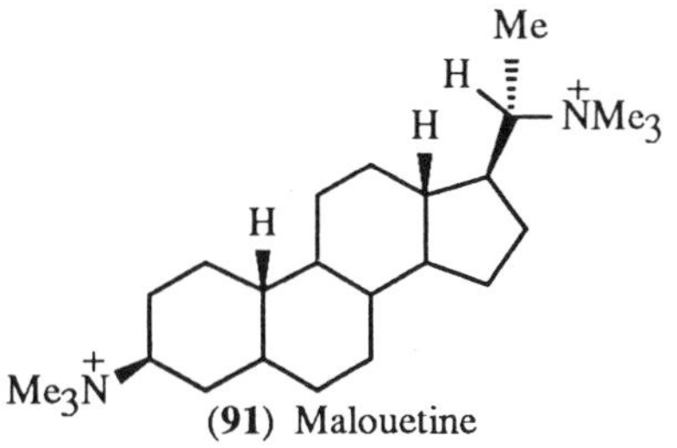

(91) Malouetine

Introduction of two cyclohexyl groups into the polymethylene chain of decamethonium leads to a compound (90) with stabilizing properties. Similarly, diquaternary compounds with linking chains comprising piperazine or benzoquinone moieties competitively block neuromuscular nAChRs.[356] In addition, several steroids carrying quaternary ammonium substituents, mostly at rings A and D, have stabilizing neuromuscular blocking properties. The steroidal alkaloid malouetine (91), for example, is almost as potent as (+)-tubocurarine (96).[373]

Incorporation of the decamethonium quaternary nitrogen atoms into ring systems greatly reduces potency and changes the type of action from depolarizing to stabilizing [*e.g.* decamethylenedipyridinium (92), decamethylenediquinolinium (93) and decamethyleneditetrahydroisoquinolinium (94)].[373] Introduction of methoxy substituents in these compounds produces, however, a marked increase in activity: (95) is almost two orders of magnitude more potent than its unsubstituted analog (94; see Table 17).[356] The most potent agents in this series are laudexium (97) and atracurium (244). Both contain two benzyltetrahydroisoquinolinium moieties, each of them carrying four methoxy substituents (see Table 46). Both agents produce a typical stabilizing block, laudexium being about half as potent as (+)-tubocurarine.[373] Likewise, the neuromuscular blocking activity of (+)-tubocurarine and of other phenolic compounds is increased by conversion of their phenolic hydroxyl into methoxy groups.[376]

From potency differences between stereoisomers of neuromuscular blockers it is obvious that stereochemical factors play an important role in the interaction between the nAChR and its antagonists. Thus, (−)-tubocurarine is about 20- to 60-fold less potent than the naturally occurring (+)-tubocurarine (96).[374] For several other compounds, including laudanosine and glaucine methiodide as well as pavinium, potency differences between stereoisomers have also been reported.[377−379] However, the interpretation of relationships between stereochemistry and activity is complicated by the conformational flexibility of large molecules.[380] Therefore, only few attempts have been made to develop general models to explain stereochemistry–activity relationships,[373] even for single structural classes of neuromuscular blocking agents.

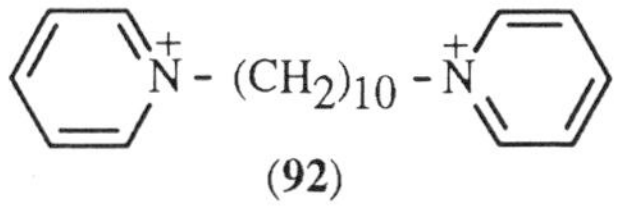

(92)

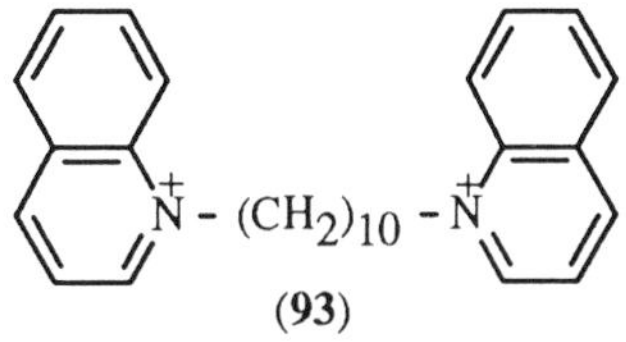

(93)

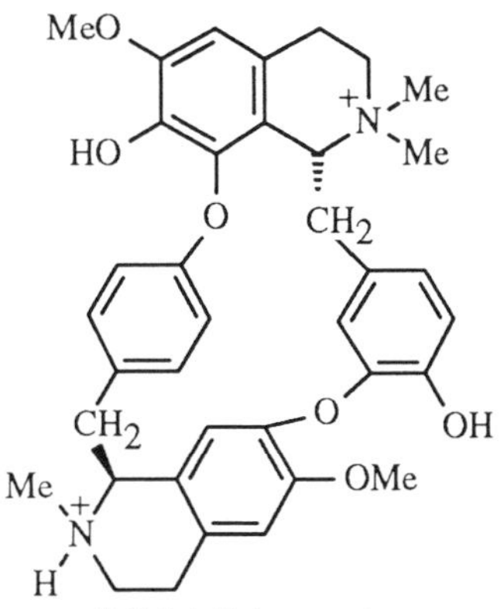

(96) (+)-Tubocurarine

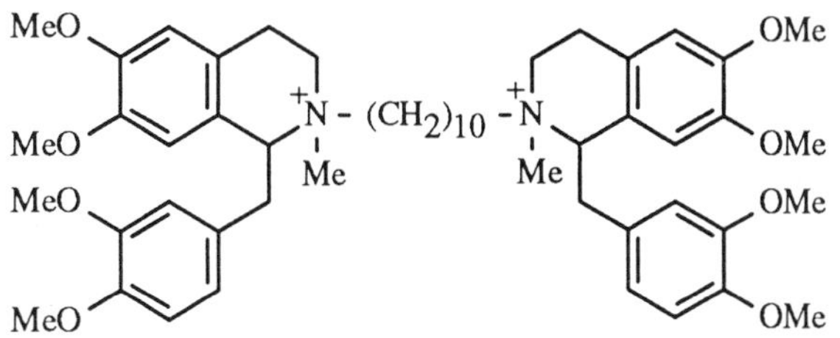

(97) Laudexium

Table 17 Neuromuscular Blocking Agents[356]

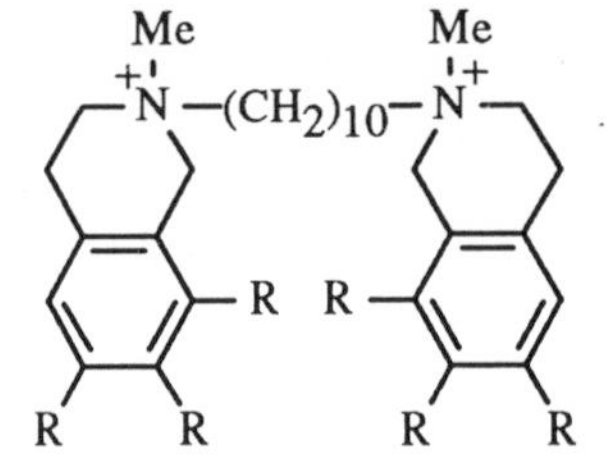

Compound	R	ED_{50}^a (mg kg^{-1})
(94)	H	1.5
(95)	OMe	0.02

^{a} Dose paralyzing 50% of rabbits.

12.6.7.2 Drugs Acting Preferentially at Muscarinic Receptors

12.6.7.2.1 *Agonists*

Similar to nicotinic receptors, the minimum requirement for activity at muscarinic receptors seems to be the presence of a positively charged 'head' group. Thus, even the tetramethylammonium ion is a muscarinic stimulant, although a rather weak one.[356] This 'head' group need not always be a quaternary ammonium function. There are several highly potent tertiary amines which are decidedly more potent at mAChRs than their quaternary counterparts (*e.g.* **98–103**).[328] Their extraordinary potency is explicable by reason of their relatively rigid ring structure which makes an intramolecular interaction between the protonated nitrogen atom and a negatively charged group (*e.g.* C=O) impossible. In conformationally flexible molecules like dimethylaminoethyl acetate (**104**) such an interaction may stabilize a conformation which is not favorable for the interaction with mAChRs, resulting in markedly lower potencies for the protonated tertiary amine compared to the quaternary analog (Table 18).[381–383]

Besides a positively charged head group, other moieties, either lipophilic (alkyl groups, *e.g.* *n*-pentyl), or bearing an electron rich center (ester group, triple bond, *etc.*), are a necessary requirement for potent muscarinic agonists. Ing's 'five-atom rule'[384] is a very general rule governing the properties of these moieties required for high muscarinic activity. It holds true for quite a few muscarinic agonists, *e.g.* muscarine (**60**), methylfurtrethonium (**105**), *n*-pentyltrimethylammonium

Table 18 Potency of Muscarinic Agonists[381, 382]

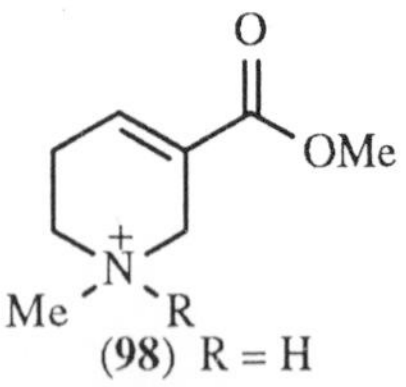

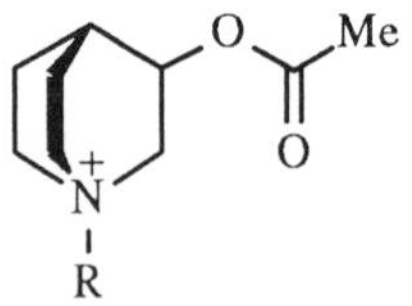

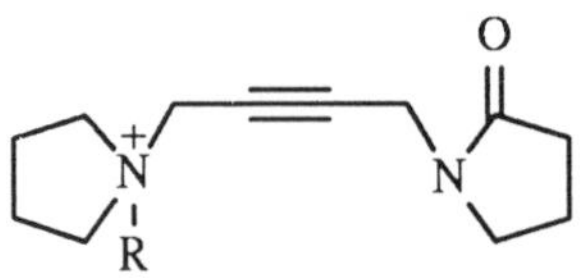

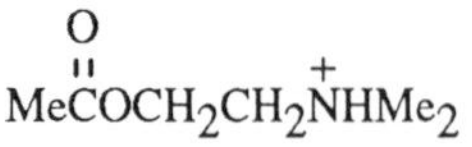

Compound	EPMR, bethanechol = 1, guinea pig ileum	Ratio quaternary/tertiary
(98)	0.06	
(99)	1.04	17
(100)	0.12	
(101)	26.3	220
(102)	0.02	
(103)	0.20	10
(104)	3.80	
(3) ACh	0.03	0.008

(106), and many others. According to the five-atom rule, maximum stimulant activity at mAChRs in a series of compounds is associated with a five-atom chain which is attached to the quaternary nitrogen function and terminates in a methyl group. Although this rule played an important role for the interpretation of SAR and for the design of muscarinic agonists, there are numerous exceptions, and the underlying assumption that all compounds meeting the requirements of the five-atom rule bind to the same site at the receptor surface, seems not to be justified.[328]

(60) Muscarine   (105)   (106)

In addition to critical moieties required for muscarinic activity, the stereochemical features of molecules interacting with mAChRs are decisive for their potency. The usually very high stereo- and enantio-selectivity of the mAChR gave rise to numerous investigations and theories directed towards the elucidation of stereochemical requirements for high muscarinic potency and of the active conformation(s) of muscarinic agonists. As a thorough analysis of these general theories, except special aspects particularly interesting for those structural classes of agonists and antagonists treated below, lies beyond the scope of this overview, the reader is referred to several excellent reviews covering these topics in depth.[325,327,331–334,385,386]

Most of the SAR data presented below have an essentially qualitative character. Nevertheless, there have been attempts to delineate QSAR at least for limited structural classes of muscarinic agonists. Pratesi and coworkers have systematically investigated the topology of the muscarinic receptor through appropriately designed structures. Starting from an 'archetypical structure' for muscarinic ligands they performed correlation analyses which provided clues to the specific role of the structural features of the ligands acting at mAChRs. Most interesting are the results they obtained in a large series of 3-substituted benzyltrimethylammonium salts (cf. ref. 487 and refs. therein). In this study, the choice of substituents was planned on the basis of equally weighted parameters for hydrophobic–lipophilic, polar, electronic and steric effects on the basis of cluster analysis following the principles of variance and collinearity problems. The results obtained were achieved by using the known substituent constants and Sterimol parameters; π values were determined experimentally. In summary, the results clearly show the heterogeneous nature of the active site of the receptor which seems to be made up of apolar and polar residues. There is one hydrophobic region of limited size, and two polar spaces extending beyond this hydrophobic pocket which interact with hydrophilic ligand component parts. The extensive material presented by Pratesi has been dealt with in depth in recent reviews.[387,488]

As pointed out above, a cationic center is essential for muscarinic activity in acyclic ACh analogs. The quaternary ammonium function may be substituted for by a dimethylsulfonium, trimethylphosphonium or -arsonium group (reduction of potency),[331] but not by trimethylsilane or tertiary butyl moieties. Acetylcarbocholine and acetylsilicocholine both are indirectly acting agonists that release ACh from presynaptic nerve terminals.[388] Replacement of ACh methyl groups by higher alkyl residues markedly reduces potency. In ACh and related compounds the formal charge is largely distributed among the N-methyl groups, which form a ball of positive charge around the central nitrogen atom.[331] N-Methoxy analogs of ACh as well as those of methacholine and carbachol are less potent than their parent compounds (22, 112).[389] Amine oxide analogs generally display only weak muscarinic activity.[331] Increasing the length of the choline 'ethylene bridge' in ACh results in analogs with weak muscarinic activity and ultimately leads to antagonists.[331,348,349]

β-Methyl substitution (for the effects of α-methyl substitution (21a,b), see Section 12.6.7.1.1) only slightly reduces potency at mAChRs but nearly abolishes nicotinic activity. (S)-(+)-Acetyl-β-methylcholine [(S)-(+)-methacholine; 22b] is at least 200 times more potent than its (R)-(−)-enantiomer (22a) at mAChRs, thus demonstrating the high degree of enantioselectivity displayed by the mAChR for potent agonists. The absolute configuration of the corresponding chiral centers in the eutomers of methacholine and muscarine is identical, which is indicative of a common binding site. In α,β-dimethylated analogs, ca. 1/7 of ACh muscarinic potency is preserved in *erythro*-acetyl-α,β-dimethylcholine (107a), while the *threo* analog (107b) is almost inert as a cholinergic agent. *gem*-Dimethyl substitution or the introduction of longer alkyl chains markedly reduces muscarinic activity (Table 19).[331,348,349]

Table 19 Enantioselectivity of Muscarinic Agonists[348, 349]

$$\underset{\text{MeCOCHR}^1\text{CHR}^2\overset{+}{\text{NMe}}_3}{\overset{\displaystyle\overset{\text{O}}{\underset{\|}{}}}{}}$$

Compound	R^1	R^2	Configuration	EPMR, ACh = 1, guinea pig ileum
(21a)	H	Me	(R)-(+)	42
(21b)	H	Me	(S)-(−)	223
(22a)	Me	H	(R)-(−)	240
(22b)	Me	H	(S)-(+)	1.0
(107a)	Me	Me	erythro, $\alpha(R)$, $\beta(S)$	7
(107b)	Me	Me	threo, $\alpha(S)$, $\beta(S)$	2800

Choline itself has some residual muscarinic activity (1/200 to 1/20000 compared to ACh),[348, 349] but esterification usually increases potency.[331] Among choline esters, formylcholine (**108**), as well as esters with higher homologs of acetic acid (**109, 110**), are less potent than ACh itself. In higher homologs, however, introduction of double or triple bonds (*e.g.* **111**) may considerably increase muscarinic potency (Table 20).[348, 349]

Replacement of the methyl group by an amino group in the acetyl moiety of ACh and methacholine (**22**) leads to the respective carbamates, carbachol (**112**) and bethanechol (**113**). Both agents are less potent at mAChRs than their acetyl analogs, but are less sensitive to cleavage by AChE (Table 20).[348, 349]

The closely related amide congener (**114**) of ACh has little or no cholinergic activity. Its remarkably low potency might be related to the stiffness of the amide bond, which greatly reduces conformational flexibility and consequently makes the compound less able to fit the mAChR.[390] The methoxycarbonylcholine analog (**115**) of ACh is a muscarinic agonist about 1/20 as potent as ACh.[391] Among quaternary aminocarboxylic acid esters, the 'reverse ACh' (**116**) is almost as potent as ACh itself (Table 21).[348, 349] It is interesting to note that, in contrast to ACh, α- and β-methyl substitution in the corresponding positions of the quaternary aminopropionic acid moiety both lead to a considerable loss of muscarinic activity.[348, 349] Alkyltrimethylammonium analogs, quaternary amino ethers and quaternary amino ketones related to ACh are generally less potent at mAChRs than ACh. For further details, the reader is referred to several extensive reviews.[328, 331, 347–349, 356]

Among carbocyclic ACh congeners, high muscarinic potency is found only with the cyclopropane analog (1*S*,2*S*)-(+)-*trans*-acetoxycyclopropyltrimethylammonium (**117**), which is equipotent to ACh. Its absolute configuration at the 2-position of the cyclopropane ring is identical to that of the corresponding chiral centers in (*S*)-(+)-methacholine (**22b**) and (2*S*,3*R*,5*S*)-(+)-muscarine (**60a**). All other stereoisomers of (**117**) are several hundred times weaker than the (+)-*trans* enantiomer. Incorporation of the choline methylene groups of ACh into ring systems larger than cyclopropane results in analogs with only feeble muscarinic effects. This finding can be interpreted in terms of a steric hindrance in their interaction with mAChRs and a different stereochemistry of larger ring systems (Table 21).[327, 331]

In acetoxypiperidine analogs (**118, 119, 121, 122**) of ACh, the choline methylene groups and the nitrogen atom are part of the ring system, which brings about rigidization. The generally weak activities of the 3- and 4-isomers of acetoxypiperidine can be explained by an unfavorable conformational equilibrium for those conformers being active at mAChRs.[334, 386] In acetoxythiacyclohexane analogs (**120, 123**), replacement of the nitrogen by sulfur allows the isolation of further

Table 20 Muscarinic Activity of Choline Esters and Carbamates[348, 349]

$$\underset{\text{RCOCH}_2\text{CH}_2\overset{+}{\text{NMe}}_3}{\overset{\displaystyle\overset{\text{O}}{\underset{\|}{}}}{}} \qquad\qquad \underset{\text{H}_2\text{NCOCHRCH}_2\overset{+}{\text{NMe}}_3}{\overset{\displaystyle\overset{\text{O}}{\underset{\|}{}}}{}}$$

Compound	R	EPMR, ACh = 1, rat jejunum	i.a.	Compound	R	EPMR, ACh = 1, guinea pig ileum
(108)	H	250	1.0	**(112)**	H	0.6
(109)	Et	400	0.9	**(113)**	Me	11
(110)	Prⁿ	6400	0.3			
(111)	CH=CH₂	5	1.0			

Table 21 Muscarinic Activity of ACh Analogs

Compound	EPMR, ACh = 1	Preparation	Ref.
$\underset{(114)}{MeCNHCH_2CH_2\overset{+}{N}Me_3}$ (with O double-bonded to C)	10 000	Rat jejunum	390
$\underset{(115)}{MeOCOCH_2CH_2\overset{+}{N}Me_3}$ (with O double-bonded to C)	17	Guinea pig atrium (force)	391
$\underset{(116)}{MeOCCH_2CH_2\overset{+}{N}Me_3}$ (with O double-bonded to C)	~1	Guinea pig ileum	348, 349
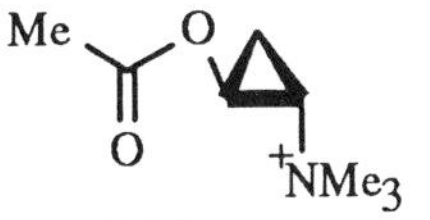 (117) cyclopropane acetoxy $\overset{+}{N}Me_3$ structure	1.13	Guinea pig ileum	328

geometrical and optical isomers, as the energy barrier for pyramidal inversion is much higher in tertiary sulfonium compounds compared to tertiary amines. Furthermore, in 1-methyl-substituted thiacyclohexanes the solute concentrations of conformers with an axial methyl group are several hundredfold higher than in the corresponding *N*-methylpiperidines.[334,350,392] The extraordinarily potent *cis*-4-acetoxy-1-methylthianium (**120**) and (1*R*,3*R*)-(+)-*trans*-3-acetoxy-1-methylthianium (**123**),[350] seem to comprise the 'muscarinic essential' conformations of this class of compounds,[332-334,350,386,392-394] which is illustrated for (**123**) in conformation (**123a**) (see Table 22).

In acetoxyquinuclidine analogs (**100, 101**) of ACh, the acetoxypiperidine ring system is further constrained in a 'boat' conformation.[332,334,386,392,395] In contrast to acetoxypiperidine and acetoxythiacyclohexane congeners (**118–123**), higher muscarinic activity is found with the 3-acetoxy analog; 4-acetoxyquinuclidine is about 100-fold less potent.[396,397] (*S*)-(+)-3-Acetoxyquinuclidine (**100a**) is at least 10 times more potent than its (*R*)-(−)-enantiomer (**100b**).[334,343,386,395] *N*-Methylation reduces potency of the stronger (*S*)-(+)-enantiomer more than 1000-fold (**101a**), whereas the quaternary (*R*)-(−)-3-acetoxyquinuclidine (**101b**) is about 1/20 as potent as the tertiary base, thus leading to an inversion of enantioselectivity.[332,334,395,398,399] Quantum chemical calculations suggest a similar receptor-interaction pattern for (*S*)-(+)-3-acetoxyquinuclidine (**100a**) and ACh; the interaction pharmacophore of the *N*-methyl derivative (**101b**) seems to be less compatible with the requirements of the mAChR (Table 23).[343]

Arecoline (**98**) is a naturally occurring, semirigid analog of the 'inverse' ACh (**116**). Arecoline and several of its congeners are potent muscarinic agonists.[400] This is an indication for a favorable steric arrangement of its functional groups for the interaction with mAChRs. Hydrogenation of the arecoline double bond (**128–130**) decreases potency,[400] probably due to changes in the ring geometry of the molecule rather than to changes in electron density on the ester carbonyl oxygen.[401] In agreement with this suggestion, hydrogenation in the isoarecaidine ester series (**131–134**) leads to compounds with similar changes in electron density but different steric properties, in which muscarinic activity is largely preserved (**135–137**).[402] Similarly, in a series of 3-alkoxycarbonyl-*N*-methylpyrrolines (**138, 139**), where hydrogenation of the ring double bond is not accompanied by changes in ring geometry as pronounced as in arecaidine analogs, muscarinic activity in saturated analogs (**140, 141**) is lowered to a much smaller extent than in the corresponding dihydroarecaidine congeners (Table 24).[401]

In arecaidine ester analogs, quaternization (**99, 124, 125**) reduces muscarinic potency, the extent being dependent on the size of the *N*-alkyl moiety.[400] Replacement of the *N*-methyl group in arecoline (**98**) and in arecaidine propargyl ester (APE; **144**) by higher alkyl groups (**142, 143, 145, 146**) also results in a loss of potency and intrinsic activity.[245,403,465] Interestingly, ileal mAChRs are more sensitive to structural variations of the *N*-alkyl group in these agents: for example, (**145**) is still

Table 22 Muscarinic Activity of Cyclic ACh Analogs[333, 350, 386, 392, 393]

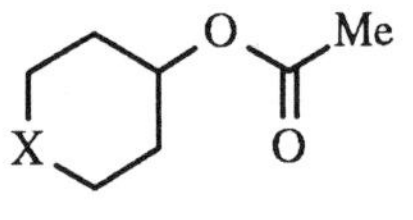

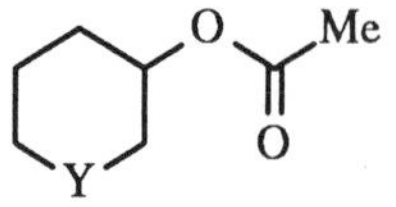

Compound	X	EPMR, ACh = 1, guinea pig ileum	Compound	Y	EPMR, ACh = 1, guinea pig ileum
(118)	N^+HMe	127	**(121)**	N^+HMe	4800
(119)	N^+Me_2	63	**(122)**	N^+Me_2	3100
(120)	S^+Me (*cis*)	0.8	**(123)**	S^+Me (*trans*-1*R*, 3*R*)	9

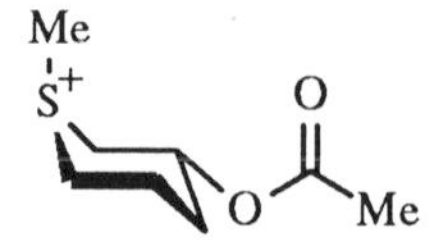

(123a)

Table 23 Muscarinic Activity of Acetoxyquinuclidine ACh Analogs[395, 399]

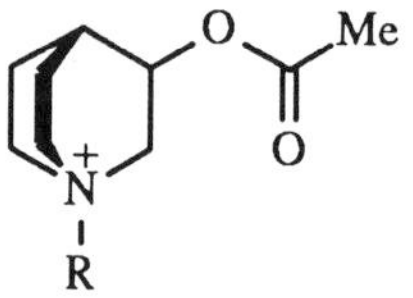

Compound	R	Configuration	EPMR, oxotremorine = 1, guinea pig ileum
(100a)	H	(*S*)-(+)	5
(100b)	H	(*R*)-(−)	71
(101a)	Me	(*S*)-(+)	>10 000
(101b)	Me	(*R*)-(−)	1280

a rather potent partial agonist at atrial ($M_{2\alpha}$) mAChRs, whereas it is an antagonist at ileal ($M_{2\beta}$) mAChRs (Table 25).[245, 403, 465]

In the isoarecaidine ester series, higher potencies of quaternary congeners (**132, 136**) compared to their tertiary counterparts (**131, 135**) show that the above-mentioned rule for the relative potencies of tertiary and quaternary cyclic ACh analogs is not generally applicable.[402] As for acetoxypiperidine analogs (**118, 119, 121, 122**), studies with sulfonium analogs of arecoline (**98**) and isoarecoline (**131**) provided further insights into structural requirements for mAChR activation.[404-406] In both the arecaidine and isoarecaidine ester series, a single methyl group in the onium center suffices for high muscarinic potency; the methyl group must be oriented axially in isoarecoline analogs, contrasting with ethyl or higher esters of arecaidine where an equatorial methyl group is required for an effective interaction with mAChRs. In arecoline itself, a single methyl group in the onium center is equally efficient in axial or equatorial position. In the isoarecaidine ester series, a second methyl group is tolerated, but does not increase potency, whereas in arecoline analogs introduction of a second methyl group lowers potency, apparently by steric hindrance.[406]

Among the great many variations of the arecaidine ester side chain, unsaturated esters generally display higher potencies than their saturated analogs.[407] Arecaidine propargyl ester (APE; **144**) is considerably more potent than arecoline (**98**) and even ACh. The extraordinarily high potencies of unsaturated esters of this type is thought to result from an additional interaction of the electron rich triple bond with an electron acceptor at the receptor surface, possibly similar to oxotremorine analogs (see below).[407] In APE analogs, potency is highly dependent on the position of the triple bond (*cf.* **147, 150**), whereas elongation of the propargyl ester side chain does not diminish potency in (**147**) and (**148**).[408] However, introduction of a C(1) methyl group in the APE ester side chain (**149**) results in a nearly complete loss of agonistic activity (Table 26).[408]

Replacement of the methyl ester group of arecoline by the hydrolysis-resistant 3-methoxyisoxazole moiety leads to arecoline bioisosteres containing the 4,5,6,7-tetrahydroisoxazolo[4,5-*c*]pyridin-

Table 24 Muscarinic Activity of Cyclic ACh Analogs[400-402]

	Compound	R^1	R^2	EPMR, ACh = 1
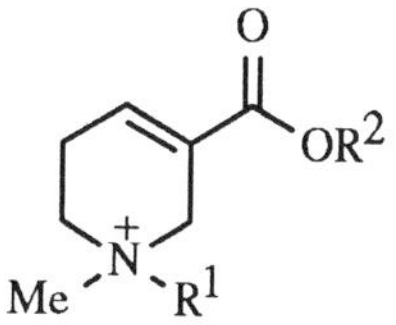	**(98)**	H	Me	10[a]
	(99)	Me	Me	83[a]
	(124)	Et	Me	3300[a]
	(125)	Pr^n	Me	50 000[a]
	(126)	H	Et	2.9[a]
	(127)	H	Pr^n	330[a]
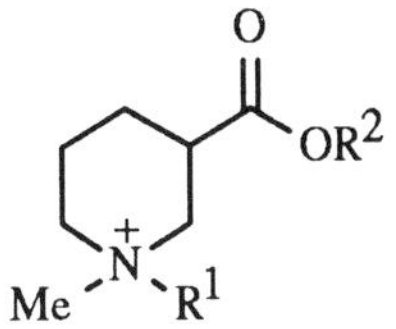	**(128)**	H	Me	2500[a]
	(129)	Me	Me	1000[a]
	(130)	H	Et	5000[a]
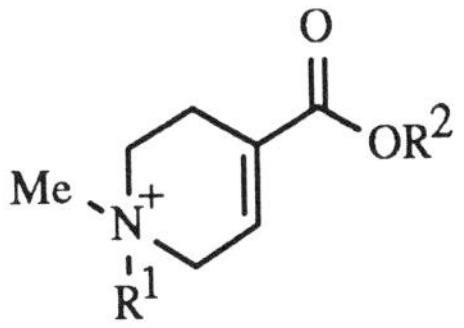	**(131)**	H	Me	160[b]
	(132)	Me	Me	3.2[b]
	(133)	H	Et	Partial agonist[b,c]
	(134)	H	Pr^n	Partial agonist[b,d]
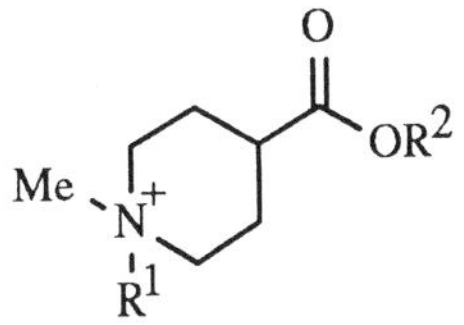	**(135)**	H	Me	500[b]
	(136)	Me	Me	16[b]
	(137)	H	Et	Partial agonist[b,e]
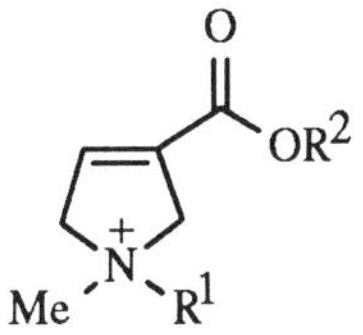	**(138)**	H	Me	20[b]
	(139)	Me	Me	20[b]
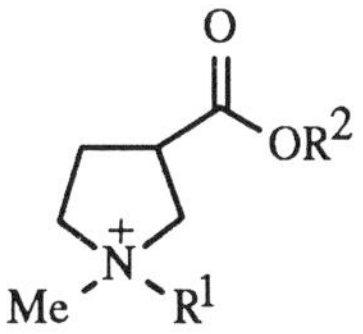	**(140)**	H	Me	320[b]
	(141)	Me	Me	8[b]

[a] Guinea pig ileum. [b] Rat ileum. [c] i.a. = 0.31. [d] i.a. = 0.12. [e] i.a. = 0.2.

Table 25 Effect of *N*-Alkyl Chain Length of Muscarinic Potency[403]

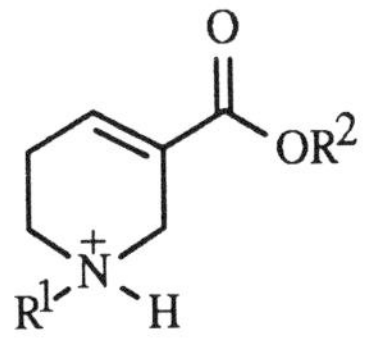

Compound	R^1	R^2	pD_2 rat atrium	i.a. rat atrium	pD_2 rat ileum	i.a. rat ileum
(98)	Me	Me	6.9	1.0	6.5	1.0
(142)	Et	Me	5.5	0.7	4.8	0.3
(143)	Pr^n	Me	5.3	0.8	4.3	0.7
(144) APE	Me	CH$_2$C≡CH	8.1	1.0	7.5	1.0
(145)	Et	CH$_2$C≡CH	6.6	0.8	pA$_2$ = 6.1	0.0
(146)	Pr^n	CH$_2$C≡CH	6.3	0.7	5.8	0.1

Table 26 Muscarinic Potency of Unsaturated Arecaidine Esters[408]

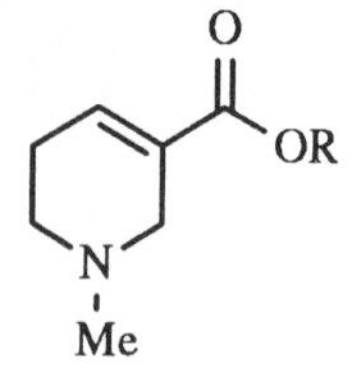

Compound	R	$pD_2{}^a$	$pA_2{}^a$
(144) APE	$CH_2-C\equiv CH$	7.8	—
(147)	$CH_2-C\equiv C-CH_3$	7.7	—
(148)	$CH_2-C\equiv C-CH_2-CH_3$	8.0	—
(149)	$CH(CH_3)-C\equiv CH$	—	6.7
(150)	$CH_2-CH_2-C\equiv CH$	—	6.8

^{a} Guinea pig ileum.

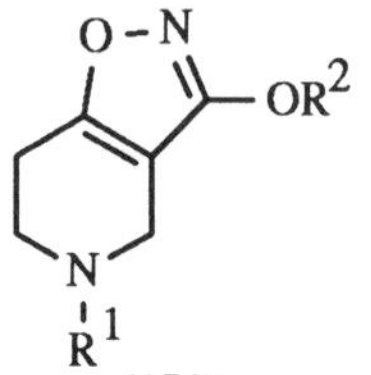

(151)

3-ol (THPO) skeleton (*cf.* general formula, **151**).[409,410] Several analogs in the THPO series are muscarinic stimulants, although less potent than the corresponding arecaidine esters. SAR for THPO analogs have been reviewed recently.[411]

Since the discovery of its physiological actions, muscarine (**60**) and its pentatomic cyclic analogs have always attracted great interest with regard to their unique SAR.[412] Several agents with an outstanding potency at mAChRs can be found within this group.[362] Muscarine may be regarded as a conformationally restrained analog of ACh.[327] Due to its rotational freedom, the trimethylammoniummethyl side chain can adopt several conformations; in dioxolane analogs of muscarine, agonistic activity seems to be associated with an extended conformation of the side chain.[328]

Strict stereochemical requirements determine muscarinic activity of muscarine and most of its congeners. All stereoisomers of muscarine are at least 200 times less potent than the naturally occurring (2S,3R,5S)-(+) isomer (**60a**).[327] In several analogs, stereochemical requirements are strictly the same as in muscarine.[362] One of the most remarkable exceptions to this rule is the high muscarinic activity of (2R,5R)-(−)-muscarone (**61b**), which has the same absolute configuration as the weakly active (2R,3S,5R)-(−)-muscarine (**60b**).[385] The almost complete loss of stereoselectivity [(2S,5S)-(+)-muscarone (**61a**) is nearly equipotent to its (2R,5R)-(−) enantiomer (**61b**)] is accompanied by the occurrence of considerable nicotinic activity (*cf.* Section 12.6.7.1.1). The reasons underlying this apparent anomaly still remain a point at issue (Table 27).

Modifications of the muscarine ring system may lead to several highly potent agonists at mAChRs. The cyclopentane analog (**66**) retains considerable muscarinic activity (about 1/10 to 1/3 compared to ACh),[362,413] which is in contrast to earlier speculations ascribing an important role to the ether oxygen as a primary site of interaction with the mAChR.[412] Likewise, high potencies and low stereoselectivity of several cyclopentene analogs provide evidence for an interaction of these compounds with a nonpolar area at the agonist recognition site of mAChRs.[362]

Some highly potent heterocyclic muscarine analogs are derived from the 1,3-dioxolane (*e.g.* **152**) and 1,3-oxathiolane nucleus (*e.g.* **62**, **64**).[414,415] SAR among these compounds substantiate the importance of ring position X (corresponding to the CHOH moiety of muscarine) for an effective interaction with the mAChR.[362,363] The outstanding potency of the 1,3-oxathiolane analog (**62**) cannot be accounted for by stronger hydrogen bonding or dipole–dipole interaction of the sulfur with a corresponding group at the receptor surface, as both interactions should be much stronger for the corresponding sulfoxide (**64**), which is however clearly less potent than (**62**). Yet, determinations of affinity values for (**62**) and (**64**) in fact revealed a lower affinity for (**62**), but a much higher efficacy.[416] This indicates that an easily polarizable atom in the position corresponding to the muscarine CHOH group greatly enhances the ability of the ligand to induce a productive conformational change in the receptor molecule.

The muscarine 2-methyl group also plays a very significant role for muscarinic potency: its removal in 2-demethylmuscarine results in a very significant decrease in activity (five-atom rule, see above). Addition of a second methyl group gives an even greater reduction in activity.[363] Furthermore, the steric arrangement of the methyl group seems to be very important as potency drops when the carbon carrying the methyl group is engaged in a double bond.[362] Similarly, the effects on muscarinic activity of various substituents in the 2-position of the dioxolane ring system clearly show a very specific interaction of the 2-methyl group with the receptor. Absence of the methyl group (153) results in an almost 100-fold loss in activity, introduction of a second methyl group (154) or of two ethyl groups (155) decreases potency by more than three orders of magnitude (Table 27).[417]

At first glance, there are only a few similarities between ACh and muscarine (60) on one hand, and oxotremorine (102) on the other. Nevertheless, oxotremorine is a highly potent muscarinic agonist devoid of any nicotinic activity.[418] In oxotremorine the pyrrolidine nitrogen, which is largely protonated at physiological pH, substitutes for the muscarine and ACh quaternary ammonium function. The oxotremorine triple bond coincides with the tetrahydrofuran oxygen of muscarine as a center of high electron density, and the lactam oxygen is considered to interact with a third polar site at the receptor surface.[419] The important role of the pyrrolidone carbonyl group is emphasized by the complete absence of muscarinic activity in tremorine (156; Table 28).[420]

Structural modifications in the oxotremorine butynyl chain almost inevitably reduce muscarinic potency. The corresponding butenyl and butyl analogs are more than two orders of magnitude less potent than oxotremorine itself.[347] Introduction of a 1-methyl group into the oxotremorine butynyl chain abolishes intrinsic efficacy, but increases affinity in one of the enantiomers, thus resulting in potent antagonists (*cf.* Section 12.6.7.2.2).[422] Methyl substitution in the 4-position of the butynyl chain leads to antagonists with affinities considerably lower than that of oxotremorine.[422]

The structural requirements with respect to the size of the oxotremorine lactam ring seem to be very strict, as minor structural modifications generally reduce muscarinic potency.[418] Replacement of the pyrrolidone ring by the smaller β-lactam ring, for example, brings about a seven-fold reduction of potency.[418] However, opening of the β-lactam ring leads to the corresponding acetamides (*e.g.* 157) in which muscarinic potency is largely preserved. Interestingly, some of these analogs (158, 159) show higher relative efficacies than oxotremorine (102).[423] Replacement of the methylene group in the 5-position of the pyrrolidone ring by another oxygen or nitrogen heteroatom largely preserves muscarinic activity, introduction of lipophilic or bulky moieties in this position results in antagonists with remarkably high affinities (*cf.* Section 12.6.7.2.2).[424]

Structural modifications at the pyrrolidine nitrogen, like quaternization (103) or replacement of the whole pyrrolidine ring system by aminoalkyl groups or by larger ring systems[425,426] generally reduce potency, mainly by lowering relative intrinsic efficacy; affinities of higher homologs are still similar to oxotremorine. Higher potencies, caused by a prominent rise in intrinsic efficacies, are

Table 27 Muscarinic Potency of Muscarine (60) and Analogs[362,412,417]

Compound	Stereochemistry	X	Y	R^1	R^2	EPMR, ACh = 1
(60a)	(2S,3R,5S)-(+)	CHOH	O	Me	H	0.3^a
(60b)	(2R,3S,5R)-(−)	CHOH	O	H	Me	130^a
(61a)	(2S,5S)-(+)	CO	O	Me	H	0.2^a
(61b)	(2R,5R)-(−)	CO	O	H	Me	0.1^a
(66)	Same as (±)-(60)	CHOH	CH_2	Me	H	$\sim 10^b$
(152)	(2S,4R)-(+)	O	O	Me	H	0.7^b
(153)	(4RS)-(±)	O	O	H	H	55^b
(154)	(4R)	O	O	Me	Me	1300^b
(155)	(4R)	O	O	Et	Et	3600^b
(62)	Cis	S	O	Me	H	0.43^b
(64)	Same as (±)-(60)	SO	O	Me	H	1.05^b

[a] Rabbit ileum. [b] Guinea pig ileum.

observed after replacement of the pyrrolidine ring by a smaller azetidine ring system (**160**) or a quaternary trimethylammonium group (**161**; oxotremorine-M).[426]

In acetamides related to oxotremorine (**157–159**), the pyrrolidine analogs (*e.g.* **157**) display high affinity but relatively low intrinsic efficacy at mAChRs. Replacement of the pyrrolidine ring by a dimethylamino group (**158**) leads to lower affinities but higher intrinsic efficacies. In dimethylamino analogs, affinity and intrinsic efficacy both are enhanced on quaternization (*e.g.* **159**; see Table 28).[423]

Table 28 Muscarinic Activity of Oxotremorine (**102**) and Related Compounds[421]

$$R^1CH_2C{\equiv}CCH_2R^2$$

Compound	R^1	R^2	Guinea pig ileum		
			$-log\,ED_{50}$	$log\,K^a$	$e_r^{\,b}$
(**102**)	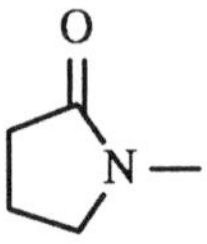	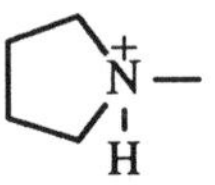	7.61	6.17	1.00
(**156**)	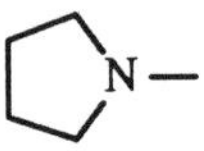	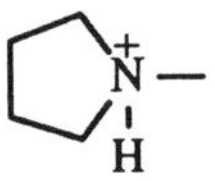	Not active at mAChRs		
(**157**)	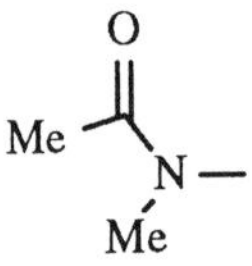	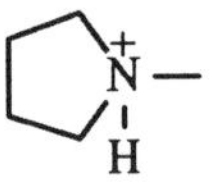	7.16	5.66	1.14
(**158**)	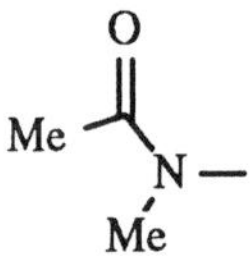	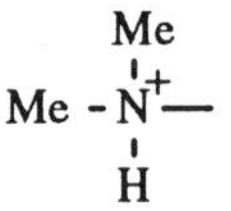	6.41	4.16	6.46
(**159**)	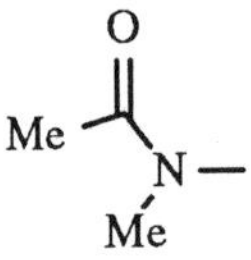	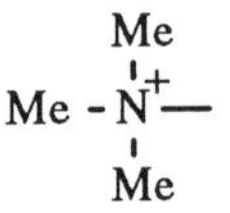	7.43	5.00	9.50
(**103**)	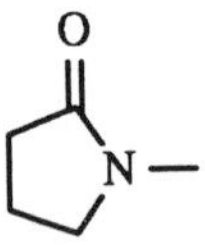	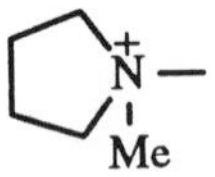	6.50	5.17	0.78
(**160**)	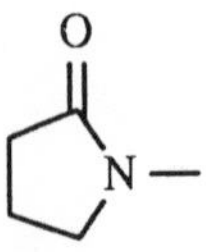	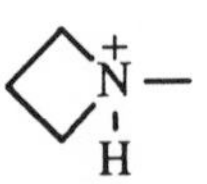	7.96	5.86	4.38
(**161**)	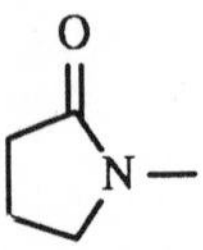	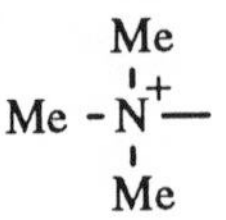	7.87	5.53	7.28

[a] K = equilibrium association constant (L mol^{-1}). [b] e_r = relative intrinsic efficacy (oxotremorine (**102**) = 1.0).

Butynyl carbamates do not exhibit extraordinarily high potency at mAChRs. The primary interest for McN-A-343 (**11**) and its analogs arose from the observation that several of these agents selectively stimulate a minor population of mAChRs present in sympathetic ganglia (M_1 receptors).[195] The selectivity of these compounds is strictly coupled to several structural requirements. Modification of the substitution pattern at the phenyl ring generally reduces potency; only the 4-chloro-substituted McN-A-343 analog (**162**) is about three times as potent at muscarinic M_1 receptors as McN-A-343 itself.[245] Replacement of the phenyl ring or of the phenylcarbamate moiety as a whole by polar groups always abolishes M_1 stimulating properties. Several of these analogs, however, are classical muscarinic M_2 receptor stimulants.[427]

After partial hydrogenation of the triple bond, high activity at M_1 receptors is preserved only in the *trans* alkenic analog (**163**), which can closely approximate a nearly fully extended conformation of McN-A-343 (**11**) where the quaternary ammonium group and the carbamate ether oxygen are about 0.57 nm apart.[262,428] In this conformation, McN-A-343 (**11**) and the *trans* alkenic analog (**163**) display a similar spatial arrangement of ether oxygen, unsaturation between C-2 and C-3 and the quaternary nitrogen. The alkynic triple bond can also be replaced by an electron rich center such as the *trans* epoxide moiety (**164**) without significant loss of M_1 agonistic potency. In contrast, the *trans* cyclopropyl (**165**) and the fully saturated analog are inactive as M_1 receptor stimulants (Table 29).[429]

Among cyclic analogs of McN-A-343, the quaternary 3- and 4-chloro-substituted isoarecolinol derivatives (**166**, **167**) displayed considerable potency as M_1 receptor stimulants (Table 30).[430] The propargyl esters of arecaidine (APE; **144**) and of isoarecaidine also proved to be rather potent M_1 receptor stimulants, indicating that this property is not confined to quaternary compounds. The considerable activity of arecoline (**98**) and isoarecoline (**131**) at ganglionic M_1 receptors further

Table 29 Muscarinic Activity of McN-A-343 (**11**) and Related Compounds[427-429]

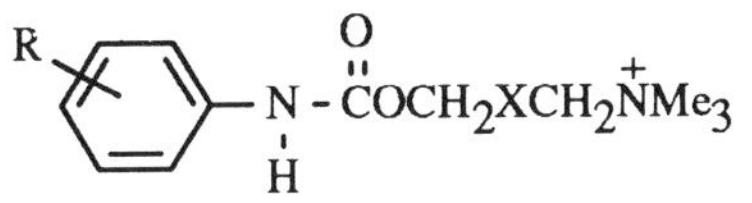

Compound	R	X	EPMR, McN-A-343 = 1
(**11**) McN-A-343	3-Cl	C≡C	1.0^a
(**162**)	4-Cl	C≡C	0.34^a
(**163**)	3-Cl	CH≡CH, *trans*	$\sim 2.0^b$
(**164**)	4-Cl	HC-CH (O, *trans*)	$\sim 1.0^b$
(**165**)	4-Cl	HC-CH (CH_2, *cis/trans*)	Inactive^b

^{a} Dog blood pressure. ^{b} Cat blood pressure.

Table 30 Muscarinic Activity of Cyclic Analogs of McN-A-343 (**11**)[430]

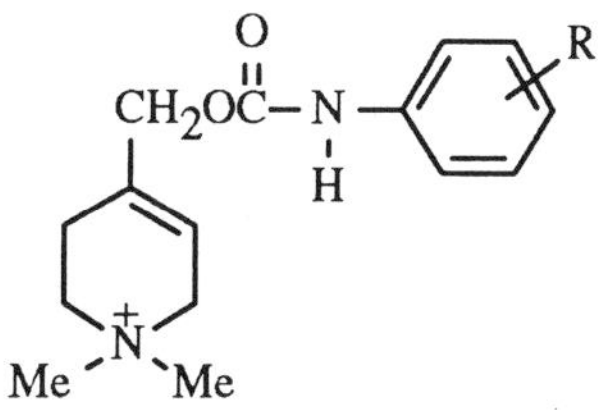

Compound	R	EPMR, McN-A-343 = 1, pithed rat
(**166**)	3-Cl	~ 6
(**167**)	4-Cl	~ 4

suggests that the triple bond in the ester side chain is not an essential requirement for M_1 receptor activation.[431]

The incorporation of a reactive chemical moiety into the structure of an agent with a selective pharmacological action enables it to bind covalently to the receptor. Acetylcholine mustard (*N*-2-chloroethyl-*N*-methyl-2-acetoxyethylamine; **168**) in its cyclized aziridinium ion form (**169**) is a potent muscarinic agonist and binds irreversibly to mAChRs.[432] Its use as an irreversible probe of the mAChR is, however, limited, since it also has nicotinic actions[433] and is rapidly hydrolyzed by cholinesterases.[434]

The recently developed 2-chloro- (**170**) and 2-bromo-ethylamino (**171**) analogs of oxotremorine-M (**161**), are more suitable for an irreversible blockade of mAChRs as both agents are highly selective for mAChRs.[435-437] In both cases, the aziridinium ion (**172**) which is formed by spontaneous cyclization in aqueous solution is responsible for muscarinic actions. The aziridinium ion (**172**) is approximately equipotent to oxotremorine-M (**161**), which is not very surprising as the aziridinium and trimethylammonium moiety are structurally very similar. Differences in pharmacological properties between (**170**) and (**171**) are related to much higher peak levels of the aziridinium ion concentration reached after application of (**171**), due to an approximately 50-fold higher reaction velocity of the 2-bromoethylamino analog compared to the 2-chloroethylamino analog (**170**; see scheme below).[436]

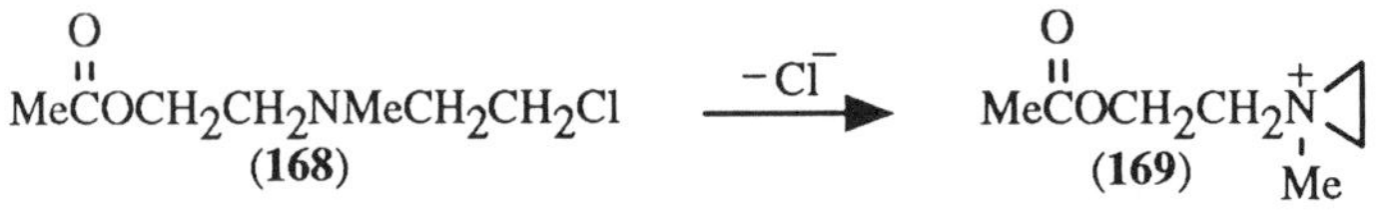

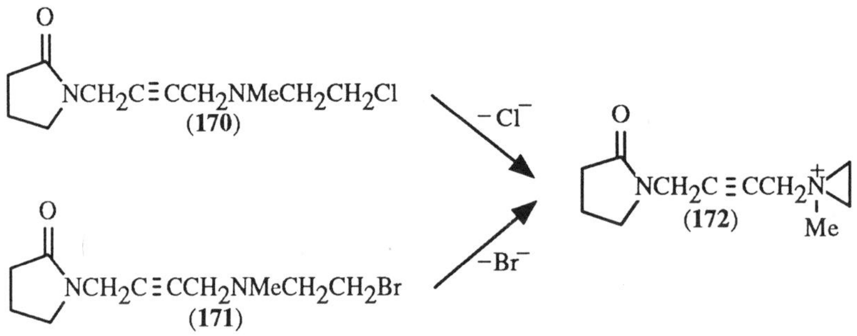

12.6.7.2.2 Antagonists

In muscarinic antagonists, several structural elements common to most of these agents can be identified: a cationic 'head group' and some 'heavy blocking moieties' (*e.g.* alicyclic or aromatic ring systems) are connected by a structural element (*e.g.* ester group) of definite length. Additionally, so-called 'anchoring groups' (*e.g.* hydroxyl) are often present at key positions of antagonist molecules; although nonessential, they often contribute significantly to total binding energy.[438]

Binding to the receptor is apparently initiated by an interaction between the positively charged 'head group' of the antagonist molecule and an anionic site at the receptor surface. Effects of N substitution on affinity show that size and shape of the cationic group also play a critical role in drug–receptor interaction (for reviews see refs. 325, 327, 328, 438 and 439). However, significant antimuscarinic activities of 3,3-dimethylbutan-1-ol (the carbon analog of choline) esters (**174, 176, 178**) demonstrate that a cationic group is not necessarily required in muscarinic antagonists (Table 31).[440]

Introduction of large lipophilic moieties into agonist molecules drastically reduces intrinsic efficacy, whereas affinity is often preserved or even increased. As a general rule, incorporation of cyclic moieties, often phenyl groups, leads to more potent antagonists than the introduction of aliphatic substituents. In antagonists comprising more than one lipophilic moiety, these groups do not contribute additively to overall affinity. Moreover, in these agents the mode of linkage of the substituents is very important for antimuscarinic activity.[328,438,439]

The chain connecting cationic head and cyclic moieties determines the mutual arrangement of these groups. Besides length and form, affinity for mAChRs is determined by functional groups and lateral branching of the chain.[438,439] Although an ester group is present in many potent antimuscarinic agents, such as in atropine (**179**), it is not essential for high affinity. In many potent antagonists

Table 31 Activity of Various Muscarinic Antagonists[440]

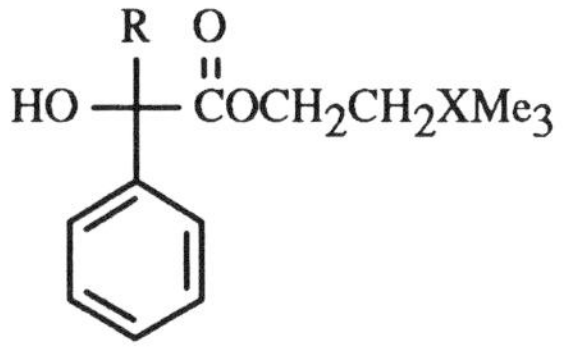

$$HO-\underset{\underset{\displaystyle C_6H_5}{|}}{\overset{\displaystyle R}{\underset{|}{C}}}-\overset{\displaystyle O}{\overset{||}{C}}OCH_2CH_2XMe_3$$

Compound	X	R	Log K, guinea pig ileum
(173)	N^+	C_6H_{11}	9.4
(174)	C	C_6H_{11}	7.6
(175)	N^+	Ph	8.5
(176)	C	Ph	7.5
(177)	N^+	H	5.3
(178)	C	H	5.5

blocking moieties and basic nitrogen are linked by a polymethylene chain (for examples, see below). Nevertheless, if an effective interaction is not sterically prevented, the contribution to antagonist affinities of hydroxyl or other polar groups attached to the linking chain can be very significant (for an example, see below).

Similar to agonists, the spatial arrangement of the moieties interacting with mAChRs plays a decisive role for affinity to the receptor. High eudismic ratios have been reported, *e.g.* for atropine enantiomers, (S)-(−)- and (R)-(+)-hyoscyamine (179a,b),[454] for procyclidine (180a,b),[333,441,442] benzetimide (181a,b),[443] and many other chiral antagonists (Table 32).[328] Nevertheless, it seems to be a necessary condition for the appearance of enantioselectivity that an asymmetric center is present in a part of the molecule that actually contributes to receptor binding.[444] For a more profound, general discussion of stereochemical aspects regarding the interaction of muscarinic antagonists with their receptors, the reader is referred to the recent review of Triggle.[385]

Although most SAR studies of muscarinic antagonists have a more or less qualitative or semiquantitative character, several attempts have been made to quantitatively correlate (QSAR) the antimuscarinic activities with the physicochemical constants of the ligands.[445-447,449] Several of these studies were limited from the beginning to a class of closely related compounds.[445,446] Other attempts to quantitatively predict antagonist affinities are based on the assumption that the molecular components of the antagonists additively contribute to the total free energy of the

Table 32 Enantioselectivity of Muscarinic Antagonists[441-443,454]

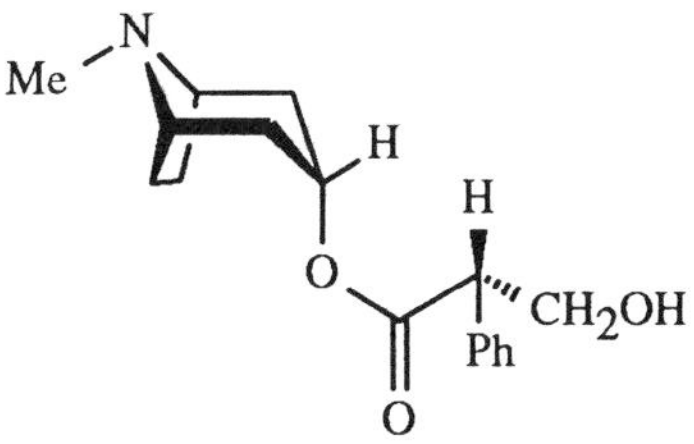

(179a) 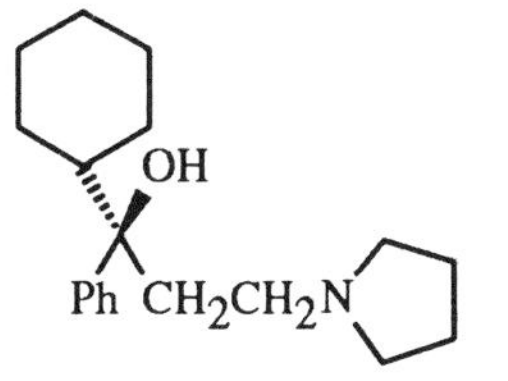   (180a) 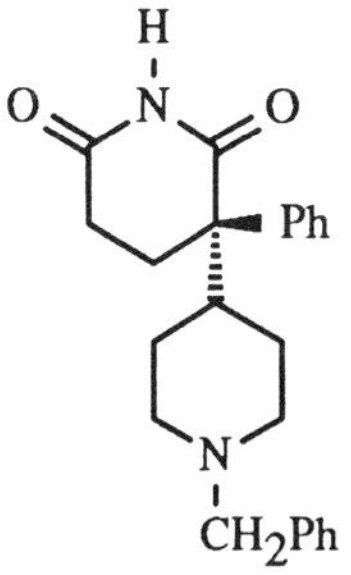   (181a)

Compound	Configuration	Log K, guinea pig ileum	Affinity ratio (S)/(R)
(179a)	(S)-(−)	9.38	330
(179b)	(R)-(+)	6.86	
(180a)	(S)-(−)	5.69	0.003
(180b)	(R)-(+)	8.27	
(181a)	(S)-(+)	9.05	>4000
(181b)	(R)-(−)	<5.4	

interaction with mAChRs.[447] Yet, there are serious doubts about the justification of this supposition.[328] One of the most comprehensive studies, which is based on the quantitative approach of Hansch[448] (for review, see ref. 439), has been undertaken by Lien *et al.*,[449] using affinity data of Abramson *et al.*[450] Based on equations correlating affinity values with physicochemical constants, Lien *et al.* proposed structures of compounds with prospective very high affinity for mAChRs.[449] However, synthesis and pharmacological testing of these agents showed that their affinity for mAChRs is several orders of magnitude lower than that predicted.[451]

Atropine (**179**) and its eutomer, (*S*)-(−)-hyoscyamine (**179a**), are among the most extensively studied muscarinic antagonists. Recent studies emphasized the important contribution of the hydroxyl group to the remarkable high affinity of atropine and its congeners to mAChRs. The affinity of (**182**) for mAChRs is more than two orders of magnitude lower than that of atropine itself (Table 33).[452]

It is well known that *N*-methylation of atropine further increases affinity for mAChRs. Quaternization with alkyl moieties other than methyl produces two stereoisomers (*e.g.* **183**, **184**); in *N*-ethylatropinium, the isomer with an axial ethyl group (**183**) is more potent than that with the ethyl substituent oriented equatorially (**184**; see Table 33).[454]

Replacement of the atropine *N*-methyl group by a chiral N substituent leads to a new series of analogs with asymmetric centers in both the tropanol and tropic acid part of the molecule (**185a–d**). Among the four *N*-(α-phenethyl)atropine stereoisomers, the *RR* isomer (**185a**) is the most potent, which is in contrast to atropine itself, where the eutomer, (−)-hyoscyamine (**179a**), is of the *S* configuration. The complete loss of stereoselectivity in analogs of (**185**) lacking the asymmetric center in the ester moiety is suggestive of an intimate interrelation between the amino alcohol and ester moiety in these compounds upon binding to mAChRs (Table 34).[453]

Introducing an epoxide moiety into the tropanol part of (*S*)-(−)-hyoscyamine leads to (*S*)-(−)-hyoscine (scopolamine; **186a**) which, although it is a weaker base, is even more potent than atropine.[454,455] Comparison of partial molal volumes in various solvents gives significantly smaller values for (*S*)-(−)-hyoscine (**186a**) than for (*S*)-(−)-hyoscyamine (**179a**). The resulting differences in enthalpies in the absorption to the receptor may be responsible for the observed affinity differences (Table 35).[456]

Several hydroxypiperidine esters of acetic or glycolic acids substituted with lipophilic moieties, like phenyl or cyclohexyl, have remarkably high affinity for mAChRs (**16**, **194–196**, **201–204**, **207**, **208**).[450] In this series, 4-hydroxypiperidine esters (**189**, **190**, **196**, **16**, **203**, **204**) usually display 6- to 100-fold higher affinities than their 3-substituted isomers (**187**, **188**, **194**, **195**, **201**, **202**). Successive introduction of lipophilic substituents into the acid moiety apparently improves interaction with the lipophilic receptor area. Consequently, diphenylacetic esters (**16**, **194–196**) are generally more potent than phenylacetic esters (**187–190**). Even higher affinities are observed with the corresponding benzilates (**201–204**) or esters of phenylcyclohexylglycolic acid (**207**, **208**). Upon quaternization of the nitrogen, affinity is further enhanced. Affinity can also be increased by bridging the piperidine ring system: 3-quinuclidinol esters (**191**, **192**, **197**, **198**, **205**, **206**) display up to 100-fold higher affinities for mAChRs than their 3-hydroxypiperidine analogs. In contrast to hydroxypiperidine esters, tertiary 3-

Table 33 Muscarinic Antagonist Activity of Atropine (179) and Analogs[452,454]

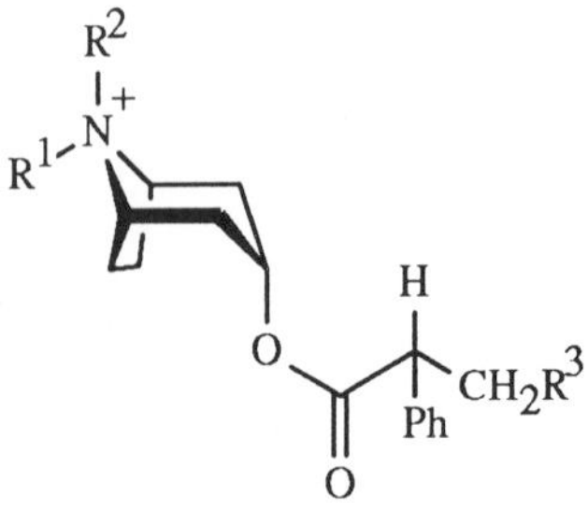

Compound	Configuration	R^1	R^2	R^3	Log K, guinea pig ileum
(**179**) Atropine	(*RS*)	Me	H	OH	9.01
(**182**)	(*RS*)	Me	H	H	6.95
(**183**)	(*S*)	Me	Et	OH	9.59
(**184**)	(*S*)	Et	Me	OH	8.79

Table 34 Muscarinic Antagonist Activity and Stereochemistry of an Atropine Analog[453]

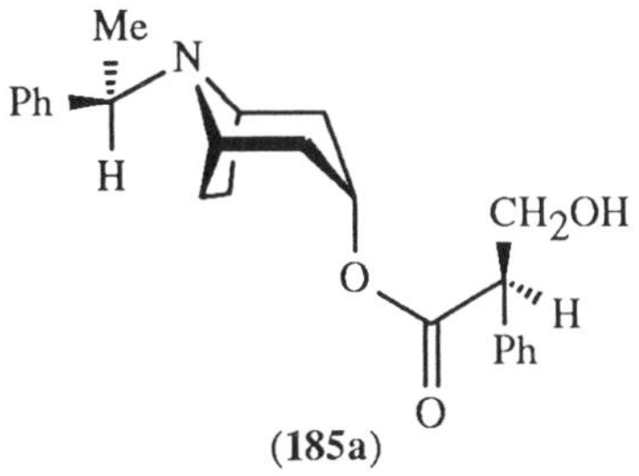

(185a)

Compound	Configuration of N-substituent	Configuration of tropic acid	Log K, guinea pig ileum
(185a)	(R)	(R)	8.68
(185c)	(R)	(S)	7.40
(185d)	(S)	(R)	7.40
(185b)	(S)	(S)	6.51

Table 35 Muscarinic Antagonist Activity of Scopolamine (186a)

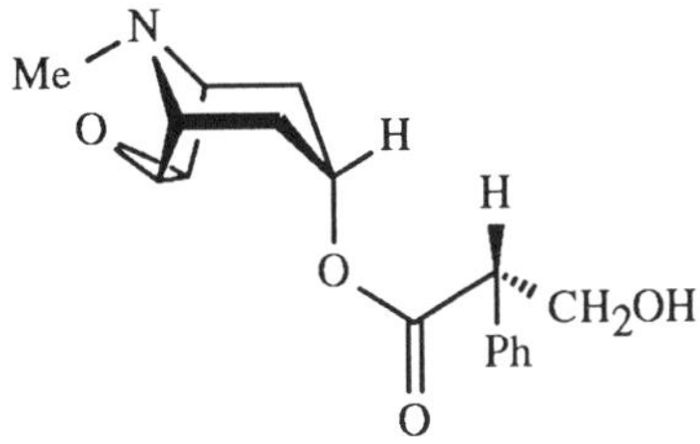

(186a)

Compound	Configuration	Log K, guinea pig ileum[a]	pK_a (10 mM)[b]
(179a)	(S)	9.38	9.53
(186a)	(S)	9.58	7.53

[a] Refs. 454, 455. [b] Ref. 455.

quinuclidinol esters (197) are much more potent than the corresponding 4-substituted analogs (199).[350] Quaternization of the nitrogen has completely opposed effects upon affinity in 3- and 4-quinuclidinol esters: in 3-substituted analogs (192, 198, 206) affinity is reduced, whereas quaternization drastically improves affinity in 4-quinuclidinol esters (200; Table 36).[350,450] In 3-quinuclidinylbenzilate (QNB; 205) the R enantiomer (205a) displays more than 50 times higher affinity than its distomer (205b). Quaternization (206) reduces the eudismic ratio by a factor of about 10 (Table 37).[457,458] By structural variations of the potent muscarinic antagonist 3-quinuclidinylbenzilate (205), several analogs with similarly high affinities can be obtained.[459,460]

Interestingly, affinity differences between atrial ($M_{2\alpha}$) and ileal ($M_{2\beta}$) mAChRs have been observed with certain hydroxypiperidine and quinuclidinol esters. These differences are most pronounced with 4-diphenylacetoxy-N-methylpiperidine methiodide (4-DAMP; 16).[259,461] Compared to cardiac $M_{2\alpha}$ receptors, 4-DAMP displays an approximately 10–20-fold higher affinity for ileal $M_{2\beta}$ receptors.[259–261] In contrast, conformationally more flexible (e.g. 175) as well as even more constrained analogs (e.g. 198) of 4-DAMP do not discriminate between these two M_2 receptor subtypes.[259] Linking together two molecules of 4-DAMP by a pentamethylene chain (209) generally reduces affinity for mAChRs, but slightly increases selectivity for $M_{2\beta}$ receptors (Table 38).[260]

Unlike classical muscarinic antagonists, where introduction of hydrophobic ring systems into agonist molecules abolishes intrinsic efficacy and significantly increases affinity, antagonists related to oxotremorine (102) usually do not carry the structural elements required for strong hydrophobic

Table 36 Comparison of Structure and Muscarinic Antagonist Activity

R^1	R^2	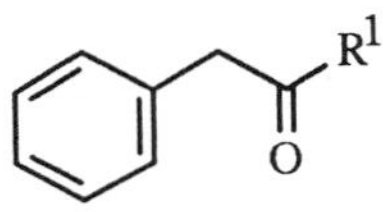 Compound	$\log K^a$	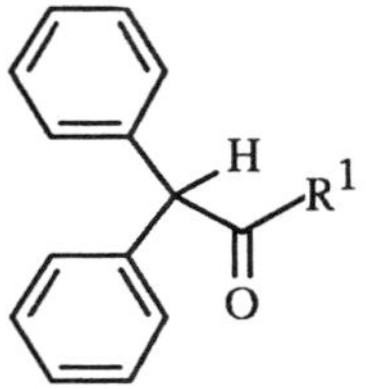 Compound	$\log K^a$	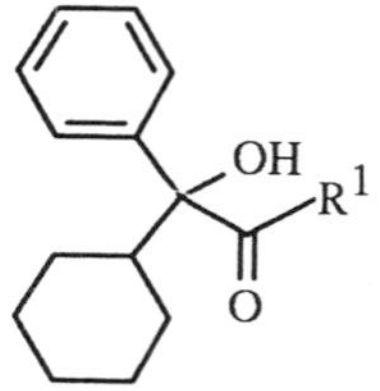 Compound	$\log K^b$	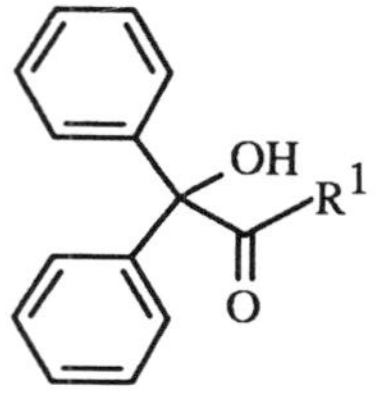 Compound	$\log K^b$
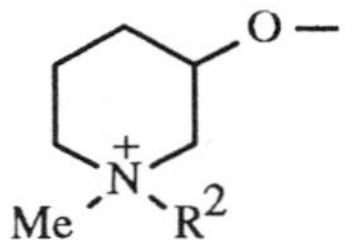 (N-Me-piperidinol, 3-O)	$R^2 = H$	(187)	4.82	(194)	6.77	(201)	8.70	(207)	~10.6–11
	$R^2 = Me$	(188)	5.11	(195)	7.09	(202)	8.85	(208)	~10–11
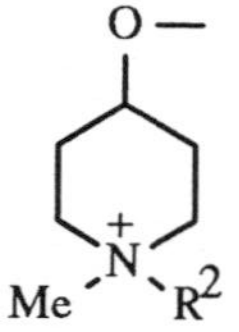 (N-Me-piperidinol, 4-O)	$R^2 = H$	(189)	5.59	(196)	8.36	(203)	9.93		
	$R^2 = Me$	(190)	6.19	(16)	9.06	(204)	10.25		
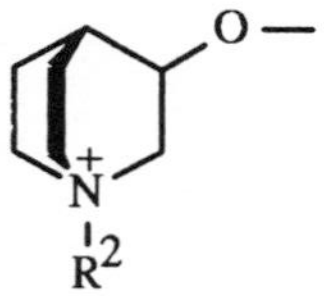 (quinuclidinol, 3-O)	$R^2 = H$	(191)	6.76	(197)	9.29	(205)	~10–11		
	$R^2 = Me$	(192)	5.50	(198)	7.86	(206)	9.43		
(quinuclidinol, 4-O)	$R^2 = Me$	(193)	6.23						
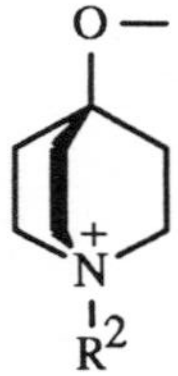	$R^2 = H$			(199)	6.83				
	$R^2 = Me$			(200)	9.60				

[a] Guinea pig ileum, refs. 395 and 450.   [b] Guinea pig ileum, ref. 450.

Table 37 Stereochemistry and Muscarinic Antagonist Activity[458]

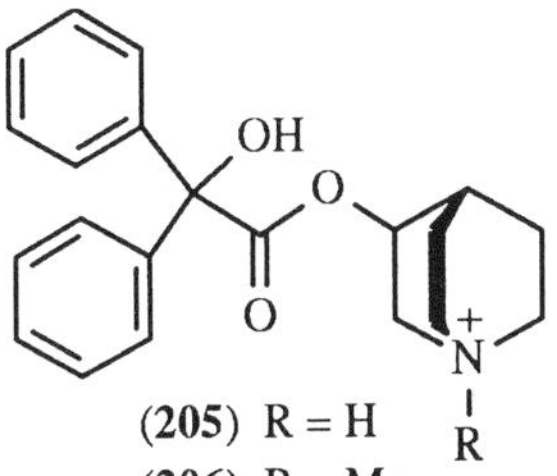

(205) R = H
(206) R = Me

Compound	Configuration	Log K, guinea pig ileum
(205a)	(R)	>10
(205b)	(S)	8.21
(206a)	(R)	9.73
(206b)	(S)	8.75

Table 38 Affinity Differences between Atrial ($M_{2\alpha}$) and Ileal ($M_{2\beta}$) mAChRs[259, 260]

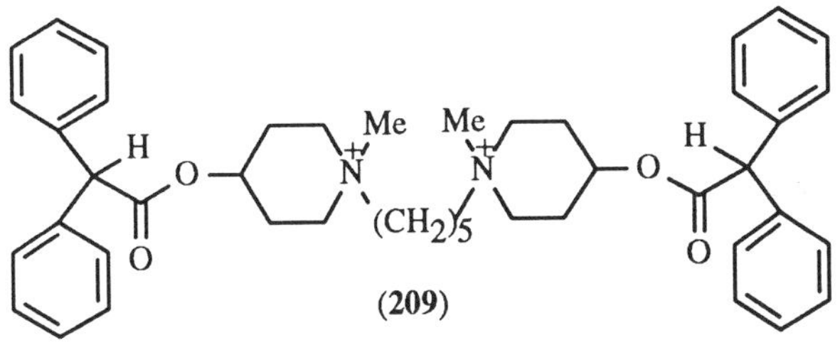

(209)

Compound	Log K Guinea pig		Affinity ratio ileum/atrium
	Atrium (force)	Ileum	
(175)	7.65	7.97	2.1
(16) 4-DAMP	7.81[a]	9.11[a]	20.0
(198)	7.62[a]	7.95[a]	2.1
(209)	7.32[a]	8.69[a]	23.4

[a] Calculated from dose ratios given in ref. 259.

binding to accessory receptor areas. In contrast, close structural similarities and identical stereochemical requirements suggest that both agonists and antagonists interact with a common receptor site.[421] Introduction of a single methyl group in the 1-position of the butynyl chain considerably reduces intrinsic efficacy in all oxotremorine analogs.[421] The 1-methyl-substituted oxotremorine analog (210) is a competitive antagonist; its R enantiomer (210a) has a more than tenfold higher affinity to mAChRs than oxotremorine itself. Moreover, the high eudismic ratio suggests a very specific interaction of the 1-methyl group with mAChRs.[421,462] Interestingly, increasing the chain length of the 1-alkyl substituent reduces affinities of the R enantiomers (211a, 212a), and enantiomeric affinity ratios,[422] which is indicative of spatial limitations at the receptor subsite interacting with the alkyl moiety (Table 39).

5-Methyl substitution in the oxotremorine pyrrolidone moiety also abolishes intrinsic efficacy and increases affinity for ileal mAChRs about tenfold. Antimuscarinic activity is mainly inherent in the R enantiomer (213a), which has an approximately 20-fold higher affinity than its distomer.[463] Most interesting is an enormous increase in affinity for ganglionic M_1 receptors, which is effected by such a minor structural modification. Compared to ileal $M_{2\beta}$ receptors, (213a) has an approximately 100-fold higher affinity for ganglionic M_1 receptors. As in 5-methyl substitution, replacement of the methylene group in the 5-position of the pyrrolidone ring system by an N-formyl moiety leads to a competitive antagonist (214), and compared to (213a) affinity to both M_1 and $M_{2\beta}$ receptor subtypes is reduced. However, the decrease in affinity is more pronounced at ileal mAChRs, thus further enhancing the selectivity of (214) for ganglionic M_1 receptors (Table 40).[424]

Table 39 Analogs of Oxotremorine (**102**) and Stereochemical Requirements

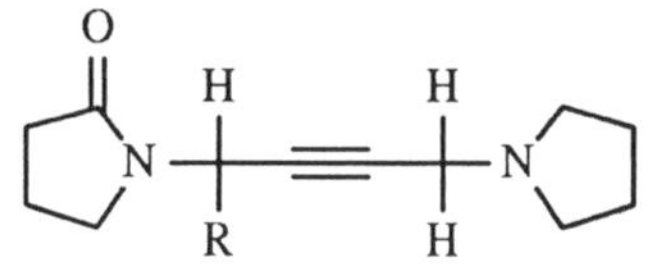

Compound	R	Configuration	Log K, guinea pig ileum[421]	Eudismic ratio
(**102**)	H	—	6.17	
(**210a**)	Me	(R)	7.34	
(**210b**)	Me	(S)	5.02	209
(**211a**)	Et	(R)	7.09	
(**211b**)	Et	(S)	5.42	47
(**212a**)	Pr^n	(R)	6.79	
(**212b**)	Pr^n	(S)	5.63	14

Table 40 Compounds Selective for Ganglionic M_1 Receptors[424]

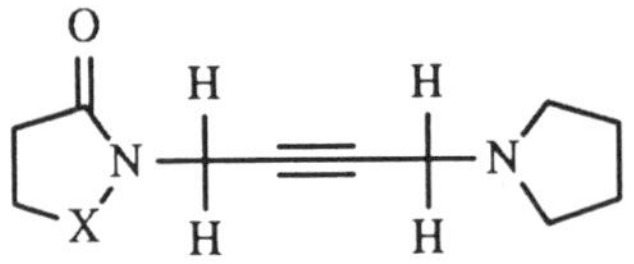

Compound	X	Configuration	log K^a	log K^b	Affinity ratio ganglion/ileum
(**213a**)	CHMe	(R)	7.18	9.2	105
(**214**)	NCHO	—	5.20	7.9	500

^{a} Guinea pig ileum. ^{b} Rat ganglion cervicale sup.

Among unsymmetrically substituted carbinols carrying a phenyl and a cyclohexyl group, many potent muscarinic antagonists can be found, such as trihexyphenidyl (**215**), procyclidine (**180**), or pridinol (**218**), which are widely used for the treatment of Parkinson's disease. Several of these agents (*e.g.* **215**, **180**, **14**) have higher affinity for mAChRs in the ileum compared to those in the atrium.[262,263] Replacement of the central carbinol carbon atom by a silicon atom increases OH acidity, which would be expected to result in stronger hydrogen bonding of the silanols to a basic center of the mAChR.[464] On the whole this holds true for ileal mAChRs: Silapridinol (**219**), for example, displays higher affinity for ileal mAChRs than pridinol (**218**). At cardiac mAChRs ($M_{2\alpha}$) receptors, however, silasubstitution leaves affinities largely unaffected, which results in an enhanced selectivity of the silanols for ileal mAChRs. Hexahydrosiladifenidol (**17**), for example, displays a 27-fold higher affinity for ileal ($M_{2\beta}$) than for atrial ($M_{2\alpha}$) receptors.[262] Quaternization of the nitrogen in hexahydrosiladifenidol (**221**) and in its carbon analog (**220**) considerably increases affinity to cardiac $M_{2\alpha}$ receptors, thereby abolishing selectivity.[243,245,465] Shortening (**222**) or lengthening (**223**) of the carbon chain connecting silicon and nitrogen generally diminishes affinities for both mAChR subtypes. As the reduction is more pronounced at ileal ($M_{2\beta}$) mAChRs, these analogs are less selective than hexahydrosiladifenidol (**17**) itself (Table 41).[243,245]

Comparison of the enantiomers of procyclidine (**180a,b**) and silaprocyclidine (**217a,b**) suggests marked differences for the mode of interaction between chiral carbinols and silanols, and M_2 receptor subtypes: the eudismic ratio is generally low (2–4) for the silanol enantiomers, whereas it amounts to 34 and 380 for the carbinol at $M_{2\alpha}$ and $M_{2\beta}$ receptors, respectively. Moreover, differences in eudismic ratios for procyclidine (**180a,b**) in atria and ileal smooth muscle further substantiate the $M_{2\alpha}/M_{2\beta}$ subclassification.[244,333,442,465] Similarly, trihexyphenidyl enantiomers (**215a,b**) discriminate between M_1, $M_{2\alpha}$ and $M_{2\beta}$ receptors by different affinity ratios (Table 42).[466]

Pirenzepine (**12**) and several of its analogs comprise the characteristic features of muscarinic antagonists (lipophilic moieties, hydrophilic 'anchoring group' and basic nitrogen) in the rigidized framework of a tricyclic ring system and a 4-methyl-1-piperazinyl moiety. Rotational freedom around the exocyclic amide bond is limited in comparison to the conformationally more flexible ester group present in many potent muscarinic antagonists. These conformational restrictions

Table 41 Comparison of Structure and Muscarinic Antagonist Activity

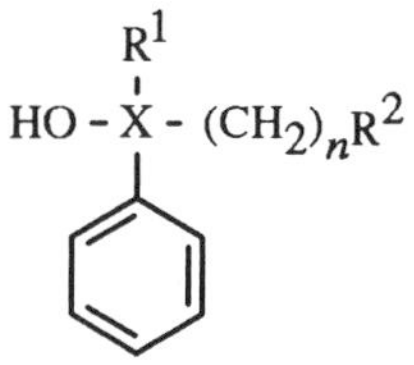

$$HO - \underset{\underset{R^1}{|}}{X} - (CH_2)_n R^2$$

Compound	n	X	R^1	R^2	Guinea pig log K^a	log K^b	Affinity ratio ileum/atrium
(215)	2	C	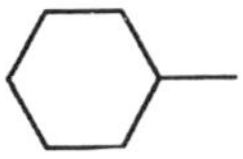 cyclohexyl	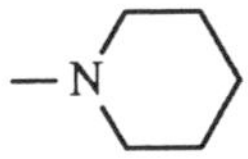 piperidino	7.30	7.91	4.0
(216)	2	Si	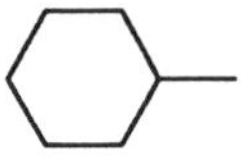 cyclohexyl	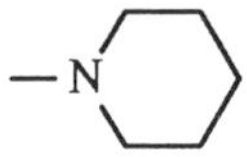 piperidino	7.12	7.78	4.6
(180)	2	C	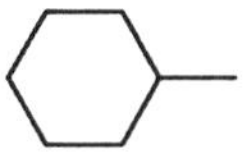 cyclohexyl	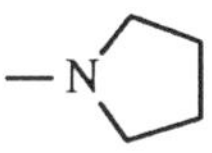 pyrrolidino	6.76	7.75	9.8
(217)	2	Si	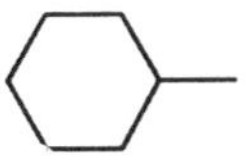 cyclohexyl	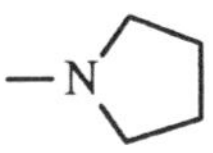 pyrrolidino	6.92	8.04	13
(218)	2	C	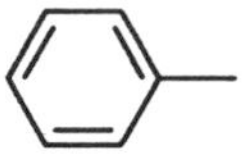 cyclohexenyl	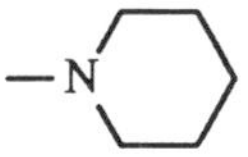 piperidino	7.23	7.65	2.6
(219)	2	Si	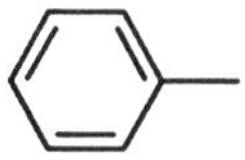 cyclohexenyl	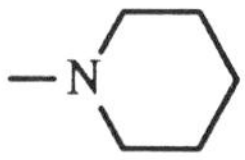 piperidino	7.24	8.29	11.3
(14)	3	C	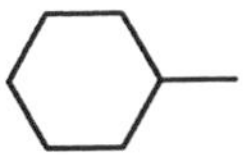 cyclohexyl	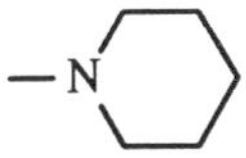 piperidino	6.71	7.98	19
(17)	3	Si	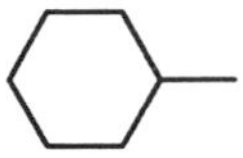 cyclohexyl	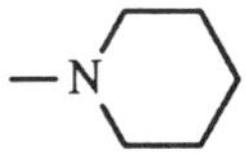 piperidino	6.53	7.96	27
(220)	3	C	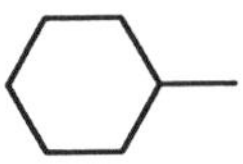 cyclohexyl	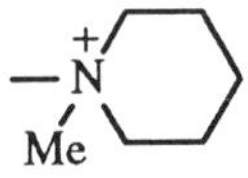 N$^+$-Me piperidino	7.93	8.00	1.2
(221)	3	Si	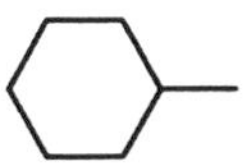 cyclohexyl	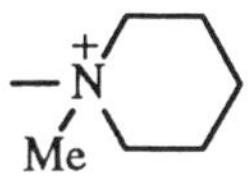 N$^+$-Me piperidino	7.99	8.18	1.5
(222)	1	Si	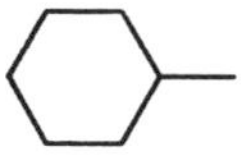 cyclohexyl	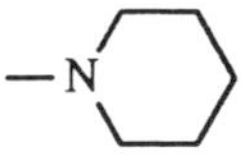 piperidino	5.68	6.53	7.2
(223)	4	Si	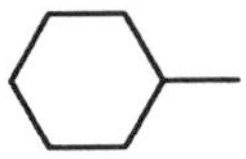 cyclohexyl	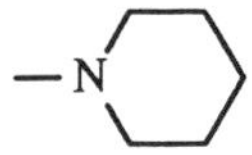 piperidino	5.95	6.92	9.3

[a] Atrium, refs. 243, 245, 252 and 465. [b] Ileum, refs. 243, 245, 262 and 465.

apparently impede an effective interaction with muscarinic M_2 receptors, thus resulting in relatively low affinities. At neuronal M_1 receptors, however, pirenzepine (12) displays much higher affinity, which suggests a more efficient interaction of pirenzepine with this receptor subtype.[199, 201] Bioisosteric replacement of the pirenzepine exocyclic amido function by polar moieties like carbamate (224), ester (225) or even a dioxolane ring system (226) largely preserves affinities and M_1

Table 42 Enantioselectivity at M_1, $M_{2\alpha}$ and $M_{2\beta}$ Receptors

		Rabbit vas deferens[a]		Guinea pig atrium		Guinea pig ileum	
Compound	Configuration	log K^b	Affinity ratio (R)/(S)	log K^c	Affinity ratio (R)/(S)	log K^c	Affinity ratio (R)/(S)
(180a)	(R)	—		7.04		8.04	
(180b)	(S)	—	—	5.51	34	5.46	380
(217a)	(R)	—		7.15		8.26	
(217b)	(S)	—	—	6.89	2	7.66	4
(215a)	(R)	10.1		8.2		8.8	
(215b)	(S)	6.9	1600	6.4	63	5.9	790

[a] Ref. 467. [b] Ref. 466. [c] Refs. 244, 333, 442, 465 and 466.

receptor selectivity. Substitution of the polar exocyclic carbamido group by an apolar alkylene moiety (**227**), however, leads to a loss of M_1 receptor selectivity (Table 43). Moreover, (**227**) has a high affinity for histamine and 5-HT receptors.[468] Introducing a 2-methylthiophene instead of the phenyl moiety and replacing the pyridyl by a phenyl ring in pirenzepine enhances affinity to both M_1 and M_2 receptors by about one order of magnitude, thereby preserving M_1 receptor selectivity in the pirenzepine analog telenzepine (**13**).[208, 286] In another pirenzepine analog, AF-DX 116 (**18**), affinity for cardiac $M_{2\alpha}$ receptors is increased upon replacement of the 4-methyl-1-piperazine by the conformationally more flexible 2-(diethylamino)methyl-1-piperidine side chain, whereas affinity for other mAChR subtypes is up to 30 times lower, making AF-DX 116 a cardioselective muscarinic antagonist. The (+)-enantiomer of AF-DX 116 (**18a**), is somewhat more potent than the racemate (**18**) and shows a slightly enhanced selectivity towards cardiac $M_{2\alpha}$ receptors (Table 44).[275,276]

Several polymethylene tetraamines (**20, 228–233**), structurally unrelated to any class of classical muscarinic antagonists, display significant muscarinic blocking activity.[279–282] In these compounds

Table 43 Muscarinic Receptor Selectivity of Pirenzepine (**12**) and Analogs[468].

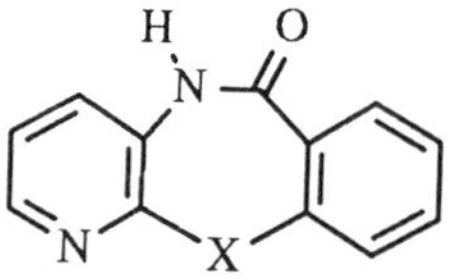

Compound	X	log K, rat cortex	log K, rat atrium	Affinity ratio cortex/atrium
(12)	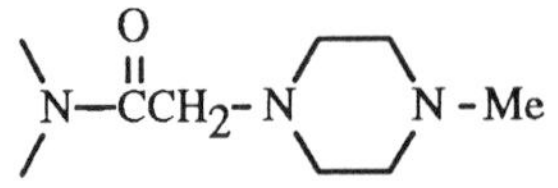	7.89	6.26	43
(224)	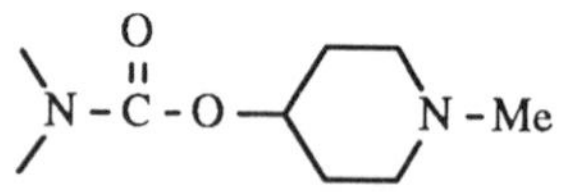	7.55	6.48	12
(225)	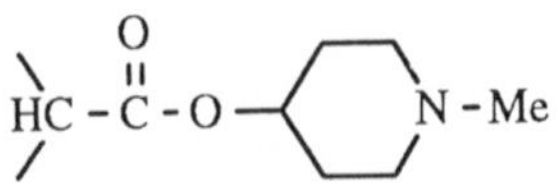	8.05	6.48	37
(226)	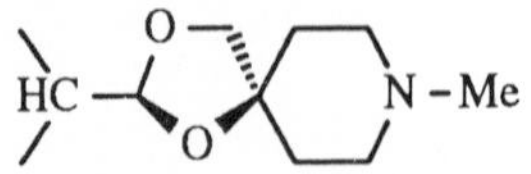	8.40	7.48	8.3
(227)	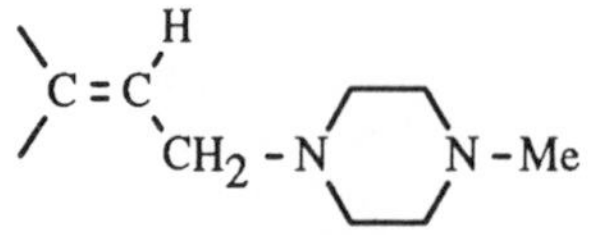	8.40	8.40	1

Table 44 Muscarinic Receptor Selectivity of Pirenzepine (**12**), Telenzepine (**13**) and AF-DX 116 (**18**)[286]

Compound	pK_i^a	pK_i^b	pK_i^c
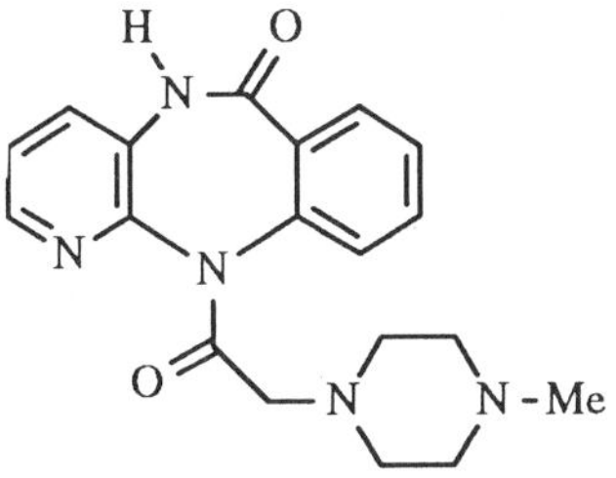 (**12**) Pirenzepine	5.86	6.38	7.43
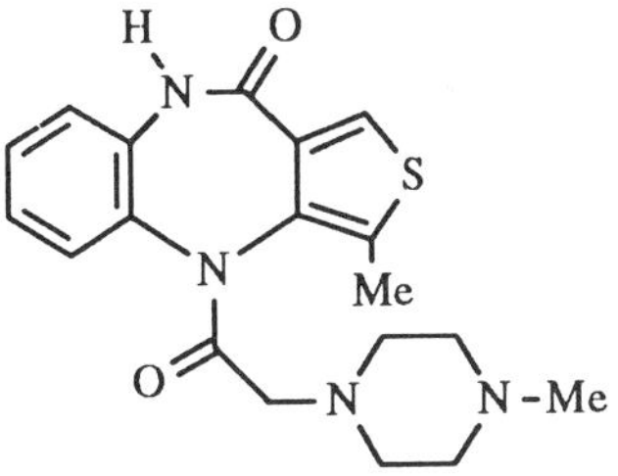 (**13**) Telenzepine	7.04	7.80	8.46
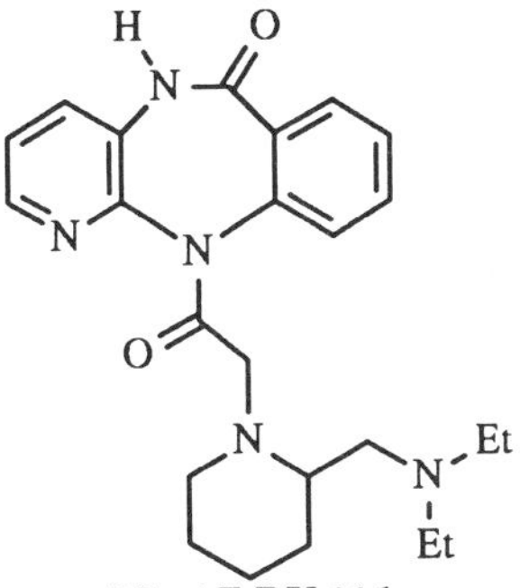 (**18**) AF-DX 116	6.71	5.30	6.09

[a] Rat atria. [b] Rat submandibular gland. [c] Rat hippocampus (M_1).

structural modifications such as removal of the 2-methoxy group, substitution of the phenyl moiety with hydroxyl groups or methylation of the secondary amino groups lead to a decrease in affinity. Optimum affinity to mAChRs depends on the length n of the carbon chain separating the two inner nitrogens. Most interestingly, mAChRs in atria and in smooth muscle make different structural demands regarding the length of the carbon chain separating the two inner nitrogens. Thus, methoctramine (**20**), which is the most selective agent in this series of compounds, has an affinity about two orders of magnitude higher for atrial ($M_{2\alpha}$) mAChRs than for smooth muscle ($M_{2\beta}$) mAChRs (Table 45).[279-281]

As with muscarinic agonists (*cf.* Section 12.6.7.2.1), introduction of reactive chemical moieties into antagonist molecules enables them to bind covalently to mAChRs. In solution, β-haloethylamino compounds (**234–237**) easily form aziridinium ions (*cf.* Section 12.6.7.2.1), which bind covalently to nucleophilic groups of biomolecules, such as mAChRs. The nonspecific antagonists dibenamine (**234**) and phenoxybenzamine (**235**) are largely replaced by benzilyl- (**236**)[469] and propylbenzilyl-choline mustard (**237**),[470] which are highly specific for mAChRs and, unlike dibenamine or phenoxybenzamine, do not interact with effector molecules.[471] (**236**) and (**237**) are practically equipotent in blocking mAChRs; the rate of reaction with the mAChR drops markedly when the N-alkyl group is larger than *n*-propyl.[470]

Table 45 Muscarinic Antagonist Activity of Polymethylene Tetraamines[279]

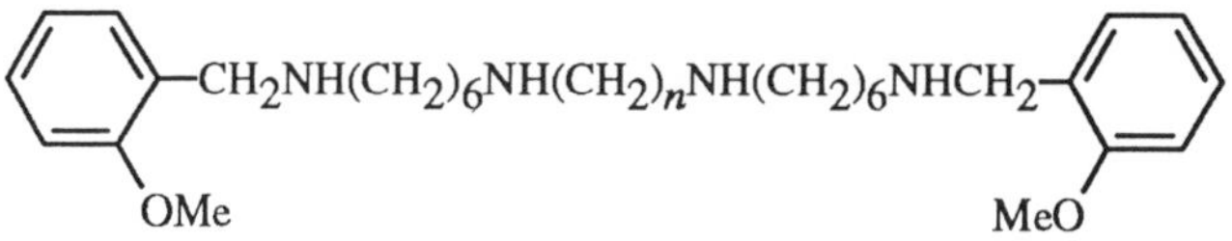

$$\text{—CH}_2\text{NH(CH}_2)_6\text{NH(CH}_2)_n\text{NH(CH}_2)_6\text{NHCH}_2\text{—}$$

OMe   MeO

Compound	n	pA_2, guinea pig atrium (force)	pA_2, rat ileum	Affinity ratio atrium/ileum
(228)	5	6.71	5.42	19
(229)	6	6.87	5.29	38
(230)	7	7.80	5.37	269
(20)	8	8.13	5.69	275
(231)	9	7.96	5.81	141
(232)	10	7.71	5.73	95
(233)	12	7.35	7.62	0.54

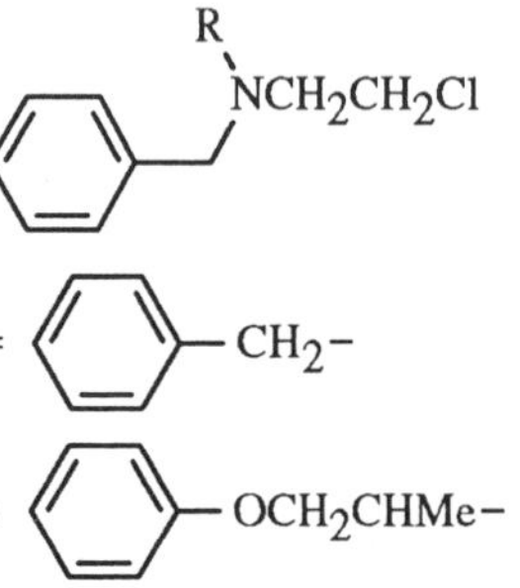

(234) R = [phenyl]—CH$_2$—

(235) R = [phenyl]—OCH$_2$CHMe—

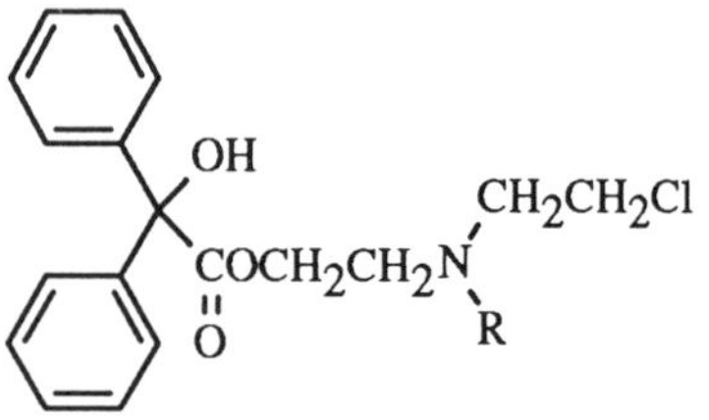

(236) R = Me
(237) R = Pr^n

12.6.8 BIOLOGICAL ACTIONS AND THERAPEUTIC USES OF CHOLINERGIC AGONISTS AND ANTAGONISTS

This section deals with the biological actions and therapeutic uses of clinically applied cholinergic agonists and antagonists, including limitations and side effects. For detailed information concerning the pharmacokinetic behavior, dosage regimens or trade names of the drugs mentioned below, the reader is referred to pharmacology textbooks.

12.6.8.1 Nicotinic Agonists

The physiological events following nAChR activation have been summarized in Section 12.6.4.2. The acute pharmacological actions of nicotinic agonists are complex and often unpredictable, mainly due to the broad range of physiological functions mediated by nAChR and the fact that nAChR stimulation may be rapidly followed by receptor blockade (receptor desensitization).[30] As nicotinic agonists are virtually without any therapeutic relevance, their biological actions are not discussed in more detail here. Nevertheless, due to its presence in tobacco, nicotine itself is of great toxicological relevance because of the well-documented adverse effects associated with smoking.

It should be mentioned, however, that cholinesterase inhibitors of the carbamate type (*e.g.* neostigmine), although they do not stimulate cholinergic receptors directly, act by accumulation of ACh at skeletal muscle nAChRs (and also other cholinergic receptors) when used in treating myasthenia gravis or as antagonists of neuromuscular blocking drugs (see Section 12.6.8.2.2).

12.6.8.2 Nicotinic Antagonists

12.6.8.2.1 Ganglion-blocking drugs

Agents which selectively block the actions of ACh at nAChRs of autonomic ganglia by competitive antagonism are generally referred to as ganglion-blocking drugs. Due to the fact that these agents nonselectively inhibit neurotransmission in all sympathetic and parasympathetic ganglia, they produce a large variety of physiological effects. These can be anticipated by knowing which part of the autonomic nervous system exerts dominant control of the individual organs or organ systems. The arterioles, for example, which are under predominant sympathetic vasomotor tone, will dilate after application of ganglion-blocking drugs, resulting in hypotension. Other physiological alterations following ganglionic blockade are atony of the urinary bladder and the gastrointestinal tract, cycloplegia (paralysis of the ciliary muscle), dry mouth, impairment of sexual functions such as penile erection or ejaculation, or postural hypotension. As these effects are intolerable for most patients, ganglion-blocking agents, such as trimethaphan (**238**) or mecamylamine (**10**), have been almost abandoned for clinical use today. Their major therapeutic applications were to control blood pressure in the treatment of hypertensive emergencies, to produce controlled hypotension during surgery to reduce bleeding in the operative field,[472] and to combat autonomic hyperreflexia.[473]

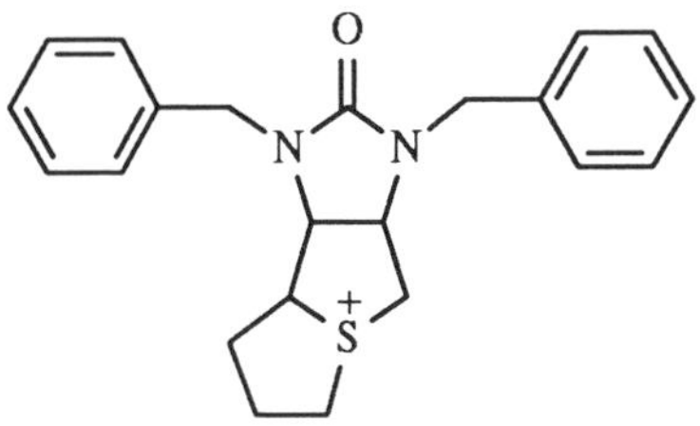

(**238**) Trimethaphan

12.6.8.2.2 *Neuromuscular blocking agents*

Neuromuscular blocking drugs lead to skeletal muscle relaxation by selective interaction with nAChRs located at the neuromuscular junction. Blockade of skeletal muscle endplate function by these agents can occur by two different mechanisms. Stabilizing (competitive) neuromuscular blocking drugs, such as (+)-tubocurarine (**96**), dimethyltubocurarine (metocurine; **239**), gallamine (**240**), alcuronium (**241**), vecuronium (**242**), pancuronium (**243**), atracurium (**244**) or fazadinium (**245**; Table 46), combine with endplate nAChRs without leading to receptor activation and thus represent competitive antagonists of the neurotransmitter ACh. On the other hand, depolarizing neuromuscular blocking drugs, of which succinylcholine (suxamethonium; **85**; Table 46) is the only one in common clinical use today, act in the same manner as ACh by depolarizing the endplate membrane through nAChR activation. However, because succinylcholine is metabolically considerably more stable than ACh, the endplate remains depolarized. Since repolarization and repetitive firing are required to maintain muscle tension, skeletal muscle relaxation results (phase I or depolarization block).[474] Despite the continued exposure to succinylcholine, the membrane may become repolarized gradually, but as long as succinylcholine is present the endplate region does not respond to ACh (phase II or desensitization block).[474] The mechanism involved in this latter process remains unclear.

Consistent with the competitive nature of antagonism, skeletal muscle relaxation induced by (+)-tubocurarine and other stabilizing neuromuscular blocking drugs can be effectively reversed by cholinesterase inhibitors such as neostigmine. In contrast, the depolarization block (phase I block) induced by succinylcholine is not antagonized but is even potentiated by cholinesterase inhibitors. Due to the fact that neuromuscular blocking agents may paralyze all skeletal muscles including the diaphragm and the intercostal muscles, they are potentially hazardous drugs and should only be employed when facilities for immediate respiratory and cardiovascular resuscitation are at hand. As all neuromuscular blocking drugs are quaternary ammonium compounds, they are poorly absorbed from the gastrointestinal tract and are thus administered parenterally, usually *via* the intravenous route.

Stabilizing neuromuscular blocking agents are extensively used as an adjuvant in anesthesia in order to facilitate surgery by relaxation of skeletal muscles, particularly those of the abdominal wall. Furthermore, the application of such drugs, combined with controlled respiration, may be lifesaving in patients with severe muscle spasms (*e.g.* status epilepticus or tetanus) or with ventilatory failure from various causes such as obstructive airway disease.

Intravenous injection of (+)-tubocurarine (0.12–0.4 mg kg^{-1}), which is the prototype of a stabilizing neuromuscular blocking agent, first causes motor weakness followed by total flaccid

Table 46 Structural Formulae of Clinically Used Neuromuscular Blocking Agents

Depolarizing agent

$$Me_3\overset{+}{N}CH_2CH_2O\overset{O}{\overset{\|}{C}}CH_2CH_2\overset{O}{\overset{\|}{C}}OCH_2CH_2\overset{+}{N}Me_3$$

(**85**) Succinylcholine (suxamethonium)

Stabilizing agents

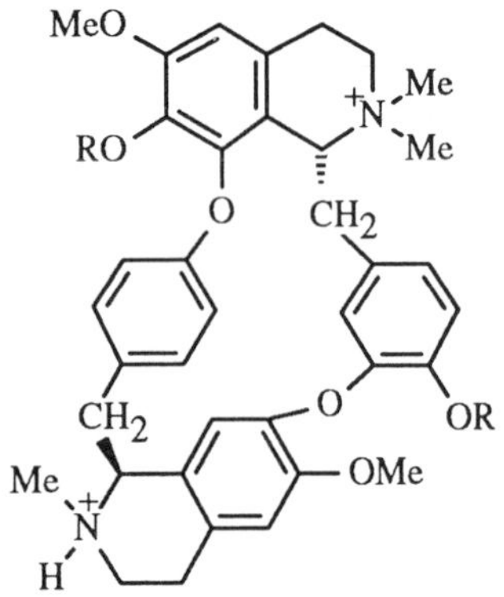

(**96**) R = H, *d*-Tubocurarine
(**239**) R = Me, Dimethyltubocurarine

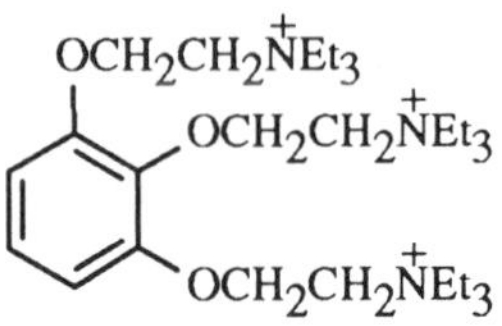

(**240**) Gallamine

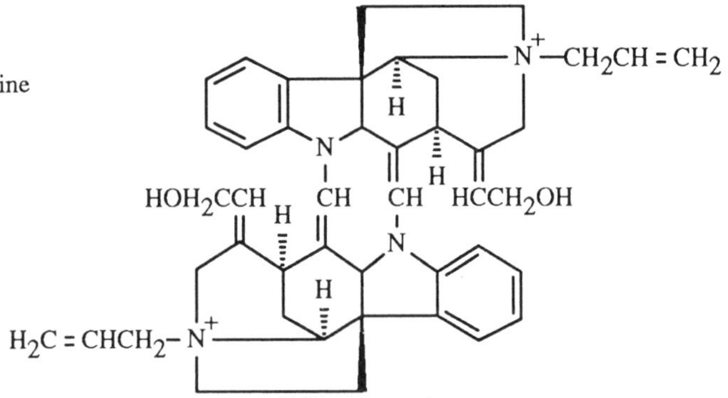

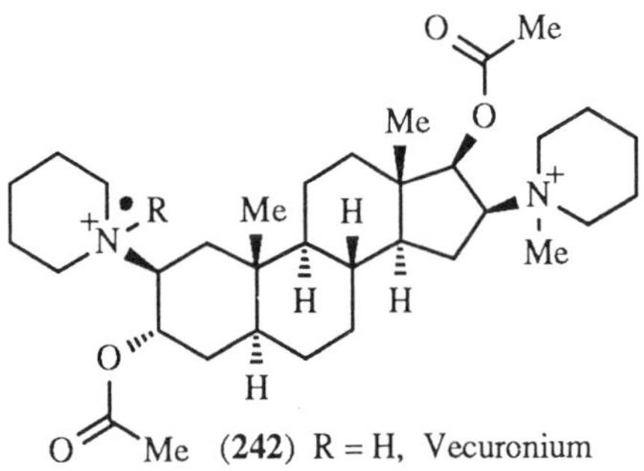

(**242**) R = H, Vecuronium
(**243**) R = Me, Pancuronium

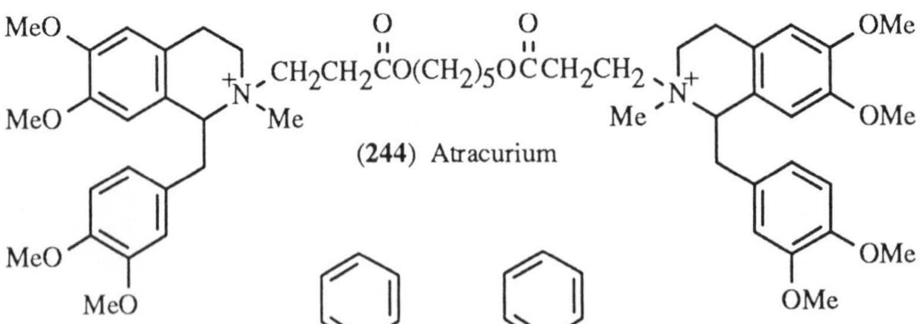

(**241**) Alcuronium

(**244**) Atracurium

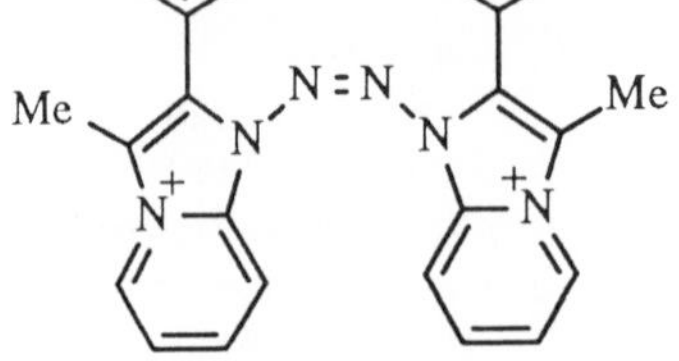

(**245**) Fazadinium

paralysis lasting for about 30 min. Muscles capable of rapid movements, such as those of the fingers and eyes, are affected prior to the larger muscles of the limbs and trunk. Finally, respiration ceases due to paralysis of the intercostal muscles and the diaphragm. Recovery of muscles usually occurs in the reverse order of their paralysis. In some patients, (+)-tubocurarine induces the release of histamine which may lead to bronchospasm, excessive bronchial and salivary secretion, and hypotension as well. However, severe hypotension seen after administration of (+)-tubocurarine may also result from ganglionic blockade. These side effects are shared by several other neuromuscular blocking agents, although to a lesser extent, but they are usually not seen in newer drugs such as vecuronium.[475,476] In addition, several stabilizing skeletal muscle relaxants, such as gallamine, alcuronium or pancuronium, may lead to an increase in heart rate, which appears to be primarily due to blockade of cardiac mAChRs (see Section 12.6.5.5.5).

Due to its brevity of action, the depolarizing neuromuscular blocking agent succinylcholine is the drug of choice if skeletal muscle relaxation is required for short-lasting manipulations, such as endotracheal intubation or psychiatric electroshock therapy to prevent muscle and bone damage. Several seconds after the intravenous administration of succinylcholine ($0.5-1$ mg kg^{-1}), endplate depolarization frequently leads to transient muscle fasciculations, particularly over the chest and the abdomen. However, skeletal muscle relaxation follows within 1 min but lasts for only about 5 min, mainly due to the rapid hydrolysis of succinylcholine by pseudocholinesterase in plasma and liver (*cf.* Section 12.6.2). Occasionally, prolonged neuromuscular blockade is observed in patients with an atypical pseudocholinesterase of genetic origin or a deficiency of the enzyme (estimated incidence $1:1000-1:3000$). Besides various disturbances in cardiac rhythm, the application of succinylcholine is frequently followed by muscle pain, which most probably results from the unsynchronized contraction of muscle fibers just before the onset of paralysis. Furthermore, as muscle cells may lose significant amounts of K$^+$ during prolonged depolarization, succinylcholine may lead to life-threatening increases in plasma K$^+$ levels, particularly in patients with electrolyte imbalances or extensive soft-tissue trauma or burns.

12.6.8.3 Muscarinic Agonists

Despite its many physiological functions (Table 2), ACh (3) itself has little therapeutic value, since it is metabolized too rapidly and its actions are too widespread. The only therapeutic use of ACh is as an intraocular solution to rapidly produce miosis during ocular surgery. However, several metabolically more stable muscarinic agonists, such as the ACh derivatives methacholine (22), carbachol (112) and bethanechol (113; Table 47), are available for clinical use today. In contrast to ACh, methacholine and bethanechol are rather selective stimulants of mAChRs, while carbachol retains considerable nicotinic activity, particularly on autonomic ganglia. Other clinically employed muscarinic agonists are the alkaloid pilocarpine (246) and the quinuclidine derivative aceclidine (100; Table 47).

Pilocarpine, carbachol and aceclidine are widely used in the treatment of glaucoma in order to reduce intraocular pressure. They are applied locally to the eye, frequently in combination with β-adrenergic blocking drugs or sympathomimetic agents. Moreover, alternated with mydriatics (*e.g.* atropine), pilocarpine (or other muscarinic agonists) can also be used to break adhesions between the iris and the lens. The most common side effects of pilocarpine (and other muscarinic agonists)

Table 47 Structural Formulae of Clinically Used Muscarinic Agonists

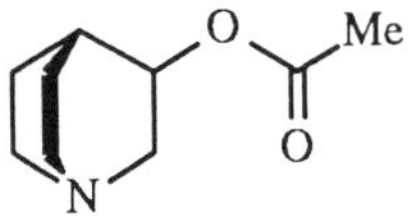

(22) Methacholine   (100) Aceclidine   (112) Carbachol

(113) Bethanechol   (246) Pilocarpine

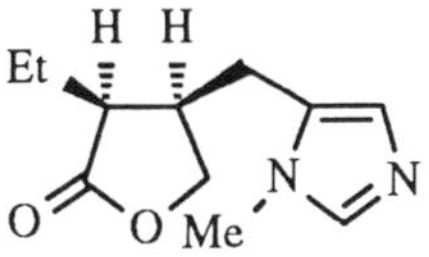

when applied locally to the conjunctiva are the stinging sensation and the myopia (contraction of the ciliary muscle) experienced immediately after the application of the drug.

While methacholine is rarely used clinically today, carbachol and particularly bethanechol are employed in various clinical disorders which involve depression of smooth muscle activity without obstruction. After oral or subcutaneous administration, both agents show some selectivity in stimulating smooth muscle activity in the urinary and gastrointestinal tract. However, bethanechol and carbachol should not be given intravenously or intramuscularly, because serious toxic responses such as bronchoconstriction or cardiovascular depression may readily occur. Both agents may be useful in the treatment of postoperative atonia of the stomach or bowel, gastric retention following bilateral vagotomy, and selected cases of congenital megacolon. Moreover, bethanechol may also be valuable in combating esophageal reflux.[477] Likewise, bethanechol and carbachol have been shown to be of benefit in the treatment of various cases of urinary retention and inadequate emptying of the bladder. Such conditions may, for example, occur postoperatively or post partum, or may be secondary to spinal cord injury or disease (neurogenic bladder).[478]

Side effects of systemically applied muscarinic agonists reflect raised parasympathetic tone and include nausea, intestinal cramps, diarrhea, bronchoconstriction, bradycardia, hypotension, as well as increased gastric secretion, sweating and saliva production. However, serious toxic reactions can be readily overcome by the administration of atropine (0.5–1 mg i.v. or i.m.). Among the major contraindications to the use of direct-acting parasympathomimetic agents are asthma, coronary insufficiency, peptic ulcer and hyperthyroidism (risk of atrial fibrillation).

More recently, muscarinic agonists which readily enter the CNS, such as arecoline (**98**) or RS 86 (2-ethyl-8-methyl-2,8-diazaspiro[4,5]decan-1,3-dione hydrobromide; **247**), have been employed in several clinical trials to combat the decline in cognitive functions observed in patients with Alzheimer's disease (AD).[479] This approach has mainly been encouraged by the finding that AD is usually accompanied by a profound loss of cholinergic neurons and a marked decrease in ChAT activity in various forebrain regions, while the number of central mAChRs appears to be little affected.[96–98] Although clinical studies have shown that muscarinic agonists may lead to small improvements in at least some AD patients, the utility of these agents is mainly limited by considerable parasympathomimetic side effects.[96,98,479] It has therefore been suggested that centrally acting, selective M_1 receptor agonists (*cf.* Section 12.6.5.5), which, however, are not yet available for clinical use, might be more effective in the therapy of AD.[479] Interestingly, the usefulness of the 'cholinergic approach' to the treatment of AD has been confirmed in a recent study, in which several AD patients experienced a significant increase in intellectual functions after oral intake of tetrahydroaminoacridine (THA; **248**), a centrally acting cholinesterase inhibitor.[480]

(**98**) Arecoline   (**247**) RS 86   (**248**) Tetrahydroaminoacridine (THA)

12.6.8.4 Muscarinic Antagonists

Clinically used muscarinic antagonists competitively block the physiological actions of ACh mediated by mAChRs. As most of their effects are predictable from the reduction in parasympathetic tone, these agents are also referred to as parasympatholytics. The prototypical antimuscarinic agents are the plant alkaloids atropine (**179**) and scopolamine (**186**; Table 48) which are found in several Solanaceae species (*e.g. Atropa belladonna* or *Hyoscyamus niger*).

The most conspicuous pharmacological effects seen after administration of atropine (or other antimuscarinic agents) are: reduction of lacrimal, salivary, bronchial and gastrointestinal secretion; suppression of sweating; increase in heart rate; depression of smooth muscle activity in the bronchial, gastrointestinal and genitourinary tract; mydriasis and cycloplegia. In addition, clinically used doses of atropine (0.5–1 mg) may also induce various central effects such as mild vagal excitation and slight sedation. Scopolamine, however, has considerably more pronounced sedative effects, usually producing drowsiness and amnesia in therapeutic doses. In toxic doses, atropine causes central excitation leading to restlessness, hallucinations or delirium, which, with still larger doses, may be followed by death due to medullary paralysis.

The broad range of physiological responses caused by atropine has led to intense efforts to develop antimuscarinic agents which display selectivity for certain organs or organ systems. Nevertheless, success has been limited and, with very few exceptions (see below), the large variety of semisynthetic and synthetic antimuscarinic drugs available for clinical use today display essentially the same pharmacological profile as atropine. However, based on the availability of novel pharmacological tools which have proved useful in the subclassification of mAChRs in experimental pharmacology (*cf.* Section 12.6.5.5), it is hoped that antimuscarinic agents endowed with organ or tissue selectivity will be introduced into therapy in the near future.

Among the great number of antimuscarinic drugs used in therapy today, the quaternary ammonium compounds, *e.g.* N-methylscopolamine (**249**), methantheline (**250**), propantheline (**251**), glycopyrrolate (**252**) and oxyphenonium (**253**) (Table 48), share several pharmacological properties, which, however, are mainly pharmacokinetic in nature. These agents, in contrast to atropine and most other uncharged muscarinic antagonists, are poorly and unreliably absorbed after oral administration. However, they produce virtually no CNS effects, as they scarcely penetrate the blood–brain barrier. In addition quaternary antimuscarinic agents may exhibit considerable ganglion-blocking activity, which may occasionally lead to impotence and postural hypotension.

Antimuscarinic agents are widely used in ophthalmology, where they are applied locally to the eye to produce mydriasis and/or cycloplegia. Mydriasis may be necessary for accurate examination of the retina and the optic disc, as well as in the treatment of acute iritis, iridocyclitis and keratitis. Complete cycloplegia may be useful in certain clinical conditions such as iridocyclitis, and for precise measurement of refractive errors. Shorter-acting antimuscarinic drugs such as homatropine (**254**), cyclopentolate (**255**) or tropicamide (**256**) (Table 48) are preferable to atropine and scopolamine when prolonged mydriasis and cycloplegia are not required.

Prior to the introduction of H_2-receptor blocking drugs, conventional antimuscarinic agents such as propantheline or glycopyrrolate had been widely used in the management of peptic ulcer disease. However, these agents are rarely used in this condition today, as the doses required to significantly reduce gastric acid secretion are usually associated with pronounced parasympatholytic side effects such as dry mouth, blurred vision, constipation or impaired micturition. In contrast, the newly developed, selective M_1 receptor antagonist pirenzepine (**12**; *cf.* Section 12.6.5.5) is effective in the treatment of peptic ulcer disease, while causing fewer side effects.[198] It has been shown that pirenzepine selectively inhibits gastric acid secretion, possibly by preferential blockade of neuronal M_1 receptors in intramural ganglia of the stomach wall.[228,229] A similar pharmacological profile has been found in several clinical trials for the pirenzepine derivative, telenzepine (**13**).[481]

In addition, antimuscarinic agents are also of value in the treatment of certain clinical disorders involving increased tone or motility of the gastrointestinal tract, such as, for example, diarrheas associated with mild dysenteries or diverticulitis. Furthermore, antimuscarinic agents are often used to combat biliary and renal colics where they are frequently applied in combination with an analgesic drug.

The quaternary ammonium antimuscarinic compounds ipratropium (**257**) and oxitropium (**258**; Table 48) are used in the therapy of obstructive pulmonary diseases such as chronic bronchitis or bronchial asthma. As these agents are applied locally as aerosols, they produce bronchial dilatation without significant systemic side effects.[482] The main cardiac indications for the application of atropine and related antimuscarinic agents (*e.g.* ipratropium) are symptomatic sinus bradycardia (e.g. in acute myocardial infarction), selected cases of higher degree heart block and certain types of ventricular arrhythmias which may be exacerbated by slowing of the heart (*e.g.* torsade de pointes).[483,484] The use of conventional antimuscarinic drugs in long-term cardiac therapy is frequently limited by annoying parasympatholytic side effects. However, a novel, cardioselective antimuscarinic agent, the pirenzepine derivative AF-DX 116 (**18**; *cf.* Section 12.6.5.5.5), has recently entered clinical trials. Initial findings indicate that AF-DX 116 produces few noncardiac side effects and may thus also be employed chronically, *e.g.* in patients with symptomatic sinus bradycardia or higher degree heart block.[485]

In addition, the belladonna alkaloids atropine and scopolamine are frequently used as part of routine preoperative medication, mainly to counteract the vagal effects that may occur during general anesthesia (*e.g.* reflex bradycardia) and to reduce excessive bronchial secretion, which, however, with the advent of less irritating anesthetic agents, has become a minor problem. Furthermore, the sedation and amnesia produced by preoperatively administered scopolamine may be of value, too.

Table 48 Structural Formulae of Some Clinically Used Antimuscarinic Agents

Belladonna alkaloids

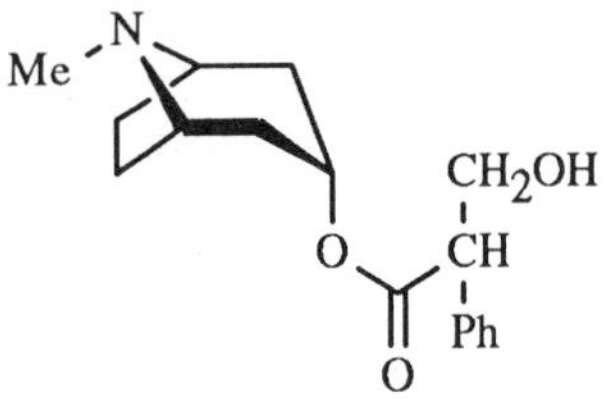

(**179**) Atropine

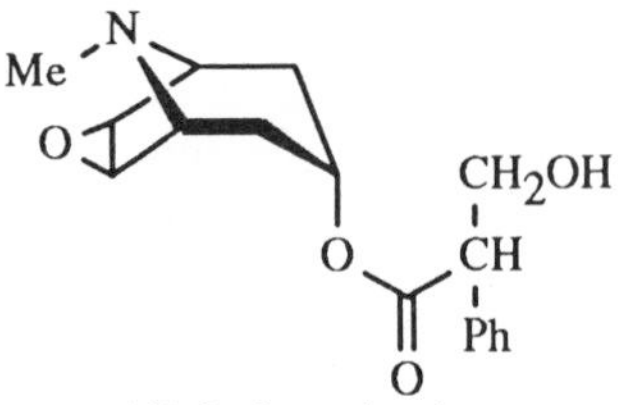

(**186**) Scopolamine

Quaternary ammonium compounds

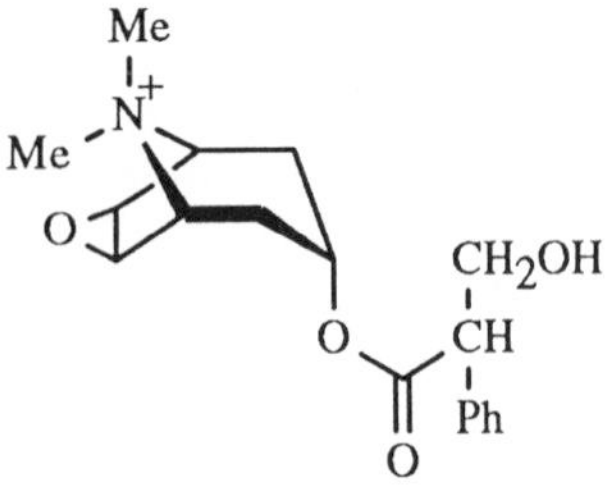

(**249**) *N*-Methylscopolamine

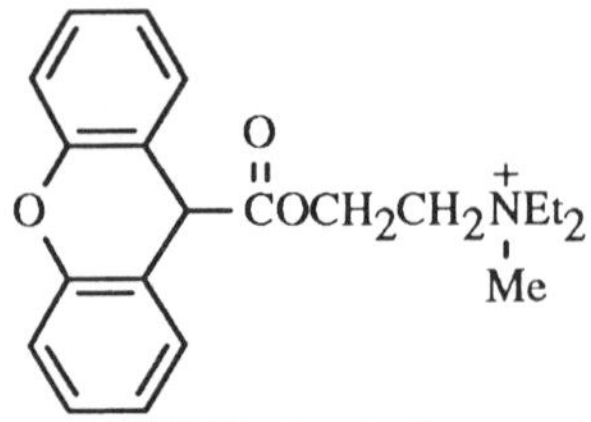

(**250**) Methantheline

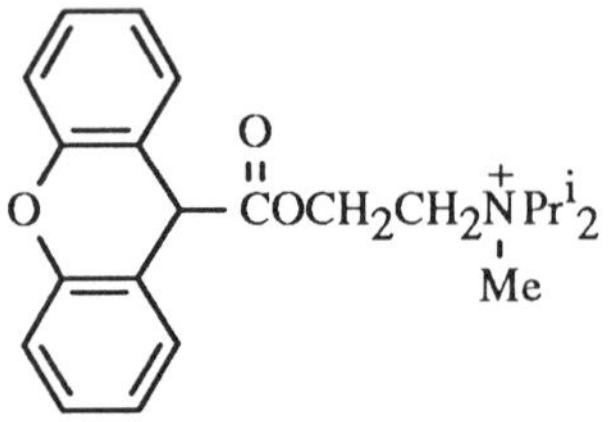

(**251**) Propantheline

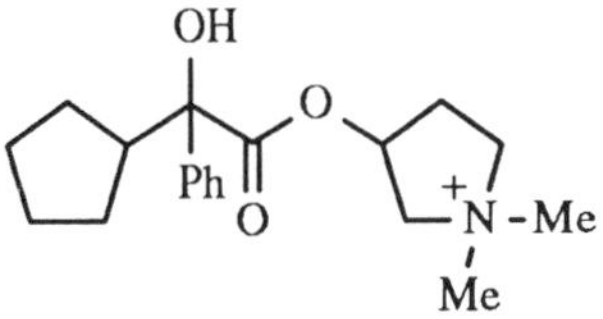

(**252**) Glycopyrrolate

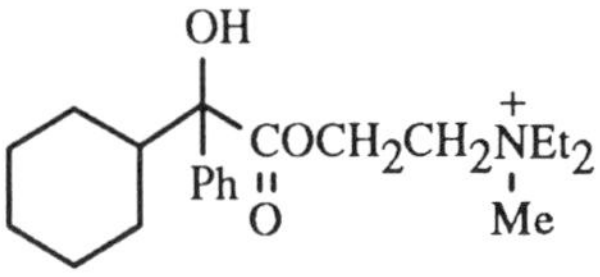

(**253**) Oxyphenonium

Agents used in ophthalmology

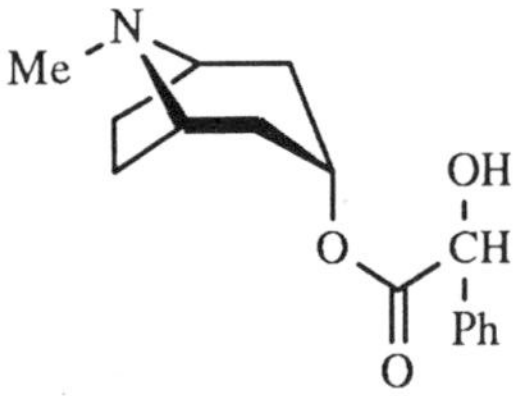

(**254**) Homatropine

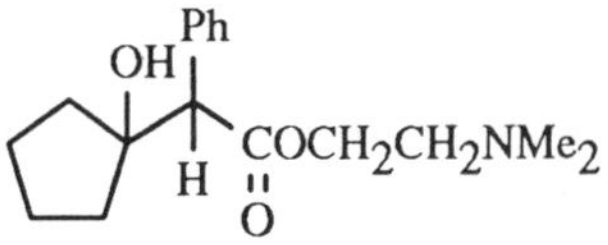

(**255**) Cyclopentolate

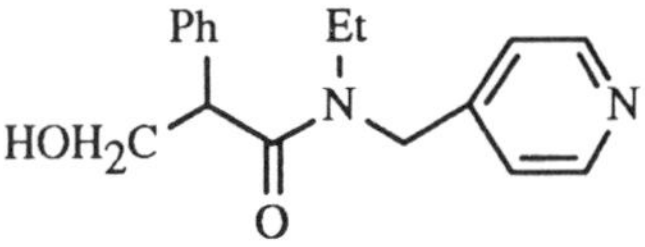

(**256**) Tropicamide

Agents for obstructive pulmonary diseases

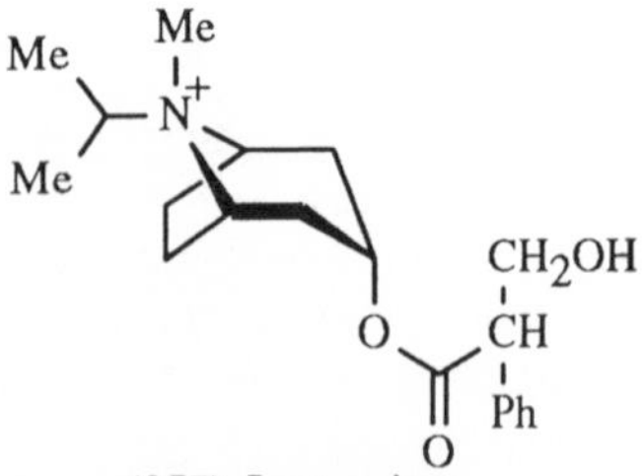

(**257**) Ipratropium

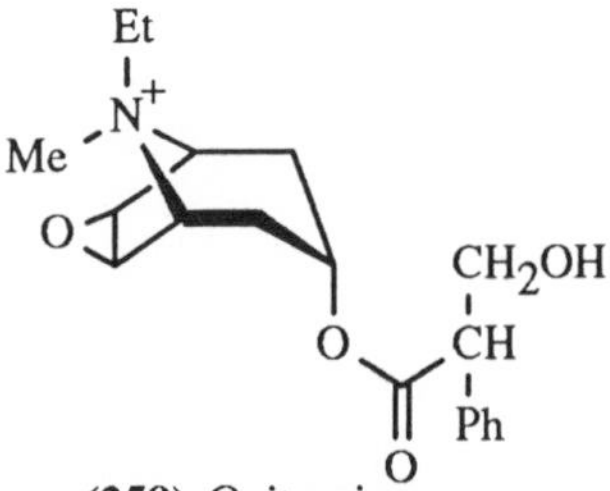

(**258**) Oxitropium

Agents for Parkinson's disease

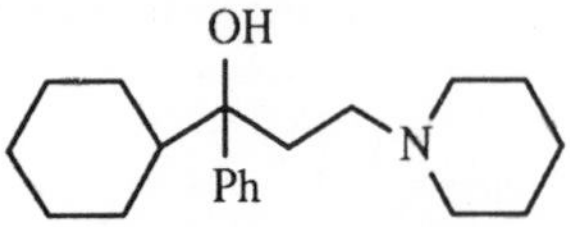

(**215**) Trihexyphenidyl

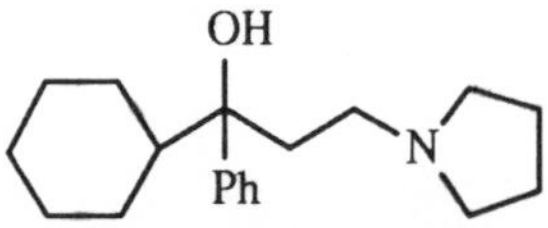

(**180**) Procyclidine

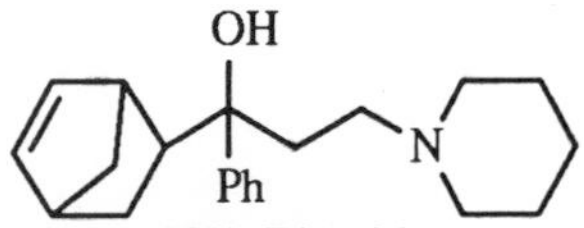

(**259**) Biperiden

Centrally acting antimuscarinic agents, such as, for example, trihexyphenidyl (**215**), procyclidine (**180**) or biperiden (**259**) (Table 48), play a supportive role in the treatment of Parkinson's disease by restoring the normal balance of cholinergic and dopaminergic neurotransmission in the basal ganglia. Moreover, these drugs may also be of value to combat the parkinsonism-like syndrome induced by antipsychotic agents. However, the utility of antimuscarinic agents in these clinical conditions may be limited by undesired CNS reactions such as somnolence, mental confusion and hallucinations, or by side effects attributable to the blockade of peripheral mAChRs.

Likewise, antimuscarinic drugs penetrating the blood–brain barrier, particularly scopolamine, are highly effective in preventing motion sickness. Recently, a new dosage form (transdermal patch) of scopolamine has become available for clinical use in which the drug is incorporated into an adhesive unit that is applied behind the ear.[486] The use of this preparation (duration of action $\approx$ 72 h) is less frequently associated with sedation, dry mouth or blurred vision.

Finally, atropine can be applied to counteract the parasympathomimetic side effects seen after the administration of carbamate cholinesterase inhibitors (*e.g.* neostigmine) when used to relieve the symptoms of myasthenia gravis or to antagonize the skeletal muscle relaxant effects of neuromuscular blocking drugs. Moreover, the judicious use of large doses of atropine (up to 50 mg d^{-1}) can be life saving in the treatment of poisoning by organophosphate cholinesterase inhibitors, which are widely used as insecticides.

Antimuscarinic drugs are contraindicated in patients with glaucoma, especially narrow-angle glaucoma, obstructive gastrointestinal diseases (*e.g.* pyloric stenosis or paralytic ileus) and prostatic hypertropy. Moreover, in patients with coronary insufficiency, these agents should only be applied in doses that do not increase heart rate.

12.6.9 REFERENCES

1. N. Weiner and P. Taylor, in 'Goodman and Gilman's: The Pharmacological Basis of Therapeutics', 7th edn., ed. A. G. Gilman, L. S. Goodman, T. W. Rall and F. Murad, Macmillan, New York, 1985, p. 66.
2. J. K. Blusztajn and R. J. Wurtman, *Science (Washington, D.C.)*, 1983, **221**, 614.
3. Y. Dunant, *Prog. Neurobiol. (Oxford)*, 1986, **26**, 55.
4. V. P. Whittaker, *Trends Pharmacol. Sci.*, 1986, **7**, 312.
5. J. M. Lundberg, *Acta Physiol. Scand.*, 1981, **496**, Suppl., 1.
6. D. V. Ágoston, M. Ballmann, J. M. Conlon, G. H. C. Dowe and V. P. Whittaker, *J. Neurochem.*, 1985, **45**, 398.
7. G. C. Augustine, M. P. Charlton and S. J. Smith, *Annu. Rev. Neurosci.*, 1987, **10**, 633.
8. L. L. Simpson, *Pharmacol. Rev.*, 1981, **33**, 155.
9. M. Schumacher, S. Camp, Y. Maulet, M. Newton, K. MacPhee-Quigley, S. S. Taylor, T. Friedmann and P. Taylor, *Nature (London)*, 1986, **319**, 407.
10. J. Massoulié and S. Bon, *Annu. Rev. Neurosci.*, 1982, **5**, 57.
11. B. N. La Du and O. Lockridge, *Fed. Proc., Fed. Am. Soc. Exp. Biol.*, 1986, **45**, 2965.
12. H. H. Dale, *J. Pharmacol. Exp. Ther.*, 1914, **6**, 147.
13. J. Lindstrom and P. Dau, *Annu. Rev. Pharmacol. Toxicol.*, 1980, **20**, 337.
14. J. P. Merlie, *Cell*, 1984, **36**, 573.
15. J. P. Merlie and M. M. Smith, *J. Membr. Biol.*, 1986, **91**, 1.
16. M. M. Salpeter and R. H. Loring, *Prog. Neurobiol. (Oxford)*, 1985, **25**, 297.
17. S. M. Schuetze and L. W. Role, *Annu. Rev. Neurosci.*, 1987, **10**, 403.
18. E. A. Barnard, D. M. W. Beeson, V. B. Cockcroft, M. G. Darlison, A. A. Hicks, F. A. Lai, S. J. Moss and M. D. Squire, in 'Cellular and Molecular Basis of Cholinergic Function', ed. M. J. Dowdall and J. N. Hawthorne, Horwood, Chichester, 1987, p. 15.
19. C. Y. Lee, in 'Neurotoxins: Tools in Neurobiology', ed. B. Ceccarelli and F. Clementi, Raven Press, New York, 1979, p. 1.
20. A. Karlin, *Cell Surf. Rev.*, 1980, **6**, 191.
21. P. B. S. Clarke, *Trends Pharmacol. Sci.*, 1987, **8**, 32.
22. J. P. Long and C. Y. Chiou, *J. Pharm. Sci.*, 1970, **59**, 133.
23. P. R. Adams, *J. Membr. Biol.*, 1981, **58**, 161.
24. B. J. Barrantes, *Int. Rev. Neurobiol.*, 1983, **24**, 259.
25. B. Sakmann and E. Neher, *Annu. Rev. Physiol.*, 1984, **46**, 455.
26. S. J. Tzartos, *Trends Biochem. Sci. (Pers. Ed.)*, 1984, **9**, 63.
27. T. Claudio, *Trends Pharmacol. Sci.*, 1986, **7**, 308.
28. K. Peper, R. J. Bradley and F. Dreyer, *Physiol. Rev.*, 1982, **62**, 1271.
29. R. L. Volle, in 'Pharmacology of Ganglionic Transmission', 'Handbook of Experimental Pharmacology', ed. D. A. Kharkevich, Springer-Verlag, Berlin, 1980, vol. 53, p. 281.
30. P. Taylor, in 'Goodman and Gilman's: The Pharmacological Basis of Therapeutics', 7th edn., ed. A. G. Gilman, L. S. Goodman, T. W. Rall and F. Murad, Macmillan, New York, 1985, p. 215.
31. K. Starke, *Rev. Physiol., Biochem. Pharmacol.*, 1977, **77**, 1.
32. S. Nishi, H. Higashi, K. Odawara and K. Ikeda, in 'Neurobiology of Acetylcholine', ed. N. J. Dun and R. L. Perlman, Plenum Press, New York, 1987, p. 239.
33. W. C. Bowman, *Anesth. Analg. (Cleveland)*, 1980, **59**, 935.
34. I. Wessler and H. Kilbinger, in 'Cellular and Molecular Basis of Cholinergic Function', ed. M. J. Dowdall and J. N. Hawthorne, Horwood, Chichester, 1987, p. 152.

35. M. D. Aceto and B. R. Martin, *Med. Res. Rev.*, 1982, **2**, 43.
36. D. A. McCormick and D. A. Prince, *J. Neurosci.*, 1987, **7**, 742.
37. D. A. Brown, R. J. Docherty and J. V. Halliwell, *J. Physiol. (London)*, 1983, **341**, 655.
38. D. R. Curtis and R. W. Ryall, *Exp. Brain Res.*, 1966, **2**, 49.
39. P. R. Rowell and D. L. Winkler, *J. Neurochem.*, 1984, **43**, 1593.
40. T. C. Westfall, H. Grant and H. Perry, *Gen. Pharmacol.*, 1983, **14**, 321.
41. M.-F. Chesselet, *Neuroscience*, 1984, **12**, 347.
42. S. Wonnacott, C. Rapier and G. G. Lunt, in 'Cellular and Molecular Basis of Cholinergic Function', ed. M. J. Dowdall and J. N. Hawthorne, Horwood, Chichester, 1987, p. 33.
43. S. Shimohama, T. Taniguchi, M. Fujiwara and M. Kameyama, *J. Neurochem.*, 1985, **45**, 604.
44. E. D. London, S. B. Waller and J. K. Wamsley, *Neurosci. Lett.*, 1985, **53**, 179.
45. P. B. S. Clarke, R. D. Schwartz, S. M. Paul, C. B. Pert and A. Pert, *J. Neurosci.*, 1985, **5**, 1307.
46. R. D. Schwartz, *Life Sci.*, 1986, **38**, 2111.
47. M. J. Marks, J. A. Stitzel, E. Romm, J. M. Wehner and A. C. Collins, *Mol. Pharmacol.*, 1986, **30**, 427.
48. A. M. Martino-Barrows and K. J. Kellar, *Mol. Pharmacol.*, 1987, **31**, 169.
49. J.-P. Changeux, *Harvey Lect.*, 1981, **75**, 85.
50. B. M. Conti-Tronconi and M. A. Raftery, *Annu. Rev. Biochem.*, 1982, **51**, 491.
51. J.-P. Changeux, A. Devillers-Thiéry and P. Chemouilli, *Science (Washington, D.C.)*, 1984, **225**, 1335.
52. J.-L. Popot and J.-P. Changeux, *Physiol. Rev.*, 1984, **64**, 1162.
53. A. Maelicke, *Angew. Chem., Int. Ed. Engl.*, 1984, **23**, 195.
54. R. M. Stroud and J. Finer-Moore, *Annu. Rev. Cell Biol.*, 1985, **1**, 317.
55. F. Hucho, *Eur. J. Biochem.*, 1986, **158**, 211.
56. M. P. McCarthy, J. P. Earnest, E. F. Young, S. Choe and R. M. Stroud, *Annu. Rev. Neurosci.*, 1986, **9**, 383.
57. A. Karlin, P. N. Kao and M. DiPaola, *Trends Pharmacol. Sci.*, 1986, **7**, 304.
58. D. Colquhoun and B. Sakmann, *Nature (London)*, 1981, **294**, 464.
59. D. Colquhoun and B. Sakmann, *J. Physiol. (London)*, 1985, **369**, 501.
60. R. L. Huganir, A. H. Delcour, P. Greengard and G. P. Hess, *Nature (London)*, 1986, **321**, 774.
61. E. X. Albuquerque, S. S. Deshpande, Y. Aracava, M. Alkondon and J. W. Daly, *FEBS Lett.*, 1986, **199**, 113.
62. R. L. Huganir and P. Greengard, *Trends Pharmacol. Sci.*, 1987, **8**, 472.
63. B. J. Morley, G. R. Farley and E. Javel, *Trends Pharmacol. Sci.*, 1983, **4**, 225.
64. G. Kemp and B. J. Morley, *FEBS Lett.*, 1986, **205**, 265.
65. R. E. Oswald and J. A. Freeman, *Neuroscience*, 1981, **6**, 1.
66. T. Heidmann and J.-P. Changeux, *Annu. Rev. Biochem.*, 1978, **47**, 317.
67. P. J. Whiting and J. M. Lindstrom, *Biochemistry*, 1986, **25**, 2082.
68. P. Whiting and J. Lindstrom, *Proc. Natl. Acad. Sci. U.S.A.*, 1987, **84**, 595.
69. M. G. McNamee and E. L. M. Ochoa, *Neuroscience*, 1982, **7**, 2305.
70. M. A. Raftery, M. W. Hunkapiller, C. D. Strader and L. E. Hood, *Science (Washington, D.C)*, 1980, **208**, 1454.
71. B. M. Conti-Tronconi, C. M. Gotti, M. W. Hunkapiller and M. A. Raftery, *Science (Washington, D.C.)*, 1982, **218**, 1227.
72. E. N. Olson, L. Glaser and J. P. Merlie, *J. Biol. Chem.*, 1984, **259**, 5364.
73. A. Brisson and P. N. T. Unwin, *Nature (London)*, 1985, **315**, 474.
74. A. Karlin, R. Cox, R.-R. Kaldany, P. Lobel and E. Holtzman, *Cold Spring Harbor Symp. Quant. Biol.*, 1983, **48**, 1.
75. S. Numa, M. Noda, H. Takahashi, T. Tanabe, M. Toyosato, Y. Furutani and S. Kikyotani, *Cold Spring Harbor Symp. Quant. Biol.*, 1983, **48**, 57.
76. T. Kubo, M. Noda, T. Takai, T. Tanabe, T. Kayano, S. Shimizu, K. Tanaka, H. Takahashi, T. Hirose, S. Inayama, R. Kikuno, T. Miyata and S. Numa, *Eur. J. Biochem.*, 1985, **149**, 5.
77. J. Finer-Moore and R. M. Stroud, *Proc. Natl. Acad. Sci. U.S.A.*, 1984, **81**, 155.
78. H. R. Guy, *Biophys. J.*, 1984, **45**, 249.
79. J. Lindstrom, M. Criado, S. Hochschwender, J. L. Fox and V. Sarin, *Nature (London)*, 1984, **311**, 573.
80. E. F. Young, E. Ralston, J. Blake, J. Ramachandran, Z. W. Hall and R. M. Stroud, *Proc. Natl. Acad. Sci. U.S.A.*, 1985, **82**, 626.
81. F. Hucho, W. Oberthür and F. Lottspeich, *FEBS Lett.*, 1986, **205**, 137.
82. M. Mishina, T. Kurosaki, T. Tobimatsu, Y. Morimoto, M. Noda, T. Yamamoto, M. Terao, J. Lindstrom, T. Takahashi, M. Kuno and S. Numa, *Nature (London)*, 1984, **307**, 604.
83. B. Sakmann, C. Methfessel, M. Mishina, T. Takahashi, T. Takai, M. Kurasaki, K. Fukuda and S. Numa, *Nature (London)*, 1985, **318**, 538.
84. K. Imoto, C. Methfessel, B. Sakmann, M. Mishina, Y. Mori, T. Konno, K. Fukuda, M. Kurasaki, H. Bujo, Y. Fujita and S. Numa, *Nature (London)*, 1986, **324**, 670.
85. T. Takai, M. Noda, M. Mishina, S. Shimizu, Y. Furutani, T. Kayano, T. Ikeda, T. Kubo, H. Takahashi, T. Takahashi, M. Kuno and S. Numa, *Nature (London)*, 1985, **315**, 761.
86. M. Mishina, T. Takai, K. Imoto, M. Noda, T. Takahashi, S. Numa, C. Methfessel and B. Sakmann, *Nature (London)*, 1986, **321**, 406.
87. P. Whiting and J. Lindstrom, *J. Neurosci.*, 1986, **6**, 3061.
88. B. M. Conti-Tronconi, S. M. J. Dunn, E. A. Barnard, J. O. Dolly, F. A. Lai, N. Ray and M. A. Raftery, *Proc. Natl. Acad. Sci. U.S.A.*, 1985, **82**, 5208.
89. J. Boulter, K. Evans, D. Goldman, G. Martin, D. Treco, S. Heinemann and J. Patrick, *Nature (London)*, 1986, **319**, 368.
90. P. N. Kao, A. J. Dwork, R.-R. J. Kaldany, M. L. Silver, J. Wideman, S. Stein and A. Karlin, *J. Biol. Chem.*, 1984, **259**, 11 662.
91. M. Mishina, T. Tobimatsu, K. Imoto, K. Tanaka, Y. Fujita, K. Fukuda, M. Kurasaki, H. Takahashi, Y. Morimoto, T. Hirose, S. Inayama, T. Takahashi, M. Kuno and S. Numa, *Nature (London)*, 1985, **313**, 364.
92. D. Neumann, D. Barchan, A. Safran, J. M. Gershoni and S. Fuchs, *Proc. Natl. Acad. Sci. U.S.A.*, 1986, **83**, 3008.
93. P. T. Wilson, T. L. Lentz and E. Hawrot, *Proc. Natl. Acad. Sci. U.S.A.*, 1985, **82**, 8790.
94. T. Barkas, A. Mauron, B. Roth, C. Alliod, S. J. Tzartos and M. Ballivet, *Science (Washington, D.C.)*, 1987, **235**, 77.
95. D. Collerton, *Neuroscience*, 1986, **19**, 1.

96. R. T. Bartus, R. L. Dean, B. Beer and A. S. Lippa, *Science (Washington, D.C.)*, 1982, **217**, 408.
97. J. T. Coyle, D. L. Price and M. R. DeLong, *Science (Washington, D.C.)*, 1983, **219**, 1184.
98. R. T. Bartus, R. L. Dean, M. J. Pontecorvo and C. Flicker, *Ann. N.Y. Acad. Sci.*, 1985, **444**, 332.
99. W. D. M. Paton and H. P. Rang, *Proc. R. Soc. London, Ser. B*, 1965, **163**, 1.
100. H. I. Yamamura and S. H. Snyder, *Mol. Pharmacol.*, 1974, **10**, 861.
101. A. J. Beld and E. J. Ariëns, *Eur. J. Pharmacol.*, 1974, **25**, 203.
102. E. C. Hulme, N. J. M. Birdsall, A. S. V. Burgen and P. Mehta, *Mol. Pharmacol.*, 1978, **14**, 737.
103. A. S. V. Burgen, C. R. Hiley and J. M. Young, *Br. J. Pharmacol.*, 1974, **50**, 145.
104. N. J. M. Birdsall, A. S. V. Burgen and E. C. Hulme, *Mol. Pharmacol.*, 1978, **14**, 723.
105. F. J. Ehlert, Y. Dumont, W. R. Roeske and H. I. Yamamura, *Life Sci.*, 1980, **26**, 961.
106. A. R. Kerlavage, C. M. Fraser and J. C. Venter, *Trends Pharmacol. Sci.*, 1987, **8**, 426.
107. M. Sokolovsky, D. Gurwitz and J. Kloog, in 'Advances in Enzymology and Related Areas of Molecular Biology', ed. A. Meister, Wiley, New York, 1983, vol. 55, p. 137.
108. W. E. Haefely, in 'Pharmacology of Ganglionic Transmission', 'Handbook of Experimental Pharmacology', ed. D. A. Kharkevich, Springer-Verlag, Berlin, 1980, vol. 53, p. 313.
109. H. Kilbinger, *Trends Pharmacol. Sci.*, 1984, **5**, 103.
110. E. Muscholl, *Am. J. Physiol.*, 1980, **239**, H713.
111. P. M. Vanhoutte and J. T. Shepherd, *Gen. Pharmacol.*, 1983, **14**, 35.
112. K. Krnjević, *Physiol. Rev.*, 1974, **54**, 418.
113. M. Raiteri, M. Marchi and G. Maura, in 'Handbook of Neurochemistry', ed. A. Lajtha, Plenum Press, New York, 1984, vol. 6, p. 431.
114. P. Kása, *Prog. Neurobiol. (Oxford)*, 1986, **26**, 211.
115. P. L. McGeer, E. G. McGeer, K. Mizukawa, H. Tago and J. H. Peng, in 'Neurobiology of Acetylcholine', ed. N. J. Dun and R. L. Perlman, Plenum Press, New York, 1987, p. 3.
116. A. Rotter, N. J. M. Birdsall, A. S. V. Burgen, P. M. Field, E. C. Hulme and G. Raisman, *Brain Res. Rev.*, 1979, **1**, 141.
117. A. Rotter, N. J. M. Birdsall, P. M. Field and G. Raisman, *Brain Res. Rev.*, 1979, **1**, 167.
118. R. Cortés, A. Probst and J. M. Palacios, *Neuroscience*, 1984, **12**, 1003.
119. R. Cortés, A. Probst and J. M. Palacios, *Neuroscience*, 1987, **20**, 65.
120. P. G. Green and I. Kitchen, *Prog. Neurobiol. (Oxford)*, 1986, **26**, 119.
121. A. G. Karczmar, in 'Cholinergic Mechanisms and Psychopharmacology', 'Advances in Behavioral Biology', ed. D. J. Jenden, Plenum Press, New York, 1978, vol. 24, p. 679.
122. D. S. Janowsky and S. C. Risch, *Drug Dev. Res.*, 1984, **4**, 125.
123. S. C. Dilsaver, *Acta Psychiatr. Scand.*, 1986, **74**, 312.
124. S. C. Dilsaver, *Brain Res. Rev.*, 1986, **11**, 285.
125. P. J. Shiromani, J. C. Gillin and S. J. Henriksen, *Annu. Rev. Pharmacol. Toxicol.*, 1987, **27**, 137.
126. H. C. Hartzell, *Trends Pharmacol. Sci.*, 1982, **3**, 213.
127. J. Y. Jeremy, D. P. Mikhailidis and P. Dandona, *Eur. J. Pharmacol.*, 1986, **123**, 67.
128. C. O. Feddersen, M. M. Mathias, I. F. McMurtry and N. F. Voelkel, *Prostaglandins*, 1986, **31**, 973.
129. J. Y. Jeremy, D. P. Mikhailidis and P. Dandona, *Naunyn-Schmiedeberg's Arch. Pharmacol.*, 1986, **334**, 463.
130. R. H. Michell, *Biochim. Biophys. Acta*, 1975, **415**, 81.
131. R. H. Michell and C. K. Kirk, *Trends Pharmacol. Sci.*, 1981, **2**, 86.
132. J. H. Brown and S. Brown-Masters, *Trends Pharmacol. Sci.*, 1984, **5**, 417.
133. M. J. Berridge, *Biochem. J.*, 1984, **220**, 345.
134. M. J. Berridge and R. F. Irvine, *Nature (London)*, 1984, **312**, 315.
135. M. J. Berridge, *Annu. Rev. Biochem.*, 1987, **56**, 159.
136. Y. Nishizuka, *Science (Washington, D.C.)*, 1986, **233**, 305.
137. B. M. Grandordy, F. M. Cuss, A. S. Sampson, J. B. Palmer and P. J. Barnes, *J. Pharmacol. Exp. Ther.*, 1986, **238**, 273.
138. F. Miot, C. Erneux, J. N. Wells and J. E. Dumont, *Mol. Pharmacol.*, 1984, **25**, 261.
139. L. I. Tanner, T. K. Harden, J. N. Wells and M. W. Martin, *J. Pharmacol. Exp. Ther.*, 1986, **29**, 455.
140. Y. Oron, N. Dascal, E. Nadler and M. Lupu, *Nature (London)*, 1985, **313**, 141.
141. C. W. Taylor and J. E. Merritt, *Trends Pharmacol. Sci.*, 1986, **7**, 238.
142. A. R. Hughes, M. W. Martin and T. K. Harden, *Proc. Natl. Acad. Sci. U.S.A.*, 1984, **81**, 5680.
143. M. W. Martin, T. Evans and T. K. Harden, *Biochem. J.*, 1985, **229**, 539.
144. M. E. Dunlop and R. G. Larkins, *Biochem. J.*, 1986, **240**, 731.
145. T. Sasaguri, M. Hirata, T. Itoh, T. Koga and H. Kuriyama, *Biochem. J.*, 1986, **239**, 567.
146. W. Hoss and J. Ellis, *Int. Rev. Neurobiol.*, 1985, **26**, 151.
147. N. M. Nathanson, *Annu. Rev. Neurosci.*, 1987, **10**, 195.
148. A. G. Gilman, *Annu. Rev. Biochem.*, 1987, **56**, 615.
149. M. Ui, *Trends Pharmacol. Sci.*, 1984, **5**, 277.
150. O. Hazeki and M. Ui, *J. Biol. Chem.*, 1981, **256**, 2856.
151. H. Kurose, T. Katada, T. Amano and M. Ui, *J. Biol. Chem.*, 1983, **258**, 4870.
152. M. Endoh, M. Maruyama and T. Iijima, *Am. J. Physiol.*, 1985, **249**, H309.
153. S. Tuček, V. Doležal, J. Folbergrová, S. Hynie, F. Kolář and B. Oštádal, *Pflügers Arch. (Eur. J. Physiol)*, 1987, **408**, 167.
154. V. A. Florio and P. C. Sternweis, *J. Biol. Chem.*, 1985, **260**, 3477.
155. J. M. Martin, E. M. Subers, S. W. Halvorsen and N. M. Nathanson, *J. Pharmacol. Exp. Ther.*, 1987, **240**, 683.
156. B. T. Liang and J. B. Galper, *J. Biol. Chem.*, 1987, **262**, 2494.
157. K. H. Jakobs, K. Aktories and G. Schultz, *Naunyn-Schmiedeberg's Arch. Pharmacol.*, 1979, **310**, 113.
158. M. C. Olianas, P. Onali, N. H. Neff and E. Costa, *Mol. Pharmacol.*, 1983, **23**, 393.
159. T. J. Torphy, C. Zheng, S. M. Peterson, R. R. Fiscus, G. A. Rinard and S. E. Mayer, *J. Pharmacol. Exp. Ther.*, 1985, **233**, 409.
160. K. Löffelholz and A. J. Pappano, *Pharmacol. Rev.*, 1985, **37**, 1.
161. H. C. Hartzell, in 'Neurobiology of Acetylcholine', ed. N. J. Dun and R. L. Perlman, Plenum Press, New York, 1987, p. 159.

162. T. Bartfai, R. E. Study and P. Greengard, in 'Cholinergic Mechanisms and Psychopharmacology', 'Advances in Behavioral Biology', ed. D. J. Jenden, Plenum Press, New York, 1978, vol. 24, p. 285.
163. M. McKinney and E. Richelson, *Annu. Rev. Pharmacol. Toxicol.*, 1984, **24**, 121.
164. B. E. Swartz and C. D. Woody, *J. Neurobiol.*, 1979, **10**, 465.
165. G. J. Wastek, J. R. Lopez and E. Richelson, *Mol. Pharmacol.*, 1980, **19**, 15.
166. Ö. Nordström and T. Bartfai, *Brain. Res.*, 1981, **213**, 467.
167. H. Nawrath, *Nature (London)*, 1977, **267**, 72.
168. N. Dascal, E. M. Landau and Y. Lass, *J. Physiol. (London)*, 1984, **352**, 551.
169. G. Bkaily and N. Sperelakis, *Am. J. Physiol.*, 1985, **248**, H745.
170. R. M. Rapoport, M. B. Draznin and F. Murad, *Nature (London)*, 1983, **306**, 174.
171. L. J. Ignarro and P. J. Kadowitz, *Annu. Rev. Pharmacol. Toxicol.*, 1985, **25**, 171.
172. R. F. Furchgott and J. V. Zawadzki, *Nature (London)*, 1980, **288**, 373.
173. R. F. Furchgott, *Annu. Rev. Pharmacol. Toxicol.*, 1984, **24**, 175.
174. S. Moncada, A. G. Herman and P. Vanhoutte, *Trends Pharmacol. Sci.*, 1987, **8**, 365.
175. R. A. North, *Trends Pharmacol. Sci.*, 1986, **7**, Suppl., 19.
176. J. Dodd and J. P. Horn, *J. Physiol. (London)*, 1983, **334**, 271.
177. T. M. Egan and R. A. North, *Nature (London)*, 1986, **319**, 405.
178. A. E. Cole and P. Shinnick-Gallagher, *Nature (London)*, 1984, **307**, 270.
179. D. A. McCormick and D. A. Prince, *Nature (London)*, 1986, **319**, 402.
180. P. J. Pfaffinger, J. M. Martin, D. D. Hunter, N. M. Nathanson and B. Hille, *Nature (London)*, 1985, **317**, 536.
181. G. E. Breitwieser and G. Szabo, *Nature (London)*, 1985, **317**, 538.
182. A. Yatani, J. Codina, A. M. Brown and L. Birnbaumer, *Science (Washington, D.C.)*, 1987, **235**, 207.
183. D. E. Logothetis, Y. Kurachi, J. Galper, E. J. Neer and D. E. Clapham, *Nature (London)*, 1987, **325**, 321.
184. D. A. Brown, B. H. Gähwiler, S. J. Marsh and A. A. Selyanko, *Trends Pharmacol. Sci.*, 1986, **7**, Suppl., 66.
185. K. Morita, R. A. North and T. Tokimasa, *J. Physiol. (London)*, 1982, **333**, 125.
186. D. A. Brown and P. R. Adams, *Nature (London)*, 1980, **283**, 673.
187. A. Constanti and D. A. Brown, *Neurosci. Lett.*, 1981, **24**, 289.
188. J. V. Halliwell and P. R. Adams, *Brain Res.*, 1982, **250**, 71.
189. A. Constanti and M. Galvan, *Neurosci. Lett.*, 1983, **39**, 65.
190. C. D. Benham, T. B. Bolton and R. J. Lang, *Nature (London)*, 1985, **316**, 345.
191. Y. Maruyama and O. H. Petersen, *Nature (London)*, 1982, **300**, 61.
192. A. Marty, M. G. Evans, Y. P. Tan and A. Trautmann, *J. Exp. Biol.*, 1986, **124**, 15.
193. T. Iijima, H. Irisawa and M. Kameyama, *J. Physiol. (London)*, 1985, **359**, 485.
194. J. Hescheler, M. Kameyama and W. Trautwein, *Pflügers Arch. (Eur. J. Physiol.)*, 1986, **407**, 182.
195. A. P. Roszkowski, *J. Pharmacol. Exp. Ther.*, 1961, **132**, 156.
196. G. N. Woodruff and R. J. Walker, *Eur. J. Pharmacol.*, 1971, **14**, 81.
197. R. K. Goyal and S. Rattan, *Gastroenterology*, 1978, **74**, 598.
198. A. A. Carmine and R. N. Brogden, *Drugs*, 1985, **30**, 85.
199. R. Hammer, C. P. Berrie, N. J. M. Birdsall, A. S. V. Burgen and E. C. Hulme, *Nature (London)*, 1980, **283**, 90.
200. A. J. Beld, S. van den Hoven, A. C. Wouterse and M. A. P. Zegers, *Eur. J. Pharmacol.*, 1975, **30**, 360.
201. R. Hammer and A. Giachetti, *Life Sci.*, 1982, **31**, 2991.
202. R. Hammer and A. Giachetti, *Trends Pharmacol. Sci.*, 1984, **5**, 18.
203. J. Wess, G. Lambrecht, U. Moser and E. Mutschler, *Life Sci.*, 1984, **35**, 553.
204. R. Gilbert, S. Rattan and R. K. Goyal, *J. Pharmacol. Exp. Ther.*, 1984, **230**, 284.
205. R. M. Eglen and R. L. Whiting, *J. Auton. Pharmacol.*, 1986, **5**, 323.
206. R. M. Eglen, B. A. Kenny, A. D. Michel and R. L. Whiting, *Br. J. Pharmacol.*, 1987, **90**, 693.
207. D. W. Gil and B. B. Wolfe, *J. Pharmacol. Exp. Ther.*, 1985, **232**, 608.
208. M. Eltze, S. Gönne, R. Riedel, B. Schlotke, C. Schudt and W. A. Simon, *Eur. J. Pharmacol.*, 1985, **112**, 211.
209. J. M. Garvey, M. Rossor and L. L. Iversen, *J. Neurochem.*, 1984, **43**, 299.
210. D. C. Mash and L. T. Potter, *Neuroscience*, 1986, **19**, 551.
211. R. Cortés and J. M. Palacios, *Brain Res.*, 1986, **362**, 227.
212. M. Watson, W. R. Roeske and H. I. Yamamura, *Life Sci.*, 1982, **31**, 2019.
213. M. Watson, H. I. Yamamura and W. R. Roeske, *Life Sci.*, 1983, **32**, 3001.
214. G. R. Luthin and B. B. Wolfe, *J. Pharmacol. Exp. Ther.*, 1984, **228**, 648.
215. J. K. Wamsley, D. R. Gehlert, W. R. Roeske and H. I. Yamamura, *Life Sci.*, 1984, **34**, 1395.
216. M. Watson, W. R. Roeske and H. I. Yamamura, *J. Pharmacol. Exp. Ther.*, 1986, **237**, 419.
217. S.-C. Lin, K. C. Olson, H. Okazaki and E. Richelson, *J. Neurochem.*, 1986, **46**, 274.
218. R. Cortés, A. Probst, H.-J. Tobler and J. M. Palacios, *Brain Res.*, 1986, **362**, 239.
219. D. G. Spencer, Jr., E. Horváth and J. Traber, *Brain Res.*, 1986, **380**, 59.
220. D. A. McCormick and D. A. Prince, *Proc. Natl. Acad. Sci. U.S.A.*, 1985, **82**, 6344.
221. A. Constanti and S. H. Williams, *Br. J. Pharmacol.*, 1988, **93**, 855.
222. M. Raiteri, R. Leardi and M. Marchi, *J. Pharmacol. Exp. Ther.*, 1984, **228**, 209.
223. M. Marchi and M. Raiteri, *J. Pharmacol. Exp. Ther.*, 1985, **235**, 230.
224. A. Giachetti, E. Monferini, A. Schiavone, R. Micheletti, R. Hammer and H. Ladinsky, in 'Muscarinic Receptor Subtypes in the GI Tract', ed. G. Lux and E. E. Daniel, Springer-Verlag, Berlin, 1985, p. 14.
225. N. J. Buckley and G. Burnstock, *Brain Res.*, 1986, **375**, 83.
226. R. A. North, B. E. Slack and A. Surprenant, *J. Physiol. (London)*, 1985, **368**, 435.
227. H. Kilbinger and M. Nafziger, *Naunyn-Schmiedeberg's Arch. Pharmacol.*, 1985, **328**, 304.
228. M. Feldman, *Gastroenterology*, 1984, **86**, 361.
229. F. Pagani, A. Schiavone, E. Monferini, R. Hammer and A. Giachetti, *Trends Pharmacol. Sci.*, 1984, **5**, Suppl., 66.
230. J. W. Black and N. P. Shankley, *Br. J. Pharmacol.*, 1985, **86**, 601.
231. J. W. Black and N. P. Shankley, *Br. J. Pharmacol.*, 1986, **88**, 291.
232. M. Watson, W. R. Roeske, P. C. Johnson and H. I. Yamamura, *Brain Res.*, 1984, **290**, 179.
233. E. Giraldo, E. Monferini and R. Hammer, *Arzneim.-Forsch.*, 1985, **35** (I), 325.

234. D. A. Brown, A. Forward and S. Marsh, *Br. J. Pharmacol.*, 1980, **71**, 362.
235. N. R. Newberry, T. Priestley and G. N. Woodruff, *Eur. J. Pharmacol.*, 1985, **116**, 191.
236. M. Watson, T. W. Vickroy, W. R. Roeske and H. I. Yamamura, *Trends Pharmacol. Sci.*, 1984, **5**, Suppl., 9.
237. T. L. Smith and H. I. Yamamura, *Biochem. Biophys. Res. Commun.*, 1985, **130**, 282.
238. S. Lazareno, D. A. Kendall and S. R. Nahorski, *Neuropharmacology*, 1985, **24**, 593.
239. S. K. Fisher and R. T. Bartus, *J. Neurochem.*, 1985, **45**, 1085.
240. J. H. Brown, D. Goldstein and S. Brown Masters, *Mol. Pharmacol.*, 1985, **27**, 525.
241. A. Pfeiffer, G. Paumgartner and A. Herz, *FEBS Lett.*, 1986, **204**, 352.
242. M. McKinney, S. Stenstrom and E. Richelson, *Mol. Pharmacol.*, 1985, **27**, 223.
243. G. Lambrecht, E. Mutschler, U. Moser, J. Riotte, M. Wagner, J. Wess, G. Gmelin, R. Tacke and H. Zilch, in 'International Symposium on Muscarinic Cholinergic Mechanisms', ed. S. Cohen and M. Sokolovsky, Freund, London, 1987, p. 245.
244. E. Mutschler, U. Moser, J. Wess and G. Lambrecht, *Prog. Pharmacol. Clin. Pharmacol.*, 1989, **7** (1), 13.
245. E. Mutschler, G. Gmelin, U. Moser, J. Wess and G. Lambrecht, in 'Pharmacology', ed. M. J. Rand and C. Raper, International Congress Series No. 750, Elsevier, Amsterdam, 1987, p. 67.
246. T. I. Bonner, N. J. Buckley, A. C. Young and M. R. Brann, *Science (Washington, D.C.)*, 1987, **237**, 527.
247. G. Lambrecht, U. Moser, M. Wagner, J. Wess, G. Gmelin, K. Raseiner, C. Strohmann, R. Tacke and E. Mutschler, *Trends Pharmacol. Sci.*, 1988, **9**, Suppl., 82.
248. T. M. Egan and R. A. North, *Br. J. Pharmacol.*, 1985, **85**, 733.
249. A. Constanti and J. A. Sim, *Br. J. Pharmacol.*, 1987, **90**, 3.
250. E. M. Meyer and D. H. Otero, *J. Neurosci.*, 1985, **5**, 1202.
251. M. K. James and L. X. Cubeddu, *J. Pharmacol. Exp. Ther.*, 1987, **240**, 203.
252. F. Mitchelson, *Trends Pharmacol. Sci.*, 1984, **5**, 12.
253. H. Fuder, D. Rink and E. Muscholl, *Naunyn-Schmiedeberg's Arch. Pharmacol.*, 1982, **318**, 210.
254. H. Fuder, *Scand. J. Gastroenterol.*, 1982, **17**, Suppl. 72, 79.
255. L. K. Choo, F. Mitchelson and Y. M. Vong, *Br. J. Pharmacol.*, 1986, **87**, 733.
256. S. Halim, H. Kilbinger and I. Wessler, *Scand. J. Gastroenterol.*, 1982, **17**, Suppl. 72, 87.
257. H. Kilbinger, S. Halim, G. Lambrecht, W. Weiler and I. Wessler, *Eur. J. Pharmacol.*, 1984, **103**, 313.
258. A. Surprenant, *Trends Pharmacol. Sci.*, 1986, **7**, Suppl., 23.
259. R. B. Barlow, K. J. Berry, P. A. M. Glenton, N. M. Nikolaou and K. S. Soh, *Br. J. Pharmacol.*, 1976, **58**, 613.
260. R. B. Barlow and M. K. Shepherd, *Br. J. Pharmacol.*, 1985, **85**, 427.
261. R. U. Clague, R. M. Eglen, A. C. Strachan and R. L. Whiting, *Br. J. Pharmacol.*, 1985, **86**, 163.
262. E. Mutschler and G. Lambrecht, *Trends Pharmacol. Sci.*, 1984, **5**, Suppl., 39.
263. G. Lambrecht and E. Mutschler, in 'Muscarinic Receptor Subtypes in the GI Tract', ed. G. Lux and E. E. Daniel, Springer-Verlag, Berlin, 1985, p. 20.
264. H. Fuder, H. Kilbinger and H. Müller, *Eur. J. Pharmacol.*, 1985, **113**, 125.
265. D. S. Louie and C. Owyang, *Am. J. Physiol.*, 1986, **251**, G275.
266. M. Waelbroeck, J. Camus, M. Tastenoy and J. Christophe, *FEBS Lett.*, 1988, **226**, 287.
267. L. Nilvebrant and B. Sparf, *Eur. J. Pharmacol.*, 1988, **151**, 83.
268. A. F. Roffel, W. G. in't Hout, R. A. de Zeeuw and J. Zaagsma, *Naunyn-Schmiedeberg's Arch. Pharmacol.*, 1987, **335**, 593.
269. E. Giraldo, M. A. Viganò, R. Hammer and H. Ladinsky, *Mol. Pharmacol.*, 1988, **33**, 617.
270. P. R. Saxena and I. L. Bonta, *Eur. J. Pharmacol.*, 1970, **11**, 332.
271. A. L. Clark and F. Mitchelson, *Br. J. Pharmacol.*, 1976, **58**, 323.
272. J. M. Stockton, N. J. M. Birdsall, A. S. V. Burgen and E. C. Hulme, *Mol. Pharmacol.*, 1983, **23**, 551.
273. J. Nedoma, N. A. Dorofeeva, S. Tuček, S. A. Shelkovnikov and A. F. Danilov, *Naunyn-Schmiedeberg's Arch. Pharmacol.*, 1985, **329**, 176.
274. J. Nedoma, S. Tuček, A. F. Danilov and S. A. Shelkovnikov, *J. Pharmacol. Exp. Ther.*, 1986, **236**, 219.
275. R. Hammer, E. Giraldo, G. B. Schiavi, E. Monferini and H. Ladinsky, *Life Sci.*, 1986, **38**, 1653.
276. A. Giachetti, R. Micheletti and E. Montagna, *Life Sci.*, 1986, **38**, 1663.
277. R. Micheletti, E. Montagna and A. Giachetti, *J. Pharmacol. Exp. Ther.*, 1987, **241**, 628.
278. S. A. H. Gilani and L. B. Cobbin, *Naunyn-Schmiedeberg's Arch. Pharmacol.*, 1986, **332**, 16.
279. C. Melchiorre, A. Cassinelli and W. Quaglia, *J. Med. Chem.*, 1987, **30**, 201.
280. W. Quaglia, A. Cassinelli and C. Melchiorre, in 'International Symposium on Muscarinic Cholinergic Mechanisms', ed. S. Cohen and M. Sokolovsky, Freund, London, 1987, p. 302.
281. C. Melchiorre, P. Angeli, G. Lambrecht, E. Mutschler, M. T. Picchio and J. Wess, *Eur. J. Pharmacol.*, 1987, **144**, 117.
282. J. Wess, G. Lambrecht, E. Mutschler, C. Melchiorre and P. Angeli, *Eur. J. Pharmacol.*, 1987, **142**, 475.
283. A. D. Michel and R. L. Whiting, *Eur. J. Pharmacol.*, 1988, **145**, 61.
284. N. J. M. Birdsall and E. C. Hulme, *Trends Pharmacol Sci.*, 1983, **4**, 459.
285. N. J. M. Birdsall, C. A. M. Curtis, P. Eveleigh, E. C. Hulme, E. K. Pedder, D. Poyner, J. M. Stockton and M. Wheatley, in 'Cellular and Molecular Basis of Cholinergic Function', ed. M. J. Dowdall and J. N. Hawthorne, Horwood, Chichester, 1987, p. 46.
286. H. N. Doods, M.-J. Mathy, D. Davidesko, K. J. van Charldorp, A. de Jonge and P. A. van Zwieten, *J. Pharmacol. Exp. Ther.*, 1987, **242**, 257.
287. E. Giraldo, R. Hammer and H. Ladinsky, *Life Sci.*, 1987, **40**, 833.
288. H. N. Doods, H. D. Batink, K. J. van Charldorp, D. Davidesko, A. de Jonge and P. A. van Zwieten, in 'International Symposium on Muscarinic Cholinergic Mechanisms', ed. S. Cohen and M. Sokolovsky, Freund, London, 1987, p. 109.
289. F. J. Ehlert, W. R. Roeske and H. I. Yamamura, *Trends Neurosci.*, 1982, **5**, 336.
290. M. Sokolovsky, *Int. Rev. Neurobiol.*, 1984, **25**, 139.
291. N. J. M. Birdsall and E. C. Hulme, *J. Neurochem.*, 1976, **27**, 7.
292. N. J. M. Birdsall, E. C. Hulme and A. S. V. Burgen, *Proc. R. Soc. London, Ser. B*, 1980, **207**, 1.
293. J. F. Rodrigues de Miranda, H. M. E. Scheres, H. J. M. Salden, A. J. Beld, A. B. M. Klaasen and W. Kuijpers, *Eur. J. Pharmacol.*, 1985, **113**, 441.
294. T. Buhl, J. F. Rodrigues de Miranda, A. J. Beld, G. Lambrecht and E. Mutschler, *Eur. J. Pharmacol.*, 1987, **140**, 221.

295. F. J. Ehlert, *Mol. Pharmacol.*, 1985, **28**, 410.
296. E. C. Hulme, N. J. M. Birdsall, M. Wheatley, C. Curtis, E. K. Pedder, D. Poyner, J. M. Stockton and P. Eveleigh, *Postgrad. Med. J.*, 1987, **63**, Suppl. 1, 5.
297. K. Haga, T. Haga and A. Ichiyama, *J. Biol. Chem.*, 1986, **261**, 10 133.
298. F. J. Ehlert and D. J. Jenden, *Mol. Pharmacol.*, 1985, **28**, 107.
299. J. Christophe, P. de Neef, P. Robberecht and M. Waelbroeck, *Br. J. Pharmacol.*, 1986, **88**, 63.
300. M. Watson, T. W. Vickroy, W. R. Roeske and H. I. Yamamura, *Prog. Neuro-Psychopharmacol. Biol. Psychiatry*, 1985, **9**, 569.
301. K. J. Kellar, A. M. Martino, D. P. Hall, Jr., R. D. Schwartz and R. L. Taylor, *J. Neurosci.*, 1985, **5**, 1577.
302. H. I. Yamamura, T. W. Vickroy, D. R. Gehlert, J. K. Wamsley and W. R. Roeske, *Brain Res.*, 1985, **325**, 340.
303. W. S. Messer, Jr. and W. Hoss, *Brain Res.*, 1987, **407**, 27.
304. K.-P. Ruess and M. Liefländer, *Biochem. Biophys. Res. Commun.*, 1979, **88**, 627.
305. N. J. M. Birdsall, A. S. V. Burgen and E. C. Hulme, *Br. J. Pharmacol.*, 1979, **66**, 337.
306. J. C. Venter, *J. Biol. Chem.*, 1983, **258**, 4842.
307. C. Cremo and M. I. Schimerlik, *Biochemistry*, 1984, **23**, 3494.
308. S. Avissar, G. Amitai and M. Sokolovsky, *Proc. Natl. Acad. Sci. U.S.A.*, 1983, **80**, 156.
309. S. R. Hootman, T. M. Picado-Leonard and D. B. Burnham, *J. Biol. Chem.*, 1985, **260**, 4186.
310. H. K. Dadi, D. Batteiger, M. Keen and R. J. Morris, *J. Neurochem.*, 1986, **47**, 1700.
311. P. M. Laduron and B. Ilien, *Biochem. Pharmacol.*, 1982, **31**, 2145.
312. O. Shirakawa, T. Kuno and C. Tanaka, *Biochem. Biophys. Res. Commun.*, 1983, **115**, 814.
313. G. S. Herron and M. I. Schimerlik, *J. Neurochem.*, 1983, **41**, 1414.
314. J. J. Rauh, M. P. Lambert, N. J. Cho, H. Chin and W. L. Klein, *J. Neurochem.*, 1986, **46**, 23.
315. C. André, J. P. De Backer, J. C. Guillet, P. Vanderheyden, G. Vauquelin and A. D. Strosberg, *EMBO J.*, 1983, **2**, 499.
316. K. Haga and T. Haga, *J. Biol. Chem.*, 1985, **260**, 7927.
317. K. Haga and T. Haga, *J. Biol. Chem.*, 1983, **258**, 13 575.
318. G. L. Peterson, G. S. Herron, M. Yamaki, D. S. Fullerton and M. I. Schimerlik, *Proc. Natl. Acad. Sci. U.S.A.*, 1984, **81**, 4993.
319. G. L. Peterson, L. C. Rosenbaum, D. J. Broderick and M. I. Schimerlik, *Biochemistry*, 1986, **25**, 3189.
320. T. Kubo, K. Fukuda, A. Mikami, A. Maeda, H. Takahashi, M. Mishina, T. Haga, K. Haga, A. Ichiyama, K. Kangawa, M. Kojima, H. Matsuo, T. Hirose and S. Numa, *Nature (London)*, 1986, **323**, 411.
321. T. Kubo, A. Maeda, K. Sugimoto, I. Akiba, A. Mikami, H. Takahashi, T. Haga, K. Haga, A. Ichiyama, K. Kangawa, H. Matsuo, T. Hirose and S. Numa, *FEBS Lett.*, 1986, **209**, 367.
322. E. G. Peralta, J. W. Winslow, G. L. Peterson, D. H. Smith, A. Ashkenazi, J. Ramachandran, M. I. Schimerlik and D. J. Capon, *Science (Washington, D.C.)*, 1987, **236**, 600.
323. E. C. Hulme, M. Wheatley, C. Curtis and N. J. M. Birdsall, in 'International Symposium on Muscarinic Cholinergic Mechanisms', ed. S. Cohen and M. Sokolovsky, Freund, London, 1987, p. 192.
324. K. Fukuda, T. Kubo, I. Akiba, A. Maeda, M. Mishina and S. Numa, *Nature (London)*, 1987, **327**, 623.
325. B. Jensen, 'Aspects of the Molecular Structure of Acetylcholine and of Related Compounds', Fadl's Forlag, Copenhagen, 1984.
326. E. D. Bergmann and B. Pullman, 'Molecular and Quantum Pharmacology', Reidel, Dordrecht, 1974.
327. A. F. Casy, *Prog. Med. Chem.*, 1975, **11**, 1.
328. D. J. Triggle, in 'Chemical Pharmacology of the Synapse', ed. D. J. Triggle and C. R. Triggle, Academic Press, London, 1976, p. 291.
329. A. J. Hopfinger, 'Intermolecular Interactions and Biomolecular Organization', Wiley, New York, 1977.
330. A. F. Casy, 'PMR Spectroscopy in Medicinal and Biological Chemistry', Academic Press, London, 1971.
331. J. G. Cannon, in 'Burger's Medicinal Chemistry', 4th edn., ed. M. E. Wolff, Wiley, New York, 1981, vol. 3, p. 339.
332. G. Lambrecht and E. Mutschler, in 'Medicinal Chemistry Advances', ed. F. G. De Las Heras and S. Vega, Pergamon Press, Oxford, 1981, p. 117.
333. G. Lambrecht and E. Mutschler, in 'Innovative Approaches in Drug Research', ed. A. F. Harms, Elsevier, Amsterdam, 1986, p. 353.
334. E. Mutschler and G. Lambrecht, in 'Stereochemistry and Biological Activity of Drugs', ed. E. J. Ariens, W. Soudijn and P. B. M. W. M. Timmermans, Blackwell Scientific, Oxford, 1983, p. 63.
335. B. Pullman, Ph. Courrière and J. L. Coubeils, *Mol. Pharmacol.*, 1971, **7**, 397.
336. J. Langlet, P. Claverie, B. Pullman, D. Piazzola and J. P. Daudey, *Theor. Chim. Acta*, 1977, **46**, 105.
337. A. Pullman and G. N. J. Port, *Theor. Chim. Acta*, 1973, **32**, 77.
338. D. Lichtenberg, P. A. Kroon and S. J. Chan, *J. Am. Chem. Soc.*, 1974, **96**, 5934.
339. Y. Terui, M. Ueyama, S. Satoh and K. Tori, *Tetrahedron*, 1974, **30**, 1465.
340. A. Makriyannis, J. M. Theard and H. G. Mautner, *Biochem. Pharmacol.*, 1979, **28**, 1911.
341. P. Partington, J. Feeney and A. S. V. Burgen, *Mol. Pharmacol.*, 1972, **8**, 269.
342. D. Aslanian, *Life Sci.*, 1983, **32**, 2809.
343. H. Weinstein, S. Maayani, S. Srebrenik, S. Cohen and M. Sokolovsky, *Mol. Pharmacol.*, 1975, **11**, 671.
344. J. A. Waters, C. E. Spivak, M. Hermsmeier, J. S. Yadav, R. F. Liang and T. M. Gund, *J. Med. Chem.*, 1988, **31**, 545.
345. D. L. Beveridge and R. J. Radna, *J. Am. Chem. Soc.*, 1971, **93**, 3759.
346. D. Ajò, M. Bossa, A. Damiani, R. Fidenzi, S. Gigli, L. Lanzi and A. Lapiccirella, *J. Theor. Biol.*, 1972, **34**, 15.
347. R. W. Brimblecombe, 'Drug Actions on Cholinergic Systems', Macmillan, London, 1974, p. 43.
348. G. Lambrecht, *Pharm. Ztg.*, 1975, **120**, 1063.
349. G. Lambrecht, *Pharm. Ztg.*, 1975, **120**, 1411.
350. G. Lambrecht, *Arzneim.-Forsch.*, 1981, **31**, 634.
351. C. E. Spivak, J. Waters, B. Witkop and E. X. Albuquerque, *Mol. Pharmacol.*, 1983, **23**, 337.
352. R. B. Barlow, in 'Tobacco Alkaloids and Related Compounds', ed. U. S. von Euler, Pergamon Press, Oxford, 1965, p. 277.
353. R. B. Barlow and J. T. Hamilton, *Br. J. Pharmacol.*, 1965, **25**, 206.
354. J. W. Sloan, G. D. Todd and W. R. Martin, *Pharmacol. Biochem. Behav.*, 1984, **20**, 899.
355. S. Wonnacott, *J. Neurochem.*, 1986, **47**, 1706.

356. D. J. Triggle, 'Neurotransmitter–Receptor Interactions', Academic Press, London, 1971, p. 209.
357. W. E. Ormerod, *Br. J. Pharmacol.*, 1956, **11**, 267.
358. K. A. Scott and H. G. Mautner, *Biochem. Pharmacol.*, 1964, **13**, 907.
359. P. Hey, *Br. J. Pharmacol.*, 1952, **7**, 117.
360. W. C. Holland, in 'Proceedings of the International Pharmacology Meeting', ed. E. J. Ariens, Pergamon Press, Oxford, 1966, vol. 7, p. 295.
361. R. B. Barlow and F. M. Franks, *Br. J. Pharmacol.*, 1973, **49**, 480.
362. F. Gualtieri, P. Angeli, L. Brasili, M. Giannella and M. Pigini, in 'Proceedings of the VIIIth International Symposium on Medicinal Chemistry', ed. R. Dahlbom and J. L. G. Nilsson, Swedish Pharmaceutical Press, Stockholm, 1985, p. 404.
363. R. F. Timoney, *Int. J. Pharm.*, 1983, **15**, 223.
364. C. E. Spivak, B. Witkop and E. X. Albuquerque, *Mol. Pharmacol.*, 1980, **18**, 384.
365. R. B. Barlow and L. J. McLeod, *Br. J. Pharmacol.*, 1969, **35**, 161.
366. C. E. Spivak, T. M. Gund, R. F. Liang and J. A. Waters, *Eur. J. Pharmacol.*, 1986, **120**, 127.
367. R. Jannasch, *Pharmazie*, 1967, **22**, 198.
368. V. Trčka, in 'Pharmacology of Ganglionic Transmission', 'Handbook of Experimental Pharmacology', ed. D. A. Kharkevich, Springer-Verlag, Berlin, 1980, vol. 53, p. 124.
369. V. Trčka, in 'Pharmacology of Gangalionic Transmission', 'Handbook of Experimental Pharmacology', ed. D. A. Kharkevich, Springer-Verlag, Berlin, 1980, vol. 53, p. 156.
370. R. B. Barlow and A. Zoller, *Br. J. Pharmacol.*, 1964, **23**, 131.
371. D. M. Brown and B. H. Turner, *J. Pharm. Pharmacol.*, 1959, **11**, Suppl., 95.
372. D. Bovet, *Ann. N.Y. Acad. Sci.*, 1951, **54**, 407.
373. J. B. Stenlake, in 'Burger's Medicinal Chemistry', 4th edn., ed. M. E. Wolff, Wiley, New York, 1981, vol. 3, p. 431.
374. P. Taylor, in 'Goodman and Gilman's: The Pharmacological Basis of Therapeutics', 7th edn., ed. A. G. Gilman, L. S. Goodman, T. W. Rall and F. Murad, Macmillan, New York, 1985, p. 222.
375. D. A. Kharkevich, *Trends Pharmacol. Sci.*, 1981, **2**, 218.
376. J. B. Stenlake, *Prog. Med. Chem.*, 1963, **3**, 1.
377. J. B. Stenlake, W. D. Williams, N. C. Dhar and I. G. Marshall, *Eur. J. Med. Chem.*, 1974, **9**, 233.
378. P. W. Erhardt and T. O. Soine, *J. Pharm. Sci.*, 1975, **64**, 53.
379. A. A. Genenah, T. O. Soine and N. A. Shaath, *J. Pharm. Sci.*, 1975, **64**, 62.
380. J. B. Stenlake, *Prog. Med. Chem.*, 1979, **16**, 257.
381. I. Hanin, D. J. Jenden and A. K. Cho, *Mol. Pharmacol.*, 1966, **2**, 352.
382. A. K. Cho, D. J. Jenden and S. I. Lamb, *J. Med. Chem.*, 1972, **15**, 391.
383. F. J. Ehlert and D. J. Jenden, *Mol. Pharmacol.*, 1984, **25**, 46.
384. H. R. Ing, *Science (Washington, D.C.)*, 1949, **109**, 264.
385. D. J. Triggle, in 'CRC Handbook of Stereoisomers: Drugs in Psychopharmacology', ed. D. F. Smith, CRC Press, Boca Raton, FL, 1984, p. 31.
386. H.-D. Höltje, B. Jensen and G. Lambrecht, in 'Recent Advances in Receptor Chemistry', ed. F. Gualtieri, M. Giannella and C. Melchiorre, Elsevier, Amsterdam, 1979, p. 281.
387. P. Pratesi, L. Villa, V. Ferri, C. De Micheli, E. Grana, C. Silipo and A. Vittoria, in 'Highlights in Receptor Chemistry', ed. C. Melchiorre and M. Giannella, Elsevier, Amsterdam, 1984, p. 225.
388. P. T. Henderson, E. J. Ariens, B. W. J. Ellenbroek and A. M. Simonis, *J. Pharm. Pharmacol.*, 1968, **20**, 26.
389. L. L. Darko and J. G. Cannon, *J. Med. Chem.*, 1965, **8**, 841.
390. R. B. Barlow, J. B. Bremner and K. S. Soh, *Br. J. Pharmacol.*, 1978, **62**, 39.
391. B. Jensen and G. Lambrecht, *Naunyn-Schmiedeberg's Arch. Pharmacol.*, 1979, **307**, Suppl., R54.
392. H.-D. Höltje, B. Jensen and G. Lambrecht, *Eur. J. Med. Chem.*, 1978, **13**, 453.
393. G. Lambrecht, *Experientia*, 1976, **32**, 365.
394. K. Jim, G. T. Bolger, D. J. Triggle and G. Lambrecht, *Can. J. Physiol. Pharmacol.*, 1982, **60**, 1707.
395. G. Lambrecht, *Eur. J. Med. Chem.*, 1976, **11**, 461.
396. R. B. Barlow and R. Kitchen, *Br. J. Pharmacol.*, 1982, **77**, 549.
397. G. Lambrecht, *Arzneim.-Forsch.*, 1982, **32**, 130.
398. R. B. Barlow and A. F. Casy, *Mol. Pharmacol.*, 1975, **11**, 690.
399. B. Ringdahl, F. J. Ehlert and D. J. Jenden, *Mol. Pharmacol.*, 1982, **21**, 594.
400. H. Gloge, H. Lüllmann and E. Mutschler, *Br. J. Pharmacol.*, 1966, **27**, 185.
401. K. Hultzsch, U. Moser, W. Back and E. Mutschler, *Arzneim.-Forsch.*, 1971, **21**, 1979.
402. G. Lambrecht and E. Mutschler, *Arzneim.-Forsch.*, 1973, **23**, 1427.
403. M. Wolf-Pflugmann, G. Lambrecht, J. Wess and E. Mutschler, *Arzneim.-Forsch.*, 1988, 1989, **39**, 539.
404. U. Moser, G. Lambrecht, E. Mutschler and J. Sombroek, *Arch. Pharm. (Weinheim, Ger.)*, 1983, **316**, 670.
405. E. Mutschler, H.-D. Höltje, G. Lambrecht and U. Moser, *Arzneim.-Forsch.*, 1983, **33**, 806.
406. H.-D. Höltje, G. Lambrecht, U. Moser and E. Mutschler, *Arzneim.-Forsch.*, 1983, **33**, 190.
407. E. Mutschler and K. Hultzsch, *Arzneim.-Forsch.*, 1973, **23**, 732.
408. U. Moser, G. Lambrecht, M. Wagner, J. Wess and E. Mutschler, *Br. J. Pharmacol.*, 1988, 1989, **96**, 319.
409. P. Sauerberg, J.-J. Larsen, E. Falch and P. Krogsgaard-Larsen, *J. Med. Chem.*, 1986, **29**, 1004.
410. P. Sauerberg, B. Fjalland, J.-J. Larsen, T. Bach-Lauritsen, E. Falch and P. Krogsgaard-Larsen, *Eur. J. Pharmacol.*, 1986, **130**, 125.
411. P. Krogsgaard-Larsen, E. Falch, P. Sauerberg, S. B. Freedman, H. L. Lembol and E. Meier, *Trends Pharmacol. Sci.*, 1988, **9**, Suppl., 69.
412. P. G. Waser, *Pharmacol. Rev.*, 1961, **13**, 465.
413. K. G. R. Sundelin, R. A. Wiley, R. A. Givens and D. R. Rademacher, *J. Med. Chem.*, 1973, **16**, 235.
414. D. J. Triggle and B. Belleau, *Can. J. Chem.*, 1962, **40**, 1201.
415. J. G. R. Elferink and C. A. Salemink, *Arzneim.-Forsch.*, 1975, **25**, 1702.
416. P. Angeli, L. Brasili, M. Giannella, F. Gualtieri and M. Pigini, *Br. J. Pharmacol.*, 1985, **85**, 783.
417. K.-J. Chang and D. J. Triggle, *J. Med. Chem.*, 1973, **16**, 718.
418. B. Ringdahl and D. J. Jenden, *Life Sci.*, 1983, **32**, 2401.

419. M. Martin-Smith, G. A. Smail and J. B. Stenlake, *J. Pharm. Pharmacol.*, 1967, **19**, 561.
420. A. K. Cho, W. L. Haslett and D. J. Jenden, *J. Pharmacol. Exp. Ther.*, 1962, **138**, 249.
421. B. Ringdahl, in 'Proceedings of the VIIIth International Symposium on Medicinal Chemistry', ed. R. Dahlbom and J. L. G. Nilsson, Swedish Pharmaceutical Press, Stockholm, 1985, p. 391.
422. B. Ringdahl and D. J. Jenden, *Mol. Pharmacol.*, 1983, **23**, 17.
423. B. Ringdahl, *Br. J. Pharmacol.*, 1984, **82**, 269.
424. R. Amstutz, A. Closse and G. Gmelin, *Helv. Chim. Acta*, 1987, **70**, 2232.
425. B. Resul, B. Ringdahl, R. Dahlbom and D. J. Jenden, *Eur. J. Pharmacol.*, 1983, **87**, 387.
426. B. Ringdahl, *J. Pharmacol. Exp. Ther.*, 1985, **232**, 67.
427. A. P. Roszkowski and J. Yelnosky, *J. Pharmacol. Exp. Ther.*, 1967, **156**, 238.
428. W. L. Nelson, D. S. Freeman, P. D. Wilkinson and F. F. Vincenzi, *J. Med. Chem.*, 1973, **16**, 506.
429. W. L. Nelson, D. S. Freeman and F. F. Vincenzi, *J. Med. Chem.*, 1976, **19**, 153.
430. G. Lambrecht, U. Moser, E. Mutschler, G. Walther and J. Wess, *J. Med. Chem.*, 1986, **29**, 1309.
431. J. Wess, G. Lambrecht, U. Moser and E. Mutschler, *Eur. J. Pharmacol.*, 1987, **134**, 61.
432. D. A. Robinson, J. G. Taylor and J. M. Young, *Br. J. Pharmacol.*, 1975, **53**, 363.
433. W. S. Willcockson, M. Kahlid, A. E. Ahmed and G. R. Hillman, *J. Pharmacol. Exp. Ther.*, 1981, **218**, 330.
434. P. M. Hudgins and J. F. Stubbins, *J. Pharm. Sci.*, 1975, **64**, 1419.
435. F. J. Ehlert, D. J. Jenden and B. Ringdahl, *Life Sci.*, 1984, **34**, 985.
436. B. Ringdahl and D. J. Jenden, *J. Med. Chem.*, 1987, **30**, 852.
437. B. Ringdahl and D. J. Jenden, *J. Pharmacol. Exp. Ther.*, 1987, **240**, 370.
438. B. V. Rama Sastry, in 'Burger's Medicinal Chemistry', 4th edn., ed. M. E. Wolff, Wiley, New York, 1981, vol. 3, p. 361.
439. T. D. Inch and R. W. Brimblecombe, *Int. Rev. Neurobiol.*, 1974, **14**, 67.
440. R. B. Barlow and J. H. Tubby, *Br. J. Pharmacol.*, 1974, **51**, 95.
441. R. B. Barlow, *J. Pharm. Pharmacol.*, 1971, **23**, 90.
442. R. Tacke, H. Linoh, D. Schomburg, L. Ernst, U. Moser, E. Mutschler and G. Lambrecht, *Liebigs Ann. Chem.*, 1986, 242.
443. W. Soudijn, I. van Wijngaarden and E. J. Ariens, *Eur. J. Pharmacol.*, 1973, **24**, 43.
444. E. J. Ariens, *Adv. Drug Res.*, 1966, **3**, 325.
445. K. J. Chang, R. C. Deth and D. J. Triggle, *J. Med. Chem.*, 1972, **15**, 243.
446. B. Cappello, C. Silipo, A. Vittoria and P. Pratesi, *Farmaco, Ed. Sci.*, 1984, **39**, 991.
447. L. B. Kier and L. H. Hall, *J. Pharm. Sci.*, 1978, **67**, 1408.
448. C. Hansch, P. P. Maloney, T. Fujita and R. M. Muir, *Nature (London)*, 1962, **194**, 178.
449. E. J. Lien, E. J. Ariens and A. J. Beld, *Eur. J. Pharmacol.*, 1976, **35**, 245.
450. F. B. Abramson, R. B. Barlow, F. M. Franks and J. D. M. Pearson, *Br. J. Pharmacol.*, 1974, **51**, 81.
451. G. Lambrecht, U. Moser and E. Mutschler, *Eur. J. Med. Chem.*, 1980, **15**, 305.
452. R. B. Barlow and S. Ramtoola, *Br. J. Pharmacol.*, 1980, **71**, 31.
453. S. Cherkez, H. Yellin, Y. Kashman, B. Yaavetz and M. Sokolovsky, *Mol. Pharmacol.*, 1978, **14**, 781.
454. R. B. Barlow, F. M. Franks and J. D. M. Pearson, *J. Med. Chem.*, 1973, **16**, 439
455. R. B. Barlow and E. A. Winter, *Br. J. Pharmacol.*, 1981, **72**, 657.
456. S. Cohen and F. Haberman, *Br. J. Pharmacol.*, 1984, **83**, 807.
457. G. Lambrecht, *Arzneim.-Forsch.*, 1980, **30**, 2113.
458. G. Lambrecht, *Eur. J. Med. Chem.*, 1979, **14**, 111.
459. W. J. Rzeszotarski, R. E. Gibson, W. C. Eckelman, D. A. Simms, E. M. Jagoda, N. L. Ferreira and R. C. Reba, *J. Med. Chem.*, 1982, **25**, 1103.
460. R. E. Gibson, W. J. Rzeszotarski, W. C. Eckelman, E. M. Jagoda, D. J. Weckstein and R. C. Reba, *Biochem. Pharmacol.*, 1983, **32**, 1851.
461. R. B. Barlow and M. K. Shepherd, *Br. J. Pharmacol.*, 1986, **89**, 837.
462. B. Ringdahl, *J. Pharmacol. Exp. Ther.*, 1984, **229**, 199.
463. R. Amstutz, B. Ringdahl, B. Karlen, M. Roch and D. J. Jenden, *J. Med. Chem.*, 1985, **28**, 1760.
464. R. Tacke and U. Wannagat, *Top. Curr. Chem.*, 1979, **84**, 58.
465. E. Mutschler, U. Moser, J. Wess and G. Lambrecht, in 'Recent Advances in Receptor Chemistry', ed. C. Melchiorre and M. Giannella, Elsevier, Amsterdam, 1988, p. 195.
466. G. Lambrecht, R. Feifel, U. Moser, A. J. Aasen, M. Waelbroeck, J. Christophe and E. Mutschler, *Eur. J. Pharmacol.*, 1988, **155**, 167.
467. M. Eltze, *Eur. J. Pharmacol.*, 1988, **151**, 205.
468. M. Gil Quintero, A. Donetti, P. Limonta, A. Giachetti, G. B. Schiavi, R. Micheletti and H. Ladinsky, IXth International Symposium on Medicinal Chemistry, 1986, Berlin (West), Poster Abstract No. 204.
469. E. W. Gill and H. P. Rang, *Mol. Pharmacol.*, 1966, **2**, 284.
470. J. M. Young, R. Hiley and A. S. V. Burgen, *J. Pharm. Pharmacol.*, 1972, **24**, 950.
471. E. El-Fakahany and E. Richelson, *Mol. Pharmacol.*, 1981, **20**, 519.
472. M. R. Salem, *Int. Anesthesiol. Clin.*, 1978, **16**, 171.
473. J. W. Basta, K. Nlejadlik and V. Pallares, *Br. J. Anaesth.* 1977, **49**, 1087.
474. N. N. Durant and R. L. Katz, *Br. J. Anaesth.*, 1982, **54**, 195.
475. P. M. Ertama, *Ann. Clin. Res.*, 1982, **14**, 27.
476. G. A. Sutherland, J. B. Squire, A. J. Gibb and I. G. Marshall, *Br. J. Anaesth.*, 1983, **55**, 1119.
477. K. Thanik, W. K. Chey, A. Shak, D. Hamilton and N. Nadelson, *Arch. Intern. Med.*, 1982, **142**, 1479.
478. A. E. Finkbeiner and N. K. Bissada, *Urol. Clin. North Am.*, 1980, **7**, 3.
479. E. Hollander, R. C. Mohs and K. L. Davis, *Br. Med. Bull.*, 1986, **42**, 97.
480. W. K. Summers, L. V. Majovski, G. M. Marsh, K. Tachiki and A. Kling, *New Engl. J. Med.*, 1986, **315**, 1241.
481. W. Londong, V. Londong, A. Meierl and U. Voderholzer, *Gut*, 1987, **28**, 885.
482. N. J. Gross and M. S. Skorodin, *Am. Rev. Respir. Dis.*, 1984, **129**, 856.
483. A. M. Watanabe, in 'Cardiac Therapy', ed. B. F. Hoffman and M. R. Rosen, Nijhoff, New York, 1983, p. 95.
484. D. P. Zipes, in 'Heart Disease. A Textbook of Cardiovascular Medicine', ed. E. Braunwald, Saunders, Philadelphia, 1984, p. 683.

485. H. F. Pitschner, B. Schulte, A. Wellstein, B. Kiesow, M. Schlepper and H. Franke, *Naunyn-Schmiedeberg's Arch. Pharmacol.*, 1988, **337**, Suppl., R91.
486. N. M. Price, L. G. Schmitt, J. McGuire, J. E. Shaw and G. Trobough, *Clin. Pharmacol. Ther.*, 1981, **29**, 414.
487. M. De Amici, C. De Micheli, P. Pratesi, E. Grana, M. G. Santagostino Barbone, B. Cappello, C. Silipo and A. Vittoria, *Farmaco, Ed. Sci.*, 1987, **42**, 409.
488. P. Pratesi, L. Villa, V. Ferri, C. De Micheli, E. Grana, C. Grieco, C. Silipo and A. Vittoria, in 'Recent Advances in Receptor Chemistry', ed. F. Gualtieri, M. Giannella and C. Melchiorre, Elsevier, Amsterdam, 1979, p. 303.

12.7

Amino Acid Receptors

POVL KROGSGAARD-LARSEN

The Royal Danish School of Pharmacy, Copenhagen, Denmark

12.7.1 4-AMINOBUTANOIC ACID (GABA)

4-Aminobutanoic acid (GABA) was first identified in the mammalian central nervous system (CNS) over 30 years ago. However, it was not until the latter part of the 1960s that sufficient evidence accumulated to allow the conclusion that this amino acid serves a neurotransmitter function.

During the past decade a great deal of information has been gathered with respect to the anatomical, physiological, biochemical and behavioural characteristics of the GABA neurotransmitter system.[1-11] Moreover, GABA has been implicated in a variety of neurological and neuropsychiatric disorders.[3, 4, 6, 8, 12-14] These observations have led to the design of a variety of agents capable of specifically manipulating this system.[4, 8, 15-17] Some of these compounds, which have been developed on the basis of bioisosteric principles and modern approaches to design of enzyme inhibitors, are or have been subject to clinical exploitation.

12.7.1.1 GABA, an Inhibitory Neurotransmitter with Multiple Functions

GABA is now considered to be the major inhibitory amino acid neurotransmitter, playing a key role in the control of neuronal activity in the mammalian CNS, notably in the brain. Virtually all central neurones seem to be under inhibitory control by GABA, and it has been estimated that perhaps more than 30% of central neurones utilize GABA as a neurotransmitter.

GABA is involved in the regulation of many physiological mechanisms including the secretion of a number of hormones such as prolactin and growth hormone.[18, 19] GABA also plays a role in the control of cardiovascular functions,[20-22] and the mechanisms underlying the involvement of GABA in pain processes have been extensively studied in recent years.[23-28] These studies have included the role of GABA in anaesthesia.[29] GABA appears to play an important part in the synaptic mechanisms associated with anxiety[30, 31] and with aggressive[32] and feeding behaviour.[33]

12.7.1.2 Pathophysiological Roles of GABA

The growing interest in the pharmacology of GABA has been stimulated by the suggestion that GABA dysfunctions may play important roles in certain diseases. Analyses of brain tissue samples from sites near seizure foci in epileptic patients or in animals made epileptic have revealed severe impairments of the GABA system.[34-36] Low levels of the GABA-synthesizing enzyme (S)-glutamate decarboxylase (GAD) and the reduced GABA uptake capacity measured in different models of epilepsy probably reflect degeneration of GABA neurones.[37-40] Indirect evidence derived from numerous animal studies supports the view that impairments of GABA-mediated neurotransmission is a major factor underlying epileptic phenomena.[41]

Low levels of GABA and GAD have been measured in post mortem brain tissues from patients who died with Huntington's chorea, and neurochemical studies have disclosed abnormalities of GABA receptors in certain regions of brains of choreic patients.[13, 42, 43] Earlier circumstantial evidence for GABA dysfunctions in schizophrenia[44] has recently been supported by the demonstration of GABA receptor abnormalities in autopsied brains of chronic schizophrenics.[45] There is experimental evidence for a critical role of GABA neurones in the pathophysiology of tardive dyskinesia.[46] A GABAergic contribution to the symptoms in Parkinsonian[47, 48] and depressed[49] patients has been proposed. Remarkably low plasma GABA levels have been measured in alcoholics,[50] and accumulating evidence supports the view that ethanol has severe effects on GABA receptors.[51, 52]

These aspects clearly focus attention on the various processes and mechanisms associated with GABA-mediated neurotransmission in the CNS as potential targets for clinically useful drugs.

12.7.1.3 Biosynthesis and Metabolism

GABA is synthesized in the CNS from (S)-glutamic acid (Glu) by decarboxylation catalyzed by the pyridoxal phosphate-dependent enzyme GAD (EC 4.1.1.15). Glu is produced from the tricarboxylic acid cycle intermediate 2-oxoglutaric acid (1) by the enzymatic catalysis of a variety of transaminases or from (S)-glutamine (2; Gln) catalyzed by glutaminase (Figure 1).[3, 53-56] The rate of GABA synthesis appears to be largely governed by the activity of GAD rather than the availability of Glu.

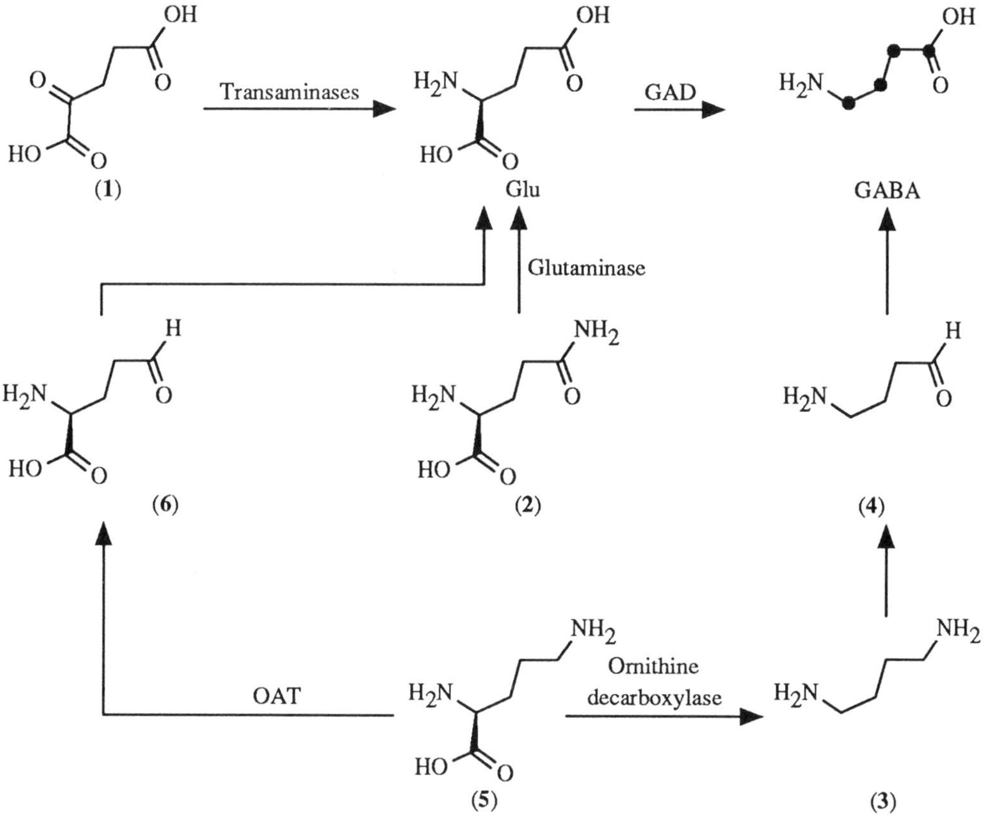

Figure 1 Outline of the biosynthesis of GABA

While Glu is considered to be the major source of GABA, the polyamine putrescine (**3**) may be an alternate source of GABA *via* 4-aminobutanal (**4**; GABA aldehyde, see Figure 1).[57, 58] In turn, ornithine (**5**) may be an important source of (**3**) and also of Glu *via* γ-glutamaldehydic acid (**6**; glutamic γ-semialdehyde). Interestingly, GABA may exert feedback inhibition on ornithine δ-aminotransferase (OAT; EC 2.6.1.13). This inhibition may indicate an important link between amino acid and carbohydrate metabolism in the brain, but its quantitative significance for GABA synthesis is as yet unknown. It appears that (**1**) and (**2**) are used more extensively than (**5**) to replenish transmitter pools of GABA.[56]

GABA is metabolized to the tricarboxylic acid intermediate succinic acid (**7**; Figure 2).[3, 55, 56] GABA aminotransferase (GABA-T; EC 2.6.1.19), a pyridoxal phosphate-dependent enzyme found in neurones and glia cells, catalyzes the formation from GABA of succinaldehydic acid (**8**; succinic acid semialdehyde), which is further metabolized to (**7**) by succinic acid semialdehyde dehydrogenase (SSD; EC 1.2.1.24). Compound (**8**) may be further reduced to 4-hydroxybutanoic acid (**9**), which may function as a neurotransmitter or neuromodulator in the CNS.[59, 60]

12.7.1.3.1 Inhibitors of biosynthesis and metabolism

As one would expect, inhibitors of GAD usually produce convulsions on systemic administration, and such compounds are useful tools in experimental pharmacology. The (*R*) and (*S*) forms of the most widely used inhibitor of GAD, 2-amino-4-pentenoic acid (**10**; allylglycine), are much more active *in vivo* than *in vitro*, reflecting the fact that the metabolite 2-oxo-4-pentenoic acid (**11**), formed by amino acid oxidase-induced decomposition of (*R*)- or (*S*)-(**10**), is the active inhibitor of GAD.[61, 62] While chelidonic acid (**12**) is one of the most potent competitive inhibitors of GAD,[63] the mechanism-based irreversible inhibitor (2*RS*,3*E*)-2-methyl-3,4-didehydroglutamic acid (**13**) appears to be the most specific GAD inactivator.[64] Although 3-mercaptopropanoic acid (**14**) is an inhibitor

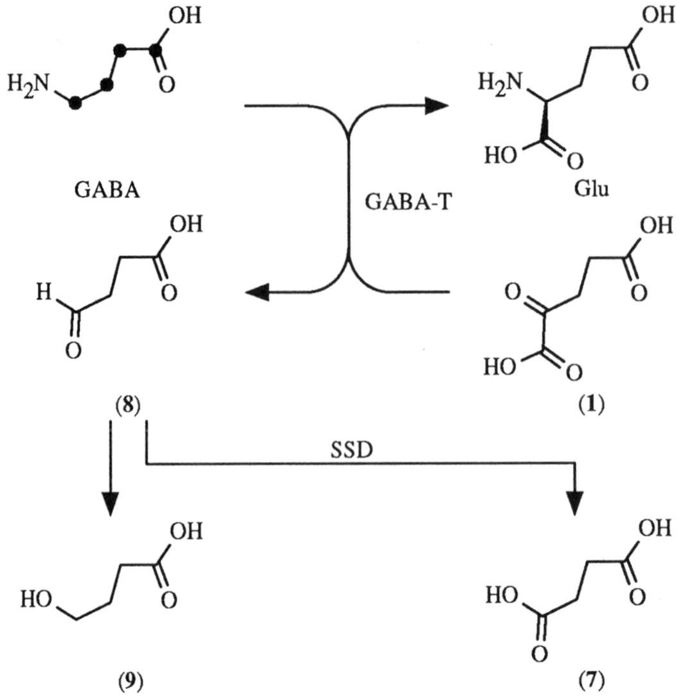

Figure 2 Outline of the metabolism of GABA

of GAD, its rapid convulsant action is likely to result from inhibition of GABA release and enhancement of the release of excitatory amino acids.[65]

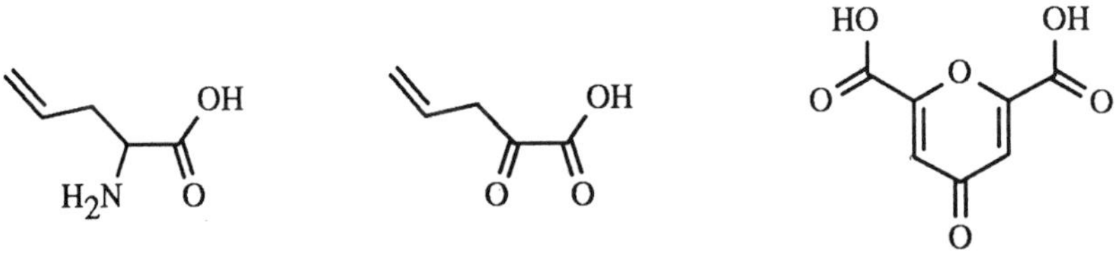

A number of analogues of GABA affect the activity of GABA-T,[66-68] including (E)-4-amino-2-butenoic acid (**15**) and (E)-4-amino-2-methyl-2-butenoic acid (**16**), which are substrates for the enzyme and are more effectively transaminated than GABA itself.[69] The (Z) form of (**15**), on the other hand, does not interact significantly with GABA-T.[69] The 2-chloromethyl analogue (**17**) of (**15**), which was designed as a mechanism-based irreversible inactivator of GABA-T, proved to be a competitive GABA-T inhibitor.[70] Methyl substituents at C-4 of (**15**) effectively prevent binding to GABA-T, (S)- and (R)-(**18**) showing no significant affinity for GABA-T.[69] Since the (S) and (R) isomers of (**18**) bind tightly to GABA-A receptors and GABA uptake mechanisms, respectively, the structural requirements for binding to the active site of GABA-T would seem to be different from those required for binding to these GABA-A synaptic mechanisms. On the other hand, the powerful GABA-A agonists 5-aminomethyl-3-hydroxyisoxazole (**19**; muscimol) and 5-aminomethyl-3-hydroxyisothiazole (**20**; thiomuscimol) bind more tightly to GABA-A than GABA itself; but the rates of transamination of these heterocyclic GABA analogues are some two orders of magnitude lower than that measured for GABA.[71,72] The (S) and (R) forms of dihydromuscimol (**21**) seem to interact with the active site of GABA-T in a similar manner, but both of these enantiomers bind less tightly than (19) or (20).[72]

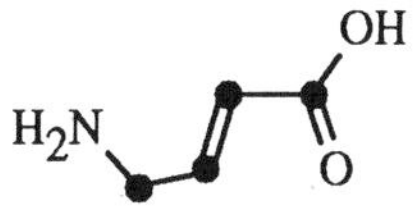

These structure–activity studies seem to suggest that GABA adopts a relatively planar conformation during its initial binding to the active site of GABA-T, and that it undergoes conformational changes during the transamination process which the heterocyclic analogues of GABA, (19) and (20), may find it difficult to mimic. The conformationally immobilized specific GABA-A agonist 4,5,6,7-tetrahydroisoxazolo[5,4-*c*]pyridin-3-ol (22; THIP), which has a secondary amino group, does not interact with GABA-T *in vitro*, as expected.[73]

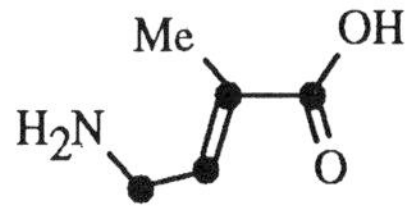

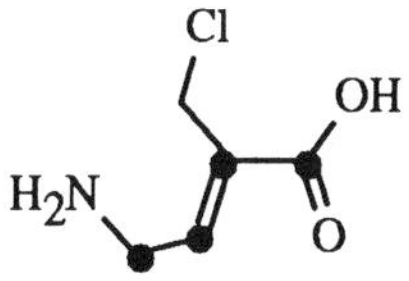

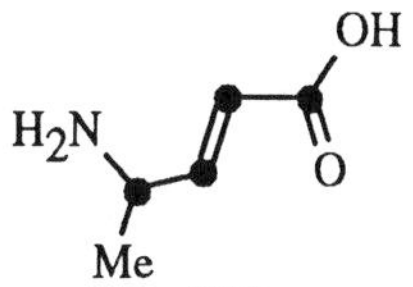

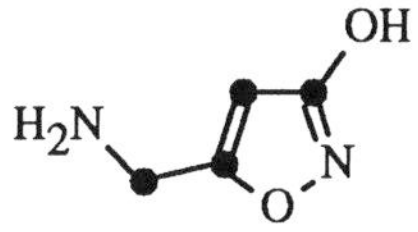

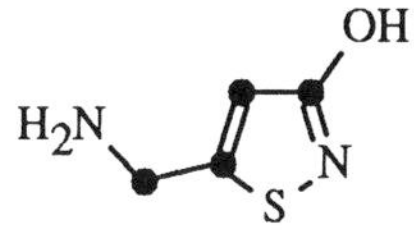

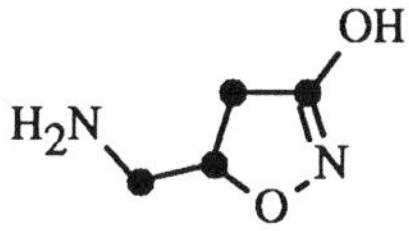

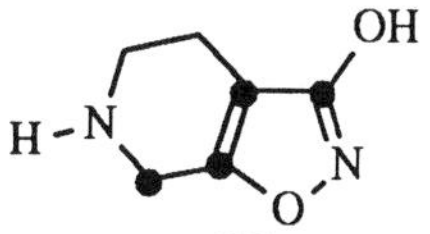

A number of mechanism-based inactivators of GABA-T have been developed and shown to inactivate the enzyme *in vitro* and *in vivo*.[66-68] These compounds are typically analogues of GABA or (15) containing appropriate functional groups at C-4 of the GABA backbone, and they are converted by GABA-T into electrophiles which react with nucleophilic groups at or near the active site of the enzyme and inactivate the enzyme irreversibly. Although GABA-T, like other pyridoxal phosphate-dependent enzymes, does not show strict stereospecificity with respect to inactivation by mechanism-based inactivators (suicide substrates),[74] such inhibitors do react with the enzyme in a stereoselective manner. Thus, the (*S*) form of the GABA-T suicide substrates 4-amino-5-hexenoic acid (23; GVG),[74] 4-amino-5-hexynoic acid (24; GAG),[75] 4-amino-5,6-heptadienoic acid (25; 4-allenyl-GABA)[76] and the 4-fluoromethyl analogue of (15), compound (26),[77] are more active as GABA-T inactivators than the respective (*R*) isomers. GVG has clinical interest as an antiepileptic agent.[78] In this regard it is interesting and fortunate that the active (*S*) isomers of GVG and GAG are actively taken up by the neuronal as well as the glial transport mechanisms, whereas the (*R*) isomers are not transported.[79]

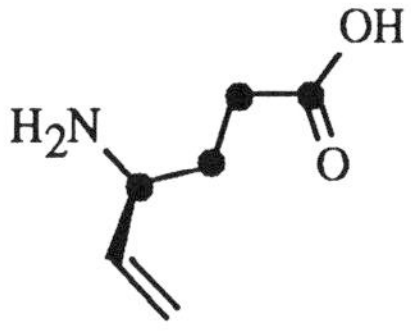

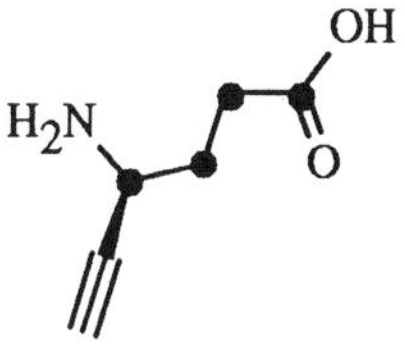

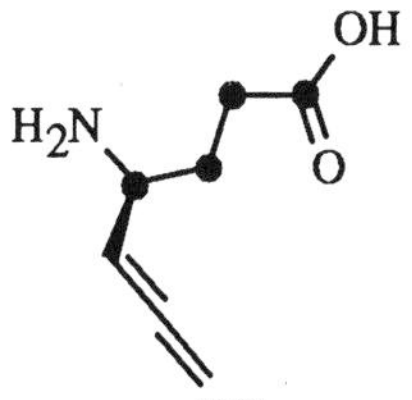

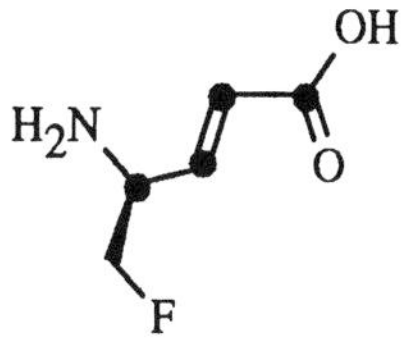

The cyclic GABA analogues gabaculine (27)[80] and isogabaculine (28)[81] are also mechanism-based inhibitors of GABA-T but, in contrast to the suicide substrates GVG (23) and GAG (24), (27) and (28) do not alkylate the enzyme. As a result of enzymatic processing by GABA-T these compounds are converted into aromatic pyridoxamine 5-phosphate adducts, which do not desorb from the active site of the enzyme. The GABA-T inhibitor 4-amino-4,5-dihydro-2-furancarboxylic acid (29)[82] probably inactivates the enzyme by a similar mechanism.

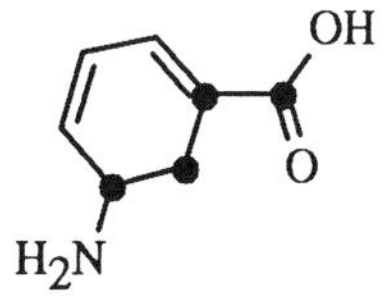

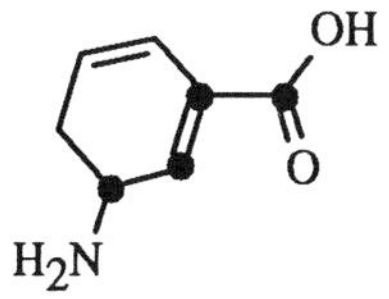

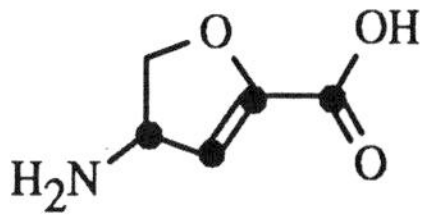

12.7.1.4 Biological *In Vivo* and *In Vitro* Test Systems

The *in vivo* and *in vitro* test systems mentioned below are of primary importance for evaluation of GABA agonists and GABA uptake inhibitors. Such compounds have been studied in a variety of other biochemical, neurochemical and pharmacological systems,[8-10] but, so far, no animal behavioural model has been shown to give responses specific for GABAergic compounds.

12.7.1.4.1 *Electrophysiological techniques*

The microelectrophoretic studies on the compounds discussed in this chapter have been performed on lumbar dorsal horn interneurones and Renshaw cells of cats anaesthetized with pentobarbitone.[83] Extracellular action potentials were recorded by means of the centre barrel of seven-barrel micropipettes. The compounds tested were administered electrophoretically from the outer barrels of the micropipettes, which contained solutions of the compounds ($100-200 \text{ mmol dm}^{-3}$, adjusted to pH 3-4) or a GABA antagonist (see Section 12.7.1.7.2). Firing of the spinal neurones was induced by electrophoretically administered (*RS*)-homocysteic acid (200 mmol dm^{-3}, adjusted to pH 7.5).

Similarly, microelectrophoretic techniques offer the most direct approach to examination of the effects of GABA uptake inhibitors on GABA synaptic mechanisms *in vivo*. The depressant effect of GABA, administered microelectrophoretically on single central neurones, can be enhanced by GABA uptake inhibitors administered simultaneously using the same technique.[84-86] Furthermore, electrophoretically administered uptake inhibitors have been shown to enhance the GABA-mediated inhibition of hippocampal neurones.[87] This technique, however, does not distinguish between inhibitors of the neuronal and glial uptake systems.

In recent years, cultures of mammalian central neurones have been used as model systems for a variety of electrophysiological studies based on voltage-clamp[88] and patch-clamp[89] techniques. These and other types of electrophysiological studies[90] have provided insight into the mechanisms underlying different GABA-mediated synaptic functions.

12.7.1.4.2 *GABA-A and GABA-B receptor binding*

There are many studies on the binding of radioactive GABA, GABA agonists and GABA antagonists.[8-10] Fractionation studies show that most GABA binding is associated with synaptic membranes, and high affinity GABA receptor sites are particularly enriched in postsynaptic densities.[15,91] Membranes prepared from rat brains are typically extensively washed, rapidly frozen at about $-70\,^{\circ}$C and kept at about $-20\,^{\circ}$C for some time before use in binding studies, and for such studies aliquots of synaptic membranes (*ca.* 1 mg of protein) are normally incubated in tricitrate buffer at pH *ca.* 7 containing the radioactive ligand at concentrations of $1-20 \text{ nmol dm}^{-3}$ and the test substance. Procedures have been developed for GABA-A receptor binding studies using radioactive forms of GABA[91-93] and the GABA agonists muscimol (**19**),[94] THIP (**22**),[95] 1,2,3,6-tetrahydro-4-pyridinecarboxylic acid (**30**; isoguvacine)[96] and 4-piperidinesulfonic acid (**31**; P4S).[97] Whereas (**22**) selectively labels low affinity GABA receptor sites,[95,98] the other GABA agonist ligands interact with both high and low affinity receptor sites (see Figure 7). In recent years cultured neurones have been used as model systems for biochemical and pharmacological studies of GABA-A receptors for other amino acid neurotransmitters.[99]

GABA 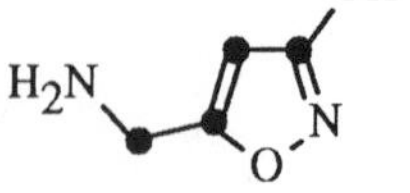   (19) 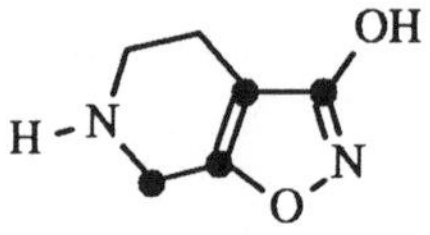   (22) 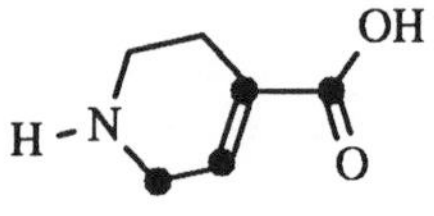   (30) 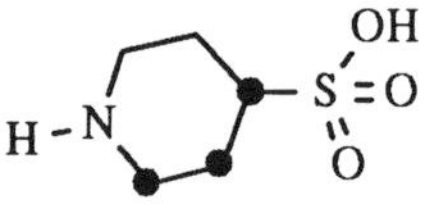   (31)

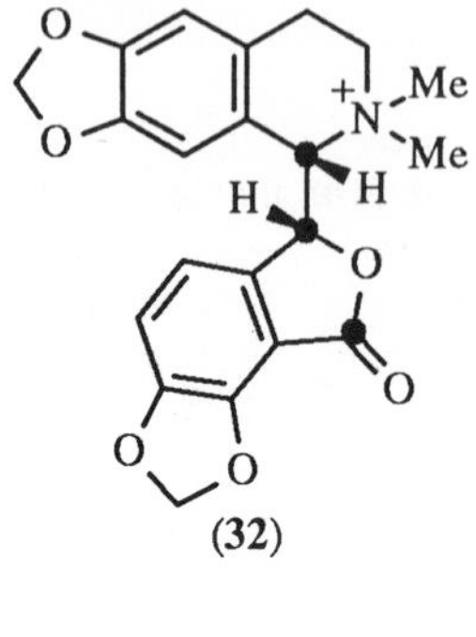

(32) 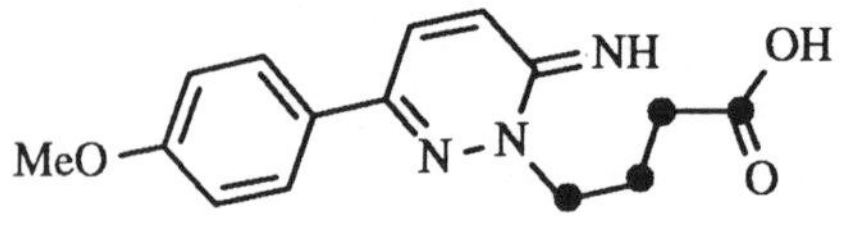   (33) 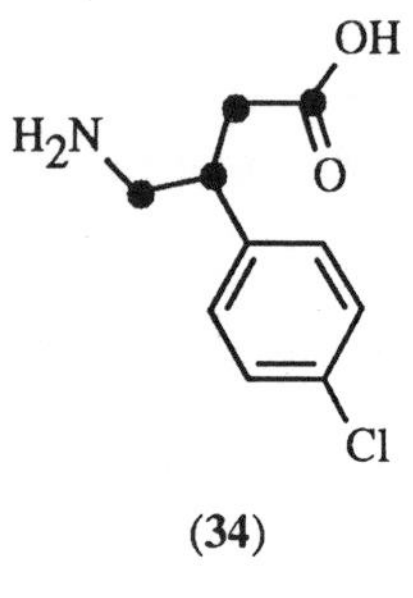   (34)

The GABA-A receptor antagonists bicuculline methochloride (**32**; BMC)[100, 101] and the amino-pyridazine derivative SR 95531 (**33**)[102] have been tritiated and used for studies of GABA-A receptor sites under various experimental conditions. While (**32**) interacts preferentially with low affinity GABA-A receptor sites, (**33**) has been shown to selectively label high affinity sites (see Figure 7).

In the presence of physiological concentrations of calcium, the selective GABA-B receptor agonist baclofen (**34**) binds to receptor sites in brain synaptic membranes showing a pharmacological profile distinctly different from those of GABA-A sites.[103] These GABA-B receptor sites can also be studied using GABA as the radioactive ligand in the presence of (**30**) to block GABA-A sites and using incubation media containing appropriate concentrations of calcium ions.[104]

12.7.1.4.3 Modulation of benzodiazepine binding

Different procedures for studies of GABA-A-agonist-induced enhancement of benzodiazepine (BZD) binding have been developed.[105] Rat brain synaptic membranes are frequently used for these studies. Aliquots of membrane preparations are incubated with radioactive BZD ligands such as diazepam (**35**), flunitrazepam (**36**) or propyl β-carboline-3-carboxylate (**37**) in the presence of the GABA-A agonists under study. The effects of GABAergic compounds on BZD binding is dependent on a variety of factors, notably temperature and concentration of chloride ions in the incubation media.[93; 105-108]

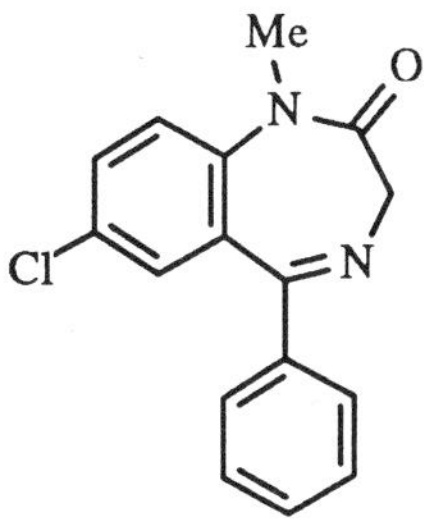

(35) 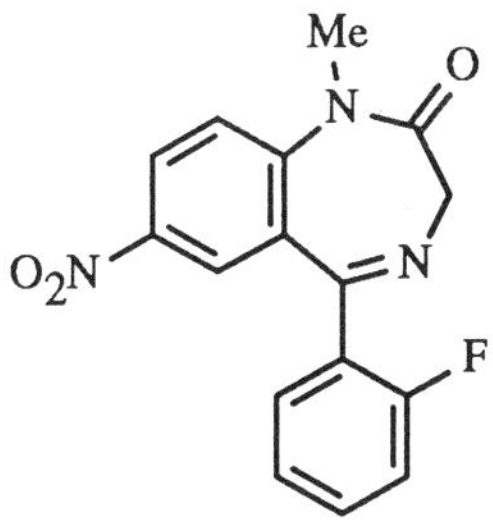   (36) 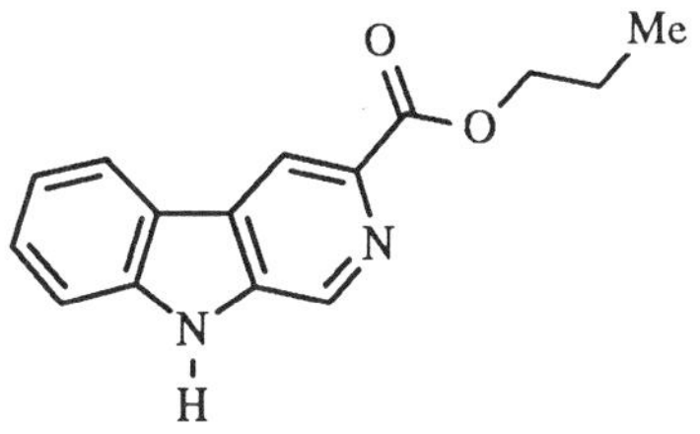   (37)

12.7.1.4.4 Neuronal and glial uptake test systems

Studies of the selectivity of GABA uptake inhibitors with respect to neuronal and glial transport systems have, so far, been performed using *in vitro* test systems. While synaptosomes and minislices prepared from brain tissue using different techniques represent models for studies of neuronal transport mechanisms,[109] primary cultures of neurones and astrocyte cells have proved to be a very useful model system for studies of neuronal and glial GABA transport, respectively.[110] The potency of GABA uptake inhibitors in different test systems is dependent on many factors, including preincubation times and concentration of radioactive GABA.[111] GABA uptake studies in synaptosomal preparations are typically carried out with preincubation of the synaptosomes in the presence of inhibitor for 10 min before addition of the radioactive substrate, GABA, at concentrations of 20–50 nmol dm^{-3}. Studies on inhibition of the uptake of GABA into cultured neurones or astrocyte cells are normally performed at GABA concentrations of 1 μmol dm^{-3} and without preincubation of the cells with inhibitor. IC$_{50}$ or K_i values for GABA uptake inhibitors determined under the former conditions are typically 10–20 times lower than those measured at higher concentrations of radioactive GABA and without preincubation.[111-113]

12.7.1.5 Uptake Mechanisms

Since the discovery of high affinity GABA uptake systems in brain tissue preparations, the physiological role of these membrane processes has been the subject of extensive studies.[109] It is now generally accepted that these mechanisms are concerned with the removal of synaptically released GABA as part of the termination of the GABA neurotransmission process, but the precise mechanism of action, including the time course and capacity, of these mechanisms *in vivo* is not fully understood. The involvement of neuronal as well as glial cells in high affinity GABA uptake has been demonstrated using a variety of different techniques and model systems.[55, 109-111] Studies of the uptake of GABA into isolated nerve endings (synaptosomes) have revealed the presence of both high

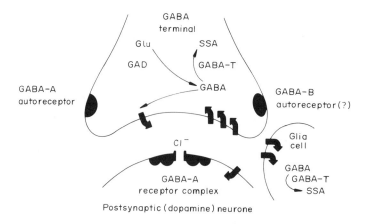

Figure 3 Schematic illustration of an axo-somatic GABA synapse

and low affinity transport systems.[114, 115] Recent GABA uptake data have been interpreted in terms of the existence of three rather than two transport systems for GABA in nerve terminals (Figure 3).[116, 117] GABA uptake data obtained from studies using cultured cells from the mammalian CNS are consistent with heterogeneity not only of neuronal but also of glial transport mechanisms.[113, 118] It has recently been proposed that facilitated diffusion of GABA into the postsynaptic membrane rather than carrier-mediated transport into terminals and glia cells may constitute the primary event in termination of the synaptic actions of GABA with subsequent transfer of GABA from the postsynaptic cell to nerve terminals and/or glia cells.[119] The amount of GABA accumulated in terminals, but not that taken up by glia cells, is partially re-used as neurotransmitter substance (Figure 3).[109, 110]

12.7.1.5.1 Uptake inhibitors and substrates

A large number of compounds have been tested as inhibitors of GABA uptake systems. Whereas most simple analogues of GABA interact non-selectively with all GABA synaptic mechanisms,[15, 69] 2,4-diaminobutanoic acid (**38**; DABA) and 3-hydroxy-5-aminopentanoic acid (**39**) are relatively selective inhibitors of the neuronal GABA uptake system, (**38**) being a substrate for this mechanism (Figure 4).[109, 120, 121] 3-Piperidinecarboxylic acid (**40**; nipecotic acid),[122] on the other hand, is an effective inhibitor of neuronal as well as glial GABA uptake, being slightly more potent at the latter system.[111, 120] Furthermore, (**40**) has been shown to be a substrate for both neuronal[113, 123] and glial[113] GABA transport carriers, and (**40**) appears to provide a retrograde tracer specific to neurones whose terminals exhibit preferential GABA uptake.[124] 1,2,5,6-Tetrahydro-3-pyridine-carboxylic acid (**41**; guvacine) shows an *in vitro* pharmacological profile very similar to that of (**40**), being, perhaps, a slightly more selective inhibitor of the glial GABA uptake system,[120] and, based on kinetic data, (**41**) seems to be a substrate for the neuronal GABA transport carrier.[125]

Like (**42**),[126] 4,5,6,7-tetrahydroisoxazolo[4,5-*c*]pyridin-3-ol (**43**; THPO) has an oxygen function in the 4-position of the piperidine ring, which for unknown reasons may contribute to the selectivity of (**42**) and in particular (**43**) for the glial GABA uptake system (Figure 4). In contrast to (**42**), which is a substrate for neuronal as well as glial GABA transport mechanisms, the more rigid compound (**43**) does not seem to be a substrate for the glial transport carrier.[113] Thus, a prerequisite for transport by, but not for binding to, the glial uptake system by GABA analogues appears to be a certain degree of rotational freedom of the acid functionalities. The ring homologue (**44**) of (**43**) is equipotent with (**43**) as a glia-selective GABA uptake inhibitor, but the mechanism of action of (**44**) is not known in detail.[111]

The depressant action of microelectrophoretically applied GABA on spinal, cerebellar and cortical neurones was reversibly enhanced by simultaneously administered (**40**).[84-86] The (*R*) form of (**40**) is more potent than the (*S*) isomer in enhancing the depressant action of GABA on spinal neurones,[84] in agreement with the relative potency of these optical isomers as uptake inhibitors *in vitro*.[111, 120] Using the same technique, (**41**) has been shown to enhance the depressant action of exogenous GABA on single cat spinal neurones.[127]

Electrophoretically applied (**43**), a selective inhibitor of glial GABA uptake, also enhances the action of similarly administered GABA on cat spinal neurones.[86, 128] These effects compared with

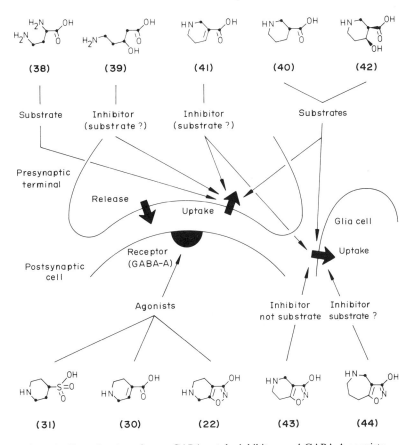

Figure 4 Sites of action of some GABA uptake inhibitors and GABA-A agonists

those of **(40)** and a number of other GABA uptake inhibitors are consistent with both glial and neuronal GABA transport systems playing a role in the termination of GABA-mediated neurotransmission.[109-111]

Studies on the rat hippocampal dentate gyrus demonstrated pronounced enhancement of the duration of recurrent inhibition of granule cells by electrophoretically applied **(41)**.[87] Similar effects on GABA-mediated inhibition in the hippocampus by GABA uptake inhibitors have recently been demonstrated *in situ*[129] and using slice preparations.[90] The predominant effect of the uptake inhibitors was a marked prolongation of the falling phase of the inhibitory postsynaptic potential (IPSP),[90,129] an effect which may become of major importance during repetitive activation of GABA-mediated inhibitory processes.[130] Compound **(40)** was shown to abolish the fading of the inhibitory action of GABA in the stratum pyramidale of CA1,[129,130] suggesting that, to a large extent, GABA fading may be caused by GABA uptake rather than true desensitization of GABA receptors.[130] The structure–activity relationships depicted in Figure 4 illustrate that neuronal and glial GABA uptake have dissimilar inhibitor/substrate characteristics, which are distinctly different from the structural requirements for agonist activity at GABA-A receptors.[16,72,111,131]

Introduction of small substituents on the amino groups of **(40)** or **(41)** normally results in compounds with decreased affinity for the GABA transport carriers.[111,112,132] In the light of these observations, the very potent effects on synaptosomal GABA uptake of a series of amino acids containing bulky substituents on the amino groups is remarkable.[133,134] These compounds, **(47)**, (*R*)-SKF 89976-A **(48)**, (*S*)-SKF 89976-A **(49)**, SKF 100330-A **(50)** and SKF 100591-A **(51)**, have been prepared by introduction of the 4,4-diphenyl-3-butenyl (DPB) substituent on the nitrogen atoms of GABA and the classical GABA uptake inhibitors such as the (*R*) and (*S*) forms, **(45)** and **(46)**, of nipecotic acid **(40)** and the related compounds **(41)** and **(42**; Figure 5). The DPB analogues of these GABA uptake inhibitors containing a secondary amino group are typically at least an order of magnitude more potent than the parent amino acids as inhibitors of synaptosomal GABA uptake.[111,133,134]

The precise mechanisms underlying the interaction of this series of analogues with GABA uptake systems are, as yet, unknown. The relative potencies of these DPB analogues and of the respective

Parent amino acids

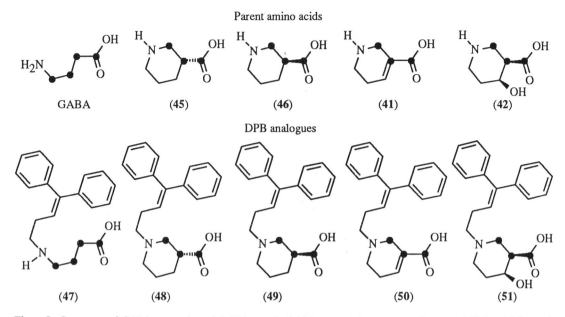

DPB analogues

Figure 5 Structures of GABA, a number of GABA uptake inhibitors and the corresponding *N*-4,4-diphenyl-3-butenyl (DPB) analogues

parent amino acid uptake inhibitors are, however, very similar, suggesting that the amino acid moieties of these DPB analogues are recognized and bound by the GABA transport carriers with which the parent amino acids interact. On the other hand, introduction of the DPB substituent on the amino groups of GABA and other GABA uptake inhibitors containing primary amino groups did not lead to analogues with increased affinity for GABA uptake mechanisms in synaptosomes. These DPB analogues containing secondary amino groups, as exemplified by compound (**47**), actually proved to be weaker than the parent amino acids.[133]

It has recently been demonstrated that the racemate of (**48**) and (**49**), SKF 89976-A, in contrast to the parent amino acid (**40**),[113,123] is acting as a simple competitive inhibitor of neuronal as well as glial GABA uptake and is not transported by the uptake carriers concerned, and, furthermore, the DPB analogues of glia-selective GABA uptake inhibitors actually seem to be approximately equipotent as inhibitors of neuronal and glial GABA uptake.[111,135]

Alterations of the structure of the DPB substituent of the compounds (**47**)–(**51**) normally result in substantial or complete loss of affinity for GABA uptake mechanisms. Thus, removal of the double bond or shortening of the carbon chain of this group gives compounds with much lower affinity for synaptosomal GABA uptake.[111,133] In contrast to the parent amino acid GABA uptake inhibitors, the lipophilic DPB analogues are pharmacologically active after systemic administration to animals and are of great interest as antiepileptic drugs.[111]

12.7.1.6 Classification of GABA Receptors

Electrophysiological and receptor binding studies have been used to detect GABA receptors and to identify subtypes of these receptors.[8-10] GABA receptors are now divided into two main classes: GABA-A receptors, which are blocked by BMC (**32**), and BMC-insensitive GABA receptors, including GABA-B receptors.[104] Both classes of GABA receptors are probably heterogeneous.

GABA-A receptors are coupled to a chloride ion channel (Figure 3),[1,2] and activation of this receptor results in a net influx or efflux of chloride ions, depending on the prevailing concentration gradient. GABA-A receptors include postsynaptic (axo-somatic or axo-dendritic) as well as pre-synaptic (axo-axonic) receptors (Figure 6). The postsynaptic GABA-A receptor, which is actually a receptor complex containing a number of subsynaptic receptors (see Section 12.7.1.8, Figure 7), regulates the passage of chloride ions in such a way that receptor activation causes hyperpolarization of the cell membrane and, thus, decreased sensitivity of the neurone to excitatory input. Activation of presynaptic GABA-A receptors normally leads to net efflux of chloride ions, causing partial depolarization.

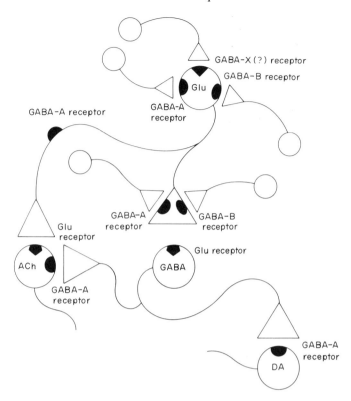

Figure 6 Schematic illustration of the localization of different types of GABA receptors

GABA-A receptors also include extrasynaptic receptors (Figure 6), and there are reports supporting the view that GABA-A receptors can be further subdivided. Thus, the agonist profile and sensitivity to antagonists of GABA-A receptors in the mammalian spinal cord and cerebral cortex appear to be different,[136] and some pharmacological effects of GABA-A agonists have shown resistance to antagonism by BMC (**32**) or the non-quaternized alkaloid bicuculline (see Section 12.7.1.7.2).[137,138]

Within the group of central bicuculline- and BMC (**32**)-insensitive GABA receptors, the GABA-B receptors have been most extensively studied.[9] These receptors are activated by GABA and, in contrast to GABA-A receptors, also by the GABA analogue baclofen (**34**). Although very little is known about the physiological role of GABA-B receptors, they seem to regulate the release of certain neurotransmitters, including Glu (Figure 6; see Section 12.7.3). Accumulating evidence suggests that GABA-B receptors are predominantly located presynaptically and that they affect neurotransmitter release *via* regulation of a calcium ion channel.[104] In a recent report, postsynaptically located GABA-B receptors linked to potassium channels have been described.[139] GABA-B receptors have also been detected and characterized in a variety of tissue preparations of peripheral origin,[11] and neurochemical data have been interpreted in terms of the presence of presynaptic GABA-B receptors, perhaps autoreceptors, on GABA terminals (Figure 3).[140] Accumulating evidence derived from neurochemical and pharmacological studies suggests that GABA-operated receptors different from GABA-A and GABA-B receptor subtypes ('GABA-X receptors'; Figure 6) exist in the mammalian CNS.[137,138,141]

Although the existence of GABA autoreceptors (Figure 3) has not yet been supported by studies employing electrophysiological techniques, neurochemical data are consistent with the existence of such receptors.[104,142-144] Studies on the effects of GABA itself on the depolarization-induced release of labelled GABA from preloaded slices or synaptosomes prepared from brain tissue are hampered by homoexchange phenomena. Thus, uptake of GABA applied to the exterior surface of the tissue preparations produces an apparent influx of the labelled transmitter because of 1:1 exchange.

The most convincing evidence for the existence of GABA autoreceptors is derived from *in vitro* studies on GABA release using GABA-A agonists such as (**22**), (**30**) and (**31**) which are not substrates for GABA uptake mechanisms.[16,145] The sensitivity of receptors mediating this phenomenon to GABA-A agonists and GABA-A antagonists, such as BMC (**32**), appears to be very similar to that of postsynaptic GABA-A receptors. The absolute as well as the relative potencies of GABA-A agonists such as muscimol (**19**), THIP (**22**), isoguvacine (**30**) and P4S (**31**) as inhibitors of synaptosomal GABA release and as inhibitors of the binding of GABA to postsynaptic receptor sites are virtually identical. The GABA-B agonist (**34**) is inactive at the receptors concerned.[146] In contrast to postsynaptic GABA-A receptors (see Figure 7), autoreceptors do not seem to be coupled to BZD receptor sites.[147]

In addition to the different pharmacological profiles of the GABA-A and GABA-B receptors, major differences between these receptor systems have been disclosed.[8,9] While pre- as well as postsynaptic GABA-A receptors are coupled to chloride channels, GABA-B receptors are coupled to calcium channels, and, in contrast to GABA-A receptors, GABA-B receptors appear to be associated with a second messenger system. Thus GABA and (**34**) are capable of potentiating the response to stimulation of adenyl cyclase by catecholamines, whereas neither compound has any significant effect on basal adenyl cyclase activity in brain slices or membranes.[148–150] On the other hand, GABA and (**34**) were shown to inhibit forskolin-induced cAMP production.[148–150] While an association between a large population of postsynaptic GABA-A receptors and BZD receptor sites is well documented (see Section 12.7.1.8), it seems unlikely that GABA-B receptors are linked to BZD receptor sites, and the regional distributions of GABA-A and GABA-B receptors in the CNS are different.[104]

12.7.1.7 Agonists and Antagonists

A considerable degree of conformational flexibility is a trait of the molecule of GABA, and molecular orbital calculations have disclosed a relatively high degree of delocalization of the positive as well as negative charges of GABA.[151,152] These molecular characteristics are apparently essential for the synaptic activity of GABA, and there is strong evidence supporting the view that GABA adopts dissimilar active conformations at different GABA-A synaptic recognition sites.[16,72] Structure–activity studies on conformationally restricted GABA analogues supporting this view are summarized in Figure 4 (see Section 12.7.1.5.1). As a result of such studies a number of compounds with specific actions at different GABA receptors are now available.[15,16,72]

12.7.1.7.1 GABA-A agonists

The observation that muscimol (**19**) is a very powerful neuronal depressant which acts through activation of GABA-A receptors[83,86,153] prompted the synthesis and structure–activity studies of a variety of aminoalkyl-substituted acidic heterocyclic compounds. These studies have shown that the effects of such conformationally restricted analogues of GABA are strictly dependent on the structure of the heterocyclic rings. It must be emphasized that although these compounds are depicted in the unionized forms all of them exist predominantly in the zwitterion form, the degree of zwitterion formation being a function of the pK_a values of the compounds. Alterations of the carbon skeleton of muscimol along different lines result in pronounced, and frequently complete, loss of GABA-A agonist activity. Thus, the analogue (**52**) is totally inactive as a GABA-A agonist.[86]

Thiomuscimol (**20**) and dihydromuscimol (**21**) are potent GABA-A agonists,[153] the (S) isomer (**53**) being the most powerful agonist at GABA-A receptors so far described (Table 1).[154] Isomuscimol (**55**) is several orders of magnitude weaker than muscimol (**19**).[153] Similarly, the triazole muscimol analogue (**56**) is inactive.[155] 2-Aminomethyl-5-hydroxy-4-pyranone (**57**; kojic amine) is a moderately potent but non-specific GABA-A agonist,[156] whereas its five-membered ring analogue 5-aminomethyl-3-hydroxyfuran-2 (5H)-one (**58**)[157] and the aza analogue (**59**)[156] are totally inactive.

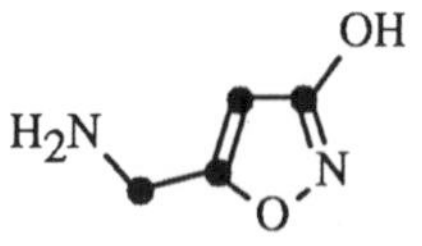

(**19**) 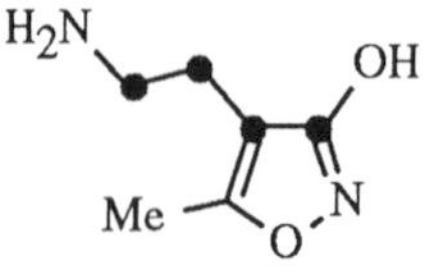   (**52**) 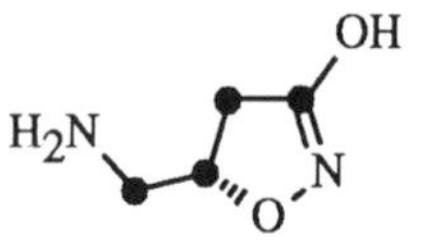   (**53**) 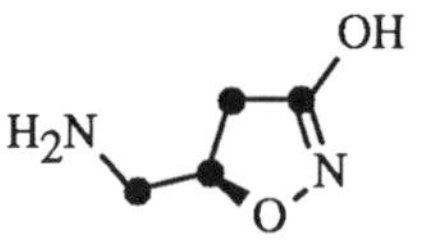   (**54**) 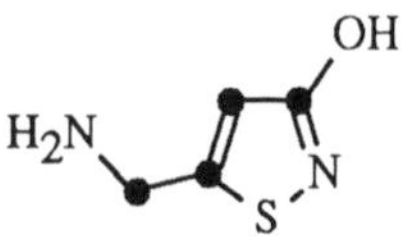   (**20**)

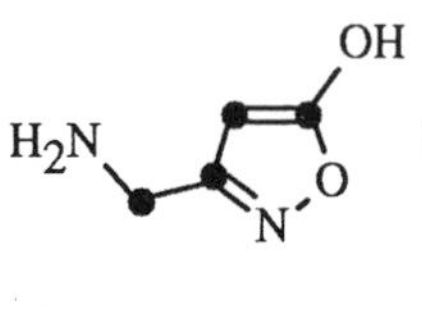

(**55**) 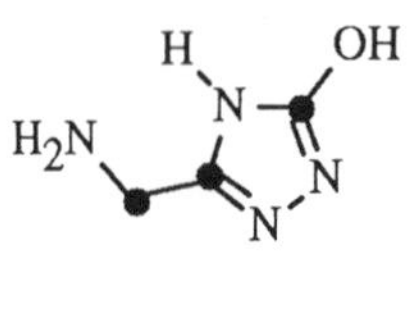   (**56**) 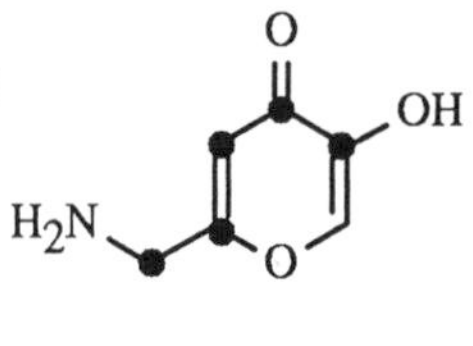   (**57**) 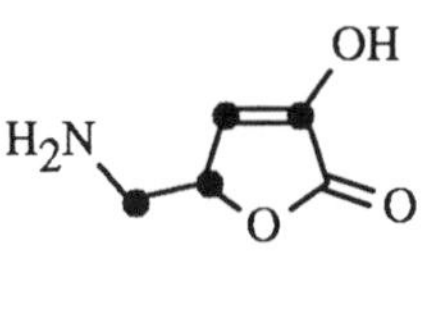   (**58**) 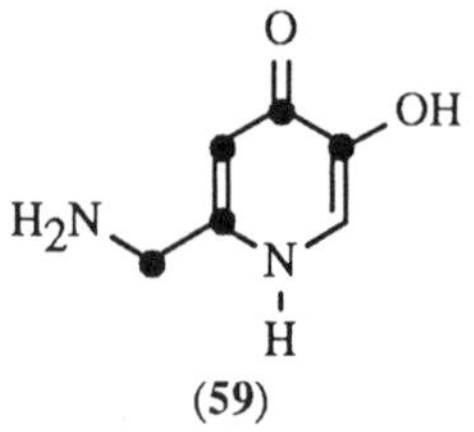   (**59**)

Table 1 Structure–Activity Relationships for GABA, Muscimol and Some Muscimol Analogues

Compound	GABA-A agonist activity (relative potency)	Receptor binding (IC$_{50}$, μmol dm^{-3})		Inhibition (in vitro) of GABA uptake (IC$_{50}$, μmol dm^{-3})			GABA-T activity (K$_m$, mmol dm^{-3})	Ref.
		GABA-A	GABA-B	Synaptosomal	Neuronal	Glial		
GABA	—	0.03	0.03	3	15	35	1.92	120
Muscimol (19)	—	0.006	2.5	240	2500	2000	1.27	73, 120, 153
Thiomuscimol (20)	—	0.02	45	>300	>5000	>5000	ca. 1	16, 153
(S)-Dihydromuscimol (53)	—	0.004	12.5	>300	>5000	>5000	2.2	16, 153, 154
(R)-Dihydromuscimol (54)	—	0.3	4.5	70	800	2000	2.2	16, 153, 154

Although the structural parameters of importance for the effect, or lack of effect, on GABA-A receptors of these heterocyclic analogues of GABA have not yet been mapped out in detail, the degree of delocalization of their negative charges seems to be a factor of major importance.[16,153,155] Thus, the negative charge of (55) and probably also that of (56) are delocalized to a larger extent than those of muscimol (19), thiomuscimol (20) and the isomers of dihydromuscimol (53) and (54).

These structure–activity studies indicate that 3-isoxazolol, 3-isothiazolol and 2-isoxazolin-3-ol heterocyclic systems are effective bioisosteres of the acid moiety of GABA, making the respective GABA analogues (19), (20), (53) and (54) important tools for molecular pharmacological studies and leads for the design of new GABA-A agonists (Table 1). In order to elucidate the pharmacological importance of these compounds, their effects on different GABA synaptic mechanisms have been studied.[16,72,111] Whereas muscimol (19) interacts very effectively with GABA-A receptors *in vivo* and *in vitro*, it binds much less tightly to GABA-B receptor sites and to GABA transport mechanisms. The potent GABA-A agonist thiomuscimol (20) does not affect GABA uptake *in vitro*, but the K_m values for this GABA analogue and for (19) as substrates for GABA-T are lower than the K_m value of 1.92 mmol dm^{-3} for GABA (see Section 12.7.1.3.3). Thus, the fact that (19)[158] and (20) are metabolized *in vivo* by GABA-T reduces the value of these GABA-A agonists for pharmacological studies. The relatively weak GABA uptake affinity of racemic dihydromuscimol resides exclusively in the (R) isomer (54), and (54) is slightly more potent than the (S) isomer (53) as an inhibitor of GABA-B binding.[159] Interestingly, however, (53) and (54) show similar affinities for GABA-T, the K_m values being slightly higher than that of GABA.[72] Although the (S) isomer (53) appears to be only a relatively poor substrate for GABA-T, metabolic decomposition *in vivo* is likely to limit the pharmacological importance of this very potent GABA-A agonist.

The heterocyclic GABA analogue imidazole-4-acetic acid (60; IAA) is a relatively potent depressant of the firing of cat cortical neurones (Table 2).[160] IAA (60) is present in the mammalian CNS, being a metabolite of histamine, and, consequently, it may play a role in regulating the central GABA system.[12] It actually does affect the level of Glu (the precursor for GABA) in the brain but, so far, it has not been shown to alter the steady-state concentrations of GABA. The pharmacological profile of (60) includes hypnotic and analgesic effects.[12] In these studies, the correlation between blood and CNS levels of (60) was not studied in detail but, since (60) is a naturally occurring metabolite in the brain, it may be rapidly excreted from the CNS. In any case, (60) is an interesting GABA-A agonist, the pharmacological and clinical potential of which has not yet been exhaustively studied.

(60)   (61)   (62)   (63)   (64)

The degree of charge delocalization of the imidazole unit of (60) is different from that of the amino group of GABA, indicating that the GABA-A receptors show some tolerance with respect to this structural parameter.

Even minor structural modifications of (60) result in compounds with lower activity as GABA-A agonists.[131] A number of analogues containing basic groups with protolytic properties similar to that of the imidazole nucleus of (60) have been synthesized and tested as GABA-A agonists. Whereas 2-aminothiazole-4-acetic acid (61) shows very low affinity for GABA-A receptor sites,[161] its unsaturated analogue (RS)-2-aminothiazoline-4-acetic acid (62) is a potent GABA-A agonist.[162] Similarly, the structurally related aliphatic compound (Z)-3-[(aminoiminomethyl)thio]propenoic acid (63) has properties reflecting effective interaction with GABA-A receptors, in particular with low affinity GABA receptor sites.[163] The (E) isomer (64) is inactive.[163]

These structure–activity relationships illustrate that certain bioisosteric modifications of different structure elements of GABA are tolerated by GABA-A receptors, and that some heterocyclic bioisosteres of GABA actually show higher affinity for and efficacy at such receptors than GABA itself.

A number of analogues of the potent and specific GABA-A agonist THIP (22)[153,164] have been synthesized and tested. These structure–activity studies include analogues such as (65)–(68), in which

Table 2 Structure–Activity Relationships for GABA and a Number of Heterocyclic GABA Analogues

Compound	GABA-A agonist activity (relative potency)	Receptor binding (IC$_{50}$, μmol dm^{-3})		Inhibition (in vitro) of GABA uptake (IC$_{50}$, μmol dm^{-3})			GABA-T activity (K_m, mmol dm^{-3})	Ref.
		GABA-A	GABA-B	Synaptosomal	Neuronal	Glial		
GABA	— — —	0.03	0.03	3	15	35	1.92	120
THIP (**22**)	— — (−)	0.1	>300	>300	>5000	>5000	No effect	73, 145
Isoguvacine (**30**)	— — —	0.04	>300	>300	>5000	>5000	No effect	73, 120, 145
Isonipecotic acid (**78**)	— — —	0.3	>300	>300	>5000	>5000	No effect	73, 120
P4S (**31**)	— — —	0.03	>300	>300	>5000	>5000	No effect	107, 176
DH-P4S (**80**)	— — —	0.3	>300	>300	>5000	>5000	No effect	107
IAA (**60**)	— — —	0.2	>300	>300	>5000	>5000	No effect	16, 120

the 3-isoxazolol unit of (22) has been replaced by other heterocyclic systems. With the exception of thio-THIP (65), which is a very weak GABA-A agonist,[128] none of these analogues show significant GABA-A receptor affinities.[165,166] Neither the bicyclic GABA analogue (69),[167] combining the structural characteristics of THIP (22) and kojic amine (57), nor compound (70)[168] interact significantly with GABA-A receptors. The ring homologues of (22), THAZ (71) and THIA (72), have very little affinity for GABA-A receptors,[73,86] but these compounds are antagonists for glycine receptors (see Section 12.7.2.2).[169,170] The 5-isoxazolol zwitterion iso-THIP (68) blocks GABA-A receptors in rat brains (see Section 12.7.1.7.2).[171] The non-fused bicyclic THIP analogue 5-(4-piperidyl)-3-isoxazolol (73; 4-PIOL) has recently been synthesized and tested.[172] In spite of the fact that (73) is not a GABA analogue in the strict sense of the word, it is a moderately potent agonist at GABA-A receptors in the cat spinal cord and it inhibits the binding of GABA to GABA-A receptor sites in rat brains. 4-PIOL (73) is, however, the first example of a GABA-A agonist without stimulatory effect on the binding of BZD (see Section 12.7.1.8.1).[172]

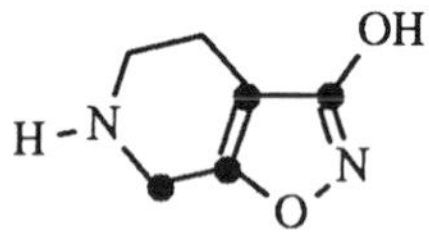

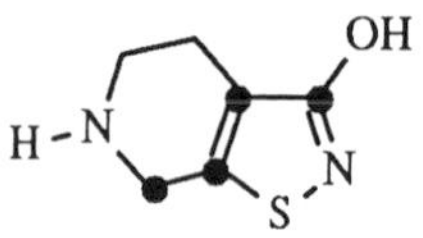

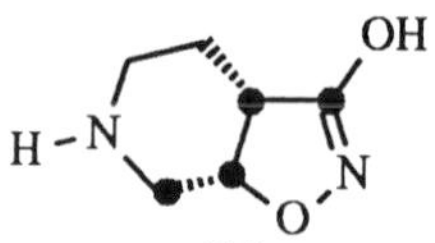

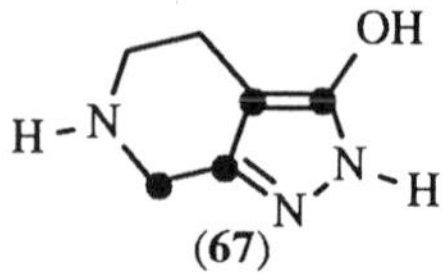

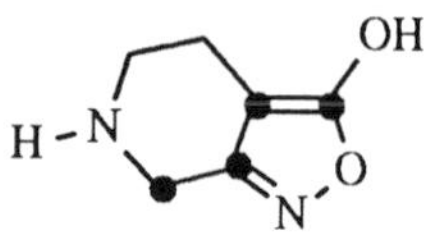

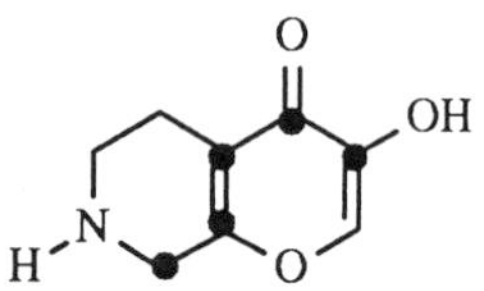

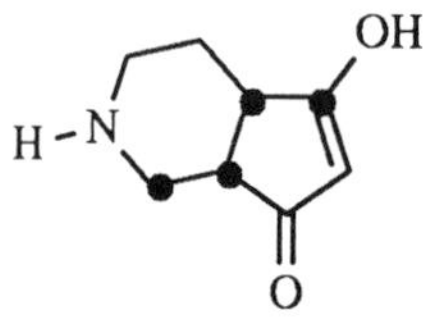

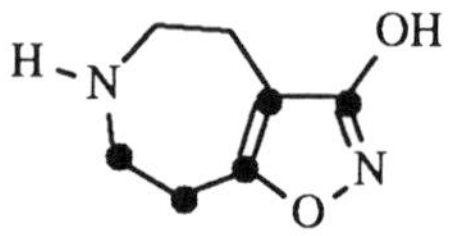

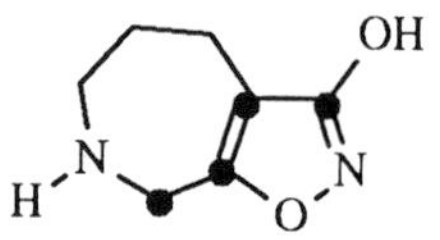

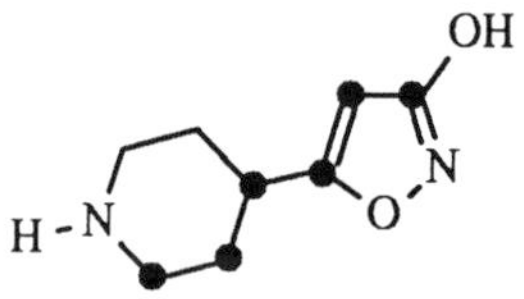

The development of THIP (22) and the demonstration of its potency and specificity as a GABA-A agonist (Table 2) prompted the synthesis and testing of the structurally related monocyclic amino acid isoguvacine (30),[16] which is a very powerful GABA-A agonist showing specificity identical with that of THIP (22).[145,153,164] The affinity of the lower ring homologue of (30), 3-pyrroline-3-carboxylic acid (74), for GABA-A receptor sites is some two orders of magnitude lower than that of (30), and, whereas (30) has no affinity for neuronal or glial GABA uptake, (74) interacts with both of these transport systems.[120] The higher ring homologues of isoguvacine, (75) and (76), do not affect GABA uptake *in vitro*, and these compounds are even weaker than (74) as inhibitors of GABA-A receptor binding.[165] In agreement with the findings for the 3-isoxazolol bioisosteres of (75) and (76), THIA (72) and THAZ (71) respectively, (75) and (76) block glycine-induced depressant effects on cat spinal neurones.[170] 1,2,3,6-Tetrahydropyridine-4-acetic acid (77) is a very weak inhibitor of GABA-A receptor binding.[173]

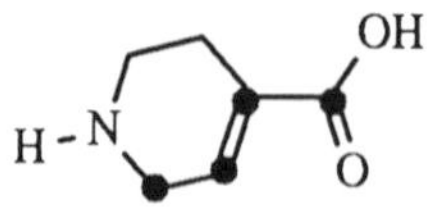

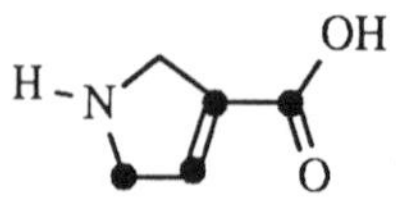

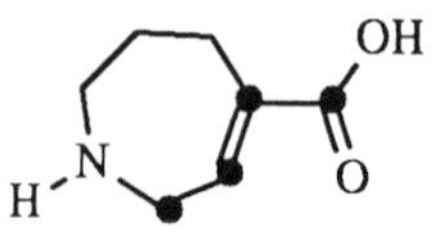

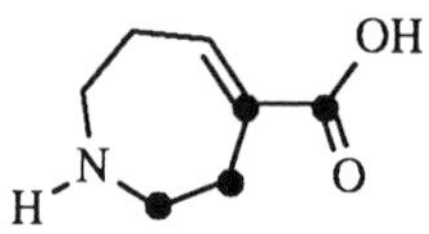

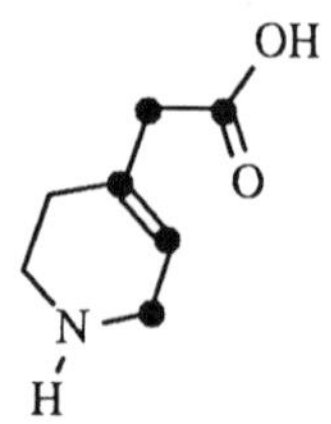

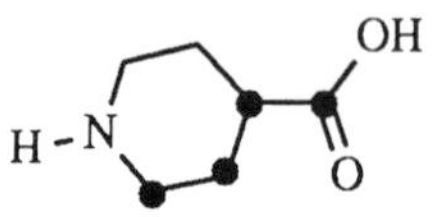

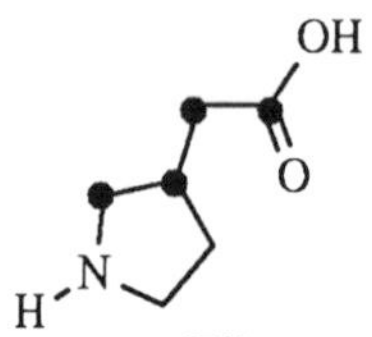

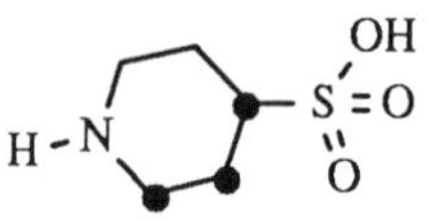

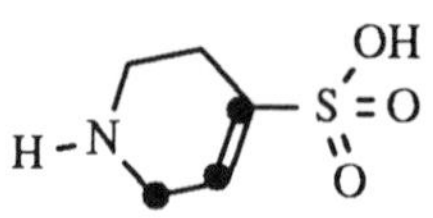

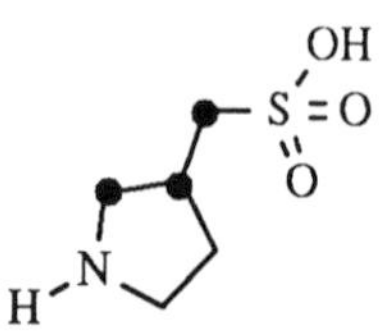

4-Piperidinecarboxylic acid (**78**; isonipecotic acid) is a specific GABA-A agonist slightly weaker than isoguvacine (**30**),[153,164] whereas the isomeric amino acid 3-pyrrolidineacetic acid (**79**; homo-β-proline) is a potent inhibitor of neuronal as well as glial GABA uptake in addition to its effect on GABA-A receptors, which is equipotent with that of isonipecotic acid (**78**).[159,174] Isonipecotic acid (**78**), isoguvacine (**30**) and THIP (**22**) show no affinity for GABA-B receptors,[175] supporting the view that these compounds reflect the active conformation of GABA at GABA-A receptors and, furthermore, that GABA adopts different conformations during its interaction with GABA-A and GABA-B receptors.[16,72] The sulfonic acid analogue P4S (**31**) of (**78**), the corresponding unsaturated analogue DH-P4S (**80**) and the sulfonic acid analogue of homo-β-proline 3-pyrrolidinemethylsulfonic acid (**81**; PMSA) are very active GABA-A agonists with no or, in the case of PMSA, very little effect on GABA uptake mechanisms.[107,176] The mechanisms underlying the interaction of these amino sulfonic acid GABA agonists with the GABA-A receptor complex do, however, seem to be different from those of the corresponding amino acid GABA agonists.[16] Thus, whereas isoguvacine (**30**) is an order of magnitude more potent than its saturated analogue isonipecotic acid (**78**), the opposite relative potency of DH-P4S (**80**) and its saturated analogue P4S (**31**) was observed (Table 2).[131] Furthermore, stereostructure–activity studies on the inhibition of GABA-A receptor binding of radioactive GABA and (**31**) disclosed striking differences.[95] These comparative studies revealed that the relative potencies of chiral GABA analogues as inhibitors of the binding of these two agonist ligands were comparable, whereas their absolute potencies in these two series of experiments were substantially different. The mechanism(s) underlying this difference are still unknown, but it is interesting to note that under certain conditions the binding of P4S (**31**) is more sensitive than that of GABA to stimulation by barbiturates, which interact with a distinct binding site at the GABA-A receptor complex (see Figure 7).[10]

12.7.1.7.2 *GABA-A antagonists*

The classical GABA-A antagonists BMC (**32**) and the parent alkaloid (1*S*,9*R*)-bicuculline (**82**) appear to interact directly with the GABA-A receptor,[177–179] possibly with an antagonist conformational state of this receptor.[100] As mentioned earlier (see Section 12.7.1.4.2), (**32**) binds selectively to low affinity sites at the GABA-A receptor (see Figure 7).[179]

In agreement with the stereoselectivity of the activation of GABA-A receptors in the CNS,[16,72] these receptors are blocked in a stereoselective manner;[100] thus the (1*R*,9*S*) isomer of (**82**) has only weak GABA-A antagonist properties and it does not significantly affect the binding of radioactive BMC (**32**). The relatively strict structural constraints imposed on antagonists for GABA-A receptors have been emphasized *via* structure–activity studies on a comprehensive series of synthetic analogues of (**82**).[180] In summary, the (1*S*,9*R*) stereochemistry of bicuculline is essential for potent GABA-A antagonism. Inversion of the stereochemistry at one or both of these chiral centres results in substantial or complete loss of activity. Introduction of substituents into the 8-position reduces the GABA-A antagonist effect considerably, and the hydroxy amino acid bicucine, obtained by opening the lactone ring of (**82**), is inactive. Esterification of bicucine, however, does restore activity, the methyl ester of bicucine being a GABA-A receptor antagonist. The C(6)–C(7) methylenedioxy group of (**82**) may be replaced by two methoxy groups without significant loss of activity.

A number of GABA-A antagonists with structures more or less different from that of bicuculline (**82**) have been discovered. The alkaloid securinine (**83**) is somewhat weaker than bicuculline in displacing GABA from its receptor sites, but the molecular pharmacology of securinine is similar to that of (**82**).[181] The steroid derivative R 5135 (**84**) is a GABA-A antagonist, which also interacts with the BZD receptor site (see Figure 7) as well as with glycine receptors.[182] A similar pharmacological profile is shown by the polycyclic 5-piperazinyl-1,2,4-triazole derivative pitrazepin (**85**).[183,184] Although the GABA-A antagonists (**82**)–(**85**) have quite different structures, certain parts of these molecules have comparable structural features, as emphasized by heavy lines.

In agreement with the findings for R 5135 (**84**) and pitrazepin (**85**), iso-THAZ (**86**), which is more potent than iso-THIP (**68**), is an antagonist at GABA-A as well as at glycine receptors (see Section 12.7.2.2).[170] Dopamine 3-*O*-sulfate (**87**) and its 4-*O* isomer, both of which are dopamine metabolites, have been shown to possess GABA-A antagonist profiles.[185] Evidence derived from electroencephalographic studies suggests that 5-guanidinopentanoic acid (**88**) is an endogenous GABA antagonist.[186]

In contrast to R 5135 (**84**) and pitrazepin (**85**), the aminopyridazine GABA-A antagonist SR 95103 (**89**) does not interact directly with BZD binding sites but, like BMC (**32**), it antagonizes the GABA-induced enhancement of BZDs *via* blockade of the BZD-coupled GABA-A receptors (see

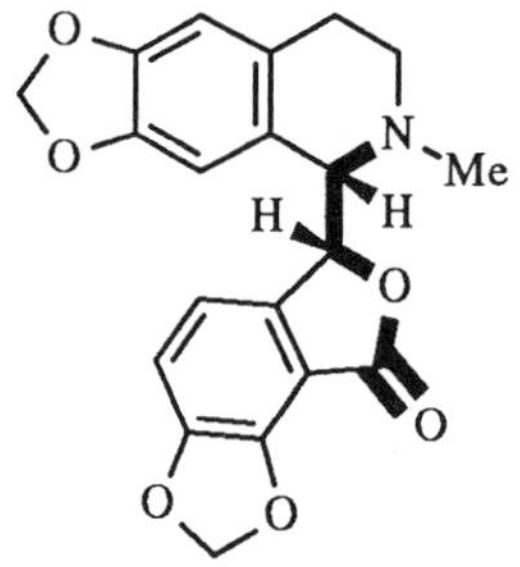

(82) 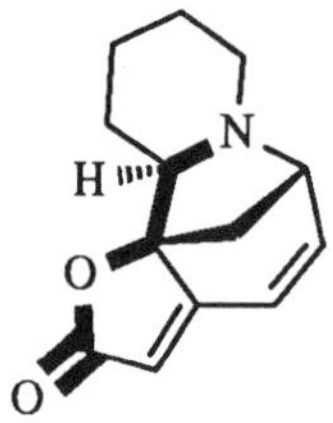   (83) 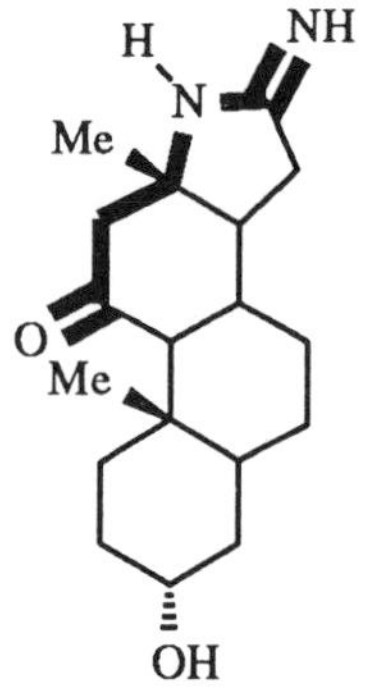   (84) 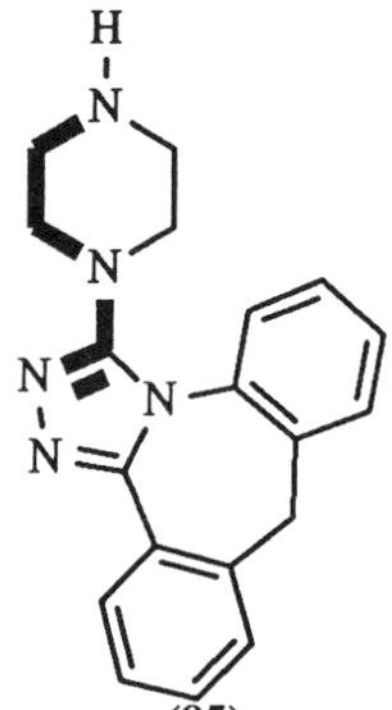   (85)

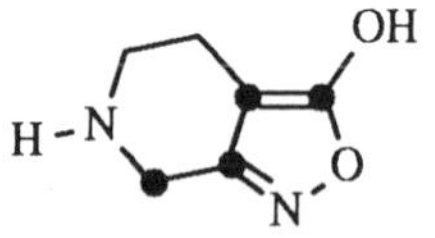

(68) 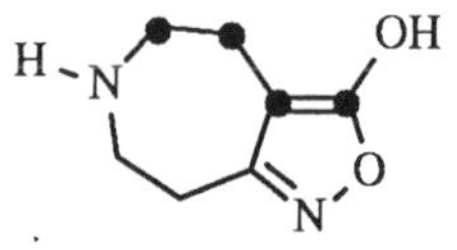   (86) 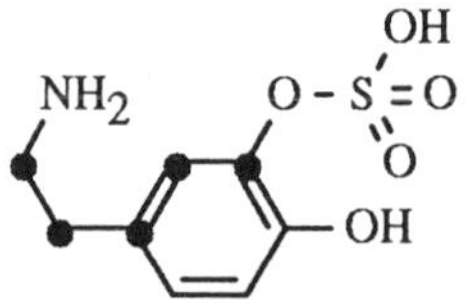   (87) 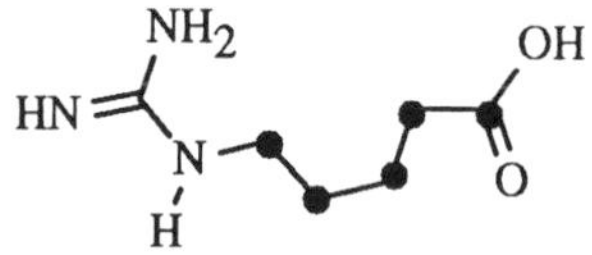   (88)

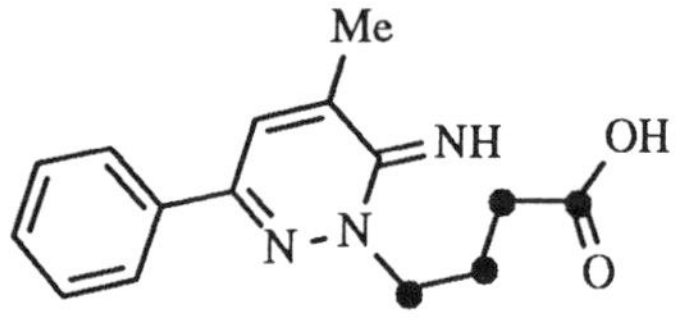

(89) 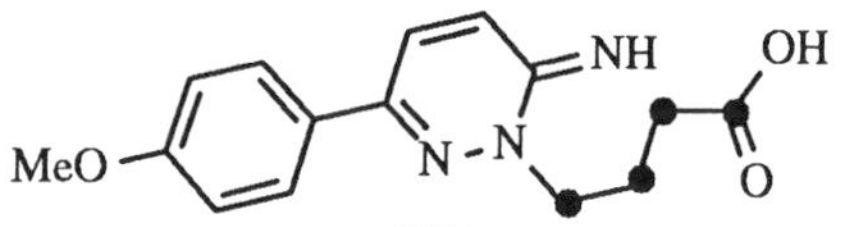   (33)

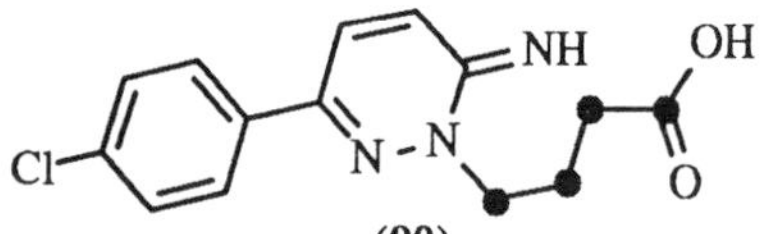

(90) 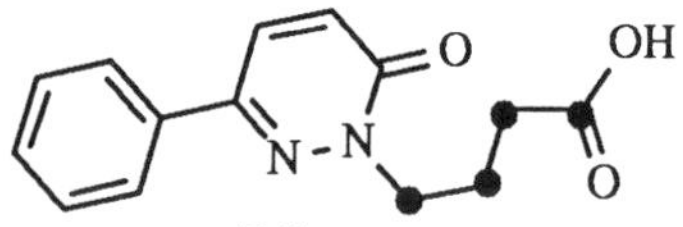   (91)

Figure 7).[187] On the other hand, like (84) and (85), (89) is also an antagonist at central glycine receptors,[188,189] but other pyridazinyl GABA analogues closely related to (89), notably SR 42641 (90) and the corresponding 4-methoxyphenyl analogue SR 95531 (33), are more selective GABA-A antagonists.[189,190] The binding characteristics of these novel GABA-A antagonists which contain a GABA structure element suggest that these compounds bind to an antagonist conformational state of the high affinity GABA-A receptor sites (see Figure 7 and Section 12.7.1.4.2), making this class of GABA analogues valuable tools for studies of GABA-A receptors.[102] The inactivity of compound (91) emphasizes the importance of the aminopyridazine structure element, and thus the zwitterionic character, of the 'SR-series' of GABA analogues for GABA-A antagonist activity.[191]

In general, the availability of antagonists with specific or highly selective effects on receptors is essential for elucidation of the physiological role and pharmacological importance of the receptors concerned, and, in many areas of neuropharmacology, antagonists have proved to be extremely useful therapeutic agents. The fact that all GABA-A antagonists pharmacologically studied so far are convulsants makes it unlikely that such compounds are going to play an important role in future psychotherapy. On the other hand, GABA-A agonists have been shown to aggravate symptoms in certain neurological diseases (see also Section 12.7.1.10),[16,47] and in such cases GABA-A antagonist therapies may, at least theoretically, be beneficial.

12.7.1.7.3   GABA-B agonists

Baclofen (34) is clinically effective in certain types of spasticity.[192,193] Furthermore, (34) has non-opioid analgesic effects, showing a pharmacological profile in different test systems different from that of the GABA-A agonist THIP (22; see Section 12.7.1.10),[25,28,138,194] and (34) has anticonvulsant properties which are not identical with those of (22) or the BZDs in terms of antiseizure effects and profile of side effects.[72,137] All pharmacological effects of (34) reside in the (R) form (92), the (S) isomer (93) being very weak or inactive in different pharmacological test systems.[104] These aspects have prompted the synthesis of a variety of analogues of (34) and an intense search for GABA-B agonists with structures different from that of (34), and for GABA-B antagonists (see Section 12.7.1.7.4). The latter group of agents are essential as tools for basic studies of GABA-B receptor functions and for studies of the mechanisms underlying the pharmacological and therapeutic effects of (34), some of which may not be mediated by GABA-B receptors.[193] The pharmacological profiles of a variety of baclofen (34) analogues including (94) have been assessed on the basis of microelectrophoretic experiments on single neurones and pharmacological studies on reflexes in the cat.[195] Alterations of the amino acid as well as the aromatic moiety of (34) result in substantial or complete loss of pharmacological effects. Replacement of the chloro atom of baclofen by a trifluoromethyl group led to complete loss of activity, and compound (94), containing an unsubstituted phenyl group, was much weaker than baclofen in terms of reflex-inhibiting properties, and somewhat weaker as a depressant of the spontaneous firing of single neurones.[195] Shortening or extension of the amino acid backbone of (34) also gave much weaker compounds. Unsaturated analogues of (34) such as (*E*)-4-amino-3-(4-chlorophenyl)-2-butenoic acid (95) have been synthesized[196] and shown to be inactive.

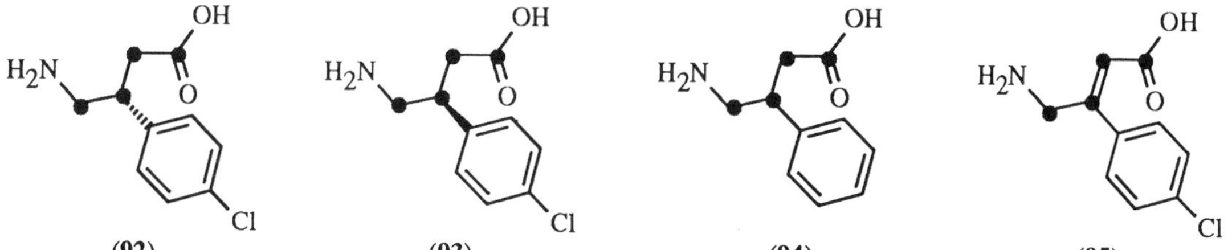

(92)   (93)   (94)   (95)

A number of simple GABA analogues have been studied as inhibitors of GABA-B binding, including the enantiomers of 3-hydroxy-4-aminobutanoic acid, of which the (*R*) form (96) is the most potent one, and a variety of structurally related hydroxylated GABA analogues, including (97)–(99).[159] With the exception of 2-hydroxy-5-aminopentanoic acid (98; 2-OH-DAVA), these compounds did not affect GABA-B binding.[159] 3-Methoxy-4-aminobutanoic acid (100) also does not significantly affect GABA-B receptor binding.[159]

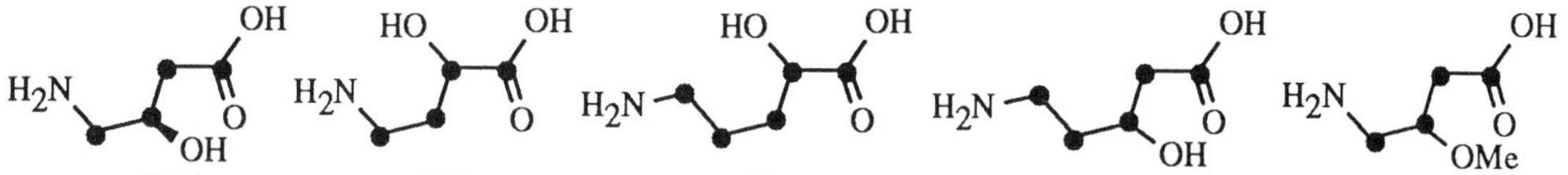

(96)   (97)   (98)   (99)   (100)

Comparative stereostructure–activity studies have disclosed that GABA-A and GABA-B receptor sites exhibit opposite stereoselectivity.[159] Compound (96) is actually a potent inhibitor of GABA-B binding, showing about one-fifth of the affinity of (*R*)-baclofen (92) for GABA-B sites.[159] Furthermore, (*R*)-dihydromuscimol (54) is somewhat more potent as an inhibitor of GABA-B binding than (*S*)-dihydromuscimol (53), the most powerful GABA-A agonist so far described (see Section 12.7.1.7.1).

The GABA analogue (53) evidently almost perfectly mimics the active conformation(s) of GABA at the GABA-A receptors, whereas (*R*)-3-hydroxy-4-aminobutanoic acid (96) and (*R*)-baclofen (92) seem to reflect the conformation(s) adopted by GABA during its binding to GABA-B receptor sites. Due to the considerable conformational mobility of both of these compounds it is, however, not possible to deduce the active conformation(s) of GABA at the GABA-B receptors from these structure–activity studies. (*R*)-3-Hydroxy-4-aminobutanoic acid (96) and (*R*)-baclofen (92) have opposite stereochemical orientations of the hydroxy and 4-chlorophenyl groups, respectively. This observation strongly suggests that the polar hydroxy group in the former GABA analogue interacts with a structure element of the GABA-B receptor site different from that which binds the lipophilic 4-chlorophenyl group of (92) during its interaction with GABA-B receptor sites. The recent observation that baclofen apparently activates two distinct GABA-B receptors[197] does, however, complicate structure–activity studies on compounds interacting with these receptor sites.

Evidence derived from different lines of research strongly suggests that hyperactivity of the central excitatory neurotransmitter Glu is a major causal factor in certain neurodegenerative disorders (see Section 12.7.3.2).[198,199] The results of numerous neurochemical studies have demonstrated that the release of Glu may be regulated by GABA-B receptors located on terminals of Glu-utilizing neurones (Figure 6).[104] Such findings have focused much pharmacological and therapeutic interest on these presynaptic receptors, which may actually represent a subclass of GABA-B receptors,[197] and selective activation of presynaptic GABA-B receptors may represent a flexible way of reducing excessive stimulation of neurones in the brain by Glu.

12.7.1.7.4 *GABA-B antagonists*

There is also a pharmacological and therapeutic interest in GABA-B receptor antagonists. Thus, extensive neurochemical studies indicate that the *in vitro* release of monoamine neurotransmitters such as dopamine (DA), serotonin and noradrenaline may also be regulated by presynaptically located GABA-B receptors,[104] and, in principle, administration of GABA-B antagonists would stimulate the release of such neurotransmitters, which may have therapeutic prospects in certain psychiatric diseases.

The GABA homologue 5-aminopentanoic acid (**101**; DAVA), which is an endogenous amino acid, has been shown to possess a weak antagonist profile at peripheral GABA-B receptors.[200] Furthermore, (**101**) and (*S*)-baclofen (**93**) inhibited the antinociceptive effect of (*R*)-baclofen (**92**) after intrathecal injection.[197] Under these conditions 3-aminopropanesulfonic acid (**102**; 3-APS), which has GABA-B antagonist properties on peripheral GABA-B receptors,[201] did not significantly antagonize (*R*)-baclofen (**92**)-induced antinociception.[197] On the other hand, (**101**) and (**102**), but not (**93**), antagonized the inhibitory effect of (**92**) on a guinea pig muscle preparation.[197] Neither DAVA (**101**) nor (**102**) interact selectively with GABA-B receptors, (**101**) showing affinity for all GABA-A synaptic mechanisms and (**102**) being a very potent agonist at GABA-A receptors in the mammalian CNS.[15, 16] There is evidence suggesting that the antagonism by (**101**) at GABA-B receptors in the guinea pig ileum may be due to an interaction between GABA-A and GABA-B receptors.[202] In any case, lack of selectivity reduces the value of (**101**) and (**102**) as tools for studies of GABA-B receptor mechanisms.

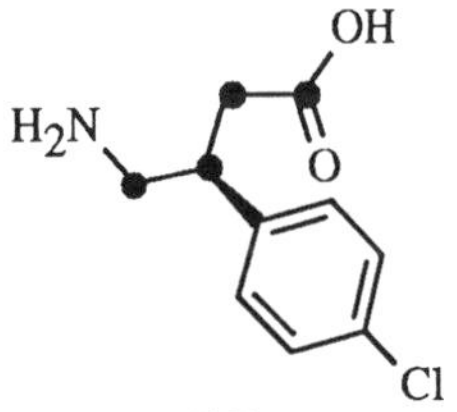

(**93**) 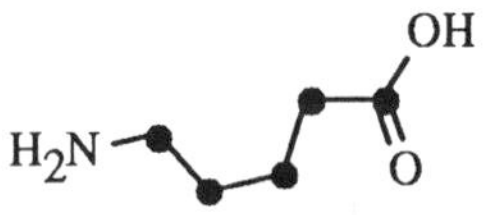   (**101**) 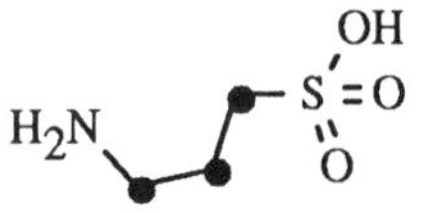   (**102**)

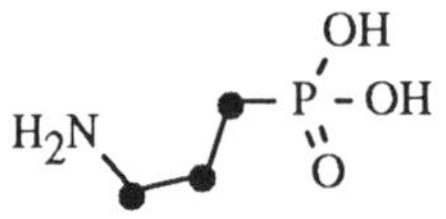

(**103**) 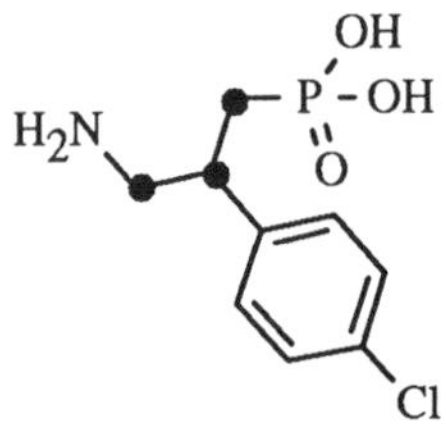   (**104**)

It has been demonstrated that 3-aminopropanephosphonic acid (**103**) has weak GABA-B antagonist properties in a guinea pig muscle preparation,[203] and the phosphonic acid analogue of baclofen (**34**), phaclofen (**104**), shows antagonist effects on central as well as peripheral GABA-B receptors.[204] These observations are likely to accelerate studies of the physiological role of GABA-B receptors and may stimulate the development of therapeutically useful GABA-B antagonists. In the GABA-B field much interest has recently been focused on phosphinic acid analogues of GABA as GABA-B agonists or antagonists.[205]

12.7.1.8 Postsynaptic GABA-A Receptor Complex

Computer-aided analyses of receptor binding data for radioactive GABA, muscimol (**19**), THIP (**22**), isoguvacine (**30**), P4S (**31**), BMC (**32**) and SR 95531 (**33**; see Section 12.7.1.4.2) are consistent

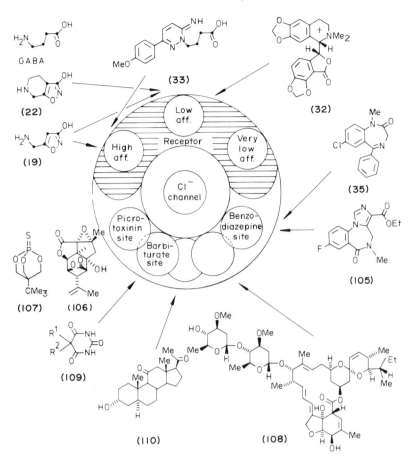

Figure 7 Schematic illustration of the GABA-A receptor complex and the sites of action of different drugs and compounds

with the presence of two or, perhaps more likely, three GABA receptor binding sites (Figure 7). Such analyses of the binding data for radioactive P4S (**31**), THIP (**22**) and GABA revealed that a receptor model with three independent binding sites was statistically preferable to receptor models containing one or two sites.[95] These receptor sites are not interconvertible under the assay conditions.[206] Normally, the affinity of ligands for the very low affinity binding site is too low for satisfactory characterization.[10,95,206]

The physiological relevance of these multiple binding sites is unknown. In general, low or very low affinity receptor sites for neurotransmitters are likely to correspond to functional receptors.[10] In the case of GABA, this view may be supported by the observation that coupling between the GABA-A receptors and the benzodiazepine (BZD) sites (Figure 7) seems to involve very low affinity GABA receptor sites.[10,206] It has been proposed that the different affinities may reflect anatomical rather than functional differences; thus, high affinity GABA binding sites were proposed to relate to postsynaptic GABA-A receptors, whereas low affinity sites were supposed to reflect presynaptic GABA-A receptors.[177,178] This view, however, has not been supported by subsequent electrophysiological or receptor binding studies.

The GABA receptor function is associated with[10,207,208] and appears to be modulated by various additional units[9,10] which can be detected *in vitro* as distinct binding sites for BZDs[209,210] such as diazepam (**35**) or the BZD antagonist Ro 15-1788 (**105**) and for picrotoxinin (**106**) or the cage convulsant *t*-butylbicyclophosphothionate (**107**; TBPS).[211,212] There is some evidence of heterogeneity for both of these binding sites,[10,213] and for the existence of a distinct binding site at the postsynaptic GABA-A receptor complex for the avermectines, including ivermectin and avermectin B_{1a} (**108**).[214,215] A number of binding data support the view that the picrotoxinin/TBPS binding sites represent the pharmacological receptors for the barbiturates (**109**).[10,93,211] Evidence derived from binding data using radioactive TBPS (**107**) are, however, consistent with an allosterical interaction between the picrotoxinin site and a separate binding site for the barbiturates (Figure 7).[216,217]

The physiological role of these additional sites ('pharmacological receptors') at the GABA receptor complex, which can be co-solubilized to different extents depending on the nature of the detergent used,[10,218] is unknown. The intimate contact and allosteric interactions between these units and the GABA-A receptor site *in vitro* may, however, reflect certain aspects of the dynamic properties of the GABA-A receptor complex.[219] The binding sites for GABA-A agonists such as muscimol (19) and the BZDs have been shown to be associated with different subunits of the GABA-A receptor complex.[220]

It has recently been demonstrated that this receptor complex also comprises a site which binds different steroids with very high affinity.[221] The anaesthetic steroid alfaxalone (110) selectively enhances the binding of radioactive muscimol (19) to GABA-A receptor sites, and (110) potentiates the inhibitory responses of GABA without affecting those of glycine.[222] Compound (110) and a variety of other steroids including metabolites of progesterone and deoxycorticosterone interact with the GABA-A receptor complex in a manner resembling that of hypnotic barbiturates (109),[223,224] but these two classes of compounds seem to modulate GABA-mediated neurotransmission *via* different sites of action (Figure 7).[221] It is possible that the 'up-regulation' of GABA receptors by oestrogens is mediated by the steroid site of the GABA-A receptor complex.[225] The physiological relevance and pharmacological importance of this steroid–GABA-A receptor interaction are under intense investigation.

12.7.1.8.1 GABA agonist–benzodiazepine interactions

Studies *in vitro* have revealed striking differences between the effects on BZD binding of different structural classes of GABA-A agonists.[107,174,226,227] GABA and the GABA-A agonists (S)-dihydromuscimol (53), muscimol (19) and thiomuscimol (20) are very effective activators of BZD binding in the absence of chloride ions and at 0 °C. Other GABA-A agonists such as THIP (22) are much weaker, and P4S (31) is actually a deactivator of BZD binding under these conditions. This conspicuous lack of correlation between the potent GABA-A agonist effects of these latter compounds and their effects on BZD binding at 0 °C and in the absence of chloride ions was explained in terms of partial GABA agonist/antagonist properties of (22) and (31),[226] or in terms of the existence of a distinct type of GABA-A receptor coupled to the BZD receptors.[227] It is now generally accepted that the effects concerned are initiated by activation of the physiological GABA-A receptor.[9,10]

The effects of GABA-A agonists on BZD binding *in vitro* are strongly dependent on the experimental conditions. Thus, elevation of the temperature to 30 °C and, in particular, addition of appropriate concentrations of chloride to the incubation medium have pronounced effects. Under these conditions, P4S (31) as well as DH-P4S (80) are converted from deactivators into activators of BZD binding.[106,107] In general, the maximal levels of BZD stimulation attainable by GABA-A agonists are increased in the presence of chloride ions, reflecting the close association between the GABA-A and BZD receptors and the chloride channel in the GABA receptor complex. The efficacy of GABA agonists as stimulators of BZD binding appears to be determined by at least two structural parameters of the GABA-A agonists: (i) the conformational mobility of the GABA analogue and (ii) the structure of the acid moiety of the GABA analogue.

4-PIOL (73) is a moderately potent agonist at GABA-A receptors in the spinal cord.[172] In spite of the GABA-A agonist effect of (73), it does not significantly affect the binding of BZD under different experimental conditions. The apparent deactivation of BZD binding by (73) seen at low temperature and in the absence of chloride ions probably reflects blockade of the stimulatory effects of the very low concentrations of GABA present in the brain synaptic membranes used. These effects of (73) are observed at surprisingly low concentrations when compared with its relatively weak effects as an inhibitor of GABA-A binding ($IC_{50} = 6\ \mu mol\ dm^{-3}$). The effects of (73) on BZD binding are, qualitatively and quantitatively, very similar to those of the GABA-A antagonist BMC (32).[226]

This unique profile may reflect that 4-PIOL (73) is an agonist at spinal GABA-A receptors, whereas an antagonist profile of (73) is expressed by supraspinal GABA-A receptors. Alternatively, (73) may interact with a subpopulation of GABA-A receptors which are not coupled to BZD receptors.

12.7.1.8.2 Efficacy scale for benzodiazepine receptor ligands

Since the discovery of the BZDs and the pharmacological effects of these compounds,[228] numerous analogues have been synthesized and tested *in vitro* and *in vivo* and a number of BZDs with slightly different pharmacological profiles are used therapeutically, mainly as anticonvulsants, anxiolytics and sedatives.[105] In addition to the BZDs, a wide variety of other structural classes of compounds have been shown to interact potently with BZD receptors,[105] as exemplified in Figure 8. The structure of the classical BZD flunitrazepam (**36**) is compared with the triazolopyridazine CL 218.872 (**111**), the pyrrolopyrazine zopiclone (**112**), the β-carboline derivative ZK 93123 (**113**), the pyrazoloquinoline CGS 9896 (**114**) and the imidazobenzodiazepine Ro 15-1788 (**105**). In addition to (**113**), the structurally related β-carboline analogues (**115**)–(**119**) are illustrated.

These compounds which bind tightly to BZD receptor sites *in vitro* exhibit a broad spectrum of behavioural pharmacological effects.[105, 229, 230] The classical BZDs typically show anticonvulsant, anticonflict and sedative effects, and similar pharmacological profiles characterize compounds (**111**)–(**113**). These compounds are classified as BZD receptor agonists (Figure 8).[229, 230] Partial agonists at BZD receptors such as (**114**), (**115**) and related compounds typically lack the sedative pharmacological profile but show anticonvulsant properties, and the BZD receptor antagonists, as exemplified by (**105**) and (**116**), block all pharmacological effects of compounds acting *via* BZD receptors, including the inverse and partial inverse agonists (Figure 8).[229, 230] Whereas partial inverse BZD agonists such as FG 7142 (**117**) typically show anxiogenic and proconvulsant effects, the inverse agonists DMCM (**118**) and β-CCM (**119**) are powerful convulsants.[105, 229, 230] The structural parameters characterizing these different classes of BZD-receptor-active compounds have been mapped out in some detail.[230]

12.7.1.9 Pharmacokinetic Aspects and Prodrugs

All compounds so far known with specific actions on GABA receptors have zwitterionic structures. Small, and frequently negligible, fractions of amino acids exist as unionized molecules in solution, the ratio between the concentrations of ionized (zwitterionic) and unionized molecules (I/U ratio, zwitterionic constant) being a function of the difference between the pK_a I and II values.[128, 231] A large difference between the pK_a values of neutral amino acids is tantamount to high I/U ratios for the compounds.

Since amino acids are likely to penetrate the blood–brain barrier (BBB) in the unionized form, it is of pharmacological interest to develop analogues of GABA with small differences in pK_a values, and thus lower I/U ratios, compared to GABA. Like GABA (I/U 800 000), isoguvacine (**30**; I/U 200 000) and, in particular, P4S (**31**; I/U > 1 000 000) have high I/U ratios, and none of these compounds penetrate the BBB. THIP (**22**; I/U 1500) and muscimol (**19**; I/U 900), on the other hand, have much lower I/U ratios, and approximately 0.1 and 0.2%, respectively, of doses of (**22**) or (**19**) exist as unionized molecules in aqueous solution, and these values explain why (**22**) and (**19**) enter the brain very easily after peripheral administration in mice, rats[232] and humans.[233]

In addition to its lack of specificity as a GABA agonist, muscimol (**19**) is relatively toxic and, as mentioned earlier, it is rapidly metabolized after peripheral administration.[158, 232, 233] THIP (**22**), on the other hand, is well tolerated by various animal species, is active after oral administration and is excreted unchanged and to some extent in a conjugated form in the urine from animals and humans.[233]

As discussed in previous sections, a variety of heterocyclic bioisosteres of GABA have been synthesized and tested for GABAergic activities. Some of these GABA bioisosteres, notably THIP (**22**), have pharmacokinetic and toxicological properties making behavioural pharmacological and clinical studies possible.

Like GABA itself, most of the specific GABA-A agonists, especially isonipecotic acid (**78**), isoguvacine (**30**) and P4S (**31**), do not easily penetrate the BBB, as mentioned earlier. The pharmacological interest in GABA and these GABA analogues has prompted the development and pharmacological testing of a variety of prodrugs of these compounds. This approach may, in principle, be particularly attractive in the central amino acid neurotransmitter field. Ideally, the active amino acid would be 'trapped' within the brain following cleavage of the lipophilic transport-facilitating group(s).

The most exhaustively studied GABA prodrug is progabide (**120**), in which the amino group of GABA-amide forms an imino group with a benzophenone derivative.[234] *In vivo*, (**120**) appears to be partially converted into the corresponding carboxylic acid (SL 75.102), which has GABA agonist properties, whereas GABA-amide is hydrolyzed to give GABA.[235] These aspects make a detailed analysis of the mechanisms underlying the pharmacological and clinical effects of progabide difficult.[236] At rather high doses (**120**) has a broad spectrum of anticonvulsant activities in a variety of experimental models of epilepsy, and (**120**) shows anticonvulsant activity in different types of

BZD agonists

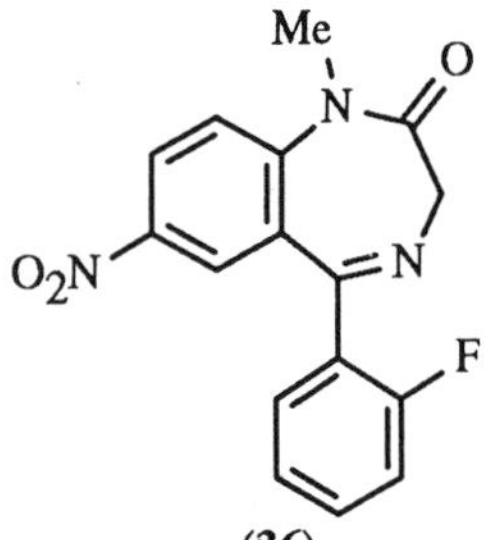

(36) 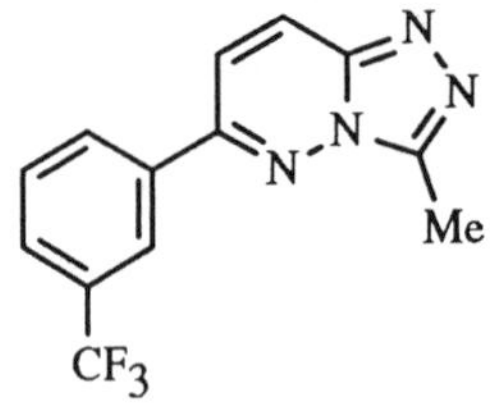   (111) 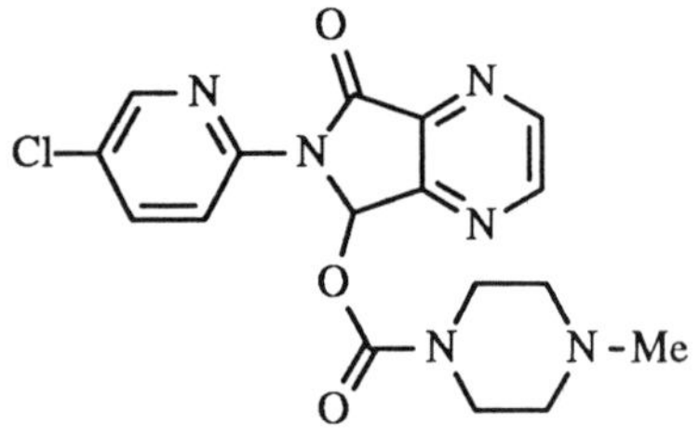   (112)

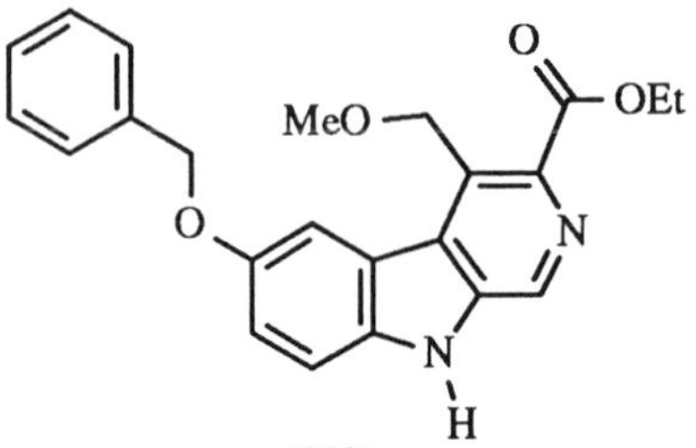

(113)

BZD partial agonists

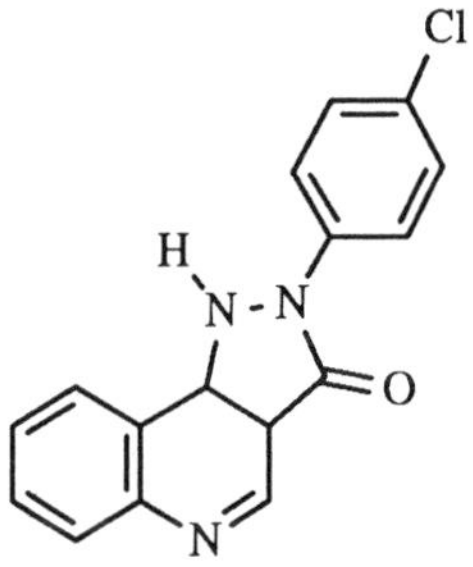

(114) 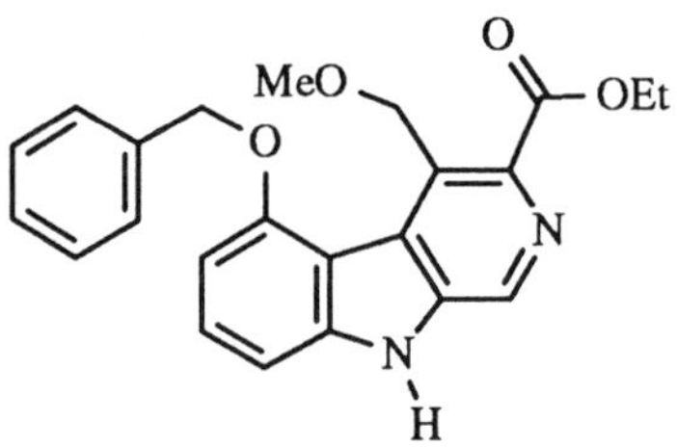   (115)

BZD antagonists   BZD partial inverse agonist

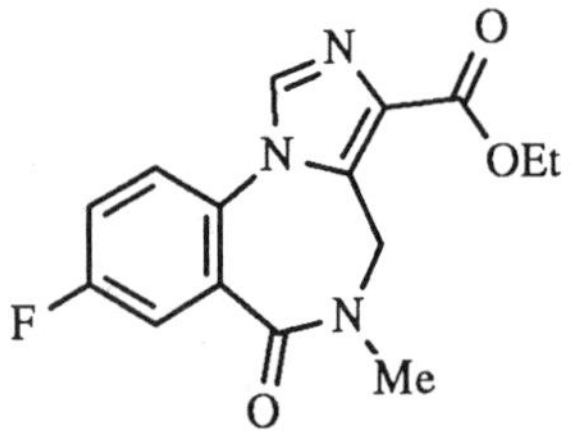

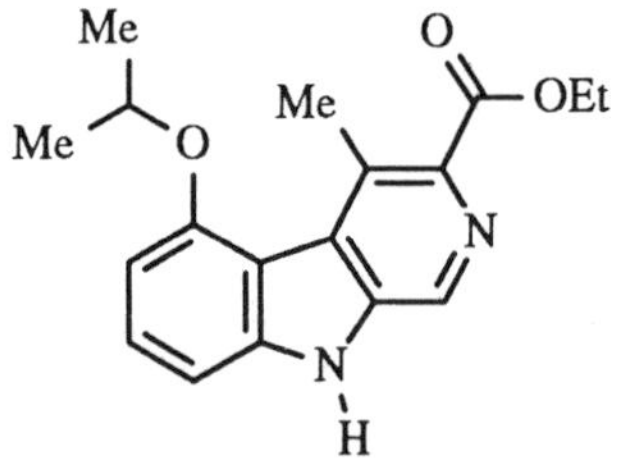

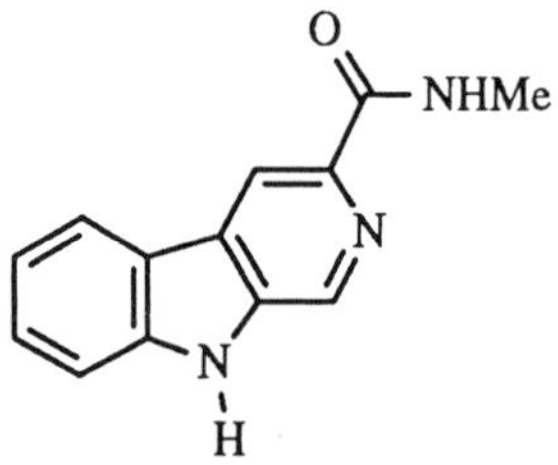

(105)   (116)   (117)

BZD inverse agonists

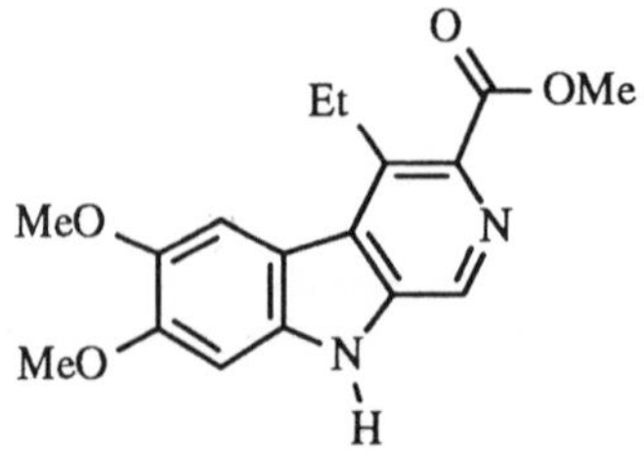

(118) 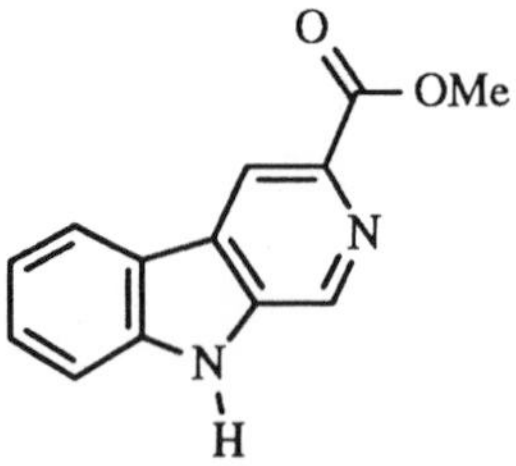   (119)

Figure 8   Structures of some compounds with different actions on benzodiazepine (BZD) receptors

epilepsy.[34,36] So far, there are no reports on the potential toxicity of the benzophenone moiety of (120).

The *N*-pivaloyl-leucyl-GABA derivative (121) is capable of crossing the BBB in rats with subsequent increases of central GABA levels.[237] (121) shows persistent anticonvulsant effects in rats, probably as a result of decomposition in the brain to give GABA, although (121) itself and/or partially hydrolyzed products from (121) seem to be pharmacologically active.[237] A number of simple esters of GABA have been tested as potential prodrugs of GABA.[17]

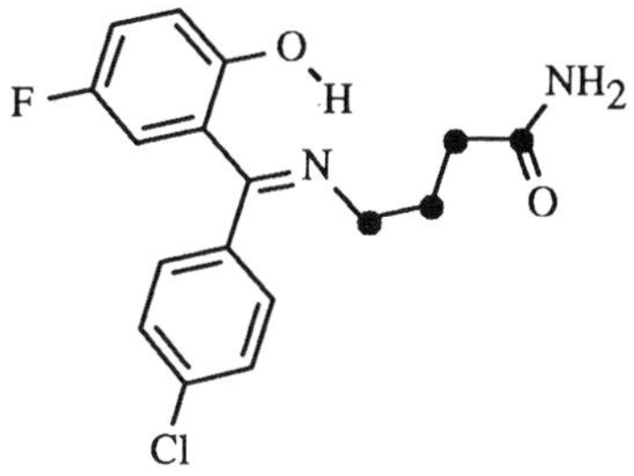

(120) 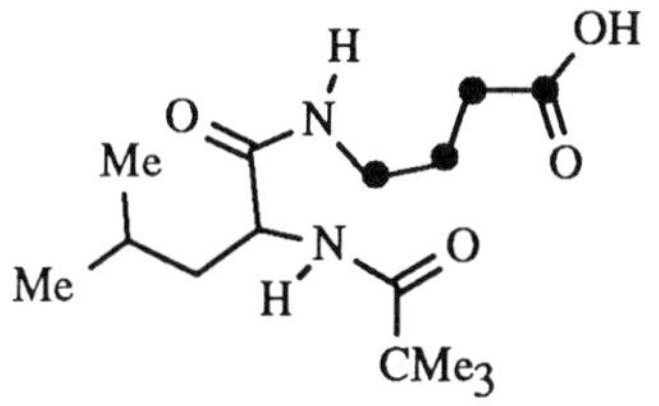   (121) 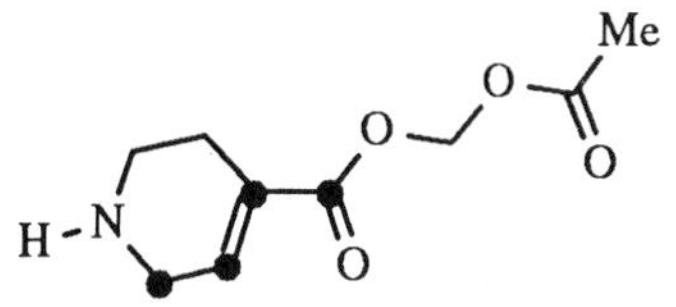   (122)

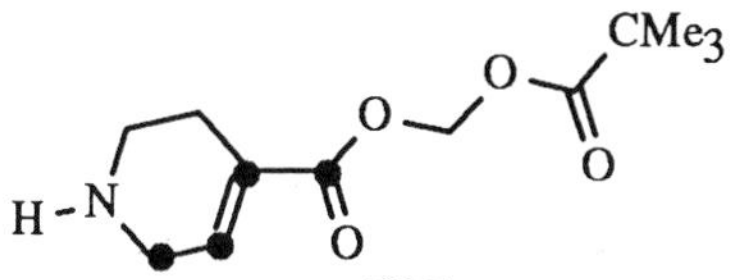

(123)

The potency and specificity of isoguvacine (30) as a GABA-A agonist have made prodrugs of this compound pharmacologically interesting. A number of simple esters of (30) and a series of double esters including the acetyloxymethyl (122) and pivaloyloxymethyl (123) esters of (30) have been synthesized and tested.[238] The half-lives of these double esters were strongly dependent on the structure of the acyloxy moieties in the ester groups, and a certain degree of correlation of the half-lives of these compounds and their anticonvulsant effects was observed.[238]

12.7.1.10 Pharmacological and Clinical Effects of GABA-A Agonists

The very effective GABA-A agonist muscimol (19) has been administered to patients suffering from certain neurological and psychiatric disorders in short-term clinical trials.[18,47] However, the toxicity and rapid metabolism of (19) make interpretation of such pharmacological and clinical data difficult, and these aspects may explain the conflicting pharmacological observations which, in some cases, have been reported for (19).

The potency and specificity of THIP (22) as a GABA-A agonist and its favourable pharmacokinetic and animal toxicological properties have made this compound the 'classical' GABA-A agonist for pharmacological and clinical studies.

The anticonvulsant effects of THIP (22) and muscimol (19) have been compared in a variety of animal models. THIP (22) is typically two to five times weaker than (19) in suppressing seizure activities. In mice and gerbils with genetically determined epilepsy, systemically administered (22) has proved very effective in suppressing seizure activity and it is capable of reducing audiogenic seizures in DBA/2 mice.[239-241] However, (22) failed to protect baboons with photosensitive epilepsy against photically induced myoclonic responses.[241] THIP (22) has been subjected to a single-blind controlled trial in patients with epilepsy, in which it was added to the concomitant antiepileptic treatment. Under these conditions no significant effects of (22) were detected, although a trend was observed for lower seizure frequency during a period of submaximal doses.[242]

The demonstration of very potent analgesic effects of (22) in different animal models has made studies of the clinical prospects of GABA-mediated analgesia possible. Analgesia induced by (22) is insensitive to naloxone,[243-245] indicating that the effect is not mediated by opiate receptors. Quite surprisingly, THIP (22) analgesia cannot be reversed by bicuculline (82) but it can be reduced by atropine, reflecting as yet unclarified functional interactions between GABA and acetylcholine neurones rather than a direct action of (22) on muscarinic receptors.[243,244]

THIP (**22**) and morphine are approximately equipotent as analgesics, although their relative potencies are dependent on the animal species and experimental models used.[243] Chronic administration of (**22**) produces a certain degree of functional tolerance to its analgesic effects,[23] and there may be some cross-tolerance between (**22**) and morphine.[23] In contrast to morphine, (**22**) does not cause respiratory depression.[246] Clinical studies on post-operation patients and patients with chronic pain of malignant origin have disclosed the potent analgesic effects of (**22**) in the latter group of patients at doses of 5–30 mg (i.m.).[247] In these cancer patients and also in patients with chronic anxiety[30] the desired effects of (**22**) were accompanied by side effects, notably sedation, nausea and, in a few cases, euphoria.

Muscimol (**19**) has proved effective in conflict tests, though with a pharmacological profile different from that of diazepam (**35**);[248] in humans, (**19**) in low doses was found to sedate and calm schizophrenic patients.[249] In patients with chronic anxiety the effects of (**22**) were assessed on several measures of anxiety.[30] Although these effects were accompanied by side effects, the combination of analgesic and anxiolytic effects of (**22**) would seem to have therapeutic prospects.

The results of pharmacological studies on the spastic mouse are consistent with a role for GABA in spasticity.[250] Systemic administration of the GABA-A agonists muscimol (**19**), THIP (**22**) and isoguvacine (**30**) to cats affected spinal cord activities.[251] Since (**30**) does not readily penetrate the BBB, its pharmacological effects in this animal model may suggest that some parts of the spinal cord are not effectively protected by a BBB. Compound (**22**) has been studied in spastic patients.[252] At oral doses of 15–25 mg it clearly reduced the monosynaptic T-reflexes without affecting the flexor threshold significantly.[252]

Studies in recent years have disclosed very complex interactions between different neurotransmitter systems in the basal ganglia.[14] These interactions have been extensively studied with the intention of achieving a better insight into the mechanisms underlying schizophrenia, Parkinson's disease and different dyskinetic syndromes and, furthermore, of developing new strategies for the treatment of these severe diseases. Much interest has been focused on the nigrostriatal DA neurones, which form part of the nigrostriatal 'feedback' pathway, of which the striatonigral GABA neurones terminate within the substantia nigra (SN) pars reticulata, possibly on cholinergic neurones.

While activation of GABA receptors in SN pars reticulata of rats has dramatic behavioural consequences,[253] the DA neurones in SN pars compacta and the mesolimbic DA neurones are much less sensitive. Direct application of (**22**) in the respective brain areas actually has weak inhibitory effects on both types of DA neurones, whereas systemically administered (**22**) weakly stimulated these DA neurones.[254] No simple explanation of these apparently self-contradictory observations has, so far, been forwarded. The behavioural effects of acute and chronic administration of (**22**) have been studied.[255] DA-agonist-induced locomotor activity and stereotypies are altered by simultaneous treatment with GABA agonists, the former activity being depressed and the latter intensified. From a clinical point of view the interactions between (**22**) and neuroleptics may be particularly interesting. Most neuroleptic drugs inhibit DA-induced stereotypy and induce catalepsy in animals, the former effect being related to clinical antipsychotic effects and the latter to extrapyramidal side effects of neuroleptics.[256] Since (**22**) and also scopolamine antagonize the antistereotypic effects of some neuroleptics, it has been tentatively concluded that GABA-A agonists such as (**22**) would probably not potentiate the antipsychotic effect of neuroleptics but rather would antagonize it.[256]

The interactions between (**22**) and the central DA systems have also been studied in monkeys.[257] Analyses of the complex pharmacological profile in this animal of (**22**), which to some extent was similar to that of diazepam (**35**), led to the conclusion that (**22**) would probably have limited therapeutic effect in different kinds of dyskinesia, and (**22**) actually proved ineffective in reducing the symptoms of some dyskinetic patients.[258] Interestingly, (**22**) has recently been shown to reduce significantly the symptoms in patients suffering from tardive dyskinesia.[46]

12.7.2 GLYCINE

12.7.2.1 Physiological and Pathophysiological Roles of Glycine

The most fully documented case of an amino acid neurotransmitter is that of GABA in different areas of the mammalian brain. The pharmacology of this inhibitory system has been outlined in the previous sections of this chapter. In the spinal cord, glycine fulfils the majority of criteria expected for a neurotransmitter candidate.[1,2,259] Although the biochemical pathways for the biosynthesis of glycine are far from being mapped out in detail, a number of reactions involved in these processes have been characterized.[1,260] The rate-controlling step in the synthesis of glycine from glucose appears to be conversion of D-glycerate into hydroxypyruvate, a process which is catalyzed by D-glycerate dehydrogenase (EC 1.1.1.29). Two major possibilities exist for the production of glycine from hydroxypyruvate, the more obvious one being that *via* serine by means of the enzymes hydroxypyruvate:α-alanine (glutamate/glutamine) transferase and, subsequently, serine hydroxy-methyltransferase (EC 2.1.2.1). Alternatively, hydroxypyruvate may be transformed into glycine *via* glycolaldehyde (hydroxyacetaldehyde), glycollate and glyoxylate, the final transamination of gly-oxylate to give glycine being catalyzed by extracts of CNS tissues.

Levels of glycine are highest in the spinal cord and the brain stem, and the content of glycine in ventral grey matter is greater than that of other inhibitory amino acids including GABA, and there is evidence for *in vivo* release of endogenous glycine after physiological stimulation.[1,259,260] Two kinetically distinct transport systems appear to mediate the uptake of glycine in CNS tissues.[1,261] Although there is strong evidence for a predominantly presynaptic location of specific high affinity glycine uptake, glial components may also play a role in these processes assumed to be responsible for termination of glycine-mediated neurotransmission.[1,261]

The ability of a substance to mimic the action of the endogenous transmitter is an essential criterion for identification of the particular transmitter. Microelectrophoretic application of glycine near spinal interneurones or Renshaw cells induces a strong depressant action.[1] The underlying hyperpolarization is associated with a fall in membrane resistance and an influx of chloride ions[262] similar to the effects of electrophoretically applied GABA on single cells. However, whereas these GABA-A-receptor-mediated effects of GABA are antagonized by BMC (32) or bicuculline (82), the receptors mediating the effects of glycine are effectively blocked by strychnine (124; see Section 12.7.2.2) but not by (32) or (82).[1,263]

Since interruptions of glycine-mediated neurotransmission, such as blockade of glycine receptors, cause severe convulsions,[260] dysfunctions of the glycine system might be assumed to be implicated in epileptic phenomena. These aspects have been studied in some detail, but so far there is no convincing evidence of a role for glycine in epilepsy.[264] Nevertheless, compounds capable of stimulating glycine neurotransmission may prove to have clinically useful anticonvulsant properties. Studies in the spastic mutant mouse have disclosed marked deficits in the binding of the glycine receptor antagonist (124),[265] suggesting a pathophysiological role for glycine in spasticity.[266] Glycine appears to play an important role in the regulation of the activity of mesolimbic DA neurones,[267] indicating that glycine receptors in this supraspinal region are potential targets for therapeutic attack in disorders characterized by dysfunctions of central DA neurotransmitter systems.

12.7.2.2 Glycine Receptors, Agonists and Antagonists

Glycine[268] as well as GABA receptors[220] are coupled to membrane chloride channels which have very similar multiconductance properties.[269] These observations, combined with the distinctly different sensitivity of these receptors to agonists and antagonists, suggest that the structures of the receptor macromolecules concerned are very similar in those regions that form the channel lining, possibly differing only in the receptor units which carry the transmitter recognition sites.[269]

Based on the potency and high degree of selectivity of the alkaloid strychnine (124) as a glycine receptor antagonist,[1,262,263] this compound has been extensively used for *in vivo* and *in vitro* studies of glycine receptors.[270] Low concentrations of (124) administered microelectrophoretically on single neurones block the inhibitory effects of glycine without affecting significantly those of GABA, and tritiated (124) binds with high affinity to synaptic membranes in a saturable manner.[271] Although these binding sites show the pharmacological characteristics expected for glycine receptor sites, further studies have indicated that glycine and (124) bind to separate but mutually interactive sites at the glycine receptor–ion channel complex.[272] Additionally, the results of extensive studies using radioactive glycine and (124) are consistent with the existence of glycine receptors insensitive to (124).[273-275] There is some evidence suggesting that (124) not only blocks glycine receptors but also interacts with receptors unrelated to glycine.[270] These studies cast doubt on the utility of radioactive (124) as a specific tool for studies of synaptic glycine receptors, and the results of autoradiographic studies using this ligand[276] should be interpreted with care.

In addition to antagonizing glycine, strychnine (124) also blocks the depressant effects of a number of structurally related amino acids, including alanine (125) and proline (126).[1,277] The potent depressant effects on central neurones of β-alanine (127) are sensitive to bicuculline (82) as well as (124),[1,278] whereas the cyclic analogue of (127), β-proline (128), does not show significant neuronal depressant effects.[278] The 3-amino analogue of (128), compound (129), on the other hand, is an effective depressant of neuronal firing sensitive to (124) and has about half the potency of glycine.[278]

Compound (129) may be a useful lead structure for the development of glycine agonists of therapeutic interest.

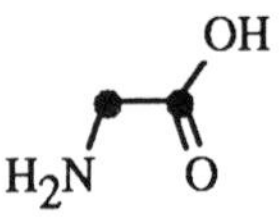

Glycine 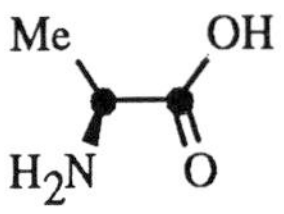   (125) 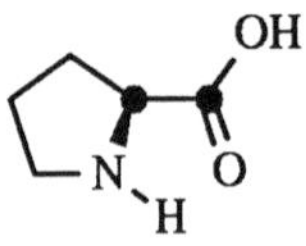   (126) 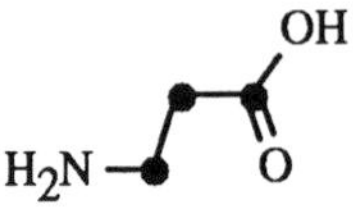   (127) 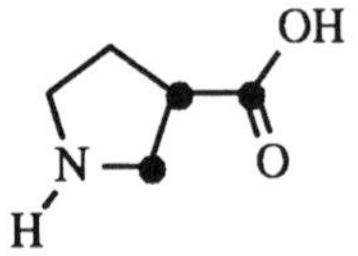   (128) 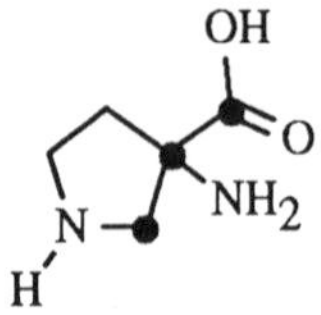   (129)

The depressant actions of glycine are also antagonized by a variety of other compounds including the strychnine (124) analogue diaboline (130).[1] Furthermore, laudanosine (131) and 1-methyl-4-formyl-4-phenylpiperidine (132) are glycine antagonists, though less potent and selective than (124).[1] Although a glycine-like fragment of the molecule of (124) which does not include the basic nitrogen atom has been tentatively identified,[279] there is a striking lack of similarity between the structures of glycine and the glycine antagonists (124) and (130)–(132).

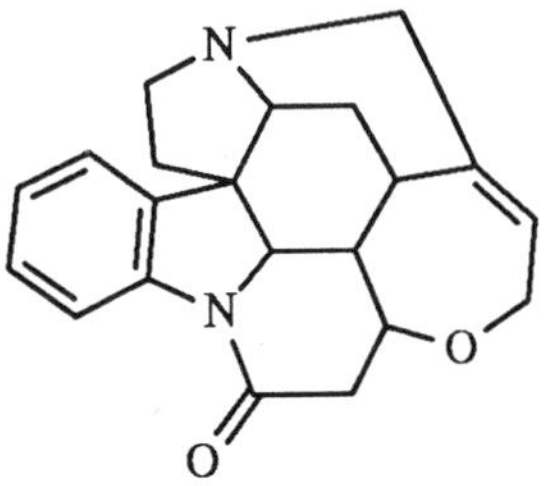

(124) 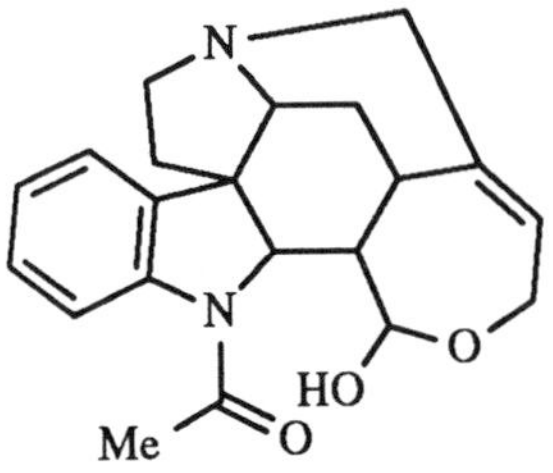   (130) 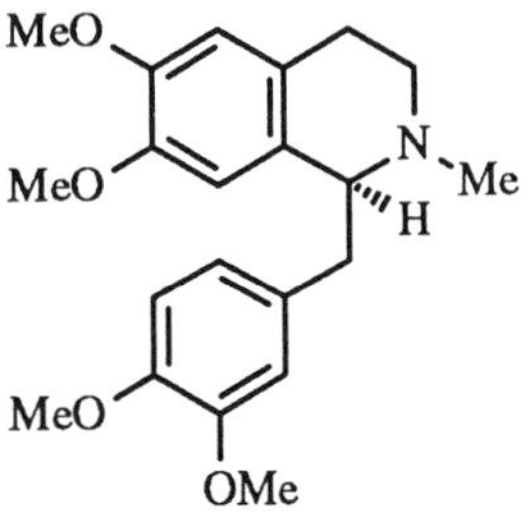   (131)

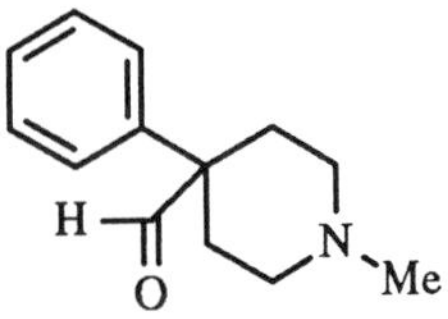

(132) 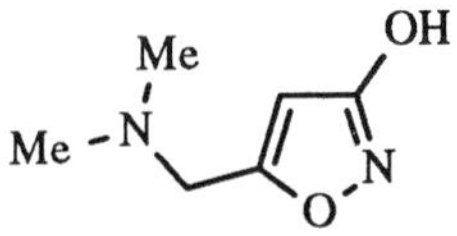   (133) 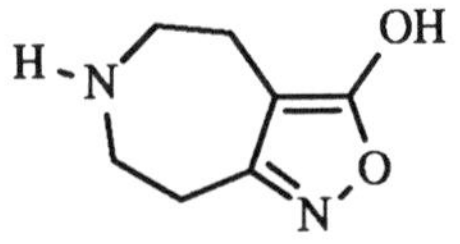   (134) 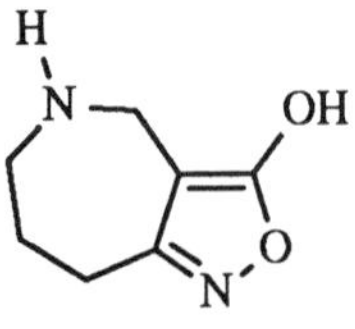   (135)

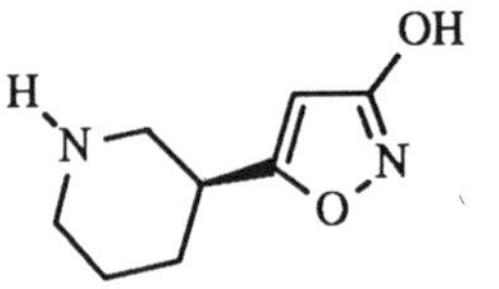

(136) 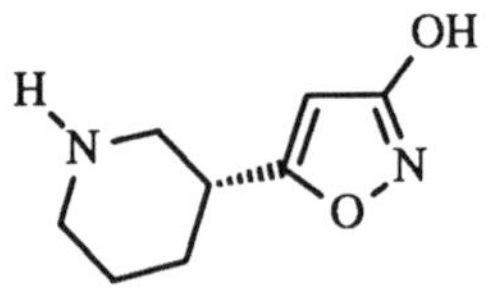   (137)

Whereas muscimol (19; see Section 12.7.1.7.1) as well as *N*-methylmuscimol[170] are GABA-A agonists, (19) being the more potent one, *N,N*-dimethylmuscimol (133) is a glycine antagonist showing no affinity for GABA-A receptors.[170] In agreement with the glycine antagonist effects of the ring homologues of the specific GABA-A agonist THIP (22), compounds (71) and (72), the 5-isoxazolol zwitterions iso-THAZ (134)[170] and iso-THAO (135)[169] block glycine-induced depression of spinal neurones. Within this class of zwitterionic glycine antagonists, the analogues (136) and (137) of the GABA-A agonist 4-PIOL (73) have recently been shown to act as glycine antagonists, the two optical isomers showing no difference in potency.[172] Although these glycine antagonists are moderately potent inhibitors of strychnine (124) binding,[280] their zwitterionic structures suggest an interaction directly with the glycine receptor rather than with the associated chloride channel, which is probably the primary site of action for (124) and related glycine antagonists.[270,272]

12.7.2.3 Glycine–GABA–Excitatory Amino Acid Interactions

There are many reports describing apparent functional interactions between GABA and glycine, in particular in certain brain regions,[281] and there is electrophysiological evidence that GABA and glycine may share the same chloride conductance channel (see Section 12.7.2.2).[282]

As discussed in previous sections, there are also many examples of 'pharmacological similarities' between GABA and glycine receptor mechanisms. Thus, a number of compounds are almost equally as effective as GABA and glycine antagonists (see Section 12.7.1.7.2), and minor alterations of GABA-A agonists frequently result in compounds with glycine antagonist properties (see Sections 12.7.1.7.1 and 12.7.2.2).

In recent years a number of observations of pharmacological interactions between GABA and glycine neurotransmitter systems have been reported. Thus, synergistic anticonvulsant effects of GABA-T inhibitors and glycine have been described[283] and, similarly, glycine amplifies the protective effect of the GABA-A agonist muscimol (**19**) against seizures caused by impairment of GABA-A-mediated neurotransmission.[284] Glycine administered concomitantly with the GABA uptake inhibitor THPO (**43**; see Section 12.7.1.5.1) also greatly enhanced the anticonvulsant effects of this latter compound.[285] Even the epileptiform EEG activities of the GABA-A antagonist SR 95103 (**89**; see Section 12.7.1.7.2) were facilitated by glycine.[286]

The mechanism(s) underlying these synergistic effects of systemically administered glycine on different types of GABAergic drugs, also administered systemically, are unknown. Pharmacokinetic factors can hardly explain these pronounced effects, which may be the result of interactions between the activated glycine and GABA-A receptors, perhaps through the chloride channel, which may be shared by these receptors.

In the case of THPO (**43**), which in addition to its effect on GABA uptake (see Section 12.7.1.5.1) has very weak glycine antagonist properties,[86,128] it is possible that abolition of this weak profile by glycine is sufficient to explain the enhanced anticonvulsant effect of this compound resulting from its inhibition of glial GABA uptake. It has recently been shown that glycine exerts a pronounced positive modulatory effect on the receptor subtype at which the excitatory amino acid *N*-methyl-D-aspartic acid (NMDA) is a selective agonist (see Section 12.7.3.5).[287] This remarkable effect of glycine has been shown to be mediated by strychnine (**124**)-insensitive glycine receptors, which form part of the NMDA receptor complex (see Figure 11).

12.7.3 EXCITATORY AMINO ACIDS

12.7.3.1 Glutamic Acid, Aspartic Acid and Related Amino Acids as Excitatory Neurotransmitters

The acidic amino acids Glu and aspartic acid (Asp) exert strong neuroexcitatory actions on most neurones in the CNS. These excitatory amino acids (EAAs) are present in all neurones, where they participate in protein and nucleotide metabolism as well as energy regulation. This ubiquitous presence and general effect on central neurones together with the precursor function of Glu in the biosynthesis of GABA (see Section 12.7.1.3) have complicated neurochemical research on these amino acids. There is, however, today a virtual consensus that Glu and probably also Asp are excitatory transmitters in the CNS.[1,7,198,199] This consensus is not based on unequivocal proof, but it is supported by a wealth of evidence obtained during the last three decades by a variety of anatomical, physiological and biochemical techniques including microelectrophoresis, receptor binding and autoradiographic techniques, and using tissue preparation and cell culture procedures.

Other amino acids with neuroexcitatory actions have been detected in the CNS and some of these compounds may also play a role in central excitatory neurotransmission mechanisms, notably (*S*)-homocysteic acid (**138**) and serine *O*-sulfate (**139**).[288] The dipeptide derivative *N*-acetylaspartyl-glutamic acid (**140**; NAAG) exists in high concentrations in the brain; it excites certain types of neurones and binds effectively to EAA receptors in the CNS.[289] Compound (**140**) and related dipeptides which are inactivated by the enzyme *N*-acetylated α-linked acidic dipeptidase (NAALA dipeptidase)[290] may have a neurotransmitter or rather a neuromodulator function in the CNS. Quinolinic acid (**141**) is an agonist at NMDA receptors (see Section 12.7.3.5.1), notably in the brain,[291] but, whereas (**141**) is unlikely to be a neurotransmitter, this endogenous compound may play a role in excitotoxic processes in the brain (see Section 12.7.3.2).[292] Similarly, methyltetra-hydrofolic acid (**142**) may be an endogenous excitotoxin[293] but, like (**141**), compound (**142**) does not seem to be an excitatory neurotransmitter in the CNS.[198,199]

12.7.3.2 Pathophysiological Roles of Excitatory Amino Acids and Excitotoxicity

Excitatory amino acids are neurotoxic, causing neuronal degeneration and ultimately cell death after local administration in brain tissues or on different types of cultured neurones.[294] There is a certain degree of correlation between the neuroexcitatory and neurotoxic potency of EAA agonists,

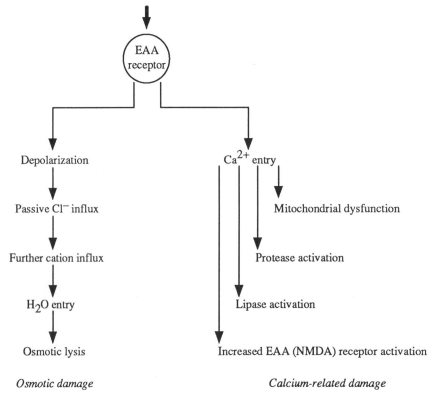

Glu   Asp   (138)   (139)

(140)   (141)   (142)

suggesting that the EAA receptors to a large extent mediate neurodegenerative processes.[294] Although the mechanisms underlying excitotoxicity are not fully understood, extensive studies in recent years have shed much light on these very complex processes causing neuronal injury (Figure 9).[295]

In the light of these findings, hyperactivity at EAA synapses has been associated with the etiology of certain neurological disorders characterized by neuronal degeneration such as epilepsy, Huntington's chorea and dementia of the Alzheimer type.[13,296,297] It must be emphasized that neurodegenerative processes are extremely complex, and overstimulation of EAA receptors certainly is only one of many possible mechanisms. The excitotoxic hypothesis is based almost exclusively on indirect evidence.[295] Glu and other EAAs can induce epileptiform neuronal activity and convulsions in animal studies,[298,299] and cause neuropathological changes similar to those observed after epileptic seizures.[300] Furthermore, antagonists at EAA receptors can prevent convulsions in animal

EAA receptor

Depolarization Ca^{2+} entry

Passive Cl^- influx   Mitochondrial dysfunction

Further cation influx   Protease activation

H_2O entry   Lipase activation

Osmotic lysis   Increased EAA (NMDA) receptor activation

Osmotic damage   *Calcium-related damage*

Figure 9   Outline of the processes involved in the neuronal degeneration induced by excitatory amino acids (EAAs)

models of epilepsy.[301,302] Huntington's chorea is characterized by degeneration of certain types of neurones, notably neurones utilizing GABA as transmitter. A similar pattern of neuronal degeneration can be observed in animal models after administration of Glu and certain agonists for central EAA receptors.[303-305] Post mortem studies of brains from Huntington's chorea patients show pronounced reduction in the number of uptake sites for Glu[306] and a decreased activity of the enzyme glutamine synthetase.[307] Both of these synaptic alterations would increase the excitotoxic activity of endogenous Glu. Alzheimer's disease is characterized by region-selective degeneration of cholinergic neurones in particular, but there also is loss of noradrenergic and serotonergic neurones in certain brain areas.[308] These alterations may be the result of dysfunctions of central Glu neurotransmitter functions.[309]

Excitotoxic mechanisms are also likely to underlie the severe neuronal injury caused by ischaemia, anoxia and hypoglycaemia.[310,311] Lathyrism is a pathological condition which may involve malfunction of EAA synaptic mechanisms. The severe neuronal degeneration characterizing this disease is probably caused by the potent neuroexcitant (*S*)-2-amino-3-(*N*-oxalylamino)propanoic acid (ODAP) present in *Lathyrus sativus*.[312]

Thus, several lines of evidence implicate hyperactivity at central EAA synapses in different pathological conditions. In principle, a number of sites at such synapses are potential sites for therapeutic attack in these disorders. The pharmacological interest has, so far, been focused primarily on the central EAA receptors. The structural requirements for activation and blockade of subtypes of EAA receptors (see Section 12.7.3.5) have been extensively studied in recent years with the aim of designing agents suitable for pharmacological manipulation of EAA receptor mechanisms in the neurological diseases and pathological conditions discussed above.

12.7.3.3 Biosynthesis, Metabolism and Uptake

The biochemistry of the central EAA neurotransmitter systems has been the subject of extensive studies during the past three decades.[1,7,55,198,199,313] Nevertheless, many aspects of the biosynthesis, metabolism and uptake of Glu, Asp and other putative central excitatory neurotransmitters are far from being completely elucidated. The most likely biosynthetic pathways for neurotransmitter Glu are those catalyzed by any one of the enzymes Asp aminotransferase (AAT), Glu dehydrogenase (GLDH), and phosphate-activated glutaminase (PAG). The high activity of AAT in Glu neurones together with the immunocytochemical localization of AAT in brain areas with known glutamatergic activity may be indicative of a special, but as yet not fully understood, role for this enzyme in neurones utilizing Glu as neurotransmitter.

The termination of the neurotransmitter action of Glu, as well as that of GABA (see Section 12.7.1.5), is accomplished by high affinity uptake into both presynaptic terminals and astroglial cells.[7,110] The relative importance of these two uptake mechanisms, in terms of capacity, at GABA- and Glu-operated synapses is, however, different, the inactivation mechanism of primary importance for Glu being the glial uptake system. In contrast to the different inhibitor/substrate characteristics of the neuronal and glial GABA uptake systems (see Section 12.7.1.5.1),[111,112] a number of analogues of Glu show very similar effects on neuronal and glial Glu uptake mechanisms.[55] (*R*)-Aspartic acid (**143**; D-Asp) is a competitive inhibitor of the uptake of Glu and Asp into neurones, but (**143**) interacts in a more complex manner with the glial uptake system(s) for these amino acids. This metabolism-resistant amino acid (**143**), which is a substrate for Glu and Asp uptake mechanisms, has been extensively used as a tracer molecule for these transmitters and a number of EAA pathways in the brain have been mapped out based on retrograde transport studies using (**143**).[313]

The metabolism of Glu in neurones and glia cells appears to differ somewhat, depending on cell type.[55] In both GABAergic neurones and glia cells, exogenously supplied Glu is metabolized primarily to carbon dioxide *via* a concerted action of GLDH and α-ketoglutarate dehydrogenase, but in Glu neurones this process appears to play only a minor role. In glia cells which, in contrast to neurones, express glutamine synthetase, Glu is predominantly metabolized to glutamine which appears to be released from these cells.[7,55]

12.7.3.4 Biological *In Vivo* and *In Vitro* Test Systems

12.7.3.4.1 *Electrophysiological techniques*

Electrophysiological techniques have been extensively used for studies of the potency and pharmacological profile of a variety of agonists at central EAA receptors.[1,2,198,199,314-319]

Multibarrel micropipettes are normally used for microelectrophoretic (microionophoretic) application of test compounds near neurones in the spinal cord or brain of animals, frequently cats or rats, and for determination of the neuronal responses to the compounds. Other preparations of CNS tissues such as brain slices, hemisected spinal cords or cultured cells have been extensively used for pharmacological and mechanistic studies of EAA receptors. In recent years, patch-clamp recording techniques have been used to provide insight into the mechanisms underlying the coupling between EAA receptors and the associated channels and the conductance states of the single channels concerned.[269,287]

12.7.3.4.2   *Receptor binding assays*

The EAA receptors are at present most conveniently subdivided into four main classes: NMDA, QUIS/AMPA, KAIN and AP4 receptors (see Section 12.7.3.5). The pharmacological characterization of these receptors is based on electrophysiological and receptor binding studies. During the last few years a wide variety of EAA agonists and antagonists have been labelled and used for receptor binding and autoradiographic studies.[198,199,314,315]

Whereas Glu and Asp show little discrimination among the various subtypes of EAA receptors, different analogues of these amino acids and a number of compounds structurally unrelated to Glu or Asp have been effectively used to characterize these receptors. Quite surprisingly, radioactive NMDA (144) cannot be used for receptor binding studies, probably due to its relatively low affinity for NMDA receptor sites.[315] On the other hand, the potent competitive NMDA antagonist 3-(2-carboxypiperazin-4-yl)propyl-1-phosphonic acid (145; CPP)[320] has proved to be a useful ligand for studies of NMDA receptor sites.[321] The non-competitive NMDA antagonists 1-(1-phenylcyclohexyl)piperidine (146; phencyclidine, PCP) and its thienyl analogue (147; TCP) have also been used as radioactive ligands for studies of the NMDA receptor complex.[322,323] The dibenzocyclohepteneimine MK-801 (148), which is the most potent non-competitive NMDA antagonist so far described,[324] has also been labelled and shown to bind effectively to the NMDA receptor complex (see Figure 11).[325] Although (2S,3S,4S)-2-carboxy-4-isopropenyl-3-pyrrolidineacetic acid (149; kainic acid, KAIN) is not a specific agonist for KAIN receptors, also showing affinity for QUIS/AMPA receptor sites,[326] radioactive (149) is a useful KAIN receptor ligand reflecting its very high affinity for this subclass of receptor sites.[327,328] The isoxazole amino acid α-amino-3-hydroxy-4-isoxazolepropionic acid (150; AMPA), which is a potent and highly selective agonist for QUIS/AMPA receptors,[316] is an effective ligand for studies of particular binding sites.[326,329] Radioactive Glu can be used as a ligand for studies of distinct subtypes of EAA receptor sites under experimental conditions where the other receptor sites are blocked by selective agonists.[315]

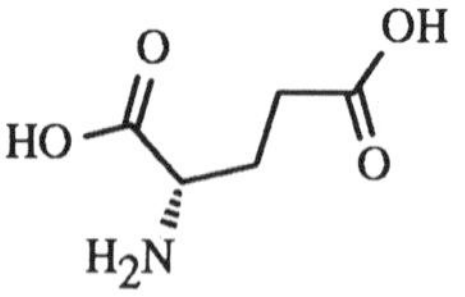

Glu 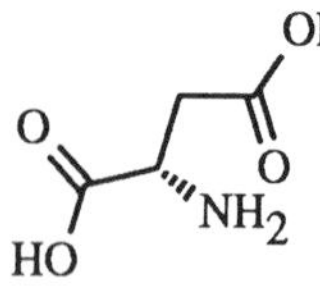   Asp 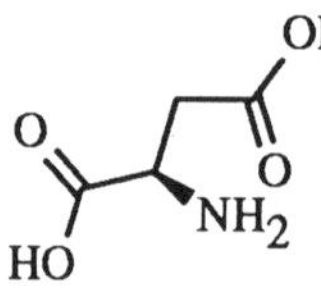   (143) 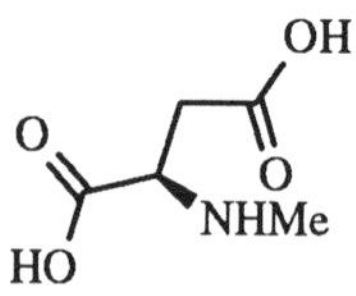   (144) 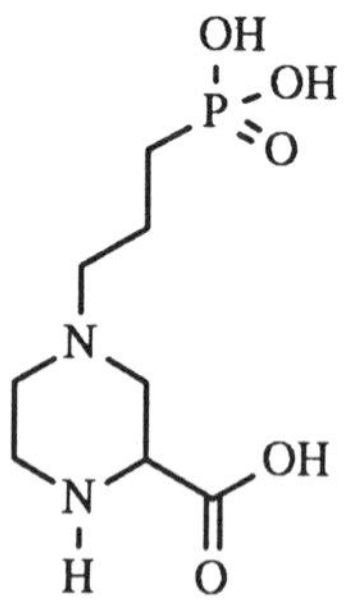   (145)

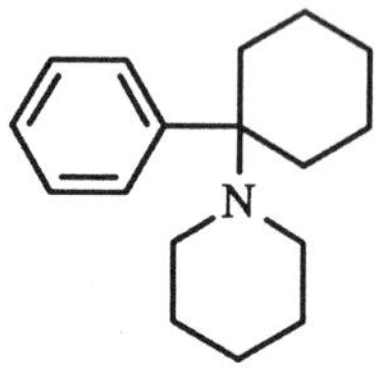

(146) 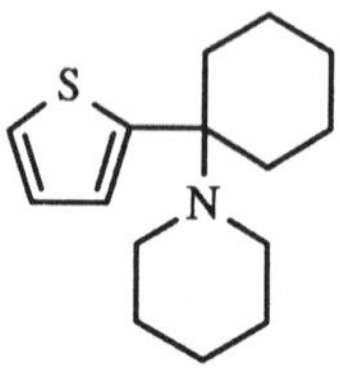   (147) 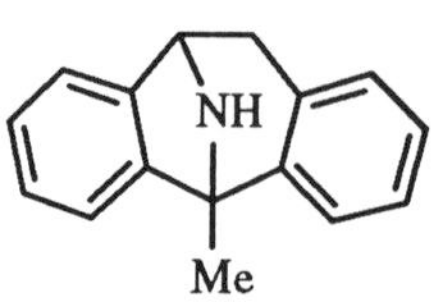   (148) 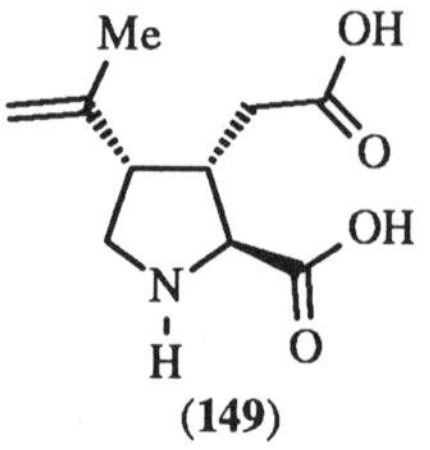   (149) 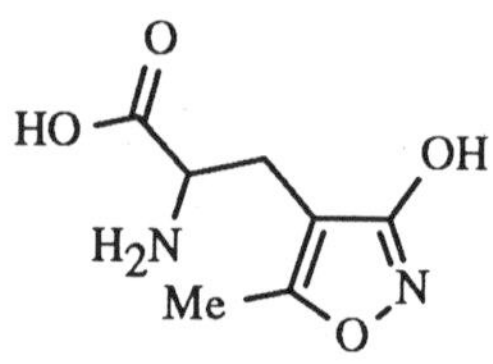   (150)

12.7.3.5 Classification of Excitatory Amino Acid Receptors

By analogy with other neurotransmitters, multiple receptors seem to exist for EAA in the CNS (Figure 10). These receptors were originally classified on the basis of electrophysiological experiments,[318,330] but this classification has since been supported by membrane receptor binding and autoradiographic studies (see Section 12.7.3.4.2).[315] It is generally accepted that Glu is an endogenous ligand for all subtypes of EAA receptors, and Asp probably also acts as a neuro-transmitter for all types of such receptors so far detected. The earlier view that the neuroexcitatory actions of Asp are selectively mediated by NMDA receptors has not been supported by receptor binding and electrophysiological studies in recent years. The endogenous sulfur-containing EAAs (138) and (139) may play a role as neurotransmitters, primarily at NMDA receptors.[288]

In addition to NMDA (144), the *Amanita muscaria* constituent ibotenic acid (151) is a potent, though not selective, agonist for NMDA receptors.[316] Interestingly, AMPA (150), which is a synthetic analogue of (151),[331] does not show any affinity for NMDA receptors.[316] As shown in Figure 10, quisqualic acid (152; QUIS) interacts with QUIS/AMPA receptors as well as with KAIN receptors.[328] The lack of selectivity of QUIS is emphasized by the observations that (152), in contrast to (150), interacts with Glu uptake mechanisms,[332] and (152) is a potent inhibitor of the enzyme NAALA dipeptidase (see Section 12.7.3.1).[290]

A number of potent and highly selective NMDA receptor antagonists, notably (R)-2-amino-5-phosphonopentanoic acid (153; D-AP5), have been developed,[333,334] and these compounds have been extremely useful for studies of NMDA receptors. A variety of compounds, including the dipeptide γ-(R)-glutamylglycine (154; γDGG), with non-selective antagonist effects on EAA receptors have been described.[333,334] QUIS/AMPA receptors were originally distinguished from KAIN receptors by the selective antagonism by the diethyl ester of Glu (155; GDEE) of the former class of receptors,[330] but lack of potency and specificity of (155) reduces its value as a pharmacological tool.[315] Further distinctions between these two subtypes of receptors have been provided by their different localizations, as demonstrated by autoradiography.[333,336] While no consistent evidence exists for a coupling of EAA receptors to adenylate cyclase, NMDA receptor activation can lead to an increase in cerebellar cGMP production,[337] and NMDA agonists, and perhaps also QUIS/AMPA receptor agonists, can increase phosphatidylinositol turnover.[338]

Although the three receptor classes are reasonably well-characterized pharmacologically, they are by no means well-defined molecular entities, and subclassification of both NMDA and QUIS/AMPA has been suggested.[339,340] In addition, other receptor types have been

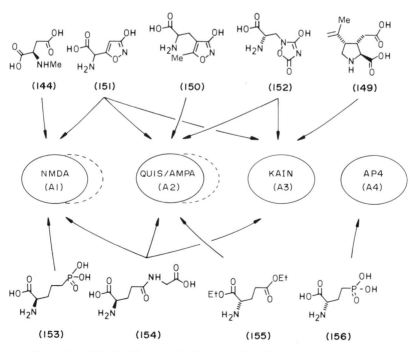

Figure 10 Schematic illustration of the classification of excitatory amino acid receptors and structures of some agonists and antagonists

proposed,[314,341] notably one which appears to mediate the antagonism of synaptic excitation by (*S*)-2-amino-4-phosphonobutanoic acid (**156**; L-APB) in the hippocampus.[342] NMDA receptor antagonists do not antagonize synaptic excitation at this proposed L-APB receptor (Figure 10), and (**156**) does not affect excitations induced by (**144**), (**149**) or (**152**), nor does it affect Glu-induced excitation. The lack of effect of (**156**) on excitations induced by NMDA, QUIS/AMPA or KAIN agonists may indicate a presynaptic localization of L-APB receptors.[315]

In the light of the lack of specificity of some of the compounds which have given names to the EAA receptors, notably KAIN (**149**) and QUIS (**152**), the traditional nomenclature for EAA receptors is rather unfortunate and alternative nomenclature systems have been proposed,[315,340] as exemplified in Figure 10. However, none of these proposals has become widely recognized as yet.

The physiological relevance of the receptor classification depicted in Figure 10 is not clear, and there is an urgent need for selective antagonists at QUIS/AMPA and KAIN receptors for studies of the physiological functions and pharmacological importance of these receptors. There are some indications that QUIS/AMPA receptors are playing an important role in monosynaptic excitatory transmission, whereas NMDA receptors are probably mediating polysynaptic excitatory mechanisms.[343]

The NMDA receptor is actually a receptor complex (Figure 11).[315,337,344] There are some indications that the site of action of the competitive NMDA receptor antagonists is not identical with the agonist recognition site of this receptor.[345] The NMDA receptor is probably not activated by fast low-frequency excitatory transmission.[344] It is coupled to ion channels which, in contrast to those associated with QUIS/AMPA or KAIN receptors, show a voltage-dependent blockade by magnesium, which is released following increasing depolarization of the neuronal membranes.[346] At physiological concentrations of magnesium and resting membrane potential or low frequency stimulation, the postsynaptic cells are insufficiently depolarized to release the magnesium blockade of the ion channel, rendering the NMDA receptor complex virtually inactivated. Following membrane depolarization, for example *via* activation of QUIS/AMPA or KAIN receptors in the cell membrane, the magnesium blockade is released causing further depolarization.[315,344] Thus, the NMDA receptor appears to function as an amplification system capable of generating long-lasting physiological changes, and it has been associated with the phenomenon of long-term potentiation (LTP), which is a sustained increase in synaptic sensitivity following high frequency

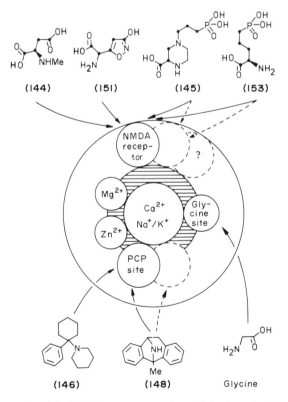

Figure 11   Schematic illustration of the NMDA receptor complex and the sites of action of different compounds

stimulation.[344,347] LTP can last for weeks and may play a key role in memory and learning processes.[348] This component of synaptic plasticity mediated by NMDA receptors may be involved in the processes causing neuronal damage and epileptiform activity (see Section 12.7.3.2), and these aspects have brought the NMDA receptor complex into focus as a potential target for therapeutic attack in certain neurological diseases.[337]

The NMDA receptor complex also contains distinct binding sites for zinc ions[349] and for glycine[287] which are closely associated with the ion channel of this complex (Figure 11). The physiological roles of these additional sites are unknown, but activation of the latter site, which is distinctly different from the strychnine-sensitive glycine receptor (see Section 12.7.2.2), strongly potentiates the responses to NMDA (**144**) *via* allosteric interactions with the NMDA receptor site.[350]

The dissociative anaesthetics such as PCP (**146**) selectively inhibit NMDA (**144**)-associated excitatory effects without affecting excitation induced by agonists at QUIS/AMPA or KAIN receptors.[337,344,351,352] These effects correlate with the ability of such compounds to displace the binding of radioactive PCP (**146**) or TCP (**147**; see Section 12.7.3.4.2).[337,344] The binding site for MK-801 (**148**) is closely associated with that for (**146**) and (**147**), but these two binding sites are apparently non-identical.[337,344] In agreement with the findings for blockade by magnesium of NMDA (**144**) responses, (**148**), (**146**) and other dissociative anaesthetics block NMDA responses in a voltage-dependent manner, indicating a close association between the binding sites concerned and the ion channel (Figure 11).[337] Furthermore, the blockade of binding sites for (**146**) and (**148**) is use-dependent, in that a prerequisite for this antagonist effect is the presence of an NMDA receptor agonist, suggesting that opening of the ion channel uncovers these binding sites, which are distinctly different from σ-opiate receptor sites.[344]

12.7.3.5.1 NMDA receptor agonists

Besides Glu, Asp and NMDA (**144**), a number of structurally related compounds show NMDA receptor agonist profiles.[334] The *trans* forms of piperidine-2,4-dicarboxylic acid and piperidine-2,3-dicarboxylic acid, (**157**) and (**158**) respectively, are NMDA receptor agonists, whereas the *cis* form of (**158**), compound (**159**), is a relatively selective antagonist at NMDA receptors.[334] This difference in pharmacological profile may be related to different degrees of conformational mobility of these cyclic amino acids.[353] Whereas the agonists (**157**) and (**158**) are conformationally flexible compounds, the antagonist (**159**) is much more rigid, suggesting that the NMDA agonist–receptor complex undergoes a conformational change during activation of the receptor. The conformational mobility of the NMDA agonist 1-amino-*cis*-cyclopentane-1,3-dicarboxylic acid (**160**; c-1,3-ADCP)[314] has not been studied, but the glycine moiety of the potent NMDA agonist ibotenic acid (**151**) can adopt a variety of energetically similar conformations.[354] While (**151**), which is a Glu analogue, is a potent but non-selective NMDA agonist, the corresponding analogue of Asp, α-amino-3-hydroxy-5-methyl-4-isoxazoleacetic acid (**161**; AMAA) is a more selective but weaker agonist at NMDA receptors.[316] Similarly, the Glu analogue homoquinolinic acid (**162**) is more potent than quinolinic acid (**141**), which is structurally related to Asp, as an agonist at NMDA receptors.[355] The physicochemical and conformational properties of (**141**) and (**162**) are obviously

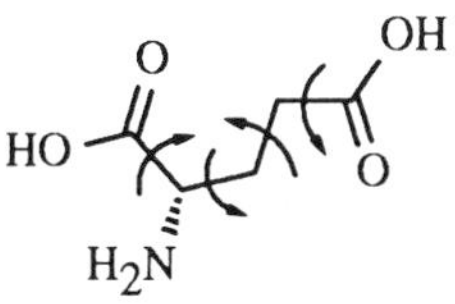

Glu 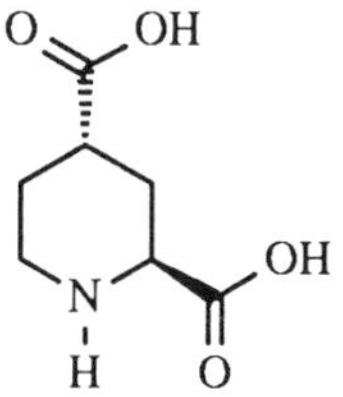 (157) 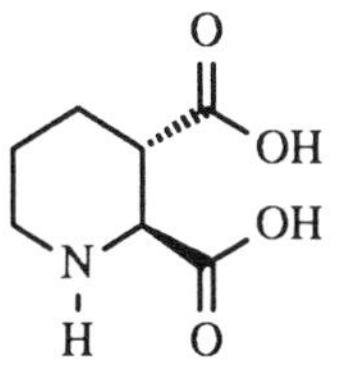 (158) 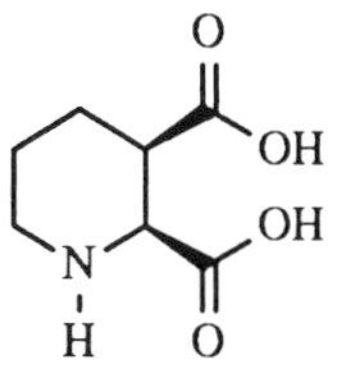 (159) 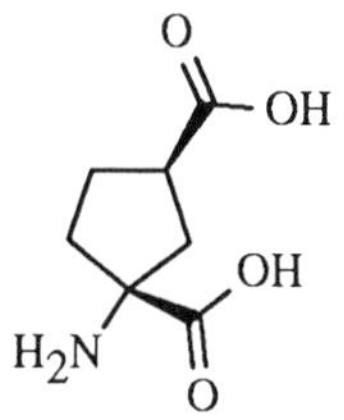 (160)

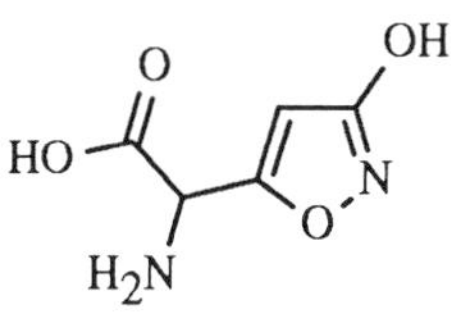

(151) 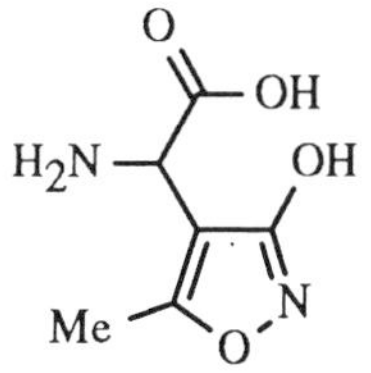 (161) 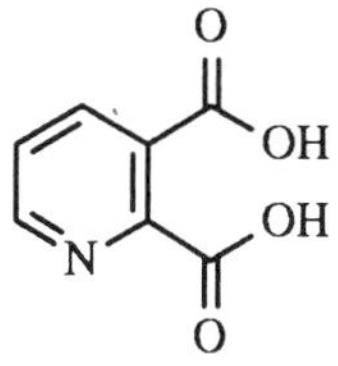 (141) 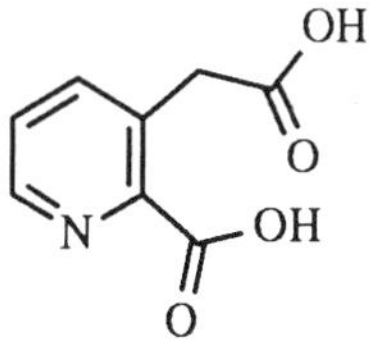 (162)

very different from those of other NMDA receptor agonists. These aspects compared with the regional variations in sensitivity of NMDA receptors to NMDA (144) and (141) may reflect that these two ligands interact with different receptors which show very similar sensitivity to NMDA antagonists.[356] This apparent heterogeneity of NMDA receptors (Figure 10) is interesting in the light of the considerable therapeutic interest in NMDA antagonists and, perhaps, agonists, the latter compounds being potential drugs in disorders characterized by learning and memory impairments.

12.7.3.5.2 *Competitive and non-competitive NMDA receptor antagonists*

The discovery of the potent and highly selective NMDA receptor antagonist effects of D-AP5 (153) and AP7 (163)[333,334] prompted the development of a variety of structurally related phosphono amino acids.[337] This interest was greatly stimulated by the observation that the neutral analogue of (163), CPP (145), is a very active competitive NMDA antagonist showing a surprisingly high capacity for penetrating the BBB.[320,321] More recently, the aromatic analogue of (163), NPC 451 (164), and the piperidine analogue of (153), CGS 19755 (165), have been developed and shown to be selective and very potent competitive NMDA antagonists, which, like (145) and (163), have therapeutic interest.[337]

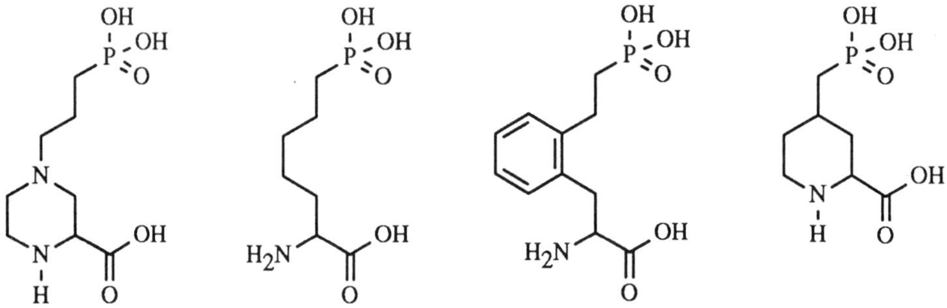

MK-801 (148) is probably the most potent and selective non-competitive antagonist at the PCP site or a closely associated site at the NMDA receptor complex (Figure 11).[344] Furthermore, the agonist dependency (use dependency) of (148) is more pronounced than that determined for other members of this particular class of compounds, including ketamine (166), the morphinan derivative dextrorphan (167), dexoxadrol (168) and MLV 5860 (169).[337,344] None of the compounds (166)–(169) interact selectively with the NMDA receptor complex, showing more or less pronounced affinity for σ-opiate and other receptor sites.[344]

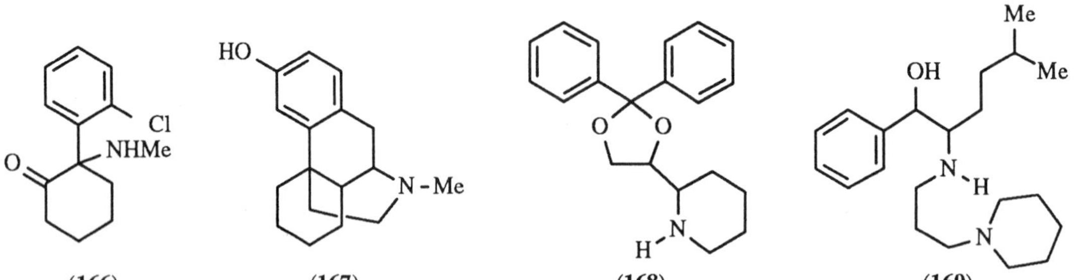

12.7.3.5.3 *QUIS/AMPA receptor agonists*

The pharmacological profile of the heterocyclic amino acid willardiine (170) appears to be similar to that of the potent but non-selective QUIS/AMPA agonist QUIS (152).[357] The potency and high degree of selectivity of AMPA (150) as a QUIS/AMPA receptor agonist[316] form the basis of its increasing use as a ligand for studies of this particular class of receptors (see Section 12.7.3.5) and as a lead for the design of other agonists for these receptors.[354] The conformationally restricted analogue of (150), 3-hydroxy-4,5,6,7-tetrahydroisoxazolo[5,4-*c*]pyridine-5-carboxylic acid (171; 5-HPCA)[358] and the isomeric compound 7-HPCA (172)[359] are QUIS/AMPA receptor agonists with potencies and degrees of selectivity similar to that of (**150**). Similarly, analogues of homoibotenic acid containing substituents in the 4-position of the ring, such as 4-bromohomoibotenic acid (**173**), are very active QUIS/AMPA receptor agonists.[316,340] Structure–activity studies on (**171**) and (**172**) indicate that conformational mobility is not a necessary condition for agonist action at QUIS/AMPA receptors as it was suggested to be for NMDA receptors (see Section 12.7.3.5.1). It is reasonable to assume that 5-HPCA (**171**) essentially reflects the receptor-active conformation of AMPA (**150**).[358]

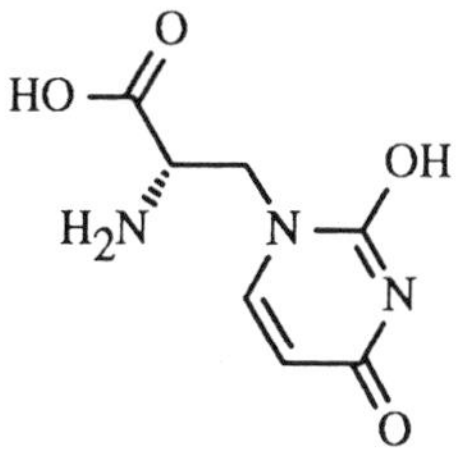

(**170**) 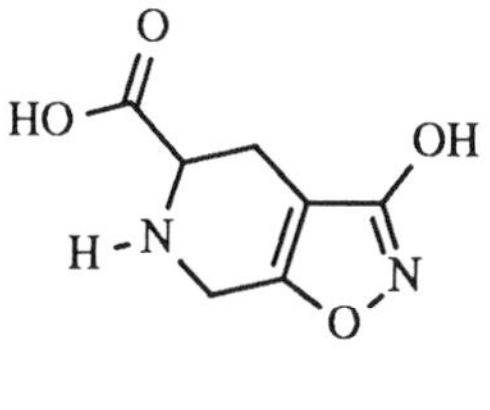   (**171**) 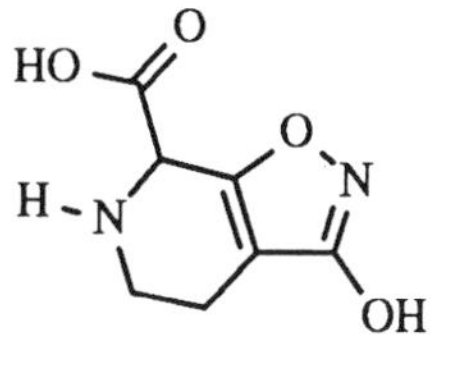   (**172**) 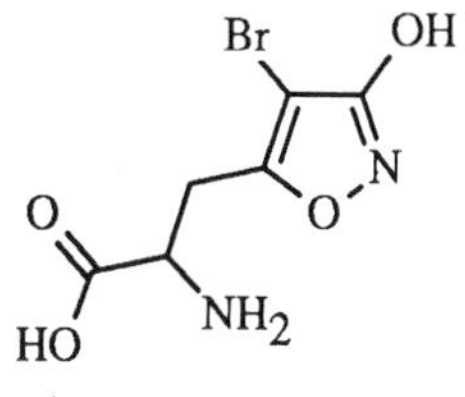   (**173**)

12.7.3.5.4 KAIN receptor agonists

The prototypic agonist at KAIN receptors is KAIN (**149**) itself (see Section 12.7.3.5). The β analogue of (**149**), compound (**174**), is virtually devoid of affinity for KAIN receptor sites,[360] whereas the naturally occurring amino acid domoic acid (**175**) is at least as potent as (**149**) as an agonist at KAIN receptors.[317,328] More recently, the mushroom constituent acromelic acid *A* (**176**), which like (**175**) is an analogue of (**149**), has been shown to depolarize crayfish opener muscle fibres more potently than (**149**) or (**175**) and to reduce the response of this preparation to QUIS (**152**).[361]

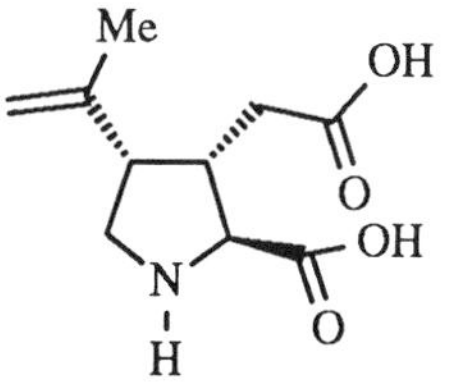

(**149**) 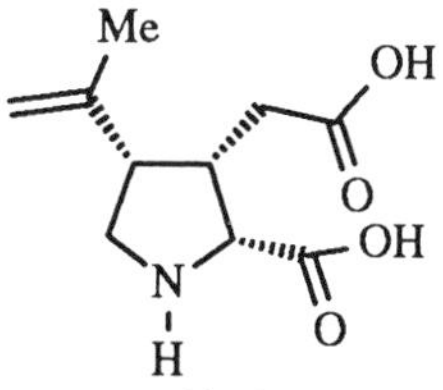   (**174**)

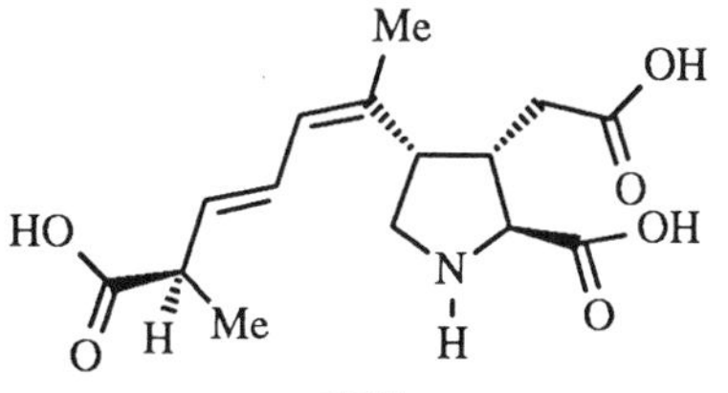

(**175**) 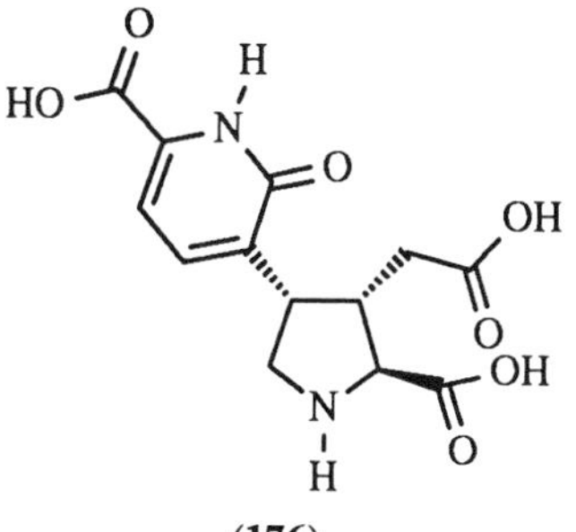   (**176**)

12.7.3.5.5 Non-selective antagonists at QUIS/AMPA and KAIN receptors

So far, selective antagonists for QUIS/AMPA or KAIN receptors have not been described. GDEE (**155**) shows selective antagonism at the former class of receptors in some but not all biological systems.[1,314] A number of compounds including γ-D-glutamylaminomethylsulfonic acid (**177**; GAMS), 1-(4-bromobenzoyl)piperazine-2,3-dicarboxylic acid (**178**) and the tryptophan metabolite 4-hydroxy-2-quinolinecarboxylic acid (**179**; kynurenic acid) are broad spectrum antagonists, which, like (**154**; Figure 10) interact non-selectively with all classes of EAA receptors, though with somewhat different pharmacological profiles.[334] It is possible that the endogenous EAA receptor antagonist (**179**)[362,363] plays a role in the regulation of central excitatory neurotransmission processes.

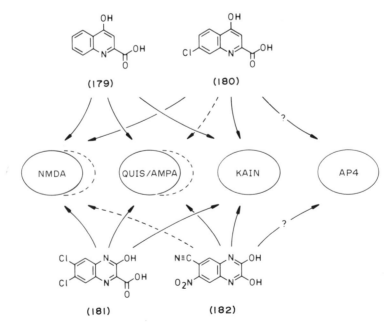

A number of compounds structurally related to **(179)** have been shown to interact potently with central EAA receptors as antagonists (Figure 12). In general, the members of this rapidly growing family of compounds, showing a striking lack of structural similarity with Glu and EAA agonists, interact more or less non-selectively with EAA receptors. 7-Chlorokynurenic acid **(180)** does, however, show some selectivity for NMDA and KAIN receptors,[364] whereas CNQX/FG 9065 **(182)** blocks excitation mediated by QUIS/AMPA and KAIN receptors more effectively than NMDA-induced excitation.[365, 366]

Using AMPA **(150)** as a lead structure, a variety of structurally related 3-isoxazolol amino acids have been synthesized and tested, including α-amino-3-hydroxy-5-*t*-butyl-4-isoxazolepropionic acid **(183;** ATPA**)** and α-amino-3-hydroxy-5-bromomethyl-4-isoxazolepropionic acid **(184;** ABPA; Figure 13).[358, 359] ATPA **(183)** is only slightly weaker than AMPA **(150)**, and ABPA **(184)** is actually at least as potent as **(150)** as a specific QUIS/AMPA receptor agonist, suggesting that this receptor has a 'cavity' capable of accommodating bulky substituents of agonist molecules (Figure 13).[367, 368] The fact that **(184)**, which has the chemically reactive bromomethyl moiety in a position corresponding to that of the bulky *t*-butyl group of **(183)**, does not interact irreversibly with QUIS/AMPA receptors *in vivo* or *in vitro*[358] seems to support this view. These structure–activity studies have led to the development of the hypothetical model for the recognition site of the QUIS/AMPA receptor illustrated in Figure 13.[367, 368] Assisted by this primitive receptor model, it has very recently been possible to 'convert' the potent and highly selective QUIS/AMPA agonist AMPA **(150)** into non-NMDA antagonists.[369] This line of research is in a state of extensive investigation.

Figure 12 Structures and sites of action of kynurenic acid **(179)** and a number of structurally related non-selective EAA receptor antagonists

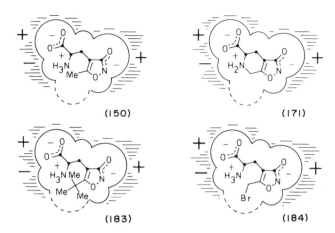

(150)   (171)

(183)   (184)

Figure 13 A hypothetical model of the QUIS/AMPA receptor based on structure–activity studies of AMPA (150) and a number of structurally related QUIS/AMPA receptor agonists

12.7.3.6 Pharmacology of Excitatory Amino Acid Antagonists

The therapeutic prospects of EAA antagonists and, perhaps, agonists have almost exclusively been discussed in relation to the NMDA receptors as a reflection of the compounds available. NMDA antagonists were first recognized as having clinical potential as anticonvulsants.[297, 370] Competitive NMDA antagonists such as CPP (145) produce anticonflict animal behaviour suggestive of anxiolytic potential.[371] After systemic administration, NMDA antagonists produce effects in animal studies that have been ascribed to central muscle relaxant effects,[372] and such compounds actually produce muscle relaxation after intrathecal administration.[373] This pharmacological profile of NMDA antagonists may have therapeutic application, but it does, on the other hand, represent an undesired side effect in other potential clinical situations.

The possible role of EAAs in neurodegenerative diseases (see Section 12.7.3.2) has brought EAA receptor antagonists, and in particular NMDA antagonists, into focus as neuroprotective drugs. When administered systemically or intracerebrally, competitive as well as non-competitive NMDA antagonists can block the neurodegeneration caused by hypoglycaemia or induced in animal models of stroke.[295, 344]

Competitive as well as non-competitive NMDA antagonists obviously have therapeutic potential. The therapeutic utility of such compounds is, however, not straightforward, since NMDA receptors probably play an important role in LTP and, thus, in learning processes (see Section 12.7.3.5).[374] In general, both types of NMDA antagonists induce confusional states, amnesia and muscle relaxation.[337] Non-competitive NMDA antagonists may have psychomimetic properties in man which raises doubts about their therapeutic prospects.[344] These aspects have not been fully elucidated yet, and it is not known whether competitive and non-competitive NMDA antagonists show identical pharmacological profiles in man. It will be interesting to compare the pharmacological properties of NMDA antagonists with antagonists at QUIS/AMPA and KAIN receptors which are at present under development.

12.7.4 REFERENCES

1. D. R. Curtis and G. A. R. Johnston, *Ergeb. Physiol., Biol. Chem. Exp. Pharmakol.*, 1974, **69**, 97.
2. K. Krnjevic, *Physiol. Rev.*, 1974, **54**, 418.
3. E. Roberts, T. N. Chase and D. B. Tower (eds.), 'GABA in Nervous System Function', Raven Press, New York, 1976.
4. P. Krogsgaard-Larsen, J. Scheel-Krüger and H. Kofod (eds.), 'GABA-Neurotransmitters. Pharmacochemical, Biochemical and Pharmacological Aspects', Munksgaard, Copenhagen, 1979.
5. P. Mandel and F. V. DeFeudis (eds.), 'GABA—Biochemistry and CNS Functions', Plenum Press, New York, 1979.
6. Y. Okada and E. Roberts (eds.), 'Problems in GABA Research from Brain to Bacteria', Excerpta Medica, Amsterdam, 1982.
7. L. Hertz, E. Kvamme, E. G. McGeer and A. Schousboe (eds.), 'Glutamine, Glutamate, and GABA in the Central Nervous System', Liss, New York, 1983.
8. S. J. Enna (ed.), 'The GABA Receptors', Humana Press, Clifton, NJ, 1983.
9. N. G. Bowery (ed.), 'Actions and Interactions of GABA and Benzodiazepines', Raven Press, New York, 1984.

10. R. W. Olsen and J. C. Venter (eds.), 'Benzodiazepine/GABA Receptors and Chloride Channels. Structural and Functional Properties', Liss, New York, 1986.
11. S. L. Erdö and N. G. Bowery (eds.), 'GABAergic Mechanisms in Mammalian Periphery', Raven Press, New York, 1986.
12. T. N. Chase and J. R. Walters, in 'GABA in Nervous System Function', ed. E. Roberts, T. N. Chase and D. B. Tower, Raven Press, New York, 1976, p. 497.
13. T. N. Chase, N. S. Wexler and A. Barbeau (eds.), 'Huntington's Disease', Raven Press, New York, 1979.
14. G. DiChiara and G. L. Gessa (eds.), 'GABA and the Basal Ganglia', Raven Press, New York, 1981.
15. R. D. Allan and G. A. R. Johnston, *Med. Res. Rev.*, 1983, **3**, 91.
16. P. Krogsgaard-Larsen, E. Falch and H. Hjeds, *Prog. Med. Chem.*, 1985, **22**, 67.
17. P. Krogsgaard-Larsen, H. Hjeds, E. Falch, F. S. Jørgensen and L. Nielsen, *Adv. Drug Res.*, 1988, **17**, 381.
18. S. J. Enna, *Biochem. Pharmacol.*, 1981, **30**, 907.
19. G. Racagni and A. O. Donoso (eds.), 'GABA and Endocrine Function', Raven Press, New York, 1986.
20. F. V. DeFeudis, *Neurochem. Int.*, 1981, **3**, 113.
21. E. Mesdjian, F. V. DeFeudis, G. Jadot, M. Valli, B. Brugerolle and P. Bouyard, *Drug Dev. Res.*, 1983, **3**, 311.
22. G. K. Matheson, E. Freed and G. Tunnicliff, *Gen. Pharmacol.*, 1987, **18**, 269.
23. T. Andree, D. A. Kendall and S. J. Enna, *Life Sci.*, 1983, **32**, 2265.
24. M. D. Hynes, J. D. Leander, R. C. A. Frederickson, P. P. K. Ho, D. W. Johnson and R. A. Archer, *Drug Dev. Res.*, 1984, **4**, 405.
25. S. P. Sivam and I. K. Ho, *Life Sci.*, 1985, **37**, 199.
26. J.-L. Moreau and H. L. Fields, *Brain Res.*, 1986, **397**, 37.
27. S. H. Zorn and S. J. Enna, *Neuropharmacology*, 1987, **26**, 433.
28. J. Sawynok, *Pharmacol., Biochem. Behav.*, 1987, **26**, 463.
29. S.-C. Cheng and E. A. Brunner, *Anesthesiology*, 1985, **63**, 147.
30. R. Hoehn-Saric, *Psychopharmacology*, 1983, **80**, 338.
31. G. Biggio and E. Costa (eds.), 'GABAergic Transmission and Anxiety', Raven Press, New York, 1986.
32. L. Ciesielski, S. Simler, J. Clement and P. Mandel, *J. Neurochem.*, 1985, **45**, 244.
33. N. Blavet, F. V. DeFeudis and F. Clostre, *Psychopharmacology*, 1982, **76**, 75.
34. P. L. Morselli, W. Löscher, K. G. Lloyd, B. Meldrum and E. H. Reynolds (eds.), 'Neurotransmitters, Seizures, and Epilepsy', Raven Press, New York, 1981.
35. R. G. Fariello, P. L. Morselli, K. G. Lloyd, L. F. Quesney and J. Engel (eds.), 'Neurotransmitters, Seizures, and Epilepsy II', Raven Press, New York, 1984.
36. G. Nistico, P. L. Morselli, K. G. Lloyd, R. G. Fariello and J. Engel (eds.), 'Neurotransmitters, Seizures, and Epilepsy III', Raven Press, New York, 1986.
37. C. E Ribak, *Brain Res.*, 1985, **326**, 251.
38. R. W. Olsen, J. K. Wamsley, R. T. McCabe, J. L. Randall and P. Lomax, *Proc. Natl. Acad. Sci. U.S.A.*, 1985, **82**, 6701.
39. C. R. Houser, A. B. Harris and J. E. Vaughn, *Brain Res.*, 1986, **383**, 129.
40. S. Piredda, M. Pavlick and K. Gale, *Epilepsy Res.*, 1987, **1**, 102.
41. B. Meldrum, *Clin. Neuropharmacol.*, 1982, **5**, 293.
42. P. C. Van Ness, A. E. Watkins, M. O. Bergman, W. W. Tourtellotte and R. W. Olsen, *Neurology*, 1982, **32**, 63.
43. S. J. Kish, K. S. Shannak, T. L. Perry and O. Hornykiewicz, *J. Neurochem.*, 1983, **41**, 1495.
44. D. P. Van Kammen, D. E. Sternberg, T. A. Hare and R. N. Waters, *Arch. Gen. Psychiatry*, 1982, **39**, 91.
45. S. Hanada, T. Mita, N. Nishino and C. Tanaka, *Life Sci.*, 1987, **40**, 259.
46. G. K. Thaker, C. A. Tamminga, L. D. Alphs, J. Lafferman, T. N. Ferraro and T. A. Hare, *Arch. Gen. Psychiatry*, 1987, **44**, 522.
47. C. D. Marsden and M. P. Sheehy, in 'GABA and the Basal Ganglia', ed. G. DiChiara and G. L. Gessa, Raven Press, New York, 1981, p. 225.
48. J. P. Bennett, M. B. Ferrari and C. J. Cruz, *Ann. Neurol.*, 1987, **21**, 41.
49. K. G. Lloyd and A. Pilc, *Neuropharmacology*, 1984, **23**, 841.
50. F. Petty and J. A. Coffman, *Neuropharmacology*, 1984, **23**, 859.
51. G. D. Frye, T. J. McCown and G. R. Breese, *J. Pharmacol. Exp. Ther.*, 1983, **226**, 720.
52. S. K. Rastogi, S. Thyagarajan, J. Clothier and M. K. Ticku, *Neuropharmacology*, 1986, **25**, 1179.
53. R. Balazs, Y. Machiyama, B. J. Hammond, T. Julian and D. Richter, *Biochem. J.*, 1970, **116**, 445.
54. S. Lindgren and N.-E. Anden, *J. Neural Transm.*, 1985, **61**, 21.
55. A. Schousboe, *Biochem. Soc. Trans.*, 1987, **15**, 205.
56. G. A. R. Johnston and V. J. Balcar, In 'GABA: From Basic Research to Clinical Implications', ed. N. G. Bowery, Pythagora Press, Rome, 1989, in press.
57. N. Seiler, *Neurochem. Res.*, 1981, **6**, 95.
58. S. Matsushima, S. Hori and M. Matsuda, *Neurochem. Res.*, 1986, **11**, 1313.
59. O. Carter Snead, III, *J. Neurochem.*, 1987, **48**, 196.
60. V. Hechler, D. Weissmann, E. Mach, J.-F. Pujol and M. Maitre, *J. Neurochem.*, 1987, **49**, 1025.
61. R. W. Horton, A. G. Chapman and B. S. Meldrum, *J. Neurochem.*, 1978, **30**, 1501.
62. R. W. Horton, *Biochem. Pharmacol.*, 1978, **27**, 1471.
63. T. G. Porter and D. L. Martin, *Biochem. Pharmacol.*, 1985, **34**, 4145.
64. E. Crystal, P. Bey and R. R. Rando, *J. Neurochem.*, 1979, **32**, 1501.
65. J. H. Skerritt and G. A. R. Johnston, *Brain Res.*, 1983, **258**, 165.
66. R. B. Silverman and S. J. Hoffman, *Med. Res. Rev.*, 1984, **4**, 415.
67. R. R. Rando, *Pharmacol. Rev.*, 1984, **36**, 111.
68. C. Walsh, *Annu. Rev. Biochem.*, 1984, **53**, 493.
69. G. A. R. Johnston, R. D. Allan, S. M. E. Kennedy and B. Twitchin, in 'GABA-Neurotransmitters. Pharmacochemical, Biochemical and Pharmacological Aspects', ed. P. Krogsgaard-Larsen, J. Scheel-Krüger and H. Kofod, Munksgaard, Copenhagen, 1979, p. 149.
70. R. B. Silverman, S. C. Durkee and B. J. Invergo, *J. Med. Chem.*, 1986, **29**, 764.
71. L. J. Fowler, D. H. Lovell and R. A. John, *J. Neurochem.*, 1983, **41**, 1751.
72. P. Krogsgaard-Larsen, *Med. Res. Rev.*, 1988, **8**, 27.

73. P. Krogsgaard-Larsen and G. A. R. Johnston, *J. Neurochem.*, 1978, **30**, 1377.
74. C. Danzig and M. J. Jung, in 'Chemical and Biological Aspects of Vitamin B$_6$ Catalysis: Part A', ed. A. E. Evangelopoulos, Liss, New York, 1984, p. 377.
75. B. W. Metcalf, M. J. Jung, B. Lippert, P. Casara, P. Böhlen and P. J. Schechter, in 'GABA-Neurotransmitters. Pharmacochemical, Biochemical and Pharmacological Aspects', ed. P. Krogsgaard-Larsen, J. Scheel-Krüger and H. Kofod, Munksgaard, Copenhagen, 1979, p. 236.
76. M. J. Jung, J. G. Heydt and P. Casara, *Biochem. Pharmacol.*, 1984, **33**, 3717.
77. R. B. Silverman, B. J. Invergo and J. Mathew, *J. Med. Chem.*, 1986, **29**, 1840.
78. B. S. Meldrum and K. Murugaiah, *Eur. J. Pharmacol.*, 1983, **89**, 149.
79. A. Schousboe, O. M. Larsson and N. Seiler, *Neurochem. Res.*, 1986, **11**, 1497.
80. R. R. Rando, *Biochemistry*, 1977, **16**, 4604.
81. B. W. Metcalf and M. J. Jung, *Mol. Pharmacol.*, 1979, **16**, 539.
82. J. P. Burkhart, G. W. Holbert and B. W. Metcalf, *Tetrahedron Lett.*, 1984, **25**, 5267.
83. D. R. Curtis, A. W. Duggan, D. Felix and G. A. R. Johnston, *Brain Res.*, 1971, **32**, 69.
84. D. R. Curtis, C. J. A. Game and D. Lodge, *Exp. Brain Res.*, 1976, **25**, 413.
85. G. G. Yarbrough, *Can. J. Physiol. Pharmacol.*, 1978, **56**, 443.
86. P. Krogsgaard-Larsen, G. A. R. Johnston, D. R. Curtis, C. J. A. Game and R. M. McCulloch, *J. Neurochem.*, 1975, **25**, 803.
87. W. D. Matthews, G. P. McCafferty and P. E. Setler, *Neuropharmacology*, 1981, **20**, 561.
88. M. S. Jensen and J. D. C. Lambert, *Neuropharmacology*, 1984, **23**, 1441.
89. J. L. Barker, N. L. Harrison and A. P. Mariani, *Life Sci.*, 1986, **39**, 1959.
90. S. J. Korn and R. Dingledine, *Brain Res.*, 1986, **368**, 247.
91. G. A. R. Johnston, in 'The GABA Receptors', ed S. J. Enna, Humana Press, Clifton, NJ, 1983, p. 107.
92. S. J. Enna and S. H. Snyder, *Brain Res.*, 1975, **100**, 81.
93. R. W. Olsen, *J. Neurochem.*, 1981, **37**, 1.
94. F. V. DeFeudis, *Neuroscience*, 1980, **5**, 675.
95. E. Falch and P. Krogsgaard-Larsen, *J. Neurochem.*, 1982, **38**, 1123.
96. A. M. Morin and C. G. Wasterlain, *Life Sci.*, 1980, **26**, 1239.
97. P. Krogsgaard-Larsen, A. Snowman, S. C. Lummis and R. W. Olsen, *J. Neurochem.*, 1981, **37**, 401.
98. J. H. Skerritt and G. A. R. Johnston, *Neurosci. Lett.*, 1983, **38**, 315.
99. A. Schousboe, J. Drejer, G. H. Hansen and E. Meier, *Dev. Neurosci.*, 1985, **7**, 252.
100. H. Möhler and T. Okada, *Nature (London)*, 1977, **267**, 65.
101. R. W. Olsen and A. M. Snowman, *J. Neurochem.*, 1983, **41**, 1653.
102. M. Heaulme, J.-P. Chambon, R. Leyris, J.-C. Molimard, C. G. Wermuth and K. Biziere, *Brain Res.*, 1986, **384**, 224.
103. N. G. Bowery, D. R. Hill and A. L. Hudson, *Br. J. Pharmacol.*, 1983, **78**, 191.
104. N. G. Bowery, in 'The GABA Receptors', ed. S. J. Enna, Humana Press, Clifton, NJ, 1983, p. 177.
105. C. Braestrup and M. Nielsen, in 'Handbook of Psychopharmacology', ed. L. L. Iversen, S. D. Iversen and S. H. Snyder, Plenum Press, New York, 1983, vol. 17, p. 285.
106. P. Supavilai and M. Karobath, *Neurosci. Lett.*, 1980, **19**, 337.
107. E. Falch, P. Jacobsen, P. Krogsgaard-Larsen and D. R. Curtis, *J. Neurochem.*, 1985, **44**, 68.
108. E. H. F. Wong and L. L. Iversen, *J. Neurochem.*, 1985, **44**, 1162.
109. D. L. Martin, in 'GABA in Nervous System Function', ed. E. Roberts, T. N. Chase and D. B. Tower, Raven Press, New York, 1976, p. 347.
110. A. Schousboe, *Int. Rev. Neurobiol.*, 1981, **22**, 1.
111. P. Krogsgaard-Larsen, E. Falch, O. M. Larsson and A. Schousboe, *Epilepsy Res.*, 1987, **1**, 77.
112. P. Krogsgaard-Larsen, *Mol. Cell. Biochem.*, 1980, **31**, 105.
113. O. M. Larsson, P. Krogsgaard-Larsen and A. Schousboe, *Neurochem. Int.*, 1985, **7**, 853.
114. G. Levi and M. Raiteri, *Life Sci.*, 1973, **12**, 81.
115. R. J. Hitzemann and H. H. Loh, *J. Neurochem.*, 1978, **30**, 471.
116. J. D. Wood and H. S. Sidhu, *J. Neurochem.*, 1986, **46**, 739.
117. J. D. Wood and H. S. Sidhu, *J. Neurochem.*, 1987, **49**, 1202.
118. O. M. Larsson, G. A. R. Johnston and A. Schousboe, *Brain Res.*, 1983, **260**, 279.
119. A. Cupello and H. Hyden, *Cell. Mol. Neurobiol.*, 1986, **6**, 1.
120. A. Schousboe, P. Thorbek, L. Hertz and P. Krogsgaard-Larsen, *J. Neurochem.*, 1979, **33**, 181.
121. L. L. Iversen and J. S. Kelly, *Biochem. Pharmacol.*, 1975, **24**, 933.
122. P. Krogsgaard-Larsen and G. A. R. Johnston, *J. Neurochem.*, 1975, **25**, 797.
123. G. A. R. Johnston, A. L. Stephanson and B. Twitchin, *J. Neurochem.*, 1976, **26**, 83.
124. A. F. Ryan and I. R. Schwartz, *Brain Res.*, 1986, **399**, 399.
125. G. A. R. Johnston, P. Krogsgaard-Larsen and A. Stephanson, *Nature (London)*, 1975, **258**, 627.
126. P. Krogsgaard-Larsen, in 'Amino Acids as Chemical Transmitters', ed. F. Fonnum, Plenum Press, New York, 1978, p. 305.
127. D. Lodge, G. A. R. Johnston, D. R. Curtis and S. J. Brand, *Brain Res.*, 1977, **136**, 513.
128. P. Krogsgaard-Larsen, H. Mikkelsen, P. Jacobsen, E. Falch, D. R. Curtis, M. J. Peet and J. D. Leah, *J. Med. Chem.*, 1983, **26**, 895.
129. C. Rovira, Y. Ben-Ari and E. Cherubini, *Neuroscience*, 1984, **12**, 543.
130. K. Krnjevic, *Neurosci. Lett.*, 1984, **47**, 283.
131. P. Krogsgaard-Larsen, P. Jacobsen and E. Falch, in 'The GABA Receptors', ed. S. J. Enna, Humana Press, Clifton, NJ, 1983, p. 149.
132. J. D. Wood, D. Tsui and J. W. Phillis, *Can. J. Physiol. Pharmacol.*, 1979, **57**, 581.
133. F. E. Ali, W. E. Bondinell, P. A. Dandridge, J. S. Frazee, E. Garvey, G. R. Girard, C. Kaiser, T. W. Ku, J. J. Lafferty, G. I. Moonsammy, H.-J. Oh, J. A. Rush, P. E. Setler, O. D. Stringer, J. W. Venslavsky, B. W. Volpe, L. M. Yunger and C. L. Zirkle, *J. Med. Chem.*, 1985, **28**, 653.
134. L. M. Yunger, P. J. Fowler, P. Zarevics and P. E. Setler, *J. Pharmacol. Exp. Ther.*, 1984, **228**, 109.
135. O. M. Larsson, E. Falch, P. Krogsgaard-Larsen and A. Schousboe, *J. Neurochem.*, 1988, **50**, 818.

136. P. Krogsgaard-Larsen, in 'Glutamine, Glutamate and GABA in the Central Nervous System', ed. L. Hertz, E. Kvamme, E. G. McGeer and A. Schousboe, Liss, New York, 1983, p. 537.
137. P. Krogsgaard-Larsen, E. Falch, A. Schousboe and D. R. Curtis, in 'Neurotransmitters, Seizures, and Epilepsy III', ed. G. Nistico, P. L. Morselli, K. G. Lloyd, R. G. Fariello and J. Engel, Raven Press, New York, 1986, p. 135.
138. S. H. Zorn, L. J. Willmore, C. M. Bailey and S. J. Enna, in 'Neurotransmitters, Seizures, and Epilepsy III', ed. G. Nistico, P. L. Morselli, K. G. Lloyd, R. G. Fariello and J. Engel, Raven Press, New York, 1986, p. 123.
139. N. Ogata, M. Inoue and T. Matsuo, *Synapse*, 1987, **1**, 62.
140. R. A. Anderson and R. Mitchell, *Eur. J. Pharmacol.*, 1985, **118**, 355.
141. G. A. R. Johnston and R. D. Allan, *Neuropharmacology*, 1984, **23**, 831.
142. M. J. W. Brennan and R. C. Cantrill, *Nature (London)*, 1979, **280**, 514.
143. S. R. Snodgrass, *Nature (London)*, 1978, **274**, 392.
144. P. R. Mitchell and I. L. Martin, *Nature (London)*, 1978, **274**, 904.
145. A. Schousboe, O. M. Larsson and P. Krogsgaard-Larsen, *Neurochem. Int.*, 1985, **7**, 505.
146. R. O. Lockerbie and P. R. Gordon-Weeks, *Neurosci. Lett.*, 1985, **55**, 273.
147. M. J. W. Brennan, *J. Neurochem.*, 1982, **38**, 264.
148. D. R. Hill, N. G. Bowery and A. L. Hudson, *J. Neurochem.*, 1984, **42**, 652.
149. S. J. Enna and E. W. Karbon, *Neuropharmacology*, 1984, **23**, 821.
150. K. J. Watling and D. R. Bristow, *J. Neurochem.*, 1986, **46**, 1755.
151. E. G. Steward, P. W. Borthwick, G. R. Clarke and D. Warner, *Nature (London)*, 1975, **256**, 600.
152. D. Warner and E. G. Steward, *J. Mol. Struct.*, 1975, **25**, 403.
153. P. Krogsgaard-Larsen, H. Hjeds, D. R. Curtis, D. Lodge and G. A. R. Johnston, *J. Neurochem.*, 1979, **32**, 1717.
154. P. Krogsgaard-Larsen, L. Nielsen, E. Falch and D. R. Curtis, *J. Med. Chem.*, 1985, **28**, 1612.
155. D. R. Armstrong, R. J. Breckenridge and C. J. Suckling, *J. Theor. Biol.*, 1982, **97**, 267.
156. J. G. Atkinson, Y. Girard, J. Rokach, C. S. Rooney, C. S. McFarlane, A. Rackham and N. N. Share, *J. Med. Chem.*, 1979, **22**, 99.
157. R. D. Allan, G. A. R. Johnston, R. Kazlauskas and H. Tran, *Aust. J. Chem.*, 1983, **36**, 977.
158. A. Maggi and S. J. Enna, *Neuropharmacology*, 1979, **18**, 361.
159. E. Falch, A. Hedegaard, L. Nielsen, B. R. Jensen, H. Hjeds and P. Krogsgaard-Larsen, *J. Neurochem.*, 1986, **47**, 898.
160. J. M. Godfraind, K. Krnjevic, H. Maretic and R. Pumain, *Can. J. Physiol. Pharmacol.*, 1973, **51**, 790.
161. R. J. Breckenridge, S. H. Nicholson, A. J. Nicol, C. J. Suckling, B. Leigh and L. L. Iversen, *J. Neurochem.*, 1981, **37**, 837.
162. D. R. Bristow, M. M. Campbell, L. L. Iversen, J. A. Kemp, G. R. Marshall, K. J. Watling and E. H. F. Wong, *Proc. Br. Pharmacol. Soc.*, April, 1985.
163. R. D. Allan, H. W. Dickenson, B. P. Hiern, G. A. R. Johnston and R. Kazlauskas, *Br. J. Pharmacol.*, 1986, **88**, 379.
164. P. Krogsgaard-Larsen, G. A. R. Johnston, D. Lodge and D. R. Curtis, *Nature (London)*, 1977, **268**, 53.
165. P. Krogsgaard-Larsen and T. R. Christiansen, *Eur. J. Med. Chem.—Chim. Ther.*, 1979, **14**, 157.
166. R. Nordmann, P. Graff, R. Maurer and B. H. Gähwiler, *J. Med. Chem.*, 1985, **28**, 1109.
167. W. Haefliger, L. Révész, R. Maurer, D. Römer and H.-H. Büscher, *Eur. J. Med. Chem.—Chim. Ther.*, 1984, **19**, 149.
168. R. D. Allan and J. Fong, *Aust. J. Chem.*, 1983, **36**, 1221.
169. L. Brehm, P. Krogsgaard-Larsen, K. Schaumburg, J. S. Johansen, E. Falch and D. R. Curtis, *J. Med. Chem.*, 1986, **29**, 224.
170. P. Krogsgaard-Larsen, H. Hjeds, D. R. Curtis, J. D. Leah and M. J. Peet, *J. Neurochem.*, 1982, **39**, 1319.
171. J. Arnt and P. Krogsgaard-Larsen, *Brain Res.*, 1979, **177**, 395.
172. J. R. Byberg, I. M. Labouta, E. Falch, H. Hjeds, P. Krogsgaard-Larsen, D. R. Curtis and B. D. Gynther, *Drug Design and Delivery*, 1987, **1**, 261.
173. I. M. Labouta, E. Falch, H. Hjeds and P. Krogsgaard-Larsen, *Eur. J. Med. Chem.—Chim. Ther.*, 1982, **17**, 531.
174. E. Falch, P. Krogsgaard-Larsen, P. Jacobsen, A. Engesgaard, C. Braestrup and D. R. Curtis, *Eur. J. Med. Chem.—Chim. Ther.*, 1985, **20**, 447.
175. N. G. Bowery, D. R. Hill, A. L. Hudson, A. Doble, D. N. Middlemiss, J. Shaw and M. Turnbull, *Nature (London)*, 1980, **283**, 92.
176. P. Krogsgaard-Larsen, E. Falch, A. Schousboe, D. R. Curtis and D. Lodge, *J. Neurochem.*, 1980, **34**, 756.
177. R. C. Frere, R. L. Macdonald and A. B. Young, *Brain Res.*, 1982, **244**, 145.
178. L. M. Nowak, A. B. Young and R. L. Macdonald, *Brain Res.*, 1982, **244**, 155.
179. R. W. Olsen, E. W. Snowhill and J. K. Wamsley, *Eur. J. Pharmacol.*, 1984, **99**, 247.
180. J. Kardos, G. Blasko, P. Kerekes, I. Kovacs and M. Simonyi, *Biochem. Pharmacol.*, 1984, **33**, 3545.
181. J. A. Beutler, E. W. Karbon, A. N. Brubaker, R. Malik, D. R. Curtis and S. J. Enna, *Brain Res.*, 1985, **330**, 135.
182. P. Hunt and S. Clements-Jewery, *Neuropharmacology*, 1981, **20**, 357.
183. B. H. Gähwiler, R. Maurer and H. J. Wüthrich, *Neurosci. Lett.*, 1984, **45**, 311.
184. D. R. Curtis and B. D. Gynther, *Eur. J. Pharmacol.*, 1986, **131**, 311.
185. N. T. Buu, J. Duhaime and O. Kuchel, *Life Sci.*, 1984, **35**, 1083.
186. I. Yokoi, K. Tsuruta, H. Shigara and A. Mori, *Epilepsy Res.*, 1987, **1**, 114.
187. J.-P. Chambon, P. Feltz, M. Heaulme, S. Restle, R. Schlichter, K. Biziere and C. G. Wermuth, *Proc. Natl. Acad. Sci. U.S.A.*, 1985, **82**, 1832.
188. B. D. Gynther and D. R. Curtis, *Neurosci. Lett.*, 1986, **68**, 211.
189. J. C. Michaud, J. M. Mienville, J.-P. Chambon and K. Biziere, *Neuropharmacology*, 1986, **25**, 1197.
190. D. R. Curtis and B. D. Gynther, *Trends Pharmacol. Sci.*, 1987, **8**, 90.
191. C.-G. Wermuth, J.-J. Bourguignon, G. Schlewer, J.-P. Gies, A. Schoenfelder, A. Melikian, M.-J. Bouchet, D. Chantreux, J.-C. Molimard, M. Heaulme, J.-P. Chambon and K. Biziere, *J. Med. Chem.*, 1987, **30**, 239.
192. D. Burke, C. J. Andrews and L. Knowles, *J. Neurol. Sci.*, 1971, **14**, 199.
193. N. G. Bowery, *Trends Pharmacol. Sci.*, 1982, **3**, 400.
194. F. V. DeFeudis, *Trends Pharmacol. Sci.*, 1982, **3**, 444.
195. H.-R. Olpe, A. Glatt and W. Bencze, *Brain Res. Bull.*, 1980, **5** (Suppl. 2), 507.
196. R. D. Allan and H. Tran, *Aust. J. Chem.*, 1981, **34**, 2641.
197. J. Sawynok, *Neuropharmacology*, 1986, **25**, 795.

198. P. J. Roberts, J. Storm-Mathisen and H. F. Bradford (eds.), 'Excitatory Amino Acids', Macmillan Press, London, 1986.
199. T. P. Hicks, D. Lodge and H. McLennan (eds.), 'Excitatory Amino Acid Transmission', Liss, New York, 1987.
200. M. Muhyaddin, P. J. Roberts and G. N. Woodruff, *Br. J. Pharmacol.*, 1982, **77**, 163.
201. A. Giotti, S. Luzzi, S. Spagnesi and L. Zilletti, *Br. J. Pharmacol.*, 1983, **79**, 855.
202. R. D. Allan and H. W. Dickenson, *Eur. J. Pharmacol.*, 1986, **120**, 119.
203. S. Luzzi, S. Franchi-Micheli, M. Ciuffi, A. Pajani and L. Zilletti, *J. Auton. Pharmacol.*, 1986, **6**, 163.
204. D. I. B. Kerr, J. Ong, R. H. Prager, B. D. Gynther and D. R. Curtis, *Brain Res.*, 1987, **405**, 150.
205. J. G. Dingwall, J. Ehrenfreund, R. G. Hall and J. Jack, *Phosphorus Sulfur*, 1987, **30**, 571.
206. R. W. Olsen, O. Bergman, P. C. Van Ness, S. C. Lummis, A. E. Watkins, C. Napias and D. V. Greenlee, *Mol. Pharmacol.*, 1981, **19**, 217.
207. E. Sigel, F. A. Stephanson, C. Mamalaki and E. A. Barnard, *J. Biol. Chem.*, 1983, **258**, 6965.
208. P. Schoch, J. G. Richards, P. Häring, B. Takacs, C. Stähli, T. Staehelin, W. Haefely and H. Möhler, *Nature (London)*, 1985, **314**, 168.
209. R. F. Squires and C. Braestrup, *Nature (London)*, 1977, **266**, 732.
210. H. Möhler and T. Okada, *Science (Washington, D.C.)*, 1977, **198**, 849.
211. R. F. Squires, J. E. Casida, M. Richardson and E. Saederup, *Mol. Pharmacol.*, 1983, **23**, 326.
212. J. Seifert and J. E. Casida, *J. Neurochem.*, 1985, **44**, 110.
213. J. Hebebrand, W. Friedl, B. Unverzagt and P. Propping, *J. Neurochem.*, 1986, **47**, 790.
214. P. Supavilai and M. Karobath, *J. Neurochem.*, 1981, **36**, 798.
215. M. Williams and E. A. Risley, *J. Neurochem.*, 1984, **42**, 745.
216. M. K. Ticku and R. Ramanjaneyulu, *Pharmacol., Biochem. Behav.*, 1984, **21**, 151.
217. R. R. Trifiletti, A. M. Snowman and S. H. Snyder, *Eur. J. Pharmacol.*, 1985, **106**, 441.
218. J. R. Hammond and I. L. Martin, *J. Neurochem.*, 1986, **47**, 1161.
219. R. W. Olsen, J. Yang, R. G. King, A. Dilber, G. B. Stauber and R. W. Ransom, *Life Sci.*, 1986, **39**, 1969.
220. P. R. Schofield, M. G. Darlison, N. Fujita, D. R. Burt, F. A. Stephenson, H. Rodriguez, L. M. Rhee, J. Ramachandran, V. Reale, T. A. Glencorse, P. H. Seeburg and E. A. Barnard, *Nature (London)*, 1987, **328**, 221.
221. J. J. Lambert, J. A. Peters and G. A. Cottrell, *Trends Pharmacol. Sci.*, 1987, **8**, 224.
222. N. L. Harrison and M. A. Simmonds, *Brain Res.*, 1984, **323**, 287.
223. M. D. Majewska, N. L. Harrison, R. D. Schwartz, J. L. Barker and S. M. Paul, *Science (Washington, D.C.)*, 1986, **323**, 1004.
224. N. L. Harrison, M. D. Majewska, J. W. Harrington and J. L. Barker, *J. Pharmacol. Exp. Ther.*, 1987, **241**, 346.
225. A. Maggi and J. Perez, *J. Neurochem.*, 1986, **47**, 1793.
226. C. Braestrup, M. Nielsen, P. Krogsgaard-Larsen and E. Falch, *Nature (London)*, 1979, **280**, 331.
227. M. Karobath, P. Placheta, M. Lippitsch and P. Krogsgaard-Larsen, *Nature (London)*, 1979, **278**, 748.
228. L. H. Sternbach, *J. Med. Chem.*, 1979, **22**, 1979.
229. C. Braestrup, T. Honoré, M. Nielsen, E. N. Petersen and L. H. Jensen, *Biochem. Pharmacol.*, 1984, **33**, 859.
230. R. I. Fryer, C. Cook, N. W. Gilman and A. Walser, *Life Sci.*, 1986, **39**, 1947.
231. J. T. Edsall and J. Wyman, in 'Biophysical Chemistry', Academic Press, New York, 1958, vol. 1, p. 485.
232. F. Moroni, M. C. Forchetti, P. Krogsgaard-Larsen and A. Guidotti, *J. Pharm. Pharmacol.*, 1982, **34**, 676.
233. P. Krogsgaard-Larsen, E. Falch and A. V. Christensen, *Drugs of the Future*, 1984, **9**, 597.
234. J.-P. Kaplan, B. M. Raizon, M. Desarmenien, P. Feltz, P. M. Headley, P. Worms, K. G. Lloyd and G. Bartholini, *J. Med. Chem.*, 1980, **23**, 702.
235. P. Worms, H. Depoortere, A. Durand, P. L. Morselli, K. G. Lloyd and G. Bartholini, *J. Pharmacol. Exp. Ther.*, 1982, **220**, 660.
236. K. G. Lloyd, S. Arbilla, K. Beaumont, M. Briley, G. De Montis, B. Scatton, S. Z. Langer and G. Bartholini, *J. Pharmacol. Exp. Ther.*, 1982, **220**, 672.
237. L. Galzigna, M. Bianchi, A. Bertazzon, A. Barthez, G. Quadro and M. A. Coletti-Previero, *J. Neurochem.*, 1984, **42**, 1762.
238. E. Falch, P. Krogsgaard-Larsen and A. V. Christensen, *J. Med. Chem.*, 1981, **24**, 285.
239. W. Löscher, *Neuropharmacology*, 1982, **21**, 803.
240. W. Löscher, H.-H. Frey, R. Reiche and D. Schultz, *J. Pharmacol. Exp. Ther.*, 1983, **226**, 839.
241. B. Meldrum and R. Horton, *Eur. J. Pharmacol.*, 1980, **61**, 231.
242. H. R. Petersen, I. Jensen and M. Dam, *Acta Neurol. Scand.*, 1983, **67**, 114.
243. A. Grognet, F. Hertz and F. V. DeFeudis, *Gen. Pharmacol.*, 1983, **14**, 585.
244. D. A. Kendall, M. Browner and S. J. Enna, *J. Pharmacol. Exp. Ther.*, 1982, **220**, 482.
245. R. C. Hill, R. Maurer, H. H. Buescher and D. Roemer, *Eur. J. Pharmacol.*, 1981, **69**, 221.
246. T. Lindeburg, S. Foelsgaard, H. Sillesen, E. Jacobsen and H. Kehlet, *Acta Anaesthesiol. Scand.*, 1983, **27**, 10.
247. M. Kjaer and H. Nielsen, *Br. J. Clin. Pharmacol.*, 1983, **16**, 477.
248. V. Cuomo, I. Cortese and G. Siro-Brigiani, *Arzneim.-Forsch.*, 1981, **31**, 1724.
249. C. A. Tamminga, J. W. Crayton and T. N. Chase, *Arch. Gen. Psychiatry*, 1979, **36**, 595.
250. T. J. Biscoe and J. P. Fry, *Br. J. Pharmacol.*, 1982, **75**, 23.
251. P. Polc, *Prog. Neuro-Psychopharmacol.*, 1979, **3**, 345.
252. K. Mondrup and E. Pedersen, *Acta Neurol. Scand.*, 1983, **67**, 48.
253. J. Arnt, J. Scheel-Krüger, G. Magelund and P. Krogsgaard-Larsen, *J. Pharm. Pharmacol.*, 1979, **31**, 306.
254. B. L. Waszczak, R. E. Hruska and J. R. Walters, *Eur. J. Pharmacol.*, 1980, **65**, 21.
255. A. V. Christensen, O. Svendsen and P. Krogsgaard-Larsen, *Pharm. Weekbl., Sci. Ed.*, 1982, **4**, 145.
256. J. Arnt and A. V. Christensen, *Eur. J. Pharmacol.*, 1981, **69**, 107.
257. N. Bjoerndal, J. Gerlach, D. E. Casey and E. Christensson, *Psychopharmacology*, 1983, **79**, 220.
258. S. Korgsgaard, D. E. Casey, J. Gerlach, O. Hetmar, B. Kaldan and L. B. Mikkelsen, *Arch. Gen. Psychiatry*, 1982, **39**, 1017.
259. C. J. Pycock and R. W. Kerwin, *Life Sci.*, 1981, **28**, 2679.
260. E. C. Dale and M. H. Aprison, in 'Handbook of Neurochemistry', 2nd edn., ed. A. Lajtha, Plenum Press, New York, 1983, vol. 3, p. 467.
261. J. A. Hardy, A. Barton, E. Lofdahl, S. C. Cheetman, G. A. R. Johnston and P. R. Dodd, *J. Neurochem.*, 1986, **47**, 460.

262. D. R. Curtis, L. Hösli, G. A. R. Johnston and I. H. Johnston, *Exp. Brain Res.*, 1968, **5**, 235.
263. D. R. Curtis, C. J. A. Game, D. Lodge and R. M. McCulloch, *J. Physiol. (London)*, 1976, **258**, 227.
264. S. S. Oja, P. Kontro and P. Lähdesmäki, *Prog. Pharmacol.*, 1977, **1**, 1.
265. W. F. White, *Brain Res.*, 1985, **329**. 1.
266. W. F. White and A. H. Heller, *Nature (London)*, 1982, **298**, 655.
267. A. L. Gundlach and P. M. Beart, *J. Neurochem.*, 1982, **38**, 574.
268. G. Grenningloh, A. Rienitz, B. Schmitt, C. Methfessel, M. Zensen, K. Beyreuther, E. D. Gundelfinger and H. Betz, *Nature (London)*, 1987, **328**, 215.
269. S. G. Cull-Candy and M. M. Usowicz, *Trends Pharmacol. Sci.*, 1987, **8**, 218.
270. S. E. Barron and P. S. Guth, *Trends Pharmacol. Sci.*, 1987, **8**, 204.
271. A. B. Young and S. H. Snyder, *Proc. Natl. Acad. Sci. U.S.A.*, 1973, **70**, 2382.
272. S. H. Snyder, *Br. J. Pharmacol.*, 1975, **53**, 473.
273. F. V. DeFeudis, *Gen. Pharmacol.*, 1978, **9**, 139.
274. H. Kishimoto, J. R. Simon and M. H. Aprison, *J. Neurochem.*, 1981, **37**, 1015.
275. D. R. Bristow, N. G. Bowery and G. N. Woodruff, *Eur. J. Pharmacol.*, 1986, **126**, 303.
276. A. Probst, R. Cortes and J. M. Palacios, *Neuroscience*, 1986, **17**, 11.
277. D. R. Curtis, L. Hösli and G. A. R. Johnston, *Exp. Brain Res.*, 1968, **6**, 1.
278. M. A. Simmonds, *Br. J. Pharmacol.*, 1983, **79**, 799.
279. M. H. Aprison, K. B. Lipkowitz and J. R. Simon, *J. Neurosci. Res.*, 1987, **17**, 209.
280. C. Braestrup, M. Nielsen and P. Krogsgaard-Larsen, *J. Neurochem.*, 1986, **47**, 691.
281. C. Braestrup and M. Nielsen, *Brain Res. Bull.*, 1980, **5** (Suppl. 2), 681.
282. J. L. Barker and R. N. McBurney, *Nature (London)*, 1979, **277**, 234.
283. S. Sarhan, M. Kolb and N. Seiler, *Drug Res.*, 1984, **34**, 687.
284. N. Seiler and S. Sarhan, *Gen. Pharmacol.*, 1984, **15**, 367.
285. N. Seiler, S. Sarhan, P. Krogsgaard-Larsen, H. Hjeds and A. Schousboe, *Gen. Pharmacol.*, 1985, **16**, 509.
286. V. Santucci, M. Fournier, J.-P. Chambon and K. Biziere, *Eur. J. Pharmacol.*, 1985, **114**, 219.
287. J. W. Johnson and P. Ascher, *Nature (London)*, 1987, **325**, 529.
288. L. M. Pullan, J. W. Olney, M. T. Price, R. P. Compton, W. F. Hood, J. Michel and J. B. Monahan, *J. Neurochem.*, 1987, **49**, 1301.
289. J. Bernstein, R. S. Fisher, R. Zaczek and J. T. Coyle, *J. Neurosci.*, 1985, **5**, 1429.
290. M. B. Robinson, R. D. Blakely, R. Couto and J. T. Coyle, *J. Biol. Chem.*, 1987, **262**, 14 498.
291. T. W. Stone and J. H. Connick, *Neuroscience*, 1985, **15**, 597.
292. P. J. Roberts and S. W. Davies, *Biochem. Soc. Trans.*, 1987, **15**, 218.
293. A. Ruck, S. Kramer, J. Metz and M. J. W. Brennan, *Nature (London)*, 1980, **287**, 852.
294. K. Fuxe, P. Roberts and R. Schwarcz (eds.), 'Excitotoxins', MacMillan Press, London, 1983.
295. S. M. Rothman and J. W. Olney, *Trends Neurosci.*, 1987, **10**, 299.
296. J. T. Greenamyre, *Arch. Neurol. (Chicago)*, 1986, **43**, 1058.
297. B. Meldrum, *Clin. Sci.*, 1985, **68**, 113.
298. H. F. Bradford and P. R. Dodd, *Biochem. Pharmacol.*, 1977, **26**, 253.
299. T. Hayashi, *Keio J. Med.*, 1953, **3**, 183.
300. R. S. Sloviter and D. W. Dempster, *Brain Res. Bull.*, 1985, **15**, 39.
301. M. J. Croucher, J. F. Collins and B. S. Meldrum, *Science (Washington, D.C.)*, 1982, **216**, 899.
302. C. E. Herron, R. Williamson and G. L. Collingridge, *Neurosci. Lett.*, 1985, **61**, 255.
303. E. G. McGeer and P. L. McGeer, *Nature (London)*, 1976, **263**, 517.
304. M. F. Beal, N. W. Kowall, D. W. Ellison, M. F. Mazurek, K. J. Schwartz and J. B. Martin, *Nature (London)*, 1986, **321**, 168.
305. J. T. Coyle, *J. Neurochem.*, 1983, **41**, 1.
306. A. J. Cross, P. Slater and G. P. Reynolds, *Neurosci. Lett.*, 1986, **67**, 198.
307. C. J. Carter, *Life Sci.*, 1982, **31**, 1151.
308. P. K. Narang and N. R. Cutler, *Prog. Neuro-Psychopharmacol. Biol. Psychiatr.*, 1986, **10**, 519.
309. J. T. Greenamyre, J. B. Penney, A. B. Young, C. J. D'Amato, S. P. Hicks and I. Shoulson, *Science (Washington, D.C.)*, 1985, **227**, 1496.
310. B. Meldrum, *Trends Neurosci. (Pers. Ed.)*, 1985, **8**, 47.
311. S. M. Rothman and J. W. Olney, *Ann. Neurol.*, 1986, **19**, 105.
312. J. C. Watkins, D. R. Curtis and T. J. Biscoe, *Nature (London)*, 1966, **211**, 637.
313. F. Fonnum, *J. Neurochem.*, 1984, **42**, 1.
314. H. McLennan, *Prog. Neurobiol. (Oxford)*, 1983, **20**, 251.
315. A. C. Foster and G. E. Fagg, *Brain Res. Rev.*, 1984, **7**, 103.
316. P. Krogsgaard-Larsen, T. Honoré, J. J. Hansen, D. R. Curtis and D. Lodge, *Nature (London)*, 1980, **284**, 64.
317. T. J. Biscoe, R. H. Evans, P. M. Headley, M. R. Martin and J. C. Watkins, *Br. J. Pharmacol.*, 1976, **58**, 373.
318. J. Davies and J. C. Watkins, *J. Physiol. (London)*, 1979, **297**, 621.
319. D. Lodge and N. A. Anis, *Eur. J. Pharmacol.*, 1982, **77**, 203.
320. J. Davies, R. H. Evans, P. L. Herrling, A. W. Jones, H. J. Olverman, P. Pook and J. C. Watkins, *Brain Res.*, 1986, **382**, 169.
321. D. E. Murphy, J. Schneider, C. Boehn, J. Lehmann and M. Williams, *J. Pharmacol. Exp. Ther.*, 1987, **240**, 778.
322. J. Vignon, A. Privat, I. Chaudieu, A. Thierry, J.-M. Kamenka and R. Chicheportiche, *Brain Res.*, 1986, **378**, 133.
323. P. Loo, A. Braunwalder, J. Lehmann and M. Williams, *Eur. J. Pharmacol.*, 1986, **123**, 467.
324. E. H. F. Wong, J. A. Kemp, T. Priestley, A. R. Knight, G. N. Woodruff and L. L. Iversen, *Proc. Natl. Acad. Sci. U.S.A.*, 1986, **83**, 7104.
325. A. C. Foster and E. H. F. Wong, *Br. J. Pharmacol.*, 1987, **91**, 403.
326. T. Honoré, J. Lauridsen and P. Krogsgaard-Larsen, *J. Neurochem.*, 1982, **38**, 173.
327. J. R. Simon, J. F. Contrera and M. J. Kuhar, *J. Neurochem.*, 1976, **26**, 141.
328. J. T. Slevin, J. F. Collins and J. T. Coyle, *Brain Res.*, 1983, **265**, 169.

329. T. Honoré and M. Nielsen, *Neurosci. Lett.*, 1985, **54**, 27.
330. H. McLennan and D. Lodge, *Brain Res.*, 1979, **169**, 83.
331. J. J. Hansen and P. Krogsgaard-Larsen, *J. Chem. Soc., Perkin Trans. 1*, 1980, 1826.
332. D. W. G. Cox, P. M. Headley and J. C. Watkins, *J. Neurochem.*, 1977, **29**, 579.
333. J. C. Watkins and R. H. Evans, *Annu. Rev. Pharmacol. Toxicol.*, 1981, **21**, 165.
334. J. C. Watkins and H. J. Olverman, *Trends Neurosci. (Pers. Ed.)*, 1987, **10**, 265.
335. D. T. Monaghan, D. Yao and C. W. Cotman, *Brain Res.*, 1985, **340**, 378.
336. J. T. Greenamyre, J. M. M. Olson, J. B. Penney and A. B. Young, *J. Pharmacol. Exp. Ther.*, 1985, **233**, 254.
337. J. Lehmann, J. A. Schneider and M. Williams, *Annu. Rep. Med. Chem.*, 1987, **22**, 31.
338. F. Nicoletti, J. T. Wroblewski, A. Novelli, H. Alho, A. Guidotti and E. Costa, *J. Neurosci.*, 1986, **6**, 1905.
339. L. Fagni, M. Baudry and G. Lynch, *J. Neurosci.*, 1983, **3**, 1538.
340. L. L. Werling, K. A. Doman and J. V. Nadler, *J. Neurochem.*, 1983, **41**, 586.
341. A. Luini, O. Goldberg and V. Teichberg, *Proc. Natl. Acad. Sci. U.S.A.*, 1981, **78**, 3250.
342. J. F. Koerner and C. W. Cotman, *Brain Res.*, 1981, **216**, 192.
343. G. E. Fagg, A. C. Foster and A. H. Ganong, *Trends Pharmacol. Sci.*, 1986, **7**, 357.
344. J. A. Kemp, A. C. Foster and E. H. F. Wong, *Trends Neurosci. (Pers. Ed.)*, 1987, **10**, 294.
345. D. Lodge, *Trends Pharmacol. Sci.*, 1987, **8**, 243.
346. L. Nowak, P. Bregestovski, P. Ascher, A. Herbet and A. Prochiantz, *Nature (London)*, 1984, **307**, 462.
347. G. L. Collingridge, S. J. Kehl and H. McLennan, *J. Physiol. (London)*, 1983, **334**, 33.
348. G. Lynch and M. Baudry, *Science (Washington, D.C.)*, 1984, **224**, 1057.
349. S. Peters, J. Koh and D. W. Choi, *Science (Washington, D.C.)*, 1987, **236**, 589.
350. P. Ascher and L. Novak, *Trends Neurosci. (Pers. Ed.)*, 1987, **10**, 284.
351. N. A. Anis, S. C. Berry, N. R. Burton and D. Lodge, *Br. J. Pharmacol.*, 1983, **79**, 565.
352. S. C. Berry and D. Lodge, *Biochem. Pharmacol.*, 1984, **33**, 3829.
353. U. Madsen, K. Schaumburg, L. Brehm, F. S. Jørgensen and P. Krogsgaard-Larsen, in 'NMR Spectroscopy and Drug Development', ed. J. Jaroszewski, K. Schaumburg and H. Kofod, Munksgaard, Copenhagen, 1988, p. 57.
354. P. Krogsgaard-Larsen, E. Ø. Nielsen, A. Engesgaard, J. Lauridsen, L. Brehm and J. J. Hansen, in 'Natural Products and Drug Development', ed., P. Krogsgaard-Larsen, S. B. Christensen and H. Kofod, Munksgaard, Copenhagen, 1984, p. 525.
355. T. W. Stone, *Br. J. Pharmacol.*, 1984, **81**, 175.
356. M. N. Perkins and T. W. Stone, *J. Pharmacol. Exp. Ther.*, 1983, **226**, 551.
357. R. H. Evans, A. W. Jones and J. C. Watkins, *J. Physiol. (London)*, 1980, **308**, 71P.
358. P. Krogsgaard-Larsen, L. Brehm, J. S. Johansen, P. Vinzents, J. Lauridsen and D. R. Curtis, *J. Med. Chem.*, 1985, **28**, 673.
359. P. Krogsgaard-Larsen, E. Ø. Nielsen and D. R. Curtis, *J. Med. Chem.*, 1984, **27**, 585.
360. H. Shinozaki and I. Shibuya, *Neuropharmacology*, 1976, **15**, 145.
361. H. Shinozaki, M. Ishida and T. Okamoto, *Brain Res.*, 1986, **399**, 395.
362. M. N. Perkins and T. W. Stone, *Brain Res.*, 1982, **247**, 184.
363. F. Moroni, P. Russi, G. Lombardi, M. Beni and V. Carla, *J. Neurochem.*, 1988, **51**, 177.
364. P. Frey, D. Berney, W. Mueller, P. L. Herrling and S. Urwyler, in 'Abstr. Amino Acid Transmitters', Canberra, Australia, 19–21 August 1987, p. 12.
365. J. Drejer and T. Honoré, *Neurosci. Lett.*, 1988, **87**, 104.
366. T. Honoré, S. N. Davies, J. Drejer, E. J. Fletcher, P. Jacobsen, D. Lodge and F. E. Nielsen, *Science (Washington, D.C.)*, 1988, **241**, 701.
367. P. Krogsgaard-Larsen, U. Madsen, B. Nielsen, J. J. Hansen, E. Ø. Nielsen, L. Brehm and D. R. Curtis, in 'Proceedings of the International Congress of Pharmacology, 10th', ed. M. J. Rand and C. Raper, Elsevier, Amsterdam, 1987, p. 113.
368. L. Brehm, F. S. Jørgensen, J. J. Hansen and P. Krogsgaard-Larsen, *Drug News and Perspectives*, 1988, **1**, 138.
369. P. Krogsgaard-Larsen, unpublished results.
370. S. J. Cruczwar and B. Meldrum, *Eur. J. Pharmacol.*, 1982, **83**, 335.
371. D. A. Bennett and C. L. Amrick, *Life Sci.*, 1986, **39**, 2461.
372. L. Turski, T. Klockgether, K.-H. Sontag, P. L. Herrling and J. C. Watkins, *Neurosci. Lett.*, 1987, **73**, 143.
373. J. Lehmann, J. Schneider, S. McPherson, D. E. Murphy, P. Bernard, C. Tsai, D. A. Bennett, G. Pastor, D. J. Steel, C. Boehm, D. L. Cheney, J. M. Liebman, M. Williams and P. L. Wood, *J. Pharmacol. Exp. Ther.*, 1987, **240**, 737.
374. G. L. Collingridge and T. V. P. Bliss, *Trends Neurosci.*, 1987, **10**, 288.

12.8

Ligand Interactions at the Benzodiazepine Receptor

R. IAN FRYER

Rutgers University, Newark, NJ, USA

12.8.1 INTRODUCTION

This chapter has been written to illustrate briefly the historical development of a qualitative structure–activity relationship (SAR) for 1,4-benzodiazepines that is still ongoing after a period of more than 30 years, and, in addition, to describe the methods currently being used to develop and refine a predictive structural model which can be employed in the design of biologically active compounds.

The biological activity of the benzodiazepines (BZDs) was found by an evaluation of results obtained by random screening through a battery of *in vivo* tests designed to find compounds that would exhibit anxiolytic activity in humans.[1] The synthesis of one of the first active members of this chemical class of compounds (chlordiazepoxide) was rapidly followed by the preparation of diazepam, the *N*-methyl analog of the degradation product of chlordiazepoxide (7-chloro-5-phenyl-1,4-benzodiazepin-2-one), which was used in early structural elucidation work.[2] At this time many hypotheses for the mechanism of activity were proposed and chemical SAR work followed the classical methods in use in the early 1960s, *i.e.* by an examination of the effects of different substituents attached to all possible ring positions and then by ring modifications in order to define further structural requirements for activity.

At least three problems can arise by the use of only *in vivo* data for SAR work: (i) some compounds which are inherently inactive may appear to be active due to *in vivo* metabolic conversion to active compounds (see Table 1); (ii) since it is probable that few changes are made to the original basic ring system, the model that can be derived from such closely related compounds would have to mimic the original lead;[3] and (iii) it is unlikely that antagonists without *in vivo* biological activity will be discovered. Although some differences in the biological profile (Table 2) for the BZDs were noted during this early 'classical' work, these differences were, in general, quantitative rather than qualitative.

Table 1 Comparison of *In Vitro* Binding Data with an *In Vivo* Test for Anticonvulsant Activity, Indicating that the Level of Activity Shown is Probably Due to *In Vivo* Metabolism

Structure	Name/code no.	Inhibition of [³H]diazepam binding (IC_{50} nM)[a]	Antipentylenetetrazole activity[a]	Possible active metabolite
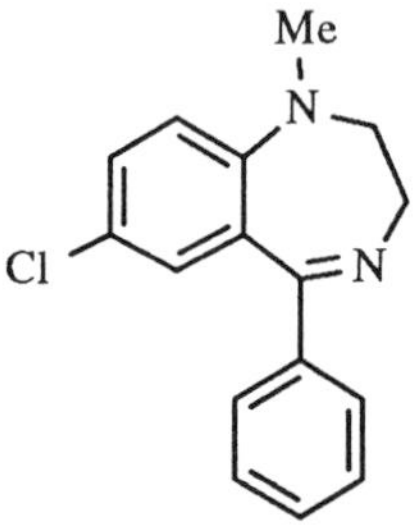	Medazepam	870	+ + +	Diazepam
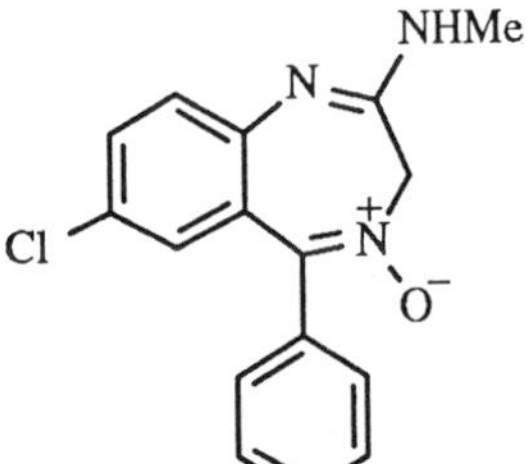	Chlordiazepoxide	352	+ +	*N*-Oxide of Ro5-2180
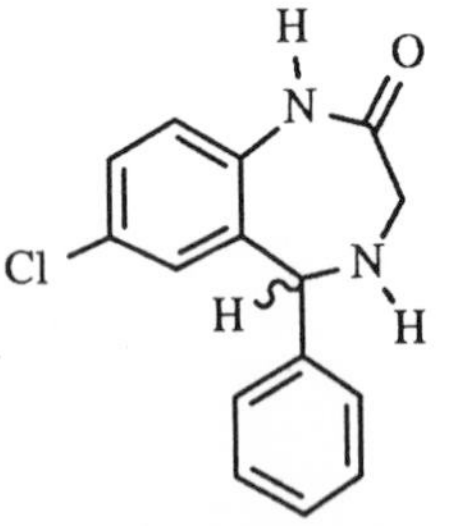	4,5-Dihydro-Ro5-2181	> 5000	+ + +	Ro5-2180
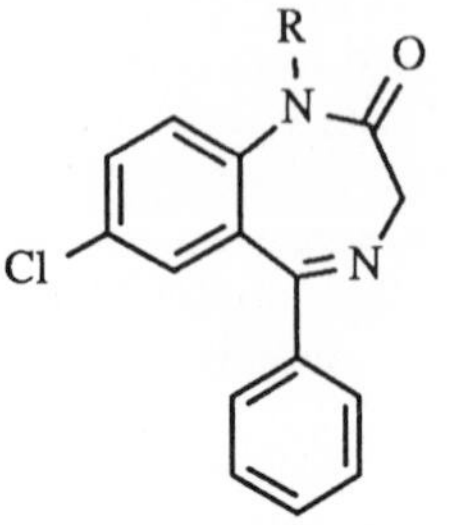	R = Me; Diazepam R = H; Ro5-2180	8.1 9.4	+ + + + + + +	Ro5-2180 —

[a] Data selected from various sources; see, for example, refs. 48a and 48b.

Table 2 Biological Properties of Full Agonists, Antagonists and Inverse Agonists
Acting Through the Benzodiazepine Receptor

Full agonist	*Full antagonist*	*Full inverse agonist*
Sedative	None	Stimulant
Amnestic	None	Enhance cognition
Anxiolytic	None	Anxiogenic
Anticonvulsant	None	Convulsant
Ataxia	None	Not determined
Muscle relaxant	None	Not determined
Alcohol potentiation	None	Reversal of alcohol effects

Approximately 20 years after the first synthesis of chlordiazepoxide came the discovery and characterization of the benzodiazepine receptor (BZR) from brain tissue,[4,5] which was followed rapidly by the development of the *in vitro* BZR binding assay[6,7] capable of expeditiously screening a large number of compounds, regardless of structural type. It was not long before many compounds, whose structures were apparently unrelated to the BZDs, were found to bind competitively to the BZR and *in vivo* were agonists like diazepam.[3] Other BZR ligands were found that exhibited a biological profile which was the reverse of that for benzodiazepine agonists (called inverse agonists, see Section 12.8.2.2), and in addition a third type of ligand was found which was capable of competitive displacement of both agonist and inverse agonist at the BZR and had no overt biological effects (called antagonists, see Section 12.8.2.2).

Attempts to correlate all of this new data in terms of structures and what might be a mechanistically viable explanation for the differing types of biological activity were started in the late 1970s. At first this was done by examining the possible chirality of the BZR, and then by comparing three-dimensional models, or by overlaying two-dimensional pictures of structures derived from single-crystal X-ray analysis. The rapid development of interactive real time computer graphics analysis in the past few years has greatly facilitated this type of correlation. The three-dimensional model resulting from this type of approach is discussed in detail in Sections 12.8.3.1–12.8.3.5.

12.8.2 THE BENZODIAZEPINE RECEPTOR

12.8.2.1 Function and Interaction with the γ-Aminobutyric Acid Receptor

The finding that the BZR is coupled to the γ-aminobutyric acid (GABA) receptor and is part of the $GABA_A$-controlled chloride ion channel ($BZD/GABA_A/Cl^-$) supramolecular complex led to the discovery that BZDs are not directly responsible for their observed biological activity but act as modulators of GABA binding to its receptor, which then directly alters the gating of the GABA dependent transmembrane chloride ion channel.[8,9]

12.8.2.2 Full Agonists, Antagonists and Inverse Agonists

The BZR is unique in the way it responds to three different types of ligands, two of which act as allosteric modulators of the $GABA_A$ receptor complex, resulting in mirror image biological effects. The third ligand is a true antagonist at the BZR for the other two types, but shows no effect on the binding of GABA (see Figure 1). Because of these unusual properties, it is necessary to define terms to be used for these three different ligands for the BZR. A slight paraphrase of the definitions given by Haefely[10] follows. BZR ligands that exert a positive cooperative effect on GABA binding to its receptor complex, resulting in a full biological response over the complete agonist profile of activity (positive intrinsic efficacy) are defined as *full agonists*. *Full antagonists* at the BZR are defined as ligands with a high affinity for the BZR, having no modulatory effect on GABA binding to its receptor complex, and showing no relevant biological effects of their own other than to block the effects of both agonist and inverse agonist ligands (have no intrinsic efficacy). Finally, *full inverse agonists* are defined as ligands that exert a negative cooperative effect on GABA binding to its

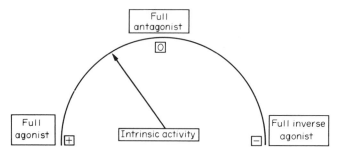

Figure 1 The BZR as a modulator of GABA binding to the GABA/Cl ion channel supramolecular complex

receptor complex and, when compared to agonists, show a mirror image biological response over the full inverse profile of activity (negative intrinsic efficacy).

12.8.2.3 Two-state or Three-state Model?

The interrelationship of these three types of ligands of the BZR can be explained on the basis of changes in the conformation of the receptor from its unoccupied resting state. Such a model has been proposed previously[11,12] and is shown schematically in Figure 2, in a slightly modified form. After primary recognition of the essential binding pharmacophores, the receptor will undergo a shift to either an agonist or an inverse agonist conformation, based on the geometry and hydrophobic characteristics of the ligand. This conformational change, probably energy driven, then allosterically modulates the binding of GABA to the GABA$_A$ receptor. It is proposed that no conformational shift occurs when a full antagonist binds to the resting state of the BZR, and it would therefore be expected that such a receptor–ligand complex would show zero efficacy at the GABA$_A$ receptor. Evidence for a multistep model for receptor binding has been given by a comparative thermodynamic analysis of binding for the antagonist Ro15-1788 and for the agonist clonazepam (the 7-nitro-5-(2-chlorophenyl) analog of Ro5-2180; Table 1). Using extensively washed synaptic membranes of rat cerebral cortex, Mohler and Richards[68] obtained a linear Van't Hoff plot for thermodynamic parameters of Ro15-1788 binding over a range of temperatures from 0 to 37 °C (enthalpy- and entropy-driven). The corresponding plot for clonazepam was almost identical at temperatures below 21 °C (enthalpy- and entropy-driven), but above this temperature agonist binding was found to be enthalpy-driven.

An alternative two-state receptor model, in which the unoccupied receptor is in equilibrium with agonist and inverse agonist conformations (positive and negative modulation of the GABA receptor complex), proposed by Braestrup,[13] is a viable alternative to the three-state model discussed above

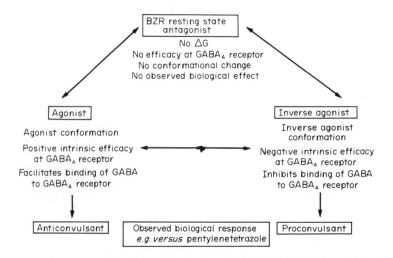

Figure 2 Schematic representation of a three-state model for ligand interactions at the BZR

and there is currently no evidence to support one hypothesis over the other. In this instance the binding of a ligand would alter the equilibrium in favor of either positive or negative efficacy at the $GABA_A$ receptor, depending on the nature of the ligand that binds.

12.8.2.4 Partial Agonists and Inverse Agonists

A discussion of the rationale for the ability of ligands to act as partial agonists should also be applicable to partial inverse agonists. For this reason, and also because the size of the current database for (partial) inverse agonists is relatively small, this section consists mainly of a discussion of the structural relationships for BZR partial agonists. The utility of this rationale in the design of three-dimensional models for SAR and the potential clinical importance of both partial agonists and inverse agonists is discussed in Section 12.8.4.

While some compounds are known to be either full agonists, full antagonists or full inverse agonists, the majority of the compounds that have been synthesized and found to bind to the BZR, regardless of structure, show less than either full positive or full negative GABA shift effects. Their biological profiles would therefore be expected to differ, depending on the relative intrinsic efficacies between the two extremes of full agonist and full inverse agonist. The receptor reserve theory has been used[10] in order to explain the profiles of such compounds where, for a particular effect, an ED_{100} is never reached.

Simply stated, the receptor reserve concept requires that the relative percentage occupancy of receptors is different for every individual part of a ligand's biological profile. In the case of the BZR it has been suggested that for anxiolytic and anticonvulsant properties a smaller percentage receptor occupancy is necessary in order to obtain a full biological response (positive GABA shift) than for the sedative or muscle relaxant properties. While different neurons in different brain areas may require a different percentage occupancy for full biological effect, the relative rank order of the profile should be unchanged.

The receptor reserve concept does explain quite well the effects of partial agonists, in which certain ligands show less than an ED_{100} for tests indicative of sedation and muscle relaxation.[14] Some

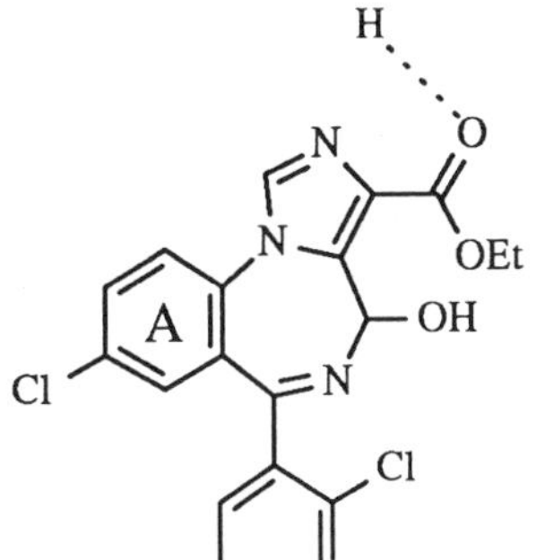

Ro23-0364
Mixed type

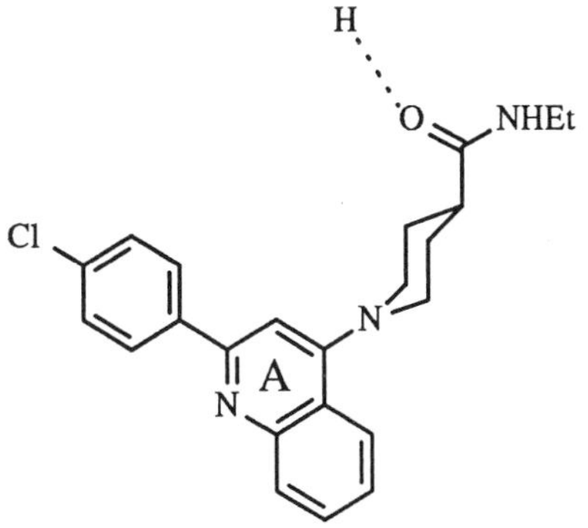

Ro23-1590
Selective anxiolytic, anticonvulsant

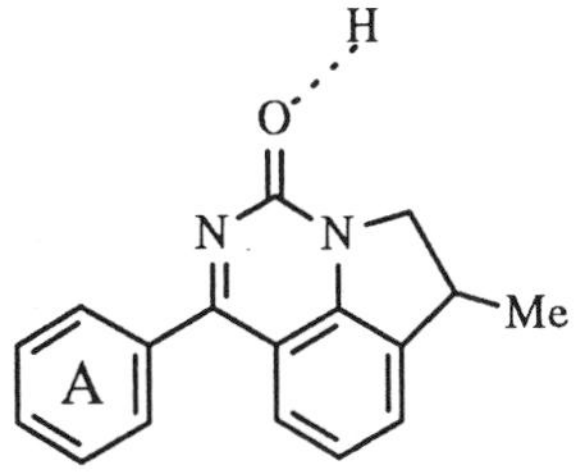

AHR11797
Selective muscle relaxant

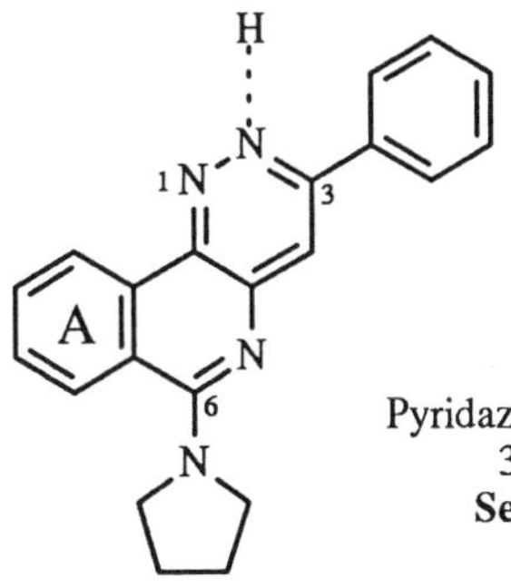

Pyridazinyl[4,3-*c*]isoquinoline,
3,6-disubstituted
Selective anxiolytic

Figure 3 Partial agonist BZR ligands, with unusual profiles of *in vivo* activity. Orientation indicates one possible fit with the receptor

compounds which may also be considered as partial antagonists are capable of reversing the full agonist effect of other ligands in that same test.[10] Taken to an extreme case, this would mean that it is possible for ligands to exist as full agonists for one biological effect and as full antagonists for another. Such compounds have been reported (Ro23-0364)[15,16] and have been referred to as mixed agonist/antagonists (the biological significance of this class of partial agonist would only be apparent in the presence of an exogenous or endogenous agonist ligand). In addition, there exist many compounds with very different pharmacological profiles of activity, all classified within the partial agonist (or partial inverse agonist) definition. There are compounds within this group whose profiles are very different, achieving less than full positive efficacy, and that possibly act through different mechanisms, *e.g.* a pyridazino[4,3-*c*]isoquinoline derivative (binding, $K_i = 11.4$ nM), which is an anxiolytic with no anticonvulsant properties[17] and an anxiolytic/anticonvulsant that has none of the other effects usually associated with compounds that bind to the BZR.[18-20] Also to be included with these latter compounds should be compounds reported to show selective binding properties for the BZR_1 and BZR_2 subgroups located in different brain areas (*e.g.* CL218,872;[21] see Figure 3 for structures). According to receptor reserve theory, it should be impossible to find a BZR ligand with sedative and muscle relaxant activity which does not also have anxiolytic and anticonvulsant activity. However, a compound having this type of profile (muscle relaxant, but not anxiolytic or anticonvulsant) has been reported, with an IC_{50} value for the displacement of [^{3}H]-diazepam of 82 nM L^{-1} (AHR11797).[22]

While all of these compounds are classified as partial agonists, with less than a full positive intrinsic activity, for our purposes (that of drug design), it might be conceivable that not all compounds follow the principle of receptor reserve. This realization facilitates a rational approach to the design of such compounds as those that exhibit mixed agonist/antagonist properties and is discussed in Section 12.8.4.

It is felt that by defining subsets of partial agonists it should be possible to evaluate structurally those ligands having unusual profiles of activity, and as the corresponding database is enlarged, perhaps the corresponding partial inverse agonists. The complete biological characterization of these compounds requires a full pharmacological profile of testing, which is a time-consuming task, but one that has been routinely accomplished within the pharmaceutical industry.[14]

12.8.2.5 Homogeneity of the Benzodiazepine Receptor

The question as to whether the receptor sites for agonists, antagonists and for inverse agonists are the same or different is, to a certain extent, semantic. Each ligand to the receptor can competitively displace the others and therefore in the worst case the three receptors, if 'different', must be allosterically coupled. Work carried out by Sweetman and Tallman[23] demonstrated that the BZR/GABA$_A$ complex, isolated from different brain areas, is covalently bound to different amounts (or types) of carbohydrate. The affinities of these different complexes differ for a particular ligand. However, once the carbohydrates are removed, the IC_{50}s become identical. This could be interpreted as a mechanism for the selective admittance of ligands to neurons affecting different biological pathways. It could well be argued that while the BZR is homogeneous, the environment is not. Homogeneity of the receptor should be defined in the chemical sense, *i.e.* it is the amino acid sequence for the BZR protein that should be identical.

By an examination of steric effects (Section 12.8.3.4) it has been proven that the ligand/receptor complexes for agonists and antagonists are conformationally distinct (and therefore when occupied are 'different').[12] It has thus been possible to corroborate in a (tertiary) structural sense, the work described in two papers, one by Mohler[24] and the other by Yamamura,[25] in which the authors explain their photoaffinity labelling results by proposing that, when the full agonist flunitrazepam (FLU) is irradiated in the presence of BZD receptor membranes, for each receptor that is photolabelled, four additional, closely associated receptors are conformationally altered. That is to say, when 20% of the available receptors have been irreversibly labelled by this technique, a complete loss of additional agonist binding results (with a corresponding reduction in B_{max}). Specific binding of an antagonist (Ro15-1788) was unchanged under conditions in which 80% of specific binding [^{3}H]FLU was lost. It is stated that 'since BZD agonists and antagonists may stabilize the receptors in different conformations, it is possible that receptors that are not irreversibly bound to FLU may retain their ability to bind antagonists but not agonists'. This explanation would fit with the three-state model discussed above, in which it was proposed that the antagonist/ligand fit requires no conformational change from the resting state of the receptor.

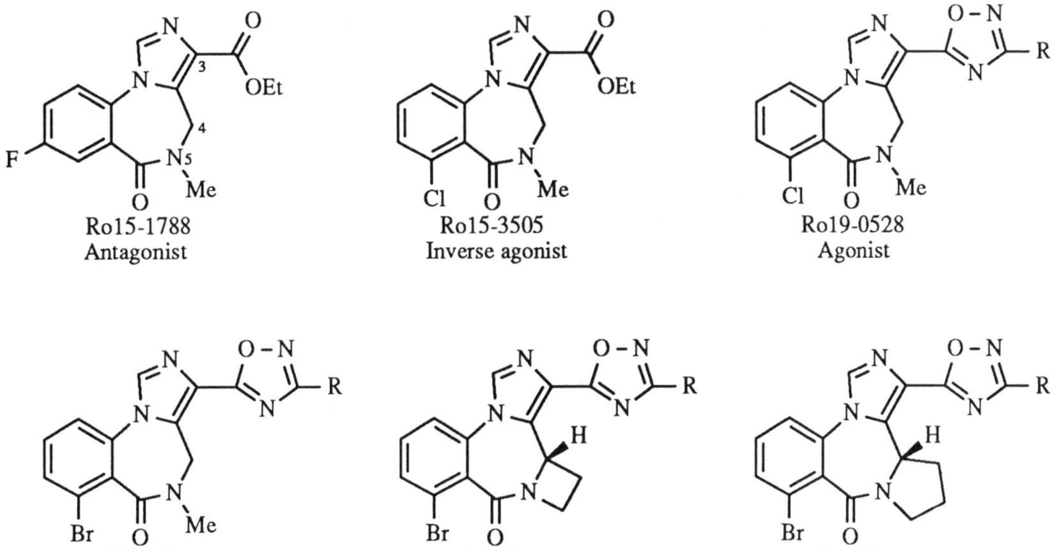

Figure 4 Variations of intrinsic activity within closely related series of 1,4-benzodiazepin-6-ones: obvious steric interactions in the region of the 3,4,5-positions can be seen;[14,59] less apparent are possible (rotational?) effects of 'A' ring substituents (see Figure 11)

Additional arguments for the homogeneity of BZR binding sites can be made from the modelling studies discussed below, which provide evidence demonstrating a commonality of groups involved in binding site interactions for all three types of activity. It has also been shown that conformational shifts within the receptor can either be allowed or disallowed on the basis of differing steric interactions. This was further demonstrated for compounds having only minor structural modifications, which showed similar binding interactions (IC_{50}) but which displayed activities across the full spectrum from agonist to antagonist to inverse agonist. Examples are given for the imidazobenzodiazepin-6-one series of compounds, where a change from an 8-fluoro to a 7-chloro substituent (Ro15-1788 to Ro15-3505) shifts activity from antagonist to (partial) inverse agonist. Replacement of the 3-carboxylic ester function by a bioisosteric 3-oxadiazolo group (Ro19-0528) again shifted the *in vivo* profile, but in this case to that of an agonist[14] (see Figure 4). Analogous observations have been made with β-carbolines,[26–28] pyrazoloquinolines[29–32] and the triazolopyridazines.[33,34]

The proposed BZ_1 and BZ_2 receptor subclasses[35] do not militate against the above hypothesis for receptor homogeneity, since all known ligands are recognized by both BZ_1 and BZ_2, with the preferential affinity for some structural classes of ligands reaching a maximum of a 10-fold difference.[36] Furthermore it has been proposed that these differences may be due to only one class of receptors, existing in two conformations.[37] Finally, an examination of Scatchard plots[38] for equilibrium binding studies on [^{3}H]-β-carbolines has given no clear indication of multiple components.[39] Many of these same supporting arguments for the homogeneity of the BZR have also been discussed by other workers carrying out SAR studies at the BZR (see, for example, ref. 47).

12.8.3 DEVELOPMENT OF A PREDICTIVE MODEL

12.8.3.1 Use of *In Vitro* Data

The pitfalls of using only *in vivo* data for the construction of a meaningful SAR for compounds acting through receptor mechanisms have been adequately described, both here (see Section 12.8.1) and elsewhere.[12] Some of the problems inherent in using only *in vivo* data also exist in the collation and interpretation of published data from various sources, whether *in vitro* or *in vivo*. Many published *in vitro* results, particularly in review articles, are given without references to the original experimental work and unless these data are compared with known standards, the reported values should be used only in a qualitative sense rather than attempting to rely on absolute values. Large changes in IC_{50} values, reported for standard compounds, can quite often signal procedural changes in the *in vitro* experiment, *e.g.* buffer, pH, temperature, composition of the medium *etc.*, and if possible should be traced to reports giving experimental details.

The minimal requirements for binding at the BZR have been determined to be relatively simple (see Section 12.8.3.2) and therefore it is felt that compounds that bind in the micromolar range may have no biological significance. For this reason only compounds with reported IC_{50} values in the nanomolar range have been used for SAR correlations. Again, with GABA shift experiments, the use of standard compounds as controls with each set of data used is essential for anything other than qualitative comparisons (see Section 12.8.3.1.1). Haefely (footnote a, Table 1) has drawn attention to the fact that even within one company (Hoffmann-La Roche), procedural changes in carrying out the antipentylenetetrazole test has given them (even *with* the consistent use of diazepam as a positive control) a large amount of data that can only be compared by use of the semiquantitative notations (0, +, + +, + + + and + + + +), indicating changes in orders of magnitude for activity.

It was decided to examine the concept that all compounds that bind to the BZR should have certain common characteristics that allow for recognition by the receptor without regard to the type of *in vivo* activity (agonist, antagonist, or inverse agonist; either full or partial) and without regard to gross structural features. Thus by an examination of widely differing structures, known to bind to the BZR in the nanomolar range, it should be feasible to develop a three-dimensional model for minimum binding requirements at the BZR, discounting, in the first instance, all of the possible auxiliary binding sites. Once this model has been defined, it should be possible to examine and differentiate structural features that would force conformational shifts within the receptor corresponding to *in vivo* profiles of activity.

12.8.3.1.1 *Biological testing*

Good procedures, already in place and available for use, can give the answer to the critical questions necessary both to validate and refine the model. Reliable determinations of binding activity at the BZR[4] and either a biochemical or an electrophysiological evaluation of intrinsic activity have been well described.[42,43] It is extremely important to carry out the validation procedure in order to confirm or reject and modify the proposed conformational models for the full agonist, full antagonist and full inverse agonist. The design of partial agonists or partial inverse agonists, based on structural requirements for all three types of activities, can then be considered (see Section 12.8.4).

As mentioned above, in the characterization of synthetic ligands at the BZR, the consistent use of only those structures that show binding affinities in the nanomolar range ($IC_{50} < 100$ nM L^{-1}) is indicative of a concern for the relative simplicity of the agonist model that has been derived from minimum requirements for receptor binding. This model might allow for micromolar nonspecific protein binding, or, even worse, binding at the BZR that does not have biological relevance. It should also be noticed that on a thermodynamic basis IC_{50} values within one order of magnitude are considered to be directly comparable. This means that compounds which show small differences in binding affinities are not ranked. In refining any model, a probe compound which does not bind to the receptor gives only negative data and positive conclusions regarding its SAR should not be drawn without other, corroborative evidence. If a BZR ligand does bind in the nanomolar range, it becomes necessary to determine efficacy, either positive, negative or zero. Initially, a qualitative sense of efficacy may be sufficient and can be obtained by biochemical methods. For analogs with expected full receptor activity, such qualitative measurements will later require augmentation by an examination of chloride flux within a single neuron by electrophysiological techniques.

It must be recognized that GABA shifts are not the most definitive means of assessing intrinsic activity and, regardless of which way this procedure is carried out, it suffers greatly from a very low time resolution due to $GABA_A$ receptor desensitization,[40] a fault common to $GABA_A$ receptor biochemical techniques. A related method, that of determining PAL (photoaffinity labelling) ratios has also some limited value.[41] Another technique, derived from the fact that BZR agonists have been found to decrease cGMP levels in the cerebellum (and inverse agonists to increase levels of cGMP), could be used as a measure of intrinisic activity even though it is not known how this second messenger system interacts with the $GABA_A$ receptor.[42]

Perhaps the most direct and accurate way to assess intrinsic activity is to measure the dose–response curve for chloride conductance increasing activity of GABA in single neurons, in the presence of increasing concentrations of ligand and in the presence of a fixed concentration of ligand.

This is not a trivial procedure but could be used to give far more definitive data on compounds of interest, after the initial GABA shift experiments had been performed. The procedure can be simplified by using a single submaximal dose of GABA for various doses of ligand.[43]

12.8.3.2 Conformational Chirality of 1,4-Benzodiazepines

The chirality of dihydro-1,4-benzodiazepines related to diazepam, due to the 'flipping' of the seven-membered ring, has been widely recognized and the conformational requirement believed to be necessary for receptor recognition of the benzodiazepines has been established.[44-46] This apparent requirement has been used to propose that the ligand binding sites, *i.e.* aromatic 'A' ring and proton-accepting groups, are not coplanar. Reports in the literature[47] which still relate the chirality of (*R*)- and (*S*)-3-methyl-1,4-benzodiazepines directly to binding activity are erroneous. These reports have neglected the fact that, for steric reasons, the methyl group of all possible conformational diasteriomers adopts a pseudo-equatorial orientation on the seven-membered ring, regardless of whether the absolute configuration at the 3-position is (*R*)- or (*S*)-derived. It has been shown by an X-ray analysis, carried out for both (*R*) and (*S*) compounds, that in order for the molecule to achieve this lower energy conformation, the seven-membered ring will flip, thus giving one active and one inactive conformation.[3, 44] It is of interest to note (and perhaps predictable) that crowding an inactive, (*R*)-alanine-derived equatorial methyl group at the 4-position of an imidazo-benzodiazepine, by the addition of bulky substituents at the two adjacent ring atoms (positions 3 and 5), the inactive equatorial methyl derivative (*R*) could be forced to flip to the now active pseudo-axial (*R*) conformer.[48]

It is now clear that there exist a variety of nonbenzodiazepine molecules that are either completely planar, or have the capability of being planar, that bind in the nanomolar range to the BZR, and demonstrate *in vivo* activity either as agonists, antagonists or inverse agonists[32,49a-d] (see also some of the compounds shown in Table 6 and Figure 5). If the active site on the BZR for the three types of ligand is one and the same, with *in vivo* activity differences being due to conformational shifts within the receptor, and if these binding sites are essentially coplanar, then the chiral requirements for the BZDs can be explained on the basis that the out of plane 3-methylene group of the inactive conformer is sterically inaccessible to the active site (see Section 12.8.6, the Borea model, for a further discussion and see Section 12.8.3.5.3 for a further discussion of planarity *versus* nonplanarity of the receptor pocket).

12.8.3.3 Minimum Requirements for *In Vitro* Binding to the Benzodiazepine Receptor

A comparison of *in vitro* binding properties was carried out for a variety of structures in which a seven-membered ring is attached to an aromatic 'A' ring and in this way fixing, in the three-dimensional sense discussed above, the relationship between the 'A' ring and a proton-accepting source in the vicinity of the amide carbonyl group (for diazepam). Compounds were selected in order to confirm or exclude different substituent atoms or groups as primary binding sites. Table 3 illustrates, for some specific examples, that portion of the diazepam structure believed to be responsible for initial receptor recognition. (i) Substituents on the 'A' ring: while substituents on the 'A' ring are certainly known to have a varied effect on the binding properties of the benzodiazepines, such effects are not predictable either on the basis of electronic or (within limits) steric properties, and it can be seen from an examination of Table 3 that this ring need not be substituted in order to obtain compounds that bind to the receptor in the nanomolar range. The old belief (based as it was on *in vivo* data) that the substituent had to be electron withdrawing and located only on the 7-position of the 1,4-benzodiazepine ring nucleus, has been shown to be invalid in terms of binding ability (intrinsic activity not determined).[12] (ii) The 4,5-(methyleneimino) group: neither the double bond nor the 4-position nitrogen is required for the *in vitro* binding of ligands (see also Section 12.8.3.4.2). (iii) 5-Phenyl ring: this substituent is also not a requirement for binding and its possible function will be discussed below. (iv) 1-Position nitrogen: finally, neither the amide nitrogen nor its methyl substituent are prerequisites for *in vitro* binding.

It was proposed that only by looking for the minimum requirements for *in vitro* binding might it be possible to identify common active binding sites for all of the varied structures now known to interact with the BZR. Initial correlations were carried out using structures derived from single-crystal X-ray analysis and were examined by creating a database for use on a high resolution computer graphics system together with a commercially available molecular modelling system.[50] By superpositioning one molecule on another and looking at surface electrostatic potentials, it became clear that the common features of all of these structures were: (i) the presence of an aromatic or heteroaromatic ring ('A'), believed to undergo π/π stacking within the receptor (probably with amino acid aromatic residues); and (ii) a proton-accepting group spatially related to the plane of the aromatic ring and arbitrarily labeled π_1.[3,12,51] Since there is no evidence at the present time for intercalation of the 'A' ring within the receptor, this interaction could take place in a receptor pocket and be only hydrophobic in nature; such a pocket would require sufficient flexibility/size in order to accommodate possible aromatic substituents. A publication has described evidence that a histidine residue, implicated in BZD binding, as part of the receptor could serve as such a proton source.[52] The three-dimensionality, given by the relative locations of the plane of the aromatic ring and the

Table 3   Minimum Structural Requirements for Binding at the Benzodiazepine Receptor[a]

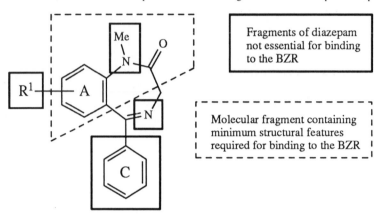

Fragment missing	Structure/ code no.	[^3H]Diazepam binding (IC$_{50}$ nM)	Antipentylene- tetrazole activity
R^1	Ro5-4336	19	+ +
$\equiv$N	Ro14-0609	24.4	+ +
C	Ro15-1788	2.5	Antagonist

Table 3 (*Contd.*)

Fragment missing	Structure/ code no.	[³H]Diazepam binding (IC₅₀ nM)	Antipentylene- tetrazole activity
	Ro23-5090	12.5	Not determined
	Ro22-8515	0.1	+ + + +

ᵃ Biological data from refs. 12, 46 and 60.

electrons of the proton-accepting group, has been depicted by placing the center of the aromatic 'A' ring (in this instance phenyl) as the 0,0,0 point of a set of cartesian coordinates, oriented in the x, y plane as shown in Figure 5 and Table 4.

The model allows for the determination of the mid 'A' to π_1 distance and for the measurement of the z coordinate value for any out of plane atoms. The π_2 group illustrated in Figure 5 is shown as being positionally related to π_1. At the present time, this group (π_2) is not one of the minimum requirements for binding and is thought to be directly related to ligand binding in the antagonist conformation (see Section 12.8.3.5). Since the π_2 proton-accepting group has always been observed in conjuction with a π_1 proton-accepting group, it is shown in Figure 5 attached to π_1. However, measurements for π_2 on the cartesian coordinates (see Table 4) are measured from "mid 'A'". The aromatic or heteroaromatic group labelled as π_3 is also not required for binding and in this instance

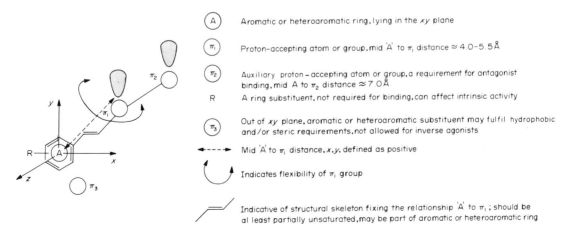

(A)	Aromatic or heteroaromatic ring, lying in the xy plane
(π_1)	Proton-accepting atom or group, mid 'A' to π_1 distance ≈ 4.0-5.5Å
(π_2)	Auxiliary proton-accepting atom or group, a requirement for antagonist binding, mid A to π_2 distance ≈ 7.0Å
R	A ring substituent, not required for binding, can affect intrinsic activity
(π_3)	Out of xy plane, aromatic or heteroaromatic substituent may fulfil hydrophobic and/or steric requirements, not allowed for inverse agonists
◄- - - -	Mid 'A' to π_1 distance, x, y, defined as positive
↺	Indicates flexibility of π_1 group
	Indicative of structural skeleton fixing the relationship 'A' to π_1; should be at least partially unsaturated, may be part of aromatic or heteroaromatic ring

Figure 5 Schematic three-dimensional model for binding of ligands at the BZR

Table 4 Coordinates for π_1 and π_2 for Various Ligands at the Benzodiazepine Receptor[a]

Compound	x (Å)	y (Å)	Mid 'A'–π_1 (Å)	Mid 'A'–π_2 (Å)
Diazepam	4.50	1.76	4.91	—
Midazolam	3.88	2.75	4.78	—
Ro22-8515	4.83	2.36	5.44	—
Ro22-9187	3.82	2.81	4.75	—
Ro22-7244	4.71	3.85	6.11	—
Zopiclone	3.56	3.56	5.00	—
ZK 93423	3.20	4.34	5.45	—
CGS-17867A	3.16	2.28	3.90	—
CL218,872	4.6	1.0	4.8	—
Ro15-1788	3.79	2.93	4.93	—
	6.18	3.16	—	7.27
Ro15-1624	3.82	2.80	4.74	—
	6.02	3.38	—	6.94
Ro16-6028	3.63	3.07	4.75	—
	5.76	3.67	—	6.96
Ro17-1812	3.65	3.03	4.74	—
	5.84	3.59	—	6.99

[a] Data taken from M.S. thesis of N. Pleshko, Rutgers State University, New Jersey, 1988.

represents the 5-phenyl substituent found on 1,4-diazepines related to diazepam. It may also represent a steric or hydrophobic substituent. Its geometric relationship to the 'A' ring is as yet undefined.

Based on assumptions made at that time, some of our previously reported measurements were taken from points other than atoms directly involved in hydrogen bonding (see Table 4 for corrected values). It is now also clear that the value of the z coordinate for the proton-accepting group does not have to be greater than or equal to zero since it is becoming more and more apparent that 'A' and π_1 are essentially coplanar, with values of z for π_1 being either positive or negative.

While x and y values for π_1 of each structure examined were determined, the angles from the mid 'A' to π_1 vectors, measured in the xy plane, from the x axis were not determined. [While there is no hard evidence to support such a proposal, it is possible that one of the effects of any of the various substituents, located at any of the different positions on the 'A' ring, would be to affect the orientation of this ring rotationally, within its π/π stacking position in the BZR, thus altering both the relative position of π_1 in relation to the proton source in the receptor and the conformation of the BZR (see Section 12.8.3.5.2)]. The effect of this might be to ignore any ligand or receptor plasticity. As discussed above, the modified values assigned to some of the compounds used in current correlations are given in Table 4. The structures used in these correlations are shown in Tables 5 and 6, together with the assumed positions of 'A' and π_1.

It has been shown by a computer graphics analysis carried out for diazepam that if both mirror image conformers are depicted with the 'A' rings superpositioned, and if the electrostatic potential map calculated for both carbonyl oxygen atoms at -10 kcal M^{-1} (1 cal = 4.18 J) is displayed, then the volume of contour overlap would encompass both possible receptor protons capable of hydrogen bonding with lone pair electrons from either of the oxygen atoms.[53] These results indicate that the inactivity demonstrated by the (R) conformer must be due to steric inhibition within the receptor pocket and not due to the inability of the oxygen lone pair electrons to interact with the receptor proton.

It has been stated that nonbenzodiazepines, such as the phenyl-substituted bicyclic ring systems of quinolines and of triazolopyridazines (Table 6), are not conformationally chiral and therefore cannot bind to the BZR in the same manner as the 1,4-benzodiazepines.[45] The fallacy here is that if both the phenyl ('A' ring) and the heterocyclic (π_1) rings are involved in BZR interactions, there is free rotation about the bond joining the two systems such that any geometry defined by Figure 5 can be overlapped.

It has been pointed out that there is a two-fold axis of symmetry within this model for minimal binding requirements[12] (Figure 6). This becomes an important factor in determining which of various heteroaromatic groups can be the 'A' ring and which can act as the proton-accepting group. In turn, this becomes important in the consideration of modes of binding for ligands with differing spectra of biological activity (see Section 12.8.4).

Table 5 Benzodiazepine Derivatives used in Correlations shown in Table 4

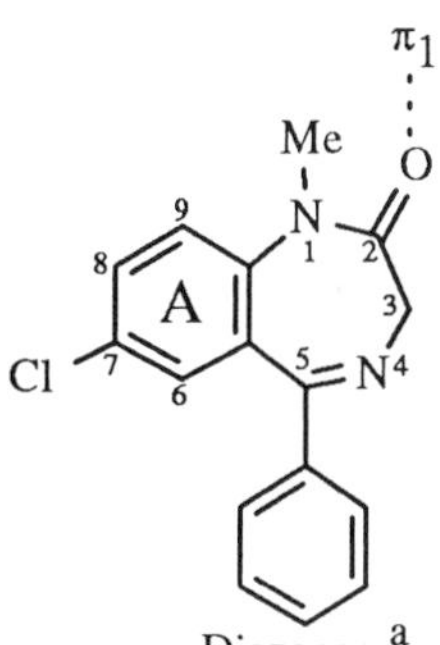

Diazepam[a]

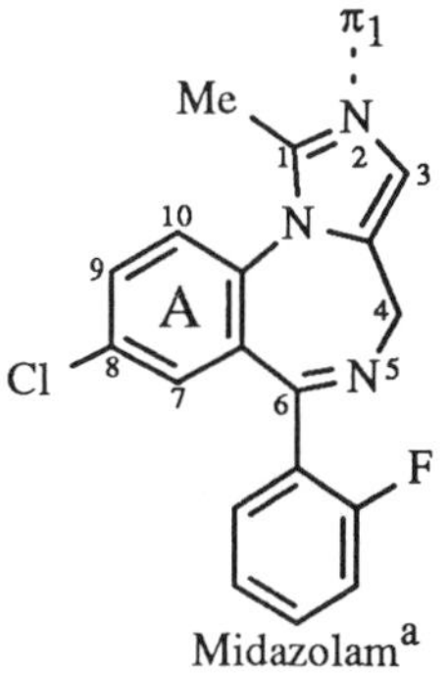

Midazolam[a]

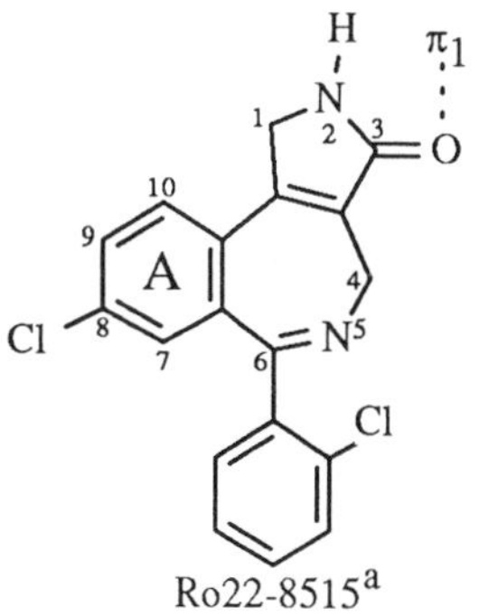

Ro22-8515[a]

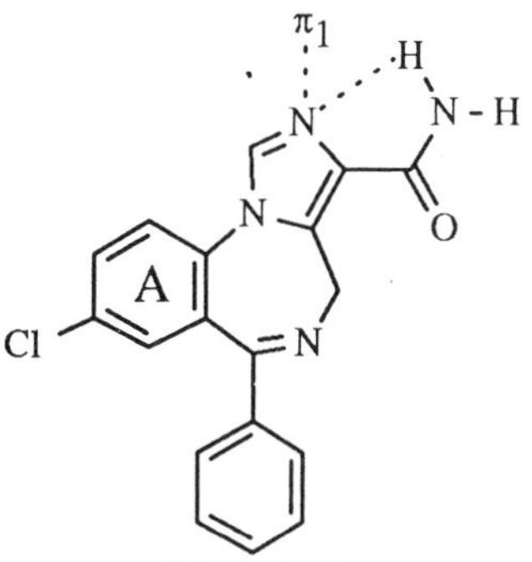

Ro22-9187

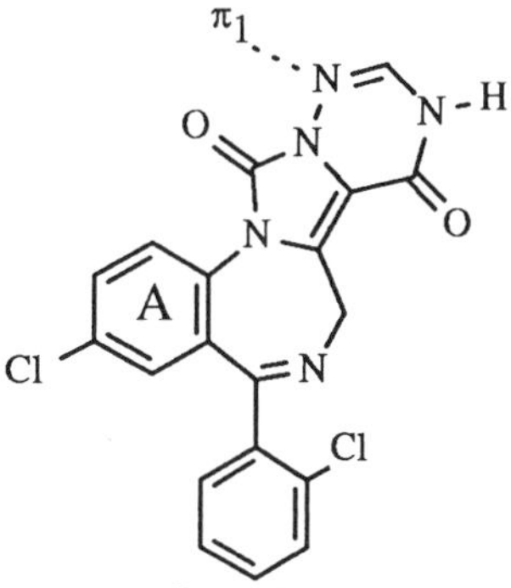

Ro22-7244

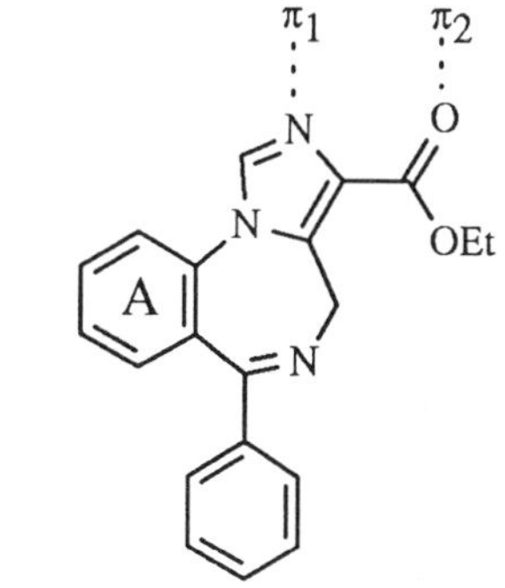

Ro15-1624

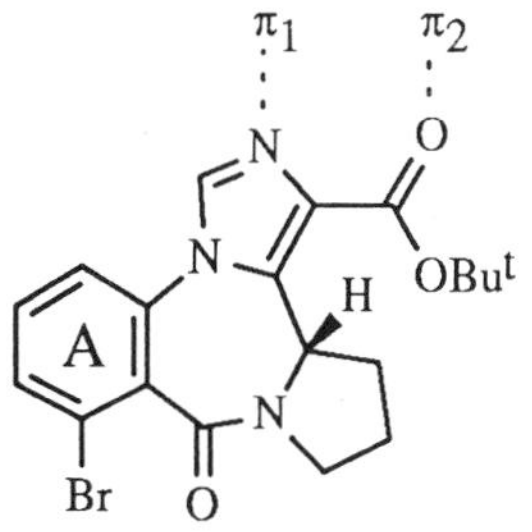

Ro16-6028

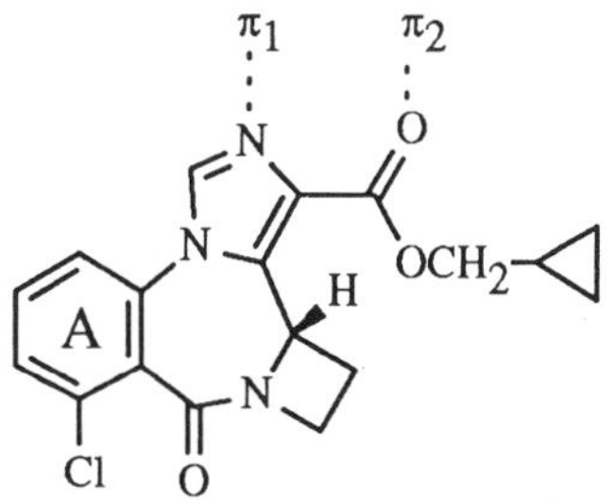

Ro17-1812

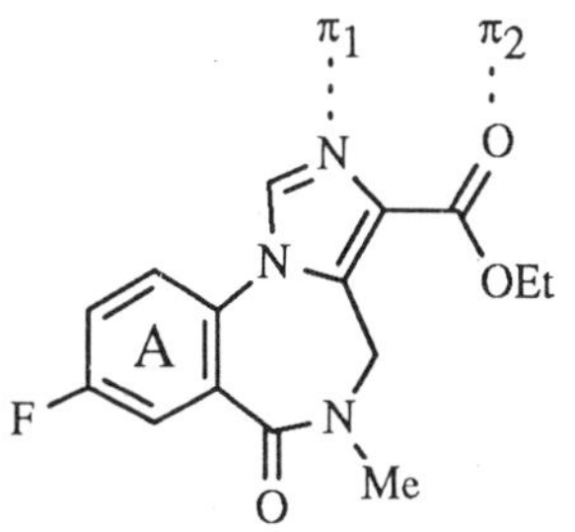

Flumazenil (Ro15-1788)

[a] Please note the numbering of the different seven-membered ring systems.

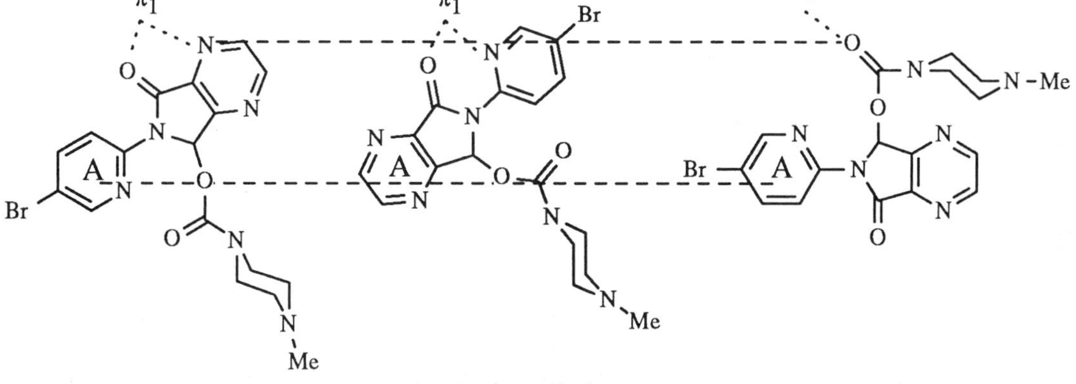

Figure 6 Zopiclone shown in three possible agonist binding modes, due to two-fold axis of symmetry in three-dimensional model. Three-dimensional freedom is given by the free rotation of the *p*-bromopyridine ring

Table 6 Nonbenzodiazepine Structures Listed in Table 4

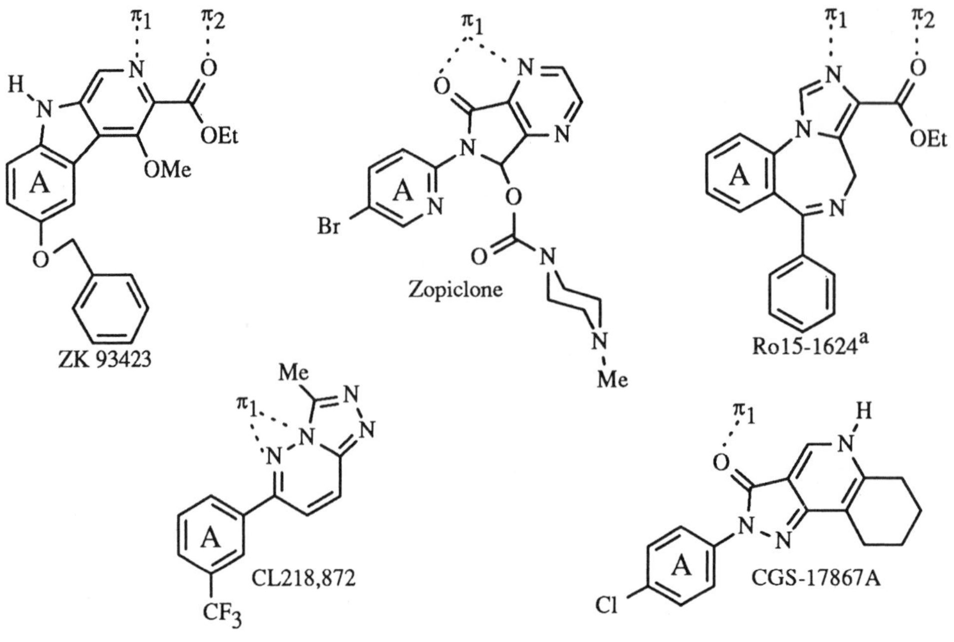

[a] Ro15-1624 is shown in order to allow for a comparison of orientations.

12.8.3.4 Predictive Use for *In Vitro* Binding

In order to determine the validity and/or utility of the model described above, a number of compounds were designed which encompassed the minimal binding requirements and relative geometry determined by the model, without regard to gross skeletal features. For the purposes of design with the computer graphics molecular modelling program,[50] the structure of midazolam was used as a template. Compounds that were synthesized and had nanomolar IC_{50} values in [^{3}H]diazepam-binding experiments are shown in Table 7. Not all of the compounds that were designed and synthesized were ligands at the BZR. This can be ascribed to the 'necessary but not sufficient' concept, in that while the model for minimal binding requirements describes the necessary (common) receptor–ligand interactions, it does not take into account other possible auxiliary binding sites or hydrophobic or steric groups. While an overview of several SAR studies given in Section 12.8.6 is more definitive, it is worth a brief examination of two of these at this point in regard to the number of interactive binding sites that are proposed for ligand–receptor interactions. Crippen,[54] using distance geometry analysis, in an evaluation of the essential binding sites for BZR ligands of differing structures, has proposed a site model with nine attractive site points for binding. Codding and Muir[55] have proposed a model in which seven, conformationally mobile, binding sites have been determined for compounds related to the antagonist Ro15-1788. It was suggested that the mobility of the sites would allow for the differentiation of ligands of different biological activity. It seems clear that the interaction of all of such sites cannot be consistent within different structural entities (otherwise they would be requisites for minimal binding) and therefore should be determined individually for each heterocyclic system known to bind to the BZR.

12.8.3.5 *In Vivo* Activity

Once the relationship between the sites essential for *in vitro* binding has been determined, it becomes necessary to find the factors that differentiate the three types of BZR ligands. Thus, the structurally unique characteristics, such as steric, hydrophobic and/or electronic effects, that correspond to the conformational differences correlating structures with *in vivo* activity have to be defined. While this has been accomplished to a great extent for BZR agonists and antago-

Table 7 Benzodiazepine Receptor Ligands, Designed on the Basis of the Three-dimensional Model (Figure 5), Synthesized and Tested in the *In Vitro* [^{3}H]Diazepam Binding Assay[12,60]

Code number	[^3H] Diazepam binding assay (IC$_{50}$ nM L^{-1})
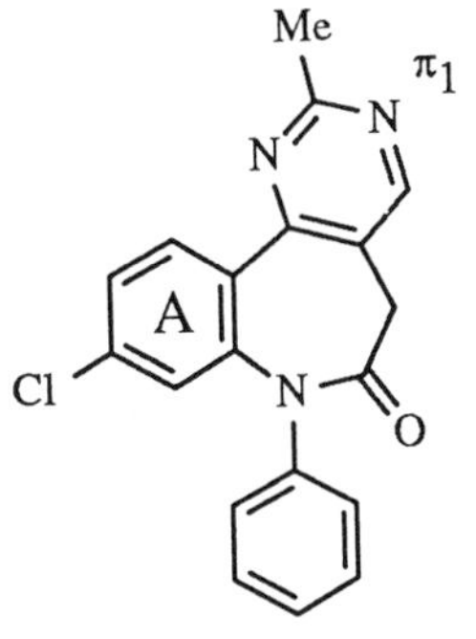 Ro22-6417	79
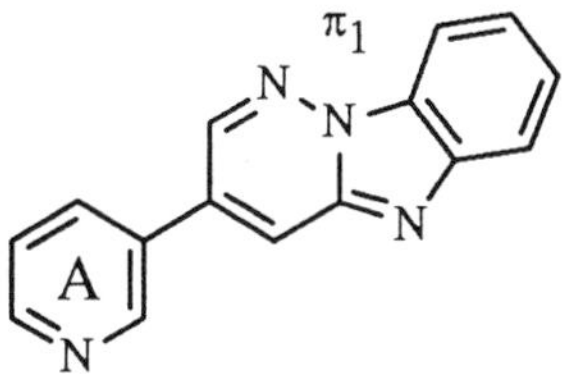 Ro22-9134	24
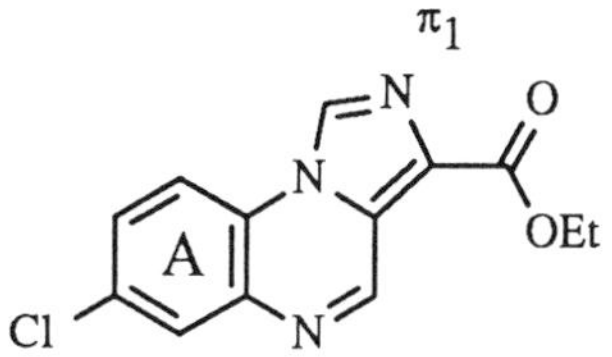 Ro22-1683	4.3
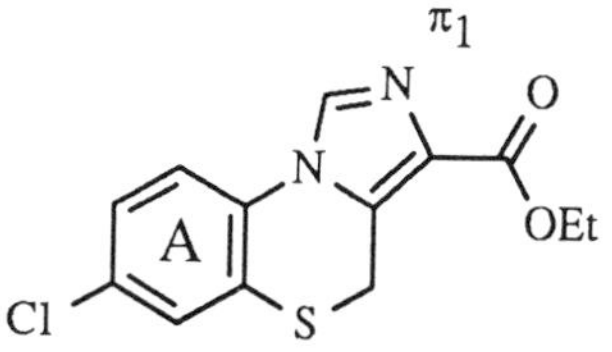 Ro22-5867	25

nists, inverse agonists, because of their relatively small database, still await a more complete interpretation.

As discussed above, an examination of Table 4 for the known antagonist ligands listed (Ro15-1788, Ro15-1624, Ro16-6028 and Ro17-1812), shows that there is a second proton-accepting group or binding site present, labelled π_2. Initial correlations[3,12,51,55] had depicted π_2 as an extension of the π_1 value. Since there is no evidence to the contrary π_2 could exist independently of π_1, providing two possible proton acceptors (π_1 and π_2) which are always present in antagonist ligands. Until additional synthetic work has been undertaken to unambiguously resolve this point, it is felt that the data shown in Table 4 probably best represent differences in ligand-binding interactions for agonists and antagonists. Once again the database for inverse agonists is not yet large enough to be used for differentiating differences in binding requirements with absolute confidence (see Section 12.8.3.5.3).

12.8.3.5.1 Full agonists

A discussion of the electronic, steric and hydrophobic requirements for full agonist activity at the BZR is in essence a discussion of the prohibitive interactions for full antagonists at that same receptor. So far five major structural features have been found to differentiate a full agonist from a full antagonist. These are: (i) for 3-substituted imidazobenzodiazepines, differences between 3-carboxamides and their corresponding esters; (ii) substituent effects at the 1-position of imidazobenzodiazepines; (iii) differences between 6-(4-substituted-phenyl)-imidazobenzodiazepines; (iv) variations in the substitution (geometry) at the 4,5,6-positions of the imidazobenzodiazepine; and (v) steric limitations caused by the addition of bulky substituents to the 3-position of imidazobenzo-diazepines.

(i) Amides versus esters

One of the more unusual SAR observations that differentiated full agonists and full antagonists concerned the 3-position substituent on the imidazole ring of an imidazobenzodiazepine. When the substituent was a primary amide, the *in vivo* activity for such a compound was always found to be that of a full agonist (with one known exception, see Section 12.8.4). If, however, the substituent was an ester, the activity was found to be either an antagonist or a partial agonist. A reasonable explanation of this phenomenon is based on an examination of X-ray structures for a variety of both types of compound,[56] in which all of the primary amides that were examined show a conformation in which the amino group is hydrogen bonded to the imidazole nitrogen and is coplanar with it. There is also some minor rotational steric interference between the two methylene protons on the seven-membered ring and the protons of the primary amide, based on rotation about the carbon–carbon bond between the imidazole and the amide. The ester, on the other hand, has free rotation about the carbon–carbon bond, no steric interaction with the methylene protons and there is no hydrogen bonding with the imidazole nitrogen. X-Ray analyses were carried out for several structures of this type and showed no preference for the orientation of the ester carbonyl group. In addition, energy calculations have shown that there is little difference between various possible conformational positions for the carbonyl group (Figure 7). It therefore seems reasonable to propose that the conformational binding properties of these primary amides are such that the carbonyl oxygen cannot participate in binding to the BZR (for this reason, the mid 'A' to π_2 distance for the primary amide carbonyl oxygen is not included in Table 4). Esters, on the other hand, depending on the relative conformation of the carbonyl group, may bind to the receptor in such a way that the carbonyl oxygen acts as a second proton-accepting group labelled π_2. In this binding mode the receptor/ligand adopts the conformationally different antagonist form.

(ii) The 1-substituent

By examining many structures of the imidazobenzodiazepine class of agonists and antagonists, it was observed that only full agonists could be substituted at the 1-position of the imidazo ring. The extent for maximum size of this substituent for agonists has not been reported. The 3-carboxamido derivatives of the bulky 1-(2-pyridyl)-, the 1-(6-methyl-2-pyridyl)- or 1-phenyl-imidazobenzo-diazepines (Ro21-8098, Ro21-8591 and Ro21-7518 respectively) were approximately as active as diazepam.[57] On the other hand, all known imidazo antagonists substituted by anything other than hydrogen (*e.g.* methyl), no longer bound to the receptor (Table 8).

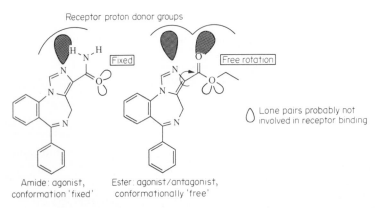

Figure 7 Imidazobenzodiazepines substituted at the 3-position with either a primary amide (agonist conformation) or by an ester (agonist, antagonist or partial agonist conformation). Esters have rotational freedom about the carbon–carbon bond that joins the carbonyl group to the imidazole ring; amides are 'fixed' by hydrogen bonding

Table 8 The Effect of 1-Substituents on the Biological Activity of Imidazo-1,4-benzodiazepine-3-carboxylic Esters and Amides

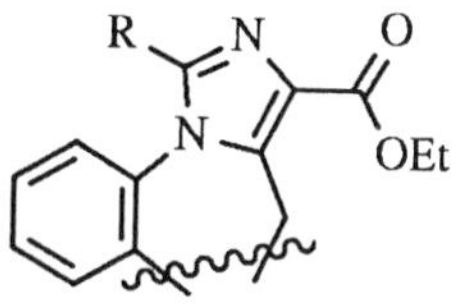

Binding and in vivo *activity for imidazoesters with following partial structure at 5, 6*

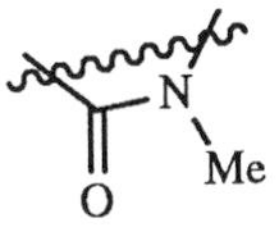

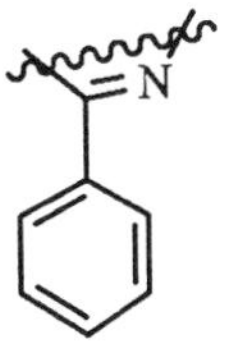

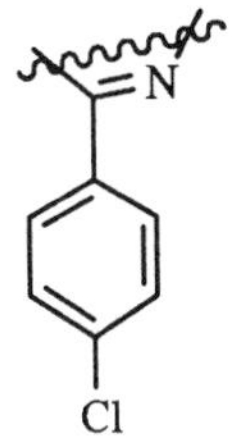

R = H

R = Me

If compound has nM *in vitro* binding, then 6-substituted phenyl is antagonist; others may be antagonists or partial agonists.

None bind and none show *in vivo* activity

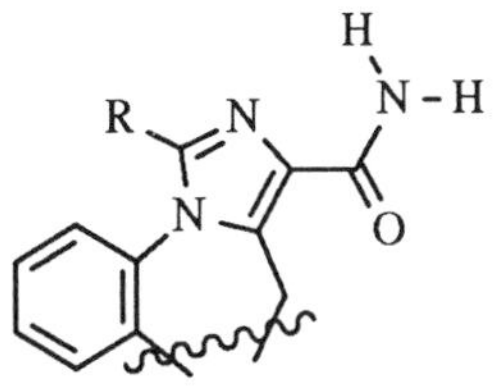

Binding and in vivo *activity for imidazoamides with following partial structure at 5, 6*

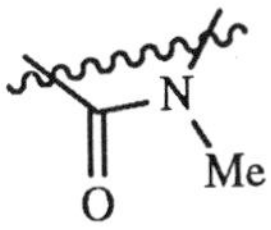

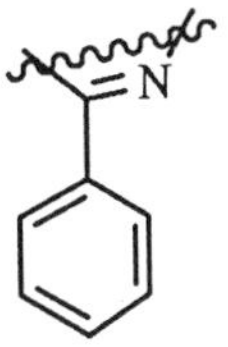

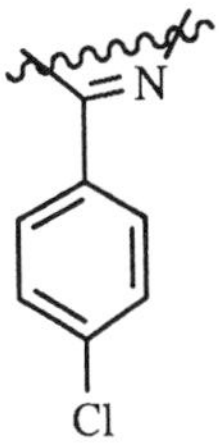

R = H	Inactive	Active (agonist)	Inactive
R = Me	Inactive	Active (agonist)	Inactive

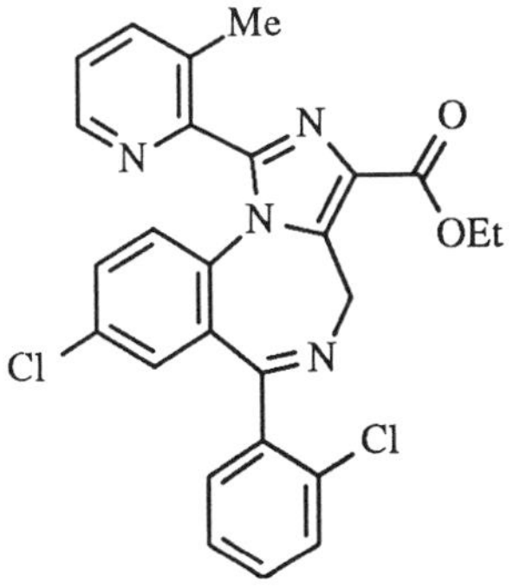

Ro21-8495
Inactive[60,63]

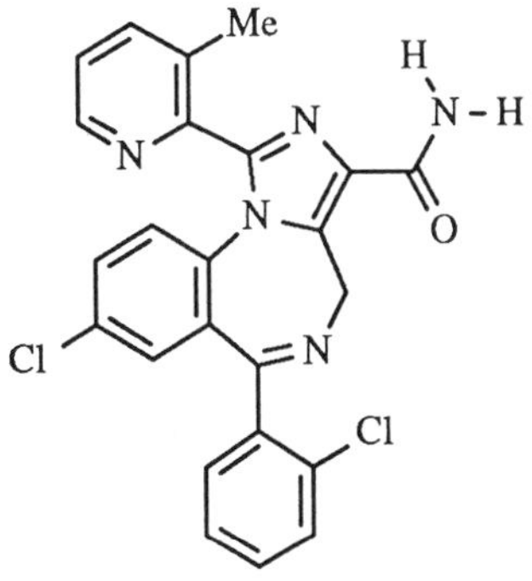

Ro21-8591
Active (agonist)[60,63]

(iii) The 4'-substituent

In very early 'classical' SAR work, it was noted that for any 5-phenyl-substituted BZD agonist, no substituent was allowed at the 4' (*para*) position. This effect does not appear to be electronic since the same substituent attached to the corresponding 2' (*ortho*) position either had no effect on binding or enhanced the binding properties. It is therefore believed that the agonist conformation of the receptor is sterically inhibited from accepting any substituent at the 4'-position, other than hydrogen (Tables 9 and 10). Antagonist 6-phenylimidazobenzodiazepines do not show any steric restrictions at the 4'-position and are capable of both *in vitro* binding and of *in vivo* antagonist activity.[12]

(iv) Modification of the 4,5,6 region

Modification of the skeleton of the seven-membered ring by alteration of the 4, 5 and 6 position geometry has little or no effect on the activity for antagonists (Table 10), but with only one exception

Table 9   Effect of 4′-Substituent on 6-Phenyl Ring of Imidazobenzodiazepine Carboxylic Esters (A) and Amides (B)

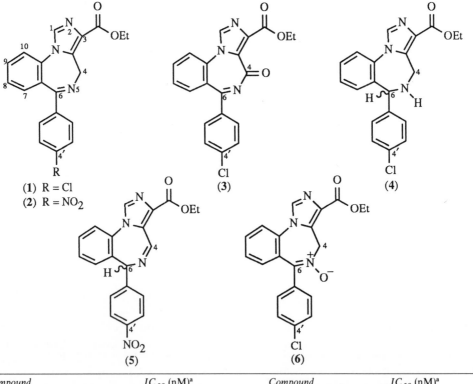

Compound	R	IC_{50}(nM)[a]	Activity	Compound	R	IC_{50}(nM)[a]	Activity
Ro22-9735	Cl	7.4	Antagonist	Ro22-9395	Cl	0	None
Ro15-1625	H	7.2	Antagonist	Ro22-8476	H	45	Agonist
Ro23-2896	NO_2	1.8	Antagonist				

[a] [³H]Diazepam binding assay.[16,60]

Table 10   Allowed Variations at the 4,5,6-Positions of Antagonist 6-(4′-substituted-phenyl)imidazo-1,4-benzo-diazepine-3-carboxylic Esters

Compound	IC_{50} (nM)[a]	Compound	IC_{50} (nM)[a]
(1)	7.4	(4)	18.5
(2)	1.8	(5)	1.5
(3)	31	(6)	4.6

[a] [³H]Diazepam binding assay.[16,60]

(*N*-oxide) these same modifications to agonist BZDs will destroy activity. Since the stereochemical requirements for structurally rigid agonists and antagonists are identical for benzodiazepine analogs,[44] this might indicate a less important role for receptor geometry in this region for the antagonist conformation.

(v) Steric effects related to substituents attached to π_2

Reported changes in the biological profile of activity for certain ester analogs, from antagonist, to partial agonist and/or to full agonist,[58] caused by the addition of four- or five-membered rings to the 4,5-positions of the imidazobenzodiazepine ring (see Figure 4), can be ascribed to steric properties that influence the relative positioning of π_2 at the receptor (see Figure 11). For the oxadiazole compounds (Figure 4), in which the same type of effect was noted,[59] the out of plane twist of the oxadiazole ring caused by the additional ring has, to our knowledge, not yet been investigated.

(vi) Other factors

Substitution at the 3-position of the seven-membered ring is sterically unfavorable and activity for agonists decreases as the bulk increases. This is possibly due to deformation of the ring with concomitant misalignment of the relative positions of the 'A' ring and π_1. The effect of substitution on the 'A' ring is important, but is not consistent either for agonists or antagonists and has been discussed elsewhere.[12]

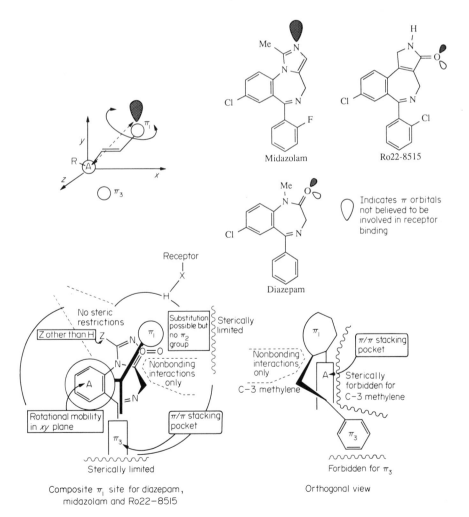

Figure 8 A model for agonist ligands at the BZR: steric considerations. π_3 is not one of the minimal requirements for the binding of agonist compounds, but is included in order to show its position relative to the 'A' ring of 1,4-BZDs

Based on the factors discussed above, and being careful to include functionality that is known to prohibit antagonist activity (prohibiting the ability of the ligand–receptor complex to adopt an antagonist conformation), a modified model for full agonists at the BZR is depicted in Figure 8.

12.8.3.5.2 *Full antagonists*

A distillation of the structural effects previously discussed gives a model for a full antagonist that would encompass both the required functionality for antagonist activity, together with all of the 'forbidden' features for agonists. The first requirement will ensure that the antagonist conformation prevails, while the second will prohibit the receptor from adopting an agonist conformation.

While the conformational chirality (absolute stereochemistry) is the same for both agonists and antagonists, the binding requirements differ, and for antagonists they are as follows: (i) an aromatic or heteroaromatic 'A' ring; (ii) a π_1 proton-accepting group or function spatially related to and connected with 'A' in the same manner as for the agonist conformation; and (iii) a second electron-rich, proton-accepting source, π_2, that can interact with and form a (second) hydrogen bond with a receptor proton.

(i) *Steric interactions*

An examination of the structural variations for antagonists shown in Tables 4, 5 and 6 indicates that antagonists can well support hydrophobic groups in the vicinity of the 4-, 5- and 6-positions of the imidazobenzodiazepine ring. While the limits for the bulk of the substituent at position 6 has not yet been determined, the model would call for: (i) a 4'-substituted phenyl ring in order to prohibit agonist activity and ensure full antagonist properties (Figure 9), or (ii) a variation of the 4,5,6 geometry [*e.g.* a 4,5 double bond, and a phenyl substituent at the trigonal C-6 carbon atom (Ro23-3812; **5**, Table 10)].

Based on the differences in binding properties for primary 3-carboxamides and their corresponding esters, it is felt that there is no hydrogen bonding with the receptor below a plane $x'z'$, which at the moment is arbitrarily defined as passing through atoms 1 and 3 of the imidazole ring and is parallel to the xz plane defined in Figure 5. The location of π_2 probably can best be placed within a hemisphere whose center is given by the atom attached to the 3-position of the imidazole ring of the model compound Ro15-1788, whose base is defined as lying on the $x'z'$, with radius of approximately 1.2 Å and is described in a positive 'y' sense above the $x'z'$ plane (see Figure 10). If π_2 is a carbonyl group, as in Ro15-1788, the above definition would limit free rotation of this group to within about

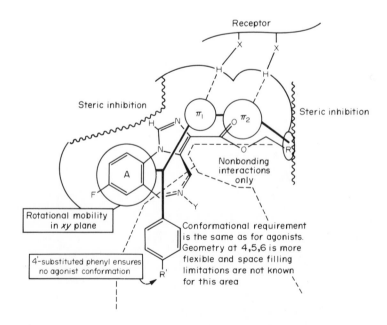

Figure 9 A model for full antagonist ligands at the BZR: steric considerations

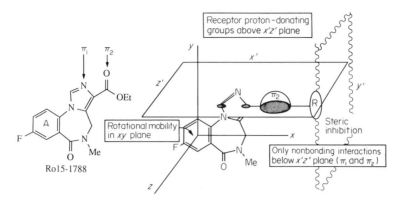

Figure 10 Schematic representation of the steric interactions of R groups attached to π_2

± 90° of coplanarity with π_1. It must be pointed out, however, that the limits of flexibility for continued interaction with the BZR proton source have not been experimentally determined.

Special consideration must now be given to interactions (steric and hydrophobic) for groups attached to the π_2 functionality and in the case of compounds related to Ro15-1788, to the 4-carbon and 5-nitrogen positions. Reports of changes in *in vivo* profile depending on the type and size of substituents[58,59] can be rationalized by proposing that such interactions between the receptor cleft and the π_2 terminal group or a 4,5-annelated ring would force a rotation of the 'A' ring within its π/π stacking pocket in an anticlockwise direction as shown in Figure 11. While the original $\pi_{1,2}$ atoms are not labelled (for the sake of clarity) it can be seen that a small rotational shift of approximately 20° would cause a relatively large shift in the groups capable of undergoing hydrogen bonding, such that it is conceivable that what was once the π_2 group now becomes the π_1 proton-accepting group and the 'old' π_1 group is no longer able to bind to the receptor. Added to this, is the fact that as rotation occurs, the 1-carbon atom of the imidazole ring now moves into the region that is disallowed for antagonist binding (Figure 11).

An additional consideration is one that would require a rotation of the π_2 function about the bond attaching π_2 to the imidazole ring, to a point below the $x'z'$ plane, where it would be unable to bind to the receptor as an antagonist (*e.g.* the carboxamide carbonyl oxygen). Furthermore, rotation

Figure 11 Possible rotational effects on *in vivo* activity: a rationale to explain the *in vivo* antagonist, partial agonist or full agonist activity of structurally related compounds, based on the relative positioning of interactive groups at the BZR by steric control of the π_2 terminal substituent

Table 11   Effect of 'A' Ring Substituent on *In Vivo* Profile for 3-Substituted Imidazobenzodiazepines

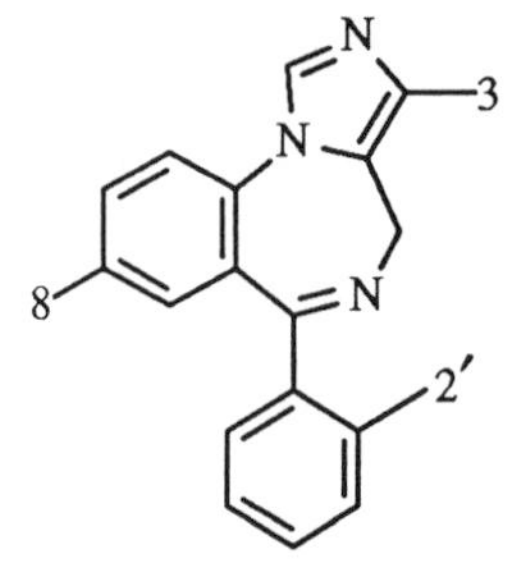

Compound	Structure substituent			IC_{50} (nM)[a]	*In vivo profile*
	3	*2'*	*8*		
Ro15-1624	—CO_2Et	H	H	7.2	Antagonist
Ro15-8670	—CO_2Et	H	Cl	15	Agonist
Ro23-0373	—CN	Cl	H	27	Antagonist
Ro21-9753	—CN	Cl	Cl	b	Agonist

[a] [^{3}H]Diazepam binding assay.[60]
[b] *In vivo* data only (antipentylenetetrazole activity, by mouth).[60]

about the middle point of the 'A' ring as discussed in the previous paragraph, caused by a possible rotational effect of the 'A' ring substituent, would have the same effect. This rationale would perhaps explain the agonist properties of some compounds structurally related to the antagonist ester Ro15-1624 (Table 6). An analog, substituted on the 'A' ring with 8-Cl (Ro15-8670), is an agonist with a reported binding IC_{50} of 15 nM and oral activity in an anticonvulsant test[48b,60] (Table 11). Since in this instance there are no apparent steric limitations at π_2, it seems reasonable to invoke one of these two different rotational effects as the cause for the change in profile. However, since no systematic evaluation of such proposals has been undertaken for compounds with full antagonist activity, the terminal group (if any) attached to π_2 should be kept small in order to avoid full agonist activity. Even then, there is no guarantee that (partial) agonist effects will not be found unless more is known about the possible rotational effects of the 'A' ring substituent.

12.8.3.5.3   *Full inverse agonists*

As mentioned in previous sections, the database for full inverse agonists is relatively small; most of these compounds have the characteristics of partial inverse agonists. The compounds initially found to exhibit negative efficacy at the $GABA_A$ receptor were β-carboline derivatives, isolated as artifacts from urine in studies directed towards the characterization of a putative endogenous ligand.[61] A large number of analogs of this ring system have now been synthesized and biologically evaluated.[49] Some of these compounds are shown in Figure 12, together with an indication of their *in vivo* profile. Three fused ring diazepines have also been reported to show activity as partial inverse agonists.[10,14] The β-carbolines are planar molecules and any 'out of plane' interaction of a π (proton-accepting) group with the receptor is only possible by rotation of the carboxylate ester group. Extended ring systems based on the carbolines have also shown good affinity to the receptor and for these structures there is no possible out of plane interaction.[49c] Borea *et al.* have suggested that the active site on the BZR is most probably almost planar[62] and, as discussed in Sections 12.8.3.2 and 12.8.3.3, it is becoming clear that within the receptor cleft it now appears that there is an almost coplanar relationship between the 'A' ring and the π_1 group. Thus the inverse agonists still fit the model proposed for minimal requirements for receptor binding (see Figure 4).

The factors that force the necessary conformational shift within the receptor, responsible for the inverse agonist effects seen for CCE (ethyl β-carboline-3-carboxylate), which, by definition, are different from those effecting agonist and antagonist conformations, are difficult to discern and at the present time only some general comments regarding classical SAR work are known (see Figure 12).

The conformational relationship between the β-carbolines with partial agonist activity (benzyloxy substituted) and agonist imidazobenzodiazepines has been reported.[51] A fit of molar volumes was

β-Carbolines, showing possible relative receptor orientations

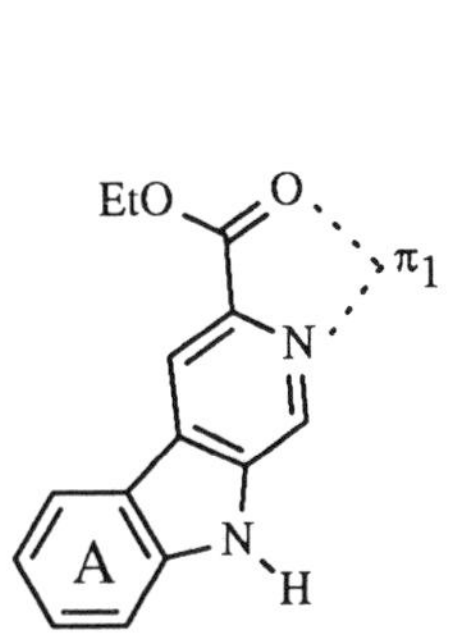

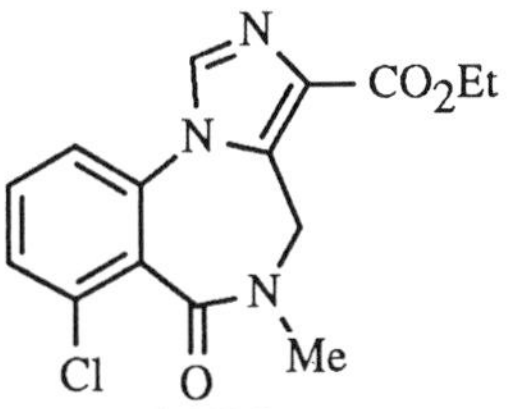

CCE — Inverse agonist

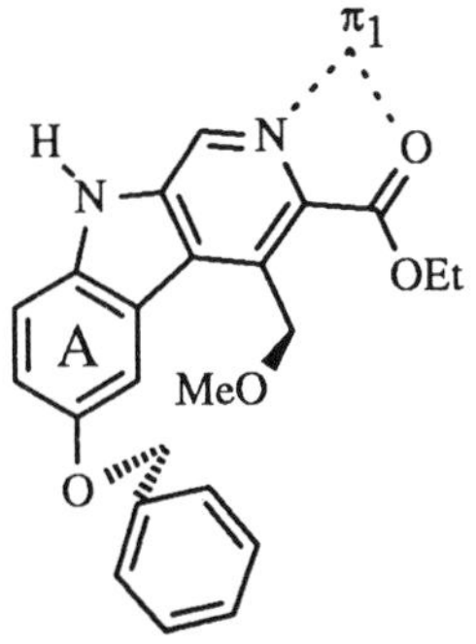

ZK 93423 — Agonist

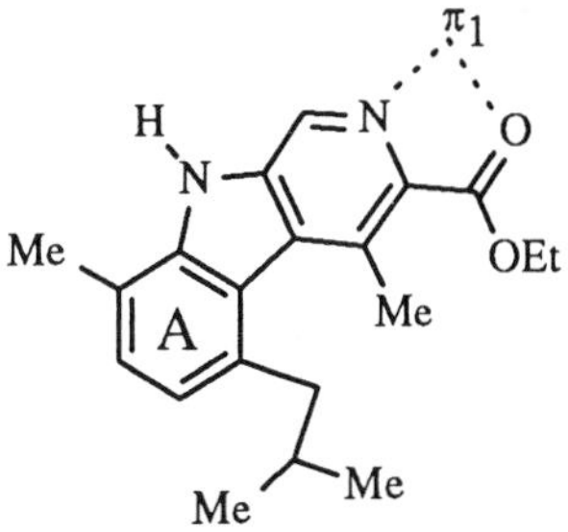

ZK 93426 — Partial antagonist

Benzodiazepine partial inverse agonists

Ro15-3505

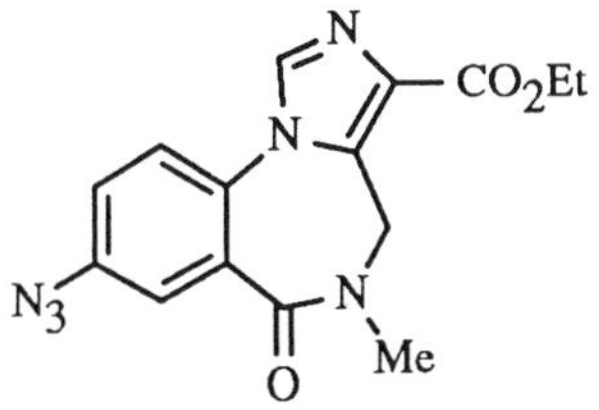

Ro15-4513

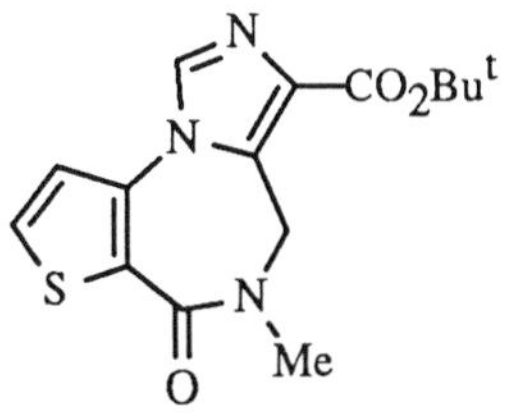

Ro19-4603

Figure 12 Selected (partial) inverse agonist structures for β-carbolines and imidazo-1,4-benzodiazepin-6-ones

carried out in which the corresponding 'A' ring, π_1, π_2 and π_3 groups for both molecules were required to coincide. The fit showed the β-carboline oriented in such a manner that the indole N–H portion of the molecule overlapped the 'allowed' 1-position of the imidazole region. Presumably this orientation within the receptor cleft is either not required for an inverse agonist, or, more likely, not even allowed (Section 12.8.5). The presence of the benzyloxy substituent may affect the receptor conformation in such a manner that possible binding of the indole N–H (proton donor) cannot take place. An indication that the N–H proton is important for binding activity has been shown by the reported inactivity of analogs substituted in this position by alkyl groups. Structural considerations must also be given to the first three benzodiazepines with reported partial inverse agonist properties. Two of these compounds are electron rich in the vicinity of the 'A' ring but are also close structural relatives of the Ro15-1788 series of antagonists (Figure 12). None of these compounds have a proton-donating group. Further correlations will be obtained by additional synthetic work, hopefully forthcoming in the near future.

12.8.4 RATIONALE FOR THE DESIGN OF PARTIAL AGONISTS

If a particular molecular structure has the ability to fit both the agonist and the antagonist conformations of the BZR, and is energetically capable of forcing different conformational shifts, either (i) in different receptor populations (subsets), or (ii) by altering the kinetics within a specific receptor population, or (iii) by any other mechanism, the net result in terms of *in vivo* activity would be that of a partial agonist of the mixed agonist/antagonist type (Section 12.8.2.4).

The design of such compounds should be feasible within any known structural class of BZR agonist or antagonist, providing that (i) all of the requirements for binding as both an agonist and as an antagonist are present and that (ii) none of the 'forbidden' groups or substituents for either type of activity are present. Under (i) would be: (a) the requirement for an aromatic or heteroaromatic 'A' ring, joined to both π_1 and π_2 groups in a manner described under Section 12.8.3.5; (b) rotational flexibility of π_2 should be allowed and/or balanced by steric limitations for substituent groups attached to it (note the use of 3-CN as the π_2 group, shown in Table 11); and (c) possible rotational effects of 'A' ring substituents should be considered and probably should either be H or a halogen on either the 7- or 8-positions corresponding to an imidazobenzodiazepine related to Ro15-1788.

Under (ii): (a) the exclusion of substituents at the 1-position for the imidazobenzodiazepines; (b) no substitution is allowed at the 4'-position of a 6-phenyl derivative; and (c) finally there should be only very limited modification of the geometry at the 4,5,6-positions of the diazepine ring.

12.8.5 RATIONALE FOR THE DESIGN OF PARTIAL INVERSE AGONISTS

Due to the overwhelming preponderance of adverse biological effects of the full inverse agonist class of BZR ligand (*e.g.* anxiogenic, proconvulsant activity), it would seem that the only type of compound that might have a therapeutic value within this type of BZR ligand would have to be derived from partial inverse agonist ligands. The methodological basis for the design of such a structure is identical to that described for the partial agonists. At this time however, with perhaps one exception, the complete steric/hydrophobic requirements for changing the profile from that of a full inverse agonist to either that of a full agonist or to that of a full antagonist have not been delineated. The possible exception is that, for full inverse agonist activity, an out of plane aromatic (aralkyl, *e.g.* benzyl, benzyloxy) group located such that it could correspond to π_3 in its relationship to π_1 and the 'A' ring of the agonist model (Figure 8), is forbidden. This is based only on two observations, one negative and one positive, namely (i) a search of the literature has failed to reveal the present existence of π_3-substituted compounds that both bind to the BZR and show negative intrinsic activity, and (ii) the addition of such aralkyl substituents to either the 5- or 6-positions of an ethyl β-carboline-3-carboxylate (*e.g.* ZK 93423, Table 6) has been demonstrated to force a conformational shift within the receptor,[51] an explanation compatible with its change in intrinsic activity from negative to positive. With the number of synthetic analogs rapidly increasing, confirmation of this hypothesis as well as the finding of additional conformational limits should be possible in the near future.

12.8.6 OTHER CORRELATIONS: AN OVERVIEW

There have been many attempts to carry out SAR for the BZDs since their discovery in the late 1950s. At first, structures were compared with the biological activity demonstrated in animal models. Then with the discovery of the BZR, the database was enlarged to include all BZDs that were able to recognize the receptor, regardless of efficacy. More recently all of the known different structural classes of compounds capable of binding to the BZR in the nanomolar range have been included.

Two of the recent attempts to correlate these SAR were mentioned earlier (see Section 12.8.3.4). One of these, the application of the distance geometry approach as devised by Crippen,[54] resulted in a determination of 15 site points (five adjustable energy parameters), for the receptor site. A total of 29 compounds, selected from five structural classes, were used in these correlations. Crippen, who did not consider conformational shifts within the receptor for differing efficacies, does warn, however, of the possibility of errors that can be introduced in his analysis by relatively small magnitudinal errors in binding data. He also points out that related structures do not necessarily have to be oriented in the same way when bound to the receptor (see two-fold axis of symmetry, Section 12.8.3.3).

The second SAR mentioned above was carried out by Codding and Muir,[55] whose model for binding contained seven conformationally mobile binding sites and was determined for compounds related to the antagonist Ro15-1788. The view that the mobility of the sites within the receptor would allow for the differentiation of ligands of different biological activity was expressed by Codding and Muir and independently reflected our own opinions held at that time[12] (*i.e.* antagonist activity was due to a conformational shift within the receptor, caused by an increase in the mid 'A' to π_1 distance, rather than what is our currently held view, that this shift is caused by the introduction of the additional site, π_2). It is of interest to note that a hydrophobic side chain or substituent (located close to the 3-position of the diazepam nucleus), indicated as the ester hydrocarbon in Ro15-1788 and by a phenyl group in the CGS series, is also noted by Wermuth and coworkers (see below).[47] The major difficulty here is that the reason for the observed large swings in efficacy, caused by changing the *para* substituent on the phenyl ring is not easily explained. In the models proposed for both antagonist and agonist interactions, the authors were probably hampered by the fact that they were unaware of: (i) the existence of BZR ligands which have heteroaromatic as well as aromatic rings (five-membered as well as six-membered rings);[28] (ii) the nonrequirement for the imine nitrogen to function as a primary electron donor to a receptor proton[28] (Table 3); (iii) the lack of steric inhibition in the region of the 1-position of imidazobenzodiazepine agonists;[63] (iv) the lack of a requirement for the electronegative substituent on the 'A' ring[12] (Table 3); and (v) the finding that compounds related to the antagonist Ro15-1788 (without the phenyl attached to the 6-position) can be receptor agonists.[14,59]

An interesting but perhaps, in its scope, somewhat limited 'active analog approach' to SAR at the BZR was carried out for seven structurally different ligands, using a superpositioning of structures displayed by computer graphics.[47] The results of this study were stated to be largely in agreement with our own, but a new possibility for ligand interaction located in the region of the 3-position for 1,4-BZDs has been proposed (see also Codding and Muir,[55] above). This was found by allowing for a different orientation of the ligand by changing the location of the 'A' ring within the molecule, for a group of nonBZDs (see also Figure 6) substituted with a freely rotating aromatic group (FRA). The axis of the FRA is generally in the plane of the 'A' ring. Wermuth and co-workers required the presence of a substituent in either the FRA region or in the so-called OPR or out of plane region (equivalent to the 5-phenyl substituent of a 1,4-BZD) in order to elicit agonist properties. Such a proposal should be capable of being tested experimentally and the results of such experiments would be of great value in validating this site.

Some points raised by these authors in their discussion of BZD SAR need some clarification: (i) the argument advanced in order to explain stereochemical and conformational requirements is not correct (for the reason discussed in detail in Section 12.8.3.2, and structures b and d in figure 13 of ref. 47 do not correspond to published X-ray structures[44]); and (ii) the presence of the azomethine group (positions 4, 5 of diazepam) is not a requirement for recognition at the BZR (Table 3).[42] The saturated antagonists and other variations at the 3-, 4- and 5-positions are shown in Table 10.

Since this model was derived by using as templates the most active and most rigid analogs of a structural series, neither receptor mobility nor conformational shifts within the receptor were taken into account. Thus it would be anticipated that volume matching for these analogs might refine this model considerably. For the many reasons cited in Section 12.8.3, the d_2 site as a required binding site has been discounted. For the antagonist ligands we have added the π_2 site in the direction of d_1 (our π_1) but further away from the 'A' ring centroid.[64] Perhaps due to the very limited selection of compounds from within structurally related classes that are known to be capable of exhibiting different degrees of efficacy at the BZR, this model was unable to pick up π_2 as a receptor proton acceptor distinct from π_1.

Borea *et al.*[62] have described five 'basic concepts' of BZD SAR that are utilized in their modelling approach. The evidence presented in their textual summary for the following statements does not appear to be well substantiated and the use of negative evidence to draw a positive conclusion should be used with extreme care.

(i) The decrease in binding activity for a 4-*N*-oxide derivative does not indicate the necessity of the 4-nitrogen as a 'basic' binding requirement. BZD derivatives with 5,4 partial structures –C(Ph)CH– and –CH(Ph)CH$_2$– have been reported to bind to the BZR in the nanomolar range. Of 15 such compounds listed in Table 10 of the review article by Haefely *et al.*,[46] 13 have binding IC$_{50}$ values ranging between 1.5 and 70 nM.

(ii) The lack of binding of medazepam (or of any compound) has no bearing on whether or not the 2-C=O oxygen is a basic requirement for binding (see, for example, Ro22-1274, a 2-benzazepine, IC$_{50}$ 75 nM[46]).

(iii) The assertion that the 2'-substituent on phenyl always enhances activity is not substantiated by an examination of data tables given by Haefely *et al.*[46] These data show that when the only variable is the 2'-substituent, the activating effect on binding activity is not consistent. The belief that all 4'-substituted phenyl-substituted benzodiazepines are inactive is also incorrect; an examination of Tables 9 and 10 will illustrate 4'-substituted phenyl compounds that have excellent binding properties.

(iv) The discussion of the stereochemical requirements for activity, centering around (*R*) and (*S*) enantiomers of the chiral 3-methyl derivative (only (*S*) enantiomer active), leads to the proposal by the authors that this difference can be ascribed to out of plane receptor interactions by the 5-phenyl substituent for the active enantiomer. These same methyl substituents are described under 'Summary of General Features of Proposed Model' as being in the axial position. It has been shown by single-crystal X-ray analysis that, for both enantiomers, the methyl groups, as expected, occupy the pseudo-equatorial position.[44] This has even been confirmed in solution for the active enantiomer, from NMR studies carried out by Sunjic *et al.*[45] The authors propose that for the active (*S*) compound, the out of plane 5-phenyl group is a requirement for agonist activity. It is known that this substituent is neither a requirement for binding, nor is its presence needed in order to obtain positive efficacy at the BZR.[59] Also known is that the identical stereochemical requirement exists for antagonists or partial agonists related to Ro15-1788[46] (no phenyl substituent present), as for compounds related to diazepam. This means that although the 5-phenyl substituent can fit within the receptor, it does not represent a primary binding site. Further, the stereospecificity for the BZDs must then lie in the relative positioning of the conformationally distinct methylene groups.

(v) Unfortunately, the authors were not aware of the existing data regarding the effects of electron-releasing substituents attached to the 7-position of the 'A' ring, reported earlier[12] (see also Ro23-5090, Table 3), and were unable to use this information in the design of their model. Such substitution has been found to exert little influence on *in vitro* binding properties, but may affect the intrinsic activity.

Borea *et al.*[62] have described a model based on the correlation of three 'groups' of compounds: (i) 7-substituted-2,3-dihydro-5-phenyl-1,4-benzodiazepin-2-ones, closely related and all with the same positive intrinsic activity; (ii) variously substituted β-carboline derivatives with, in general, partial intrinsic properties; and (iii) Zopiclone, Suriclone, CGS-9896, CGS-8216 and Ro15-1788. In a simplistic interpretation of this model axes are drawn on a two-dimensional view (*xy* plane) in order to divide the molecule into four quadrants (segments), with one of the two proton-donating groups lying on one axis. Each quarter is then labelled according to the effect on efficacy of substituents in that quadrant. The molecules are now superpositioned for the different classes by matching quadrant substituent effects. It appears that in order to account for differing intrinsic activities within closely related compounds, this model requires that these structures must bind in a differing orientation within the receptor. This might be interpreted by the view that neither the receptor nor the ligand is conformationally mobile, but that the conformations required for the different intrinsic activities already reside within the receptor complex.

This modelling technique requires the interaction between two proposed electron-donating atoms within molecules believed to interact with the BZR. All other interactions are thought to be hydrophobic. Because of the way in which the compounds were selected for this study, it is possible that this might result in a skewed, or at least a biased model. It would have been of interest to examine compounds within each of the three chemical classes that have different intrinsic activities and to obtain confirmation by the predictive use of the model for the design, synthesis and testing of probes.[12]

12.8.7 CONCLUSION

The complexity of the biological mechanisms involved in the action of ligands at the BZR, and the resulting modulatory interaction with the coupled $GABA_A$ receptor/chloride ion channel, make the SAR work extremely difficult. The absence of any knowledge regarding the tertiary structure of the BZR adds to these difficulties, and the resolution of this problem requires the definition of 'reverse mapped' sites for two or three different conformations (corresponding to either a two-state or a three-state model for binding) in order to develop a predictive model useful for the design of profile specific ligands.

From earlier discussions (Section 12.8.2), it is clear that binding affinities at the BZR are not related to efficacy at the $GABA_A$ receptor and therefore attempts at quantitative SAR (QSAR) determinations are hampered by the necessity for the evaluation of a ligand in a number of biochemical and pharmacological tests in order to determine its profile.[14] QSAR work is further complicated by the fact that the majority of ligands are of the partial agonist (or partial inverse agonist) type, and the flexibility of both ligand and/or the BZR, together with requirements for changes in entropy and enthalpy must also be considered (see Section 12.8.2.3).

It was the result of an attempt to simplify many of these problems that the decision was made, in the first instance, to study only the minimum requirements for binding at the BZR, considering only *in vitro* binding data for compounds, regardless of structure, that have IC_{50} activities in the [^{3}H]diazepam binding assay in the nanomolar range. Subsequent evaluation of additional binding properties, followed by an examination of steric and hydrophobic effects, for compounds with different biological profiles, has led to the development of the models presented in this chapter.

Many of the hypotheses put forward in Sections 12.8.3 and 12.8.4 should be capable of confirmation by the synthesis and biological evaluation of predictive probe compounds. This work is being actively pursued as a means of refining and extending the SAR of the BZR. The correlations discussed in Section 12.8.6 would all seem to be restricted in scope by a choice of rather narrow databases. This has led, in some instances, to some oversimplification of what has turned out to be a very complex biological story. None of these correlations seem to have been used predictively, and the FRA group noted by Wermuth and coworkers[47] certainly deserves additional study in terms of its suggested importance as an alternative conformational constraint for agonist activity.

Even with the progress made in the understanding of the effects of ligand interactions at the BZR, much remains to be done, especially in the area of full and partial inverse agonists. New information on the tertiary structure of the BZR, either bound by ligands (with positive, negative and zero efficacy at the GABA$_A$ receptor), or unbound, should be available in the foreseeable future.[65] It is now apparent that the GABA$_A$ receptor/chloride ion channel complex isolated from different parts of the brain are heterogeneous.[66,67] The relevance of this information to the question of homogeneity of the BZR has still to be answered.

12.8.8 REFERENCES

1. L. O. Randall and B. Kappell, in 'The Benzodiazepines', ed. S. Garattini, E. Mussini and L. O. Randall, Raven Press, New York, 1973, p. 27 and review articles cited therein.
2. L. H. Sternbach and E. Reeder, *J. Org. Chem.*, 1960, **26**, 1111.
3. R. I. Fryer, in 'The Benzodiazepines: From Molecular Biology to Clinical Practice', ed. E. Costa, Raven Press, New York, 1983, p. 7.
4. H. Mohler and T. Okada, *Science (Washington, D.C.)*, 1977, **198**, 849.
5. R. F. Squires and C. Braestrup, *Nature (London)*, 1977, **266**, 737.
6. C. Braestrup and R. F. Squires, *Proc. Natl. Acad. Sci. U.S.A.*, 1977, **74**, 3805.
7. H. Mohler and T. Okada, *Life Sci.*, 1977, **20**, 2101.
8. W. Haefely, L. Pieri, P. Polc and R. Schaffner, in 'Handbook of Experimental Pharmacology', ed. F. Hoffmeister and G. Stille, Springer-Verlag, Berlin, 1981, vol. 55/II, p. 13.
9. W. Haefely and P. Polc, in 'Benzodiazepine–GABA Receptors and Chloride Channels: Structure and Functional Properties', ed. R. W. Olson and J. C. Venter, Liss, New York, 1986, p. 97.
10. W. Haefely, *Chimia*, 1987, **41**, 389.
11. P. Polc, E. Bonetti, R. Schaffner and W. Haefely, *Arch. Pharmacol.*, 1982, **321**, 260.
12. R. I. Fryer, N. W. Gilman, V. Madison and A. Walser, in 'Proceedings of the VIIIth International Symposium on Medicinal Chemistry', ed. R. Dahlbom and J. Lars Nilsson, Swedish Pharmaceutical Press, Stockholm, 1985, vol. 2, p. 265.
13. C. Braestrup, M. Nielsen and T. Honore, in 'CNS Receptors: From Molecular Pharmacology to Behaviour', ed. P. Mandel and F. V. DeFeudis, Raven Press, New York, 1983, p. 237.
14. E. Kyburz, *Pharm. Weekbl.*, 1986, **121**, 893.
15. J. Sepinwall, J. Sullivan, G. Glinka, L. Gold, E. Boff, E. Gamzu, K. Keim, N. Petrusiak and T. Smart, *Neurosci. Abstr.*, 1986, **12**, part 1, 181.9.
16. R. M. Mangano, G. Bautz, N. Spirt, R. O'Brien and D. Horst, *Neurosci. Abstr.*, 1986, **12**, part 1, 181.10.
17. E. Toja, G. Tarzia, D. Barone, F. Luzzani and L. Gallico, *J. Med. Chem.*, 1985, **28**, 1314.
18. C. Anderson, J. Sullivan, E. Boff, D. Horst, S. Furman, N. Pietrusiak, E. Zavatsky, K. Keim, L. Gold and J. Sepinwall, *Neurosci. Abstr.*, 1986, **12**, part 1, 181.7.
19. J. W. Sullivan, L. Gold, R. Cumin, K. Keim, T. Smart, G. Vincent, A. Verderese, E. Gamzu, D. McNeill, J. D'Amico and J. Sepinwall, *Neurosci. Abstr.*, 1986, **12** part 1, 181.8.
20. G. Bautz, N. Spirt, R. Mangano, R. O'Brien and D. Horst, *Neurosci. Abstr.*, 1986, **12**, part 1, 181.11.
21. H. E. Shannon and S. Herling, *Eur. J. Pharmacol.*, 1983, **92**, 155.
22. D. N. Johnson, B. Kilpatrick and P. Hannaman, *Fed. Proc. Fed. Am. Soc. Exp. Biol.*, 1986, **45**, 674.
23. P. Sweetman and J. Tallman, *Mol. Pharmacol.*, 1986, **29**, 299; P. Sweetman, private communication.
24. H. Mohler, *Eur. J. Pharmacol.*, 1982, **80**, 435.
25. H. Yamamura, *Eur. J. Pharmacol.*, 1982, **82**, 239.
26. M. Cain, R. Weber, F. Guzman, J. Cook, J. Barker, K. Rice, J. Crawley, S. Paul and P. Skolnik, *J. Med. Chem.*, 1982, **25**, 1081.
27. S. Cooper, *Trends Pharmacol. Sci.*, 1986, **7**, 210.
28. C. Braestrup, T. Honore, M. Nielsen, E. Petersen and L. Jensen, *Biochem. Pharmacol.*, 1984, **33**, 859.
29. P. Wood, T. Loo, A. Braunwalder and N. Yokoyama, *J. Pharmacol. Exp. Ther.*, 1984, **231**, 572.
30. N. Yokohama, B. Ritter and A. D. Neubert, *J. Med. Chem.*, 1982, **12**, 337.
31. C. Boast, E. Snowhill and J. Smike, *J. Pharmacol. Biochem. Behav.*, 1985, **23**, 639.
32. A. J. Czernik, B. Tetrack, H. Kalinsky, S. Psychoyos, W. Cash, C. Tsai, R. Rinehart, F. Granat, R. Lovell, D. Brundish and R. Wade, *Life Sci.*, 1982, **30**, 363.
33. J. Albright, D. Moran, W. Wright, Jr., J. Collins, B. Beer, A. Lippa and E. Greenblatt, *J. Med. Chem.*, 1981, **24**, 592.
34. K. Biziere, J. Bourguignon, J. Chambon, M. Heaulme, A. Perio, S. Tebib and C. -G. Wermuth, *Br. J. Pharmacol.*, 1987, **90**, 1983.
35. W. Seighart and M. Karobath, *Nature (London)*, 1980, **286**, 285.
36. C. Braestrup and M. Nielsen, in 'Handbook of Pharmacology', ed. L. Iverson, S. Iverson and S. Snyder, Plenum Press, New York, 1983, p. 258.
37. T. Chiu and H. C. Rosenberg, *Trends Pharmacol. Sci.*, 1983, **4**, 348.
38. J. P. Bennett, Jr., in 'Neurotransmitter Receptor Binding', ed. H. Yamamura, S. Enna and M. Kuhar, Raven Press, New York, 1978, p. 57.
39. P. Skolnick and S. Paul, *Int. Rev. Neurobiol.*, 1983, **23**, 348.
40. J. Boorman, O. Hamill and B. Sakmann, *J. Physiol.*, 1987, **385**, 243.
41. M. Karobath and P. Supavilai, *Neurosci. Lett.*, 1982, **31**, 65.
42. W. Haefely, in 'Chloride Channels and their Modulation by Neurotransmitters and Drugs', ed. G. Biaggio and E. Costa, Raven Press, New York, 1988, p. 275.
43. D. Farb, L. Borden, C. Chan, C. Czajkowski, C. Gibbs and G. Schiller, *Ann. N.Y. Acad. Sci.*, 1984, **435**, 1.

44. J. F. Blount, R.I. Fryer, N. W. Gilman and L. Todaro, *Mol. Pharmacol.*, 1983, **24**, 425.
45. V. Sunjic, A. Visini, A. Sega, T. Kovac, F. Kajfez and B. Ruscic, *J. Heterocycl. Chem.*, 1979, **16**, 757.
46. W. Haefely, K. Kyburz, M. Gerecke and H. Mohler, *Adv. Drug Res.*, 1985, **14**, 165.
47. S. Tebib, J.-J. Bourguignon and C.-G. Wermuth, *J. Computer-aided Mol. Design*, 1987, **1**, 153.
48. (a) W. Haefely, E. Kyburz, M. Gerecke and H. Mohler, *Adv. Drug Res.*, 1985, **14**, 223; (b) A. Wakser, Hoffmann-La Roche, Nutley, NJ, personal communication.
49. (a) J. C. Fong, K. Okada and M. Goldstein, *Eur. J. Pharmacol.*, 1982, **77**, 57; (b) M. Trudell, A. Basile, H. Shannon, P. Skolnick and J. M. Cook, *J. Med. Chem.*, 1987, **30**, 456; (c) S. Takeda, H. Shindo, T. Sasatani, N. Chomei, A. Matsushita, M. Eigyo, K. Kawasaki, S. Murata, Y. Takahara and H. Shintaku, *J. Med. Chem.*, 1988, **31**, 1738; (d) M. Allen, T. Hagen, M. Trudell, P. Codding, P. Skolnick and J. M. Cook, *J. Med. Chem.*, 1988, **31**, 1855.
50. Molecular Modeling Software: Sybyl, version 5.1, Tripos Associates, St. Louis, MO.
51. R. I. Fryer, C. Cook, N. W. Gilman and A. Walser, *Life Sci.*, 1986, **39**, 1947.
52. B. Lambolez and J. Rossier, *FEBS Lett.*, 1987, **219**, 301.
53. J. C. Pinto and R. I. Fryer, 196th Meeting of the American Chemical Society, Los Angeles, Sept. 1988, Div. Med. Chem., Abstr. 84.
54. G. M. Crippen, *Mol. Pharmacol.*, 1982, **22**, 11.
55. P. W. Codding and A. K. Muir, *Mol. Pharmacol.*, 1985, **28**, 178.
56. L. Todardo and J. F. Blount, personal communication.
57. A. Walser, R. Lauer and R. I. Fryer, *J. Heterocycl. Chem.*, 1978, **15**, 855 and unpublished results.
58. E. Kyburz, in 'Symposium on Antianxiety Agents, 194th ACS National Meeting', New Orleans, 1987, Div. Med. Chem., Abstr. 94.
59. F. Waetjen, M. Engelstoff and J. Hamsen, *Eur. Pat. Appl.*, 202 441 (1986) (*Chem. Abstr.*, 1987, **106**, 33133).
60. W. Dairman, K. Keim, R. Mangano, R. O'Brien and J. Sullivan, Hoffmann-La Roche, Nutley, NJ, personal communication.
61. C. Braestrup and M. Nielsen, *Proc. Natl. Acad. Sci. U.S.A.*, 1980, **77**, 2288.
62. P. A. Borea, G. Gilli, V. Bertolasi and V. Ferretti, *Mol. Pharmacol.*, 1987, **31**, 334.
63. A. Walser, R. Lauer and R. I. Fryer, *J. Heterocycl. Chem.*, 1978, **15**, 855.
64. R. I. Fryer and Z.-Q. Gu, 196th Meeting of the American Chemical Society, Los Angeles, Sept. 1988, Div. Med. Chem., Abstr. 83.
65. See, for example, E. A. Barnard and P. H. Seeburg, in 'Chloride Channels and their Modulation by Neurotransmitters and Drugs', ed. G. Baggio and E. Costa, Raven Press, New York, 1988, p. 1.
66. D. B. Pritchett, H. Sontheimer, B. D. Shivers, S. Ymer, H. Kettenmann, P. R. Schofield and P. H. Seeburg, *Nature (London)*, 1989, **338**, 582.
67. D. B. Pritchett, H. Sontheimer, C. M. Gorman, H. Kettenmann, P. H. Seeburg and P. R. Schofield, *Science (Washington, D.C.)*, 1988, **242**, 1306.
68. H. Mohler and J. G. Richards, *Nature (London)*, 1981, **294**, 763.

12.9

Serotonin (5-HT) Receptors

MARCEL F. HIBERT

Merrell Dow Research Institute, Strasbourg, France

ANIS K. MIR and JOHN R. FOZARD

Sandoz Ltd, Basel, Switzerland

12.9.1 INTRODUCTION

There can be no area of receptor pharmacology where progress has been as dramatic in recent years as that in the field of 5-hydroxytryptamine (5-HT; **1**) receptors. From the initial concept of just two functional sites,[1] the pace has increased, fuelled in the last decade particularly by perceptive radioligand-binding studies,[2-5] to the point where three major groups, with at least seven distinct 5-HT receptor subtypes, are generally conceded.[6-8] Such dynamic progress reflects in large part the development (or recognition) of molecules with high affinities and, in some instances, selectivities for the individual receptor subtypes.[6]

The purpose of this chapter is to describe the important properties of the major 5-HT receptor subtypes. For obvious reasons, emphasis will be placed on the chemistry and structure–activity relationships (SAR) of the 5-HT receptor ligands. To facilitate and, indeed, in some instances to permit, comparisons 'activity' will be represented in the main by affinities obtained from radiolig- and-binding assays. However, a number of extensive accounts of the biological sequelae of 5-HT receptor activation have recently appeared,[9–14] and the reader is referred to these publications for additional information.

12.9.2 PHYSICOCHEMICAL PROPERTIES AND METABOLISM OF 5-HT

12.9.2.1 Physicochemical Properties

5-HT (**1**) is a hydroxyethylaminoindole (also known as serotonin), whose structure has been determined by X-ray analysis. Using this technique, different salts have been studied, which correspond to different conformations of 5-HT in the crystal form, as illustrated in Table 1.

The pharmacological actions of 5-HT have been attributed to the alkylamino side chain and to electronic interactions of the indole ring with the different 5-HT receptors. It follows that, at the recognition sites, the protonation of the alkylamino nitrogen and its orientation with respect to the aromatic ring are of prime importance in accounting for the recognition and activation processes. At physiological pH and in aqueous solution 5-HT would mostly be in the cationic form, protonated at the side chain amine.

Although it seems likely, there is no definitive evidence that 5-HT interacts in its protonated form with the receptor. On the other hand, there is no reason to consider that the 5-HT conformers observed in the crystal form, or found as the energetically preferred configurations in the gas phase, or in solution, might correspond to the receptor-bound conformation.

Following contact with the receptor, 5-HT can adopt a conformation which costs energy as long as this intramolecular energy is balanced by intermolecular interactions. A good example of this would be methotrexate, whose dehydrofolate reductase-bound conformation has an energy 27 kcal mol^{-1} (1 kcal = 4.18 kJ) higher than the global minimum.[36] Molecular orbital methods of various degrees of approximation have nevertheless been used to generate relative potential energy diagrams for 5-HT which could serve as guides in the stereochemical mapping of 5-HT recognition sites.

Table 1 5-HT Lowest Energy Conformations[a]

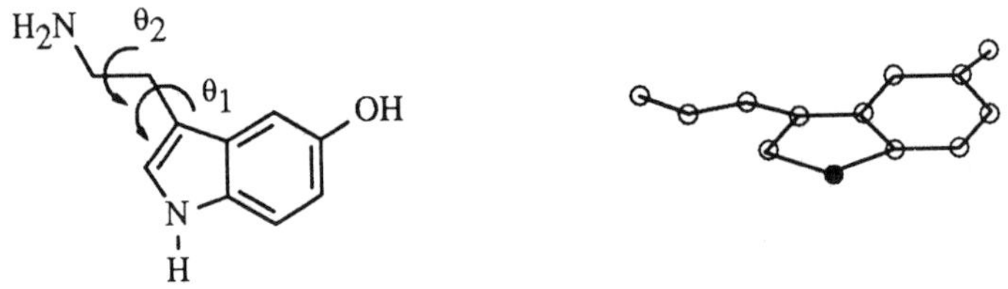

Method	θ_1 (°)	θ_2 (°)	Ref.
X-Ray analysis of the creatinine sulfate	166.7	187.4	26
X-Ray analysis of the picrate	−67.5	−66.6	27
X-Ray analysis of the hydrogen oxalate	172	176	28
EHT[b] of cation	90	180	29, 30
INDO[c] of neutral form	90	60	31
INDO[c] of cation	60	0	31
PCILO[d] of cation	40	20	32
Empirical method	−100	180	33
^{1}H NMR of the oxalate		180 ± 60	34
^{13}C NMR	?	?	35

[a] Modified from Arvidsson *et al.*[25] [b] Extended Hückel theory. [c] Intermediate neglect of differential overlap. [d] Perturbative configuration interaction using localized orbitals.

Several conformational studies of 5-HT have been performed, leading to different minimal energy conformations (Table 1). In addition, small energy differences among a large population of conformers do not support a single preferred conformer likely to correspond to the receptor-bound conformation. As will be discussed in the following sections, analysis of rigid systems containing the 5-HT skeleton may provide better tools to study the stereochemical requirements of the different 5-HT receptors.

12.9.2.2 Biosynthesis and Catabolism of 5-HT

5-HT has a widespread occurrence in plants and animals. Its distribution in tissues and body fluids of several mammalian species has been repeatedly reviewed.[37] 5-HT is synthesized in most of the tissues in which it is stored and has a rapid turnover in the majority of these; platelets are an important exception, since 5-HT originates from other tissues, such as the gastrointestinal tract. 5-HT is formed from the essential amino acid L-tryptophan (**2**). Tryptophan enters the 5-HT neurones of the brain by two nonselective uptake systems, with high and low affinity respectively;[38] the significance of these is not yet elucidated but it has been suggested that the high affinity uptake process is important in the regulation of 5-HT biosynthesis. The biosynthesis and metabolism of 5-HT, which have been extensively reviewed,[39] are summarized in Scheme 1.

The rate-limiting step in the synthesis of 5-HT is the reaction catalyzed by tryptophan-5-hydroxylase, an enzyme which exists only in cells synthesizing 5-HT. In the brain this enzyme is localized in 5-HT neurones, where it regulates 5-HT synthesis.[40] Molecular oxygen and tetrahydro-biopteridine cofactor are necessary for the hydroxylation, leading to the intermediate product, 5-hydroxy-L-tryptophan (5-HTP; **3**). 5-HTP is normally decarboxylated almost immediately it is produced, and thus does not accumulate in tissues. The decarboxylation is performed by aromatic-L-amino acid decarboxylase, which is a nonspecific pyridoxal enzyme, widely distributed in many tissues. The same enzyme catalyzes the decarboxylation of several important amino acids, including tyrosine, phenylalanine, tryptophan and L-3,4-dihydroxyphenylalanine (L-DOPA).

5-HT is stored in granules within neurones, possibly by binding to a specific protein (serotonin-binding protein; SBP),[41] before being released by nerve impulses into the synaptic cleft. 5-HT storage and release have been recently reviewed by Verbeuren.[37] Inactivation is achieved by removal of 5-HT from the cleft by a membrane uptake carrier present on the 5-HT nerve terminals. Once back within the neurone, 5-HT is degraded by different metabolic pathways. Oxidation by monoamine oxidase type A (MAO-A) constitutes the major route of 5-HT elimination. MAO-A is ubiquitous flavin-containing enzyme, present both intra- and extra-neuronally. It preferentially catalyzes the oxidative deamination of substrates such as 5-HT and noradrenaline, while type B MAO metabolizes amines like phenylethylamine and benzylamine. MAO-B is found in 5-HT neurones and platelets and is capable of acting on 5-HT *in vitro*, but there is evidence that this enzyme does not contribute significantly to 5-HT degradation *in vivo*.[42] 5-Hydroxy-1*H*-indole-3-acetaldehyde (**4**), formed from 5-HT by MAO-A, is rapidly oxidized to 5-hydroxy-1*H*-indole-3-acetic acid (5-HIAA; **5**) by a reaction catalyzed by the enzyme aldehyde dehydrogenase, which uses nicotinamide adenine dinucleotide as a coenzyme. 5-HIAA can also be reduced to the alcohol 5-hydroxytryptophol (**6**). A number of other minor catabolic pathways have been described, including 5-HT sulfation, glucuronidation, *N*-acetylation, *O*- and *N*-methylation and conversion to tetrahydro-β-carbolines.[43]

Several drugs which alter the synthesis and metabolism of 5-HT have been described and extensively studied, including inhibitors of tryptophan-5-hydroxylase, monoamine oxidase and the membrane uptake process. These compounds have recently been reviewed by Fuller.[44]

12.9.3 CLASSIFICATION OF 5-HT RECEPTOR SUBTYPES

The classification of functional 5-HT receptors proposed by Bradley *et al.*,[15] in which three major groups of 5-HT receptors ('5-HT$_1$-like', 5-HT$_2$, 5-HT$_3$) were identified, has been generally accepted as a useful, although necessarily interim, classification scheme. As clearly anticipated by Bradley *et al.*, the '5-HT$_1$-like' category is now recognized to comprise several subtypes and the terminology introduced on the basis of radioligand-binding studies (5-HT$_{1A}$, 5-HT$_{1B}$, 5-HT$_{1C}$, 5-HT$_{1D}$) is routinely applied to the analogous functional receptors.[6-8] Similarly, the 5-HT$_3$ receptor category seems likely to be heterogeneous,[16,17] although neither a suitable terminology nor a satisfactory means of discriminating the sites has yet been agreed.[8] At present there is no good evidence that the 5-HT$_2$ receptor is not a single entity.

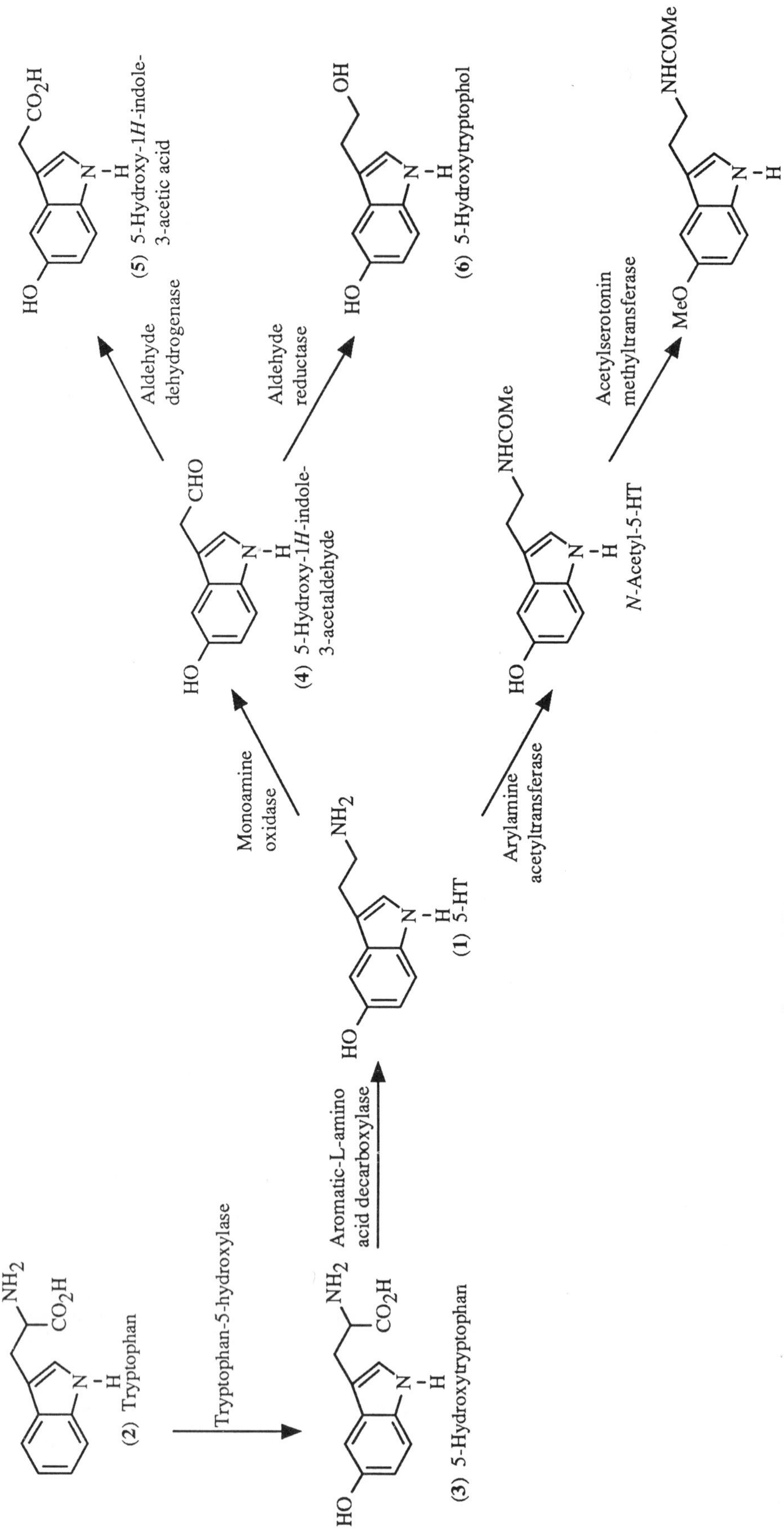

Scheme 1 Biosynthesis and catabolism of 5-HT

A major recent development, which cannot be accommodated in the original Bradley *et al.* classification, is the recognition and pharmacological characterization of a 5-HT receptor present in embryonic mouse colliculi and linked positively to adenylate cyclase.[18-20] This receptor, designated 5-HT$_4$, is closely similar, if not identical, pharmacologically to the high potency neuronal 5-HT receptor in the guinea pig ileum, which releases acetylcholine when activated, and is resistant to 5-HT$_3$ receptor blockade.[21,22]

A summary of the important features of the major 5-HT receptor subtypes is presented in Table 2. Information on discriminatory ligands, location and functional responses has been kept to a minimum since these aspects will be dealt with in detail in the sections which follow.

12.9.4 5-HT RECEPTOR SUBTYPES AS TARGET PROTEINS FOR DRUG ACTION

12.9.4.1 Introduction

In recent years, medicinal chemistry has developed from a random process of screening hundreds of compounds for therapeutically interesting agents, to one relying on a more rational, mechanistic approach. It is very important to emphasize that the mechanisms of action of different ligands can reasonably be discussed only when their host binding protein is characterized without ambiguity. Similarly, a drug design process may claim to be rational only if the target protein is unique and well defined.

Very little has been published in the way of SAR, and what has been reported should be interpreted with caution due to the discovery of multiple 5-HT receptor subtypes. Thus, a large number of early studies have been performed using nonspecific radioligands which, as has been demonstrated since, do not allow discrimination between different 5-HT receptor subtypes. For example, [^{3}H]LSD (26) possesses similar affinity for the 5-HT$_{1A}$, 5-HT$_{1C}$ and 5-HT$_2$ receptors, while [^{3}H]-5-HT labels 5-HT$_{1A}$, 5-HT$_{1B}$, 5-HT$_{1C}$ and 5-HT$_{1D}$ recognition sites at similar concentrations. For this reason, the significance of all the studies performed using these nonspecific markers is unclear and the results obtained will not be discussed in detail in this review.

In very recent years, several compounds have been tested as putative 5-HT receptor ligands with more relevant techniques. Affinity constants and complete functional studies are nevertheless not always available in all cases, which renders difficult their comparison in terms of potency, selectivity and efficacy as agonist or antagonist. In addition, binding experiments have often been performed in different species and brain areas, with different radioligands and using varied conditions of assay (GTP, Ca^{2+}, *etc.*). As a consequence, the discussion of the results of different studies poses certain problems.

Nevertheless, we have attempted to present the biological characteristics of the established 5-HT receptor subtypes and to discuss the design, SAR and the biological properties of their known ligands with respect to the state of the art. As mentioned above, emphasis has necessarily been placed on data from radioligand binding assays since relatively little data suitable for comparison are available from functional test systems. The binding affinities of ligands for 5-HT receptor subtypes, expressed as pK_D, pK_I or pIC$_{50}$ are given in Table 3 and in certain instances repeated in the text.

12.9.4.2 5-HT$_{1A}$ Receptors

12.9.4.2.1 *Identification and functional correlates*

The central 5-HT$_{1A}$ recognition site was first identified on the basis that the neuroleptic spiperone (82) showed a high affinity for a proportion of [^{3}H]-5-HT-labelled sites.[3] However, the remarkable progress that has been made in establishing the biochemical and pharmacological properties of this 5-HT$_{1A}$ site resulted from the discovery that 8-OH-DPAT (38), an aminotetralin with central 5-HT receptor agonist properties,[58] had a high affinity and selectivity for the 5-HT$_{1A}$ recognition site *vis à vis* 5-HT$_{1B}$ and 5-HT$_2$ sites.[59] Subsequently [^{3}H]-8-OH-DPAT was introduced as a radioligand.[60] Since then, several other radioligands, which selectively label 5-HT$_{1A}$ recognition sites, have been developed, such as [^{3}H]ipsapirone (65),[61] [^{3}H]PAPP (1-[2-(4-aminophenyl)ethyl]-4-(3-trifluoromethylphenyl)piperazine; 66).[53] Recently [^{3}H]spiroxatrine (76) has also been reported to label 5-HT$_{1A}$ sites, but it is nonselective, having a higher affinity for dopamine D$_2$ and opiate receptors.[62] The radioligands described above are based on compounds which act either as agonists or partial agonists; no antagonist radioligand for the 5-HT$_{1A}$ site has yet been described.

Table 2 Important Features of the Major 5-HT Receptor Subtypes[20,23,24]

	5-HT$_1$-like				5-HT$_2$	5-HT$_3$	5-HT$_4$
	5-HT$_{1A}$	5-HT$_{1B}$	5-HT$_{1C}$	5-HT$_{1D}$			
G-protein linked	Yes	Yes	Yes	Yes	Yes	No	Yes
Transduction mechanism	Cyclase (+) Cyclase (−) K$^+$ channel	Cyclase (−)	PI	Cyclase (−)	PI	Cation channels (Na$^+$/K$^+$)	Cyclase (+)
Discriminatory ligands	8-OH-DPAT (**38**) 5-CT (**13**)	5-CT (**13**)	*m*CPP (**57**) Mesulergine (**30**)	5-CT (**13**)	Ketanserin (**85**)	MDL 72222 (**104**) ICS 205-930 (**107**)	5-Methoxytryptamine (**11**) Substituted benzamides
Structure known	Yes	No	Yes	No	Yes	No	No

Table 3 Binding Affinities for 5-HT Receptor Subtypes

	5-HT$_{1A}$	5-HT$_{1B}$	5-HT$_{1C}$	5-HT$_{1D}$	5-HT$_2$	Ref.
		(pK_D or pK_I or pIC$_{50}$)				
5-HT analogues						
(**1**) 5-HT	8.5	7.6	7.5	8.4	5.5	23
(**7**) T	6.8	5.0	7.3	7.4	6.0	23
(**8**) 4-HT	7.0	6.0	7.4		6.1	45
(**9**) 6-HT	5.8	5.2	5.3		4.9	45
(**11**) 5-MeO-T	8.0	6.4	7.6	8.4	5.6	45
(**12**) 5-NH$_2$-T	6.3	6.3	7.1		5.5	23
(**13**) 5-CT	9.5	8.3	6.2	8.6	4.7	23
(**14**) 5,6-DHT	6.0	5.2	6.2		5.0	45
(**15**) 5,7-DHT	4.9	3.7	4.3		<4	45
(**16**) 2-Me-5-HT	5.6	4.4	5.8		5.0	45
(**17**) α-Me-5-HT	7.0	6.0	7.2		6.9	45
(**18**) β-Me-5-HT	7.1	5.5	6.3		5.6	45
(**19**) *N*-Me-5-HT	8.3	7.4	6.6		6.7	45
(**20**) *N*-Me$_2$-5-HT	7.6	6.0	7.2	8.1	6.4	23
(**21**) *N*-Et$_2$-5-HT	7.8	6.0				23
(**22**) *N*-Pr$_2$-5-HT	8.0	5.7				23
(**23**) DP-5-CT	9.5	4.9	4.5	7.2	5.3	23
Other indole-containing structures						
(**25**) RU 24969	8.6	9.4			6.0	46
	8.2	8.4	6.5			47
	8.1	8.4	6.5	7.3	6.0	23
(**26**) (+)-LSD	8.4	6.8	7.0			46
	8.6	6.8	7.9	8.2	8.6	23
(−)-LSD	4.4	<4	<4	<4		46
(**27**) Lisuride	9.1	6.7	7.7	7.5	8.3	23
(**28**) Methysergide	7.6	5.8	8.6	8.4	8.6	23
(**29**) Metergoline	8.1	7.4	9.2	9.1	9.0	23
	7.9	7.3	7.0			46
(**30**) Mesulergine	6.2	4.9	8.8	5.2	8.4	23
(**31**) 2-I-LSD	7.7	6.3	7.4		8.9	23
(**32**) Me-I-LSD					9.8	48
(**33**) LY 53857	6.4	5.5	8.1		7.3	23
					10.3	48
(**34**) (±) 21009	7.8	8.5	5.1		5.5	45
(−) 21009	8.0	9.4	5.3	6.4	5.0	23
(+) 21009	6.2	7.5	5.0		4.7	23
(**35**) (−) Pindolol	7.7	7.8	4.2	5.2	4.4	23
(+) Pindolol	5.9	5.0	4.4		4.9	23
(**36**) (±) Cyanopindolol	8.3	8.3	4.4	6.9	4.5	23
(−) Cyanopindolol	8.6	8.7				45
(+) Cyanopindolol	7.3	7.3				45
(**37**) (±) ICYP	8.3	9.5	5.0	6.8	4.9	23
Aminotetraline derivatives						
(**38**) (±) 8-OH-DPAT	8.7	4.2	5.2	5.9	5.0	23
(+) 8-OH-DPAT	8.9	5.1	4.6			49
(−) 8-OH-DPAT	8.0	4.8	4.7			49
(**39**) 8-MeO-DPAT	8.5					49
(**40**) 8-MeO-PAT	8.3					49
(**41**) 8-MeO-AT	6.7					49
(**42**) 8-MeO-piperidino-AT	7.1					49
(**43**) 8-OH-AT	6.8	5.1	5.2			50
(**46**) 8-MeO-CLEPAT	7.4	5.1			5.0	51
Arylpiperazine derivatives						
(**51**) Quipazine	5.5	6.5	6.7	5.9	6.2	23
(**52**) MK 212	5.3	5.0	6.2			45
(**53**) TFMPP	6.9	7.3	6.0	6.6		46
	6.3	6.4	7.2	6.2	6.6	23
(**57**) *m*CPP	6.5	6.6	7.7	5.8	6.7	23, 52
(**63**) Buspirone	7.6	3.9	5.1	4.5	6.1	23
(**64**) Gepirone	7.1	3.9	4.6		5.4	23
(**65**) Ipsapirone	7.7	3.9	4.5	4.9	5.1	23
(**66**) PAPP	8.5	6.5				53
(**67**) BrAcTFMPP	9.3	6.8			7.4	54
(**68**) CGS 12066B	6.1	7.3			5.2	55

Table 3 (*Continued*)

	$5\text{-}HT_{1A}$	$5\text{-}HT_{1B}$	$5\text{-}HT_{1C}$	$5\text{-}HT_{1D}$	$5\text{-}HT_2$	Ref.
		(pK_D or pK_I or pIC_{50})				
Benzodioxane derivatives						
(72) (±) MDL 72832	9.1	6.2	6.3	6.4	6.8	23
(+) MDL 72832	7.7	5.3			6.1	56
(−) MDL 72832	9.2	6.1			6.7	56
(73) (±) MDL 72975	8.3	6.4			6.8	56
(74) (±) MDL 73005	8.6	4.5	6.2	6.0	5.5	57[a]
(75) WB 4101	8.7	5.4	6.0	6.2	5.9	23
	7.9	5.7	6.4			46
(76) Spiroxatrine	8.1	3.9	5.1		6.2	23
Miscellaneous						
(82) Spiperone	7.2	5.3	5.9	5.3	8.8	23
(90) Pirenperone	5.9	5.3	7.3		8.8	23
(78) Methiothepin	7.1	7.3	7.6	7.3	8.8	23
(77) Mianserin	6.0	5.2	8.0	6.4	8.1	23
(85) Ketanserin	5.9	5.7	7.0	6.0	8.9	23
(91) (±) Atenolol	3.3	3.8	4.0		4.0	23
(92) (±) Betaxolol	3.8	4.8	4.0		4.2	23
(93) (±) ICI 118551	4.3	5.6	4.6		5.1	23
(94) (±) ICI 89-406	6.5	5.9	5.0		5.5	23
(95) Phentolamine	5.8	5.3	6.1			50
(96) Indorenate	7.8	5.4	6.5			50
(79) Pizotifen	6.2	5.5	8.1	5.6	7.8	23
(97) Cinanserin	6.1	5.2	6.7	5.8	7.7	23

[a] D. Hoyer, personal communication.

Autoradiographic and biochemical studies of the regional distribution of [³H]-8-OH-DPAT binding sites have revealed that $5\text{-}HT_{1A}$ sites are present in the brains of rodents and several mammalian species and are particularly abundant in limbic areas such as hippocampus and raphe nuclei.[60,63] A curious finding concerning 8-OH-DPAT binding to brain membranes is that it has been reported to bind to the 5-HT neuronal membrane uptake site.[64] However, its affinity in this respect is in the micromolar range and the functional significance is as yet obscure. In the rat brain $5\text{-}HT_{1A}$ sites are located both presynaptically[60,65] and postsynaptically.[65] In addition, the 5-HT autoreceptors located on 5-HT neuronal cell bodies in the raphe, but not those on the nerve terminals, are of the $5\text{-}HT_{1A}$ subtype.[66]

Concerning the biochemical mechanisms involved in receptor–effector coupling, the transduction mechanism coupled to $5\text{-}HT_{1A}$ receptors has been shown to be the enzyme adenylate cyclase, which is linked both in a positive and negative manner, depending upon the preexisting state of activation (see Table 2). $5\text{-}HT_{1A}$ receptors are not, however, exclusively coupled to adenylate cyclase. A recent report suggests that carbachol-induced stimulation of phosphoinositide turnover in rat hippocampus can be inhibited by $5\text{-}HT_{1A}$ receptor activation, implying negative coupling to the enzyme phosphoinositide phosphodiesterase.[67] Further, hippocampal pyramidal cell $5\text{-}HT_{1A}$ receptors are directly coupled to neuronal K^+ channels by a pertussis toxin-sensitive G protein which is neither N_s nor N_i.[68]

An impressive number of potential $5\text{-}HT_{1A}$ receptor-mediated functional/biological responses have now been documented. Two areas which have received particular attention over the last five years are the cardiovascular system and anxiety. As regards the former, there is growing evidence for a key role for central $5\text{-}HT_{1A}$ receptors in cardiovascular control (see ref. 69 for a review). Thus, selective $5\text{-}HT_{1A}$ receptor agonists, such as 8-OH-DPAT, flesinoxan and ipsapirone show hypotensive activity associated with an increase in vagal tone and sympathetic inhibition. The question whether this novel central mode of blood pressure control is of therapeutic importance awaits the outcome of clinical experience with flesinoxan, which is undergoing development in essential hypertension.

Concerning the role of 5-HT in the control of anxiety, a decrease of 5-HT neurotransmission forms the most rational basis for achieving a reduction in 'anxiety' (see refs. 70 and 71 for a review). In this context, central $5\text{-}HT_{1A}$ receptors have been implicated in the actions of certain putative anxiolytic agents buspirone (63), gepirone (64), ipsapirone (65) and MDL 73005 (74).[57,70] In theory, a decrease in 5-HT transmission by these partial agonists at $5\text{-}HT_{1A}$ receptors could be achieved either by inhibition of 5-HT neuronal firing by activation of somatodendritic 5-HT_{1A} receptors in the hippocampal region, or by blocking postsynaptic 5-HT_{1A} receptors.

Recent evidence suggests that central 5-HT_{1A} receptors are also involved in the control of endocrinological function; for example, 5-HT_{1A} receptor activation results in changes in the levels of plasma ACTH, corticosterone, β-endorphin, prolactin and growth hormone in rats,[72-74] indicating activation of the hypothalamic–pituitary–adrenal axis. Another interesting development in this area is the discovery that central 5-HT_{1A} receptor activation leads to inhibition of the basal hyper-insulinaemia of the genetically obese/insulin resistant fa/fa rat and the hyperinsulinaemia in response to a glucose load in fa/fa and normal rats.[75,76] A remarkable feature of this effect is that although 5-HT_{1A} receptor agonists induce some hyperglycaemia *per se*, no worsening of the glucose tolerance is observed despite a marked inhibition of insulin release.

Centrally acting 5-HT_{1A} receptor agonists also induce aspects of the 5-HT behavioural syndrome such as forepaw treading, hindlimb abduction and Straub tail (see ref. 77 for review); the intensity of these behaviours varies, depending on whether the compounds are full or partial agonists. Central 5-HT_{1A} receptor activation also induces a discriminative stimulus.[78] 5-HT_{1A} receptor agonists attenuate stress-induced open field deficits[79] and induce hyperphagia in satiated rats;[80] the latter effect shows a long-lasting desensitization following a single dose of the agonist.

12.9.4.2.2 *5-HT$_{1A}$ receptor ligands*

A large number of putative 5-HT receptor agonists and antagonists has been designed and tested as ligands at the 5-HT_1 site. However, it is only in recent years that the 5-HT_{1A} receptor site has been recognized. Of crucial importance in this respect was the discovery by Arvidsson *et al.* of the first nonindole potent 5-HT receptor agonist, the tetralin derivative 8-OH-DPAT (**38**),[81] and the demonstration by Middlemiss and Fozard[59] that this compound displayed high affinity and selectivity for the 5-HT_{1A} site. 8-OH-DPAT has subsequently become a useful tool in exploring the significance of the 5-HT_{1A} receptor. In radioligand-binding studies, this compound was more than 500 times more potent at 5-HT_{1A} sites than at 5-HT_{1B}, 5-HT_{1C} or 5-HT_2 sites. [^{3}H]-8-OH-DPAT was prepared[60] and is now used routinely to label selectively the 5-HT_{1A} recognition site.

(i) Indole derivatives

5-HT is, of course, the endogenous 5-HT_{1A} receptor agonist and displays a high affinity for this site, as indicated by binding assays using [^{3}H]-8-OH-DPAT as radioligand (8.7).

Many closely related analogues of 5-HT have been prepared, their binding constants at the 5-HT_{1A} site measured (Table 3), and a number of observations can be made. The 5-hydroxy substituent seems to contribute importantly to the binding process, since tryptamine (**7**) is 65 times less potent than 5-HT at the 5-HT_{1A} binding site. Chemically very diverse groups can be introduced in the 5-indole position, leading to compounds in which, sometimes, a very high affinity is retained. Thus, 5-carboxamidotryptamine (5-CT; **13**) is more potent than 5-HT itself. In contrast, 5-aminotryptamine (5-NH_2-T; **12**) is considerably less active. The position of the substituent is also crucial, since 4-hydroxy- and 6-hydroxy-tryptamine (4-HT; **8** and 6-HT; **9**) are 32 and 525 times less active than 5-HT, respectively. Disubstitution also leads to loss of activity since 5,6-dihydroxytryptamine (5,6-DHT; **14**) and 6,7-dihydroxytryptamine (6,7-DHT; **15**) have affinities in the micromolar range.

Introduction of methyl substituents in different positions modulates both potency and selectivity: thus the affinity of 2-Me-5-HT (**16**) is considerably less than 5-HT for all the 5-HT_1 receptor subtypes as well as for the 5-HT_2 site. As will be discussed later (see Section 12.9.4.7.2), 2-Me-5-HT has high activity and some selectivity for 5-HT_3 receptors. Methylation in the ethylamine chain on the carbon atoms generally decreases the affinity for the 5-HT_{1A} site by a factor of 30, and modifies the selectivity, since α-Me-5-HT (**17**) is slightly more potent than 5-HT on the 5-HT_{1C} site, while β-Me-5-HT (**18**) displays a limited but significant selectivity for the 5-HT_{1A} site, in particular *versus* the 5-HT_{1B} site.

The consequences of *N* substitution are more clear and interesting: 5-HT *N*-methylation, *N*-ethylation or *N*-*n*-propylation provides compounds (**19–22**) with reasonably high affinities (10 nM range), but with a dramatically decreased potency at the 5-HT_{1B} sites. The selectivity ratio is optimal for the *N*,*N*-di-*n*-propyl substitution. What was true in the 5-HT series is confirmed for the 5-carboxamidotryptamine analogues since the most potent and selective 5-HT_{1A} receptor agonist described to date is *N*,*N*-di-*n*-propyl-5-carboxamidotryptamine (DP-5-CT; **23**), which has an affinity of 0.3 nM (9.5) at the 5-HT$_{1A}$ site and selectivity ratios of 126 000 and 631 000 *versus* the 5-HT$_{1B}$ and 5-HT$_{1C}$ sites, respectively.

With the exception of DP-5-CT, about which little is yet known, 5-HT analogues generally do not display any significant selectivity for a given 5-HT receptor subtype, at least as indicated by binding data. For this reason, the numerous studies describing the biological properties of these nonspecific ligands are very difficult to discuss in terms of the receptor which could be involved. As a consequence, the mechanistic significance of these studies is unclear, and the results obtained will not, therefore, be presented in detail.

(ii) Other indole-containing structures

RU 24969 (**25**) is a compound which, although structurally related to 5-HT, is not directly interchangeable with 5-HT: it is indeed impossible to find conformations of RU 24969 and 5-HT where the indole rings and the basic nitrogen atoms overlap. Whereas Peroutka[46] has reported that this molecule possesses a 70-fold selectivity for 5-HT$_{1B}$ sites relative to 5-HT$_{1A}$ sites, Middlemiss,[47] and more recently Hoyer,[23] have found that whilst this agent is selective for 5-HT$_1$ *versus* 5-HT$_2$ sites (8.2 and 6.0, respectively), it demonstrates almost no selectivity for 5-HT$_{1A}$ (8.2) over 5-HT$_{1B}$ (8.4) sites. Several analogues of RU 24969 with hydrogen or hydroxy substituents in position 5, hydrogen or methyl substituents on the basic nitrogen atom, and with or without intracyclic double bonds, have been tested at [^{3}H]-5-HT binding sites without any improved potency. 5-HT$_1$ subsite selectivity has not been investigated.

Another major chemical class of indole-containing compounds, whose affinity at the 5-HT$_{1A}$ site has been measured, comprises a number of ergoline derivatives. (+)-LSD (**26**) has an affinity comparable to 5-HT for 5-HT$_{1A}$ sites and selectivity ratios of 59, 4.5, 9 and 1 *versus* 5-HT$_{1B}$-, 5-HT$_{1C}$-, 5-HT$_{1D}$- and 5-HT$_2$-binding sites, respectively. It should be noted that (−)-LSD, the optical isomer, displays negligible affinity for all the 5-HT sites. Lisuride (**27**) is a very potent 5-HT$_{1A}$ receptor ligand, with an affinity superior to 5-HT (9.14) but its affinity for the 5-HT$_2$ receptors is comparable (8.3) and its selectivity towards other 5-HT$_1$ subsites has not been established.

Table 4   Structures of 5-HT analogues

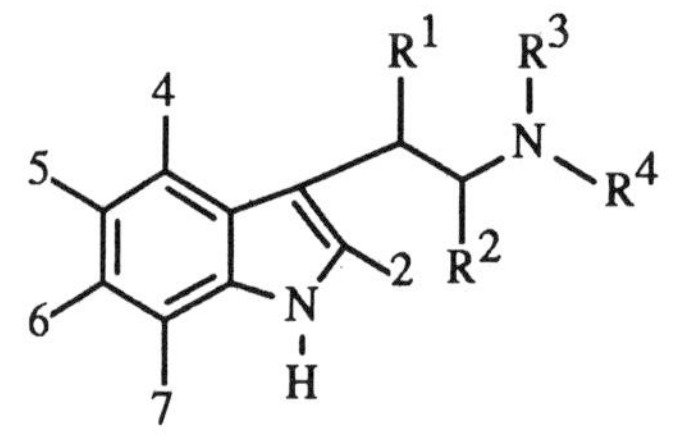

Compound	2-	4-	5-	6-	7-	R^1	R^2	R^3	R^4
(**7**) T	H	H	H	H	H	H	H	H	H
(**8**) 4-HT	H	OH	H	H	H	H	H	H	H
(**1**) 5-HT	H	H	OH	H	H	H	H	H	H
(**9**) 6-HT	H	H	H	OH	H	H	H	H	H
(**10**) 7-HT	H	H	H	H	OH	H	H	H	H
(**11**) 5-MeO-T	H	H	OMe	H	H	H	H	H	H
(**12**) 5-NH$_2$-T	H	H	NH$_2$	H	H	H	H	H	H
(**13**) 5-CT	H	H	CONH$_2$	H	H	H	H	H	H
(**14**) 5,6-DHT	H	H	OH	OH	H	H	H	H	H
(**15**) 5,7-DHT	H	H	OH	H	OH	H	H	H	H
(**16**) 2-Me-5-HT	Me	H	OH	H	H	H	H	H	H
(**17**) α-Me-5-HT	H.	H	OH	H	H	H	Me	H	H
(**18**) β-Me-5-HT	H	H	OH	H	H	Me	H	H	H
(**19**) N-Me-5-HT	H	H	OH	H	H	H	H	Me	H
(**20**) N-Me$_2$-5-HT	H	H	OH	H	H	H	H	Me	Me
(**21**) N-Et$_2$-5-HT	H	H	OH	H	H	H	H	Et	Et
(**22**) N-Pr$_2$-5-HT	H	H	OH	H	H	H	H	Pr	Pr
(**23**) DP-5-CT	H	H	CONH$_2$	H	H	H	H	Pr	Pr
(**24**) 5-MeO-DMT	H	H	MeO	H	H	H	H	Me	Me

Other classical ergoline derivatives such as methysergide (28) and metergoline (29), which may display agonist or antagonist properties, have lower affinity constants than LSD and lisuride at 5-HT_{1A} sites, and much higher ones at 5-HT_{1C} or 5-HT_2 sites. Mesulergine (30) shows good selectivity for the 5-HT_{1C} recognition site and, as will be discussed later, is used as a selective radioligand to label this site. It should be noted that ergoline derivatives also interact with noradrenaline and dopamine receptors with very high affinities (*cf.* Chapters 12.1–12.4)

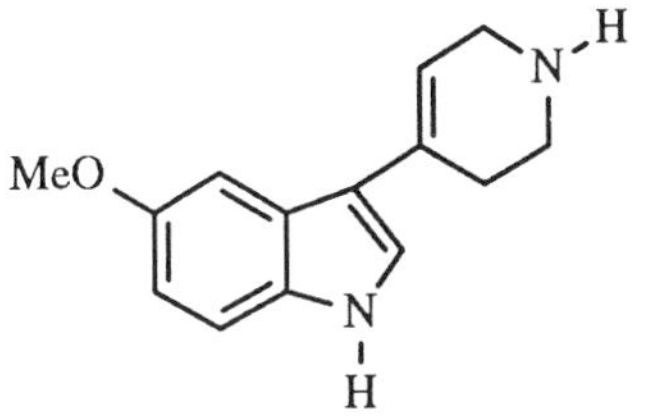

(25) RU 24969

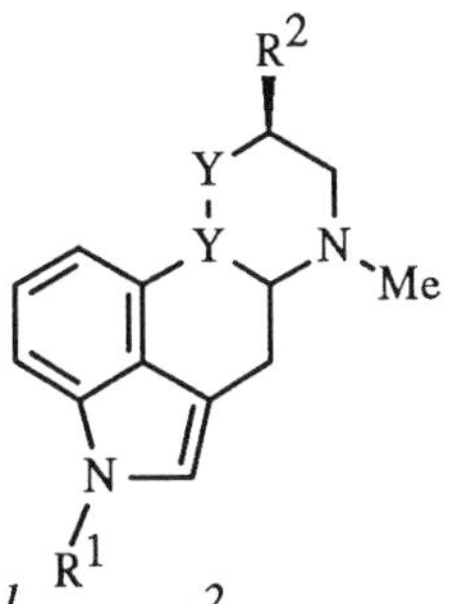

		R^1	R^2	Y–Y
(26)	LSD	H	$CONEt_2$	C=CH
(27)	Lisuride	H	$NHCONEt_2$	C=CH
(28)	Methysergide	Me	$CONHCH(CH_2OH)Et$	C=CH
(29)	Metergoline	Me	$CH_2NHCO_2CH_2Ph$	CH–CH_2
(30)	Mesulergine	Me	$NHSO_2NMe_2$	CH–CH_2

(iii) Aminotetralin derivatives

It has been known for some time that the ergoline skeleton contains in its rigid structure the key elements of both dopamine and 5-HT (mainframes). This has been exploited by medicinal chemists, who have designed and synthesized potent and selective rigid dopamine analogues belonging to the aminotetralin chemical class. Thus, 5-, 7-, 5,6-, 6,7-hydroxy- or dihydroxy-aminotetralin were prepared and displayed the expected dopamine receptor agonist properties. In 1981 Arvidsson *et al.*,[81] whilst investigating the dopamine receptor stimulant properties of *N*-substituted mono-hydroxylated aminotetralins, discovered that 8-hydroxy-*N*,*N*-di-*n*-propyl-2-aminotetralin (8-OH-DPAT; 38) showed very potent central 5-HT receptor stimulant properties both in behavioural and biochemical tests. Conversely, the 5-, 6-, or 7-hydroxy analogues were devoid of significant 5-HT receptor stimulant properties.

As mentioned above, 8-OH-DPAT became a very important pharmacological tool to characterize 5-HT receptor subtypes, since it was demonstrated to possess a low affinity for 5-HT_2 (5.04), 5-HT_{1B} (4.2) and 5-HT_{1C} (5.2) sites but very high affinity for 5-HT_{1A} sites (pIC_{50} = 8.7). In addition, as will be discussed later, this compound was the first nonindole-containing agent with full agonist properties. A limited number of analogues of 8-OH-DPAT have been tested in binding assays using [^{3}H]-8-OH-DPAT itself to label selectively the 5-HT_{1A} sites. Thus, the two enantiomers of 8-OH-DPAT have been tested, indicating a weak but significant stereospecificity of the recognition site.[49] This weak difference of affinity between the two enantiomers could be related to their similar topography in space.

Binding experiments also indicate that the 8-methoxy analogue (8-MeO-DPAT; 39) of 8-OH-DPAT displays a similar profile to 8-OH-DPAT, with only a 1.5-fold decrease in the 5-HT_{1A} receptor affinity. The affinity of a limited series of analogues with diverse *N*-substituents has been investigated. The potency rapidly decreases in the series 8-MeO-DPAT (39), 8-methoxy-*N*-*n*-propyl-2-aminotetralin (8-MeO-PAT; 40, pIC_{50} = 8.32) and 8-methoxy-2-aminotetralin (8-MeO-AT; 41, 6.7). 8-OH-AT (43) is also very weakly active. This suggests an important positive contribution to the binding process of these *N*-substituted linear hydrophobic chains. Surprisingly, the 8-methoxy-2-piperidinotetralin analogue (42) presented a much lower affinity (7.11) than was expected.

The chroman analogue of 8-OH-DPAT, where an oxygen atom replaces the carbon atom C-4 of the aminotetralin skeleton, has recently been described.[82] This agent, 5-hydroxy-3-*N*,*N*-di-*n*-propylaminochroman (44), possesses an affinity comparable to 8-OH-DPAT for the 5-HT site, but is claimed to be 10 to 20 times less active at the presynaptic sites in the striatum.

Finally, two chlorinated analogues of 8-OH-DPAT have been prepared as putative irreversible antagonists of the 5-HT_{1A} sites. While 8-methoxy-2-(N-2-chloro-n-propyl-N-n-propylamino)-tetralin (**45**) is indeed reported to bind selectively and irreversibly to the $[^3\text{H}]$-8-OH-DPAT recognition site,[83] the other derivative, 8-methoxy-2-(N-2-chloroethyl-N-n-propylamino)tetralin (8-MeO-CLEPAT; **46**), is a selective antagonist of the cardiovascular response to 8-OH-DPAT, but the effects are not irreversible.[51] A moderate affinity (7.40) has been determined for (**46**) at the 5-HT_{1A} site compared to a very low potency (5.1) at the 5-HT_{1B} site.[51]

Most of these binding studies simply confirm some elements of an extensive structure–activity study which has been performed in this series by Arvidsson *et al.* using mainly biochemical and behavioural experiments; this work has recently been comprehensively reviewed.[25] Essentially, the effects of the subcutaneous administration of 2-aminotetralin derivatives on 5-HTP accumulation in different rat brain regions have been determined. The main conclusions are the following: (i) (R)-$(+)$-8-OH-DPAT is the most potent compound in the series ($ED_{50} = 0.05\ \mu\text{mol kg}^{-1}$), the (S)-$(-)$ enantiomer being two times less active; (ii) the 5-, 6- and 7-hydroxy analogues of 8-OH-DPAT are practically inactive; (iii) N,N-diethyl- and N,N-di-n-propyl-substituted aminotetralins are equipotent, while longer or branched chains reduce the potency; and (iv) the 8-methoxy analogue (**39**) of 8-OH-DPAT is six times less active than its parent compound, a ratio of potency which agrees well with their relative potencies *in vitro*.

8-OH-DPAT analogues, methylated in position 1, have been tested in the same system. This substitution creates a second chiral centre in the molecule and Arvidsson *et al.* found that only (**47**), the *cis*-$(1S,2R)$-$(+)$-enantiomer [(+)-ALK-3], possessed a high agonist activity *in vivo* ($ED_{50} = 0.09\ \mu\text{mol kg}^{-1}$), while all the other isomers were inactive at doses up to $50\ \mu\text{mol kg}^{-1}$. This result clearly demonstrates the high stereochemical requirements of the 5-HT_{1A} agonist recognition site, in the region of space corresponding to these chiral centres.

In the same context, 2-phenylcyclopropylamine derivatives have also been tested in the 5-HTP accumulation assay. Two of the most potent compounds in the series are the 2-OH- and 3-OH-*trans*-$(1R,2S)$-$(-)$ isomers (**48** and **49**). Conformational calculations performed by Arvidsson *et al.* indicate that these compounds, and the most active methyl derivative of 8-OH-DPAT, $(+)$-ALK-3 (**47**), can have their hydroxy groups, benzene rings and nitrogen atoms in a similar spatial arrangement, which may correspond to the 5-HT_{1A} receptor requirements. It should be noted that the methylene group of the cyclopropyl ring of $(1R, 2S)$-2-OH-DPCA (**48**) and the C-1 methyl group of $(1S, 2R)$-ALK-3 (**47**) then coincide. Thus, data obtained in this series confirm and complete the results obtained in the indolethylamine and aminotetralin series, concerning the SAR.

(iv) Arylpiperazine derivatives

For several years, arylpiperazine derivatives were known to possess moderate affinity for the 5-HT_1 sites. It is only recently, with the characterization of subsites, that the activity of certain of them has been reinvestigated. As can be observed in Table 3, most of the arylpiperazine compounds display only weak affinity (micromolar range) for the 5-HT_{1A} sites. It should be noted that quipazine (**51**), which has been extensively studied, displays very weak potency at 5-HT_1 sites. More recently, compounds with more complex chemical structures have been described as potent 5HT_{1A} receptor ligands. Buspirone (**63**), which was developed as an antipsychotic in a series of dopamine receptor ligands, has been characterized as a selective 5-HT_{1A} receptor ligand, with respect to other 5-HT recognition sites. Nevertheless, its affinity constant is less than $10^{-8}\ \text{mol L}^{-1}$ (7.6). In addition, this agent displays moderate effects on dopamine and α_1-adrenoceptors, but negligible activity on α_2- or β-adrenoceptors, muscarine, 5-HT_2, GABA or benzodiazepine receptors. Buspirone is reported to be a clinically effective anxiolytic drug, whose action may be mediated by 5-HT_{1A} receptors.[84] Gepirone (**64**), an analogue of buspirone, which is devoid of significant effects at dopamine receptors, shows selective, albeit relatively weak (7.1), activity at the 5-HT_{1A} recognition site.[23] Many other structural analogues of buspirone have been described, but no SAR for activities at the 5-HT_{1A} site have yet been reported.

Ipsapirone (**65**), another pyrimidylpiperazine derivative, possesses an analogous binding profile to buspirone, and shows anxiolytic properties in animal models. This compound has been tritiated, and is claimed to be a useful ligand for the 5-HT_{1A} recognition site.[61] However, more potent, similarly selective compounds have been reported more recently by Ransom *et al.*, while 1-(3-trifluoromethylphenyl)piperazine (TFMPP; **53**) has greater affinity for the 5-HT_{1B} site than for the 5-HT_{1A} site, two of its derivatives, PAPP (**66**) and BrAcTFMPP (**67**), show affinity in the nanomolar range for the 5-HT_{1A} site and good selectivity (Table 3). $[^3\text{H}]$PAPP was synthesized, and its binding to central 5-HT receptors examined; this ligand binds to a single class of sites in rat cortical

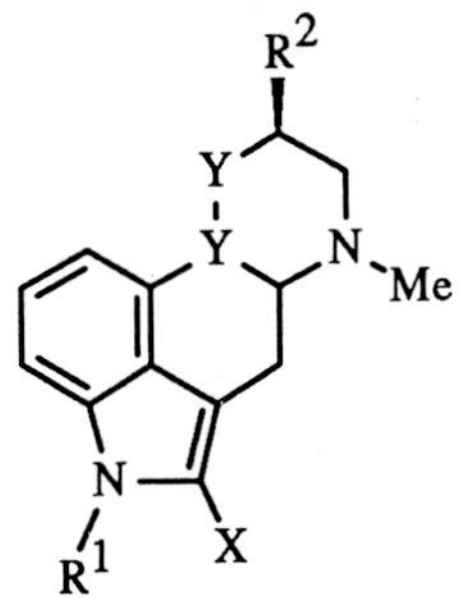

		X	R^1	R^2	Y–Y
(31)	2-I-LSD	I	H	CONEt$_2$	C=CH
(32)	Me-I-LSD	I	Me	CONEt$_2$	C=CH
(33)	Ly 53587	H	Pr^i	CO$_2$CHMeCHOHMe	CH–CH$_2$

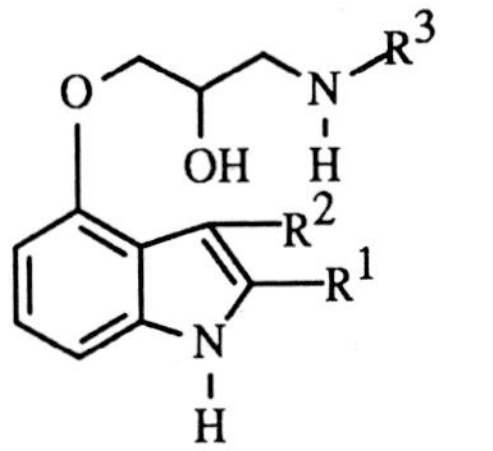

		R^1	R^2	R^3
(34)	21009	CO$_2$Pr^i	H	Bu^t
(35)	Pindolol	H	H	Pr^i
(36)	Cyanopindolol	CN	H	Pr^i
(37)	ICYP	CN	I	Pr^i

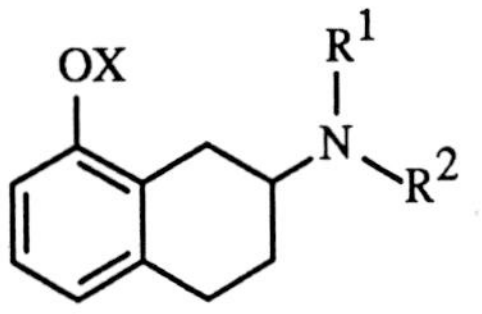

		R^1	R^2	X
(38)	8-OH-DPAT	Pr^n	Pr^n	H
(39)	8-MeO-DPAT	Pr^n	Pr^n	Me
(40)	8-MeO-PAT	H	Pr^n	Me
(41)	8-MeO-AT	H	H	Me
(42)	8-MeO-piperidino-AT	–(CH$_2$)$_5$–		Me
(43)	8-OH-AT	H	H	H

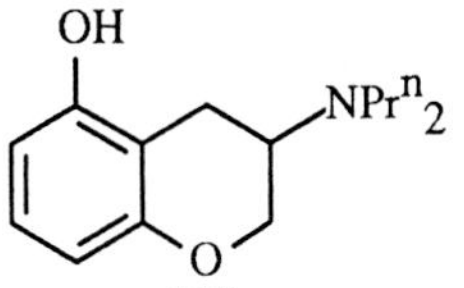

(44)

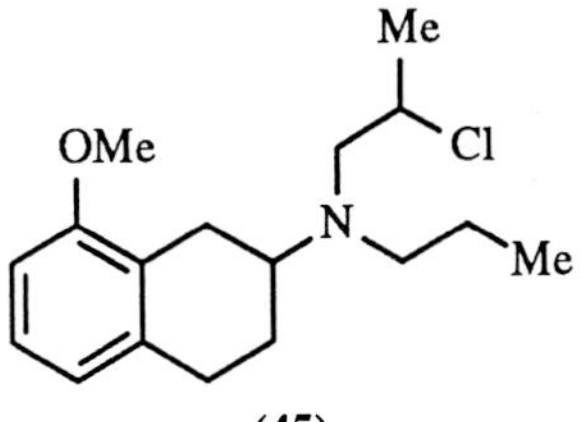

(45)

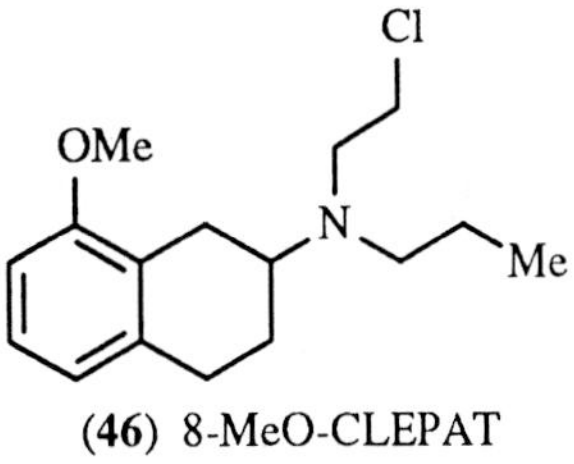

(46) 8-MeO-CLEPAT

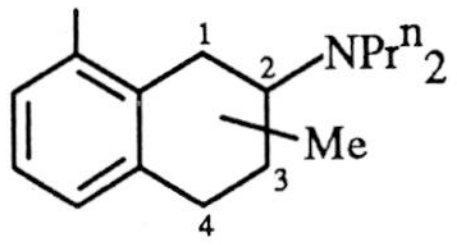

(47) (+)-ALK-3

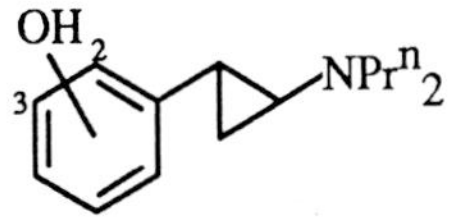

(48) (1R,2S)-2-OH-DPCA
(49) (1R,2S)-3-OH-DPCA

membranes, with a K_D of 1.6 nM. Competition experiments and regional distribution studies indicate that [^{3}H]PAPP binds selectively, and with high affinity, to 5-HT$_{1A}$ receptors.[53]

BrAcTFMPP also allows discrimination of two subpopulations of [^{3}H]-5-HT binding sites, namely 5-HT$_{1A}$ and 5-HT$_{1B}$, with dissociation constants of 9.30 and 6.83, respectively. This compound displayed only a moderate affinity (7.38) for 5-HT$_2$ sites.

The binding of a series of arylpiperazines to central 5-HT$_1$ recognition sites was investigated in conjunction with drug discrimination studies.[25] Unfortunately, affinity for the 5-HT$_1$ receptor subsites was not presented, which renders any conclusive discussion difficult. Rigid analogues of

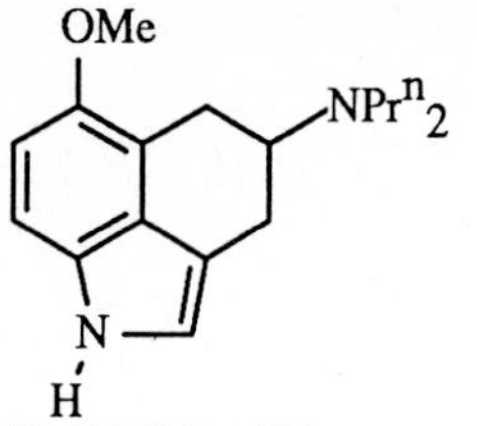

(50) BAY R 1531

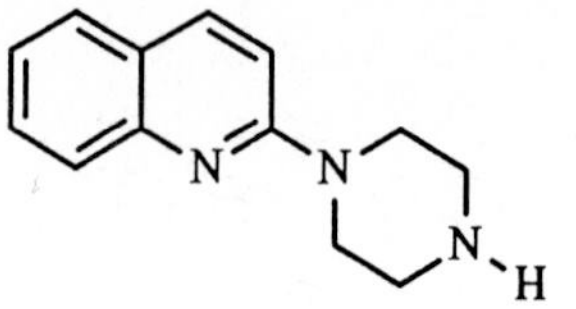

(51) Quipazine

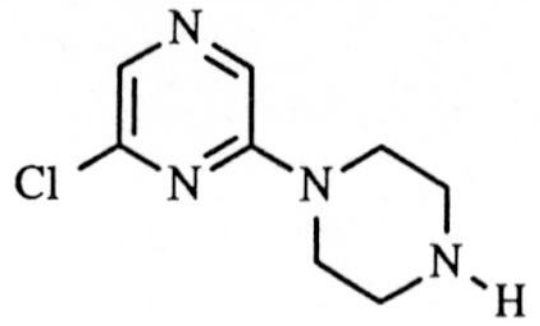

(52) MK 212

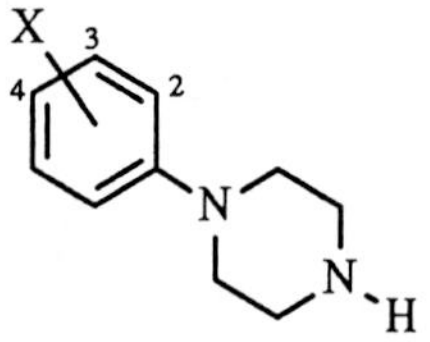

X		X
(53) 2-CF$_3$; TFMPP		(58) 3-MeO
(54) 2-MeO		(59) 2,3-diMe
(55) 2-Cl		(60) 4-Cl
(56) 2-Me		(61) 2,4-diMe
(57) 3-Cl; *m*CPP		(62) 3-NHCOMe

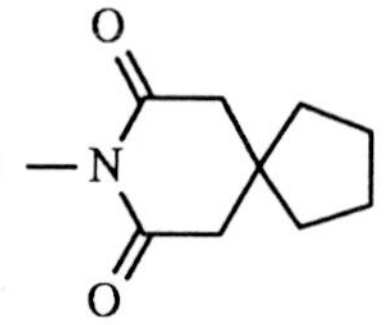

(63) Buspirone; X =

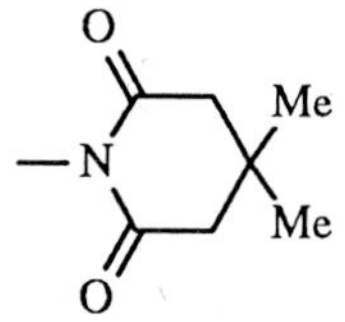

(64) Gepirone; X =

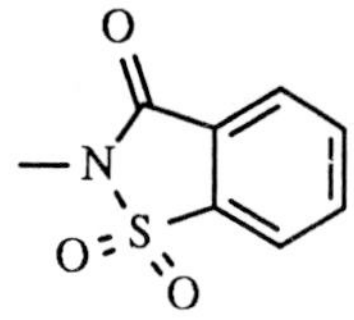

(65) Ipsapirone: X =

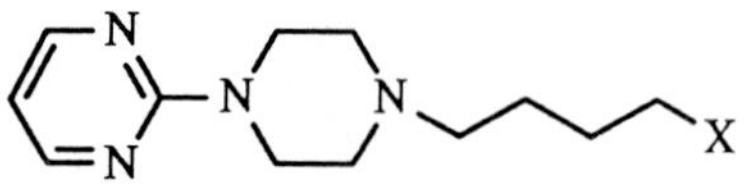

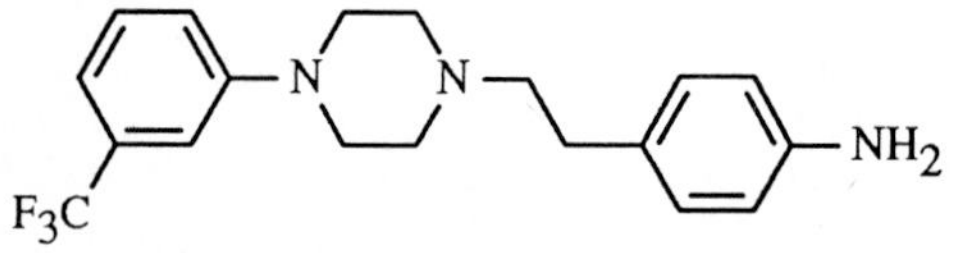

(66) PAPP

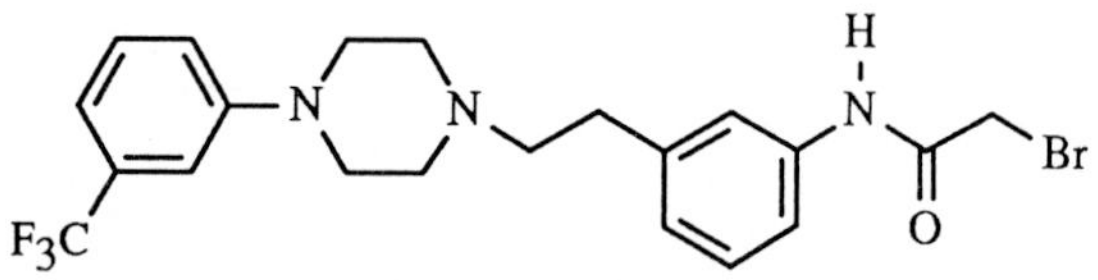

(67) BrAcTFMPP

arylpiperazines have also been prepared,[85] suggesting that the two rings of 1-arylpiperazines are relatively coplanar in the agonist bioactive conformation, as predicted from molecular modelling.[49]

(v) Tentative models of the 5-HT$_{1A}$ agonist recognition site

In recent years, the challenge for medicinal chemists has been to understand the mechanisms of molecular recognition, in order to design new putative ligands on a more rational basis. Of importance for this new drug design strategy are the following points: (i) the target protein must be unambiguously defined, and its ligands compared on the basis of affinity constants; (ii) the receptor-bound conformation of all the known active ligands must ideally be defined; and (iii) a steric and electronic model of the recognition site should be proposed as a working hypothesis and should be validated by experiments. Considering the complication of pharmacological test systems, these conditions are sometimes difficult to fulfil, particularly in the early stage of the discovery of a new biological system, when selective ligands are not available and receptor subtypes are not yet characterized.

As discussed above (Section 12.9.2.1), X-ray analysis and conformational studies of 5-HT, the natural endogenous substrate, do not provide conclusive information regarding the receptor-bound conformer of 5-HT, since numerous side chain conformations are separated only by low energy barriers. Consequently, scientists turned to rigid active molecules as probes to investigate receptors. In this respect, (+)-LSD (26) proved to be an important compound; as early as 1959, Karreman *et al.*[86] suggested that (+)-LSD could interact with putative central nervous tissue receptors as an electron donor in a charge transfer complex. Snyder and Merril[87] subsequently found that the region of highest frontier electron density in (+)-LSD was located at the C-2 atom and they suggested that this position was the site for charge transfer reactivity. Kang and Green[88] proposed that the α-face of (+)-LSD interacts with the receptor; the A-ring and the N-6 nitrogen atom being the essential groups for the binding process to a '5-HT-LSD receptor' responsible for hallucinogenic responses. They also emphasized the probable electronic importance of the pyrrole ring (B-ring) and the C(9)-C(10) double bond. Furthermore, they proposed that 2-aminotetralin derivatives, having electron-donating groups on the aromatic ring, would be hallucinogenic by acting at 5-HT receptors.

As is illustrated by the SAR discussed above, the explanation and hypothesis advanced in these early days happened to be only partially valid since, while 2-aminotetralins such as 8-OH-DPAT did indeed interact with 5-HT receptors, they did not display hallucinogenic properties. This result fits with the observation that $5-HT_2$ receptors seem more likely, rather than other 5-HT receptor subtypes, to be involved in the hallucinogenic response.[89] This discrepancy clearly illustrates the weakness of models defined using nonselective ligands of receptors ambiguously characterized. Thus, (+)-LSD binds equally well at $5-HT_{1A}$, $5-HT_{1C}$ or $5-HT_2$ receptors, which nevertheless have different physicochemical and structural requirements and mediate different functional responses.

It cannot be overemphasized that models relying on nonspecific [^{3}H]-5-HT and [^{3}H]LSD binding assays, or comparing ligands active at different 5-HT receptor subtypes must be evaluated with great care. This restriction applies to the studies performed by Weinstein *et al.*[90] which are nevertheless worth considering in detail since they introduce original molecular determinants to account for the SAR in a limited series of 5-HT analogues. Weinstein *et al.* calculated the molecular electrostatic potentials (MEP) of a number of hydroxylated tryptamines and (+)-LSD. It has been suggested that the MEP contour map generated by chosen structural parts of a 'receptor' agonist should closely resemble the contour map generated around the corresponding parts of the natural neurotransmitter itself. Thus, they showed that the MEP map for (+)-LSD resembles that for 5-HT since the C-(9)-C(10) double bond of (+)-LSD produces the same electronic effects as the 5-OH group of 5-HT. This idea was supported by the decreased '5-HT activity' of *trans*-dihydrolisuride; equally, however, the observation could be accounted for by a modified structural geometry subsequent to the double bond reduction. For the analysis of the early stages of drug–receptor interaction, the electrostatic potential fields calculated for various congeners were compared to the field generated by the most active compound, 5-HT. A model for the comparative orientation of the active molecules in the series was obtained on the basis of a requirement for matching electrostatic interaction fields. These requirements were qualitatively translated into observed differences in the affinity of the molecules for an 'LSD receptor'. The considerable difference between the electrostatic orientation vectors of 5-HT (1) and 6-HT (9), and the similarity in the directions of the vectors in 4-HT (8) and tryptamine (7), were reported to correlate well with the measured affinity of these compounds to the 'LSD receptor' (5-HT ≫ 4-HT ≫ tryptamine ≫ 6-HT). However, it is now known that the so-called 'LSD receptor' corresponds to at least three different binding sites, for which the predicted rank order of potency does not correlate so well (5-HT$_2$ site for which LSD has the highest affinity, 4-HT ≫ 5-HT ≫ 6-HT; 5-HT$_{1A}$ site, 5-HT ≫ 4-HT ≫ tryptamine ≫ 6-HT; 5-HT$_{1C}$ site, 5-HT = 4-HT = tryptamine ≫ 6-HT). This very sophisticated method remains to be applied exhaustively to all the 5-HT$_{1A}$ receptor agonists, and will have to account for their activity determined in more specific tests, in order to prove its relevance to this particular 5-HT receptor subtype.

In a more recent study, Arvidsson *et al.*[91] discussed a model on the basis of the original suggestion of Kang *et al.* but used more complete and relevant pharmacological data. They proposed that 5-HT and 8-OH-DPAT may interact with the 5-HT$_{1A}$ receptor in conformations fitting with the ergoline skeleton. Several experimental results could be accounted for in this way, including the stereospecificity of the recognition process. The authors used the model of Nichols *et al.*[92] to explain the activity of certain compounds, but it should be noted that this model is more relevant to the 5-HT$_2$ agonist recognition site, as will be discussed later.

We have carried out a similar conformation–activity study using ligands whose affinity for the rat frontal cortex 5-HT$_{1A}$ sites was determined exclusively in [^{3}H]-8-OH-DPAT binding assays.[49] The most active 5-HT$_{1A}$ receptor agonists, belonging to the four chemical classes described above, were considered. Conformational searches have been performed on 5-HT, 8-OH-DPAT and pyrimidyl piperazine to evaluate their global internal energy minimum. (+)-LSD was then used as a template to characterize the conformers of the other flexible agonists whose aromatic ring and nitrogen lone pair of electrons would best overlap those of LSD (A-ring and N-6 nitrogen). A very good fit was obtained at the cost of reasonable conformational energy. It was thus possible to account qualitatively for the 5-HT$_{1A}$ receptor affinity of 5-HT (**1**), 5-MeO-T (**11**), 5-CT (**13**), DP-5-CT (**23**), RU 24969 (**25**), LSD (**26**), lisuride (**27**), buspirone (**63**), ipsapirone (**65**), 8-OH-DPAT (**38**) and 8-MeO-DPAT (**39**). An envelope designating the volumes putatively accessible and inaccessible to ligands was defined (Figure 1). It is readily conceded that this model may be an oversimplification, since electronic components of the binding process have not been explicitly considered. However, the good affinity of BAY R 1531 (**50**) for the 5-HT$_{1A}$ site provides strong support for the model, as do recent data and discussion reported by Arvidsson *et al.*[25] Ongoing synthesis of compounds designed using this model should confirm or deny the present working hypothesis.

(vi) Putative 5-HT$_{1A}$ receptor antagonists

Of crucial importance for the pharmacological characterization of a putative receptor is the existence of potent and selective antagonists. At the early stage of the evaluation of the 5-HT$_{1A}$ site no selective antagonist was known. Most of the 'classical' 5-HT receptor antagonists (*e.g.* methysergide, cyproheptadine and cinanserin) displayed a much higher affinity for 5-HT$_2$ sites than for other 5-HT receptors. Compounds such as the β-adrenoceptor antagonist $(-)$-propranolol, the dopamine receptor antagonist spiperone (**82**), buspirone (**63**) or the particularly nonselective ligand methiothepin (**78**) displayed moderate affinity for the central 5-HT$_{1A}$ receptor, as well as pure or mixed antagonist properties; however, their nonselectivity in this respect diminished interest in these compounds as exploratory probes.

As early as 1983, we defined a model using these four ligands as reference compounds.[56] For all the compounds, stable conformations were found where the aromatic rings on one hand and the nitrogen atoms on the other overlapped with a good fit index (Figure 2). Using this model, several compounds belonging to diverse chemical classes were designed and found to present the expected activity. Thus, it was predicted that 2-aminomethylbenzodioxane derivatives might display a good affinity for the 5-HT$_{1A}$ site. This was indeed observed since a compound such as MDL 72832 (**72**) bound with a very high affinity constant (9.14) to the [^{3}H]-8-OH-DPAT binding site. Moreover, this compound was extremely selective since it was 870, 870, 550, 34 500, 218, 550 and 100 000 times less active at the 5-HT$_{1B}$, 5-HT$_2$, α_2- and β-adrenoceptors, dopamine D$_1$ and D$_2$ receptors and benzodiazepine receptors, respectively. However, this compound was only 21 times less potent at the α_1-adrenoceptor than at the 5-HT$_{1A}$ site. By comparison of the structural requirements of both sites, it was predicted that (**73**), a naphthyl analogue of MDL 72832, might be much more selective for the 5-HT$_{1A}$ site. This was confirmed by experiment since the selectivity ratio 5-HT$_{1A}$/α_1-adrenoceptor affinity for this compound reached 140; the compound was thus extremely selective when compared with any classical receptor. MDL 73005 (**74**), the ethylene analogue of MDL 72832, also presented a high potency for the 5-HT$_{1A}$ sites, weak activity at α_1-adrenoceptors, and an overall very selective

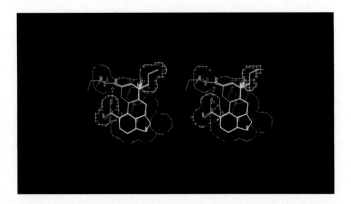

Figure 1   5-HT$_{1A}$ receptor agonists superimposed in their putative receptor-bound conformations with a representation of the binding domains accessible (blue, green, yellow) and forbidden (red, magenta) to ligands: stereoview (reproduced from ref. 49 by permission of the Société de Chimie Thérapeutique)

binding profile (8.4, 5.5, 5.6, 5.8, 5.5, 6.3 and <4 for 5-HT$_{1A}$, 5-HT$_{1B}$, 5-HT$_2$, α_1- and α_2-adrenoceptors, dopamine D$_2$ receptors and benzodiazepine receptors, respectively).[57]

The proposed model of the 5-HT$_{1A}$ recognition site was precise enough to allow prediction that the (*S*) enantiomer of MDL 72832 would be more potent than the (*R*) enantiomer. Again, this prediction has been verified: the (*S*)-(−) enantiomer is indeed at least 36-fold more active than the (*R*)-(+) enantiomer (9.21 and 7.7, respectively). It is likely that most of the residual activity of the (*R*)-(+) optical isomer reflects a 3% contamination by the (*S*)-(−) active isomer. This is one of the first examples where a graphics computer-generated receptor map has been used with success as a predictive tool, to design totally novel structures with improved activity and selectivity at a recognition site. The pharmacology of certain of these compounds is very interesting and predictive of potential clinical relevance.[57,93]

More recently, a second 2-aminomethylbenzodioxane-containing compound was found to bind to 5-HT$_{1A}$ sites. [^{3}H]WB 4101 (**75**) was considered to label selectively α_1-adrenoceptors, but Norman *et al.*[94] demonstrated that concentrations of [^{3}H]WB 4101 (3 nM) actually label, in addition to α_1-adrenoceptors, 5-HT receptors. [^{3}H]8-OH-DPAT binding studies indicated a high affinity of WB 4101 (8.69) for the 5-HT$_{1A}$ site, while affinity for the other 5-HT sites was much lower. Similarly, while screening putative 5-HT-like activity among a series of spiperone analogues, a further 2-aminomethylbenzodioxane-containing compound, spiroxatrine (**76**), was shown to possess a high affinity for the 5-HT$_{1A}$ binding site (8.4). For both WB 4101 and spiroxatrine, significant activity at other, non-5-HT receptors limits the pharmacological interest in these compounds.

12.9.4.3 5-HT$_{1B}$ Receptors

12.9.4.3.1 Identification and functional correlates

5-HT$_{1B}$ sites were originally defined by Pedigo *et al.*[3] as the sites labelled by [^{3}H]-5-HT showing low affinity for the neuroleptic spiperone. However, the indole β-adrenoceptor antagonist [^{125}I]-iodocyanopindolol (ICYP; **37**), in the presence of 30 μM isoprenaline, has been used extensively to label these sites. There is no selective ligand available for the 5-HT$_{1B}$ site, although indole β-adrenoceptor antagonists (21 009; **34**, cyanopindolol; **36** and pindolol; **35**), the indole containing agonist (RU 24969; **25**) and the piperazine agonist (CGS 12066B; **68**) show appreciable affinity for these sites.

5-HT$_{1B}$ receptors are present both in the periphery and various regions of the rat brain, being particularly enriched in the globus pallidus, dorsal subculicum and substantia nigra. However, 5-HT$_{1B}$ sites have only been found in the rat and mouse brain and appear to be absent in guinea pig, cow, chicken, turtle, frog, pig, bovine and human brain.[7] 5-HT$_{1B}$ receptors have been found to be

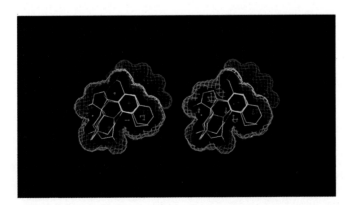

Figure 2 5-HT$_{1A}$ receptor ligands superimposed in their antagonist conformation; the defined areas represent the accessible (blue) and forbidden (red) zones of the recognition site: stereoview (reproduced from ref. 56 by permission of the American Chemical Society)

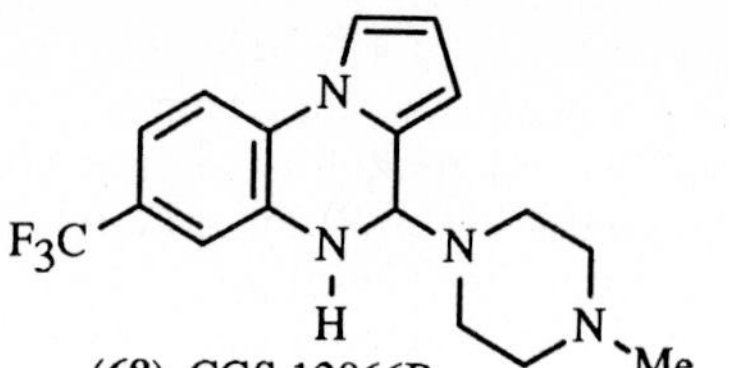

(68) CGS 12066B

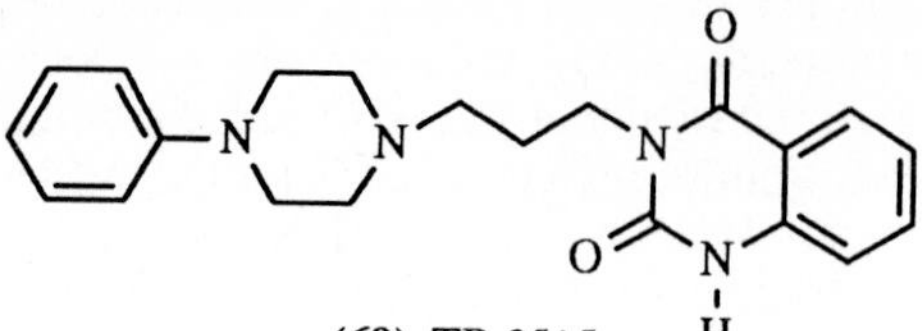

(69) TR 2515

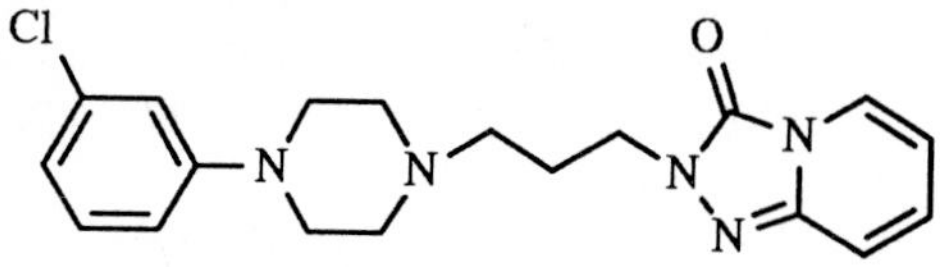

(70) Trazodone

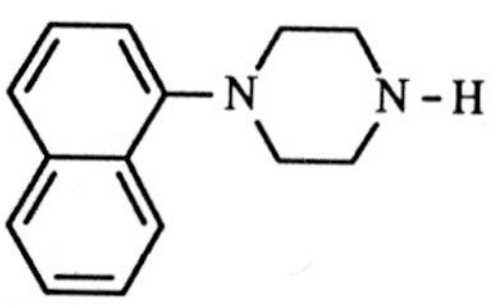

(71) 1-(1-Naphthyl)piperazine

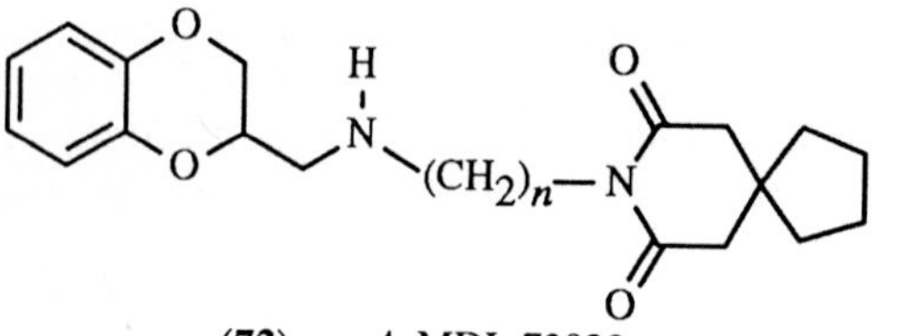

(72) $n = 4$, MDL 72832
(74) $n = 2$, MDL 73005

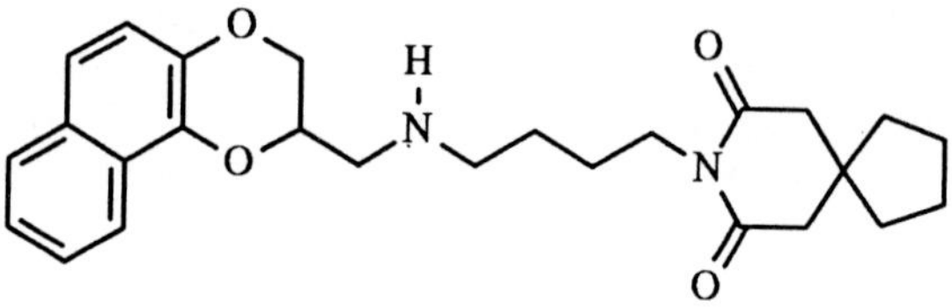

(73) MDL 72975

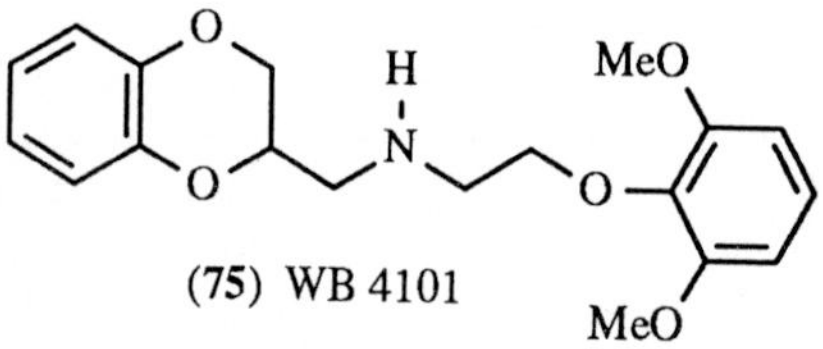

(75) WB 4101

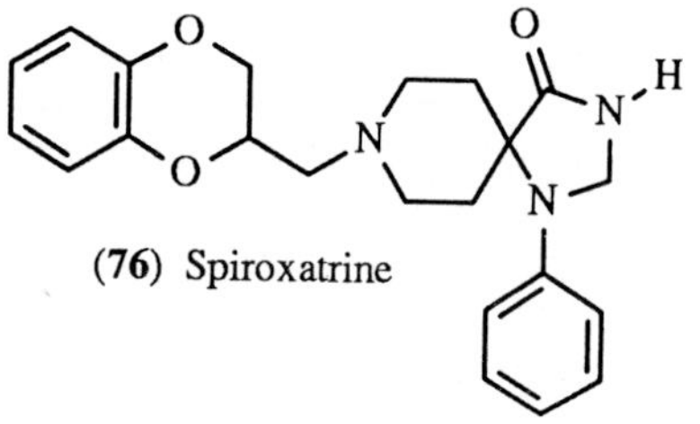

(76) Spiroxatrine

coupled negatively to adenylate cyclase in homogenates of rat substantia nigra.[95] In the rat brain 5-HT_{1B} sites are located both presynaptically, as autoreceptors controlling the release of 5-HT,[45] and postsynaptically, as heteroreceptors which control the release of acetylcholine.[96] In the periphery, 5-HT_{1B} receptors modulate the release of noradrenaline from sympathetic nerves in rat vascular tissue.[97]

12.9.4.3.2 5-HT$_{1B}$ receptor agonists

A number of compounds has now been evaluated as putative ligands at 5-HT_{1B} recognition sites using previously described binding assays or measurement of depolarization-induced 5-HT release. For this site, the lead compounds have usually been discovered by reevaluation of the 'classical' 5-HT_1 receptor ligands such as 5-HT itself and its analogues, arylpiperazines, ergoline derivatives, β-adrenoceptor antagonists and a number of miscellaneous compounds. As can be seen from Table 3, the structural requirements for 5-HT_{1A} and 5-HT_{1B} sites are completely different, as confirmed by the recent disclosure of selective 5-HT_{1B} receptor agonists and antagonists. The affinity of 5-HT itself for the 5-HT_{1B} sites (7.6) is almost 10 times less than its affinity for the 5-HT_{1A} sites but 100 times greater than its affinity for the 5-HT_2 sites. The activity is very sensitive to any structural modifications. Thus, in contrast to other 5-HT receptors, replacement of the 5-hydroxy substituent of 5-HT by a methoxy group (11) results in a strongly decreased affinity (6.4). Displacement of the 5-hydroxy group to the 4- (8) or 6-position (9) leads similarly to a dramatic decrease in affinity. Interestingly, a 5-carboxamide substituent can advantageously replace the 5-hydroxy group, affording a 5-HT_{1B} receptor agonist (13) with much higher affinity (8.29) than 5-HT.

In contrast to the 5-HT$_{1A}$ receptor agonists, N substitution is an unfavourable activity determinant. If one excepts (**19**) (N-Me-5-HT, 7.35) all the other N-substituted analogues of 5-HT are almost inactive. Of interest is the dramatically decreased affinity (4.4) of the N, N-di-n-propyl analogue of 5-carboxamidotryptamine (DP-5-CT; **23**) for the 5-HT$_{1B}$ recognition site. This difference between the structural requirements at the level of the nitrogen atom between the 5-HT$_{1A}$ and 5-HT$_{1B}$ sites is of prime importance for the design of selective 5-HT$_{1A}$ receptor agonists. Thus, DP-5-CT and 8-OH-DPAT, two very potent 5-HT$_{1A}$ receptor agonists, are virtually inactive at the 5-HT$_{1B}$ binding site or the autoreceptor. It should be noted that 8-OH-AT (**43**), which is a primary amine, is also devoid of any significant 5-HT$_{1B}$ receptor activity.

RU 24969 (**25**) is presently the most potent 5-HT$_{1B}$ receptor agonist (8.4), although it is reported to be equally active at 5-HT$_{1A}$ sites. The question of equivalent potency at the two sites is controversial. As discussed above, Sills *et al.*[98] have reported a 70-fold selectivity for 5-HT$_{1B}$ *versus* 5-HT$_{1A}$ binding, whereas Middlemiss[47] found that RU 24969 possesses only a twofold selectivity for 5-HT$_{1B}$ sites. More recent studies of Peroutka tend to support the former results,[46] while those of Hoyer[23] confirm the latter. In contrast, most would agree on a certain selectivity of certain arylpiperazines. Thus, 1-(3-trifluoromethylphenyl)piperazine (TFMPP; **53**) and 1-(3-chlorophenyl)piperazine (*m*CPP; **57**), while possessing a rather low (*i.e.* 3- to 18-fold) selectivity for 5-HT$_{1A}$ *versus* 5-HT$_2$ sites, do appear to possess a 30- to 70-fold selectivity for 5-HT$_{1B}$ *versus* 5-HT$_{1A}$ sites. Much lower selectivity ratios have nevertheless been found by several other investigators. Moreover, it is now becoming clear that the affinity of these compounds for the 5-HT$_{1C}$ sites is relatively high.[23]

Very recently, a more original and selective 5-HT$_{1B}$ agonist, CGS 12066B (**68**), has been described by Neale *et al.*[55] CGS 12066B is a pyrroloquinoxaline derivative with a pIC$_{50}$ value of 7.29 at the 5-HT$_{1B}$ recognition site and a 5-HT$_{1A}$/5-HT$_{1B}$ ratio of 17. The affinity of this compound for 5-HT$_2$ receptors, α_1-, α_2- and β-adrenoceptors and dopamine D$_1$ and D$_2$ receptors is negligible. It thus represents a potentially very useful tool for evaluating the physiological role of 5-HT$_{1B}$ receptors in the mammalian CNS.

12.9.4.3.3 *5-HT$_{1B}$ receptor antagonists*

A number of compounds with a high affinity for the 5-HT$_{1B}$ site, and which antagonize the effects of 5-HT at the autoreceptor, has been characterized by screening agents previously known as 'classical' 5-HT antagonists. Thus, methiothepin (**78**) was the first product showing a moderate affinity (7.28) for the 5-HT$_{1B}$ site and antagonizing K$^+$-induced 5-HT release with a pA$_2$ value of 6.99. This compound is not selective since it also displays moderate to high affinity for a number of central monoamine receptors. Nevertheless, the interaction with the 5-HT$_{1B}$ site is stereospecific, and the order of potency of its enantiomers suggests that the 5-HT$_{1B}$ site could correspond to the 5-HT autoreceptor.[99] This hypothesis received some support from correlation analysis performed on a range of some 30 drugs of diverse structures, affinity and degrees of selectivity at the central 5-HT recognition sites.[45]

A moderate 5-HT$_{1B}$ receptor antagonist activity has been measured for metergoline (**29**), an ergot derivative, but again this compound is not selective. Much more interesting results in terms of potency were obtained with a series of β-adrenoceptor antagonists.[100] (−)-Propranolol was studied first and presented only a moderate potency (7.33). Replacement of the naphthyl aromatic ring by an indole nucleus, more similar to 5-HT, led to a compound, pindolol (**35**), with a comparable affinity and a good stereoselectivity [(−) isomer, 7.1; (+) isomer, 5.33]. Introduction of a cyano group in position 2 of the indole ring afforded 2-cyanopindolol (**36**), which presented a much higher affinity [(−) isomer, 8.74].[101]

In addition to their activity as β-adrenoceptor antagonists, these ligands had the additional disadvantage of not being capable of discriminating 5-HT$_{1B}$ from 5-HT$_{1A}$ sites. The latter problem was somewhat reduced with the more potent and selective analogues such as (−)-21009 (**34**), a 2-amide analogue of 2-cyanopindolol, and 3-iodo-2-cyanopindolol (ICYP; **37**).[102] (−)-21009 has a value of 9.38 for 5-HT$_{1B}$ and an 18-fold selectivity for 5-HT$_{1B}$ *versus* 5-HT$_{1A}$ sites. ICYP shows even higher affinity for 5-HT$_{1B}$ sites (9.49) but shows a similar degree of selectivity (5-HT$_{1B}$/ 5-HT$_{1A}$ = 13). As mentioned earlier, [^{125}I]ICYP has been prepared and is used as a radioligand specifically to label 5-HT$_{1B}$ sites. Nevertheless the β-adrenoceptor-blocking properties of these compounds detracts from their value as tools in functional studies.

A conformation–activity relationship study has been performed with the literature compounds. Metergoline has been used as a template to define a pharmacophore and a topographical model of the 5-HT$_{1B}$ recognition site, which accounts for the activity of all the known potent 5-HT$_{1B}$

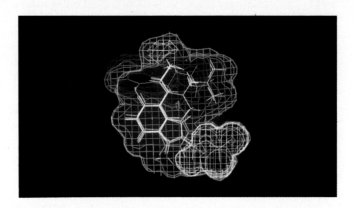

Figure 3 5-HT$_{1B}$ receptor antagonists superimposed in their putative receptor-bound conformations; the defined areas represent the accessible (blue, yellow, green) and forbidden (pink, magenta) domains of the recognition site (reproduced from ref. 125 by permission of the Société de Chimie Thérapeutique)

antagonists (Figure 3).[103] Obviously, the basic common features defining the pharmacophore are similar to those of the 5-HT$_{1A}$ site. Nevertheless, clearcut differences exist at the secondary binding sites. For instance, from the SAR discussed above, it is clear that the hydrophobic pocket in the vicinity of the N atom, which was characterized in the 5-HT$_{1A}$ site, does not seem to exist in the 5-HT$_{1B}$ site. Substituents such as cyano- or *N*-dipropylcarboxamide increase affinity for the 5-HT$_{1B}$ sites, thus defining a putative secondary binding zone.

This 5-HT$_{1B}$ receptor map has remained at the level of working hypothesis since no compound has yet been designed, made and tested to validate the model. This may reflect the fact that 5-HT$_{1B}$ receptors do not appear to exist in humans[104] and hence may have no therapeutic relevance.

12.9.4.4 5-HT$_{1C}$ Receptors

12.9.4.4.1 Identification of functional correlates

The existence of 5-HT$_{1C}$ binding sites was first detected using [^{3}H]-5-HT in pig choroid plexus and cortex.[4] These sites are also labelled by [^{3}H]mesulergine (**30**), [^{3}H]- and [^{125}I]-LSD (**26**), all of which also label 5-HT$_2$ sites in addition to 5-HT$_{1C}$ sites. There is no agonist which shows high affinity and selectivity for these sites although *m*CPP (**57**) has a certain affinity and selectivity.[23,52] It is noteworthy that 5-CT is at least 100 times less potent at 5-HT$_{1C}$ sites compared to the other 5-HT$_1$ receptor subtypes (Table 3). Amongst the antagonists, mesulergine, mianserin (**77**) and LY 53857 (**33**) show high affinity.

There is good evidence that in the mouse and rat choroid plexus 5-HT$_{1C}$ receptor activation leads to stimulation of phosphatidylinositol hydrolysis. A highly significant correlation was found for a large series of agonists and antagonists between their affinity for 5-HT$_{1C}$ sites and their potency to stimulate or antagonize inositol phosphate accumulation in pig choroid plexus.[105] It also appears that 5-HT$_{1C}$ receptors, expressed in *Xenopus* oocytes by injections of mRNA, modulate a chloride conductance;[106] the effect is mediated *via* a pertussis toxin-sensitive G protein. At the whole animal level functional correlates of 5-HT$_{1C}$ sites are beginning to emerge. Recent data suggest that, in the rat, feeding behaviour can be suppressed following 5-HT$_{1C}$ receptor activation[107] and behavioural inhibition and an 'anxiety-like' state may also reflect activation of 5-HT$_{1C}$ receptors.[108] Evidence consistent with 5-HT$_{1C}$ receptor activation being an important trigger for migraine has been obtained.[109]

12.9.4.4.2 5-HT$_{1C}$ receptor ligands

At this relatively early stage of the 5-HT$_{1C}$ site characterization, it is difficult to perform a comprehensive SAR analysis. A number of binding studies using [^{3}H]mesulergine or other radioligands have, however, recently been reported (Table 3). 5-HT appears to be the most potent agonist at this site (7.48). Interestingly, in contrast to other 5-HT$_1$ receptor subtypes, the 5-indole substituent does not seem crucial for the activity. Thus 5-MeO- (**11**), 5-NH$_2$- (**12**), 4-OH-tryptamine (**4**) and tryptamine itself (**7**) are equipotent to 5-HT (**1**) (Table 3). Surprisingly, 5-CT (**13**) is much less active than 5-HT (6.21), in contrast to the 5-HT$_{1A}$ and 5-HT$_{1B}$ sites where the 5-carboxamide substituents increased the activity considerably. 8-OH-DPAT (**38**) and RU 24969 (**25**) also displayed weak affinity for 5-HT$_{1C}$ receptors, which are thus clearly different from the other 5-HT$_1$ receptor subtypes. α-Methylation of 5-HT does not significantly modify the affinity while β- and N-methylation result in a 10-fold decrease. N-Methylation seems to affect potency to a much lesser extent. As noted above, evidence is emerging from both binding and functional studies for selective activity of the phenylpiperazine derivatives TFMPP and *m*CPP, at 5-HT$_{1C}$ receptors.

A number of very potent putative antagonists have been characterized. All are ergoline derivatives and include compounds such as metergoline (**29**) and mesulergine (**30**). As discussed above, mesulergine displays good selectivity for the 5-HT$_{1C}$ receptor subtype since it is 128 times and 6000 times less active at 5-HT$_{1A}$ and 5-HT$_{1B}$ receptors, respectively. For this reason, mesulergine has been tritiated and is used to label selectively the 5-HT$_{1C}$ site. In addition to metergoline and mesulergine, which are both active in the nanomolar range, two nonergoline derivatives, mianserin (**77**) and methiothepin (**78**), show high affinity constants (10 nM range) but no selectivity for the 5-HT$_{1C}$ site. Many other 5-HT receptor antagonists display much lower affinity constants: ketanserin (**85**), pirenperone (**90**), quipazine (**51**), spiperone (**82**; 100 to 1000 nM range), 21009 (**34**), pindolol (**35**), cyanopindolol (**36**), buspirone (**63**) and ipsapirone (**65**; IC$_{50}$ < 10 000 nM).

The structure–activity study presented above needs to be validated by correlating binding data and functional responses such as phosphatidylinositol turnover; this being the second messenger system coupled to the 5-HT$_{1C}$ receptor.[105]

12.9.4.5 5-HT$_{1D}$ Receptor

12.9.4.5.1 Identification and functional correlates

A fourth subtype of the 5-HT$_1$ site has recently been identified by Heuring and Peroutka[5] in bovine brain using [^{3}H]-5-HT. The pharmacology of the 5-HT$_{1D}$ recognition sites in calf, pig and human brain[110] is similar to that described in the bovine brain. There is no selective ligand for these sites. 5-CT, 5-MeO-T, metergoline and 5-HT show nanomolar affinity, while yohimbine and corynanthine, although less potent, show stereoselectivity for these sites. Many compounds which show selectivity for 5-HT$_{1A}$ (8-OH-DPAT; **38** and ipsapirone; **65**), 5-HT$_{1B}$ (pindolol; **35** and RU 24969; **25**) and 5-HT$_{1C}$ (mianserin; **77** and mesulergine; **30**) sites are substantially less potent at 5-HT$_{1D}$ sites, as are 5-HT$_2$ and 5-HT$_3$ receptor selective compounds.

The anatomical distribution of 5-HT$_{1D}$ sites in the bovine brain bears similarities to that of 5-HT$_{1B}$ sites in the rodent brain, being particularly enriched in the substantia nigra. Moreover, the 5-HT$_{1D}$ sites in the calf substantia nigra have been shown to be negatively coupled to adenylate cyclase. The rank order of potency of agonists and antagonists in this model was in good agreement with their affinities for the 5-HT$_{1D}$ recognition site.[111] The terminal 5-HT autoreceptors in the guinea pig, like those in pigs and humans bear pharmacological similarities to the 5-HT$_{1D}$ recognition site.[112] Finally, a topic of current interest is the possibility that 5-HT$_{1D}$ receptor agonist activity may be relevant to the major functional responses and the reported antimigraine effects of the novel '5-HT$_1$-like' receptor agonist, sumatriptan.[113]

12.9.4.5.2 5-HT$_{1D}$ receptor ligands

Binding experiments using [^{3}H]-5-HT as a radioligand in the presence of 100 nM 8-OH-DPAT and 100 nM mesulergine have been performed and the data allow discussion of the structure–activity features of the 5-HT$_{1D}$ site.

5-HT displays a very high affinity for these sites (8.4). Few analogues have yet been evaluated in this assay. However, 5-CT (**13**) the carboxamido analogue of 5-HT, shows a very high affinity (8.6). As for 5-HT$_{1A}$ and 5-HT$_{1B}$ receptor subtypes, a significant increase in affinity resulted from the substitution of 5-carboxamide for 5-hydroxy. In contrast to all the other 5-HT$_1$ receptor subtypes, the 5-HT$_{1D}$ site shows a higher affinity (8.4) for 5-MeOT (**11**). Removal of the 5-substituent (tryptamine) or N-dimethylation (**20**) results in a significant decrease in affinity. Among putative antagonists, only metergoline (**29**) is potent (9.1), while (+)-LSD (**26**) is markedly less active (8.2). 5-HT_{1A} selective agents, such as 8-OH-DPAT, buspirone (**63**) and ipsapirone, display only weak (micromolar) affinity for this site. RU 24969 and (−)-pindolol are approximately two times less potent at these sites, while compounds displaying nanomolar potencies for $5-HT_{1C}$ sites, such as mianserin and mesulergine, are two to three orders of magnitude less potent at the $[^3H]$-5-HT binding sites in bovine caudate. In addition, representative $5-HT_2$ and $5-HT_3$ receptor selective agents (*e.g.* cyproheptadine; **81** and MDL 72222; **104**) are essentially inactive at these binding sites. These data suggest that we are actually dealing with a new 5-HT receptor subtype.

12.9.4.6 $5-HT_2$ Receptors

12.9.4.6.1   Identification and functional correlates

Although 5-HT$_2$ recognition sites were first identified using $[^3H]$spiperone,[114] $[^3H]$ketanserin[115] has been used most extensively for labelling $5-HT_2$ receptors. Several other radioligands, including $[^3H]$mianserin, $[^{125}I]$LSD and $[^3H]$mesulergine, can be used to label 5-HT_2 sites, but they have the disadvantage that they also bind to the $5-HT_{1C}$ receptors. While no selective agonists are as yet available for $5-HT_2$ receptors, several potent and relatively selective antagonists exist, such as ketanserin, setoperone, altanserin, pirenperone and ritanserin. The highest densities of $5-HT_2$ receptors are found in the cerebral cortex and caudate, and the $[^3H]$ketanserin-labelled sites show a closely similar pharmacology in brain tissue from a number of species, including human.

5-HT-stimulated phosphoinositol hydrolysis has been reported to occur *via* $5-HT_2$ receptor activation both in the brain and peripheral tissues. Moreover, in cultures of smooth muscle cells and aortic myocytes, 5-HT appears to stimulate phosphoinositide turnover *via* receptors pharmacologically similar to the $5-HT_2$ binding site (see ref. 23 for review, and Table 2).

In the CNS, 5-HT-induced facilitation of the excitatory effects of glutamate in the facial motor nucleus has been attributed to the activation of $5-HT_2$ receptors.[116] The increased excitability is due to a slow depolarization of the motor neurone membrane associated with decreased membrane conductance. Excitatory 5-HT receptors of the $5-HT_2$ subtype are also located on sympathetic preganglionic neurones. Activation of spinal $5-HT_2$ receptors in the rat have been reported to result in inhibition of sympathetic nerve activity (see ref. 69 for review). In the therapeutic context, however, a role for central (or peripheral) $5-HT_2$ receptors in the maintenance or control of blood pressure is far from clear and appears unlikely.[69]

12.9.4.6.2 $5-HT_2$ receptor agonists

Although ketanserin (**85**) is only 25 times less active at H_1 histamine and α_1-adrenoceptors than at $5-HT_2$ receptors[115] the $[^3H]$ derivative is the ligand most commonly used to label $5-HT_2$ sites, with mianserin being used to define the nonspecific binding. Several reviews describing various characteristics of the $5-HT_2$ receptor and its ligands have been published.[25,117−119] The affinities and selectivities of the most interesting agonists are given in Table 5.

The first striking observation concerns 5-HT, whose affinity for $5-HT_2$ sites is very low (5.53) compared to its affinity for '$5-HT_1$-like' receptors (7.5–8.5). These binding data have been used as arguments pro and contra the allocation of a receptor role to $5-HT_1$ or $5-HT_2$ sites. Leysen has argued that according to the concept of humoral neurotransmission, the receptor-binding affinity of the endogeneous neurotransmitter must be of the same order of magnitude as its local concentration in the synaptic cleft, which is in the micromolar range. This condition seems to be better fulfilled at the $5-HT_2$ site. Nevertheless, the validity of this argument may be challenged by the recent discovery that the affinity of 5-HT for $5-HT_2$ sites can also reach the nanomolar range when tritiated agonists are used as radioligands.[120] Moreover, all the $5-HT_1$ recognition sites have been shown to have functional correlates[6,7] and can be legitimately labelled 'receptors'.

Examination of the affinities displayed by 5-HT analogues in $[^3H]$ketanserin-binding assays leads to the following observations. Surprisingly, perhaps, many of these compounds, more or less structurally related to 5-HT, display a much higher potency than 5-HT itself. Thus, in contrast to the situation at other 5-HT-binding sites, 4-HT is much more potent than 5-HT, which is equipotent to 5-MeO-T and tryptamine. In addition, α- or β-methylation of 5-HT increases (by factors of 23 and

Table 5 Agonist $5-HT_2$ Receptor Affinities Determined in $[^3H]$Ketanserin Binding Studies[a]

Compound	$5-HT_2$	$5-HT_2/5-HT_{1A}$	$5-HT_2/5-HT_{1B}$	$5-HT_2/5-HT_{1C}$	Ref.
(7) T	2895	17	0.28	57.9	45
(8) 4-HT	725	7.6	0.69	18	45
(1) 5-HT	2951	983	128	89	45
(9) 6-HT	11500	7.2	1.95	2.1	45
(11) 5-MeO-T	2570	285	6.4	57	45
(13) 5-CT	14790	73950	2900	20.5	45
(16) 2-Me-5-HT	10233	4	0.28	0.70	45
(17) α-Me-5-HT	126	1.5	0.12	2.1	45
(18) β-Me-5-HT	2512	28.2	0.81	5.1	45
(19) N-Me-5-HT	180	36	1.24	0.6	45
(24) 5-MeO-DMT	1200	60	13.3	—	119
(25) RU 24969	1000	200	250	2.5	23
(51) Quipazine	645	0.19	2.0	3.2	45
(53) TFMPP	160	0.08	5.3	—	119
(98) (R)-(−)DOM	60	—	0.017	—	25
(99) (R)-(−)DOB	24	—	0.005	—	25, 119
(100) (R)-(−)DOI	10	—	0.004	—	25, 119
(38) 8-OH-DPAT	7100	3550	0.11	0.97	45

[a] K_i values in nM, selectivities expressed as ratios of K_i values.

1.2, respectively) the affinity for $5-HT_2$ receptors; this contrasts with what is observed at $5-HT_1$ receptors (*cf.* Table 3). *N*-Methylation also results in an increase in affinity since *N*-Me-5-HT is 16 times more active than 5-HT and 5-MeO-DMT (5-methoxy-*N*, *N*-dimethyltryptamine; **24**) is two to three times more potent than 5-MeO-T or 5-HT. This suggests that the endogenous neurotransmitter is far from being the optimal ligand of its presumed natural receptor.

It is interesting to observe that while replacement of the 5-hydroxy or 5-methoxy substituent in tryptamine by a 5-carboxamido group leads to a marked increase in affinity at $5-HT_1$ receptor subsites, this substitution dramatically decreases the potency at $5-HT_2$ sites, conferring a high selectivity to this 5-HT analogue (**13**). Similarly, 2-methyl substitution of 5-HT provides a compound (2-Me-5-HT; **16**) which is only weakly active at certain $5-HT_1$ and $5-HT_2$ sites, but has potent $5-HT_3$ receptor agonist properties.

Interestingly, the most potent 5-HT analogue at the $5-HT_2$ site is α-Me-5-HT (pIC_{50} = 6.9). This result should be put into context by considering another series of very potent, selective and stereospecific 5-HT receptor agonists, the 4-substituted derivatives of α-methyl-2,5-dimethoxyphenylethylamine.[119] The (*R*)-(−)-4-Me derivative, (−)-DOM (**98**), is 50 times more active than 5-HT (pIC_{50} = 7.2). The 4-bromo and 4-iodo derivatives (*R*)-(−)-DOB (**99**) and (*R*)-(−)-DOI (**100**) are the most potent $5-HT_2$ receptor agonists, with pIC_{50} values of 7.6 and 8.0 respectively. In addition, these compounds discriminate $5-HT_2$ from $5-HT_1$ sites with a selectivity ratio superior to 60. Glennon and coworkers have performed a SAR study in this series, showing that DOB (**99**) displays optimal affinity/selectivity for $5-HT_2$ sites. All these molecules have been identified as $5-HT_2$ receptor agonists in different functional tests.[25]

$[^3H]$DOB has been prepared and evaluated as a radioligand in order to label specifically the $5-HT_2$ agonist recognition site.[119] Glennon and coworkers distinguished two states of the $5-HT_2$ receptor: a high affinity state ($5-HT_{2H}$) labelled by the agonist $[^3H]$DOB, and a low affinity state ($5-HT_{2L}$) labelled by $[^3H]$ketanserin in the presence of guanine nucleotides. The affinity pattern of the $5-HT_2$ antagonists seems to be similar in binding assays using $[^3H]$DOB or $[^3H]$ketanserin as marker; in contrast, agonists such as (−)-DOB, 5-HT and 5-MeOT generally display higher affinity for $[^3H]$DOB-labelled sites compared to $[^3H]$ketanserin-labelled sites. Although these data have been interpreted in terms of different 'states' of the $5-HT_2$ receptor, the possibility of there being two quite distinct $5-HT_2$ binding sites has been suggested.[121]

12.9.4.6.3 *5-HT₂ receptor antagonists*

A structure–activity relationship study of the $5-HT_2$ receptor antagonists is a complex procedure because of the abundance and structural diversity of such potent compounds. The affinities and efficacies of numerous $5-HT_2$ antagonists have been recently reviewed.[25,118] Excellent correlations were reported between $[^3H]$ketanserin binding data and several functional tests such as cat platelet

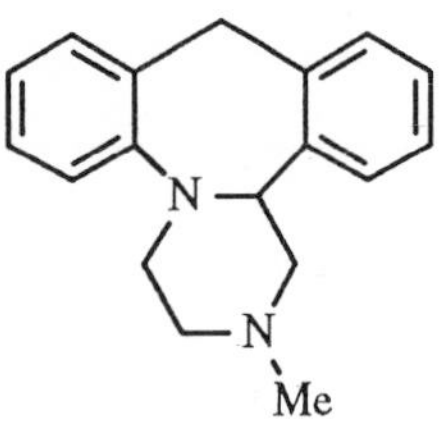

(**77**) Mianserin

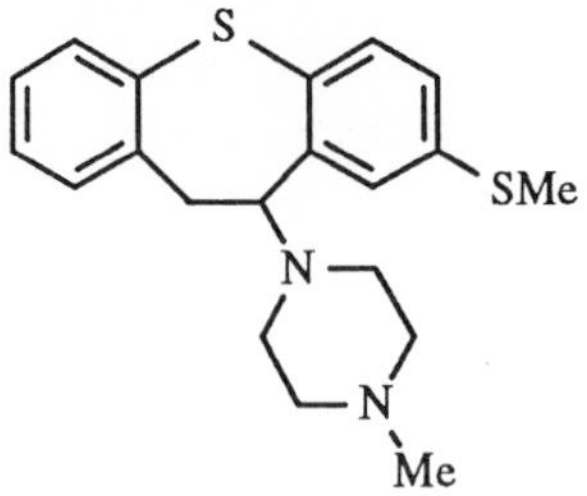

(**78**) Methiothepin

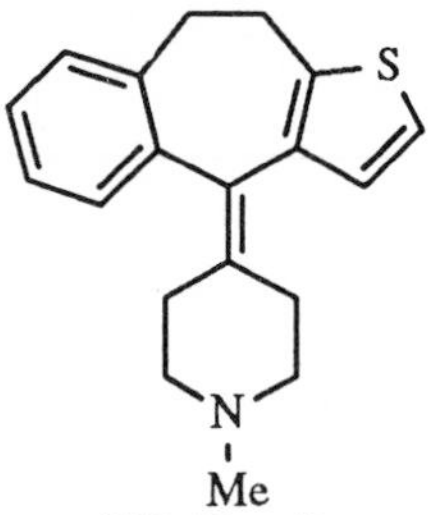

(**79**) Pizotifen

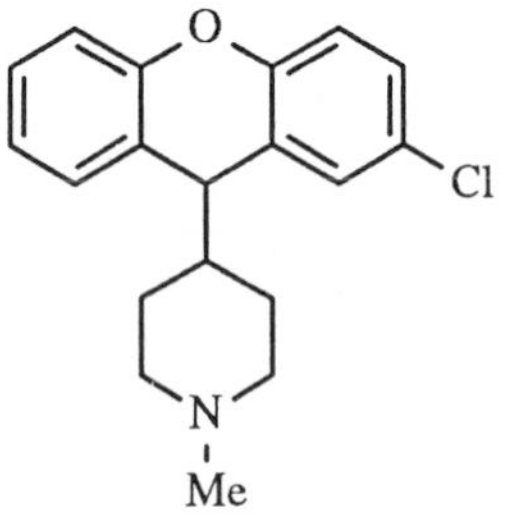

(**80**) Clopipazan

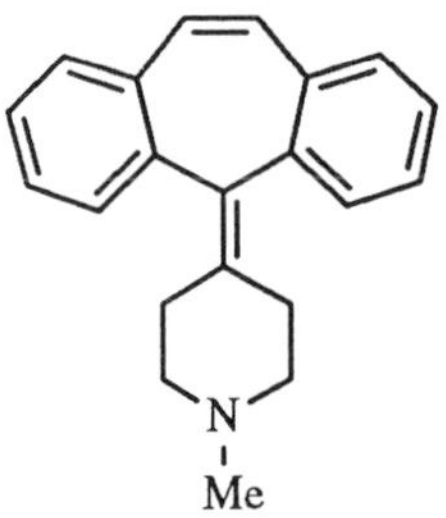

(**81**) Cyproheptadine

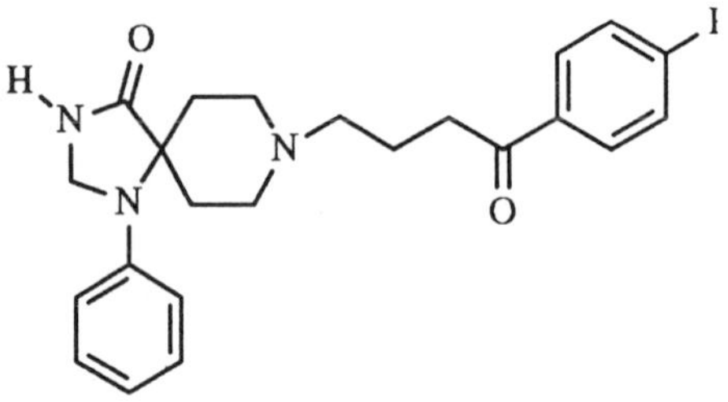

(**82**) Spiperone

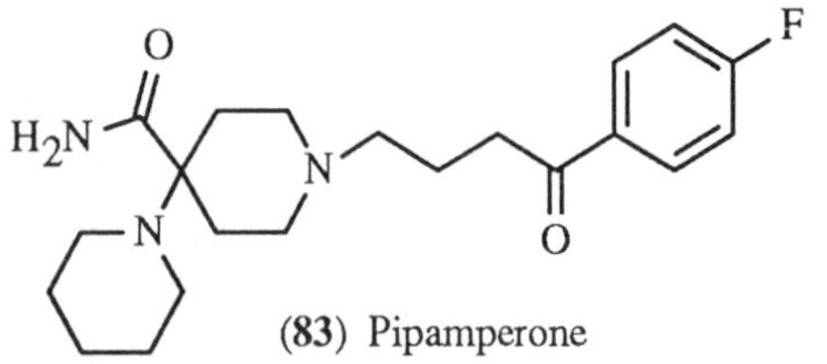

(**83**) Pipamperone

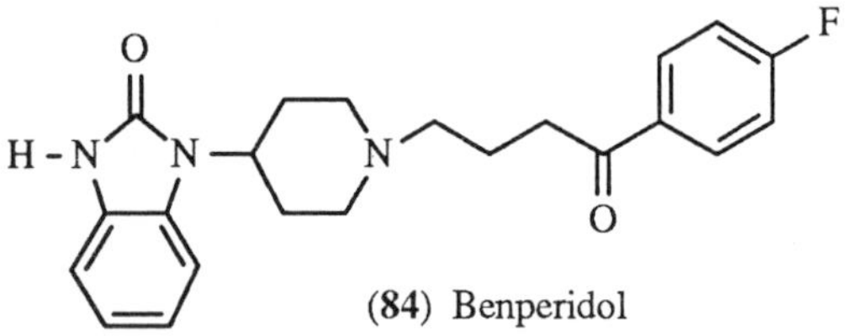

(**84**) Benperidol

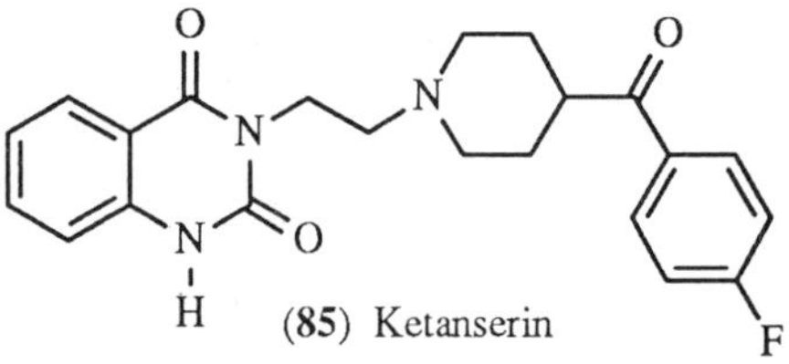

(**85**) Ketanserin

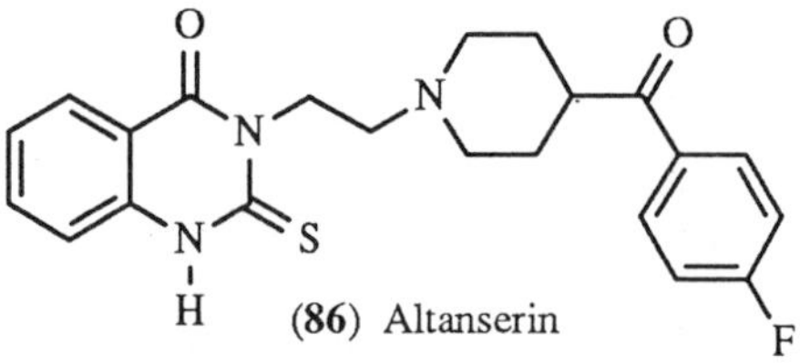

(**86**) Altanserin

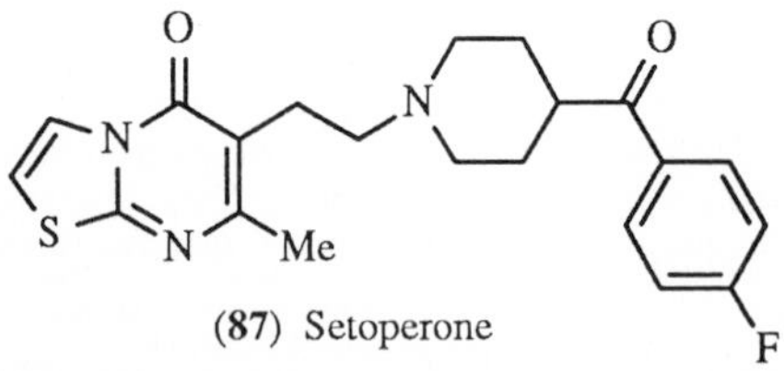

(**87**) Setoperone

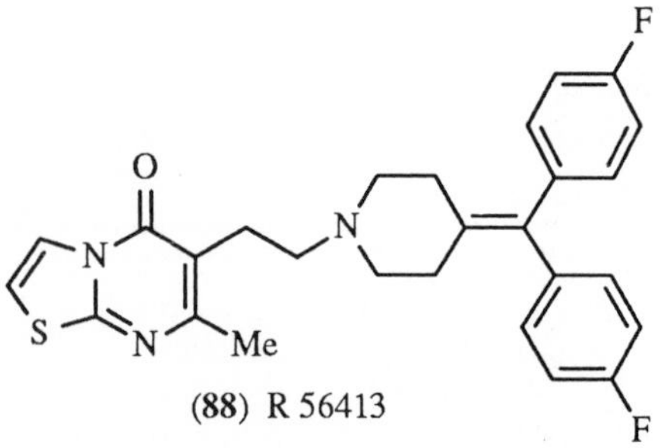

(**88**) R 56413

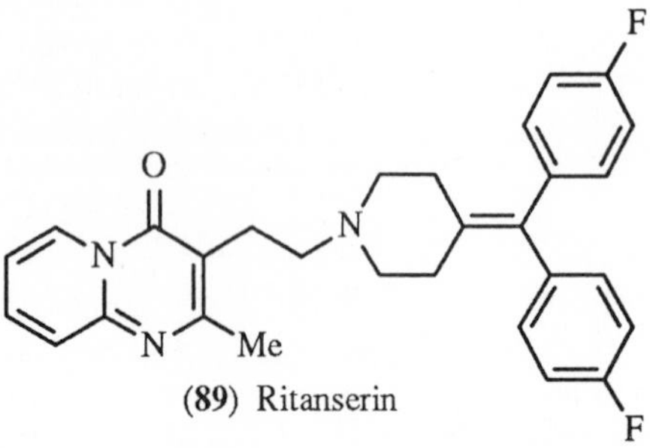

(**89**) Ritanserin

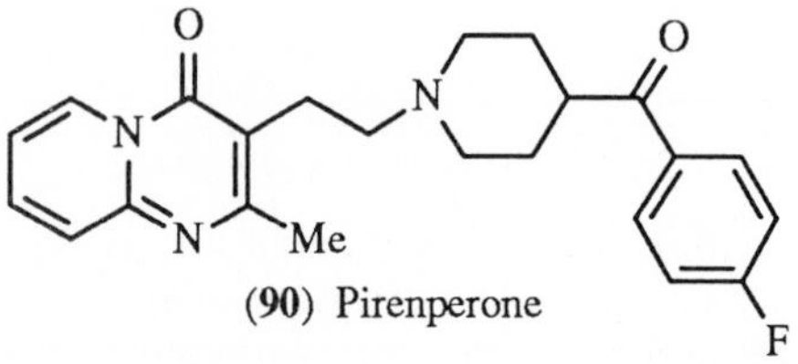

(**90**) Pirenperone

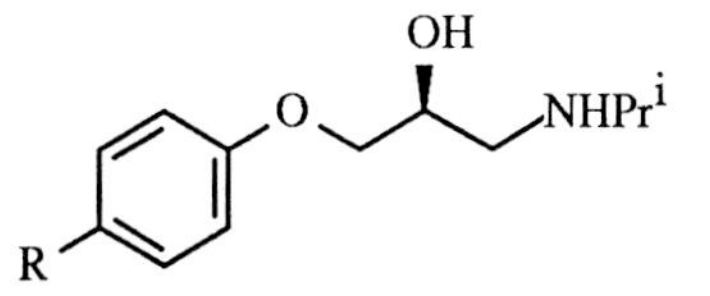

(91) Atenolol; R = CH$_2$CONH$_2$

(92) Betaxolol; R = (CH$_2$)$_2$O

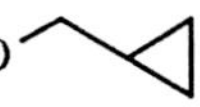

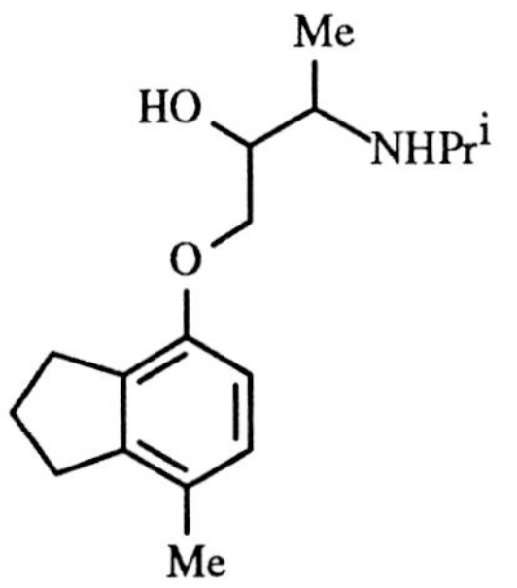

(93) ICI 118551

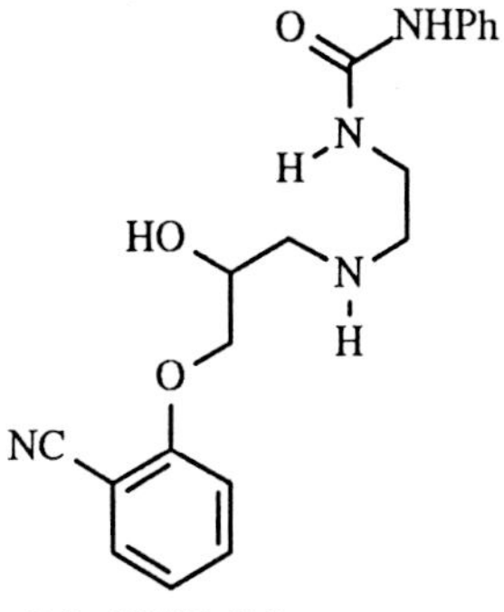

(94) ICI 89406

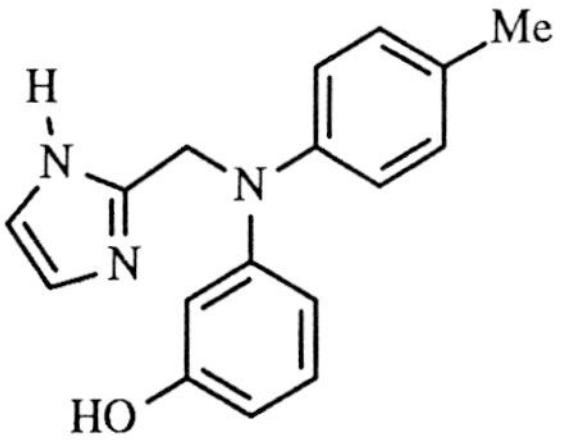

(95) Phentolamine

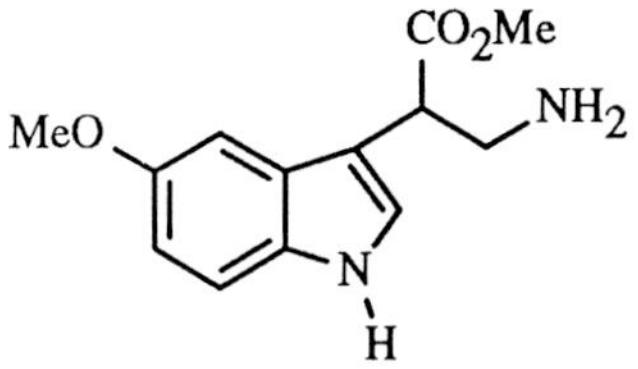

(96) Indorenate

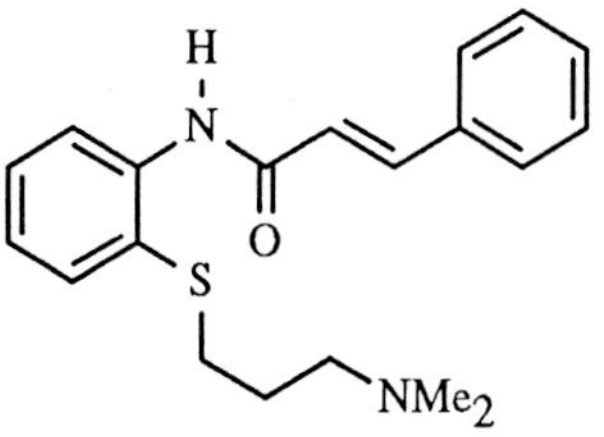

(97) Cinanserin

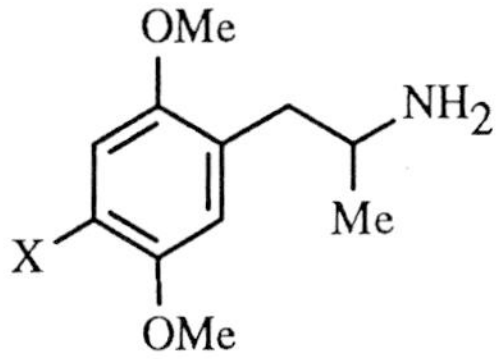

(98) (R)-(−)-DOM; X = Me
(99) (R)-(−)-DOB; X = Br
(100) (R)-(−)-DOI; X = I

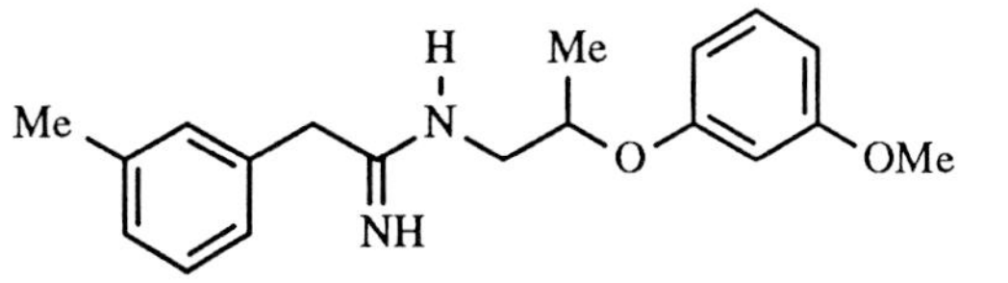

(101) Xylamidine

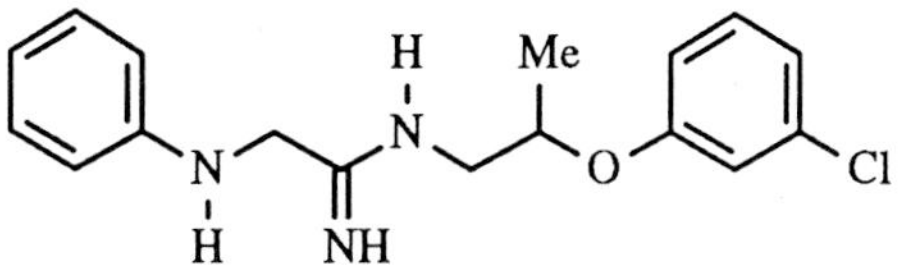

(102) BW 501C67

aggregation, 5-HT-induced [^{32}P]phosphatidic acid formation in human platelets or 5-HT-induced contractions in rat caudal arteries.[122] However, no obvious correlation seemed to exist between the structures of very potent antagonists such as cyproheptadine (81), metergoline (29), ketanserin (85) and spiperone (82).[117] In describing the SAR, it may be helpful to distinguish five chemical classes of 5-HT$_2$ receptor antagonists (Table 6).

(i) Butyrophenone derivatives

One of the first compounds used to discriminate 5-HT receptor subtypes was spiperone (82), a butyrophenone derivative originally developed as a dopamine receptor antagonist. The compound has very high affinity for the 5-HT$_2$ sites (IC$_{50}$ = 0.53 × 10^{-9} mol^{-1}), but is 33 times more active at the D$_2$ dopamine receptor. Analogues such as pipamperone (83) or benperidol (84) display broadly similar binding profiles.

(ii) Tricyclic compounds

Among the 'classical' 5-HT receptor antagonists, cyproheptadine (81) is a very potent 5-HT$_2$ receptor antagonist (pIC$_{50}$ = 9.3). Its close analogue, pizotifen (79), is the tricyclic ligand with the

Table 6 Antagonist 5-HT$_2$ Receptor Affinities,[a] Determined in [^{3}H] Ketanserin Binding Studies, and Selectivities *vis à vis* other Central Monoamine Receptors

Compound	5-HT$_2$	5-HT$_1$/5-HT$_2$	H$_1$/5-HT$_2$	α$_1$/5-HT$_2$	α$_2$/5-HT$_2$	D$_2$/5-HT$_2$	Ref.
Butyrophenone derivatives							
(82) Spiperone	0.53	190	>1800	18	>1800	0.3	115
(83) Pipamperone	0.78	—	—	—	—	—	115
(84) Benperidol	1.20	—	—	—	—	—	115
Tricyclic derivatives							
(79) Pizotifen	0.28	—	—	—	—	—	115
(80) Clopipazan	0.39	—	—	—	—	—	115
(78) Methiothepin	0.39	95	14	1	80	10	115
(81) Cyproheptadine	0.44	—	—	—	—	—	115
(77) Mianserin	1.4	710	2.0	58	43	442	115
Ergoline derivatives							
(31) 2-I-LSD	0.9	35[b]	1300	110	110	44	127
(29) Metergoline	0.28	46	3900	135	1300	80	115
(28) Methysergide	0.94	—	—	—	—	—	115
(26) (+)-LSD	2.50	8	>440	65	35	8	115
(30) Mesulergine	3.16	—	—	—	—	—	128
(32) Me-I-LSD	0.26[c]	180	—	60	280	34	129
(33) LY 53587	0.05	No effect	260000	5800	—	—	123
Ketanserin derivatives							
(86) Altanserin	0.16	>6000[b]	200	25	620	350	122
(89) Ritanserin	0.19	>5000[b]	125	185	315	115	122
(88) R 56413	0.26	>3000[b]	75	280	250	480	122
(90) Pirenperone	0.28	—	—	—	—	—	115
(87) Setoperone	0.37	>2500[b]	145	35	65	70	122
(85) Ketanserin	0.39	>2500[b]	25	25	>2500	565	122

[a] K_i values in nM, selectivities expressed as ratios of K_i values. [b] Selectivity *versus* the high affinity 5-HT$_1$ site. [c] Dissociation constant.

highest affinity at this site (pIC$_{50}$ = 9.5). Other tricyclic compounds, less directly related to the previous ones, such as clopipazan (**80**), methiothepin (**78**) and mianserin (**77**) also display binding constants in the nanomolar range. However, none of these shows satisfactory selectivity.

(iii) Ergoline derivatives

Ergoline derivatives represent a further class of 5-HT antagonists. [^{3}H]LSD (**26**) has been used as a radioligand to label 5-HT$_2$ sites. Nevertheless, as is the case for LSD, many analogues also have a high affinity but are not selective on the subsites. Thus, the affinities of (+)-LSD for 5-HT$_2$ and 5-HT$_1$ receptors are very similar. Analogues such as methysergide (**28**), metergoline (**29**), 2-iodo-LSD (**31**) and N-Me-2-iodo-LSD (**32**) are more potent 5-HT$_2$ receptor ligands and display various degrees of selectivity for these *versus* 5-HT$_1$, dopamine and adrenoceptors. Compounds such as metergoline or mesulergine possess very high affinity for 5-HT$_{1C}$ sites (pIC$_{50}$ = 9.19 and 8.67, respectively). Of particular interest is the recently disclosed compound LY 53857 (**33**), which is claimed to be an extremely potent 5-HT$_2$ receptor ligand (pIC$_{50}$ = 10.3) without significant effect at 5-HT$_1$ receptors, dopamine or adrenoceptors.[123] It is not clear yet if the *in vitro* potency and selectivity of this compound are related to the indole nitrogen isopropyl substitution, to its C-8 side chain, or to both. LY 53857 shows activity in animal models predictive of antidepressant activity.[124].

(iv) Ketanserin derivatives

The discovery of the 5-HT receptor antagonist properties of ketanserin (**85**), originally designed as a histamine H$_1$ receptor antagonist, was a key development in this field. The important feature of ketanserin was that it could clearly discriminate 5-HT$_2$ from 5-HT$_1$ sites. Nevertheless, its affinity for histamine H$_1$ and α$_1$-adrenoceptors is only 25 times lower than for 5-HT sites and its affinity for 5-HT$_{1C}$ and dopamine receptors is far from negligible. Numerous analogues have been developed with the aim of improving selectivity. For instance, altanserin (**86**), setoperone (**87**), R 56413 (**88**), ritanserin (**89**) and pirenperone (**90**) have recently been described.[122] All display high affinity for 5-

HT$_2$ receptors, with various selectivity profiles *vis à vis* other receptors. Ritanserin seems rather more selective than its congeners and is of particular interest as an extremely potent, long-acting and centrally active 5-HT$_2$ receptor angatonist which shows anxiolytic effects in preliminary clinical trials. It does, however, have meaningful activity at 5-HT$_{1C}$ sites (pK_D = 8.6).[23]

(v) Miscellaneous

In addition to compounds belonging to the four previous classes, diverse chemical structures have been reported to have 5-HT$_2$ receptor antagonist properties. Thus several arylpiperazine derivatives such as TR 2515 (69) or trazodone (70) induce 5-HT$_2$-receptor-mediated responses. 1-(1-Naphthyl)piperazine (71) shows good affinity for the 5-HT$_2$ receptor and, being 2000 times less active at α_1-adrenoceptors, is markedly selective. Two related amidines, xylamidine (101) and BW 501C67 (102), display high affinity and selectivity for 5-HT$_2$ receptors. BW 501C67 is of particular interest as it appears not to penetrate the central nervous system. Cinanserin is a very flexible molecule with reasonable affinity for the 5-HT$_2$ site.

Despite these complexities, we have defined a model of the 5-HT$_2$ recognition site using cyproheptadine, LSD and ketanserin as templates to characterize the basic pharmacophore (Figure 4).[125] Thus the activity of all the 5-HT$_2$ receptor antagonists mentioned above can be qualitatively accounted for by the common structural features represented in Figure 5: one nitrogen atom located at 6.30 Å and 5.17 Å from two aromatic rings; the nitrogen atom is almost coplanar with the first aromatic ring (0.32 Å above the plane), while its lone pair of electrons points perpendicularly to this plane. In contrast, this nitrogen atom is located at 3.28 Å above the plane of the second basic aromatic ring, its lone pair of electrons being about parallel to the plane.

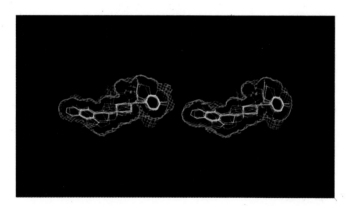

Figure 4   5-HT$_2$ receptor antagonists superimposed in their putative receptor-bound conformations; the blue area defines a possible volume accessible to ligands

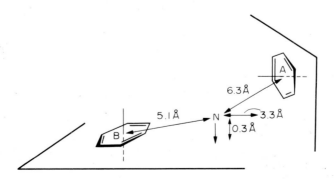

Figure 5   Basic pharmacophore of the 5-HT$_2$ antagonist recognition site (reproduced from ref. 125 by permission of the Société de Chimie Thérapeutique)

It is interesting to note that only two of these three basic anchoring points seem sufficient to confer a high affinity to ligands having a rigid skeleton, while the three structural features seem necessary for more flexible structures. This model remains to be validated by the design of appropriate compounds.

The efficacy of some of the 5-HT$_2$ receptor antagonists has been evaluated in numerous functional tests, and excellent correlations have been reported between *in vitro* and *in vivo* data, suggesting that the 5-HT$_2$ binding sites are indeed receptors playing a functional role. The reader is referred to the several excellent reviews of this topic for detailed information.[25,126]

Several 5-HT$_2$ receptor antagonists with various degrees of potency and selectivity which have been presented above are currently undergoing clinical evaluation.

12.9.4.7 5-HT$_3$ Receptors

12.9.4.7.1 Identification and functional correlates

The field of 5-HT$_3$ receptors is where perhaps the most spectacular developments have occurred during the last five years. The biochemical, pharmacological and clinical properties of the most interesting 5-HT$_3$ receptor ligands have been repeatedly reviewed[130, 131] and will, as a consequence, be dealt with only briefly here.

A number of functional responses was first used to characterize the 5-HT$_3$ receptor and to study the SAR at these sites.[130,131] These include the release of transmitter from the terminal sympathetic fibres of the rabbit heart, depolarization of the vagal afferent fibres and sympathetic ganglion cell bodies and contraction of the guinea pig ileum (in the presence of methysergide). The Bezold–Jarisch effect of 5-HT in a number of species has provided a simple test for evaluating 5-HT$_3$ receptor actions *in vivo*.

More recently, four radioligands have been described which label selectively the 5-HT$_3$ receptors in a number of tissues.[131] These are [^{3}H]GR 65630, [^{3}H]zacopride, [^{3}H]quipazine and [^{3}H]-*N*-Me-ICS 205-930. There appear to be marked differences between species with respect to 5-HT$_3$ receptor densities. For instance, using [^{3}H]GR 65630, higher levels of specific binding were observed in a variety of brain areas of rat and mouse than in the corresponding areas in rabbit, ferret or monkey brains.[132] In contrast, [^{3}H]quipazine labels 5-HT$_3$ receptors in both rat and pig cortical membranes but not membranes prepared from rabbit, mouse, guinea pig, chicken, turtle, dog, cow or human.[133] However, the area postrema seems to contain high densities of 5-HT$_3$ receptors, irrespective of species.[132,133] Cell lines such as murine neuroblastoma cells have been shown to contain recognition sites labelled by [^{3}H]ICS 205-930, which may correspond to 5-HT$_3$ receptors.[134] The affinities of a number of agonists and antagonists have been evaluated in the different systems described above.[134,135]

12.9.4.7.2 5-HT$_3$ receptor agonists

A limited number of agonists have been evaluated for their activity at the 5-HT$_3$ receptors[134–136] (Table 7). 5-HT itself displays only a moderate affinity in rat brain preparations (pK_D = 6.89) or in cells (pK_D = 6.42). These binding data correlate with the activity observed in diverse functional assays.[130,131] It is interesting to note the good affinity of 2-Me-5-HT (**16**), although there are some discrepancies between the available binding data (Table 7). If one considers the lower affinity value (pK_D = 5.9), 2-Me-5-HT does not discriminate 5-HT$_3$ from 5-HT$_{1A}$ and 5-HT$_{1C}$ sites.[23] Nevertheless, it has been reported that this molecule is a more potent agonist at autonomic, afferent and enteric neuronal 5-HT$_3$ receptors than at the 'non-5-HT$_3$' receptors present in rat uterus or rat cerebral cortex membranes.[136] Further, 2-Me-5-HT appears to be a partial 5-HT$_3$ receptor agonist in several preparations.[137] *m*CPP (**57**) is a reasonably potent 5-HT$_3$ receptor ligand (pK_D = 6.99–7.3) but whether this compound is an agonist or an antagonist at this site remains to be determined.

Of interest is the fact that 8-OH-DPAT (**38**), 5-CT (**13**) and 5-MeO-T (**11**) are virtually inactive, thus illustrating the clear pharmacological difference between the '5-HT$_1$-like' and 5-HT$_2$ receptors on the one hand and 5-HT$_3$ receptors on the other. Phenylbiguanide also interacts selectively with the 5-HT$_3$ receptors of autonomic and afferent neurones.[131] Its potency is slightly less than that of 5-HT (pK_D = 6.1). Unfortunately, there are few data from binding or functional tests with which to establish a more precise SAR for phenylbiguanide and related compounds.

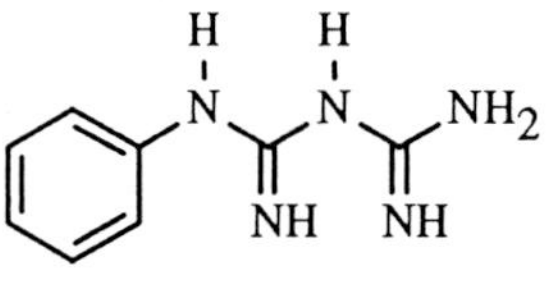

(**103**) Phenylbiguanide

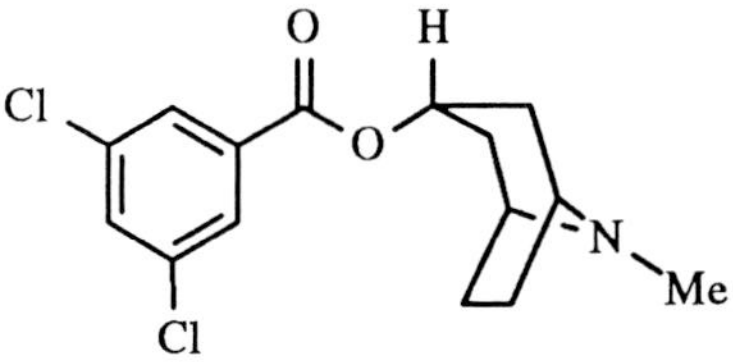

(**104**) MDL 72222

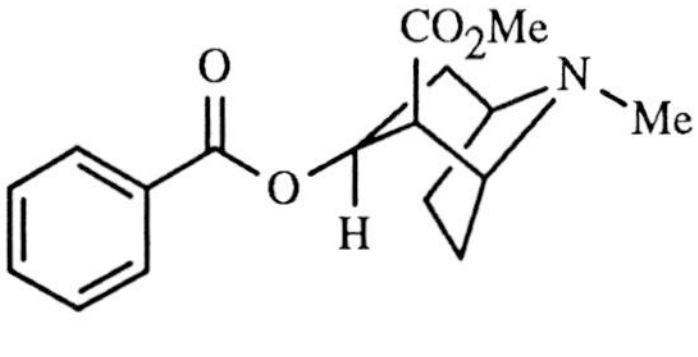

(**105**) Cocaine

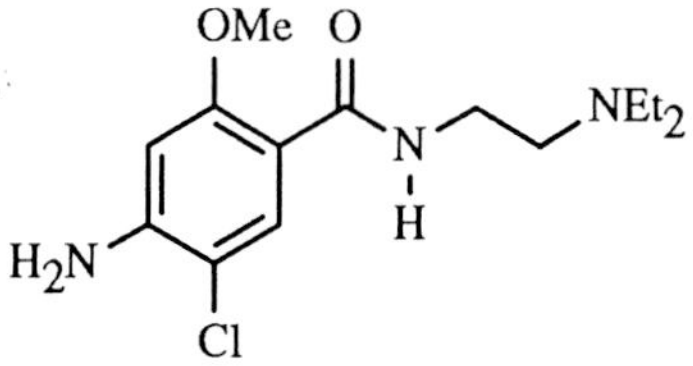

(**106**) Metoclopramide

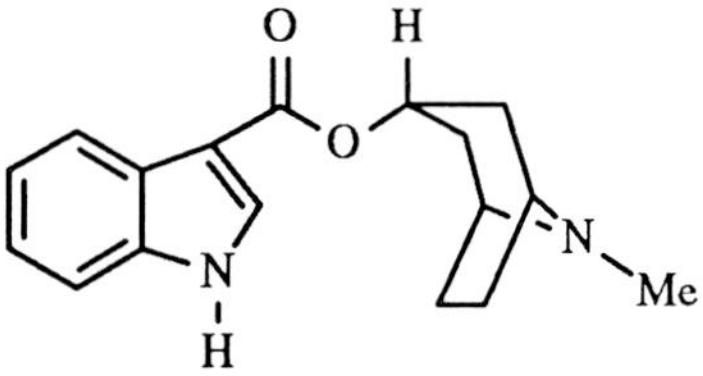

(**107**) ICS 205-930

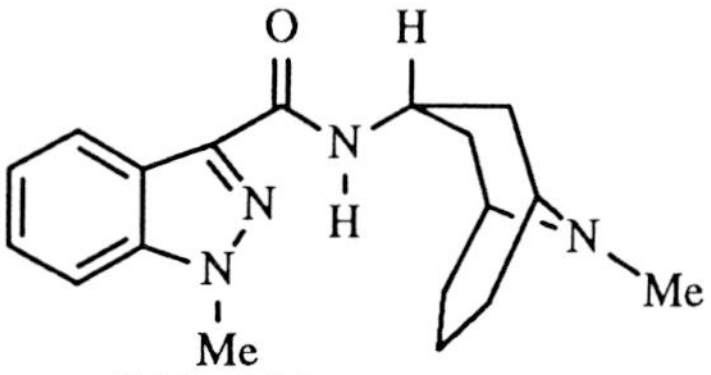

(**108**) BRL 43694

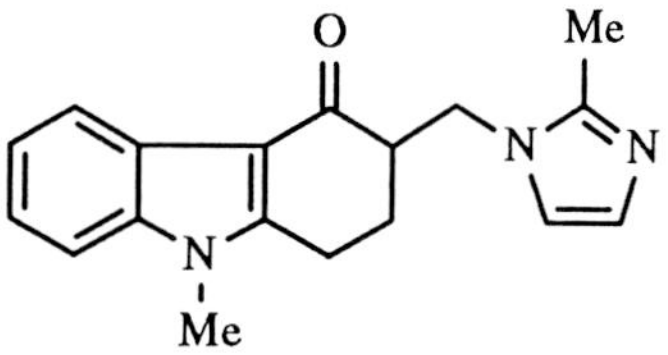

(**109**) GR 38032

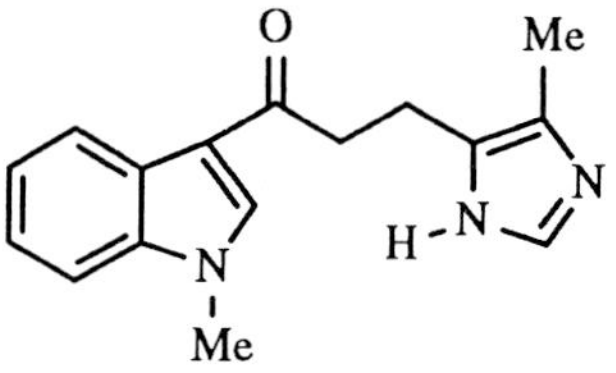

(**110**) GR 65630

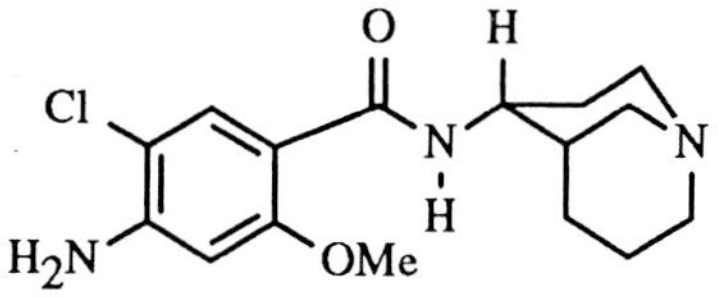

(**111**)

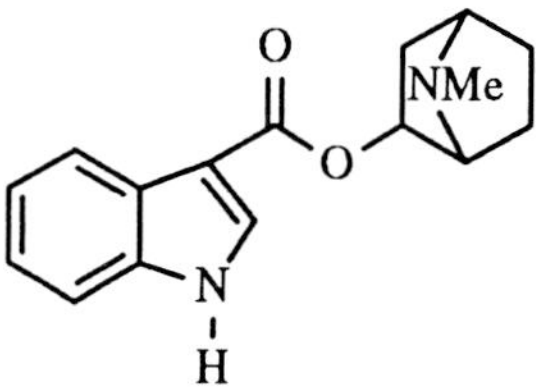

(**112**) SDZ 210-205

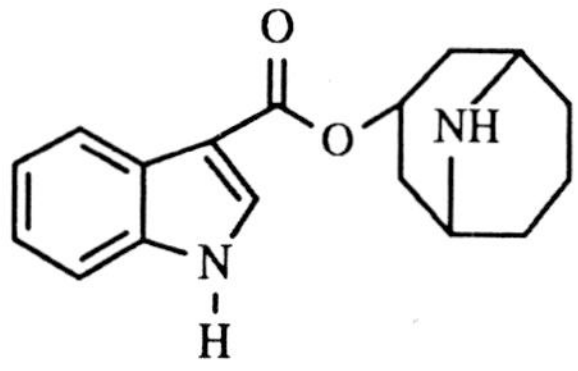

(**113**) SDZ 206-792

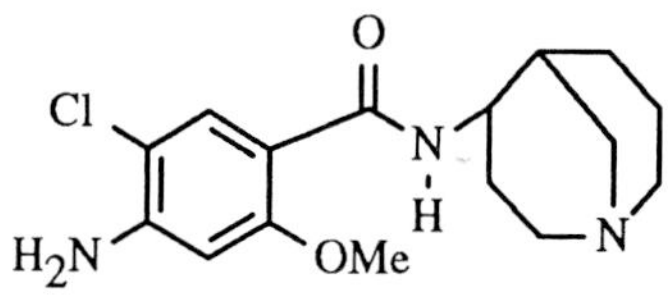

(**114**) BRL 24924

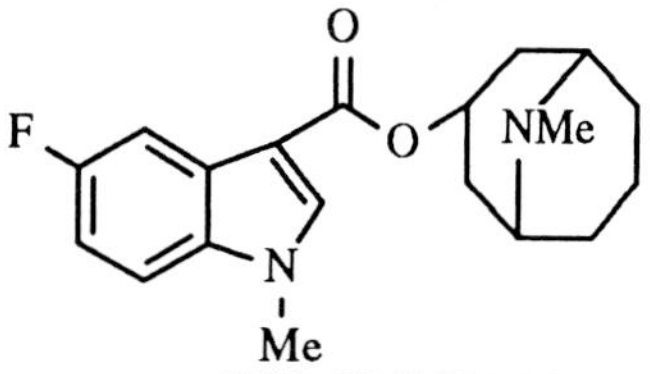

(**115**) SDZ 206-830

12.9.4.7.3 *5-HT$_3$ receptor antagonists*

The design and development of the first potent and highly selective 5-HT$_3$ receptor antagonist, MDL 72222 (**104**), has been previously reviewed in detail.[130]

After the characterization by Fozard *et al.* of the dissimilarity between the neuronal receptor of the sympathetic nerve terminals of the rabbit heart and the M or D receptors of Gaddum and Picarelli, a number of compounds were screened, among which (−)-cocaine (**105**) was found to be a

Table 7 Affinities of 5-HT$_3$ Receptor Agonists in Neuroblastoma Cells Compared to Rat Brain

Compound	pK_D (cells)[a]	pK_i (brain)[b]
(57) mCPP	6.99	7.3
(1) 5-HT	6.42	6.89
(103) Phenylbiguanide	6.14	—
(16) 2-Me-5-HT	5.89	7.06
(13) 5-CT	4.71	—
(38) 8-OH-DPAT	4.58	—
(11) 5-MeO-T	4.48	—

[a] [^{3}H]ICS 205-930 (107) used as radioligand.[138] [b] [^{3}H]GR 65630 (110) used as radioligand.[135]

Table 8 Affinities of 5-HT$_3$ Receptor Antagonists for [^{3}H]ICS 205-930 Binding Sites (Cells) and [^{3}H]GR 65630 Binding Sites (Rat Brain)

Compound	pK_D (Cells)[138]	pK_i (Brain)[135]
(104) MDL 72222	8.21	7.26
(107) ICS 205-930	9.09	8.50
(51) Quipazine	8.69	8.85
(108) BRL 43694	8.85	9.23
(113) SDZ 206-792	9.14	—
(114) BRL 24924	8.50	—
(115) SDZ 206-830	9.80	—
(106) Metoclopramide	6.65	6.46
(105) Cocaine	—	5.44
(110) GR 65630	—	8.79
(109) GR 38032	7.87	8.53
(111) (R)-GR 38032	—	8.48
(S)-GR 38032	—	8.27
(112) SDZ 210-205	7.48	
(78) Methiothepin	7.41	
(77) Mianserin	7.19	
(81) Cyproheptadin	6.58	
(−)-Propranolol	4.46	
(85) Ketanserin	3.90	
(82) Spiperone	3.64	

surmountable, reasonably potent (pA_2 = 6.21) antagonist at the rabbit heart site. A number of cocaine analogues were then evaluated yielding compounds with pA_2 values ranging from 7.0 (pseudotropine benzoate) to 7.7 [(−)-cocaine; **105**]. In addition, metoclopramide (**106**) was characterized as a potent antagonist of the sympathetic neuronal 5-HT$_3$ receptor of the rabbit heart.[139] Using this information, MDL 72222 was designed and synthesized as one of several substituted benzoic acid esters of tropine.[130] As predicted, this compound showed high affinity and selectivity for 5-HT$_3$ receptors *in vitro* and *in vivo* (Table 8).[140]

A number of analogues of MDL 72222 was prepared (*e.g.* the 3-chloro, 3-methyl, 3,5-dimethyl derivatives); all displayed high potency for the 5-HT$_3$ receptor with pA_2 values ranging from 8.2 to 9.3. This series is, however, too limited to draw any conclusions regarding the SAR.[130]

Richardson *et al.*[136] have described the approach which led to the design of ICS 205-930 (**107**). They claim that the structure of this potent 5-HT$_3$ antagonist was derived from the structure of 5-HT itself by extending the ethylene side chain and incorporating the terminal nitrogen in a tropine or homotropine ring system. Of interest is the fact that the 1-methyl-5-fluoro analogue of ICS 205-930 gives a substantially higher pA_2 value in the rabbit vagus preparation (pA_2 = 13.5) than in either the rabbit heart or the guinea pig ileum.[136] This observation has been used with other data to support the case for the existence of 5-HT$_3$ receptor subtypes.[17]

Little information is available concerning the development of two other 5-HT$_3$ receptor antagonists currently in clinical development, BRL 43694 (**108**) and GR 38032 (**109**). Chemically, BRL 43694 clearly retains the amide bridge of metoclopramide and structural moieties related to ICS 205-930. GR 38032 is of particular interest in that it is structurally quite dissimilar to any of the other classes of 5-HT$_3$ receptor antagonists. Both the carbazole and imidazole moieties are original.

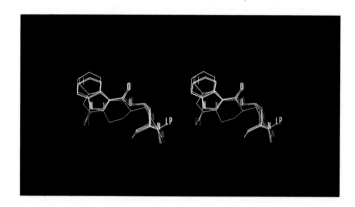

Figure 6 5-HT$_3$ receptor antagonists in their putative receptor-bound conformation (reproduced from ref. 125 by permission of the Société de Chimie Thérapeutique)

A three-dimensional pharmacophore and a 'receptor map' qualitatively accounting for the 5-HT$_3$-receptor-binding properties of the molecules described above has been proposed (Figure 6).[125] The common basic pharmacophore consists of an aromatic ring, a carbonyl group and a basic centre, occupying the relative positions illustrated in Figure 6. The fit between the different molecules is good and the considered conformers quite stable. A corresponding volume accessible to agonist ligands in the 5-HT$_3$ antagonist recognition site has been defined.

Recently, a new MDL 72222 analogue, MDL 73147, has been described.[141] This compound contains a new rigid bridged system and also fits well to the proposed model. In addition, there is a fortuitous perfect fit between the X-ray structure of this compound and its postulated receptor-bound conformation deduced from the previous model.

All the above compounds are impressively potent and selective as 5-HT$_3$ receptor antagonists: no meaningful activity, other than 5-HT$_3$ receptor blockade, has been reported for any of these agents at concentrations below micromolar. In contrast, compounds such as BRL 24924, metoclopramide and zacopride, in addition to being 5-HT$_3$ receptor antagonists, appear to have partial agonist activity at the high potency 'non-5-HT$_3$' neuronal receptor of the ileum.[22]

In contrast to all other 5-HT$_3$ receptor antagonists, MDL 72222 and, in particular, MDL 73147 show little or no activity at the 5-HT$_3$ receptor of guinea-pig ileum,[140, 142] thus strongly supporting the existence of 5-HT$_3$ receptor subtypes;[17] such selectivity could have practical significance for the development of 5-HT$_3$ receptor ligands with novel clinical applications in the future.

12.9.5 CONCLUDING REMARKS

The major objective of this chapter has been to give an account of the principal recognized 5-HT receptor subtypes and the more important compounds which interact with them. Inevitably, despite its length and detail, the account must be incomplete. In particular, there remain both functional responses[143] and [^{3}H]-5-HT binding sites[144] which defy classification under the headings described in this chapter. Time alone will tell whether these will turn out to be new 5-HT receptor subtypes with meaningful functional significance. However, the clear lesson of the last decade is that the scepticism which often greeted the advent of more and more 5-HT receptor subtypes was misplaced. Not only do multiple 5-HT receptors exist, as proved by clear structural differences,[24] but mounting evidence points to their important roles in physiological and pathophysiological processes.

12.9.6 REFERENCES

1. J. H. Gaddum and Z. P. Picarelli, *Br. J. Pharmacol. Chemother.*, 1957, **12**, 323.
2. S. J. Peroutka and S. H. Snyder, *Mol. Pharmacol.*, 1979, **16**, 687.
3. N. W. Pedigo, H. I. Yamamura and D. L. Nelson, *J. Neurochem.*, 1981, **36**, 220.
4. A. Pazos, D. Hoyer and J. M. Palacios, *Eur. J. Pharmacol.*, 1984, **106**, 539.
5. R. E. Heuring and S. J. Peroutka, *J. Neurosci.*, 1987, **7**, 894.
6. J. R. Fozard, *Trends Pharmacol. Sci.*, 1987, **8**, 501.

7. S. J. Peroutka, *Trends NeuroSci. (Pers. Ed.)*, 1988, **11**, 496.
8. P. P. A. Humphrey and B. P. Richardson, in 'Serotonin: Actions, Receptors, Pathophysiology', ed. E. J. Mylecharane *et al.*, Macmillan, London, 1989, in press.
9. B. P. Richardson and K. H. Buchheit, in 'Neuronal Serotonin', ed. N. N. Osborne, Wiley, Chichester, 1988, p. 465.
10. C. T. Dourish (ed.), 'Brain 5-HT$_{1A}$ Receptors, Behavioural and Neurochemical Pharmacology', Ellis Horwood, Chichester, 1987.
11. J. R. Fozard (ed.), 'The Peripheral Actions of 5-Hydroxytryptamine', Oxford University Press, Oxford, 1989.
12. E. Sanders-Bush (ed.), 'The Serotonin Receptors', Humana Press, Clifton, 1989.
13. E. J. Mylecharane *et al.* (eds), 'Serotonin: Actions, Receptors, Pathophysiology', Macmillan, London, 1989.
14. P. R. Saxena *et al.* (eds.), 'Cardiovascular Pharmacology of 5-Hydroxytryptamine: Prospective Therapeutic Applications', Kluwer, Dordrecht, 1989.
15. P. B. Bradley, G. Engel, W. Feniuk, J. R. Fozard, P. P. A. Humphrey, D. N. Middlemiss, E. J. Mylecharane, B. P. Richardson and P. R. Saxena, *Neuropharmacology*, 1986, **25**, 563.
16. J. R. Fozard, in 'Proceedings of the 3rd SCI/RSC Medicinal Chemistry Symposium', ed. R. W. Lambert, Royal Society of Chemistry, London, 1986, p. 37.
17. B. P. Richardson and G. Engel, *Trends NeuroSci.*, 1986, **9**, 424.
18. A. Dumuis, R. Bouhelal, M. Sebben, R. Cory and J. Bockaert, *Mol. Pharmacol.*, 1988, **34**, 880.
19. A. Dumuis, M. Sebben and J. Bockaert, *Eur. J. Pharmacol.*, 1989, **162**, 381.
20. A. Dumuis, M. Sebben and J. Bockaert, *Naunyn-Schmiedeberg's Arch. Pharmacol.*, 1989, in press.
21. K. H. Buchheit, G. Engel, E. Mutschler and B. P. Richardson, *Naunyn-Schmiedeberg's Arch. Pharmacol.*, 1985, **329**, 36.
22. G. J. Sanger and K. A. Wardle, in 'Serotonin: From Cell Biology to Pharmacology and Therapeutics', ed. R. Paoletti and P. Vanhoutte, Kluwer, Dordrecht, 1989, in press.
23. D. Hoyer, in 'The Peripheral Actions of 5-Hydroxytryptamine', ed. J. R. Fozard, Oxford University Press, Oxford, 1989, p. 72.
24. P. R. Hartig, *Trends Pharmacol. Sci.*, 1989, **10**, 64.
25. L.-E. Arvidson, U. Hacksell and R. A. Glennon, *Prog. Drug Res.*, 1986, **30**, 365.
26. I. L. Karle, K. S. Dragonette and S. A. Brenner, *Acta Crystallogr.*, 1965, **19**, 713.
27. C. E. Bugg and U. Thewalt, *Science (Washington, D.C.)*, 1970, **170**, 852.
28. A. Amit, L. Mester, B. Klewe and S. Farberg, *Acta Chem. Scand., Ser A*, 1978, **32**, 267.
29. L. B. Kier, *J. Pharm. Sci.*, 1968, **57**, 118.
30. C. L. Johnson, S. Kang and J. P. Green, *Jerusalem Symp. Quantum Chem. Biochem.*, 1973, **5**, 517.
31. S. Kang and M. H. Cho, *Theor. Chim. Acta*, 1971, **22**, 176.
32. P. Courrière, J. L. Coubeils and B. Pullmann, *C. R. Hebd. Seances Acad. Sci., Ser. D*, 1971, **272**, 1697.
33. M. Kumbar and D. V. Siva Sankar, *Res. Commun. Chem. Pathol. Pharmacol.*, 1975, **10**, 433.
34. R. R. Ison, P. Partington and G. C. K. Roberts, *J. Pharm. Pharmacol.*, 1972, **24**, 82.
35. S. Kang, L. Ernst, H. Weinstein and R. Osman, *Mol. Pharmacol.*, 1979, **16**, 1031.
36. M. J. Spark, D. A. Winkler and P. A. Andrews, *Int. J. Quantum Chem.*, 1982, **9**, 321.
37. T. J. Verbeuren, in 'The Peripheral Action of 5-Hydroxytryptamine', ed. J. R. Fozard, Oxford University Press, Oxford, 1989, p. 1.
38. J. Mandel and S. Knapp, *Fed. Proc. Fed. Am. Soc. Exp. Biol.*, 1977, **36**, 2142.
39. M. B. H. Joudim and R. Ashkenazi, *Adv. Biochem. Psychopharmacol.*, 1982, **34**, 35.
40. M. Hamon, S. Bourgoin, F. Artaud and J. Glowinski, *J. Neurochem.*, 1979, **33**, 1031.
41. M. D. Gershon, K. P. Liu, S. E. Karpiak and H. Tamir, *J. Neurosci.*, 1983, **3**, 1901.
42. D. D. Schoepp and A. J. Azzaro, *J. Neurochem.*, 1981, **36**, 2025.
43. G. M. Tyce, in 'Serotonin and the Cardiovascular System', ed. P. M. Vanhoutte, Raven Press, New York, 1985, p. 1.
44. R. W. Fuller, in 'Neuropharmacology of Serotonin', ed. A. R. Green, Oxford University Press, Oxford, 1985, p. 1.
45. G. Engel, M. Göthert, D. Hoyer, E. Schlicker and K. Hillenbrand, *Naunyn-Schmiedeberg's Arch. Pharmacol.*, 1986, **332**, 1.
46. S. Peroutka, *J. Neurochem.*, 1986, **47**, 529.
47. D. N. Middlemiss, *J. Pharm. Pharmacol.*, 1985, **37**, 434.
48. D. N. Middlemiss, M. F. Hibert and J. R. Fozard, *Annu. Rep. Med. Chem.*, 1986, **21**, 41.
49. M. F. Hibert, I. McDermott, D. N. Middlemiss, A. K. Mir and J. R. Fozard, *Eur. J. Med. Chem.*, 1989, **24**, 31.
50. D. Hoyer, G. Engel and H. O. Kalkman, *Eur. J. Pharmacol.*, 1985, **118**, 13.
51. J. R. Fozard, A. K. Mir and D. N. Middlemiss, *J. Cardiovasc. Pharmacol.*, 1987, **9**, 328.
52. D. Hoyer and P. Schoeffter, *Br. J. Pharmacol.*, 1989, **96**, 9P.
53. R. W. Ransom, K. B. Asarch and J. Shih, *J. Neurochem.*, 1986, **46**, 68.
54. R. W. Ransom, K. B. Asarch and J. Shih, *J. Neurochem.*, 1985, **44**, 875.
55. R. F. Neale, S. L. Fallon, W. C. Boyar, J. W. F. Wasley, L. L. Martin, G. A. Stone, B. S. Glaeser, C. M. Sinton and M. Williams, *Eur. J. Pharmacol.*, 1987, **136**, 1.
56. M. H. Hibert, M. W. Gittos, D. N. Middlemiss, A. K. Mir and J. R. Fozard, *J. Med. Chem.*, 1988, **31**, 1087.
57. P. Moser, M. Hibert, D. N. Middlemiss, A. K. Mir, M. D. Tricklebank and J. R. Fozard, *Br. J. Pharmacol.*, in press.
58. S. Hjorth, A. Carlsson, P. Lindberg, D. Sanchez, H. Wikström, L.-E. Arvidsson, U. Hacksell and J. L. G. Nilsson, *J. Neural Transm.*, 1982, **55**, 169.
59. D. N. Middlemiss and J. R. Fozard, *Eur. J. Pharmacol.*, 1983, **78**, 1071.
60. H. Gozlan, S. E. P. El Mestikawy, L. Pichat, J. Glowinski and M. Hamon, *Nature (London)*, 1983, **305**, 140.
61. W. U. Dompert, T. G. Gläser and J. Traber, *Naunyn-Schmiedeberg's Arch. Pharmacol.*, 1985, **328**, 467.
62. D. L. Nelson, G. Lambert, J. H. Yamamura and P. J. Monroe, *Life Sci.*, 1987, **41**, 1567.
63. A. Pazos and J. M. Palacios, *Brain Res.*, 1985, **346**, 205.
64. H. Shoemaker and S. Z. Langer, *Eur. J. Pharmacol.*, 1986, **124**, 371.
65. M. D. Hall, S. El Mestikawy, M. D. Emerit, L. Pichat, M. Hamon and H. Gozlan, *J. Neurochem.*, 1985, **44**, 1685.
66. C. T. Dourish, P. H. Hutson and G. Curzon, *Trends Pharmacol. Sci.*, 1986, **8**, 212.
67. Y. Claustre, J. Benavides and B. Scatton, *Eur. J. Pharmacol.*, 1987, **149**, 149.
68. R. Andrade, R. C. Malenka and R. A. Nicoll, *Science (Washington, D.C.)*, 1986, **234**, 1261.

69. A. K. Mir and J. R. Fozard, in 'Cardiovascular Pharmacology of 5-Hydroxytryptamine: Prospective Therapeutic Applications', ed. P. R. Saxena *et al.*, Kluwer, Dordrecht, 1989, in press.
70. J. Traber and T. Gläser, *Trends Pharmacol. Sci.*, 1987, **8**, 432.
71. P. Chopin and M. Briley, *Trends Pharmacol. Sci.*, 1987, **8**, 383.
72. F. Gilbert, C. Brazell, M. D. Tricklebank and S. M. Stahl, *Eur. J. Pharmacol.* 1988, **147**, 431.
73. J. I. Koenig, G. A. Gudelsky and H. Y. Meltzer, *Eur. J. Pharmacol.*, 1987, **137**, 1.
74. C. S. Aulakh, K. M. Wozniak, M. Haas, J. L. Hill, J. Zohar and D. N. Murphy, *Eur. J. Pharmacol.*, 1988, **146**, 253.
75. F. Chaouloff and B. Jeanrenaud, *J. Pharmacol. Exp. Ther.*, 1987, **243**, 1159.
76. F. Chaouloff and B. Jeanrenaud, *Eur. J. Pharmacol.*, 1988, **147**, 111.
77. M. D. Tricklebank, *Trends Pharmacol. Sci.*, 1985, **6**, 403.
78. M. D. Tricklebank, J. Neill, E. J. Kidd and J. R. Fozard, *Eur. J. Pharmacol.*, 1987, **133**, 47.
79. G. A. Kennett, C. T. Dourish and G. Curzon, *Eur. J. Pharmacol.*, 1989, in press.
80. G. A. Kennett, M. Marcou, C. T. Dourish and G. Curzon, *Eur. J. Pharmacol.*, 1987, **138**, 53.
81. L.-E. Arvidsson, U. Hacksell, J. L. G. Nilsson, S. Hjorth, A. Carlsson, P. Lindberg, D. Sanchez and H. Wikström, *J. Med. Chem.*, 1981, **24**, 9.
82. G. M. Cossery, H. Gozlan, E. Sampinato, C. Perdicakis, G. Guillaumet, L. Pichat and M. Hamon, *Eur. J. Pharmacol.*, 1987, **144**, 140.
83. M. B. Emerit, H. Gozlan, M. D. Hall, M. Hamon and A. Marquet, *Biochem. Pharmacol.*, 1985, **34**, 883.
84. S. J. Peroutka, *Biol. Psychiatry*, 1985, **20**, 971.
85. J. R. Huff, S. W. King, W. S. Saari, J. P. Springer, G. E. Martin and M. Williams, *J. Med. Chem.*, 1985, **28**, 945.
86. G. Karreman, I. Isenberg and A. Szent-Györgyi, *Science (Washington, D.C.)*, 1959, **130**, 1191.
87. S. H. Snyder and C. R. Merril, *Proc. Natl. Acad. Sci. USA*, 1965, **54**, 258.
88. S. Kang and J. P. Green, *Proc. Natl. Acad. Sci. USA*, 1970, **67**, 62.
89. R. A. Glennon, J. P. McKenney, R A. Lyon and M. J. Titeler, *J. Med. Chem.*, 1986, **29**, 194.
90. H. Weinstein, R. Osman, S. Topiol and J. P. Green, *Ann. N.Y. Acad. Sci.*, 1981, **367**, 434.
91. L.-E. Arvidsson, U. Hacksell, A. M. Johansson, J. L. G. Nilsson, P. Linberg, D. Sanchez, H. Wikström, K. Svensson, S. Hjorth and A. Carlsson, *J. Med. Chem.*, 1984, **27**, 45.
92. D. E. Nichols, W. R. Pfister and G. K. Yim, *Life Sci.*, 1978, **22**; 2165.
93. A. K. Mir, M. Hibert, M. D. Tricklebank, D. N. Middlemiss, E. J. Kidd and J. R. Fozard, *Eur. J. Pharmacol.*, 1988, **149**, 107.
94. A. B. Norman, G. Battaglia, A. L. Morrow and I. Creese, *Eur. J. Pharmacol.*, 1985, **106**, 461.
95. R. Bouhelal, L. Smounya and J. Bockaert, *Eur. J. Pharmacol.*, 1988, **155**, 189.
96. G. Maura, E. Roccataglia and M. Raiteri, *Naunyn-Schmiedeberg's Arch. Pharmacol.*, 1986, **334**, 323.
97. G. J. Molderings, K. Flink, E. Schlicker and M. Göthert, *Naunyn-Schmiedeberg's Arch. Pharmacol.*, 1987, **336**, 245.
98. M. A. Sills, B. B. Wolfe and A. Frazer, *J. Pharmacol. Exp. Ther.*, 1984, **231**, 480.
99. M. F. Hibert and D. N. Middlemiss, *Neuropharmacology*, 1986, **25**, 1.
100. D. N. Middlemiss, *Eur. J. Pharmacol.*, 1986, **120**, 51.
101. E. Schlicker, M. Göthert and K. Hillenbrand, *Naunyn-Schmiedeberg's Arch. Pharmacol.*, 1985, **331**, 398.
102. E. Edwards and P. M. Whitaker-Azmitia, *Neuropharmacology*, 1987, **26**, 93.
103. M. F. Hibert, in 'Topics in Pharmaceutical Sciences', ed. D. D. Breimer and P. Speiser, Elsevier, Amsterdam, 1987, p. 367.
104. D. Hoyer, A. Pazos, A. Probst and J. M. Palacios, *Brain Res.*, 1986, **376**, 85.
105. D. Hoyer, *Trends Pharmacol. Sci.*, 1988, **9**, 89.
106. T. Takahashi, E. Heher and B. Sakmann, *Proc. Natl. Acad. Sci. USA*, 1987, **84**, 5063.
107. G. A. Kennett and G. Curzon, *Br. J. Pharmacol.*, 1988, **94**, 137.
108. G. A. Kennett, P. Whitton, K. Shah and G. Curzon, *Eur. J. Pharmacol.*, 1989, **164**, 445.
109. J. R. Fozard and J. A. Gray, *Trends Pharmacol. Sci.*, 1989, **10**, 307.
110. C. Waeber, P. Schoeffter, J. M. Palacios and D. Hoyer, *Naunyn-Schmiedeberg's Arch. Pharmacol.*, 1988, **337**, 595.
111. P. Schoeffter, C. Waeber, J. M. Palacios and D. Hoyer, *Naunyn-Schmiedeberg's Arch. Pharmacol.*, 1988, **337**, 602.
112. D. Hoyer and D. N. Middlemiss, *Trends Pharmacol. Sci.*, 1989, **10**, 130.
113. P. Schoeffter and D. Hoyer, *Naunyn-Schmiedeberg's Arch. Pharmacol.*, 1989, **340**, 135.
114. J. E. Leysen, C. J. E. Niemegeers, J. P. Tollenaere and P. M. Laduron, *Nature (London)*, 1978, **272**, 168.
115. J. E. Leysen, C. J. E. Niemegeers, J. M., Van Nueten and P. M. Laduron, *Mol. Pharmacol.*, 1982, **21**, 301.
116. R. B. McCall and G. K. Aghajanian, *Eur. J. Pharmacol.*, 1980, **65**, 175.
117. J. E. Leysen and J. P. Tollenaere, *Annu. Rep. Med. Chem.*, 1982, **17**, 1.
118. D. W. Robertson and R. W. Fuller, *Annu. Rep. Med. Chem.*, 1988, **23**, 49.
119. R. A. Glennon, *J. Med. Chem.*, 1987, **30**, 1.
120. R. A. Lyon, K. H. Davis and M. Titeler, *Mol. Pharmacol.*, 1987, **21**, 301.
121. P. A. Pierce and S. J. Peroutka, *J. Neurochem.*, 1989, **52**, 656.
122. P. A. Janssen, *J. Cardiovasc. Pharmacol.*, 1985, **7**, 52.
123. M. L. Cohen, W. Colbert and L. A. Wittenauer, *Drug Dev. Res.*, 1985, **5**, 313.
124. J. M. Hingtgen, R. W. Fuller, M. R. Mason and M. H. Aprison, *Biol. Psychiatry*, 1985, **20**, 592.
125. M. F. Hibert, *Actual. Chim. Ther.*, 1989, **16**, 37.
126. J. E. Leysen, in 'Neuropharmacology of Serotonin', ed. A. R. Green, Oxford University Press, Oxford, 1985, p. 79.
127. G. Engel, E. Müller-Schweinitzer and J. M. Palacios, *Naunyn-Schmiedeberg's Arch. Pharmacol.*, 1984, **325**, 328.
128. A. Pazos, D. Hoyer and J. M. Palacios, *Eur. J. Pharmacol.*, 1985, **106**, 531.
129. B. J. Hoffman, M. D. Karpa, J. R. Lever and P. R. Hartig, *Eur. J. Pharmacol.*, 1985, **110**, 147.
130. J. R. Fozard, in 'The Peripheral Actions of 5-Hydroxytryptamine', ed. J. R. Fozard, Oxford University Press, Oxford, 1989, p. 354
131. J. R. Fozard, in 'Cardiovascular Pharmacology of 5-Hydroxytryptamine: Prospective Therapeutic Applications', ed. P. R. Saxena *et al.*, Kluwer, 1989, in press.
132. G. J. Kilpatrick, B. J. Jones and M. B. Tyers, *Eur. J. Pharmacol.*, 1989, in press.
133. S. J. Peroutka and A. Hamik, *Eur. J. Pharmacol.*, 1988, **148**, 297.

134. D. Hoyer, H. C. Neijt and A. Karpf, *J. Recept. Res.*, 1989, **9**, 65.
135. G. J. Kilpatrick, B. J. Jones and M. B. Tyers, *Nature (London)*, 1987, **330**, 746.
136. B. P. Richardson, G. Engel, P. Donatsch and P. A. Stadler, *Nature (London)*, 1985, **316**, 126.
137. S. J. Ireland and M. B. Tyers, *Br. J. Pharmacol.*, 1987, **90**, 229.
138. D. Hoyer and H. C. Neijt, *Mol. Pharmacol.*, 1988, **33**, 303.
139. J. R. Fozard and A. T. M. Mobarok Ali, *Eur. J. Pharmacol.*, 1978, **49**, 109.
140. J. R. Fozard, *Naunyn-Schmiedeberg's Arch. Pharmacol.*, 1984, **326**, 36.
141. M. W. Gittos and M. Fatmi, *Actual Chim. Ther.*, 1989, **16**, 187.
142. J. R. Fozard, in 'Serotonin: From Cell Biology to Pharmacology and Therapeutics', ed. R. Paoletti and P. Vanhoutte, Kluwer, Dordrecht, 1989, in press.
143. D. van Heuven-Nolsen, *Trends Pharmacol. Sci.*, 1989, **9**, 423.
144. J. D. Keyser, *Eur. J. Pharmacol.*, 1989, **162**, 437.

12.10

Adenosine (P₁) and ATP (P₂) Receptors

KENNETH A. JACOBSON
National Institutes of Health, Bethesda, MD, USA

12.10.1 INTRODUCTION

Derivatives of adenosine (**1**) occupy a central and crucial role in the homeostasis and reproduction of living cells and complex organisms (Figure 1). Adenosine 5′-monophosphate (AMP; **2**), or adenylic acid, is one of the four bases which compose polymeric ribonucleic acids. Adenosine 3′,5′-cyclic monophosphate (cAMP; **3**) was the earliest known example of a second messenger in the biochemical response to hormones. Adenosine 5′-triphosphate (ATP; **4**) is the immediate cytosolic

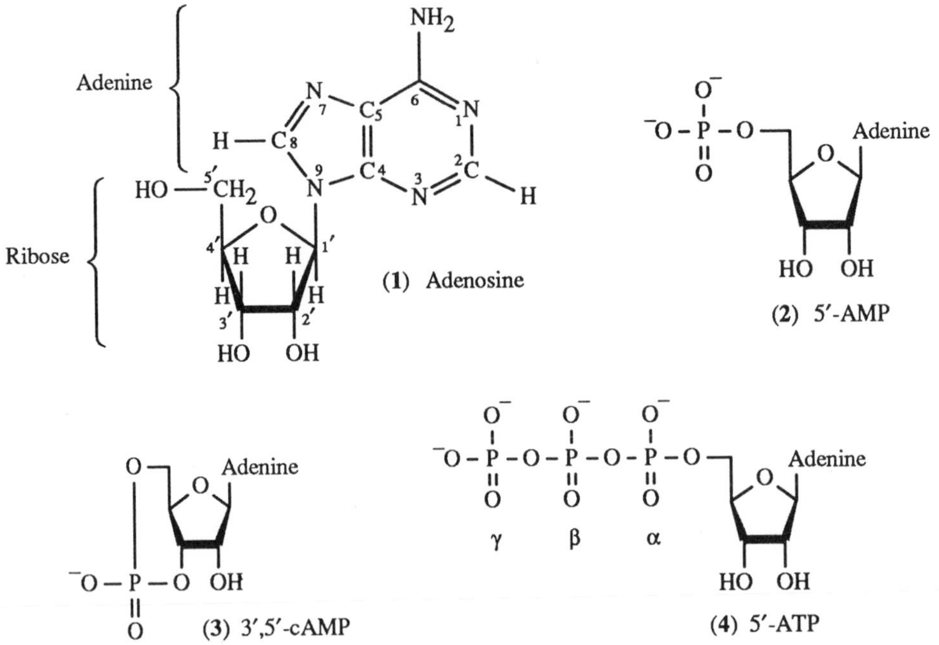

Figure 1 Structure of adenosine (**1**) and phosphate derivatives: 5'-AMP (**2**), 3',5'-cyclic AMP (**3**) and 5'-ATP (**4**)

source of energy required for muscle contraction and other biochemical work, as shown originally by Lipmann[1] and others. As the 'energy currency' of the cell ATP is ubiquitous, present in relatively high intracellular concentrations (> 1 mM), and readily metabolized. In addition to his work on the role of ATP in muscle, Szent-Györgyi[2] first recognized, with coworker Drury, that the purine nucleoside and ATP metabolite adenosine elicited intense biological effects in the cardiovascular system. Adenosine caused bradycardia and vasodilation, leading to hypotension. The depressant effects of adenosine were not explicable at that time by any known mechanism.

ATP was also found to have effects on the vascular systems, and to contract or relax various muscle preparations,[3,4] independent of its role in the storage of energy. In 1972 Burnstock[5] proposed that ATP is the principal neurotransmitter in nonadrenergic, noncholinergic neurons innervating the intestines, bladder, and rabbit portal vein.

The mechanism of action of adenosine and ATP as modulators of neural and muscular function began to be clarified with the association of these purines with discrete 'purinergic' (in that they respond to purines) cell surface receptors, also known as 'purinoceptors'. The discovery of stimulation of the second messenger cAMP system by adenosine and antagonism of adenosine by caffeine and theophylline[6] was a milestone in the purinergic field. Later work clarified the inhibitory effects of adenosine on cAMP systems, and revealed that adenosine recognition sites could be either stimulatory or inhibitory to the enzyme adenylate cyclase.[7,8]

Adenosine is thought to have a role as a feedback autoregulator in organs such as the heart.[9] Under conditions of excessive activity or of hypoxia,[10] the concentration of adenosine in the extracellular fluid rises dramatically, mainly through the breakdown of ATP. It has been estimated that the adenosine concentration in the heart in the resting state is roughly 1 μM, whereas intense activity can raise the level by at least an order of magnitude.[11] This higher local concentration of adenosine would have a depressant effect on the muscle or organ, thus moderating the state of overactivity. The differential concentration of adenosine in a particular organ is sufficiently long-lasting to account for a biological effect, prior to equilibration through circulation and metabolism.

12.10.2 PRODUCTION AND METABOLISM OF ADENOSINE AND ADENINE NUCLEOTIDES *IN VIVO*

The principal intermediates and enzyme-catalyzed transformations involved in purine metabolism are shown in Scheme 1. There are three major cycles or pathways of adenosine formation: (i) the pathway of enzymatic hydrolysis of adenine nucleotides which leads to adenosine (the reverse phosphorylations also occur); extracellular hydrolyses of ATP to ADP, ADP to AMP, and AMP to adenosine are catalyzed by endonucleotidases;[12] (ii) the methylation cycle, through which the sulfonium species *S*-adenosyl-L-methionine (SAM; **9**) acts as a ready source of methyl groups in alkylations of proteins, phospholipids, *etc*; the resulting *S*-adenosyl-L-homocysteine (SAH; **10**) may be converted enzymatically[13] by adenosylhomocysteinase into adenosine; and (iii) *de novo* biosynthesis which essentially consists of the assembly of the purine ring (Figure 2), leading to inosine 5'-monophosphate (IMP; **5**), which is then converted to adenosine 5'-monophosphate. The *de novo* biosynthesis of adenosine, which consumes six equivalents of high energy phosphate (ATP) from the starting point of α-D-ribose 5-phosphate (**6**), occurs with the purine ring precursors already mounted on a ribose molecule, at the pro-9-position nitrogen atom. The first two pathways, hydrolysis of ATP and the methylation cycle, are the largest contributors to metabolic pools of adenosine. The degree of oxygen depletion in the organ affects the relative contributions of ATP and SAM pathways. Only in the normoxic state does SAM serve as a significant source of adenosine.[14]

Removal of adenosine from the extracellular space is accomplished either by metabolic processes or by a specific uptake carrier protein[15] (see below), which internalizes adenosine through an energy independent process of facilitated diffusion. Metabolic routes for removal of adenosine include the enzymatic conversion to inosine (**7**) by adenosine deaminase,[16,17] found inside or outside the cell, and to a lesser extent by phosphorylation to AMP, by a predominantly intracellular kinase.[18] Although structurally similar to adenosine, inosine is inactive at purinergic receptors. Inosine may be converted to hypoxanthine (**8**) which is subsequently either excreted in the form of nitrogenous metabolites (uric acid, urea, *etc*.), or returned to nucleotide pools *via* the 'salvage pathway'.

A specific carrier protein[15,235] (the adenosine uptake site) is responsible for shuttling adenosine molecules across cell membranes in either direction. Drugs of a variety of classes[19] are known to be potent inhibitors of adenosine uptake and/or release (Figure 3), these include dipyridamole (**11**),[20] papaverine (**12**) and dilazep (**13**). Purines derived from 6-thioinosine, *e.g.* 6-(*p*-nitrobenzyl)-thioinosine[21] (NBTI; **14**), are also adenosine uptake inhibitors but, in spite of the structural resemblance to adenosine, are nearly inactive at adenosine A₁ and A₂ receptors (see Section 12.10.5). Adenosine uptake inhibitors are widely used clinically for their action as coronary vasodilators, which, at least in the case of dipyridamole, is thought to be elicited in large part through blockade of the uptake site. The transport of adenosine in the cytosolic direction is facilitated by the rapid conversion of intracellular adenosine to 5'-AMP.

Enzymes involved in purine metabolism (Scheme 1) are inhibited by a variety of compounds, some of which are shown in Figure 3. 9-*erythro*-(2-Hydroxy-3-nonyl)adenine (EHNA; **15**) and deoxycoformycin (**16**) inhibit adenosine deaminase.[22] 3-Deazaadenosine[23] inhibits adenosylhomocysteinase, and 5'-iodotubercidin[18] inhibits adenosine kinase.

One of the major problems in investigating the physiological role of purines has been the accurate measurement of the levels of adenosine, ATP, *etc*. due to degradation during sampling. Techniques of analysis of purines have been described.[24] In measuring plasma adenosine concentrations it is advisable to add dipyridamole, EHNA and EDTA to prevent loss by uptake and metabolism.[25]

ATP is released into the circulation (*e.g.* by endothelial cells)[12,26] as a result of hypoxia, injury, selective cellular stimulation (such as from blood cells during intravascular platelet aggregation), or in other circumstances. The concentration of ATP may be as much as four orders of magnitude greater than that of adenosine. Extracellular ATP is rapidly metabolized by stepwise enzymatic

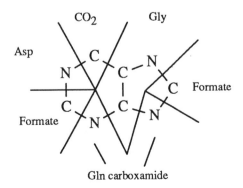

Figure 2 Purine precursors

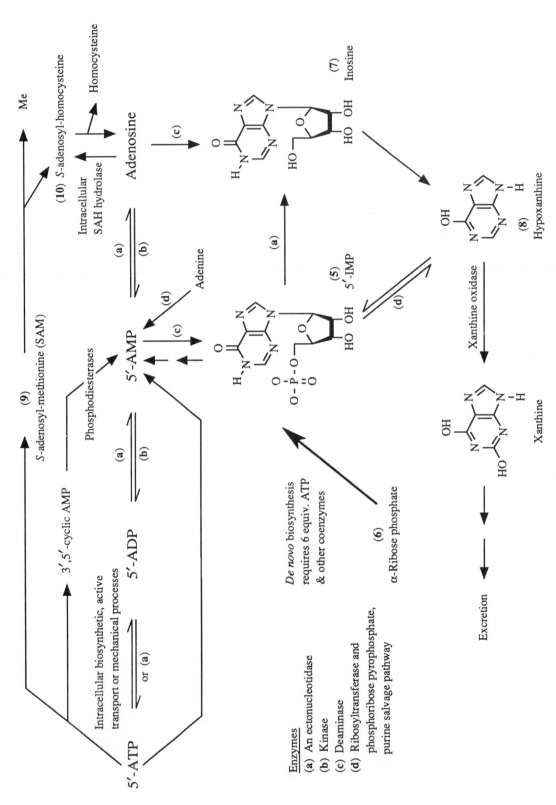

Scheme 1 Metabolic pathways for adenosine and adenine nucleotides

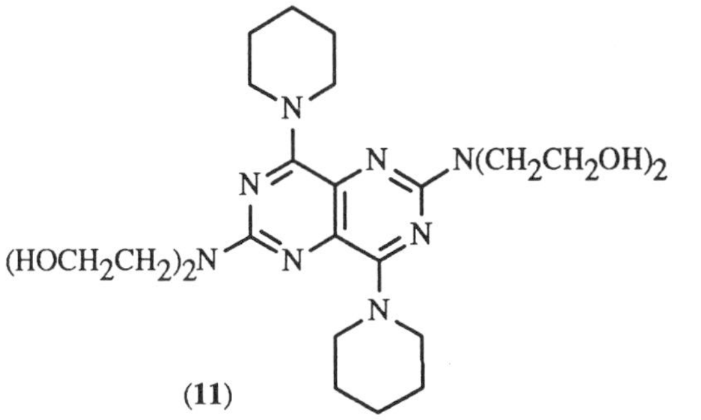

Figure 3 Inhibitors of adenosine uptake and metabolism

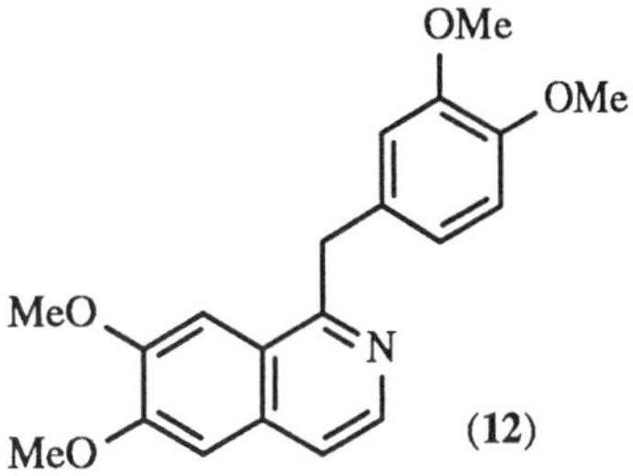

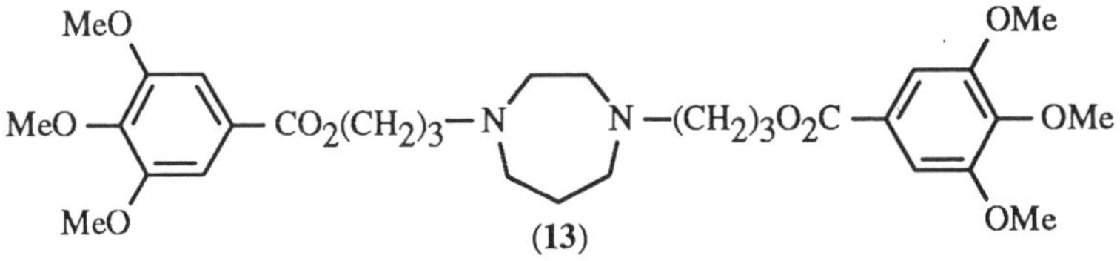

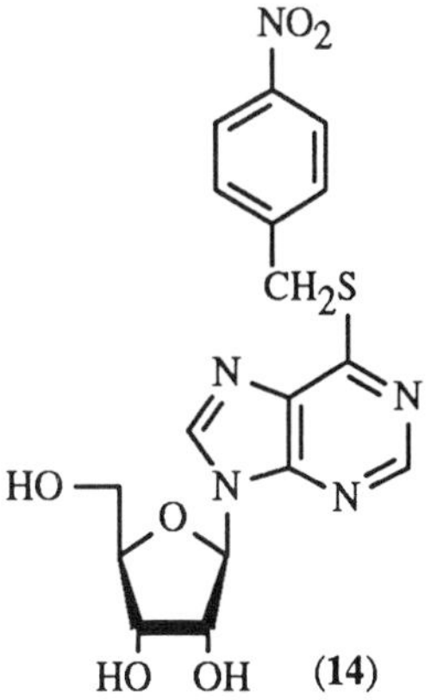

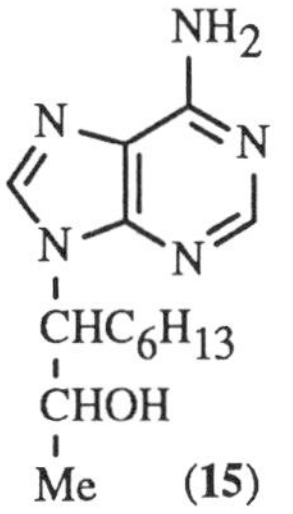

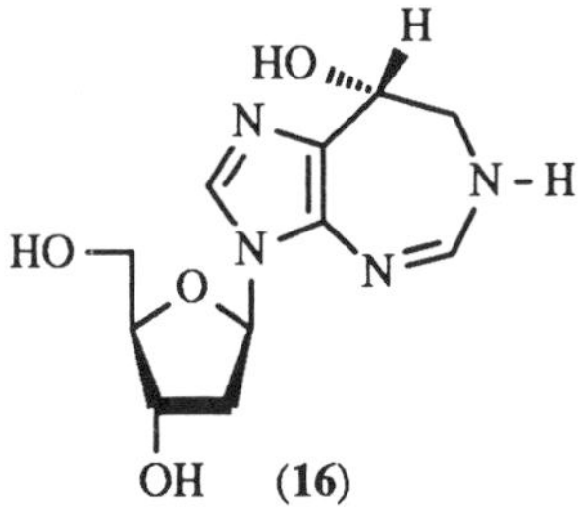

reactions[12] to ADP (by an ecto-ATPase), AMP (by an ecto-ADPase), and adenosine (by a 5'-nucleotidase). These endonucleotidases are present on the outer surface of the plasma membrane in vascular endothelial cells, smooth muscles, lymphocytes and many other cells. Given the rapid rate of ATP degradation, any physiological role proposed for ATP is limited to sites local to the source of ATP.

12.10.3 CHEMICAL STRUCTURE AND PROPERTIES OF PURINES

The chemistry and properties of purines have been described.[27-29] Purine (**17a**) is a bicyclic organic base consisting of fused imidazole (5-membered) and pyrimidine (6-membered) rings. The imidazole ring contains a weakly acidic proton, shared between two tautomeric forms (equation 1), at N-7 (**17**) or at N-9 (**18**). This proton is more acidic ($pK_a = 8.9$) than the N—H of imidazole ($pK_a = 14$) or benzimidazole ($pK_a = 12$), due to electron withdrawal by the pyrimidine ring. C-2 and C-6 of this heterocycle are electron deficient, indicative of the contribution of resonance structures (equation 2) in which a positive charge resides on C-2 or C-6 (and a negative charge resides on N-1 or N-3), as in (**19**). Thus, purine derivatives undergo nucleophilic attack at these positions (C-6 more active than C-2), especially when substituted with a good leaving group, such as a halogen. Electrophilic attack on the purine ring system does not occur readily (although it may occur in the C-8 position in xanthine derivatives).

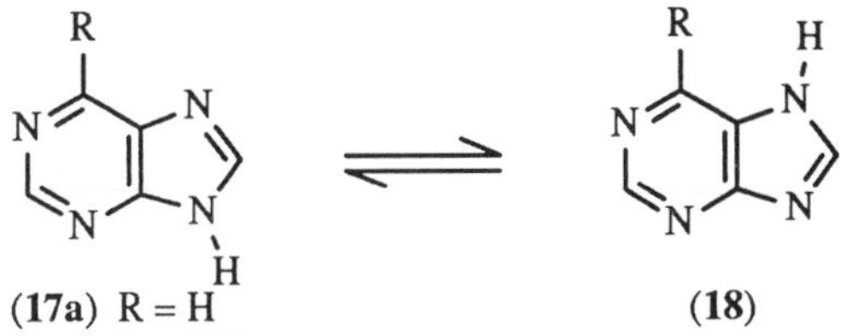

$$(1)$$

(**17a**) R = H
(**17b**) R = NH₂

(**18**)

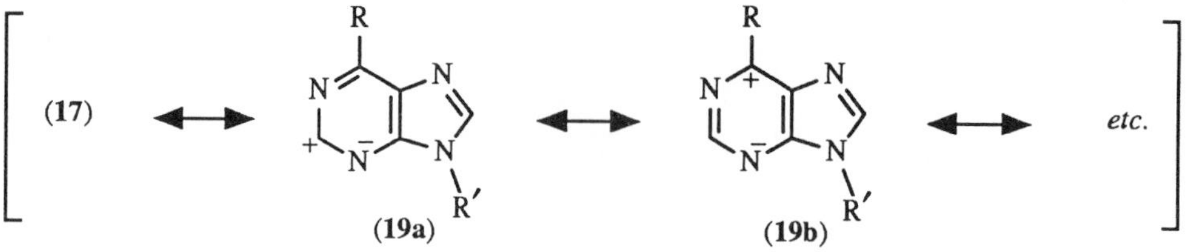

$$\left[(17) \quad \longleftrightarrow \quad (19a) \quad \longleftrightarrow \quad (19b) \quad \longleftrightarrow \quad etc. \right] \qquad (2)$$

Adenine (**17b**) is a purine, bearing an amine substituent at C-6. The nucleoside adenosine (**1**) in addition contains at N-9 an *N*-glycosidic linkage to ribose, in the furanoside form. The ribosyl residue of adenosine is linked in the β-configuration at C-1'. Due to inductive electron withdrawal by the ring nitrogens and by resonance, the N-6 amino group of adenine and adenosine is only weakly nucleophilic relative to other arylamines, such as aniline, in the uncharged state. The N-6 amino group undergoes acylation and reacts with difficulty with carbonyl compounds, forming imines.[30] The pK_a for the conjugate acid of this amine (3.45 for adenosine)[31] is well below physiological pH, thus less than 0.1% of the adenosine exists as the cationic species *in vivo*. Adenine, but not adenosine, is a weak acid, through removal of the proton of the 5-membered ring, having a pK_a of 9.83.

The nucleotide ATP (**4**) consists of a triphosphate ester of adenosine at the 5'-position of the ribosyl residue. Thus, as a multiple anion, ATP is much more polar than adenosine. The pK_a[31,32] for protonation of the N-6 amino group of ATP is 4.00, and protonation of the terminal phosphate has a pK_a of 6.48.

The *N*-glycosidic bond of adenosine is stable to base, but is cleaved in strong acid.[33] In 1M HCl at 41 °C adenosine is hydrolyzed with a $t_{\frac{1}{2}}$ of 8 h. Purine nucleosides, guanosine and, to a lesser extent, adenosine, are more labile in acid than pyrimidine nucleosides, *i.e.* cytosine and uracil, because N-3 of the purine ring facilitates the catalytic protonation of the ribosyl ether group.

The triphosphate ester moiety of ATP, a major reservoir of high energy bonds in nature, is sensitive[34] to either strongly basic or acidic conditions. The triphosphate linkage is an anhydride and thus susceptible to hydrolysis in dilute alkali, giving AMP and inorganic pyrophosphate. In acid, ATP decomposes more rapidly to adenine, ribose 5-phosphate and two equivalents of phosphate. In acid, the mechanism for hydrolysis may involve initial protonation of an interconnecting O atom, creating phosphoric acid as a good leaving group. In aqueous solution, ATP is most stable around pH 10, with the triphosphate group in the fully ionized state. The phosphorus atoms may act as electrophilic centers resulting in biochemical phosphorylations, such as transfer of phosphate to creatine in muscle, or hydrolysis when attacked by hydroxyl ions. Divalent cations, including calcium and magnesium, catalyze the hydrolysis and phosphorylation reactions of ATP.[34] The mechanism for catalysis, which occurs fastest at pH 5–6, involves the formation of complexes. Metals such as magnesium form complexes with ATP; sodium and potassium do not have this effect. Different configurations of metal chelates of ATP are defined using the lambda, delta, *exo* and *endo* nomenclature.

Xanthine (**20**) is a purine derivative oxygenated at C-2 and C-6. As deduced from the absence of OH-stretching bands in IR spectra, the molecule exists mainly as the keto tautomer (**20b**), in which protons reside on N-1 and N-3 (equation 3). *N*-Alkylxanthine derivatives act as antagonists at adenosine receptors. Xanthines are generally stable at the extremes of pH. In 1,3-dialkylxanthines, the imidazole ring N—H exists mainly as the N-7 tautomer, as indicated by the similarity to 1,3,7-trialkylxanthines in UV absorption. The nucleophilic nitrogen atoms of xanthine may be alkylated in base according to the order of decreasing acidity, *i.e.* N-3 > N-7 > N-1. The pK_a for deprotonation at N-7 of theophylline (1,3-dimethylxanthine; **21**) is 8.68.[31] Thus, theophylline analogs are soluble in aqueous base. Theophylline is often administered clinically in a salt form, aminophylline, which contains one-half equivalent of ethylene diamine. The conjugate base of theophylline exists in solution predominantly as (**22b**; equation 4). 8-Aryl substitution causes a slight increase in the acidity of the N-7 proton. Alkylxanthines are protonated to cationic species only in strong acid (pH < 1).

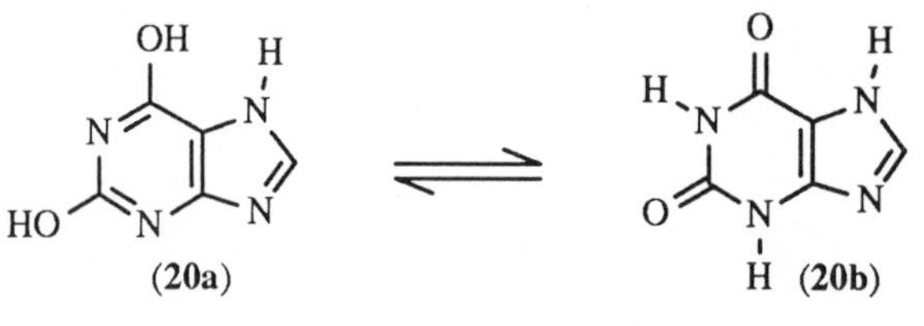

$$(20a) \quad \rightleftharpoons \quad (20b) \qquad (3)$$

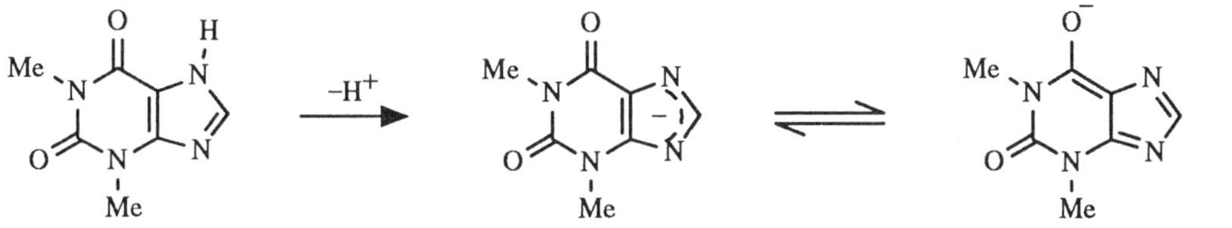

(4)

The spectral properties of purines have been described.[35] Neutral adenosine absorbs UV light at 190, 206 and 259 nm, with log ε values of 4.30, 4.33 and 4.17, respectively. Theophylline at pH 6.0 has an absorption peak at 270 nm, log ε 4.02. The fluorescence of purine is weak in neutral solution and increases upon ionization in acid or base.[27] The cation of adenine emits at 380 nm with a quantum efficiency of 0.005. Substituted xanthines are more strongly fluorescent in the visible range; for example, XAC (see Section 12.10.6.1), an 8-aryl-1,3-dialkylxanthine, absorbs at 315 nm (ε 28 180 in MeOH) and emits at 366 nm. This characteristic blue fluorescence of xanthines allows their visual detection under ultraviolet light, *e.g.* for TLC purposes. Mass spectroscopy also has been used to characterize purines.[36,37] Many adenosine nucleosides and xanthines readily give molecular ions; certain higher molecular weight analogs have required characterization using FAB or californium plasma desorption mass spectroscopy.[38]

12.10.4 CLASSIFICATION OF ADENOSINE AND ATP RECEPTORS

There are two major categories of purinergic receptors,[39] those at which adenosine acts *in vivo* as the principal agonist (P₁) and those at which ATP fills this role (P₂). Adenosine acting at P₁ receptors generally depresses the activity of a particular tissue or organ (*e.g.* heart, brain, or kidneys). The physiological role of adenosine is thought to be in adjusting the energy demand in a tissue to be commensurate with the local oxygen supply. ATP acting at P₂ receptors has both inhibitory and stimulatory effects, principally in muscles, including the smooth muscle of the vasculature. Burnstock and Kennedy[26] have suggested that ATP has the role of regulating vascular tone, particularly during pathophysiological conditions. Adenine nucleotides, particularly 5'-di- and tri-phosphates are nearly inactive at P₁ receptors, while adenosine is very weak at P₂ receptors. The criteria upon which Burnstock[39] originally classified two purinergic receptor subtypes were based on differential actions of adenosine at P₁ receptors (Ado ≫ ATP), ATP at P₂ receptors

Table 1 Classification of Purinergic Receptors

Subtype		Agonist effect	Agonist, antagonist potencies
P₁ (external adenosine receptors)	A₁ (= R_i) inhibitory	Inhibition of neurotransmitter release, cardiac depression, inhibition of lipolysis, renal vasoconstriction	CHA ≈ R-PIA > S-PIA XAC ≈ CPX (antagonists)
	A₂ (= R_a) stimulatory	Vasodilation, immunosuppression, inhibition of platelet aggregation (A₂ₐ in striatum, A₂_b in fibroblasts)	NECA > 2-Cl-Ado > R-PIA ≈ S-PIA ≥ CHA XAC ≫ CPX (antagonists)
ADP receptors		Platelet aggregation	see ref. 40
P₂ (ATP receptors)	P₂ₓ	Contraction of urinary bladder vas deferens, smooth muscle of femoral artery, central ear artery	α,β-methylene-ATP, β,τ-methylene-ATP > ATP = 2-methylthio-ATP; xanthines—no effect
	P₂ᵧ	Relaxation of taenia coli, aorta; contraction of longitudinal muscle of portal vein, regulation of vascular tone (EDRF dependent)	2-methylthio-ATP ≫ ATP > α,β-methylene-ATP, β,τ-methylene-ATP xanthines—no effect
P site (internal adenosine receptor)		Inhibition of cAMP production	2',5'-dideoxyadenosine > 2-fluoroadenosine > adenosine; xanthines—no effect

(ATP ≫ Ado) and the antagonism of P_1 receptors by methylxanthines. cAMP can act as a second messenger at P_1 receptors, while adenine nucleotides can induce the formation of prostaglandins at P_2 receptors. However, adenosine 5'-diphosphate (ADP) acts as a powerful platelet-aggregating agent, through inhibition of adenylate cyclase at a receptor that by Burnstock's classification would be considered as a P_2 subtype, but perhaps should be considered an ADP receptor.[40] Table 1 summarizes major categories and further subdivisions of receptors for adenosine and adenine nucleotides.

12.10.4.1 Subtypes of Adenosine Receptors

Adenosine receptors are linked to adenylate cyclase in many, but not all,[41-43] of the systems investigated. Initially, two subclasses of adenosine receptors were defined on the basis of either inhibition[7,8] (A_1) or stimulation (A_2) of cAMP accumulation. The A_1 and A_2 receptors (preferred terminology) are alternatively termed R_i and R_a respectively (the two subclasses of purinergic receptors proposed to require an unchanged *r*ibose moiety, that are either *i*nhibitory or *a*ctivating towards adenylate cyclase). Further studies have shown that an intact ribose moiety is not strictly required at extracellular adenosine receptors (*e.g.* NECA and 5'-deoxyadenosine, see Section 12.10.5). A_1 and A_2 adenosine receptors are now operationally defined by pharmacological potencies of selective agonists or antagonists.[44-47] In addition to the extracellular A_1 and A_2 adenosine receptors, an intracellular P site,[8,287] at which adenosine inhibits adenylate cyclase in adipocytes, has been detected. The P site was so-named since an intact purine moiety was thought to be required. Subsequently, adenosine analogs with substituted purine moieties,[48] *e.g.* 2-chloro- and 2-fluoro-adenosine, were shown to act at this site. The physiological relevance of the P site is uncertain.

Stimulatory A_2 adenosine receptors have been divided further into two categories, based on potencies of agonists in different tissues. In the striatum a high affinity A_{2a} receptor has been characterized.[44] NECA binds to this site with a K_i of 10.3 nM. In early studies of comparative structure–activity relationships (SAR) of adenosine derivatives by Bruns,[49,50] a lower affinity A_2 receptor was found in human fibroblasts, since termed the A_{2b} receptor.

An A_1 adenosine receptor glycoprotein of molecular weight 38 000 has been radiolabeled using affinity techniques (see Section 12.10.8.1).[51] Peptide mapping and glycosidase treatment have uncovered aspects of the chemical structure of this protein and its pendant carbohydrates.[52] Recently, the A_2 adenosine receptor of bovine brain was shown to be a distinct glycoprotein of molecular weight 45 000.[288] Adenosine receptors are coupled to guanine nucleotide regulatory proteins (G_i and G_s; Figure 4), which mediate the biological effects of adenosine on adenylate cyclase and other second messenger systems. Desensitization of adenosine receptor activation has been observed upon prolonged exposure to adenosine agonists.[53]

Unlike the inhibition of platelet aggregation and the inhibition of lipolysis in adipocytes, the inhibition of neurotransmitter release by adenosine in hippocampal slices and other regions of the nervous system[54-57] does not appear dependent on changes in cAMP levels.[43,58] The mechanism does involve A_1 receptors, which are coupled to a guanine nucleotide regulatory protein, as indicated by sensitivity to pertussis toxin and *N*-ethylmaleimide. Which other second messenger system constitutes the next step of the mechanism in the hippocampus is unclear. Neither protein kinases nor L-type calcium channels are involved in this A_1 effect. There is evidence that in the hippocampus an A_1 receptor mediates the opening of potassium channels.[58] In other systems stimulation of potassium channels,[59] inhibition of phosphatidyl inositol turnover,[60] inhibition of

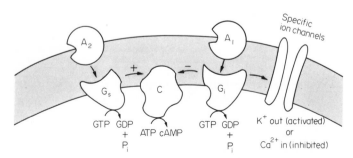

Figure 4 Multiple effector systems for adenosine receptors

calcium influx into neurons,[61] a decrease in free intracellular calcium,[62] and stimulation of guanylate cyclase[170] have been implicated as mechanisms for the action of adenosine. Models for how A$_1$ adenosine receptors may couple to multiple effector systems have been proposed.[43] Ribeiro and Sebastião[63] have studied a class of adenosine receptors in peripheral nerves, which they termed 'A$_3$', associated with the closure of calcium channels but not changes in cAMP, and in one respect anomalous in the order of potency of agonists expected for A$_1$ receptors. Thus, NECA is much more potent than expected for A$_1$ receptors, as measured through binding or the inhibition of adenylate cyclase. Whether the receptor or effector system is responsible for the difference is uncertain.

12.10.4.2 Subtypes of Receptors for Adenine Nucleotides

A receptor for adenosine 5'-diphosphate (ADP), apparently distinct from adenosine and ATP receptors, has been described in the platelet.[40] ADP stimulates platelet aggregation, an action which is not shared by other naturally occurring nucleoside diphosphates. Certain synthetic analogs, such as 2-chloroadenosine 5'-diphosphate and 2-methylthioadenosine 5'-diphosphate,[64] have been found to be more potent than ADP at this receptor. Other analogs of ADP appear to antagonize actions of ADP, but the mechanism is unclear.[40] The action of ADP is associated with inhibition of cAMP production in platelets and rat hepatocytes[65,71] and increased phosphatidyl inositol turnover.[66,71]

Defining subtypes among ATP (P$_2$) receptors has been impeded until recently by a lack of selective agents. ATP was shown to produce contraction in certain tissues (*e.g.* urinary bladder and vas deferens) and relaxation in others (*e.g.* guinea pig taenia coli and the longitudinal muscle of the rabbit portal vein). In the vasculature, two separate actions of ATP in regulating vascular tone have been delineated[26] as shown in Figure 5. Intraluminal ATP acting on P$_2$ receptors on the endothelium produces vasodilation indirectly through the release of endothelium-derived releasing factor (EDRF, now identified as NO[276]). EDRF serves as an inhibitory signal on the vascular smooth muscle to produce vasodilation. An excitatory response of ATP on muscle contraction occurs following its release from sympathetic perivascular nerves. This release of ATP accompanies the release of noradrenaline (norepinephrine), another excitatory transmitter, from the same prejunctional nerve terminal. Due to the simultaneous release and possible synergistic postjunctional effects

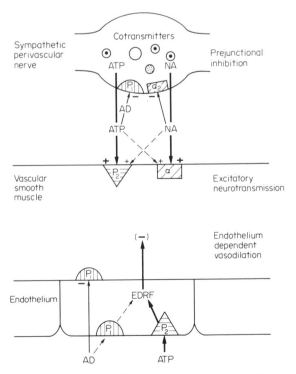

Figure 5 Schematic representation of pathways by which purines may regulate vascular tone. Broken lines between ATP and α, and between NA and P$_2$ indicate the possibility of postjunctional synergistic interactions between noradrenaline and ATP. Broken lines between AD, P$_1$ and EDRF indicate that this pathway is less common (reproduced from ref. 26 by permission of the American Heart Association, Inc.)

of the two substances, ATP and noradrenaline are designated 'cotransmitters'. This excitatory effect of ATP occurs through stimulation of P_2 receptors located directly on the vascular smooth muscle.

Recently these divergent responses have been shown to correspond to distinct receptor sub-types,[67] based on selective ATP agonists (see below). The P_{2x} site is associated with contraction of smooth muscle, and the P_{2y} is associated with the relaxation response. The ATP receptor of platelets is termed the P_{2z} receptor. Biochemical intermediates modulated by ATP include prostaglandins[68] (although not related to the endothelium dependent relaxation induced by ATP) and EDRF.[69,70] Inhibition of formation of the intracellular messenger cAMP and stimulation of phosphoinositide breakdown have recently been implicated in the mechanism of action of ATP in hepatocytes, perhaps through an ADP receptor.[71]

12.10.4.3 Biochemical and Biological Assay Systems

12.10.4.3.1 *Binding assays*

The development of synthetic analogs as radioligands (Table 2) for assays of competitive binding to adenosine receptors has aided tremendously in the evaluation of new analogs. Tritiated

Table 2 Radioligands for Adenosine Receptors (Affinity Measured at A_1 Receptors in Rat brain Membranes, unless noted)

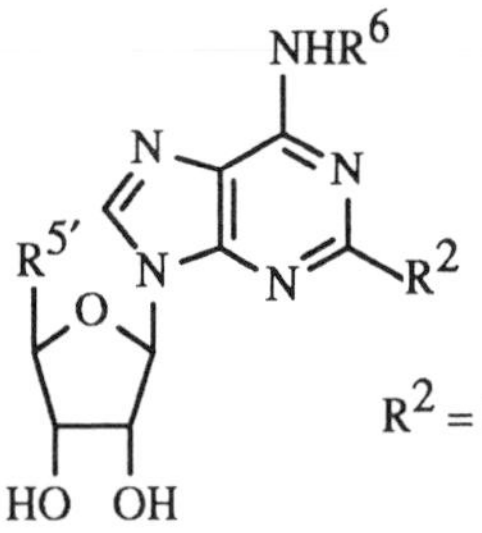

$R^2 = R^6 = H$ and $R^{5'} = CH_2OH$, unless noted

Compound	Structure	K_D (nM)	A_1 selectivity	Ref.
Tritiated				
(23) 2-CADO	$R^2 = Cl$	5	7	72
(24) R-PIA	$R^6 = CHMeCH_2Ph$	1.0	110	73
(25) CPA	$R^6 =$ 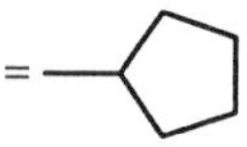 (cyclopentyl)	0.48	500	75
(26) CHA	$R^6 =$ 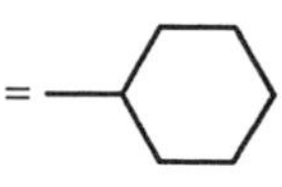 (cyclohexyl)	1.0	300	74
(27) ADAC	$R^6 = (-\text{phenyl}-CH_2CONH)_2CH_2CH_2NH_2$ 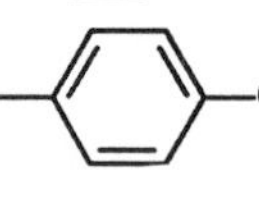	1.4	200	76
(28) NECA	$R^{5'} = CONHEt$	10[a]	1.6	44
(29) CPCA	$R^{5'} = CONHPr^i$	13[a]	2.1	106, 44
Iodinated (^{125}I)				
(30) I-HPIA	$R^6 = CHMeCH_2-\text{phenyl}(I)-OH$ 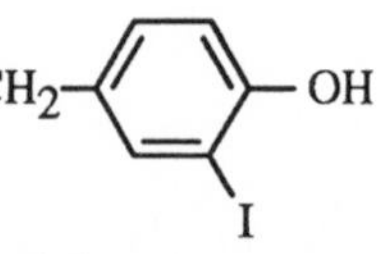	0.94	—	77, 78, 107
(31) I-ABA	$R^6 = CH_2-\text{phenyl}(I)-NH_2$ 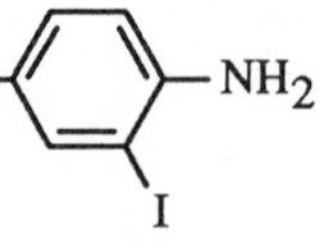	0.7	—	80, 92, 108
(32) I-APNEA	$R^6 = CH_2CH_2-\text{phenyl}(I)-NH_2$ 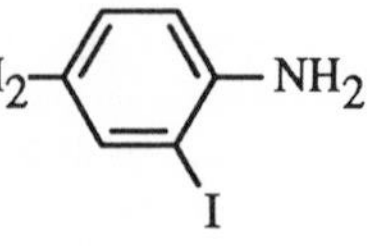	2.0	—	51, 81

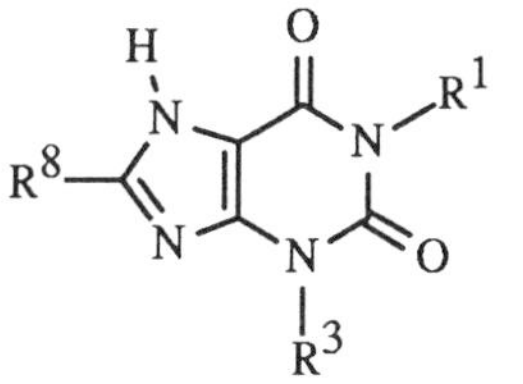

$R^1 = R^3 = Pr^n$, unless noted

Antagonists (xanthine derivatives)

(33) DPX	$R^1 = R^3 = Et, R^6 = Ph$	68	7.9	74
(34) XCC	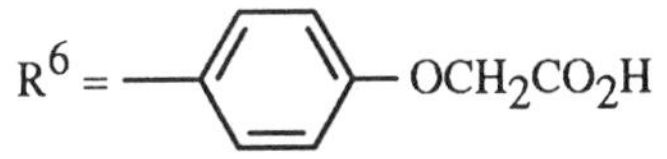 $R^6 = \text{—}\langle\text{phenyl}\rangle\text{—OCH}_2\text{CO}_2\text{H}$	3.5	630	90
(35) XAC	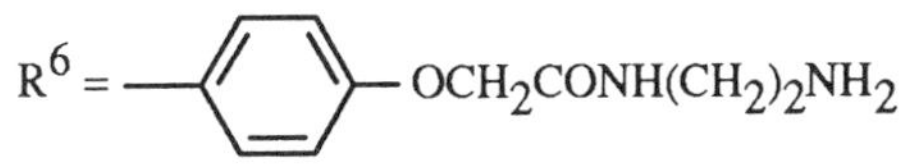 $R^6 = \text{—}\langle\text{phenyl}\rangle\text{—OCH}_2\text{CONH(CH}_2)_2\text{NH}_2$	1.2	60	83–85
(36) PD115, 119	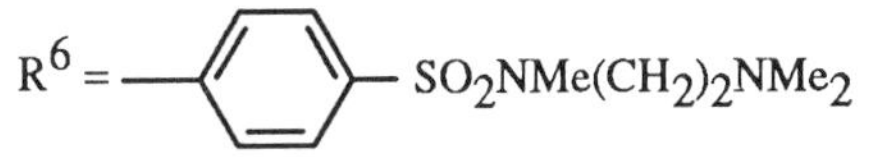 $R^6 = \text{—}\langle\text{phenyl}\rangle\text{—SO}_2\text{NMe(CH}_2)_2\text{NMe}_2$	2.6[a]	1.1	102
(37) CPX	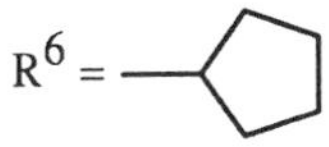 $R^6 = \text{—}\langle\text{cyclopentyl}\rangle$	0.42	740	87–89

125-iodinated (^{125}I)

(38) I-PAPA-XAC	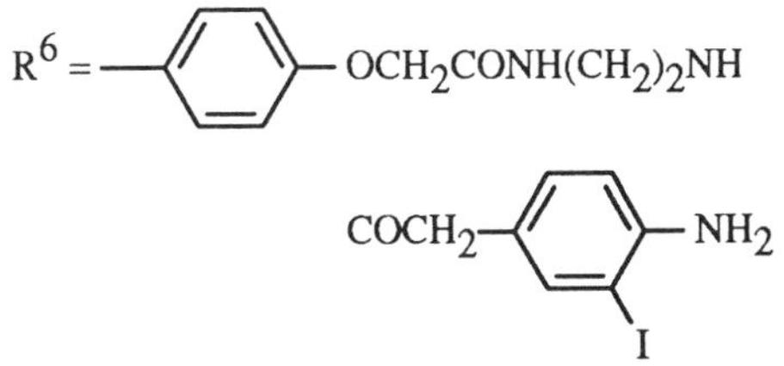 $R^6 = \text{—}\langle\text{phenyl}\rangle\text{—OCH}_2\text{CONH(CH}_2)_2\text{NH}$ — $\text{COCH}_2\text{—}\langle\text{aryl-I}\rangle\text{—NH}_2$	0.10[b]	—	91
(39) BW A827	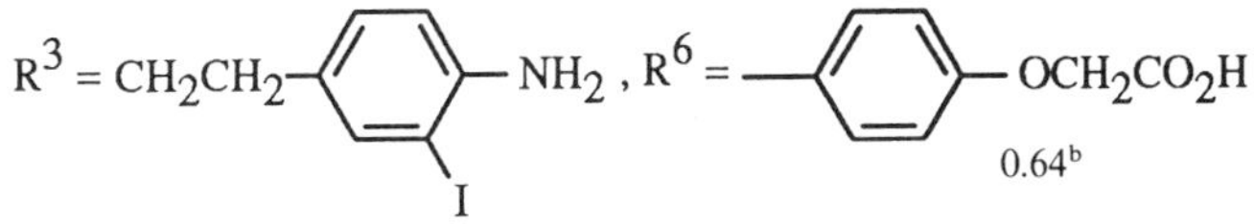 $R^3 = CH_2CH_2\text{—}\langle\text{aryl-I}\rangle\text{—NH}_2, R^6 = \text{—}\langle\text{phenyl}\rangle\text{—OCH}_2\text{CO}_2\text{H}$	0.64[b]	—	92
(40) BW A844U	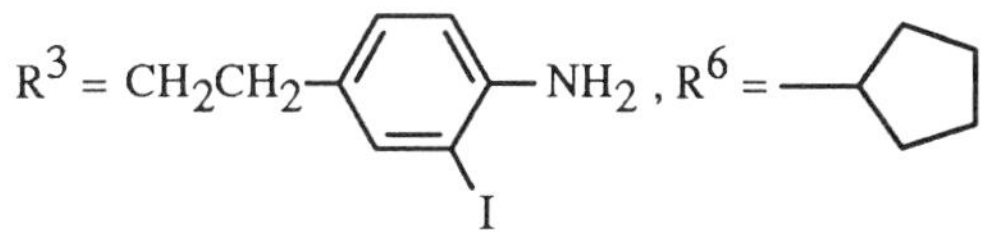 $R^3 = CH_2CH_2\text{—}\langle\text{aryl-I}\rangle\text{—NH}_2, R^6 = \text{—}\langle\text{cyclopentyl}\rangle$	0.14[b]	—	93

---

[a] A_2 adenosine receptors in rat striatum. [b] A_1 adenosine receptors in bovine brain (the intrinsic affinity of many substituted purines is one order of magnitude greater than in rat brain).

adenosine has been tried as a radioligand with unsatisfactory results, due to rapid metabolism (see Section 12.10.2).

[³H]-2-Chloroadenosine (23) was introduced by Williams and Risley[72] and by Wu *et al.*[171] as a radioligand for A_1 adenosine receptors, but it was found to lack chemical stability. Presently, affinity at A_1 receptors is most readily assayed in competitive binding assays on brain membranes (since this organ has relatively high receptor densities, with B_{max} reported as roughly 0.6 pmol mg^{-1} protein) using [³H]-(R)-N^6-phenylisopropyladenosine[73] (R-PIA; 24) or [³H]N^6-cyclohexyladenosine[74] (CHA; 26). These two radioligands gave very similar results in competition studies for K_i values for agonist or antagonist analogs. The high affinity of these N^6-substituted ligands (nanomolar K_d compared to an estimated K_d of 20 nM for adenosine) permits the use of rapid filtration methodology. [³H]-N^6-Cyclopentyladenosine[75] (CPA; 25) was found to be of higher affinity than CHA for A_1 receptors, and to have superior properties for carrying out autoradiography of adenosine receptors. An adenosine amine congener, [³H]N^6-(4-(4-(2-aminoethyl)-aminocarbonylmethyl)phenylaminocarbonylmethyl)phenyladenosine[76] (ADAC; 27), synthesized as a functionalized congener (see Section 12.10.5.1.2), has an affinity comparable to PIA and an acceptably low level of nonspecific binding.

Several groups have introduced iodinated agonist radioligands. (R)-N^6-(3-iodo-4-hydroxy-phenyl)isopropyladenosine (I-HPIA; **30**) binds specifically to A_1 adenosine receptors in rat brain.[77,78,107] The precursor of this ligand is identical in structure to R-PIA, except for the presence of a *p*-hydroxy group on the phenyl ring, present to facilitate iodination. Due to its high specific activity, [^{125}I]HPIA has been useful for binding studies in peripheral tissues having a low density of adenosine receptors, for example in the kidney glomeruli and microvessels,[79] in which a B_{max} of 7 fmol mg^{-1} protein has been reported. Several arylamine derivatives of adenosine, *i.e.* N^6-aminobenzyladenosine[80] (ABA) and N^6-aminophenylethyladenosine[81] (APNEA), have been introduced as ligands for radioiodination, producing compounds (**31**) and (**32**), and as intermediates for irreversible binding to the receptor protein (see Section 12.10.8.1).

The first antagonist radioligand for A_1 adenosine receptors was [^{3}H]-1,3-diethyl-8-phenyl-xanthine (DPX; **33**).[74,82] The use of [^{3}H]DPX is limited, due to a relatively low affinity for the receptor in brain membranes from several species, except for calf. In addition, the binding of [^{3}H]DPX in guinea pig brain appeared to contain two components.[74]

High affinity antagonist radioligands have been developed more recently. [^{3}H]-8-(4-Aminoethyl-aminocarbonylmethoxy)phenyl-1,3-dipropylxanthine (XAC; **35**) was found to display specific, saturable binding to central A_1 receptors in homogenates and tissue slices of at least six species.[83,85,86] In bovine, rat, and guinea pig brain membranes, the K_D values were found to be 0.17, 1.2, and 3.0 nM, respectively. The density of adenosine receptor sites was in close agreement with values obtained using agonist radioligands. [^{3}H]-8-Cyclopentyl-1,3-dipropylxanthine (**37**), also known as CPX, DPCPX or PD 116,948, is of comparable high affinity (K_D in rat brain of 0.5 nM), is highly A_1 selective, and has been used to detect peripheral A_1 sites and in autoradiography.[87–89] [^{3}H]-8-(4-Carboxymethoxy)phenyl-1,3-dipropylxanthine (XCC; **34**) also has been used to identify A_1 adenosine binding sites by autoradiography.[90] An additional advantage of [^{3}H]XCC, [^{3}H]XAC and [^{3}H]CPX over previous radioligands is a relatively high specific activity (100–160 Ci mmol^{-1}).

The structures of several iodinated xanthines synthesized as high affinity radioligands[91–93] are shown in Table 2. [^{125}I]PAPA-XAC (**38**) utilized a prosthetic group methodology for introduction of the radioisotope. The prosthetic group consisted of a *p*-aminophenyl moiety, which was coupled to compound (**34**).

At A_2 receptors, binding methodology has recently undergone refinement. The agonist radioligand [^{3}H]-5'-N-ethylcarboxamidoadenosine (NECA; **28**) has been used to characterize A_2 receptors in membranes derived from the striatum of rat brain.[44,94] In this region, A_1 and A_2 receptors are present in approximately equal densities. In order to eliminate the A_1 component of [^{3}H]NECA binding (K_i at A_1 sites = 6 nM), an A_1 selective agonist, N^6-cyclopentyladenosine, is added[44] at a concentration of 50 nM (a concentration approximately 100-times the K_i). Alternatively,[94] N-ethylmaleimide, which irreversibly blocks action of the G_i regulatory protein, may be added to the NECA binding assay. This results in uncoupling of the G_i protein from the A_1 receptor. In various peripheral tissues (lung,[172] placenta,[173] microvessels[96] and platelets[97–99]) a large fraction of [^{3}H]NECA binding is to sites other than adenosine receptors. The result is an unrealistically high density of 'specific' binding sites, a lack of inhibition by N^6-substituted adenosines, and a relatively low potency of 8-phenyl-substituted and certain other xanthines in competition studies. Two distinct fractions of NECA binding sites have been separated by gel filtration of solubilized components of platelet membranes.[99] Only the minor fraction, responsible for 10–25% of the combined specific [^{3}H]NECA binding, resembled adenosine receptors pharmacologically. Williams *et al.*[100] have used [^{3}H]NECA as a radioligand in membranes from PC12 (rat pheochromocytoma) cells, a cell that contains only A_2 receptors.

The first A_2 selective radioligand was [^{3}H]CGS 21680 (**48a**; see Section 12.10.5.1.2).[290] Use of this ligand (K_D = 15 nM) eliminates the need to block the A_1 component, as with [^{3}H]NECA. An arylamine congener, PAPA-APEC (**48c**), has been radioiodinated and shown to bind specifically to A_2 receptors with a K_D value of 1.6 nM in bovine brain.[288]

Binding assays for A_2 receptors using antagonist radioligands also are under development. [^{3}H]XAC binds to A_2 receptors in human platelet membranes with a K_D of 12 nM and a B_{max} of 1.1 pmol mg^{-1} protein.[101] In this assay the inhibition constants for various agonists and antagonists corresponded closely to functional potencies. [^{3}H]XAC binding to A_2 receptors has the disadvantage of a high degree of binding to glass fiber filters, which is partly overcome by presoaking the filters in a solution of polyethyleneimine. Bruns *et al.*[102] have introduced [^{3}H]PD 115,199, another 8-phenyl-substituted xanthine containing an amino functionality, as a radioligand for A_{2a} receptors in the striatum. The K_i of PD 115,199 for [^{3}H]NECA binding in the striatum was found to be

15 nM, and the K_D of the tritiated compound to sites not blocked by 1,3-dipropyl-8-cyclopentyl-xanthine was 2.6 nM.

12.10.4.3.2 *Biological assay systems*

There are well-characterized biochemical assay systems useful for screening drug analogs for activity at adenosine receptors. Studies of inhibition or stimulation of adenylate cyclase have been carried out in many tissues and cell lines (see Section 12.10.8); the initial definition of stimulatory and inhibitory effects was in fetal brain cells[7] and in liver cells.[8] Early comprehensive studies utilized intact fibroblast cells and measured the elevations of cAMP elicited by adenosine agonists in the presence of a phosphodiesterase inhibitor.[49,50] Membranes from adipocytes (A_1) and PC12 pheochromocytoma cells or platelets (A_2) are good model systems for comparison of biological activity of analogs at adenosine receptor subtypes. The potency of adenosine analogs in PC12 cells correlates closely with an *in vivo* assay of vasodilation.[103] Binding at A_1 and A_2 receptors has been correlated with potencies in an isolated heart preparation.[104] In the brain, Fredholm *et al.*[105] have measured both stimulatory and inhibitory effects (the latter in the presence of forskolin) of N^6-substituted adenosines on cAMP accumulation in hippocampal slices.

12.10.5 STRUCTURE–ACTIVITY RELATIONSHIPS FOR PURINERGIC AGONISTS

Nearly all adenosine agonists yet reported are closely related in structure to adenosine. Similarly, at P_2 receptors, the known agonists are derivatives of ATP.

12.10.5.1 A_1 and A_2 Adenosine Agonists

12.10.5.1.1 *Ribose modifications*

Few alterations of the ribose moiety (Figure 6) are tolerated at the adenosine receptor binding site.[109] Except for a limited number of modifications of the 5′ position, the intact ribose moiety generally is required for adenosine agonist activity. Certain adenine derivatives, which lack the ribose altogether, such as 9-methyladenine[106] and 9-phenyl-7-deazaadenine[174] derivatives (see Section 12.10.6.2) are adenosine antagonists. Inversion of the glycosidic bond results in the loss of receptor affinity. Most modifications at the 2′ and 3′ positions of the ribose ring or inversions of chiral centers on the ribose diminish adenosine receptor binding.[49] For example, 2′-deoxy-2′-fluoro-adenosine (**41**) and adenine-9-β-D-arabinofuranoside (**42**), are inactive as agonists or antagonists at A_2 receptors. 5′-Deoxy-5′-methylthioadenosine (**43**), an endogenous nucleoside formed during synthesis of spermine and spermidine,[111] was originally discovered to be an antagonist at cyclase-linked A_2 receptors.[49] Recently, it was found to be an *agonist* at A_1 receptors (Daly *et al.*, unpublished results) and at putative A_2 receptors that relax smooth muscle.[112] 2′,5′-Dideoxyadenosine (**44**), while inactive at adenosine receptors, is the most potent activator known of another mechanism of action of adenosine, namely suppression of cAMP accumulation through the intracellular P site,[113] at a site at which many, but not all, modifications of the ribose are tolerated.[287] A number of adenosine 5′-modified analogs, including esters such as compound (**45b**), were identified as low efficacy partial A_2 agonists.

5′-ATP, 5′-ADP and 5′-AMP are very weak antagonists at A_1 and A_2 adenosine receptors. It appears that adenosine agonist activity, ascribed previously to 5′-AMP in physiological systems, results mainly from enzymatic conversion to adenosine. However, even the low affinity of these adenine nucleotides for P_1 receptors may have implications when ATP is present in high concentration in adenylate cyclase assays.[114]

The 5′-carboxylate derivative of adenosine (**45a**) and several esters were reported to be active *in vivo* at cardiovascular A_2 receptors,[115] but were later shown to be inactive at fibroblast A_2 receptors coupled to adenylate cyclase.[49] The 5′-hydroxymethyl group of adenosine may be substituted also by an *N*-methylcarboxamide (**45c**) or *N*-ethylcarboxamide (**45d**),[116] which resulted in enhanced A_2 activity as a vasodilator[115] or as an inhibitor of platelet aggregation.[117,118] 5′-*N*-Ethyl-carboxamidoadenosine (NECA; **45d**) and the closely related cyclopropyl analog, CPCA (**45e**), are among the most potent known adenosine derivatives at A_2 receptors (EC_{50} in coronary vasodilation = 7.3 nM). However, NECA is not A_2 selective, since it is very potent at A_1 receptors

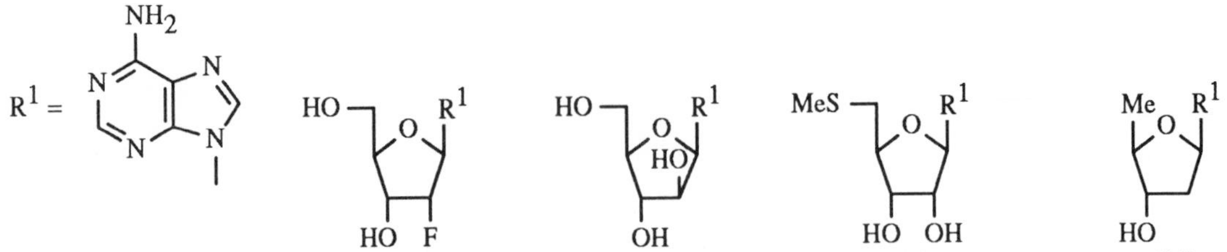

$R^1 = $ [adenine structure with NH_2]

(41) (42) (43) (44)

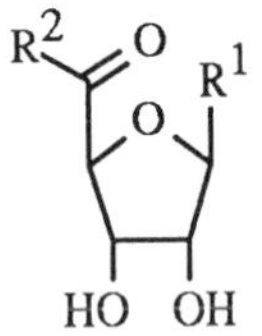

(45a) $R^2 = OH$
(45b) $R^2 = CO_2^-$
(45c) $R^2 = NHMe$; MECA
(45d) $R^2 = NHEt$; NECA
(45e) $R^2 = NH$ —◁ ; CPCA

Figure 6 Selected ribose-modified adenosine analogs, evaluated as agonists

($K_i = 6.3$ nM in rat brain).[44] Thus, potencies at A_2 and A_1 adenosine receptors are nearly equivalent and, except in model systems, NECA will activate both receptors.

The binding region for the *N*-ethyl group of NECA is highly restricted sterically. At the coronary A_2 adenosine receptor simple alkyl groups larger than propyl[116] greatly diminish biological activity. 5'-*N*-Methylcarboxamidoadenosine (MECA; **45c**) is similarly nonselective, although it is at least 5-times less potent in PC12 cells[105] and in binding to A_2 sites in striatum.[95] The 5'-*N*-cyclopropyl group of the very potent agonist (**45e**) is roughly equivalent in size to an ethyl group, and is well tolerated in this pocket of the A_2 receptor. 5'-*N*,*N*-Dialkyluronamide groups are not tolerated in this binding region. Curiously, several diadenosine uronamide derivatives, linked through *n*-alkyl chains 10 or more carbons in length, were active in coronary vasodilation.[115] A computer-based quantitative model for SAR of adenosine 5'-carboxamides has been shown to be predictive of biological potency.[119]

12.10.5.1.2 *Adenine substitutions*

The adenine moiety is more amenable to substitutions (Table 3) than is the ribose moiety. A number of useful modifications may be made at C-2 and at the N^6-amino group. 2-Chloroadenosine (**46**) binds to A_1 receptors with a K_i of 5.8 nM. At the coronary A_2 receptor it is also highly potent (60-times greater than adenosine). 2-Alkyne derivatives of adenosine are more hypotensive (A_2) than cardiac depressant (A_1).[175] 2-Phenylaminoadenosine (CV-1808; **47**) and its analog 2-(4-methoxyphenyl)adenosine (CV-1674), first reported by Marumoto *et al.*,[120,121] were the first truly A_2 selective agonists.[44,103] CV-1808 is about five fold A_2 selective in comparative binding studies. Thus, it appears that large alkylamino or arylamino substituents at the 2-position are tolerated better by A_2 receptors than by A_1 receptors.

CGS 21680, a 2-substituted adenosine derivative which also contains the 5'-*N*-ethylcarboxamido group of NECA, is 140-fold A_2 selective as an adenosine agonist.[289] It has been introduced as a radioligand, with a K_D at central A_2 receptors of 15 nM.[290] This series is amenable to a functionalized congener approach (see below), which has led to the amine derivative, APEC (**48b**) and an aryl amine for radioiodination, PAPA-APEC (**48c**).[288] [^{125}I]PAPA-APEC has a K_D at bovine brain A_2 receptors of 1.5 nM and has been photoaffinity crosslinked to the receptor.

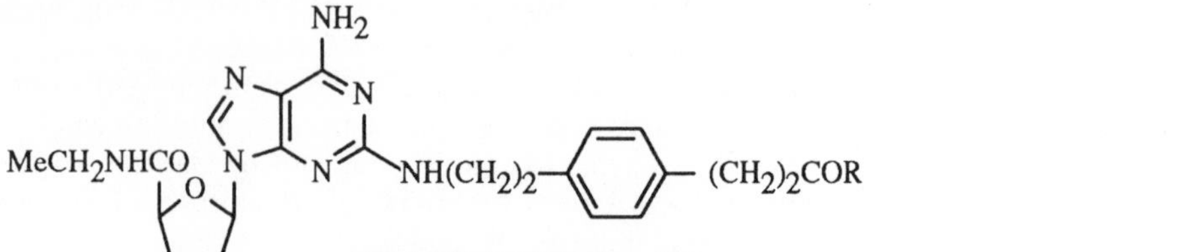

$MeCH_2NHCO$ ... $NH(CH_2)_2$—⬡—$(CH_2)_2COR$

HO OH

(48a) CGS 21680; R = -OH
(48b) APEC; R = -NH(CH_2)_2NH_2
(48c) PAPA-APEC; R = -NH(CH_2)_2NHCOCH_2—⬡—NH_2

Table 3 C-2- and N^6-substituted Adenosine Analogs as Agonists at A_1 and A_2 Adenosine Receptors[44,103,133,134,136]

	Compound	K_i at A_1 (nM)[a]	K_i at A_2 (nM)[a]
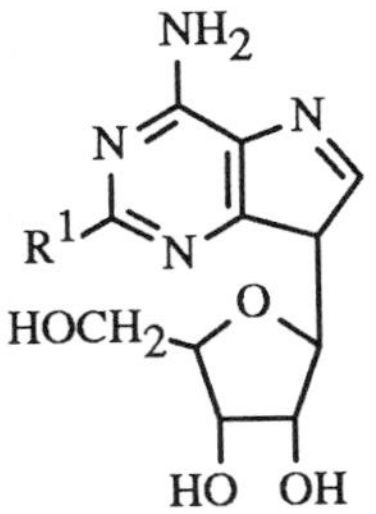 $R^1 =$ —Cl	(46)	9.3	63
$R^1 =$ —NH(phenyl) 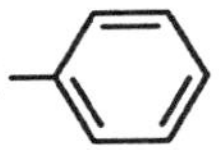	(47)	560	119
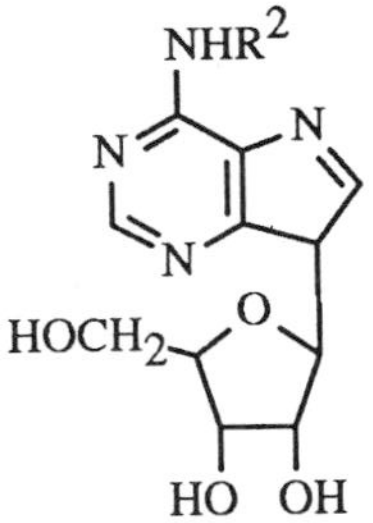 $R^2 =$ 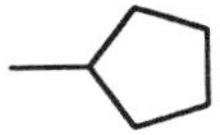 (cyclopentyl)	(49)	0.59	462
$R^2 =$  (cyclohexenyl)	(50)	1.3	514
$R^2 =$  (cyclohexyl)	(51)	1.7	—
$R^2 =$  (hydroxybutyl, OH)	(52)	7.0	4920
$R^2 =$ 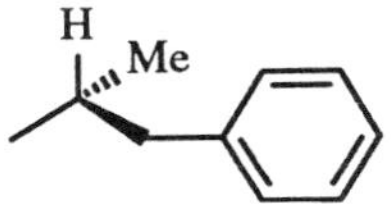 (H, Me, benzyl)	(53)	1.2	124
$R^2 =$ 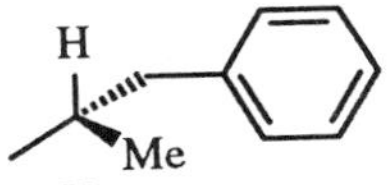 (H, Me, benzyl)	(54)	49	1820
$R^2 =$ 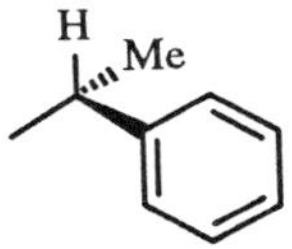 (H, Me, phenyl)	(55)	3.4	—

Table 3 (*Contd.*)

Compound	K_i at A_2 (nm)[a]	K_i at A_2 (nm)[a]
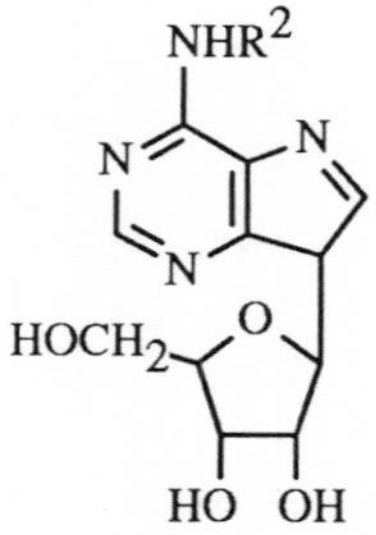 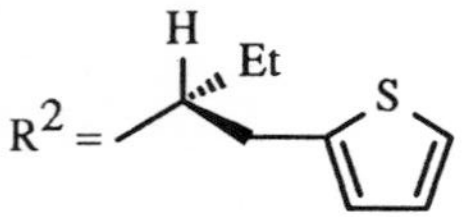 (56)	0.15	—
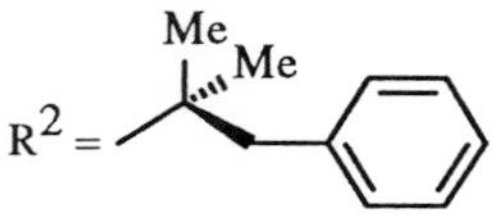 (57)	29	—
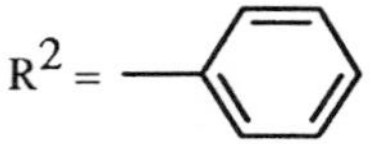 (58)	4.6	663
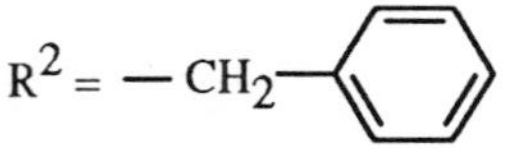 (59)	120	285
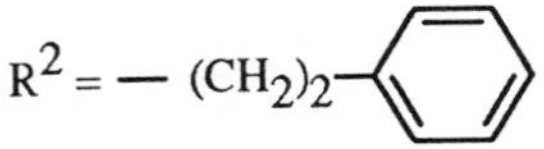 (60)	4.1	—
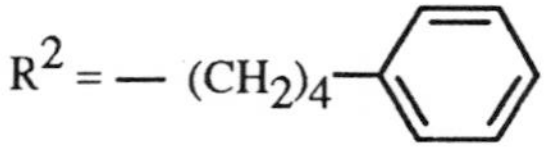 (61)	7.5	—
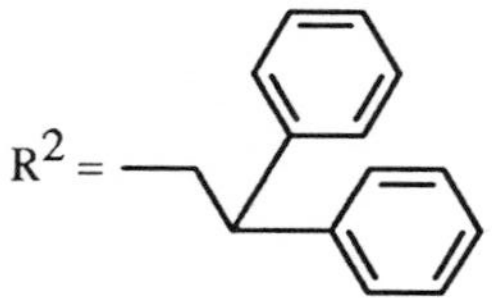 (62)	6.8	25
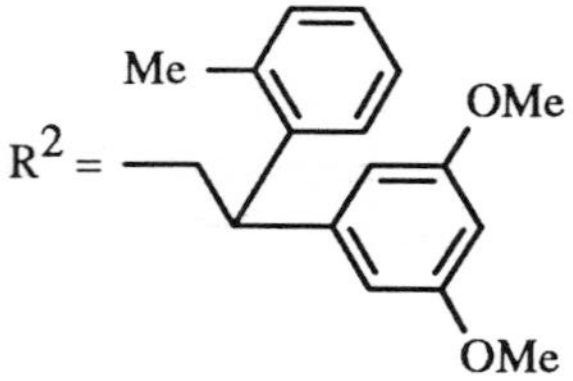 (63)	118	3.1

R^2 = (56) thiophene-substituted H, Et group

R^2 = (57) Me, Me phenyl group

R^2 = (58) CH-diphenyl group

R^2 = —CH$_2$— phenyl (59)

R^2 = —(CH$_2$)$_2$— phenyl (60)

R^2 = —(CH$_2$)$_4$— phenyl (61)

R^2 = (62) diphenylpropyl

R^2 = (63) Me, OMe, OMe substituted

Compound	R²		
(64)	(fluoren-9-yl)ethyl	5.2	4.9
(65)	CH_2CO_2H (phenyl)	210	—
(66)	$CH_2CONHMe$ (phenyl)	16	—
(67)	CH_2CONH-C$_6$H$_4$-CH_2CO_2Me	2.5	—
(68)	CH_2CONH-C$_6$H$_4$-$CH_2CONHMe$	6.7	—
(69)	CH_2CONH-C$_6$H$_4$-$CH_2CONH(CH_2)_2NH_2$	0.85	210
(70)	CH_2CONH-C$_6$H$_4$-$CH_2CONH(CH_2)_2NHCO$-CH=CH-$(CH_2)_7$/$Me(CH_2)_7$	0.69	—
(71)	$-(CH_2)_nNH_2$	0.32[b]	—
(72)	$-(CH_2)_n$-adenosin-N^6-yl	0.72[b]	—

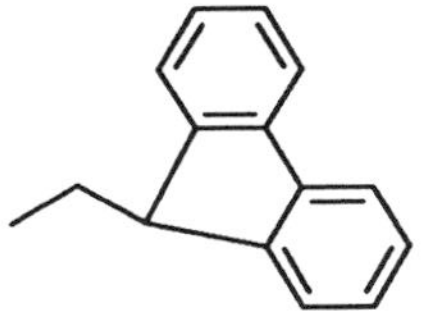

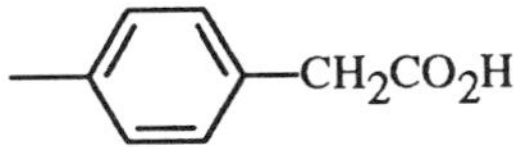

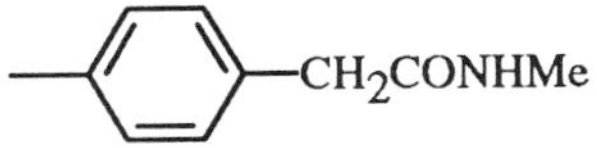

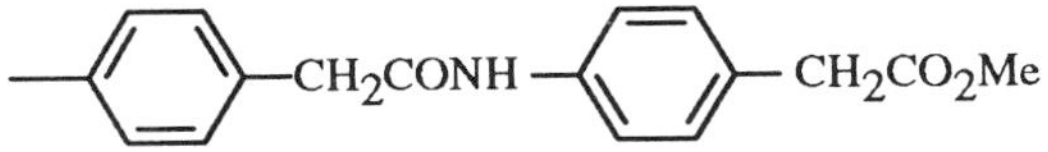

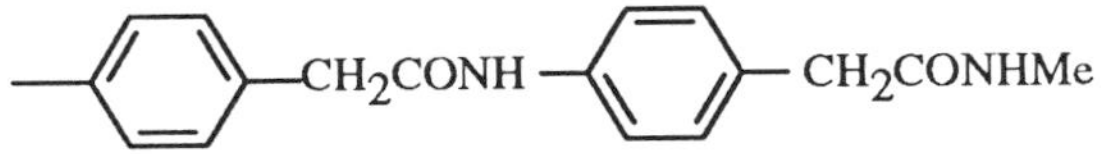

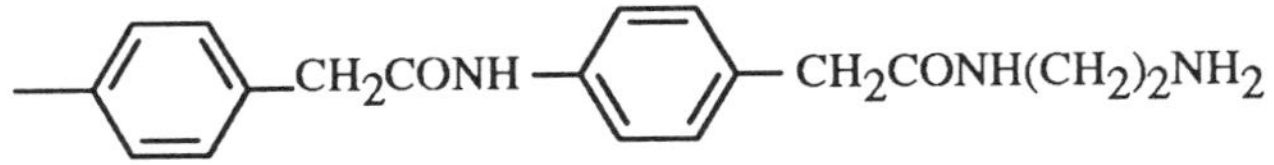

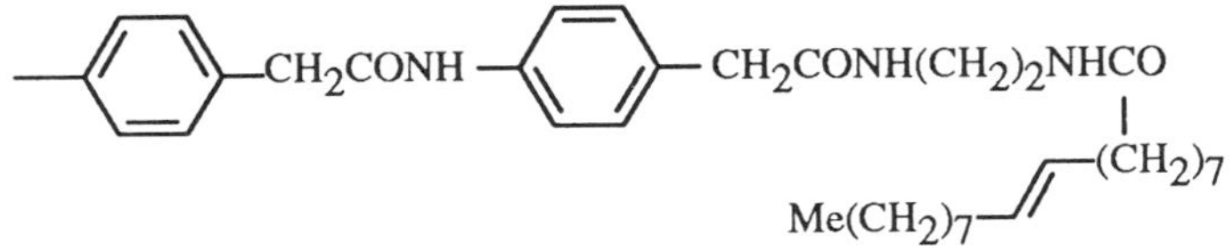

^{a} K_i values for binding experiments, using [^{3}H]CHA or [^{3}H]NECA, in rat brain. ^{b} $n = 9$, measured in bovine brain membranes.

Substitution at the 8-position (imidazole portion of the adenine ring) usually results in loss of activity. For example, 8-bromoadenosine and a number of 8-(ω-aminoalkyl)amino derivatives, available commercially as reagents for affinity chromatography, are inactive at A_1 and A_2 adenosine receptors.

The reason for low affinity of 8-substituted adenosine derivatives may be related to the conformation about the glycosidic bond. It appears that adenosine derivatives bind to adenosine receptors in the *anti* conformation at the ribosidic bond.[49] Bulky substituents, such as bromine, at the 8-position make the *anti* conformation energetically unfavorable. Additional evidence that the *anti* conformation corresponds to a conformation of receptor bound adenosine is found in semirigid cyclic analogs. Within a series of conformationally restricted analogs in which a ribose oxygen is bound to a purine carbon, 8,5′-cycloadenosine (**72**), which is forced into the *anti* conformation, binds to the A_2 receptor of fibroblasts as an antagonist.

(72)

At the N^6-amino group of adenosine substitution by an alkyl, arylalkyl, or aryl group (Table 3; **49–71**) often results in selectivity of the agonists for A_1 receptors. The N^6 region of the A_1 adenosine receptor has been mapped with computer graphics.[291] N^6-Cyclohexyladenosine (CHA; **50**)[74] was identified as a high affinity ligand at A_1 sites ($K_i = 1$ nM in rat brain). Its affinity for brain A_2 sites is very low ($K_i = 510$ nM),[44] thus it represents a highly selective (390-fold) A_1 agonist. From a series of N^6-cycloalkyladenosine derivatives, Moos *et al.*[122] found that the cyclopentyl analog (CPA; **49**) has the greatest A_1 selectivity at central adenosine receptors (780-fold). In competition by CPA for [³H]NECA binding sites (A_1 and A_2) in striatal membranes, separate A_1 and A_2 components are seen in a biphasic curve.[44] N^6-(3-Hydroxypropyl)adenosine (**52**) is also very A_1 selective (700-fold).[44] Recently, Lohse *et al.*[142] characterized 2-chloro-N^6-cyclopentyladenosine as being nearly 10 000-fold A_1 selective with a K_i of 0.4 nM.

Substitution at the 6-position by either antipode of amphetamine produces N^6-(phenylisopropyl)adenosine (PIA). The isomer having the (R) configuration at the isopropyl 2-position, (**53**) has an affinity similar to CHA at central A_1 sites ($K_i = 1.2$ nM) and is also relatively potent ($EC_{50} = 280$ nM) at coronary A_2 receptors.[123] (R)-PIA is 106-fold A_1 selective at central adenosine receptors.[44] The two diastereomers of PIA (**53** and **54**) differ in potency. In A_1 receptor binding (R)-($-$)PIA (equivalent to L-PIA) is 23 times more potent than the (S) isomer (**54**). At A_2 receptors the difference between activity of (R)- and (S)-PIA diastereomers is diminished (11-fold in coronary vasoactivity; 3.6-fold in PC12 cells; 1.9-fold in platelets). The diastereomeric pair of (R)- and (S)-PIA has been useful in distinguishing A_1 from A_2 receptors in uncharacterized systems (potency ratios of 20–200-fold at A_1 receptors and 2–10-fold at A_2 receptors). An iodinated radioligand related to PIA (I-HPIA; **30**; see Section 12.10.4.3.1) has been described.[77,78]

The potency of N^6-substituted adenosine analogs has been investigated with respect to the effects of structural elements in the N^6 subregion. Binding to A_1 receptors of brain membranes and potency at A_2 receptors controlling coronary blood flow were compared.[123–125] While some of the binding requirements for N^6-alkyl and N^6-aryl substituents at the brain A_1 receptor are conserved at the A_2 receptor, there are many marked differences.

Proposed interactions of the chiral phenylisopropyl group of (R)-PIA (**53**) at the coronary A_2 receptor[124] were analyzed. The phenylisopropyl group was divided into one aromatic and three hydrophobic aliphatic subregions (S-1, S-2, and S-3; corresponding to the carbons of the propyl group of PIA, numbering from position of the phenyl ring), comprising a Y-shaped groove at the receptor. Because of the preference for (R)- over (S)-PIA by the receptor, subregions corresponding to S-1 (a methylene attached to phenyl in PIA) and S-3 (a methyl in PIA) must be nonequivalent. A phenyl binding region within the Y-shaped groove was explored in great detail by Kusachi *et al.*[125] This type of analysis was later extended to the brain A_1 receptor.[123] For A_2 receptors, the S-1 region can accommodate up to three carbon atoms without losing activity in coronary vasodilation. Omission of the S-1 group of (R)-PIA gives (R)-N^6-(1-phenylethyl)adenosine (**55**). In nearly all S-2 chiral analogs examined, the potency at both A_1 and A_2 receptors was greater for the isomer with the (R) configuration at the S-2 carbon, consistent with the results for (R)- and (S)-PIA.

Similar stereoselectivity for the chiral center attached to the nitrogen was found for the A_1 receptor, at which agonists depress excitatory neurotransmission in rat hippocampal slices.[126] At A_2 receptors the S-3 center appears to accommodate an ethyl group most readily, and the activity is greatly diminished for larger substituents. Optimization of aryl and alkyl portions of the N^6 substituent has led to analogs, such as N^6-1-(2-thienyl)-2-(R)-butyladenosine (**56**), which are very potent at both receptor subtypes.[103,125] Consistent with previous observations, N^6-cycloalkyl analogs of adenosine (wherein the S-1 and S-3 subregions are thus doubly bridged), particularly N^6-cyclooctyladenosine (**51**), were highly A_1 selective when comparing coronary A_2 activity *versus* binding to central A_1 receptors. A spacially limited subregion termed S-4 was also defined. The S-4 subregion corresponded to the hydrogen on S-2 of (R)-PIA or to a methyl group of (**57**) which has a tertiary carbon attached to the N^6 nitrogen. This subregion appears sterically constrained and accommodates a carbon poorly in the A_1 receptor and virtually not at all in the A_2 receptor.

Although many N^6-alkyladenosine derivatives are A_1 selective, certain N^6-(2-phenylethyl) derivatives are highly potent at the A_2 receptor. At the coronary A_2 receptor, derivatives of N^6-(2-phenylethyl)adenosine (**60**; S-3 group of PIA omitted), and to some extent derivatives of N^6-phenyladenosine (**58**), show the greatest potency. However, the intermediate homologues, derivatives of N^6-benzyladenosine (**59**) tend to have weak activity at coronary receptors. N^6-(2,2-Diphenylethyl)adenosine (CI936; **62**), having K_i values at A_1 and A_2 receptors of 6.8 and 25 nM, respectively,[127] has an antipsychotic activity in behavioral tests. Computer conformational simulations suggest that one of the phenyl rings of CI936 occupies the phenyl binding region for (R)-PIA. The related, asymmetrically substituted, N^6-(2-(3,5-dimethoxyphenyl)-2-(2-methylphenyl)-ethyl)adenosine (**63**) and its 5'-uronamide derivatives were found to be A_2 selective agonists.[128] (**63**) had a K_i at central A_1 receptors of 4.4 nM, with a 32-fold A_2 selectivity. The bridged derivative of CI936, N^6-(9-fluorenylmethyl)adenosine (**64**)[129] is also a very potent A_2 agonist ($K_i = 4.9$ nM).

Analysis of the data for N^6-substituted adenosines at A_1 receptors (binding to rat brain) and A_2 receptors (coronary vasoactivity in dogs) suggested a number of pairs of physically similar compounds with divergent selectivities at A_1 and A_2 receptors that may be useful for defining adenosine receptor subtypes *in vivo*. Examples of comparable pairs are: N^6-benzyladenosine (**59**) and N^6-(p-chlorobenzyl)adenosine (adding the Cl substituent increases A_1 potency 2-fold and decreases A_2 potency 10-fold); and (**59**) and N^6-(1-phenylbutyl)adenosine (**61**) (an extension by three methylene groups increases A_1 potency 17-fold and decreases A_2 potency 11-fold).

The SAR of agonists at various A_1 and A_2 receptors linked to adenylate cyclase have been compared.[103] There were marked similarities among A_2 receptors from different sites (PC12, platelet and coronary). A_1 receptors from rat brain cells and adipocytes were also very similar. The SAR of N^6-substituted adenosine derivatives have also been studied at A_1 receptors in hippocampal slices[126] and in peripheral neuronal systems.[130]

N^6-Alkyladenosines that also contain the 5'-uronamido modification tend to lose the high potency at A_2 receptors typical of the latter.[103,131] The marked contribution of the uronamide to A_2 receptor vasoactivity is nearly completely suppressed by the N^6 substituent. However, at A_1 receptors the combination of 5'-uronamide and N^6-alkyl modifications can enhance potency. The combination of N^6-alkyl and C-2 substitutions also has been studied.[295] The substituent effects were additive only for groups known to favor A_1 selectivity.

EMD 28422, a diastereomeric pair of N^6-2-(4-chlorophenyl)-bicyclo[2,2,2]octyladenosines, which is a potent modulator at central benzodiazepine receptors, was found to be a weak, nonselective agonist at adenosine receptors.[132]

N^6,N^6-Dialkyl substituents are not well-tolerated at either receptor subtype. This suggests that a hydrogen bond to the NH may be involved in binding of adenosine analogs or, alternatively, that steric requirements at this site are violated.

A nonclassical approach to the design of purine analogs is that of functionalized (in the sense of bearing chemically reactive groups) congeners. A site on the adenosine molecule for elaboration of functionalized side chains ('functionalized congener approach', for the purpose of synthesizing covalent drug conjugates which may have unique receptor binding properties[83,198]) was created at the para position of N^6-phenyladenosine by introduction of a carboxymethyl substituent.[133] The resulting adenosine carboxylic acid congener (**65**; Table 3) and, to a greater degree, various amide derivatives (*e.g.* **66**–**70**) retained affinity for adenosine receptors. It was found that aryl amides (*e.g.* **67**) of N^6-phenylmethylcarboxylic acid tended to be more potent in A_1 receptor binding than similar alkyl amides. For this reason, an additional aryl group was included at this point, leading to extended structures. An *adenosine amine* congener (ADAC; **69**), derived from the action of ethylenediamine on the methyl ester (67), could be acylated readily using active esters, such as N-hydroxysuccinimide esters, to give amides. To investigate the utility of this site as a position for attachment to a wide variety of molecules for specific purposes, the amine congener was coupled to p-hydroxyphenylpropionic acid, known for its application as a prosthetic group for augmenting iodination sites on proteins.The resulting amide adduct bound to the A_1 adenosine receptor with a K_i in [^{3}H]CHA competition experiments on rat cerebral cortex membranes of 4.5 nM.

ADAC was a highly potent agonist ligand at A_1 receptors, with a K_i of 0.85 nM. Thus, the affinity was enhanced by a factor of five over that of the parent N^6-phenyladenosine. The enhancement was dependent on the presence of an alkylamino group, perhaps in the ammonium form predominant at physiological pH, since, after N acetylation, the affinity was somewhat diminished. The pattern of a free amino group producing high affinity at A_1 sites was paralleled in a series of functionalized congeners of 1,3-dialkylxanthines as adenosine antagonists (see below). This effect may be due to a charge attraction of the drug to an anionic site on the receptor or on another membrane component, such as a phospholipid. An electrostatic explanation is also consistent with the low potency of anionic functionalized congeners (e.g. 65). A study of straight chain N^6-alkyl- and N^6-Ω-alkyl-adenosine derivatives and dimeric adenosine derivatives (e.g. 72) has shown the dependency of potency on chain length, questioning the hypothesis of a generalized electrostatic interaction.[134] Within a series of straight chain N^6-aminoalkyladenosine derivatives, the optimal chain length for high affinity at A_1 adenosine receptors was found in compound (71).

A number of adenosine derivatives, designed through the functionalized congener approach, were found to have enhanced A_2 coronary vasoactivity[135] although not to the degree of NECA. A structural feature of several of these analogs, including (66–69), is the presence of functional groups, such as an amino group, which can be linked to other molecules or to solid supports for affinity chromatography (see below). In an *in vivo* study, compounds bearing distal carboxamides, (66 and 68), and a biotin conjugate (185; see Figure 10) were considerably more potent than adenosine (estimated EC_{50} values for these analogs were between 120 and 240 nM, compared to 1200 nM for adenosine) in causing coronary vasodilation upon intracoronary infusion in anesthetized, open-chest dogs. Although most N^6-substituted adenosines are highly selective for A_1 receptors, certain of the conjugates had much lower A_2/A_1 selectivity ratios when comparing A_2 coronary and A_1 brain adenosine receptors. The biotinyl-ε-aminocaproyl conjugate of ADAC (185; see Section 12.10.7.2) had approximately the same A_2/A_1 selectivity ratio as 2-chloroadenosine, although 2-chloroadenosine was nearly three times more potent in these systems.

A series of lipid amides of ADAC were found to be among the most potent competitors of [^{3}H]PIA binding to central A_1 receptors known.[136] A dependence of the K_i on the length of the attached fatty acid, but not on the degree of unsaturation was noted. The most potent lipid amides of ADAC contained fatty acids 18 carbons in length, for example elaidoyl-ADAC (70), which has a K_i of 70 pM in rat brain. It was hypothesized that the hydrophobic tail of the analogs is embedded in the phospholipid bilayer in the vicinity of the receptor and acts as a distal 'anchor', thus accounting for the difficulty of dissociation of the ligand.

12.10.5.1.3 *Nucleosides other than adenosine*

6-O-Alkyl- or 6-S-alkyl-purine ribosides (e.g. 14) are not active at coronary A_2 receptors or at A_1 receptors. Inosine (6-hydroxypurine riboside; 7; Scheme 1), produced by enzymatic degradation of adenosine, is inactive at adenosine receptors. For this reason, adenosine deaminase is frequently used in assays of adenosine-mediated mechanisms to eliminate any contributions from endogenous adenosine.

The marine natural product 1-methylisoguanosine (73), closely related in structure to adenosine, acts as an adenosine receptor agonist in the relaxation of striated muscle[137] and in the central nervous system.[138] In adenylate cyclase systems, it is several times more potent at A_1 receptors (adipocytes) than at A_2 receptors (PC12 cells greater than platelets).[103]

Most modifications of the heterocyclic adenine ring structure greatly diminish or abolish agonist activity of adenosine analogs (Figure 7). A number of pyrazolopyrimidine ribosides (74), while closely resembling adenosine in structural features, were practically inactive at adenosine receptors.[139] The only isosteric N for C replacement on the adenine ring that results in a full agonist is 2-azaadenosine (75). Using a series of analogs of 1-deazaadenosine (76a) and 2-chloroadenosine (46)[140] it was concluded that the relative contribution of nitrogen atoms of the purine moiety to A_1 receptor affinity follows the order N-7 > N-3 > N-1. N^6-cyclopentyl-2-chloro-1-deazaadenosine (76b), is 3000-fold selective for A_1 adenosine receptors.[141]

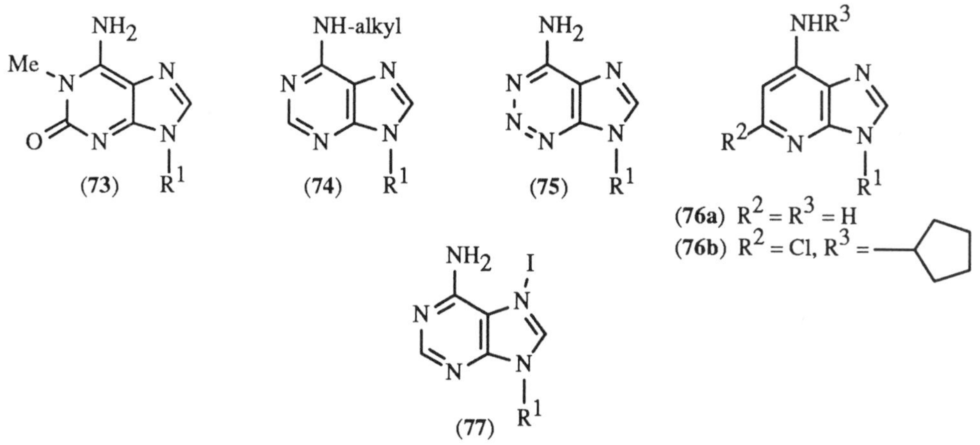

Figure 7   Adenosine analogs with modified purine structures (R = ribosyl)

Davies *et al.*[143] isolated novel halogenated adenosine derivatives from sponges. 5'-Deoxy-5-iodotubercidin and the synthetic 5'-hydroxy analog (77) were inactive at adenosine receptors, but proved to be the most potent inhibitors of adenosine kinase (Scheme 1) yet reported.

12.10.5.2   ATP Agonists

The naturally occurring nonadenine nucleotide triphosphates, 5'-UTP, 5'-CTP, and 5'-GTP (containing uridine, cytidine, or guanine, respectively), cause relaxation of the taenia coli and contraction of the urinary bladder, but are less potent than ATP.[144,145] Nucleotide diphosphates and monophosphates (Table 4) are active at P_2 receptors only for the adenine series.[146] 5'-AMP (2) is active (weakly) only at P_{2y} receptors.[152] Modifications of 5'-ADP (79), such as 2-chloro or 2-methylthio groups as in (80–82) enhance potency at P_{2y} receptors.[146]

The structures of synthetic ATP analogs which are of interest as ligands at P_2 receptors are shown in Table 5. In general, adenine C-2 and C-8, but not N-6, modifications are tolerated at P_2 receptors. 2-Methylthio-ATP (85), a selective P_{2y} agonist,[146,153] is as much as 500 times more potent than ATP at P_{2y} receptors. 2-Chloro-ATP (86)[146,153] and 2-azido-ATP (87)[150] are also more active than ATP at P_{2y} receptors, but equipotent at P_{2x} receptors. 8-Bromo-ATP (94) is equipotent at the receptor subtypes (half as active as ATP).[147,156,157]

Ribose modifications are better tolerated at P_2 than at P_1 receptors. Inversion of all of the chiral centers of ribose produces L-ATP (89), which is three times less potent than ATP at P_{2y} receptors.[150,153] The stereoselectivity of the P_{2y} receptor becomes more pronounced in the 2-substituted series. L-2-Methylthio-ATP (90) and L-2-azido-ATP (91) are both two orders of magnitude less potent than the corresponding D-enantiomers.[150,153,154] Another azido derivative, ANAPP₃ (arylazidoaminopropionyl-ATP; 92) was synthesized as a ribose-modified photoaffinity probe.[159-161] In the unphotolyzed state it acts as an apparent antagonist. Ara-ATP (93) and 2-deoxy-ATP (94), having modifications in the 2'-ribose position, are less potent than ATP at P_{2y} receptors.[146]

Numerous phosphate-modified analogs of ATP have been synthesized. One aim of phosphate modification is to render the derivative more stable to enzymatic dephosphorylation by 5'-ecto-nucleotidases, which otherwise have a large influence on the observed biological potencies. The interphosphate oxygen linkages have been replaced by methylene or halomethylene groups in the series of phosphonate analogs (95–102). At P_{2y} receptors, the potencies relative to ATP of homo-ATP (95),[146,157] α,β-methylene-ATP (AMP-CPP; 96),[157,162] and β,τ-methylene-ATP (AMP-PCP; 97)[144,164] are 70, 0.3, and 0.2, respectively. α,β-Methylene-ATP (96) is as potent as ATP at P_{2x} receptors[163] and is used in physiological studies to desensitize P_{2x} receptors. Through desensitization it antagonizes the biological effects of ATP, but is not a competitive antagonist at the receptor. As with the triphosphate analogs, purine 2-position modification further enhances potency in the β,γ-methylene series (*e.g.* 98), but only for the P_{2y} receptor subtype.

AMP-PCP (97), and to a lesser degree AMP-CPP (96), are resistant to dephosphorylation. In these phosphonate analogs a highly electronegative oxygen atom has been replaced by a CH_2

Table 4 Activity of AMP, ADP and Analogs at ATP Receptors in Guinea Pig Tissue

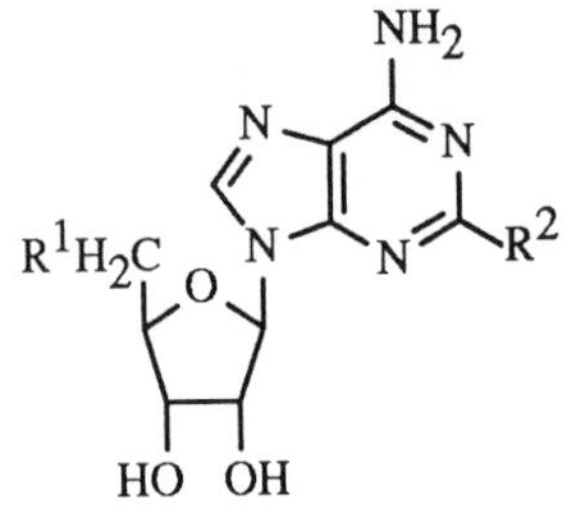

Compound	R^1 5′-substituent	R^2 2-substituent	Taenia coli (ATP = 1)[a]	Vas deferens (ATP = 1)[b]	Bladder (ATP = 1)[c]	Ref.
(2)	PO_3O-	H	0.03	very weak	inactive	146–148
(78)	PO_3O-	Cl	0.8	—	—	
(79)	PO_3OPO_2O- (ADP)	H	0.25–0.93 or > ATP	< ATP	≤ ATP	144, 148–152
(80)	PO_3OPO_2O-	Cl	4	—	—	146
(81)	PO_3OPO_2O-	MeS	30	—	—	146
(82)	$PO_3CH_2PO_2O-$ (ADPCH$_2$P)	H	0.7	< ATP	—	146, 147
(83)	$PO_3CH_2PO_2O-$	Cl	4	—	—	146,
(84a)	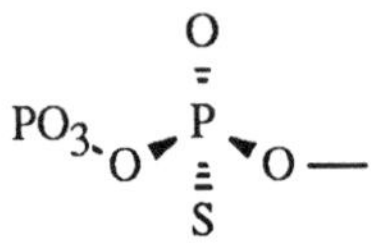 $PO_3-O-\overset{O}{\underset{S}{P}}-O-$ (R_p)-ADP-α-S	H	50	—	≈ ATP	148
(84b)	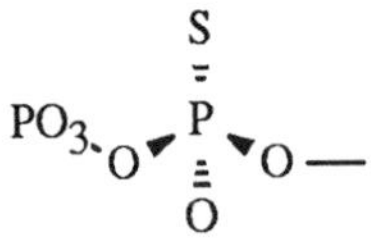 $PO_3-O-\overset{S}{\underset{O}{P}}-O-$ (S_p)-ADP-α-S	H	14.4	—	≈ ATP	148

[a] PD$_2$ for ATP = 6.1, ED$_{50}$ = 1 μM, value or range of values reported. [b] ED$_{50}$ for ATP ≈ 10 μM. [c] ED$_{50}$ for ATP ≈ 10–30 μM.

linkage, which in effect raises the pK_a of the adjacent phosphoric acid protons. To restore the degree of ionization to roughly that of ATP) electron-withdrawing halogen atoms, Cl and F, have been added to the methylene linkage. The 'isopolar' β,γ-dichloro- and difluoro-methylene-ATP, **(99)** and **(100)**, were synthesized and found to be potent ATP agonists at P$_{2y}$ receptors in smooth muscle preparations.[165] In another study,[155] **(97)** and **(99)** were found to be competitive antagonists at P$_2$ receptors.

In the isopolar β,τ-phosphonate series, additional modifications at the purine 2-position are potency-enhancing at P$_{2y}$ receptors. 2-Methylthio-β,γ-difluoromethyl-ATP **(101)** is twice as potent as ATP, but is still less potent than 2-methylthio-ATP **(85)**.[165]

L-AMP-PCP **(102)** is a highly potent and specific agonist at P$_{2x}$ receptors, which are involved in contraction of the urinary bladder.[164,166] L-AMP-PCP causes P$_{2x}$ specific desensitization to nerve stimulation in that tissue. Isopolar analogs of L-AMP-PCP, such as **(103)**, are also P$_{2x}$ selective agents.[165]

β,γ-Imido-ATP **(104)** is more potent than ATP at P$_{2x}$ receptors and only weakly active at P$_{2y}$ receptors.[146,167]

The charged atoms of the triphosphate group also may be modified without loss of biological activity. A series of phosphorothioates **(105–107)**, in which anionic sulfur has been substituted for an anionic oxygen at the α, β, or γ position, has been synthesized. Each α- or β-phosphorothioate represents a pair of diastereomers, since the affected phosphorus atom is now chiral, containing four nonequivalent substituents. A stereoselectivity is observed at P$_{2y}$ receptors, which applies only to the α-substituted phosphorothioate **(105)**.[148] For the ATP-α-(S)-pair, the (R) configuration at phosphate, designated (R_p), is preferred (8-fold). (R_p)-ATP-α-(S) is 50 times more potent than ATP at P$_{2y}$ receptors. At P$_{2x}$ receptors, only the β-phosphorothioate **(106)** is more much potent than ATP.

Table 5 Structures of ATP Analogs and their Activity at P_2 Purinergic Receptors

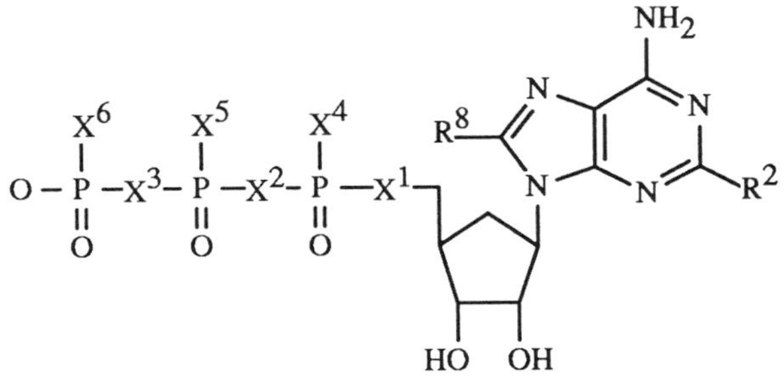

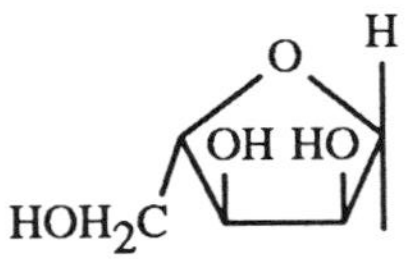

Compound	X^1–X^6	Sugar	R^2	R^8	Abbreviation	Taenia Coli $(ATP = 1)$ [a]	Vas Deferens $(ATP = 1)$ [b]	Bladder $(ATP = 1)$ [c]	Ref.
(85)	O	D-ribose	SMe	H	2-methylthio-ATP	50–200	≈ ATP	≈ ATP	146, 152–154
(86)	O	D-ribose	Cl	H		3–36	> ATP	> ATP	146, 153–154
(87)	O	D-ribose	N₃	H		22	—	—	150
(88)	O	D-ribose	H	Br	L-ATP	0.37	≈ ATP	—	147, 158
(89)	O	L-ribose	H	H		0.4–0.7	≈ 0.1	≈ ATP	150, 153, 154
(90)	O	L-ribose	SMe	H		0.22	≈ 0	≈ ATP, high dose	153, 154
(91)	O	L-ribose	N₃	H		0.18	—	—	153, 154
(92)	O	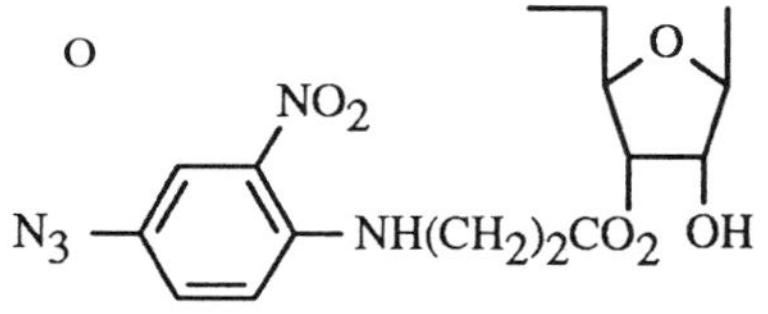	H	H	ANAPP₃	—	d	d	159–161
(93)	O	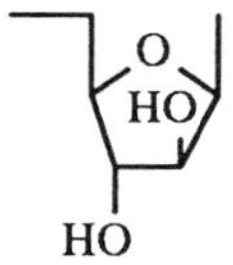	H	H	ara-ATP	0.3–0.8	—	—	146, 158
(94)	O	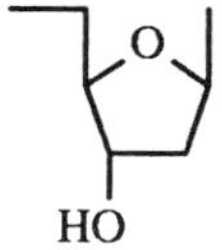	H	H	2-deoxy-ATP	0.46	≈ ATP, high dose	—	147, 158

Table 5 (Contd.)

X⁴–X⁶ are O

Compound	X¹	X²	X³	Sugar	R^2	R^8	Abbreviation	Taenia Coli $(ATP=1)$[a]	Vas Deferens $(ATP=1)$[b]	Bladder $(ATP=1)$[c]	Ref.
(95)	CH_2	O	O	D-ribose	H	H	homo-ATP	71	—	—	146
(96)	O	CH_2	O	D-ribose	H	H	AMP-CPP	0.3	> ATP, low dose	100	146, 147, 163
(97)	O	O	CH_2	D-ribose	H		AMP-PCP	0.04	> ATP	≥ATP	146, 147, 155, 163, 164
(98)	O	O	CH_2	D-ribose	Cl			6	—	—	146
(99)	O	O	CCl_2	D-ribose	H			—	—	—	155, 165
(100)	O	O	CF_2	D-ribose	H			—	—	—	155, 165
(101)	O	O	CF_2	D-ribose	SMe			—	—	—	165
(102)	O	O	CH_2	L-ribose	H		L-AMP-PCP	0	—	> ATP	164, 166
(103)	O	O	CF_2	L-ribose	H			—	—	—	
(104)	O	O	NH	D-ribose	H		β, τ-imido-ATP	0.06	> ATP	—	146, 147

X¹–X³ are O

Compound	X⁴	X⁵	X⁶	Sugar	R^2	R^8	Abbreviation	Taenia Coli $(ATP=1)$[a]	Vas Deferens $(ATP=1)$[b]	Bladder $(ATP=1)$[c]	Ref.
(105)	S	O	O	D-ribose	H		ATP-α-(S)	(R_p) 53 / (S_p) 6.9	≈ATP / ≈ATP	≈ATP / ≈ATP	148, 154 / 148, 154
(106)	O	S	O	D-ribose	H		ATP-β-(S)	(R_p) > ATP / (S_p) > ATP	≫ ATP (> S_p isomer) / ≫ ATP (< R_p isomer)	> ATP / > ATP	148, 154 / 148, 154
(107)	O	O	S	D-ribose	H			—	—	> ATP	148
(108)	O	O	F	D-ribose	H			—	—	—	167
(109)	O	O	NHφ	D-ribose	H			—	—	—	167

[a]PD_2 for ATP = 6.1, ED_{50} = 1 μM, value or range values reported. [b]ED_{50} for ATP ≈ 10 μM. ED_{50} for ATP ≈ 10–30 μM. [c]Qualitatively similar to ATP in vas deferens, also antagonized ATP noncompetitively.

Modifications of the τ phosphate group of ATP which lend resistance to degradation by nucleotidases are thio, fluoro and aminophenyl, found in analogs (**107**), (**108**) and (**109**), respectively.[148,168]

ADP and some of its analogs are active at P_2 receptors. ADP-β-F (**110**) is a specific P_{2y} receptor agonist and is not readily dephosphorylated by nucleotidases.[169]

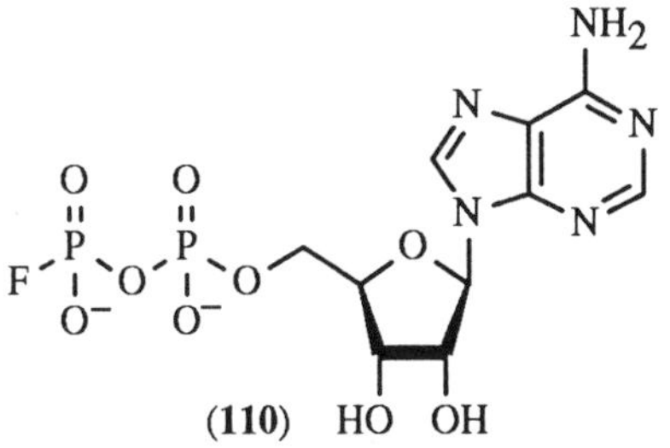

(**110**)   HO   OH

12.10.6   STRUCTURE–ACTIVITY RELATIONSHIPS FOR PURINERGIC ANTAGONISTS

Many synthetic analogs of caffeine and theophylline (alkylxanthines) have been found to be adenosine antagonists with increased affinity as great as ten thousand-fold.

Recently, β,γ-dichloromethylene-ATP (**99**) was found to block ATP receptors on rat sensory neurones with a K_i of 21 μM.[155] Previously, there were no reports of true competitive antagonists of ATP at P_2 receptors. Instead, (**92**), (**96**) and (**102**) have been used as apparent antagonists (see Section 12.10.5.2), *i.e.* in a physiological system they lead to desensitization of the purine effects. Reactive blue (**111**) has been used recently by Burnstock as a weak blocker of ATP effects.[176] Apamine also blocks ATP effects but is not a specific receptor antagonist.

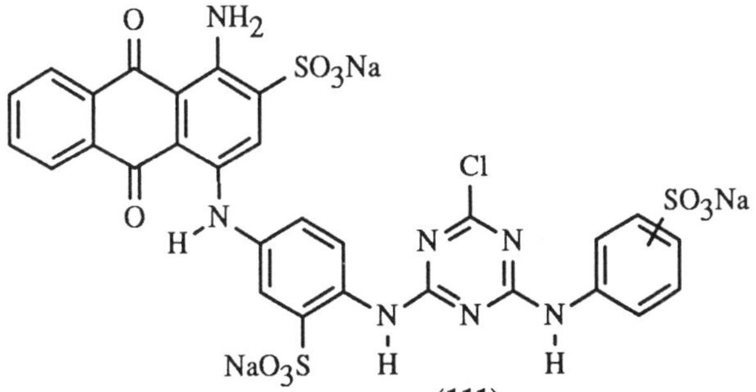

(**111**)

12.10.6.1   Xanthines as A_1 and A_2 Adenosine Antagonists

Most of the adenosine receptor antagonists reported are analogs of caffeine and theophylline, *i.e.* xanthine derivatives. Many modifications have been made at the N-1, N-3, N-7 and C-8 positions of xanthines. At the 2-position, replacement of oxygen with sulfur is tolerated at adenosine receptors, even for 8-substituted analogs.[292]

12.10.6.1.1   *Nitrogen-substituted xanthines*

Most xanthines having only NH groups or *N*-methyl substitution (Table 6), including caffeine (**116**), theophylline (**115**), and theobromine (**112**), occur naturally. Theophylline is the most potent naturally occurring xanthine at adenosine receptors,[177] with a K_i of 14 μM against [³H]CHA binding to rat brain membranes. Caffeine is significantly less potent with a K_i of 55 μM. Paraxanthine (**114**) is a major metabolite of caffeine which is nearly as potent as theophylline. Caffeine, theophylline and paraxanthine are nonselective for adenosine receptor subtypes. Theobromine, although considerably less potent, is somewhat A_1 selective. The simple methylxanthines are also weak phosphodiesterase inhibitors.[178] The unnatural 1,9-dimethylxanthine and 1,3,9-trimethyl-caffeine (isocaffeine) are inactive at adenosine receptors. 7-Chloroethyltheophylline is a 5-fold more potent antagonist than the parent caffeine.

Table 6 Affinity at Adenosine Receptors (Rat or Mouse Brain) of Xanthine Derivatives Substituted at the 1, 3 and 7 Positions (Inhibition of Binding of [^{3}H]PIA or [^{3}H]NECA)[44,178]

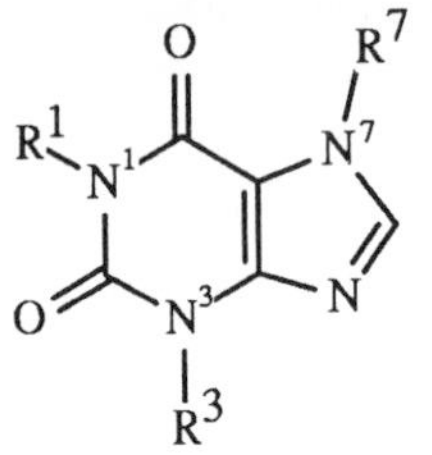

Compound	R^1	R^3	R^7	K_i (μM) A_1	A_2
(112)	H	Me	Me	120	—
(113)	H	Pr^n	H	55	120
(114)	Me	H	Me	30	—
(115)	Me	Me	H	15	17
(116)	Me	Me	Me	59	37
(117)	Me	Me	Pr^n	31	8.2
(118)	Me	$CH_2C\equiv CH$	Me	20	21
(119)	Me	Pr^n	Me	18	15
(120)	Me	CH_2CHMe_2	Me	2.5	14
(121)	Et	Et	H	2.7	—
(122)	$CH_2C\equiv CH$	Me	Me	22	9.6
(123)	$CH_2C\equiv CH$	$CH_2C\equiv CH$	$CH_2C\equiv CH$	3.8	1.9
(124)	Pr^n	Pr^n	H	1.4	5.4
(125)	Pr^n	Pr^n	Me	3.2	5.3
(126)	Pr^n	Pr^n	Pr^n	3.0	6.5
(127)	$(CH_2)_2CHMe_2$	CH_2CHMe_2	H	37	—

Enprofylline (3-propylxanthine; **113**) is a more potent smooth muscle relaxant and antiasthmatic drug than theophylline, but with fewer CNS stimulant, diuretic and gastric secretory side effects.[179] The lack of side effects was proposed to be due to inactivity as an adenosine antagonist. However, at higher than therapeutic plasma concentrations, enprofylline is a weak competitive antagonist at both A_1 and A_2 receptors.[178,180]

3-Isobutyl-1-methylxanthine (IBMX; **120**) is a potent phosphodiesterase inhibitor and is a nonselective competitive antagonist at adenosine receptors.[178]

Certain *N*-alkyl modifications in a series of caffeine analogs can result in slight A_2 selectivity,[46] based on comparison of brain [^{3}H]CHA binding (A_1) and measurement of inhibition of cAMP accumulation stimulated by 2-chloroadenosine in guinea pig brain slices (A_2). Single replacements of the methyl groups at the N-1 position (by *n*-propyl, allyl, or propargyl groups) or at the N-7 position (by allyl or propargyl groups) give A_2 selectivity between 3- and 10-fold. Selectivity was in some instances more pronounced in cyclase experiments[110] in which activities in adipocytes (A_1), PC12 cells (A_2), and platelets (A_2) were compared. (**122**) and (**117**) were 24- and 12-fold selective for A_2 receptors, respectively. Modifications of more than one *N*-alkyl residue of the caffeine molecule not only failed to enhance selectivity additively, but also in some cases eliminated the A_2 selectivity.

3,7-Dimethyl-1-propargylxanthine (**122**) selectively blocked the *in vivo* effects (temperature and locomotor depression) of NECA (**45d**) compared to blockade of the same responses elicited by CHA (**50**).[181]

Affinity to A_1 receptors was enhanced by homologation of the 1,3-dialkyl substituents of theophylline.[182] 1,3-Diethylxanthine (**121**) and the 1,3-dipropyl analog (**123**) were 1.1- and 16-times more potent, respectively, than theophylline. The A_1 potency order of Pr > Et > Me also holds for most 8-substituted analogs. At A_2 receptors affinity does not increase to the same extent with increasing size of the alkyl group. Thus the higher homologs, in particular 1,3-dipropylxanthine analogs, including those with 8-aryl substituents (see below), are somewhat A_1 selective. 1,3-Dipropylxanthine, itself, is 4-fold A_1 selective. There is an apparent size limitation for alkyl groups at the 1- and 3-positions, particularly at A_2 receptors. Thus 1-isoamyl-3-isobutylxanthine (**127**) is inactive at central A_2 receptors at its limit of solubility, and is equipotent to theophylline at brain A_1 adenosine receptors. (**127**) is also a potent inhibitor of phosphodiesterases.

It has been suggested that the orientation of the purine ring of xanthines and adenosines is inverted with respect to binding at the receptor site.[183] Thus, structurally analogous nitrogens of adenosine and xanthines would not interact with the same position on the receptor during binding. This proposal was based originally on considerations of the effects of certain substituents on the overall dipole moment of the purine. There is an approximately 180° difference in the purine C-4/C-5 dipole axis when adenosine and theophylline are compared. If orientation of the heterocyclic ring is, in fact, determined by this dipole, then it is reasonable that the N-7 of theophylline would be located near the binding site for the N-9 of adenosine. In the case of caffeine, the 7-methyl group would occupy a similar position to the ribose C-1 (bonded to N-9) of adenosine. Consistent with this hypothesis, the N^7-riboside of theophylline binds to the receptor[183] while the N^9-riboside has very low activity.[184] Such an orientation would place the N-3 methyl group of theophylline at the position of the N^6-alkyl region of potent adenosine analogs.

An alternative hypothesis for binding of xanthines would place the N^6-alkyl substituent of adenosine analogs at the same position in the receptor binding site as the C-8 substituent of xanthine derivatives. This hypothesis is based on similarities between the large hydrophobic pockets into which 8-cycloalkyl- or 8-aryl-xanthine substituents and N^6-alkyl- or N^6-aryl-adenosine substituents fit (see discussion of interspecies differences below).

12.10.6.1.2 *8-Position modifications*

At the 8-position, considerable latitude of substitution (Table 7) is possible without loss of competitive binding at adenosine receptors. Although 8-halo-substituted theophylline analogs are nearly inactive, 8-alkyl substitutions are tolerated.[50] Among 8-cycloalkyl substituents, unsubstituted cyclopentyl and cyclohexyl substituents result in the highest potency. 8-Cyclopentyltheophylline (CPT; **128**)[44] and the 1,3-dipropyl analog, CPX (**129**)[87,185] are highly A$_1$ selective (133- and 740-fold) respectively). [^{3}H]CPX is used as a radioligand (see Section 12.10.4.2) for labeling A$_1$ receptors. The aqueous solubility of CPT and to a lesser extent CPX has enabled the use of 8-cyclopentylxanthines in physiological studies.[186] The inclusion of unsaturation, as in (**130**), or halogen groups on the distal position of the cyclopentyl ring is detrimental to potency in A$_1$ receptor binding.[47]

Table 7 Affinity at Adenosine Receptors (Rat or Mouse Brain) of Xanthine Derivatives Substituted at the 1, 3 and 8 positions (Inhibition of Binding of [^{3}H]PIA or [^{3}H]NECA)[44,46,187,198]

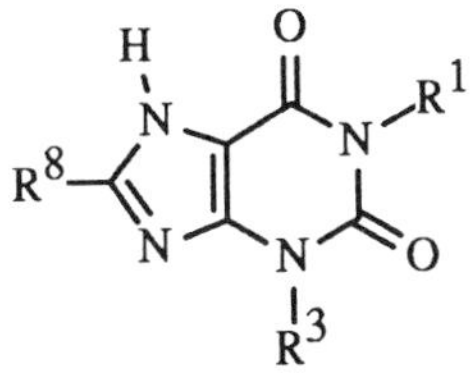

Compound	R^1	R^3	R^8	K_i (nM) A$_1$	A$_2$
(**128**)	Me	Me	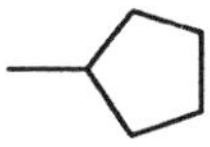	11	1440
(**129**)	Pr^n	Pr^n	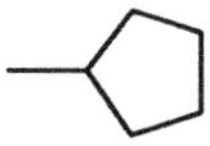	0.9	410
(**130**)	Pr^n	Pr^n	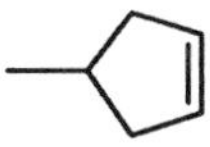	45	—
(**131**)	Me	Me	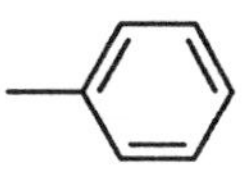	400	550
(**132**)	Et	Et	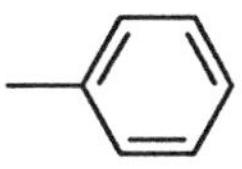	45	860

Table 7 *(Contd.)*

Compound	R^1	R^3	R^8	K_i (nM) A_1	A_2
(133)	Pr^n	Pr^n	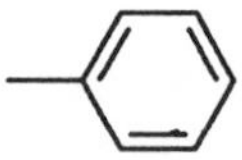 (phenyl)	13	300
(134)	Pr^n	Pr^n	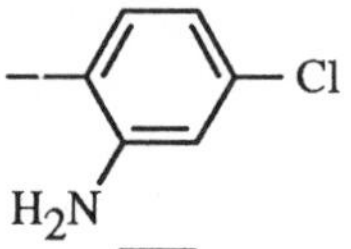 (phenyl, Cl, H_2N)	2.5	92
(135)	Pr^n	Pr^n	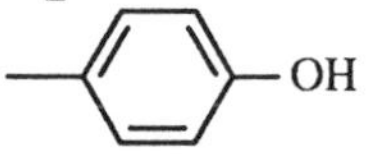 (phenyl—OH)	2.9	50
(136)	Pr^n	Pr^n	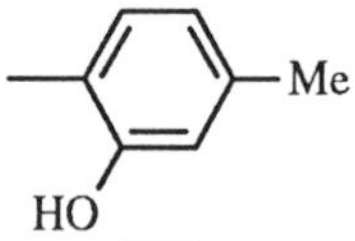 (phenyl—Me, HO)	11	980
(137)	Me	Me	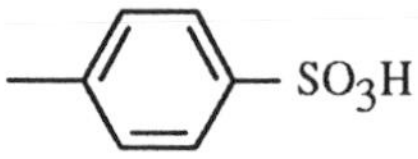 (phenyl—SO_3H)	2630	15 300
(138)	Pr^n	Pr^n		210	710

$R_1 = R_3 = Pr^n$; R_7 (phenyl—X)

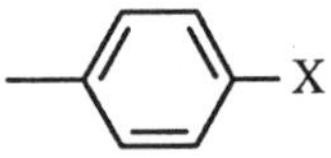

Compound	X	A_1	A_2
(139)	SO_2NH_2	8.5	115
(140)	$SO_2NH(CH_2)_3NMe_2$	5.6	70
(141)	$SO_2NMe(CH_2)_2NMe_2$	14	16
(142)	CO_2H	170	110
(143)	$CONH_2$	7	72
(144)	OCH_2CO_2H	58	2200
(145)	$OCH_2CONH(CH_2)_2NH_2$	1.2	70
(146)	$OCH_2CONH(CH_2)_2NHCOMe$	24	530
(147)	$OCH_2CONH(CH_2)_2OH$	10	—
(148)	$OCH_2CONH(CH_2)_2SH$	16	—
(149)	$OCH_2CONH(CH_2)_2NHCOCH_2NH_2$	2	—
(150)	$OCH_2CONH(CH_2)_2NH(COCH_2NH)_3H$	2	—
(151)	$OCH_2CONH(CH_2)_2NHCOCHNH_2$ (L) $(CH_2)_3NHCONH_2$	2.9	—
(152)	$OCH_2CONH(CH_2)_2NHCOCHNH_2$ (L) $(CH_2)_4NH_2$	1.0	—
(153)	$OCH_2CONH(CH_2)_2NHCOCHNH_2$ (D) $(CH_2)_4NH_2$	0.87	180
(154)	$OCH_2CONH(CH_2)_2NHCOCHNH_2$ (D) $(CH_2)_4NHCO(CH_2)_2C_6H_4$-4-OH	1.9	—
(155)	$OCH_2CONH(CH_2)_2NHCO(CH_2)_2CH(NH_2)CO_2H$ (L)	21	—
(156)	$OCH_2CONH(CH_2)_2NHCOCHNH_2$ (all L) CH_2CO-Phe$_2$-Gly-Leu-Met-NH_2	35	—

Various 8-aryl substituents greatly increase the potency of 1,3-dialkylxanthines; much freedom of substitution of an 8-phenyl ring (**131–156**) is tolerated at the receptor. 8-Phenyltheophylline (**131**) is 35 times more potent in CHA binding than theophylline, but shows no receptor subtype selectivity in brain.[187] 8-Phenyltheophylline has been described as highly selective for A_1 receptors, based on a comparison of activity in platelets *versus* binding to bovine brain.[188] In this regard it should be noted that 8-arylxanthines bind to central A_1 receptors with considerably greater affinity in bovine than in rat brain. The species dependence of affinity of 8-phenylxanthines has been explored.[189,190] K_i values for a given antagonist may vary over a range of two orders of magnitude depending on species; the general order of potency is calf > rat ≈ mouse > guinea pig > chick.

Effects of substitution at the 1-, 3- and 7-positions and on the 8-phenyl substituent are not independent. 8-Phenylcaffeine is only slightly more potent than caffeine at both A_1 and A_2 receptors.[191] At A_1 receptors, the order of potency in the caffeine series is 8-phenyl-caffeine > caffeine ≥ to 8-(*p*-carboxyphenyl)caffeine. In contrast, the potency order in the theophylline series is 8-phenyl- > 8-*p*-carboxyphenyl- ≫ unsubstituted-theophylline. 8-Cycloalkyl derivatives of caffeine appear to be A_2 selective by comparing K_i values obtained from A_1 binding assays in rat brain with A_2 cyclase assays in human platelets. By these criteria (**157**) is 150-fold selective for A_2 receptors, while the 8-phenyl analog (**158**) is nonselective. However, the margin of selectivity is diminished or absent when comparing biological potencies for (**157**) in studies of both A_1 and A_2 receptor mediated adenylate cyclase.[191]

(**157**) R = cyclohexyl
(**158**) R = phenyl

The potency-enhancing effect of 8-phenyl substituents is evident also with larger 1,3-dialkyl substituents. Tritiated 1,3-diethyl-8-phenylxanthine (DPX; **132**) has been used as a low affinity radioligand.[74] 1,3-Dipropyl-8-phenyltheophylline (**133**) is 1100 times more potent than theophylline at A_1 receptors and 47 times more potent at A_2 receptors.[187] The potency and A_1 selectivity of this analog was the basis for investigation of the effects on A_1 and A_2 activity of mono- and di-substitution on the 8-phenyl ring.[46,182,187] Such studies have led to the development of 1,3-di-propyl-8-(2-amino-4-chlorophenyl)xanthine (PACPX; **134**) as a ligand having a very high potency at A_1 receptors combined with a 37-fold margin of selectivity for A_1 receptors.[44]

In a study of QSAR Hamilton *et al.*[192] have concluded that in 8-phenyl-substituted xanthines, high A_1 potency can be enhanced by the presence of small electron-donating substituents, such as hydroxy and amino, in the *ortho* position. These have an even greater effect on potency than *para* substitution. This *ortho* effect is consistent with the high potency of PACPX and certain other disubstituted 8-phenylxanthines, such as (**136**).[46]

Simple uncharged 8-phenyl-substituted xanthines, including PACPX, have extremely high potency and in some cases A_1 selectivity in *in vitro* screening.[182] Unfortunately, they have very low water solubility (in the range of 1 μM) due to the hydrophobic substituents at the 1-, 3- and 8-positions. Thus, the maximum aqueous solubility at neutral pH of 1,3-dipropyl-8-(*p*-hydroxy-phenyl)xanthine (**135**) is 3 μM. The low solubility of some potent 8-phenylxanthine derivatives, including PACPX, has interfered with *in vivo* testing in muscular action, resulting in apparently irreversible effects.[193] PACPX was found to bind to A_2 receptors in an apparently irreversible manner,[194] perhaps also due to the inability to wash out such a lipid soluble compound from membrane sites.

One approach to enhancing the water solubility of xanthines has been to incorporate aryl sulfonate, carboxylate, or other charged groups into the molecule. These functional groups are completely (sulfonate) or almost completely (carboxylate) ionized at physiological pH. The 1,3-dialkyl-8-(*p*-sulfophenyl)xanthines, (**137** and **138**), are considerably more water soluble than the 8-phenyl parent compounds, but in the case of (**138**) the A_1 selectivity of the unsulfonated compound (**133**) is lost.[187] Similarly, 1,3-dipropyl-8-(*p*-carboxyphenyl)xanthine (**142**) is nonselective. When the anionic group is structurally separated from the phenyl ring (as in the carboxymethyloxy analog; **144**) or replaced by sulfonamido (**151**) or carboxamido groups (**155**), a modest degree of A_1 selectivity is restored. (**144**) was reported to be nonselective in initial screening, but later found to be A_1 selective in cyclase assays[195] and by autoradiography.[90] An additional result of charged groups on the phenyl ring (for example in **137**, **138**, **140** and **145**) is exclusion from passage across cell membranes and the blood–brain barrier.[186,196] Bristol and Badger[197] have synthesized a series of derivatives of 8-(sulfophenyl)xanthine, including sulfonates and sulfonamides. A particularly potent analog reported in the sulfonamide series was 8-(4-*N*-(3-dimethylaminopropyl)sulfonamido)phenyl-1,3-dipropylxanthine (PD 113,297; **140**) which had an IC_{50} for inhibition of binding of [^{3}H]CHA to rat brain membranes of 5.6 nM.[44] Enhancement of affinity at A_2 receptors in a tertiary amine derivative led to the introduction of (**141**) as a radioligand.[102]

Functionalized congeners of 1,3-dialkyl-8-phenylxanthines[84,198] have been designed as a means of improving potency, A_1 selectivity, and water solubility. A series of functionalized congeners derived from 8-phenyl-substituted xanthines were synthesized as adenosine antagonists. Based on the high receptor affinity associated with 8-phenyl substitutions, including *p*-hydroxyphenyl analogs, the *p*-carboxymethoxy substituent was introduced to form a *x*anthine *c*arboxylic acid *c*ongener (abbreviated XCC: for R = *n*-propyl; **144**; Table 7) wherein the carboxylic acid was intended to be coupled to carriers. Consistent with previous findings, replacement of the 1- and 3-position methyl groups with *n*-propyl groups increased the A_1 receptor affinity of the carboxylic acid congener and simple related amides.

Coupling of the carboxylic acid congener to diamines produced a series of amine derivatives, including a 1,3-dipropylxanthine *a*mine *c*ongener (XAC; **145**). XAC was designed initially to be a synthetic intermediate in the synthesis of conjugates but was, itself, of sufficiently high potency to warrant further *in vitro* and *in vivo* studies. The rise in A_1 affinity due to the presence of an amino group in XAC was greater relative to the affinity enhancement at A_2 receptors, resulting in a 40–60-fold selectivity for brain A_1 adenosine receptors compared to brain A_2 receptors. The high potency at A_1 sites has been observed with many other amine derivatives, including those with additional alkyl substitution on the amine, or longer spacer groups separating the amine from the primary pharmacophore, (*e.g.* **149** and **150**). The A_1 selectivity of XAC *in vivo* was demonstrated by Fredholm and coworkers.[199,200] In antagonizing the cardiovascular effects of NECA, at low doses XAC reversed the cardiodepressant effects, but not the antihypertensive effects. The cardioselectivity of this potent xanthine derivative suggested *in vivo* A_1 subtype selectivity. XCC was not selective in the cardiovascular studies *in vivo* in rats. [^{3}H]XAC was developed as a high affinity antagonist radioligand (see Section 12.10.3.2).[83]

The pronounced effects on the potency of binding and on the receptor subtype selectivity produced by the presence of charged groups on the chain suggested the synthesis of a series of amino acid and peptide conjugates (**149–156**)[198] derived from XCC and XAC. Conjugates in which the attached chain contained a free amino group tended towards high A_1 potency and, in some cases, selectivity. The potency was not necessarily diminished as the size of the conjugate was increased.

The functionalized congener approach provided a means for enhancing the water solubility of xanthine derivatives. The 1-citrullyl conjugate (**151**) was nearly three times as soluble as XAC. The D-lysyl conjugate of XAC (**153**) had an aqueous solubility of 0.52 mM. The enantiomers (**152**) and (**153**) were equipotent, emphasizing the relaxation of steric restrictions in receptor binding at this distal site on the ligand. The ε-amino group also served as the site of attachment for reporter groups, such as for radioiodination (**154**).

In a prodrug scheme, designed to achieve kidney selectivity in an adenosine antagonist, XAC has been coupled to γ-L-glutamic acid to form (**155**). The γ-amide is effectively cleaved enzymatically in the kidney to regenerate XAC, a considerably more potent antagonist, resulting in *in vivo* diuretic effects.[201]

XAC has been coupled to a biologically active sequence of the putative neurotransmitter substance P, resulting in a binary drug conjugate (**156**), which is capable of binding to either adenosine or substance P receptors.[202]

The activity of synthetic 8-phenylxanthine analogs as inhibitors of phosphodiesterases has been investigated.[203] The 8-phenyl substitution tends to diminish this activity.

12.10.6.2 Nonxanthine Heterocycles as Adenosine Antagonists

Bruns identified a number of purine glycosides which act as competitive inhibitors at A_2 receptors (Figure 6). 5′-Deoxy-5′-methylthioadenosine (**43**; see Section 12.10.4.1.1) which binds to the A_2 adenosine receptor with the same affinity as theophylline, lacks agonist action at the human fibroblast A_2 receptor, although it acts as an agonist at the smooth muscle adenosine receptor in rabbit gut.[112] Other antagonists similar in structure to adenosine (Figure 8), and with K_i values in the fibroblast assay of 10 μM or less, include 5′-deoxy-5′-(methyloxycarbonyl)methyladenosine

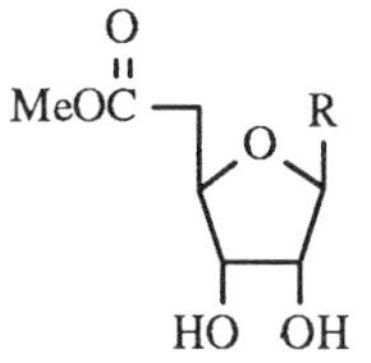

Figure 8 Modified adenosine derivatives having antagonist properties (P = adenine)

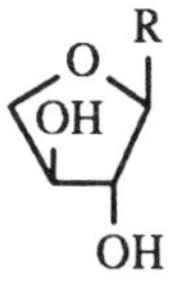

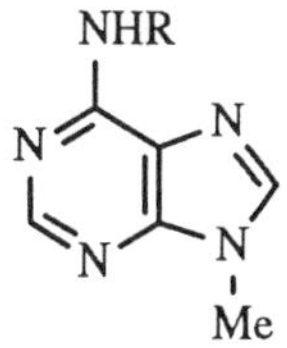

(**159**), adenine-9-β-D-*erythro*furanoside (**160**), adenine-9-α-L-*threo*furanoside (**161**), and the 5'-thio analog of the cycloadenosine derivative (**72**).

9-Methyladenine (**162a**)[50] and a series of *N*-alkyl derivatives[106] were shown to be adenosine antagonists. The N^6-cyclohexyl analog (**162b**), was moderately A$_1$ selective. The structural requirements for N^6 substituents of adenine as antagonists are similar to those for N^6-substituted adenosine agonists, suggesting a common binding domain.

A number of nonxanthine heterocyclic antagonists, similar to purines in that they contain planar, nitrogen hetero rings, have been identified (Figure 9). Some of these compounds are known for biological activity not directly related to adenosine receptors.

Davies *et al.*[204] tested a variety of nonxanthine nitrogen and sulfur heterocyclic compounds for the ability to displace [^{3}H]PIA from rat brain membranes, and for antagonism of adenosine-stimulated adenylate cyclase. A pyrazolopyrimidine derivative containing thio substituents, DJB-KK (**163**), was approximately one order of magnitude more potent than theophylline as an antagonist at A$_1$ and A$_2$ adenosine receptors.

Williams *et al.*[205] found that the pyrazolopyridine etazolate (**164**) and the related analog tracazolate, which enhances the binding of diazepam to benzodiazepine receptors, are competitive inhibitors of binding to central A$_1$ adenosine receptors.

Alloxazine (**165**), a nitrogen tricyclic (benzo[*g*]pteridine-2,4-dione), is more potent than theophylline in competitive inhibition of binding to both A$_1$ and A$_2$ adenosine receptors, showing a slight selectivity for the latter.[44]

The anticonvulsant carbamazepine was found to inhibit binding of [^{3}H]CHA to A$_1$ receptors in brain membranes (K_i = 25 μM) with much weaker activity at central A$_2$ receptors.[206–208]

Levallois *et al.*[209] studied a series of imidazo[1,2-*a*]-pyrazine derivatives which displayed theophylline like spasmolytic and bronchodilator properties. The compounds inhibited NECA-stimulated adenylate cyclase in mouse thymocytes (weaker than theophylline), but the antiallergenic potency paralleled the potency of phosphodiesterase inhibition, rather than adenosine antagonism.

A variety of mesoionic bicyclic derivatives of pyrimidine having structural similarities to xanthines were synthesized originally as phosphodiesterase inhibitors. Most of the compounds displaced [^{3}H]CHA from rat brain membranes, but were less potent than theophylline.[210] Only a set of benzothiazolo[3,2-*a*]pyrimidines, (*e.g.* **166**) approached theophylline in potency at adenosine receptors, with a slight selectivity for A$_2$ receptors.

CGS 8216 (**167**), a phenyl-substituted pyrazoloquinoline derivative, acted as a potent benzodiazepine antagonist and as a moderately potent adenosine antagonist.[211]

A potent nonxanthine adenosine receptor antagonist has been reported recently by Williams *et al.*[212] The triazoloquinoline derivative CGS 15943A (**168**) has a K_i at brain A$_1$ receptors of 20.5 nM and is 6-fold selective for A$_2$ receptors in binding assays. It is orally active *in vivo* and acts as an A$_2$ selective adenosine antagonist in coronary artery strips and in the trachea.[213] The structure–activity profile of triazoloquinazoline derivatives has been explored.[214]

The α$_2$-adrenergic agonist clonidine acts as an apparent adenosine antagonist under physiological conditions,[215] but failed to inhibit the binding of [^{3}H]CHA to brain membranes or at A$_2$ receptor mediated activation of adenylate cyclase in PC12 cells. Adenosine analogs were nearly inactive in competing for clonidine binding sites in brain membranes.[216]

The imidazopyridine derivative (**169**) and related analogs act as adenosine antagonists,[217] but the potency does not account for associated cardiotonic action in this series.

Hamilton *et al.*[218] have found similarities in the structural requirements of the phenyl substitution pattern for pyrazolopyrimidinones, such as (**170**), as adenosine antagonists and the requirements for 8-phenylxanthines.

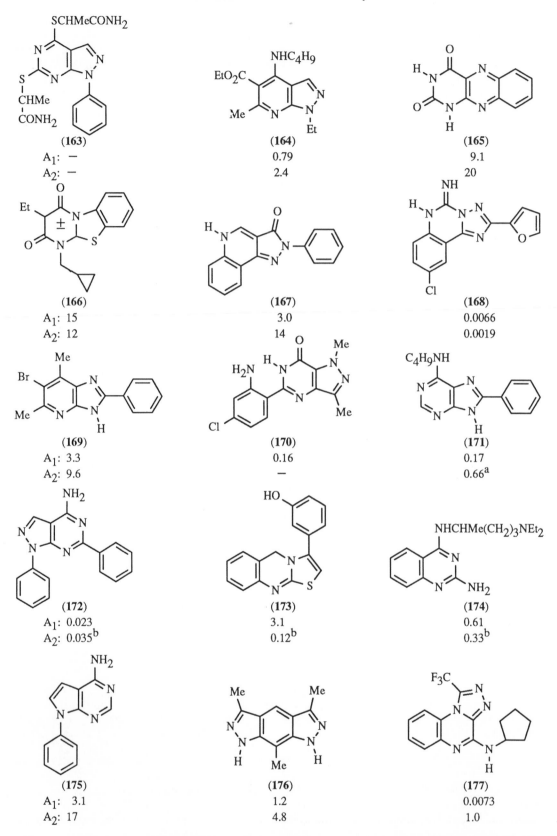

Figure 9 Nonpurine heterocycles which act as adenosine antagonists. K_i values for A_1 receptor binding in rat brain using [³H]CHA or PIA and K_B values for inhibition of adenylate cyclase stimulation *via* A_2 receptors in rat pheochromocytoma (PC12) cell membranes are given, unless noted. [a] [³H]NECA binding in rat striatum (K_i), [b] adenylate cyclase in human platelets (K_B)

Bruns[219] has identified four nonxanthine adenosine antagonists (**171–174**) in the screening of previously synthesized compounds. The 4-aminopyrazolo[3,4-*d*]pyrimidine, APPP (**172**) is a potent, nonselective adenosine antagonist of low water solubility. A hydroxy derivative of the thiazoloquinazoline, HTQZ (**173**) is 25-fold A_2 selective. The nonselective antagonist ADQZ (**174**) is water soluble.

Daly and coworkers have identified several new classes of nonselective nonxanthine adenosine antagonists, 7-deaza-9-phenyladenines[174] (*e.g.* **175**) and benzodipyrazoles[220] (*e.g.* **176**).

Trivedi and Bruns[221] have identified a new class of A_1 receptor selective antagonists related to [1,2,4]triazolo[4,3-*a*]quinoxalin-4-amine. A trifluoromethyl derivative (**177**) containing a cyclopentyl group, is 138-fold A_1 selective.

12.10.7 MOLECULAR PROBES FOR PURINERGIC RECEPTORS

'Molecular probes' signify ligands designed for detection or characterization of the receptor by physicochemical techniques. Markers present on the molecules may be for spectroscopic or microscopic detection. Examples of molecular probes are fluorescent-labeled analogs, chemically and photochemically reactive affinity labels, and polymer bound ligands (coupled to biopolymers or immobilized on insoluble polymeric matrices).

12.10.7.1 Affinity Labels

Adenosine receptor glycoproteins have been studied using affinity labeling techniques.[81,84,91–93,95,223] The introduction of a radioactive label (preferably ^{125}I, through a covalent bond) has made it possible to identify the A_1 receptor protein (molecular weight estimates are in the 34 000 to 40 000 Da range) in electrophoretic gels and to study its regulation and posttranslational modifications.

Stiles *et al.*,[84] using photoaffinity crosslinking through a multistep reaction, were the first to covalently label A_1 adenosine receptors (Scheme 2). The method uses an arylamine-functionalized derivative of adenosine, N^6-(*p*-aminophenylethyl)adenosine (APNEA; **178a**). The arylamino group of the receptor-bound APNEA is accessible to the surrounding aqueous environment and reacts specifically with a commercial, bifunctional photo-crosslinking reagent, *N*-succinimidyl-6-(4-azido-2-nitrophenylamino)hexanoate (SANPAH). After the formation of an amide bond with the bound APNEA, the azido group of (**180a**) is photolyzed,[222] resulting in a nitrene intermediate which crosslinks to the receptor protein. A_2 adenosine receptors of bovine brain (M_r 45 000) were covalently labeled in a similar fashion by photoaffinity crosslinking using [^{125}I]PAPA-APEC (**48c**).

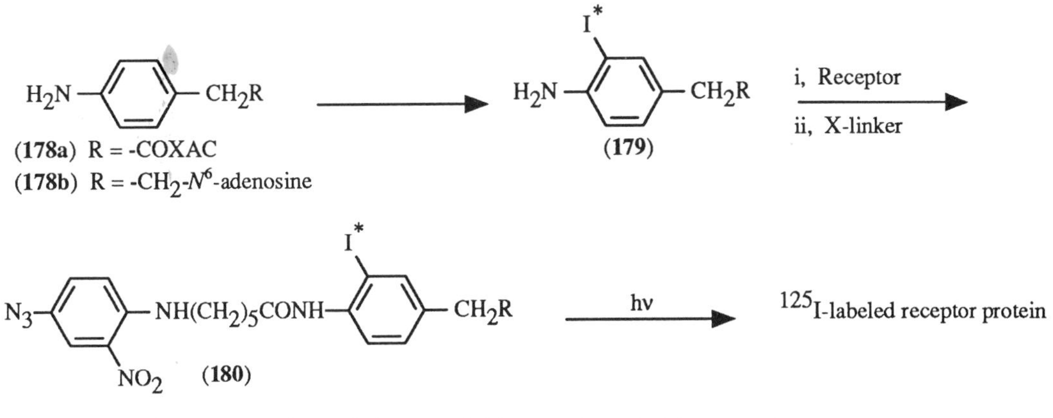

Scheme 2 Photoaffinity crosslinking, used to label A_1 adenosine receptors

Adenosine derivatives already containing arylazido groups (Figure 10) have been used as photoaffinity probes for adenosine receptors. Choca *et al.*[95] have reported the direct photoaffinity labeling of A_1 adenosine receptors using the agonist ligand N^6-(3-iodo-4-azidobenzyl)adenosine (IAzBA; **181**). Stiles labeled the A_1 adenosine receptor using [^{125}I]AZPNEA (**182**).[81] Klotz *et al.*[223] have synthesized (*R*)-2-azido-N^6-phenylisopropyladenosine (*R*-AHPIA), which can be iodinated to give

(**183**). Similar to the previous labeling studies, binding to the A_1 receptor (with a K_i of 1.6 nM in the dark) becomes irreversible upon irradiation with ultraviolet light (absorption maximum at 227 nm). *R*-AHPIA produces a persistent activation of adenosine receptors in isolated rat adipocytes.[224]

Covalent labeling of antagonists to A_1 adenosine receptors has been carried out using the photoaffinity crosslinking method (Scheme 2).[91] A prosthetic group (*p*-aminophenylacetyl; PAPA) for iodination was attached to the antagonist XAC, leading to covalent labeling of adenosine

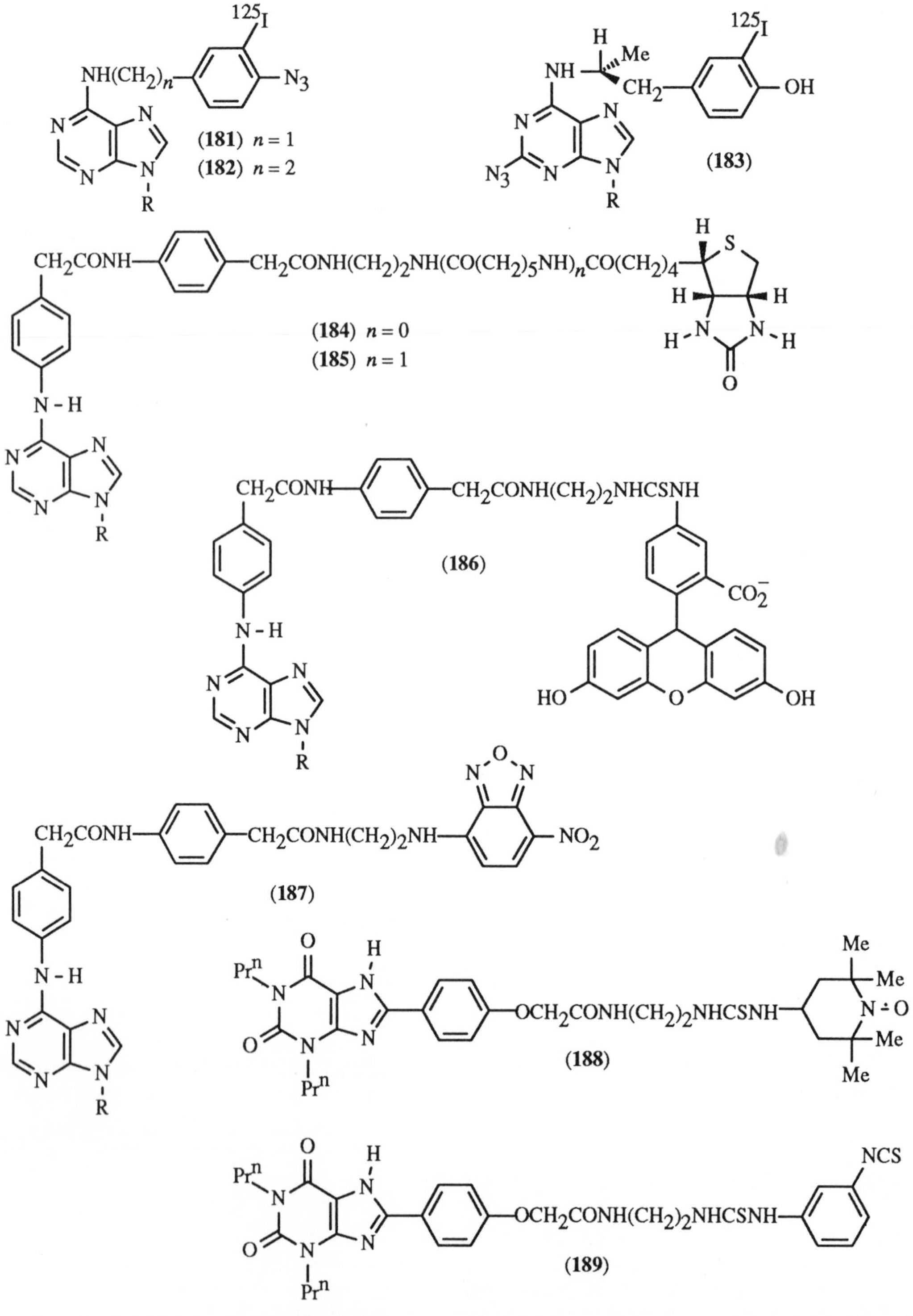

Figure 10 Structures of irreversible ligands and spectroscopic probes for adenosine receptors (R = ribosyl)

receptors. PAPA-XAC (**178b**) is iodinated using ^{125}I on the arylamine group (see Section 12.10.3.2). By virtue of its nucleophilic, uncharged amino group, [^{125}I]PAPA-XAC, when bound to adenosine receptors, reacts chemically with SANPAH, present at a concentration of 38 μM. Irradiation at 290 nm results in irreversible cross-linking of the radioactive label to a polypeptide of $M_r \approx 40\,000$, which has pharmacological characteristics of the A_1 receptor. Thus, covalent labeling is inhibited in the presence of *R*-PIA and other known competitors at adenosine receptors.

At P_2 receptors, the ATP derivative ANAPP$_3$ has been shown to be an effective photoaffinity label (see Section 12.10.5.2).[159-161]

Chemical affinity labels for A_1 receptors have been described.[225,226] *m*-DITC-XAC (**189**) and the *p*-isomer contain an isothiocyanate group (Figure 10) which reacts covalently with the receptor protein, as has been demonstrated using tritiated (**189**).[226]

12.10.7.2 Macromolecular and Spectroscopic Probes

The retention of biological activity in macromolecular conjugates of adenosine receptor ligands has been used as evidence for the extracellular nature of the receptor. Adenosine nucleotides were covalently attached to carbonic anhydrase and the conjugates were active as vasodilators *in vivo*.[227] Olsson and coworkers[228] attached adenosine analogs, through N^6-aminoalkylamino substituents, or xanthines, through aminoalkylamino and other C-8 substituents, to the oligosaccharide stachyose. The amine attachment point on the stachyose was created by periodate oxidation. The resulting dialdehydes were subject to reclosure by reductive amination. The stachyose conjugates displayed diminished but similar coronary vasoactivity to the parent drugs.

With efforts underway to isolate adenosine receptors using affinity chromatography, immobilized analogs are of renewed interest for affinity supports. Functionalized congeners of adenosine[133] (*e.g.* **65–69**) and xanthine (*e.g.* **144–154**) derivatives include analogs with carboxyl, amino, hydrazido, phenolic and other groups suitable for attachment to affinity matrices, such as sepharose resins. A series of biotin conjugates, *e.g.* adenosine derivatives (**184** and **185**), were designed for the potential use in the affinity isolation of adenosine receptors.[135] Covalent conjugates of adenosine and biotin bound simultaneously to avidin and the A_1 receptor.[229] However, a series of xanthine–biotin conjugates including long spacer chains were not capable of simultaneously bridging the two proteins. This suggested a difference in the receptor conformation or ligand orientation between agonist and antagonist bound states. Vasoactivity of biotinyl conjugates complexed to avidin (M_r 66 000) was dependent on the length of the spacer chain.[135] Such biotin conjugates are of use in estimating the depth of the binding site.

The biotin–adenosine conjugates may also serve as fluorescent or enzymatic probes for the receptor.[229] It was shown that even various conjugates of avidin, containing covalently bound fluorescein dye or horseradish peroxidase, will bind to the A_1 receptor bound adenosine–biotin conjugates. At the coronary A_2 receptor, biological activity of adenosine–biotin complexes with avidin appeared to be dependent on the spacer chain length. Attempts to use the adenosine–biotin probes in the histochemical localization of adenosine receptors have been hampered by low receptor density combined with problems associated with nonspecific tissue-binding of avidin.

An alternative approach to high affinity spectroscopic probes for adenosine receptors has been the covalent coupling of spectroscopic reporter groups. Fluorescent conjugates (*e.g.* fluorescein in **186**, having a K_i of 7 nM at rat A_1 receptors, and 4-nitrobenz-2-oxa-1,3-diazole, NBD, in **187**) have been derived from functionalized congeners of agonists or antagonists.[76] A number of other potent spectroscopic probes (K_i between 10^{-9} and 10^{-8} in rat brain) were obtained, including the spin label probe (**188**), which contains the stable free radical moiety TEMPO (K_i of 1.4 nM in rat brain).

12.10.8 BIOLOGICAL PROPERTIES OF AGONISTS AND ANTAGONISTS IN ANIMALS AND MAN

Purines, acting through P_1 and P_2 receptors have numerous physiological effects, which have been reviewed elsewhere.[63,230-232]

12.10.8.1 Adenosine Effects

12.10.8.1.1 Central nervous system responses

In the central nervous system, adenosine is thought to function as a neuromodulator.[233] Adenosine, acting through prejunctional receptors, causes an inhibition of the release of neurotransmitters,[234] including noradrenaline,[55] serotonin,[55] dopamine,[55] acetylcholine,[236] glutamate[237] and aspartate.[238] There is evidence that adenosine can act in an inhibitory manner also at postjunctional receptors.[239] In the spinal cord, the action of peptide neurotransmitters, such as substance P (mediating the pain response)[241] and opioids[242] may be mediated by release of adenosine. Modulation of pain pathways suggests that novel adenosine agonists eventually may be useful in the control of pain.

In vivo, potent adenosine agonists such as NECA and CHA cause a depression of locomotor activity and a form of sedation.[243-246] The central effects suggest that adenosine agonists may be useful as anxiolytic or sedative agents. A potent A_2 adenosine agonist (**84**; see Section 12.10.5.1.2) has promise as an antipsychotic agent, but its exact mechanism of action is unclear. Adenosine has also been implicated in the retardation of associative learning.[251]

Xanthines acting as adenosine antagonists have a central stimulatory effect. This is evident in their stimulation of locomotor activity and in the reversal of depressant effects of agonists.[178,181,243-246] 8-*p*-Sulfophenyltheophylline (**137**) and XAC (**145**) have been identified as peripherally active antagonists over a wide dose range.[196] In contrast, 8-cyclopentyltheophylline (**128**) is active both peripherally and in the central nervous system when administered peripherally.[186] Potent adenosine antagonists including xanthines may have application as central stimulants or cognitive enhancers.

Among the toxic effects of certain xanthines, including caffeine, are seizures.[247] It has been suggested that adenosine is released during seizures and functions as an endogenous antiepileptic.[248] XAC (**145**), upon rapid intravenous infusion in mice at doses greater than $30 \, mg \, kg^{-1}$, induces seizures.[249] CPX (**126**) prolongs epileptic seizures in rats.[250]

12.10.8.1.2 Cardiovascular responses

The effects of adenosine on brain stem sites that control blood pressure have been explored.[252] In addition to centrally mediated effects, nonselective adenosine agonists, acting directly on the cardiovascular system, have intense, parallel bradycardiac (related to A_1 receptors) and hypotensive (related to A_2 receptors) effects, as described in several reviews.[253,293] These effects are reversed by xanthines. The effects of adenosine on signal conduction in the heart have been studied.[255] Curiously, adenosine infusion in man is known to cause a rise in heart rate, the mechanism being an activation of the sympathoadrenal system.[256] Adenosine agonists can influence sympathetic transmission *in vivo* at several sites.[254]

The selectivity of xanthine analogs in blocking the cardiovascular effects of adenosine agonists has been studied. Fredholm *et al.*[200] found that, in contrast to theophylline which was nonselective, XAC (**145**) was approximately 20-fold selective for the blockade of cardiac depressant action (A_1) in rats *in vivo*, compared to the blockade of hypotensive effects. In isolated atrial (A_1) and aortic (A_2) tissues from guinea pig, XAC was nearly nonselective.[240] CPX (**126**) was highly A_1 selective in the isolated heart preparation.[185] Thus, there are potential applications of selective agents, both adenosine agonists (as antiarrhythmics or antihypertensives) and adenosine antagonists (as inotropic agents), in the cardiovascular system.

12.10.8.1.3 Renal responses

In the kidney there are several sites of action of adenosine.[257] Theophylline is known to have diuretic properties.[258] Moreover, theophylline and 8-phenyltheophylline have been shown to have kidney protective properties in renal failure models.[259,260] In addition to tubular effects on solute transport (an A_2 receptor has been characterized in tubules[261]), adenosine has marked hemodynamic effects. Churchill and Churchill[262] have delineated a biphasic response to adenosine agonists in renin release in kidney slices, corresponding to inhibitory A_1 (less than 1 µM CHA) and stimulatory A_2 (greater than 1 µM) effects.

12.10.8.1.4 Respiratory responses

The major clinical application of theophylline is in relieving the bronchoconstriction of asthma. Although there are adenosine receptors present in the lung,[172] it does not appear that they are involved in the antiasthmatic effect of theophylline. Enprofylline[179,180] is superior to theophylline for the treatment of asthma, but it is a much weaker adenosine antagonist; in certain systems it does not antagonize adenosine at all. Instead, there is evidence for the involvement of phosphodiesterase inhibition and perhaps other mechanisms in the actions of xanthines. On the other hand, adenosine produces bronchoconstriction in asthmatic, but not in normal, subjects.[263]

Adenosine also causes respiratory depression, through increased discharge of the carotid body chemoceptor.[265] Theophylline is used in the treatment of infant apnea.

12.10.8.1.5 Immune responses

In the immune system adenosine agonists act as immunosuppressants[266] through A_2 receptors, and appear to protect vascular endothelial cells from neutrophil-mediated injury.[267] In addition, adenosine can increase the release of mediators of inflammation, such as histamine.[172]

12.10.8.1.6 Other responses

Other physiological actions of adenosine, as outlined in Table 8, include effects in the gastro-intestinal system,[268] the retina[269] and body temperature regulation.[277]

Thus, adenosine receptor ligands have numerous potential therapeutic applications. To avoid side effects it would be desirable to achieve organ selectivity, through selective receptor affinity and/or the use of prodrugs[201] or other drug delivery systems.

12.10.8.2 ATP Effects

The organ systems in which ATP analogs have been studied most commonly are mentioned in Table 1. Burnstock and coworkers have developed the concept of ATP as a neurotransmitter. It has excitatory effects in the CNS.[278] In the periphery, ATP has an excitatory or relaxant effect on muscles (see Section 12.10.4.1). It is released by motor nerves and also postsynaptically.

The negative chronotropic and dromotropic effects of ATP on the heart have been studied.[255] In addition, ATP has inhibitory responses on the taenia coli, duodenum,[279] anal sphincter[280] and other organs.

There is evidence that ATP serves as an excitatory cotransmitter with noradrenaline in vascular sympathetic nerves. Also, excitatory responses of ATP on the frog atrium[281] and sympathetic ganglia, bladder detrussor,[282] vas deferens and other sites have been described.

The therapeutic possibilities of selective ATP agonists and antagonists in the cardiovascular system have been discussed.[3] Selective P_{2y} agonists or P_{2x} antagonists would enhance vasodilation.

Various transformed and untransformed cell lines respond to extracellular ATP.[283–286] In mouse fibroblasts, ATP induces membrane permeability to phosphorylated metabolites and other polar solutes.[284] ATP increases DNA synthesis, acts synergistically with platelet-derived growth factor and enhances rises in intracellular Ca^{2+}.[286]

Table 8 Selected Physiological Effects of Adenosine Agonists

Organ or tissue	Agonist effect	Ref.
Bone	cAMP effects	270
Brain	Sedation, inhibition of release of neurotransmitters (A_1)	43, 55, 56, 112, 196
Fat	Inhibition of lipolysis (A_1)	8
Heart	Cardiac depression (A_1)	185, 199, 200, 255
Immune system	Immunosuppression (A_2)	172, 266, 267
Kidneys	Inhibition of renin secretion (A_1), antidiuresis, vasoconstriction (A_1), vasodilation (A_2)	201
Liver	Stimulation of gluconeogenesis, vasoconstriction (A_2)	271
Muscle		63, 78
Pancreas	Inhibits glucose-induced insulin secretion	273
Retina	cAMP effects	269
Skin	Vasoconstriction (A_1)	274
Testes	High density of A_1 receptors,	275
Trachea (lungs)	Bronchoconstriction (A_1), relaxation of airway smooth muscle (A_2), A_1 present	172
Vasculature	Vasodilation (A_2)	199, 200

ACKNOWLEDGEMENTS

The author wishes to thank John W. Daly and Noel Cusack for helpful comments on this manuscript.

12.10.9 REFERENCES

1. F. Lipmann, *Adv. Enzymol. Relat. Subj. Biochem.*, 1941, **18**, 99.
2. A. N. Drury and A. Szent-Györgyi, *J. Physiol. (London)*, 1929, **68**, 213.
3. G. Burnstock, *Trends Med. Chem.*, 1986, 369.
4. J. L. Gordon, *Biochem. J.*, 1986, **233**, 309.
5. G. Burnstock, *Pharmacol. Rev.*, 1972, **24**, 509.
6. A. Sattin and T. Rall, *Mol. Pharmacol.*, 1970, **6**, 13.
7. D. van Calker, M. Müller and B. Hamprecht, *Nature (London)*, 1978, **276**, 839.
8. C. Londos, D. M. F. Cooper and J. Wolff, *Proc. Natl. Acad. Sci. U.S.A.*, 1980, **77**, 2551.
9. A. C. Newby, *Trends Biochem. Sci. (Pers. Ed.)*, 1984, **9**, 42.
10. H. Hagberg, P. Andersson, J. Lacarewicz, I. Jacobson, S. Butcher and M. Sandberg, *J. Neurochem.*, 1987, **49**, 227.
11. L. J. Heller and D. E. Mohrmann, in 'Topics and Perspectives in Adenosine Research', ed. E. Gerlach and B. F. Becker, Springer-Verlag, Berlin, p. 425.
12. J. D. Pearson, *Methods Pharmacol.*, 1985, **6**, 83.
13. M. Miyake and T. Innami, *J. Neurochem.*, 1987, **49**, 355.
14. H. G. E. Lloyd and J. Schrader, in 'Topics and Perspectives in Adenosine Research', ed. E. Gerlach and B. F. Becker, Springer-Verlag, Berlin, p. 199.
15. J. D. Young and S. M. Jarvis, *Methods Pharmacol.*, 1985, **6**, 181.
16. D. Saito, C. R. Steinhart, D. G. Nixon and R. A. Olsson, *Circ. Res.*, 1981, **47**, 875.
17. R. Rubio, R. M. Knabb, S. W. Ely, and R. M. Berne, in 'Topics and Perspectives in Adenosine Research', ed. E. Gerlach and B. F. Becker, Springer-Verlag, Berlin, p. 445.
18. A. C. Newby and C. A. Holmquist, *Biochem. J.*, 1981, **200**, 399.
19. J. W. Daly, *J. Med. Chem.*, 1982, **25**, 197.
20. A. C. Newby, *Biochem. J.*, 1986, **237**, 845.
21. B. Paul, M. F. Chen and A. R. P. Paterson, *J. Med. Chem.*, 1975, **18**, 968.
22. R. P. Agarwal, *Biochem. Pharmacol.*, 1977, **26**, 359.
23. P. W. Achterberg, R. J. Stroeve and J. W. DeJong, *Biochem. J.*, 1986, **253**, 13.
24. B. B. Fredholm, *Life Sci.*, 1987, **41**, 837.
25. H. Gewirtz, P. Brown and A. S. Most, *Proc. Soc. Exp. Biol. Med.*, 1987, **185**, 93.
26. G. Burnstock and C. Kennedy, *Circ. Res.*, 1986, **58**, 319.
27. J. H. Lister, in 'The Chemistry of Heterocyclic Compounds, Fused Pyrimidines', ed. A. Weissenberger and E. C. Taylor, Wiley, New York, 1971, part 2.
28. 'Synthetic Procedures in Nucleic Acid Chemistry', ed. W. W. Zorbach and R. S. Tipson, Wiley, New York, 1973, vol. 2.
29. G. Shaw, in 'Rodd's Chemistry of Carbon Compounds', Elsevier, Amsterdam, 1980, vol. 4, part L, p. 1.
30. E. W. Badger, D. S. Szotek and W. H. Moos, *Nucleosides Nucleotides*, 1986, **5**, 201.
31. A. Albert, in 'Synthetic Procedures in Nucleic Acid Chemistry', ed. W. W. Zorbach and R. S. Tipson, Wiley, New York, 1973, vol. 2, p. 47.
32. M. M. T. Khan and A. E. Martell, *J. Am. Chem. Soc.*, 1966, **88**, 668.
33. N. K. Kochetkov and E. I. Budovskii, 'Organic Chemistry of Nucleic Acids, Part B', Plenum Press, London, 1972, p. 439.
34. A. M. Michelson (ed.), 'The Chemistry of Nucleosides and Nucleotides', Academic Press, London, 1963, p. 153.
35. A. Albert, in 'Synthetic Procedures in Nucleic Acid Chemistry', ed. W. W. Zorbach and R. S. Tipson, Wiley, New York, 1973, vol. 2, chap. 2.
36. D. C. Dejongh, in: 'Synthetic Procedures in Nucleic Acid Chemistry', ed. W. W. Zorbach and R. S. Tipson, Wiley, New York, 1973, vol. 2, p. 145.
37. J. A. McCloskey, in 'Basic Principles in Nucleic Acid Chemistry', ed. P. O. P. Ts'o, Academic Press, New York, 1974, vol. 1, p. 209.
38. K. A. Jacobson, L. K. Pannell, K. L. Kirk, H. M. Fales and E. A. Sokoloski, *J. Chem. Soc., Perkin Trans. I*, 1986, 2143.
39. G. Burnstock, in 'Cell Membrane Receptors for Drugs and Hormones: A Multidisciplinary Approach', ed. L. Bolis and R. W. Straub, Raven Press, New York, 1978, p. 107.
40. R. J. Haslam and N. J. Cusack, in 'Purinergic Receptors (Receptors and Recognition, Series B)', ed. G. Burnstock, Chapman and Hall, London, 1981, vol. 12, p. 223.
41. R. Brückner, A. Fenner, W. Meyer, T.-M. Nobis, W. Schmitz and H. Scholz, *J. Pharmacol. Exp. Ther.*, 1985, **234**, 766.
42. B. B. Fredholm, E. Lindgren, M. Dunerr-Engstrom, J. Fastbom, J. Wang, J. Häggblad, I. van der Ploeg, T. Andersson, M. Jondal, J. Ng and C. Nordstedt, in 'Adenosine and Adenine Nucleotides', ed. D. Paton, Taylor and Francis, London, 1988, p. 121.
43. B. B. Fredholm and T. V. Dunwiddie, *Trends Pharmacol. Sci.*, 1988, **9**, 130.
44. R. F. Bruns, G. H. Lu and T. A. Pugsley, *Mol. Pharmacol.*, 1986, **29**, 331.
45. J. W. Daly, W. Padgett, R. D. Thompson, S. Kusachi, W. J. Bugni and R. A. Olsson, *Biochem. Pharmacol.*, 1986, **35**, 2467.
46. J. W. Daly, W. L. Padgett and M. T. Shamim, *J. Med. Chem.*, 1986, **29**, 1305.
47. K. A. Jacobson, R. de la Cruz, R. Schulick, L. Kiriasis, W. Padgett, W. Pfleiderer, K. L. Kirk, J. L. Neumeyer and J. W. Daly, *Biochem. Pharmacol.*, 1988, **37**, 3653.
48. Y. Nimit, J. Law and J. W. Daly, *Biochem. Pharmacol.*, 1982, **31**, 3279.
49. R. F. Bruns, *Can. J. Physiol. Pharmacol.*, 1980, **58**, 673.
50. R. F. Bruns, *Biochem. Pharmacol.*, 1981, **30**, 325.
51. G. L. Stiles, D. T. Daly and R. A. Olsson, *J. Biol. Chem.*, 1985, **260**, 10806.

52. G. L. Stiles, *J. Biol. Chem.*, 1986, **261**, 10 839.
53. W. J. Parsons and G. L. Stiles, *J. Biol. Chem.*, 1987, **262**, 841.
54. B. L. Ginsborg and G. D. S. Hirst, *J. Physiol. (London)*, 1972, **224**, 629.
55. H. H. Harms *et al.*, *Neuropharmacology*, 1979, **18**, 577.
56. R. Jackisch *et al.*, *Neuropharmacology*, 1984, **23**, 1363.
57. A. C. Dolphin and S. A. Prestwich, *Nature (London)*, 1985, **316**, 148.
58. L. O. Trussel and M. B. Jackson, *J. Neurosci.*, 1987, **7**, 3306.
59. M. Böhm, R. Brückner, J. Neumann, W. Schmitz, H. Scholz and J. Starbatty, *Naunyn-Schmeideberg's Arch. Pharmacol.*, 1986, **332**, 403.
60. D. W. Petcoff and D. M. F. Cooper, *Eur. J. Pharmacol.*, 1987, **137**, 269.
61. A. C. Dolphin, S. R. Forda and R. H. Scott, *J. Physiol. (London)*, 1986, **373**, 47.
62. H. Kai, H. Kanaide, T. Matsumoto, Y. Shogakiuchi and M. Nakamura, *FEBS Lett.*, 1987, **212**, 119.
63. J. A. Ribeiro and A. M. Sebastião, *Prog. Neurobiol.*, 1986, **26**, 179.
64. G. Gough, M. H. Maguire and F. Penglis, *Mol. Pharmacol.*, 1972, **8**, 170.
65. D. M. F. Cooper and M. Rodbell, *Nature (London)*, 1979, **282**, 517.
66. N. L. Leung, J. D. Vickers, R. L. Kinlough-Rathbone, H.-J. Reimers and J. F. Mustard, *Biochem. Biophys. Res. Commun.*, 1983, **113**, 483.
67. G. Burnstock and C. Kennedy, *Gen. Pharmacol.*, 1985, **16**, 433.
68. J. L. Gordon and W. Martin, *Br. J. Pharmacol.*, 1983, **80**, 179.
69. R. F. Furchgott, *Circ. Res.*, 1983, **53**, 557.
70. T. M. Griffith, D. H. Edwards, M. J. Lewis, A. C. Newby and A. H. Henderson, *Nature (London)*, 1984, **308**, 645.
71. F. Okajima, Y. Tokumitsu, Y. Kondo and M. Ui, *J. Biol. Chem.*, 1987, **262**, 13 483.
72. M. Williams and E. A. Risley, *Proc. Natl. Acad. Sci. U.S.A.*, 1980, **77**, 6892.
73. U. Schwabe and T. Trost, *Naunyn Schmiedeberg's Arch. Pharmacol.*, 1980, **313**, 179.
74. R. F. Bruns, J. W. Daly and S. H. Snyder, *Proc. Natl. Acad. Sci. U.S.A.*, 1980, **77**, 5547.
75. M. Williams, A. Braunwalder and T. E. Erikson, *Naunyn Schmiedeberg's Arch. Pharmacol.*, 1986, **332**, 179.
76. K. A. Jacobson, D. Ukena, W. Padgett, K. L. Kirk and J. W. Daly, *Biochem. Pharmacol.*, 1987, **36**, 1697.
77. D. Ukena, R. Furler, M. J. Lohse, G. Engel and U. Schwabe, *Naunyn Schmiedeberg's Arch. Pharmacol.*, 1984, **326**, 233.
78. R. Munshi, F. Hansske and H. P. Baer, *Eur. J. Pharmacol.*, 1985, **111**, 107.
79. M. Freissmuth, V. Hausleithner, E. Tuisl, C. Nanoff and W. Schütz, *Naunyn Schmiedeberg's Arch. Pharmacol.*, 1987, **335**, 438.
80. J. Linden, A. Patel and S. Sadek, *Circ. Res.*, 1984, **56**, 279.
81. G. L. Stiles, D. T. Daly and R. A. Olsson, *J. Neurochem.*, 1986, **47**, 1020.
82. P. J. Marangos, J. Patel, W. D. Smith and R. M. Post, *Epilepsia*, 1987, **28**, 387.
83. K. A. Jacobson, D. Ukena, K. L. Kirk and J. W. Daly, *Proc. Natl. Acad. Sci. U.S.A.*, 1986, **83**, 4089.
84. G. L. Stiles, D. T. Daly and R. A. Olsson, *J. Biol. Chem.*, 1985, **260**, 10 806.
85. J. Deckert, P. Morgan, J.-C. Bisserbe, K. A. Jacobson, K. L. Kirk, J. W. Daly and P. J. Marangos, *Neurosci. Lett.*, 1988, **86**, 121.
86. E. Leung, K. A. Jacobson and R. D. Green, in 'Adenosine and Adenine Nucleotides', ed. D. Paton, Taylor and Francis, London, 1988, p. 291.
87. R. F. Bruns, J. H. Fergus, E. W. Badger, J. A. Bristol, L. Santay, J. D. Hartman, S. J. Hays and C. C. Huang, *Naunyn Schmiedeberg's Arch. Pharmacol.*, 1987, **335**, 59.
88. J.-C. Bisserbe, O. Pascal and B. Maziere, in 'Purine Nucleosides and Nucleotides in Cell Signalling', Rockville, MD, 19th Sept. 1989, Abstract E-12.
89. M. Leid, M. I. Schimerlik and T. F. Murray, *Mol. Pharmacol.*, 1988, **34**, 334.
90. M. F. Jarvis, K. A. Jacobson and M. Williams, *Neurosci. Lett.*, 1987, **81**, 69.
91. G. L. Stiles and K. A. Jacobson, *Mol. Pharmacol.*, 1987, **32**, 184.
92. J. Linden, A. Patel, C. Q. Earl, R. H. Craig and S. M. Daluge, *J. Med. Chem.*, 1988, **31**, 745.
93. A. Patel, R. H. Craig, S. M. Daluge and J. Linden, *Mol. Pharmacol.*, 1988, **33**, 585.
94. S.-M. H. Yeung and R. D. Green, *Naunyn Schmiedeberg's Arch. Pharmacol.*, 1984, **325**, 247.
95. J. I. Choca, M. M. Kwatra, M. M. Hosey and R. D. Green, *Biochem. Biophys. Res. Commun.*, 1985, **131**, 115.
96. W. Schütz, G. Steurer and E. Tuisl, *Eur. J. Pharmacol.*, 1982, **85**, 177.
97. E. Hütteman, D. Ukena, V. Lenschow and U. Schwabe, *Naunyn Schmiedeberg's Arch. Pharmacol.*, 1984, **325**, 226.
98. D. Ukena, C. G. Schirren, K.-N. Klotz and U. Schwabe, *Naunyn Schmiedeberg's Arch. Pharmacol.*, 1985, **331**, 89.
99. M. Lohse, B. Elger, J. Lindenborn-Fotinos, K.-N. Klotz and U. Schwabe, *Naunyn Schmiedeberg's Arch. Pharmacol.*, 1988, **337**, 64.
100. M. Williams, M. Abreu, M. F. Jarvis and L. Noronha-Blob, *J. Neurochem.*, 1986, **48**, 498.
101. D. Ukena, K. A. Jacobson, K. L. Kirk and J. W. Daly, *FEBS Lett.*, 1986, **209**, 122.
102. R. F. Bruns, J. H. Fergus, E. W. Badger, J. A. Bristol, L. Santay and S. J. Hays, *Naunyn Schmiedeberg's Arch. Pharmacol.*, 1987, **335**, 64.
103. D. Ukena, R. A. Olsson and J. W. Daly, *Can. J. Physiol. Pharmacol.*, 1987, **65**, 365.
104. H. W. Hamilton, M. D. Taylor, R. P. Steffen, S. J. Haleen and R. F. Bruns, *Life Sci.*, 1987, **41**, 2295.
105. B. B. Fredholm, E. Lingren and K. Lindström, *Br. J. Pharmacol.*, 1985, **86**, 509.
106. D. Ukena, W. L. Pagett, O. Hong, J. W. Daly, D. T. Daly and R. A. Olsson, *FEBS Lett.*, 1987, **215**, 203.
107. J. Linden, *Mol. Pharmacol.*, 1984, **26**, 414.
108. E. Leung, M. M. Kwatra, M. M. Hosey and R. D. Green, *Mol. Pharmacol.*, 1988, **244**, 1150.
109. M. D. Taylor, W. H. Moos, H. W. Hamilton, D. S. Szotek, W. C. Patt, E. W. Badger, J. A. Bristol, R. F. Bruns, T. G. Heffner and T. E. Mertz, *J. Med. Chem.*, 1986, **29**, 346.
110. D. Ukena, M. T. Shamim, W. Padgett and J. W. Daly, *Life Sci.*, 1986, **39**, 743.
111. Williams-Ashman *et al.*, *Biochem. Pharmacol.*, 1982, **31**, 277.
112. R. Munshi, A. S. Clanachan and H. P. Baer, *Biochem. Pharmacol.*, 1988, **37**, 2085.
113. Y. Nimit, J. Law and J. Daly, *Biochem. Pharmacol.*, 1982, **31**, 3279.
114. W. Schütz, G. Steurer, E. Tuisl and H. Plass, *Biochem. J.*, 1984, **220**, 207.

115. G. Raberger, W. Schütz, and O. Kraupp, *Arch. Int. Pharmacodyn.*, 1977, **230**, 140
116. R. N. Prasad, D. S. Bariani, A. Fung, M. Savic and K. Tietje, *J. Med. Chem.*, 1980, **23**, 313.
117. N. J. Cusack and S. M. O. Hourani, *Br. J. Pharmacol.*, 1981, **72**, 443.
118. D. Ukena, R. Furler, M. J. Lohse, G. Engel and U. Schwabe, *Naunyn Schmiedeberg's Arch. Pharmacol.*, 1984, **326**, 233.
119. Y. C. Martin, K. H. Kim, T. Koschmann and T. J. O'Donnell, in 'Computer Applications in Chemistry', ed. S. R. Heller and R. Potenzone, Jr., Elsevier, Amsterdam, 1983, p. 285.
120. R. Marumoto, Y. Yoshioka, O. Miyashita, S. Shima, K. Imai, K. Kawazoe and M. Honjo, *Chem. Pharm. Bull.*, 1975, **23**, 759.
121. *U.S. Pat.* 3 936 439, 4 225 591 (1980) and 4 258 033 (1981).
122. W. H. Moos, D. S. Szotek and R. F. Bruns, *J. Med. Chem.*, 1985, **28**, 1383.
123. J. W. Daly, W. Padgett, R. D. Thompson, S. Kusachi, W. J. Bugni and R. A. Olsson, *Biochem. Pharmacol.*, 1986, **35**, 2467.
124. S. Kusachi, R. D. Thompson, W. J. Bugni, N. Yamada and R. A. Olsson, *J. Med. Chem.*, 1985, **28**, 1636.
125. S. Kusachi, R. D. Thompson, N. Yamada, D. T. Daly and R. A. Olsson, *J. Med. Chem.*, 1986, **29**, 989.
126. T. V. Dunwiddie, T. S. Worth and R. A. Olsson, *Naunyn Schmiedeberg's Arch. Pharmacol.*, 1986, **334**, 77.
127. A. J. Bridges, W. H. Moos, D. L. Szotek, B. K. Trivedi, J. A. Bristol, T. G. Heffner, R. F. Bruns and D. A. Downs, *J. Med. Chem.*, 1987, **30**, 1709.
128. A. J. Bridges, R. F. Bruns, D. F. Ortwine, S. R. Priebe, D. L. Szotek and B. K. Trivedi, *J. Med. Chem.*, 1988, **31**, 1282.
129. B. K. Trivedi, J. A. Bristol, R. F. Bruns, S. J. Haleen and R. P. Steffen, *J. Med. Chem.*, 1988, **31**, 271.
130. D. M. Paton, R. A. Olsson, R. T. Thompson, *Naunyn Schmiedeberg's Arch. Pharmacol.*, 1986, **333**, 313.
131. R. A. Olsson, S. Kusachi, R. D. Thompson, D. Ukena, W. Padgett and J. W. Daly, *J. Med. Chem.*, 1986, **29**.
132. T. V. Dunwiddie, B. B. Fredholm, B. Jonzon and G. Sandberg, *Br. J. Pharmacol.*, 1985, **84**, 625.
133. K. A. Jacobson, K. L. Kirk, W. L. Padgett and J. W. Daly, *J. Med. Chem.*, 1985, **28**, 1341.
134. P. M. J. van Galen, A. P. Ijzerman and W. Soudijn, *FEBS Lett.*, 1987, **223**, 197.
135. K. A. Jacobson, N. Yamada, K. L. Kirk, J. W. Daly and R. A. Olsson, *Biochem. Biophys. Res. Commun.*, 1986, **136**, 1097 and **139**, 375 (erratum).
136. K. A. Jacobson, J. Zimmet, R. Schulick, S. Barone, J. W. Daly and K. L. Kirk, *FEBS Lett.*, 1987, **225**, 97.
137. P. J. Buckle and I. Spence, *Naunyn Schmiedeberg's Arch. Pharmacol.*, 1981, **316**, 64.
138. L. P. Davies, J. Baird-Lambert and J. G. Hall, *Neuropharmacology*, 1987, **26**, 493.
139. H. W. Hamilton and J. A. Bristol, *J. Med. Chem.*, 1983, **26**, 1601.
140. G. Cristalli, M. Grifantini and S. Vittori, *Nucleosides Nucleotides*, 1985, **4**, 625.
141. G. Cristalli, P. Franchetti, M. Grifantini, S. Vittori, K.-N. Klotz and M. J. Lohse, *J. Med. Chem.*, 1988, **31**, 1179.
142. M. J. Lohse, K.-N. Klotz, U. Schwabe, G. Cristalli, S. Vittori and M. Grifantini, *Naunyn Schmiedeberg's Arch. Pharmacol.*, 1988, **337**, 687.
143. L. P. Davies, D. D. Jamieson, J. A. Baird-Lambert and R. Kazlauskas, *Biochem. Pharmacol.*, 1984, **33**, 347.
144. P. Lukasco and R. D. Krell, *Eur. J. Pharmacol.*, 1982, **80**, 401.
145. C. M. Brown and G. Burnstock, *Eur. J. Pharmacol.*, 1981, **69**, 81.
146. M. H. Maguire and D. G. Satchell, *Regul. Funct. Adenosine Adenine Nucleotides*, 1979, 33.
147. J. S. Fedan, G. K. Hogaboom, D. P. Westfall and J. P. O'Donnel, *Eur. J. Pharmacol.*, 1982, **81**, 193.
148. G. Burnstock, N. J. Cusack and L. A. Meldrum, *Br. J. Pharmacol.*, 1984, **82**, 369.
149. D. P. Westfall, G. K. Hogaboom, J. Colby, J. P. O'Donnel and J. S. Fedan, *Proc. Natl. Acad. Sci. U.S.A.*, 1982, **79**, 7041.
150. N. J. Cusack and M. Planker, *Br. J. Pharmacol.*, 1979, **67**, 153.
151. C. M. Brown and B. Burnstock, *Br. J. Pharmacol.*, 1981, **73**, 617.
152. D. G. Satchell and M. H. Maguire, *J. Pharmacol. Exp. Ther.*, 1975, **195**, 5430.
153. G. Burnstock, N. J. Cusack, J. M. Hills, I. MacKensie and P. Meghii, *Br. J. Pharmacol.*, 1983, **79**, 907.
154. G. Burnstock, N. J. Cusack and L. A. Meldrum, *Br. J. Pharmacol.*, 1985, **84**, 431.
155. O. Krishtal, S. M. Marchenko, A. G. Obukhov and T. M. Volkova, *Br. J. Pharmacol.*, 1988, **95**, 1957.
156. D. G. Satchell and M. H. Maguire, *Physiol. Pharmacol. Adenosine Deriv.*, 1983, 85.
157. L. A. Welford, N. J. Cusack and S. M. O. Hourani, *Eur. J. Pharmacol.*, 1987.
158. D. G. Satchell and M. H. Maguire, *Eur. J. Pharmacol.*, 1982, **81**, 669.
159. G. K. Hogaboom, J. P. O'Donnell and J. S. Fedon, *Science (Washington, D.C.)*, 1980, **208**, 1273.
160. J. S. Fedan, G. K. Hogaboom, J. P. O'Donnell, J. Colby and D. P. Westfall, *Eur. J. Pharmacol.*, 1981, **69**, 41.
161. D. P. Westfall, J. S. Fedan, J. Colby, G. K. Hogaboom and J. P. O'Donnell, *Eur. J. Pharmacol.*, 1983, **87**, 415.
162. L. Kasakov and G. Burnstock, *Eur. J. Pharmacol.*, 1983, **86**, 291.
163. R. M. Levin, R. Jacoby and A. J. Wein, *Mol. Pharmacol.*, 1981, **19**, 525.
164. N. J. Cusack and S. M. O. Hourani, *Br. J. Pharmacol.*, 1984, **82**, 155.
165. N. J. Cusack, S. M. O. Hourani, G. D. Loizou and L. A. Welford, *Br. J. Pharmacol.*, 1987, **90**, 971.
166. S. M. O. Hourani, L. A. Welford and N. J. Cusack, *Eur. J. Pharmacol.*, 1985, **108**, 197.
167. R. G. Yount, D. Babcock, W. Ballantyne and D. Ojala, *Biochemistry*, 1971, **10**, 2484.
168. N. J. Cusack, L. A. Welford and S. M. O. Hourani, in 'Adenosine and Adenine Nucleotides', ed. D. Paton, Taylor and Francis, London, 1988, p. 73.
169. S. M. O. Hourani, L. A. Welford, G. D. Loizou and N. J. Cusack, *Eur. J. Pharmacol.*, 1989, in press.
170. A. Kurtz, *J. Biol. Chem.*, 1987, **262**, 6296.
171. P. H. Wu, J. W. Phillis, K. Balls and B. Rinaldi, *Can. J. Physiol. Pharmacol.*, 1980, **58**, 576.
172. A. Leoutsakos and F. L. Pearce, *Biochem. Pharmacol.*, 1986, **35**, 1373.
173. I. Fox and L. Kurpis, *J. Biol. Chem.*, 1983, **258**, 6952.
174. J. W. Daly, W. L. Padgett and K. Eger, *Biochem. Pharmacol.*, 1988, **37**, 3749.
175. A. Matsuda and T. Ueda, *Nucleosides Nucleotides*, 1987, **6**, 85.
176. G. Burnstock and J. J. Warland, *Br. J. Pharmacol.*, 1987, **90**, 383.
177. J. W. Daly, P. Butts-Lamb and W. Padgett, *Cell. Mol. Neurobiol.*, 1983, **3**, 69.
178. O. H. Choi, M. T. Shamim, W. L. Padgett and J. W. Daly, *Life Sci.*, 1988, **43**, 387.
179. C. G. A. Persson, U.-E. Anderson and G. Kjellin, *Life Sci.*, 1986, **38**, 1057.
180. C. G. A. Persson, *J. Allergy Clin. Immunol.*, 1986, **78**, 780.
181. T. W. Seale, K. A. Abla, M. T. Shamim, J. M. Carney and J. W. Daly, *Life Sci.*, 1988, **43**, 1671.

182. R. F. Bruns, J. W. Daly and S. H. Snyder, *Proc. Natl. Acad. U.S.A.*, 1983, **80**, 2077.
183. R. A. Olsson, R. D. Thompson and S. Kusachi, *Methods Pharmacol.*, 1985, **6**, 293.
184. A. S. Clanachan, *Can. J. Physiol. Pharmacol.*, 1981, **59**, 603.
185. S. J. Haleen, R. P. Steffen and H. W. Hamilton, *Life Sci.*, 1987, **40**, 555.
186. R. F. Bruns, R. E. Davis, F. W. Ninteman, B. P. H. Poschel, J. N. Wiley and T. G. Heffner, in 'Adenosine and Adenine Nucleotides', ed. D. M. Paton, Taylor and Francis, London, 1988, p. 39.
187. J. W. Daly, W. Padgett, M. T. Shamim, P. Butts-Lamb and J. Waters, *J. Med. Chem.*, 1985, **28**, 487.
188. U. Schwabe, D. Ukena and M. J. Lohse, *Naunyn Schmiedeberg's Arch. Pharmacol.*, 1985, **330**, 212.
189. J. W. Ferkany, H. L. Valentine, G. A. Stone and M. Williams, *Drug Dev. Res.*, 1986, **9**, 85.
190. D. Ukena, K. A. Jacobson, W. L. Padgett, C. Ayala, M. T. Shamim, K. L. Kirk, R. A. Olsson and J. W. Daly, *FEBS Lett.*, 209, **122**, 1986.
191. M. T. Shamim, D. Ukena, W. L. Padgett and J. W. Daly, *J. Med. Chem.*, 1989, **32**, 1231.
192. H. W. Hamilton, D. F. Ortwine, D. F. Worth, E. W. Badger, J. A. Bristol, R. F. Bruns, S. J. Haleen and R. P. Steffen, *J. Med. Chem.*, 1985, **28**, 1071.
193. G. Burnstock and C. H. V. Hoyle, *Br. J. Pharmacol.*, 1985, **85**, 291.
194. M. Williams, M. F. Jarvis, M. A. Sills, J. W. Ferkany and A. Braunwalder, *Biochem. Pharmacol.*, 1987, **36**, 4042.
195. D. Ukena, K. L. Kirk and J. W. Daly, *Life Sci.*, 1986, **39**, 743.
196. T. W. Seale, K. A. Abla, K. A. Jacobson and J. M. Carney, *Pharmacol., Biochem. Behav.*, in press.
197. J. A. Bristol and E. W. Badger, *US Pat.* 4 452 788 (1984).
198. K. A. Jacobson, K. L. Kirk, W. L. Padgett and J. W. Daly, *Mol. Pharmacol.*, 1986, **29**, 126.
199. K. A. Jacobson, K. L. Kirk, J. W. Daly, B. Jonzon, Y.-O. Li and B. B. Fredholm, *Acta. Physiol. Scand.*, 1985, **125**, 341.
200. B. B. Fredholm, K. A. Jacobson, K. L. Kirk, B. Jonzon, Y.-O. Li and J. W. Daly, *J. Cardiovasc. Pharmacol.*, 1987, **9**, 396.
201. S. Barone, P. C. Churchill and K. A. Jacobson, *J. Pharmacol. Exp. Ther.*, 1989, **250**, 79.
202. K. A. Jacobson, A. W. Lipkowski, T. W. Moody, W. Padgett, E. Pijl, K. L. Kirk and J. W. Daly, *J. Med. Chem.*, 1987, **30**, 1529.
203. E. A. Martinson, R. A. Johnson and J. N. Wells, *Mol. Pharmacol.*, 1987, **31**, 247.
204. L. P. Davies, S. Chen Chow, J. H. Skerrit, D. J. Brown and G. A. R. Johnson, *Life Sci.*, 1984, **34**, 2117.
205. M. Williams, E. A. Risley and J. R. Huff, *Can. J. Physiol. Pharmacol.*, 1981, **59**, 897.
206. J. H. Skerritt, L. P. Davies and G. A. R. Johnson, *Eur. J. Pharmacol.*, 1982, **82**, 195.
207. P. J. Marangos, R. M. Post, J. Patel, K. Zander, A. Parma and S. Weiss, *Eur. J. Pharmacol.*, 1983, **93**, 175.
208. R. L. Weir, W. Padgett, J. W. Daly and S. M. Anderson, *Epilepsia*, 1984, **25**, 492.
209. C. Levallois, J. Bonnafous, M. Francoise, C. Sablayrolles, J. Chapat and J. Mani, *Biochem. Pharmacol.*, 1984, **33**, 2253.
210. R. A. Glennon, S. M. Tejani-Butt, W. Padgett and J. W. Daly, *J. Med. Chem.*, 1984, **27**, 1364.
211. A. J. Czernik, B. Petrack, H. J. Kalinsky, S. Psychoyos, W. D. Cash, C. Tsia, R. K. Rinehart, F. R. Granat, R. A. Lovell, D. E. Brundish and R. Wade, *Life Sci.*, 1982, **30**, 363.
212. M. Williams, J. Francis, G. Ghai, A. Braunwalder, S. Psychoyos, G. A. Stone and W. D. Cash, *J. Pharmacol. Exp. Ther.*, 1987, **241**, 415.
213. G. Ghai, J. E. Francis, M. Williams, R. A. Dotson, M. F. Hopkins, D. T. Cote, F. R. Goodman and M. B. Zimmerman, *J. Pharmacol. Exp. Ther.*, 1987, **242**, 784.
214. J. E. Francis, W. D. Cash, S. Psychoyos, G. Ghai, P. Wenk, R. C. Friedmann, C. Atkins, V. Warren, P. Furness, J. L. Hyun, G. A. Stone, M. Desai and M. Williams, *J. Med. Chem.*, 1988, **31**, 1014.
215. T. Katsuragi, Inoue and T. Furukawa, *Eur. J. Pharmacol.*, 1985, **108**, 151.
216. T. W. Stone and P. Forster, *Biochem. Pharmacol.*, 1986, **35**, 1757.
217. J. W. Daly, O. Hong, W. L. Padgett, M. T. Shamim, K. A. Jacobson and D. Ukena, *Biochem. Pharmacol.*, 1988, **37**, 655.
218. H. W. Hamilton, D. F. Ortwine, D. F. Worth and J. A. Bristol, *J. Med. Chem.*, 1987, **30**, 91.
219. R. F. Bruns and L. L. Coughenour, *Pharmacologist*, 1987.
220. N. P. Peet, G. A. Dickerson, A. H. Abdallah, J. W. Daly and D. Ukena, *J. Med. Chem.*, 1988, **31**, 2034.
221. B. K. Trivedi and R. F. Bruns, *J. Med. Chem.*, 1988, **31**, 1011.
222. H. Bayley, in 'Laboratory Techniques in Biochemistry and Molecular Biology', 1984, p. 29.
223. K.-N. Klotz, G. Cristalli, M. Grifantini, S. Vittori and M. J. Lohse, *J. Biol. Chem.*, 1979, **260**, 14 659.
224. M. J. Lohse, K.-N. Klotz and U. Schwabe, *Mol. Pharmacol.*, 1986, **30**, 403.
225. K. A. Jacobson, S. Barone, U. Kammula and G. Stiles, *J. Med. Chem.*, 1989, **32**, 1043.
226. G. L. Stiles and K. A. Jacobson, *Mol. Pharmacol.*, 1988, **34**, 724.
227. J. Schrader, S. Nees and E. Gerlach, *Pflügers Arch.*, 1977, **369**, 251.
228. R. A. Olsson, C. J. Davis, E. M. Khoury and R. E. Patterson, *Circ. Res.*, 1976, **39**, 93.
229. K. A. Jacobson, K. L. Kirk, W. Padgett and J. W. Daly, *FEBS Lett.*, 1985, **184**, 30.
230. M. Williams, *Annu. Rev. Pharmacol. Toxicol.*, 1987, **27**, 315.
231. G. Burnstock and N. J. Buckley, *Methods Pharmacol.*, 1985, **6**, 193.
232. T. D. White, *Pharmacol. Ther.*, 1988, **38**, 129.
233. S. H. Snyder, *Annu. Rev. Neurosci.*, 1985, **8**, 103.
234. T. W. Stone, *Neuroscience*, 1981, **6**, 523.
235. J. Deckert, J.-C. Bisserbe, E. Klein and P. J. Marangos, *J. Neurosci.*, 1988, **8**, 2338.
236. F. Pedata, L. Giovannelli, P. De Sarno and G. Pepeu, *J. Neurochem.*, 1986, **46**, 1593.
237. A. C. Dolphin and E. R. Archer, *Neurosci. Lett.*, 1983, **43**, 49.
238. J. Drejer, A. Frandsen, T. Honoré and A. Schousboe, *Neurochem. Int.*, 1987, **11**, 77.
239. T. V. Dunwiddie, unpublished results.
240. M. G. Collis, K. A. Jacobson and D. M. Tompkins, *Br. J. Pharmacol.*, 1987, **92**, 69.
241. M. I. Sweeney, T. D. White, K. H. Jhamandas and J. Sawynok, *Eur. J. Pharmacol.*, 1987, **141**, 169.
242. G. E. Delander and C. J. Hopkins, *J. Pharmacol. Exp. Ther.*, 1986, **239**, 88.
243. R. A. Barraco, V. L. Coffin, H. J. Altman and J. W. Phillis, *Brain Res.*, 1983, **272**, 392.
244. J. J. Katims, Z. Annau and S. H. Snyder, *J. Pharmacol. Exp. Ther.*, 1983, **227**, 167.
245. S. H. Snyder, J. J. Katims, Z. Annau, R. F. Bruns and J. W. Daly, *Proc. Natl. Acad. Sci. U.S.A.*, 1981, **78**, 3260.
246. H. Vapaatalo, D. Onken, P. J. Neuvonen and E. Westerman, *Arzneim-Forsch.*, 1975, **25**, 407.

247. J. L. Katz and J. M. Carney, *Pharmacol. Biochem. Behav.*, 1988, **29**, 409.
248. M. Dragunow, G. V. Godard and R. Laverty, *Epilepsia*, 1985, **26**, 480.
249. P. F. Morgan, J. Deckert, K. A. Jacobson, P. J. Marangos and J. W. Daly, *Life Sci.*, 1989, **45**, 719.
250. M. Dragunow and H. A. Robertson, *Brain Res.*, 1987, **417**, 377.
251. L. Winsky and J. A. Harvey, *J. Neurosci.*, 1986, **6**, 2684.
252. R. A. Barraco, J. W. Phillis, W. R. Campell, D. R. Marcantonio and R. S. Salah, *Neuropharmacology*, 1986, **25**, 675.
253. A. Sollevi, *Prog. Neurobiol.*, 1986, **27**, 319.
254. G. E. Evoniuk, R. W. von Borstel and R. J. Wurtman, *J. Pharmacol. Exp. Ther.*, 1986, **236**, 350.
255. A. Pelleg, E. L. Michelson and L. S. Dreifus, 'Cardiac Electrophysiology and Pharmacology of Adenosine and ATP: Basic and Clinical Aspects', Liss, New York, 1987.
256. I. Biaggioni, J. Onrot, A. S. Hollister and D. Robertson, *Life Sci.*, 1986, **39**, 2229.
257. H. Osswald, *Trends Pharmacol. Sci.*, 1984, 94.
258. M. G. Collis, D. B. Palmer and G. S. Baxter, *Eur. J. Pharmacol.*, 1986, **121**, 141.
259. A. K. Bidani and P. C. Churchill, *Can. J. Physiol. Pharmacol.*, 1983, **61**, 567.
260. C. J. Bowmer, M. G. Collis and M. S. Yates, *Br. J. Pharmacol.*, 1986, **88**, 205.
261. M. Freissmuth, C. Nanoff, E. Tuisl and W. Schuetz, *Eur. J. Pharmacol.*, 1987, **138**, 137.
262. P. C. Churchill and M. C. Churchill, *J. Exp. Pharmacol. Ther.*, 1985, **232**, 589.
263. M. K. Church, R. L. Featherstone, M. J. Cushley, J. S. Mann and S. T. Holgate, *J. Allergy Clin. Immunol.*, 1986, **78**, 670.
264. K. A. Jacobson, unpublished results.
265. J. A. Ribeiro, E. C. Monteiro and D. S. McQueen, in 'Adenosine and Adenine Nucleotides', ed. D. M. Paton, Taylor and Francis, London, 1988, p. 225.
266. R. Mandler, R. E. Birch, S. H. Polamr, G. M. Kammer and S. A. Rudolph, *Proc. Natl. Acad. Sci. U.S.A.*, 1982, **79**, 7542.
267. B. N. Cronstein, S. B. Kramer, E. D. Rosenstein, G. Weissmann and R. Hirschhorn, *Ann. N. Y. Acad. Sci.*, **451**, 292.
268. J. G. Gerber, A. S. Nies and N. A. Payne, *J. Pharmacol. Exp. Ther.*, 1984, **31**, 109.
269. C. Blazynski, *J. Neurosci.*, 1987, **7**, 2522.
270. K. A. Jacobson, unpublished results.
271. C. Londos and T. Wolff, *Proc. Natl. Acad. Sci. U.S.A.*, 1977, **74**, 5482.
272. W. W. Lautt, in 'Adenosine and Adenine Nucleotides', ed. D. M. Paton, Taylor and Francis, London, 1988, p. 185.
273. K. A. Jacobson, unpublished results.
274. K. A. Jacobson, unpublished results.
275. L. Monaco and M. Conti, *Biol. Reprod.*, 1986, **35**, 258.
276. R. M. J. Palmer, A. G. Ferrige and S. Moncada, *Nature (London)*, 1987, 327, 524.
277. L. C. H. Wang and E. C. Anholt, *J. Appl. Physiol.: Respir. Environ. Exercise Physiol.*, 1982, **53**, 16.
278. J. W. Phillis and P. H. Wu, *Prog. Neurobiol.*, 1981, **16**, 187.
279. S. Manzini, C. A. Maggi and A. Meli, *Eur. J. Pharmacol.*, 1986, **123**, 229.
280. S. P. Lim and T. C. Muir, *Eur. J. Pharmacol.*, 1986, **128**, 17.
281. C. H. V. Hoyle and G. Burnstock, *Eur. J. Pharmacol.*, 1986, **124**, 285.
282. R. J. Theobald, *Life Sci.*, 1983, **32**, 2479.
283. E. Rosengurt and L. A. Heppel, *J. Biol. Chem.*, 1979, **254**, 708.
284. Z. Sternberg and L. A. Heppel, *Biochem. Biophys. Res. Commun.*, 1987, **148**, 560.
285. G. R. Dubyak and M. B. DeYoung, *J. Biol. Chem.*, 1985, **260**, 10653.
286. F. A. Gonzales, L. A. Heppel, D. J. Gross, W. W. Webb and G. Parries, *Biochem. Biophys. Res. Commun.*, 1988, **151**, 1205.
287. R. A. Johnson, S.-M. H. Yeung, D. Stübner, M. Bushfield and I. Shoshani, *Mol. Pharmacol.*, 1989, **35**, 681.
288. W. W. Barrington, K. A. Jacobson, M. Williams, A. J. Hutchison and G. L. Stiles, *Proc. Natl. Acad. Sci. U.S.A.*, 1989, **86**, 6572.
289. A. J. Hutchison, M. Williams, R. de Jesus, H. H. Oei, G. R. Ghai, R. L. Webb, H. C. Zoganas, G. A. Stone and M. F. Jarvis, *J. Med. Chem.*, submitted.
290. M. Jarvis, R. Schutz, A. J. Hutchison, E. Do, M. A. Sills and M. Williams, *J. Pharmacol. Exp. Ther.*, 1989, in press.
291. P. J. M. van Galen, F. J. J. Leusen, A. P. Ijzerman and W. Soudijn, *Eur. J. Pharmacol.*, 1989, **172**, 19.
292. K. A. Jacobson, L. Kiriasis, S. Barone, B. J. Bradbury, U. Kammula, J. M. Campagne, S. Secunda, J. W. Daly, J. L. Neumeyer and W. Pfleiderer, *J. Med. Chem.*, 1989, **32**, 1873.
293. L. Belardinelli, J. Linden and R. M. Berne, *Prog. Cardiovasc. Dis.*, 1989, **32**, 73.
294. H. Nakata, *Mol. Pharmacol.*, 1989, **35**, 780.
295. B. K. Trivedi and R. F. Bruns, *J. Med. Chem.*, 1989, **32**, 1667.

12.11

Prostanoids and their Receptors

ROBERT A. COLEMAN, IAN KENNEDY, PATRICK P. A. HUMPHREY, KEITH BUNCE AND PHILIP LUMLEY

Glaxo Group Research Ltd, Ware, UK

12.11.1   PROSTANOID BIOCHEMISTRY

12.11.1.1   Definition, Structure and Nomenclature

The prostanoids are oxygenated derivatives of C_{20} fatty acids, principally arachidonic acid. Five pathways of arachidonic acid metabolism are currently recognized (for a review see Needleman *et al.*[1]), and prostanoids are the products of the first of these to be discovered, the cyclooxygenase pathway. There are two major classes of prostanoid, the prostaglandins (PGs) and the thromboxanes (Txs).

Prostaglandins may be regarded as substituted derivatives of prostanoic acid (**1**),[2] and are classified according to the substitution pattern on the cyclopentane ring. Currently 10 types, designated A–J, are known (see structures **2–11**). Prostaglandins E (**6**) and F_α (**7**), the first to be discovered, were so named because they partitioned into ether and phosphate buffer (Swedish fosfat) respectively,[3] whereas prostaglandins A (**2**) and B (**3**) were so named because they can be produced by treatment of PGE with acid and base respectively.[4] Thereafter, PGs were named to fill in and extend the alphabetical sequence. Prostaglandins G (**8**) and H (**9**) are exceptional in that both have the same endoperoxide ring structure, differing only at C-15, having hydroperoxy and hydroxy groups respectively.

Thromboxanes may be regarded as derivatives of thrombanoic acid (**12**).[5] Thromboxane A has an oxetane–oxane structure (**13**), which is highly unstable and rapidly decomposes ($t_{1/2}$ at $37\,^\circ C \approx 32$ s)

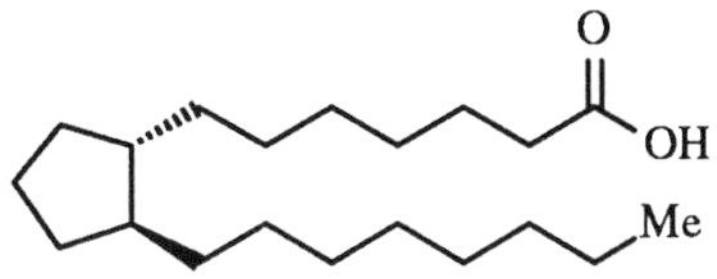

(**1**) Prostanoic acid

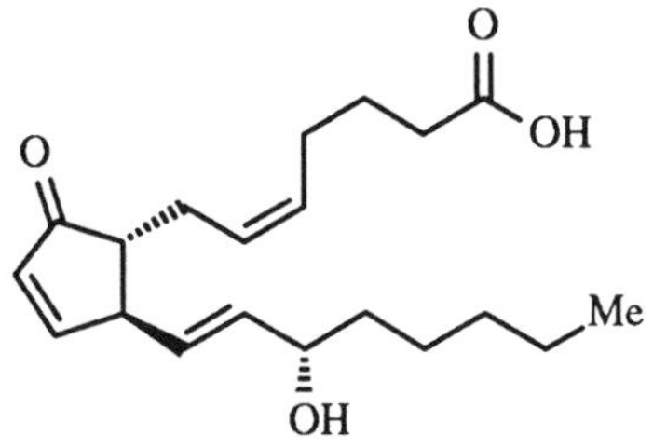

(**2**) Prostaglandin A$_2$

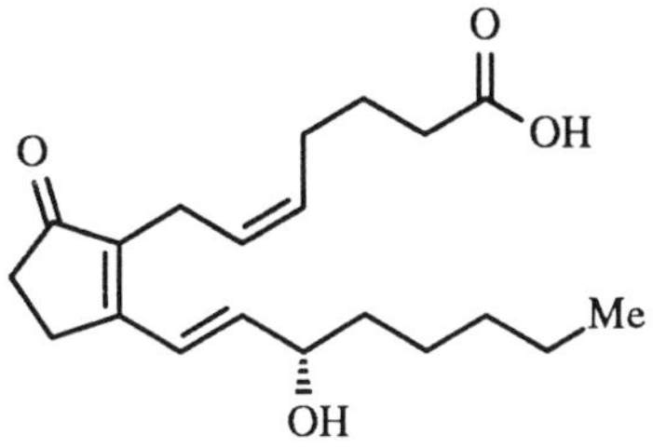

(**3**) Prostaglandin B$_2$

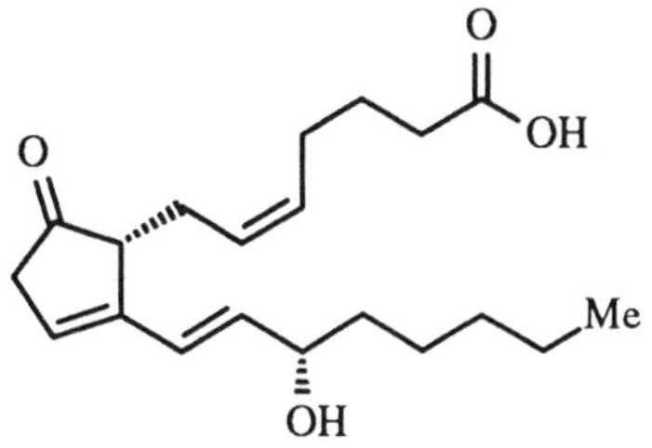

(**4**) Prostaglandin C$_2$

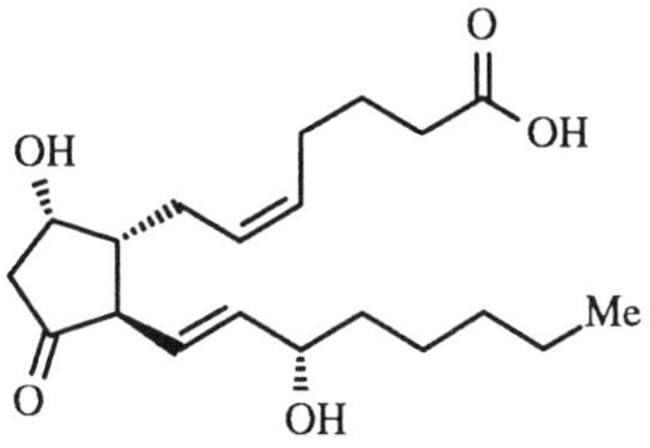

(**5**) Prostaglandin D$_2$

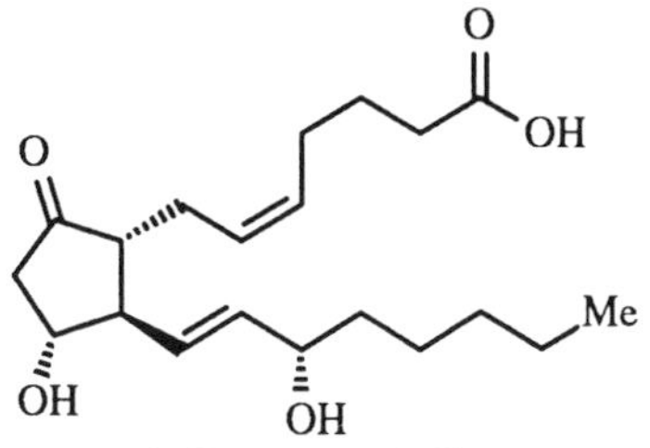

(**6**) Prostaglandin E$_2$

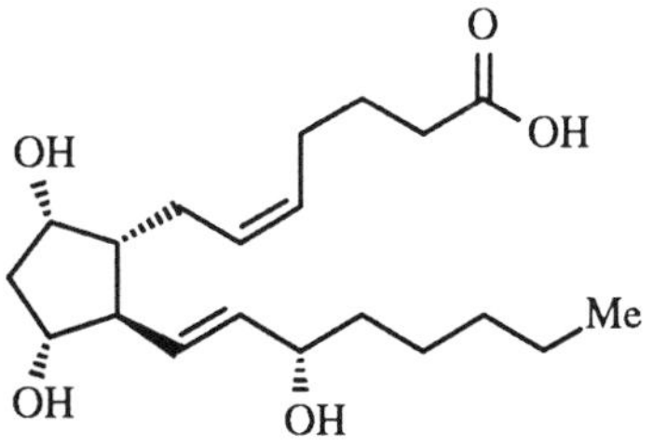

(**7**) Prostaglandin F$_{2\alpha}$

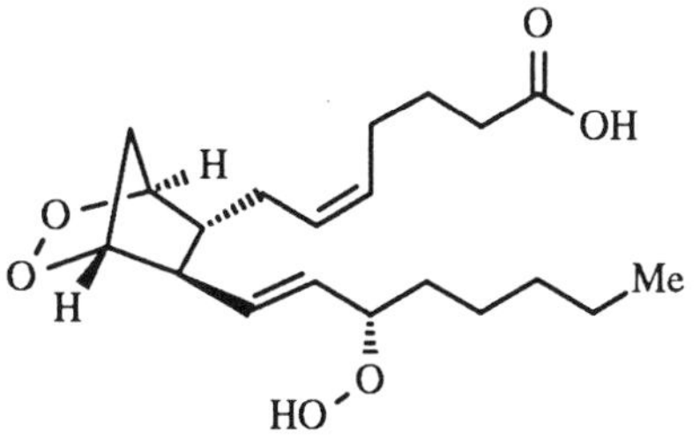

(**8**) Prostaglandin G$_2$

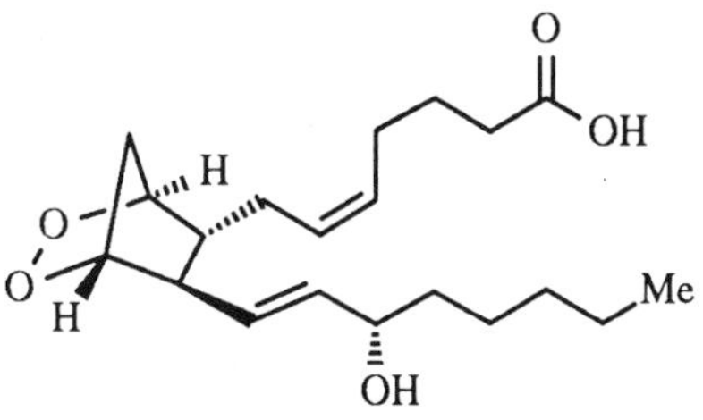

(**9**) Prostaglandin H$_2$

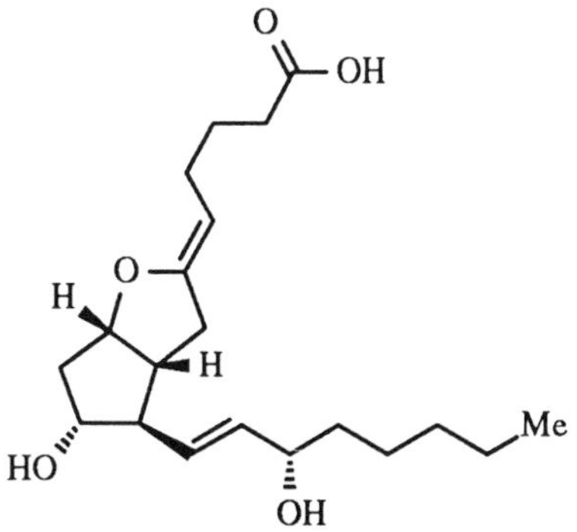

(**10**) Prostaglandin I$_2$

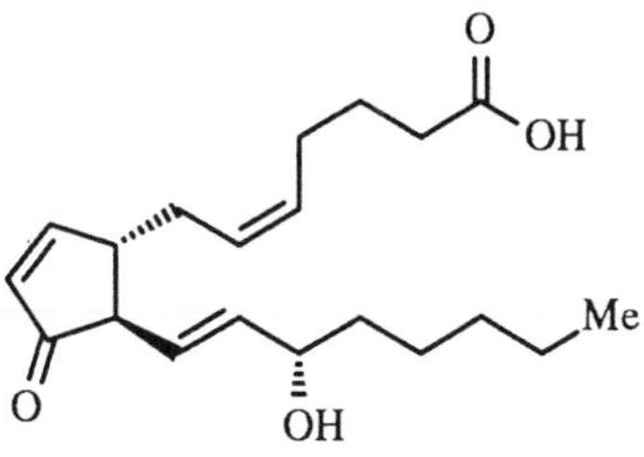

(**11**) Prostaglandin J$_2$

in aqueous medium yielding the dihydroxy-substituted oxane TxB (**14**).[6] Like the prostaglandins, thromboxanes have a hydroxy group at C-15.

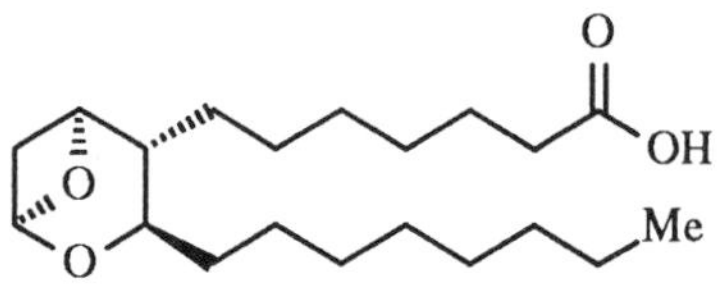

(**12**) Thrombanoic acid

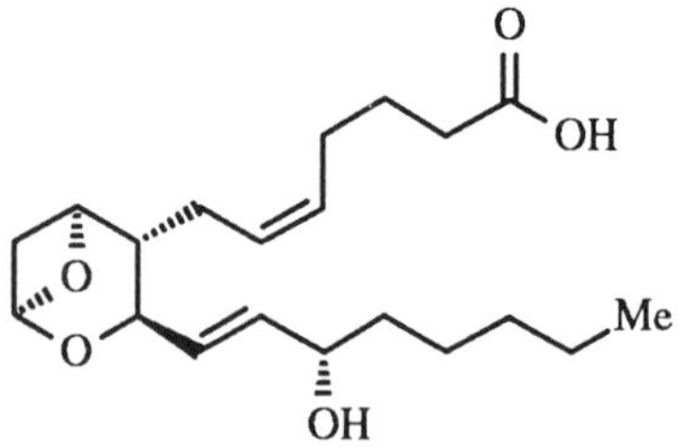

(**13**) Thromboxane A$_2$

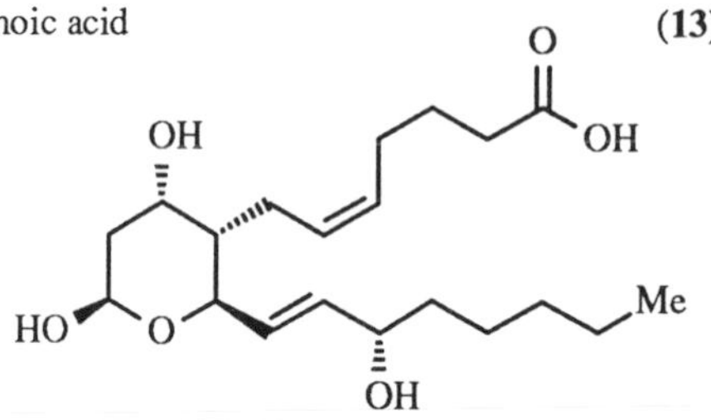

(**14**) Thromboxane B$_2$

Prostanoids are also classified into three series according to the number of double bonds in their side chains. The 1-series compounds have a *trans*-13 double bond, the 2-series *cis*-5 and *trans*-13 double bonds and the 3-series *cis*-5, *trans*-13 and *cis*-17 double bonds.[1]

12.11.1.2 Biosynthesis

12.11.1.2.1 Substrates for prostanoid biosynthesis

Most types of mammalian cells are capable of releasing prostanoids in response to a wide variety of stimuli ranging from activation of hormone receptors to simple mechanical trauma. They are synthesized from fatty acid constituents of membrane phospholipids. Thus the 1-, 2- and 3-series prostanoids are formed from γ-homolinolenic acid (8,11,14-icosatrienoic acid; **15**), arachidonic acid (5,8,11,14-icosatetraenoic acid; **16**) and EPA (timodonic acid; 5,8,11,14,17-icosapentaenoic acid; **17**), respectively.[7] Prostanoids are not stored, but are synthesized *de novo* and released in response to a stimulus.

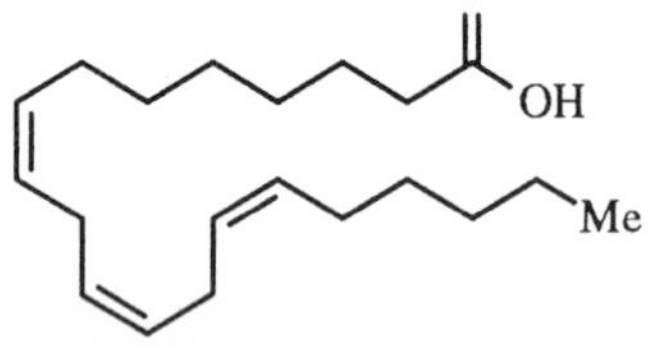

(**15**) Dihomo-γ-linolenic acid

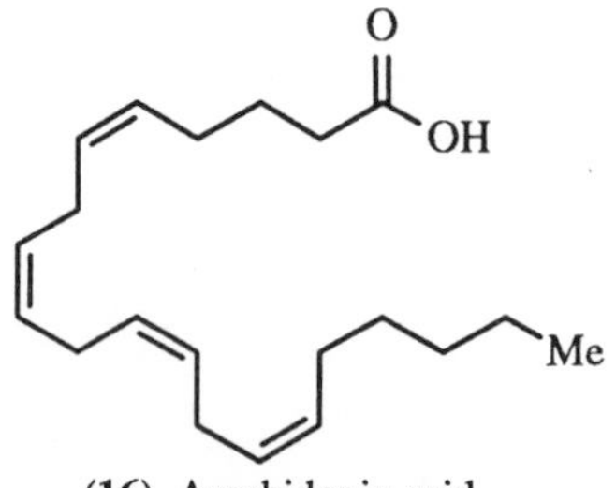

(**16**) Arachidonic acid

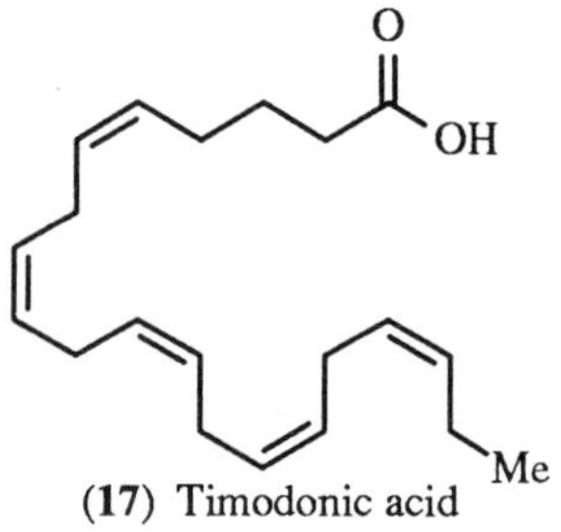

(**17**) Timodonic acid

Arachidonic acid is the most abundant of the prostanoid precursors and consequently it is the 2-series prostanoids that are formed almost exclusively in most mammals, including humans.[8] There is little evidence that 1-series prostanoids occur naturally; however, in recent years there has been some interest in the 3-series. This is because the bodies of fish and other marine animals, in contrast to those of freshwater and land animals, contain large amounts of highly polyunsaturated fatty acids including EPA. As a consequence of this a number of fish-eating populations, notably Greenland

Eskimos, have high concentrations of EPA in their phospholipids, and this may explain the resistance of such populations to atherosclerotic and thrombotic diseases.[9]

12.11.1.2.2 *Release of substrate*

Prostanoid formation requires free, unesterified arachidonic acid. Therefore, since cytoplasmic levels of this fatty acid are very low, liberation of substrate is a necessary first step. The principal source of arachidonic acid for prostanoid formation is that esterified at the 2-acyl position in fatty acyl chains of glycophospholipids. A phospholipase enzyme is probably responsible for liberation of arachidonic acid from phospholipids, and a phospholipase A_2 (PLA_2) enzyme is the most likely candidate.[10] However, there is evidence that in human platelets at least, phospholipase C (PLC) may release 1,2-diacylglycerol from the membrane phospholipid, from which arachidonic acid is then liberated by diglyceride lipase.[11] Despite the existence of this alternative pathway, it is most likely that the PLA_2 pathway is in fact the more important.[12] Once liberated, any arachidonic acid not metabolized to prostanoids or other icosanoids is rapidly reesterified by acyltransferase enzymes.[13]

In view of the importance of PLA_2 in the formation of prostanoids and other icosanoids, agents which inhibit this enzyme are of considerable interest. While most of such agents are of low potency and doubtful specificity,[14] an interesting recent development in this area has been the recognition that corticosteroids inhibit icosanoid formation by stimulating the intracellular release of a protein, variously known as lipomodulin, macrocortin and renocortin, which inhibits PLA_2.[15] However, it is by no means certain that all of the effects of these proteins can be attributed to inhibition of PLA_2.

12.11.1.2.3 *Formation of prostanoids from arachidonic acid*

The pathways leading to the formation of the primary prostanoids, PGD_2, PGE_2, $PGF_{2\alpha}$, PGI_2 and TxA_2 are shown in Figure 1. Pivotal in their formation is the generation of the endoperoxide intermediates PGG_2 and PGH_2. The sequential formation of PGG_2 and PGH_2 is catalyzed by the enzyme prostaglandin endoperoxide synthase.[1] The cyclooxygenase activity of this enzyme catalyzes the insertion of two molecules of oxygen into arachidonic acid to give the 15-hydroperoxy compound PGG_2, and the peroxidase activity of the enzyme then reduces the hydroperoxy group to hydroxy, giving PGH_2. The cyclooxygenase and peroxidase activities of endoperoxide synthase reside in a single protein. Nonsteroidal antiinflammatory ('aspirin-like') drugs inhibit prostanoid biosynthesis *via* inhibition of the enzyme cyclooxygenase and it is now accepted that this is the basis of the antiinflammatory action of these drugs (see Section 12.11.6.1).[16]

12.11.1.2.4 *Transformation of endoperoxides*

The endoperoxides PGG_2 and PGH_2 are unstable in aqueous media and decompose ($t_{1/2} \approx 4$–5 min at 37 °C) to a mixture of PGD_2, PGE_2, $PGF_{2\alpha}$, 12-L-hydroxy-5,8,10-heptadecatrienoic acid and malondialdehyde. However, formation of the so-called 'primary' prostanoids, PGD_2, PGE_2, $PGF_{2\alpha}$, PGI_2 and TxA_2, is normally catalyzed by specific enzymes.

12.11.1.2.5 *Formation of PGD_2*

Serum albumin can catalyze the formation of PGD_2 from PGH_2 released by platelets, and this mechanism may be involved in the regulation of platelet function.[17] Prostaglandin D synthase enzymes have been isolated from rat brain.[18] This enzyme has specific activity two orders of magnitude higher than that of albumin.

12.11.1.2.6. *Formation of PGE_2*

The isomerase enzyme that converts PGH_2 to PGE_2 is widely distributed in animal tissues. PGE_2 synthase is unstable, and this has hampered studies of its properties. Recently however, the use of monoclonal antibodies has shown the presence of three PGE_2 synthase isoenzymes in sheep vesicular gland.[19]

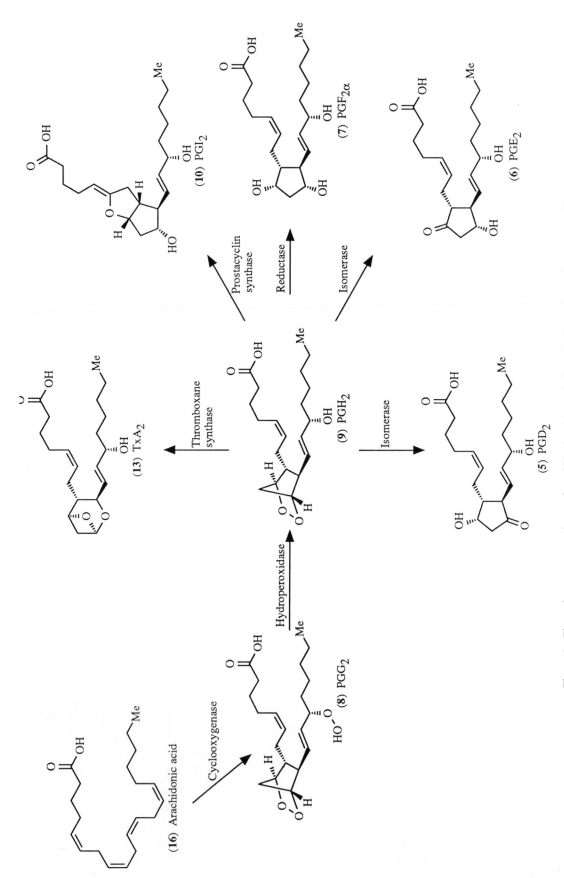

Figure 1 The cyclooxygenase pathway of arachidonic acid metabolism: the biosynthesis of the prostanoids

12.11.1.2.7 Formation of PGF₂ₐ

Although $PGF_{2\alpha}$, along with PGE_2, was among the first prostaglandins to be isolated, the mechanisms involved in the biosynthesis of this potent substance are poorly understood. Indeed, it has been suggested that $PGF_{2\alpha}$ formation is simply a result of chemical decomposition of PGH_2,[20] although this does not appear to be a widely held view. Three enzymatic pathways have been proposed: (i) direct conversion of PGH_2, (ii) 9-keto reduction of PGE_2 and (iii) 11-keto reduction of PGD_2. Direct conversion of PGH_2 to $PGF_{2\alpha}$ has been demonstrated in a number of tissues, although the enzymes(s) involved have not been characterized. Recently however, it has been shown that rat liver glutathione *S*-transferase can catalyze the reaction.[21] A cytoplasmic PGE 9-keto reductase enzyme has been isolated, but its biological significance is unclear since, in rabbit renal medulla, which is a rich source of the enzyme, $PGF_{2\alpha}$ synthesis does not occur *via* PGE_2.[22] An enzyme which converts PGD_2 to $PGF_{2\alpha}$ has been isolated from rat lung and rabbit liver.[23] Interestingly, an enzyme, for which the name PGF synthase has been proposed, has been isolated from bovine lung which can convert either PGD_2 or PGH_2 to $PGF_{2\alpha}$.[24] Clearly further work is necessary to establish the pathway(s) involved in $PGF_{2\alpha}$ synthesis *in vivo*.

12.11.1.2.8 Formation of PGI₂

Vascular endothelial cells contain an enzyme, PGI_2 synthase, which converts PGH_2 to PGI_2 (prostacyclin). PGI_2 synthase has been purified and is a ferrihemoprotein with a subunit molecular weight of about 52 000.[25] There is evidence to indicate that it is a cytochrome *P*-450-type enzyme.

12.11.1.2.9 Formation of TxA₂

The blood platelet is the principal source of TxA_2, where it is synthesized from PGH_2 by the enzyme thromboxane synthase. Like PGI_2 synthase, thromboxane synthase appears to be a cytochrome P-450-type hemoprotein.[26]

12.11.1.2.10 Formation of PGA₂, PGB₂, PGC₂ and PGJ₂

Although PGA_2 and PGB_2 can be produced by the action of acid and base respectively on PGE_2, there is little or no evidence that such transformations occur *in vivo*, and these prostaglandins are not now considered to occur naturally.[3] It is therefore surprising that an enzyme has been identified which can catalyze the isomerization of PGA_2 to PGC_2, which itself further isomerizes, either spontaneously or enzymatically, to PGB_2.[27] The biological significance, if any, of these pathways is unclear. The most recently discovered prostaglandin, PGJ_2, a dehydration product of PGD_2, has been the focus of some interest because of its potential antineoplastic activity (see Section 12.11.6.2). Whether such a transformation from PGD_2 occurs *in vivo*, and whether PGJ_2 occurs naturally, remains to be established.

12.11.1.3 Catabolism

The catabolism of the naturally occurring prostanoids is well documented.[28] They generally have short durations of action because of the efficiency of the processes which exist for their inactivation. For example, about 95% of a single dose of PGE_2 or $PGF_{2\alpha}$ is inactivated during one passage through the lungs.

Since the enzymes involved in the catabolism of prostanoids are located intracellularly, the substrate must first be transported across the cell membrane. Little is known about this transport process; however, in the lung at least, it displays different specificity from that of the prostanoid-metabolizing enzymes. Thus, for example, 15-methyl-PGE_2 and 16,16-dimethyl-PGE_2, which can be transported across the cell membrane, are not substrates for the metabolizing enzymes, while PGI_2, which is readily metabolized in broken cell preparations, is not transported.

The enzymatic breakdown of prostanoids consists of two steps: firstly a relatively rapid process catalyzed by enzymes specific for prostanoids with biological activity usually, but not always, lost at this stage; secondly, a slower process in which products of the first stage are oxidized by enzymes presumed to be those responsible for β and ω oxidation of fatty acids in general.

The first step in the catabolism of PGE_2 and $PGF_{2\alpha}$ involves the transformation to the 15-oxo-PG, which is catalyzed by the NAD-dependent enzyme, 15-hydroxyprostaglandin dehydrogenase (PGDH). 15-Oxo-PGE_2 and 15-oxo-$PGF_{2\alpha}$ are devoid of biological activity. Transformation of these compounds to 13,14-dihydro-15-oxo-PGs is catalyzed by the enzyme Δ^{13}-prostaglandin reductase. β and ω oxidation leads to the formation of a variety of products, quantitatively the most important of which is 7α-hydroxy-5,11-dioxotetranorprosta-1,6-dioic acid.

In the case of PGD_2, the basic processes involved are the same, but it has been found in monkeys and humans that more than 30% of the urinary metabolites contain the PGF ring structure. This is a consequence of the action of a 9-keto reductase enzyme. The PGF metabolites could be produced by the action of the 9-keto reductase enzyme on PGD_2 itself or on one or more of the subsequent metabolites. Interestingly, subsequent work has shown that some, if not all, of the metabolites do not have the PGF_α (9α,11β-PGF) structure. Rather they have a 9α,11β-PGF (also known as 11-epi-PGF) ring. Both human and rabbit liver, together with bovine lung, contain a 9-keto reductase enzyme which can convert PGD_2 to 9α,11β-PGF_2 (18). 9α,11β-PGF_2 has marked biological activity (see Section 12.11.3.1); it is a vasoconstrictor, a bronchoconstrictor and inhibits platelet aggregation. However, the full pathophysiological significance of this metabolite remains to be determined.

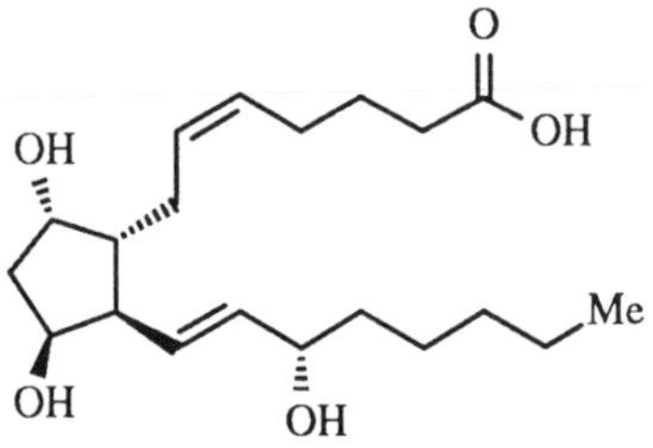

(18) 9α,11β-Prostaglandin F_2

PGI_2 is chemically unstable, and rapidly decomposed to 6-oxo-$PGF_{1\alpha}$ (19), which is devoid of significant biological activity. Both PGI_2 and 6-oxo-$PGF_{1\alpha}$ are rapidly metabolized *in vivo*, the major urinary metabolite in man being dinor-6-oxo-$PGF_{1\alpha}$. In addition however, a number of tissues, including platelets, kidney and lung, contain a 9-hydroxydehydrogenase enzyme which can convert PGI_2 to 6-oxo-PGE_1 (20). This substance is a potent vasodilator and inhibitor of platelet aggregation, but, unlike PGI_2, is chemically stable. It has been suggested that it may have an important role in the regulation of the cardiovascular system, but this remains to be established.

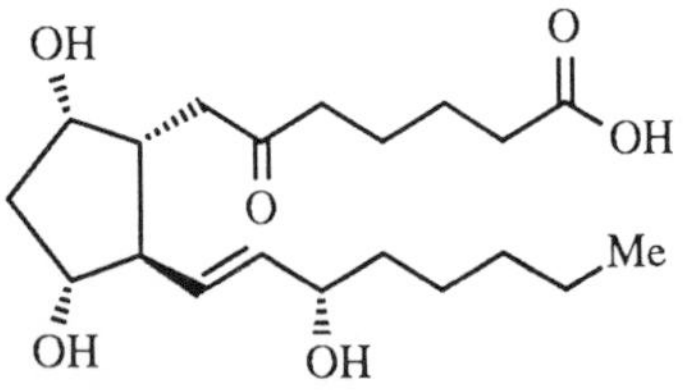

(19) 6-Oxo-prostaglandin $F_{1\alpha}$

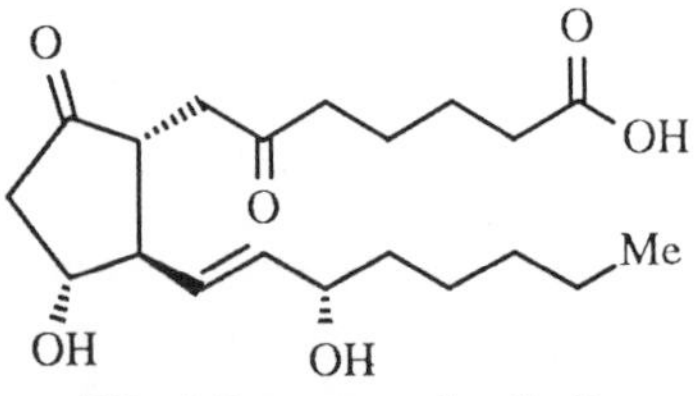

(20) 6-Oxo-prostaglandin E_1

As already described, TxA_2 rapidly decomposes to TxB_2, which has little or no biological activity. TxB_2 is readily metabolized, and over 20 metabolites have been identified, the most abundant of which is 2,3-dinor-TxB_2.

12.11.2 PROSTANOID RECEPTOR CLASSIFICATION

12.11.2.1 Introduction and History

Prostanoids, like other local hormones, produce their effects by interacting with specific receptors on cell membranes. Even in the absence of direct evidence, the presence of such receptors may be inferred from the properties of prostanoids. Thus, for example, they display high potency, sometimes being active at concentrations as low as 10^{-11} M, and small chemical modifications can have profound effects on their potency and profile of biological activity.[29] These observations imply the existence of specific recognition sites. Furthermore, it is common to find that different prostanoids can have different effects on the same cell type, for example TxA_2 causes platelet aggregation, whilst

PGI_2 inhibits this process.[5, 30] The simplest way to rationalize these observations is to postulate that TxA_2 and PGI_2 act at different types of receptor.

Studies on the classification of the different types of receptors for local hormones and neuro-transmitters have led to important advances. For example, work on the classification of adrenoceptors and histamine receptors led to the development of β-adrenoceptor-blocking drugs[31] and histamine H_2 receptor-blocking drugs respectively.[32] These agents have proved to be valuable, not only as therapeutic agents, but also as tools for probing the physiological functions of the sympathetic nervous system and histamine. It is therefore surprising in view of the large volume of research on prostanoids carried out over the last 20 or more years that more attention has not been paid to the classification of prostanoid receptors. Indeed, the absence of a logical framework for the analysis of the selectivity of action of agonists and antagonists provided by a receptor classification is an important reason why research into prostanoids has so far produced few major therapeutic advances.

Nevertheless, in recent years, progress has been made towards establishing the broad outlines of a workable classification of prostanoid receptors. According to this classification, distinct receptors exist for each of the five naturally occurring prostanoids, PGD_2, PGE_2, $PGF_{2\alpha}$, PGI_2 and TxA_2. Furthermore, evidence is beginning to accumulate that, at least in the case of receptors for PGE_2 and TxA_2, further subdivision is possible.

Before going on to discuss the current state of knowledge of the classification of prostanoids, it is valuable to outline the techniques used for receptor classification and consider their limitations.

12.11.2.1.1 *Techniques for the classification of receptors*

(i) *Pharmacological comparisons of agonist and antagonist potency*

Two procedures are used for the pharmacological classification of receptors, these are comparison of the relative potencies of a series of agonists and comparison of potencies of competitive antagonists. Provided that a number of conditions are satisfied (see below),[33, 34] then a finding in two different test systems of similar relative potencies for a series of agonists and/or a finding of similar potency for a competitive antagonist suggests that both test systems contain the same type of receptor. Conversely, dissimilar relative potencies for agonists and/or antagonists suggest that the test systems contain different receptors. It is necessary to compare relative potencies of agonists, because absolute agonist potency is at least in part determined by tissue-related factors such as receptor density and efficiency of coupling between receptor and effector mechanism. On any given preparation, tissue-related factors are assumed to be the same for all agonists, and therefore relative potencies in producing a response are assumed to reflect relative potencies at the receptor level. In the case of competitive antagonists however, potency is theoretically not tissue dependent. Furthermore, if the necessary criteria are satisfied, namely that in the presence of an antagonist the agonist concentration–effect curve is shifted to the right in a parallel fashion with no change in the maximum response and the Schild regression is linear and of unit slope, then the pA_2 can be taken as a measure of the affinity of that antagonist for the receptor.

Since in practice the potencies of both agonists and antagonist can be influenced by a variety of factors unrelated to receptor differences, care in the choice of test systems, and rigorous control of experimental conditions is necessary before potency differences can reliably be attributed to receptor differences. Such problems have been considered at length by Furchgott[33] and Kenakin.[34]

The optimal conditions required for receptor characterization are difficult, if not impossible, to satisfy in whole animal experiments. Thus, although studies in whole animals can be valuable, in general, receptor classification studies are best carried out using isolated tissue. A further important point to bear in mind is that agonist potencies are in general more susceptible to distortion by tissue-related factors than antagonist potencies. Furthermore, such distortions are more readily detected with antagonists than with agonists. This is because they are often reflected in deviations from the predicted behaviour for competitive antagonists, *i.e* nonparallel shifts of the agonists' concentration–effect curves and Schild regressions which are not linear or are not of unit slope. Such internal checks on the validity of agonist potency ratios are not generally possible. For these reasons, receptor classifications based on agonist potencies are best regarded as working hypotheses until they can be verified using antagonists.

(ii) *Biochemical ligand-binding studies*

Over the last 10 to 15 years, substantial progress has been made in the measurement of the binding of agonists and antagonists to receptors in cell membrane preparations using radiolabelled ligands.

Measurement of the ability of compounds to compete with labelled ligand for occupation of the receptors can be used to estimate the affinity of the competing drug for the receptor. This technique has a number of attractions, not the least of which are that it is simple to use and that it allows the direct study of receptors uncomplicated by postreceptor events. However, as will become apparent, this divorce between receptor and response can also have its drawbacks.[34]

Thus, although ligand-binding studies have proved valuable, particularly in understanding the mechanism of action of receptors at the molecular level, the technique has a number of limitations, both theoretical and practical. These limitations relate to the fundamental question of how to determine whether a particular binding site is the receptor mediating a given functional response. To demonstrate that it is, it is essential that ligand-binding data be shown to correlate with appropriate functional data. In the case of competitive antagonists, the comparison is in principle straightforward; as both pharmacological (see Section 12.11.2.1.1.i) and ligand-binding studies can give estimates of the affinity of an antagonist for a receptor, the two can be readily compared. However, this is less easy in the case of agonists, as agonist potency is, according to the generally accepted model introduced by Stephenson,[35] determined not only by affinity, but also by efficacy. Thus for a given series of agonists, affinities will only correlate with potencies if efficacies are equal.

Such caution in the interpretation of ligand-binding data is important as many of the labelled ligands used in binding studies can interact with specific recognition sites which are not receptors. In practice, this problem seems to be most often encountered when agonists are used as ligands. For this reason, high affinity antagonists are usually considered to be the most satisfactory ligands although even these can give misleading results.

12.11.2.1.2 Development and current status of prostanoid receptor classification

Historically, the earliest evidence for the existence of more than one type of prostanoid receptor came from the work of Pickles,[36] who examined the effects of six PGE and PGF analogues on three isolated tissues, guinea pig uterus, human myometrium and rabbit jejunum. He concluded that at least three and possibly four different types of receptor were required to explain his results. The work of Andersen and Ramwell[37] on structure–activity relationships for PGA, PGE and PGF analogues, although not interpreted in this light, pointed to the existence of multiple receptor types. An early attempt to classify prostanoid receptors was made by Gardiner and Collier,[38] using a range of natural and synthetic prostanoid agonists. These workers postulated the existence of three types of receptor, termed ψ, χ and ω. However, this classification was restricted to receptors present in the lung, and no attempt was made to apply it more generally.

Our own work was undertaken with the aim of producing a comprehensive classification of prostanoid receptors. We compared the potencies of the natural prostanoids PGD_2, PGE_2, $PGF_{2\alpha}$ and PGI_2, together with the stable TxA_2-like agonist U-46619 (**21**).[39] The results of these studies led us to the conclusion that distinct receptors exist for each of the naturally occurring prostanoids.[40] Support for this conclusion was provided initially by the work of Jones *et al.*,[41] using pharmacological techniques, and subsequently by that of Andersen and coworkers[42] who used both pharmacological and ligand-binding techniques.

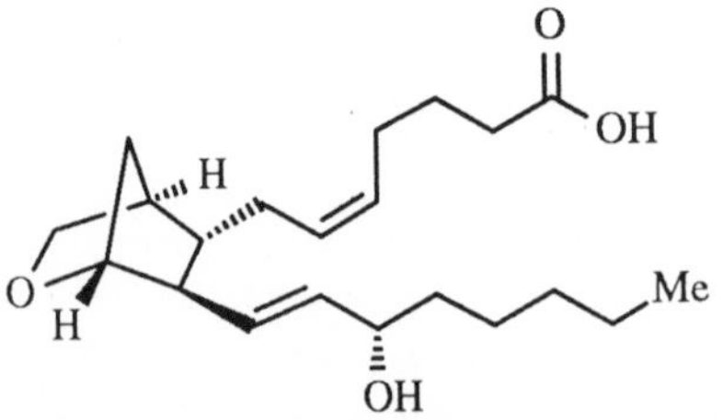

(**21**) U-46619

In our studies, isolated tissues and experimental conditions were chosen to approximate as closely as possible the ideal conditions for receptor classification outlined by Furchgott[33] and Kenakin.[34] Furthermore, being aware of the limitations of agonists as tools for receptor classification, we set out to attempt to identify specific prostanoid-receptor-blocking drugs, which constitute the most powerful tools in receptor classification (see Section 12.11.2.1.1.i).

Comparisons of agonist potency led to the identification of three groups of tissues containing what were hypothesized to be specific receptors for PGE_2, $PGF_{2\alpha}$ and TxA_2. A survey of the literature led us to conclude that specific receptors exist also for the other two naturally occurring prostanoids, PGD_2 and PGI_2. Since these results were consistent with the conclusion that distinct receptors exist for each of the five naturally occurring prostanoids, we proposed a nomenclature for prostanoid receptors based on this hypothesis.[40] This is shown in Table 1.

Investigation of a wide range of compounds led to the identification of two specific prostanoid-receptor-blocking drugs, AH 19437 (**22**)[43] and SC-19220 (**23**).[44,45] AH 19437 behaved as a specific competitive antagonist on tissues classified as containing thromboxane-sensitive (TP) receptors, but was devoid of activity on tissues containing other types of prostanoid receptor (see Table 1). Therefore, AH 19437 was classified as a TP-receptor-blocking drug. In contrast, SC-19220 was a weak, but specific, competitive antagonist only on tissues containing PGE_2 sensitive (EP) receptors.

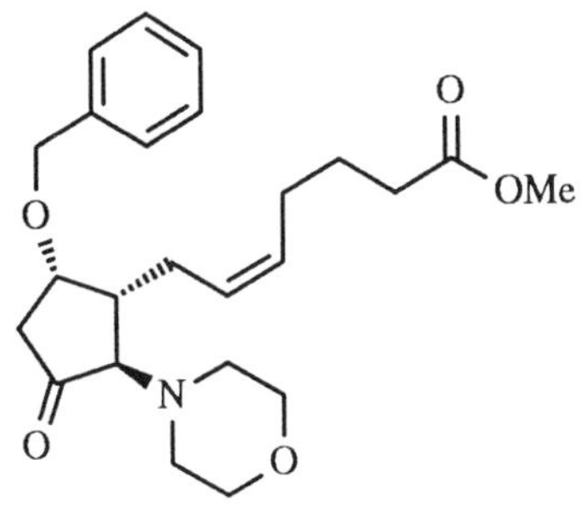

(**22**) AH 19437 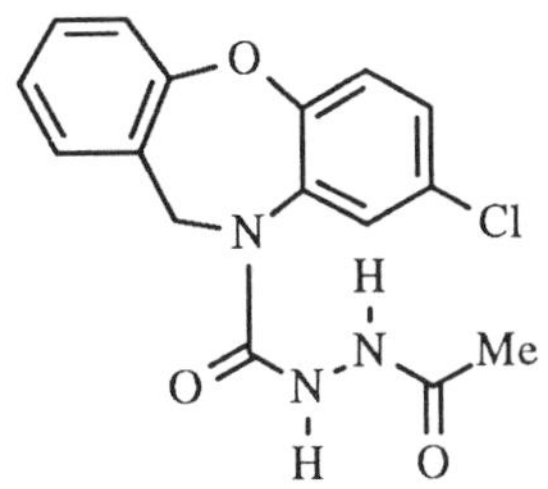   (**23**) SC-19220

Interestingly however, SC-19220 was only effective on some EP-receptor-containing tissues (see Table 1), a finding which led us to conclude that there is more than one type of EP receptor. Thus EP receptors which are blocked by SC-19220 were termed EP_1 receptors. While the usefulness of SC-19220 is limited by its low potency and solubility, we subsequently identified another compound, AH 6809 (**24**)[46] with a similar profile of activity at EP receptors (see Table 1) but which is about 10 times more potent than SC-19220 and is more soluble. The subclassification of EP receptors was confirmed and extended by the identification of the selective agonists, sulprostone (**25**) and AY 23626 (**26**).[47]

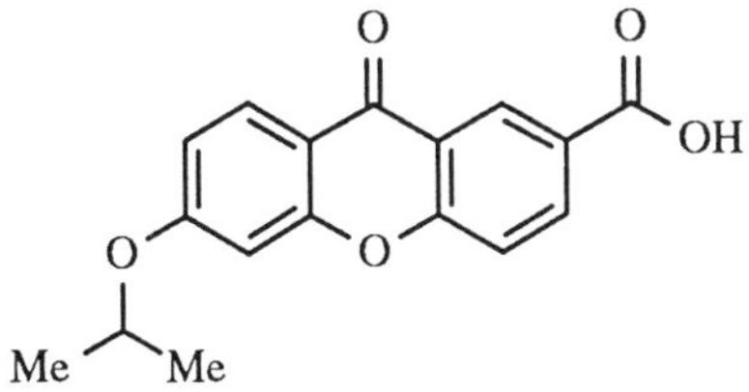

(**24**) AH 6809 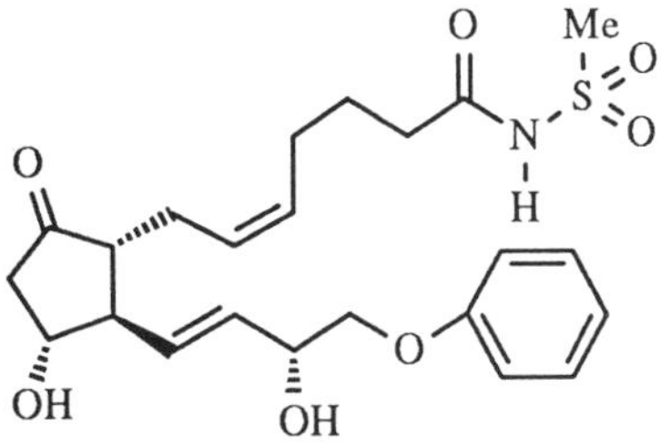   (**25**) Sulprostone

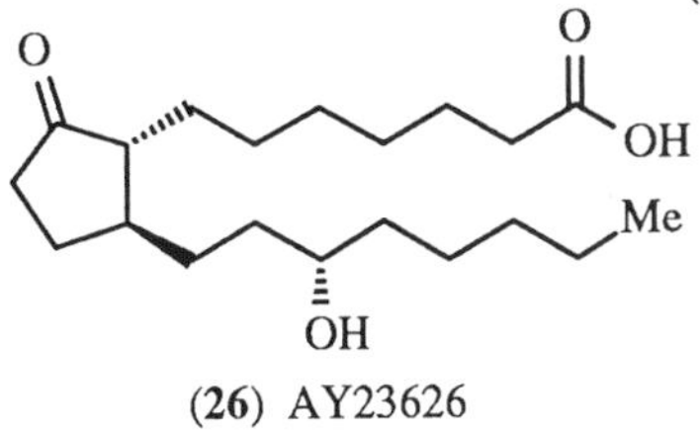

(**26**) AY23626

Data obtained with these two compounds suggested that 'nonEP$_1$' EP receptors comprised two subtypes which we have termed EP_2 and EP_3.[48] Thus sulprostone has high potency at EP_1 and EP_3 receptors, but is inactive at EP_2 receptors, while AY23626 is a potent agonist at EP_2 and EP_3 receptors, but is weak or inactive at EP_1 receptors.

Jones *et al.*,[41] in an extensive series of studies, have provided further substantial evidence for the existence of receptors for each of the natural prostanoids. Furthermore, they have also obtained evidence with selective agonists for the existence of subtypes of EP receptor. Interestingly, they have also suggested that there is more than one type of DP receptor (see Section 12.11.3.1).

Thromboxane receptors are probably the most extensively studied of all prostanoid receptors. A large number of potent and selective TP receptor agonists and antagonists have been described. Work with these compounds has led to suggestions that subtypes of TP receptor may exist, although

Table 1 Characterization of the Five Types of Prostanoid Receptor and the Three Subtypes of the PGE-sensitive (EP) Type

Receptor type		Rank order of potency of natural agonists[a]	Selective agonists	Selective antagonists
DP		$D_2 > E_2, F_{2\alpha}, I_2,$ U-46619		
	EP$_1$	$E_2 > F_{2\alpha} \approx I_2 > D_2 >$ U-46619	Sulprostone	SC-19220, AH 6809
EP	EP$_2$	$E_2 > F_{2\alpha} \approx D_2 \approx I_2 >$ U-46619	AY23626	
	EP$_3$	$E_2 > I_2 > F_{2\alpha} \gg D_2 >$ U-46619	Sulprostone, AY23626	
FP		$F_{2\alpha} > D_2 > E_2 \approx$ U-46619 $> I_2$		
IP		$I_2 > D_2, E_2, F_{2\alpha} >$ U-46619		
TP		U-46619 $\gg D_2, E_2, F_{2\alpha}, I_2$	U-46619	AH 19437

[a] TxA$_2$ mimetic, U-46619, used instead of authentic TxA$_2$.

a comprehensive subclassification of TP receptors has yet to be proposed (see Sections 12.11.3.5 and 12.11.4.5).

In conclusion, there is now a substantial body of evidence in support of the view that distinct receptors exist for each of the five naturally occurring prostanoids. Furthermore, it is evident that, at least in the case of EP receptors and possibly DP and TP receptors, further subdivision exists.

12.11.2.2 Ligand Binding

A study of the literature on prostanoid ligand-binding studies reveals the interesting fact that binding sites have been identified which are characterized by a high affinity for each of the natural prostanoids, that is, for each site, one of the natural prostanoids has a higher affinity than any of the others, an observation consistent with our proposed pharmacological characterization of prostanoid receptors.

12.11.2.2.1 PGD$_2$-specific binding sites

As there is substantial pharmacological evidence that distinct receptors exist for PGD$_2$ in platelets from some but by no means all species,[49] it is interesting that high affinity PGD$_2$-specific binding sites have been isolated from human platelets.[50] The rank order of binding affinity for PGs D$_2$, E$_1$, E$_2$, F$_{2\alpha}$ and I$_2$ at these sites is: D$_2$ (1) > I$_2$ (25) > E$_1$ (75) > F$_{2\alpha}$ (100) > E$_2$ (> 100)[50] (relative binding affinities, PGD$_2$ = 1).

This rank order of binding affinity contrasts not only with that for PGI$_2$ binding sites also from platelets (see Section 12.11.2.2.4), but also with those for PGF$_{2\alpha}$ and PGE$_2$ binding sites. That these binding sites are identical to the DP receptor is given strong support by the finding that the selective DP agonist, BW 245C (see Section 12.11.3.1), has affinity for PGD$_2$ binding sites in human platelets but has no affinity for PGI$_2$ binding sites in these same cells.[51]

Specific PGD$_2$ binding sites have also been identified in rat brain synaptic membranes,[52] with PGD$_2$ itself and its methyl ester being the most potent ligands tested. However these binding sites do not appear to resemble the DP receptor present on human platelets or in the cardiovascular system of the sheep since neither BW 245C nor 13,14-dihydro-15-oxo-PGD$_2$ (see Section 12.11.3.1) were able to displace [^{3}H]PGD$_2$. Only the use of specific blocking drugs will clarify whether these receptors represent pharmacologically different subtypes of the DP receptor.

12.11.2.2.2 PGE-specific binding sites

There is now a large body of evidence for the existence of high affinity ($K_D < 10$ nM) PGE-specific binding sites in a wide range of tissues. Such binding sites have been identified in adipocytes, corpora lutea, myometrium, kidney, intestinal epithelium, liver, heart, brain and blood platelets.[53-61] In some of these cases, the presence of these high affinity binding sites has been associated with a functional response, usually an effect on adenylate cyclase, giving some support to the proposition that these binding sites are indeed functional receptors. Futhermore, in a number of studies, rank orders of binding affinities for at least some of the natural prostanoids as well as the two synthetic PGE analogues, sulprostone and AY23626,[59,61] have been reported, these being determined from their abilities to displace labelled ligand from the binding sites. Such rank orders are summarized in Table 2.

Table 2 Comparison of Relative Affinities at PGE-specific Binding Sites in Various Tissues with Relative Potencies at EP Receptors

Tissue			*Relative binding affinity* ($PGE_2 = 100$)					
	PGE_2	PGE_1	$PGF_{2\alpha}$	$PGF_{1\alpha}$	PGD_2	*Sulprostone*	*AY23626*	*Ref.*
Rat adipocyte	100	125–167	1.9–6.3	0.5	NT[a]	270	12.5	53–55
Bovine corpus luteum	100	124–179	1.6–2.5	0.2–0.4	0.2	NT	NT	56, 57
Hamster myometrium	100	50	2.0	NT	NT	NT	NT	55, 58
Guinea pig myometrium	100	NT	8.0	NT	NT	530	NT	55, 59
Human myometrium	100	NT	NT	NT	NT	280	NT	59
Cow heart	100	91	2.3	NT	0.01	NT	NT	60
Rat kidney	100	164	4.4	0.08	0.18	NT	NT	61

Tissue	Receptor	PGE_2	*Relative agonist potency* ($PGE_2 = 100$)					
			PGE_1	$PGF_{2\alpha}$	$PGF_{1\alpha}$	PGD_2	*Sulprostone*	*AY23626*	*Ref.*
Guinea pig ileum Guinea pig fundus	EP_1	100	7–20	2–4	0.02–0.2	0.1–0.4	22–27	<0.24	62
Cat trachea Guinea pig ileum (circ. muscle)	EP_2	100	77–200	0.1–0.3	<0.3	0.5–0.7	<0.03	7–83	62
Chick ileum Guinea pig vas deferens	EP_3	100	125–400	0.9–1.7	0.2–2.5	<0.1	111–200	14–19	62

[a]NT = not tested.

It is clear that there are marked similarities between the PGE-specific sites from the different tissues in that the affinities of PGE_1 and PGE_2 are similar, any differences being no more than two-fold, and that while the affinity of $PGF_{2\alpha}$ is lower than that of the PGEs, it is higher than those of $PGF_{1\alpha}$ and PGD_2. Lastly, where studied, both sulprostone and AY23626 are highly potent in displacing PGE binding.

Although the data are limited, there are similarities between the results of the binding and pharmacological studies, suggesting that the binding sites may be identical to EP receptors. The particular subtype that they correspond to is suggested by the binding data obtained with PGE_1 and the two synthetic agonists, sulprostone and AY23626. Thus the fact that the selective EP_1 and EP_3 receptor agonist, sulprostone (see Sections 12.11.2.1.2 and 12.11.3.2), has a binding affinity between three- and five-fold higher than that of PGE_2 at the PGE-specific binding sites in human and guinea pig uterus and in rat adipocytes implicates EP_1 and/or EP_3 receptors. However, the fact that the selective EP_2 and EP_3 receptor agonist AY23626 (see Sections 12.11.2.1.2 and 12.11.3.2) also has a relatively high affinity at least in rat adipocytes, together with the fact that PGE_1 has a binding affinity similar to PGE_2 in all of the binding sites included in Table 2, suggests that EP_1 receptors are not involved. Thus the rank order of binding affinity of sulprostone, PGE_2, PGE_1 and AY23626 is similar to their rank order of agonist activity on EP_3-receptor-containing preparations (see Table 2).

12.11.2.2.3 *PGF-specific binding sites*

Virtually all studies into PGF-specific binding sites have been conducted on fractions from corpora lutea.[55,57,58,63–68] It is significant therefore that $PGF_{2\alpha}$ is a luteolytic agent in a range of animal species (see Section 12.11.5.5), being, as far as is known, the most potent of the naturally occurring prostanoids in this respect. Similarly, a number of structural analogues of $PGF_{2\alpha}$, *e.g.* cloprostenol, fluprostenol and prostalene, are also potent, selective FP receptor agonists (see Section 12.11.3.3) and are highly potent luteolytic agents. The relative binding affinities of a range of both natural prostanoids and, in some cases, also fluprostenol and cloprostenol at luteal binding sites have been determined and compared with their FP agonist potencies (see Table 3). It is clear that the compounds with potent FP receptor agonist activity have high affinities for the luteal binding sites, while those that are weaker FP receptor agonists have correspondingly lower affinities for the binding sites. It appears therefore that the PGF-specific binding sites in luteal membranes are similar to FP receptors, and further suggests that FP receptors are responsible for prostanoid-induced luteolysis, at least in animals (see Section 12.11.5.5).

Table 3 Comparison of Relative Affinities at $PGF_{2\alpha}$-specific Binding Sites in Corpora Lutea from Various Species with Relative FP Receptor Agonist Potency

	Cloprostenol	Fluprostenol	$PGF_{2\alpha}$	PGD_2	$PGF_{1\alpha}$	PGE_2	$PGF_{2\beta}$	Ref.
Luteal binding affinities ($PGF_{2\alpha}$ = 100)								
Cow	NT[a]	69.3	100	0.1	4.3	3.7	0.1	57
Cow	NT	NT	100	11	2.5	2.1	NT	64
Cow	210	51.2	100	NT	15	19	NT	65
Sheep	NT	NT	100	NT	5.0	3.7	1.4	64
Sheep	NT	NT	100	NT	3.0	2.0	NT	66
Horse	NT	300	100	18	2.4	0.8	0.2	58
Horse	NT	NT	100	3.3	2.1	2.4	0.2	65
Rabbit	NT	NT	100	NT	NT	1.3	NT	55
Rat	NT	100	100	NT	9.2	1.8	NT	68
FP agonist potency ($PGF_{2\alpha}$ = 100)								
Dog iris	250	200	100	7.7	4.2	0.3	0.04	62
Cat iris	100	333	100	3.8	3.4	2.5	0.01	62

[a]NT = not tested.

12.11.2.2.4 PGI-specific binding sites

Prostanoid IP receptors have been identified extensively in blood platelets and vascular smooth muscle (see Sections 12.11.5.1 and 12 11.5.3), and, similarly, most PGI-specific binding sites have been identified in these same tissues.

Studies have been performed on human and bovine platelets, and on homogenates of bovine coronary arteries as well as on NCB-20 neuronal somatic hybrid cell membranes and homogenates of guinea pig lung with $[^3H]PGI_2$, $[^3H]PGE_1$ and/or $[^3H]$iloprost as the ligand.[69-78] In these tissues, similar rank orders of binding affinity were obtained (see Table 4).

It is interesting from the data in Table 4 that not only are the rank orders of prostanoid binding similar for all of the PGI_2 binding sites isolated, but, omitting only PGD_2 for which distinct receptors exist on platelets, they also reflect the rank order of potency of the prostanoids in inhibiting platelet aggregation. These data are therefore consistent with the specific PGI_2 binding sites in vascular smooth muscle, blood platelets, cultured neuronal cells and guinea pig lung being identical to IP receptors. It is not clear in guinea pig lung from which cell type the binding sites originate, particularly as PGI_2 is only a weak agonist on guinea pig airways smooth muscle. Possibly the binding sites derive from the bronchial/pulmonary vasculature.

12.11.2.2.5 TxA₂-specific binding sites

Of all of the studies on prostanoid-specific binding sites reported in the literature, those concerned with TxA_2-specific sites have produced the most convincing evidence that these binding sites are the same as the TP receptors identified in functional studies. The reason for this is that, in addition to a range of potent selective TP receptor agonists, there exist a wide variety of specific TP-receptor-blocking drugs, and it is such agents which are the ideal ligands for binding studies (see Section 12.11.2.1.1.ii). Thus, studies have been carried out using both labelled agonists and antagonists as ligands, and their binding has been displaced with both unlabelled agonists and antagonists (see Table 5).[79-84]

All of the data in Table 5 are derived from experiments with platelet membranes, and the ligands used include ^3H-labelled 9,11- and 11,9-epoxymethano-PGH_2 (U-44069 and U-46619 respectively), both of which are potent selective TP receptor agonists (see Section 12.11.3.5), $[^3H]$-13-azaprostanoic acid (13-APA) and $[^{125}I]$-13-aza,16-*p*-hydroxyphenylpinane-TxA_2 (PTA-OH), both of which are TP-receptor-blocking drugs (see Section 12.11.4.5). The K_D value for PTA-OH determined on platelets from binding studies and the K_B value determined from pharmacological studies are very similar, being 14.5–40 nM and 11 nM respectively. This similarity is consistent with the common identity of binding site and receptor. Interestingly, while 13-APA has two binding sites on platelet membranes with affinities of 100 nM and 35 μM,[82] it is the lower affinity value that corresponds to the pharmacologically derived K_B.[85]

Table 4 Relative Binding Affinities of Prostanoids at PGI-specific Binding Sites Isolated from Various Tissues

Tissue	Ligand	Relative binding affinities (PGI_2 = 100)							
		ZK	PGI_2	6β-PGI_1	PGE_1	PGE_2	$PGF_{2\alpha}$	PGD_2	Ref.
Human platelets	[^{3}H]PGE$_1$	NT[a]	100	NT	50	5	0.07	0.07	69
	[^{3}H]PGI$_2$	NT	100	NT	5	0.3	0.3	0.3	70
	[^{3}H]ZK[b]	100	100	NT	9	NT	NT	NT	71
	[^{3}H]PGI$_2$	NT	100	12.5	50	NT	NT	NT	72
	[^{3}H]ZK	200	100	NT	14	0.2	NT	NT	73
Bovine platelets	[^{3}H]PGI$_2$	NT	100	NT	5.4	0.4	0.2	NT	74
	[^{3}H]ZK	100	100	NT	30	NT	NT	NT	71
NCB-20 hybrid cells	[^{3}H]PGI$_2$	NT	100	NT	8.3	0.13	0.01	NT	75
	[^{3}H]ZK	125	100	22	3.6	0.5	<0.25	<0.25	76
Guinea pig lung	[^{3}H]PGI$_2$	NT	100	317	3.3	0.13	<0.01	<0.01	77
Bovine coronary artery	[^{3}H]ZK	100	NT	NT	14	1	0.01	2	78

[a] NT = not tested. [b] [^{3}H]ZK = [^{3}H]iloprost.

Table 5 Detail of Studies on TxA$_2$-specific Binding Sites

Tissue	Ligand	K_D (nM)	Displacing agents		Ref.
			TP agonists	TP antagonists	
Guinea pig platelets	[^{125}I]PTA-OH	14.5	U-44069, U-46619, 9,11-azo-PGH$_2$, SQ 26,655, MB 28767	13-Aza,16-phenyl-PTA analogues	79
Human platelets	[^{3}H]U-46619	108		13-APA, BM 13.177 ONO 3708, SQ 29,548	80
Human platelets	[^{125}I]PTA-OH	40			81
Human platelets	[^{3}H]-13-APA	100	U-46619	PGF$_{2\alpha}$[a]	82
Dog platelets	[^{125}I]PTA-OH	24		13-Aza,16-phenyl-PTA analogues	83
Human platelets	[^{3}H]U-44069	65	PGH$_2$, TxA$_2$, U-44069, U-46619		84

[a] PGF$_{2\alpha}$ acts as an antagonist in platelets, blocking TP agonist-induced aggregation.

In some of these studies, the abilities of ranges of agonists and/or antagonists to inhibit ligand binding were studied and compared to the pharmacological activities in platelet aggregation studies.[79,80,83,86] In human washed platelets, binding of [^{3}H]-U-44069 was displaced by unlabelled U-44069 and its close analogue, U-46619, but also by both PGH$_2$ and authentic TxA$_2$.[84] This provides strong evidence that the binding sites are indeed TP receptors. Kattelman *et al.*[80] examined a range of structurally unrelated TP-receptor-blocking drugs, SQ 29,548, ONO 3708, BM 13.177 and 13-APA on human platelet membranes, and again obtained identical rank orders of binding affinity and TP antagonist potency using the two techniques. In their study on guinea pig platelets, Halushka *et al.*[79] displaced [^{125}I] PTA-OH binding with a range of synthetic TP receptor agonists and antagonists. While all of the agonists both aggregated platelets and displaced labelled ligand from the platelet binding sites, the rank orders of potency for the two effects were different, whereas for the antagonists there was an excellent correlation. The apparent inconsistency with the agonist data presumably results from a difference in the respective efficacies of the agonists. Interestingly, these authors compared similar data for the antagonists in both guinea pig and dog platelets, and found an excellent correlation in each species, but differences between species. This suggests that while the binding sites are indeed the same as functional TP receptors, the TP receptors in dog and guinea pig platelets may be different.

12.11.2.2.6 Summary

In summary, therefore, binding characteristics for prostanoid agonists and, in some cases, antagonists at PGD$_2$-, PGE$_2$-, PGF$_{2\alpha}$-, PGI$_2$- and TxA$_2$-specific binding sites have been described.

The impressive correlation between relative binding affinities and pharmacological activity at DP, EP, FP, IP and TP receptors suggests that the binding sites studied are similar if not identical to the functional receptors identified by pharmacological means. Such binding studies therefore represent a potentially valuable alternative means of investigating prostanoid receptors.

12.11.2.3 Intracellular Second Messengers

At least four prostanoid receptor types can mediate contraction of smooth muscle, *i.e.* EP_1, EP_3, TP and FP. Since contraction of smooth muscle is dependent on the concentration of free Ca^{2+} in the myoplasm, it is clearly possible that activity at these receptors is transduced *via* intracellular Ca^{2+}. Direct evidence for Ca^{2+} as the second messenger is abundant for TP receptors, but more restricted for FP and EP receptors. TxA_2 mimetics cause contraction of smooth muscle by increasing intracellular free Ca^{2+} which is achieved by both opening receptor-operated channels in the plasma membrane and mobilizing intracellular Ca^{2+} from the sarcoplasmic reticulum;[87,88] although the exact mechanism of the latter effect is not entirely clear, it could be triggered by influx of extracellular Ca^{2+} and/or involve phosphatidylinositol turnover.[89] The main body of work relating TP receptor activation to Ca^{2+} mobilization is in human platelets, where TxA_2 mimetics induce platelet aggregation also by elevating free intracellular Ca^{2+}, possibly through an influx of extracellular Ca^{2+} and/or by the mobilization of Ca^{2+} from intracellular stores.[90,91] This latter release of Ca^{2+} is thought to be mediated *via* the hydrolysis of phosphatidylinositol 4,5-diphosphate (PI) in the plasma membrane. For example, a good correlation exists between the degree of TP receptor occupancy with U-44069, PI hydrolysis and the rise in cytosolic free Ca^{2+}. Significantly, all of these effects as well as platelet aggregation to U-44069 are antagonized by the TP-receptor-blocking drug EP 045.

Direct evidence that activation of FP receptors mobilizes Ca^{2+} is difficult to find. Contraction of vascular smooth muscle by $PGF_{2\alpha}$ is Ca^{2+}-dependent,[92] but this is believed to be mediated by TP receptors. However, there is much evidence that stimulation of luteolysis by $PGF_{2\alpha}$ is mediated by FP receptors (see Sections 12.11.2.2.3 and 12.11.3.3), and that this response is associated with an increase in intracellular Ca^{2+} in the luteal cells.[93] As removal of extracellular Ca^{2+} had no effect on the luteolytic action of $PGF_{2\alpha}$, mobilization of intracellular Ca^{2+} appears to be involved.[93] Indeed, Raymond *et al.*[94] have shown that $PGF_{2\alpha}$ stimulates phosphatidylinositol turnover in isolated luteal cells, implicating Ca^{2+} as the second messenger. This latter work in the corpus luteum, taken with the association of FP receptors with smooth muscle contraction, provides strong evidence that changes in the concentration of free intracellular Ca^{2+} mediate the responses to FP receptor activation.

EP_1 receptors mediate contraction of smooth muscle in, for example, guinea pig trachea. Creese and Denborough[95] have reported that contraction of guinea pig trachea induced by PGE_2 is absolutely dependent on extracellular Ca^{2+}, and this result, taken with the general observation that smooth muscle contraction involves Ca^{2+},[89] indicates that extracellular Ca^{2+} mediates the response to EP_1 receptor stimulation.

As to EP_3 receptors, there is no clear evidence linking their activity with alterations of intracellular Ca^{2+} levels. However, it has been shown that EP_3 receptors mediate inhibition of transmitter release in guinea pig vas deferens and also that such an effect is associated with a decrease in the intracellular levels of cAMP.[96] Also, prostanoid-induced antilipolytic activity in adipocytes is associated with a decrease in adenylate cyclase activity and this latter effect exhibits a rank order of potency of $PGE_2 > PGF_{2\alpha} = PGI_2 > PGD_2$,[97] indicating an EP-receptor-mediated response. The observations that sulprostone is slightly more potent than PGE_2 as an antilipolytic, and that like PGE_2 it inhibits the adrenaline-stimulated increase in cAMP levels in adipocytes,[98] and that adipocytes contain EP_3-receptor-like binding sites (see Section 12.11.2.2), all indicate that EP_3 receptors are involved. Thus these data all point to EP_3 receptors mediating their effects through inhibition of adenylate cyclase. However, such a conclusion appears to be at odds with the fact that EP_3 receptors can also mediate the contraction of smooth muscle preparations, *e.g.* chick ileum,[99] an event usually associated with an increase in intracellular levels of free Ca^{2+} rather than a change in cAMP. The explanation for this apparent inconsistency is not as yet clear.

There is conflicting evidence regarding the ability of TP receptor stimulation to inhibit platelet adenylate cyclase activity. However, the possible role of adenylate cyclase inhibition in the process of platelet aggregation remains controversial.

Three prostanoid receptor types mediate relaxation of smooth muscle, *i.e.* EP_2, DP and IP. Since relaxation of smooth muscle is mediated intracellularly by an increase in cAMP it is clearly possible that activity at EP_2, DP and IP receptors is transduced *via* intracellular cAMP. Indirect evidence associating EP_2 receptors with cAMP is derived from the observation that PGE_2-induced relaxation of vascular and intestinal smooth muscle is accompanied by increases in intracellular cAMP.[95,100] However, unequivocal evidence that such responses are mediated by EP_2 receptors is lacking. A more direct association between EP_2 receptors and cAMP may be found in enterocytes. Hardcastle *et al.*[101] have reported that PGE_2 increases cAMP levels in rat isolated enterocytes, and that dibutyryl cAMP stimulates intestinal secretion. Our own experiments (Section 12.11.5.8) have shown that PGE_2, but not sulprostone, stimulates intestinal secretion. These data indicate that increase in intestinal secretion is mediated by EP_2 receptors *via* increased levels of intracellular cAMP.

Further evidence that DP and IP receptors are associated with increases in cAMP is derived from experiments on platelets and on intestinal mucosa. Inhibition of platelet aggregation is mediated by DP and IP receptors. In both cases there is a good correlation between stimulation of adenylate cyclase and this inhibition.[102] Taken with the observation that exogenous dibutyryl cAMP inhibits platelet aggregation,[103] these results link DP and IP receptor stimulation with adenylate cyclase stimulation and cAMP elevation. Additional, albeit indirect, evidence relating DP and IP receptors with cAMP is the observation of Simon *et al.*[104] that PGE_2, PGI_2 and PGD_2 are approximately equipotent in stimulating adenylate cyclase activity in human colonic mucosa, indicating that EP, IP and DP receptors may all be involved. Unfortunately, complementary studies on colonic secretion were not carried out.

In summary, an attempt has been made to rationalize the pharmacological characterization of prostaglandin receptors in terms of the intracellular messenger mediating the cellular end response. Although it is possible to strongly implicate each receptor type with a characteristic intracellular response, it must be pointed out that an unequivocal functional association between the two has not always been established. Nevertheless, a tentative characterization of prostaglandin receptors in terms of intracellular messengers is given in Table 6.

Table 6 A Possible Association between Prostanoid Receptors and Intracellular Responses

Intracellular response	Tissue response	Receptor type
Increased intracellular free Ca^{2+}	Smooth muscle contraction	TP, FP, EP_1, EP_3
	Platelet aggregation	TP
	Luteolysis	FP
Decreased intracellular cAMP	Inhibition of neurotransmitter release	EP_3
	Inhibition of lipolysis	EP_3
Increased intracellular cAMP	Smooth muscle relaxation	EP_2, DP, IP
	Inhibition of platelet aggregation	DP, IP
	Stimulation of intestinal secretion	EP_2

12.11.3 SELECTIVE PROSTANOID AGONISTS

12.11.3.1 DP Receptor Agonists

PGD_2 probably represents the least studied of the natural prostanoids, and, as recently as 1973, PGD_2 was considered to have negligible pharmacological activity.[105] However, a variety of diverse actions have now been identified for this prostaglandin, ranging from inhibition of platelet aggregation, vasodilatation, vasoconstriction, bronchoconstriction, modulation of allergen-induced mediator release and a central effect in the control of sleep. However, some of these actions of PGD_2 may not be mediated *via* DP receptors. For example, the bronchoconstriction produced by PGD_2 in man is antagonized by the specific TP-receptor-blocking drug GR 32191.[107] The most thoroughly characterized PGD_2-sensitive system is that which is found on the human platelets (see Section 12.11.5.3). A comprehensive review of the biological actions of PGD_2 and mimetics has been produced by Giles and Leff.[106]

PGD_2, like the other natural prostanoids, is only relatively selective, and possesses moderately potent activity at both FP and TP receptors.[107,108] Although weaker, PGD_1 possesses a similar profile to PGD_2, as does PGD_3.[109] In addition, for a given degree of platelet inhibition, the PGD_2 metabolite $9\alpha,11\beta$-PGF_2 (**18**) appears to possess relatively more TP-receptor agonist activity than PGD_2.[110] In contrast, 9-deoxy-Δ^9-PGD_2 (PGJ_2; **11**), a dehydration product of PGD_2, has been reported to be equipotent with the parent compound at inhibiting platelet aggregation and producing vasodilatation. However, it is more specific, possessing relatively less activity on EP and

FP receptors.[109] Similarly, the 9β derivative of PGD_2 (27) possesses a more specific profile than the parent compound,[109] and is a relatively potent agonist in a range of DP-receptor-containing preparations.[111] Various PGD_2 analogues have also been synthesized and their actions compared with those of PGD_2 in a variety of test systems. Such an analysis was performed with a range of C-15 modified analogues.[112] One of the effects analyzed was the PGD_2-sensitive pressor response in the anaesthetized sheep, an action unaffected by TP-receptor-blocking drugs and possibly mediated *via* a DP receptor.[41] A similar response has been identified in the rabbit and rat. Of the analogues tested, 15-methoxy-PGD_2 (28) and 13,14-dihydro-15-oxo-PGD_2 (29) were amongst the most potent pressor agents in the sheep, but were at least 3000-times weaker than PGD_2 as inhibitors of human platelet aggregation.[112,113] This finding led Jones *et al.* to propose the existence of subtypes of DP receptor.[41] These analogues were also much weaker than PGD_2 on other prostanoid-receptor-containing smooth muscle preparations such as the rabbit oviduct and jejunum, rabbit aorta and guinea pig ileum which contain FP, TP and EP receptors respectively.[112,113] Both compounds would appear, therefore, to be more specific DP agonists than PGD_2. The hydantoin analogue, BW 245C (30) is a potent inhibitor of aggregation of human platelets,[114] but, unlike PGI_2, it is inactive on rat platelets.[51,115] BW 245C displaces [³H]PGD_2 but not [³H]PGI_2 or [³H]iloprost from bovine and human platelets respectively,[51] and its antiaggregatory action on human platelets is antagonized by the DP-receptor-blocking drugs, N-0164 and AH 6809 (see Section 12.11.4.1), a profile consistent with an action on platelet DP receptors. In terms of its actions at other prostanoid receptors, this compound is also much more specific for DP receptors than is PGD_2 itself. In addition, in a study conducted by Narumiya and Toda, BW 245C and 9β-PGD_2 were shown, like PGD_2, to potently inhibit human platelet aggregation, elevate rat peritoneal mast cell cAMP and relax the rabbit transverse stomach strip.[111] The similarity of the equipotent concentrations of the compounds was indicative of a single subtype of DP receptor existing in the three systems, and this being different from that mediating vasopressor effects in the sheep.

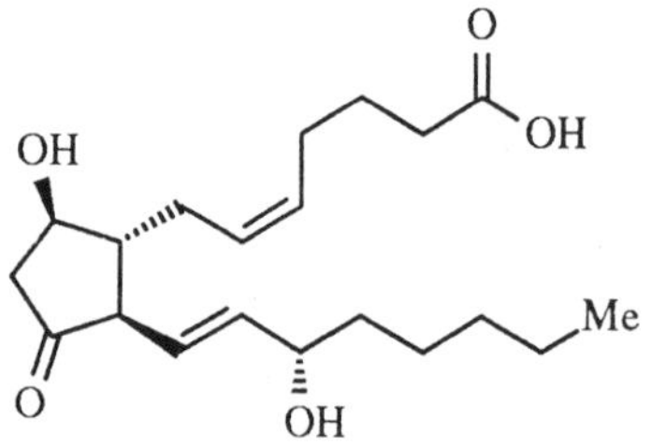

(27) 9β-Hydroxy-PGD_2

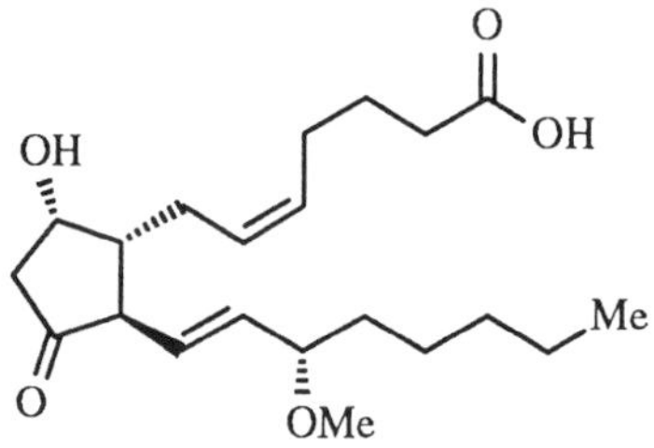

(28) 15-Methoxy-PGD_2

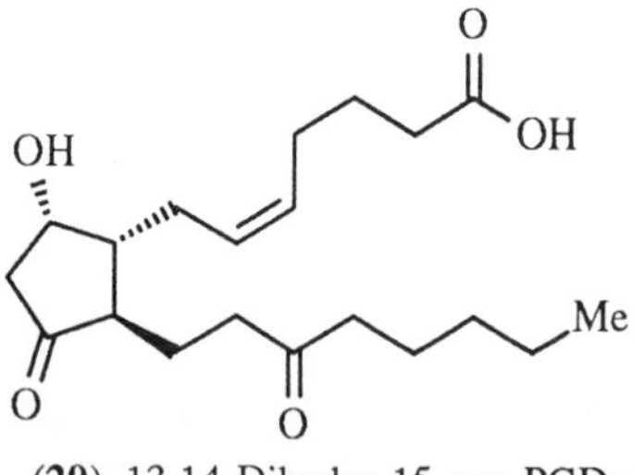

(29) 13,14-Dihydro-15-oxo-PGD_2

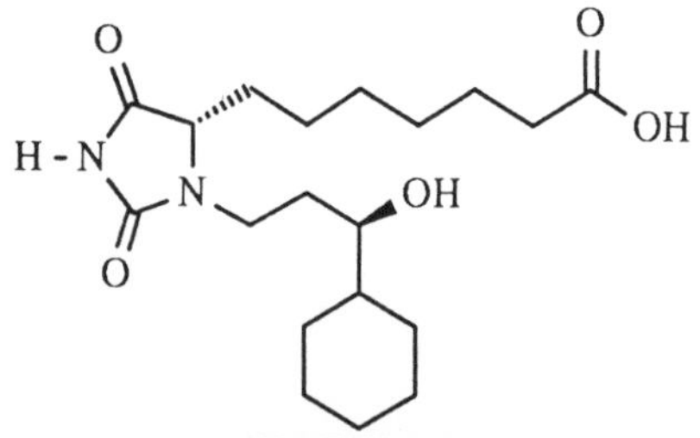

(30) BW 245C

Little is known concerning structural requirements for the DP-receptor-mediated pressor activity in the sheep. On the platelet, the antiaggregatory activity of PGD_2 is reduced by bulky substitution (*e.g.* 15-methyl-16,16-dimethyl-17-phenyl-) at or near C-15.[116] However, recent studies have shown that replacement of the *n*-pentyl moiety in PGD_2 by 15-cyclohexyl, either alone or in the presence of a 9β-halo group, produces compounds with activity at platelet DP receptors equal to or greater than that of PGD_2 itself.[116] The importance of the unnatural configuration of substituion at C-9 is further illustrated by the highly potent activity of the 9β-hydroxy derivative of PGD_2. The ability of the 15-cyclohexyl moiety to impart or enhance DP receptor agonist activity in prostanoid analogues has been recognized by others.[116] For example, the TP-receptor-blocking drug, SQ 27,427[117] (see Section 12.11.4.5) which contains a 15-cyclohexyl moiety has been reported to elevate human platelet cAMP. Consistent with this effect, the drug also inhibits ADP-induced platelet aggregation, an effect prevented by the DP receptor antagonist AH 6809 (see Section 12.11.4.1). It is interesting however, to note the presence of this group in the recently described potent DP-receptor-blocking drug BW A868C (see Section 12.11.4.1).[118]

12.11.3.2 EP Receptor Agonists

While there are many prostanoid agonists which are analogues of PGE_2, it is important to stress however that the biological actions of these agonists are not necessarily all mediated by EP receptors. Thus, for example, three such analogues, 16,16-dimethyl-PGE_2 (31), ICI 80,205 (32) and Wy17186 (33), all have TP agonist activity on vascular smooth muscle and blood platelets, while PGE_1 has IP agonist activity.[119]

(31) 16,16-Dimethyl-PGE_2

(32) ICI 80,205

(33) Wy17186

Although there are a number of reports on structure–activity relationships for EP agonists,[120–139] they have not been conducted or interpreted with reference to the prostanoid receptor classification. Therefore in an analysis of the data in such reports, it is necessary to apply our knowledge of the classification to determine receptor activity from functional findings. In this analysis, we have made certain assumptions which we believe to be true, but may not necessarily be valid in all instances, *e.g.* contractile activity on guinea pig ileum and uterus reflects EP_1 receptor agonist activity (see Sections 12.11.5.1.2 and 12.11.5.1.4); broncho- and vaso-dilatation, EP_2 receptor activity (see Sections 12.11.5.1.1 and 12.11.5.1.3); and inhibition of gastric acid secretion, EP_3 receptor activity (see Section 12.11.5.8). Bearing this in mind, it appears that certain structural features are essential for EP agonist activity generally, whereas others promote a degree of selectivity between the various EP receptor subtypes.

The length of the α-chain appears to be critical; addition or removal of a single carbon atom results in a loss of EP agonist activity.[120] Substitutions at C-1, where the carboxylic acid is replaced by a variety of esters or acidic imino or methanesulfonamido groups, result in maintained agonist activity at EP_1 and EP_3 receptors, but a tendency for a reduction in EP_2 agonist activity.[120,125,138] Substitutions at C(2)–(6) appears to be incompatible with EP agonist activity.[120,122,135] While a *cis* Δ^4 or Δ^5 bond or both are optimal as far as activities at EP_2 and EP_3 receptors are concerned,[120,121] such unsaturation in the α-chain is known to enhance potency at EP_1 receptors. Interestingly, introduction of an alkynic link at C(4)–(5) reduces EP_3 agonist activity,[121] and an interphenylene between C-3 and C-7[127] appears to result in EP_2 receptor selectivity.

Expanding the cyclopentyl ring to cyclohexyl leads to a substantial loss in agonist activity at all EP receptors.[120] A substituent at C-9 also appears to be critical for EP agonist activity; such a group is preferably a carbonyl, but a methylene group permits potent EP_1 and EP_3 agonist activity,[124,126,133] and a halogen, activity at EP_2 receptors.[120] Substitution of a hydroxy group reduces potency at all EP receptors.[120,128,137] The 11-hydroxy group is important for EP_1 receptor agonist activity, but is not essential for activity of either EP_2 or EP_3 agonists.[120,126,131] However, loss of the hydroxy group at C-11 can lead to an increase in TP receptor agonist activity.

The length of the β-chain is not critical to activity, there being many examples of compounds with β-chains extended or reduced, but with maintained biological activity.[120,126,127,134] Similarly, the presence or absence of a C(13)–(14) double bond has little influence on activity at EP_2 or EP_3 receptors; if present, however, it must be of the *trans* conformation.[120,127,134] A hydroxy group at either C-15 or C-16 appears to be essential for EP agonist activity,[120,131] however hydroxy groups at both lead to a decline in EP_2 agonist potency.[120] Although addition of methyl groups at C-15 and C-16 results in a selective loss in EP_2 receptor agonist potency, the introduction of a vinyl group at C-16 has given rise to the potent, selective EP_2 receptor agonist viprostol (34).[130] Like removal of

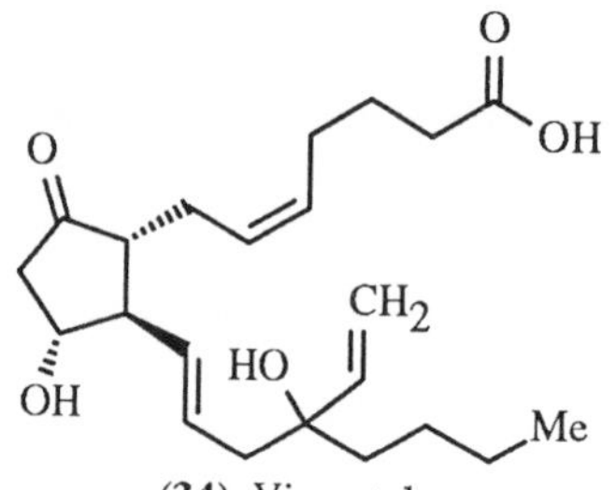

(34) Viprostol

the 11-hydroxy group, the presence of a methyl group at C-15 or C-16 appears to enhance TP receptor agonist potency.[136]

Many PGE analogues have been synthesized in which the final 2–4 carbon atoms in the β-chain have been omitted and replaced by a cyclic structure.[120,126,127,132] Thus 16-phenyltetranor-PGE$_2$ is a potent EP$_2$ agonist with substantially reduced EP$_1$ and EP$_3$ activity, while 17-phenyltrinor-PGE$_2$ is a potent, selective EP$_1$ receptor agonist, although data on EP$_3$ receptors are not available. Finally 18-phenyldinor-PGE$_2$ is nonselective, but somewhat weaker than PGE$_2$.[125,127] The presence of a 16-phenoxy group in tetranor-PGE analogues leads to compounds with high EP$_1$ and EP$_3$ but low EP$_2$ agonist potency and such selectivity is enhanced by introducing a *p*-chloro or *m*-trifluoromethyl group into the phenyl ring.[132,138]

These studies reveal a number of apparent 'rules', first for EP receptor agonist activity in general, and then for selective activity at each of the three subtypes. For general EP receptor agonist activity, the requirements are: (i) an α-chain of seven carbon atoms, (ii) a cyclopentane ring, (iii) a substituent at C-9, usually carbonyl, and (iv) hydroxy groups at C-15 or C-16. Some features resulting in selectivity of agonist activity within the three EP receptor subtypes are summarized in Table 7.

In addition to the systematic studies on structure–activity relationships dealt with above, there are many reports on pharmacological results obtained with selectively acting EP receptor agonists on various isolated tissue preparations for which the receptor populations are well characterized. Some of these compounds have already been dealt with in the preceding section, while others have not. The results with some such compounds are summarized in Table 8.

Two features emerge from these data. Firstly, the selectivity of action exhibited by some of the agonists between the preparations containing different EP receptors supports some of the conclusions drawn from the structure–activity studies above. Secondly, there is broad consistency of the data obtained within groups of preparations containing the same prostanoid receptor type. These agonists show various profiles of selectivity. Thus 16,16-dimethyl-PGE$_2$ (31), 9-methylene-PGE$_2$ (35) and ICI 80,205 (32) demonstrate some degree of EP$_1$ receptor selectivity, although only limited data are available on EP$_3$-receptor-containing preparations. Butaprost (TR4979; 36) is clearly an interesting compound in that it is the only reported analogue to demonstrate selective EP$_2$ agonist

Table 7 Some Structural Features Leading to Selectivity of Action at the EP Receptor Subtypes from Published Data

Receptor selectivity	Structural feature	Ref.
EP$_1$	1-Methanesulfonamido	125, 138
	1-Acidic imino	125, 138
	cis Δ^4 or Δ^5 bond	121
	9-Deoxy,9-methylene	139
	Methyl groups at C-15 or C-16	136, 137
	16-Phenoxy-tetranor	127
	17-Phenyl-trinor	127
EP$_2$	3,7-Interphenylene	127
	Alkynic link at C(5)–C(6)	121
	11-Deoxy	120, 131
	16-Vinyl	130
	16-Phenyl-tetranor	120, 126, 127
EP$_3$	1-Methanesulfonamido	125, 138
	1-Acidic imino	125, 138
	11-Deoxy	126
	Methyl groups at C-15 or C-16	121, 129, 133
	16-Phenoxy-tetranor	126, 132

Table 8 Agonist Potencies of Some PGE Analogues on a Range of Preparations Containing EP Receptors[55,62,119,140,141]

Preparation	Response	Receptor	AY23626	PGE_1	16,16-Dimethyl-PGE_2	9-Methylene-PGE_2	Wy17186	Butaprost	ICI 80,205	Sulprostone
					Equipotent concentrations ($PGE_2 = 1$)					
Guinea pig ileum	↑[a]	EP_1	>500	12	0.8	7.6	830	>1000	4.5	
Guinea pig fundus	↑	EP_1	410	5	0.08	5	436			3.6
Dog fundus	↑	EP_1	>100	14	0.3	8.1			5.6	
Guinea pig trachea	↑	EP_1	6000	11	0.5	1.3		>3000	0.23	5.6
Rat fundus	↑	EP_1		2.6	0.3			>10 000	0.05	
Bovine iris	↑	EP_1		3.1	0.4				0.16	
Guinea pig uterus	↑	EP_1		1.1						≈0.1
Rat uterus	↓[b]	EP_1		0.5				>50		≈1.0
Cat trachea	↓	EP_2	1.2	1.3	50	54	56	>500	70	>10 000
Guinea pig ileum (circ. muscle)	→	EP_2	14	0.5	15	127	433	30		>30 000
Guinea pig trachea	→	EP_2	21	0.5	4.4	78		1.6		>100
Dog saphenous vein	→	EP_2	1.4	2.3	280	50				>2100
Human bronchus	→	EP_2						6		
Chick ileum	↑	EP_3	5.3	0.25			19	>1000	0.9	
Guinea pig vas deferens	↓NT[c]	EP_3	7.4	0.8	0.12		5.6		0.5	0.02

[a] ↑ Smooth muscle contraction. [b] ↓ Smooth muscle relaxation. [c] ↓NT Inhibition of neurotransmitter release.

activity.[141] Although not a highly potent compound, the degree of butaprost's EP_2 selectivity is dramatic, being apparently inactive on preparations containing EP_1 and EP_3 receptors. Wy17186 acts as a moderately potent and selective EP_3 agonist, but the usefulness of this compound is limited by its TP agonist activity. Two of the agonists in Table 8 are selective for two of the EP receptor subtypes over the other one, thus sulprostone is a potent EP_1/EP_3 agonist, but with dramatically reduced potency at EP_2 receptors, whereas AY23626 is a potent EP_2/EP_3 agonist, but is weak at EP_1 receptors. These two compounds have proved invaluable in the characterization of the various subtypes of EP receptor (see Section 12.11.2.1.2). In contrast, two other PGE_2 analogues, PGE_1 and 11-deoxy-PGE_1, are essentially nonselective, although they may be somewhat weaker on EP_1 than on EP_2 and EP_3 receptors, and PGE_1 is also a moderately potent agonist at IP receptors.[62]

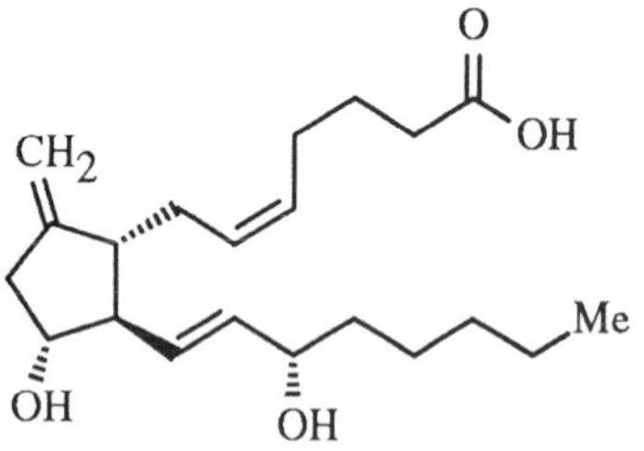

(35) 9-Methylene-PGE_2 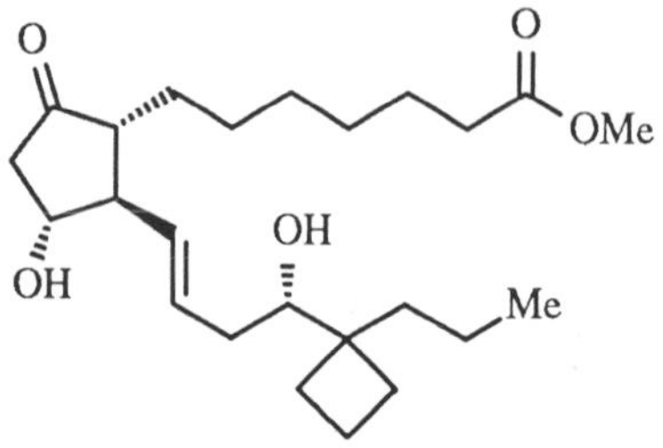   (36) Butaprost

Thus some of the PGE_2 analogues in Table 8 serve as useful tools in the investigation of the distribution of the various EP receptor subtypes in different tissues. However, until more is known about the action of these agonists at the other prostanoid receptor types, any such conclusions must be regarded as tentative.

In addition to the agonists in Table 8, there are a number of PGE_2 analogues developed for particular therapeutic applications, but for which there is little or no published pharmacological information on which to identify their sites of action. Of such agonists, most are gastric cytoprotective agents, *e.g.* enprostil (37), misoprostol (38) and rioprostil (39) but one, 9-methylene-16,16-dimethyl-PGE_2 is a uterine stimulant,[139] CS-412 (40) is a bronchodilator[142] and viprostol (34) is a vasodilator.[143] Although all of these actions are mimicked by PGE_2, it is not certain that the effects of the analogues are mediated by EP receptors. Thus while such compounds may represent potent, selective EP receptor agonists, we must await further pharmacological data on preparations with well-characterized receptor profiles before this can be established.

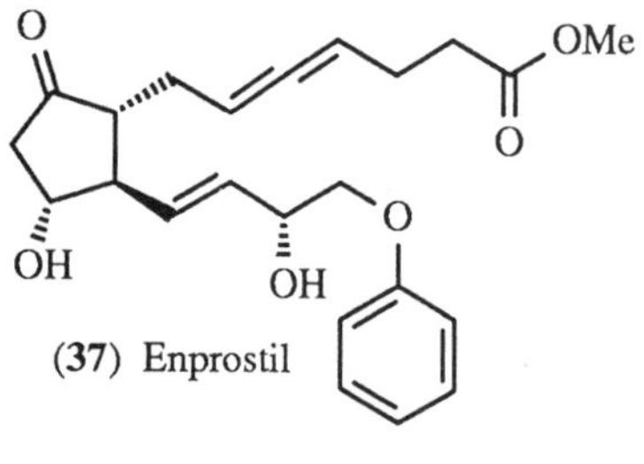

(37) Enprostil 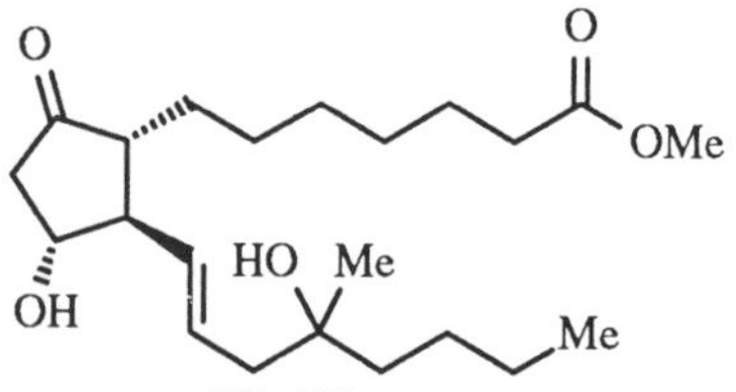   (38) Misoprostol

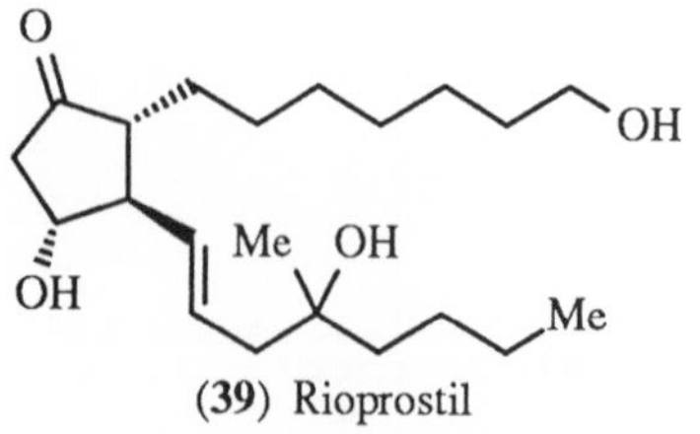

(39) Rioprostil 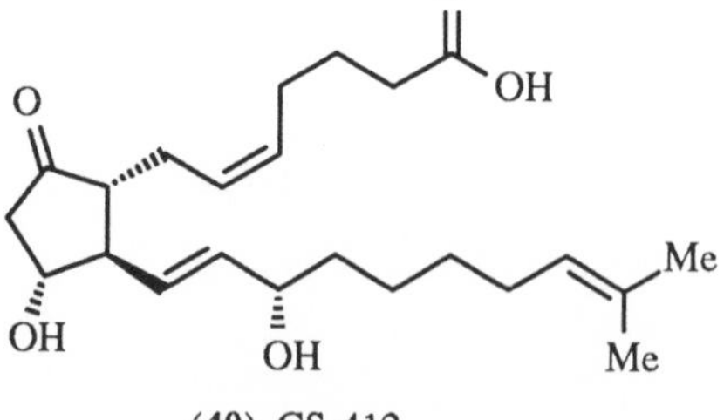   (40) CS-412

Finally, it is not essential that an agonist should be a PGE_2 analogue for it to behave as an EP agonist. A good example of this is the stable PGI_2 analogue, iloprost (ZK 36374; 41), which is not only a potent IP receptor agonist on both platelets and vascular smooth muscle (see Section 12.11.3.4), but also a potent agonist at EP_1 receptors. Thus iloprost potently contracts bovine iris sphincter and guinea pig trachea, actions antagonized by the EP_1-receptor-blocking drugs SC-19220 and AH 6809 respectively.[119,144] In contrast, iloprost is only a weak agonist on preparations containing EP_2 or EP_3 receptors.[144]

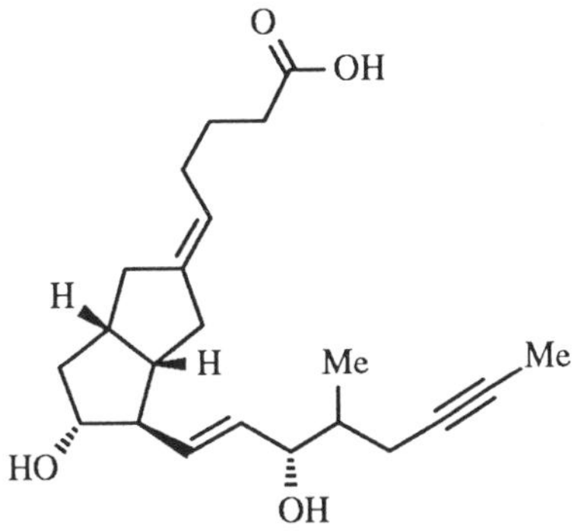

(**41**) Iloprost

12.11.3.3 FP Receptor Agonists

In 1974, Dukes *et al.* from ICI described a novel series of substituted 16-phenoxy analogues of PGF$_{2\alpha}$, which, like PGF$_{2\alpha}$ itself, were potent luteolytic agents in a range of animal species.[145] Of the natural prostanoids, PGF$_{2\alpha}$ is by far the most potent in this action, and FP receptors are therefore believed to be involved. The high potency of two of the ICI analogues, fluprostenol (**42**) and cloprostenol (**43**), as contractile agents on the FP-receptor-containing preparations, dog and cat iris sphincter muscle, characterize these two compounds as potent FP receptor agonists.[146] Since the discovery of these two compounds, a number of other PGF$_{2\alpha}$ analogues have been developed as luteolytic agents. Of these compounds, we have evaluated fluprostenol, cloprostenol, prostalene (**44**) and PGF$_{2\alpha}$ as well as some closer analogues, PGF$_{1\alpha}$ (**45**), PGF$_{2\beta}$ (**46**) and PGD$_2$ on a range of prostanoid-receptor-containing tissues.[62,146] Others have reported data with tiaprost (**47**) and fenprostalene (**48**).[147,148] These data, summarized in Table 9, give some indication as to the FP receptor selectivity of these various PGF$_{2\alpha}$ analogues. Quite clearly, the most selective of the FP agonists is fluprostenol, which shows not only high potency at FP receptors, but a quite remarkable degree of selectivity, being essentially inactive at DP, EP, IP and TP receptors. While some of the other compounds also exhibit potent, selective actions at FP receptors, none equals fluprostenol. We regard this compound as diagnostic in establishing whether FP receptors exist in any particular tissue. The most important study into the structure–activity relationship in FP agonists is that of Crossley[149] who detailed the structural modifications of PGF$_{2\alpha}$ which led to the discovery of fluprostenol. He described the importance of the length of the β-chain, which can vary between 8 and 11 carbon atoms, yet maintain activity. He also reported the effect of replacing carbon atoms 17–21 in the β-chain one at a time with oxygen in natural and bishomo analogues. In these studies, the 17-oxa derivative was the most potent FP agonist, with the least EP agonist activity. Finally, and perhaps most importantly, he demonstrated the effect of replacing C(17)–(20) with a phenoxy group to which were added *meta* and *para* substituents. While the *p*-fluorophenoxy analogue is possibly the most potent FP receptor agonist, it is also a potent TP receptor agonist, and the compound is highly

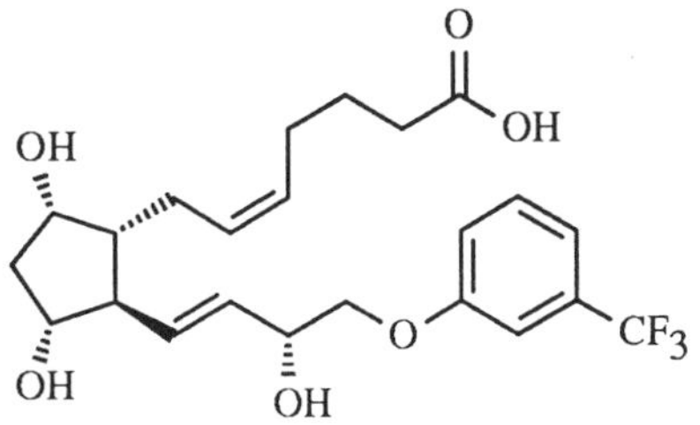

(**42**) Fluprostenol

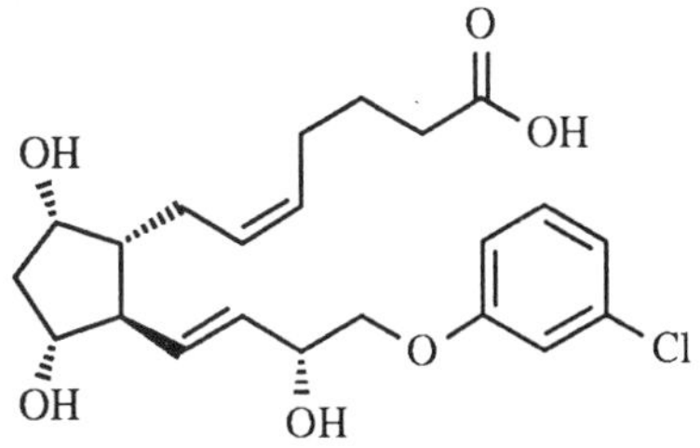

(**43**) Cloprostenol

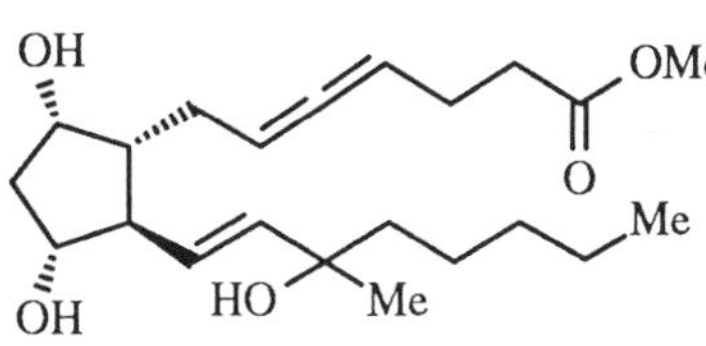

(**44**) Prostalene

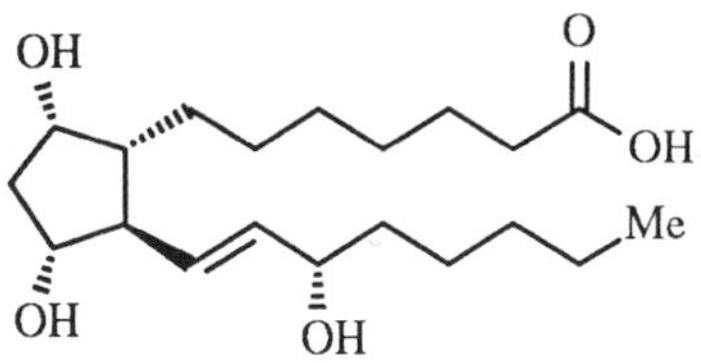

(**45**) PGF$_{1\alpha}$

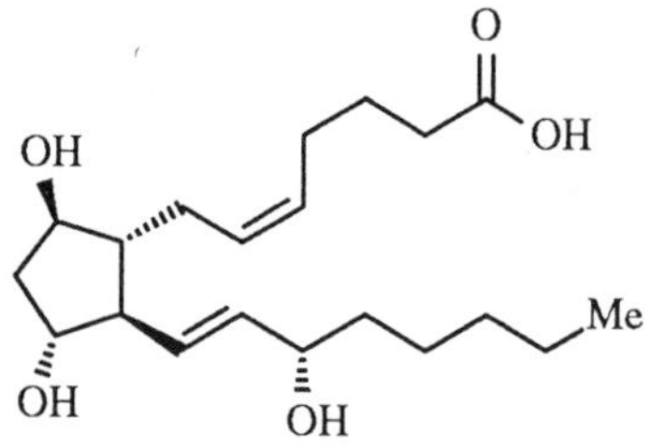

(46) PGF$_{2\beta}$

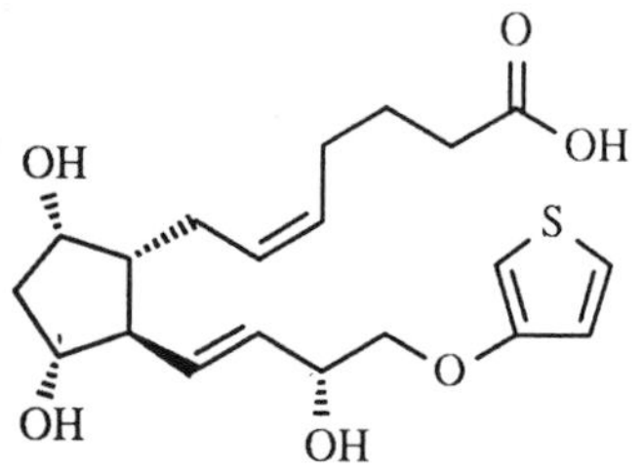

(47) Tiaprost

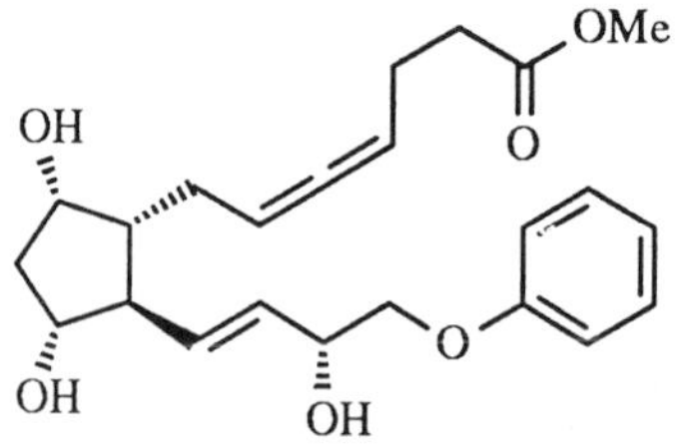

(48) Fenprostalene

toxic. In contrast, the *m*-chlorophenoxy (cloprostenol) and *m*-trifuoromethylphenoxy (fluprostenol) analogues proved both highly potent and selective. While other structure–activity studies have presumably been conducted with analogues of PGF$_{2\alpha}$, none has yielded compounds which have been shown to be as selective in their FP agonist actions as cloprostenol and fluprostenol. With the exception of PGF$_{2\alpha}$ and prostalene, all reported luteolytic prostanoids to date are either tetranoraryloxy or trinoraryl analogues, and therefore represent no advance on the structure–activity requirements demonstrated by Crossley.[149]

12.11.3.4   IP Receptor Agonists

The selectivity of action of PGI$_2$ itself is relatively low since, in addition to its IP receptor agonist activity, PGI$_2$ itself has also been shown to stimulate both EP$_1$ and TP receptors.[62,119] Despite the fact that many PGI$_2$ analogues have been synthesized and many comprehensive structure–activity studies have been performed with them, little information is available regarding their specificity for the IP receptor. The emphasis of the chemical effort in this area has centred on attempts to produce chemically and metabolically stable PGI$_2$ analogues which retain the platelet inhibitory effect but not the blood-pressure-lowering effect of the parent compound. PGI$_2$ is chemically highly unstable due to the strained enol ether structure in close proximity to a carboxylic function. PGI$_2$ is also metabolically unstable (see Section 12.11.1.3). Major attempts to confer chemical and metabolic stability upon PGI$_2$ have centred on substitution of its enol ether function as well as modification of the ω-side chain.[148,150,151] Thus, substitution of the oxygen of the enol ether moiety in PGI$_2$ by sulfur, nitrogen and carbon have led to more chemically stable analogues such as, for example carbacyclin [(5*E*)-6a-carba-PGI$_2$; 49]. However, the retention of 1-carboxy, 11- and 15-hydroxy groups and unsaturation at C-5, as well as maintainance of the stereochemistry of the parent compound in these analogues is important for maintaining biological activity. Introduction of a single methyl group at C-16 or C-17 increases activity, which along with inclusion of an alkynic group at C-18, as in iloprost (41), also confers increased metabolic stability.

Iloprost was the first stable analogue synthesized which was at least as potent as the parent compound at inhibiting platelet aggregation and relaxing vascular smooth muscle.[152] It appeared to be more specific than PGI$_2$ since, unlike the latter, it failed to contract the bovine coronary vein.[152] However, more extensive studies have shown iloprost to possess potent, albeit partial, agonist activity at the EP$_1$ receptor, mediating contraction of the guinea pig trachea, rat stomach fundus and bovine iris sphincter muscle (see Section 12.11.3.2).[119] Caution must therefore clearly be exercised with the compound when dealing with tissues known to contain EP receptors.

Attempts to improve the metabolic stability of iloprost yielded cicaprost (50).[153,154a] This compound was found to be more potent than either PGI$_2$ or iloprost as an inhibitor of platelet aggregation, as a relaxant of bovine coronary artery strip and as a hypotensive agent. However, in contrast to the actions of iloprost, cicaprost was found to exhibit weak or negligible activity upon EP receptors and appears to be the most selective IP receptor agonist yet described.[119]

Table 9 Agonist Potencies of Some PGF Analogues, PGE_2 and U-46619 on a Range of Preparations Containing Prostanoid Receptors[62,119,140,147].

Preparation	Receptor	Response	PGE_2	U-46619	$PGF_{2\alpha}$	PGD_2	$PGF_{1\alpha}$	Fluprostenol	Cloprostenol	Prostalene	Tiaprost	Fenprostalene
Guinea pig ileum	EP_1	↑[a]	1	>5000	50	1600	4750	>5000	[650–4500][e]	[600–700]	105	80
Guinea pig trachea	EP_1+TP	↑	1	1	20	140	360	>6000	328	NT[f]	3.8	0.16
Guinea pig uterus	EP_1+TP	↑[b]	1	3.7	16							
Cat trachea	EP_2	↑	1	2500	1000	150	380	>900	70			
Chick ileum	EP_3	↑	1	<400	116	>1500	43	>100[g]	100[g]			
Guinea pig lung	TP	↑	19 000	1	1110	155	8300	40 000	1700	900		
Rabbit aorta	TP	↑	800	1	167	585	850	4000	4500	NT	22	4
Human platelets	TP	↑AG[c]				1			334			
	IP+DP	↓AG[d]				1						
Rat uterus	FP+EP	↑	2.7	43	1	40	15.6	0.6				
Human uterus	FP+EP+TP	↑	95	2.3	1	13	24	3.4	0.7	3.3		
Dog iris	FP	↑	515	131	1	26	29	0.8	0.5	0.7		
Cat iris	FP		40	63				0.5	0.3	2.7		

[a] ↑ Smooth muscle contraction. [b] ↓ Smooth muscle relaxation. [c] ↑ AG Platelet aggregation. [d] AG ↓ Inhibition of platelet aggregation. [e] [ ] unpublished data. [f] NT = not tested. [g] Partial agonist.

Other potent, stable analogues of carbacyclin such as 15-cyclopentylcarbacyclin (OP-41483; **51**), 9β-methylcarbacyclin (ciprostene; **52**), CG 4203 (**53**) and FCE-22509 (**54**) have also been synthesized and are under development . However, attempts to obtain stable PGI$_2$ mimetics have not resulted in any clear examples of agonists which show a separation of platelet antiaggregatory activity and vasodepressor activity. Furthermore, little attention has been paid to studying the classification and distribution of IP receptors and so provide a rational framework for the design of selective IP agonists. Indeed it is not certain whether all IP receptors are the same, or whether subtypes of IP receptor exist. Various pharmacological studies have been interpreted to indicate that differences may exist between IP receptors upon platelets from different species[154b] and upon platelets and vascular smooth muscle.[155] However, in the case of the latter study, differences in stimulus–response coupling or receptor density in the two biological systems may have been responsible for the differences observed. In addition to the possible existence of IP receptor subtypes, a marked variation in their distribution has been reported in, for example, vascular smooth muscle.[156]

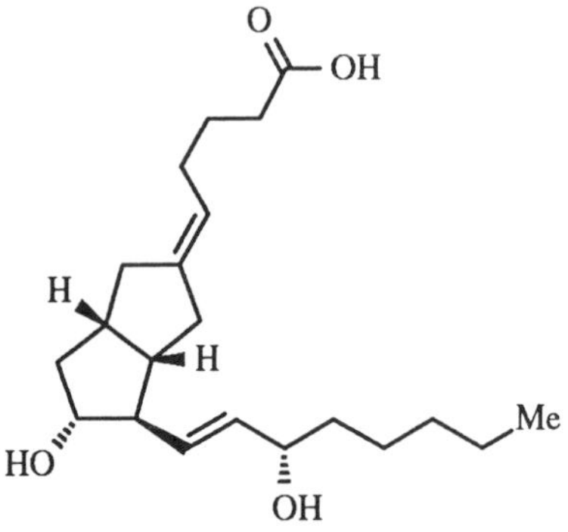

(49) (5*E*)-6a-Carba-PGI$_2$

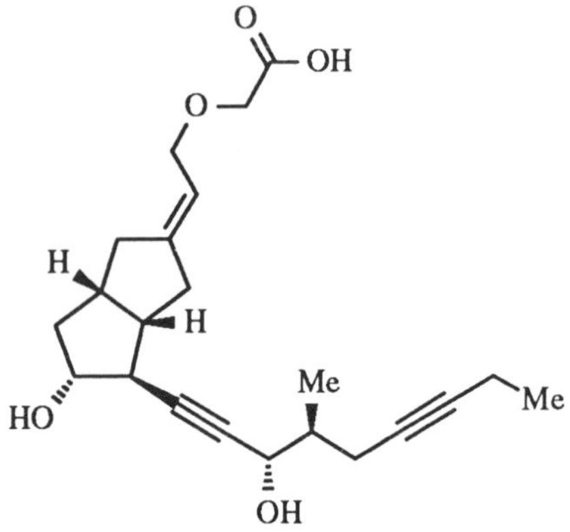

(50) Cicaprost

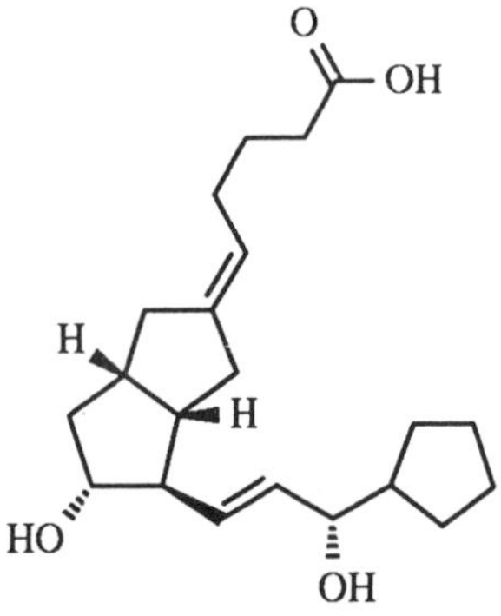

(51) OP-41483

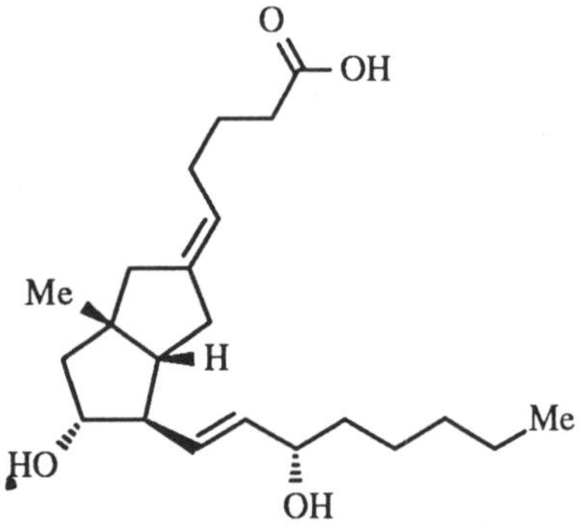

(52) Ciprostene

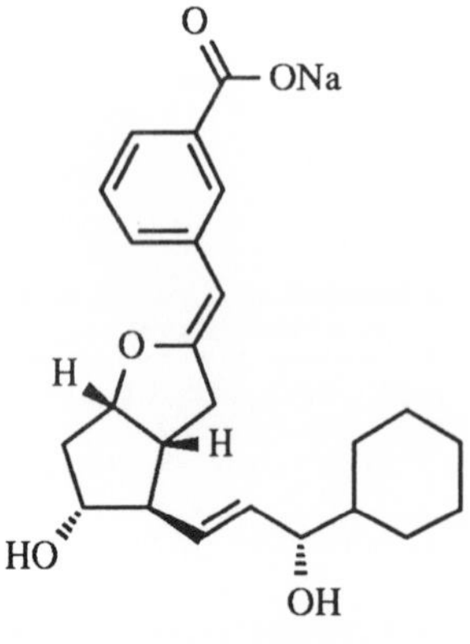

(53) CG 4203

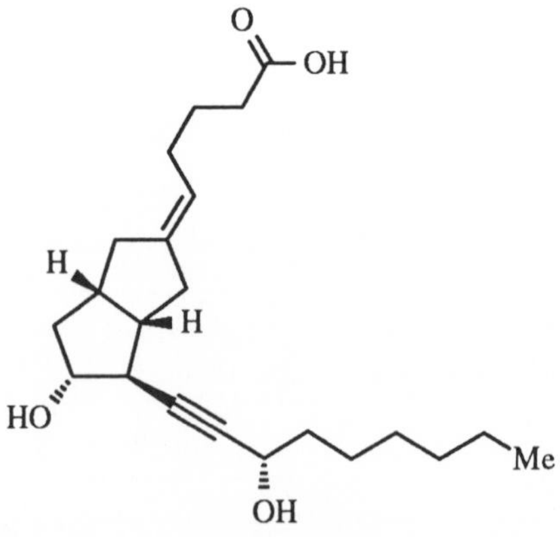

(54) FCE-22509

12.11.3.5 TP Receptor Agonists

Although many studies have been conducted with biosynthetically generated TxA$_2$, its instability, with a half-life at 37 °C and pH 7.4 of approximately 32 s in aqueous solution, renders it virtually unusable for quantitative pharmacological studies. Furthermore, the fact that PGH$_2$, from which TxA$_2$ is generated and with which it is inevitably contaminated, can spontaneously degrade or be enzymatically converted to other prostaglandins, makes interpretation and quantification of the activity of TxA$_2$ even more difficult. Recently, the synthesis of synthetic TxA$_2$ has been described.[157,158] This has allowed the structure of TxA$_2$, proposed by Hamberg *et al.*,[6] to be confirmed and has also allowed its biology to be investigated without contamination by the prostaglandin endoperoxides.[158-160] However, the extreme lability of the compound still makes it unsuitable for quantitative studies. Several of the stable prostaglandins such as PGF$_{2\alpha}$, PGE$_2$, PGA$_2$ and PGB$_2$ contract rat and rabbit aortic strips *via* stimulation of TP receptors.[40,41] In contrast, with the exception of PGE$_2$ under certain circumstances (see Section 12.11.5.3), these prostaglandins fail to induce platelet aggregation, although PGA$_2$ and PGB$_2$ may have weak TP-receptor-blocking activity.[161] Additionally of course, the natural prostaglandins have limited use as TP agonists because of their lack of specificity.

Shortly after the isolation and chemical characterization of PGG$_2$ and PGH$_2$ (see Section 12.11.1.1), stable analogues of PGH$_2$ were successfully synthesized. Of these, U-46619 (11α,9α-epoxymethano-PGH$_2$; **21**) and its corresponding 9α,11α-epoxymethano analogue (U-44069; **55**) potently mimicked the actions of TxA$_2$ in causing aggregation of human platelets and contraction of vascular smooth muscle.[162] To date, U-46619 and U-44069 remain the best characterized and most widely used TP agonists. U-46619 has been shown to closely mimic the contractile actions of TxA$_2$, being a potent and full contractile agonist on a wide range of TP-receptor-containing preparations, but is weak on preparations containing only other prostanoid receptor types.[39-41,163,164] The compound has been reported to be some 2–3 times less potent than synthetic TxA$_2$, but some 4–6 times more potent than PGG$_2$ or PGH$_2$ at causing human platelet aggregation and contraction of vascular smooth muscle respectively *in vitro*.[159,162] *In vivo*, U-46619 appears to be equipotent with synthetic TxA$_2$ at causing bronchoconstriction and vasoconstriction.[160] U-44069 possesses a similar profile of action to U-46619,[41,162,163] although it is less potent and appears to be a partial agonist on human platelets as well as on various vascular smooth muscle preparations.[41,163,165]

(21) U-46619   (55) U-44069

Whilst the similarity in the profiles of activity of U-46619 and TxA$_2$ is an indication that U-46619 may act at the TP receptor, it is not conclusive evidence in itself. The discovery of potent and highly specific TP-receptor-blocking drugs has, however, partly helped to resolve this question. Thus, compounds such as EP 045 and AH 23848 (see Section 12.11.4.5) antagonize the actions of U-46619 (and U-44069) at the same concentrations at which they antagonize the actions of TxA$_2$.[163,166,167] The availability of both [^{3}H]U-44069 and [^{3}H]U-46619 has confirmed that U-46619 interacts with a single class of stereospecific, saturable, high affinity binding sites which have the pharmacological characteristics of TP receptors.[84,168] Similarly, both U-46619 and U-44069 compete with specific TP receptor ligands in platelet preparations (see Section 12.11.2.2.5). The greater similarity in structure of U-46619 to PGH$_2$ than to TxA$_2$ has prompted some discussion as to whether, in preparations where PGH$_2$ and TxA$_2$ produce similar effects (*e.g.* platelets), U-46619 is acting as a PGH$_2$ mimetic *via* PGH$_2$ receptors or as a TxA$_2$ mimetic *via* TP receptors. The evidence cited above and that presented by Armstrong *et al.*[84,169] strongly supports the contention that both U-46619 and PGH$_2$ are TxA$_2$ mimetics, and act at TP receptors.

As mentioned above, other potent TP agonists were discovered at or about the same time as U-46619, such as 9,11-azo-PGH$_2$ (U-51093; **56**) and PGF$_{2\alpha}$-acetal (**57**). For example, 9,11-azo-PGH$_2$ was shown to be a highly potent TP agonist, being some 7–8 times more potent than PGG$_2$ and PGH$_2$ at producing platelet aggregation and contraction of rabbit aortic strips respectively.[170] It is of similar potency to U-46619 at causing aggregation of human washed platelets, and at contracting rabbit aorta and dog saphenous vein.[41,163,164,171] Compared with U-46619 it is a full agonist on the TP-receptor-containing preparations tested,[163,164,172] where it is antagonized by TP-receptor-blocking drugs[163,171,173] and competes with labelled TP receptor agonists and antagonists for TP-receptor-binding sites on human platelets.[84,168] Other analogues which display agonist activity at both platelet and smooth muscle TP receptors have also been described, such as 9,11-etheno-PGH$_2$ (**58**), 9,11-ethano-PGH$_2$ (**59**) and its ω-tetranor-16-*p*-fluorophenoxy derivative, EP 011 (**60**), the more potent 9α,11α-oxa-10a-homo analogues, EP 171 (**61**) and SQ 26,655 (**62**), and the various thia derivatives of TxA$_2$, including STA$_2$ (**63**).[164] The TP agonist activity of various analogues of PGE$_2$ such as 11-deoxy-15(*RS*)-15-methyl-PGE$_2$ (Wy17186; **33**), its 15(*S*) epimer (Wy40659) and 11-deoxy-15(*S*)-16(*RS*)-methyl-PGE$_2$ (Wy19110) upon human platelets has also been described.[161] Unfortunately, only limited characterization of the agonist activity has been performed on many of these analogues. Jones *et al.* have examined the speed of onset and offset of several of these TP agonists on vascular smooth muscle and have classified them into three groups.[163] The first type of compound is rapid in onset and offset, more than one concentration–effect curve being obtainable on a single preparation. The second and third groups are characterized by a progressively slower onset and offset of action, making construction of more than one concentration–effect curve or even, in some cases, determination of more than a single response on a single preparation impossible. The first group includes U-46619 and various analogues of PGF$_{2α}$ such as the 15-methyl, 16,16-dimethyl, 11-deoxy, and the 16-*p*-chlorophenoxy (ICI 79,492) and 16-*p*-fluorophenoxy (ICI 79,939) analogues.

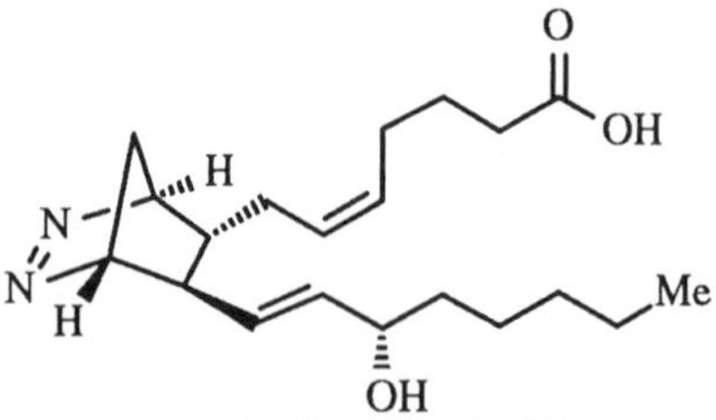

(**56**) 9,11-Azo-PGH$_2$

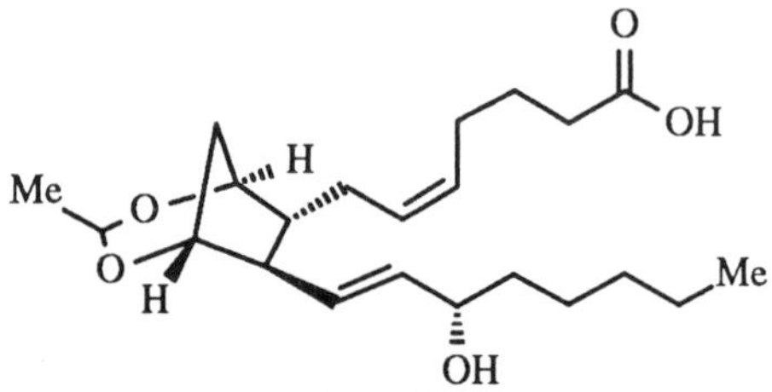

(**57**) PGF$_{2α}$-acetal

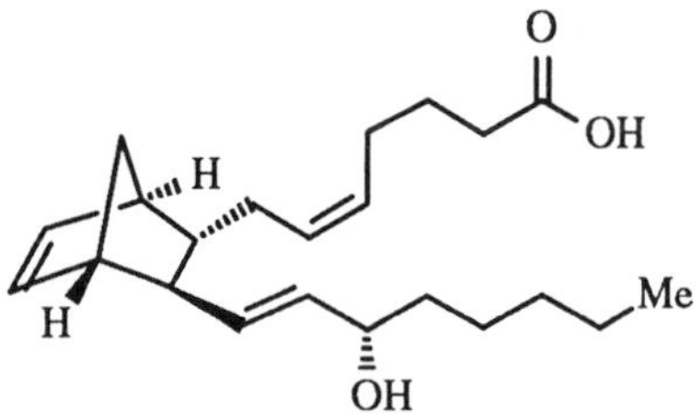

(**58**) 9,11-Etheno-PGH$_2$

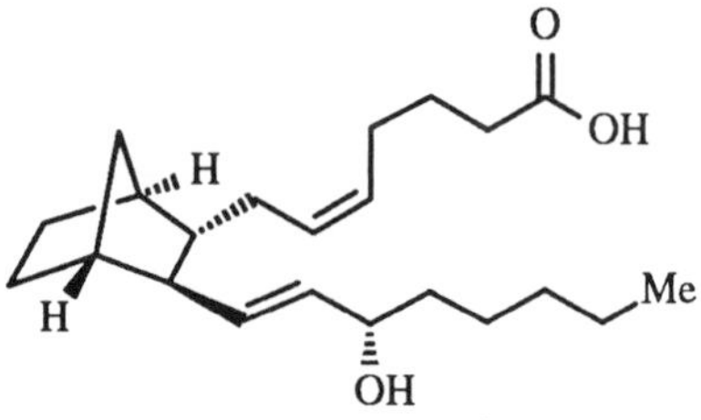

(**59**) 9,11-Ethano-PGH$_2$

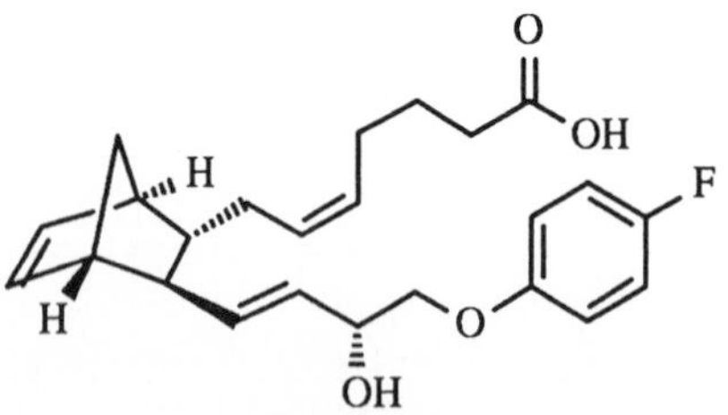

(**60**) EP 011

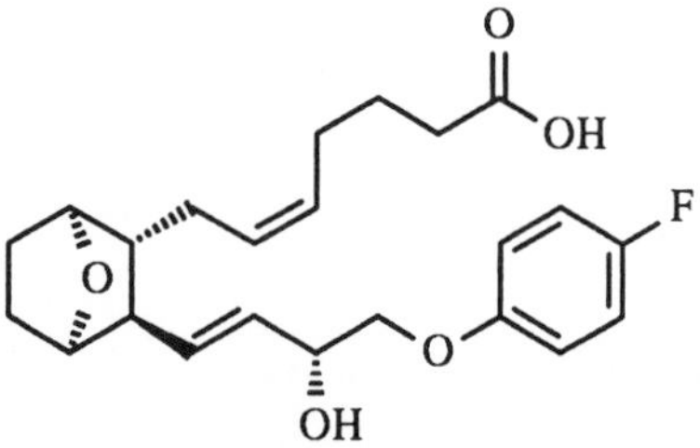

(**61**) EP 171

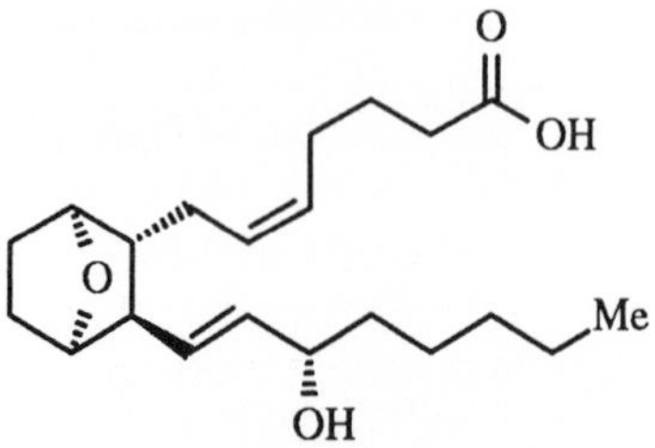

(**62**) SQ 26,655

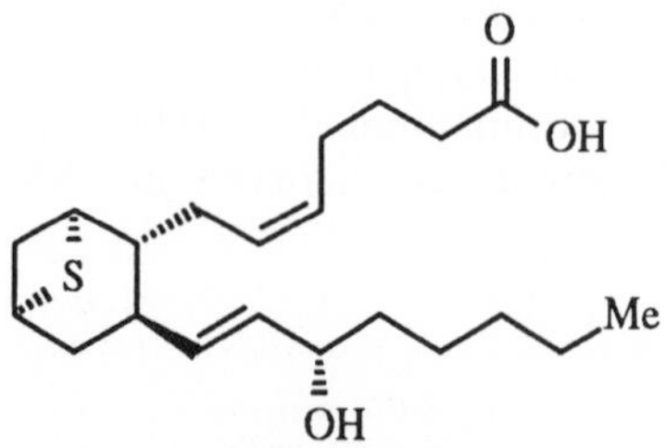

(**63**) STA$_2$

Although in some cases these latter analogues display potent TP agonist activity, they are of limited usefulness as they also possess EP agonist activity. The second and third groups of slow-acting analogues include several extremely potent TP agonists, including 9,11-azo-PGH$_2$, EP 011, the 16-*p*-fluorophenoxy and 16-*p*-chlorophenoxy analogues of 9,11-ethano-PGH$_2$ (EP 031 and EP 032 respectively). In particular, of this group, the more recently described EP 171, the 16-*p*-fluorophenoxy analogue of SQ 26,655 (see below), is the most potent TP agonist described to date.[41,164,174,175] The slow onset and offset of action of these agonists, possibly related to their high degree of lipophilicity, severely limits their usefulness for quantitative studies of TP receptors.

Other potent TP agonists have been described; these include the 7-oxabicyclo[2.2.1]heptane analogues of PGH$_2$, for example SQ 26,538, and the more potent 9α,11α-oxa-10a-homo derivative, SQ 26,655 (**62**),[176,177] as well as 11a-carba-9α,11α-thia-TxA$_2$ (STA$_2$; ONO 11113). These compounds are characterized as TP agonists by their profile of agonist activity, and their competition with radiolabelled TP receptor agonists and antagonists for specific binding sites. While STA$_2$ exhibits slow rates of onset and offset of action, SQ 26,655 is much more rapid in both aspects and is therefore potentially a more valuable agonist for quantitative purposes. No specificity data for either STA$_2$ or SQ 26,655 appear to have been published.

The TP receptor agonists available fall into two main categories, analogues of TxA$_2$ and of PGH$_2$, and some comments can be made concerning the optimal structure for biological activity in these series. Interestingly, straightforward isosteric replacement of the very hydrolytically sensitive acetal moiety of TxA$_2$, whilst conferring stability on the molecule, can also lead to both agonist and antagonist activity. Thus, whilst the thia analogue STA$_2$ is a full agonist, the corresponding 11α-carba[178] and 9α,11α-dicarba (CTA$_2$; **77**) derivatives are antagonists and partial agonists at the platelet TP receptor respectively (see Section 12.11.4.5). Similar isosteric replacement of the dioxygen bridge in PGH$_2$ generally results in a TP agonist profile. Thus replacement of either oxygen by a methylene group (U-44069 and U-46619), or both oxygens by an azo, etheno or ethano group, provides potent TP agonists. In most instances, the natural α- and β-chains are retained, but incorporation of a *p*-fluorophenoxy moiety into the terminal portion of the β-chain seems to impart enhanced potency (*e.g.* EP 011 and EP 171). The most important feature for retention of activity of TP agonists appears to be the conformation which is imposed on the α- and β-side chains by their attachment to a highly rigid bicyclic template.

Studies utilizing TP agonists have been less successful than those using TP-receptor-blocking drugs (Section 12.11.4.5) in demonstrating differences between TP receptors in different biological systems.[41,163,179,180] Whilst there are many instances of TP agonists which display agonist activity upon vascular smooth muscle and antagonist activity upon platelets,[41,163,172,181a] a clearly factors other than differences in receptors can account for this profile of action of partial agonists (see Section 12.11.2.1.1). Claims of differences in agonist potency between platelets and vascular smooth muscle are also difficult to interpret, for example in the study of Mais *et al.*[182b] where plasma proteins were present in only one of the two test systems examined. Clearly further careful studies are necessary before a conclusion can be reached regarding the existence of subtypes of TP receptors.

12.11.4 SELECTIVE PROSTANOID RECEPTOR ANTAGONISTS

12.11.4.1 DP-receptor-blocking Drugs

The first compounds to be identified as DP-receptor-blocking drugs were the phloretin derivatives, N-0164 (**64**)[182] and close structural analogues N-0057 and N-0161. The compounds antagonized the antiaggregatory action of PGD$_2$ on human platelets, 10-fold higher concentrations being required to antagonize the effects of PGI$_2$ and PGE$_1$. N-0164 was also shown to antagonize the antiaggregatory effect of BW 245C (see Section 12.11.3.1) and inhibit PGD$_2$-induced elevation of cAMP in human platelets. However, N-0164 also possesses other actions and was in fact first identified, like the parent compound, polyphloretin phosphate, as an EP-receptor-blocking drug antagonizing contractions of gastrointestinal smooth muscle induced by PGE$_2$ and PGF$_{2\alpha}$.[183] The compound was also subsequently shown to exhibit thromboxane synthase inhibitory activity,[184] TP-receptor-blocking activity[185] and cAMP phosphodiesterase inhibitory activity.[186] A derivative of tetrahydrocannabinol, deacetyl-($-$)-nantradol (**65**), has also been reported to inhibit PGD$_2$- but not PGE$_1$-stimulated increases in cAMP in human platelet membranes, and to compete with [^{3}H]PGD$_2$ but not [^{3}H]PGE$_1$ binding on human platelet membranes at concentrations of 10 μM and above.[187] However, we have failed to show antagonism of the antiaggregatory effect of PGD$_2$ on human platelets with this compound at concentrations of up to 300 μM.

We have also recently identified a compound, AH 6809 (**24**), which antagonizes the antiaggregatory effects of PGD$_2$ and its mimetics, BW 245C and 9α,11β-PGF$_2$ (see Section 12.11.3.1), but not

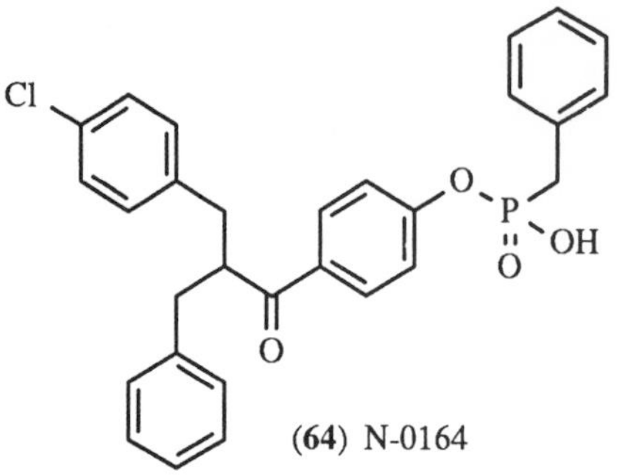

(64) N-0164

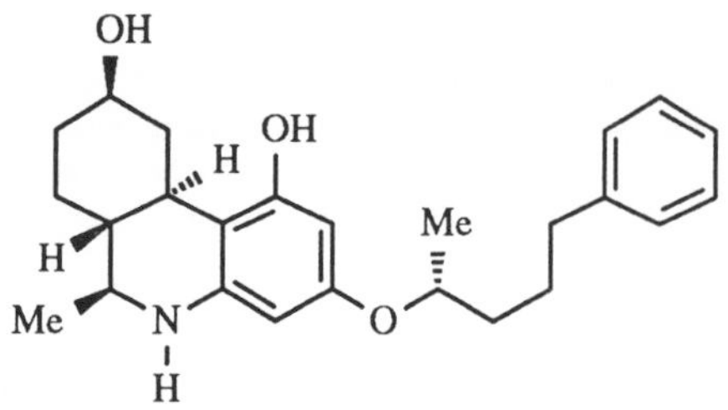

(65) Deacetyl-(−)-nantradol

those of PGI_2 or the adenosine mimetic, NECA, upon human platelets.[114] The compound also displaces [^{3}H]PGD_2 from platelet binding sites.[188] However, AH 6809 also displays EP-receptor-blocking activity upon smooth muscle (see Section 12.11.4.2) as well as weak TP-receptor-blocking activity upon platelets and vascular smooth muscle. Whilst the compound can be used experimentally for characterizing DP receptors, more specific compounds are clearly needed.

Because of the diverse structures of the DP-receptor-blocking drugs discussed so far, it is not possible to make any comment upon structure–activity relationships. However, reports have appeared very recently describing the pharmacology of BW A868C **(66)**,[118,189] a structural analogue of BW 245C (see Section 12.11.3.1). This compound displayed high potency for antagonizing the antiaggregatory effects of PGD_2 upon human platelets (pK_B 9.3), but was specific, being without effect upon other prostanoid receptor types. BW A868C is also active *in vivo*,[190] and should prove to be a major advance in studying the pharmacology of PGD_2 and its analogues.

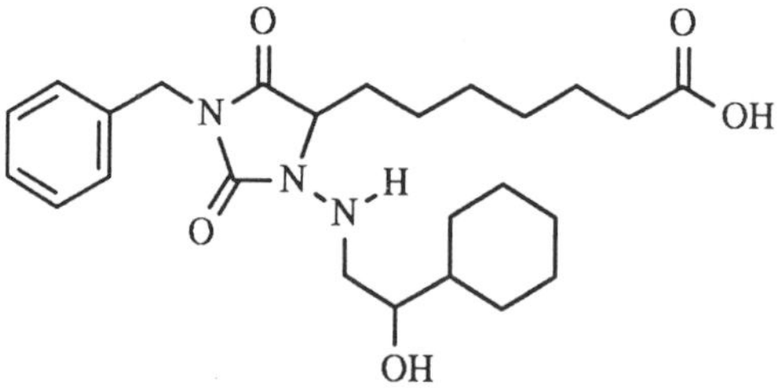

(66) BW A868C

12.11.4.2 EP-receptor-blocking Drugs

Although at present we have evidence for the existence of three different subtypes of EP receptors, to date there exist specific antagonists for only one them, namely the EP_1 receptor subtype. One of the first specific prostanoid antagonists reported was SC-19220 **(23)**,[44] and this has since been identified as a specific EP_1-receptor-blocking drug.[191] Since then, another compound has been identified which possesses a similar profile of action, AH 6809 **(24)**.[191] The pharmacological profiles of SC-19220 and AH 6809 have been extensively reported elsewhere.[191] AH 6809 is more potent than SC-19220 as an EP_1-receptor-blocking drug, but unlike SC-19220, it possesses blocking activity at receptors other than EP_1. Thus AH 6809 also possesses some blocking activity at both DP receptors and TP receptors (see Sections 12.11.4.1 and 12.11.4.5). While both compounds have proved valuable in the characterization of prostanoid receptors, both have their limitations. For example, the combination of poor aqueous solubility and low potency of SC-19220 means that its usefulness *in vivo* is limited.[146] Furthermore, despite its higher potency and aqueous solubility, AH 6809 also has limited usefulness *in vivo*, since in the presence of 4% bovine serum albumen, AH 6809 is approximately 97% protein bound.

Various analogues of SC-19220 have been tested for antiprostaglandin (EP_1 antagonist) activity on both guinea pig ileum and rat fundus. In these compounds, the acetyl function of SC-19220 was replaced with *n*-butanolyl, isobutanoyl and *n*-hexanyl functions. While increase in length of this function was associated with higher EP_1 antagonist potency, it was also associated with a reduced specificity of action. Thus despite its low potency, SC-19220 remains the most useful of this series of compounds.[192] While one further analogue, the *n*-chloropentanoyl derivative, SC-25469 **(67)**,[193] has been reported to exhibit EP_1-receptor-blocking activity, there is no published information relating to its potency. Both SC-19220 and SC-25469 have been demonstrated to possess *in vivo* activity,

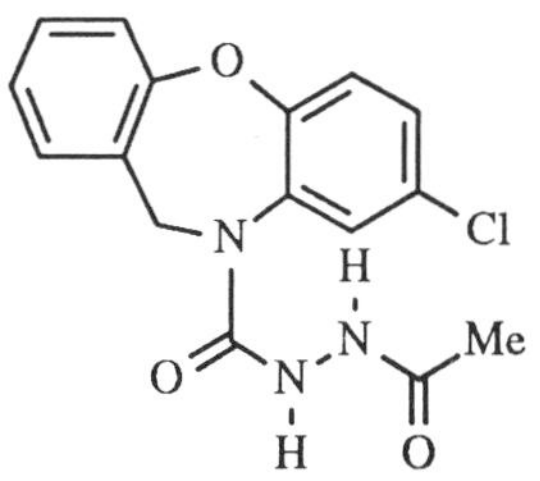

(**23**) SC-19220

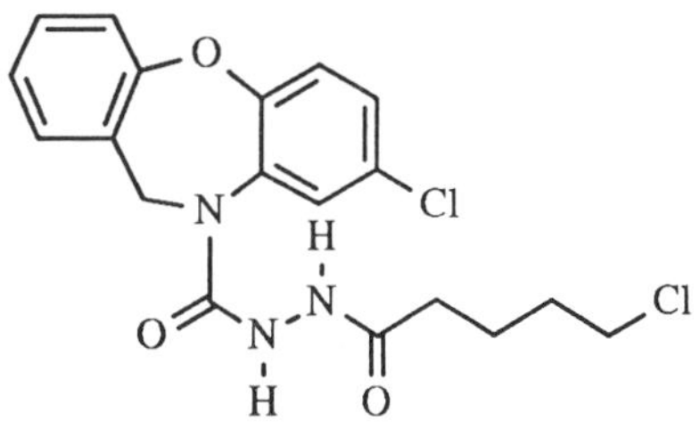

(**67**) SC-25469

exhibiting antinociceptive activity in a range of tests.[193] This activity suggests that EP receptors may be involved in prostanoid-induced hyperalgesia.

Three other prostanoid antagonists which undoubtedly inhibit at least some EP_1-receptor-mediated effects include the phloretin (**68**) derivatives, polyphloretin phosphate (PPP), diphloretin phosphate (DPP) and N-0164. Additionally, there is evidence that, between them, these three compounds, like AH 6809, also possess some antagonist activity against responses mediated by DP and TP receptors. However, none of these three compounds clearly behaves as a competitive receptor-blocking drug, as where they are active, rightward shifts of concentration–effect curves are often associated with depressions of response maxima. Nevertheless, their apparent specificity of action would be expected to make them useful for the pharmacological characterization of prostanoid receptors. However, they are not generally very highly regarded as pharmacological tools and are now seldom used.

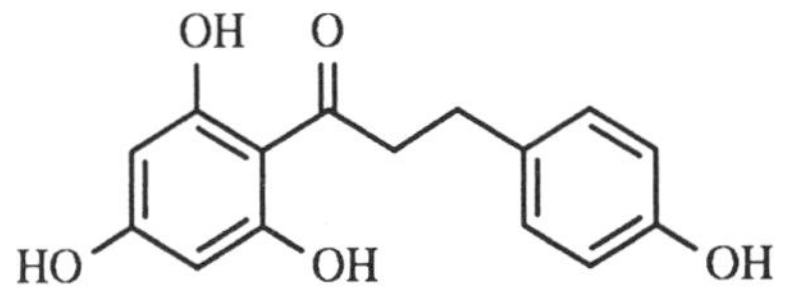

(**68**) Phloretin

Of the various agents with established EP-receptor-blocking activity described so far, none is obviously structurally related to prostanoids. However, a prostanoid analogue has recently been described that may possess EP_1-receptor-blocking activity. Interestingly, however, the compound, 13,14-didehydro-20-methylcarbaprostacyclin, FCE-22176 (**69**) is a PGI_2 analogue.[194] This compound was originally described as a PGI_2-receptor-blocking drug because it antagonized PGI_2-induced contractions of guinea pig trachea. However, guinea pig tracheal smooth muscle contains no IP receptors, prostanoid-induced contraction of this preparation being mediated by EP_1 and TP receptors, and PGI_2[195] has modest potency at EP_1 receptors.[62] Additionally, Wilkins and MacDermot failed to demonstrate any IP-receptor-blocking activity with FCE-22176 on either human platelets or NCB-20 hybrid cells.[196] Indeed, on both preparations, FCE-22176 exhibited IP agonist activity, although the compound was somewhat weak. If indeed FCE-22176 is an EP_1-receptor-blocking drug, it is not only the first prostanoid analogue for which such activity has been reported, but is also the most potent, with an approximate pA_2 of 7.2, determined from published data. The possibility of this PGI_2 analogue possessing potent EP_1-receptor-blocking activity is interesting in the light of the high EP_1 agonist activity observed with another PGI_2 analogue, iloprost (see Sections 12.11.3.2 and 12.11.3.4).

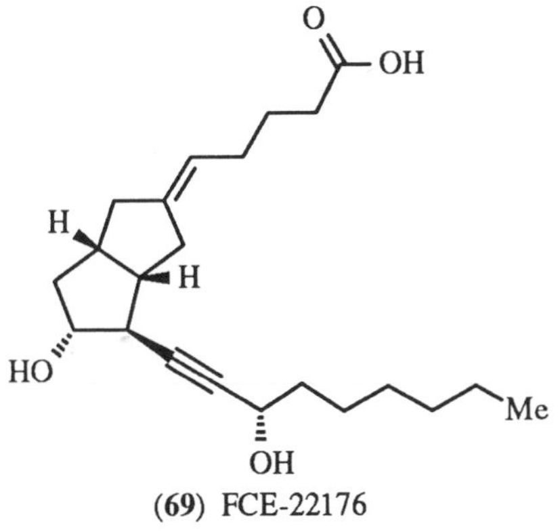

(**69**) FCE-22176

Finally, a compound that may be an EP-receptor-blocking drug is the cannabinoid, deacetyl-(−)-nantradol (see Section 12.11.4.1), which has been reported to inhibit the hyperalgesic and diarrhoeagenic actions of PGE_2,[197,198] as well as inhibiting PGD_2-induced activity on human platelets. Whether the antagonism is of a competitive, pharmacological or noncompetitive, physiological nature is not certain as there is no evidence as to the specificity of its activity. Although it has been suggested that there is a structural similarity between PGE_2 and deacetyl-(−)-nantradol, the evidence that it is an EP-receptor-blocking drug can only be regarded as tenuous.

12.11.4.3 FP-receptor-blocking Drugs

Although a wide range of compounds has been reported to antagonize various actions of $PGF_{2\alpha}$, many such actions are mediated by prostanoid receptors other than the FP type. Thus EP_1-receptor-blocking drugs antagonize $PGF_{2\alpha}$-induced contractions of such preparations as guinea pig ileum, fundus and trachea, and TP-receptor-blocking drugs antagonize $PGF_{2\alpha}$-induced contractions of many vascular smooth muscle preparations.[40] To date, no compounds have been reported which specifically antagonize prostanoid-induced effects where FP receptors are known to be involved, *e.g.* luteolysis, contraction of dog and cat isolated iris sphincter and $PGF_{2\alpha}$-induced bronchoconstriction in the dog. There are, however, three compounds which have been reported to inhibit prostanoid agonist activity on preparations that we believe to contain FP receptors. One such compound, 13,14-didehydro-20-methyl-$PGF_{2\alpha}$ (K10136; **70**), has been reported to inhibit contractions of rat isolated uterine smooth muscle to $PGF_{2\alpha}$ but not PGE_2, acetylcholine, histamine or 5-hydroxytryptamine.[199] Since the prostanoid receptors mediating contraction of rat uterus are believed to be a mixed population of EP and FP types (see Section 12.11.5.1.5), the antagonist activity of K10136 appears to be *via* an action at FP receptors. Similarly, two other close analogues of $PGF_{2\alpha}$, N,N-dimethylamino-$PGF_{2\alpha}$ (amino-$PGF_{2\alpha}$; **71**) and N,N-dimethylamido-$PGF_{2\alpha}$ (amido-$PGF_{2\alpha}$; **72**), are both reported to exhibit specific prostanoid antagonist activity on gerbil colon,[200] a preparation on which $PGF_{2\alpha}$ and fluprostenol both exhibit high agonist potency. These data are therefore consistent with these two analogues being FP-receptor-blocking drugs.

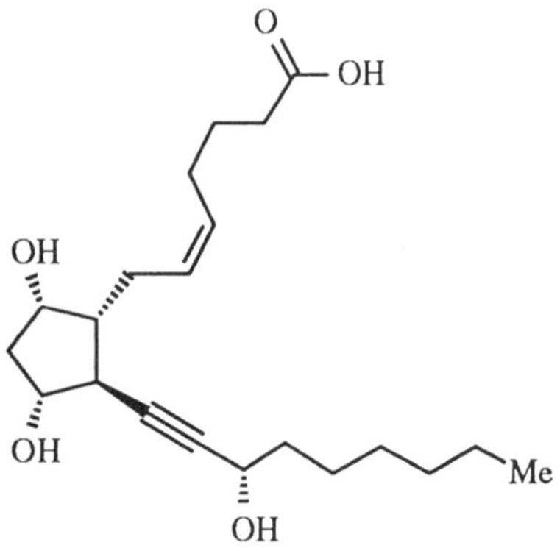

(**70**) K10136

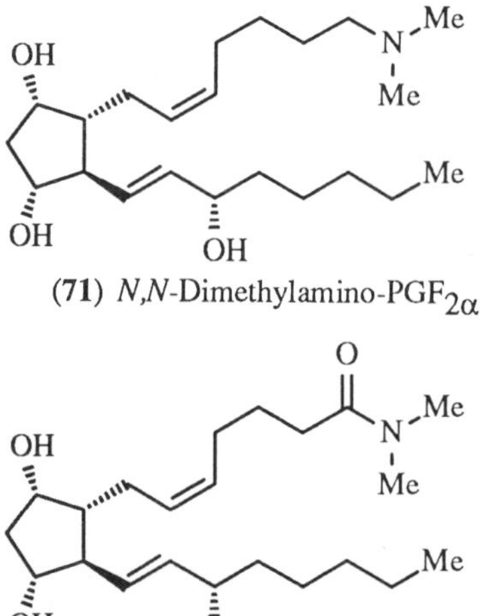

(**71**) *N,N*-Dimethylamino-PGF$_{2\alpha}$

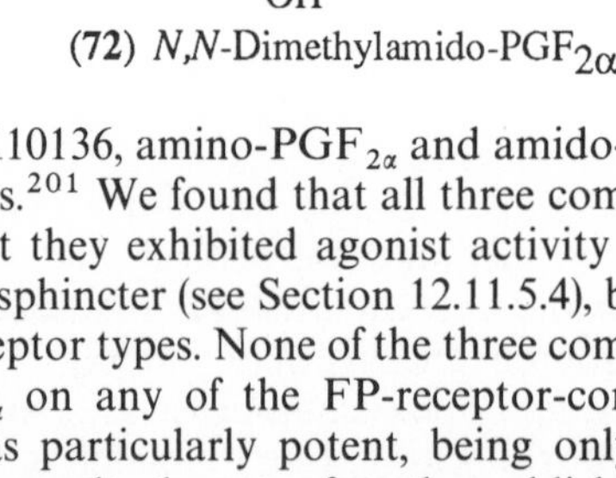

(**72**) *N,N*-Dimethylamido-PGF$_{2\alpha}$

We have, however, evaluated these three compounds, K10136, amino-$PGF_{2\alpha}$ and amido-$PGF_{2\alpha}$, on a range of prostanoid-receptor-containing preparations.[201] We found that all three compounds broadly resembled the parent compound, $PGF_{2\alpha}$, in that they exhibited agonist activity on FP-receptor-containing preparations such as dog and cat iris sphincter (see Section 12.11.5.4), but were weak or inactive on those containing other prostanoid receptor types. None of the three compounds was obviously a partial agonist with respect to $PGF_{2\alpha}$ on any of the FP-receptor-containing preparations, and, of the three compounds, K10136 was particularly potent, being only about fivefold less potent than $PGF_{2\alpha}$. While on their own these results do not refute the published data, they do suggest that none of the three agents is a potentially useful FP-receptor-blocking drug. The published antagonist data may indicate that different subtypes of FP receptors exist, or alternatively they may indicate that the compounds can behave as partial agonists or that they can induce FP receptor desensitization/down-regulation.

12.11.4.4 IP-receptor-blocking Drugs

Over the last few years, the intensive search for IP receptor agonists for use as antithrombotic drugs has yielded several compounds with therapeutic potential. However, as yet, no specific IP-receptor-blocking drug has been identified, although a small number of compounds have been reported which might serve as chemical starting points. For example, while (5Z)-6a-carba-PGI$_2$ [(5Z)-carbacyclin] behaved as a full IP agonist in human platelets, in rat mesenteric arterial myocytes, it displayed partial agonist activity and was able to antagonize adenylate cyclase stimulation produced by PGI$_2$, PGE$_1$ and (5E)-carbacyclin.[155] In addition, the compound antagonized the PGI$_2$-induced relaxation of the rabbit isolated mesentric artery.[155] Andersen and coworkers reported briefly upon the antagonistic properties of several PGI$_2$ analogues.[202] One analogue, 17,17-dimethyl-8,9,12-epi-PGI$_2$ (73), was without effect itself upon blood pressure in the anaesthetized rat but appeared to antagonize the hypotensive response to PGI$_2$ and PGE$_2$. A second analogue, 17-perfluorobutyl-18,19,20-trinor-PGI$_2$ methyl ester, was claimed to display some antagonistic effect against the hypotensive response to PGI$_2$ in the conscious baboon. However, no further investigations have been carried out on these analogues.

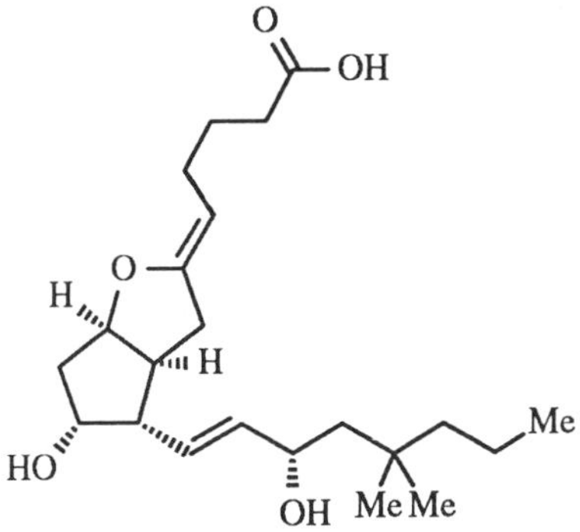

(73) 17,17-Dimethyl-8,9,12-epi-PGI$_2$

Fassina *et al.* recently reported on the ability of FCE-22176 [(5Z)-(+)-13,14-didehydro-20-methyl-carbaprostacyclin; 69] to antagonize the contractile actions of PGI$_2$ on guinea pig trachea and atria.[194] These authors suggested that FCE-22176 was an IP-receptor-blocking drug in these tissues. However, the contractile action of PGI$_2$ on the guinea pig trachea results predominantly from an action at EP$_1$ receptors, thus it appears unlikely that FCE-22176 represents an IP-receptor-blocking drug (see Section 12.11.4.2).

12.11.4.5 TP-receptor-blocking Drugs

Many compounds, of widely differing chemical structures, have been claimed to possess TP-receptor-blocking activity. However, for the purposes of the following discussion, detailed description will be largely reserved for compounds which exhibit a specific action. Thus, within this definition, compounds should only interact with the TP receptor, and be without effect on other prostanoid receptors, be devoid of activity upon cyclooxygenase, thromboxane synthase, prostacyclin synthase, or cAMP phosphodiesterase.

With the elucidation of the chemical structures of the prostaglandin endoperoxide intermediates, the ensuing discovery of thromboxane A$_2$ and a proposal for its structure, attempts were soon in progress to synthesize structural analogues of these compounds as stable mimetics (see Section 12.11.3.5) and antagonists. 9,11-Azoprosta-5,13-dienoic acid (azo analogue I) was shown to possess both thromboxane synthase inhibitory activity[203] and TP-receptor-blocking activity.[161] Subsequently, 9,11-epoxyiminoprosta-5,13-dienoic acid was described, and this appeared to be a 'pure' TP-receptor-blocking drug on platelets.[204] However, the compound should be classed as a partial TP receptor agonist since it also caused contraction of the rat aorta. In addition, several other compounds, structurally unrelated to prostaglandins, namely the phloretin derivative N-0164 and the tetrahydroisoquinoline trimethoquinol (74) were described at this time which possessed, amongst other varied actions, weak TP-receptor-blocking activity.[161] There followed the discovery of several other prostanoid-related compounds with reported TP-receptor-blocking activity. Thus,

Le Breton *et al.* demonstrated that 13-azaprostanoic acid (**75**) inhibited human platelet aggregation to arachidonic acid, PGH_2 and U-44069, but was without effect upon primary aggregation to ADP or thrombin and did not affect TxA_2 synthesis,[205] a profile consistent with specific TP-receptor-blocking activity (Table 10). Nicolaou *et al.* reported a similar profile of action for pinane thromboxane A_2 (PTA$_2$; **76**), although this compound,[206] at marginally higher concentrations than those required to block the platelet TP receptor, also inhibited thromboxane synthase. Recently, Armstrong *et al.* showed that on human platelets, PTA$_2$ possessed weak partial TP receptor agonist activity and also increased platelet cAMP content.[207] This latter action correlated with an inhibition of platelet aggregation to both ADP and platelet activating factor (PAF). Carbocyclic thromboxane A_2 (CTA$_2$; **77**) was originally claimed to be a TP-receptor-blocking drug on human platelets with additional thromboxane synthase inhibitory activity.[181] However, it also possesses TP agonist activity on vascular smooth muscle, a finding often cited as evidence of a difference between the platelet and vascular TP receptors (see below). However, it is now known that CTA$_2$ can also exhibit TP agonist activity on human platelets.[207] The profile of action of the compound upon platelets is further complicated by its ability, like PTA$_2$, to raise cAMP to functionally significant levels.[207]

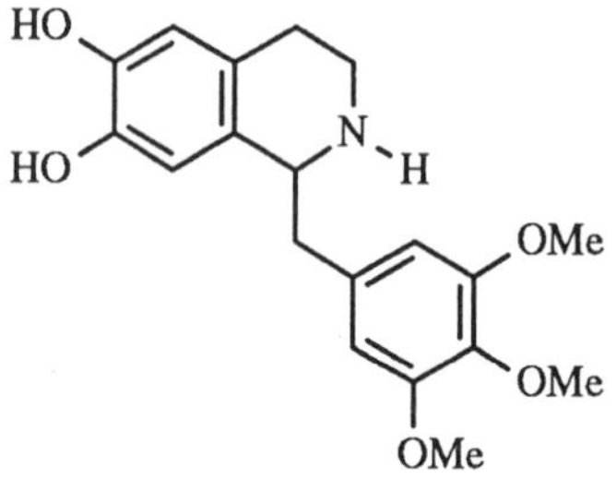

(**74**) Trimethoquinol

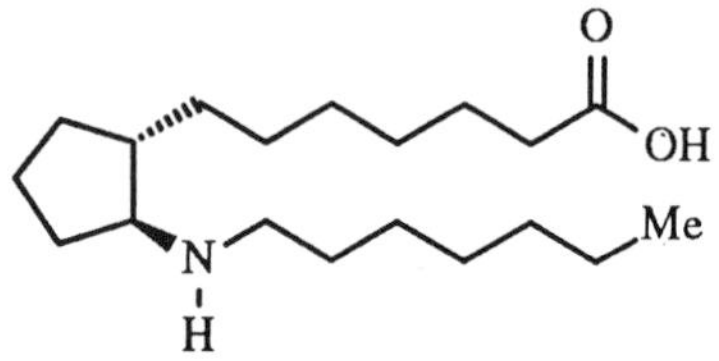

(**75**) 13-Azaprostanoic acid

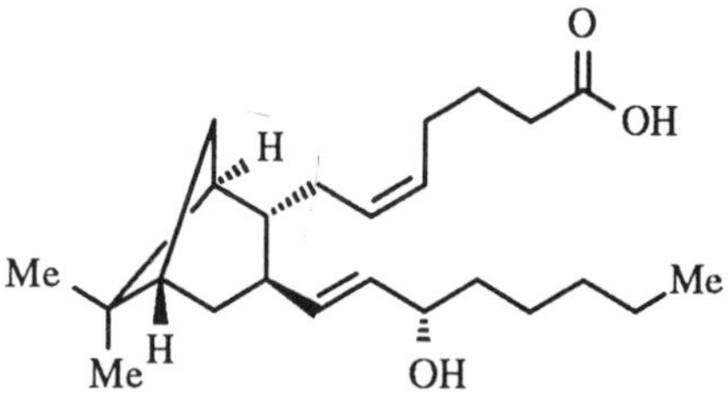

(**76**) Pinane-TxA$_2$

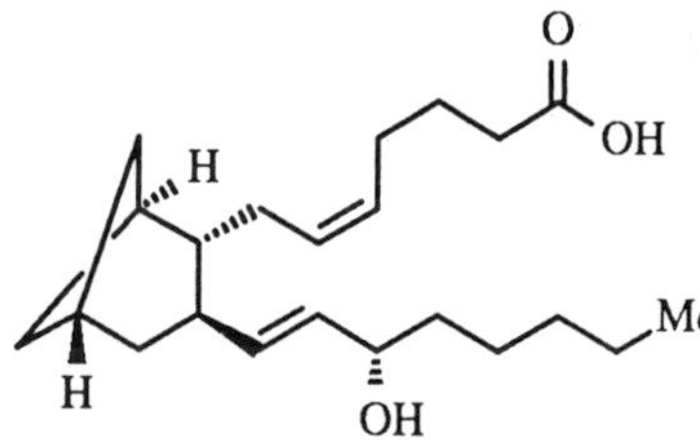

(**77**) Carbocyclic-TxA$_2$

Since these early attempts to obtain specific TP-receptor-blocking drugs, there has been a proliferation of such compounds of diverse chemical structure making any rational comments upon structure–activity relationships in this class of compounds difficult. However, in general, most analogues to be described possess a carboxylic acid function which presumably acts as a primary recognition site. In most instances, this carboxylic acid moiety is linked, *via* a six carbon atom chain, to a cyclic or bicyclic system and thus mimics a large portion of the TxA_2 molecule. The presence of a *cis* Δ^5, or preferably Δ^4, double bond in the linking unit is usually favoured over a fully saturated chain. Secondary binding and subsequent receptor affinity is probably achieved *via* the β-chain replacements, which vary widely in structure. Thus, they encompass substituted amino, hydrazino and amido moieties with many incorporating additional aromatic functionality.

The Squibb group initially reported on a series of 7-oxabicyclo[2.2.1]heptane prostaglandin analogues as TP-receptor-blocking drugs.[176] This work led to the discovery of more potent analogues such as SQ 26,536, SQ 27,427 SQ 28,668 (**78**) and recently SQ 29,548 (**79**).[117,173,177,208,209] The latter compound combines features of both this structural series and the analogue EP 045 (**80**) (see below). SQ 27,427 is an interesting analogue since in human platelets, in addition to blocking TP receptors, the compound also elevates cAMP (see Section 12.11.3.1). The detailed structure–activity relationships of this series of compounds have been comprehensively reviewed elsewhere.[176]

At the same time as the Squibb group were carrying out their studies, we at Glaxo had discovered the chemically novel TP-receptor-blocking drug AH 19437 (**22**).[43,146,210] Collington *et al.*[211] studied the effect of modification of the benzyloxy group in AH 19437 upon its airways smooth muscle and platelet TP-receptor-blocking activity (see structures **81–87**; Table 10). Modifications at C-9 established no firm correlation between size of the substituent and pharmacological activity.

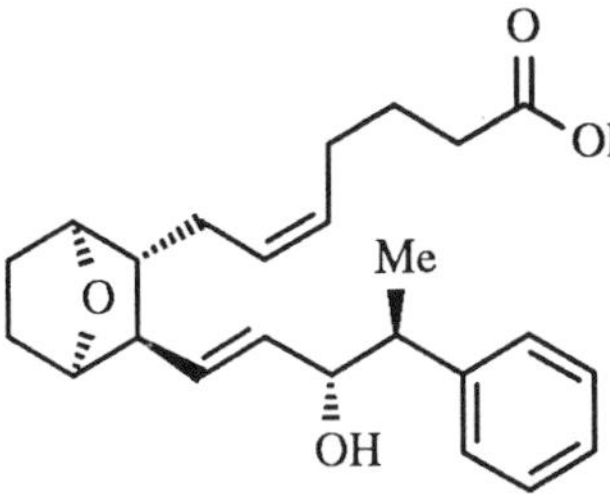

(78) SQ 28,668

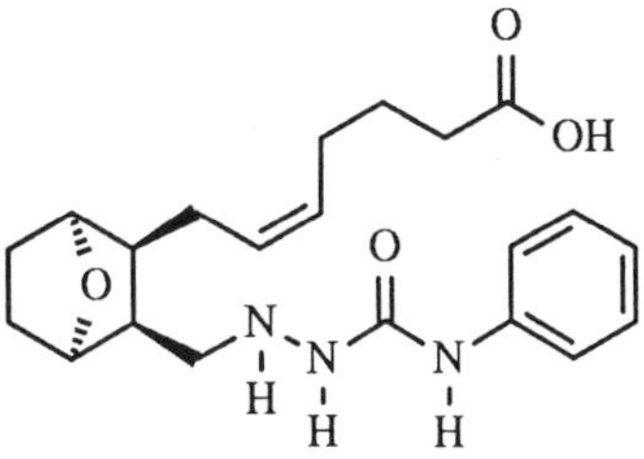

(79) SQ 29,548

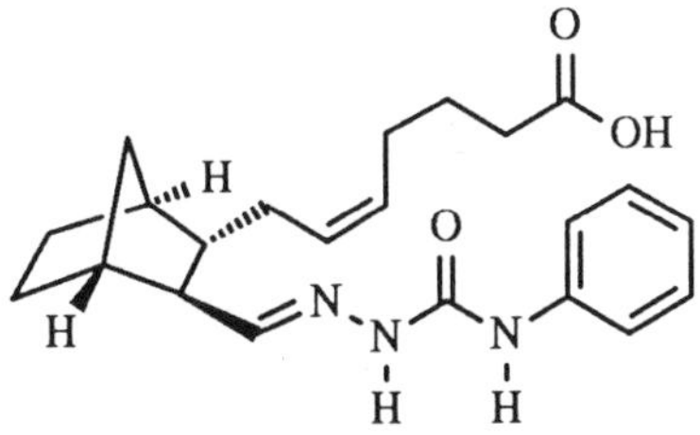

(80) EP 045

Table 10 Antagonist Activities of Some Analogues of AH 19437 (**22**) on Guinea Pig Lung Strip and Human Platelets[211]

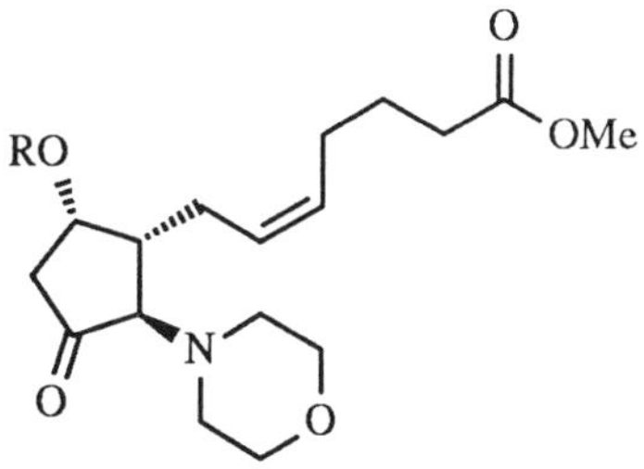

Compound	R	Potency relative to AH 19437	
		Guinea pig lung vs $PGF_{2\alpha}$ *or U-46619 contractions*	*Human platelets vs collagen-induced aggregation*
(**22**) AH 19437	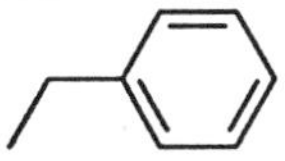	1	1
(**81**)	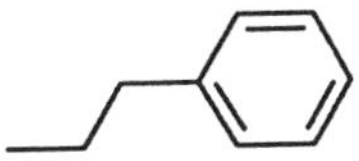	1.3	0.4
(**82**)		3	1.6
(**83**)	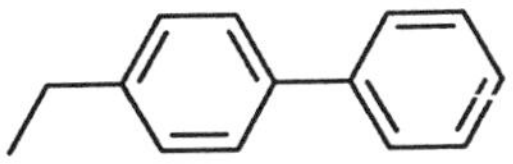	15	1
(**84**)	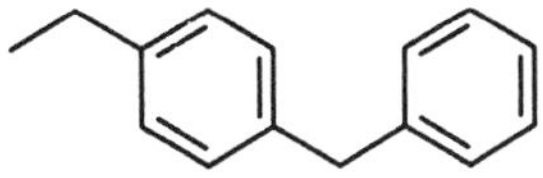	10	2.6
(**85**)	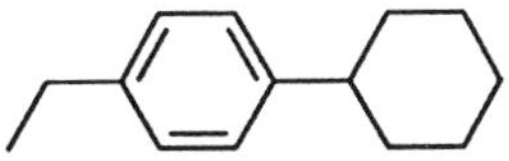	12	1
(**86**)	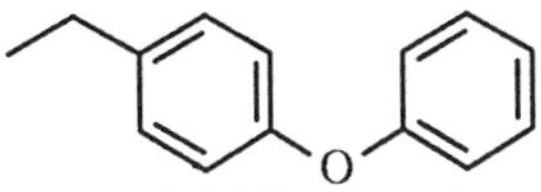	5	0.6
(**87**)	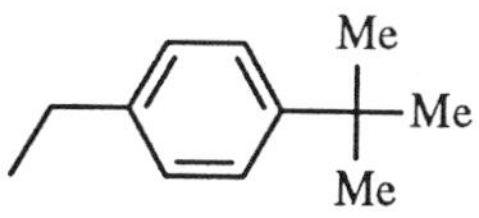	6	1.6

However, a trend was apparent for increased blocking potency at the smooth muscle TP receptor with increasing lipophilicity and possibly a decrease in the relative ability of the *para* substituent to donate electrons to the aromatic ring. Interestingly, there was no increase in potency of these C-9-modified analogues as antagonists at the platelet TP receptor. However, preparation of the corresponding acids of (83)–(85) (Table 10) revealed the importance of this group for activity upon the platelet TP receptor (Table 11). Thus, for example, (88) was found to be between one to two orders of magnitude more potent than AH 19437 at both smooth muscle and platelet TP receptors (Table 11). It is well known that a double bond at the Δ^4 position confers greater metabolic stability upon compounds than when in the Δ^5 position. This Δ^4 modification yielded AH 23848 (93)[212,213] and eventually GR 32191 (94)[214] which have both been previously reported to be potent and long lasting TP-receptor-blocking drugs in humans.[215,216] Whilst of similar potency to AH 23848, GR 32191 lacks the partial agonist activity of the former compound.

Jones *et al.* were also successful in performing structural refinements to various PGH$_2$ analogues which acted as partial TP agonists on platelets and vascular smooth muscle to produce the specific, albeit relatively weak, TP-receptor-blocking drug, EP 045,[41,163,217] and latterly the more potent compound, EP 092 (95; Table 12).[207,218] Further structural modifications in this series have resulted in analogues, which, like SQ 27,427, are reasonably potent TP-receptor-blocking drugs but which also stimulate increases in platelet cAMP *via*, it has been proposed, the IP receptor.[219] In addition to these compounds, both the Ono company and ICI have also recently produced potent antagonists such as ONO 11120, ONO 3708 (96), ICI 159,995, ICI 180,080, ICI 185,282 (97) and recently, ICI 192,605 (98). In the ICI series of 1,3-dioxan-TxA$_2$ antagonists, where the side chains need to be *cis* for maximal activity, the introduction of an *o*-hydroxy group on to the pendant aromatic ring (ICI

Table 11 Antagonist Activities of Some Analogues of AH 19437 (22) on Guinea Pig Lung Strip and Human Platelets[211]

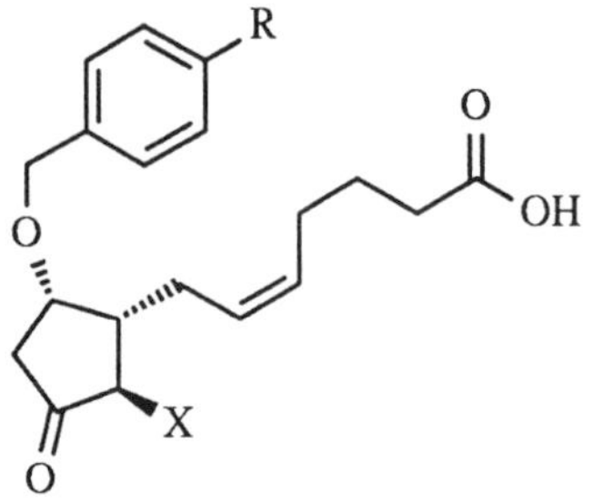

Compound	X	R	Potency relative to AH 19437 = 1 Guinea pig lung	Human platelets
(88)	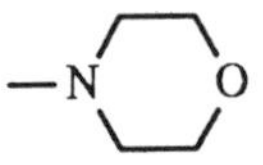 —N(morpholine, O)	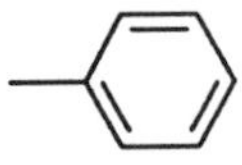 phenyl	32	> 30
(89)	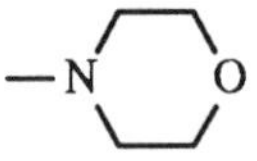 —N(morpholine, O)	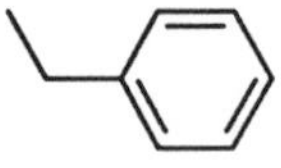 CH₂-phenyl	10	24
(90)	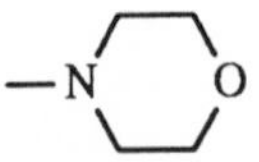 —N(morpholine, O)	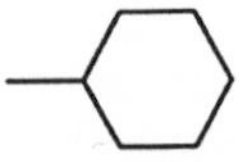 cyclohexyl	20	2.7
(91)	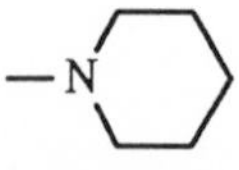 —N(piperidine)	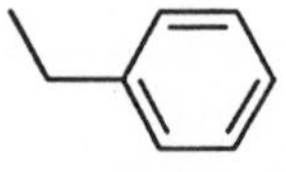 CH₂-phenyl	2.5	18
(92)	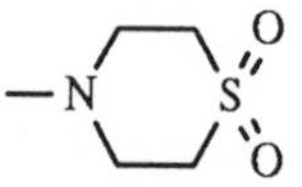 —N(thiomorpholine-S,S-dioxide)	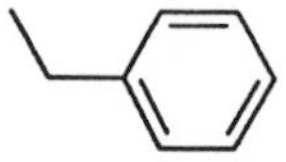 CH₂-phenyl	79	2.6

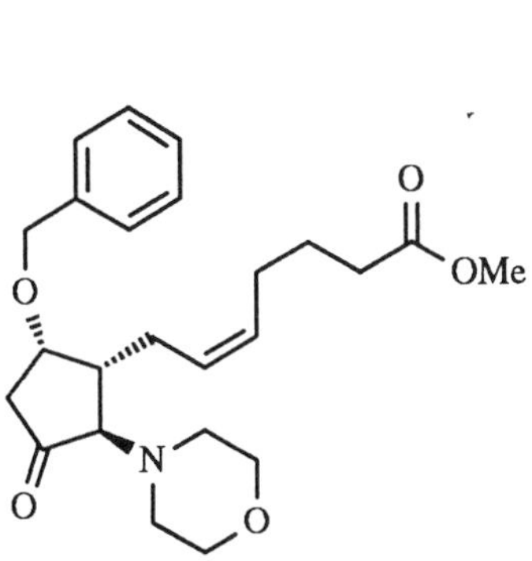

(22) AH 19437

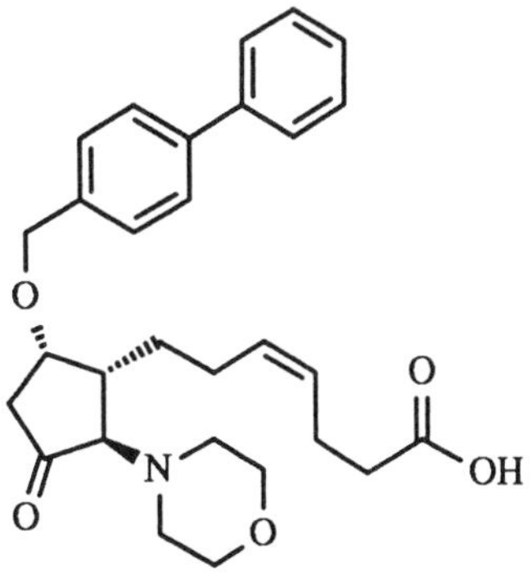

(93) AH 23848

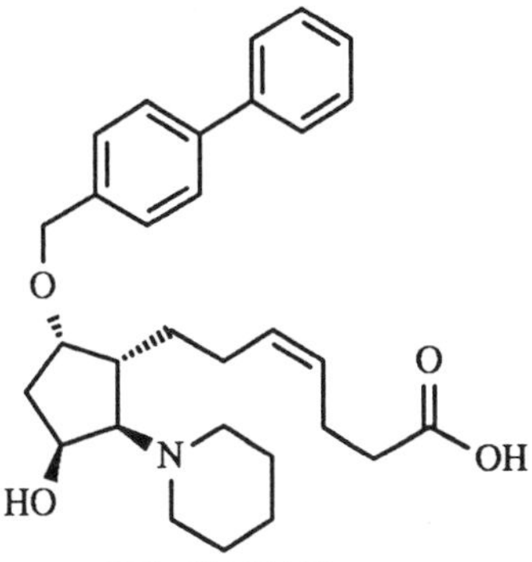

(94) GR 32191

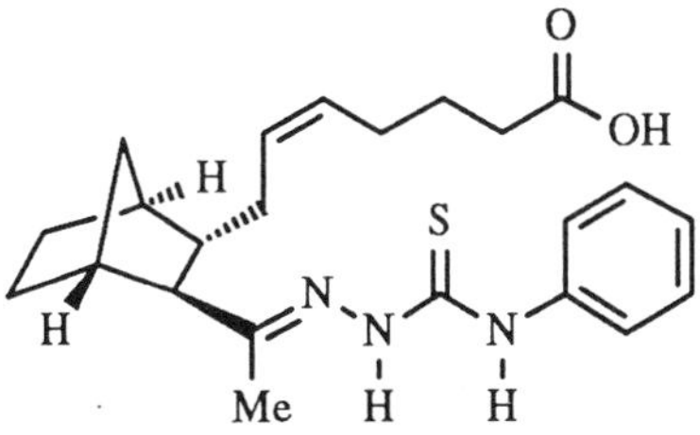

(95) EP 092

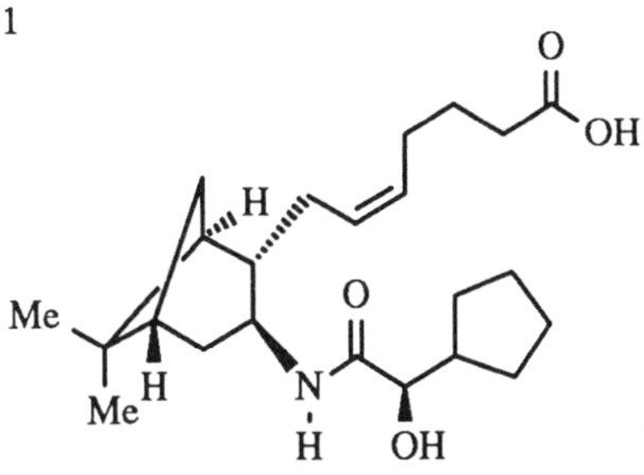

(96) ONO 3708

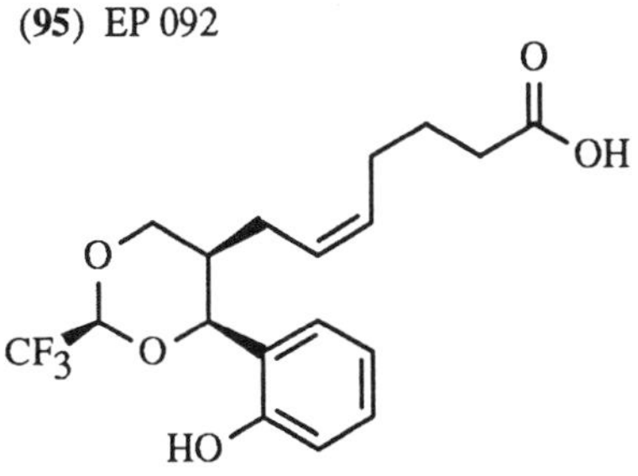

(97) ICI 185,282

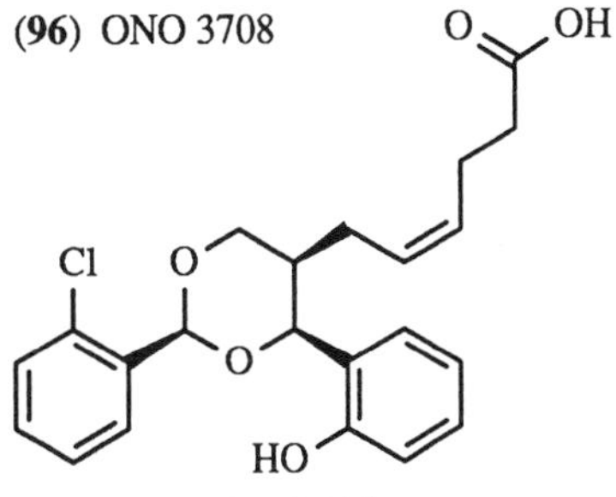

(98) ICI 192,605

180,080) enhances activity. This could be envisaged as enabling additional binding to the site on the receptor normally occupied by the C-15 hydroxy moiety in the natural agonist. Alternatively, an intramolecular hydrogen bond to the proximal ring oxygen may promote conformational rigidity. Hydrolytic stability is imparted by replacing the dimethyl ketal unit by the trifluoromethyl acetal moiety.

Finally, several interesting compounds which are structurally unrelated to prostaglandins have been reported to possess specific TP-receptor-blocking activity. Among these are the benzylsulfon-amido analogue BM 13.177 (99)[220,221] and its more potent chloro analogue BM 13.505 (100).[222,223] These compounds possess the profile of TP-receptor-blocking drugs, although there is now evidence that the latter compound displays weak partial agonist activity on platelets and vascular smooth muscle.[223] Detailed structure–activity relationships have been reported on the series of TxA$_2$ antagonists such as L-655,240 (101) derived from indole-2-propanoic acid.[224] Besides delineating the structural requirements for potent antagonist activity, they have prepared a conformationally restricted analogue and shown that activity only resides in the $(-)$-(R)-isomer, L-657,925. For the

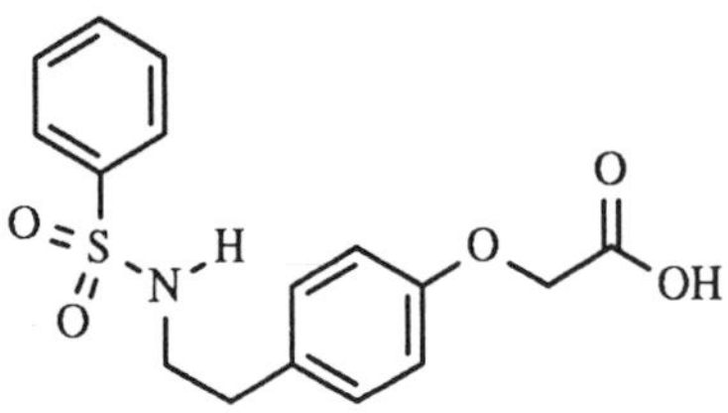

(99) BM 13.177

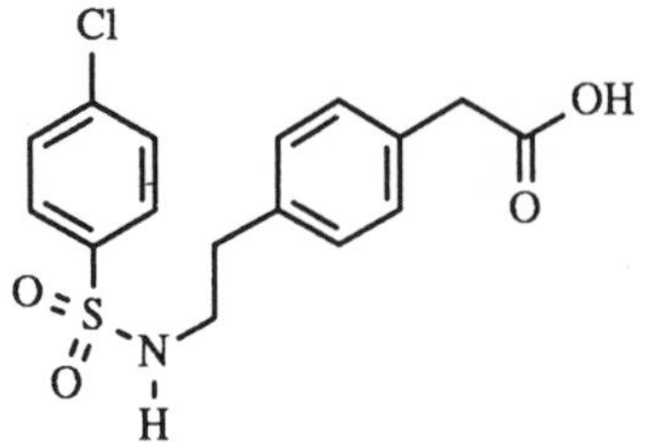

(100) BM 13.505

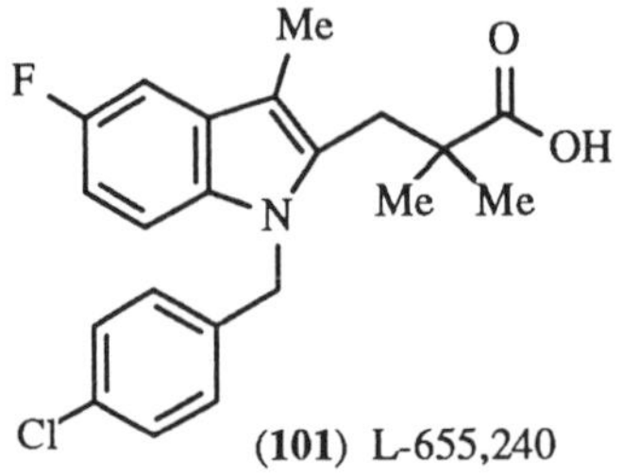

(101) L-655,240

main compounds of interest a full profile of TP and other prostanoid and nonprostanoid receptor-blocking activity is shown in Table 12.

As can be seen from Table 12, for most of the compounds cited, comprehensive information on the profile of action upon other prostanoid receptor types is lacking. The exceptions are GR 32191 and AH 23848, which have been shown, up to concentrations of 10 μM, to be without effect upon IP and DP receptors (human platelets), FP receptors (dog iris) and EP_1, EP_2 and EP_3 receptors (guinea pig fundus, cat trachea and guinea pig vas deferens, respectively).

Despite the apparent similarity in their profiles of action, there appear to be some differences in the apparent nature of the antagonism produced by these compounds. Upon vascular and airways smooth muscle, the compounds listed in Table 12 appear to exhibit competitive reversible receptor antagonism against TP agonists such as U-46619, with slopes of Schild regression not differing significantly from unity.[163,167,173,214] However, upon platelets, compounds such as EP 092, AH 23848 and GR 32191 slow the rate of attainment of the aggregatory response. Slight suppression of the maximum achievable response to the agonist has also been observed with other compounds[173] as well as antagonism of aggregation greater than that anticipated by competitive antagonism. This results in slopes of the Schild regression significantly greater than unity.[167,214] The slowing of the attainment of the aggregatory response has been suggested to reflect a slow dissociation of the antagonists from the TP receptor, thus slowing the approach to equilibrium occupancy by the agonist. This may in turn allow disaggregation to intervene in the attainment of the full aggregatory response. The suppression of the maximum aggregatory response and the apparently greater than predicted antagonism may also be related to the aggregatory agonist used since, for example, the high concentrations of U-46619 needed in the presence of TP receptor blockade can also elevate platelet cAMP.[233] This effect would lead to an apparent enhancement of the magnitude of the antagonism observed (see Section 12.11.2.3).

The availability of potent TP-receptor-blocking drugs has led to some preliminary studies on TP receptor subclassification. As can be seen from Table 12, the TP receptors in rabbit aorta appear to be different from those in other species, with pA_2 values for several compounds being almost one order of magnitude lower than on vascular smooth muscle preparations from other species. Evidence for the existence of a subtype of TP receptor in the rabbit has been reported by others on vascular smooth muscle,[163] airways smooth muscle[234] and platelets.[86,179,235] Interestingly, not all blocking drugs differentiate rabbit TP receptors from those of other species, for example BM 13.177 and BM 13.505 show no such differentiation (see Table 12). Few studies have attempted to systematically characterize TP receptors in a quantitative manner excluding complications from factors such as plasma protein binding of drugs, nor has a range of TP-receptor-containing preparations from different species been thoroughly examined. Plasma protein binding is a particular problem in platelet studies, and thus many of the compounds in Table 12 appear to undergo some plasma protein binding (compare data in platelet-rich plasma with that in resuspended platelets). In addition, the use of partial agonists, which appear as agonists on one system and antagonists on another, to characterize receptors (e.g. CTA_2 and PTA_2, see above)[235] poses interpretational problems, since such apparent differences can be explained by differences in receptor density and/or

Table 12 Prostanoid-receptor-blocking Activity of a Range of TP-receptor-blocking Drugs *in vitro*

Drug	TP-receptor-blocking activity pA_2 v U-46–619					Activity against nonprostanoid agonists pA_2 vs		Activity at other prostanoid receptors pA_2 vs				Ref.
	Human platelets		Vascular Smooth muscle			Human platelets	Vascular 5-	PGI_2	PGD_2	PGE_2	$PGF_{2\alpha}$	
	HWB/PRP[a]	RP[b]	Various	RbA[c]	Airways Guinea pig	ADP/ADR[d]	HT/KCl/NA[e]	(IP)	(DP)	(EP)	(FP)	
AH 19437	6.1	ND[f]	5.9	ND	6.6	< 4.1	< 4.1	< 4.6	ND	< 4.6	< 4.6	43,146,210
AH 23848	7.8	8.3	7.8	[6.9][g]	8.2	< 5.0	< 5.0	< 5.0	< 5.0	< 5.0	< 5.0	167,212,213
GR 32191	8.2	8.8	8.2	7.2	[8.2]	< 5.0	< 5.0	< 5.0	< 5.0	< 5.0	< 5.0	214
BM 13.177	6.0	5.8	6.2	6.3	ND	< 4.7	< 4.5	ND	ND	ND	ND	214, 220, 225
BM 13.505	6.7	7.8	7.9	7.4	ND	[< 5.0]	ND	ND	ND	ND	ND	214, 222
SQ 29,548	7.8	8.7	8.9	[8.1]	9.1	< 3.0	[< 5.0]	ND	< 3.6	< 5.0	ND	173
SQ 28,668	5.5	5.7	6.0	ND	ND	< 4.0	[< 5.0]	ND	ND	ND	ND	177, 214
ONO 3708	6.7[h]	ND	8.9	ND	ND	ND	< 6.0	ND	ND	ND	ND	226, 227
EP 045	5.9	7.1	7.2	6.3	7.5	< 4.7	< 4.7	< 4.7	< 4.7	< 5.6	ND	163, 217
EP 092	7.2	≈7.9	8.4	7.3	8.0	< 5.3	ND	< 4.7	< 4.7	ND	ND	207
L-655,240	6.8[h]	8.2[h]	8.4	ND	8.0	< 4.1	ND	ND	ND	ND	ND	228
ICI 185, 282	7.0	ND	8.5	7.9	>7.0	< 4.0	< 4.7	< 5.0	< 5.0	< 5.0	< 5.0	229, 230
ICI 192,605	8.2	ND	8.4	ND	>8.0	< 4.0	< 5.0	< 5.0	< 5.0	< 5.0	< 5.0	231, 232
13-APA	5.3	ND	4.8	[< 4.0]	ND	[< 4.0]	[< 4.0]	< 4.3	ND	ND	ND	205, 214

[a] HWB = human whole blood; PRP = platelet-rich plasma. [b] RP = resuspended platelets. [c] RbA = rabbit aorta. [d] ADP = adenosine diphosphate; ADR = adrenaline. [e] 5-HT = 5-hydroxytryptamine, KCl = potassium Chloride, NA = noradrenaline. [f] ND = no data available. [g] [ ] = Lumley, unpublished data. [h] log IC_{50} *vs* U-44069.

receptor–effector coupling between the different systems. Nevertheless, various groups have suggested that there are differences between platelet and vascular TP receptors both between and within species.[82,161,181,236,237] However, it is clear that further, more carefully controlled studies are necessary before a firm conclusion can be drawn regarding the possible existence of subtypes of TP receptors. Further characterization of TP receptors and confirmation of the mode of action of the TP-receptor-blocking drugs may come from ligand-binding experiments (see Section 12.11.2.2). Such studies, utilizing various ligands, have also indicated possible differences in TP receptors between species (see Section 12.11.2.2.5) and recent attempts have been made to utilize these ligands to isolate and purify TP receptors.[238]

12.11.5 DISTRIBUTION AND PHYSIOLOGICAL ROLES OF PROSTANOID RECEPTORS

12.11.5.1 Smooth Muscle

Of the biological actions of the prostanoids, probably the best documented are their contractile and relaxant effects on smooth muscle. Few smooth muscle preparations fail to respond to prostanoids in some fashion. While there is probably little merit in simply listing the effects of all of the prostanoids on all of the smooth muscle preparations on which they have been tested, we will instead attempt to indicate the distribution of prostanoid receptors mediating contraction and relaxation of smooth muscle from vascular, gastrointestinal, respiratory, reproductive and urinary systems and the eye, in which smooth muscle is extensively present, stressing where possible the findings in human tissue.

12.11.5.1.1 Vascular

Prostanoids, particularly TxA_2 and PGI_2, are well known for their vasoconstrictor and vasodilator activities. Although both TP and IP receptors are widely distributed in vascular smooth muscle from many species including humans, they are not the only prostanoid receptors present in this tissue, as there is evidence for the presence of DP and EP receptors mediating vasodilatation in various blood vessels and vascular beds, and for DP, EP and FP receptors mediating vasoconstriction. Typical contractile and relaxant responses of dog isolated saphenous vein preparations to prostanoids are illustrated in Figure 2.

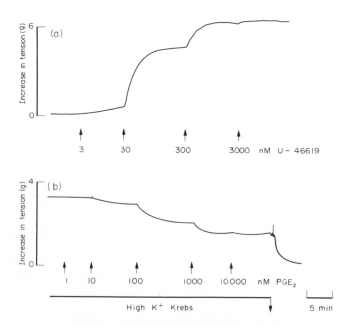

Figure 2 Dog saphenous vein preparation: (a) contractile concentration–effect curve to U-46619; (b) relaxant concentration–effect curve to PGE_2 on a K^+ (60 mM) contracted preparation

(i) Relaxation

Vasodilator DP receptors are found in dog isolated saphenous vein and rabbit jugular vein, where they coexist with EP_2 receptors.[146] Furthermore, administration of both PGD_2 and the potent, selective DP agonist BW 245C to humans is associated with a pronounced but selective vasodilatation of the blush area and also an intense nasal congestion which is believed to result from dilatation of the nasal vasculature.[239,240] In contrast, PGI_2 causes a more general vasodilatation with no evidence of nasal congestion.[241] We have previously demonstrated the coexistence of EP and IP receptors in various canine vascular beds,[156] but although PGE_2 is a vasodilator agent in humans, it has not been established that this effect is mediated through EP receptors. However, the vasodilator activity of the proposed EP_2 agonist, viprostol, in humans provides some circumstantial evidence that this is so.[242]

It is an interesting observation that vasodilator IP receptors appear to be restricted to arterial smooth muscle; we have been unable to find a single clear example of venous dilatation mediated by IP receptors. Both Schrör *et al.*[152] and Ceserani *et al.*[243] found that while PGI_2 and the selective IP agonists iloprost and FCE-22509 all relaxed bovine coronary artery, on the corresponding venous preparation PGI_2 caused a small contraction, FCE-22509 was inactive and iloprost exhibited only very weak relaxant activity. Various other groups have also failed to demonstrate IP receptors mediating relaxation of venous smooth muscle from a range of species including man.[146,243,244] In contrast, vasodilator EP receptors exist in both venous and arterial preparations. This apparent arterioselectivity of PGI_2 is particularly interesting in the light of the observation that in the rat at least, venous homogenates have a much lower synthetic capacity for PGI_2 than do arterial homogenates.[245]

(ii) Contraction

Evidence for the existence of vasoconstrictor DP receptors is somewhat indirect, and has been provided by Jones who showed that PGD_2 and various close analogues are potent pressor agents in the sheep, and exhibit a rank order of potency different from that associated with other DP-receptor-mediated effects (see Section 12.11.3.1).[246] Indeed this is the only apparent evidence for a subdivision of DP receptors.

Like DP receptors, EP receptors are usually associated with vasodilatation, but there is evidence that EP receptors can also mediate vasoconstriction. We have found that EP receptors mediate constriction of rabbit renal and guinea pig uterine artery preparations, and these appear to be of the EP_3 subtype.[247,248] It is not clear how widespread vasoconstrictor EP receptors are, the scarcity of reports of their existence may in part be due to the abundance of vasodilator EP_2 receptors which could tend to mask them. Thus in order to determine the distribution of vasoconstrictor EP receptors, it will be necessary to use some of the more selective agonists that are becoming available (see Section 12.11.3.2)

FP receptors are not normally associated with vascular smooth muscle, but it has been suggested that in the rat at least, FP-agonist-induced luteolysis may result from a vasoconstrictor response in the omentum artery.[249] There is some evidence that FP receptors may mediate vasoconstriction of pulmonary lobular artery preparations from the dog,[250] but this has not been confirmed by the use of selective FP agonists such as fluprostenol.

Vasoconstrictor TP receptors appear to occur in nearly all vascular smooth muscle from a wide variety of mammalian and nonmammalian species. In humans they have been shown to occur in cerebral, pulmonary and umbilical vessels. Interestingly, TP-receptor-mediated umbilical vasoconstriction may be regarded as the one physiological rather than pathological role for TxA_2; at birth high local levels of TxA_2 result in profound umbilical vasoconstriction, preventing the potential extensive blood loss from both mother and young when the cord is severed.[251]

12.11.5.1.2 Gastrointestinal

Prostanoids have both contractile and relaxant effects on gastrointestinal smooth muscle from all levels of the alimentary canal, and there exist differences in receptor populations both between and within species at different levels of the tract. The alimentary tract is complicated in that smooth muscle is arranged in both longitudinal and circular fashion, and the receptor populations in the two layers can differ widely. In the small intestine, longitudinal muscle is generally populated by excitatory receptors, whereas circular muscle tends to contain relaxant receptors. Figure 3 illustrates

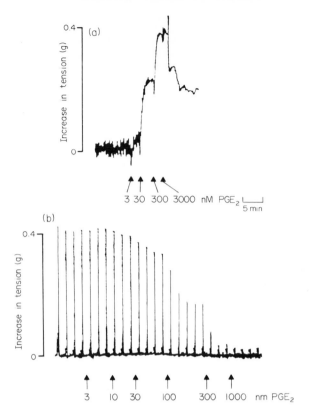

Figure 3 Guinea pig ileum: (a) contractile concentration–effect curve to PGE$_2$ on a longitudinal muscle preparation; (b) relaxant concentration–effect curve to PGE$_2$ on an electrically stimulated circular muscle preparation

typical contractile and relaxant effects to PGE$_2$ on longitudinal and circular muscle preparations of guinea pig ileum. A notable feature of certain gastrointestinal smooth muscle preparations is the number of different receptors that can coexist mediating either the same or opposing effects. It is this multiplicity of prostanoid receptors which has led to such preparations as rat stomach fundus strip and gerbil colon to be so useful for bioassay purposes. In these cases, several different types of receptor present within the preparation subserve smooth muscle contraction. Such preparations, while useful for bioassay, are too complicated for studying gastrointestinal prostanoid receptors.

(i) Relaxation

The high potency of PGD$_2$ in relaxing the transverse stomach strip preparation of the rabbit[252] suggests the presence of relaxant DP receptors in this preparation. This may also be the case with the circular muscle preparation of chick duodenum. In this latter tissue, further support has been provided by the demonstration that the selective DP agonist BW 245C is also a potent relaxant agent.[253]

EP receptors mediating relaxant actions in small intestinal smooth muscle are commonplace, occurring in a range of species, particularly in circular muscle. They are usually masked to some degree by their association with other prostanoid receptors, sometimes also EP receptors, mediating contraction. However in the guinea pig ileum circular muscle, inhibitory EP$_2$ receptors appear to exist as a homogeneous population, and this preparation has proven valuable in the characterization of EP$_2$ receptors.[62]

Inhibitory IP receptors are not widely found in gastrointestinal smooth muscle. However, rat colon, which has long been used as a bioassay preparation for PGI$_2$, does appear to contain inhibitory IP receptors.[119] Thus in this preparation, while most prostanoids cause contraction, PGI$_2$ inhibits spontaneous myogenic activity.

(ii) Contraction

There are many examples of EP receptors mediating gastrointestinal smooth muscle contraction, particularly in longitudinal muscle from all levels of the gastrointestinal tract, in a wide range of species. In guinea pig, they appear to be of the EP_1 subtype,[46,146,191] as they are also in stomach fundus preparations from dog and cat.[146] In similar preparations from rat and pig, while EP_1 receptors are undoubtedly present, they coexist with EP_3 receptors,[62,146] TP receptors and, in the case of the rat, also FP receptors. EP_3 receptors mediating a contractile response have also been found in chick ileum[99] where they appear to represent at least the bulk of the receptors present. Whether excitatory EP receptors occur in human gut is not certain.

FP receptors mediating smooth muscle contraction are found in rat stomach fundus and gerbil colon, which are potently contracted by such selective FP agonists as fluprostenol and cloprostenol.[119,146,254]

Finally, while TP receptors do occur in animal gastrointestinal smooth muscle, *e.g.* rat fundus, pig fundus and gerbil colon, they are very much more prevalent in gut preparations from humans.[255]

12.11.5.1.3 Respiratory

The airways and lungs from a wide range of species are highly responsive to prostanoids, this group of compounds having been regarded both as mediators and potential therapeutic agents in chronic, obstructive lung disease, particularly asthma.

(i) Relaxation

While there is little evidence that DP receptors play any inhibitory role in the control of bronchial smooth muscle tone, in cat trachea DP receptors coexist with the predominant EP_2 receptors mediating smooth muscle relaxation. Their presence is indicated by the relatively high agonist potencies of PGD_2 and BW 245C.[256]

In contrast, inhibitory EP receptors are widespread throughout the bronchial tree of mammalian species. These receptors have been identified as being of the EP_2 subtype in tracheobronchial preparations of guinea pig, cat and human, with the synthetic PGE analogue butaprost (TR4979) being a particularly selective agonist at these receptors.[47,141]

Interestingly, to date there are no documented examples of IP receptors mediating relaxation of tracheobronchial smooth muscle in any species, and where PGI_2 has activity it is weak and probably acting *via* EP_2 receptors.

(ii) Contraction

Although PGE_2 is a well-known bronchodilator agent, in certain species it also possesses potent contractile activity on tracheobronchial smooth muscle. Thus on guinea pig trachea, there coexist EP_1 and EP_2 receptors mediating contraction and relaxation respectively,[195] and the response observed to exogenously administered PGE_2 depends on both the preexisting level of smooth muscle tone in the preparation, and the concentration of PGE_2 tested. Whether bronchoconstrictor EP receptors exist in human airways is not clear, but the fact that the EP receptor agonist 16,16-dimethyl-PGE_2 (see Section 12.11.3.2) contracts human bronchial smooth muscle, an effect resistant to TP-receptor-blocking drugs,[257] suggests that this could be so.

Bronchoconstrictor FP receptors have been demonstrated in the lungs of cats and dogs, with $PGF_{2\alpha}$, fluprostenol and cloprostenol being highly potent bronchoconstrictors *in vitro* and *in vivo*.[258,259] Despite the fact that $PGF_{2\alpha}$ is an effective bronchoconstrictor agent in humans, this effect is mediated by TP receptors (see below).

Bronchoconstrictor TP receptors are extensively distributed in airways smooth muscle from many species.[62] Thus they are found in the lung parenchyma of guinea pig and rat as homogeneous populations, and in that of cat and dog in combination with FP receptors (see above), while in guinea pig trachea, they coexist with EP receptors (see above and Figure 4). TP receptors are the predominant prostanoid receptors mediating contraction in human lung parenchyma and bronchial smooth muscle. While both $PGF_{2\alpha}$ and PGD_2 are effective constrictor agents of human airways smooth muscle both *in vitro* and *in vivo*, their effects are mediated by TP receptors.[258,260]

12.11.5.1.4 Reproductive

Prostanoids are potent agents in contracting and relaxing smooth muscle from both male and female reproductive systems, and may well exert profound effects on reproductive function (see Section 12.11.5.5).

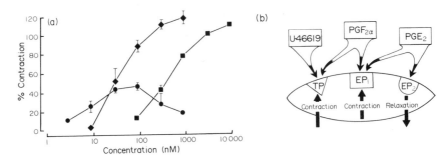

Figure 4 Guinea pig trachea: (a) mean contractile concentration–effect curves to PGE_2 (●), U-46619 (◆) and $PGF_{2\alpha}$ (■); note the bell-shaped curve to PGE_2, contraction at lower concentrations (3–100 nM) and relaxation at higher concentrations (100–1000 nM); (b) schematic representation of prostanoid receptors present in guinea pig tracheal smooth muscle (EP_1 and TP mediating contraction, and EP_2 mediating relaxation), and of the interactions of PGE_2, U-46619 and $PGF_{2\alpha}$ with them

(i)   Male

Despite the close association between prostanoids and the male reproductive system (prostaglandins, and hence prostanoids, were so-called because they were believed to be derived from the prostate gland, and human seminal fluid contains enormous concentrations of E- and F-type prostaglandins), little is known about the actions of prostanoids on smooth muscle from the male reproductive system. What information that there is refers to seminiferous tubules, vasa deferentia and penile erectile tissue, largely of human origin.

(a)   Seminiferous tubules. Prostanoids cause both concentration-related contraction ($PGF_{2\alpha}$) and relaxation (PGE_1, PGE_2 and $PGF_{1\alpha}$) of human isolated seminiferous tubules.[261] The high potency of $PGF_{2\alpha}$ (threshold effect $\simeq$ 1 nM) is consistent with the involvement of FP receptors, but this is by no means certain. Secondly, the high relaxant potency of PGE_1 both in absolute terms (threshold effect $\simeq$ 1 nM) and relative to PGE_2 (> 10 times more potent) suggests the involvement of IP receptors, but again this is only a tentative conclusion.

(b)   Vasa deferentia. Although prostanoid-induced inhibition of autonomic neurotransmission in guinea pig vasa deferentia is well known,[262] less is known about their direct effects on smooth muscle in this tissue. However, although prostanoids have little direct effect on the basal tone of guinea pig and human vasa, in preparations from guinea pig, but not humans, PGE_2 induces a postsynaptic enhancement of spasmogenic responses to both nerve stimulation and exogenous noradrenaline.[263] This enhancement is reported to be inhibited by SC-19220,[262] and is therefore likely to be mediated by EP_1 receptors.

(c)   Penile erectile tissue. Human penile erectile tissue appears to contain TP receptors mediating contraction of corpus cavernosum and corpus spongiosum as well as of the cavernous artery.[264] Inhibitory prostanoid receptors in these structures may be classified as EP in corpora cavernosum and spongiosum and IP in the cavernous artery. Indeed it has been suggested that PGI_2 plays a vasodilator role in the process of erection.[265]

(ii)   Female

In the female reproductive system smooth muscle exists in the ovary, in the fallopian tubes, in the uterus and in the associated blood vessels.

(a)   Ovary and fallopian tubes. $PGF_{2\alpha}$ is a rather weak contractile agonist upon human ovary *in vivo*, and PGE_2 is seemingly without effect.[266] It is not clear whether the action of $PGF_{2\alpha}$ is mediated by FP receptors or by a weak action at some other receptor type.

Although little is known regarding the effects of prostanoids on tubular contractility, $PGF_{2\alpha}$ has been reported to enhance, and PGE_1, PGE_2 and PGI_2 to inhibit, human tubular activity *in vivo*,[266] but this information is insufficient to determine which prostanoid receptors are involved.

(b)   Uterus. In contrast, there is a wealth of information relating to the relaxant and contractile actions of a wide range of prostanoids on both animal and human myometrium, and conclusions may be drawn as to the receptors involved.

The presence of inhibitory DP receptors in nonpregnant human myometrium has been indicated by Sanger *et al.* who demonstrated the potent relaxant action of the DP agonist, BW 245C.[267] Inhibitory EP receptors also clearly exist in human myometrium, and the relaxant activity of two EP_2 receptor agonists, butaprost[141,268a] and misoprostol,[268b] indicate that these are of the EP_2

Table 13 Distribution of Prostanoid Receptors in the Myometrium from Various Species [62,141,267,268,270]

Species	Relaxant			Contractile			
	DP	EP$_2$	IP	EP$_1$	EP$_3$	FP	TP
Guinea pig	X[a]	X	X	√[b]	√	X	√
Rat	X	X	X	√	√	√	X
Hamster	X	√	X	√	√	√	√
Cat	X	X	X	X	√	X	X
Human	√	√	√	√	√	√	√

[a] X = absent. [b] √ = present.

type. EP$_2$ receptors also mediate relaxation of hamster uterus *in vitro*.[62] PGI$_2$, iloprost and cicaprost all potently relax human isolated myometrium.[268a] Although this strongly supports the presence of inhibitory IP receptors, it contrasts with the lack of activity of PGI$_2$ on human uterus *in vivo*.[269] The reason for this *in vivo/in vitro* difference is not clear.

Myometrial preparations from the various different species studied contain a range of different prostanoid receptors mediating contraction. These receptors are found generally as heterogeneous populations, but the receptor types which constitute these populations differ between all species studied to date. Their distribution in five species, guinea pig, rat, hamster, cat and human is summarized in Table 13.

Excitatory EP receptors are found in uterine preparations from guinea pig, rat, hamster, cat and human. It appears that the predominant subtype of EP receptor found in guinea pig uterus is EP$_1$, but EP$_3$ receptors are also believed to be present. In contrast, the predominant EP receptor subtype present in rat, hamster and human is probably EP$_3$ with a minor contribution of EP$_1$, while those in cat and possibly human are exclusively EP$_3$.[62,268a,270]

FP receptors also exist in myometrium from rat, hamster and probably human, but not from guinea pig and cat.[268a,270] probably not from human, although this is not certain. And finally, TP receptors are present in uterine preparations from guinea pig, hamster and human, but not from rat or cat.[62,268,270]

What is clear from this is that in terms of myometrial prostanoid receptors, no two species are the same. The simplest case is the cat, where it appears that prostanoids can only cause excitatory effects, and that these are mediated through a single receptor type, the EP$_3$ receptor. The most complex are probably the hamster and the human, where prostanoids can cause both inhibitory and excitatory effects, and there is evidence that as many as four different prostanoid receptor types are present mediating the same response.

12.11.5.1.5 Urinary system

Prostanoids have profound effects on smooth muscle from all levels of the urinary system, the ureters, the bladder and the urethra.

(i) Ureters

Little work has been carried out on ureteric smooth muscle, but what evidence there is suggests that PGF$_{2\alpha}$ both causes some contraction and enhances spontaneous rhythmic activity, while PGE$_1$ and PGE$_2$ both exhibit an inhibitory effect.[271,272] In the sheep ureter, it has been proposed that prostanoids play a permissive role in ureteric activity.[273] Thus spontaneous rhythmic activity may be abolished by administration of nonsteroidal antiinflammatory agents, albeit by high concentrations, an effect reversed by application of low concentrations of PGE$_2$.

(ii) Bladder

There are many reports of studies with prostanoids on smooth muscle from the urinary bladder. Both E and F series PGs have excitatory effects on bladder preparations from a wide range of species including humans.[274] They cause not only direct contractions, but may also be involved in the maintenance of spontaneous tone.[275] It is not clear which particular prostanoid receptors are involved, but it appears that on rabbit detrusor smooth muscle, PGE$_2$ is between five- and ten-fold more potent than PGF$_{2\alpha}$,[276] consistent with EP receptor mediation. Interestingly, the prostanoid antagonist N-0164 (see Section 12.11.4.2) caused concentration-related inhibition of detrusor contractions induced by both prostanoids. While this observation is consistent with EP_1 receptor mediation, further studies with another EP_1-receptor-blocking drug, SC-19220, showed it to have no antagonistic effect against either PGE_2 or $PGF_{2\alpha}$. However, the concentration of this agent used (1 μM) was lower than that at which antagonism could be expected, bearing in mind the fact that its pA_2 is only about 5.5.

(iii)   Urethra

As with ureteral smooth muscle, on urethral smooth muscle from a wide range of species, $PGF_{2\alpha}$ induces contraction, and PGE_2 causes relaxation.[274,277] Again there is little information on which to base any characterization of the prostanoid receptors involved.

12.11.5.1.6   Eye

Smooth muscle in the mammalian eye controls the diameter of both the pupil and the lens. The muscles controlling pupil diameter are the iris sphincter (circular) and dilator (radial) muscles, and that controlling the shape of the lens is the ciliary muscle. The effects of prostanoids have been studied on isolated preparations of all three muscles from a range of species.[62,278,279] The nature of the prostanoid-induced effects on the three muscle types, sphincter, dilator and ciliary muscles, from these species are summarized in Table 14.

(i)   Sphincter muscle

The prostanoid receptors mediating contraction of dog and cat iris sphincter muscle are homogeneous populations of FP receptors, with $PGF_{2\alpha}$ and the potent selective FP agonists such as fluprostenol, cloprostenol and prostalene all being more potent than any of the other standard agonists.[62] In this same preparation from the rabbit, it appears that IP receptors mediate contraction, albeit in indirect fashion, through stimulation of irritant receptors, and may involve local substance P release.[280] Prostanoid-induced relaxation of this preparation appears to involve EP receptors, but the subtype is not known. In the cow, iris sphincter contraction is mediated by a heterogeneous population of EP_1 and TP receptors. This is demonstrated by the high contractile agonist potencies of PGE_2 and such potent TP agonists as U-46619 and the selective inhibition of these agonists by the EP_1- and TP-receptor-blocking drugs, SC-19220 and EP 092, respectively.[119] $PGF_{2\alpha}$ and FP agonists are only weak contractile agonists on bovine iris sphincter.

On primate (monkey and human) iris sphincter muscle preparations, the higher spasmogenic potencies of PGE_2 and PGE_1 than that of $PGF_{2\alpha}$[278] suggest the involvement of EP rather than FP receptors. However, the possible involvement of the other prostanoid receptor types is unknown.

(ii)   Dilator muscle

There is little direct information relating to dilator muscles. However, it appears that in the cat at least, as in sphincter muscles, contraction is mediated by FP receptors. While $PGF_{2\alpha}$ also contracts dilator muscles of rabbit and primate, it does not appear to be very potent, and therefore may not involve FP receptors. Both PGE_1 and PGE_2 relax these preparations,[278] which implicates EP receptors, but gives no indication of which particular subtype.

Table 14   Effects of Prostanoids on Intraocular Muscle Preparations from a Range of
Animal Species

Species	Intraocular muscle			Ref.
	Sphincter	Dilator	Ciliary	
Cat	↑ᵃ	↑	↓ᵇ	62, 278
Dog	↑	↑	NTᶜ	62, 279
Rabbit	↑↓	↑↓	↓	41, 278
Cow	↑	NT	NT	279
Monkey	↑	↑↓	↓	278
Human	↑	↑↓	↓	278

ᵃ↑ = contraction.   ᵇ↓ = relaxation.   ᶜNT = not tested.

(iii) Ciliary muscle

Again, the information relating to prostanoid-induced relaxation of ciliary muscle is scant, but it appears that in every case, E series prostanoids are more potent than those of the F series, and PGE_2 is either equipotent with or more potent than PGE_1.[278] These results suggest the involvement of EP receptors, possibly of the EP_2 subtype.

12.11.5.2 Neurones

Prostanoids are known to markedly affect the function of sensory and motor neurones, exhibiting both inhibitory and excitatory actions.

12.11.5.2.1 *Inhibition of neuronal activity*

Like α_2-adrenoceptor agonists and adenosine A_1 agonists, prostanoids can exert potent inhibitory effects on autonomic neurotransmitter release in a range of tissues. Thus prostanoids, particularly PGE_1 and PGE_2, cause inhibition of sympathetic neurotransmitter release in heart, vasculature, spleen, vas deferens and seminal vesicle of various species.[281,282] In these tissues, where studied, $PGF_{2\alpha}$ and PGD_2 are very much weaker than the E series prostanoids. As much of this work predates the discovery of PGI_2, it is not clear how potent this prostanoid is in these preparations. However, PGI_2 has been shown to be particularly potent in inhibiting sympathetic neurotransmitter release in rabbit heart,[283] and may even play a physiological role in the modulation of neurotransmitter release in this tissue.

Despite the early observations of a lack of activity of PGD_2 on sympathetic neurotransmission, PGD_2 has been found to potently inhibit sympathetic neurotransmission in cat nictitating membrane,[284] a preparation in which PGE_2 is without effect.

Reports of prostanoid-induced inhibition of parasympathetic neurotransmission are few. However, there are reports that E series prostanoids inhibit vagally mediated bradycardia in the rabbit[285] and cholinergically mediated contractile responses of dog intestine[286] and dog and guinea pig trachea.[287]

While the evidence as to the receptors involved in these inhibitory responses is somewhat sparse, we have identified those in guinea pig vas deferens, and guinea pig and dog trachea, as EP receptors, and these specifically of the EP_3 subtype.[287,288] However, it is clear that other types of prostanoid receptor must be involved in other tissues; for example the high potencies of PGI_2 in rabbit heart and of PGD_2 in cat nictitating membrane raise the possibility of the involvement of IP and DP receptors respectively. In the latter case, a role for DP receptors is given additional weight by the observation that PGD_3, a potent DP agonist in human platelets (see Section 12.11.3.1), is equipotent with PGD_2 in inhibiting neuronally mediated membrane contractions.[284]

12.11.5.2.2 *Enhancement of neuronal activity*

The excitatory actions of prostanoids on neuronal activity take a number of forms; for example, prostanoids have been shown to enhance neurotransmitter release, to elicit neuronal depolarization and induce hyperalgesia through a lowering of the excitation threshold of peripheral nociceptors.[289] Additionally, prostanoids induce upper airways irritancy and cough[290] as well as gastric irritancy, nausea and vomiting. Whether all of these actions are manifestations of the same effect is not clear, but what is clear is that prostanoids can profoundly enhance nerve function in many tissues.

Probably the best documented example of prostanoid-induced enhancement of neurotransmitter release is that which occurs in the guinea pig ileum myenteric plexus preparation.[291] In this preparation, E series prostanoids potently enhance parasympathetic neurotransmission through an increase in the release of acetylcholine. Furthermore, nonsteroidal antiinflammatory drugs and the prostanoid-receptor-blocking drug SC-19220 inhibit neurotransmission in a concentration-related fashion, effects potently reversed by exogenously administered prostanoids. It is possible therefore that endogenous prostanoids play a permissive role in cholinergic neurotransmission in this tissue. Indeed it has been established that E series prostanoids can play more than just a potentiating role, as they can actually elicit acetylcholine release from parasympathetic nerves. Similarly, in dog tracheobronchial smooth muscle, the TxA_2 mimetic U-46619 potently enhances acetylcholine release from parasympathetic nerves,[292,293] an action which contrasts with the inhibition seen with PGE$_2$ (see above).

Possibly the best known and most obvious manifestation of the neuronal excitation produced by prostanoids is their ability to cause hyperalgesia.[294] The mechanism of prostanoids' hyperalgesic actions may well involve a lowering of the excitatory threshold of polymodal nociceptors associated with sensory C-fibres. Thus the ability of prostanoids to enhance the algogenic actions of such agents as bradykinin, 5-HT and acetylcholine is well known. Various workers have demonstrated that low concentrations of E series prostanoids markedly potentiate the excitability of peripheral sensory nerves *in vivo* and *in vitro*, and even in cell culture.[295] The hyperalgesic actions of prostanoids are not limited to the periphery, as both intracerebroventricular and intracisternal injections of PGE$_2$ and PGD$_2$ have been shown to enhance peripheral nociception.[296-298] As with inhibition of neuro-transmitter release, many of the studies into neuronal excitation predate the discovery of PGI$_2$, thus the effects of this prostanoid are incompletely understood.

Stimulation of neuronal action potentials is not limited to hyperalgesia, as there is a substantial body of evidence that in dogs both PGE$_2$ and PGI$_2$ initiate cardiac reflexes *via* vagal afferent C-fibre stimulation, resulting in bradycardia.[284,301] Similarly, in cats, PGF$_{2\alpha}$ and PGD$_2$ both cause reflex bradycardia.[284,301] Prostanoid stimulation of afferent C-fibres also occurs in dog lung, where prostanoids of the E type potently evoke sensory afferent neuronal discharge.[302] It is believed that such C-fibre stimulation is responsible for the irritant effects of the E series prostanoids.

The only receptors involved in prostanoid-induced neuronal excitation which can be identified with any certainty are the U-46619-sensitive receptors present in dog airways, as these have been shown to be sensitive to blockade by the TP-receptor-blocking drug SQ 29,548,[293] thus implicating TP receptors. As to the various other effects, it appears that generally PGE$_2$ and PGI$_2$ are most potent, implicating EP and/or IP receptors, while the reported inhibition of these effects by the EP$_1$-receptor-blocking drug SC-19220[303] suggests that if EP receptors are involved, they are of the EP$_1$ subtype. It is interesting in this context therefore that SC-19220 and its close analogue pinadoline both exhibit antihyperalgesic activity (see Section 12.11.6.1).

12.11.5.3 Blood Platelets

Platelet aggregation in response to a variety of natural stimuli such as thrombin and collagen is associated with the generation of prostanoids, mainly TxA$_2$ and the prostaglandin endoperoxi-des,[304] but also significant amounts of PGE$_2$, PGF$_{2\alpha}$ and PGD$_2$,[305-307] from platelet phospholipids. Of these prostanoids, PGG$_2$, PGH$_2$ and TxA$_2$ can all induce aggregation of human platelets. However, other natural prostanoids, for example PGI$_2$, PGD$_2$, 6-oxo-PGE$_1$ and PGE$_1$ all inhibit human platelet aggregation, although the relative physiological importance of each prostaglandin is not yet established. In addition, it is becoming increasingly apparent that while PGE$_2$ has little direct aggregatory or antiaggregatory activity, it may have a profound modulatory role upon platelet function, offsetting the antiaggregatory action of endogenous platelet inhibitory agents.

There are several lines of evidence that TxA$_2$, PGI$_2$ and PGD$_2$ act at specific receptors to induce their effects upon platelets.[161,308] In the case of the platelet TP receptors, potent specific receptor-blocking drugs, radioligands and agonists have proliferated in the last few years, all serving to strengthen the concept of a specific common recognition site for TxA$_2$, PGG$_2$ and PGH$_2$ (see Section 12.11.3.5). In fact, in recent studies with radiolabelled 13-APA, a 60 KDa protein has been isolated and partially purified from human platelet membranes. This protein has the characteristics of the TP receptor.[238] In the case of PGI$_2$ and PGD$_2$, the selective effects of antagonists suggest the existence of distinct IP and DP receptors on human platelets.[114,117,182,189,309] In addition, differences in the responsiveness of platelets from different species, as well as results of desensitiz-ation[49,50] and radioligand-binding experiments,[310,311] all support this view.

TP receptor stimulation of human platelets with, for example, U-46619 results in shape change, exposure of fibrinogen receptors, aggregation and selective liberation of α-granule and dense granule constituents.[162,312] In contrast, stimulation of IP or DP receptors leads to an inhibition of all these processes. As described in Section 12.11.2.3, the intracellular mediators linked to TP and IP/DP receptor stimulation are thought to be cytosolic free Ca^{2+} and cAMP respectively.

While detectable amounts of both PGF$_{2\alpha}$ and PGE$_2$ are formed during irreversible platelet aggregation (see above), it is unlikely that endogenously produced PGF$_{2\alpha}$ exerts any significant pharmacological effect upon the platelet, as only at high concentrations can it modify platelet function. In contrast to PGF$_{2\alpha}$, the amounts of PGE$_2$ (approximately 10–30 nM) produced during platelet activation by collagen or thrombin[306,313] would be expected to be sufficient to modify platelet function. The effect of endogenously produced PGE_2 may become even more significant in the presence of thromboxane synthase inhibition when the concentrations of PGE_2 can increase some 20-fold.[313,314] The pharmacological action of PGE_2 upon human platelets is complex. At concentrations above 1 μM it inhibits aggregation of human platelets,[315,316] which, based on evidence from ligand-binding experiments, is probably an effect mediated by IP receptors. At intermediate concentrations (0.1–1 μM), PGE_2 potentiates secondary aggregation to a range of agents, and in pig platelets, under certain conditions, it actually induces aggregation.[317] These actions of PGE_2 may be mediated *via* TP receptor stimulation.[318] In addition to these actions, low concentrations (10–100 nM) of PGE_2 have also been reported to inhibit platelet adenylate cyclase[319,320] and antagonize the antiaggregatory action of PGE_1 and PGI_2.[321] The latter effect was suggested to arise from a partial agonist action of PGE_2 on the platelet IP receptor.[320] However, since this inhibitory effect is also observed against PGD_2[321] and the adenosine mimetic NECA,[322] this mechanism of action seems unlikely. Andersen *et al.* have suggested a distinct EP receptor linked to inhibition of adenylate cyclase.[323] In summary, at low concentration, PGE_2 exerts a powerful modulating effect on human platelets, inhibiting the antiaggregatory effects of a wide range of agents, possibly *via* stimulation of an as yet uncharacterized EP receptor. Higher concentrations of PGE_2 can inhibit aggregation, possibly *via* IP receptor stimulation, whilst under certain circumstances potentiation of aggregation can occur possibly *via* either EP or TP receptor stimulation or both.

12.11.5.4 Kidney

The major prostaglandins produced by the mammalian kidney are PGE_2, PGI_2, $PGF_{2\alpha}$ and TxA_2.[324–326] There appears, however, to be a marked regional variation in prostaglandin production, with medullary synthesis exceeding that of the cortex.[324,326] In addition, the production of each prostaglandin is also highly anatomically localized. In the cortex, apart from the arteries and arterioles which predominantly synthesize PGI_2 and PGE_2, the glomerulus is the major site of prostaglandin synthesis.[327] Human glomeruli synthesize mainly PGI_2 with relatively less PGE_2, TxA_2 and $PGF_{2\alpha}$. Within the glomerulus, the major nonvascular site of prostaglandin synthesis appears to be the mesangial cell.[327] The remainder of the nephron produces mainly PGE_2, and this predominantly in the collecting duct and papilla.[326] If the major action of renal prostaglandins is at their site of synthesis, then this pattern of localized production should give a clue as to their physiological function. In the human kidney, therefore, it is believed that PGI_2 is primarily involved in modulation of cortical events such as renal blood flow, renin release and glomerular filtration rate. In contrast, PGE_2 is largely confined to controlling medullary blood flow, collecting tubule response to vasopressin and Na^+ and Cl^- reabsorption in the loop of Henle.[328] The function of prostaglandins in the kidney appears to be a protective one, effects under normal physiological conditions being difficult to demonstrate. Thus in normal healthy humans, the inhibition of renal prostaglandin synthesis with cyclooxygenase inhibitors has little effect upon glomerular filtration rate or renal function.[329] However, under conditions of renal stress, where perfusion of the kidney is compromised as a result of various circulatory disorders and pathological states, the situation changes. Under such conditions, vasoactive hormones such as angiotensin II, arginine vasopressin and catecholamines are produced, all of which are potent stimuli of renal prostanoid synthesis. The released prostanoids are critical in the maintenance of renal function by offsetting the detrimental actions of the vasoactive agents on the kidney. Under such conditions, therefore, inhibition of prostanoid synthesis by cyclooxygenase inhibitors can result in a substantial decline in renal function.[329] Renal prostaglandins, particularly cortical PGI_2, are also thought to play a role in the action of high-ceiling diuretics such as furosemide. The latter induces prostaglandin synthesis, temporally related to the increase in renin release and natriuresis. Indomethacin abolishes the furosemide-induced release of prostaglandins and blunts the vasodilatation and renin release, but not the natriuresis.

Characterization of the receptors through which prostanoids mediate their effects upon renal function is limited. However, the abilities of PGI_2 and PGE_2 to antagonize vasoconstrictor effects on afferent and efferent arterioles have been shown to differ. Thus, whilst both prostaglandins are effective against afferent arteriolar vasoconstriction, only PGI_2 is effective on efferent arterioles.[331] These data suggest that while EP and IP receptors coexist in the preglomerular microcirculation, only IP receptors exist in the postglomerular vessels. In the glomerulus, one of the determinants of filtration rate is the surface area available for filtration and this may be substantially affected by the 'smooth muscle-like' mesangial cells. It has been shown that both angiotensin II and arginine vasopressin increase glomerular and mesangial cell production of PGI_2 and PGE_2.[327] It has also been demonstrated that these prostaglandins potently counteract the contraction of mesangial cells produced by these peptides.[327,332] Both PGI_2 and PGE_2 elevate cAMP in cultured mesangial cells,[333] although the nature of the receptor involved has not been elucidated. The mesangial cell can also produce TxA_2 and the production can become markedly elevated in certain renal disease states (see Section 12.11.6.6). TxA_2 and its mimetics, U-46619 and U-44069, potently contract isolated mesangial cells in culture and such contractions are antagonized by the TP-receptor-blocking drugs EP 092 and SQ 27,427.[334] Thus the glomerulus, and in particular the mesangial cell, appears to be a major site for prostaglandin interactions with both inhibitory EP or IP receptors and excitatory TP receptors capable of influencing glomerular filtration rate.[332]

Finally, as mentioned above, the major site of PGE_2 production in the nephron is in the collecting duct. There are several reports of an effect of PGE_2 upon tubular ionic transport, although many studies appear contradictory.[325,326] In addition it has been proposed that an inhibitory EP receptor linked to adenylate cyclase is localized in the outer medulla and an excitatory EP receptor in the papilla.[326,335] However, further characterization studies are necessary before the existence of such receptors can be confirmed.

12.11.5.5 Ovary

During the oestrous cycle, the ovaries undergo structural and functional changes in which prostaglandins are closely involved.

The growth of the ovarian follicle is controlled by follicle stimulating hormone (FSH) and luteinizing hormone (LH). FSH initiates follicle growth, and further follicular changes, together with ovary maturation and ovulation, are under the control of LH. In cultured follicles *in vitro*, LH induces meiotic division of the oocyte and accompanying changes in the granulosa cells of the follicle *i.e.* cAMP production and changes in steroidogenesis.[336,337] In addition, LH increases the rate of prostaglandin formation in the follicle, but the follicular response to LH is not blocked by indomethacin treatment, suggesting that endogenous prostanoids are not obligatory intermediates of LH in this respect.[336,337]

Once the oocyte has matured, ovulation is initated by a surge of LH secretion from the pituitary. This LH secretion stimulates an increase of follicular prostanoids: the peak prostaglandin change coincides with ovulation; both PGE_2 and $PGF_{2\alpha}$ increase but PGE_2 predominates. Ovulation is prevented by administration of indomethacin, an effect reversed by PGE_2 administration.[336] Thus, PGE_2 may well be an obligatory intermediate in ovulation, although which prostanoid receptor type is involved is not known. Most of this information relating to prostanoids and ovulation has been obtained in rats and rabbits; at present there is no conclusive evidence that prostaglandins are involved in ovulation in women.[337]

Following ovulation, the ruptured follicle becomes the corpus luteum, which in many species is responsible for the maintenance of pregnancy. The formation of the corpus luteum, luteinization, is characterized by increased intracellular cAMP content and increased progesterone formation. Although in human isolated luteal cells these changes can be produced by addition of either LH or PGE_2 (but not $PGF_{2\alpha}$), PGE_2 does not appear to be an obligatory intermediate, as doses of indomethacin sufficient to block ovulation fail to prevent luteinization.[337]

If pregnancy fails to occur, the corpus luteum regresses (luteolysis), a process associated with a fall in cAMP content and decreased progesterone formation.[336,338] There is convincing evidence that $PGF_{2\alpha}$ is the endogenous luteolytic hormone in animals. Thus, inhibition of $PGF_{2\alpha}$ formation by indomethacin maintains the corpus luteum, whereas administration of $PGF_{2\alpha}$, but not PGE_2, induces luteolysis. The release of $PGF_{2\alpha}$ from the endometrium is probably controlled by ovarian steroids (estrogen and progesterone).[339] $PGF_{2\alpha}$ is believed to induce luteolysis by inhibiting LH-induced cAMP accumulation, as well as inhibiting progesterone production.[338] Evidence obtained with several synthetic $PGF_{2\alpha}$ analogues in a range of animal species suggests that prostanoid-induced luteolysis is mediated by FP receptors (see Section 12.11.3.3). While *in vitro* experiments suggest that $PGF_{2\alpha}$ may fulfill such a luteolytic function in women,[337] such a role is not supported by clinical findings.

This discussion shows that prostaglandins may be involved in several aspects of ovarian function, and there is convincing evidence of an obligatory role for PGE_2 inducing ovulation and for $PGF_{2\alpha}$

in inducing luteolysis in animals. Indeed, analogues of $PGF_{2\alpha}$ have been used successfully to induce luteolysis and to synchronize oestrous in horses, cows and pigs.[340]

12.11.5.6 Eye

In 1955 Ambache extracted an unsaturated fatty acid material from rabbit irises which contracted smooth muscle.[341] This substance was termed irin and was later shown to contain PGE and PGF. It is now known that several different tissues in the eye synthesize PGE_2, $PGF_{2\alpha}$, PGI_2, PGD_2 and TxA_2 and that these prostaglandins affect ocular function; such effects are the subject of an excellent review by Bito[342] and a brief overview is given here.

In the amphibian cornea, active Cl^- (and fluid) transport across the epithelium maintains normal hydration and transparency.[343] Both E and F prostaglandins stimulate this Cl^- transport and thus contribute to the maintenance of corneal transparency.[344,345] However, a similar role for prostaglandins in the mammalian cornea remains to be established.

The effect of prostaglandins on intraocular pressure (IOP) is uncertain; acute administration of E and F prostaglandins may produce an increase or a decrease in IOP depending on the experimental procedure and anaesthetic used.[342] In cats and primates, application of PGE_2 or $PGF_{2\alpha}$ to the eyes reduces IOP by increasing the rate of outflow of aqueous humour from the anterior chamber of the eye.[342] Interestingly, this reduction in IOP observed with PGE_2 occurs despite the fact that PGE_2 also stimulates secretion of aqueous humour. This stimulation results from changes in both active transport and membrane permeability.[346,347] Clearly more work is required in this area to clarify the actions of prostanoids on IOP, but it is possible that provided side effects such as miosis are not produced, they may provide a new class of potential antiglaucoma agents.

Although irin causes pupillary constriction, and prostanoids can cause contraction of iris smooth muscle from a range of species (see Section 12.11.5.1), a detailed reassessment by Bito[342] of a number of studies suggest that, in general, E and F prostaglandins cannot be regarded as miotic agents in all species. However, it is possible that prostaglandins potentiate the miotic responses to other substances present in irin or to substances released into the eye as a result of experimental trauma.[342]

In summary, the various tissues of the eye form prostaglandins which affect function. However, these actions of prostaglandins appear to depend on the species used and the experimental techniques employed, and considerably more work is required before we can speculate as to the prostaglandin receptors controlling ocular function.

12.11.5.7 Bone

The skeleton acts as a store of calcium, thus calcium may be taken up to form new bone, or conversely bone may be resorbed (broken down) to release calcium into the extracellular fluid. This calcium may then be used to balance Ca^{2+} loss by the kidney or to form new bone in other parts of the body as required. The control of bone resorption is believed to involve prostaglandins as 'local mediators'.

The process of bone resorption is controlled by osteoclasts which are believed to remove bone by secretion of a combination of the enzyme acid hydrolase and H^+ ions. This combination enhances the dissolution of calcium phosphate from bone.[348] The major blood-borne hormone controlling bone resorption is parathyroid hormone (PTH), and *in vitro* experiments have indicated that prostaglandins are the local mediators of the PTH-induced response; there are several lines of evidence which support this. First, the osteoblast cells in bone synthesize prostaglandins, the rate of this synthesis is increased by substances which stimulate bone resorption, most notably PTH, but also epidermal growth factor and phorbol esters. In addition, indomethacin inhibits the stimulation of prostaglandin synthesis and of bone resorption.[348] Finally, prostaglandins stimulate bone resorption *in vitro* with a rank order of agonist potency of $PGE_2 > PGF_{2\alpha} > U\text{-}46619 > PGD_2$,[349] which suggests that this action is mediated by EP receptors.

Prostaglandins probably increase the rate of bone resorption by stimulating the formation of new osteoclasts, and by increasing the activity of preexisting osteoclasts.[348] The intracellular messenger mediating the action of prostaglandins on osteoclast function is not entirely clear, but is probably cAMP since prostaglandins stimulate cAMP formation in osteoclasts with the same rank order potency as described above for bone resorption.[349] An involvement of cAMP as intracellular messenger permits the tentative conclusion that the EP receptors mediating bone resorption are of the EP_2 subtype (see Section 12.11.2.3).

12.11.5.8 Gastrointestinal Absorption and Secretion

12.11.5.8.1 Stomach

In gastric mucosa, prostaglandins cause both inhibition of gastric acid secretion and stimulation of the secretion of an alkaline NaCl-rich juice.

In the rat, inhibition of gastric acid secretion is mediated by EP receptors, with no evidence for the involvement of FP, TP, IP or DP receptors.[350] Prostanoid-induced inhibition of acid secretion is associated with a reduction in histamine-induced cAMP accumulation in the parietal cell,[351,352] an effect which suggests the involvement of EP_3 receptors (see Section 12.11.2.3). Indeed, there is now direct evidence obtained with a range of potent antisecretory prostanoids indicating that this is so.[353] In experiments on canine parietal cells, measuring aminopyrine accumulation as an index of acid secretion, it was found that while PGE_2 and PGI_2 were both inhibitory, PGE_2 was between 10–100-fold more potent than PGI_2,[352] a finding consistent with PGI_2 acting at EP receptors.

It is well-established that E prostaglandins stimulate gastric nonparietal secretion, and this effect appears to be associated with an increase in cAMP levels,[351,354] implicating EP_2 receptors (see Section 12.11.2.3). However, in guinea pig gastric mucosa it has also been shown that TP receptors mediate stimulation of gastric nonparietal secretion, seen as an increase in short circuit current;[355] typical responses to PGE_2 and U-46619 are illustrated in Figure 5. It is even possible that in human gastric mucosa, IP receptors are also involved, since PGI_2 is equipotent with PGE_2 in stimulating adenylate cyclase activity in this tissue.[356] Our own studies indicate that FP receptors do not mediate nonparietal secretion, and measurement of adenylate cyclase activity has revealed a similar absence of DP receptors.[357]

12.11.5.8.2 Intestine

Prostaglandins both stimulate secretion and inhibit absorption in the intestine. In rabbit isolated ileum, using short circuit current (Isc) as an index of secretion, the rank order of potency was PGE_2 > PGI_2 > PGD_2 > $PGF_{2\alpha}$, thus implicating EP receptors in the control of secretion.[358] In rat ileum, sulprostone had no effect on Isc in tissues that responded to PGE_2,[359] and, taken with the increase in mucosal cAMP levels associated with prostanoid-induced secretion, this suggests that secretion is mediated by EP_2 receptors (see Sections 12.11.2.3 and 12.11.3.2). The weak activity of $PGF_{2\alpha}$ described above suggests that FP receptors are absent from secretory (crypt) cells, and this is

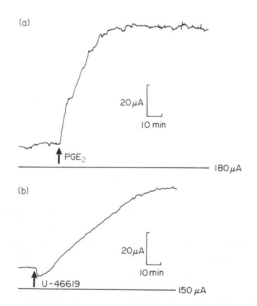

Figure 5 Guinea pig isolated gastric mucosa: stimulation of gastric nonparietal secretion, seen as changes in short circuit current in response to (a) PGE_2 (1 μM) and (b) U-46619 (1 μM)

Table 15 A Scheme for the Distribution of Prostanoid Receptors
Affecting Secretion and Absorption within Gastrointestinal Mucosa

	Stimulation of secretion	*Inhibition of absorption*	*Inhibition of secretion*
Stomach	EP_2, TP, IP	—	EP_3
Small intestine	EP_2	EP_1 and/or EP_3	—
Large intestine	EP, IP, DP	TP	—

confirmed in experiments in human jejunal mucosa.[360a] Although sulprostone does not affect Isc in rat ileum, it does inhibit Na^+ absorption in this tissue,[359] and this result indicates that different EP receptors control secretion and absorption, the latter response probably involving EP_1 and/or EP_3 receptors.

The question of the involvement of DP and IP receptors in intestinal secretory mechanisms is more contentious. The weak activity of PGD_2 in rabbit ileum[358] indicates the absence of DP receptors; similarly, the weak agonist response to PGI_2 compared with PGE_2 on Isc in rat ileum and colon[360b] suggests the lack of IP receptors. In contrast with these results, Simon *et al.* found that PGE_2, PGI_2 and PGD_2 were equipotent as stimulants of adenylate cyclase activity in human colonic mucosa;[357,361] these apparent anomalies may reflect species differences. The TP agonist, U-46619, had no effect on Isc in guinea pig and rat intestine,[362a] but U-46619 did stimulate rat colonic secretion *in vivo*, an effect blocked by the TP antagonist GR 32191 (see Section 12.11.4.5). These data suggest that stimulation of TP receptors affects net secretion by controlling absorptive rather than secretory mechanisms.[362b]

A suggested scheme for the distribution of prostanoid receptors modulating gastrointestinal absorption and secretion is shown in Table 15.

12.11.6 PATHOPHYSIOLOGICAL ACTIONS OF PROSTANOIDS

12.11.6.1 Inflammation

Prostanoids play a number of important roles in both acute and chronic inflammation.[363,364] Prostanoids are produced in large quantities in inflammatory conditions, whether these are induced by mechanical trauma, corrosive chemicals, burning, radiation, antigen–antibody reactions or immune/autoimmune responses.[363] The prostanoids may be generated from a variety of invading cells, *e.g.* eosinophils and neutrophils, but macrophages appear to be the richest source. And finally, they modulate all aspects of the inflammatory response, local vasodilatation, oedema, pain and the immune response, and in cases of infection can induce pyrexia.[365]

12.11.6.1.1 Vasodilatation/oedema

Prostanoids, in particular PGE_2 and PGI_2, are potent vasodilators not only generally but also in the microcirculation, and the high local concentrations of these prostanoids in inflammatory conditions are sufficient to induce local hyperaemia through vasodilatation.[366] The ability of prostanoids to directly induce plasma extravasation, and thus oedema, has been a matter of some debate; contrary to some early reports, prostanoids on their own are poor inducers of oedema, but dramatically enhance the oedema-producing properties of agents such as bradykinin and histamine.[367] Directly acting oedema-producing agents are believed to do so by constricting venular endothelial cells, allowing plasma to escape through the intercellular spaces. While the pro-inflammatory prostanoids have little or no ability to contract endothelial cells, their potent vasodilator activity results in a substantial enhancement of the ability of agents which can cause plasma extravasation and thus oedema.[368] The rheumatoid synovium has proved a particularly useful site for studying vascular permeability associated with inflammation, concentrations of endogenous prostanoids being substantially higher than those in normal joints.[369] Furthermore, the ability of cultured cells from rheumatoid synovia to generate prostanoids is substantially elevated, with PGE_2 being the predominant product.[369,370]

As the role of prostanoids in oedema formation almost certainly results from their vasodilator activity, and PGs E, I and D are all known to exhibit such activity in various vascular beds, EP, IP and/or DP receptors could be involved in the oedema of inflammation. The substantial body of evidence for the involvement of PGE_2 would therefore support the role of EP receptors, probably of the EP_2 subtype.

12.11.6.1.2 Pain

In 1972, Ferreira demonstrated that E series PGs have hyperalgesic activity.[371] Thus, while they are not pain-producing in their own right, they sensitize pain receptors to stimulation by other agents such as bradykinin and 5-hydroxytryptamine. This observation has subsequently been confirmed by many groups.[372-374] It is this ability of prostanoids to amplify the pain-producing effects of other agents which explains the analgesic action of nonsteroidal antiinflammatory drugs (NSAID) such as aspirin and indomethacin.[373] Such agents, by reducing levels of endogenous prostanoids remove their amplifying effect. Because of this, such agents do not behave as strong analgesics like the opiates, being only effective in the pain associated for example with inflammation, where endogenous prostanoid levels are elevated.

Of the natural prostanoids, PGs E_1 and E_2 are generally the most potent hyperalgesic agents, being substantially more potent than $PGF_{2\alpha}$,[375,376] indeed $PGF_{2\alpha}$ has even been reported to inhibit PGE-induced hyperalgesic actions.[377] PGI_2 also possesses hyperalgesic activity in some models,[378] but this activity appears to differ from that induced by PGE_2, in that the effects of PGI_2 are rapid both in onset and recovery, while the effects of PGE_2 are slow in both respects, onset and duration of action being measured in hours.[378] Such a long duration of action of PGE_2 may explain the delay often experienced in the onset of action of NSAIDs as analgesic agents. There appear to be no reports of hyperalgesia induced by TxA_2 or stable mimetics, but there are a few relating to PGD_2.[297,379] Paradoxically, it has been demonstrated that at higher doses, both PGD_2 and PGE_2 can exert hypoalgesia, and that the hypoalgesic effects of PGD_2 but not those of PGE_2 appear to be mediated *via* an endogenous opioid system.[297]

There is growing evidence that the site of action of endogenous prostanoids in their hyperalgesic effects is not entirely peripheral, they may also have a central site of action.[296] Thus peripheral administration of an inflammatory agent can cause prostanoid release both locally and centrally, and both may contribute to the associated hyperalgesia.[380,381] Furthermore, central administration of prostanoids consistently induces hyperalgesia.[296,297,376,381]

Despite the well-established link between prostanoids and hyperalgesia both in the periphery and in the central nervous system, little effort has been directed towards investigating the hyperalgesic effects of more selective synthetic prostanoid analogues. There is therefore little information upon which to speculate as to the receptors involved. The consistently reported high potency of PGE_1 and PGE_2 must support the involvement of EP receptors, but the reports of high potency of PGI_2 suggest that IP receptors may also be involved. It seems unlikely that PGE and PGI are acting through the same receptor, as the time courses of the hyperalgesia induced by the two agents are so different. The one strong indication as to the identity of the hyperalgesic EP receptor is provided by the various reports of the analgesic activity of the EP_1-receptor-blocking drug SC-19220.[193,294,382] However, this suggestion of the involvement of EP_1 receptors is apparently at odds with the intracellular mechanisms believed to be responsible for hyperalgesia, *i.e.* an elevation of cAMP,[378] as to date there is no indication that EP_1 receptors are positively linked to adenylate cyclase (see Section 12.11.2.3). A final point of possible relevance to prostanoid-induced hyperalgesia is the potent analgesic effect afforded by the cannabinoid derivative deacetyl-(−)-nantradol.[198] This compound has been suggested to be a prostanoid antagonist (see Section 12.11.4) and to exhibit its analgesic activity by this mechanism.

12.11.6.1.3 Immune response

Prostanoids are believed to be important modulators of the immune response, but their effects are complicated, involving both inhibition and enhancement.[383] Prostanoids are produced in large quantities in inflammation, the most important cellular source being the macrophage.[384] Stimulated human macrophages release predominantly PGE_2 and TxA_2, of which PGE_2 appears to be the most immunologically important.[363] Thus PGE_2, in concentrations in which it occurs naturally in inflammatory conditions, can inhibit both the function and the proliferation of T cells, whether killer, helper or suppressor.[363] Interestingly, under some circumstances, PGE will also stimulate T cells, as it can both induce the development of mature T cells from immature thymocytes, and stimulate mitogenic activity of low density T cells, although it inhibits that of medium and high density T cells.[385] Such dual excitatory/inhibitory effects are also observed on B cells, natural killer (NK) cells and macrophages, and in the case of the macrophage, PGE can both stimulate and inhibit macrophage phagocytosis, spreading and adherence. PGE not only inhibits interleukin-2 (IL-2) production, but also inhibits its activity. It has in fact been proposed that macrophage-derived PGE_2 plays a negative feedback role in the immune response, although macrophages also release TxA_2 which has the opposite effect, thus suggesting that a PGE_2/TxA_2 balance is important. Interestingly, the sensitivity of lymphocytes to the inhibitory effects of PGE_2 in humans increases dramatically with age, being more than 100-fold more sensitive at age 70 than in young adults.[382] This increase in sensitivity may be responsible for some of the immunological disturbances that occur in otherwise healthy old people. Prostanoids, particularly E series PGs, seem to play such a variety of roles in the immune system, some inhibitory, some excitatory that, coupled with the lack of information with more selective synthetic analogues, it is impossible to speculate usefully upon which prostanoid receptors mediate which effects.

12.11.6.2 Cancer

Prostanoids may also play a role in tumour progression, being released in large quantities by some tumours as well as by T suppressor cells,[386] and these released prostanoids may then be responsible for the suppression of the host's immunological response, allowing tumour development to advance unchecked (see Section 12.11.6.1). Indeed there is substantial evidence that prostanoids, particularly PGE_2, play an important role in some forms of cancer progression.[387] However, PGE_2 is not restricted to a facilitatory role, as there is also evidence that the predominant effect of PGE_2 on tumour cells is inhibitory, and indeed the analogue, 16,16-dimethyl-PGE_2, has been shown to delay the appearance and growth of B16 melanoma tumours in mice and thus to increase their survival time.[388] The effects of prostanoids on tumour progression are therefore complicated, but it is significant that NSAIDs tend to reduce tumour growth, increase survival of tumour-bearing animals and enhance the therapeutic efficacy of more conventional anticancer therapy, *e.g.* radiotherapy and chemotherapy.[387] Whether NSAID-induced inhibition of tumour progression is due to a reduction of prostanoid-induced immunosuppression is not clear, as the correlation between the two effects is not always good. However, bearing in mind the manifold effects of prostanoids on the immunological system, perhaps this is not surprising. In addition, many tumours appear to be resistant to the effects of NSAIDs. A clearer picture of the role of endogenous prostanoids in tumour progression awaits the development of more selective agonists and, more importantly, receptor-blocking drugs.

There has been considerable interest in the antineoplastic activity of PGD_2 and its metabolite PGJ_2.[389] It has since become apparent that this activity is shared by nonprostanoids such as the clavulones,[390] but it appears that these agents are generally cytotoxic and do not appear to be specific for malignant cells.[391] Furthermore, prostanoids seem to owe their activity not to their prostanoid structure *per se*, but instead to the enone and dienone functions that all of the active compounds possess.

12.11.6.3 Destruction of Cartilage and Bone

Various inflammatory conditions, *e.g.* rheumatoid arthritis, osteoarthritis and peridontitis, are associated with substantial cartilage and/or bone breakdown. In such disease states, PGE_2 has been implicated as a causative factor.[363] Indeed PGE_2 has well-documented resorptive actions on both cartilage and bone (see Section 12.11.5.7). As well as being released by inflammatory cells, PGE_2 is also released in large quantities by rheumatoid synovial cells.[370] Furthermore, treatment of arthritic patients with antiinflammatory drugs has been shown to result in reduced levels of PGE_2 in the synovium.[392,393] Thus there exists strong circumstantial evidence for the involvement of PGE_2 in the bone destruction associated with inflammatory joint disease. However, the observation that PGI_2 also has potent bone resorptive activity in some, but not all, models[394,395] suggests that this prostanoid may also play a role in certain conditions. It is perhaps important to mention that the effects of PGE_2 and also of PGI_2 may not be entirely pathological in nature, as it has been suggested that both may act as modulators of normal bone turnover (see Section 12.11.5.7).

The osteolytic activity of prostanoids is of particular consequence not only in inflammatory disease, but also in some forms of cancer, where tumour formation is associated with bone loss and hypercalcaemia.[363,386,396] As many tumours release large quantities of prostanoids, it has been suggested that they are responsible for tumour-related bone breakdown,[397] and also for the metastatic spread of tumours, particularly to bone, there being, for example, a correlation between PGE_2 synthesis by human breast cancers and the development of secondary bone metastases.[387]

As with other areas of inflammation, there is too little information upon which to determine the nature of the prostanoid receptors involved beyond saying that EP and possibly in some cases IP receptors play a role.

12.11.6.4   Pyrexia

The ability of prostanoids, when administered directly into the brain, to induce an elevation of body temperature is well known,[398] and fever is a frequent side-effect of intravenous infusions of prostanoids when given as abortifacients.[399] Furthermore, it is believed that the fever induced by both endogenous and exogenous pyrogens is mediated by prostanoids, which accounts for the efficiency of NSAIDs as antipyretic agents. Indeed, NSAIDs have been shown to cause parallel inhibition of both fever and prostanoid levels within the cerebrospinal fluid (CSF).[365] While prostanoids are clearly pyretic and mediate the fevers induced by many infectious and noninfectious stimuli,[400] the question arises as to which particular prostanoid is involved. The strongest candidate is PGE_2, which appears in the CSF during fever and exhibits potent pyretic activity on administration into brains of animals.[365] In contrast, $PGF_{2\alpha}$ does not appear to cause fever, and in rats, whose brains synthesize $PGF_{2\alpha}$ rather than PGE_2, pyrogens fail to cause an increase in body temperature.[400]

Although the causative role of PGE_2 in many fevers is generally accepted, its mechanism of action is not known, and there is very little information regarding the pyrogenic effects of synthetic prostanoids. However, interestingly, intravenous infusions of the EP_1/EP_3 receptor agonist sulprostone, unlike similar infusions of PGE_2 itself, failed to consistently elevate body temperature.[401,402] Assuming that it can gain access to the thermoregulatory centres, the lack of activity of sulprostone suggests that the receptors involved in prostanoid-induced pyrexia, if EP receptors, are neither EP_1 nor EP_3 and are probably EP_2. Such a conclusion is apparently inconsistent with the observation in the rabbit that PGE_2-induced pyrexia may be prevented by the EP_1-receptor-blocking drug SC-19220.[403] Clearly more evidence is required before any firm conclusions as to the nature of the receptors mediating prostanoid-induced pyrexia can be drawn.

12.11.6.5   Thrombosis and Occlusive Vascular Disease

Early reports of the vasoactive properties of prostaglandins like $PGF_{2\alpha}$ led to the suggestion that such prostanoids might be involved in ischaemic vascular events such as cerebral vasospasm following subarachnoid haemorrhage.[404] However, the discovery in 1975 of TxA_2, and the subsequent characterization of its potent biological activity upon human platelets and vascular smooth muscle,[6,405] caused this theory to be reevaluated. In fact, TxA_2 was proposed to be the prostanoid most likely to be of pathological significance in ischaemic vascular disease, especially that in which platelet activation was implicated.[406,407] A possible role for TxA_2 in such ischaemic events as variant angina, angina pectoris and myocardial infarction was supported by evidence that in such conditions in humans, circulating levels of its primary metabolite, TxB_2, were elevated.[408] However the validity of such reports is open to question since it is now realized that during blood sampling platelet activation occurs, leading to generation of TxA_2 and hence its metabolite TxB_2.[409] Recently however, stable enzymatic degradation products of TxA_2 such as 2,3-dinor-TxB_2 and 11-dehydro-TxB_2, which are not subject to sampling artefacts, have been identified.[410] These metabolites, which are usually measured in urine and plasma respectively, and largely reflect systemic TxA_2 production, have allowed a more reliable evaluation to be made of the possible pathophysiological role of TxA_2 in disease states.

Elevated levels of these metabolites have now been reported to occur in patients with unstable angina, acute myocardial infarction, severe atherosclerosis, Raynaud's disease, as well as following venous thrombosis, pulmonary embolism, heart transplantation and insertion of prosthetic arterial grafts.[411-413] While not yet proven, it is most probable that these elevated levels of TxA_2 metabolites signify some pathological role for TxA_2 itself. However, definitive proof must await the clinical testing of drugs, such as TP-receptor-blocking drugs, in these disease states.[167]

The temporal pattern of the excretion of the systemic markers of TxA_2 production and its relation to clinical symptoms has been most thoroughly studied in patients with unstable angina. For example, in these patients over 80% of the episodes of chest pain were associated with elevated levels of 2,3-dinor-TxB$_2$.[414] However, a proportion of the observed increases in the TxA$_2$ metabolite were not associated with chest pain, and not all chest pain was associated with increased excretion of the metabolite.[414] Since the platelet is the major source of TxA$_2$ in humans,[415] these cyclical changes in TxA$_2$ biosynthesis most probably reflect episodic platelet activation. The precise pathological consequences of these cyclical TxA$_2$-dependent thrombotic episodes is uncertain. For example, in patients with unstable angina, doses of aspirin that completely inhibit platelet cyclooxygenase and hence TxA$_2$ production, failed to alter the frequency of chest pain.[416] However this lack of effect of aspirin may have arisen from the concomitant inhibition of PGI$_2$ which is also elevated in unstable angina (see below). Nevertheless, in such patients, aspirin has been shown to reduce the incidence of myocardial infarction and death by up to 50%.[417] This is consistent with an important pathological role of TxA$_2$ in the final events leading to infarction in these patients.

In many of the clinical conditions of thrombosis and occlusive vascular disease where TxA$_2$ biosynthesis is increased, levels of PGI$_2$ are also elevated. However as with TxA$_2$, sampling artefacts have led to erroneous estimates of the concentration of circulating PGI$_2$ when measured as 6-oxo-PGF$_{1\alpha}$.[409] More reliable estimates have been obtained by measuring the stable metabolite 2,3-dinor-6-oxo-PGF$_{1\alpha}$ in urine.[418] Elevated levels of this metabolite have, for example, been detected in patients with unstable angina, myocardial infarction, severe atherosclerosis and following implantation of prosthetic arterial grafts.[412,414,419] Increased PGI$_2$ synthesis often occurs concomitantly with TxA$_2$ synthesis, and is considered to occur as a result of the interaction of activated platelets with the vessel wall.[419] However, PGI$_2$ can increase independently of TxA$_2$ and therefore independently of platelet activation. This is the case following myocardial infarction, where PGI$_2$ is believed to be derived from the damaged myocardium or the vasculature in the infarcted zone.[414] Ischaemia itself is a powerful stimulus for PGI$_2$ production, whose role is probably protective. Thus, a drug which spares PGI$_2$ biosynthesis under these conditions but prevents the deleterious effects of TxA$_2$ should be superior to aspirin under these conditions (see Section 12.11.7.8).

12.11.6.6 Renal Disease

As described in Section 12.11.5.4, the effects of prostaglandins upon renal function appear to be most important under conditions in which the kidney is 'stressed'. One situation in which renal prostaglandin production is elevated is during various forms of renal disease. Several reviews have appeared recently describing the various experimental and clinical situations in which this occurs.[327,330,420,421] In these situations, the action of prostaglandins can be classed as either beneficial, such as in the maintenance of renal blood flow and glomerular filtration rate by PGI$_2$ and PGE$_2$, or deleterious, as in the reductions in these two parameters by TxA$_2$ (see Section 12.11.5.4). The pathological conditions in which a prostaglandin component has been described include immune glomerulonephritis, lupus nephritis, diabetic albuminuria, subtotal nephrectomy, acute renal failure, ureteral obstruction and renal transplant rejection.

The involvement of prostaglandins in these various diseases and experimental conditions has been demonstrated in various ways. For example, Patrono *et al.* have shown elevated urinary excretion of TxB$_2$ and PGE$_2$, but reduced excretion of 6-oxo-PGF$_{1\alpha}$ in patients with systemic lupus erythematosus, an immune-mediated renal disease.[422] In contrast, patients with chronic glomerular disease only differed from controls in having reduced 6-oxo-PGF$_{1\alpha}$ excretion. Elevated levels of urinary TxB$_2$ also occur in renal allograft rejection,[423] ureteral obstruction[424] and in cyclosporin nephrotoxicity.[425] Drugs have also been utilized to demonstrate prostanoid involvement in renal disease. Thus, for example, thromboxane synthase inhibitors improve renal function during acute allograft rejection in the rat.[423] In patients with lupus nephritis, an improvement in renal function has also been demonstrated with the thromboxane receptor-blocking drug BM 13.177.[426]

Thus, in certain forms of renal disease, the antagonism of the detrimental effects of TxA$_2$ appears to be of benefit. However in some instances a deficiency of renal prostaglandin production may be a major factor. Consequently, the use of nonspecific cyclooxygenase inhibitors would tend to be contraindicated in such clinical settings.

12.11.6.7 Asthma

While prostanoids are generally believed to play a role in the aetiology of asthma,[427] the nature and extent of that role has been the subject of considerable speculation over the last two decades. There is substantial circumstantial evidence that prostanoids are important causative agents in the impairment of lung function associated with asthma.[428] Thus several prostanoids, particularly

$PGF_{2\alpha}$, PGD_2 and TxA_2 have well-documented bronchoconstrictor activity.[429] Also a wide range of allergic stimuli release a variety of different prostanoids from human lung tissue, PGD_2 being released in particularly large amounts from human lung mast cells,[430] and, finally, a dramatic hypersensitivity to the bronchoconstrictor effects of prostanoids has been reported in asthmatics.[431]

Interest in prostanoids and asthma declined when it became apparent that NSAIDs appeared to offer little if any benefit to the majority of asthmatics. Indeed, a minor, though numerically substantial proportion of asthmatics (5–10%) actually appear to suffer an acute exacerbation of their asthma after taking aspirin or other structurally unrelated NSAIDs.[432] It is, however, important to realize that prostanoids have a variety of different effects which may be relevant to their overall contribution to the pathogenesis of asthma. In fact the first observation of the biological activity of prostanoids on respiratory smooth muscle was made by Main who reported that E series prostanoids relax isolated tracheobronchial smooth muscle from a range of species.[433] The bronchodilator effect of E series prostanoids is well established in many species including humans, and synthetic analogues of PGE_2 have been tested as potentially therapeutically useful bronchodilators in human asthmatics.[434] Examples of such compounds are CS-412 (**40**), butaprost (**36**) and the cytoprotective prostanoid, misoprostol (**38**) (see Section 12.11.3.2).

The beneficial actions of prostanoids are limited in part by the occurrence of upper airways irritancy (see Section 12.11.5.2.2) and also the occasional paradoxical occurrence of bronchoconstriction.[364]

The interest in prostanoids and asthma has been revived in recent years following two important observations. The first of these was that made by Fairfax *et al.* who, while confirming that NSAIDs have at best a modest protective effect against the early response of asthmatics to antigen challenge, demonstrated that when given before challenge, NSAIDs prevent the appearance of the late response.[435] The mechanism of this inhibition of the late response is not understood, but, interestingly, NSAIDs administered after the expression of the early response then failed to influence the progression of the late response. The second observation was that on antigen challenge, human lung mast cells generate large quantities of PGD_2, a prostanoid with marked bronchoconstrictor activity when administered by inhalation.[436,437] It is now believed that PGD_2 is metabolized to $9\alpha,11\beta$-PGF_2 (**18**) *in vivo*, and that this compound is at least as potent as PGD_2 in its bronchoconstrictor activity.[438]

Asthma is characterized by the development of airways hypersensitivity to the bronchoconstrictor effects of a wide range of bronchoactive agents. Investigators have revealed that prostanoids possess the ability to induce such non-specific hypersensitivity.[439,440] Thus *in vitro*, PGD_2, but not $PGF_{2\alpha}$, potentiates parasympathetically induced contractions of guinea pig trachea.[441] And more significantly, prostanoids, including PGD_2, are capable of inducing airways hyperreactivity to a variety of bronchoconstrictor agents in both normal and asthmatic subjects. Bearing in mind the high levels of PGD_2 released from human lung mast cells following antigen challenge, it is clearly possible that prostanoids may play an important role in the hypersensitive status of asthmatics.

It has been noted that lung appears to produce spontaneously and continuously large quantities of PGI_2.[429] As it is well established, particularly on vascular smooth muscle and blood platelets, that PGI_2 and TxA_2 exert mutually antagonistic effects, and as TxA_2 is a potent bronchoconstrictor agent,[442] PGI_2 might be expected to be an effective bronchodilator. It is interesting therefore that on respiratory smooth muscle TxA_2 and PGI_2 do not exhibit their customary 'Yin–Yang' relationship, PGI_2 being only a weak bronchodilator in both dogs and humans, and can actually contract tracheobronchial smooth muscle.[443] The role of this PGI_2 released from lung tissue is therefore uncertain. However, despite its lack of bronchodilator activity, PGI_2 does exert a powerful protective effect against both ultrasonic mist and exercise-induced bronchoconstriction, without affecting baseline airways resistance.[444] The mechanism of this effect is not understood.

Prostanoid effects in asthma are not restricted to smooth muscle; in addition they also have powerful effects on inflammatory cells (see Section 12.11.6.1). Thus prostanoids can potently inhibit and stimulate antigen-induced mediator release from a variety of cell types. Prostaglandins, particularly of the E type, potently inhibit histamine and leukotriene release from human basophils and mast cells.[445,446] The effects of PGD_2, the major prostanoid produced by human lung mast cells, are interesting in that not only can it enhance histamine release from human basophils, but, under certain conditions, it can actually induce it.[430]

Finally, prostanoids have some effect on mucus secretion. Whereas a variety of prostanoids, when present in micromolar concentrations, can increase mucous glycoprotein release, PGE_2, in nanomolar concentrations, causes an inhibition.[447]

Although much is known about the direct contractile and relaxant effects of both naturally occurring and synthetic prostanoids on airways smooth muscle from both animals and humans, there is much less information on the other aspects of the asthmatic condition, *i.e.* airways hyperreactivity, inflammatory cell mediator release, and mucus secretion. Similarly, as with other areas of inflammatory pathology, there is little information relating to the actions of synthetic prostanoid agonists and antagonists in the treatment of asthma. It is established that TxA_2 and synthetic TP agonists have potent bronchoconstrictor actions in a wide range of species including humans,[260,442] and that the bronchoconstrictor effects of TxA_2 and synthetic TP agonists are potently inhibited by a range of antagonists (TP-receptor-blocking drugs).[260]

Thus, in attempting to identify the receptors involved in the various aspects of the actions of prostanoids in the lung, we know considerably more about smooth muscle than inflammatory cells, irritant receptors and mucus secretion. It appears that relaxation of tracheobronchial smooth muscle is mediated by EP_2 receptors, with no good evidence that IP receptors play any significant role. In humans, bronchoconstriction is mediated by TP receptors, and it has recently been demonstrated that bronchoconstriction induced by $PGF_{2\alpha}$, PGD_2 and $9\alpha,11\beta$-PGF_2 are also mediated by TP receptors, there being no evidence for the involvement of either FP or DP receptors. This is not true of all species, as in dog and cat we have found that prostanoid-induced bronchoconstriction is mediated by both TP and FP receptors.[146] As far as the other prostanoid-induced aspects of inflammatory airways disease are concerned, it appears that EP, and in some cases IP, receptors are involved in inhibition of inflammatory cell mediator release, upper airways irritancy and mucus secretion. There is however no indication of which receptor subtypes are involved in any of these effects. Similarly, the ability of PGD_2 to induce hypersensitivity and to enhance or even induce histamine release from human basophils may indicate an involvement of DP receptors. However, as on bronchial smooth muscle, it could equally well reflect an action at TP receptors, and indeed TP receptors appear to be involved in prostanoid-induced increases in mucus secretion.[446] Clearly a lot more work is required using more selective tools, many of which are now available, before many of these effects can be classified with any degree of certainty.

12.11.6.8 Migraine

Prostaglandins have been implicated in the pathogenesis of migraine attacks.[449] Thus the migraine headache has long been considered to result from extracranial vasodilatation, inflammation and hyperalgesia consequent to arterial distension. Circumstantially, substantial quantities of prostaglandins can be produced by blood vessels, and they have potent biological actions which could be responsible for the pathological events associated with the migraine attack. Prostaglandins, particularly of the E series, are potent vasodilators and sensitize the algogenic actions of other mediators such as bradykinin and 5-HT, which have also been implicated in the disease. Perhaps the most intriguing claim is that PGE_1 and PGE_2 (but, interestingly, not PGI_2) uniquely produce migraine-like symptoms when administered to volunteers, even those who have never before experienced migraine.[450-452] The symptoms include flushing, nausea and severe headache, and in some instances visual disturbances.

In 1972, Sandler proposed that the 5-HT released from blood platelets at the onset of a migraine attack evokes a pulmonary release of prostaglandins which are responsible for the subsequent pathophysiological changes.[453] Consistent with this hypothesis is the finding that 5-HT will release prostaglandins from the rat or guinea pig isolated perfused lung.[454] The ability of prostaglandin synthase inhibitors, such as aspirin and paracetamol, to give some relief from the symptoms of migraine also supports the view that prostaglandins are involved.[455] However, attempts to measure circulating plasma prostaglandin levels in patients have provided no evidence for their involvement, since they could not be shown to be significantly raised during an attack.[456] This, coupled with the fact that aspirin and related drugs are of only limited value in the treatment of migraine, suggests that prostaglandins are not the primary or the only mediators involved. Thus, prostaglandins may be of secondary importance along with other mediators in the inflammatory component of the disease. Later hypotheses implicated platelet-derived TxA_2 in the pathology of migraine, but this appears to be unlikely, as the clinical evaluation of a thromboxane synthase inhibitor in the treatment of migraine showed it to be largely ineffective.[457]

12.11.7 THERAPEUTIC VALUE OF DRUGS WHICH MIMIC OR INTERFERE WITH THE SYNTHESIS OR ACTIONS OF PROSTANOIDS

12.11.7.1 Cyclooxygenase Inhibitors

Apart perhaps from caffeine, nicotine and ethyl alcohol, aspirin and related NSAIDs are the most widely used drugs in the western world.[458] It is available not only as preparations of the pure drug, but also in combination with a wide range of other entities of varying degrees of clinical utility in a whole host of over-the-counter medicines. However, despite this, the uses of this agent and other NSAIDs are rather limited. NSAIDs are used as analgesic, antiinflammatory and antipyretic agents, actions which are all believed to result from the compounds' ability to reduce the synthesis of endogenous prostanoids *via* inhibition of the enzyme cyclooxygenase. Despite the obvious popularity and wide clinical use of these compounds, their efects are generally rather modest, for example aspirin-like compounds are not truly analgesic agents, being only antihyperalgesic (see Section 12.11.5.2), reducing only amplification of nociception rather than nociception itself. Similarly, while they do possess a degree of antiinflammatory activity, concern has been expressed that they may actually exacerbate some aspects of inflammatory disease (see Section 12.11.6.1.2).

NSAIDs have also been tested for a variety of noninflammatory applications, and these include the treatment of dysmenorrhoea,[364] the prevention of acute myocardial infarction (MI),[459] and as an adjunct to chemo- and radio-therapy in the treatment of various cancers.[387] For the first of these applications, NSAIDs are now widely used, and they do provide real, albeit limited relief. Whether this relief results totally from their antihyperalgesic actions, or whether there is also an antiuterotonic action is not clear. The suggested utility of low dose aspirin for the prevention of MI results from the observation that such a regimen can effectively eliminate platelet TxA_2 generation, whilst sparing the synthesis of PGI_2 by the vascular endothelium,[460] but whether this truly offers a protective action against such incidents as acute MI is not proven. As to the use of NSAIDs as adjuncts to cancer therapy, flurbiprofen, for example, while having no antitumour effect demonstrable on its own, has been reported to significantly enhance the effectiveness of combined chemo- and radio-therapy. But whether NSAIDs represent a generally useful means of enhancing cancer regression has not been established.

12.11.7.2 Thromboxane Synthase Inhibitors

Over the past few years there has been a great deal of interest in the therapeutic potential of thromboxane synthase inhibitors. Evidence for the involvement of TxA_2 in a variety of diseases such as thrombosis and renal and occlusive vascular disease has been detailed elsewhere (see Section 12.11.6.5 and 12.11.6.6). By preventing the production of TxA_2, this class of drugs would be anticipated to be of clinical benefit in these disease states. They should also be superior to cyclooxygenase inhibitors since they spare prostaglandins such as PGI_2, PGD_2 and PGE_2 which have beneficial actions upon platelets and upon renal function. In addition, there is also evidence that production of these prostaglandins might be enhanced in the presence of thromboxane synthase inhibition, through 'redirection' of accumulated prostaglandin endoperoxides.[461,462] In fact this action may constitute the main mechanism of action of this class of compounds. Many experimental studies have been performed in animals with a variety of thromboxane synthase inhibitors, and benefit has been shown in many of these including acute thrombosis, MI, ventricular fibrillation, renal allograft rejection and immune complex glomerulonephritis, hypertension and endotoxin shock.[463] In contrast to these encouraging experimental results, this class of drugs has generally failed to show clinical benefit in humans.[464a,464b] The possible reasons for this are varied. For example, TxA_2 may not be pathologically important in the clinical situations in which thromboxane synthase inhibitors have been evaluated, such as chronic stable angina.[464,465] In this context, the TP-receptor-blocking drug AH 23848 has been found to be without effect upon pacing- and exercise-induced chest pain in patients with stable angina[465] and no elevations in stable TxA_2 metabolites have been observed during episodes of exercise-induced myocardial ischaemia.[415] In contrast, in conditions of peripheral arterial disease such as Raynaud's disease, elevated levels of TxA_2 metabolites have been detected,[466] yet the beneficial effect of thromboxane synthase inhibitors has been equivocal.[467,468] Thus, in disease states where a TxA_2 component has been demonstrated, the lack of effect of these drugs may be due to two factors, firstly the substitution of the effects of TxA_2 by accumulated prostaglandin endoperoxides, or secondly, incomplete inhibition of thromboxane synthase. The first proposal has been claimed to have been demonstrated in humans.[469] In the case of the second proposal, Reilly and coworkers have proposed that greater than 95% inhibition of the enzyme is necessary to effectively reduce TxA_2 production below pathophysiologically significant levels.[470] With many of the inhibitors tested to date, this level of inhibition has not been achieved over the full period of dosing. Thus, in reality, the concept of a thromboxane synthase inhibitor has yet to be fully evaluated in humans. Alternatively, it has recently been proposed that the therapeutic potential of this type of drug may benefit from combination with other pharmacological agents.[462,464a]

12.11.7.3 DP Receptor Agonists

While it appeared that DP agonists could represent a new class of antithrombotic agents in humans through their inhibitory effects on platelet activity, in the light of clinical data this now appears unlikely. Thus while both PGD_2 and the selective DP agonist BW 245C have been tested in healthy volunteers for activity on *ex vivo* platelet activity, both agonists have exhibited limiting side effects.[239,240] These side effects include a marked vasodilatation of the face and neck as well as an acute nasal congestion (see Section 12.11.5.1.1i). Furthermore, these effects occurred in doses below those which showed antiaggregatory activity on *ex vivo* platelet activity. Therefore, unless platelet and vascular DP receptors can be differentiated, the use of DP agonists as antiplatelet agents appears to be side effect limited.

12.11.7.4 EP Receptor Agonists

Established applications of EP agonists concern their gynaecological and gastrointestinal actions. PGE_2 itself is widely used for the induction of labour at term, with the associated ripening effect upon the cervix. While the use of the natural prostaglandin has been highly successful over the years, the occurrence of unpleasant side effects, *e.g.* nausea and diarrhoea, suggests that a more selective compound may be desirable. However, until the EP receptor subtype mediating the uterine and cervical effects is identified, it is not certain which type of agonist will be required. In addition to the induction of labour, prostanoids of the E type are also used to induce abortion. In this case, the fact that sulprostone is so effective implicates an EP_1 and/or EP_3 agonist action. Finally, EP agonists have now been developed as antiulcer agents; enprostil, misoprostol and rioprostil being examples (see Section 12.11.3.2). It is believed that these agents exhibit their antiulcer actions at least largely through EP_1 and/or EP_3 receptors. Whether such compounds will ever offer a serious challenge to histamine H_2-receptor-blocking drugs for the treatment of gastric/duodenal ulcers remains to be determined.

Potential uses of EP agonists fall into two groups: those tested but as yet not successfully exploited, and those for which there is animal experimental evidence, but which have not yet been tested. As to the first of these two groups, bronchodilatation, vasodilatation, successful treatment of urinary and sexual dysfunction and apparently even baldness have been demonstrated with EP receptor agonists, but as yet no such agonist has been approved for clinical use.

In the second group fall such potential applications as antiallergic and antiinflammatory agents, which would exploit the effects of EP agonists on inflammatory cells, antilipolytic agents of possible use in diabetes, where the target cell would be the adipocyte, and antitumour activity which may result from the ability of prostanoids to stimulate the immune system.

12.11.7.5 EP-receptor-blocking drugs

A therapeutic use for an EP-receptor-blocking drug requires the involvement of EP receptors in a pathological process. Generally, in such conditions NSAIDs will probably be of some benefit, *e.g.* pain, inflammation and pyrexia, but this need not necessarily be so (see above). Other potential uses of EP-receptor-blocking drugs are in the treatment of dysmenorrhoea and as antineoplastic and antimetastatic agents.

12.11.7.6 FP Receptor Agonists

As there is as yet no convincing evidence for the existence of FP receptors in humans, FP agonists cannot be regarded as offering any therapeutic potential in human disease. Despite this of course, FP agonists have found a place in veterinary medicine, where their luteolytic actions in farm animals have made them extremely valuable aids to animal husbandry (see Section 12.11.3.3).

12.11.7.7 IP Receptor Agonists

In their articles on the pharmacology of PGI_2 shortly after its discovery, Moncada and Vane speculated as to the potential therapeutic areas in which this prostanoid might be used.[471,472] They included MI and crescendo angina, peripheral vascular disease, organ transplantation and during the use of extracorporeal circuits such as in cardiopulmonary by-pass, charcoal haemoperfusion and renal dialysis; in short, situations in which platelet activation has been suggested to occur. More recently, two other actions of PGI_2 have been identified, namely stimulation of fibrinolysis and cytoprotection, which may offer therapeutic potential.[473] However within a short time of its discovery it was soon realized that PGI_2 itself did not represent an ideal therapeutic agent since its use in humans was severely limited by side effects upon the cardiovascular system[474] and the compound also lacked stability and oral activity. There was hope that IP receptor agonists might be developed that were selective for platelets. Nevertheless, several open studies in humans during extracorporeal circulation have indicated beneficial effects of PGI_2 in preserving circulating platelet numbers, reduction of postoperative blood loss and a heparin-sparing effect; benefit was also claimed in open studies in peripheral vascular and coronary artery disease.[475] In more closely controlled studies, some of these actions of PGI_2 have been confirmed, whilst in others, results are equivocal.[473,474] For example, intravenously administered PGI_2 was shown to be effective during extracorporeal circulation, in Raynaud's disease, in some instances in patients with unstable angina but not in stable angina, whilst in obliterative vascular disease, benefit appeared to be dependent upon the intraarterial administration of PGI_2. In contrast, in MI and ischaemic stroke, clear clinical improvement was not observed.[473] In some instances, PGI_2 is only effective during the infusion period. This led to longer and longer infusion periods being used and this in turn led to reports of 'rebound' effects with loss of inhibition of platelet aggregation and even platelet hyperaggregability.[476] Whilst suitable infusion regimes have been devised which appear to overcome this problem, the use of PGI_2 is clearly limited, but several stable analogues of PGI_2 are now available (see Section 12.11.3.4). The clinical efficacy of analogues such as iloprost is currently under evaluation.[477] However, continued lack of selectivity at IP receptors on, for example, platelets and vascular smooth muscle, has led inevitably to problematic haemodynamic side effects with these compounds.[478] Therefore, until compounds are synthesized which can differentiate between IP receptors in different biological systems and even possibly in different regional vascular beds in humans, it is unlikely that the true therapeutic potential of this class of drugs will be fully realized.

12.11.7.8   TP-receptor-blocking Drugs

We have previously proposed that TP-receptor-blocking drugs should be pharmacologically superior to cyclooxygenase and thromboxane synthase inhibitors in diseases where TxA_2 exerts a pathological action.[167] In the light of the current uncertainty regarding the therapeutic benefit of thromboxane synthase inhibitors[464b] (see Section 12.11.7.2) and an effective PGI_2-sparing dosage regimen for aspirin[415] (also see Section 12.11.7.1), the case for TP-receptor-blocking drugs remains strong. Thus a potent drug such as the recently described compound GR 32191,[214] which is long lasting in humans[216] and appears to be capable of a continuous blockade of at least 99% of platelet TP receptors, should provide protection against increments in locally produced TxA_2 approaching 100-fold. The definition of diseases in which elevated levels of TxA_2 occur has been improved with newer techniques available to measure its stable metabolites (see Section 12.11.6.5). Of the many structurally varied TP-receptor-blocking drugs described (see Section 12.11.4.5), activity has been found in a wide variety of experimental models, including MI, coronary thrombosis and other models of platelet deposition, ischaemia and reperfusion arrhythmias, cerebral vasospasm, proteinurea, endotoxin shock and antigen-induced bronchoconstriction. Of the compounds described to date, several, in addition to GR 32191 described above, have been reported to be active in man. These include BM 13.177, BM 13.505, AH 23848 and SQ 26,688.[215,223,479,480] For example, all of these compounds increase bleeding time in humans, indicating a physiological role for TxA_2 in this process.

The most thoroughly tested compound to date is BM 13.177 (sulotroban). However this compound is relatively weak and short acting.[481] To date, BM 13.177 has undergone testing in patients with atherosclerotic disease, where it reduced markers of platelet activation and in patients undergoing coronary angioplasty or bypass grafting where it reduced the incidence of reocclusion, the effect being equivalent to that of aspirin, where tested.[482–484] Studies with AH 23848 have shown the compound to be effective in preventing deposition of platelets onto arterial prostheses in humans.[485] Clearly studies with this type of drug must be performed with doses sufficient to produce a long lasting and substantial blockade of platelet and vascular smooth muscle TP receptors before comment can be made upon their therapeutic value. However, several key studies are currently underway with compounds such as GR 32191, which has the necessary profile of action to definitively evaluate the role of TxA_2 in cardiovascular disease.

12.11.8 PROSPECTS FOR FUTURE ADVANCES

12.11.8.1 Receptor Classification

The basic classification of prostanoid receptors into five main types, corresponding to the five naturally occurring hormones, is now widely accepted. However, there are two main areas in which a substantial amount of work remains to be done. Firstly, it is evident that further subdivisions of five basic receptor types exist. This is most clearly seen in the case of EP receptors, where there is evidence for the existence of at least three subtypes. However, it remains to be established that all EP-receptor-mediated effects can be rationalized in terms of these three subtypes. Subtypes of TP and possibly also DP receptors almost certainly exist, but as yet no coherent picture has emerged as to the number and characteristics of these subtypes. There is as yet little evidence for the subdivision of FP and IP receptors, but it would be premature to conclude that subtypes of these receptors do not exist.

The second major area of work outstanding concerns the classification of the receptors mediating the various actions of prostanoids in whole animals and humans. It will have already been apparent that in many cases (see Section 12.11.5) the classification of the actions of prostanoids *in vivo* in terms of receptors is at present based on little more than guesswork. Whilst to some extent solution of this problem requires the development of new tools (see below), much useful work could be done with those that are currently available. Often this would require little more than testing a wider range of agonists than has so far been utilized. In this way, some simple pitfalls can be avoided. Thus, for example, it is unwise to assume that if a given prostanoid can produce an effect, then the specific receptor for that prostanoid is involved. The bronchoconstrictor action of $PGF_{2\alpha}$ for example is a case in point; in humans this effect is mediated by TP and not FP receptors (see Section 12.11.5.1).

A further point which has emerged and which requires further exploration is that frequently the same effect is mediated by different types of receptor in different species. Again, the bronchoconstrictor action of $PGF_{2\alpha}$ is a good example. Whereas in humans this effect is mediated by TP receptors, in cat and dog FP receptors are involved. Clearly this point is highly relevant when attempts are made to extrapolate from results obtained in experimental animals to humans.

12.11.8.2 New Tools for Receptor Classification

Progress in receptor classification depends upon the availability of highly selective agonists and antagonists. It will be apparent from Sections 12.11.3 and 12.11.4 that, whilst advances in the development of selective agonists are still required, the major requirement is for potent selective antagonists. In contrast to the case of TP receptors, for which a variety of potent antagonists are available, for the other prostanoid receptors, few if any such compounds exist. Thus although the EP_1 antagonist, SC-19220, and the EP_1/DP antagonist, AH 6809, have proved valuable in the development of the classification, problems of solubility and lack of *in vivo* activity, respectively, limit their utility. The situation with respect to the other receptor types is even less satisfactory, there being no antagonists available whatsoever.

Whilst potent antagonists with 'nonprostanoid' structures, such as SC-19220 and AH 6809, may yet be discovered for the various receptor types, a more logical approach would be to systematically modify the structures of the natural hormones. In view of the large number of prostanoid analogues that have been synthesized, it is perhaps surprising that good antagonists have not already emerged. Nevertheless it should not be forgotten that no histamine H_2-receptor-blocking drugs were identified until a systematic attempt to synthesize one was undertaken, and the recent discovery of the DP receptor-blocking drug BW A868C (see Section 12.11.4.1) shows what can be achieved.

12.11.8.3 Potential New Prostanoid Drugs

It has been said of prostanoids that they have been thought of as drugs of the future for the last 25 years. It is certainly true that despite the large amount of research carried out over many years, much of it by the pharmaceutical industry, remarkably few new drugs have emerged. The discovery that NSAIDs owe their activity to inhibition of prostanoid biosynthesis was a major scientific discovery, but these drugs were introduced long before prostanoids were discovered. Apart from TP-receptor-blocking drugs, thromboxane synthase inhibitors and cytoprotective EP agonists, all of which have yet to establish their therapeutic value, use of prostanoids in human medicine is limited to PGE_2, $PGF_{2\alpha}$ and a few analogues for the induction of labour and abortion.

We believe that an important reason for this rather disappointing situation is a lack of appreciation of the importance of receptor classification in drug discovery. In the case of prostanoid agonists, although they have many actions which are therapeutically desirable, the very diversity of their actions means that unwanted side effects are a major concern. However, a proper understanding of prostanoid receptor classification would allow definition of what profiles of selectivity are achievable, and hence differentiation of those that are acceptable from those that are not. The possible therapeutic applications of prostanoid antagonists are largely a matter of speculation at present, because so few are available. It could be argued that experience with NSAIDs does not suggest that prostanoid antagonists would be important new drugs. However, it should be remembered that nonsteroidal antiinflammatories: (i) do not necessarily cause complete inhibition of prostanoid synthesis at therapeutic doses; (ii) can, at least in principle, cause diversion of substrate down other pathways of arachidonic acid metabolism; and (iii) nonselectively inhibit formation of all prostanoids. It is therefore unlikely that the effects of these drugs can be used as a basis for predicting the effects of highly selective prostanoid antagonists. In conclusion, it is to be hoped that the continuing growth in knowledge of prostanoid receptors will lead to prostanoids becoming drugs of the present in the coming years.

12.11.9 SUMMARY AND OVERVIEW

In summary, we have outlined the structures and synthesis of the family of C_{20} arachidonic acid metabolites known as the prostanoids. We have presented a scheme of classification of the receptors which mediate their biological actions, and have detailed the characterization of each of these receptor types. The scheme is based on rank orders of agonist and antagonist potencies in functional studies but has received substantial support from the results of studies using ligand-binding techniques and investigation of second messengers. In the light of this background, we have described compounds which exhibit selective agonist or antagonist activity for the various prostanoid receptor types, where such compounds exist. Where they do not exist, these shortcomings are identified. The distribution of the various prostanoid receptors in a wide range of tissues, and the extensive physiological and pharmacological actions of the prostanoids, have been discussed. Many actions of the prostanoids appear to be of a pathological nature, and where such actions have been discussed, some attempt has been made to identify the receptor type involved. From the information in these last two sections, it has been possible to speculate as to the therapeutic potential of various prostanoid receptor agonists and antagonists. To date, there are few established clinical applications for prostanoid agonists and antagonists; this we believe is due largely to the lack of receptor selectively of the compounds currently available. We hope that the next decade will see the development of many novel effective medicines which are either agonists or antagonists at one or more of the prostanoid receptors described in this chapter, or perhaps at prostanoid receptors yet to be described.

ACKNOWLEDGEMENTS

We wish to acknowledge the important contribution made by a number of our colleagues in the preparation of this chapter. Bob Sheldrick has been responsible for the generation of much of the data included, Harry Finch gave invaluable advice towards the structure–activity analyses, Graham Lock prepared all of the structural formulae and Sonya Morton typed the manuscript; it is largely thanks to Sonya's tireless efforts that this chapter has seen the light of day.

12.11.10 REFERENCES

1. P. Needleman, J. Turk, B. A. Jakschik, A. R. Morrison and J. B. Lofkowith, *Annu. Rev. Biochem.*, 1986, **55**, 69.
2. N. A. Nelson, *J. Med. Chem.*, 1974, **17**, 911.
3. E. W. Horton, in 'Chemistry, Biochemistry and Pharmacological Activity of Prostanoids', ed. S. M. Roberts and F. Scheinman, Pergamon Press, Oxford, 1979, p. 1.
4. S. Bergstrom, *Science (Washington, D. C.)*, 1967, **157**, 382.
5. B. Samuelsson, M. Hamberg, L. J. Roberts and J. A. Oates, *Prostaglandins*, 1978, **16**, 857.
6. M. Hamberg, J. Svensson and B. Samuelsson, *Proc. Natl. Acad. Sci. USA*, 1975, **72**, 2994.
7. D. A. Van Dorp, R. K. Beerthuis, D. H. Nugteren and H. Vonkeman, *Biochim. Biophys. Acta*, 1964, **90**, 204.

8. S. Moncada, R. J. Flower and J. R. Vane, in 'Goodman and Gilman's The Pharmacological Basis of Therapeutics', ed. A. Goodman Gilman, L. S. Goodman and A. Gilman, 6th edn., MacMillan, London, 1980, p. 668.
9. J. Mehta, L. M. Lopez and T. Wargovich, *Am. J. Cardiol.*, 1987, **59**, 155.
10. R. J. Flower and G. J. Blackwell, *Biochem. Pharmacol.*, 1976, **25**, 285.
11. J. B. Smith, C. Dangelmaier, A. D. Pardon and G. Mauco, in 'Mechanisms of Stimulus–Response Coupling in Platelets', ed. J. Westwick, M. F. Scully, D. E. MacIntyre and V. V. Kakkar, Plenum Press, New York, 1985, p. 281.
12. V. G. Mahadevappa and B. J. Holub, *Biochem. Biophys. Res. Commun.*, 1986, **134**, 1327.
13. R. F. Irvine, *Biochem. J.*, 1982, **204**, 3.
14. C. Y. Lee, *IUPHAR 9th Int. Congr. Pharmacol.*, London, 1984, **3**, 31.
15. M. Di Rosa, *IUPHAR 9th Int. Congr. Pharmacol.*, London, 1984, **3**, 47.
16. R. J. Flower, *Pharmacol Rev.*, 1974, **26**, 33.
17. T. Watanabe, S. Narumiya, T. Shimizu and O. Hayaishi, *J. Biol. Chem.*, 1982, **257**, 14847.
18. T. Shimizu, S. Yamamoto and O. Hayaishi, *J. Biol. Chem.*, 1979, **254**, 5222.
19. Y. Tanaka and W. L. Smith, *Adv. Prostaglandin Thromboxane Leukotriene Res.*, 1985, **15**, 147.
20. Y. S. Bakhle, *Br. Med. Bull.*, 1983, **39**, 214.
21. J. R. Burgess, H. Yang, M. Chang, M. K. Rao, C. P. D. Tu and C. C. Reddy, *Biochem. Biophys. Res. Commun.*, 1987, **162**, 441.
22. Z. Qureshi and L. M. Cagan, *Biochem. Biophys. Res. Commun.*, 1982, **104**, 1255.
23. P. Y. K. Wong, *Biochim. Biophys. Acta*, 1981, **659**, 169.
24. K. Watanabe, R. Yoshida, T. Shimizu and O. Hayaishi, *Adv. Prostaglandin Thromboxane Leukotriene Res.*, 1985, **15**, 151.
25. D. L. De Witt and W. L. Smith, *J. Biol. Chem.*, 1983, **258**, 3285.
26. V. Ullrich and M. Haurand, *Adv. Prostaglandin Thromboxane Leukotriene Res.*, 1983, **11**, 105.
27. R. L. Jones and S. Cammock, *Adv. Biosci.*, 1973, **9**, 61.
28. E. Granstöm and M. Kumlin, in 'Prostaglandins and Related Substances, a Practical Approach'. ed. C. Benedetto, R. G. McDonald-Gibson, S. Nigam and T. F. Slater, IRL Press, Oxford, 1987, p. 5.
29. W. D. M. Paton, in 'Drug Receptors and Their Function', ed. R. Porter and M. O'Connor, Churchill, New York, 1970, p. 3.
30. S. Moncada, R. J. Gryglewski, S. Bunting and J. R. Vane, *Nature (London)*, 1976, **263**, 663.
31. N. C. Moran and M. E. Perkins, *J. Pharmacol. Exp. Ther.*, 1958, **124**, 223.
32. J. W. Black, W. A. M. Duncan, G. J. Durant, C. R. Ganellin and M. E. Parsons, *Nature (London) New Biol.*, 1972, **236**, 385.
33. R. F. Furchgott, in 'Handbook of Experimental Pharmacology, Catecholamines', ed. H. Blaschko and E. Muscholl, Springer Verlag, Berlin, 1972, vol. 33, p. 283.
34. T. P. Kenakin, *Pharmacol. Rev.*, 1984, **36**, 165.
35. R. P. Stephenson, *Br. J. Pharmacol. Chemother.*, 1956, **11**, 379.
36. V. R. Pickles, *Nobel Symp.*, 1967, **2**, 79.
37. N. H. Andersen and P. W. Ramwell, *Arch. Intern. Med.*, 1974, **133**, 30.
38. P. J. Gardiner and H. O. J. Collier, *Prostaglandins*, 1980, **19**, 819.
39. R. A. Coleman, P. P. A. Humphrey, I. Kennedy, G. P. Levy and P. Lumley, *Br. J. Pharmacol.*, 1981, **73**, 773.
40. I. Kennedy, R. A. Coleman, P. P. A. Humphrey, G. P. Levy and P. Lumley, *Prostaglandins*, 1982, **24**, 667.
41. R. L. Jones, N. H. Wilson, R. A. Armstrong and Y. J. Dong, *Proc. IUPHAR 9th Int. Congr. Pharmacol.*, London, 1984, **2**, 293.
42. S. S. Tynan, N. H. Andersen, M. T. Wills, L. A. Harker and S. R. Hanson, *Prostaglandins*, 1984, **27**, 683.
43. R. A. Coleman, E. W. Collington, H. P. Geisow, E. J. Hornby, P. P. A. Humphrey, I. Kennedy, G. P. Levy, P. Lumley, P. J. McCabe and C. J. Wallis, *Br. J. Pharmacol.*, 1981, **72**, 524P.
44. J. H. Sanner, *Arch. Int. Pharmacodyn. Ther.*, 1969, **180**, 46.
45. R. A. Coleman, I. Kennedy and G. P. Levy, *Br. J. Pharmacol.*, 1980, **69**, 266P.
46. R. A. Coleman, I. Kennedy and R. L. G. Sheldrick, *Br. J. Pharmacol.*, 1985, **85**, 273P.
47. R. A. Coleman, I. Kennedy and R. L. G. Sheldrick, *Adv. Prostaglandin Thromboxane Leukotriene Res.*, 1987, **17**, 467.
48. R. A. Coleman, I. Kennedy and R. L. G. Sheldrick, *Br. J. Pharmacol.*, 1987, **91**, 323P.
49. O. V. Miller and R. R. Gorman, *J. Pharmacol. Exp. Ther.*, 1979, **210**, 134.
50. B. Cooper and D. Ahern, *J. Clin. Invest.*, 1979, **64**, 586.
51. M. H. Town, J. Casals-Stenzel and E. Schillinger, *Prostaglandins*, 1983, **25**, 13.
52. T. Shimizu, A. Yamashita and O. Hayaishi, *J. Biol. Chem.*, 1982, **257**, 13570.
53. F. A. Kuehl, *Prostaglandins*, 1974, **5**, 325.
54. H. G. Oien, L. R. Mandel, J. L. Humes, D. Talis, R. D. Hollsommer and F. A. Kuehl, *Prostaglandins*, 1975, **9**, 985.
55. W. Losert, O. Loge, E. Schillinger and J. Casals-Stenzel, in 'International Sulprostone Symposium', ed. K. Friebel, A. Schneider and H. Würfel, Schering, Berlin, 1979, p. 47.
56. C. V. Rao, *Adv. Prostaglandin Thromboxane Res.*, 1976, **1**, 247.
57. F. A. Kimball and J. W. Lauderdale, *Prostaglandins*, 1975, **10**, 313.
58. F. A. Kimball and L. J. Wyngarden, *Prostaglandins*, 1977, **13**, 553.
59. E. Schillinger, G. Prior, A. Speckenbach and S. Wellershof, *Prostaglandins*, 1979, **18**, 293.
60. P. M. Olley, P. Merchant, M. Michalek, F. Coceani and G. D. Lopaschuk, *Proc. 6th Int. Conf. Prostaglandins Relat. Compounds, Florence*, 1986, 344.
61. H. G. Oien, E. M. Babiarz, D. D. Soderman, E. A. Ham and F. A. Kuehl, *Prostaglandins*, 1979, **17**, 525.
62. R. A. Coleman, PhD Thesis, Council For National Academic Awards, London, 1983.
63. W. S. Powell, S. Hammarström and B. Samuelsson, *Eur. J. Biochem.*, 1976, **61**, 605.
64. S. Hammarström, W. S. Powell, U. Kyldén and B. Samuelsson, *Adv. Prostaglandin Thromboxane Res.*, 1976, **1**, 235.
65. M. T. Lin and C. V. Rao, *Life Sci.*, 1978, **22**, 303.
66. F. A. Kuehl, *Models Pharmacol. Toxicol.*, 1976, **9**, 385.
67. C. V. Rao, L. P. Griffin and F. R. Carman, *J. Clin Endocrinol. Metab.*, 1977, **44**, 1032.
68. K. Wright, J. L. Luborsky-Moore and H. R. Behrman, *Mol. Cell. Endocrinol.*, 1979, **13**, 25.

69. A. I. Schafer, B. Cooper, D. O'Hara and R. I. Handin, *J. Biol. Chem.*, 1979, **254**, 2914.
70. A. M. Siegl, J. B. Smith, M. J. Silver, K. C. Nicolaou and D. Ahern, *J. Clin. Invest.*, 1979, **63**, 215.
71. E. Schillinger and W. F. Losert, *Acta Ther.*, 1980, **6**, suppl. 37.
72. M. Lombroso, S. Nicosia, R. Paoletti, B. J. R. Whittle, S. Moncada and J. R. Vane, *Prostaglandins*, 1984, **27**, 321.
73. G. Steurer, K. Ettl, B. Jankovic and H. Sinzinger, *Proc. 6th Int. Conf. Prostaglandins, Florence*, 1986, p. 347.
74. E. Schillinger and G. Prior, *Biochem. Pharmacol.*, 1980, **29**, 2297.
75. I. A. Blair and J. MacDermot, *Br. J. Pharmacol.*, 1981, **72**, 435.
76. P. J. Leigh, W. A. Cramp and J. MacDermot, *J. Biol. Chem*, 1984, **259**, 12 431.
77. J. MacDermot, P. J. Barnes, K. A. Waddell, C. T. Dollery and I. A. Blair, *Eur. J. Pharmacol.*, 1981, **75**, 127.
78. M. H. Town, E. Schillinger, A. Speckenbach and G. Prior, *Prostaglandins*, 1982, **24**, 61.
79. P. V. Halushka, D. E. Mais and M. Garvin, *Eur. J. Pharmacol.*, 1986, **131**, 49.
80. E. J. Kattelman, D. L. Venton and G. C. Le Breton, *Thromb. Res.*, 1986, **41**, 471.
81. R. M. Burch, D. E. Mais, S. H. Pepkowitz and P. V. Halushka, *Biochem. Biophys. Res. Commun.*, 1985, **132**, 961.
82. S. C. Hung, N. I. Ghali, D. L. Venton and G. C. Le Breton, *Biochim. Biophys. Acta*, 1983, **728**, 171.
83. D. E. Mais, P. J. Kochel, D. L. Saussy and P. V. Halushka, *Mol. Pharmacol.*, 1985, **28**, 163.
84. R. A. Armstrong, R. L. Jones and N. H. Wilson, *Br. J. Pharmacol.*, 1983, **79**, 953.
85. Huzoor-Akbar, A. Mukhopadhyay, K. S. Anderson, S. S. Navran, K. Romstedt, D. D. Miller and D. R. Feller, *Biochem. Pharmacol.*, 1985, **34**, 641.
86. S. Narumiya, M. Okuma and F. Ushikubi, *Br. J. Pharmacol.*, 1986, **88**, 323.
87. R. Loutzenhiser and C. Van Breeman, *Am. J. Physiol.*, 1981, **241**, C243.
88. N. Toda, *Circ. Res.*, 1982, **51**, 675.
89. T. Itoh, H. Ueno and H. Kuriyama, *Experientia*, 1985, **41**, 989.
90. W. K. Pollock, R. A. Armstrong, L. J. Brydon, R. L. Jones and D. E. MacIntyre, *Biochem. J.*, 1984, **219**, 833.
91. K. J. Moffat, A. McNicol and D. E. MacIntyre, *Proc. Int. Symp. Calcium Antagonists Pharmacol. Clin. Res.*, 1987, 25.
92. T. K. Ushi, *Acta Pharmacol. Toxicol.*, 1985, **56**, 117.
93. H. R. Behrman, J. L. Luborsky, R. F. Aten, M. L. Polan, B. C. Tarlatzis, F. P. Haseltine, S. L. Preston, L. K. Soodak, G. F. Mattson and A. S. Chi, *Adv. Prostaglandin Thromboxane Leukotriene Res.*, 1985, **15**, 601.
94. V. Raymond, P. C. K. Leung and F. Labrie, *Biochem. Biophys. Res. Commun.*, 1983, **116**, 39.
95. B. R. Creese and M. A. Denborough, *Clin. Exp. Pharmacol. Physiol.*, 1981, **8**, 616.
96. Y. Gutman, P. Boonjaviroj and L. Eckstein, *Adv. Biosci.*, 1979, **18**, 341.
97. K. Aktories, G. Schultz and K. H. Jakobs, *Adv. Prostaglandin Thromboxane Leukotriene Res.*, 1983, **12**, 283.
98. W. Losert, O. Loge, E. Schillinger and J. Casals-Stenzel, in 'International Sulprostone Symposium', ed. K. Friebel, A. Schneider and H. Würfel, Schering, Berlin, 1979, p. 47.
99. R. A. Coleman, I. Kennedy and R. L. G. Sheldrick, *Br. J. Pharmacol.*, 1987, **91**, 406P.
100. L. Somova and B. Bojkov, *Acta Physiol. Pharmacol. Bulg.*, 1983, **9**, 36.
101. J. Hardcastle, P. T. Hardcastle and J. S. Redfern, *J. Pharm. Pharmacol.*, 1982, **34**, 68.
102. R. Alvarez, A. Taylor, J. J. Fazzari and J. R. Jacobs, *Mol. Pharmacol.*, 1981, **20**, 302.
103. R. J. Haslam, M. M. L. Davidson, T. Davies, J. A. Lynham and M. D. McClenaghan, in 'Advances in Cyclic Nucloetide Research', ed. W. J. George and L. J. Ignarro, Raven Press, New York, 1978, p. 553.
104. B. Simon, H. Kather and B. Kommerell, *Adv. Prostaglandin Thromboxane Res.*, 1980, **8**, 1617.
105. D. H. Nugteren and E. Hazelhof, *Biochim. Biophys. Acta*, 1973, **326**, 448.
106. H. Giles and P. Leff, *Prostaglandins*, 1988, **35**, 277.
107. R. C. W. Beasley, R. L. Featherstone, M. K. Church, P. Rafferty, J. G. Varley, A. Harris, C. Robinson and S. T. Holgate, *J. Appl. Physiol: Respir. Environ. Exercise Physiol.*, 1989, **66**, 1685.
108. S. Hamid-Bloomfield and B. J. R. Whittle, *Br. J. Pharmacol.*, 1986, **88**, 931.
109. G. L. Bundy, D. R. Morton, D. C. Peterson, E. E. Nishizawa and W. L. Miller, *J. Med. Chem.*, 1983, **26**, 790.
110. R. C. W. Beasley, M. K. Church, R. L. Featherstone, C. C. Hardy, S. T. Holgate, C. Robinson and J. G. Varley *Br. J. Pharmacol.*, 1986, **88**, 235P.
111. S. Narumiya and N. Toda, *Br. J. Pharmacol.*, 1985, **85**, 367.
112. R. L. Jones and N. H. Wilson, *Br. J. Pharmacol.*, 1977, **60**, 315P.
113. R. L. Jones, *Acta Biol. Med. Ger.*, 1978, **37**, 837.
114. R. J. Keery and P. Lumley, *Br. J. Pharmacol.*, 1988, **94**, 745.
115. B. J. R. Whittle, S. Moncada, K. Mullane and J. R. Vane, *Prostaglandins*, 1983, **25**, 205.
116. K.-H. Thierauch, C.-St. Stürzebecher, E. Schillinger, H. Rehwinkel, B. Radüchel, W. Skuballa and H. Vorbrüggen, *Prostaglandins*, 1988, **35**, 855.
117. D. N. Harris, R. Greenberg, M. B. Phillips, I. M. Michel, H. J. Goldenberg, M. F. Haslanger and T. E. Steinbacher, *Eur. J. Pharmacol.*, 1984, **103**, 9.
118. H. Giles, P. Leff, M. L. Bolofo, M. G. Kelly and A. D. Robertson, *Br. J. Pharmacol.*, 1989, **96**, 291.
119. Y. J. Dong, R. L. Jones and N. H. Wilson, *Br. J. Pharmacol.*, 1986, **87**, 97.
120. C. V. Grudzinskas, J. S. Skotnicki, S.-M. L. Chen, M. B. Floyd, Jr., W. A. Hallett, R. E. Schaub, G. J. Siuta, A. Wissner and M. J. Weiss, in 'Drugs Affecting the Respiratory System', ed. D. L. Temple, Jr., American Chemical Society, Washington, DC, 1980, p. 301.
121. P. W. Collins, E. Z. Dajani, R. Pappo, A. F. Gasiecki, R. G. Bianchi and E. M. Woods, *J. Med. Chem.*, 1983, **26**, 786.
122. P. W. Collins, S. W. Kramer and G. W. Gullikson, *J. Med. Chem.*, 1987, **30**, 1952.
123. N. A. Nelson, R. C. Kelly and R. A. Johnson, *Chem. Eng. News*, 1982, Aug. 16, 30.
124. C. H. Lin, S. J. Stein and J. E. Pike, *Prostaglandins*, 1976, **11**, 377.
125. H. J. Hess, T. K. Schaaf, J. S. Bindra, M. R. Johnson and J. W. Constantine, in 'International Sulprostone Symposium', ed. K. Friebel, A. Schneider and H. Würfel, Schering, Berlin, 1979, p. 29.
126. H. Carpio, G. F. Cooper, J. A. Edwards, J. H. Fried, G. L. Garay, A. Guzman, J. A. Mendez, J. M. Muchowski, A. P. Roszkowski, A. R. Van Horn and D. Wren, *Prostaglandins*, 1987, **33**, 169.
127. M. R. Johnson, T. K. Schaaf, J. W. Constantine and H.-J. Hess, *Prostaglandins*, 1980, **20**, 515.
128. N. A. Nelson, R. W. Jackson, A. T. Au, D. J. Wynalda and E. E. Nishizawa, *Prostaglandins*, 1975, **10**, 795.
129. P. W. Collins, *J. Med. Chem.*, 1986, **29**, 437.

130. P. Chan, P. Cervoni, M. A. Ronsberg, R. C. Accomando, G. J. Quirk, P. A. Scully and L. M. Lipchuck, *J. Pharmacol. Exp. Ther.*, 1983, **226**, 726.

131. M. B. Floyd, R. E. Schaub, G. J. Siuta, J. S. Skotnicki, C. V. Grudzinskas, M. J. Wiess, F. Dessy and L. VanHumbeeck, *J. Med. Chem.*, 1980, **23**, 903.

132. A. K. Banerjee, B. J. Broughton, T. S. Burton, M. P. L. Caton, A. J. Christmas, E. C. J. Coffee, K. Crowshaw, C. J. Hardy, M. A. Heazell, M. N. Palfreyman, T. Parker, L. C. Saunders and K. A. J. Stuttle, *Prostaglandins*, 1981, **22**, 167.

133. F. A. Kimball, G. L. Bundy, A. Robert and J. R. Weeks, *Prostaglandins*, 1979, **17**, 657.

134. P. W. Collins, E. Z. Dajani, D. R. Driskill, M. S. Bruhn, C. J. Jung and R. Pappo, *J. Med. Chem.*, 1977, **20**, 1152.

135. T. K. Schaaf, *Annu. Rep. Med. Chem.*, 1976, **11**, 80.

136. J. R. Weeks, D. W. DuCharme, W. E. Magee and W. L. Miller, *J. Pharmacol. Exp. Ther.*, 1973, **186**, 67.

137. T. K. Schaaf and H. J. Hess, *J. Med. Chem.*, 1979, **22**, 1340.

138. T. K. Schaaf, J. S. Bindra, J. F. Eggler, J. J. Plattner, A. J. Nelson, M. R. Johnson, J. W. Constantine and H. J. Hess, *J. Med. Chem.*, 1981, **24**, 1352.

139. G. L. Bundy, F. A. Kimball, A. Robert, J. W. Aiken, K. M. Maxey, O. K. Sebek, N. A. Nelson, J. C. Sih, W. L. Miller and R. S. P. Hsi, *Adv. Prostaglandin Thromboxane Res.*, 1980, **6**, 355.

140. E. T. Whalley and S. K. White, *Br. J. Pharmacol.*, 1980, **68**, 150P.

141. P. J. Gardiner, *Br. J. Pharmacol.*, 1986, **87**, 45.

142. M. Murao, K. Uchiyama, A. Shida, K. Sakai, T. Yusa and T. Yamaguchi, *Adv. Prostaglandin Thromboxane Res.*, 1980, **7**, 987.

143. S. J. Gray and S. Heptinstall, *Eur. J. Pharmacol.*, 1985, **114**, 129.

144. R. L. G. Sheldrick, R. A. Coleman and P. Lumley, *Br. J. Pharmacol.*, 1988, **94**, 334P.

145. M. Dukes, W. Russell and A. L. Walpole, *Nature (London)*, 1974, **250**, 330.

146. R. A. Coleman, in 'Prostaglandins and Related Substances, a Practical Approach', ed. C. Benedetto, R. G. McDonald-Gibson, S. Nigam and T. F. Slater, IRL Press, Oxford, 1987, p. 267.

147. P. S. Jackson and R. Jessup, *Vet. Rec.*, 1984, **114**, 168.

148. J. M. Muchowski, in 'CRC Handbook of Eicosanoids: Prostalandins and Related Lipids. Chemical and Biochemical Aspects', ed. A. L. Willis, CRC Press, Boca Raton, FL, 1987, vol. 1, part B, p. 19.

149. N. S. Crossley, *Prostaglandins*, 1975, **10**, 5.

150. B. J. R. Whittle and S. Moncada, *Prog. Med. Chem.*, 1984, **21**, 237.

151. K. Kojima and S. Kobayashi, *Sankyo Kenkyusho Nempo*, 1986, **38**, 1.

152. K. Schrör, H. Darius, R. Matzky and R. Ohlendorf, *Naunyn-Schmiedeberg's Arch. Pharmacol.*, 1981, **316**, 252.

153. C.-St. Sturzebecher, M. Haberey, B. Muller, E. Schillinger, G. Schröder, W. Skuballa and G. Stock, *Proc. 2nd Int. Symp. Nurnberg-Furth*, 1985, 485.

154. (a) C.-St. Sturzebecher, M. Harberey, B. Muller, E. Schillinger, G. Schröder, W. Skuballa, G. Stock, H. Vorbrüggen and W. Witt, *Prostaglandins*, 1986, **31**, 95; (b) N. H. Wilson, R. A. Armstrong and R. L. Jones, *Adv. Prostaglandin Thromboxane Leukotriene Res.*, 1987, **17**, 491.

155. A. Corsini, G. C. Folco, R. Fumagalli, S. Nicosia, M. A. Moe and D. Oliva, *Br. J. Pharmacol.*, 1987, **90**, 255.

156. P. Lumley, P. P. A. Humphrey, I. Kennedy and R. A. Coleman, *Eur. J. Pharmacol.*, 1982, **81**, 421.

157. S. S. Bhagwat, P. R. Hamann and W. C. Still, *J. Am. Chem. Soc.*, 1985, **107**, 6372.

158. S. S. Bhagwat, P. R. Hamann, W. C. Still, S. Bunting and F. A. Fitzpatrick, *Nature (London)*, 1985, **315**, 511.

159. S. Bunting, L. V. Buchanan, H. H. Holzgrefe and F. A. Fitzpatrick, *Adv. Prostaglandin Thromboxane Leukotriene Res.*, 1987, **17**, 192.

160. I. V. Richards, J. A. Oostveen, R. L. Griffin and S. Bunting, *Adv. Prostaglandin Thromboxane Leukotriene Res.*, 1987, **17**, 1067.

161. D. E. MacIntyre, in 'Platelets in Biology and Pathology', ed. J. L. Gordon, Elsevier, North Holland, 1981, vol. 2, p. 211.

162. C. Malmsten, *Life. Sci.*, 1976, **18**, 169.

163. R. L. Jones, V. Peesapati and N. H. Wilson, *Br. J. Pharmacol.*, 1982, **76**, 423.

164. N. H. Wilson and R. L. Jones, *Adv. Prostaglandin Thromboxane Leukotriene Res.*, 1985, **14**, 393.

165. S. M. Barr, R. L. Jones, D. E. MacIntyre, A. McNicol and N. H. Wilson, *Br. J. Pharmacol.*, 1986, **88**, 392P.

166. R. L. Jones, N. H. Wilson, R. A. Armstrong, V. Peesapati and G. M. Smith, *Adv. Prostaglandin Thromboxane Leukotriene Res.*, 1983, **11**, 245.

167. R. T. Brittain, L. Boutal, M. C. Carter, R. A. Coleman, E. W. Collington, H. P. Geisow, P. Hallett, E. J. Hornby, P. P. A. Humphrey, D. Jack, I. Kennedy, P. Lumley, P. J. McCabe, I. F. Skidmore, M. Thomas and C. J. Wallis, *Circulation*, 1985, **72**, 1208.

168. N. Liel, D. E. Mais and P. V. Halushka, *Prostaglandins*, 1987, **33**, 789.

169. R. A. Armstrong, R. L. Jones and N. H. Wilson, *Br. J. Pharmacol.*, 1983, **78**, 159P.

170. E. J. Corey, K. C. Nicolaou, Y. Machida, C. L. Malmsten and B. Samuelsson, *Proc. Natl. Acad. Sci. USA*, 1975, **72**, 3355.

171. S. McGlynn, G. Mallarkey and G. M. Smith, *Prostaglandins*, 1984, **27**, 105.

172. R. L. Jones and N. H. Wilson, *Adv. Prostaglandin Thromboxane Res.*, 1980, **6**, 467.

173. M. L. Ogletree, D. N. Harris, R. Greenberg, M. F. Haslanger and M. Nakane, *J. Pharmacol. Exp. Ther.*, 1985, **234**, 435.

174. R. L. Jones, D. E. MacIntyre, W. K. Pollock, A. M. Shaw and N. H. Wilson, *Br. J. Pharmacol.*, 1985, **84**, 148P.

175. R. L. Jones, N. H. Wilson and R. A. Lawrence, *Br. J. Pharmacol.*, 1989, **96**, 875.

176. P. W. Sprague, J. E. Heikes, J. Z. Gougoutas, M. F. Malley, D. N. Harris and R. Greenberg, *J. Med. Chem.*, 1985, **28**, 1580.

177. D. N. Harris, A. Hedberg, M. B. Phillips, I. M. Michel, H. J. Goldenberg and E. C. K. Liu, *Adv. Prostaglandin Thromboxane Leukotriene Res.*, 1987, **17**, 482.

178. K. M. Maxey and G. L. Bundy, *Tetrahedron Lett.*, 1980, **21**, 445.

179. L. Anderson and D. E. MacIntyre, *Br. J. Pharmacol.*, 1982, **77**, 546P.

180. R. L. Jones, P. Tymkewycz and N. H. Wilson, *Br. J. Pharmacol.*, 1987, **90**, 226P.

181. (a) A. M. Lefer, E. F. Smith, H. Araki, J. B. Smith, D. Aharony, D. A. Claremon, R. L. Magolda and K. C. Nicolaou, *Proc. Natl. Acad. Sci. USA*, 1980, **77**, 1706; (b) D. E. Mais, D. L. Saussy, A. Chaikhovni, P. J. Kochel, D. R. Knapp, N. Hamanaka and P. V. Halushka, *J. Pharmacol. Exp. Ther.*, 1985, **233**, 418.

182. D. E. MacIntyre and J. L. Gordon, *Thromb. Res.*, 1977, **11**, 705.

183. K. E. Eakins, V. Rajadhyaksha and R. Schroer, *Br. J. Pharmacol.*, 1976, **58**, 333.
184. K. E. Eakins and P. S. Kulkarni, *Br. J. Pharmacol.*, 1977, **60**, 135.
185. M. Kangasaho and H. Vapaatalo, *Acta Pharmacol. Toxicol.*, 1983, **53**, 130.
186. Y. Vulliemoz, M. Verosky and L. Triner, *Biochem. Pharmacol.*, 1981, **30**, 1941.
187. W. C. Horne, *Prostaglandins Leukotrienes Med.*, 1984, **15**, 129.
188. R. A. Armstrong, personal communication.
189. D. G. Trist, B. A. Collins, J. Wood, M. G. Kelly and A. D. Robertson, *Br. J. Pharmacol.*, 1989, **96**, 301.
190. S. Hamid-Bloomfield and B. J. R. Whittle, *Br. J. Pharmacol.*, 1989, **96**, 307.
191. R. A. Coleman, P. P. A. Humphrey and I. Kennedy, in 'Trends in Autonomic Pharmacology', ed. S. Kalsner, Taylor and Francis, London, 1985, vol. 3, p. 35.
192. J. H. Sanner, R. A. Mueller and R. H. Schulze, *Adv. Biosci.*, 1973, **9**, 139.
193. E. J. Drower, A. Stapelfeld, R. A. Mueller and D. L. Hammond, *Eur. J. Pharmacol.*, 1987, **133**, 249.
194. G. Fassina, G. Froldi and L. Caparrotta, *Eur. J. Pharmacol.*, 1985, **113**, 459.
195. R. A. Coleman and I. Kennedy, *Prostaglandins*, 1985, **29**, 363.
196. A. J. Wilkins and J. MacDermot, *Eur. J. Pharmacol.*, 1986, **127**, 117.
197. M. R. Johnson, L. S. Melvin, T. H. Althuis, J. S. Bindra, C. A. Harbert, G. M. Milne and A. Weissman, *J. Clin. Pharmacol.*, 1981, **21**, 2715.
198. M. R. Johnson, L. S. Melvin and G. S. Milne, *Life Sci.*, 1982, **31**, 1703.
199. R. Ceserani, C. Gandolfi, D. Longiave and V. Mandelli, *Prostaglandins Med.*, 1979, **2**, 455.
200. Y. T. Maddox, P. W. Ramwell, C. S. Shiner and E. J. Corey, *Nature (London)*, 1978, **273**, 549.
201. R. A. Coleman and R. L. G. Sheldrick, unpublished observations.
202. L. A. Harker, S. R. Hanson, N. H. Andersen, M. T. Wills, B. De, B.-S. Lin, D. A. McCrae and C. H. Wilson, *Proc. 5th Int. Conf. Prostaglandins, Florence*, 1982, 309.
203. R. R. Gorman, G. L. Bundy, D. C. Peterson, F. F. Sun, O. V. Miller and F. A. Fitzpatrick, *Proc. Natl. Acad. Sci. USA*, 1977, **74**, 4007.
204. F. A. Fitzpatrick, G. L. Bundy, R. R. Gorman and T. Honohan, *Nature (London)*, 1978, **275**, 764.
205. G. C. Le Breton, D. L. Venton, S. E. Enke and P. V. Halushka, *Proc. Natl. Acad. Sci. USA*, 1979, **76**, 4097.
206. K. Nicolaou, R. L. Magolda, J.-B. Smith, D. Aharony, E. F. Smith and A. M. Lefer, *Proc. Natl. Acad. Sci. USA*, 1979, **76**, 2566.
207. R. A. Armstrong, R. L. Jones, V. Peesapati, S. G. Will and N. H. Wilson, *Br. J. Pharmacol.*, 1985, **84**, 595.
208. D. N. Harris, M. B. Phillips, I. M. Michel, H. J. Goldenberg, J. E. Heikes, P. W. Sprague and M. J. Antoncaccio, *Prostaglandins*, 1981, **22**, 295.
209. R. Greenberg, T. E. Steinbacher, D. H. Harris and M. F. Haslanger, *Eur. J. Pharmacol.*, 1984, **103**, 19.
210. H. P. Geisow, E. J. Hornby and P. J. McCabe, *Br. J. Pharmacol.*, 1981, **73**, 219P.
211. E. W. Collington, H. Finch, P. Hallett, P. Hunt, T. Parkhouse, D. Reynolds, L. M. Smith and C. J. Wallis, in '2nd SCI–RSC Medicinal Chemistry Symposium', ed. J. C. Emmett, Royal Society of Chemistry, London, 1983, p. 299.
212. R. T. Brittain, R. A. Coleman, E. W. Collington, P. Hallett, P. P. A. Humphrey, I. Kennedy, P. Lumley, R. L. G. Sheldrick and C. J. Wallis, *Br. J. Pharmacol.*, 1984, **83**, 377P.
213. P. Lumley, *Drugs Future*, 1986, **11**, 85.
214. P. Lumley, B. P. White, and P. P. A. Humphrey, *Br. J. Pharmacol.*, 1989, **97**, 783.
215. M. Thomas, P. Lumley and P. Fowler, *Br. J. Clin. Pharmacol.*, 1985, **20**, 543P.
216. M. Thomas and P. Lumley, *Circulation*, 1990, **81** (suppl.), in press.
217. R. L. Jones and N. H. Wilson, *Br. J. Pharmacol.*, 1981, **73**, 220P.
218. R. A. Armstrong, R. L. Jones and N. H. Wilson, *Prostaglandins*, 1985, **29**, 703.
219. R. A. Armstrong, R. L. Jones, J. MacDermot and N. H. Wilson, *Br. J. Pharmacol.*, 1986, **87**, 543.
220. H. Patscheke and K. Stegmeier, *Thromb. Res.*, 1984, **33**, 277.
221. K. Stegmeier, J. Pill, B. Müller-Beckmann, F. H. Schmidt, E. C. Witte, H. P. Wolff and H. Patscheke, *Thromb. Res.*, 1984, **35**, 379.
222. K. Stegmeier, J. Pill, B. Müller-Beckmann, G. Sponer and H. Patscheke, *Proc. Int. Conf. Leukotrienes Prostanoids Health Dis.*, 1985, 10.
223. H. Patscheke, K. Stegmeier, W. Hornberger, Ch. Staiger and G. Neugebauer, *Thromb. Haemostasis*, 1987, **58**, 670.
224. H. E. Morton, J. Evans, C. Leveillé, A. Lord and J. W. Gillard, *Proc. 3rd North Am. Chem. Congr. Toronto*, 1988, 122.
225. W. J. Janssens, H. Deckmyn, P. Gresele and J. Vermylen, *Arch. Int. Pharmacodyn. Ther.*, 1985, **276**, 28.
226. N. Toda, M. Nakajima, T. Okamura and M. Miyazaki, *J. Cardiovasc. Pharmacol.*, 1986, **8**, 818.
227. K. Kondo, R. Seo, T. Kitagawa, N. Omawari, H. Kira, T. Okegawa and A. Kawasaki, *Adv. Prostaglandin Thromboxane Leukotriene Res.*, 1987, **17**, 423.
228. R. A. Hall, J. Gillard, Y. Guindon, G. Letts, E. Champion, D. Ethier, J. Evans, A. W. Ford-Hutchinson, R. Fortin, T. R. Jones, A. Lord, H. E. Morton, J. Rokach and C. Yoakim, *Eur. J. Pharmacol.*, 1987, **135**, 193.
229. E. Byland, C. L. Jessup, R. Jessup and M. Wayne, *Br. J. Pharmacol.*, 1987, **90**, 228P.
230. C. L. Jessup, R. Jessup and M. Wayne, *Br. J. Pharmacol.*, 1987, **90**, 229P.
231. C. L. Jessup, R. Jessup and M. Wayne, *Br. J. Pharmacol.*, 1988, **95**, 675P.
232. C. L. Jessup, R. Jessup and M. Wayne, *Br. J. Pharmacol.*, 1988, **95**, 676P.
233. L. C. Best, M. B. McGuire, T. J. Martin, F. E. Preston and R. G. G. Russell, *Biochim. Biophys. Acta*, 1979, **583**, 344.
234. P. P. A. Humphrey and P. Lumley, *Proc. 6th Int. Conf. Prostaglandins Relat. Compounds, Florence*, 1986, 349.
235. S. E. Burke, A. M. Lefer, K. C. Nicolaou, G. M. Smith and J. B. Smith, *Br. J. Pharmacol.*, 1983, **78**, 287.
236. R. R. Gorman, K. M. Maxey and G. L. Bundy, *Biochem. Biophys. Res. Commun.*, 1981, **100**, 184.
237. D. L. Saussy, D. E. Mais, D. R. Knapp and P. V. Halushka, *Circulation*, 1985, **72**, 1202.
238. C. T. Lim, E. J. Kattelman, S. K. Arora, D. L. Venton and G. C. Le Breton, *Fed. Proc., Fed. Am. Soc. Exp. Biol.*, 1986, **45**, 346.
239. M. A. Orchard, J. M. Ritter, G. L. Shepherd and P. J. Lewis, *Br. J. Clin. Pharmacol.*, 1983, **15**, 509.
240. D. J. Heavey, P. Lumley, S. E. Barrow, M. B. Murphy, P. P. A. Humphrey and C. T. Dollery, *Prostaglandins*, 1984, **28**, 755.
241. H. Pickles and J. O'Grady, *Br. J. Clin. Pharmacol.*, 1982, **14**, 177.

242. B. D. Given, N. A. Vita, H. Black, C. Francis, K. Lasseter, C. Mickiewicz, J. Alcester, K. Kowry and V. J. Dzan, *Circulation*, 1984, **70**, suppl. 2, 63.
243. R. Ceserani, M. Grossoni, G. Ukmar, M. Colombo and N. Mongelli, *Prostaglandins Leukotrienes Med.*, 1986, **21**, 231.
244. J. V. Levy, *Prostaglandins*, 1978, **16**, 93.
245. R. A. Skidgel and M. P. Printz, *Prostaglandins*, 1978, **16**, 1.
246. R. L. Jones, *Adv. Prostaglandin Thromboxane Res.*, 1976, **2**, 221.
247. A. Ahluwalia, S. A. Head, R. L. G. Sheldrick and R. A. Coleman, *Br. J. Pharmacol.*, 1988, **95**, 721P.
248. G. S. Baxter, R. A. Coleman, J. Senior and R. L. G. Sheldrick *Br. J. Pharmacol.*, 1989, **96**, 71P.
249. J. Csepli and A. I. Csapo, *Prostaglandins*, 1975, **10**, 689.
250. T. M. Fitzpatrick, I. Alter, E. J. Corey, P. W. Ramwell, J. C. Rose and P. A. Kot, *J. Pharmacol. Exp. Ther.*, 1978, **206**, 139.
251. T. Tuvemo, K. Strandberg, M. Hamberg and B. Samuelsson, *Adv. Prostaglandin Thromboxane Res.*, 1976, **1**, 425.
252. B. J. R. Whittle, K. G. Mugridge and S. Moncada, *Eur. J. Pharmacol.*, 1979, **53**, 167.
253. C. Penning, unpublished observations.
254. R. A. Coleman, unpublished observations.
255. L. E. Peacock, A. Bennett, R. A. Coleman and I. Kennedy, *IUPHAR 9th Int. Congr. Pharmacol., London*, 1984, 1495P.
256. R. L. G. Sheldrick, unpublished observations.
257. M. G. McKenniff, P. J. Gardiner, P. Norman and I. W. Rodger, *Br. J. Pharmacol.*, 1988, **93**, 56P.
258. R. A. Coleman, L. Feniuk and I. Kennedy, *Br. J. Pharmacol.*, 1981, **74**, 913P.
259. R. A. Coleman, unpublished observations.
260. R. A. Coleman and R. L. G. Sheldrick, *Br. J. Pharmacol.*, 1989, **96**, 688.
261. M. Yamamoto, J. Hashimoto, H. Takaba and K. Miyake, *J. Urol.*, 1987, **137**, 345.
262. P. Hedqvist and U. S. Von Euler, *Neuropharmacology*, 1972, **11**, 177.
263. M. C. Michailov, A. B. Murray, F. Zettler and H. W. Grindler-Greimel, *Urol. Int.*, 1983, **38**, 234.
264. H. Hedlund and K. E. Andersson, *J. Virol.*, 1985, **134**, 1245.
265. J. J. Jeremy, R. J. Morgan, D. P. Mikhailidis and P. Dandona, *Prostaglandins Leukotrienes Med.*, 1986, **23**, 211.
266. E. M. Coutinho and H. S. Maia, *Fertil. Steril.*, 1971, **22**, 539.
267. G. J. Sanger, A. Jackson and A. Bennett, *Eur. J. Pharmacol.*, 1982, **81**, 141.
268. (a) G. S. Baxter, Ph. D. Thesis, University of Bradford, 1989; (b) J. K. Clayton, K. Marshall and J. Senior, *Abstr. 6th Int. Conf. Prostaglandins Relat. Compounds, Florence*, 1986, 107.
269. L. Wilhelmsson, M. Wikland and N. Wiqvist, *Prostaglandins*, 1981, **21**, 277.
270. R. A. Coleman, unpublished observations.
271. P. H. Abrams and R. C. L. Feneley, *Br. J. Urol.*, 1976, **47**, 909.
272. K. E. Andersson and A. Forman, *Acta Pharmacol. Toxicol.*, 1978, **43**, suppl. 2, 90.
273. M. Angelo-Khattar, O. Thulesius and L. Ugaily-Thulesius, *Br. J. Pharmacol.*, 1986, **88**, 241P.
274. K. E. Andersson and C. Sjögren, *Prog. Neurobiol.*, 1982, **19**, 71.
275. N. H. Hills, *Br. J. Pharmacol.*, 1976, **57**, 464P.
276. O. P. Khanna, E. J. Barbieri and R. McMichael, *Urology*, 1978, **163**, 188.
277. G. Lose and J. Thorup Andersen, *Eur. Urol.*, 1986, **12**, 1.
278. G. W. H. M. Van Alphen, P. B. Wilhelm and P. W. Elsenfeld, *Doc. Ophthalmol.*, 1977, **42**, 397.
279. Y. J. Dong and R. L. Jones, *Br. J. Pharmacol.*, 1982, **76**, 149.
280. N. Ueda, I. Muramatsu and M. Fujiwara, *Brain Res.*, 1985, **337**, 347.
281. P. Hedqvist, in 'Prostaglandins', ed. P. Ramwell and J. Shaw, Plenum Press, New York, 1972, p. 101.
282. P. Hedqvist, *Adv. Biosci.*, 1973, **9**, 461.
283. M. Wennmalm, G. A. FitzGerald and A. Wennmalm, *Prostaglandins*, 1987, **33**, 675.
284. D. P. Hemker and J. W. Aiken, *Prostaglandins*, 1981, **22**, 599.
285. A. Wennmalm and P. Hedqvist, *Life Sci.*, 1971, **10**, 465.
286. N. Nakahata, H. Nakanishi and T. Suzuki, *Br. J. Pharmacol.*, 1980, **68**, 393.
287. R. A. Coleman, I. Kennedy, R. L. G. Sheldrick and I. Tolowinska, *Br. J. Pharmacol.*, 1987, **91**, 407P.
288. R. A. Coleman, unpublished observations.
289. L. A. Chahl and A. Iggo, *Br. J. Pharmacol.*, 1977, **59**, 343.
290. H. M. Coleridge, J. C. G. Coleridge, K. H. Ginzel, D. G. Baker, R. B. Banzett and M. A. Morrison, *Nature (London)*, 1976, **264**, 451.
291. S. Ehrenpreis, J. Greenberg and S. Belman, *Nature (London)*, 1973, **245**, 280.
292. K. F. Chung, T. W. Evans, P. D. Graf and J. A. Nadel, *Eur. J. Pharmacol.*, 1985, **117**, 373.
293. E. E. Daniel and R. Serio, *J. Physiol.*, 1988, **398**, 46P.
294. H. Juan and S. Seewann, *Eur. J. Pharmacol.*, 1980, **65**, 267.
295. P. I. Baccaglini and P. G. Hogen, *Neurobiology*, 1983, **80**, 594.
296. S. H. Ferreira, *Adv. Pain Res. Ther.*, 1983, **5**, 627.
297. S. Horiguchi, R. Ueno, M. Hyodo and O. Hayaishi, *Eur. J. Pharmacol.*, 1986, **122**, 173.
298. S. Okuyama and H. Aihara, *J. Pharmacobio-Dyn.*, 1986, **9**, 902.
299. H. M. Coleridge and J. C. G. Coleridge, *Annu. Rev. Physiol.*, 1980, **42**, 413.
300. J. Straszewska-Barczak, *Am. J. Cardiol.*, 1983, **52**, 36A.
301. M. C. Koss and J. Nakano, *Br. J. Pharmacol.*, 1976, **56**, 245.
302. H. M. Coleridge, J. C. G. Coleridge, D. G. Baker, K. H. Ginzel and M. A. Morrison, *Adv. Exp. Med. Biol.*, 1978, **99**, 291.
303. A. Bennett, *Prog. Drug Res.*, 1974, **8**, 83.
304. B. Samuelsson, M. Hamberg, C. Malmsten and J. Svensson, *Adv. Prostaglandin Thromboxane Res.*, 1976, **2**, 737.
305. J. B. Smith and A. L. Willis, *Br. J. Pharmacol.*, 1970, **40**, 545P.
306. J. B. Smith, C. Ingerman, J. Kocsis and M. J. Silver, *J. Clin. Invest.*, 1973, **52**, 965.
307. O. Oelz, R. Oelz, H. R. Knapp, B. J. Sweetman and J. A. Oates, *Prostaglandins*, 1977, **13**, 225.
308. D. E. MacIntyre and R. A. Armstrong, in 'Platelet Responses and Metabolism; Platelet, Receptors and Metabolism', ed. H. Holmsen, CRC Press, Boca Raton, FL, 1987, vol. 2, p. 93.
309. B. J. R. Whittle, S. Moncada and J. R. Vane, *Prostaglandins*, 1978, **16**, 373.
310. A. I. Schafer, B. Cooper, D. O'Hara and R. I. Handin, *J. Biol. Chem.*, 1979, **254**, 2914.

311. A. M. Siegl, J. B. Smith and M. J. Silver, *Adv. Prostaglandin Thromboxane Res.*, 1980, **6**, 395.
312. T. A. Moninelli, S. Niewiarowski J. L. Daniel and J. B. Smith, *Am. J. Physiol.*, 1987, **253**, H1035.
313. I. A. Blair, P. J. Lewis, M. A. Orchard and K. A. Waddell, *Br. J. Pharmacol.*, 1983, **79**, 356P.
314. M. A. Orchard, K. A. Waddell, P. J. Lewis and I. A. Blair, *Thromb. Res.*, 1985, **39**, 701.
315. J. Kloeze, *Nobel Symp.*, 1967, **2**, 241.
316. J. J. Bruno, L. A. Taylor and M. J. Doller, *Nature (London)*, 1974, **251**, 721.
317. D. E. MacIntyre and J. L. Gordon, *Nature (London)*, 1975, **258**, 337.
318. P. Lumley and P. P. A. Humphrey, *Proc. 5th Int. Conf. Prostaglandins, Florence*, 1982, 683.
319. E. W. Salzman, *Thromb. Diath. Haemorrh. Suppl.*, 1974, **60**, 311.
320. J. W. D. McDonald and R. K. Stuart, *J. Lab. Clin. Med.*, 1974, **84**, 111.
321. C. Bonne, B. Martin, M. Watada and F. Regnault, *Thromb. Res.*, 1981, **21**, 13.
322. P. Lumley, unpublished data.
323. N. H. Andersen, T. L. Eggerman, L. A. Harker, C. H. Wilson and B. De, *Prostaglandins*, 1980, **19**, 711.
324. A. Hassid and M. Dunn, in 'Prostaglandins and the Kidney', ed. M. J. Dunn, C. Patrono and G. A. Cinotti, Plenum Press, New York, 1983, p. 3.
325. D. Schlondorff, *Am. J. Med.*, 1986, **81**, 1.
326. J. P. Bonvalet, P. Praadelles and N. Farman, *Am. J. Physiol.*, 1987, **253**, F377.
327. L. Scharschmidt, M. Simonson and M. J. Dunn, *Am. J. Med.*, 1986, **81**, suppl. 2B, 30.
328. C. Patrono, G. Ciabattoni, P. Filabozzi, F. Catella, L. Forni, M. Segni, P. Patrignani, F. Pugliese, B. M. Simonetti and A. Pierrucci, *Adv. Prostaglandin Thromboxane Leukotriene Res.*, 1985, **13**, 131.
329. M. J. Dunn and E. J. Zambraski, *Kidney Int.*, 1980, **18**, 609.
330. C. Patrono and A. Pierucci, *Am J. Med.*, 1986, **81**, (suppl. 2B), 71.
331. R. M. Edwards, *Am. J. Physiol.*, 1985, **248**, F779.
332. L. A. Scharschmidt, E. Lianos and M. J. Dunn, *Fed. Proc., Fed. Am. Soc. Exp. Biol.*, 1983, **42**, 3058.
333. G. Freidlander, D. Chansel, J. Sraer, M. Bens and R. Ardaillou, *Mol. Cell. Endocrinol.*, 1983, **30**, 201.
334. P. Mené and M. J. Dunn, *Adv. Prostaglandin Thromboxane Leukotriene Res.*, 1987, **17**, 744.
335. W. L. Smith, T. Watanabe and K. Umegaki, *Kidney Int.*, 1987, **31**, 287.
336. H. R. Lindner, U. Zor, F. Kohen, S. Bauminger, A. Amsterdam, M. Lehav and Y. Saloman, *Adv. Prostaglandin Thromboxane Res.*, 1980, **8**, 1371.
337. B. Dennefors, L. Hamberger, T. Hillensjo, P. Holmes, P. O. Janson, C. Magnusson and L. Nilsson, *Acta Obstet. Gynecol. Scand., Suppl.*, 1983, **13**, 31.
338. L. J. Dorflinger, J. L. Luborsky, S. D. Gore and H. R. Behrman, *Mol. Cell. Endocrinol.*, 1988, **33**, 225.
339. J. A. McCracken, W. Schremm, B. Barciakowski and L. Wilson, *Acta Vet. Scand., Suppl.*, 1981, **77**, 71.
340. M. J. Cooper, D. Hammond and R. H. Schulz, in 'Practical Applications of Prostaglandins and their Synthesis Inhibitors', ed. S. M. M. Karim, MTP Press, Lancaster, 1979, p. 189.
341. N. Ambache, *J. Physiol.*, 1955, **129**, 65P.
342. L. Z. Bito, in 'Biological Protection with Prostaglandins', ed. M. M. Cohen, CRC Press, Boca Raton, FL, 1985, vol. 1, p. 231.
343. J. A. Zadunaisky, in 'Mechanism of Intestinal Secretion', ed. H. J. Binder, Liss, New York, 1979, p. 53.
344. B. R. Beitch, I. Beitch and J. A. Zadunaisky, *J. Membr. Biol.*, 1974, **19**, 381.
345. P. J. Bentley and M. C. McGahen, *J. Physiol.*, 1982, **325**, 481.
346. D. F. Cole and S. Nagasubramanan, *Exp. Eye Res.*, 1973, **16**, 251.
347. J. E. Pederson, *Exp. Eye Res.*, 1975, **21**, 569.
348. B. R. MacDonald, *World Rev. Nutr. Diet.*, 1986, **47**, 163.
349. T. J. Martin and N. C. Partridge, *Metab. Bone Dis. Relat. Res.*, 1980, **2**, 167.
350. J. J. Reeves and R. Stables, *Br. J. Pharmacol.*, 1985, **86**, 677.
351. J. S. Major and P. Scholes, *Agents Actions*, 1978, **8**, 324.
352. A. H. Soll, *J. Clin. Invest.*, 1980, **65**, 1222.
353. J. J. Reeves, K. T. Bunce, R. L. G. Sheldrick and R. Stables, *Br. J. Pharmacol.*, 1988, **95**, 805P.
354. A. Wollin, A. H. Soll and I. M. Samloff, *Am. J. Physiol.*, 1979, **237**, E437.
355. K. T. Bunce and C. F. Spraggs, *Br. J. Pharmacol.*, 1987, **91**, 319P.
356. B. Simon and H. Kather, *Digestion*, 1979, **19**, 137.
357. B. Simon, H. Kather and B. Kommerell, *Biochem. Pharmacol.*, 1979, **28**, 3465.
358. M. W. Munsch, M. Field, R. J. Miller and J. S. Stoff, *Am. J. Physiol.*, 1987, **252**, G120.
359. K. T. Bunce, N. M. Clayton, M. Knight, D. N. Sheppard and C. F. Spraggs, *Gastroenterology*, 1987, **92**, 1332.
360. (a) K. Bukhave and J. Rask-Madson, *Gastroenterology*, 1980, **78**, 32; (b) J. Hardcastle, P. T. Hardcastle and J. S. Redferm, *Life Sci.*, 1980, **26**, 123.
361. B. Simon and H. Kather, *Digestion*, 1980, **20**, 62.
362. (a) K. T. Bunce and C. F. Spraggs, unpublished observations; (b) N. M. Clayton, K. T. Bunce and R. Stables, *Br. J. Pharmacol.*, 1988, **95**, 725P.
363. G. P. Lewis, *Br. Med. Bull.*, 1983, **39**, 243.
364. P. K. Moore, 'Prostanoids: Pharmacological, Physiological and Clinical Relevance', Cambridge University Press, Cambridge, 1985.
365. A. S. Milton, *J. Pharm. Pharmacol.*, 1976, **28**, 393.
366. T. J. Williams, *Br. J. Pharmacol.*, 1979, **65**, 517.
367. T. J. Williams and J. Morley, *Nature (London)*, 1973, **246**, 215.
368. T. J. Williams, *Br. Med. Bull.*, 1983, **39**, 239.
369. D. R. Robinson and L. Levine, in 'Prostaglandin Synthetase Inhibitors', ed. H. J. Robinson and J. R. Vane, Raven Press, New York, 1974, p. 223.
370. E. Moilanen, E. Seppala, M. Nissila and H. Vapaatalo, *Agents Actions*, 1987, **20**, 98.
371. S. H. Ferreira, *Nature (London), New Biol.*, 1972, **240**, 200.
372. S. H. Ferreira, S. Moncada and J. R. Vane, *Br. J. Pharmacol.*, 1973, **49**, 86.
373. G. Thomas and G. B. West, *J. Pharm. Pharmacol.*, 1973, **25**, 747.

374. H. Juan and F. Lembeck, *Naunyn-Schmiedeberg's Arch. Pharmacol.*, 1974, **283**, 151.
375. R. Deraedt, S. Jouquey, F. Delevatée and M. Flahaut, *Eur. J. Pharmacol.*, 1980, **61**, 17.
376. Y. O. Taiwo and J. D. Levine, *Brain Res.*, 1986, **373**, 81.
377. H. Juan and F. Lembeck, *Br. J. Pharmacol.*, 1977, **59**, 385.
378. S. H. Ferreira, M. Nakamura and M. S. A. Castro, *Prostaglandins*, 1978, **16**, 31.
379. H. Juan, *Agents Actions*, 1979, **8**, suppl. 4, 204.
380. S. H. Ferreira, *Br. J. Clin. Pharmacol.*, 1980, **10**, 2375.
381. O. G. Berge, *Cephalalgia (Oslo)*, 1986, **6**, suppl. 4, 21.
382. K. Gyires and Z. Torma, *Arch. Int. Pharmacodyn. Ther.*, 1984, **267**, 131.
383. J. S. Goodwin and J. Ceuppens, *J. Clin. Immunol.*, 1983, **3**, 295.
384. M. Dy, M. Astoin, M. Rigand and J. Hamburger, *Eur. J. Immunol.*, 1980, **10**, 121.
385. J. S. Goodwin and D. R. Webb, in 'Suppressor Cells in Human Disease', ed. J. S. Goodwin, Dekker, New York, 1981, p. 99.
386. J. S. Goodwin, G. Husby and R. C. Wiliams, *Cancer Immunol. Immunother.*, 1980, **8**, 3.
387. A. Bennett, *NATO Adv. Study Inst. Ser., Ser. A*, 1983, **54**, 237.
388. M. G. Santoro, G. W. Philpott and B. M. Jaffe, *Prostaglandins*, 1977, **14**, 645.
389. M. Fukushima, T. Kato, K. Ota, Y. Aray, S. Narumiya and O. Hayaishi, *Biochem. Biophys. Res. Commun.*, 1982, **109**, 626.
390. R. Noroyi and M. Suzuki, *Angew. Chem., Int. Ed. Engl.*, 1984, **23**, 847.
391. S. Narumiya, K. Ohno, M. Fukushima and M. Fujiwara, *J. Pharmacol. Exp. Ther.*, 1987, **242**, 306.
392. G. A. Higgs, J. R. Vane, F. D. Hart and J. A. Wojthlewski, in 'Prostaglandin Synthetase Inhibitors', ed. H. J. Robinson and J. R. Vane, Raven Press, New York, 1974, p. 165.
393. M. Tokunaga, K. Ohuchi, S. Yoshizawa, S. Tsurufuji, A. Rikimaru and E. Wakamatsu, *Ann. Rheum. Dis.*, 1981, **40**, 462.
394. L. G. Raisz, J. Y. Vanderhock, H. A. Simmons, B. E. Kream and K. C. Nicolaou, *Prostaglandins*, 1979, **17**, 905.
395. A. Crawford, D. Atkins and T. J. Martin, *Biochem. Biophys. Res. Commun.*, 1978, **82**, 1195.
396. H. W. Seyberth, L. G. Raisz and J. A. Oates, *Annu. Rev. Med.*, 1978, **29**, 23.
397. D. C. Klein and L. G. Raisz, *Endocrinology*, 1970, **86**, 1436.
398. A. S. Milton and S. Wendlandt, *J. Physiol.*, 1971, **218**, 325.
399. R. J. Flower, *Naunyn-Schmiedeberg's Arch. Pharmacol.*, 1977, **297**, 577.
400. W. Feldberg, in 'Prostaglandin Synthetase Inhibitors', ed. H. J. Robinson and J. R. Vane, Raven Press, New York, 1974, p. 197.
401. M. Schmidt-Gollwitzer, B. Schuessler, K. Schmidt-Gollwitzer and J. Nevinring-Stickel, in 'International Sulprostone Symposium', ed. K. Friebel, A. Schneider and H. Würfel, Schering, Berlin, 1979, p. 119.
402. W. S. Gruber, in 'International Sulprostone Symposium', ed. K. Friebel, A. Schneider and H. Würfel, Schering, Berlin, 1979, p. 181.
403. W. I. Cranston, G. W. Duff, R. F. Hellon, D. Mitchell and Y. Townsend, *J. Physiol.*, 1976, **259**, 238.
404. R. P. White, A. A. Hagen, H, Morgan, W. N. Dawson and J. T. Robertson, *Stroke*, 1975, **6**, 52.
405. P. S. Kulkarni, H. H. Wang and K. E. Eakins. *Proc. 4th Int. Conf. Prostaglandins, Washington, D.C.*, 1979, 64.
406. E. F. Ellis, O. Oelz, L. J. Roberts, N. A. Payne, B. J. Sweetman, A. S. Nies and J. A. Oates, *Science (Washington, D. C.)*, 1976, **193**, 1135.
407. P. Needleman, P. Kulkarni and A. Raz, *Science (Washington. D. C.)*, 1977, **195**, 409.
408. P. D. Hirsh, W. B. Campbell, J. T. Willerson and L. D. Hillis, *Am. J. Med.*, 1981, **71**, 1009.
409. G. A. FitzGerald, A. K. Pedersen and C. Patrono, *Circulation*, 1983, **67**, 1174.
410. F. Catella, D. Healy, J. A. Lawson and G. A. FitzGerald, *Proc. Natl. Acad. Sci. USA*, 1986, **83**, 5861.
411. G. A. FitzGerald, C. Healy and J. Daugherty, *Fed. Proc., Fed. Am. Soc. Exp. Biol.*, 1987, **46**, 154.
412. K. Gréen and O. Vesterqvist, *Adv. Prostaglandin Thromboxane Leukotriene Res.*, 1986, **16**, 309.
413. F. Catella, J. A. Lawson, D. J. FitzGerald and G. A. FitzGerald, *Adv. Prostaglandin Thromboxane Leukotriene Res.*, 1987, **17**, 611.
414. D. J. FitzGerald, L. Roy, F. Catella and G. A. FitzGerald, *N. Engl. J. Med.*, 1986, **315**, 983.
415. G. A. FitzGerald, J. A. Oates, J. Hawiger, R. L. Maass, L. Jackson, L. J. Roberts, J. A. Lawson and A. R. Brash, *J. Clin. Invest.*, 1983, **71**, 676.
416. H. D. Lewis, J. W. Davis and D. G. Archibald, *N. Engl. J. Med.*, 1984, **310**, 122.
417. H. D. Lewis, J. W. Davis, D. G. Archibald, W. E. Steinke, T. C. Smitherman, J. E. Doherty, H. W. Schnaper, M. M. LeWinter, E. Linares, J. M. Pouget, S. C. Sabharwal, E. Chesler and H. DeMots, *N. Engl. J. Med.*, 1983, **309**, 396.
418. A. R. Brash, E. K. Jackson, C. A. Saggese, J. A. Lawson, J. A. Oates and G. A. FitzGerald, *J. Pharmacol. Exp. Ther.*, 1983, **226**, 78.
419. G. A. FitzGerald, B. Smith, A. K. Pedersen and A. R. Brash, *N. Engl. J. Med.*, 1984, **310**, 1065.
420. A. R. Morrison, J. E. Benabe and A. Taylor, in 'Prostaglandins and the Kidney; Biochemistry, Physiology, Pharmacology and Clinical Applications', ed. M. J. Dunn, C. Patrono and G. A. Cinotti, Plenum Press, New York, 1983, p. 309.
421. J. E. Stork, M. A. Rahman and M. J. Dunn, *Am. J. Med.*, 1986, **80**, suppl. 1A, 34.
422. C. Patrono, G. Ciabattoni, E. Remuzzi, E. Gotti, S. Bombardieri, O. Di Munno, G. Tartarelli, G. A. Cinotti, B. M. Simonetti and A. Pierucci, *J. Clin. Invest.*, 1985, **76**, 1011.
423. T. M. Coffman, W. E. Yarger and P. E. Klotman, *J. Clin. Invest.*, 1985, **75**, 1242.
424. A. R. Morrison, K. Nishikawa and P. Needleman, *Nature (London)*, 1977, **267**, 259.
425. T. M. Coffman, D. R. Carr, W. E. Yarger and P. E. Klotman, *Transplantation*, 1987, **43**, 282.
426. A. Pierucci, B. M. Simonetti, G. Pecci, G. Mavrikakis, S. Feriozzi, G. A. Cinotti, P. Patrignani, G. Ciabattoni and C. Patrono, *N. Engl. J. Med.*, 1989, **320**, 421.
427. E. W. Horton, *Physiol. Rev.*, 1969, **49**, 122.
428. C. Robinson and S. T. Holgate, *Bull. Eur. Physiopathol. Respir.*, 1986, **22**, suppl. 7, 81.
429. M. A. Wasserman, *Bull. Eur. Physiopathol. Respir.*, 1981, **17**, 675.
430. S. P. Peters, R. P. Schleimer, A. Kagey-Sobotka, R. M. Naderio, D. W. MacGlashan, E. S. Schulman, N. F. Adkinson and L. M. Lichtenstein, *Trans. Assoc. Am. Physicians*, 1982, **95**, 221.
431. A. A. Mathé, P. Hedqvist, A. Holmgren and N. Svanborg, *Br. Med. J.*, 1973, **1**, 193.

432. A. Szczeklik, *Drugs,* 1986, **32**, suppl. 4, 148.
433. I. H. M. Main, *Br. J. Pharmacol.,* 1964, **22**, 511.
434. A. Nizankowska, A. Q. Sheridan, M. H. Maile, C. J. Cross, R. Nizankowska, K. Prochowska and A. Szezeklik, *Prostaglandins,* 1985, **29**, 349.
435. A. J. Fairfax, J. M. Hanson and J. Morley, *Clin. Exp. Immunol.,* 1983, **52**, 393.
436. R. A. Lewis, N. A. Soter, P. T. Diamond, K. F. Auster, J. A. Oates and L. J. Roberts, *J. Immunol.,* 1982, **129**, 1627.
437. S. T. Holgate, G. B. Burns, C. Robinson and M. K. Church, *J. Immunol.,* 1984, **133**, 2138.
438. K. Seibert, J. R. Schiller and L. F. Roberts, *Proc. Natl. Acad. Sci. USA,* 1987, **84**, 256.
439. E. H. Walters, *Thorax,* 1983, **38**, 195.
440. R. W. Fuller, C. M. S. Dixon, C. T. Dollery and P. J. Barnes, *Am. Rev. Respir. Dis.,* 1986, **133**, 252.
441. C. Omini, G. Brunelli, L. Daffoncio, C. Mapp, L. Fabbri and F. Berti, *J. Auton. Pharmacol.,* 1986, **6**, 181.
442. J. Svensson, K. Strandberg, T. Tuvemo and M. Hamberg, *Prostaglandins,* 1977, **14**, 425.
443. C. Omini, S. Moncada and J. R. Vane, *Prostaglandins,* 1977, **14**, 628.
444. S. Bianco, M. Robuschi, R. Ceserani, C. Gandolfi and P. L. Kamburoff, *Pharmacol. Res. Commun.,* 1978, **10**, 657.
445. L. M. Lichtenstein and C. S. Henney, in 'Progress in Immunology II', ed. L. Brent and J. Holborow, North Holland, Amsterdam, 1974, vol. 2, p. 73.
446. J. L. Walker, *Adv. Biosci.,* 1974, **9**, 235.
447. P. S. Richardson, R. J. Phipps, K. Balfre and R. L. Hall, in 'Respiratory Tract Mucus', Ciba Foundation Symposium No. 54, Elsevier, Amsterdam, 1978, p. 111.
448. J. M. Yanni, W. L. Smith and M. H. Foxwell, *Prostaglandins Leukotrienes Essential Fatty Acids,* 1988, **32**, 45.
449. J. W. Lance, 'The Mechanism and Management of Headache', 2nd edn., Butterworth, Woburn, MA, 1973.
450. L. A. Carlson, L. G. Ekelund and L. Oro, *Acta Med. Scand.,* 1968, **183**, 423.
451. A. P. Smith, *Br. J. Clin. Pharmacol.,* 1974, **1**, 399.
452. R. Peatfield, *Headache,* 1981, **21**, 190.
453. M. Sandler, *Lancet,* 1972, **1**, 618.
454. V. A. Alabaster and Y. S. Bakhle, *Eur. J. Pharmacol.,* 1976, **35**, 349.
455. R. Peatfield, 'Headache', Springer-Verlag, Berlin, 1986.
456. M. Anthony, *Headache,* 1976, **16**, 58.
457. J. Rajiv, J. T. Steiner, C. J. M. Poole, J. Littlewood and F. Clifford Rose, *Headache,* 1985, **25**, 204.
458. J. G. Kelton and J. Hirst, in 'Contemporary Hematology–Oncology', ed. A. S. Gordon, R. Silber and J. Lo-Bue, Plenum Press, New York, 1981, vol. 2, p. 305.
459. H. D. Lewis, J. W. Davis, D. G. Archibald, W. E. Steinke, T. C. Smitherman, J. E. Doherty, H. W. Schraper, M. M. LeWinter, E. Linares, J. M. Pouget, S. C. Sabhawal, E. Chesler and H. DeMots, *N. Engl. J. Med.,* 1983, **309**, 396.
460. G. Masotti, G. Galanti, L. Poggesi, R. Abbate and G. G. Neriserneri, *Lancet,* 1979, **2**, 1213.
461. G. Defreyn, H. Deckmyn and J. Vermylen, *Thromb. Res.,* 1982, **26**, 389.
462. J. Vermylen, H. Deckmyn, P. Gresele and J. Arnout, *Proc. 2nd Int. Symp. Nurnberg-Furth,* 1984, 445.
463. A. M. Lefer, *Drugs of the Future,* 1986, **11**, 197.
464. (a) G. A. Fitzgerald, I. A. G. Reilly and A. K. Pedersen, *Circulation,* 1985, **2**, 1194; (b) G. I. Fiddler and P. Lumley, *Circulation,* 1990, 81 (suppl. I), in press.
465. D. P. De Bono, P. Lumley, M. Been, R. Keery, S. E. Ince and D. F. Woodings, *Br. Heart J.,* 1986, **56**, 509.
466. I. A. C. Reilly, L. Roy and G. A. Fitzgerald, *Br. Med. J.,* 1986, **292**, 1037.
467. J. J. F. Belch, P. Newman, J. K. Durury, H. Capell, P. Leiberman, W. B. James, C. D. Forbes and C. R. M. Prentice, *Thromb. Haemostasis,* 1981, **45**, 255.
468. W. H. Ettinger, R. R. Wise, D. Schaffhauser and F. M. Wigley, *Am. J. Med.,* 1984, **77**, 451.
469. P. Gresele, J. Arnout, H. Deckmyn, E. Huybrechts, G. Pieters and J. Vermylen, *J. Clin. Invest.,* 1987, **80**, 1435.
470. I. A. G. Reilly and G. A. FitzGerald, *Blood,* 1987, **69**, 180
471. S. Moncada and J. R. Vane, *Pharmacol. Rev.,* 1979, **30**, 293.
472. S. Moncada and J. R. Vane, *J. Med. Chem.,* 1980, **23**, 592.
473. A. Szczeklik and R. J. Gryglewski, *Adv. Prostaglandin Thromboxane Leukotriene Res.,* 1985, **13**, 345.
474. P. G. Lewis and C. T. Dollery, *Br. Med. Bull.,* 1983, **39**, 281.
475. J. R. Vane and S. Moncada, *Adv. Pharmacol. Ther.,* 1982, **4**, 215.
476. H. Sinzinger, K. Silberbauer, A. K. Horsch and A. Gall, *Prostaglandins,* 1981, **21**, 49.
477. *Drugs of the Future,* 1987, **12**, 1079.
478. B. J. R. Whittle and S. Moncada, *Circulation,* 1985, **72**, 1219.
479. P. Gresele, J. Arnout, W. Janssens, H. Deckmyn, H. Lemmens and J. Vermylen, *Lancet,* 1984, **1**, 991.
480. L. T. Friedhoff, J. Manning, P. T. Funke, E. Ivashkiv, J. Tu., W. Cooper and D. A. Willard, *Clin. Pharmacol. Ther.,* 1986, **40**, 634.
481. H. Patscheke, C. Staiger, G. Neugebauer, B. Kaufmann, K. Strein, R. Endele and K. Stegmeier, *Clin. Pharmacol. Ther.,* 1986, **39**, 145.
482. H. Riess, E. Hiller, B. Reinhardt and C. Brauning, *Thromb. Res.,* 1984, **35**, 371.
483. H. Riess, B. Hofling, T. Von Arnim and E. Hiller, *Thromb. Res.,* 1986, **42**, 235.
484. M. C. Torka, R. W. Hacker, I. Yüksetan, V. Pohlmann, P. Meier, T. Zimmermann, H. Etti, M. Bulitta and P. Kondor, *Eur. Heart J.,* 1988, **9** (abstr. suppl. 1), 325.
485. I. F. Lane, J. T. C. Irwin, S. A. Jennings, K. R. Poskitt, R. M. Greenhalgh and C. N. McCollum, *Br. J. Surg.,* 1984, **71**, 903.

12.12

Platelet Activating Factor Receptors

MICHAEL C. VENUTI

Syntex Research, Palo Alto, CA, USA*

* The author's current affiliation is Genentech Inc., San Francisco, CA, USA.

12.12.1   INTRODUCTION

A soluble lytic 'fluid phase mediator' released from IgE-sensitized rabbit basophils and capable of rabbit platelet stimulation was first detected in 1970, and soon after was termed 'platelet activating factor' (PAF).[1] By 1979, the lipid nature of this autocoid had been recognized, culminating in its nearly simultaneous identification by the research groups of Benveniste in Paris,[2] Hanahan in San Antonio[3] and Snyder in Oak Ridge.[4] Careful chemical and spectroscopic determinations, use of stereospecific phospholipases, semi-synthesis from bovine heart plasmalogen and eventual total synthesis established the structure as 1-*O*-alkyl-2-(*R*)-acetylglycero-3-phosphorylcholine (**1**; alkyl-acetyl-GPC), predominantly composed of the octadecyl and hexadecyl homologs of the 1-*O*-alkyl residue. Subsequently, a similar if not identical substance was isolated from renal medulla which demonstrated significant hypotensive properties and was termed antihypertensive polar renomedullary lipid (APRL).[5]

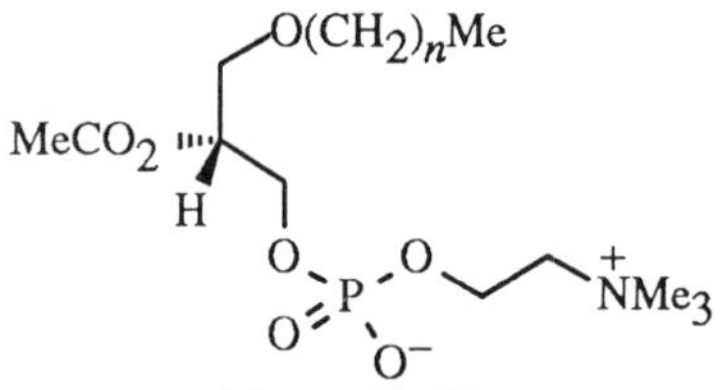

$$\text{MeCO}_2 \overset{\text{O(CH}_2)_n\text{Me}}{\underset{\text{H}}{}} \quad \quad \overset{\text{O(CH}_2)_n\text{Me}}{\underset{\text{MeCO}_2}{\text{H}}}$$

(**1**) *n* = 15, 17 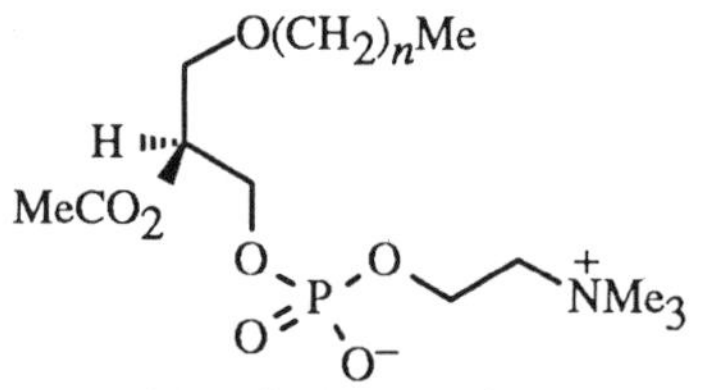   (*enantio*-**1**) *n* = 15, 17

In the decade since these pioneering studies, which culminated in the detection, isolation, structure elucidation and biochemical characterization of platelet activating factor, this ether phospholipid has emerged as an important mediator of a multitude of biological and physiological processes critical in cellular function, tissue reactivity, anaphylaxis and acute inflammation. Details of the research efforts which laid the groundwork for the current broad interest in PAF and summaries of the multitude of subsequent studies on its biological and pharmacological activities are documented in multiple comprehensive reviews and symposia proceedings[6-17] to which the reader is referred. Note that although structurally descriptive abbreviations such as AGEPC, AAGPC and PAF-acether also appear in the literature, this review of the chemistry, biochemistry and pharmacology of (**1**) and its receptor agonists and antagonists will refer to it simply as PAF.

12.12.2   CHEMISTRY

The chemistry of PAF is intimately related to the broad class of ether lipids, about which a large body of information stretching back to the 1920s is available. The analytical, synthetic and biochemical methods applied to previous investigations of ether lipids[18,19] were utilized as the basis for design of derivatization protocols and semi-synthetic procedures for the analysis and structure proof of PAF.[9,20] These methods rely heavily on separation of structurally closely related lipids

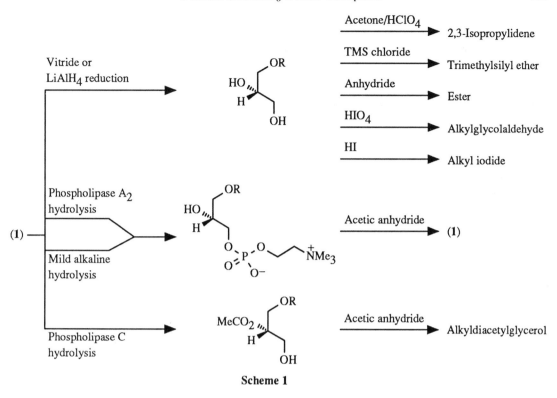

Scheme 1

produced using a series of chemically or enzymatically specific degradation or resynthesis steps (Scheme 1). Several powerful HPLC protocols have been developed to accomplish such separations of PAF from either other normally encountered phospholipids or PAF analogs, and have been used to quantitate alkyl chain length differences in PAF isolated from different tissue or species sources, stimulated with various cellular activators.[21–23]

Chemical ionization and fast-atom bombardment mass spectrometry have provided alternative analytical tools for determination of the composition of PAF from various sources.[23–25] Enhancement of such methods by combination with GLC and selective ion monitoring techniques have demonstrated wide species-specific variations and a high degree of precursor substrate specificity in PAF biosynthesis using picogram quantities.[26,27]

Analysis of the ^1H and ^{13}C NMR spectra indicates a profound influence of solvent on the formation of aggregates in water, and the lack thereof in methanol.[28] Determination of the critical micellar concentration of $1.1 \, \mu mol \, dm^{-3}$ indicates that the monomolecular species can be assumed to be responsible for biological activity since, at the subnanomolar concentrations usually observed for PAF activity, only the monomolecular species should be present.[29]

Definitive proof of the unique structure of PAF was accomplished by synthesis.[30] Exploitation of the *sn*-glycerol conformation present in ether phospholipids prompted the semi-synthesis of PAF from bovine ethanolamine or choline plasmalogens, and provided the first structural confirmations for PAF.[2–4] The first total synthesis of PAF, accomplished by Benveniste and co-workers,[31] established a pattern and set limitations followed by numerous subsequent syntheses of PAF utilizing D-mannitol as the chiral source.[32–35] Subsequent more efficient syntheses have relied on the use of alternative sources of chirality, such as D-tartaric acid[36] or (S)(−)-malic acid.[37] The desired (R)-glyceryl stereochemistry has also been obtained by asymmetric reduction of an achiral precursor.[38] Further refinements in these procedures have been extensively applied to the synthesis of analogs of PAF and other closely related compounds.

12.12.3 BIOSYNTHESIS, METABOLISM AND CATABOLISM

Pathways describing the biosynthesis, metabolism and catabolism of PAF were proposed soon after its structural determination was complete. Since that time, evidence supporting the existence of these common biochemical processes has been accumulated from the many diverse cellular sources in which PAF has been detected (Figure 1).[9,39] Of key importance was the recognition that *lyso*-PAF (**2**) was an obligatory intermediate along routes used for both the biosynthesis and metabolism of PAF (Scheme 2). This observation, coupled with the fact that *lyso*-PAF itself possesses none of the observed activities of PAF, had complicated some early studies but has become an important unifying feature in the overall understanding of PAF biosynthesis.[11,16] The biosynthesis of the ether phospholipid precursors required in the biosynthesis of PAF has been recently reviewed, providing the necessary background for subsequent discussion.[19,40-42]

12.12.3.1 The Activation–Inactivation Pathway

The diverse and potent effects of PAF on a wide variety of target cells and tissues suggest that multiple mechanisms for the precise regulation of its concentration in tissue and body fluids may

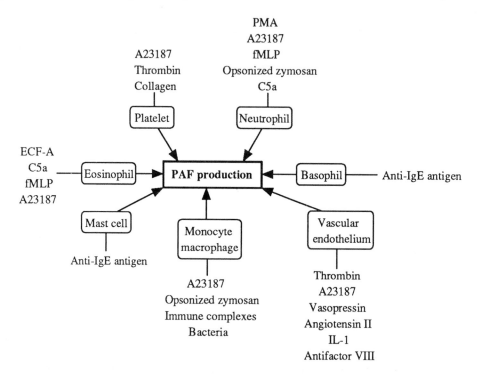

Figure 1 Cellular sources of PAF and the agents which stimulate its production. PMA = phorbol myristate acetate, A23187 = calcium ionophore, fMLP = formylmethionylleucylphenylalanine, C5a = proteolytic cleavage product of the fifth component of complement, ECF-A = eosinophil chemotactic factor of anaphylaxis (adapted from ref. 39)

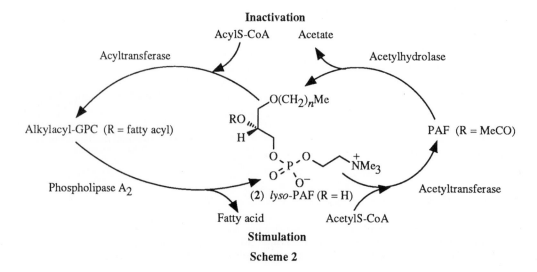

Scheme 2

exist. One such mechanism in operation balances the synthesis of PAF against its rapid clearance and metabolism *via* the bicyclic activation–inactivation pathway depicted in Scheme 2.[16]

Unstimulated cells contain little if any PAF, but a wide variety of cells synthesize and secrete PAF upon appropriate stimulation. The finding that *lyso*-PAF is both a precursor and metabolite of PAF was the product of two observations. First, the presence of a specific acetyltransferase was demonstrated in a number of cell types, including macrophages, neutrophils, natural killer lymphocytes and endothelial cells, and that cellular stimulation correlated highly with acetyltransferase activity and production of PAF. Second, inhibition of phospholipase A_2 (PLA_2) activity, which in theory should provide the required acetyltransferase substrate *lyso*-PAF from 1-*O*-alkyl-2-acyl ether phospholipid precursors, inhibited the formation of both *lyso*-PAF and PAF. These results established that, upon cellular stimulation, endogenous ether phospholipids possessing long chain acyl groups at the 2-position would be acted upon by PLA_2 to provide *lyso*-PAF, the specific acetyltransferase substrate for production of PAF.[9,11] Enhanced acetyltransferase activity has been demonstrated to be dependent on extracellular calcium in a number of cell types, and to be regulated by calmodulin by the use of calmodulin antagonists.[43] This stimulus-dependent pathway is represented by the lower half of Scheme 2.

Complementary to the activation pathway, the rapid inactivation of PAF is accomplished by a specific acetylhydrolase present in both cytosolic and extracellular compartments, especially in the plasma,[44] which produces *lyso*-PAF as product. The profile of this acetylhydrolase differs distinctly from that displayed by PLA_2, which utilizes long chain acyl groups as substrate, based on competition experiments. Regardless of its source, however, *lyso*-PAF, which is cytotoxic due to its lytic and detergent properties, is once again produced. Elimination of *lyso*-PAF is accomplished *via* a specific acyltransferase which introduces a long chain fatty acid into the 2-position. The resulting 1-*O*-alkyl-2-*O*-acyl-GPC is then reincorporated into the membrane, completing the activation–inactivation cycle, as represented by the top half of Scheme 2. The fact that acyltransferase activity results in net inactivation, even in the presence of acetyltransferase activity, suggests that reaction of the former with *lyso*-PAF is favored on kinetic or substrate binding grounds over the latter.

In studies conducted in a number of cell types, arachidonic acid (AA) itself has been found to be one of the major fatty acids incorporated into the deacylation–reacylation cycle, implying that 1-*O*-alkyl-2-*O*-arachidonyl-GPC is a precursor for both PAF and AA during cellular responses to inflammatory stimuli.[45,46] The simultaneous release of PAF and AA, a substrate for lipoxygenases (LO) which produce the chemotactic leukotrienes (LT), represents an important link between these two potent mediators of the inflammatory response.

In vivo metabolism experiments have demonstrated rapid clearance of [^{3}H]PAF after intravenous administration, with a plasma half-life of 30 s. Recovery of radiolabeled material by tissue extraction afforded both *lyso*-PAF and 1-*O*-alkyl-2-*O*-acyl-GPC, indicating that the activation–inactivation cycle may indeed be operative *in vivo* also.

12.12.3.2 The *de Novo* Pathway

Independent of the acylation–deacylation cycle described above, the biosynthesis of PAF by phosphocholine transfer to 1-*O*-alkyl-2-(R)-acetylglycerol (5) by a specific dithiothreitol-insensitive CDPcholine:cholinephosphotransferase has also been demonstrated (Scheme 3).[9,11,19] Alkylacetylglycerols of several chain lengths serve as substrates for this enzyme and have been found to exhibit the antihypertensive effects characteristic of PAF when administered to spontaneously hypertensive and normal rats.[47] However, serious doubts about the biological relevance of this pathway persisted, mainly due to the lack of evidence supporting the existence of a biosynthetic source of (5), until the demonstration that: (i) labeled hexadecanol can be incorporated into the alkylglycerol biosynthetic pathway;[48] (ii) alkyl-*lyso*-GP (3) can be converted to alkylacetyl-GP (4) by a specific alkyl-*lyso*-GP:acetyl-CoA acetyltransferase; and (iii) this intermediate is subsequently dephosphorylated to generate the required alkylacetyl-G (5).[49] Acylation of (3) by an arachidonate-specific acyltransferase, and subsequent parallel conversion to 1-*O*-alkyl-2-arachidonyl-GPC, provides an alternative source of this membrane lipid for utilization in the activation–inactivation cycle, thus making (3) an important branchpoint between the two biosynthetic pathways.[50] Detailed examination of the final two steps of the *de novo* pathway has determined that the alkylacetyl-GP phosphohydrolase necessary to convert (4) to (5) is present in rat spleen, and that sufficient (5) is present in rat kidney to permit the synthesis of PAF. This stimulus-insensitive route could be responsible for maintaining

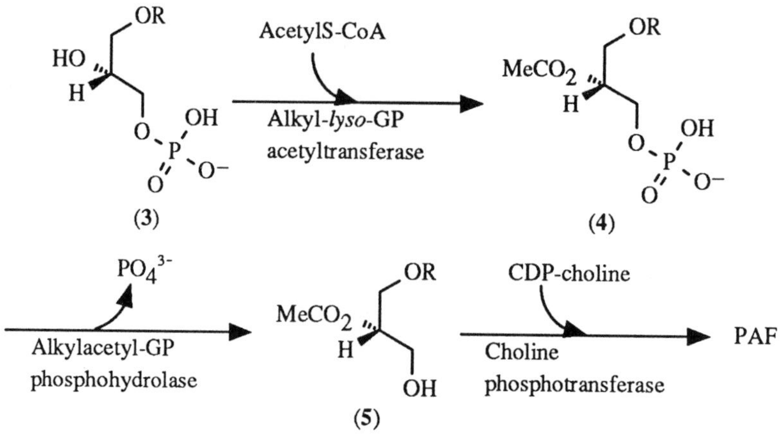

Scheme 3

physiologically relevant amounts of PAF for normal cellular function and regulation of blood pressure.[51,52]

12.12.3.3 Other Catabolic Routes

Aside from the acetylhydrolase activity incorporated into the activation–inactivation cycle described above, PAF is not directly degraded by any catabolic pathways common to ether lipids. However, *lyso*-PAF, the product of acetylhydrolase activity, is a substrate for the tetrahydropteridine-dependent alkyl-GPC monooxygenase, the enzyme responsible for the cleavage of lipid *O*-alkyl ether linkages. The products of this cleavage are long chain fatty aldehydes and GPC, effecting overall removal of *lyso*-PAF from its crucial position in the activation–inactivation cycle.[9]

12.12.4 BIOLOGICAL AND PHARMACOLOGICAL ACTIVITIES

PAF exhibits an extraordinarily wide range of biological activities in various target cells, isolated tissue preparations and *in vivo* (Figure 2). The development of this biological profile required an enormous number of individual studies, of which only the highlights are presented.[11,53–55]

12.12.4.1 Target Cells

12.12.4.1.1 Platelets

The effects of PAF on platelets include aggregation and shape change, degranulation, cross-desensitization and increases in calcium uptake, protein phosphorylation, phosphoinositide (PI) and arachidonate turnover, hydroxyeicosatetraenoic acid (HETE) and thromboxane (Tx) production, and cAMP levels. Platelet responsiveness to PAF in freshly prepared platelet-rich plasma (PRP) is highly species-selective, since PAF induces aggregation in platelets from humans, dogs, cats, rabbits, guinea pigs and horses at concentrations in the nanomolar range, but not in those from mice, rats or nonhuman primates even into the millimolar concentration range.[56,57] The inability of rat and mouse platelets to respond to PAF is not due to differences in plasma acetylhydrolase activity but to intrinsic 'platelet responsiveness', now ascribed to the absence of high affinity receptors in these species (*vide infra*).

PAF-stimulated aggregation and serotonin secretion in human platelets are concentration-dependent processes. Low concentrations of PAF induce primary aggregation, a monophasic reversible process devoid of serotonin release or TxB_2 production. At higher concentrations, however, PAF induces a distinct first wave of aggregation, followed by a second wave characterized by secretion of platelet granule contents such as serotonin.

The role of calcium ions in the biosynthesis and metabolism of PAF is also manifested at the cellular level and is intimately associated with the first steps of platelet activation. In human, rabbit and horse platelets, PAF rapidly induced a transient loss of PI by phospholipase C (PLC) activation,

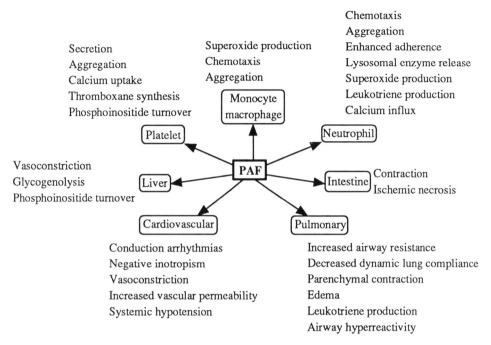

Figure 2 Biological targets of PAF and consequences (adapted from ref. 39)

producing diacylglycerols (DG) and phosphatidic acid, a calcium ionophore. Thus, the initial reduction in the PI level provides phosphatidic acid for mobilization of membrane-bound calcium ions, and DG for the activation of protein kinase C, which phosphorylates the 20 kDa light chain of platelet myosin, and a functionally unidentified 40 kDa protein, ultimately resulting in the release of serotonin from the activated platelet.[58,59] The associated preliminary shape change, the first measurable physiological platelet response, has been demonstrated to be independent of both extracellular divalent cations and AA metabolism.[60] In rabbit platelets, PAF increased the uptake of extracellular calcium in a time-, temperature- and concentration-dependent manner, effects which could be inhibited by the calcium channel blocker verapamil. This ionophoretic activity of PAF was greater than that observed with either the antipode of PAF (*enantio*-1) or intermediates along the activation–inactivation pathway, and was independent of ADP-induced platelet responses and cyclooxygenase (CO) products. Moreover, when AA was given sufficient time to be metabolized to other products, stimulation of calcium uptake also occurred.[61] Later studies in calcium-poor buffer and with calcium channel blockers suggest that PAF opens a calcium channel distinct from those present in unstimulated platelets.[62]

Although the mechanisms that couple initial stimulation of platelet aggregation to the final responses remain largely obscure, two sequences that facilitate this platelet function have been identified: (a) formation of prostaglandin (PG) endoperoxides and TxA$_2$, both products of the CO pathway in AA metabolism and potent platelet effectors at micromolar concentrations; and (b) secretion of ADP, stored in the dense granules, accelerating platelet aggregation *via* an extracellular feedback loop. Since PAF had been found to stimulate rabbit platelet aggregation in the presence of both CO inhibitors, such as aspirin and indomethacin, and the ADP-scavenging enzymes creatine phosphate-creatinephosphokinase (CP-CPK) and apyrase, and was detected upon platelet stimulation with thrombin, collagen and calcium ionophore, it was proposed as the endogenous mediator of the so-called third pathway of platelet aggregation.[63] This hypothesis, however, has been contradicted in numerous studies which have demonstrated that PAF-induced aggregation is mediated through both cyclooxygenase and ADP-dependent pathways *via* mechanisms common to a number of platelet agonists. Although early studies offered conflicting results regarding the effects of various CO inhibitors and the CP-CPK system on second wave aggregation and serotonin release, later experiments suggest that PAF-induced second wave aggregation and secretion fully depend on PG endoperoxide and TxA$_2$ formation and are facilitated by ADP secretion, especially at low PAF concentrations.[64–67] The phenomenon of positive synergism between agonists at subcritical doses demonstrated between PAF and ADP, collagen, sodium arachidonate, calcium ionophore and adrenalin, has also been shown to depend heavily on ADP and CO pathway products.[68] A similar study showed that LTB_4, LTC_4 and LTD_4, products of the LO pathway, had no direct effect on human platelet aggregation and did not modify the platelet response to PAF.[69] In human platelets from aspirin-treated volunteers, synergism is blocked post-treatment but returns within eight hours, apparently *via* a mechanism independent of both CO and LO pathways.[70] Platelets from patients with Zellweger syndrome, who manifest a virtual absence of the enzymes necessary for the biosynthesis of alkoxy lipids, displayed undetectable or low levels of PAF synthesis in isolated leukocytes but maintained their ability to respond to thrombin as an inducer of platelet aggregation, further evidence disproving PAF as the mediator of the third pathway.[71]

PAF produces a time- and dose-dependent stimulation of thromboxane synthesis, reaching a maximum coinciding with the appearance of second wave aggregation. Although PAF does not appear to have a direct effect on PGI_2-stimulated cAMP accumulation in platelets, it does attenuate such a response to exogenous PGI_2 added at the onset of second wave aggregation, a response blocked by cyclooxygenase and thromboxane synthetase inhibitors. This evidence suggests that PAF inhibition of the PGI_2-stimulated accumulation of cAMP can be attributed to the induction of TxA_2 synthesis by PAF.[72]

The interrelationship of PAF and cAMP levels has been addressed from a number of additional perspectives. In general, all agents known to increase cellular cAMP levels, such as PGE_1, PGI_2, isoproterenol, theophylline and dibutyryl-cAMP, inhibit the PAF-stimulated aggregation and serotonin release response in platelets. Incubation of PAF with rabbit platelets had no effect on the basal level of cAMP but it did inhibit the increase in cAMP produced by the addition of PGE_1 or the cAMP phosphodiesterase (PDE) inhibitor 3-isobutyl-1-methylxanthine (IBMX). Three chemically unrelated PDE inhibitors (IBMX, RA-233 and papaverine) decreased, but did not abolish, the inhibition of cAMP accumulation induced by PAF. In addition, PAF inhibited both basal adenylate cyclase activity and the increased adenylate cyclase activity resulting from PGE_1 or fluoride stimulation of the particulate fraction derived from rabbit platelets. These results established that PAF prevents the accumulation of cAMP in the presence of stimuli by both inhibiting adenylate cyclase and stimulating cAMP PDE.[73]

12.12.4.1.2 Neutrophils

The recruitment of human neutrophils to sites of local inflammation may be activated by many stimuli, including PAF which elicits a variety of responses in neutrophils, such as degranulation, aggregation, chemotaxis and chemokinesis, enhancement of the respiratory burst and associated superoxide generation, alterations in membrane cation content and surface charge, increased cell adherence and stimulation of arachidonic acid turnover. As in platelets, some of these processes are direct consequences of PAF action while others are part of integrated responses.[11,74]

Human polymorphonuclear neutrophils (PMN) undergo a PAF-induced degranulation process dependent on temperature, cellular glycolysis and available sulfhydryl groups. Extracellular calcium ions enhance this degranulation process, but it is not a requirement. However, the calmodulin antagonist trifluoperazine caused a dose-related suppression of PAF-stimulated degranulation, indicating that intracellular calcium may play a regulatory role in the process.[75] In the presence of cytochalasin B, PAF-induced degranulation is rapid, but the response in the absence of cytochalasin B is highly dependent on incubation time and PMN amounts. The degranulation response is also independent of other stimuli, since granule enzyme release can be elicited from PAF-desensitized cells.[75,76] The response in rabbit PMN occurs at doses tenfold lower than for human PMN, and is characterized by extracellular calcium uptake. The calcium channel blocker verapamil blocks both the degranulation and calcium uptake in this case.[77]

PAF induces aggregation in human, rat and mouse PMN independent of arachidonate- and ADP-mediated aggregation, requiring both extracellular calcium and magnesium. Cytochalasin B enhances the magnitude and duration of this response, while a variety of agents (CO, LO, esterase, PLA_2, PDE inhibitors, adenylate cyclase agonists and membrane-active drugs) inhibit PAF-induced PMN aggregation. PAF and *lyso*-PAF induce PMN migration, the factors being chemokinetic at low concentrations and chemotactic at high concentrations. Although *lyso*-PAF is a weaker chemotactic stimulus than PAF it has been found to be more inhibitory than PAF during cross-desensitization, a result attributed to the more potent effect of *lyso*-PAF on the less well-defined post-receptor processes operative in PMN aggregation. Since the CO-LO inhibitor BW755C but not the CO inhibitor indomethacin enhanced the chemotactic response to both PAF and *lyso*-PAF, a product of the LO pathway was proposed to exert an inhibitory effect on the PAF-induced chemotactic response in PMN.[11,78]

The relationship of PAF and LO products, particularly LTB$_4$, in the proposed mechanism of the neutrophil migration–aggregation response has evolved from one of direct PAF stimulation of LT production to that of coamplifiers of the chemotactic stimulation. When human and rabbit platelets were pretreated with AA, PAF stimulated the release and metabolism of arachidonate from PI and PC in roughly equivalent amounts and in a dose-dependent manner. The arachidonate metabolites produced were predominantly the LO products 5-hydroxyeicosatetraenoic acid (5-HETE) and LTB$_4$.[79–81] While 5-HETE potentiated only the PAF-induced degranulation response,[82] LTB$_4$ caused both degranulation and aggregation of PMN.[79–83] Evidence indicating that endogenously synthesized LTB$_4$ may mediate PAF-induced neutrophil aggregation in PMN includes: (i) LTB$_4$ was up to two orders of magnitude more potent than PAF in the aggregation response; (ii) the activity of LTB$_4$ was relatively insensitive to LO inhibitors; and (iii) LTB$_4$-desensitized cells were not responsive to PAF.[11,80–83] In studies which demonstrated no significant cross-desensitization, however, it was proposed that PAF and LTB$_4$ interact with separate receptor sites on the neutrophil surface and that PAF did not induce neutrophil aggregation by releasing LTB$_4$.[84] While LTB$_4$ was found to enhance the aggregation response to PAF, use of lipoxygenase inhibitors at concentrations sufficient to inhibit the release of LTB$_4$ did not affect the aggregation response to PAF. Moreover, the role of LTB$_4$ as a mediator of PAF-induced neutrophil degranulation was questionable, since LTB$_4$ was significantly less potent than PAF in evoking this response. Although the degranulating actions of PAF and LTB$_4$ were similarly susceptible to LO inhibitors, PMN desensitized with LTB$_4$ degranulated normally when challenged with PAF.[11,85,86]

The regulatory role of cAMP in neutrophil activation by PAF has also been investigated. Levels of cAMP were found to be elevated coincidentally with the initiation of PAF-induced PMN aggregation. Both PGI$_2$ and the PDE inhibitor Ro 20-1724 attenuated the PAF-induced aggregation response but further amplified the elevated levels of cAMP induced by PAF. Inhibition of CO enhanced the PAF-induced effects on cAMP levels and aggregation, while inhibition of LO inhibited both responses. Although LTB$_4$ also increased cAMP levels in intact cells and stimulated adenylate cyclase in cell homogenates, the increase in cAMP levels induced by either LTB$_4$ or PAF does not seem to be obligatory for the aggregation response. In fact, inhibition of adenylate cyclase blocked the PAF-stimulated increase in cAMP but enhanced the aggregation response. This evidence suggests that an increase in cAMP levels is part of a feedback mechanism through which PAF and LTB$_4$ limit their own activities in neutrophils.[11,83,87]

Yet another connection between PAF- and LTB$_4$-mediated neutrophil activation is the mobilization of protein kinase C (PKC). Nanomolar concentrations of either one caused PMN to lose cytosolic PKC-specific protein phosphorylating activity and DG/phorbol receptors. Unlike the direct activators of PKC, however, PAF and LTB$_4$ induced only moderate decreases in cytosolic PKC, acted only on cytochalasin B-activated PMN, did not mobilize PKC in disrupted PMN or activate PKC in a cell-free system, and, for PAF, induced responses reversible within 30 min. In studies with analogs of both compounds, mobilization of PKC correlated closely with the respective agonist properties and receptor affinities (*vide infra*), indicating that both were acting by indirect but receptor-mediated mechanisms. Other observations closely correlated PKC mobilization with the neutrophil degranulation response to either PAF, LTB$_4$ or 5-HETE, which could be inhibited by the PKC blocker polymyxin B. Because stimulated PMN may produce and use PAF, LTB$_4$ and 5-HETE as secondary cellular mediators, these results implicate PKC as a central and potentially critical regulator of the response to any of these stimuli.[88]

PAF elicits respiratory burst and superoxide generation responses in neutrophils treated with cytochalasin B. Pretreatment with PAF enhanced oxygen consumption when cells were subsequently treated with *N*-formylmethionylleucylphenylalanine (fMLP). As with the aggregation response, superoxide production failed to show a peak or plateau in relation to PAF dose, a direct contrast to the dose- or concentration-dependent processes of chemotaxis and degranulation.[76,79] PAF-activated superoxide generation appears to be stimulus specific, since both LTB$_4$ and fMLP were capable of inducing superoxide production in cells pretreated with PAF.[89] The enhancement of the respiratory burst after chemotactic stimulation induced by either PAF or LTB$_4$ displayed no synergism, precluding the possibility of autoactivation of neutrophils.[90]

12.12.4.1.3 *Other cellular targets*

(i) *Macrophages*

Activation of macrophages occurs upon interaction of soluble mediators, macroscopic particles or tumor cells with macrophage cell surface receptors, resulting in the secretion of a variety of products and the increased capacity to destroy the offending microbe or tumor cell. Response to both the priming signal (lymphokines, lipopolysaccharide or microbes) and the triggering signal (immune complexes, lipopolysaccharide opsonized particles or tumor cells) requires transduction into intracellular messages. Upon application to macrophages, PAF has been shown to stimulate the oxidative burst and superoxide generation, PGE and TxB_2 synthesis, glucose consumption and spreading.[91-95] Although the triggering of the oxidative burst may be directly initiated by PAF, AA metabolism modulates the response, with LO products being stimulatory and CO products inhibitory. Cells liberating PAF in close contact with macrophage populations may induce the release of oxygen species known to be highly toxic.[93] In culture for 24 hours or more, macrophages themselves display increased acetylhydrolase activity, nullifying the effects of PAF *via* the catabolic process.[96] As had been observed in platelets, PAF induces the influx of extracellular calcium and the mobilization of calcium from intracellular stores, which may provide the necessary signal transduction for macrophage activation.[97]

(ii) Eosinophils

The chemoattractant properties of PAF have also been observed in human eosinophils, with PAF eliciting directional locomotion in a time- and dose-dependent manner. Compared with PAF, the locomotory responsiveness to LTB_4, histamine and eosinophil chemotactic factor of anaphylaxis (ECF-A) tetrapeptides was negligible, suggesting that PAF may play a role in inflammation characterized by eosinophil infiltration.[98]

12.12.4.2 Isolated Tissues and Perfused Organs

12.12.4.2.1 Lung

Administration of a single acute dose of PAF caused a reduction in the luminal area of pulmonary capillaries and an increase in the size and number of plasmalemmal vesicles. Chronic dosing produced parallel changes, but did not result in more extensive lung disease.[99] Intratracheal instillation of PAF caused macrophage accumulation in alveolar spaces, degenerative changes in the alveolar epithelium, the accumulation of platelets and PMN in the alveolar capillary lumen and degenerative changes in endothelial cells, results indicative of pulmonary injury mediated by PAF.[100] Sensitized guinea pig lungs perfused through the airways, but not the pulmonary circulation, released PAF on antigen challenge, supporting a role for PAF in respiratory anaphylaxis.[101] Parenchymal lung strips from various species contract when exposed to PAF, a receptor-specific response modulated by cyclic nucleotide levels and blocked by LO and PL inhibitors.[102] Further studies indicate that LO products other than peptidoleukotrienes are involved in the contraction response to PAF and that platelet-independent release of TxA_2 may be involved.[103,104]

12.12.4.2.2 Cardiovascular tissue

The direct effects of PAF in isolated heart tissue are cardiodepressant and are characterized by a biphasic dose-dependent response. A transient positive effect on inotropism and action potential duration was followed by a marked prolonged negative effect on both parameters. In human tissue, no changes in resting membrane potential, overshoot or maximum rate of depolarization were detected after PAF challenge.[105] This profile was essentially duplicated in perfused guinea pig heart where, in addition, no increase in heart rate was observed.[106-108] In rat heart, LTC_4 was found to be largely responsible for the coronary vasoconstriction induced by PAF. CO products were proposed to play only a modulatory role in the vasoconstriction response but were found to be involved in the decrease in cardiac contractility.[109] The contrasting peripheral arterial vasodilation induced by PAF is responsible for the profound hypotensive effects observed *in vivo* (*vide infra*).[110]

12.12.4.2.3 Gastrointestinal tissue

PAF induces a slow and persistent contraction of guinea pig ileum in a dose-dependent manner at nanomolar concentrations, whereas at higher concentrations rapid contraction and relaxation result, a response independent of muscarinic, H_1 or slow-reacting substance receptors. While PAF desensitizes the ileum to restimulation by itself, it does not affect the response to C3a or C5a; the converse also holds true. These results indicate interaction with a unique receptor for muscle contraction stimulation by PAF.[111-113] PAF also caused a dose-related contraction of other regions of the intestine, including the duodenum, jejunum and colon, although the profile of contraction in the colon was qualitatively different. Over a wide range of doses, PAF desensitized all regions of the intestine to further challenge, a tachyphylactic effect specific to PAF since both acetylcholine and histamine induced normal contraction in PAF-desensitized muscle.[114]

12.12.4.2.4 *Other tissues*

(i) *Liver*

PAF causes a rise in polyphosphoinositide metabolism in rat hepatocytes upon short incubation and a significant depletion of cAMP levels on longer exposure.[115,116] The dose-response for the effect of PAF on hepatic glycogenolysis is, however, more complex. At subnanomolar concentrations, a single transient stimulatory phase is obtained, whereas at higher concentrations a rapid transient peak of glucose output is followed by a return to basal levels. Neither α nor β antagonists were able to inhibit PAF-stimulated glycogenolysis at concentrations which block adrenergic stimulation of hepatic glycogenolysis. This and other studies indicate that PAF induces glycogenolysis by a mechanism different from that utilized by vasopressin, angiotensin II or catecholamines,[117] probably involving hepatic vasoconstriction[118] and possibly involving CO products.[119]

(ii) *Kidney*

PAF is released from isolated perfused rat kidney upon stimulation with calcium ionophore.[120] Bolus injection of PAF into similarly prepared tissue caused a dose-dependent stimulation of renal PG release and an increase in renal vascular resistance.[121]

12.12.4.3 *In Vivo* **Effects and Pathobiology**

Administration of PAF to various animal species can have severe consequences, such as hypotension, pulmonary hypertension, increased airway resistance and bronchoconstriction, increased vascular permeability, thrombocytopenia, neutropenia and even death.[16] The effects observed, however, are markedly dependent on both the species involved and the route of administration.[122] A number of recent reviews have focused on the pathobiology of PAF, the highlights of which are presented.[11,16,39,123,124]

12.12.4.3.1 *Pulmonary alterations*

Intratracheal or intravenous administration of PAF to baboons or guinea pigs induces a platelet-dependent bronchoconstriction which could be partially or totally blocked by PGI_2 and LO inhibitors.[125,126] Intravenous infusion of PAF in rabbits or baboons induces a dose-dependent aggregation of platelets, thrombocytopenia, neutropenia, basopenia and the release of platelet factor 4 and TxB_2, localized in the lung.[127-130] In addition, increased pulmonary resistance, decreased dynamic lung compliance and cardiovascular complications are noted. These effects are indistinguishable from the alterations induced by IgE-anaphylaxis. Only platelet-depleted animals exhibited differences in the physiological response induced by PAF or IgE-anaphylaxis.[127] A detailed study in guinea pigs demonstrated that the histamine- and leukotriene-independent component of guinea pig anaphylaxis is mediated by PAF, but that PAF is not responsible for the anaphylaxis-induced thrombocytopenia.[131] The steroidal antiinflammatory agent budesonide, an inhibitor of anaphylactic bronchoconstriction in actively sensitized guinea pigs, suppresses the biosynthesis of PAF upon antigenic challenge in the lungs of pretreated animals, suggesting the role of PAF as a mediator of bronchial anaphylaxis.[132] The inability of β_2-adrenoreceptor antagonists to reverse the airway obstruction induced by spasmogens in PAF-treated animals has been ascribed to PAF-induced receptor down-regulation.[133] However, no change in β_2-adrenoreceptor numbers or binding affinity was observed in lungs removed from PAF-treated animals or after direct incubation with PAF *in vitro*, suggesting that the reduced responsiveness of PAF-treated animals with agents such as isoprenaline is unrelated to changes in pulmonary β_2-receptor function.[134]

12.12.4.3.2   *Cardiovascular and renal effects*

PAF displays potent dose-dependent antihypertensive properties in renal hypertensive, spontaneously hypertensive (SHR) and normotensive rats by a variety of routes of administration, and was one of the first effects of PAF to be studied intensively.[135-139] PAF-induced hypotension has been associated with elevated plasma renin activity, norepinephrine, epinephrine and TxB_2 levels and with tachycardia, but has been shown to be independent of these by blockade of cholinergic, β-adrenergic and histaminergic receptors or PG and bradykinin synthesis. Observation of these effects in SHR and platelet-depleted SHR suggested that PAF-induced hypotension was platelet independent.[140] The role of PAF as an α-adrenergic antagonist was suggested, based on results which show PAF to inhibit the pressor responses of norepinephrine but not angiotensin II. In addition, pressor responses to angiotensin II, phenylephrine and norepinephrine were attenuated by PAF.[141] However, *in vitro* studies demonstrated no effect of PAF on norepinephrine-induced contractions in both vascular and nonvascular preparations from the rat, and no affinity of PAF for α_1- or α_2-adrenergic receptors from rat brain.[135] Further studies suggested that PAF exerts its potent hypotensive effect mainly by endothelium-dependent vasodilation,[142] but this result was deemed inconclusive, since relatively high doses of PAF were required and no correlation was found between hypotensive activity and endothelium-mediated vasodilation within a series of PAF analogs.[143] Recuperation from the effects of PAF are mediated solely by the sympathetic system and β-adrenergic receptors.[144] PAF-induced peripheral vessel hyperpermeability leads to extravasation of protein-rich plasma. The resulting hemoconcentration was not blocked by Tx synthetase, CO or PDE inhibitors, calcium channel blockers or antihistamines, indicating a direct effect of PAF.[145,146] In the kidney, PAF produces decreases in blood flow, glomerular filtration and fluid and electrolyte excretion. Intrarenal injection of PAF results in glomerular accumulation of platelets and neutrophils and mild proteinuria. However, the direct role of PAF in renal pathophysiology remains in question.[147,148]

Hemodynamic studies in anesthetized open-chest dogs and pigs on the effects of intravenous administration of PAF confirmed the multiphasic response observed in isolated tissue noted above. The overall cardiodepressant profile, however, indicates that PAF has profound effects on vascular tone and the inotropic state of the myocardium. The release of PAF from aggregating platelets might also play a major role in modulating coronary blood flow.[149,150]

The consequences of the actions of PAF on the cardiovascular system, when taken together, could probably combine to result in shock, the acute circulatory collapse due to dramatic decreases in blood volume, failure of cardiac or vascular circulation or loss of neurogenic control of the circulation. The systemic hypotension, pulmonary hypertension, increased vascular permeability and extravasation of protein-rich plasma observed on administration of PAF suggests its direct involvement in such a shock state.[151,152] In anesthetized dogs, intravenous injection of PAF resulted in cardiovascular and hemodynamic changes typical of the features of acute circulatory collapse with distributive and hypovolumic etiologies.[153] Similar studies in rats concluded that, since PAF was not present in control animals but has been isolated from animals in the shock state, and since PAF mimics most of the hemodynamic changes of the shock state, its direct involvement in shock must be seriously considered.[154]

12.12.4.3.3   *Gastrointestinal alterations*

PAF has been reported to be a potent gastric ulcerogen after intravenous infusion in rats. The ulcerogenic actions of PAF are not attributable solely to its hypotensive activity and were not mediated by effects on platelets, cyclooxygenase products nor by histamine H_1, H_2 or α-adrenergic receptors.[155] Gastric mucosal damage induced by PAF was blocked by pretreatment with corticosteroids but was not inhibited by similar treatment with PGE_2 or its 16,16-dimethyl analog, shown to inhibit gastric damage induced by ethanol.[156,157] Further studies have indicated that picomole doses of PAF predispose the gastric mucosa to damage by other topical irritants, such as ethanol.[158] The effects of PAF are not limited to the gastric mucosa, however. Damage to the duodenum, jejunum and ileum, but not the colon, was observed and could be correlated with elevated acid phosphatase activity.[159] Similar results have been obtained utilizing PAF to induce necrotizing enterocolitis (ischemic bowel disease) upon coadministration with bacterial lipopolysaccharide.[160] This response was found to be mediated by LTs, since LO inhibitors ameliorated the disease course, while the CO inhibitor indomethacin aggravated it, probably by shifting arachidonate metabolism to the LO pathway.[161] These results indicate that the endogenous release of PAF during septic shock or in inflammatory gastrointestinal diseases could contribute to mucosal injury and eventual ulceration.

12.12.4.3.4 *Acute inflammatory reactions*

Subplantar injection of PAF into the rat paw produces both edema and hyperalgesia, two dissociated phenomena with regard to doses required for induction, time course of development and antagonism exerted by various classes of drugs.[162] Kinetics similar to that of the edema response have been reported for the inflammatory action of PAF in the rat pleural cavity.[163] Later pharmacological analyses on the inhibition of PAF-induced rat paw edema, however, differ widely with the original study and amongst themselves with respect to results on drug effects, especially for steroidal and nonsteroidal antiinflammatory agents.[164-166] The role of calcium fluxes and their relationship to cyclic nucleotide regulation in the edemagenic response is, however, generally considered important. Examination of the first phase of carrageenan-induced rat paw edema demonstrated release of PAF and PAF-like materials, suggesting that PAF release, together with released histamine and kinin, play important roles in the development of edema.[167]

Intradermal injection of PAF into rat, guinea pig or human skin produces an inflammatory response marked by increased vascular permeability, increased plasma protein extravasation, platelet accumulation and red blood cell accumulation.[168-171] In humans, a characteristic early weal and flare response is commonly succeeded by an area of dose-dependent late-onset erythema at the site of the resolved weal, reminiscent of the dual response to allergen in sensitized individuals.[172,173] In the guinea pig, the acute response is potentiated by the presence of serum albumin and is slightly modified by H_1 receptor antagonists, but is not significantly affected by the CO inhibitor indomethacin.[174] The response in human skin has been suggested to be more dependent on histamine release,[175] while CO products may play a larger role in rat skin.[176] In both guinea pig and human skin, significant synergism between PAF and PGE_2 has been demonstrated, an interaction which accounts for the observed increases in blood flow and vasopermeability of the edema response.[177,178] The observations that monocytes from patients with severe psoriasis or atopic eczema exhibited increased chemotaxis toward PAF[179] and that PAF has been isolated from the lesional scale of psoriatic patients[180] offer support for the hypothesis that PAF may play a significant role in acute skin inflammation and in the maintenance of chronic inflammatory dermatoses.[181]

12.12.4.3.5 *PAF-induced mortality*

Intravenous injection of microgram doses of PAF produces dose-dependent mortality in rabbits[182] and mice[183,184] within minutes, mimicking the effects of lethal anaphylactic shock. The sudden death is characterized by cessation of respiration, marked decrease in mean arterial blood pressure and, at least in rabbits, a major increase in plasma TxB_2 levels. Pretreatment with glucocorticoids consistently protected mice from these effects, whereas CO inhibitors, antihistamines and adrenergic antagonists did not. Calcium channel blockers were effective only at very high doses, consistent with nonspecific effects on calcium-dependent processes. LO inhibitors, LT antagonists and PDE inhibitors also offered protection, presenting the possibility of using PAF-induced mortality as a screening assay for such agents. In rabbits, however, both the CO inhibitor ibuprofen and the Tx synthetase inhibitor dazoxiben increased survival rates significantly, pointing to a possible difference in mechanisms between species. Later studies have demonstrated that PAF-induced mortality in mice is indeed platelet independent, and that pharmacological manipulation of β_2-adrenoreceptors modulates the response. The involvement of LO products distinct from LTs, but not arachidonate metabolites of the CO pathway or peptidoleukotrienes, has been suggested as the major cause of the bronchoconstriction and cardiovascular events associated with PAF-induced mortality.[185]

12.12.5 THE PAF RECEPTOR

The multitude of biological and pharmacological activities ascribed to PAF in which other biochemical mediators assume secondary roles, the picomolar potency of PAF in these systems, the fact that certain cells and tissues could be specifically desensitized to the effects of PAF and the many *in vitro* and *in vivo* observations that the unnatural (S) stereoisomer of PAF (*enantio*-1) was essentially inactive in stimulating the various responses elicited by the natural antipode, all suggested the existence of specific receptors for PAF in target cells and tissues.[16,186-188] This hypothesis has been confirmed by the isolation and biochemical characterization of PAF-specific membrane receptor proteins, and by the discovery of specific antagonists of PAF binding which inhibit the biological effects of PAF (*vide infra*).

12.12.5.1 Occurrence and Characterization

Since the first report of specific receptor affinity for PAF by human platelets,[189] binding studies using [^{3}H]PAF have confirmed the existence of saturable high affinity receptors in human and rabbit platelets, human PMN, and guinea pig and human lung membrane, but not in rat platelets (Table 1).[187-202] The resulting profile is consistent with the species- and tissue-specific effects exerted by PAF, since (a) both human PMN and rabbit platelets, which are more sensitive to PAF than human platelets, exhibit a larger number of binding sites per cell and (b) rat platelets, totally refractory to PAF, exhibit no detectable PAF receptors. The presence of a low affinity binding site of infinite capacity was also detected in some of the studies with human platelets and PMN,[189,192,194,197,199] first explained as an indication of the unsaturable nonspecific uptake and metabolism in these cells,[193] but later more fully characterized as a ligand-specific role of PAF sequestration in competition with nonspecific intramembraneous metabolism.[199] Full receptor occupancy is not a likely requirement for eliciting a biological response, at least in platelets, since the K_d values are ten- to a hundred-fold higher than the EC_{50} for platelet aggregation.[187]

Platelets exposed to low concentrations of PAF at 37 °C for as little as 5 min exhibit marked desensitization to subsequent doses of PAF. Desensitization is characterized by a decreased affinity of the high affinity binding site for PAF rather than a loss of binding site numbers. Under such conditions, platelets continue to exhibit normal responses to other agonists.[203] The demonstration

Table 1 Occurrence and Characteristics of the PAF Receptor[187]

Receptor source	$K_d (\times 10^{-9})^a$	Sites per cell	Ref.
Human platelet	37 ± 13	1399 ± 498	189, 190
	1.58 ± 0.36	1983 ± 391	192
	0.053 ± 0.014	242 ± 64	193
	20.1 ± 6.3	1577 ± 461	194
	0.8	160	195
	0.29 ± 0.07	351 ± 21	187
	0.295 ± 0.033	245 ± 30	197
	7.6 ± 1.9	145 ± 15	198
Rabbit platelet	1.36 ± 0.05	150–300	191
	0.9 ± 0.5	19386 ± 6588	192
	0.65 ± 0.17		187
Rat platelet	—	Not found	192
Human PMN	0.11 ± 0.02	$5.2 \pm 2.1 \times 10^6$	190
	45 ± 1.7	27391 ± 1381	194
	0.2 ± 0.04	1100 ± 220	199
	0.47 ± 0.14	313 ± 14^b	200
Bovine blood PMN	4.93 ± 0.05	1.08 ± 0.34^b	191
Guinea pig peritoneal PMN	7.58 ± 0.05	0.113 ± 0.034^b	191
Mouse macrophages	0.08 ± 0.01	7872 ± 1310	201
Rabbit ileum	4.87 ± 0.05	0.159 ± 0.034^b	191
Guinea pig ileum	c		191
Guinea pig lung	c		191
Human lung tissue	0.49 ± 0.17	140 ± 37^b	196
Gerbil brain	3.66 ± 0.92	830 ± 230^b	202
	20.4 ± 0.50	1100 ± 320^b	202

^{a} Using [^{3}H]PAF. ^{b} fmol mg^{-1} protein. ^{c} Detected, but not quantified.

of *in vitro* specific receptor desensitization correlates with the *in vivo* observations of tissue, refractory to a second PAF challenge, but remaining responsive to other stimuli.

The PAF receptor from platelet plasma membrane is heat labile and sensitive to protease activity.[191,204] Comparative studies of the effects of PAF and its 1-*O*-stearoyl analog on the endothermotropic transition behavior of multilamellar liposomes showed that they induced almost identical changes in thermal behavior, in direct contrast to their vastly dissimilar biological activities in, for example, platelet aggregation. This lack of correlation between the biological and physicochemical properties suggested that the receptor sites for PAF were not phospholipids.[191] Sepharose-bound PAF affinity chromatography of solubilized platelet plasma membranes and subsequent gel electrophoresis revealed the existence of a single protein of an apparent molecular weight of 180 kDa as a possible constituent of the PAF receptor, as judged by its ability to bind PAF.[204] Sequential chromatography of solubilized platelet plasma membranes followed by electrophoresis of the final preparation revealed a protein of 160 kDa molecular weight and an isoelectric point near 8.0 corresponding to bound labeled PAF.[205] Specific antibodies to PAF (anti-PAF IgG) have been raised in rabbits and have been shown to significantly agglutinate the PAF antigen and inhibit PAF-induced platelet aggregation. The precise chemical structure of PAF was found to be necessary for antigenic expression, since neither a 1-*O*-acyl analog nor *lyso*-PAF exhibited antigenic properties.[206]

12.12.5.2 Stimulus–Response Pathways

The membrane events and subsequent cellular responses triggered by the binding of PAF to its receptor involve some of the most important biochemical pathways in cellular regulation (Figure 3).[186,187,207] Although the hypothesis that PAF is an endogenous mediator of stimulus–response coupling, converting cell stimulation into cell function, remains vigorously contested, the array of stimulatory and inhibitory interactions of PAF on these pathways has implicated PAF as at least an important link in the etiology and maintenance of a multitude of pathobiological processes.[208] Binding of PAF induces activation of PLC and the initiation of the PI cycle, resulting in the formation of DG and inositol triphosphate (IP$_3$). The former activates PKC and subsequent phosphorylation; the latter is involved in mobilization of calcium from internal pools. Activation of protein kinase A or G by cAMP or cGMP, respectively, initiates calcium sequestration and can counteract these calcium-mobilizing effects of PAF. Release of AA and its subsequent metabolism by both the CO and LO pathways is also stimulated by PAF, resulting in the release of TxA$_2$, LTs and HETEs, implicated in acute and chronic inflammatory processes.[207]

12.12.5.2.1 Regulation of specific binding

Specific binding of [^{3}H]PAF to rabbit platelet membranes has been shown to be regulated by monovalent and divalent cations and GTP. Studies at 0 °C demonstrated that [^{3}H]PAF receptor binding is inhibited specifically by Na$^+$ ions and to a lesser extent by Li$^+$, but is potentiated by Mg^{2+}, Ca^{2+}, Mn^{2+}, K$^+$, Cs$^+$ and Rb$^+$, in order of decreasing enhancement.[209] Replacement of H$_2$O with D$_2$O in the incubation medium induces a total inhibition of PAF-induced platelet aggregation but does not affect the binding, suggesting a role for H$^+$ in the early events in the PAF-induced signaling process.[186] Radioligand binding studies also revealed specific binding inhibition by GTP; other nucleotides have little effect. Sodium-inhibitory and Mg^{2+}-potentiated effects previously reported for other membrane receptors have been attributed to a direct linkage between receptors and adenylate cyclase through an inhibitory guanyl nucleotide-binding regulatory protein.[209] Indeed, PAF has been demonstrated to inhibit human platelet adenylate cyclase by stimulation of a high-affinity hormone-sensitive GTPase, suggesting direct coupling of the PAF receptor to a GTP-binding inhibitory protein assumed to be the regulatory protein N$_i$.[210] Subsequent studies, however, showed that the degree of GTPase activity elicited by PAF was additive with that due to either of the regulatory proteins N$_i$ or N$_s$, suggesting that the effects of PAF are mediated by a guanine nucleotide regulatory protein distinct from either N$_i$ or N$_s$.[211] Pretreatment of rabbit platelets with phorbol ester or dibutyryl cAMP and desensitization to PAF itself have also been examined for their differing GTPase-mediated effects on PAF receptor binding characteristics.[212]

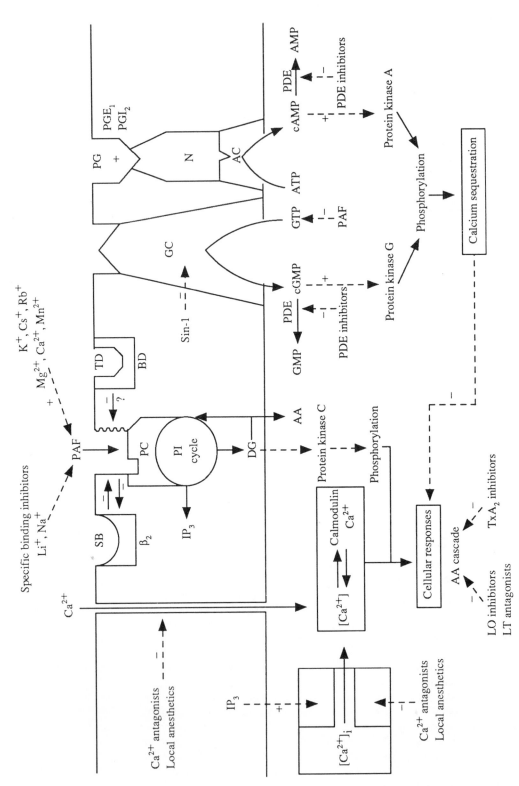

Figure 3 The biochemical signal produced by PAF and its pharmacological modulation (adapted from refs. 187 and 207)

12.12.5.2.2 Stimulus–aggregation coupling

Binding of PAF to its receptor induces exposure of fibrinogen binding sites, a stimulus–aggregation coupling mechanism.[193] In contrast to most agonists, PAF induces a more pronounced aggregation at 22 °C than at 37 °C. Studies at these two temperatures demonstrated that, at 22 °C, (i) binding of [³H]PAF was more rapid, (ii) PI monophosphate was accumulated rather than recycled and (iii) PKC-mediated phosphorylation was increased, but (iv) there was no change in AA metabolism or PI bisphosphate formation. At both temperatures, both low and high affinity fibrinogen binding sites were detected. At 22 °C, however, there were sixfold more low affinity sites than at 37 °C; the number of high affinity sites did not change, suggesting that the enhanced PAF-induced aggregation at 22 °C is the result of exposure of an increased number of low affinity fibrinogen binding sites.[213] The exposure and maintenance of these sites requires metabolic energy, but the subsequent binding of fibrinogen does not.[214] The rate at which PAF binds to its receptors and not the degree of receptor occupancy determines the amount of fibrinogen binding.[215] Preincubation of platelets with CO or Tx synthetase inhibitors completely abolished the high affinity fibrinogen binding, while, in contrast, ADP scavengers prevented low affinity fibrinogen binding. These results suggest that PAF induces little platelet aggregation under binding conditions, but that levels of TxA_2 and secreted ADP are sufficient for initiating high and low affinity binding of fibrinogen to the sites exposed by the action of PAF *via* mutually independent mechanisms.[216]

12.12.5.2.3 Nonspecific pharmacological inhibition

As can be appreciated from Figure 3, the complex web of biochemical interactions initiated by the binding of PAF to its receptor can be manipulated by any agent which intervenes along one of these pathways. Agents which interfere with intracellular calcium mobilization, such as calcium channel antagonists, calmodulin inhibitors, calcium chelators and local anesthetics, have been shown to counteract stimulation by PAF.[187] Of particular note is the possible close spatial relationship of the PAF binding site to membrane calcium channels, as determined by the inhibition of [³H]PAF binding by calcium antagonists.[217,218] The most potent of these, (+)-*cis*-diltiazem, was shown to exhibit this effect on PAF binding in a stereospecific and competitive manner, in comparison with its antipode.[217] Verapamil caused disaggregation of PAF-stimulated platelets and the reversal of the PKC-mediated phosphorylation of the 40 kDa protein substrate.[219] Verapamil also exerted a protective effect on PAF-induced cardiac and circulatory alterations in isolated guinea pig heart, and in the rabbit.[220] The weak anticalcic antithrombotic agent BN-50341 also demonstrates inhibition of PAF- and thrombin-induced platelet activation.[221] Intracellular calcium levels can also be manipulated indirectly by modulating the level of cyclic nucleotides *via* stimulation of adenylate or guanylate cyclase, or *via* inhibition of cyclic nucleotide PDE. Such effects have been noted with PGI_2, PGE_1 and the β_2 agonist salbutamol (adenylate cyclase agonism), molsidomine metabolite Sin-1 (guanylate cyclase agonism) and aminophylline (PDE inhibition).[187] Other agents counteracting the effects of PAF include selected inhibitors of arachidonate metabolism (FCE 22178[222] and *viz.* Section 12.12.7.4.4), antiallergic agents (chromoglycate,[223] amoxanox[224] and REV 2871[225]), antithrombotic agents (AD6,[226] ticlopidine,[227] amiloride[228] and 3178 AQ[229]) and peptides (thyrotropin-releasing hormone (TRH), TRH analog MK 771[230] and C-reactive protein[231]). Serine protease inhibitors acting by either chemical modification of serine residues or by competitive inhibition have also been demonstrated to inhibit PAF-induced platelet stimulation and aggregation, but the target and the specificity of the protease activity are yet to be determined.[232]

12.12.6 PAF RECEPTOR AGONISTS

Almost immediately upon determination of the structure of PAF the task of synthesizing analogs of this novel phospholipid was undertaken with three distinct goals in mind: (i) to probe the structural requirements accounting for the observed full spectrum of biological activity of PAF; (ii) to determine if specific and therapeutically selective agonists of PAF could be designed which maintained the desirable effects of PAF while eliminating its untoward effects; and (iii) to discover receptor-specific antagonists of the biological effects of PAF, providing compounds or lead structures of possible therapeutic use in the treatment of the acute and chronic pathobiological events potentially mediated by PAF.[233] The first two of these objectives have yielded enormous information regarding the operative structure–activity relationship(s) for PAF and its analogs, and will be addressed in this section; the last will be discussed separately (*viz.* Section 12.12.7).

12.12.6.1 Implications and Evaluation of Selective Agonism

The biological profile of the actions of PAF is heavily skewed toward its role as an inflammatory and immunopathological mediator. However, it was the hypotensive activity of PAF which led the Snyder group to their discovery of this phospholipid. Indeed, many of the first efforts toward the synthesis of PAF analogs were aimed at the preparation of a chemically and metabolically stable antihypertensive agent based on PAF but devoid of effects on platelet aggregation, bronchoconstriction, anaphylaxis and acute inflammation. For this reason, most compounds are evaluated as potential PAF agonists by comparison of their ability to induce hypotension *vs.* their pro-aggregatory response. In the discussion of agonist structure–activity relationships which follows, data for representative structures in these two diagnostic assays are tabulated (Table 2). The ability to selectively activate macrophage function with metabolically stable PAF agonists has also been investigated, aimed at the development of novel antitumor agents.[234,235] However, after nearly a decade of investigation into the actions of PAF,[236] the search for selective PAF agonists still remains

Table 2 Relative Potencies of PAF Agonists

Agonist	Relative agonist potency (PAF = 100)[a]	Ref.
Alterations at C-1		
(1) n = 15 (PAF)	100	239, 240
(1) n = 17	30	
(1) n = 11	20	
(6a)	80	239
(7a)	0	241
(7b)	100	
(7c)	<1	
(7d)	0.5	242
(7e)	1	
(8a)	10	243
(8b)	33	
(8c)	58	
(9a)	0.5	244
(9b)	20	
(10)	1	238
(11a)	0.005	241
(11b)	0	245
(11c)	0.03	246
(12)	0	247
Alterations at C-2		
(2; *lyso*-PAF)	0	239
(13a)	2	
(13b)	25–100	
(13c)	0	
(13d)	0.5	
(13e)	0.06	
(13f)	0	
(13g)	0	249
(13h)	0	
(14a)	<0.1	239
(14b)	2–10	
(14c)	0	
(15a)	100	
(15b)	<0.1	
(16a)	1	248
(16b)	<0.1	
(16c)	<0.1	
(17a)	0	239
(17b)	0.2–1	
(17c)	<0.1	
(17d)	0	
(18a)	0	250
(18b)	0	
(19)	0.1	246
(20)	10–100	253

Table 2 (*Contd.*)

Agonist	Relative agonist potency (PAF = 100)[a]	Ref.
Phosphorylcholine modifications		
(21)	33	246
(22)	1	
(23)	0	255
(24)	0–10	255, 256
(25a)	0.6–2	257
(25b)	100	
(26)	0	258
(27a)	0	259
(27b)	0	256
(28a)	100	256
(28b)	31	
(28c)	<0.1	
(28d)	<0.1	
(28e)	<0.1	
(29a)	730	
(29b)	56	
(30)	3.3	
(31)	41	
(32a)	40	260
(32b)	5	
(32c)	0.3	
(33a)	100	261
(33b)	300	
(33c)	1000	
(33d)	100	
(33e)	100	263
(34a)	0.04	262
(34b)	12	
Backbone modifications		
(*enantio*-1; *enantio*-PAF)	<0.1	239, 240
(35)	1[b]	268
	5[c]	
	20 000[d]	
(36a)	1	267
(36b)	1	
(37a)	<0.1	143
(37b)	<0.1	269
(38a)	<0.1	270
(38b)	0	
(39a)	<0.1	
(39b)	0	

[a] Based on a composite scale derived from assays of human or rabbit platelet activation and induction of hypotension in normotensive rats, *vs.* PAF control in the same assay, according to ref. 233. [b] Activation of rabbit platelets. [c] Hypotensive activity in normotensive rats, i.v. [d] Antihypertensive activity in SHR, p.o.

limited to these two possible therapeutically beneficial indications, based on the otherwise patho-biological actions of this molecule.

12.12.6.2 Systematic Structural Variations

The distinct characteristics of the phospholipid structure of PAF made dissection into relevant subunits a relatively straightforward intellectual exercise, but synthesis of its analogs a considerably more difficult problem. A retrospective view of these efforts reveals the four main structural components which have been investigated: (i) the substituent at position 1, with regard to chain length and connection to the glycerol backbone; (ii) the substituent at position 2, with similar objectives to those at position 1; (iii) the phosphorylcholine polar head group, with regard to chain length and ammonium and/or phosphate group replacement; and (iv) modification of the glycerol backbone by substitution, isomerization or constraint (Figure 4).[186] Each of these modifications will

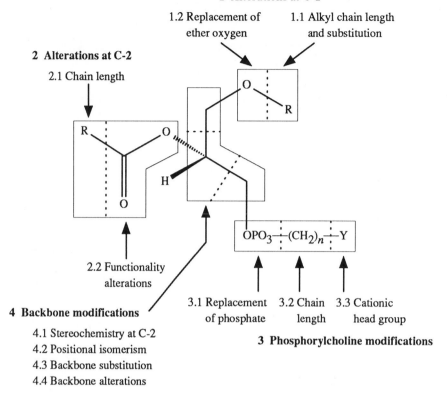

Figure 4 Systematic variation of the structure of PAF in search of agonists and antagonists (adapted from ref. 186)

be discussed in turn, with regard to their overall biological profile and their implications for the steric requirements of the PAF receptor.

12.12.6.2.1 Alterations at C-1

(i) Alkyl chain length, unsaturation and substitution

Variation of either length or degree of unsaturation in the alkyl chain of the C-1 substituent has invariably produced agonists of decreased potency relative to PAF,[237-239] with the exception of some unsaturated analogs such as (6).[239] Within these series, all agonistic activities (washed and platelet-rich plasma platelet aggregation, hypotension and thrombocytopenia) parallel each other, with maximum activity observed for the C_{16}–C_{18} chain lengths, whereas maximal bronchoconstriction was found with chain length C_{14}.[186,240] Analogs in which a phenyl spacer was inserted into the alkyl chain gave a series of compounds (7a–e) of generally overall diminished agonistic activity, but with a variable hypotension/proaggregation ratio, with only (7b) exhibiting an advantage over PAF as a hypotensive agent.[241,242] Terminal fluorination of the alkyl chain (8a–c)[143,243] and insertion of multiple oxygen atoms (9a and b)[244] also diminished activity significantly without separation of agonistic effects. The overall hydrophobic contribution of the C-1 alkyl chain to the observed agonism has been described by an elegant quantitative structure–activity relationship (SAR) compiled from a variety of sources.[240]

(ii) Ether functionality replacement

Connection of the alkyl chain to the glycerol backbone of PAF by an ether linkage is considered an absolute requirement for agonistic activity.[187] Replacement of the ether oxygen by an ester group (10) reduced activity a hundredfold,[238] while other more isosterically compatible substitutions, such as methylene (11a–c)[241,245,246] and sulfur (12),[247] essentially abolished activity. The SAR correlation of hydrophobicity with agonistic effects also accounts for the activity observed in these cases.[240]

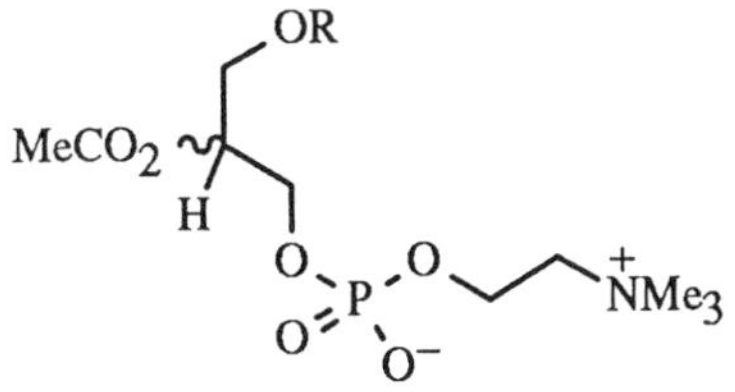

(6) a: R = oleyl
   b: R = 9-*cis*-hexadecenyl
   c: R = 9-*cis*-octadecenyl

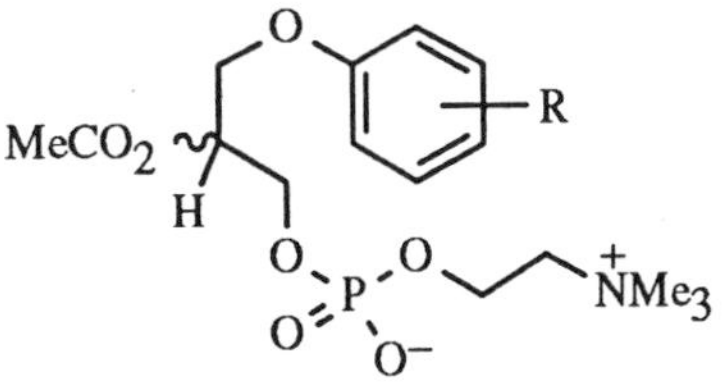

(7) e: R = OCH₂ ⟨benzene ring⟩ Me

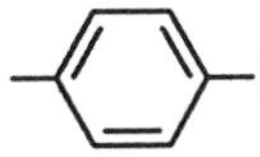

(8) a: R = $(CH_2)_{15}CF_3$
   b: R = $(CH_2)_{13}C_3F_7$
   c: R = $(CH_2)_{15}C_3F_7$
(9) a: R = $O(CH_2)_8O(CH_2)_2O(CH_2)_2OMe$
   b: R = $O(CH_2)_2O(CH_2)_2O(CH_2)_9Me$

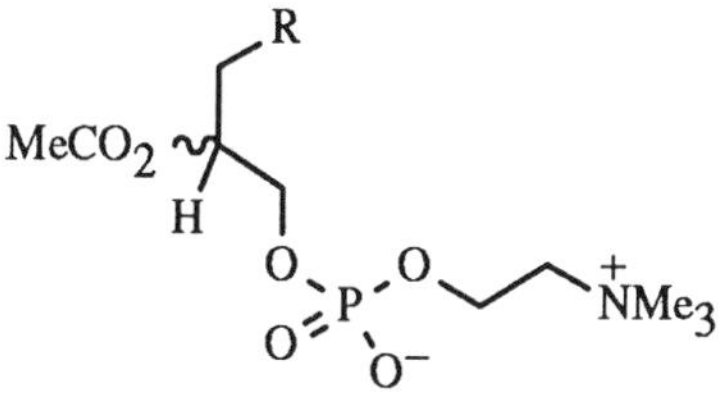

(7) a: R = 2-hexadecyl
   b: R = 3-tetradecyl
   c: R = 4-tridecyl
   d: R = $4\text{-}CH_2O(CH_2)_9Me$

(10) R = stearoyloxy
(11) a: R = hexadecyl
    b: R = heptadecyl
    c: R = nonadecyl
(12) R = $S(CH_2)_{17}Me$

12.12.6.2.2 Alterations at C-2

Initial impetus for functional modifications at C-2 was provided by the observation that PAF was transformed by cleavage of the *sn*-2-acetate into the inactivated metabolite *lyso*-PAF (2), as shown in Scheme 2.[6,187] Examination of a range of esters (13a–h), ethers (14a–c), carbamates (15a and b), 2-deoxyalkyl analogs (16a–c) and amino derivatives (17a–d), however, rapidly proved that agonistic activity did not require removal or transfer of the acetate, since metabolically stable analogs such as the nitrate ester (13e), ethyl ether (14b), methyl carbamate (15a) and 2-deoxy-2-*n*-propyl analog (16a) continued to exhibit reasonable activity.[239,248] Instead, activity at the C-2 position can be correlated with the length and bulk of the substituent, with maximal activity observed for substituents within a van der Waals radius of 6–7 Å. The SAR derived from the C-2 analog series thus accounts for the inactivity of analogs substituted with steric extremes such as trifluoro- and trichloro-acetyl (13g and h),[249] or fluorine and chlorine (18a and b),[250] as well as for structures intermediary in bulk.[187] Of the compounds possessing substitution most closely isosteric with acetoxy at C-2, such as the ketone (19),[245,251] the acetamide (17b)[239,252] and the thioester (20),[253] only the last displays activity actually comparable to PAF, *i.e.* hypotensive effects at picomolar doses.

12.12.6.2.3 Phosphorylcholine modifications

(i) Replacement of phosphate

As noted previously in Scheme 3, 1-*O*-alkyl-2-acetylglycerols (5), which result from complete removal of the phosphorylcholine moiety of PAF, display antihypertensive activity in rats, probably due to the action of a specific cholinephosphotransferase which converts them to PAF *in situ*.[47] In

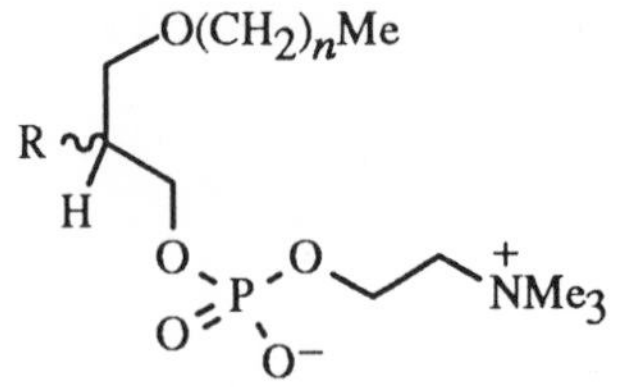

$$\text{R} \underset{\text{H}}{\overset{\text{O(CH}_2)_n\text{Me}}{\diagdown}} \quad \underset{\text{O}}{\overset{\text{O}}{\underset{\diagdown}{P}}} \overset{\text{O}}{\diagup} \diagdown \diagup \overset{+}{\text{NMe}_3}$$

(13) a: R = HCO_2	(14) a: R = Me	(17) a: R = NH_2
b: R = $EtCO_2$	b: R = Et	b: R = $NHCOMe$
c: R = Bu^tCO_2	c: R = CH_2Ph	c: R = $NHCO_2Me$
d: R = Bu^nCO_2	(15) a: R = O_2CNHMe	d: R = $NHCONHMe$
e: R = ONO_2	b: R = O_2CNHPh	(18) a: R = F
f: R = OSO_2Me	(16) a: R = n-propyl	b: R = Cl
g: R = CF_3CO_2	b: R = isopropyl	(19) R = CH_2COMe
h: R = CCl_3CO_2	c: R = isobutyl	(20) R = $SCOMe$

contrast, however, the corresponding phosphoric acid (4), biosynthetic precursor of the glycerol (5), elicited little, if any, platelet serotonin release,[254] possibly indicating the absence of this biosynthetic pathway in platelets.

Replacement of the phosphate group by phosphonate has been approached from both possible directions. Replacement of the glycerol or choline oxygen with methylene results in isosteric phosphonates (21) and (22), respectively.[246] Removal of these oxygens likewise affords phosphonates (23) and (24).[249,255,256] Of these phosphonate analogs, only the sn-3-phosphonate (21) retained reasonable activity in comparison with PAF. Comparison of activity within the series of isosteric analogs, where oxygen is replaced by methylene (11, 19, 21 and 22), reveals that, of the four oxygen atoms considered, the sn-3 oxygen plays the least important role in the SAR of PAF agonists.[246] Of the two possible chiral phosphorothioate analogs (25a and b), remarkably, only the S_P-PAF analog (25b) exhibited agonistic activity equal to that of PAF, while the R_P-PAF analog (25a) was only 0.6–2% as active, demonstrating that the phosphate oxygen makes an important contribution to the interaction of PAF with its receptor.[257] In fact, complete replacement of the phosphate by the isosteric sulfonylbismethylene (26)[258] or by ω-(trimethylamino)alkoxy groups (27a and b)[256,259] eradicated agonistic activity, suggesting that the contribution of the phosphate group to the activity of PAF lies in its ability to bear a negative charge.[258]

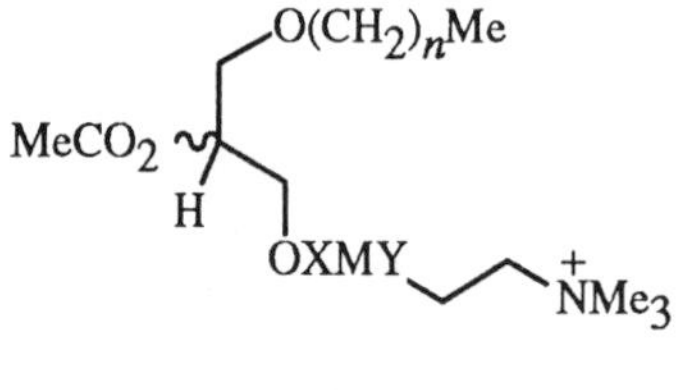

$$\text{MeCO}_2 \underset{\text{H}}{\overset{\text{O(CH}_2)_n\text{Me}}{\diagdown}} \quad \overset{}{\underset{\text{OXMY}}{\diagdown}} \diagup \diagdown \diagup \overset{+}{\text{NMe}_3}$$

$$\text{MeCO}_2 \underset{\text{H}}{\overset{\text{O(CH}_2)_{16}\text{Me}}{\diagdown}} \quad \overset{\text{X}}{\underset{\text{O}}{\overset{\|}{\underset{P}{\diagup}}}} \diagdown \text{Y} \diagdown \diagup \overset{+}{\text{NMe}_3}$$

	X	M	Y
(21)	CH_2	PO_2	O
(22)	O	PO_2	CH_2
(23)	—	PO_2	O
(24)	O	PO_2	—
(26)	CH_2	SO_2	—
(27) a:	O	—	CH_2
b:	O	CH_2	CH_2

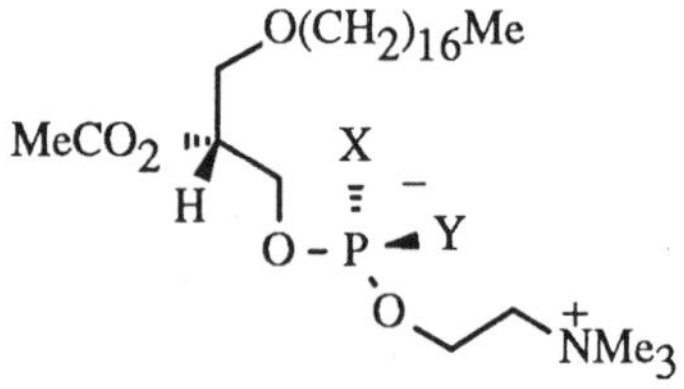

(25) a:	X = S, Y = O
b:	X = O, Y = S

(ii) Chain length and substitution

Incremental lengthening of the distance between the phosphate and quaternary ammonium group from two to 10 carbons (28a–e) results in a progressive but gradual decrease in agonistic activity. While substitution of methyl adjacent to the phosphate (29a) results in little change in activity, addition of a methyl group adjacent to the ammonium group (29b) increased activity eightfold over PAF in both hypotensive and proaggregatory responses. A similar substitution with phenyl (30) resulted in decreased activity, however. Replacement of the ethylene bridge by m-phenoxymethylene

(**31**) did little to alter activity. None of these alterations resulted in substantial improvement of agonistic selectivity.[256]

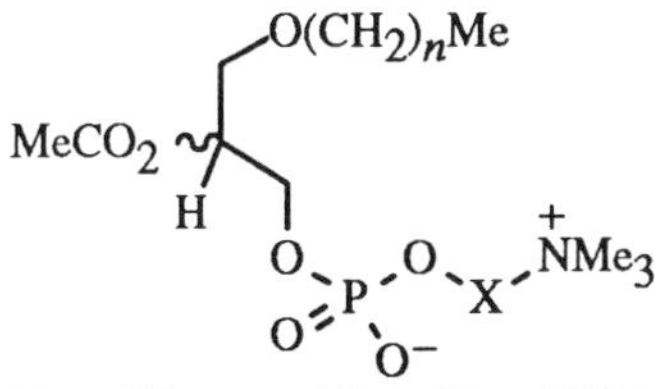

(**28**) **a**: X = (CH$_2$)$_3$ (**29**) **a**: X = CH(Me)CH$_2$
       b: X = (CH$_2$)$_4$ **b**: X = CH$_2$CH(Me)
       c: X = (CH$_2$)$_6$ (**30**) X = CH$_2$CH(Ph)
       d: X = (CH$_2$)$_8$
       e: X = (CH$_2$)$_{10}$ (**31**) X =

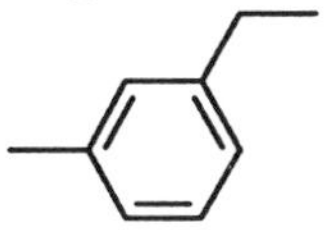

(iii) Cationic head group modifications

Sequential removal of methyl groups from the quaternary ammonium moiety of the choline tail (**32a–c**) results in a steady decrease in agonistic activity.[260] That the dimethylamino and mono-methylamino analogs (**32a** and **b**) possess reasonable activity with respect to PAF indicates that *N*-methylation may take place *in vivo*.[187] Replacement of the quaternary trimethylammonium group of choline with other cationic head groups (**33a–e**) or similar dialkylamino moieties (**34a** and **b**) results in a series of compounds which retain or exceed, by up to a factor of ten for (**33b** and **c**), the proaggregatory and hypotensive activities of PAF, but which fail to offer any meaningful selectivity advantages.[261-263] Later modifications to the cationic head group resulted in the discovery of the first analogs of PAF to display antagonistic activity (*vide infra*).

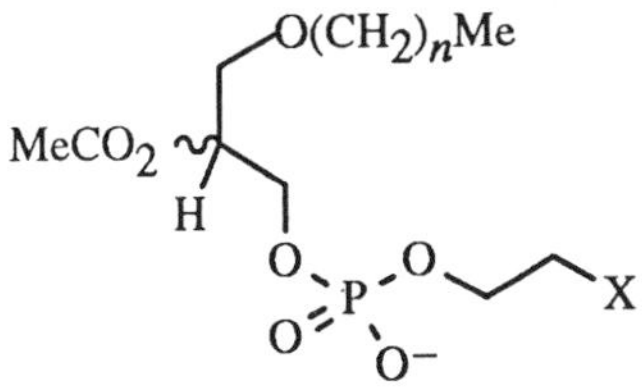

(**32**) **a**: X = NMe$_2$ (**33**) **a**: X =   (**34**) **a**: X =
       b: X = NHMe
       c: X = NH$_2$

                 b: X = 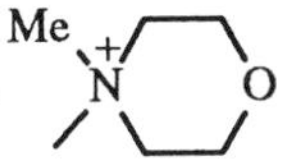   **b**: X =

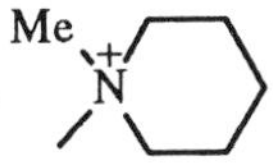

                 c: X =

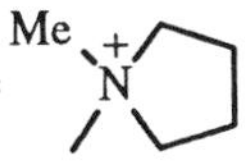

                 d: X = $^+$NEt$_3$
                 e: X = $^+$NEt$_2$Me

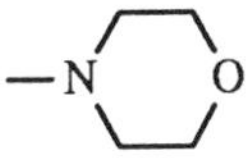

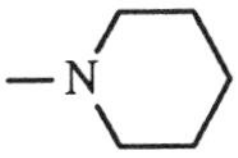

12.12.6.2.4 Glycerol backbone modifications

(i) Stereochemistry at C-2

One of the most convincing factors favoring the existence of a specific PAF receptor is the observation that, by every measure of agonistic activity, the stereospecificity requirement of (*R*)-PAF (**1**) over its unnatural antipode (*S*)-PAF (*enantio*-**1**) is maintained, most often by a factor of a thousand or more.[239,264] This difference has also been observed for a number of analogs of PAF, prompting the synthesis of many potential agonists and antagonists as racemic mixtures, under the assumptions that: (i) the agonistic activity of the antipode would be negligible and (ii) the antipode would not display activity of opposing (antagonist or agonist) character.

(ii) Positional isomerism

The strict stereospecificity requirements at C-2 would seem to dictate that there would be little tolerance for changes in the spatial arrangement of the three glyceryl substituents. However, this has been found not to be the case, since there is sometimes only one order of magnitude difference in activity between C-1/C-2 or C-2/C-3 regioisomers in comparison with the usual substitution pattern on the glycerol backbone. This can be accounted for by careful examination of the relative spatial configurations around C-2 in the positional isomers (Figure 5). The (R) configuration of natural PAF closely corresponds to the (S) configuration of both the C-1/C-2 and C-2/C-3 positional isomers, maintaining the relative spatial arrangement of the alkyl chain, acetate and choline tail by the shift of a single methylene group (boxed); the equivalent relation exists between (S)-PAF (enantio-**1**), and the C-1/C-2 and C-2/C-3 regioisomers of the (R) configuration. The decreased activity of the regioisomers may be related to the increase in bulk at the C-2 acetate imparted by the extra methylene group.[187] This is indeed what is observed when stereochemically pure positional isomers are compared; the activities of (S)-1-acetyl-2-O-alkyl-GPCs, the C-1/C-2 positional isomers of PAF, are within a factor of 50–100 of the activity of PAF itself.[239] Since, as noted above, most analogs of PAF have been prepared as racemic mixtures, racemates of such positional isomers will necessarily contain the (S) configuration corresponding to (R)-PAF, and display at least some of the activity inherent in the natural glyceryl spatial arrangement.[265] This relationship between PAF regioisomers has been found to extend also to a number of PAF analogs of varying structure.[187,245,266]

(iii) Backbone substitution

Examination of most permutations of methyl substitution at the three possible positions on the glyceryl backbone of PAF, as diastereomeric mixtures[267] or as pure diastereomers,[268] produced disappointing results in both maintenance and separation of agonistic activities. From amongst the series of monomethyl-substituted PAF analogs (eight pure diastereomers derived from positions 1 and 3, and the racemate at position 2), however, a single compound, 1-(S)-methyl-(R)-PAF (**35**), exhibited a sixfold separation of hypotensive from proaggregatory activity, suggesting potential antihypertensive activity. Upon oral administration to SHR, (**35**) was found to be approximately 200 times more potent than PAF as an oral hypotensive agent, producing significant reductions in blood pressure without effects on heart rate, at doses ten- to a hundred-fold lower than its lethal dose by the same route of administration. At this time, (**35**) remains the only PAF analog of any substitution pattern which demonstrates a potentially useful separation of agonist activities.[268]

$$
\begin{array}{c}
\text{H} \quad \text{Me} \\
\diagup \! \diagdown \text{O(CH}_2)_{16}\text{Me} \\
\text{MeCO}_2 \cdots \\
\text{H} \\
\text{O} \diagdown \, \text{P} \diagup \text{O} \diagdown \diagup \diagdown \overset{+}{\text{NMe}_3} \\
\text{O} \diagup \diagdown \\
\text{O}^-
\end{array}
$$

(**35**)

(iv) Other backbone alterations

Insertion of either a methylene[267] or an acetoxymethylene[143,269] unit between either C-1 and C-2 (**36a** and **b**) or C-2 and C-3 (**37a** and **b**) results in compounds one to three orders of magnitude poorer than PAF as hypotensive or proaggregatory agents. No separation of activities has been noted.

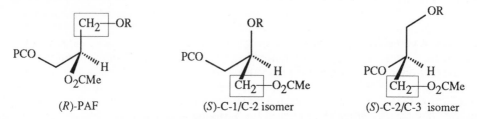

(R)-PAF   (S)-C-1/C-2 isomer   (S)-C-2/C-3 isomer

Figure 5 Configurational comparison of the (S) positional isomers of PAF with (R)-PAF (adapted from ref. 186)

Constraint of the glycerol backbone to afford γ-butyrolactones (**38a** and **b**) and tetrahydrofurans (**39a** and **b**) also had disappointing results, although it is noteworthy that only the analogs which maintained the natural sense of chirality of PAF actually induced aggregation at all.[270] It is also interesting to note that backbone constraint plays a large role in the potency of a number of structures possessing antagonist activity (*vide infra*).

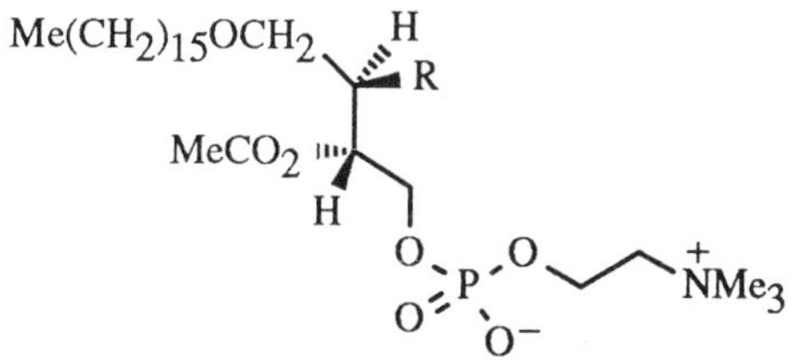

(**36**) a: R = H
       b: R = MeCO$_2$

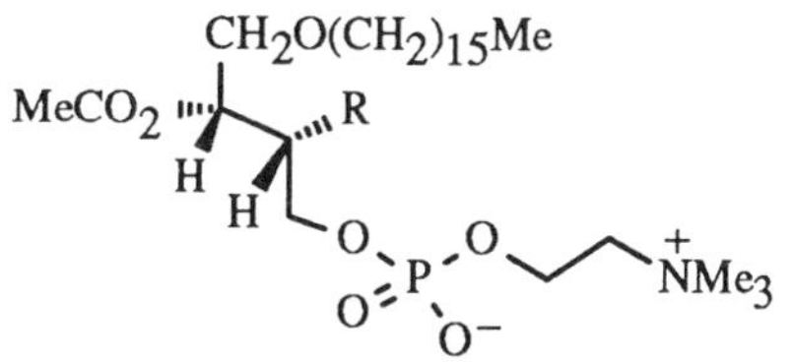

(**37**) a: R = H
       b: R = MeCO$_2$

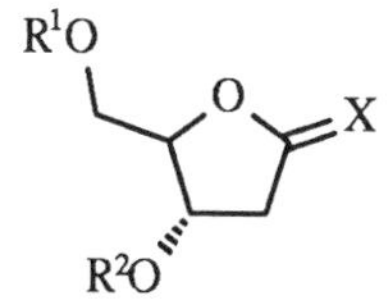

	X	R^1	R^2
(**38**) a:	O	Hexadecyl	PC
b:	O	PC	Hexadecyl
(**39**) a:	CH$_2$	Hexadecyl	PC
b:	CH$_2$	PC	Hexadecyl

(PC = phosphorylcholine)

12.12.7 PAF RECEPTOR ANTAGONISTS

12.12.7.1 Implications and Evaluation of Selective Antagonism

The discovery of antagonists of the actions of PAF lagged behind the work aimed at uncovering agonists, but gained impetus as the complex scheme of biochemical pathways acted on and potentially mediated by PAF was uncovered. The mounting evidence that most actions of PAF are receptor-mediated events, based on stereospecificity requirements in PAF and analogs, and the discovery of PAF-specific responses to stimulation and PAF-specific desensitization to further stimulus, however, confirmed the validity of this search.[271] The possibility of interfering with or blocking the actions of a molecule of such potent pathobiological effects, as described above, has become an enticing goal in the search for novel agents of potential use as treatments for such acute conditions as systemic anaphylaxis, asthma, thrombosis, atherogenesis, endotoxic shock, gastro-intestinal ulceration and graft rejection.[272,273]

Evaluation of compounds as antagonists of the actions of PAF could, in theory, be carried out by assessment of the degree of inhibition or reversal of any of the physiological effects of PAF detailed in Figure 2. In practice, however, this evaluation is carried out most often by *in vitro* assay of the inhibition of PAF-induced platelet aggregation by the potential antagonist, followed by, in the case of reasonably potent compounds, determination of its receptor binding affinity using [³H]PAF. More recently, an alternative microtiter-scale *in vitro* assay based on the inhibition of PAF-induced elastase release by human neutrophils was shown to be of comparable sensitivity and discriminative capacity to these methods, suggesting this as a suitable alternative for large-scale drug screening of PAF antagonists.[274] A compilation of comparative data available in these screens for reported antagonists is presented in Table 3, which is organized in parallel with the discussion which follows.

Evaluation of potential PAF antagonists *in vivo* is highly dependent on the nature of the disease model. Of these models, the most general is PAF-induced mortality in mice, previously described in Section 12.12.4.3.5. However, as mentioned, this screen also detects inhibitors of enzymes activated downstream from the direct actions of PAF. Specific models used to evaluate the actions of PAF antagonists, mainly under conditions of acute PAF administration, have been developed for a number of disease states cited above in which PAF is implicated. Amongst these are the inhibition of PAF-induced hypotension (data for which is included in Table 2 where available), PAF-induced

Table 3 Inhibition of PAF-induced Responses by PAF Antagonists

Antagonist	Platelet aggregation, pIC_{50}[a]	$[^3H]PAF$ binding, pIC_{50}[b]	Elastase release, pIC_{50}[c]	Hypotension, ED_{50} or %[d] (mg kg^{-1}, i.v.)	Ref.
PAF analogs					
CV-3988 (**40**)	6.0 (A)	7.17	6.56	57 (0.1)	274, 276, 280, 286
Ono-6240 (**41**)	6.62 (C)	7.31	—	0.13	292, 293, 317
Ro 19-3740 (**42**)	6.4 (B)	—	8.04	—	274, 296
SRI 63-119 (**43**)	5.42 (B)	5.87	—	—	300
SRI 63-072 (**44**)	4.65 (B)	5.85	—	0.16	300, 312
Tetrahydropyran (**45**)	5.07 (E)	—	—	0.09	301
SRI 63-073 (**46**)	4.42 (B)	5.47	—	—	302
RU-45703 (**48**)	5.10 (B)	—	—	—	304
U66985 (**49**)	6.69 (B)	—	—	—	305
CV-6209 (**50**)	6.77 (B)	—	—	0.009	309
Pyridinium ester (**51**)	5.82 (B)	—	—	51 (1.0)	310
Cyclic phosphate (**53a**)	5.67 (E)	—	—	—	311
SRI 63-441 (**54a**)	—	—	—	0.15	313
SRI 63-675 (**54b**)	5.46 (B)	6.43	—	0.032	315
Natural products					
Kadsurenone (**55**)	6.09 (A)	6.84	6.36	67 (0.5)	274, 276, 312, 317
Ginkgolide B (**62**)	6.06 (A)	6.44	6.90	100 (0.5)	274, 276, 317, 334
L-652,469 (**66**)	5.79 (D)	5.16	—	—	336
FR-49175 (**71**)	5.07 (D)	—	—	0 (10)	338, 339
FR-900452 (**73**)	6.43 (D)	—	—	57 (1.0)	341, 342
Structurally novel compounds					
L-652,731 (**74**)	7.0 (D)	6.99	—	72 (1.6)	317, 345, 346
L-653,150 (**75**)	7.52 (D)	7.05	—	—	317, 350, 351
L-659,989 (**76**)	8.96 (D)	8.04	—	—	352
Diketopiperazine (**77**)	6.75 (E)	—	—	51 (3)	353
Alprazolam (**78**)	4.86 (B)	5.42	—	—	357, 363
Triazolam (**79**)	5.11 (B)	6.09	—	—	345, 363
Brotizolam (**80**)	6.27 (B)	—	—	0.8	357
Etizolam (**81**)	5.50 (D)	7.66	—	54 (0.3)	358, 359
WEB 2086 (**82**)	6.77 (B)	8.21	—	0.052	368, 384
48740 RP (**83**)	4.80 (D)	5.64	5.19	—	274, 369
[^3H]52770 RP (**84**)	7.71 (D)	8.39	—	50 (2.0)	372
Pyrido[2,1-*b*]quinazoline-8-carboxamide (*R*)-(**87**)	—	6.60	—	—	377
(*S*)-(**87**)	—	5.22	—	—	
rac-(**87**)	—	—	—	75 (10)	
SDZ 64,412 (**88**)	7.22	7.22	—	—	378
Dioxolane (**89**)	—	6.52	—	—	381
α-Pentyl enone (**91**)	—	6.15	—	—	382

[a] PAF-induced aggregation of (A) washed human platelets, (B) human PRP, (C) guinea pig platelets, (D) washed rabbit platelets or (E) rabbit PRP. [b] Inhibition of [^3H]PAF binding to washed human platelets. [c] Inhibition of PAF-induced elastase release from neutrophils. [d] Inhibition of PAF-induced hypotension in normotensive rats, given as ED_{50} or as percent inhibition at indicated dose.

bronchospasm and endotoxin-induced shock. Since the conditions under which such *in vivo* assays are conducted vary so widely, the results for individual antagonists are also incorporated in a more qualitative manner into the discussion which follows.

12.12.7.2 Systematic Structural Variations

Using criteria identical to those described above for the design of PAF analogs as agonists, a number of specific PAF antagonists have been discovered by systematic variation of the structure of PAF. In direct contrast to the agonists, however, most of these PAF analog antagonists simultaneously incorporate multiple changes in the basic phospholipid structure of PAF. By this token, it is convenient to classify these compounds as acyclic (nonconstrained) or cyclic (constrained) analogs of the PAF structure, and merely enumerate their additional individual characteristics.[187]

12.12.7.2.1 CV-3988

The first potent and specific antagonist of PAF from any class was the racemic PAF analog from Takeda, CV-3988 (**40**), discovered as part of an investigation of carbamate analogs of *lyso*-GPC as potential antifungal and cytotoxic agents. The original report concerning (40) claimed that the compound inhibited PAF-induced platelet aggregation at micromolar concentrations, while having no effect on aggregation induced by AA, ADP, collagen or calcium ionophore.[275] More recent reports, however, have shown that (40) also inhibits the aggregation response induced by these other agents but at doses one order of magnitude greater.[276,277] This activity is also reflected *in vivo*, as (40) causes a dose-dependent inhibition of the hypotension and fall in platelet count induced by a low dose of PAF.[278] In all of these studies, however, high doses of (40) displayed PAF-agonist activities.[276-278] Binding of [³H]PAF to rabbit, human and guinea pig platelets is inhibited by submicromolar concentrations of (40).[279,280] Among the other PAF-induced or PAF-mediated effects inhibited by (40) are phosphorylation of the 20 and 40 kDa platelet proteins,[281] platelet PI turnover,[282] neutropenia and thrombocytopenia,[283] PMA-induced pleurisy,[284] increased systemic vascular[145] and cutaneous vascular[176] permeability, negative inotropism and general cardiodepression,[106] endotoxin and anaphylactic shock,[285-287] disseminated intravascular coagulation,[288] endotoxin-induced gastrointestinal erosion[289] and bronchoconstriction.[290] The efficacy and tolerability of (40) upon intravenous infusion in man has also recently been determined. Doses from 750 to 2000 μg kg⁻¹ caused a dose-dependent reduction in platelet sensitivity to PAF without major changes in blood pressure, pulse or respiratory rate, with clinically insignificant indications of plasma hemolysis.[291] As might be judged from this list, CV-3988 (40) has become somewhat of a standard for PAF antagonism and thus for studies in which PAF is considered a mediator, even though it has exhibited a potential for agonistic effects and nonspecific platelet inactivation.

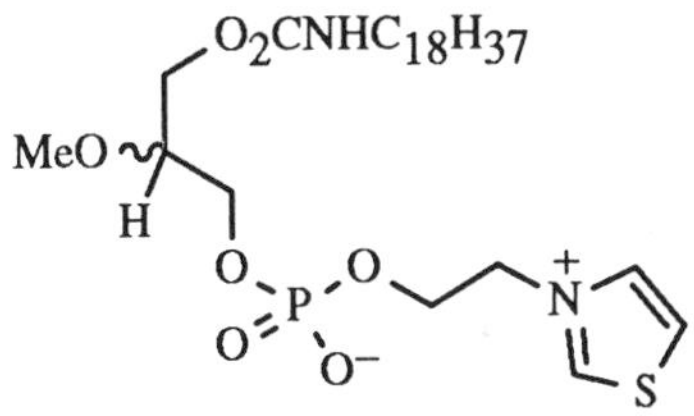

(40)

12.12.7.2.2 *Other thiazolium-type analogs*

Much as the structure of PAF was used as a model for agonists, the lead structure (40) provided a starting point for the synthetic efforts aimed at development of PAF-based antagonists. Replacement of the phosphorylethyl group of (40) by a heptamethylene bridge afforded Ono-6240 (41), a compound of similar profile[292] and active *in vivo* in models of endotoxin shock[293] and ischemic bowel necrosis.[294] From amongst a similar series of compounds, Ro 19-3704 (42) was chosen for its potency and *in vivo* stability.[295,296] Inhibition of PAF-induced rabbit, human and guinea pig platelet aggregation as well as hypotension, bronchoconstriction and thrombocytopenia have been reported for (42).[187] The pattern of potency and *in vivo* activity is also followed by the close analog SRI 63-119 (43) and its spirocyclic counterpart SRI 63-072 (44), shown to inhibit PAF-induced platelet aggregation, hypotension, bronchospasm, hemoconcentration, extravasation and ischemic bowel necrosis.[294,297-299] In the case of the latter compound, both enantiomeric forms demonstrate similar binding to the PAF receptor[300] and produce similar inhibition of PAF-induced hemoconcentration in the guinea pig.[273] Cyclization of the backbone of (40) into a tetrahydropyran ring results in a compound (45) of increased potency as an inhibitor of both platelet aggregation and hypotension. Both 2,3-positional and relative stereochemical isomerization decrease potency, while replacement of the hydroxylic carbamate oxygen by sulfur did not change activity significantly.[301] A similar but somewhat less potent compound SRI 63-073 (46) was designed by combination of thiamine phosphate with a piperidine-based PAF-like backbone.[302]

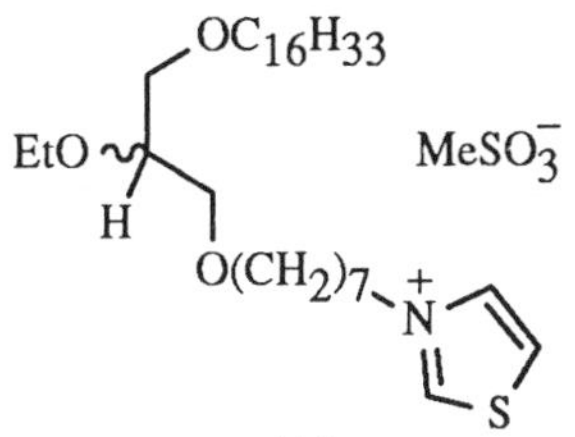

(41)

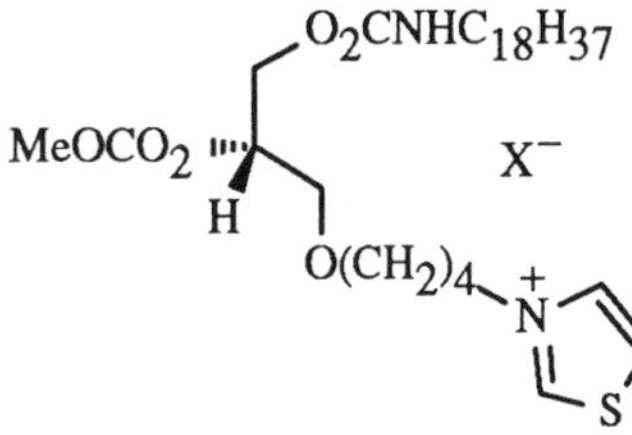

(42)

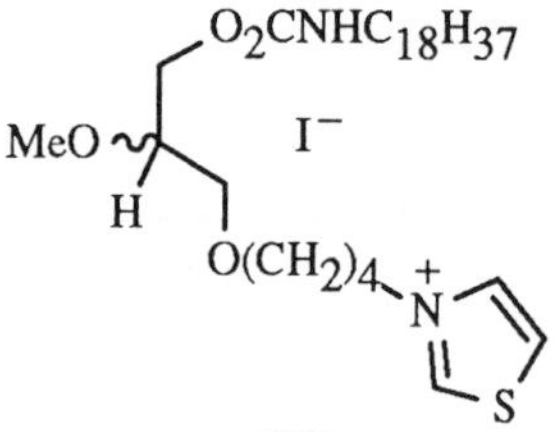

(43)

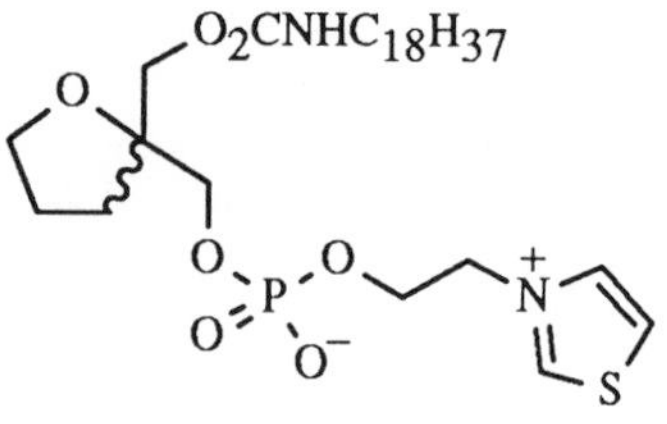

(44)

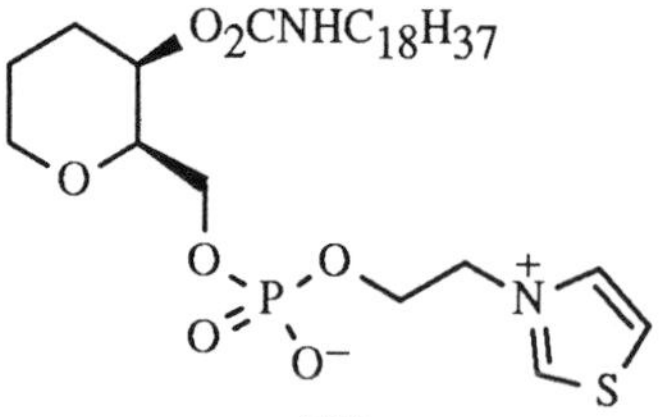

(45)

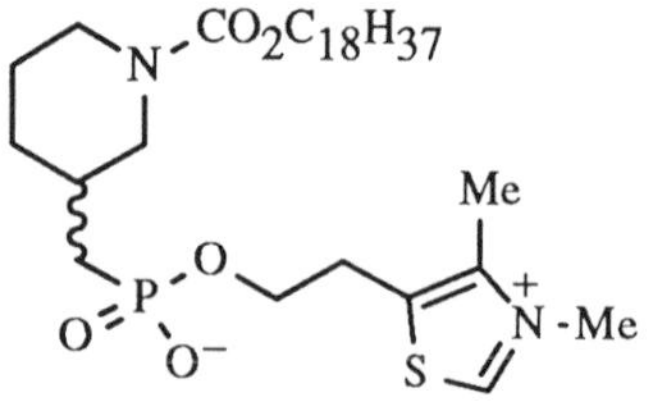

(46)

12.12.7.2.3 Trimethylammonium head groups

In comparison with thiazolium-based analogs of PAF, potential antagonists containing the trimethylammonium functionality of PAF itself have not enjoyed as much success. The amidophosphonate (47), related to the agonist (17b), inhibited platelet aggregation stimulated by PAF, AA, ADP, thrombin and calcium ionophore, but not by epinephrine or collagen. Inhibition of PLA_2 and PLC_2 activity has been suggested as an additional mode of action.[303] A more PAF-specific profile has been presented for RU-45703 (48), which shows antagonistic activity against PAF- and collagen- but not AA-induced platelet aggregation. *In vivo*, its inhibitory effect favors PAF-induced broncho-constriction over hypotension.[304] The presence of the ester moiety, however, does little for plasma stability, as has been found in the study which resulted in (42).[296] Of a series of choline chain length homologs, U66985 (49), the (R) antipode of (28c), was determined to be the most potent compound against PAF-induced platelet aggregation, secretion and phosphoinositide turnover. In direct comparison with (40), (49) was consistently one order of magnitude more potent.[305] The effects of (49) in rabbit platelets were found to be PAF specific.[306] The ability of PAF to enhance its own rate of metabolism and of (49) to inhibit the metabolism by sevenfold by a mechanism independent of competitive binding have also been investigated.[307] Both PAF-induced hemodynamic and gly-cogenolytic responses were inhibited by (49) in perfused rat liver.[308]

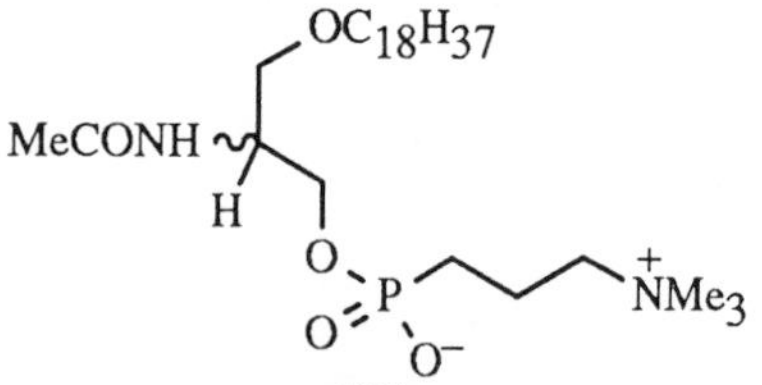

(47)

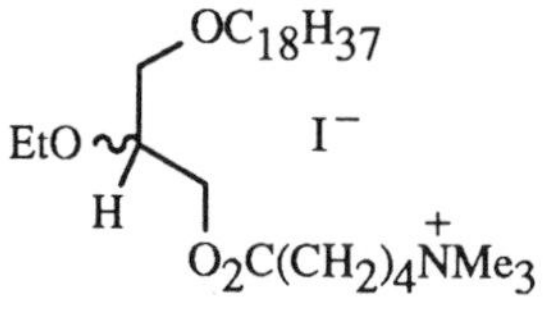

(48)

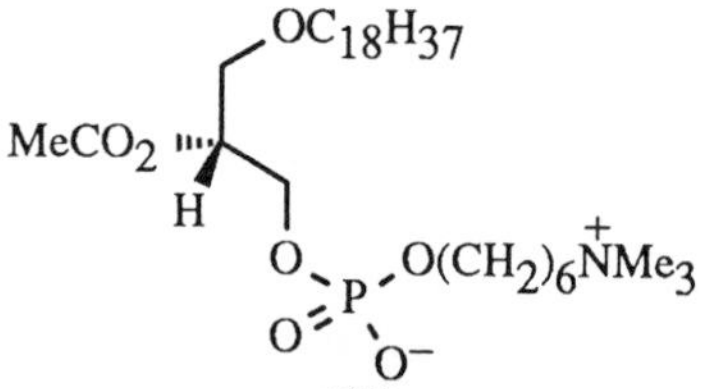

(49)

12.12.7.2.4 Other cationic head groups

Major structural changes incorporated into one molecule have been the overall hallmark of the PAF antagonists of useful potency. Replacement of the 2-(thiazolium)ethyl phosphate head group of CV-3988 (40) by the more complex pyridinium carbamate of CV-6209 (50) resulted in a hundredfold potency increase in antagonism of both PAF-induced platelet aggregation and hypotension.[309] A modest increase in antagonist activity was also observed with (51), a pyridinium analog of (48).[310] Another such example is dioxanone (52), where conformational restraint has been imposed on the PAF backbone and the cationic head group has been changed to pyridinium.[295] Of a similar series of cyclic phosphates with pyridinium or trimethylanilinium cationic head groups, compounds (53a–c) inhibited PAF-induced rabbit platelet aggregation at concentrations similar to (40).[311]

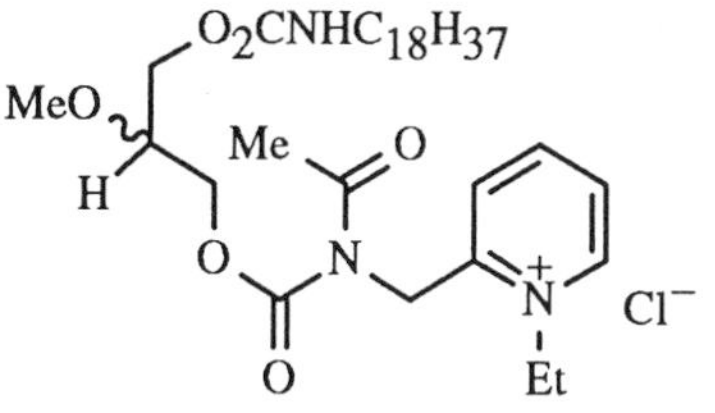

(50) 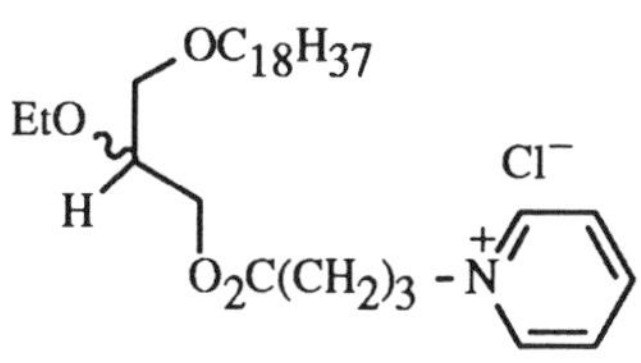   (51) 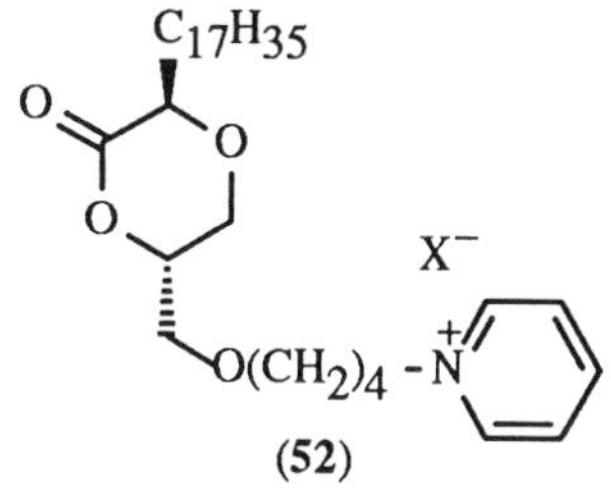   (52)

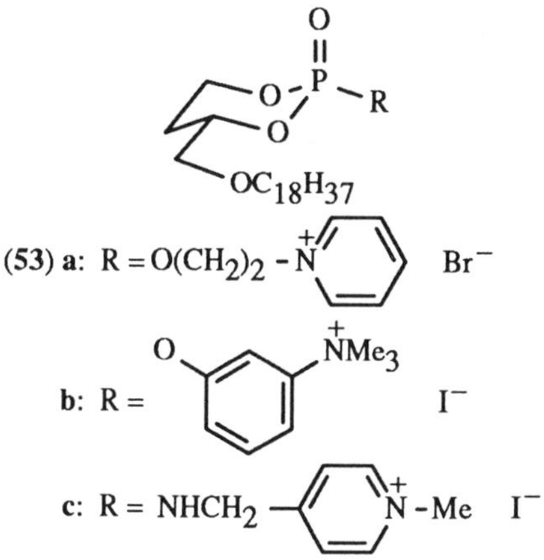

(53) a: $R = O(CH_2)_2 - \overset{+}{N}$ ... Br$^-$

b: $R =$ ... $\overset{+}{N}Me_3$ ... I$^-$

c: $R = NHCH_2 -$ ... $\overset{+}{N}-Me$ I$^-$

The combination of a backbone constrained into a 2,5-disubstituted tetrahydrofuran and a quinolinium head group in the structure of SRI 63-441 (**54a**) has been shown to potently inhibit PAF- and endotoxin-induced hypotension in the rat and dog,[312] and PAF-induced hemoconcentration and bronchoconstriction in rat, guinea pig, dog and primate species,[313] suggesting potential clinical application of (**54a**) in disease states involving hypotension, shock, hyperpermeability and pulmonary dysfunction. Treatment with (**54a**) inhibited interleukin 1 (IL-1)-induced increases in vascular permeability and leukocyte infiltration in the rabbit eye following intravitreal injection of IL-1, suggesting a role for PAF in IL-1-induced inflammation.[314] A similar profile has been reported for the 2,5-dimethyl analog of (**54a**), SRI 63-675 (**54b**), which displays an enhanced potency in primates *vs.* other species and *vs.* a wide range of PAF antagonists of all classes.[315]

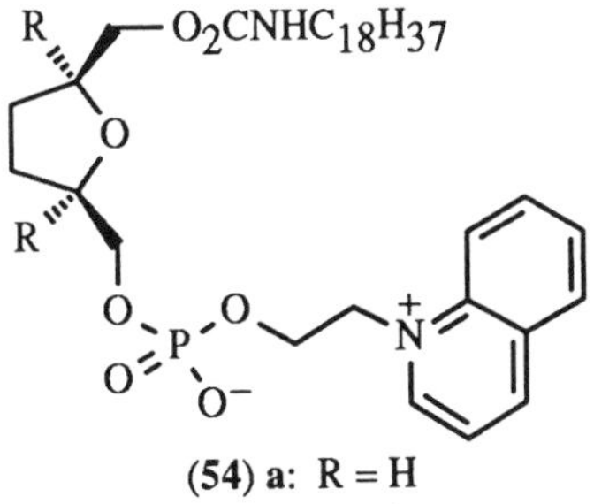

(54) a: R = H
     b: R = Me

12.12.7.3 Natural Products

Although the fact that lipid-like structures related to PAF were found to be specific antagonists of PAF receptor binding and the effects of PAF, the validity of the search for PAF antagonists of potential clinical utility was not fully realized until the discovery that several natural products whose structures are totally unrelated to PAF display potent and specific PAF antagonism. These compounds, which include lignans, terpenes, sesquiterpenes and diketopiperazines, will be considered separately by class.

12.12.7.3.1 *Kadsurenone*

The neolignan kadsurenone (**55**) was isolated from the Chinese herbal plant haifenteng (*Piper futokadsura*) used in southern China to prepare a traditional remedy for the general relief of bronchoasthma and the stiffness, inflammation and pain of rheumatic conditions. The compound is a potent and specific inhibitor of PAF-induced rabbit platelet and human neutrophil aggregation in micromolar concentrations, without exhibiting any PAF-agonist activity. It was also demonstrated to be a specific and competitive inhibitor of the binding of [^{3}H]PAF to its receptor from a number of tissue sources.[316,317] Scatchard analysis of binding data using [^{3}H]dihydrokadsurenone revealed the presence of a single class of binding sites ($K_D = 16.8$ nmol dm^{-3}).[318] Although Schild plots displaying linearity and unity of slope confirmed the competitive nature of the PAF antagonism by (55) in guinea pig peritoneal macrophages and hog leukocytes, comparison of pA_2 values showed a 91-fold lower affinity of (55) for the leukocyte *vs.* the macrophage receptor, suggesting that the PAF receptors involved are not identical.[319]

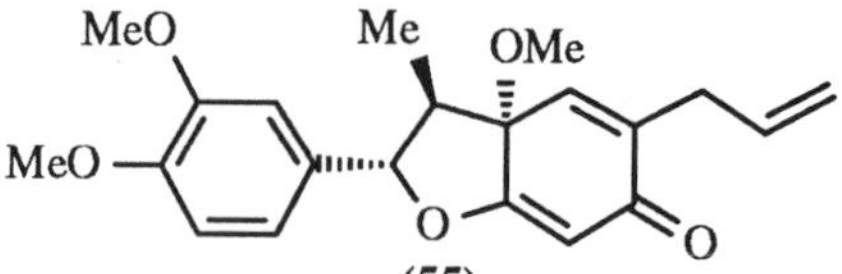

(55)

Studies *in vivo* have demonstrated that (55) is active orally in blocking PAF-induced cutaneous vascular permeability and increases in hematocrit, without any effects on histamine H$_1$, LTD$_4$ or benzodiazepine receptors, or on 5-LO or CO enzyme activity.[316] Endotoxin-induced hypotension was also partially reversed by infusion of (55).[320] In combination with an antihistaminic and a dual CO–LO inhibitor, (55) also blocked ovalbumin-induced guinea pig lung parenchymal strip contraction, suggesting that PAF, histamine and the peptidoleukotrienes act in concert to mediate anaphylaxis-induced airway constriction.[321]

The structural specificity for the binding of (55) is high, since the close structural analogs kadsurin A (56), kadsurin B (57) and piperenone (58) were significantly less active than (55) in PAF receptor binding studies.[322] The synthesis of (55) and a wide range of analogs has allowed the development of a limited SAR for this neolignan skeleton.[323] In addition, several other lignans and neolignans, including burseran (59), veraguensin (60)[187] and a family of related compounds isolated from *Magnolia biondii*,[324] have also been reported to exhibit PAF antagonistic effects.

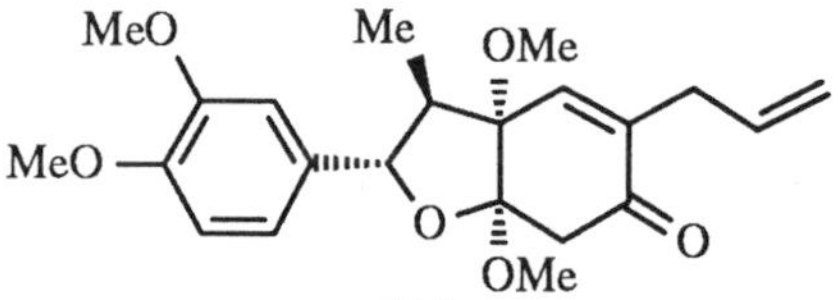

(56)

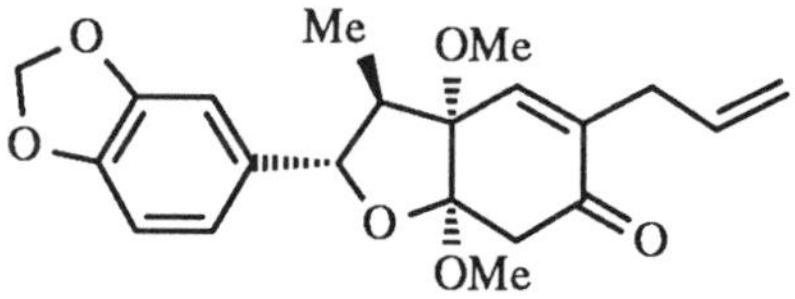

(57)

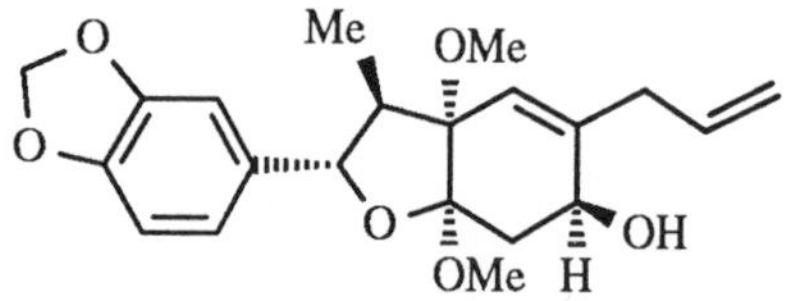

(58)

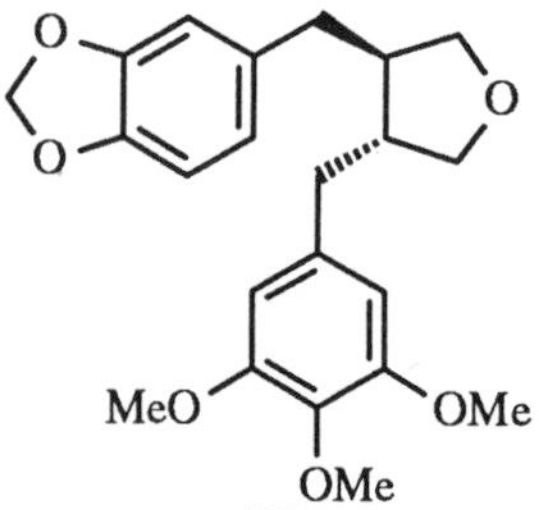

(59)

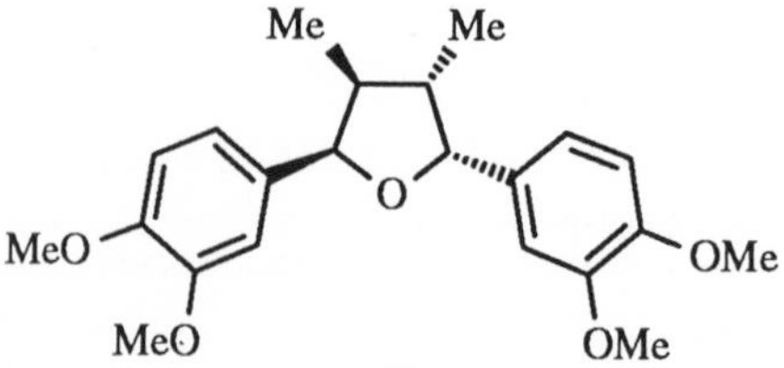

(60)

12.12.7.3.2 *Ginkgolides*

Ginkgolides A, B, C and J, also known as BN-52020 (61), BN-52021 (62), BN-52022 (63) and BN-52024 (64), respectively, are a family of C$_{20}$ hexacyclic terpenoids isolated from the Chinese tree

Ginkgo biloba L.[325,326] The cage structures of these compounds were first elucidated by Nakanishi and co-workers by chemical methods in 1967, and have been confirmed by 500 MHz NMR and X-ray crystallography,[325,327] and, more recently, by total synthesis of (62).[328] Examination of the inhibition of the binding of [³H]PAF by these compounds demonstrated a high affinity for the PAF receptor. Of these, (62) was found to be the most potent, while (63) and (64), possessing a hydroxyl group adjacent to the lipophilic *t*-butyl moiety, were significantly less active, suggesting that the hydrophilic group counteracts the antagonistic effects by interference with the lipophilic group.[207] A synthetic tricyclic analog (65) of the CDE ring system of the ginkgolides, designed as a model of the putative binding mode of (62) to the PAF receptor, was, however, inactive as a PAF antagonist.[329] A comparison of the molecular structures of kadsurenone (55) and (62) suggests that the ether–ester (lactone) carbonyl oxygen–oxygen interatomic distance common to both structures, and possibly to the PAF structure, may be favorable for antagonist activity.[330]

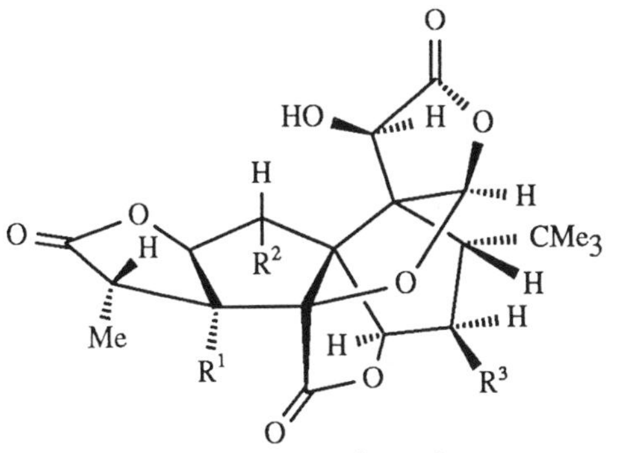

	R^1	R^2	R^3
(61)	OH	H	H
(62)	OH	OH	H
(63)	OH	OH	OH
(64)	OH	H	OH

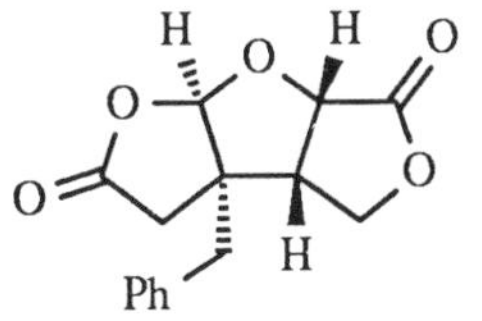

(65)

The potent binding capacity and specificity of (62) for the PAF receptor is illustrated by: (i) its ability to displace [³H]PAF from both rabbit and human platelets, (ii) the inability to reactivate treated platelets by washing and (iii) the inability of (62) to inhibit CO or LO, or to bind to TxA_2 or LTC_4 receptors.[187] This level of activity and specificity is paralleled in platelet aggregation studies, where (62) was once again the most potent of the four and did not inhibit platelet aggregation induced by ADP, AA, thrombin, collagen or calcium ionophore.[207] As had been noted for (49), the antagonist (62) blocks the incorporation of labeled PAF into the phospholipid bilayer of platelet membranes, and also slows the acceleration of PAF metabolism noted on PAF receptor binding.[331] Inhibition of both reacylation of *lyso*-PAF and phosphatidic acid synthesis and a significant decrease in PAF-induced intracellular calcium concentration has been demonstrated by (62) in intact rabbit platelets, suggesting that (62) inhibits not only the binding of PAF to its receptor but also the subsequent intracellular events mediated by the activation of the phosphoinositide cycle and calcium mobilization.[187] *Ex vivo* platelet aggregation studies in rabbits treated with (62) showed significant inhibition of platelet aggregation up to six hours after dosing, indicating favorable bioavailability and metabolism rates.[187]

In addition to platelet effects, inhibition of PAF-induced events by (62) has been noted in a variety of other cellular targets. Amongst these actions are: (i) inhibition of PAF-induced aggregation and degranulation, and reduced chemotaxis in human neutrophils; (ii) blockade of LTC_4 release in human eosinophils; and (iii) inhibition of superoxide generation in human and rabbit PMN, guinea pig macrophages and human eosinophils.[187] The reversal of PAF-induced inhibition of leukocyte proliferation and interleukin 2 production by (62) suggest an immunoregulatory role for PAF and the potential use of (62) as a biological response modifier.[332]

The ginkgolide (62) has been examined in a multitude of *in vivo* models, the results of which have been summarized.[187,207,325,326,333] These effects include: (i) prophylactic inhibition or curative reversal of PAF- or IgG-induced hypotension, hemoconcentration and extravasation in the rat;[334] (ii) inhibition of thrombus formation by PAF in the guinea pig or by electrical stimulation in the rat carotid artery; (iii) normalization of PAF-induced renaltubular sodium transport disturbances and hemodynamic changes associated with experimental cirrhosis; (iv) antagonism of tissue plasminogen activation by PAF; (v) counteraction of endotoxic shock and related hypotension, leukopenia and thrombocytopenia in rat and guinea pigs; (vi) prolongation of experimental cardiac allograft survival in the rat; (vii) inhibition of cardiac anaphylaxis in both passively and actively sensitized guinea pig hearts; (viii) antagonism of PAF-induced bronchoconstriction and ovalbumin-induced bronchospasm, with a concomitant and dose-dependent decrease in leukotriene and TxB_2 levels; and (ix) inhibition of airway hyperreactivity induced by PAF.[207] Finally, in a double-blind placebo-controlled trial in man, a mixture of ginkgolides A, B and C administered orally two hours prior to challenge antagonized the weal and flare responses to intradermal PAF injection and significantly inhibited PAF- but not ADP-induced platelet aggregation.[335] The wide spectrum of activity of (62) in animal models (comprehensively summarized in review form[325, 326]), coupled with an indication of activity in humans, stands as the best demonstration of the potential clinical viability of a PAF antagonist.

12.12.7.3.3 *Other terpenoids*

From amongst a family of sesquiterpenes (66–69) isolated from the Chinese antitussive herbal medicine *Tussilago farfara L.*, identical to products previously found as constituents of *Senecio kleinia*, L-652,469 (66) was determined to be the active constituent, inhibiting [³H]PAF specific binding to rabbit membranes more potently than its closely related coisolates. This compound also demonstrated *in vivo* PAF-antagonistic activity in platelet aggregation and, by oral administration, in PAF- and carrageenan-induced rat paw edema and in PAF-induced cutaneous vascular permeability increase. In addition, (66) potently and completely inhibited the specific binding of dihydropyridine calcium channel blockers (*e.g.* [³H]nitrendipine, $K_i = 1.2 \mu mol\, dm^{-3}$) in cardiac sarcolemmal vesicles. Partial inhibition of such binding was noted for the aromatic alkyl amine verapamil and the benzothiazepine diltiazem. The calcium-channel-related activity is manifested *in vivo* by relaxation of Ca^{2+}-induced contraction of rat thoracic aorta strips. Such a dual activity profile might provide information regarding the structural interrelationship between the PAF receptor, calcium channels and their sensitivity to ionic conditions in responding to antagonists.[336]

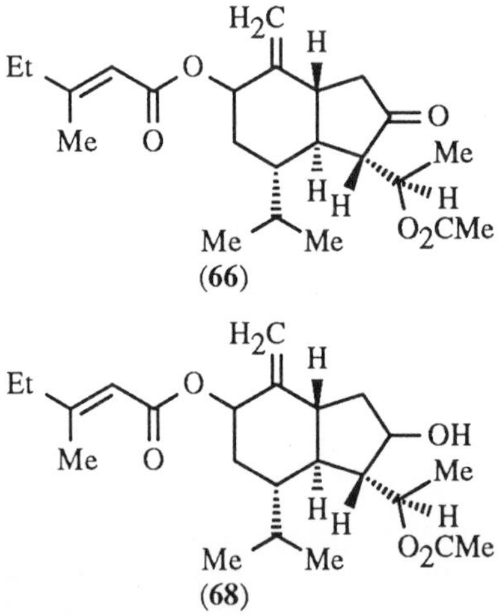

(66)

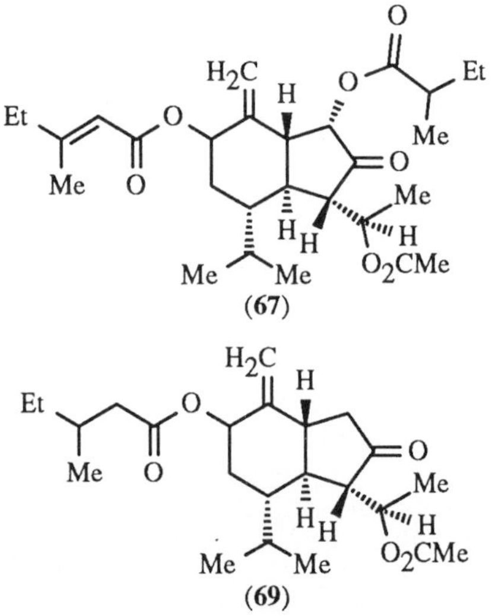

(67)

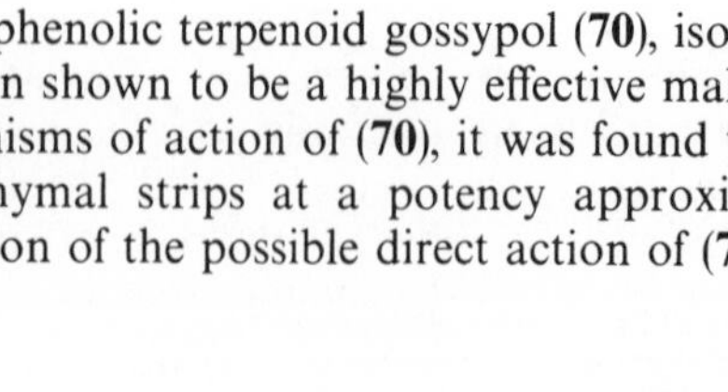

(68)

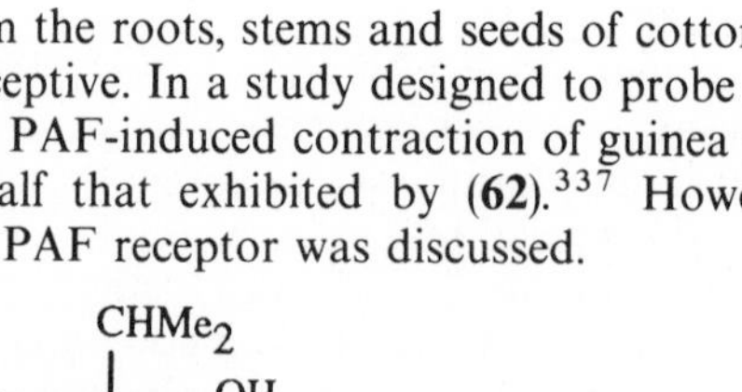

(69)

The phenolic terpenoid gossypol (70), isolated from the roots, stems and seeds of cotton plants, has been shown to be a highly effective male contraceptive. In a study designed to probe possible mechanisms of action of (70), it was found to inhibit PAF-induced contraction of guinea pig lung parenchymal strips at a potency approximately half that exhibited by (62).[337] However, no indication of the possible direct action of (70) at the PAF receptor was discussed.

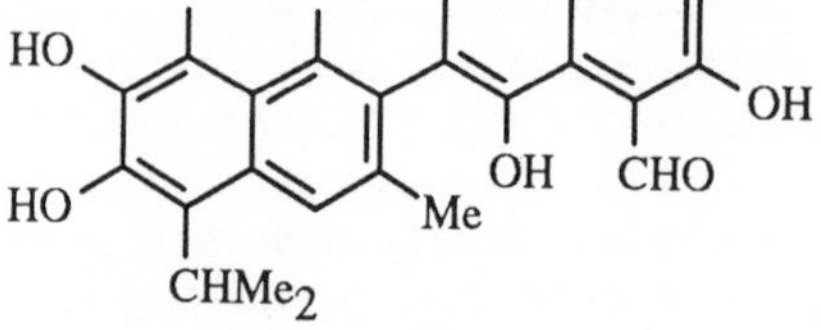

(70)

12.12.7.3.4 Diketopiperazines

Screening of microbial fermentation broths for PAF antagonistic activity identified bisdethiobis(methylthio)gliotoxin (71; FR-49175), isolated from *Penicillium terlikowskii*, as an inhibitor of platelet aggregation induced by PAF but not by collagen, AA or ADP. Of a series of semisynthetic analogs of (71), only (72) exhibited comparable activity.[338] In animal models, (71) significantly inhibited PAF-induced bronchoconstriction in guinea pigs but did not, however, prevent PAF-induced hypotension in rats, vascular permeability increase in mice nor inhibition of IgG-induced anaphylaxis, even at large doses.[339]

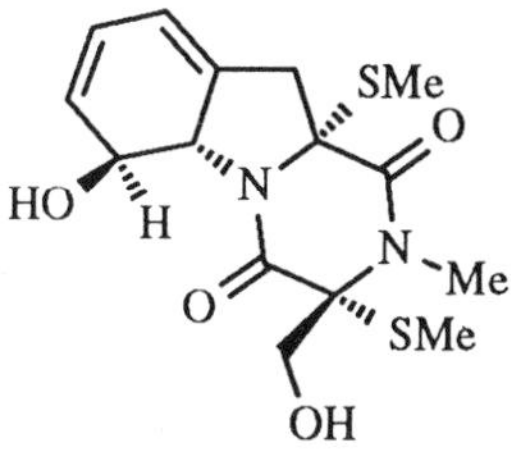

(71) 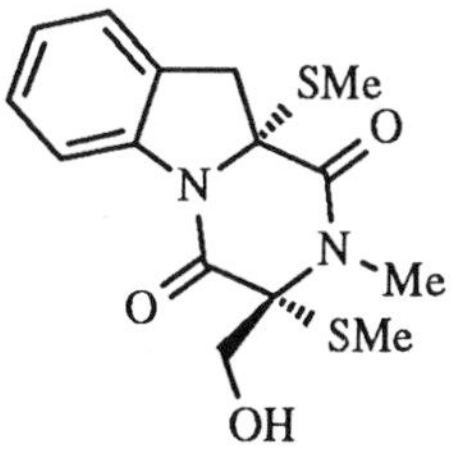   (72)

A similar *in vitro* profile was displayed by the structurally more complex diketopiperazine FR-900452 (73;[340] WS7793B), isolated from the fermentation broth of *Streptomyces phaeofaciens*.[341] Unlike (71), this compound displayed PAF antagonistic activity in guinea pig bronchoconstriction, rat hypotension, mouse vascular permeability increase and IgE-mediated anaphylaxis.[342] Prophylactic administration of (73) inhibited PAF-induced thrombocytopenia and leukopenia in rabbits. Administration prior to endotoxin-induced shock, however, reduced the thrombocytopenia but not the leukopenia associated with this event, suggesting that PAF is not completely responsible for the circulatory events in endotoxemia.[343]

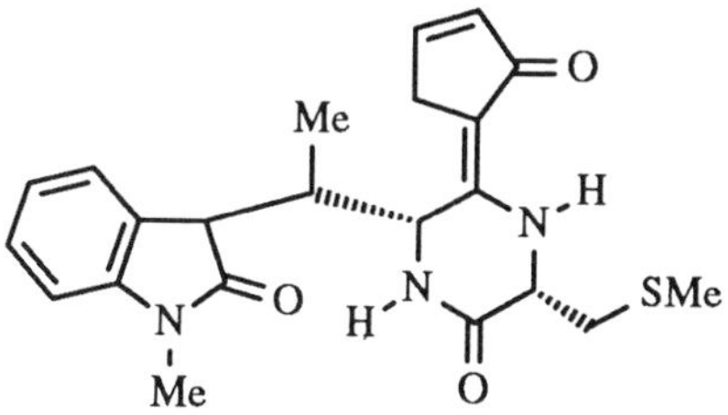

(73)

12.12.7.4 Structurally Novel Synthetic Antagonists

12.12.7.4.1 Diaryltetrahydrofurans

From a series of compounds based on the structural leads provided by the neolignans related to kadsurenone (55) and the lignans such as veraguensin (60), *trans*-2,5-bis(3,4,5-trimethoxyphenyl)-tetrahydrofuran (74; L-652,731) was determined to be the most potent PAF antagonist, displaying an IC_{50} of 0.02 μmol dm^{-3} for inhibition of [^{3}H]PAF receptor binding. The activity was shown to be affected by the overall shape of the molecule, the relative stereochemistry of the aryl substituents and the presence or absence of substituents at positions 3 and 4 of the tetrahydrofuranyl central core. Comparative studies also showed (74) to be the most potent receptor antagonist *vs.* CV-3988 (40), kadsurenone (55) or ginkgolide B (62).[344] The *in vitro* actions of (74) are specific, since platelet aggregation induced by PAF but not by histamine, serotonin, ADP, AA or calcium ionophore was inhibited, and since the binding of other ligands to their respective receptors was not inhibited.[345] The *in vivo* PAF antagonistic effects noted include inhibition of PAF-induced lysosomal hydrolase secretion and extravasation, inhibition of PAF-induced hypotension, reversal of endotoxin-induced hypotension, inhibition of edema formation in the reversed passive Arthus reaction, inhibition of PAF- or carrageenin-induced rat paw edema and inhibition of PAF-induced ocular inflammation in the rat.[167, 346-349] The corresponding tetrahydrothiophene L-653,150 (75) shares the PAF antagonist *in vitro* and *in vivo* profile of its oxygen progenitor (74), but in addition displays a potent inhibition of 5-LO from either human red blood leukocytes (RBL) or PMN. Considering that PAF-induced effects in a variety of tissues include LTB_4 generation, this combination of leukotriene and

PAF antagonistic effects may offer a potential clinical advantage in states such as asthma.[272,350,351] The most potent member of this class, however, is L-659,989 (76), in which the substitution pattern of one of the aryl rings has been greatly varied. This compound binds about tenfold more tightly than the parent (74) to PAF receptors from either rabbit or human platelets, and exhibits comparable potency increases in inhibition of both PAF-induced platelet aggregation and neutrophil degranulation. *In vivo*, a $1 \, mg \, kg^{-1}$ oral dose of (76) 90 min prior to intravenous administration of $10 \, nmol \, kg^{-1}$ of PAF had a marked inhibitory effect upon PAF-induced extravasion and enzyme release in female but not male rats, with a 12–16 h duration of action. The origin of the gender difference is not known, however. This profile of extreme potency coupled with oral activity of long duration makes (76) unique among synthetic PAF antagonists thus far.[352]

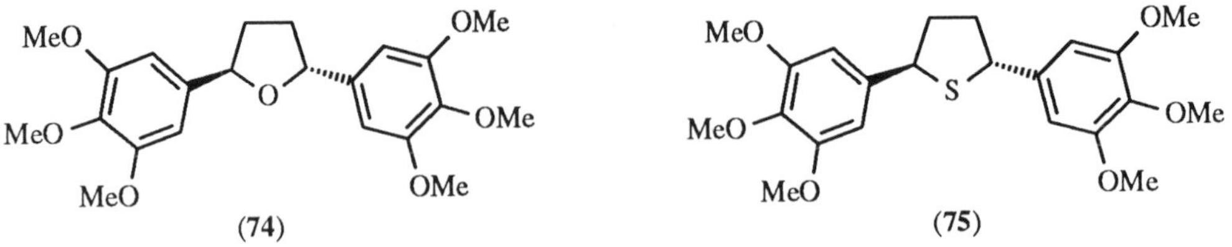

(74)

(75)

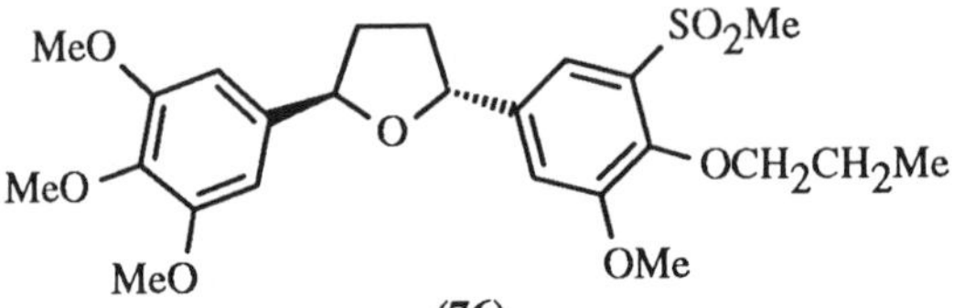

(76)

12.12.7.4.2 Diketopiperazines

The reasonable profile of activity displayed by the microbial products related to gliotoxin (*vide supra*) suggested the synthesis of a series of structurally novel diketopiperazines.[338] These compounds exhibit activity as inhibitors of PAF-induced platelet aggregation, hypotension and vascular permeability increase. Structural preferences within this series include the 3-(R),6-(R)-diastereomeric configuration derived from D-amino acids, and at least one very lipophilic side chain substituent, as exemplified by (77).[353-355]

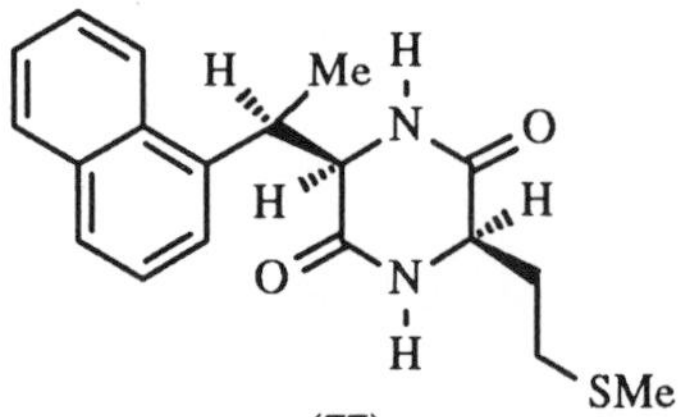

(77)

12.12.7.4.3 Triazolodiazepines

The surprising finding that certain triazolobenzodiazepine psychotropic agents, such as alprazolam (78) and triazolam (79), specifically inhibited PAF-induced platelet aggregation at submicromolar concentrations has provided yet another avenue for synthetic exploration.[356] Screening of the multitudes of such drugs already on hand as potential tranquillizers has revealed that the benzene ring present in (78) or (79) can be conveniently replaced by fused heteroaryl groups, as in such compounds as brotizolam (80),[357] etizolam (81)[358,359] and closely related analogs,[360] which show *in vivo* activity as PAF antagonists in platelet aggregation, hypotension and bronchoconstriction models. That compounds such as diazepam and chlordiazepoxide are orders of magnitude less potent as PAF antagonists certainly suggests structural specificity for an interaction independent of the benzodiazepine receptor.[361] Indeed, the PAF antagonistic activity of these triazolodiazepines can be dissociated from their CNS activity, as demonstrated by the use of specific benzodiazepine receptor ligands or antagonists which did not block or reverse the PAF inhibitory activity of either

(79) or **(80)**.[362] The probability that these compounds act directly at the PAF receptor has been shown by competitive displacement experiments using [³H]PAF.[363] Of particular interest for potential clinical application are structural analogs devoid of benzodiazepine-associated CNS activities. One such compound, WEB 2086 **(82)**, has demonstrated a wide spectrum of PAF antagonistic activities, such as inhibition of PAF-induced platelet aggregation, bronchoconstriction, hypotension, endotoxin shock, passive and active anaphylaxis and gastric damage.[364-368]

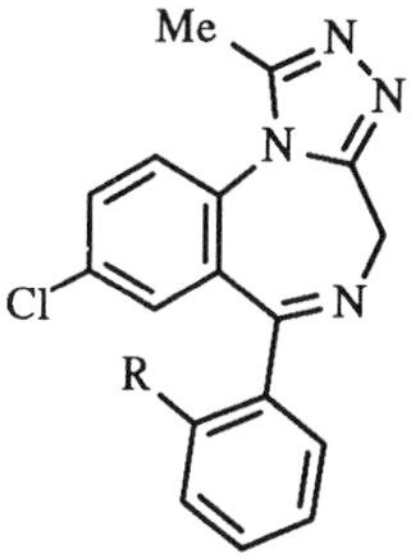

(78) R = H
(79) R = Cl

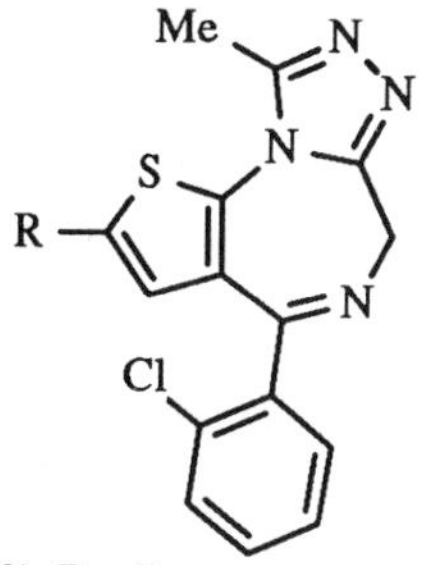

(80) R = Br
(81) R = Et

(82) R = CH₂CH₂CO - N⌒O

12.12.7.4.4 Other synthetic antagonists

The first synthetic antagonist structurally unrelated to PAF was 48740 RP **(83)**, a relatively weak inhibitor of PAF-induced platelet aggregation *in vitro*, which also exhibited *in vivo* activity against PAF-induced thrombocytopenia, bronchospasm, hypotension, vascular permeability increase and dermal edema.[369-371] A radiolabeled analog, [³H]52770 RP **(84)** was more recently used as an antagonist receptor probe, and exhibited activity *in vivo*, where it was found to be 2–200 times more potent than either **(55)** or **(62)**. When separated into its enantiomers, the (+) antipode of unlabeled **(84)** was shown to be 200–350 times more potent than the corresponding (−) antipode at displacing labeled **(84)** from the rabbit platelet PAF receptor, a demonstration of the stereospecificity demands of the PAF receptor on potential antagonists.[372] Similar results were obtained with **(84)** in studies with human PMNs.[373] A compound of similar structure SKF 86002 **(85)**, a dual inhibitor of arachidonate metabolism, has also exhibited antagonism of PAF-induced rat paw edema.[374] The resemblance of **(83)** and **(85)** to other relatively new nonacidic nonsteroidal antiinflammatory agents (NSAIDs) may provide further structural leads, and potentially a biochemical connection, to compounds within this class. However, a comparison of both acidic NSAIDs (potent CO inhibitors such as indomethacin, phenylbutazone and sulfinpyrazone) and structurally similar analogs devoid of CO inhibitory activity demonstrated that, in some cases, both classes are moderately active as inhibitors of [³H]PAF binding and, in parallel, of PAF-induced platelet aggregation, suggesting that the receptor binding site of PAF varies greatly from the site of cyclooxygenase inhibition.[375] For example, from amongst a series of sulindac derivatives, PAF antagonistic effects were separable from CO inhibitory activity. Of these, the (methylthio)ethyl analog **(86)** was found to be the most potent receptor antagonist and to be orally active in a number of animal models.[272,376] From a series of pyrido[2,1-*b*]quinazoline-8-carboxamides originally prepared as spasmolytic agents, *rac*-**(87)** was found to inhibit PAF-induced thrombocytopenia and hypotension in guinea pigs after oral administration. Binding studies using dog platelets showed that (*R*)-**(87)** was more potent than the (*S*)-**(87)** enantiomer, indicating a stereoselective preference for orientation of the lipophilic and charged extremes of the molecule.[377] Incorporation of features of the diaryltetrahydrofuran **(74)** with functional and topographical features related to the benzodiazepine ring system common to **(78–82)** suggested the synthesis of a series of variously substituted 5-aryl-2,3-dihydroimidazo-[2,1-*a*]isoquinolines. Of these, SDZ 64,412 **(88)** was found to be the most potent against PAF-induced platelet aggregation and in PAF receptor binding studies. The design of this compound is quite significant, in that it provides the first structural link between two diverse classes of synthetic PAF antagonists.[378]

(**83**) R = H

(**84**) R =

(**85**)

(**86**)

(**87**)

(**88**)

12.12.8 RECEPTOR BINDING MODEL

A model of the PAF receptor designed around the structure–activity correlations in both the agonist and antagonist series has been proposed by Braquet and Godfroid.[16,186,187,207,379,380] The salient features of this model are depicted in Figure 6.[186] The hydrophobic trough extending down into the surface of the membrane is suggested by the observations that: (i) agonistic activity decreases as the 1-*O*-alkyl residue is shortened and (ii) introduction of a polar group in the vicinity of the allyl

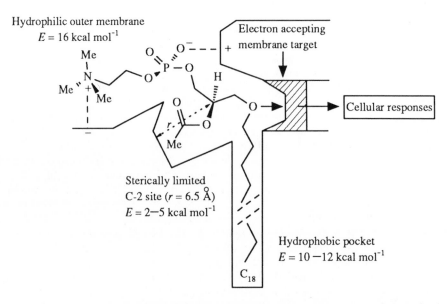

Figure 6   Putative model of the PAF receptor. Stabilization energies shown were calculated from molecular modeling studies (adapted from refs. 16, 186 and 380)

group of kadsurenone (**53**) or the *t*-butyl group of ginkgolide B (**60**) greatly reduces antagonistic effects. A lipophilic moiety thus seems essential for both agonist and antagonist activities. The anchorage of the chain or chain-substitute into the membrane pocket is proposed to occur *via* an electron transfer process from the lone pairs of the ether oxygen functionality at C-1 into an as yet unidentified electron-deficient acceptor region, possibly comprised of a hydrogen-bonding species. The existence of such an acceptor is proposed based on the reduced agonistic activities of analogs such as thioethers, methylene analogs and fatty acid esters. These substitutions for the long chain alkoxide residue are essentially isosteric and of comparable lipophilicity but are not of comparable electron density at the critical point where the interaction should take place. In the antagonist series, such an interaction is provided by, for example, the tetrahydrofuran ring oxygen atoms of (**55**), (**62**) and (**74**) or the carbamate functionality common to many of the lipid-like antagonists. A more detailed examination of the role of the oxygen in the diaryltetrahydrofuran series using enantiomerically pure analogs of (**74**) showed only slight preference for the *trans*-(*S*,*S*) enantiomer over the *trans*-(*R*,*R*) configuration, and prompted the synthesis of the 1,3-dixolane analog (**89**). In this case, the *trans* diastereomeric relationship of the aryl substituents found in (**89**) was found to be significantly more favorable for binding than in the corresponding *cis* diastereomer. Since this study demonstrates the equivalency of the aryl rings in compounds such as (**74**), the finding that the unsymmetrical diaryltetrahydrofuran (**76**) is a more potent PAF antagonist is not surprising, considering the vastly different structural demands imposed by the hydrophilic and hydrophobic domains of the receptor.[381]

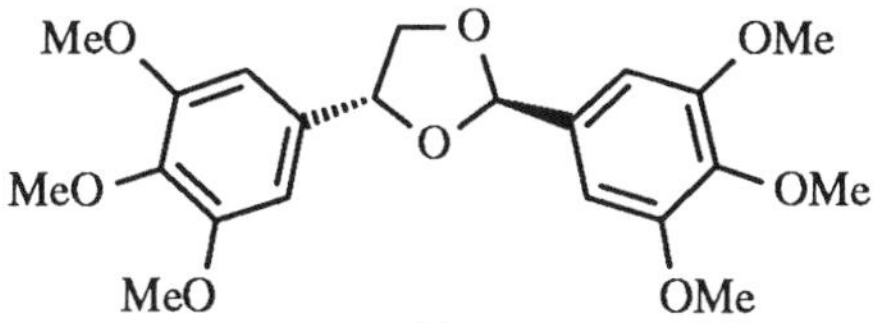

(**89**)

Some of the potential electronic and lipophilic requirements for antagonist activity have been more formally addressed in a pharmacophore model recently proposed by Schreiber.[382] In this model, based on structural features from three structurally divergent antagonists (**62**, **55** and **83**), there exist three separate functional generalizations, as depicted in Figure 7: (i) the presence of an electron-donating functionality as part of a delocalized rigid five-atom network, (ii) a hydrophobic group in the vicinity of the above functionality and (iii) the presence of a suitably disposed aryl group. These criteria, for the most part consistent with the Braquet receptor model, have been applied to the design of potential PAF antagonists (**90**–**92**) containing structural elements of (**62**) and (**55**). In the one case reported thus far, racemic (**91**) was demonstrated to bind to the PAF receptor, exhibiting a K_d nearly midway between those of (**55**) and (**62**).[382]

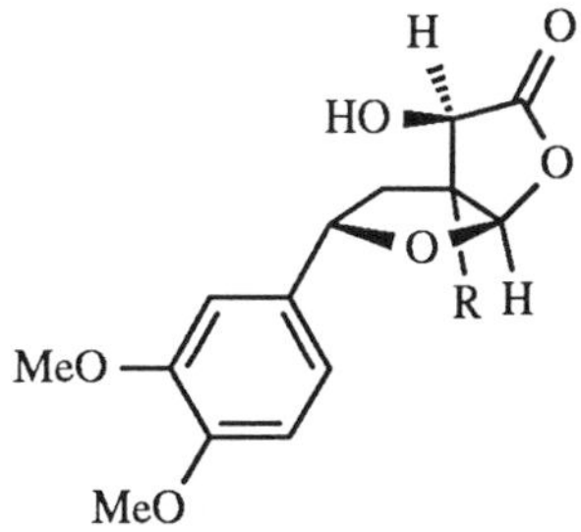

(**90**) a: R = H
       b: R = CH$_2$CMe$_3$

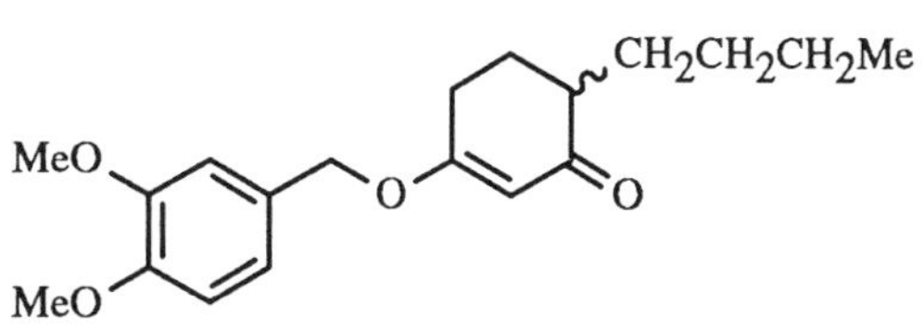

(**91**)

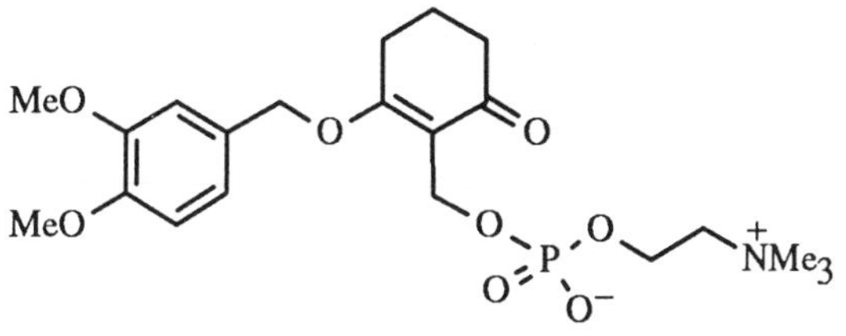

(**92**)

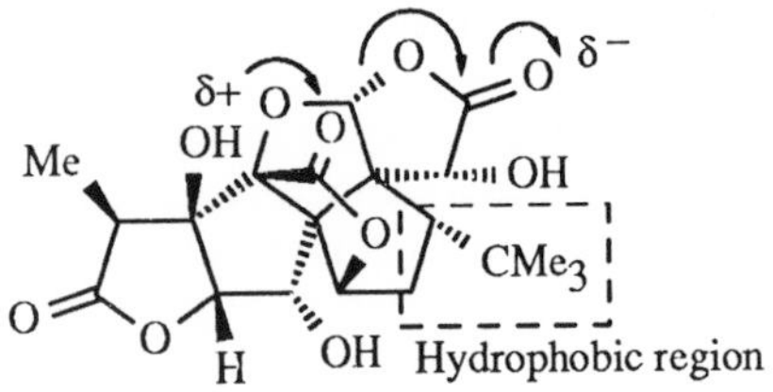

(**62**) Sigmologous ester

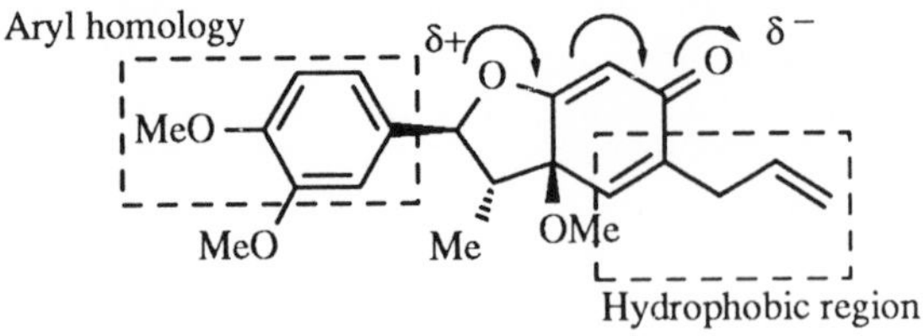

(**55**) Vinylogous ester

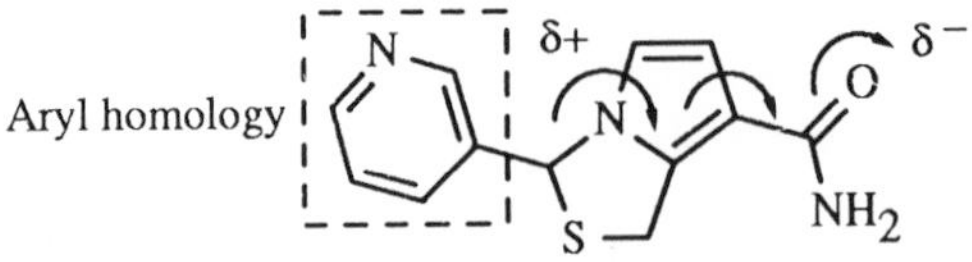

(**83**) Vinylogous urea

Figure 7 Pharmacophoric model for antagonistic activity (adapted from ref. 382)

As examined previously, the requirements for agonistic activity at C-2 seem much more dependent on overall steric bulk than on electronic factors. The short chain found to be necessary may take part in the anchorage of ligand to receptor, forcing a more favorable alignment of the polar head group with membrane phospholipids and aiming the lipophilic portion of the molecule into its pocket. In any event, the absolute requirement for the (*R*)-PAF configuration, or its close equivalent in the (*S*) positional isomers (*vide supra*), and the steric limitations in the vicinity must combine to prevent indiscriminate binding of lipophilic chains into the PAF receptor site.

The findings that modification to the phosphorylcholine polar head group are not very well tolerated in the agonist series but are extremely well tolerated in antagonist structures implies that activation of the PAF receptor may involve a necessary interaction with or penetration into the membrane bilayer for signal generation to occur. That compounds with polar tails, such as thiazolium or quinolinium, or with no tail at all are associated with antagonistic activity suggests that, while the rest of the molecule is able to bind into the lipophilic pocket and the C-2 gateway, effecting receptor blockade, the necessary receptor conformational change, induced by incorporation of the molecule by the receptor into the lipid bilayer, is inhibited by the lack of proper polar interaction, thus preventing signal generation. The synthesis of further rationally designed compounds, such as (**76**) and (**88–92**), and their evaluation in comparative PAF receptor binding or antagonism assays against other classes of agents and across a variety of membrane receptor sources[383,384] will certainly be necessary to develop a more exact model of the PAF receptor and its interactions with agonists and antagonists.

12.12.9 POTENTIAL THERAPEUTIC INDICATIONS

The pharmacological events potentially mediated in some way by PAF present the tangible possibility of a new clinical approach to a variety of therapeutic targets. Although most research concerning the therapeutic potential of PAF-related agents began by searching for ways to exploit its agonist property of induction of hypotension (*vide supra*), this approach yielded little in the way of potential antihypertensive agents. The discovery of specific antagonists of the pathophysiological actions of PAF, however, refocused attention onto the notion that PAF itself is a mediator of these events and that specific intervention at this level could provide a new entry into a number of acute inflammatory and immunopathological conditions.[385–389] The appeal arising from the novelty of such an approach, however, must be tempered by the fact that many of the models developed which demonstrate the utility of PAF antagonists do so under conditions where these compounds prevent or reverse the actions of acutely administered rather than endogenous PAF, a caveat generated by consideration of the relative ubiquity of the acetylhydrolase which inactivates PAF and by acknowledgement that PAF has yet to be demonstrated to be the sole or primary mediator of any acute inflammatory response. Nevertheless, the fact that none of these 'first generation' PAF antagonists are even 1/100th as potent as PAF as an agonist[273] suggests that there is a wide margin for improvement and the eventual development of agents of sufficient potency to be effective against the localized, even inter- or intra-cellular, effects of subnanomolar concentrations of PAF.

With these thoughts in mind, the potential therapeutic avenues for investigation will be briefly summarized.

12.12.9.1 Asthma and Other Respiratory Conditions

The airway obstruction characteristic of asthma and its spontaneous reversal or rapid response to treatment has prompted investigation of smooth-muscle-mediated mechanisms in this disease.[390,391] In the search for agents which might provoke airway smooth-muscle contraction, PAF has been the focus of recent scrutiny, since: (i) PAF can induce responses in the airway reminiscent of asthma, (ii) cells of asthmatic patients can generate PAF on stimulation, (iii) the indication exists that PAF is released in experimental and clinical asthma and (iv) the effects of PAF on pulmonary tissue can be reversed by specific PAF antagonists and by a number of other antiasthma agents.[392-397] The distinctive inflammatory profile of asthma is closely mimicked by exposure of normal lung tissue to PAF, and there is at least adequate evidence that PAF is generated during its course. The human *in vivo* response to PAF[398] and the correlation of plasma *lyso*-PAF levels with the late asthmatic response[399] also confirm this view. The intrapulmonary sequestration of platelets and subsequent pulmonary hypertension and edema of adult respiratory distress syndrome (ARDS) have also been postulated to be mediated by PAF-induced release of TxA_2.[400]

12.12.9.2 Cardiovascular and Renal Pathophysiology

The profile of cardiac function depression induced by PAF described previously is independent of the autonomic nervous system, purinergic mechanisms and AA metabolites and may be related to a regulatory role that PAF plays in the normal maintenance of blood pressure,[401] but complicates any examination of the role of PAF in renal pathophysiology.[148] The cardiovascular events associated with the shock state, including severe hypotension, myocardial contractility impairment, decreased coronary artery blood flow, systemic and pulmonary vascular changes, renal dysfunction, increased vascular permeability and hemoconcentration, metabolic acidosis, leukopenia and thrombocytopenia, have all been shown to be pathophysiological effects of PAF *in vivo*.[402-405] These symptoms of systemic anaphylaxis, induced by either PAF or endotoxin, have been reversed by a number of the PAF antagonists mentioned above, indicating a potential clinical utility for these agents in this acute situation. The role of platelets and PAF in localized vessel wall injury leading to atherogenesis has also been examined, raising the possibility of the use of PAF antagonists in the treatment of atherosclerosis.[406]

12.12.9.3 Other Indications

The cutaneous response to intradermal injection of PAF and its reversal by a PAF antagonist, along with the detection of PAF in psoriatic lesions cited above, indicate a potential for the use of PAF antagonists in inflammatory dermatological conditions, possibly one of the only chronic disease states in which a PAF antagonist may be of use. Its role in the pathogenesis of chronic arthritis, for example, seems to be limited to the acute induction phase of the disease.[407] The severe gastrointestinal erosion elicited by PAF and its reversal by PAF antagonists also suggest the possibility of their use in the control or reversal of ulcerogenesis. Prolongation of cardiac allograft survival rate by the use of an antagonist may signal the use of such agents in combination with lower doses of the immunosuppressive agents currently used after organ transplant.[408] The detection of increased plasma levels of PAF in patients with cirrhosis of the liver[409] and the increased sensitivity of platelets of migraine sufferers to PAF[410] are amongst the newest areas of potential application of PAF antagonists. While it is likely that not all of the pathophysiological states in which PAF is implicated as a mediator will be treatable with PAF antagonists, the likelihood that some of these disease states, especially those less acute in nature, might succumb to such an agent cannot be dismissed.

12.12.10 CONCLUSION

The intense research effort of the last few years into the biochemistry and pathophysiology of PAF and the potential therapeutic benefits of new antagonists of the actions of PAF have generated much enthusiasm, and some skepticism, concerning the role of PAF as a primary mediator or autocoid. The short biological half-life of PAF coupled with the minute concentrations required for cellular response have made absolute proof of its involvement in human disease difficult. The indirect evidence of such involvement provided by PAF antagonists (their reversal of the effects of deliberately administered PAF *in vivo* and their high affinities for the putative PAF receptor) has highlighted the potential role of PAF in a variety of poorly understood and mechanistically complicated disease syndromes. But its qualifications as mediator in *in vivo* situations, where release of PAF by stimulated cells into the extracellular medium must occur, can be questioned, since most PAF synthesized is, in fact, retained intracellularly. Its extreme potency as an activator, however, requires that only minute quantities be released to effect stimulation, offsetting this apparent problem. The receptor-mediated effects of extracellularly released PAF are more clear, however, because of these same low concentrations needed for activity, the structure–function specificity observed in both agonists and antagonists, the observation of stimulus-specific down-regulation of cellular responses and the existence of a varied number of synthetic PAF antagonists of structures totally disparate from PAF. The role of intracellularly-retained PAF, apart from that entering the activation–inactivation cycle to provide membrane components containing arachidonic acid, is probably the least understood action of PAF and remains to be elucidated.[411]

The intense research centered around PAF seems to have raised rather than answered more questions about the nature of this novel phospholipid since its discovery. The special challenge presented by PAF has been stated bluntly: it is a mediator in search of identification with diseases.[16] Because of its unique chemical structure, biochemical and pathophysiological profile, and the implication that it might be a primary mediator in so many poorly understood disease states, such questions will without doubt, but with good reason, continue to be raised. A definitive answer to these questions must necessarily await the eventual development and clinical evaluation of PAF antagonists of suitable bioavailability and tissue specificity in the treatment of diseases attributed to the actions of PAF.[16,272,273,411]

12.12.11 REFERENCES

1. J. Benveniste, P. M. Henson and C. G. Cochrane, *J. Exp. Med.*, 1972, **136**, 1356.
2. J. Benveniste, M. Tencé, P. Varenne, J. Bidault, C. Boullet and J. Polonsky, *C. R. Hebd. Seances Acad. Sci., Ser. D*, 1979, **289**, 1037.
3. C. A. Demopoulos, R. N. Pinckard and D. J. Hanahan, *J. Biol. Chem.*, 1979, **254**, 9355.
4. M. L. Blank, F. Snyder, L. W. Byers, B. Brooks and E. E. Muirhead, *Biochem. Biophys. Res. Commun.*, 1979, **90**, 1194.
5. E. E. Muirhead, L. W. Byers, D. M. Desiderio, B. Brooks and W. M. Brosius, *Fed. Proc., Fed. Am. Soc. Exp. Biol.*, 1981, **40**, 2285.
6. F. Snyder, *Annu. Rep. Med. Chem.*, 1982, **17**, 243.
7. J. Benveniste and B. Arnoux (eds.), 'Platelet Activating Factor and Structurally Related Ether Lipids', INSERM Symposium no. 23, Elsevier, Amsterdam, 1983.
8. B. B. Vargaftig and J. Benveniste, *Trends Pharmacol. Sci.*, 1983, **4**, 341.
9. F. Snyder, *Med. Res. Rev.*, 1985, **5**, 107.
10. M. C. Venuti, *Annu. Rep. Med. Chem.*, 1985, **20**, 193.
11. T.-C. Lee and F. Snyder, in 'Phospholipids and Cellular Regulation', ed. J. F. Kuo, CRC Press, Boca Raton, FL, 1986, chap. 1, p. 1.
12. F. H. Valone, in 'Chemical Mediators of Inflammation and Immunity', ed. S. Cohen, H. Hayashi, K. Saito and A. Takada, Academic Press, Tokyo, 1986, p. 13.
13. D. J. Hanahan, *Annu. Rev. Biochem.*, 1986, **55**, 483.
14. F. Snyder (ed.), 'Platelet Activating Factor and Related Lipid Mediators', Plenum Press, New York, 1987.
15. C. M. Winslow and M. L. Lee (eds.), 'New Horizons in Platelet Activating Factor Research', Wiley, New York, 1987.
16. P. Braquet, L. Touqui, T. Y. Shen and B. B. Vargaftig, *Pharmacol. Rev.*, 1987, **39**, 97.
17. P. Braquet, H. K. Mangold and B. B. Vargaftig (eds.), 'Biologically Active Ether Lipids: Progress in Biochemical Pharmacology', Karger, Basel, 1988, vol. 22.
18. H. K. Mangold and F. Paltauf (eds.), 'Ether Lipids: Biochemical and Biomedical Aspects', Academic Press, New York, 1983.
19. F. Snyder, T.-C. Lee and R. L. Wykle, in 'The Enzymes of Biological Membranes', ed. A. N. Martonosi, Plenum Press, New York, 1985, vol. 2, p. 1.
20. D. J. Hanahan and R. Kumar, *Prog. Lipid Res.*, 1987, **26**, 1.
21. M. C. Moschidis, *J. Chromatogr.*, 1983, **270**, 344.
22. M. L. Blank and F. Snyder, *J. Chromatogr.*, 1983, **273**, 415.
23. R. N. Pinckard, E. M. Jackson, C. Hoppens, S. T. Weintraub, J. C. Ludwig, L. M. McManus and G. E. Mott, *Biochem. Biophys. Res. Commun.*, 1984, **122**, 325.
24. K. Satouchi, M. Oda, K. Yasunaga and K. Saito, *J. Biochem. (Tokyo)*, 1983, **94**, 2067.
25. K. L. Clay, D. O. Stene and R. C. Murphy, *Biomed. Mass Spectrom.*, 1984, **11**, 47.
26. P. Varenne, B. C. Das, J. Polonsky and M. Tencé, *Biomed. Mass Spectrom.*, 1985, **12**, 6.
27. C. S. Ramesha and W. C. Pickett, *J. Immunol.*, 1987, **138**, 1559.

28. O. Convert, E. Michel, F. Heymans and J. J. Godfroid, *Biochim. Biophys. Acta*, 1984, **794**, 320.
29. W. Kramp, G. Pieroni, R. N. Pinckard and D. J. Hanahan, *Chem. Phys. Lipids*, 1984, **35**, 49.
30. R. C. Murphy and K. L. Clay, in 'Platelet Activating Factor and Related Lipid Mediators', ed. F. Snyder, Plenum Press, New York, 1987, p. 9.
31. J. J. Godfroid, F. Heymans, E. Michel, C. Redeuilh, E. Steiner and J. Benveniste, *FEBS Lett.*, 1980, **116**, 161.
32. J. J. Godfroid, C. Broquet and F. Heymans, in 'Platelet Activating Factor and Structurally Related Ether Lipids', INSERM Symposium no. 23, ed. J. Benveniste and B. Arnoux, Elsevier, Amsterdam, 1983, p. 3.
33. G. Hirth and R. Barner, *Helv. Chim. Acta*, 1982, **65**, 1059.
34. S. Takano, M. Akiyama and K. Ogasawara, *Chem. Pharm. Bull.*, 1984, **32**, 791.
35. C. A. A. van Boeckel, G. A. van der Marel, P. Westerduin and J. H. van Boom, *Synthesis*, 1982, 399.
36. M. Ohno, K. Fujita, H. Nakai, S. Kobayashi, K. Inoue and S. Nojima, *Chem. Pharm. Bull.*, 1985, **33**, 572.
37. T. Tsuri and S. Kamata, *Tetrahedron Lett.*, 1985, **26**, 5195.
38. H. Suemune, A. Akashi and K. Sakai, *Chem. Pharm. Bull.*, 1985, **33**, 1055.
39. L. M. McManus, *Pathol. Immunopathol. Res.*, 1986, **5**, 104.
40. A. K. Hajra, in 'Ether Lipids: Biochemical and Biomedical Aspects', ed. H. K. Mangold and F. Paltauf, Academic Press, New York, 1983, p. 85.
41. F. Snyder, in 'Platelet Activating Factor and Related Lipid Mediators', ed. F. Snyder, Plenum Press, New York, 1987, p. 89.
42. T.-C. Lee, in 'Platelet Activating Factor and Related Lipid Mediators', ed. F. Snyder, Plenum Press, New York, 1987, p. 115.
43. M. M. Billah and M. I. Siegel, *Biochem. Biophys. Res. Commun.*, 1984, **118**, 629.
44. D. M. Stafforini, T. M. McIntyre, M. E. Carter and S. M. Prescott, *J. Biol. Chem.*, 1987, **262**, 4215.
45. F. H. Chilton, J. M. Ellis, S. C. Olson and R. L. Wykle, *J. Biol. Chem.*, 1984, **259**, 12014.
46. M. Chignard, J.-P. LeCouedic, E. Coeffier and J. Benveniste, *Biochem. Biophys. Res. Commun.*, 1984, **124**, 637.
47. M. L. Blank, E. A. Cress and F. Snyder, *Biochem. Biophys. Res. Commun.*, 1984, **118**, 344.
48. A. Zanglis and E. A. Lianos, *Biochem. Biophys. Res. Commun.*, 1987, **144**, 666.
49. T.-C. Lee, B. Malone and F. Snyder, *J. Biol. Chem.*, 1986, **261**, 5373.
50. F. Snyder, in 'New Horizons in Platelet Activating Factor Research', ed. C. M. Winslow and M. L. Lee, Wiley, New York, 1987, p. 13.
51. D. S. Woodard, T.-C. Lee and F. Snyder, *J. Biol. Chem.*, 1987, **262**, 2520.
52. T.-C. Lee, B. Malone and F. Snyder, *J. Biol. Chem.*, 1988, **263**, 1755.
53. R. Kumar and D. J. Hanahan, in 'Platelet Activating Factor and Related Lipid Mediators', ed. F. Snyder, Plenum Press, New York, 1987, p. 239.
54. P. M. Henson, in 'Platelet Activating Factor and Related Lipid Mediators', ed. F. Snyder, Plenum Press, New York, 1987, p. 255.
55. J. T. O'Flaherty, in 'Platelet Activating Factor and Related Lipid Mediators', ed. F. Snyder, Plenum Press, New York, 1987, p. 283.
56. D. H. Namm, A. S. Tadepalli and J. A. High, *Thromb. Res.*, 1982, **25**, 341.
57. D. I. Cargill, D. S. Cohen, R. G. Van Valen, J. J. Klimek and R. P. Levin, *Thromb. Haemostasis*, 1983, **49**, 204.
58. H. Ieyasu, Y. Takai, K. Kaibuchi, M. Sawamura and Y. Nishizuka, *Biochem. Biophys. Res. Commun.*, 1982, **108**, 1701.
59. E. G. Lapetina and F. L. Siegel, *J. Biol. Chem.*, 1983, **258**, 7241.
60. W. Seiss, P. C. Weber and E. G. Lapetina, *J. Biol. Chem.*, 1984, **259**, 8286.
61. T.-C. Lee, B. Malone and F. Snyder, *Arch. Biochem. Biophys.*, 1983, **223**, 33.
62. F. H. Valone and B. Johnson, *Thromb. Res.*, 1985, **40**, 385.
63. B. B. Vargaftig, M. Chignard and J. Benveniste, *Biochem. Pharmacol.*, 1981, **30**, 263.
64. E. Kloprogge, G. H. De Haas, G. Gorter and J. W. N. Akkerman, *Thromb. Res.*, 1983, **30**, 107.
65. A. K. Rao, J. Willis, B. Hassell, C. Dangelmaier, H. Holmsen and J. B. Smith, *Am. J. Hematol.*, 1984, **17**, 153.
66. S. Krishnamurthi, J. Westwick and V. V. Kakkar, *Biochem. Pharmacol.*, 1984, **33**, 3025.
67. A. Sturk, G. M. Asyee, M. C. L. Schaap, M. van Maanen and J. W. ten Cate, *Thromb. Res.*, 1985, **40**, 359.
68. R. Altman, A. Scazziota, J. Rouvier and R. Cacchione, *Thromb. Res.*, 1986, **43**, 103.
69. J. Filep and E. Földes-Filep, *Thromb. Res.*, 1987, **45**, 865.
70. R. Altman and A. Scazziota, *Thromb. Res.*, 1986, **43**, 113.
71. A. Sturk, M. C. L. Schaap, J. W. ten Cate, H. S. A. Heymans, R. B. H. Schutgens, H. Przyrembel and P. Borst, *J. Clin. Invest.*, 1987, **79**, 344.
72. O. V. Miller, D. E. Ayer and R. R. Gorman, *Biochim. Biophys. Acta*, 1982, **711**, 445.
73. R. J. Halsam and M. Vanderwel, *J. Biol. Chem.*, 1982, **257**, 6879.
74. R. L. Wykle, in 'Platelet Activating Factor and Related Lipid Mediators', ed. F. Snyder, Plenum Press, New York, 1987, p. 273.
75. R. J. Smith, B. J. Bowman and S. S. Iden, *Clin. Immunol. Immunopathol.*, 1983, **28**, 13.
76. J. O. Shaw, R. N. Pinckard, K. S. Ferrigni, L. M. McManus and D. J. Hanahan, *J. Immunol.*, 1981, **127**, 1250.
77. J. T. O'Flaherty, C. L. Swendsen, C. J. Lees and C. E. McCall, *Am. J. Pathol.*, 1981, **105**, 107.
78. B. M. Czarnetzki and J. Benveniste, *Chem. Phys. Lipids*, 1981, **29**, 317.
79. L. M. Ingraham, T. D. Coates, J. M. Allen, C. P. Higgins, R. L. Baehner and L. A. Boxer, *Blood*, 1982, **59**, 1259.
80. A. H. Lin, D. R. Morton and R. R. Gorman, *J. Clin. Invest.*, 1982, **70**, 1058.
81. F. H. Chilton, J. T. O'Flaherty, C. E. Walsh, M. J. Thomas, R. L. Wykle, L. R. DeChatelet and B. M. Waite, *J. Biol. Chem.*, 1982, **257**, 5402.
82. J. T. O'Flaherty, M. J. Thomas, M. J. Hammett, C. Carroll, C. E. McCall and R. L. Wykle, *Biochem. Biophys. Res. Commun.*, 1983, **111**, 1.
83. R. R. Gorman, D. R. Morton, N. K. Hopkins and A. H. Lin, *Adv. Prostaglandin Thromboxane Leukotriene Res.*, 1983, **12**, 57.
84. A. W. Ford-Hutchinson, *Int. J. Immunopharmacol.*, 1983, **5**, 17.
85. J. T. O'Flaherty, R. L. Wykle, C. J. Lee, T. Shewmake, C. E. McCall and M. J. Thomas, *Am. J. Pathol.*, 1981, **105**, 264.
86. R. J. Smith and B. J. Bowman, *Biochem. Biophys. Res. Commun.*, 1982, **104**, 1495.

87. N. K. Hopkins, A. H. Lin and R. R. Gorman, *Biochim. Biophys. Acta*, 1983, **763**, 276.
88. J. T. O'Flaherty and J. Nishihira, *J. Immunol.*, 1987, **138**, 1889.
89. R. J. Smith, B. J. Bowman and S. S. Iden, *Biochem. Pharmacol.*, 1984, **33**, 973.
90. M. Baggiolini and B. Dewald, *Pharmacol. Res. Commun.*, 1986, **18** (suppl.), 51.
91. H.-P. Hartung, *FEBS Lett.*, 1983, **160**, 209.
92. H.-P. Hartung, M. J. Parnham, J. Winklemann, W. Engelberger and U. Hadding, *Int. J. Immunopharmacol.*, 1983, **5**, 115.
93. M. J. Parnham, J. Winklemann, H.-P. Hartung and U. Hadding, *Agents Actions*, 1984, **14** (suppl.), 215.
94. H. Hayashi, I. Kudo, K. Inoue, H. Nomura and S. Nojima, *J. Biochem. (Tokyo)*, 1985, **97**, 1255.
95. H. Hayashi, I. Kudo, K. Inoue, K. Onozaki, S. Tsushima, H. Nomura and S. Nojima, *J. Biochem. (Tokyo)*, 1985, **97**, 1737.
96. I. Haye-Legrand, A. Duliouet, E. Vivier, R. Roubin and J. Benveniste, *Pharmacol. Res. Commun.*, 1986, **18** (suppl.), 239.
97. G. W. Conrad and T. J. Rink, *J. Cell Biol.*, 1986, **103**, 439.
98. A. J. Wardlaw, R. Moqbel, O. Cromwell and A. B. Kay, *J. Clin. Invest.*, 1986, **78**, 1701.
99. C. J. Lewis, J. T. O'Flaherty, C. E. McCall, R. L. Wykle and M. E. Bond, *Exp. Mol. Pathol.*, 1983, **38**, 100.
100. G. Camussi, I. Pawlowski, C. Tetta, C. Roffinello, M. Alberton, J. Brentjens and G. Andres, *Am. J. Pathol.*, 1983, **112**, 78.
101. M. F. Fitzgerald, S. Moncada and L. Parente, *Br. J. Pharmacol.*, 1986, **88**, 149.
102. G. Camussi, G. Montrucchio, C. Antro, F. Bussolino, C. Tetta and G. Emanuelli, *Immunopharmacology*, 1983, **6**, 87.
103. C. Touvay, B. Villain, A. Etienne, F. Clostre and P. Braquet, *Pharmacol. Res. Commun.*, 1986, **18** (suppl.), 91.
104. J. Lefort, D. Rotilio and B. B. Vargaftig, *Br. J. Pharmacol.*, 1984, **82**, 565.
105. G. Alloatti, G. Montrucchio, F. Mariano, C. Tetta, R. DePaulis, M. Morea, G. Emanuelli and G. Camussi, *Int. Arch. Allergy Appl. Immunol.*, 1986, **79**, 108.
106. S. Saeki, F. Masugi, T. Ogihara, A. Otsuka, Y. Kumahara, K. Watanabe, K. Tamura, A. Akashi and A. Kumagai, *Life Sci.*, 1985, **37**, 325.
107. J. Tamargo, T. Tejerina, C. Delgado and S. Barrigon, *Eur. J. Pharmacol.*, 1985, **109**, 219.
108. J. Benveniste, C. Boullet, C. Brink and C. Labat, *Br. J. Pharmacol.*, 1983, **80**, 81.
109. P. J. Piper and A. G. Stewart, *Br. J. Pharmacol.*, 1986, **88**, 595.
110. S. Tanaka, Y. Kasuya, Y. Masuda and K. Shigenobu, *J. Pharmacobio-Dyn.*, 1983, **6**, 866.
111. S. R. Findlay, L. M. Lichtenstein, D. J. Hanahan and R. N. Pinckard, *Am. J. Physiol.*, 1981, **241**, C130.
112. N. P. Stimler, C. M. Bloor, T. E. Hugli, R. L. Wykle, C. E. McCall and J. T. O'Flaherty, *Am. J. Pathol.*, 1981, **105**, 64.
113. A. Tokumura, K. Harada, K. Fukuzawa and H. Tsukatani, *Lipids*, 1983, **18**, 848.
114. A. Tokumura, K. Fukuzawa and H. Tsukatani, *J. Pharm. Pharmacol.*, 1984, **36**, 210.
115. S. D. Shukla, D. B. Buxton, M. S. Olson and D. J. Hanahan, *J. Biol. Chem.*, 1983, **258**, 10212.
116. I. Hillmar and N. Zollner, *Res. Exp. Med.*, 1983, **182**, 215.
117. D. B. Buxton, S. D. Shukla, D. J. Hanahan and M. S. Olson, *J. Biol. Chem.*, 1984, **259**, 1468.
118. R. A. Fisher, R. Kumar, D. J. Hanahan and M. S. Olson, *J. Biol. Chem.*, 1986, **261**, 8817.
119. F. Mendlovic, S. Corvera and J. A. Garcia-Sainz, *Biochem. Biophys. Res. Commun.*, 1984, **123**, 507.
120. E. Pirotzky, J. Bidault, C. Burtin, M. C. Gubler and J. Benveniste, *Kidney Int.*, 1984, **25**, 404.
121. S. M. Weisman, D. Felsen and E. D. Vaughan, Jr., *J. Pharmacol. Exp. Ther.*, 1985, **235**, 10.
122. B. B. Vargaftig, J. Lefort and D. Rotilio, in 'Platelet Activating Factor and Structurally Related Ether Lipids', INSERM Symposium no. 23, ed. J. Benveniste and B. Arnoux, Elsevier, Amsterdam, 1983, p. 307.
123. P. Braquet and B. B. Vargaftig, *Transplant. Proc.*, 1986, **18** (suppl. 4), 10.
124. G. Camussi and J. R. Brentjens, in 'Platelet Activating Factor and Related Lipid Mediators', ed. F. Snyder, Plenum Press, New York, 1987, p. 299.
125. A. Denjean, B. Arnoux, J. Benveniste, A. Lockhart and R. Masse, *Agents Actions*, 1981, **11**, 567.
126. J. Bonnet, D. Thibaudeau and R. Bessin, *Prostaglandins*, 1983, **26**, 457.
127. R. N. Pinckard, L. M. McManus, M. Halonen, D. M. Humphrey and D. J. Hanahan, in 'Biological Response Mediators and Modulators', ed. J. T. August, Academic Press, New York, 1983, p. 67.
128. L. M. McManus, F. A. Fitzpatrick, D. J. Hanahan and R. N. Pinckard, *Immunopharmacology*, 1983, **5**, 197.
129. K. F. Chung, H. Aizawa, G. D. Leikauf, I. F. Ueki, T. W. Evans and J. A. Nadel, *J. Pharmacol. Exp. Ther.*, 1986, **236**, 580.
130. B. B. Vargaftig, in 'Platelet Activating Factor and Related Lipid Mediators', ed. F. Snyder, Plenum Press, New York, 1987, p. 341.
131. H. Darius, D. J. Lefer, J. B. Smith and A. M. Lefer, *Science (Washington, D.C.)*, 1986, **232**, 58.
132. M. Chignard, J. P. LeCouedic, P. Andersson and C. Brange, *Int. Arch. Allergy Appl. Immunol.*, 1986, **81**, 184.
133. P. Braquet, A. Etienne and F. Clostre, *Prostaglandins*, 1985, **30**, 721.
134. P. J. Barnes, B. M. Grandordy, C. P. Page, K. J. Rhoden and D. N. Robertson, *Br. J. Pharmacol.*, 1987, **90**, 709.
135. C. G. Caillard, S. Mondot, J. L. Zundel and L. Julou, *Agents Actions*, 1982, **12**, 725.
136. F. Masugi, T. Ogihara, A. Otsuka, S. Saeki and Y. Kumahara, *Biochem. Biophys. Res. Commun.*, 1982, **104**, 280.
137. G. Feuerstein, Z. Zukowska-Grojec, M. M. Krausz, M. L. Blank, F. Snyder and I. J. Kopin, *Clin. Exp. Hypertens. Theory Practice*, 1982, **A4**, 1335.
138. J. W. Hubbard, R. H. Cox, J. E. Lawler, M. L. Blank and F. Snyder, *Life Sci.*, 1983, **32**, 221.
139. F. M. Lai, C. A. Shepherd, P. Cervoni and A. Wissner, *Life Sci.*, 1983, **32**, 1159.
140. A. E. Randolph, T. E. Mertz and H. R. Kaplan, *Clin. Exp. Hypertens. Theory Practice*, 1983, **A5**, 741.
141. E. J. Sybertz, C. Sabin, T. Baum, E. Eynon, S. Nelson and R. Moran, *J. Pharmacol. Exp. Ther.*, 1982, **223**, 594.
142. T. Kamitani, M. Katamoto, Y. Tatsumi, K. Katsuta, T. Ono, H. Kikuchi and S. Kumada, *Eur. J. Pharmacol.*, 1984, **98**, 357.
143. K. Shigenobu, Y. Masuda, Y. Tanaka and Y. Kasuya, *J. Pharmacobio-Dyn.*, 1985, **8**, 128.
144. Z. Zukowska-Grojec, M. L. Blank, F. Snyder and G. Feuerstein, *Clin. Exp. Hypertens. Theory Practice*, 1985, **A7**, 1015.
145. D. A. Handley, R. G. Van Valen, M. K. Melden and R. N. Saunders, *Thromb. Haemostasis*, 1984, **52**, 34.
146. D. A. Handley, M. L. Lee and R. N. Saunders, *Thromb. Haemostasis*, 1985, **54**, 756.
147. D. Schlondorff and R. Neuwirth, *Am. J. Physiol.*, 1986, **251**, F1.
148. G. Camussi, *Kidney Int.*, 1986, **29**, 469.
149. J. L. Kenzora, J. E. Perez, S. R. Bergmann and L. G. Lange, *J. Clin. Invest.*, 1984, **74**, 1193.
150. G. Feuerstein, L. M. Boyd, D. Ezra and R. E. Goldstein, *Am. J. Physiol.*, 1984, **246**, H466.

151. G. Feuerstein and J. M. Hallenbeck, *Annu. Rev. Pharmacol. Toxicol.*, 1987, **27**, 301.
152. G. Feuerstein and R. E. Goldstein, in 'Platelet Activating Factor and Related Lipid Mediators', ed. F. Snyder, Plenum Press, New York, 1987, p. 403.
153. P. Bessin, J. Bonnet, D. Apffel, C. Soulard, L. Desgroux, I. Pelas and J. Benveniste, *Eur. J. Pharmacol.*, 1983, **86**, 403.
154. M. Sanchez-Crespo, P. Inarrea, M. L. Nieto and S. Fernandez-Gallardo, *Pharmacol. Res. Commun.*, 1986, **18** (suppl.), 181.
155. A. Rosam, J. L. Wallace and B. J. R. Whittle, *Nature (London)*, 1986, **319**, 54.
156. J. L. Wallace and B. J. R. Whittle, *Br. J. Pharmacol.*, 1986, **88** (Proc. suppl.), 237P.
157. G. Steel, J. L. Wallace and B. J. R. Whittle, *Br. J. Pharmacol.*, 1987, **90**, 365.
158. J. L. Wallace and B. J. R. Whittle, *Prostaglandins*, 1986, **31**, 989.
159. J. L. Wallace and B. J. R. Whittle, *Prostaglandins*, 1986, **32**, 137.
160. F. Gonzalez-Crussi and W. Hsueh, *Am. J. Pathol.*, 1983, **112**, 127.
161. W. Hsueh, F. Gonzalez-Crussi and J. L. Arroyave, *Am. J. Pathol.*, 1986, **122**, 231.
162. J. Bonnet, A. M. Loiseau, M. Orven and P. Bessin, *Agents Actions*, 1981, **11**, 559.
163. M. M. Goldenberg and R. D. Meurer, *Prostaglandins*, 1984, **28**, 271.
164. J. P. Tarayre, M. Aliaga, M. Barbara, V. Caillol and J. Tisne-Versailles, *Agents Actions*, 1985, **17**, 397.
165. K. F. Swingle and M. J. Reiter, *Agents Actions*, 1986, **18**, 359.
166. R. S. B. Cordeiro, P. M. R. Silva, M. A. Martins and B. B. Vargaftig, *Prostaglandins*, 1986, **32**, 719.
167. S.-B. Hwang, M.-H. Lam, C.-L. Ling and T.-Y. Shen, *Eur. J. Pharmacol.*, 1986, **120**, 33.
168. J. Morley, C. P. Page and W. Paul, *Br. J. Pharmacol.*, 1983, **80**, 503.
169. C. B. Archer, C. P. Page, W. Paul, J. Morley and D. M. MacDonald, *Int. J. Tissue Reac.*, 1985, **7**, 363.
170. B. Gerdin, C. Lundberg and G. Smedegard, *Inflammation (N.Y.)*, 1985, **9**, 107.
171. C. B. Archer, C. P. Page, W. Paul, J. Morley and D. M. MacDonald, *Br. J. Dermatol.*, 1985, **112**, 285.
172. C. B. Archer, C. P. Page, W. Paul, J. Morley and D. M. MacDonald, *Br. J. Dermatol.*, 1984, **110**, 45.
173. C. B. Archer, M. W. Greaves and D. M. MacDonald, *J. Invest. Dermatol.*, 1986, **87**, 127.
174. C. B. Archer, D. M. MacDonald, J. Morley, C. P. Page, W. Paul and S. Sanjar, *Br. J. Pharmacol.*, 1985, **85**, 109.
175. B. Fjellner and Ö. Hägermark, *Acta Derm.-Venereol.*, 1985, **65**, 409.
176. E. J. Kusner, C. D. Knee and R. D. Krell, *Agents Actions*, 1987, **20**, 61.
177. C. B. Archer, W. Frohlich, C. P. Page, W. Paul, J. Morley and D. M. MacDonald, *Prostaglandins*, 1984, **27**, 495.
178. D. V. McGivern and G. S. Basran, *Eur. J. Pharmacol.*, 1984, **102**, 183.
179. B. Czarnetzki, *Clin. Exp. Immunol.*, 1983, **54**, 486.
180. A. I. Mallet and F. M. Cuningham, *Biochem. Biophys. Res. Commun.*, 1985, **126**, 192.
181. E. Pirotzky, A. Pfister and J. Benveniste, *Br. J. Dermatol.*, 1985, **113** (suppl. 28), 91.
182. A. M. Lefer, H. F. Miller and J. B. Smith, *Br. J. Pharmacol.*, 1984, **83**, 125.
183. A. Myers, E. Ramey and P. Ramwell, *Br. J. Pharmacol.*, 1983, **79**, 595.
184. J. M. Young, P. J. Maloney, S. N. Jubb and J. S. Clark, *Prostaglandins*, 1985, **30**, 545.
185. M. Criscuoli and A. Subissi, *Br. J. Pharmacol.*, 1987, **90**, 203.
186. J. J. Godfroid and P. Braquet, *Trends Pharmacol. Sci.*, 1986, **7**, 368.
187. P. Braquet and J. J. Godfroid, in 'Platelet Activating Factor and Related Lipid Mediators', ed. F. Snyder, Plenum Press, New York, 1987, p. 191.
188. F. H. Valone, in 'Platelet Activating Factor and Related Lipid Mediators', ed. F. Snyder, Plenum Press, New York, 1987, p. 137.
189. F. H. Valone, E. Coles, V. R. Reinhold and E. J. Goetzl, *J. Immunol.*, 1982, **129**, 1637.
190. F. H. Valone and E. J. Goetzl, *Immunology*, 1983, **48**, 141.
191. S.-B. Hwang, C.-S. C Lee, M. J. Cheah and T.-Y. Shen, *Biochemistry*, 1983, **22**, 4756.
192. P. Iñarrea, J. Gomez-Cambronero, M. Nieto and M. Sanchez-Crespo, *Eur. J. Pharmacol.*, 1984, **105**, 309.
193. E. Kloprogge and J. W. N. Akkerman, *Biochem. J.*, 1984, **223**, 901.
194. F. Bussolino, C. Tetta and G. Camussi, *Agents Actions*, 1984, **15**, 15.
195. C. M. Winslow, S. R. Vallespir, G. E. Frisch, F. J. D'Aires, A. K. DeLillo, W. J. Houlihan, V. Parrino, G. Schmitt and R. N. Saunders, *Prostaglandins*, 1985, **30**, 697.
196. S.-B. Hwang, M.-H. Lam and T.-Y. Shen, *Biochem. Biophys. Res. Commun.*, 1985, **128**, 972.
197. D. P. Tuffin, P. Davey, R. L. Dyer, D. O. Lunt and P. J. Wade, *Adv. Exp. Med. Biol.*, 1985, **192**, 83.
198. F. H. Valone and N. M. Ruis, *Biotechnol. Appl. Biochem.*, 1986, **8**, 465.
199. J. T. O'Flaherty, J. R. Surles, J. Redman, D. Jacobson, C. Piantadosi and R. L. Wykle, *J. Clin. Invest.*, 1986, **78**, 381.
200. S.-B. Hwang, *J. Biol. Chem.*, 1988, **263**, 3225.
201. F. H. Valone, *J. Immunol.*, 1988, **140**, 2389.
202. M. T. Domingo, B. Spinnewyn, P. E. Chabrier and P. Braquet, *Biochem. Biophys. Res. Commun.*, 1988, **151**, 730.
203. C. M. Chesney, D. D. Pifer and K. M. Huch, *Biochem. Biophys. Res. Commun.*, 1985, **127**, 24.
204. F. H. Valone, *Immunology*, 1984, **52**, 169.
205. J. Nishihira, T. Ishibashi, Y. Imai and T. Muramatsu, *Tohoku J. Exp. Med.*, 1985, **147**, 145.
206. J. Nishihira, T. Ishibashi and Y. Imai, *J. Biochem. (Tokyo)*, 1984, **95**, 1247.
207. P. Braquet and J. J. Godfroid, *Trends Pharmacol. Sci.*, 1986, **7**, 397.
208. J. T. O'Flaherty, *Biochem. Pharmacol.*, 1987, **36**, 407.
209. S.-B. Hwang, M.-H. Lam and S.-S. Pong, *J. Biol. Chem.*, 1986, **261**, 532.
210. P. V. Avdonin, I. V. Svitina-Ulitina and V. I. Kulikov, *Biochem. Biophys. Res. Commun.*, 1985, **131**, 307.
211. M. D. Housley, D. Bojanic and A. Wilson, *Biochem. J.*, 1986, **234**, 737.
212. H. Homma and D. J. Hanahan, *Arch. Biochem. Biophys.*, 1988, **262**, 32.
213. E. Kloprogge, P. Hasselaar, G. Gorter and J. W. N. Akkerman, *Biochim. Biophys. Acta*, 1986, **883**, 127.
214. E. Kloprogge, P. Hasselaar and J. W. N. Akkerman, *Biochem. J.*, 1986, **238**, 885.
215. E. Kloprogge, M. Mommersteeg and J. W. N. Akkerman, *J. Biol. Chem.*, 1986, **261**, 11 071.
216. E. Kloprogge and J. W. N. Akkerman, *Biochem. J.*, 1986, **240**, 403.
217. P. J. Wade, D. O. Lunt, N. Lad, D. P. Tuffin and K. G. McCullagh, *Thromb. Res.*, 1986, **41**, 251.
218. F. H. Valone, *Thromb. Res.*, 1987, **45**, 427.

219. S. N. Khan, P. A. Lane and A. D. Smith, *Eur. J. Pharmacol.*, 1985, **107**, 189.
220. G. Alloatti, G. Montrucchio, F. Mariano, C. Tetta, G. Emanuelli and G. Camussi, *J. Cardiovasc. Pharmacol.*, 1987, **9**, 181.
221. A. Etienne, N. Baroggi, R. Andries, F. Clostre, A. Esanu, R. Bourgain and P. Braquet, *Agents Actions*, 1986, suppl. 20, 259.
222. C. Giorgetti, G. C. Cadelli, C. Ferti, P. Baroldi and L. M. Fabbri, *J. Allergy Clin. Immunol.*, 1986, **77**, 122 (abstr. 7).
223. G. S. Basran, C. P. Page, W. Paul and J. Morley, *Eur. J. Pharmacol.*, 1983, **86**, 143.
224. T. Saijo, H. Kuriki, Y. Ashida, H. Makino and Y. Maki, *Int. Arch. Allergy Appl. Immunol.*, 1985, **77**, 315.
225. A. Khandwala, S. Coutts, T. Pruss, H. Jones, E. Neiss and I. Weinryb, *Biochem. Pharmacol.*, 1987, **36**, 663.
226. A. Zanetti, A. Zatta, M. Prosdocimi and E. Dejana, *Eur. J. Pharmacol.*, 1986, **128**, 119.
227. C. Lalau Keraly, D. Delautier, D. Delabassee, M. Chignard and J. Benveniste, *Thromb. Res.*, 1984, **34**, 463.
228. W. Siffert, S. Gengenbach and P. Scheid, *Thromb. Res.*, 1986, **44**, 235.
229. M. Chignard, M. Maamer, C. Lalau Keraly, M. Greiss, M. Aurousseau and J. Benveniste, *Thromb. Res.*, 1986, **44**, 445.
230. G. Feuerstein, W. E. Lux, D. Ezra, E. C. Hayes, F. Snyder and A. I. Faden, *J. Cardiovasc. Pharmacol.*, 1985, **7**, 335.
231. C. Vigo, *J. Biol. Chem.*, 1985, **260**, 3418.
232. J. Sugatani, M. Miwa and D. J. Hanahan, *J. Biol. Chem.*, 1987, **262**, 5740.
233. T.-Y. Shen, S.-B. Hwang, T. W. Doebber and J. C. Robbins, in 'Platelet Activating Factor and Related Lipid Mediators', ed. F. Snyder, Plenum Press, New York, 1987, p. 153.
234. W. E. Berdel and P. G. Munder, in 'Platelet Activating Factor and Related Lipid Mediators', ed. F. Snyder, Plenum Press, New York, 1987, p. 449.
235. O. Westphal, *Lipids*, 1987, **22**, 787.
236. F. Snyder, in 'Platelet Activating Factor and Related Lipid Mediators', ed. F. Snyder, Plenum Press, New York, 1987, p. 1.
237. J. R. Surles, R. L. Wykle, J. T. O'Flaherty, W. L. Salzer, M. J. Thomas, F. Snyder and C. Piantadosi, *J. Med. Chem.*, 1985, **28**, 73.
238. M. Tencé, E. Coeffier, C. Lalau Keraly and C. Broquet, in 'Platelet Activating Factor and Structurally Related Ether Lipids', INSERM Symposium no. 23, ed. J. Benveniste and B. Arnoux, Elsevier, Amsterdam, 1983, p. 41.
239. P. Hadvary, J.-M. Cassal, G. Hirth, R. Barner and H. R. Baumgartner, in 'Platelet Activating Factor and Structurally Related Ether Lipids', INSERM Symposium no. 23, ed. J. Benveniste and B. Arnoux, Elsevier, Amsterdam, 1983, p. 57.
240. J.-J. Godfroid, C. Broquet, S. Jouquey, M. Lebbar, F. Heymans, C. Redeuilh, E. Steiner, E. Michel, E. Coeffier, J. Fichelle and M. Worcel, *J. Med. Chem.*, 1987, **30**, 792.
241. A. Wissner, P.-E. Sum, R. E. Schaub, C. A. Kohler and B. M. Goldstein, *J. Med. Chem.*, 1984, **27**, 1174.
242. R. C. Anderson, B. E. Reitter and C. M. Winslow, *Chem. Phys. Lipids*, 1986, **39**, 73.
243. K. Fujita, S. Kobayashi, I. Kudo, K. Inoue, S. Nojima, M. Ohno, Y. Kobayashi, M. Odagiri and T. Taguchi, *Chem. Pharm. Bull.*, 1987, **35**, 647.
244. A. Wissner, C. A. Kohler and B. M. Goldstein, *J. Med. Chem.*, 1986, **29**, 1315.
245. C. Broquet, M.-P. Teulade, C. Borghero, F. Heymans, J.-J. Godfroid, J. Lefort, E. Coeffier and E. Pirotzky, *Eur. J. Med. Chem.—Chim. Ther.*, 1984, **19**, 229.
246. N. Nakamura, H. Miyazaki, N. Ohkawa, H. Koike, T. Sada, F. Asai and S. Kobayashi, *Chem. Pharm. Bull.*, 1984, **32**, 2452.
247. I. Hillmar, T. Muramatsu and N. Zöllner, *Hoppe-Seyler's Z. Physiol. Chem.*, 1984, **365**, 33.
248. R. L. Wykle, J. R. Surles, C. Piantadosi, W. L. Salzer and J. T. O'Flaherty, *FEBS Lett.*, 1982, **141**, 29.
249. L. G. Kritikou, M. C. Mochidis, A. Siafaca and C. A. Demopoulos, in 'Platelet Activating Factor and Structurally Related Ether Lipids', INSERM Symposium no. 23, ed. J. Benveniste and B. Arnoux, Elsevier, Amsterdam, 1983, p. 65.
250. G. Ostermann, H. Brachwitz and U. Till, *Biomed. Biochim. Acta*, 1984, **43**, 349.
251. M. L. Lee, A. Frei, C. Winslow and D. A. Handley, in 'Platelet Activating Factor and Structurally Related Ether Lipids', INSERM Symposium no. 23, ed. J. Benveniste and B. Arnoux, Elsevier, Amsterdam, 1983, p. 49.
252. N. S. Chandrakumar and J. Hadju, *J. Org. Chem.*, 1983, **48**, 1197.
253. S. K. Bhatia and J. Hadju, *Tetrahedron Lett.*, 1987, **28**, 1729.
254. D. M. Humphrey, L. M. McManus, K. Satouchi, D. J. Hanahan and R. N. Pinckard, *Lab. Invest.*, 1982, **46**, 422.
255. H. Disselnkötter, F. Lieb, H. Oediger and D. Wendisch, *Arch. Pharm. (Weinheim, Ger.)*, 1985, **318**, 695.
256. A. Wissner, R. E. Schaub, P. E. Sum, C. A. Kohler and B. M. Goldstein, *J. Med. Chem.*, 1986, **29**, 328.
257. T. Rosario-Jansen, R.-T. Jiang, M.-D. Tsai and D. J. Hanahan, *Biochemistry*, 1988, **27**, 4619.
258. A. Wissner, C. A. Kohler and B. M. Goldstein, *J. Med. Chem.*, 1985, **28**, 1365.
259. F. Heymans, M.-C. Borrel, C. Broquet, J. Lefort and J.-J. Godfroid, *J. Med. Chem.*, 1985, **28**, 1094.
260. K. Satouchi, R. N. Pinckard, L. M. McManus and D. J. Hanahan, *J. Biol. Chem.*, 1981, **256**, 4425.
261. Y. Kasuya, Y. Masuda and K. Shigenobu, *Can. J. Physiol. Pharmacol.*, 1984, **62**, 457.
262. E. Coëffier, M.-C. Borrel, J. Lefort, M. Chignard, C. Broquet, F. Heymans, J.-J. Godfroid and B. B. Vargaftig, *Eur. J. Pharmacol.*, 1986, **131**, 179.
263. F. Berti, V. Ferri, M. Pallavicini, M. Pretolani, E. Tremoli, E. Valoti and L. Villa, *Pharmacol. Res. Commun.*, 1986, **18**, 557.
264. M. Tencé, E. Coëffier, J. Polonsky and J. Benveniste, *Biochim. Biophys. Acta*, 1983, **755**, 526.
265. H.-P. Kertscher and G. Ostermann, *Pharmazie*, 1985, **40**, 55.
266. G. Ostermann, H.-P. Kertscher, A. Lang and U. Till, *Thromb. Res.*, 1986, **43**, 675.
267. A. Wissner, R. E. Schaub, P.-E. Sum, C. A. Kohler and B. M. Goldstein, *J. Med. Chem.*, 1985, **28**, 1181.
268. M. Ohno, K. Fujita, M. Shiraiwa, A. Izumi, S. Kobayashi, H. Yoshiwara, I. Kudo, K. Inoue and S. Nojima, *J. Med. Chem.*, 1986, **29**, 1814.
269. R. C. Anderson and R. C. Nabinger, *Tetrahedron Lett.*, 1983, **24**, 2741.
270. M. L. Phillips and R. Bonjouklian, *Carbohydr. Res.*, 1986, **146**, 89.
271. J. Benveniste, P. Braquet, C. G. Caillard, M. Chignard, J.-J. Godfroid, P. Sedivy and B. B. Vargaftig, *Prostaglandins*, 1985, **30**, 683.
272. M. N. Chang, *Drugs Future*, 1986, **11**, 869.

273. R. N. Saunders and D. A. Handley, *Annu. Rev. Pharmacol. Toxicol.*, 1987, **27**, 237.

274. B. Dewald and M. Baggiolini, *Biochem. Pharmacol.*, 1987, **36**, 2505.

275. Z. Terashita, S. Tsushima, Y. Yoshioka, H. Nomura, Y. Inada and K. Nishikawa, *Life Sci.*, 1983, **32**, 1975.

276. D. Nunez, M. Chignard, R. Korth, J.-P. LeCouedic, X. Norel, B. Spinnewyn, P. Braquet and J. Benveniste, *Eur. J. Pharmacol.*, 1986, **123**, 197.

277. C. P. Cox, *Thromb. Res.*, 1986, **41**, 211.

278. D. N. Robertson and G. M. Smith, *Eur. J. Pharmacol.*, 1986, **123**, 91.

279. Z. Terashita, Y. Imura and K. Nishikawa, *Biochem. Pharmacol.*, 1985, **34**, 1491.

280. F. H. Valone, *Biochem. Biophys. Res. Commun.*, 1985, **126**, 502.

281. J. Sugatani and D. J. Hanahan, *Arch. Biochem. Biophys.*, 1986, **246**, 855.

282. S. D. Shukla, *Arch. Biochem. Biophys.*, 1985, **240**, 674.

283. A. C. Issekutz and M. Szpejda, *Lab. Invest.*, 1986, **54**, 275.

284. S. Oh-ishi, K. Yamaki, M. Hayashi, S. Tsushima and H. Nomura, *Chem. Pharm. Bull.*, 1986, **34**, 4896.

285. Z. Terashita, Y. Imura, K. Nishikawa and S. Sumida, *Adv. Prostaglandin Thromboxane Leukotriene Res.*, 1985, **15**, 715.

286. Z. Terashita, Y. Imura, K. Nishikawa and S. Sumida, *Eur. J. Pharmacol.*, 1985, **109**, 257.

287. P. D. Toth and A. W. Mikulaschek, *Circ. Shock*, 1986, **20**, 193.

288. Y. Imura, Z. Terashita and K. Nishikawa, *Life Sci.*, 1986, **39**, 111.

289. J. D. Wallace and B. J. R. Whittle, *Eur. J. Pharmacol.*, 1986, **124**, 209.

290. M. K. Melden, R. G. Van Valen, M. L. Lee, R. N. Saunders and D. A. Handley, *Fed. Proc., Fed. Am. Soc. Exp. Biol.*, 1985, **44**, 1268.

291. J. Arnout, A. Van Hecken, I. De Lepeleire, Y. Miyamoto, I. Holmes, P. De Schepper and J. Vermylen, *Br. J. Clin. Pharmacol.*, 1988, **25**, 445.

292. T. Miyamoto, H. Ohno, T. Yano, T. Okada, N. Hamanaka and A. Kawasaki, *Adv. Prostaglandin Thromboxane Leukotriene Res.*, 1985, **15**, 719.

293. T. Toyofuku, K. Kubo, T. Kobayashi and S. Kusama, *Prostaglandins*, 1986, **31**, 271.

294. W. Hsueh, F. Gonzalez-Crussi, J. L. Arroyave, R. C. Anderson, M. L. Lee and W. J. Houlihan, *Eur. J. Pharmacol.*, 1986, **123**, 79.

295. K. Burri, R. Barner, J.-M. Cassal, P. Hadvary, G. Hirth and K. Muller, *Prostaglandins*, 1985, **30**, 691.

296. P. Hadvary and H. R. Baumgartner, *Prostaglandins*, 1985, **30**, 694.

297. D. A. Handley, R. G. Van Valen, M. K. Melden, S. Flury, M. L. Lee and R. N. Saunders, *Immunopharmacology*, 1986, **12**, 11.

298. D. A. Handley, R. G. Van Valen and R. N. Saunders, *Immunopharmacology*, 1986, **11**, 175.

299. R. Patterson, K. E. Harris, M. L. Lee and W. J. Houlihan, *Int. Arch. Allergy Appl. Immunol.*, 1986, **81**, 265.

300. C. M. Winslow, R. C. Anderson, F. J. D'Aries, G. E. Frisch, A. K. DeLillo, M. L. Lee and R. N. Saunders, in 'New Horizons in Platelet Activating Factor Research', ed. C. M. Winslow and M. L. Lee, Wiley, New York, 1987, p. 153.

301. N. Nakamura, N. Ookawa, H. Koike, T. Sada, T. Oshima and Y. Iizuka (Sankyo Co., Ltd.), *Eur. Pat. Appl.* 210 804 (1987) (*Chem. Abstr.*, 1987, **106**, 169 044k).

302. M. L. Lee, C. M. Winslow, C. Jaeggi, F. D'Aries, G. Frisch, C. Farley, M. K. Melden, D. A. Handley and R. N. Saunders, *Prostaglandins*, 1985, **30**, 690.

303. M. Steiner, R. Landolfi, N. C. Motola and J. C. Turcotte, *Biochem. Biophys. Res. Commun.*, 1985, **133**, 851.

304. B. Wichrowski, S. Jouquey, F. Heymans, C. Broquet, J.-J. Godfroid, J. Fichelle and M. Worcel, in 'Abstracts, 6th International Conference on Prostaglandins and Related Compounds (Florence), 3–6 June, 1986', p. 309.

305. A. Tokumura, H. Homma and D. J. Hanahan, *J. Biol. Chem.*, 1985, **260**, 12 710.

306. J. Sugatani and D. J. Hanahan, *Arch. Biochem. Biophys.*, 1986, **246**, 855.

307. H. Homma, R. Kumar and D. J. Hanahan, *Arch. Biochem. Biophys.*, 1987, **252**, 259.

308. D. B. Buxton, D. J. Hanahan and M. S. Olson, *Biochem. Pharmacol.*, 1986, **35**, 893.

309. Z.-I. Terashita, Y. Imura, M. Takatani, S. Tsushima and K. Nishikawa, *J. Pharmacol. Exp. Ther.*, 1987, **242**, 263.

310. B. Wichrowski, S. Jouquey, C. Broquet, F. Heymans, J.-J. Godfroid, J. Fichelle and M. Worcel, *J. Med. Chem.*, 1988, **31**, 410.

311. P. Hadvary and T. Weller, *Helv. Chim. Acta*, 1986, **69**, 1862.

312. D. A. Handley, R. G. Van Valen, J. C. Tomesch, M. K. Melden, J. M. Jaffe, F. H. Ballard and R. N. Saunders, *Immunopharmacology*, 1987, **13**, 125.

313. D. A. Handley, J. C. Tomesch and R. N. Saunders, *Thromb. Haemostasis*, 1986, **56**, 40.

314. R. M. Rubin and J. T. Rosenbaum, *Biochem. Biophys. Res. Commun.*, 1988, **154**, 429.

315. D. A. Handley, R. G. Van Valen, C. M. Winslow, J. C. Tomesch and R. N. Saunders, *Thromb. Haemostasis*, 1987, **57**, 187.

316. T.-Y. Shen, S.-B. Hwang, M. N. Chang, T. W. Doebber, M.-H. T. Lam, M. S. Wu, X. Wang, G. Q. Han and R. Z. Li, *Proc. Natl. Acad. Sci. U.S.A.*, 1985, **82**, 672.

317. S.-B. Hwang and M.-H. Lam, *Biochem. Pharmacol.*, 1986, **35**, 4511.

318. S.-B. Hwang, M.-H. Lam and M. N. Chang, *J. Biol. Chem.*, 1986, **261**, 13 720.

319. G. Lambrecht and M. J. Parnham, *Br. J. Pharmacol.*, 1986, **87**, 287.

320. T. W. Doebber, M. S. Wu, J. C. Robbins, B. M. Choy, M. N. Chang and T.-Y. Shen, *Biochem. Biophys. Res. Commun.*, 1985, **127**, 799.

321. H. Darius, J. B. Smith and A. M. Lefer, *Int. Arch. Allergy Appl. Immunol.*, 1986, **80**, 369.

322. M. N. Chang, G.-Q. Han, B. H. Arison, J. P. Springer, S.-B. Hwang and T.-Y. Shen, *Phytochemistry*, 1985, **24**, 2079.

323. M. M. Ponpipom, R. L. Bugianesi, D. R. Brooker, B.-Z. Yue, S.-B. Hwang and T.-Y. Shen, *J. Med. Chem.*, 1987, **30**, 136.

324. J.-X. Pan. O. D. Hessens, D. L. Zink, M. N. Chang and S.-B. Hwang, *Phytochemistry*, 1987, **26**, 1377.

325. P. Braquet, *Drugs Future*, 1987, **12**, 643.

326. P. Braquet (ed.), 'Ginkgolides — Chemistry, Biology, Pharmacology and Clinical Perspectives', Prous, Barcelona, 1988, vol. 1.

327. L. Dupont, O. Dideberg, G. Germain and P. Braquet, *Acta Crystallogr., Sect. C*, 1986, **C42**, 1759.

328. E. J. Corey, M.-C. Kang, M. C. Desai, A. K. Ghosh and I. N. Houpis, *J. Am. Chem. Soc.*, 1988, **110**, 649.

329. E. B. Villhauer and R. C. Anderson, *J. Org. Chem.*, 1987, **52**, 1186.

330. L. Dupont, G. Germain and O. Dideberg, *Pharmacol. Res. Commun.*, 1986, **18** (suppl.), 25.
331. H. Lachachi, M. Plantavid, M.-F. Simon, H. Chap, P. Braquet and L. Douste-Blazy, *Biochem. Biophys. Res. Commun.*, 1985, **132**, 460.
332. M. Rola-Pleszczynski, B. Pignal, C. Pouliot and P. Braquet, *Biochem. Biophys. Res. Commun.*, 1987, **142**, 754.
333. P. Braquet, *Adv. Prostaglandin Thromboxane Leukotriene Res.*, 1986, **16**, 179.
334. J. Baranes, A. Hellegouarch, M. Le Hegarat, I. Voissat, M. Auguet, P. E. Chabrier, F. Braquet and P. Braquet, *Pharmacol. Res. Commun.*, 1986, **18**, 717.
335. K. F. Chung, M. McCusker, C. P. Page, G. Dent, P. Guinot and P. J. Barnes, *Lancet*, 1987, **1**, 248.
336. S.-B. Hwang, M. N. Chang, M. L. Garcia, Q. Q. Han, L. Huang, V. F. King, G. J. Kaczorowski and R. J. Winquist, *Eur. J. Pharmacol.*, 1987, **141**, 269.
337. C. Touvay, B. Villain, P. Sirois, M. Soufir and P. Braquet, *J. Pharm. Pharmacol.*, 1987, **39**, 454.
338. M. Okamoto, K. Yoshida, I. Uchida, M. Nishikawa, M. Kohsaka and H. Aoki, *Chem. Pharm. Bull.*, 1986, **34**, 340.
339. M. Okamoto, K. Yoshida, I. Uchida, M. Kohsaka and H. Aoki, *Chem. Pharm. Bull.*, 1986, **34**, 345.
340. S. Takase, N. Shigematsu, I. Shima, I. Uchida, M. Hashimoto, T. Tada, S. Koda and Y. Morimoto, *J. Org. Chem.*, 1987, **52**, 3485.
341. M. Okamoto, K. Yoshida, M. Nishikawa, T. Ando, M. Iwami, M. Kohsaka and H. Aoki, *J. Antibiot.*, 1986, **39**, 198.
342. M. Okamoto, K. Yoshida, M. Nishikawa, K. Hayashi, I. Uchida, M. Kohsaka and H. Aoki, *Chem. Pharm. Bull.*, 1986, **34**, 3005.
343. M. Okamoto, K. Yoshida, M. Nishikawa, M. Kohsaka and H. Aoki, *Thromb. Res.*, 1986, **42**, 661.
344. T. Biftu, N. F. Gamble, T. Doebber, S.-B. Hwang, T.-Y. Shen, J. Snyder, J. P. Springer and R. Stevenson, *J. Med. Chem.*, 1986, **29**, 1917.
345. S.-B. Hwang, M.-H. Lam, T. Biftu, T. R. Beattie and T.-Y. Shen, *J. Biol. Chem.*, 1985, **260**, 15639.
346. M. S. Wu, T. Biftu and T. W. Doebber, *J. Pharmacol. Exp. Ther.*, 1986, **239**, 841.
347. P. G. Hellewell and T. J. Williams, *J. Immunol.*, 1986, **137**, 302.
348. T. W. Doebber, M. S. Wu and T. Biftu, *J. Immunol.*, 1986, **136**, 4659.
349. P. D. Gautheron, L. Coulbault and M. F. Sugrue, *J. Pharm. Pharmacol.*, 1987, **39**, 857.
350. T. Biftu, N. F. Gamble, J. C. Chabala, A. Dallob, T. Doebber, H. W. Dougherty, S.-B. Hwang and T.-Y. Shen, in 'Abstracts, 6th International Conference on Prostaglandins and Related Compounds (Florence), 3–6 June, 1986', p. 302.
351. T. Biftu (Merck & Co., Inc.), *Eur. Pat. Appl.* 217204 (1987) (*Chem. Abstr.*, 1987, **107**, 39599e).
352. M. M. Ponpipom, S.-B. Hwang, T. W. Doebber, J. J. Acton, A. W. Alberts, T. Biftu, D. R. Brooker, R. L. Bugianesi, J. C. Chabala, N. L. Gamble, D. W. Graham, M.-H. Lam and M. S. Wu, *Biochem. Biophys. Res. Commun.*, 1988, **150**, 1213.
353. N. Shimazaki, K. Hemmi, O. Nakaguti, Y. Miyazaki and M. Hashimoto (Fujisawa Pharmaceutical Co., Ltd.), *Eur. Pat. Appl.* 181152 (1986) (*Chem. Abstr.*, 1986, **105**, 115098s).
354. N. Shimazaki, I. Shima, K. Hemmi and M. Hashimoto, *J. Med. Chem.*, 1987, **30**, 1706.
355. N. Shimazaki, I. Shima, K. Hemmi, Y. Tsurumi and M. Hashimoto, *Chem. Pharm. Bull.*, 1987, **35**, 3527.
356. E. Kornecki, Y. H. Ehrlich and R. H. Lenox, *Science (Washington, D. C.)*, 1984, **226**, 1454.
357. J. Casals-Stenzel, *Naunyn-Schmiedebergs Arch. Pharmacol.*, 1987, **335**, 351.
358. M. Terasawa, H. Mikashima, T. Tahara and Y. Maruyama, *Jpn. J. Pharmacol.*, 1987, **44**, 381.
359. H. Mikashima, S. Takehara, Y. Muramoto, T. Khomaru, M. Terasawa and Y. Maruyama, *Jpn. J. Pharmacol.*, 1987, **44**, 387.
360. T. Tahara, H. Mikashima, M. Terasawa and Y. Maruyama, *Chem. Pharm. Bull.*, 1987, **35**, 2119.
361. E. Kornecki, R. H. Lenox, D. H. Hardwick and Y. H. Ehrlich, in 'New Horizons in Platelet Activating Factor Research', ed. C. M. Winslow and M. L. Lee, Wiley, New York, 1987, p. 285.
362. J. Casals-Stenzel and K. H. Weber, *Br. J. Pharmacol.*, 1987, **90**, 139.
363. C. M. Chesney, D. D. Pifer and L. M. Cagen, *Biochem. Biophys. Res. Commun.*, 1987, **144**, 359.
364. J. Casals-Stenzel, G. Muacevic and K. H. Weber, *Naunyn-Schmiedeberg's Arch. Pharmacol.*, 1986, **334** (suppl.), R44, abstr. 175.
365. J. Casals-Stenzel, *Eur. J. Pharmacol.*, 1987, **135**, 117.
366. J. Casals-Stenzel, *Immunopharmacology*, 1987, **13**, 117.
367. A. Brambilla, A. Ghiorzi and A. Giachetti, *Pharmacol. Res. Commun.*, 1987, **19**, 147.
368. J. Casals-Stenzel, G. Muacevic and K.-H. Weber, *J. Pharmacol. Exp. Ther.*, 1987, **241**, 974.
369. P. Sedivy, C. G. Caillard, A. Floch, F. Foillard, S. Mondot, C. Robaut and B. Terlain, *Prostaglandins*, 1985, **30**, 688.
370. P. Sedivy, D. Robaut, A. Carruette, C. G. Caillard, J. Deregnaucourt and S. Mondot, *Thromb. Haemostasis*, 1985, **54**, 185.
371. J. Lefort, P. Sedivy, S. Desquand, J. Randon, E. Coeffier, I. Maridonneau-Parini, A. Floch, J. Benveniste and B. B. Vargaftig, *Eur. J. Pharmacol.*, 1988, **150**, 257.
372. C. Robaut, G. Durand, C. James, D. Lave, P. Sedivy, A. Floch, S. Mondot, D. Pacot, I. Cavero and G. Le Fur, *Biochem. Pharmacol.*, 1987, **36**, 3221.
373. O. Marquis, C. Robaut and I. Cavero, *J. Pharmacol. Exp. Ther.*, 1988, **244**, 709.
374. M. J. DiMartino, D. E. Griswold, B. A. Berkowitz, G. Poste and N. Hanna, *Agents Actions*, 1987, **20**, 113.
375. S.-B. Hwang, M. J. Cheah, C.-S. C. Lee and T.-Y. Shen, *Thromb. Res.*, 1984, **34**, 519.
376. T.-Y. Shen, S. S. Yang, and S.-B. Hwang (Merck & Co., Inc.), *Eur. Pat. Appl.* 142801 (1985) (*Chem. Abstr.*, 1986, **104**, 5652q).
377. J. W. Tilley, B. Burghardt, C. Burghardt, T. F. Mowles, F.-J. Leinweber, L. Klevans, R. Young, G. Hirkaler, K. Fahrenholtz, S. Zawoiski and L. J. Todaro, *J. Med. Chem.*, 1988, **31**, 466.
378. W. J. Houlihan, S. H. Cheon, D. A. Handley, D. Larson, V. A. Parrino, B. Reitter, G. Schmitt and C. M. Winslow, in 'Abstracts, Xth International Medicinal Chemistry Symposium, Budapest, 15–19 August, 1988', p. 93.
379. J.-J. Godfroid, J. P. Robin and P. Braquet, *Prostaglandins*, 1985, **30**, 686.
380. B. B. Vargaftig and P. G. Braquet, *Br. Med. Bull.*, 1987, **43**, 312.
381. E. J. Corey, C.-P. Chen and M. J. Parry, *Tetrahedron Lett.*, 1988, **29**, 2899.
382. S. L. Schreiber, in 'Abstracts of the 30th National Organic Chemistry Symposium, 21–25 June, 1987, Vancouver, B. C., Canada', American Chemical Society and the Canadian Society for Chemistry, 1987, p. 1.

383. A. G. Stewart and G. J. Dusting, *Br. J. Pharmacol.*, 1988, **94**, 1225.
384. D. Ukena, G. Dent, F. W. Birke, C. Robaut, G. W. Sybrecht and P. J. Barnes, *FEBS Lett.*, 1988, **228**, 285.
385. R. N. Pinckard, J. C. Ludwig and L. M. McManus, in 'Inflammation — Basic Principles and Clinical Correlates', ed. J. I. Gallin, I. M. Goldstein and R. Snyderman, Raven Press, New York, 1988, p. 139.
386. P. Braquet (ed.), 'Platelet-Activating Factor and Cell Immunology', Karger, Basel, 1988, vols. 1 and 2.
387. D. A. Handley, *Drugs Future*, 1988, **13**, 137.
388. P. J. Barnes, K. F. Chung and C. P. Page, *J. Allergy Clin. Immunol.*, 1988, **81**, 919.
389. P. Braquet and M. Rola-Pleszczynski, *Immunol. Today*, 1987, **8**, 345.
390. P. J. Barnes and K. F. Chung, *Trends Pharmacol. Sci.*, 1987, **8**, 285.
391. K. F. Chung and P. J. Barnes, *Drugs*, 1988, **35**, 93.
392. C. P. Page, C. B. Archer, W. Paul and J. Morley, *Trends Pharmacol. Sci.*, 1984, **5**, 239.
393. A. J. Lewis, A. Dervinis and J. Chang, *Agents Actions*, 1984, **15**, 636.
394. C. P. Page, R. H. H. Tomiak, S. Sanjar and J. Morley, *Agents Actions*, 1985, **16**, 33.
395. J. Morley, *Agents Actions*, 1986, **19**, 100.
396. C. P. Page and J. Morley, *Pharmacol. Res. Commun.*, 1986, **18** (suppl.), 217.
397. C. P. Page, S. Sanjar, D. Alvemini and J. Morley, *Eur. J. Respir. Dis.*, 1986, **68** (suppl. 144), 163.
398. F. M. Cuss, C. M. S. Dixon and P. J. Barnes, *Lancet*, 1986, **2**, 189.
399. T. Nakamura, Y. Morita, M. Kuriyama, K. Ishihara, K. Ito and T. Miyamoto, *Int. Arch. Allergy Appl. Immunol.*, 1987, **82**, 57.
400. J. E. Heffner, S. A. Shoemaker, E. M. Canham, M. Patel, I. F. McMurtry, H. G. Morris and J. E. Repine, *Chest*, 1983, **83** (suppl.), 78S.
401. E. J. Sybertz, R. W. Watkins, T. Baum, K. Pula and M. Rivelli, *J. Pharmacol. Exp. Ther.*, 1985, **232**, 156.
402. P. Bessin, *Pharmacol. Res. Commun.*, 1986, **18** (suppl.), 139.
403. G. E. Plante, R. L. Hebert, C. Lamoureux, P. Braquet and P. Sirois, *Pharmacol. Res. Commun.*, 1986, **18** (suppl.), 173.
404. J. Benveniste and M. Chignard, *Circulation*, 1985, **72**, 713.
405. G. Feuerstein, D. Ezra, P. W. Ramwell, G. Letts and R. E. Goldstein, in 'Prostaglandins, Leukotrienes and Lipoxins', ed. J. M. Bailey, Plenum Press, New York, 1985, p. 301.
406. D. A. Handley and R. N. Saunders, *Drug Dev. Res.*, 1986, **6**, 361.
407. E. R. Pettipher, G. A. Higgs and B. Henderson, *Agents Actions*, 1987, **21**, 98.
408. M. L. Foegh, B. S. Khirabadi, J. R. Rowles, P. Braquet and P. W. Ramwell, *Transplantation*, 1986, **42**, 86.
409. C. Caramelo, S. Fernandez-Gallardo, J. C. Santos, P. Inarrea, M. Sanchez-Crespo, J. M. Lopez-Novoa and L. Hernando, *Eur. J. Clin. Invest.*, 1987, **17**, 7.
410. R. Joseph, K. M. A. Welch, G. D'Andrea and S. R. Levine, *Thromb. Haemostasis*, 1987, **57**, 125.
411. P. M. Henson, in 'New Horizons in Platelet Activating Factor Research', ed. C. M. Winslow and M. L. Lee, Wiley, New York, 1987, p. 3.

12.13
Leukotriene Receptors

WILLIAM KINGSBURY, ROBERT DAINES and JOHN GLEASON

Smith Kline & French Laboratories, King of Prussia, PA, USA

12.13.1 INTRODUCTION

The family of bioactive lipids known as the leukotrienes exert pharmacological effects on respiratory, cardiovascular and gastrointestinal systems. The leukotrienes are generally divided into two subclasses, the peptidoleukotrienes (leukotrienes C_4, D_4 and E_4) and the hydroxyleukotrienes (leukotriene B_4). Leukotrienes C_4, D_4 and E_4 are implicated with the biological responses associated with the 'slow reacting substance of anaphylaxis' (SRS-A). These include myotropic response on various smooth muscle, potent contractile effects on human bronchus, human parenchymal strips and human trachea *in vitro*. *In vivo* they have been shown to induce prolonged bronchoconstriction. In addition, cardiovascular effects such as coronary artery vasoconstriction as well as numerous other biological responses have been attributed to these mediators. LTB_4 exerts its biological effects through stimulation of leukocyte and lymphocyte functions. It stimulates chemotaxis, chemokinesis and aggregation of polymorphonuclear leukocytes (PMNs). The pharmacology of the peptido-leukotrienes includes smooth muscle contractions, myocardial depression, increased vascular permeability, and enhanced mucous production. In contrast, LTB_4 possesses chemotactic properties that attract leukocytes to sites of cellular injury and thus contribute to inflammation. The leuko-trienes are critically involved in mediating many types of cardiovascular, pulmonary, dermatological, renal, allergic and inflammatory diseases, including asthma, adult respiratory distress syndrome, cystic fibrosis, psoriasis and inflammatory bowel disease. The implication of leukotrienes in a wide variety of disease states has stimulated a significant research effort dedicated to this class of compounds.

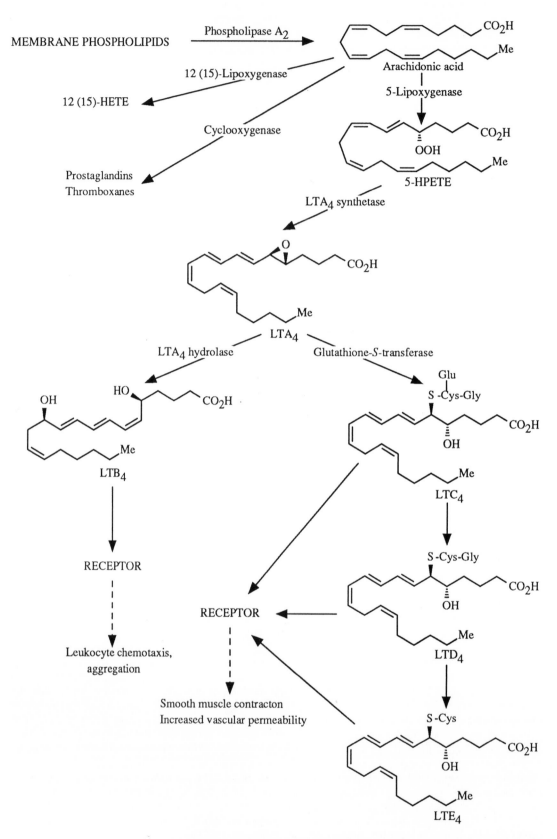

Figure 1　Biosynthesis of leukotrienes

The leukotrienes are produced by the metabolism of arachidonic acid as shown in Figure 1. Activation of phospholipase A_2, the enzyme that cleaves arachidonic acid from membrane phospholipids and provides the substrate for leukotriene biogenesis, occurs as a consequence of antigen–antibody reaction, in response to cell injury, or in response to chemical intervention. The arachidonic acid thus released is sequentially transformed into 5-hydroperoxyeicosatetraenoic acid (5-HPETE) and LTA_4 by the action of 5-lipoxygenase and LTA_4 synthetase. LTA_4 is a short-lived leukotriene intermediate that is rapidly converted into either LTB_4 or LTC_4 by an epoxide hydrolase (LTA_4 hydrolase) or by glutathione-S-transferase respectively. LTD_4 is formed from LTC_4 by γ-glutamyltranspeptidase and LTE_4 is formed from LTD_4 by an aminopeptidase.

The leukotrienes exert their biological effects through specific peptidoleukotriene and LTB_4 receptors located on a variety of cell types and various tissues (*e.g.* human lung). The potential for development of useful therapeutic agents through the design of effective leukotriene receptor antagonists has provided the basis for extensive research in this area.

This chapter will review the pathophysiological roles of the leukotrienes and briefly discuss the leukotriene receptors. The major emphasis, however, will focus on the investigations of leukotriene receptor antagonists. For the sake of clarity, the peptidoleukotrienes (LTC_4, LTD_4 and LTE_4) and the dihydroxyleukotriene (LTB_4) will be handled separately.

12.13.2 PEPTIDOLEUKOTRIENES

12.13.2.1 Peptidoleukotrienes in Disease

A detailed discussion of potential pathophysiological roles that the peptidoleukotrienes play in various disease states is beyond the scope of this chapter. However, the specific areas where evidence strongly supports the involvement of leukotrienes include the respiratory, cardiovascular and renal systems.

Of these disease states, the deleterious actions of the peptidoleukotrienes on bronchopulmonary systems are the best studied and understood. This includes an enormous amount of evidence supporting the role of peptidoleukotrienes in asthma, a disease characterized by airway obstruction, where they are implicated in bronchoconstriction, mucus hypersecretion and pulmonary edema, all factors contributing to airway obstruction. Specific reviews that deal in detail with these topics are available.[1-4] Although asthma is a complex disease with a number of potential mediators, the data supporting the role of peptidoleukotrienes are substantial and encourage the development of novel, potent and specific peptidoleukotriene synthesis inhibitors and receptor antagonists as therapeutic agents for the treatment of asthma. Data supporting the role of peptidoleukotrienes in coronary vasospasm and myocardial ischemia have also been reported.[5,6] The possibility that the peptidoleukotrienes are involved in myocardial ischemia in humans is supported by reports that human coronary arteries have the capacity to generate these mediators and that a high density of cells that produce leukotrienes were present in the artery of a patient with coronary vasospasm.[7] Recently, the potential role of peptidoleukotrienes as mediators of acute glomerulonephritis and interstitial nephritis has generated interest[8,9] along with recent evidence implicating the involvement of peptidoleukotrienes in allergic rhinitis,[10,11] cystic fibrosis[12] and in inflammatory liver diseases.[13]

12.13.2.2 Peptidoleukotriene Receptors

Considerable effort has been directed toward understanding the mechanism by which the leukotrienes exert their biological effects. Biochemical studies have demonstrated the presence of specific cell surface receptors. These receptors have been characterized and major progress has been achieved in the understanding of the signal transduction processes. The results of these efforts have led to a model that explains the interaction of LTD_4 with its receptor and the events that are induced by this interaction.[14]

Leukotrienes reversibly bind to their receptors; the binding is saturable, and the responses show stereochemical specificity.[15-17] The leukotrienes interact on a heterogeneous population of receptors between species, among different organs of the same species, and even within the same tissue.[18-20] However, a degree of commonality exists between receptors since LTE_4 is able to displace LTD_4 from its receptor, indicating that LTE_4 and LTD_4 receptors may be similar.[21] The finding that the SRS-A antagonist FPL-55712 (**30**) can specifically block LTD_4- and LTE_4-induced smooth muscle contraction further supports the involvement of common receptors in the actions of the leukotrienes.[22] In contrast, studies with LTC_4 binding support the existence of a separate receptor for LTC_4.[23,24] For example, FPL-55712 is effective in blocking both LTD_4- and LTE_4-induced guinea pig tracheal smooth muscle contraction, but fails to block LTC_4-induced contraction.[25] In fact, when the conversion of LTC_4 to LTD_4 is blocked by γ-glutamyltranspeptidase inhibitors, FPL-55712 is completely ineffective in blocking LTC_4-induced guinea pig tracheal contractions. In addition, neither SK&F-104353 (**109**) nor ICI-198615 (**126**), both potent LTD_4 receptor antagonists, is potent or specific for LTC_4-induced tissue contraction of guinea pig lung preparations.[26,27]

Human bronchiolar smooth muscle, however, responds to these LTD_4 receptor antagonists very differently from the guinea pig smooth muscle preparations. Human bronchial smooth muscle is sensitive to both LTC_4 and LTD_4 and both SK&F-104353 and ICI-198615 effectively block both LTC_4- and LTD_4-induced contractions.[28,29] These results suggest that a distinct LTC_4 receptor does not exist in human tracheal smooth muscle, but rather that a single population of receptors mediates the responses of both LTC_4 and LTD_4.

The existence of the LTD_4 receptor is supported by the use of *in vitro* smooth muscle contraction assays and by radioligand binding studies. LTD_4 induces smooth muscle contraction in a highly specific fashion.[30,31] Furthermore, guinea pig, monkey, sheep and human airway smooth muscle preparations are highly responsive to LTD_4.[32-34] These findings suggest that LTD_4 can induce smooth muscle contractions *via* specific receptors in smooth muscle tissues. The observation that FPL-55712 can specifically block LTD_4 and LTE_4 smooth muscle contractions lends further support to the hypothesis that the response to LTD_4 is receptor mediated.

The results obtained from radioligand binding studies also support the existence of specific LTD_4 receptors. $[^3H]$-LTD_4 specific binding sites are present in the plasma membrane of smooth muscle cells of sheep trachea, guinea pig lung membrane, human lung, human monocyte leukemia cells (U-937), rat basophilic leukemia cells (RBL-1) and guinea pig myocardium.[35] The binding of $[^3H]$-LTD_4 to these membranes is stereoselective, specific, and saturable. Furthermore, the specificity of high-affinity receptor antagonists such as SK&F-104353 and ICI-198615 in binding to these receptors directly correlates with the pharmacological functions of these compounds in guinea pig smooth muscle contraction assays. Thus, the specific LTD_4 binding sites in guinea pig and human lung represent the biochemically and physiologically relevant receptors and fully reflect the pharmacological specificity of agonist/antagonist-mediated responses induced by LTD_4 and its analogs.[36]

LTE_4 has been shown to bind the LTD_4 receptor in membranes from guinea pig lung, human lung and many other types of tissues.[37,38] FPL-55712, SK&F-104353 and ICI-198615 block LTE_4-induced guinea pig tracheal contraction *in vitro*. The experimental observations demonstrate that LTE_4 functions at the LTD_4 receptor. Thus, LTD_4 receptor antagonists should be effective antagonists of LTE_4-induced pharmacological responses and therefore useful in the treatment of LTD_4- as well as LTE_4-mediated disease processes.

Since the binding of the peptidoleukotrienes represents a biochemically relevant process that is reflected in a pharmacological response, peptidoleukotriene receptor antagonists represent therapeutically relevant drug targets. This chapter will describe progress to date in this area.

12.13.2.3 Peptidoleukotriene (C_4, D_4, E_4) Receptor Antagonists

Peptidoleukotriene receptor antagonists could represent a major advance in the treatment of immediate hypersensitivity diseases, including asthma and allergic rhinitis. The first receptor antagonist, however, predates the identification of the structure of the natural agonist. Discovered as an 'SRS-A' antagonist, the hydroxyacetophenone derivative FPL-55712 played a key role in the initial characterization of the peptidoleukotriene receptor and in defining its role in asthma. In addition to its pharmacological value, FPL-55712 served as a structural starting point for the discovery of a large number of related antagonists, several of which have progressed to clinical evaluation. More recently, however, antagonists based on the structures of the natural agonists, as well as structurally diverse antagonists unrelated to either the hydroxyacetophenones or the natural agonists, have emerged. These 'second generation' antagonists, generally possessing significantly enhanced affinity for the leukotriene receptor, may play a key role in defining the clinical importance of peptidoleukotriene antagonists in disease.

12.13.2.4 Hydroxyacetophenones

The first leukotriene receptor antagonist to be identified was FPL-55712 (**30**).[39] This compound was initially characterized as an 'SRS-A' antagonist in 1975, and, with the identification of the bioactive components of SRS-A as LTC_4, LTD_4 and LTE_4 by Samuelsson and Corey and their co-workers,[30,31] as a selective peptidoleukotriene antagonist. This compound was discovered by scientists at Fisons Ltd. as a result of an antiallergy screening program in which mast cell stabilizing compounds were evaluated as potential SRS-A antagonists. FPL-55712 effectively antagonizes the smooth muscle contractions induced by LTD_4 in a variety of tissues and species, and consequently has been used to define the pharmacological role of leukotrienes in immediate hypersensitivity reactions. Unfortunately, this compound was found to lack significant oral activity and has a very short half-life. Consequently, it has not been developed as a drug. Nevertheless, numerous research groups have utilized this compound as the starting point for the discovery of more potent, metabolically stable orally active antagonists.

Extensive studies by a variety of research groups have served to define the critical structure–activity relationships within the hydroxyacetophenone class. In order to determine the structural features required for activity within this class, a detailed analysis of the structural features of the molecule that are required for biological activity was undertaken. Compounds were selected in order to determine: (i) the importance of the position of the substituent group on the chromone ring; (ii) the length of the polyalkylenedioxy chain; (iii) the presence of the terminal oxygens in the chain; and (iv) the substituents on the phenyl ring.

The initial series of compounds studied involved substitution at various positions of the chromone ring (Table 1). A comparison of activities within this series led to the conclusion that substitution at the C-7 position of the chromone ring is preferred (*e.g.* compare compounds **2**, **6**, **12** and **19**, and also **3**, **7**, **13** and **20**). However, no conclusions pertaining to optimization of chain length could be made as this varied with the position of the substituent (*e.g.* compounds **4** and **13**). Furthermore, removal of the oxygens at the chain termini did not have a significant effect on the activity (*e.g.* compounds **6**, **10** and **13**, **16–18**). As an extension of these studies a number of analogs were prepared which relate activity with the chain linking the two rings and also with the positions of various substituents on the phenoxy ring (Table 2). Removal of the chain hydroxyl groups, *e.g.* compound (**27**), results in a compound with improved activity over FPL-55712 (**30**). Subsequent *in vivo* studies of (**27**) *vs.* (**30**) did not demonstrate worthwhile advantages for either compound, thus subsequent biological evaluations were conducted using the original lead, FPL-55712 (**30**). Clinical development of

Table 1 Peptidoleukotriene Receptor Antagonists: FPL-55712 Analogs

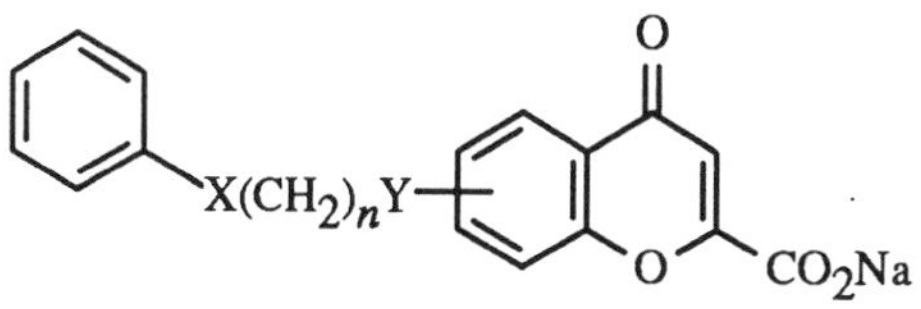

Compound	Substituent position in chromone ring	X	n	Y	Anti-SRS-A activity, IC_{50} ($\mu g\,mL^{-1}$)
(1)	5	O	2	O	100
(2)		O	3	O	35
(3)		O	5	O	17.5
(4)		O	7	O	0.8
(5)		O	9	O	6.0
(6)	6	O	3	O	3.3
(7)		O	5	O	3.3
(8)			1		6.6
(9)			3		3.0
(10)			5		4.5
(11)	7	O	2	O	15
(12)		O	3	O	1.4
(13)		O	5	O	0.4
(14)		O	7	O	1.8
(15)		O	9	O	1.8
(16)		S	5	O	0.4
(17)		O	5	S	0.3
(18)		CH_2	4	O	0.6
(19)	8	O	3	O	50
(20)		O	5	O	9

Table 2　Peptidoleukotriene Receptor Antagonists: FPL-55712 Analogs

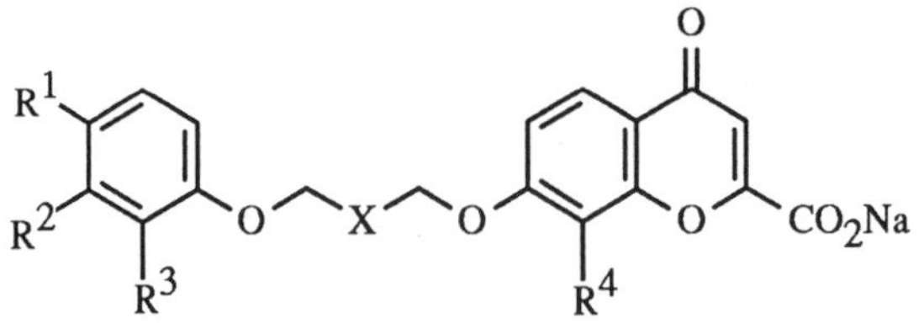

Compound	R^1	R^2	R^3	R^4	X	Anti-SRS-A activity, IC_{50} (μg mL^{-1})
(21)	Allyl	OH	Ac	H	$(CH_2)_3$	0.9
(22)	H	OH	H	H	$(CH_2)_3$	1.5
(23)	Ac	H	H	H	$(CH_2)_3$	3.5
(24)	H	OH	Ac	Allyl	$(CH_2)_3$	0.05
(25)	Ac	OH	Allyl	Allyl	$(CH_2)_3$	1.23
(26)	H	H	Pr^n	Pr^n	CH_2	0.18
(27)	Ac	OH	Pr^n	Pr^n	CH_2	0.001
(28)	Ac	OH	H	H	CH(OH)	28
(29)	Ac	OH	Pr^n	H	CH(OH)	0.08
(30)	Ac	OH	Pr^n	Pr^n	CH(OH)	0.005
(31)	H	H	Pr^n	Pr^n	CH(OH)	0.044

FPL-55712 (**30**) was hampered by the lack of oral bioavailability and short biological half-life ($t_{1/2} \approx 10$ min).[40,41] Extension of the chromone carboxylic acid group of FPL-55712 or (**27**) into a propionic acid derivative produced compounds that have longer biological half-lives, but exhibit reduced potency *in vitro*.[42]

Subsequent modifications by researchers at Beecham Pharmaceuticals, using FPL-55712 (**30**) as a structural model, led to the preparation of a series of nitrocoumarins represented by the general structure (**32**).[43] The results of extensive SAR within this class of compounds correlated with those in the FPL-55712 series (Table 3). The initial studies demonstrated that compounds with simple alkoxy substituents attached at C-7 have minimal SRS-A antagonist activity. However, the results illustrated in Table 3 reveal that substitution of the nitrocoumarin nucleus with appropriate phenoxypropoxy side chains led to compounds that possess SRS-A antagonist activity. As with FPL-55712, substitution at the C-7 ring position was favored over substitution at the other ring positions. Substitution of the coumarin ring at either the C-5 or the C-6 positions reduced activity, while substitution at C-8 had little effect on activity. SRS-A antagonist activity tended to decrease with increasing chain length, the trimethylene chain being preferred (*e.g.* compounds **33** and **34**). Addition of a lipid substituent at R^1, such as propyl, proved to be a major factor contributing to increases in antagonist activity (*e.g.* compare compounds **37** and **38**, and compounds **39** and **40**). Compounds of the nitrocoumarin class demonstrated, in addition to SRS-A antagonist activity, a high level of antiallergy activity. In this regard, the compounds were found to inhibit histamine release, the compounds with the highest SRS-A antagonist activity being the most potent inhibitors of histamine release.

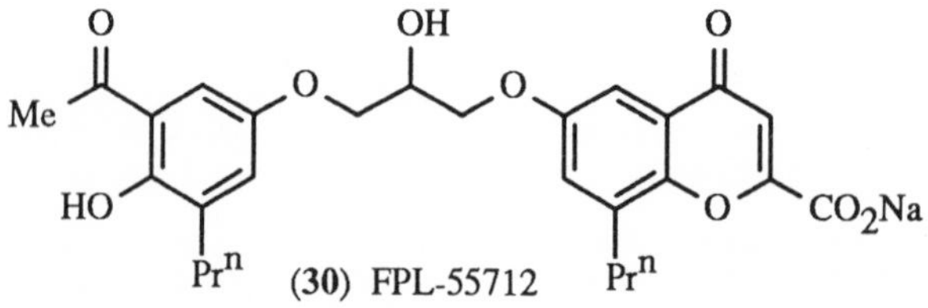

(30) FPL-55712

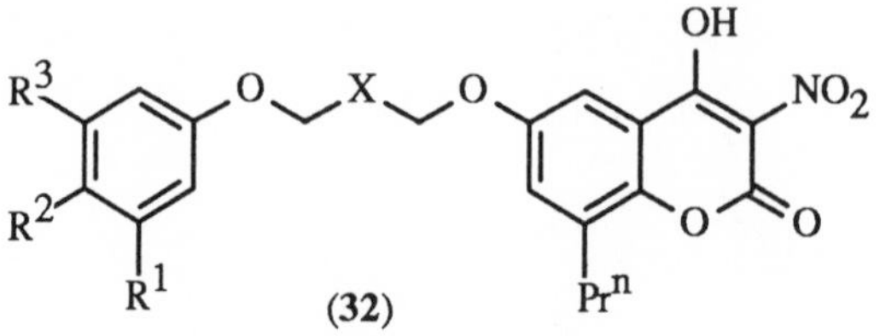

(32)

Table 3 Peptidoleukotriene Receptor Antagonists: FPL-55712 Analogs

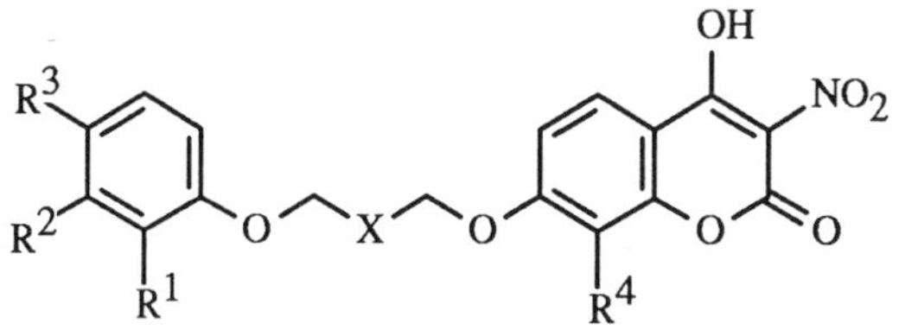

Compound	R^1	R^2	R^3	R^4	X	Anti-SRS-A activity, IC_{50} ($\mu g\,mL^{-1}$)
(33)	H	H	H	H	CH_2	1.6
(34)	H	H	H	H	$(CH_2)_3$	8.4
(35)	H	H	H	$8\text{-}Pr^n$	CH_2	0.54–3.5
(36)	H	H	Ac	H	CH_2	6.1
(37)	H	OH	Ac	H	CH_2	2.8
(38)	Pr^n	OH	Ac	H	CH_2	0.1
(39)	H	H	H	H	$CH(OH)$	12
(40)	Pr^n	H	H	H	$CH(OH)$	0.11
(41)	Pr^n	H	Ac	H	$CH(OH)$	0.7
(42)	H	OH	Ac	H	$CH(OH)$	> 20
(43)	Pr^n	OH	Ac	Pr^n	$CH(OH)$	0.08
(44)	Pr^n	OH	Ac	Pr^n	$CH(OH)$	0.20

A subsequent attempt to prepare SRS-A antagonists within the hydroxyacetophenone class was undertaken by researchers at Lilly Research Laboratories. Compounds such as (45) in which the propylhydroxyacetophenone moiety is retained but the chromone ring portion is replaced with aliphatic chains of varying lengths terminating with an acidic functional group were prepared (Table 4).[44] In this series, compounds in which the propylhydroxyacetophenone moiety is separated from a terminal carboxylic acid group (45; $X = CO_2H$) by one or two methylene chains (45; $n = 1, 2$) are inactive at the concentrations tested. Detectable activity was observed with a minimum separation of three methylene residues and maximal activity was observed with a five-methylene tether. Holding the five-methylene chain and the terminal carboxylic acid constant, an investigation of aromatic ring substituents revealed that the optimum groups were identical to those previously established in the FPL-55712 series. Variation of the terminal groups X (*i.e.* carboxyl, nitrile, hydroxyl, dimethylamino, tetrazole) revealed that compounds in which the chain was terminated with hydroxyl, dimethylamino, *N*-methylpiperizine or tetrazole had significant SRS-A antagonist activity, the most active compounds being those containing the tetrazole group (*e.g.* compounds 49–52). In contrast to the carboxylic acid compounds, in which maximum activity was obtained with a five-methylene unit spacer, the best activity in the tetrazole series was observed in compounds with a four-methylene tether (compare compounds 49 and 50 with 46 and 47). Linking the tetrazole ring to the hydroxyacetophenone nucleus by an aliphatic chain, as in compound (53), did not diminish the LTD_4 antagonist activity relative to the oxygen-linked analog (49) ($pK_B = 7.08$ *vs.* 7.2, respectively), suggesting that the oxygen atom functions primarily as a spacer.[45] Insertion of a phenoxy unit into the aliphatic side chain resulted in compounds such as (54; LY-163443) which are extremely potent LTD_4 antagonists (guinea pig ileum, $-\log IC_{50} \approx 8.0$ compared with $-\log IC_{50}$ of 7.3 for FPL-55712).[46]

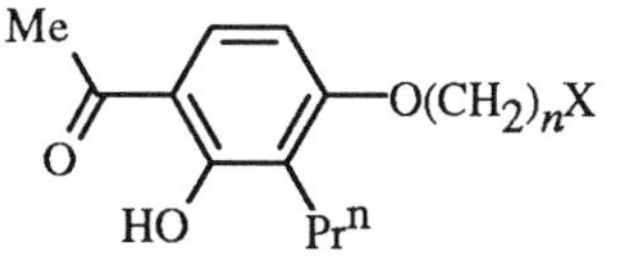

(45)

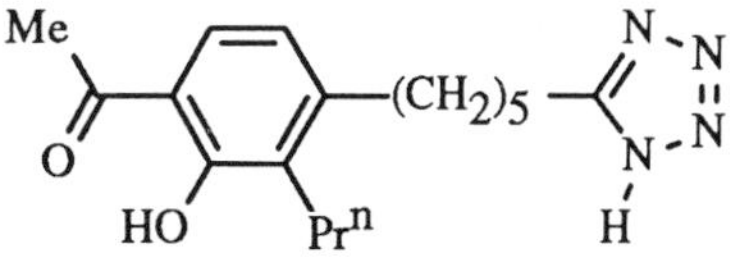

(53)

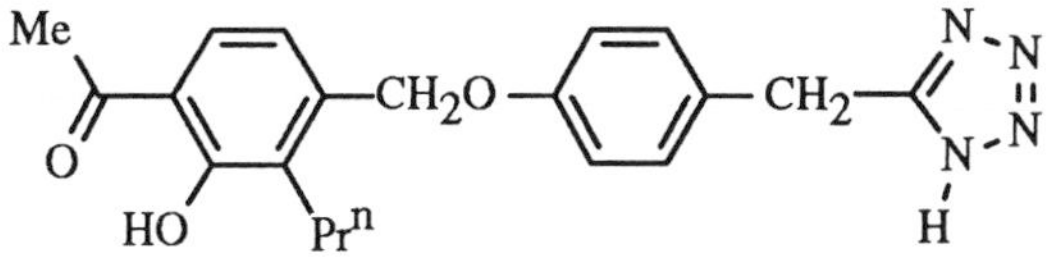

(54) LY-163443

Table 4 Peptidoleukotriene Receptor Antagonists:
LY-171883 Analogs

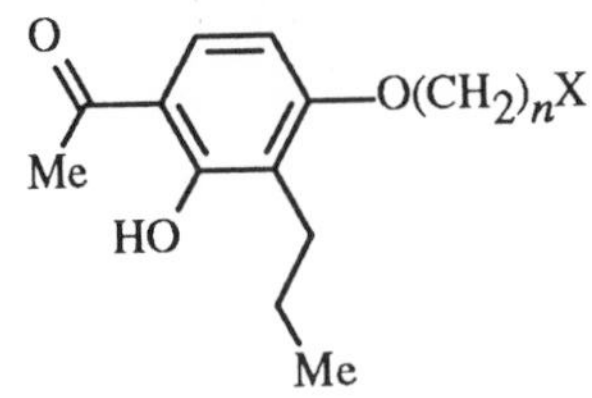

Compound	n	X	pK_B
(46)	4	CO_2H	5.8
(47)	5	CO_2H	6.0
(48)	6	CO_2H	5.7
(49)	4	Tetrazole	7.2
(50)	5	Tetrazole	6.6
(51)	6	Tetrazole	7.1
(52)	7	Tetrazole	7.0

The tetrazole-containing compounds described above are interesting biologically because they display prolonged pharmacological duration of action compared to the previous receptor antagonist analogs such as FPL-55712 (30) and they are also orally active. Because of this impressive biological profile, compound (49; LY-171883) and compound (54; LY-163443) were selected by the Lilly group for clinical evaluation. Unfortunately, the discovery of tumors in female mice resulted in the termination of the clinical trial of LY-171883; the possibility that this problem is rodent specific is currently under study.

Consideration of the possible structural similarities between LTD$_4$ and FPL-55712 by scientists at ICI Pharmaceuticals (Figure 2) led to an effort to develop simplified analogs of this compound.[47] In this comparison, the aliphatic hydroxyl groups of the two molecules coincide and the phenolic hydroxyl group of FPL-55712 mimics the C-1 carboxyl group of LTD$_4$. Thus, this model suggests that replacement of the chromone portion of FPL-55712 with mimics of the cysteinylglycine fragment of LTD$_4$ should lead to compounds with leukotriene antagonist activity. Table 5 lists a number of analogs that were prepared based on this rationale. It was subsequently established that the attachment of simple straight chain aliphatic carboxylic acids, of six to eight atoms in length, to the hydroxyacetophenone nucleus produced peptidoleukotriene antagonists of reasonable potency (*e.g.* compounds 58, 59 and 60). Further investigation resulted in the preparation of a series of benzoic acids similar to LY-163443 (Table 6). Consistent with previous studies, location of the carboxylic acid group in the *para* position provides optimal activity (compare compounds 62 and 63 with 64). Compounds (65), (66) and (68) emerged from the study as new leukotriene antagonists slightly more potent than FPL-55712 from which (68) was chosen as the lead structure. Substitution of the acetophenone ring demonstrated that all efforts to modify the propyl group, the hydroxyl group, or the acetyl group did not lead to analogs with improved activity and in most instances

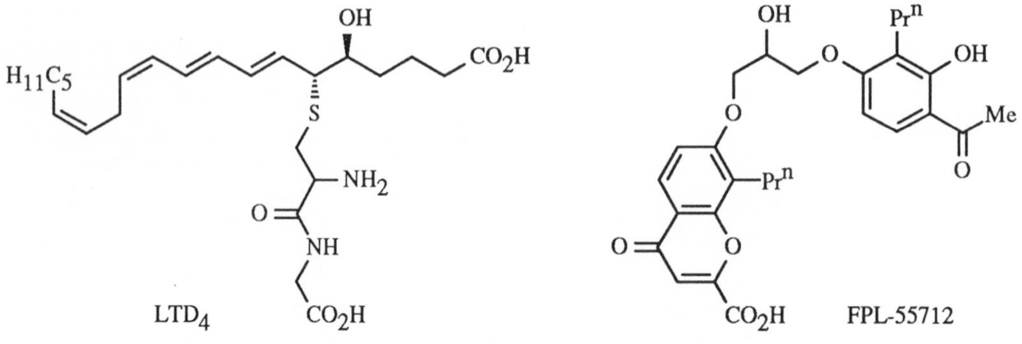

Figure 2

Table 5 Peptidoleukotriene Receptor Antagonists: Acetophenone
Analogs

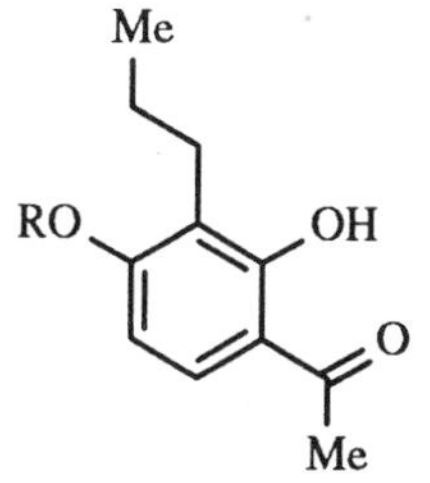

Compound	R	% Inhibition/ concentration (μM)
FPL-55712		62/4
(55)	$CH_2CH(OH)CH_2$-Cys-Gly	33/100
(56)	$CH_2CH(OH)CH_2SCH_2CO_2H$	19/10
		44/50
(57)	$(CH_2)_3SCH_2CO_2H$	62/10
		100/100
(58)	$(CH_2)_4SCH_2CO_2H$	75/10
(59)	$(CH_2)_4S(CH_2)_2CO_2H$	74/10
(60)	$(CH_2)_5CO_2H$	52/10
(61)	$(CH_2)_4CO_2H$	18/10

Table 6   Peptidoleukotriene Receptor Antagonists: Acetophenone Analogs

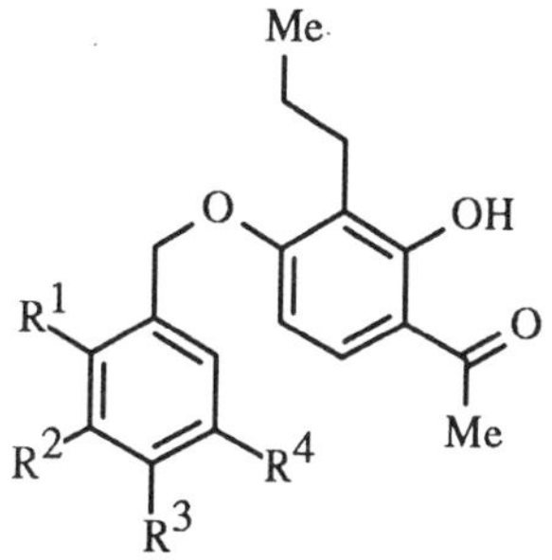

Compound	R^1	R^2	R^3	R^4	% Inhibition/ concentration (μM)
(62)	CO_2H	H	H	H	NS/10[a]
(63)	H	CO_2H	H	H	50/10
(64)	H	H	CO_2H	H	36/4
(65)	F	H	CO_2H	H	39/1
(66)	H	Br	CO_2H	H	30/1
(67)	H	OMe	CO_2H	H	NS/4
(68)	Me	H	CO_2H	H	57/1

[a] NS = not statistically significant.

caused a reduction in activity. This study by Brown and co-workers at ICI represents the most extensive investigation of the SAR of the hydroxyacetophenone class of leukotriene receptor antagonists to date and extensions of these results may provide future direction within this class as well as within other related series.

12.13.2.5 Analogs of Leukotrienes

The use of FPL-55712 as a template for the design of leukotriene antagonists, as described above, produced a number of useful lead compounds. However, this approach did not have an obvious structural connection to the natural peptidoleukotriene substances that they were intended to antagonize. The determination of the leukotriene structures provided a framework from which a rational basis for antagonist design could be established.

Extensive studies by Corey and co-workers on synthetic analogs of LTC_4 and LTD_4 provided a means to explore the structural factors within the leukotrienes that are essential for biological activity.[48,49] Corey and other investigators[50] have determined the structural requirements necessary for LTD_4 activity and this effort has provided a basis for the design and development of LTD_4 receptor antagonists. These findings indicate that it is essential to have a lipophilic chain attached at C-6, although small changes in the structure of this region can be tolerated. This is supported by the fact that hydrogenation of the C-14 alkene results in only a 34% loss of activity, whereas placement of a hydroxyl group at C-15 causes complete loss of activity. The stereochemical requirements of the lipophilic region of the receptor are sufficiently flexible to allow small geometrical changes in the C-7 through C-20 hydrocarbon unit. The correct stereochemistry at the C-5 and C-6 positions is necessary for maximum activity, although removal of the C-5 hydroxyl group results in the loss of all activity. The sulfur atom at C-6 need not be divalent, however there is significant difference in the activities of the two diastereomeric sulfoxides. This may reflect an importance in the conformational relationship between the eicosanoid and the peptide moieties. Considerable substitution can be tolerated in the peptide chain of LTD_4. Lastly, a single ionizable carboxyl group is required either at C-1 or on the peptide side chain. The data indicate, however, that the C-1 monoamide is more active than the Gly-monoamide.

Researchers at Smith Kline & French Laboratories incorporated these findings into their design of novel LTD_4 receptor antagonists. This rational design approach, based upon the natural agonist structure, eventually led to such potent antagonists as SK&F-104353 and SK&F-106203. The development of these compounds is detailed below.

The initial approach was based on structural modifications of LTD_4 in which the effect on agonist activity of altering the stereochemistry of the double bond, the distance between the C-1 carboxyl group, and the C-5 hydroxyl group (compounds **69–75**, Table 7) were determined.[51,52] The $C_{12}H_{25}$ lipid tail derivatives were selected in order to increase the chemical stability of the analogs, however there was a slight loss in agonist potency associated with this substitution (compound **72** vs. LTD_4). Lengthening the C-1 to C-5 chain by one methylene residue (compounds **70** and **71**) had little effect on the agonist activity. In contrast, deletion of a methylene unit between C-1 and C-5 adversely affected agonist activity (compounds **74** and **75**) as did altering the stereochemistry at the C-5 and C-6 functional centers (compounds **69**, **73** and **75**), (**71**) being an exception in that it retains potent agonist activity. A result that proved to be pivotal in guiding the future design of leukotriene receptor antagonists was the finding that (**75**) only weakly contracts the lung parenchymal tissue, having only 10% of the potency of LTD_4, and that pretreatment of the tissue with (**75**) significantly antagonizes the contractile activity of LTD_4. Compound (**75**) also antagonizes the leukotriene-induced contraction of guinea pig tracheal strips and the vasoconstriction of guinea pig pulmonary artery proximal to the lung. Agonist effects of (**75**) were selective as demonstrated by the lack of effect of (**75**) against contractions elicited by histamine; no agonist effects were observed with (**75**) at concentrations as high as 10^{-4}M. However (**74**), the (4S,5R) diastereomer that stereochemically resembles LTD_4, was found to possess agonist activity. These results demonstrated that the spatial separation of the C-1 carboxyl group relative to the rest of the molecule is a critical determinant since shortening the chain by one methylene residue resulted in antagonist activity. The absolute stereochemistry of the hydroxyl and sulfide groups also were found to be important, the unnatural (4R,5S) configuration being preferred for antagonist activity.

Based on the structural lead provided by the 2-nor-LTD antagonist (**75**), a series of 2-nor-LTD analogs (**76–83**; Table 8) were prepared with emphasis on determining the importance of the lipid tail, the double bond geometry, the absolute stereochemistry at C-4 and C-5, the nature of the peptide unit, and the carboxyl group on the antagonist potency.[53] The importance of the lipid tail was apparent from the lack of significant antagonist activity of compounds (**76**) and (**77**). An ionizable free carboxyl at C-1 is not an absolute requirement for activity as demonstrated by compounds (**79**) ($K_B = 7.2\,\mu M$) and (**80**) ($K_B = 14\,\mu M$). The slightly improved activity of the cysteinyl–glycyl monoamide (**78**) ($K_B = 3.5\,\mu M$) suggests that an ionizable carboxyl group in the amino acid region is not critical for antagonist activity, however the absence of a carboxyl group at this position results in compounds with agonist activity (e.g. compound **81**). Deletion of the glycine

Table 7 Peptidoleukotriene Receptor Antagonists: LTD$_4$ Analogs

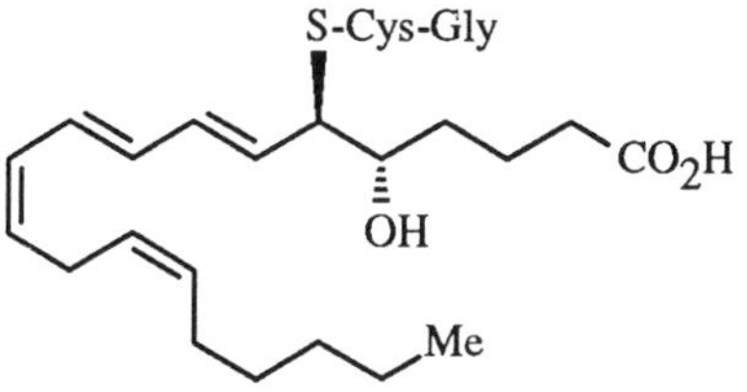

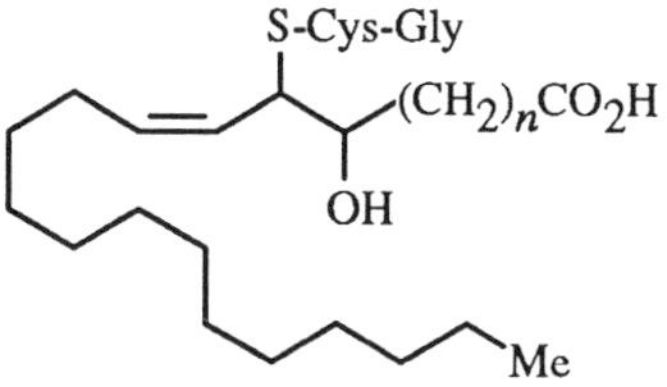

Compound	n	Stereochemistry	G. P. lung parenchyma agonist activity EC$_{50}$ (nM)	Relative contractile activity
	LTD$_4$	(5S,6R)	1.4	1
(69)	5,6-Epi-LTD$_4$	(5R,6S)	120	1
(70)	4	(6S,7R)	6.5	1
(71)	4	(6R,7S)	4.5	1
(72)	3	(5S,6R)	15	1
(73)	3	(5R,6S)	610	1
(74)	2	(4S,5R)	630	0.5
(75)	2	(4R,5S)	500	0.1

Table 8 Peptidoleukotriene Receptor Antagonists: LTD$_4$ Analogs

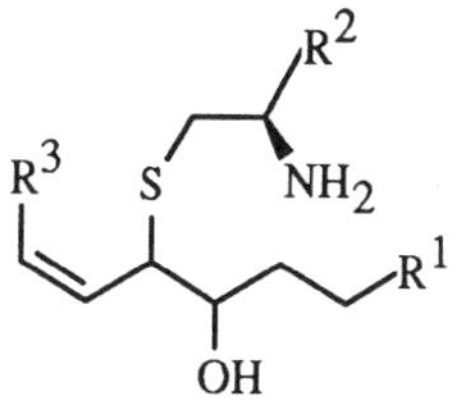

Compound	Stereochemistry	R^1	R^2	R^3	K$_B^a$ (µM)
(74)	(4S,5R)	CO$_2$H	CONHCH$_2$CO$_2$H	C$_{12}$H$_{25}$	10.0
(75)	(4R,5S)	CO$_2$H	CONHCH$_2$CO$_2$H	C$_{12}$H$_{25}$	6.3
(76)	(4R,5S)	CO$_2$H	CONHCH$_2$CO$_2$H	C$_7$H$_{15}$	Inactive
(77)	(4R,5S)	CO$_2$H	CONHCH$_2$CO$_2$H	C$_{17}$H$_{35}$	Inactive
(78)	(4R,5S)	CO$_2$H	CONHCH$_2$CONH$_2$	C$_{12}$H$_{25}$	3.5
(79)	(4R,5S)	CONH$_2$	CONHCH$_2$CO$_2$H	C$_{12}$H$_{25}$	7.2
(80)	(4R,5S)	CH$_2$OH	CONHCH$_2$CO$_2$H	C$_{12}$H$_{25}$	14.0
(81)	(4R,5S)	CH$_2$OH	CONHCH$_2$CH$_2$OH	C$_{12}$H$_{25}$	P. agonist
(82)	(4R,5S)	CO$_2$H	CO$_2$H	C$_{12}$H$_{25}$	14.0
(83)	(4S,5R)	CO$_2$H	CO$_2$H	C$_{12}$H$_{25}$	3.4
FPL-55712					0.1

^{a} Guinea pig tracheal strips.

moiety from the sulfur ligand chain only slightly reduces the LTD$_4$ antagonist activity (compound **82**; $K_B = 14$ µM), however in this case the 'natural' diastereoisomer (**83**) is more potent (compound **83**; $K_B = 3.4$ µM). The *trans* isomers (**84**; $K_B = 20.4$ µM and **85**; $K_B = 25.6$ µM), which more closely resemble the natural agonists, are less potent antagonists than the *cis* isomers. While the cysteine and cysteinyl–glycine derivatives appear equipotent as leukotriene antagonists, the 2-nor-LTC analog (**86**) is a full agonist.

Thus, analogs of LTD$_4$ having a saturated lipid tail, a shortened head group and reversal of absolute stereochemistry along the backbone provided the initial leads on which future antagonist design was based. Additional SAR studies within this series resulted in the striking finding that

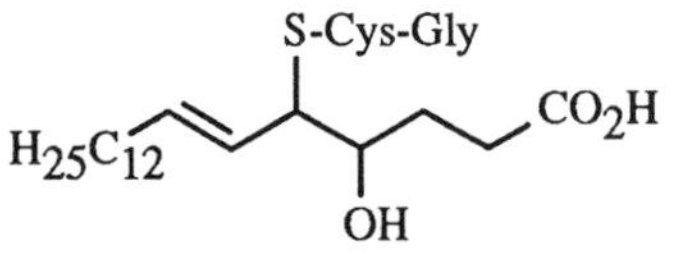

S-Cys-Gly

H$_{25}$C$_{12}$ \~\~\~\~\~/ CO$_2$H

OH

(**84**) (4*S*,5*R*)
(**85**) (4*R*,5*S*)

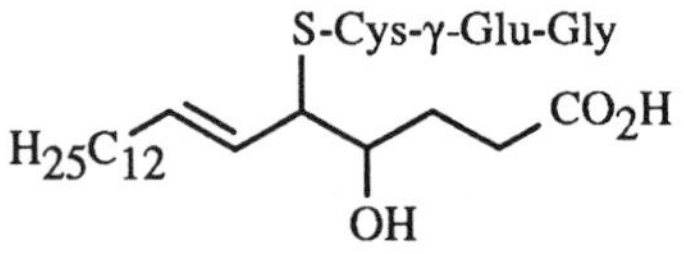

S-Cys-γ-Glu-Gly

H$_{25}$C$_{12}$ \~\~\~\~\~/ CO$_2$H

OH

(**86**) (4*RS*,5*SR*)

changes in the cysteinyl–glycyl unit in (**75**), such as (**87**) and (**89**) (Table 9), yields compounds with excellent antagonist activity and provides evidence that variation in the glycyl residue is allowed for LTD$_4$ antagonist activity.[54] In fact, removal of the glycyl residue from (**87**) produced (**89**), the most active antagonist in the series. However, although these leukotriene analogs were found to possess LTD$_4$ antagonist activity, some (*e.g.* compounds **81** and **86**) had partial agonist activity and thus they were considered to be ill-suited for *in vivo* studies.

The apparent symmetry of leukotriene antagonists such as (**89**) suggests that the two polar groups in these molecules might be interchangeable at the leukotriene receptor. Thus, researchers at SK&F undertook the synthesis of compounds in which these polar chains were identical.[55] In addition, an extensive SAR investigation was undertaken to study the effect of modifications in the polar and lipid regions of these molecules on leukotriene antagonist activity and the results are summarized in Tables 10 and 11.[61] The improved activity of (**95**) *vs.* (**93**) (Table 10) reveals the preference for a π-electron system adjacent to the sulfur groups. This observation led to the design of a novel series of antagonists in which the π-electron system was provided by an aromatic ring located adjacent to the sulfur atoms; this series of analogs is listed in Table 11. Analysis of the data revealed: (i) a preference for a specific lipid chain length of 10–12 atoms (compounds **97–100**); (ii) that use of oxygen or sulfur to attach the lipid group to the aromatic ring is acceptable (compounds **97a, 103** and **104**); (c) the lipid group can be moved to the *meta* position (compounds **105** and **106**); (iv) placing the lipid group in the *para* position abolishes activity (compound **107**). As a result of these investigations, the aromatic dithioacetal class of leukotriene antagonists was discovered and are typified by (**97a**; SKF-102081) and (**99a**; SKF-102922). These compounds were found to be competitive antagonists of LTD$_4$-induced contractions on isolated guinea pig trachea (**97a**; pK_B = 6.0; **99a**, pK_B = 6.8; FPL-55712, pK_B = 6.8). Evidence indicating that (**97a**) and (**99a**) were acting at the receptor level was demonstrated by their ability to bind to the guinea pig LTD$_4$ receptor. Both compounds displaced [³H]-LTD$_4$ from receptor sites on guinea pig lung membranes with K_i values of 445 nM and 245 nM, respectively. Significantly, (**97a**) and (**99a**) are more potent than the standard leukotriene antagonist FPL-55712 ($K_i \approx 2$ μM). Importantly, no agonist activity was observed for either compound and both compounds were found to be active *in vivo* in guinea pigs challenged with LTD$_4$ as measured by changes in airway resistance. Additionally, aerosols of (**97a**) and (**99a**) were

Table 9 Peptidoleukotriene Receptor Antagonists: LTD$_4$
Analogs

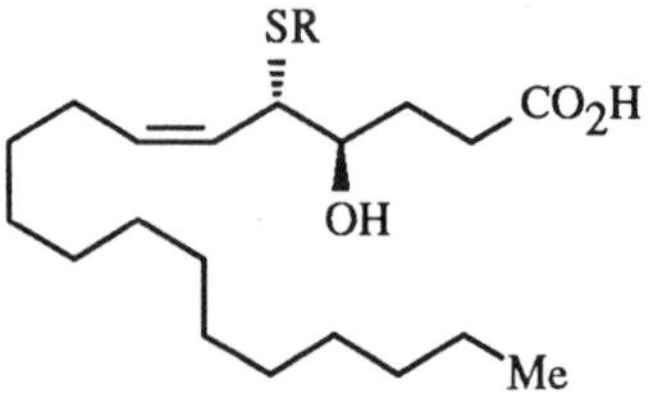

SR

\~\~\~/ CO$_2$H

OH

Me

Compound	R	$K_B{}^a$ (μM)
(**75**)	CH$_2$CH(NH$_2$)CONHCH$_2$CO$_2$H	6.3
(**87**)	CH$_2$CH$_2$CONHCH$_2$CO$_2$H	0.64
(**88**)	CH$_2$CO$_2$H	1.4
(**89**)	CH$_2$CH$_2$CO$_2$H	0.29
(**90**)	CH$_2$CH$_2$CH$_2$CO$_2$H	0.71
(**91**)	CH$_2$CH$_2$CONH$_2$	8.3

[a] Guinea pig trachea.

Table 10 Peptidoleukotriene Receptor
Antagonists: Dithioacetal Analogs of LTD_4

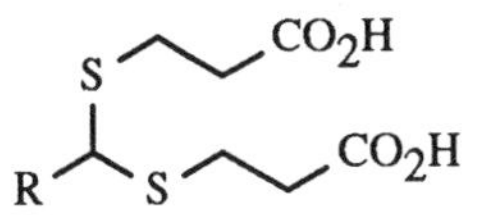

Compound	R	$-\log K_B$
(92)	$C_{14}H_{29}$	NA
(93)	$C_{12}H_{25}$	5.2
(94)	$C_{12}H_{25}C\equiv C$	5.7
(95)	$C_{10}H_{21}C\equiv C$	6.1
(96)	$C_8H_{17}C\equiv C$	5.0

Table 11 Peptidoleukotriene Receptor Antagonists: Dithioacetal
Analogs of LTD_4

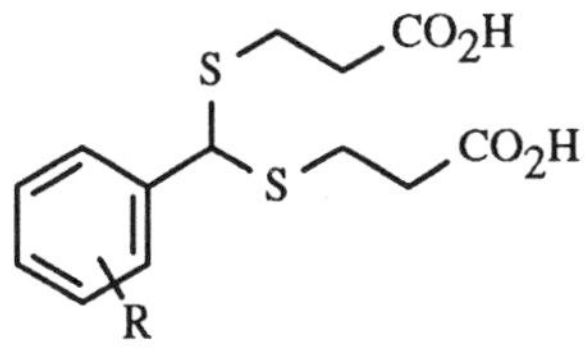

Compound	R	$-\log K_B$	K_i (nM)
(97)	$2\text{-}(C_{14}H_{29})$	NA	1246
(97a)	$2\text{-}(C_{12}H_{25})$	6.0	445
(98)	$2\text{-}(C_{10}H_{21})$	6.5	1180
(99)	$2\text{-}(C_8H_{17})$	5.2	5674
(99a)	$2\text{-}(C_8H_{16}Ph)$	6.7	245
(100)	$2\text{-}(C_{10}H_{20}C\equiv CH)$	6.8	141
(101)	$2\text{-}(Z\text{-}CH\!=\!CHC_{10}H_{21})$	NA	1380
(102)	$2\text{-}(E\text{-}CH\!=\!CHC_{10}H_{21})$	5.8	491
(103)	$2\text{-}(OC_{11}H_{23})$	6.4	287
(104)	$2\text{-}(SC_{11}H_{23})$	6.0	646
(105)	$3\text{-}(C_8H_{16}Ph)$	6.0	430
(106)	$3\text{-}(OC_{11}H_{23})$	6.1	78
(107)	$4\text{-}(C_{10}H_{21})$	NA	7565

shown to be effective antagonists of bronchoconstriction induced by LTD_4 in the guinea pig. In addition to the slightly improved activity of (99a) over (97a), it also has an additional advantage of improved metabolic stability, (97a) being subject to ω and $(\omega - 1)$ oxidation of the lipid tail.[56-60]

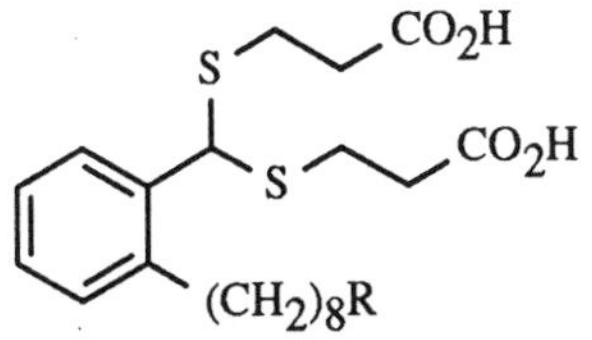

(97a) SK&F 102081, $R = Bu^n$
(99a) SK&F 102922, $R = Ph$

Two key observations made as a result of these studies are: (i) 2-nor-leukotrienes such as (75) exhibit impressive antagonist properties; and (ii) the unsaturated triene moiety of LTD_4 may be replaced by a phenyloctylphenyl group as in (99a) without losing receptor affinity. These observations were instrumental to the SK&F group's discovery of novel, potent, specific, high-affinity peptidoleukotriene receptor antagonists (**108**; SK&F-106203) and (**109**; SK&F-104353).[62] Compound (**108**; SK&F-106203) has a high affinity for the LTD_4 receptor on guinea pig lung membranes ($K_i = 60$ nM) and competitively antagonizes LTD_4-induced contractions of guinea pig trachea ($pK_B = 7.0$). The 2-(S)-hydroxy analog (**109**; SK&F-104353) is even more potent. It has high affinity for the guinea pig lung membrane ($K_i = 5$ nM) and is a competitive antagonist of LTD_4-induced contractions on the guinea pig trachea ($pK_B = 8.6$). In addition, aerosolized SK&F-104353 completely prevents pulmonary changes induced by aerosolized LTD_4. The enantiomer of SK&F-104353 is much weaker in the binding and guinea pig trachea assays, indicating a highly stereoselective interaction of these compounds at the receptor. SK&F-104353 is presently in phase III clinical trials.

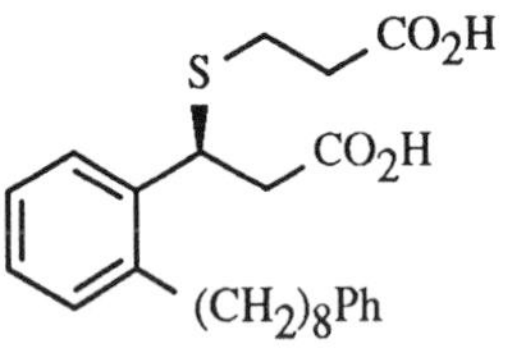

(**108**) SK&F 106203 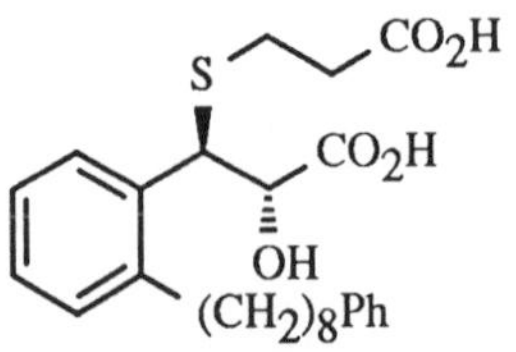   (**109**) SK&F 104353

Additional series of LTD_4 antagonists that have been designed based on the structure of the natural leukotrienes include compounds (**110**)–(**115**). Compound (**110**) was reported by ICI to have a pK_B of 6.43 on guinea pig trachea and a pK_B of 7.25 on guinea pig ileum. Agonist effects of (**110**) were not observed.[63] Compound (**111**) was reported by Ciba-Geigy (Basel) to have an IC_{50} of 0.78 µM on guinea pig ileum. Addition of a double bond to the lipid chain led to analog (**112**), which exhibited improved activity ($IC_{50} = 0.11$ µM). Consistent with previous results, the compound with the 'unnatural' leukotriene stereochemistry is more active than the one with 'natural' stereochemistry.[64] The research group at Hoechst AG found that compound (**114**) antagonizes the LTD_4-induced contraction of guinea pig lung strips with an IC_{50} of 1–3 µg mL^{-1} and (**115**) has an IC_{50} of 0.1 µg mL^{-1} in the same test system.[65] However, the antagonist response for (**114**) and (**115**) is not specific in that antagonistic responses to PAF, bradykinine and ovalbumin were also inhibited.

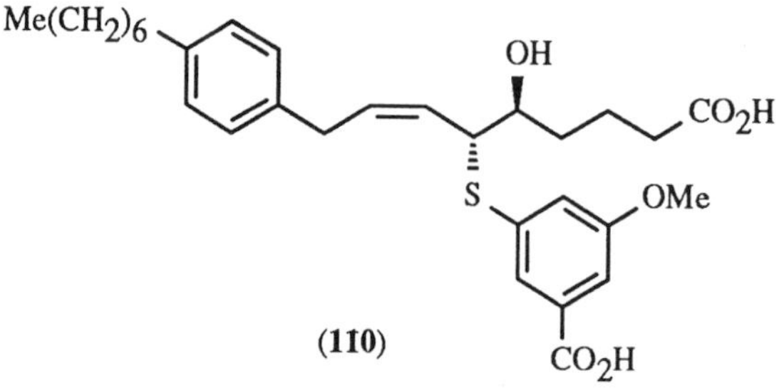

(**110**)

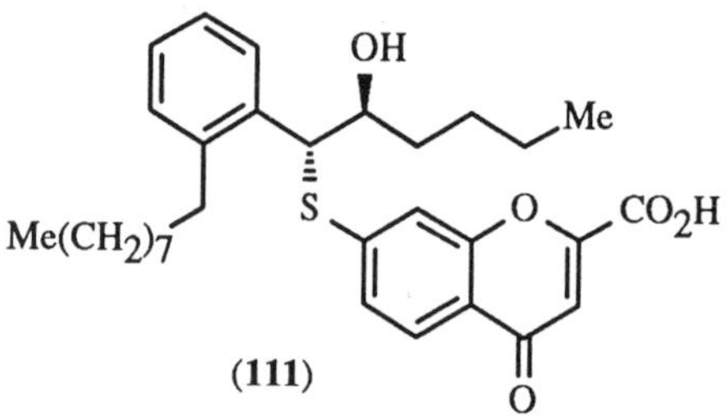

(**111**)

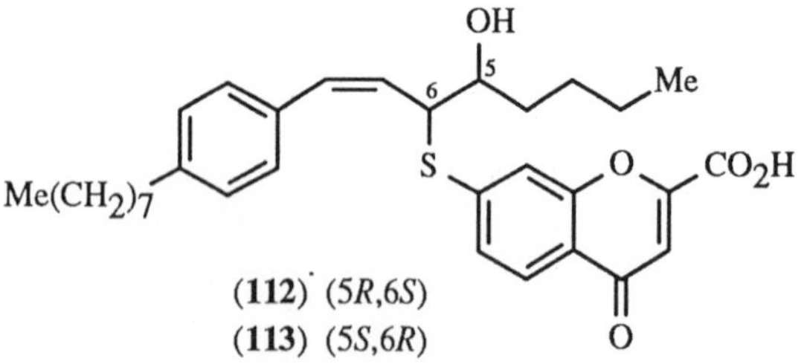

(**112**) (5R,6S)
(**113**) (5S,6R)

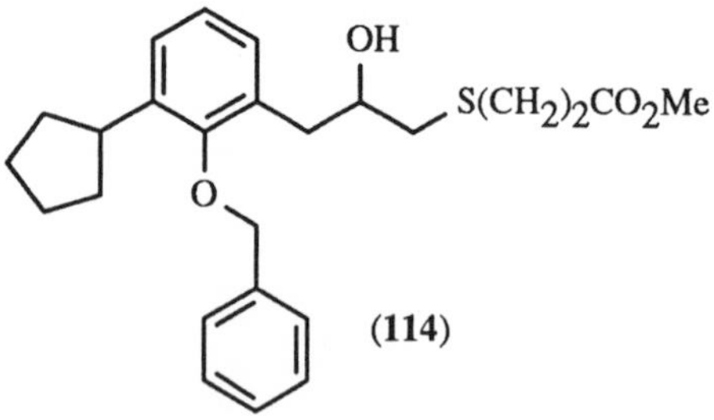

(**114**)

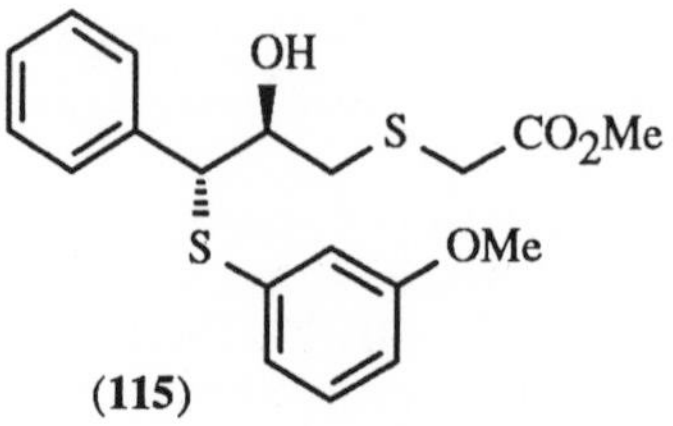

(**115**)

12.13.2.6 Quinoline Antagonists

Another major class of compounds that have been reported to be potent LTD_4 receptor antagonists are those containing a quinolylmethoxyphenyl moiety. REV-5901 (**116**) blocks LTD_4-induced contractions of guinea pig lung parenchyma strips ($IC_{50} = 2.0\,\mu M$) and also inhibits 5-lipoxygenase ($IC_{50} = 0.03$–$6.0\,\mu M$).[66] REV-5901 (RG-5901) is currently undergoing phase II clinical evaluations. A second LTD_4 receptor antagonist reported by Rorer is RG-12525 (**117**).[67] This compound is an orally active LTD_4 receptor antagonist that was developed to provide improved receptor affinity over that of RG-5901. Against [^{3}H]-LTD_4 binding to guinea pig lung membranes, RG-12525 is a competitive inhibitor with a K_i of 2.5 nM. This selective LTD_4 receptor antagonist is undergoing preclinical investigations.

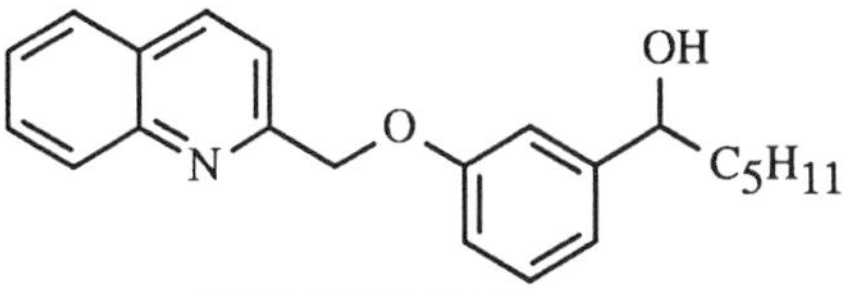

(**116**) REV-5901

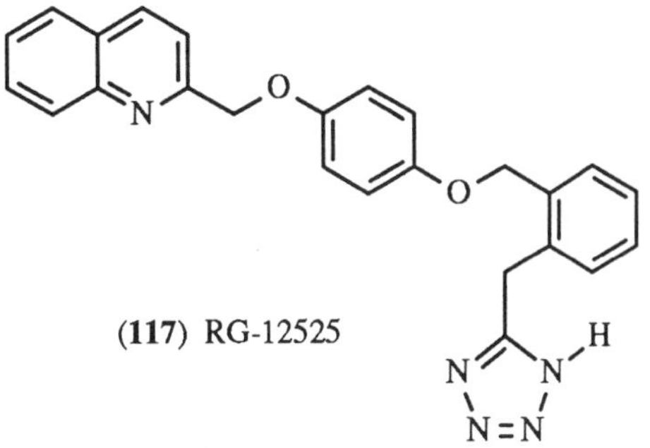

(**117**) RG-12525

WY-45911 (**118**) is a potent, orally active LTD_4 receptor antagonist with a pK_B value of 5.3 as determined in a guinea pig trachea assay. WY-45911 also has the ability to inhibit 5-lipoxygenase ($IC_{50} = 1.4\,\mu M$).[68-70] Workers at Wyeth originally designed this compound based upon the following considerations. It was speculated that a (phenylamino)-4-oxobutanoic acid group could mimic the 5-hydroxy-6-thio-6-vinylhexanoic acid portion of LTD_4. The amide pK_A is similar to that of the 5-hydroxyl group of LTD_4 and the amide–carboxylic acid distance approximates that of the C-5 hydroxyl group–C-1 carboxylic acid. Furthermore it was believed that the 2-oxomethylquinoline group could simulate either the fatty acid backbone or the cysteinylglycine portion of LTD_4. Since WY-45911 is positive in the Ames assay, alternative quinoline analogs were explored.[71,72] After several series of compounds, the phenylamino-4-oxobutanoic acid group was replaced with phenylephrine to give WY-47120 (**119**).[73] This compound is an orally active antagonist of both LTD_4 and ovalbumin-induced bronchoconstriction in the guinea pig. However, since WY-47120 was only half as potent as LY-171883 (**49**) against either bronchoconstrictor agonist, an alternative fragment corresponding to the C-1 through C-5 portion of LTD_4 was sought.

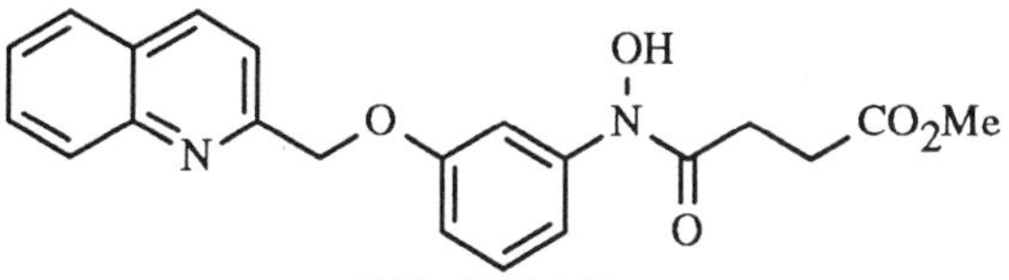

(**118**) WY-45911

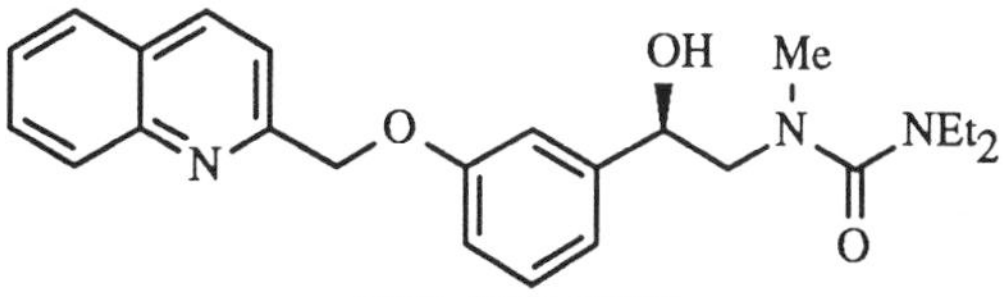

(**119**) WY-47120

The sulfonamide moiety is recognized as an isostere of a hydroxyl group. This group was therefore incorporated into the antagonist design and WY-48618 (**120**) was prepared. WY-48618 is also a potent inhibitor of LTD_4-induced bronchoconstriction in the guinea pig but exhibits erratic oral activity. Since the acidity of the hydroxamic acid of WY-45911 is greater than the corresponding group of subsequent series, analogs were considered in which the acidity of the sulfonamide NH would be increased. One such way of accomplishing this would be to replace the acetic acid portion of the molecule with groups that have greater electron-withdrawing capability. This led to the design and synthesis of WY-48252 (**121**). WY-48252 is a chemically stable and Ames-negative LTD_4 receptor antagonist with oral activity. In isolated guinea pig trachea pretreated with indomethacin and L-cysteine WY-48252 antagonizes LTD_4-induced contraction with a $pK_B = 7.6$. Studies also showed WY-48252 to be an inhibitor of both 5-lipoxygenase and 5-cyclooxygenase ($IC_{50} = 4.6\,\mu M$ and 3.3 μM, respectively). It has been reported that WY-48252 is an effective agent in reducing the severity of the immediate response and inhibiting the late response to inhaled antigen in allergic sheep.[69,71] WY-48252 is currently undergoing preclinical evaluations.

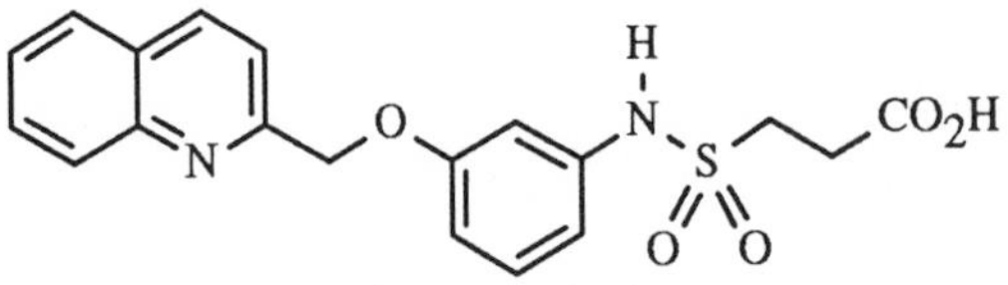

(120) WY-48618

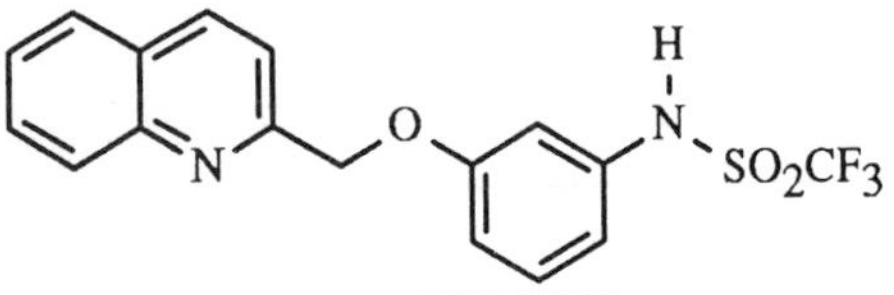

(121) WY-48252

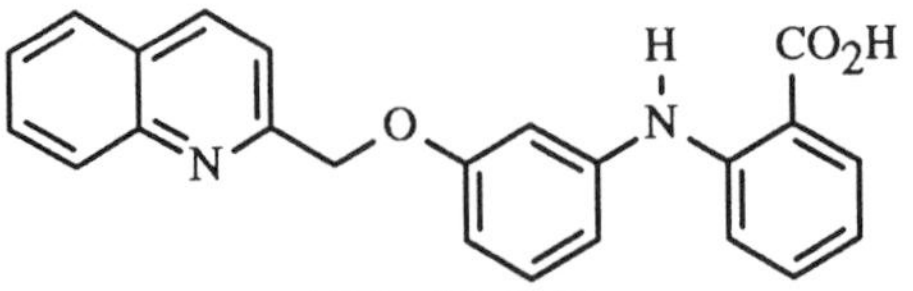

(122) SR-2640

Another quinoline-type LTD_4 receptor antagonist is SR-2640 (**122**) currently under development by Leo Pharmaceuticals (Denmark).[74] In guinea pig ileum SR-2640 inhibits LTD_4-induced contractions (IC_{50} = 3 nM), it antagonizes LTD_4-induced contraction of guinea pig trachea (pK_B = 8.8), and it inhibits the binding of $[^3H]$-LTD_4 to guinea pig lung membranes (IC_{50} = 23 nM). SR-2640 shows a poor pharmacokinetic profile in guinea pigs, however this profile does not materialize in studies with humans. In human volunteers a single dose of SR-2640 is well tolerated. The importance of this and the other quinoline-type LTD_4 receptor antagonists will become apparent as the clinical investigations progress.

12.13.2.7 Structurally Diverse Antagonists

LTD_4 receptor antagonists whose structures are unrelated to the classes already discussed (Section 12.13.2.4 through Section 12.13.2.6) will be described in this section.

ONO-RS-347 (**123**) and ONO-RS-411 (**124**) were discovered by the systematic modification of (*p*-amylcinnamoyl)anthranilic acid (**125**), the original lead compound.[75-77] *In vitro*, ONO-RS-347 and ONO-RS-411 antagonize the LTD_4-induced contraction of guinea pig ileum (IC_{50} = 0.37 nM and 0.044 nM, respectively) and *in vivo* they block the bronchoconstriction caused by administration of LTD_4 (ID_{50} = 1.2 μg kg^{-1} and 0.80 μg kg^{-1}, respectively). In addition, ONO-RS-411 was found to be a potent, orally active inhibitor of LTD_4-induced vascular permeability (75% at 0.3 mg kg^{-1}, p.o.).

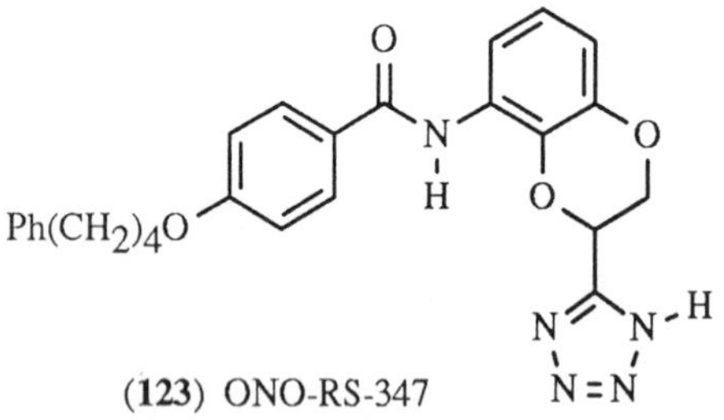

(123) ONO-RS-347

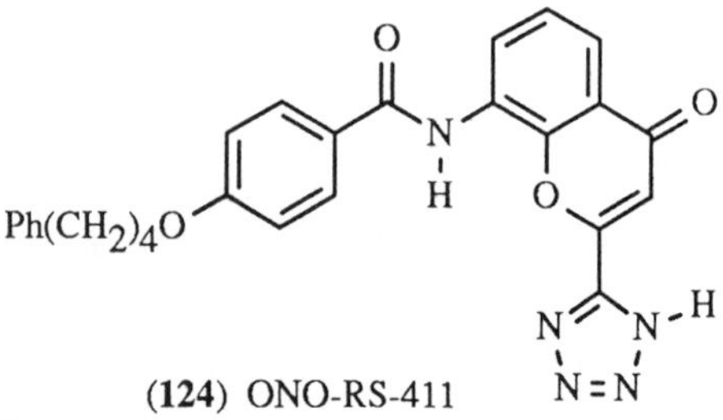

(124) ONO-RS-411

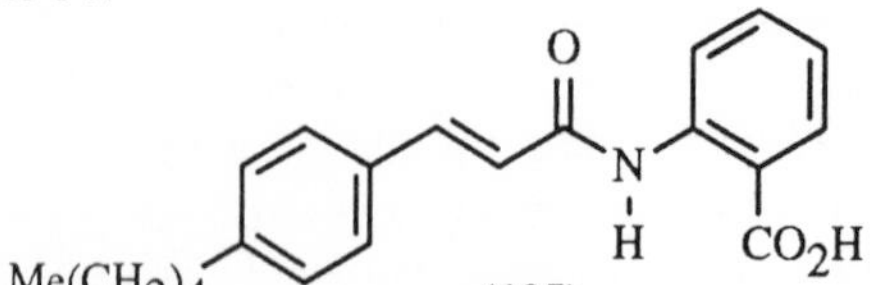

(125)

ICI-198615 (**126**) represents another class of potent leukotriene D_4/E_4 antagonists.[78] It inhibits LTD_4-induced contraction on isolated guinea pig trachea (pK_B = 9.34). *In vivo*, ICI-198615 demonstrated dose-related efficacy when administered i.v. (17 μg kg^{-1}), by aerosol (3 μM), and orally (5.7 mg kg^{-1}) to a conscious guinea pig model of LTD_4-induced dyspnea. It antagonizes both i.v. LTC_4- and LTD_4-induced increases in pulmonary resistance and decreases in dynamic lung compliance following i.v. (6–60 μg kg^{-1}) or oral (0.6–1.7 mg kg^{-1}) administration. It is also effective when administered by the aerosol route against an aerosol LTD_4 challenge and can help reverse bronchoconstriction induced by antigen. Optimization of the antagonist activity within this series involved a series of structural modifications around template structure (**127**).[79] Modification of the acylamino portion of the molecule led to the selection of the cyclopentyloxy group as the preferred substituent in this region (*e.g.* compound **132**, Table 12). Modification of the carboxylic acid portion of the molecule with a number of carboxylic acid mimics led to the selection of compound (**138**; Table 13). Variations of the heterocyclic ring led to the *N*-methylindole as the preferred hetero ring from which evolved compound (**139**; ICI-204219). This compound is a highly potent LTD_4 receptor antagonist with a pK_B of 9.5 ($pA_2 = 9.8$) on guinea pig trachea and displays excellent oral activity.[79,80]

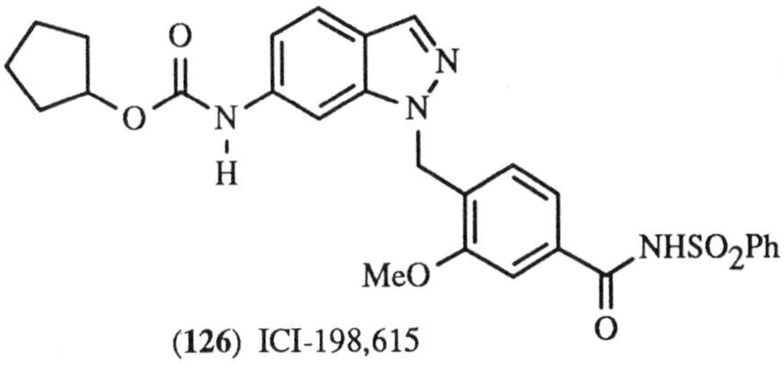

(**126**) ICI-198,615

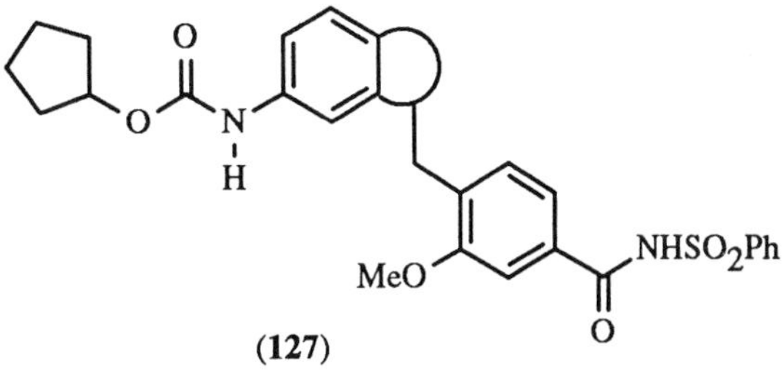

(**127**)

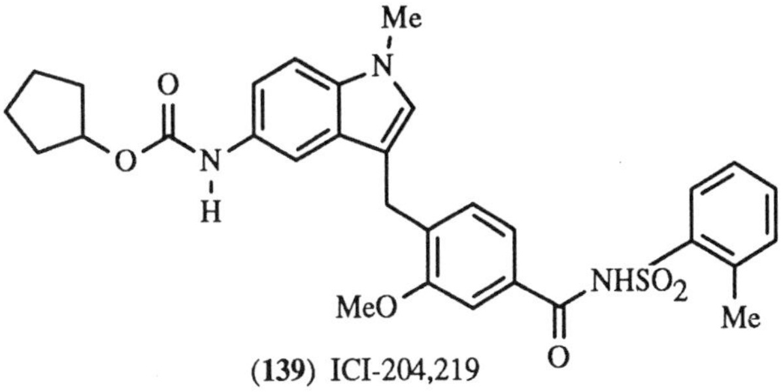

(**139**) ICI-204,219

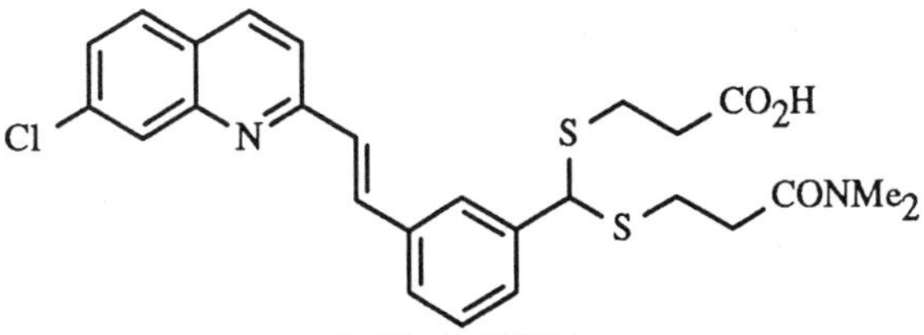

(**140**) L-660711

The quinoline L-660711 (**140**), discovered at Merck Frosst, combines a quinoline ring system with the dithioacetal moiety developed by the Smith Kline & French researchers. This compound inhibits LTD_4 binding in guinea pig ($IC_{50} = 1$ nM) and human ($IC_{50} = 10$ nM) lung homogenates but is inactive against LTC_4 binding. It antagonizes leukotriene-induced contractions of both guinea pig trachea ($pK_B = 9.3$) and guinea pig ileum ($pA_2 = 10.5$). *In vivo*, L-660711 antagonizes i.v. leukotriene-induced increases in lung resistance and decrease in lung compliance by either i.v. (0.1 mg kg^{-1}) or aerosol (3 µg mL^{-1}) administration.[81,82]

12.13.2.8 Future Design of Specific LTD_4 Receptor Antagonists

Evaluation of the numerous and structurally diverse examples of peptidoleukotriene antagonists will certainly lead to additional refinements that will be based upon semilogical functional group alterations within each known class of compound. However, the discovery of new structural leads will require new insights into the modes of molecular recognition between receptor and antagonist. Recently, a model involving the analysis of the interaction of known antagonists with the receptor was presented (Figure 3).[83] The model is based on a receptor motif that presents a flat lipophilic region on which the polyene chain of LTD_4 is arrayed in an extended planar conformation with the terminus of the chain binding in a lipophilic pocket. It is suggested that planarity is critical in the 7,8

Table 12 Peptidoleukotriene Receptor Antagonists: ICI-204219 Analogs Acylamino Chain Optimization

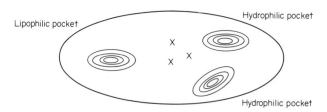

Compound	RX	pK_B
(128)	Me ~~~~	6.0
(129)	Me ~~~~ Me (Me)	6.6
(130)	Ph—CH(Me)—CH2	6.7
(131)	Me ~~~ O~	6.8
(132)	cyclopentyl—O~	7.8
(133)	cyclopentyl—CH2CH3	7.7

Figure 3

Table 13 Peptidoleukotriene Receptor Antagonists: ICI-204219 Analogs
Acid Mimics

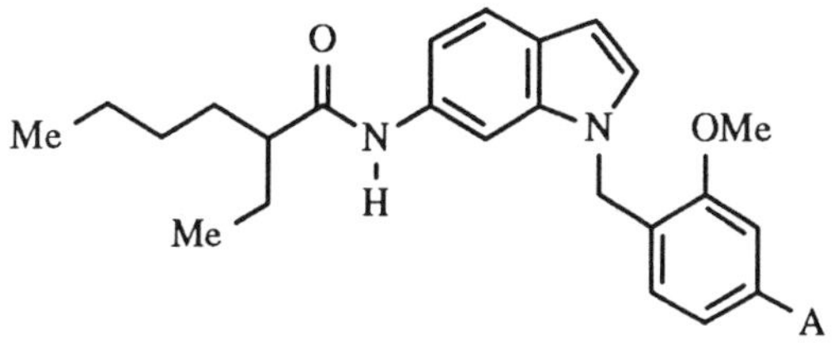

Compound	A	Activity[a]	P.o.[b]
(134)	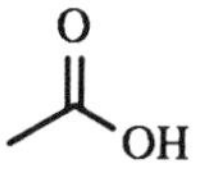 O‖C–OH	59% 1 μM	~ 100 mg kg^{-1}
(135)	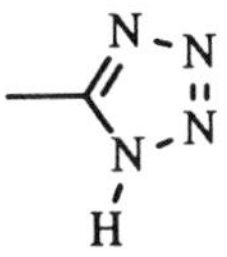 tetrazole (N-N=N-N-H)	50% 1 μM	—
(136)	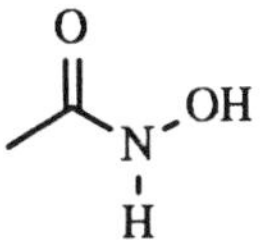 O‖C–N(H)–OH	38% 10 μM	—
(137)	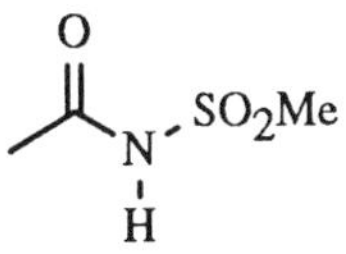 O‖C–N(H)–SO$_2$Me	60% 1 μM	—
(138)	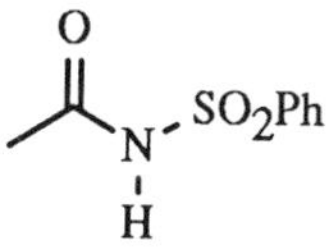 O‖C–N(H)–SO$_2$Ph	27% 0.01 μM	17 mg kg^{-1}

[a] Trachea *vs.* LTE$_4$. [b] Approximate ED$_{50}$ ('Dyspnea' model).

double bond region. The cysteinylglycine moiety is considered to involve both hydrogen bond interactions as well as ionic binding with the acid being ionized in the receptor. The model has the C-1 carboxyl group binding to the receptor through hydrogen bonds and not ionized at the receptor and the C-5 hydroxyl group binding to the receptor strongly enough to impart stereospecific recognition of both the relative and absolute stereochemistry at C-5 and C-6 of LTD$_4$.

The utility of this model is illustrated in the development of L-660711 (**140**). Random screening led to the initial discovery of (**141**) (IC$_{50}$ = 3 μM, guinea pig lung). It was postulated that (**141**) occupied the flat lipophilic binding site on the LTD$_4$ receptor and that binding could be improved by adding an acid chain in the appropriate location. This reasoning led to the preparation of (**142**), which

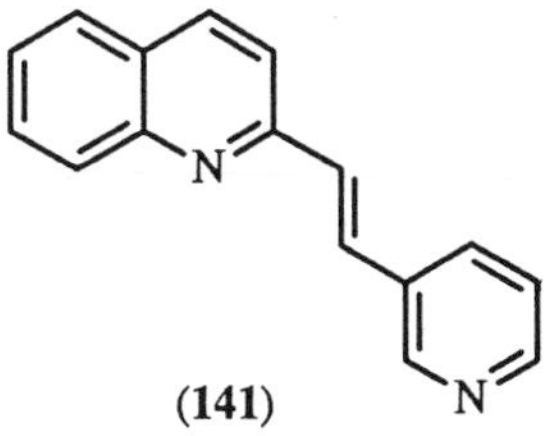

(141) 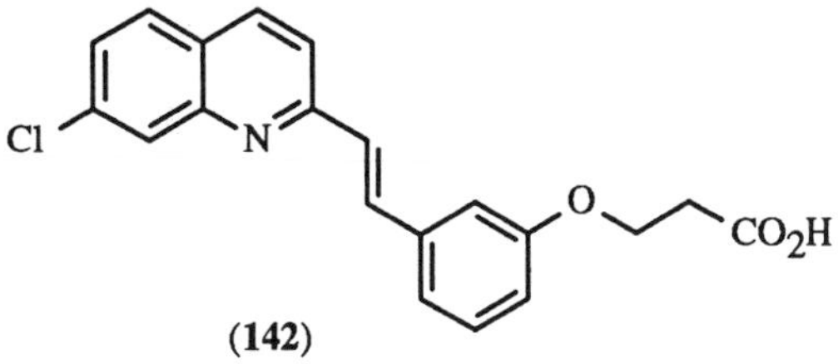 (142)

indeed exhibited improved activity (IC_{50} = 19 nM). Addition of a second acid chain, as suggested by the model, led to compound (**143**), which displayed an additional improvement in activity (IC_{50} = 1.5 nM). Finally, L-660711 (**140**) was prepared and is representative of the type of structure that would be predicted to have potent activity in the receptor model. This compound is presently undergoing clinical evaluation.

(**143**)

12.13.3 DIHYDROXYLEUKOTRIENES (LTB$_4$)

12.13.3.1 Introduction

Leukotriene B$_4$ (LTB$_4$) was first described by Borgeat and Samuelsson in 1979,[84] and was later shown by Corey and co-workers to be (5*S*,12*R*)-dihydroxy-(*Z*,*E*,*E*,*Z*)-6,8,10,14-eicosatetraenoic acid.[85] LTB$_4$ is a product of the arachidonic acid cascade, which results from the enzymic hydrolysis of LTA$_4$ (Figure 1). It has been found to be produced by mast cells, polymorphonuclear (PMN) leukocytes, monocytes and macrophages. LTB$_4$ has been shown to be a potent stimulus *in vitro* for PMN leukocytes, causing increases in chemotactic and chemokinetic migration, adherence, aggregation, degranulation, superoxide production and cytotoxicity.[86-89] The effects of LTB$_4$ are mediated through distinct receptor sites on the leukocyte cell surface which exhibit a high degree of stereospecificity.[91-93] Pharmacological studies on human blood PMN leukocytes indicate the presence of two classes of LTB$_4$ specific receptors that are separate from receptors specific for the peptide chemotactic factors. Each of the sets of receptors appears to be coupled to a separate set of PMN leukocyte functions. A high affinity class of receptors mediate chemokinesis and chemotaxis by a mechanism involving calcium mobilization. Degranulation and oxidative metabolism result from the occupancy of a low affinity receptor site. This has been demonstrated in chemotactically deactivated PMN leukocytes that are still able to degranulate in response to LTB$_4$. These cells display a selective loss of the high affinity receptors without alteration of the low affinity receptors.[94-98] One study of LTB$_4$ binding to intact human neutrophils indicates K_d values of 0.46 nM and 541 nM for the high and low affinity receptor sites, respectively.[99] The high affinity LTB$_4$ receptors appear to be coupled to a guanine nucleotide binding protein (G-protein). This has been suggested from the ability of guanosine di- and tri-phosphates to reversibly convert a portion of the high affinity receptors to a low affinity state. The involvement of a G-protein is also supported by the fact that the binding affinity of [^{3}H]-LTB$_4$ is decreased by pertussis toxin.[98,100]

The metabolic inactivation of LTB$_4$ most likely occurs at the local site of inflammation. LTB$_4$ is selectively inactivated by human neutrophils by way of ω oxidation (Figure 4). In the initial step of the inactivation process LTB$_4$ is converted to 20-hydroxy-LTB$_4$ (20-OH LTB$_4$) by the action of P-450$_{LTB}$. 20-Hydroxy-LTB$_4$ is then metabolized to 20-carbaldehyde-LTB$_4$ (20-CHO LTB$_4$) by one of two routes. The first and predominant route involves a second hydroxylation catalyzed by the same cytochrome P-450 followed by dehydration. The second route is by way of a cytosolic alcohol dehydrogenase. The final conversion of 20-carbaldehyde-LTB$_4$ to 20-carboxyl-LTB$_4$ (20-CO$_2$H LTB$_4$) can likewise be catalyzed by the same cytochrome P-450 by a third hydroxylation process or by a specific cytosolic aldehyde dehydrogenase. It would therefore appear that P-450$_{LTB}$ plays a critical role in controlling the accumulation and removal of LTB$_4$ at the inflammatory sites.[101]

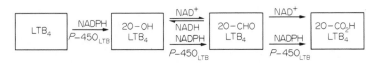

Figure 4   The two pathways of LTB$_4$ ω oxidation: (1) dehydrogenase cytosolic pathway; (2) P-450$_{LTB}$ microsomal pathway

12.13.3.2 LTB$_4$ in Disease

LTB$_4$ has been established as an inflammatory mediator *in vivo*. This is supported by the fact that LTB$_4$ has been found in elevated and biologically active concentrations in such sites as psoriatic lesions[102] and in the synovial fluid from rheumatoid arthritis patients.[103,104] Intradermal injection of LTB$_4$ causes the accumulation of neutrophils at the site of administration,[105,106] whereas intravenous injection of LTB$_4$ results in a rapid and reversible neutropenia.[107] Both of these reactions are characteristic of an inflammatory mediator. In addition, there has been evidence that the use of 5-lipoxygenase inhibitors decreases the extent of inflammatory reactions.[108,109] This suggests the importance of LTB$_4$ and the 5-lipoxygenase metabolic pathway of arachidonic acid in the inflammatory process.[110,111] LTB$_4$ has been shown to effect lymphocyte function. It has been demonstrated that LTB$_4$ binds to certain T-cell subclasses and suppresses the proliferative response of T$_4$-helper cells while augmenting that of T$_8$-suppressor cells. The net effect of LTB$_4$ on blood T-lymphocytes is immunosuppression.[112]

LTB$_4$ has been associated with airway hyperresponsiveness in dog[113] as well as being found in increased levels in lung lavages from humans with severe pulmonary dysfunction.[114] In a conscious guinea pig model, aerosol administration of LTB$_4$ resulted in an increase of neutrophils and eosinophils in mucosal/submucosal regions of trachea and bronchi as well as altered airway responsiveness.[115] Eosinophils isolated from patients with asthma have shown enhanced 5-lipoxygenase activity, producing greater levels of LTC$_4$ per cell than eosinophils isolated from normal subjects.[116,117] If this increased capacity to generate LTC$_4$ is symptomatic of inflammatory pulmonary disease, then blocking the actions of LTB$_4$ at the receptor level should prevent the recruitment of LTC$_4$-producing neutrophils and eosinophils. Other areas of possible therapeutic application include the treatment of inflammatory bowel disease,[118,119] rheumatoid arthritis,[103,104] gout[120] and psoriasis.[102] It has also been suggested that LTB$_4$ plays an important role in myocardial ischemia-reflow injury. This has been demonstrated by the accumulation of LTB$_4$ in the myocardium of rabbits and by the cardioprotection afforded by specific 5-lipoxygenase inhibitors.[121-123]

12.13.3.3 Structure–Activity Relationships of LTB$_4$ Receptor Agonists

LTB$_4$, as are the other leukotrienes, is a nonrigid molecule capable of having many conformations, several of which are illustrated in Figure 5. High-field nuclear magnetic resonance studies of the potassium salt of LTB$_4$ in aqueous solution support a conformation of LTB$_4$ in which the conjugated double bonds exist in a coplanar arrangement with *s-trans* stereochemistry about the 7,8 and 9,10 bonds (a, c–f).[124] Structure–activity relationship studies on LTB$_4$ itself have revealed the importance of this triene geometry as well as the requirement for the (5S,12R)-hydroxyl groups for biological activity. One study[125] comparing several synthetic 5,12-diHETEs with LTB$_4$ demonstrates that chemotactic activity is very dependent upon the triene geometry. The 6,10-*trans*-8,14-*cis*-eicosatetraenoic acid (*t,c,t,c*, **145**) is substantially less active than LTB$_4$ (*c,t,t,c*, **144**) in stimulating chemotaxis of human neutrophils. The 6,8-*trans*-10,14-*cis* analog (*t,t,c,c*, **146**) is very similar to (**145**) in its ability to cause chemotaxis. Both (**145**) and (**146**) lack the 6-*cis* alkene of LTB$_4$ but still permit a 'bend' in the overall geometry of the molecule. In contrast, the 6,8,10-*trans*-14-*cis*-eicosatetraenoic acid (*t,t,t,c*, **147**) has less geometrical similarity with LTB$_4$ and as a consequence exhibits even greater reduction in chemotactic activity. Additionally, the study demonstrates that the compounds lacking the correct 6-*cis* geometry show slight preference for the stereochemistry of the hydroxyl groups. The epimeric compounds are nearly equipotent as are the racemic *vs.* optically active compounds. A second report examining the structural requirements for chemotactic activity supports these observations.[126] LTB$_4$ was determined to have peak chemotactic activity at a concentration of 10^{-7} M in human PMNs. A mixture of two epimers at C-5 and C-12 shift the response curve to the right but do not lower the overall maximum activity. Similarly, increasing or decreasing the chain by one carbon between the 5-hydroxyl and the carboxyl head group also shows decreased potency but not decreased activity. The 19 carbon nor-LTB$_4$ (**148**) and the 21 carbon homo-LTB$_4$ (**149**) are indistinguishable in their activities from one another. Both require a concentration of 10^{-6} M to produce the same maximum chemotactic response as LTB$_4$. The greatest change in activity was obtained when the C-6 double bond was changed from a *cis* configuration to that of *trans*. In this case chemotactic activity was only detectable at high concentrations. These studies suggest the importance of the stereochemistry of the C-5 and C-12 hydroxyl groups, as well as the chain length between C-1 and C-5, for chemotactic activity. However, the configuration of the C-6 alkene appears to make the greatest contribution to activity. Compounds (**144**)–(**149**) were also tested for their ability to induce neutrophil aggregation. In this assay all of the compounds were found to be agonists and their potencies, relative to LTB_4, were comparable to their potencies as chemoattractants. These compounds were also able to desensitize the cells to a second challenge with LTB_4, indicating that their response is mediated by way of the LTB_4 receptor.

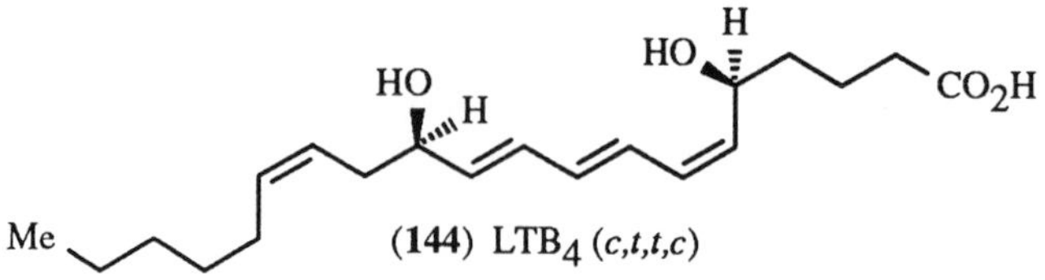

(**144**) LTB_4 (*c,t,t,c*)

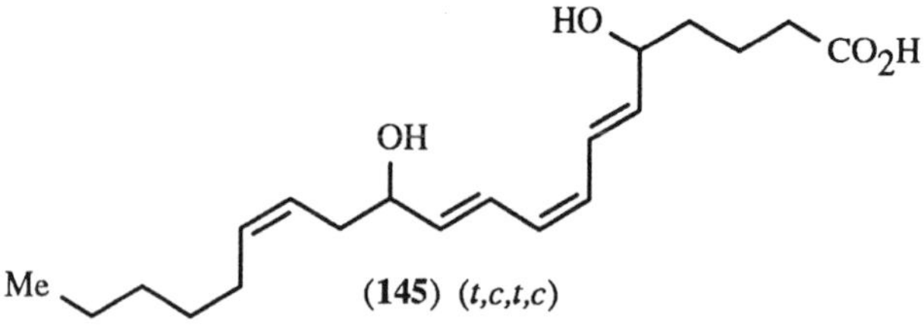

(**145**) (*t,c,t,c*)

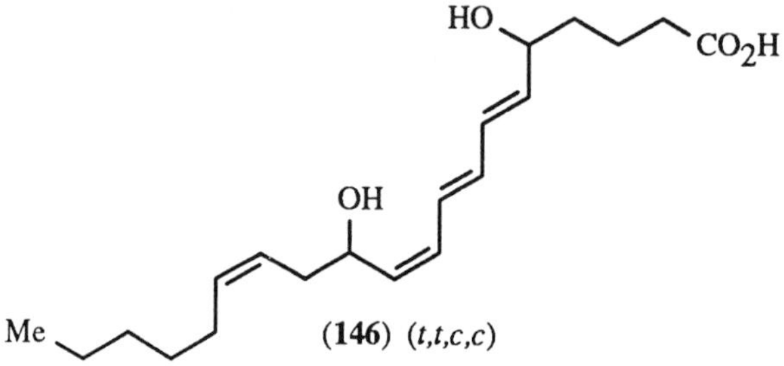

(**146**) (*t,t,c,c*)

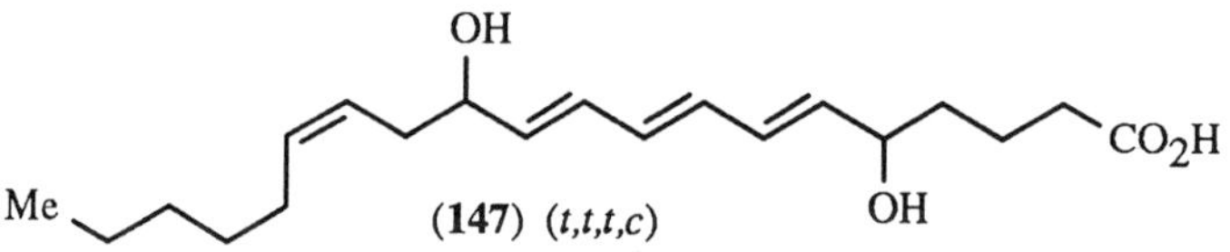

(**147**) (*t,t,t,c*)

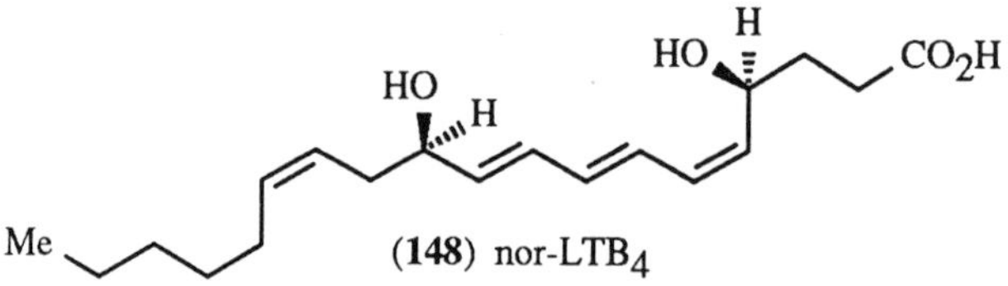

(**148**) nor-LTB_4

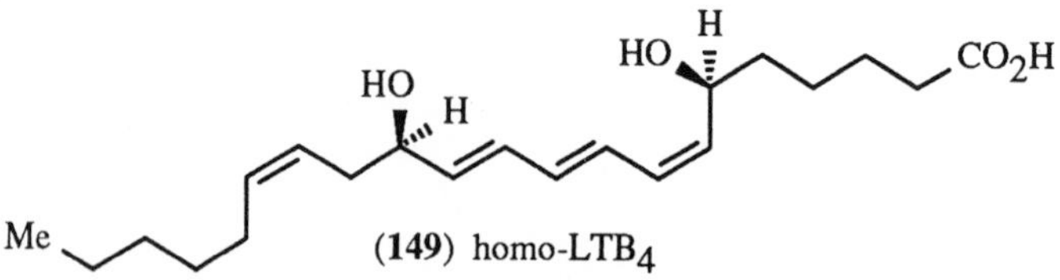

(**149**) homo-LTB_4

Whereas the *cis* double bond at C-6 is very important for activity, the C-14 *cis* double bond does not appear to play a major role.[127] In a competitive binding assay of [^{3}H]-LTB_4 *vs.* LTB_4 and LTB_3 (**150**) it was found that absence of the C-14 alkene had no effect on the activity; LTB_3 was equipotent to LTB_4 in its ability to displace [^{3}H]-LTB_4. However, if an additional double bond is placed at the C-17 position (LTB_5, **151**), the added rigidity of the molecule is disadvantageous to binding; LTB_5 was found to be 20–50 times less potent in its ability to displace [^{3}H]-LTB_4 than LTB_4 itself.

These studies clearly demonstrate the importance of the triene geometry of LTB_4 for biological activity. However, in terms of the importance of the two hydroxyl groups for activity, the data have not been definitive. Recently, synthetically pure isomers of LTB_4 (**152–156**; Table 14) were prepared having the correct *cis–trans–trans* triene geometry. The relationship of the hydroxyl groups to activity could then be unambiguously investigated.[128] The study reveals that the C-5 hydroxyl group does not play a very important role in binding or activation of the LTB_4 receptor. However,

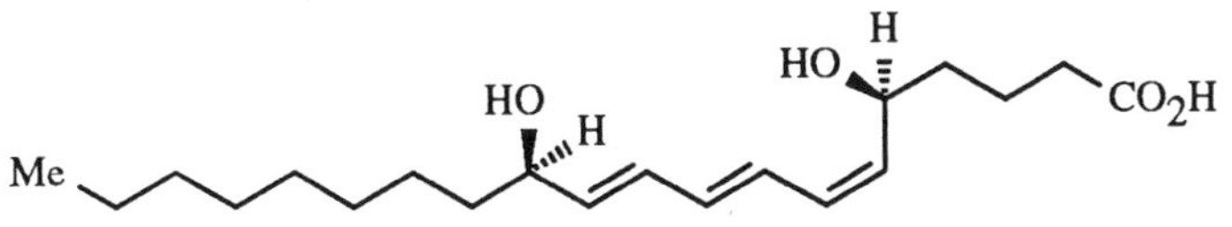

(150) LTB$_3$

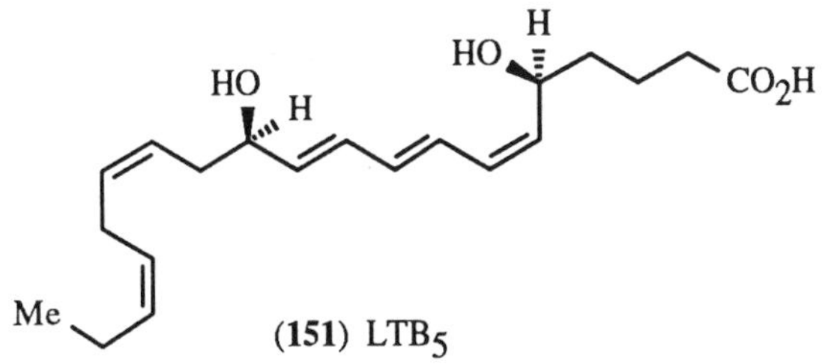

(151) LTB$_5$

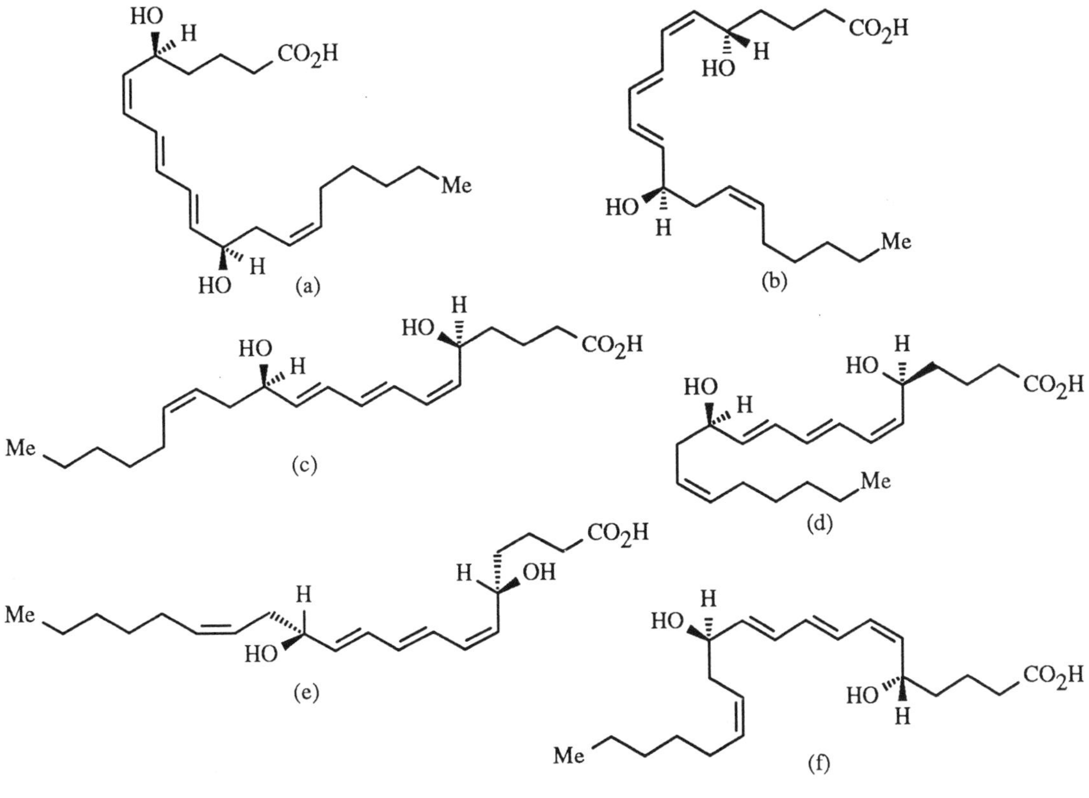

Figure 5 Some conformations of LTB$_4$

the constraints imposed by the receptor are less favorable towards the C-5 epimeric hydroxyl group. The C-12 hydroxyl group contributes far more to receptor binding than the C-5 hydroxyl group, but the requirements of the receptor appear to be less restrictive in terms of the stereochemistry. Removal of both hydroxyl groups (*e.g.* **156**) results in significant loss of activity.

12.13.3.4 LTB$_4$ Receptor Antagonists

Unlike the peptidoleukotriene receptor antagonists, the identification of LTB$_4$ receptor antagonists has proceeded slowly. Some of the reported LTB$_4$ antagonists are based upon one specific conformation of the molecule. A low energy conformation of the molecule is chosen, and then rigidity and stability are built into the system. Other compounds are merely analogs of the natural agonist itself. Most of the reported antagonists belong to this class of structure-based compounds. The other major class of LTB$_4$ antagonists appear to be derived from leads resulting from LTD$_4$ receptor antagonist research.

Table 14   LTB$_4$ Antagonists: LTB$_4$ Analogs

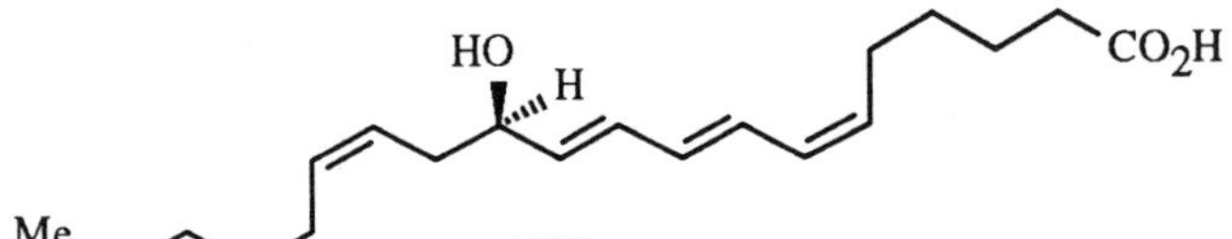

Compound	Aggregation rat PMN IC_{50} (nM)	Binding rat PMN membranes IC_{50} (nM)	Binding human PMN membranes IC_{50} (nM)
LTB$_4$	1	1	0.5
5-Deoxy-LTB$_4$ (152)	4	2.5	4
12-Epi-LTB$_4$ (153)	25	8	11
5-Epi-LTB$_4$ (154)	90	130	100
12-Deoxy-LTB$_4$ (155)	400	120	140
5,12-Dideoxy-LTB$_4$ (156)	8000	2200	870

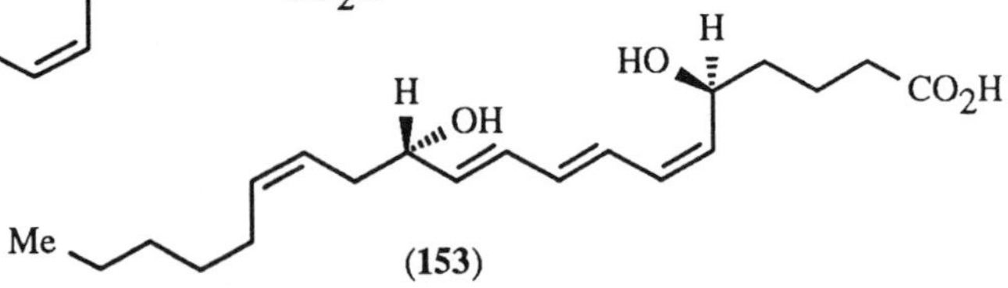

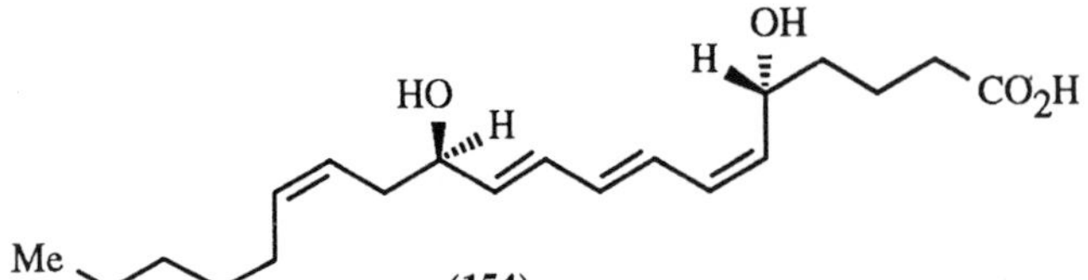

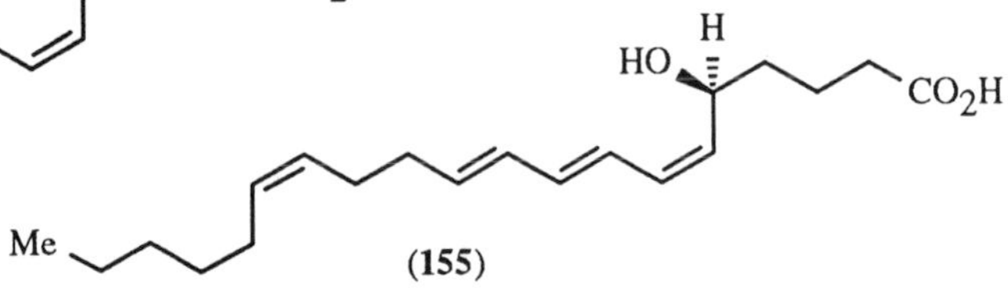

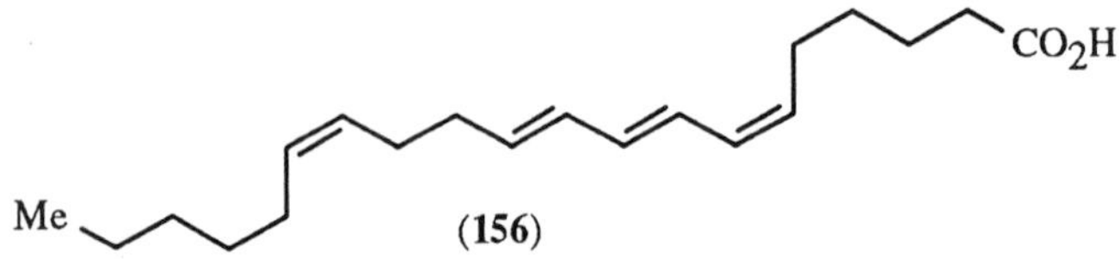

12.13.3.4.1   *Structure-based approach*

The earliest report of a leukotriene B$_4$ receptor antagonist emerged from a collaboration between E. J. Corey and Pfizer in 1982.[129] This compound, LTB$_4$ dimethylamide (LTB$_4$ DMA, **157**) was obtained as a derivative of natural LTB$_4$. This molecule was derived from the knowledge that prostaglandin F$_{2\alpha}$ dimethylamide antagonizes smooth muscle contraction induced by prostaglandin F$_{2\alpha}$. LTB$_4$ DMA was tested for its ability to inhibit the degranulation response induced by LTB$_4$ in rabbit neutrophils. At LTB$_4$ concentrations of 11 and 37 nM, LTB$_4$ DMA is shown to significantly inhibit degranulation at concentrations between 0.1 and 1.0 µM as measured by lysozyme release. At higher concentrations (5 µM) LTB$_4$ DMA is shown to exhibit partial agonist activity in a degranulation assay. The dissociation constant (K_d) of the antagonist was determined to be in the range of 34–426 nM. For maximum inhibitory activity, neutrophils first had to be exposed to LTB$_4$ DMA for 30 s prior to the introduction of LTB$_4$ into the system. No further inhibition was seen by pre-incubating the cells for longer periods of time and the effects were minimally reversed by washing the cells free of the antagonist before exposing them to LTB$_4$. This time dependency, poor reversibility, and the presence of partial agonist activity suggest that the mode of inhibition of LTB$_4$ DMA was *via* desensitization of the LTB$_4$ receptor. Despite the fact that LTB$_4$ DMA may not be a full antagonist, the report demonstrates that at concentrations of LTB$_4$ DMA that exhibit little or no agonist activity, the degranulation response due to LTB$_4$ could be dramatically reduced.

In 1986, Sumitomo Pharmaceuticals reported the LTB$_4$ antagonist SM-9064 (**158**). This compound is an analog of LTB$_4$ and its design was based upon conformation (a; Figure 5).[130] SM-9064 was reported to inhibit LTB_4-induced chemotaxis of rat PMN leukocytes with an IC_{50} of 0.13 μM. SM-9064 showed little inhibition of chemotaxis induced by *N*-formyl-Met-Leu-Phe (FMLP) and lipopolysaccharide-activated serum ($IC_{50} > 30$ μM), thus indicating that the antagonism was selective for LTB_4. When assessing the chemotactic ability of SM-9064 it was found to possess slight agonist activity. Maximum chemotactic activity occurs at a concentration of 3 μM and exhibits 20% of the response induced by 30 nM LTB_4. At higher concentrations of SM-9064 chemotactic activity decreased, suggesting possible desensitization. SM-9064 showed dose dependent suppression of paw edema due to Arthus reaction in mice but had no effect on edema induced by carrageenin.

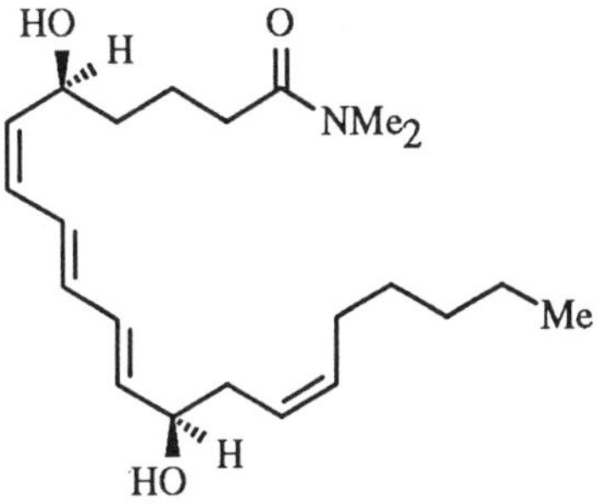

(157) LTB$_4$ DMA

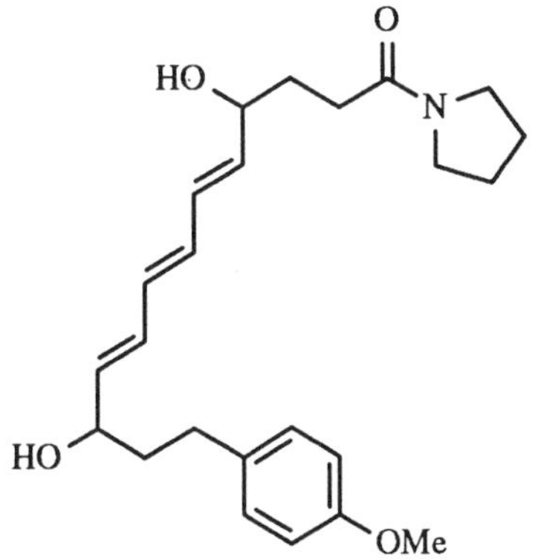

(158) SM-9064

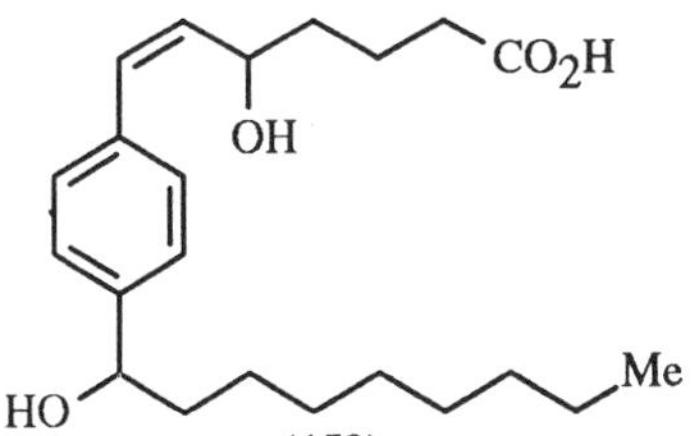

(159)

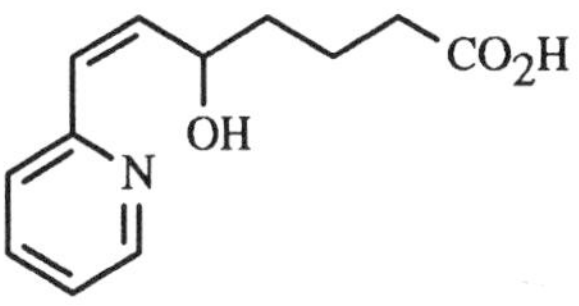

(160)

A report from the University of East Anglia (UK) in conjunction with Fisons appeared in 1987, describing the preparation of several aromatic LTB_4 analogs (159) and (160), which are based upon conformation (b) of LTB_4 (Figure 5).[131] The strategy involved the design of bridged leukotriene analogs in which the 8*E*,10*E*-diene unit is constrained by its incorporation into an aromatic ring. No biological data were reported for these analogs other than to indicate that they exhibit 'some biological activity'.

Upjohn researchers focused upon conformation (c) of LTB_4 (Figure 5).[132] Their strategy required the design of a molecule in which the triene unit corresponding to LTB_4 is modified so as to make it more stable. Specifically, compounds were synthesized in which carbons 7–9 (LTB_4 numbering) of the *cis–trans–trans* triene unit were incorporated as part of an aromatic ring system. Examples included *meta*-substituted benzenes, 2,5-disubstituted furans, and 2,6-disubstituted pyridines.[99] The most active compound (U-75302; 161) utilized a pyridine ring such that the 6,7-*cis* alkene of LTB_4 could be simulated by an intramolecular hydrogen bond between the basic nitrogen and the C-5 hydroxyl group. Twelve analogs were studied for their ability to inhibit the binding of [³H]-LTB_4 to human neutrophils. In each set of tests the pyridine analogs were found to be the most potent. Other structure–activity relationships could be discerned from the test data (Tables 15 and 16). Specifically, compounds containing a C-1 alcohol group were uniformly more potent inhibitors than the corresponding carboxylic acid analogs (Table 15), compounds in which the C-5 hydroxyl was replaced by a C-5,6 double bond show the most activity when the alkene geometry was *cis* rather than *trans* (Table 16). All of the compounds were tested at a concentration of 1 μM and no assays were described that would allow for the differentiation between agonist and antagonist activity. In addition, U-75302 was found to inhibit LTB_4-induced contraction of guinea pig lung parenchyma strips at a concentration of 0.3 μM.[132] A final point of interest was that the compounds show enhanced inhibitory activity when tested in isolated membranes over that found in whole cells. This was confirmed when several structural analogs of U-75485 (162) were tested independently. The

Table 15　LTB$_4$ Antagonists: U-75302 Analogs

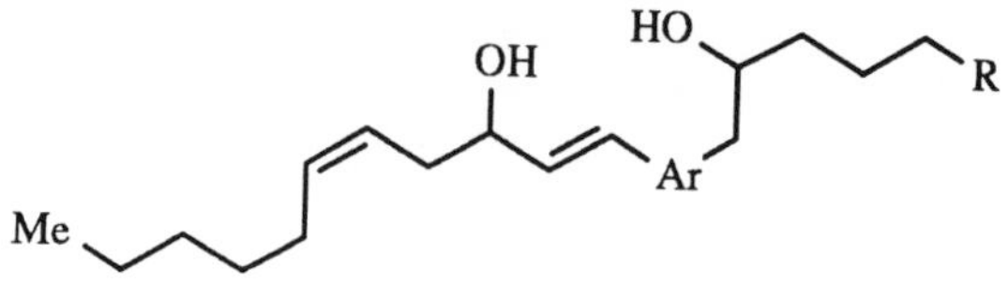

Ar	R		% Inhibition[a]
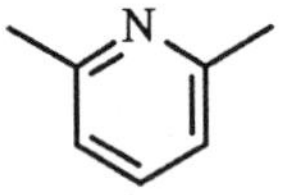 (2,6-pyridyl)	CO$_2$H	U-75305	40
	CH$_2$OH	U-75302	80
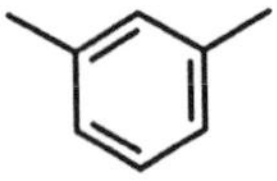 (1,3-phenyl)	CO$_2$H	U-74738	5
	CH$_2$OH	U-74675	20
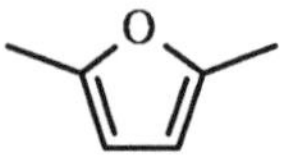 (2,5-furyl)	CO$_2$H	U-78058	10
	CH$_2$OH	U-77980	15

[a] Inhibition of 1 nM [^{3}H]-LTB$_4$ by 1 μM of antagonist.

Table 16　LTB$_4$ Antagonists: U-75360 Analogs

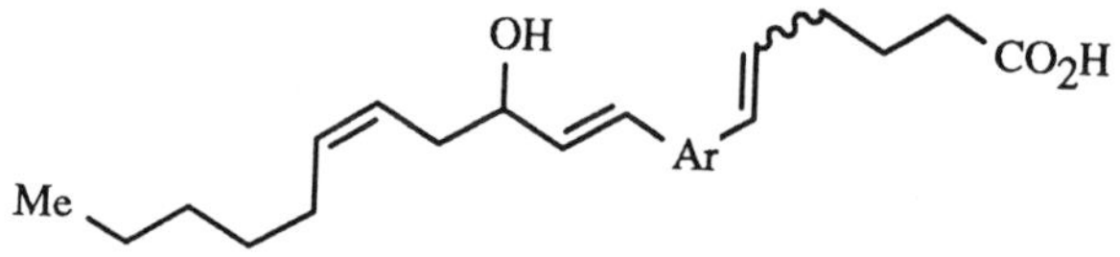

Ar	Alkene geometry		% Inhibition[a]
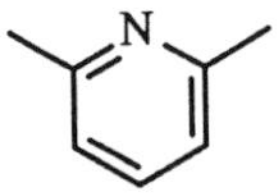 (2,6-pyridyl)	Cis	U-75360	70
	Trans	U-77860	32
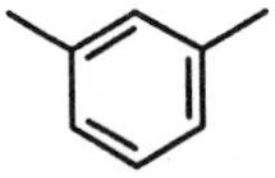 (1,3-phenyl)	Cis	U-75409	68
	Trans	U-74530	23
 (2,5-furyl)	Cis	U-76854	35
	Trans	U-76853	0

[a] Inhibition of 1 nM [^{3}H]-LTB$_4$ by 1 μM of antagonist.

results show that these compounds inhibit [^{3}H]-LTB$_4$ binding to human neutrophil membranes with nanomolar affinity (IC$_{50}$ values from 79 to 400 nM). However, they appear to be at least 10-fold less potent in the binding assay using intact human neutrophils. This report also found that these analogs do possess mixed agonist/antagonist activity as determined by an LTB$_4$-induced calcium rise assay.[133]

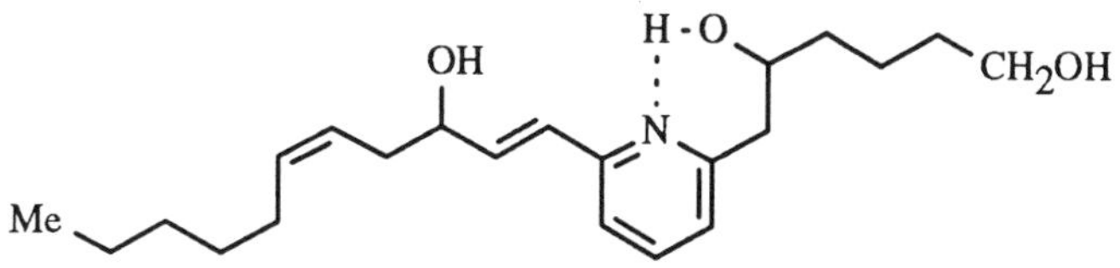

(161) U-75302

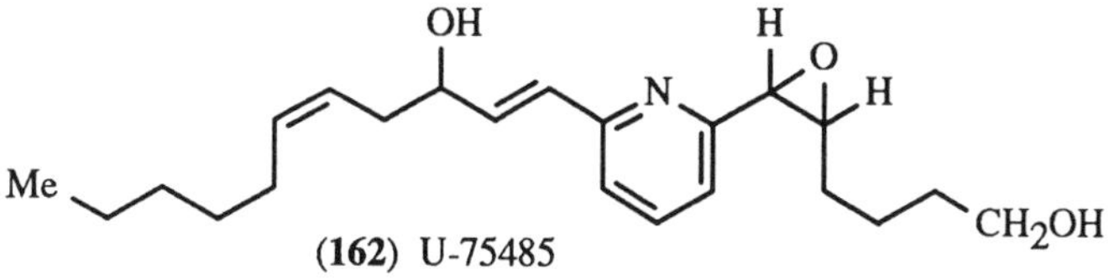

(162) U-75485

12.13.3.4.2 *LTD₄ antagonist-based leads*

Two compounds and their analogs have recently been described in the literature that appear to have been derived from analogs of the LTD$_4$ receptor antagonist FPL-55712. One of these, SC-41930 (163) from G. D. Searle, has been reported to be a potent, selective LTB$_4$ receptor antagonist with oral activity. SC-41930 was shown to have an IC$_{50}$ of 0.30 μM in a human neutrophil binding assay. The compound was an effective inhibitor of LTB$_4$-induced neutrophil degranulation and LTB$_4$-induced neutrophil chemotaxis. The results suggest the ability of SC-41930 to antagonize both high (chemotaxis) and low (degranulation) affinity LTB$_4$ receptors. SC-41930 also demonstrates efficacy in reducing inflammation in a guinea pig model of acetic acid-induced colitis having an oral ED$_{50}$ of 41 μmol kg^{-1}. It is hoped that this activity can be extended to human inflammatory bowel disease by preventing neutrophil infiltration into the affected colon. SC-41930 exhibits very poor affinity for the LTD$_4$ receptor (4% inhibition at 10 μM). This is an interesting observation due to the similarity of the molecule to the chroman carboxylic acid type of compounds (*e.g.* FPL-55712) which are known LTD$_4$ antagonists. It would appear that methylation of the phenolic hydroxyl of the acetophenone ring results in a compound having LTB$_4$ antagonist activity while preventing LTD$_4$ receptor affinity.[134-136] The second compound, Ro-23-3544 (164), has been

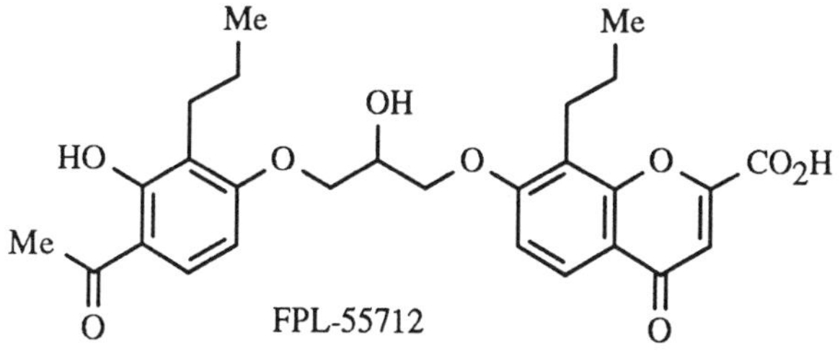

FPL-55712

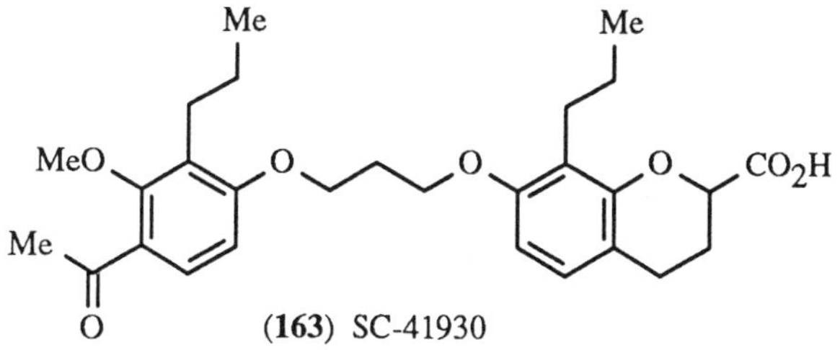

(163) SC-41930

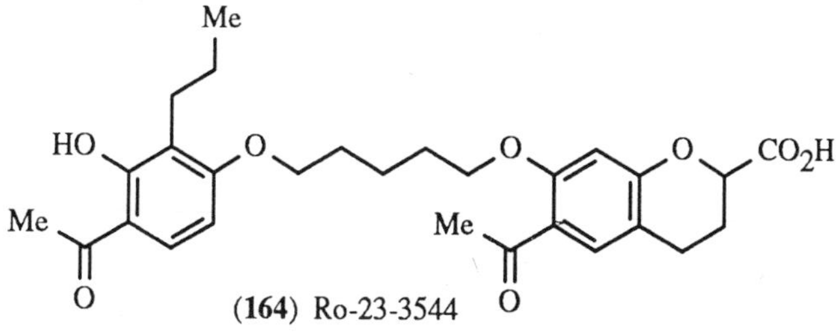

(164) Ro-23-3544

reported to be a nonselective leukotriene antagonist from Hoffmann-La Roche. Ro-23-3544 has been reported to be effective in an acetic acid-induced inflammatory bowel disease model in the rat.[137,138]

Eli Lilly and Company has reported two potent LTB_4 specific antagonists, LY-223982 (**165**), a benzophenone analog, and LY-255283 (**166**), an acetophenone analog.[139-141] Both compounds inhibit the binding of [^{3}H]-LTB_4 to human neutrophils, LY-223982 having an IC_{50} of 12 nM and LY-255283 having an IC_{50} of 87 nM. At 0.1 μM concentration both compounds were found to inhibit LTB_4-induced aggregation of guinea pig neutrophils by 50%. Neither compound caused neutrophil aggregation, indicating that they were both free of agonist activity. Recently an independent study was performed in which the *in vivo* effect of LY-223982 on injury and PMN accumulation in a rabbit model of myocardial ischemia-reflow was examined.[142] PMN specific myeloperoxidase (MPO) activity was measured as an index of PMN accumulation. Rabbits treated with LY-223982 show a reduced area of injury *vs.* control rabbits as well as significantly decreased MPO activity in the infarcted tissue. These findings provide additional evidence for the role of LTB_4 in PMN accumulation and injury during myocardial ischemia-reflow conditions. The data also demonstrate the possible therapeutic use of an LTB_4 antagonist in treating this condition. A second study using LY-223982 was performed to assess its ability to inhibit the binding of [^{3}H]-LTB_4 to human neutrophils in both whole cell and membrane preparations.[143] Whereas LTB_4 inhibits the binding of [^{3}H]-LTB_4 in both assays with equal affinity (IC_{50} = 2 nM), significant differences were found in the activity of LY-223982. In the membrane preparations LY-223982 was found to inhibit binding with only micromolar affinity. However, in whole cell systems it exhibits binding inhibition with nanomolar affinity. This effect was also demonstrated in the activity of 20-OH LTB_4. It should be noted that this difference in activity seen for LY-223982 in whole cell *vs.* membrane binding is contrary to that demonstrated by the U-75485 analogs.[133] The pharmacological significance of this discrepancy is currently not known.

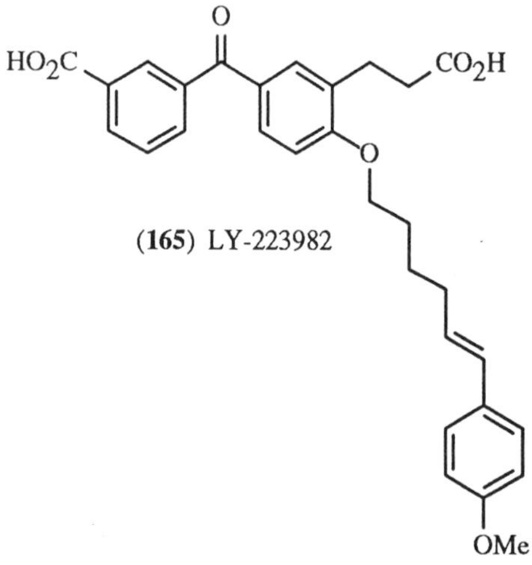

(**165**) LY-223982

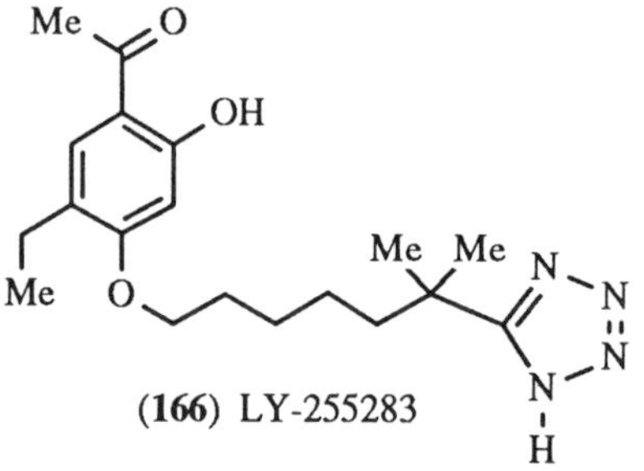

(**166**) LY-255283

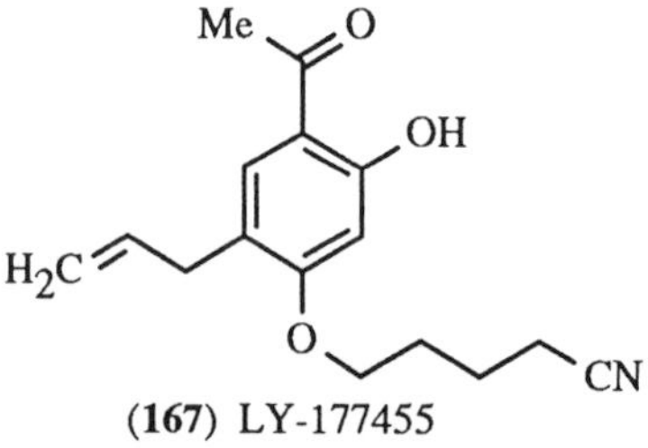

(**167**) LY-177455

Structure–activity relationships developed in the LY-223982 series reveal the requirement for both of the acidic groups.[139] Analogs with nonacidic or weakly acidic groups have greatly reduced activity. The distance between these acidic groups as well as their relative orientation is also critical for optimum activity. It was also determined that the overall length and lipophilicity of the molecule is important. A detailed examination of the 'tail' region of the molecule revealed that the most active derivatives had 'tails' that were terminated with a substituted aromatic ring (Tables 17–19).[144] LY-255283 was developed from structure–activity studies on LY-177455 (**167**), itself probably derived from an LTD_4 antagonist program.[140] The structure of LY-255283 differs from known LTD_4 receptor antagonists mainly in having a short alkyl group at the C-5 position rather than at C-3. It was found that an ethyl group at the C-5 position gave the best LTB_4 antagonist activity. Removing either the acetyl or phenolic groups reduced activity. The design of these Lilly antagonists does not appear to be based upon any particular conformation of LTB_4.

Table 17 LTB$_4$ Antagonists: LY-223982 Analogs

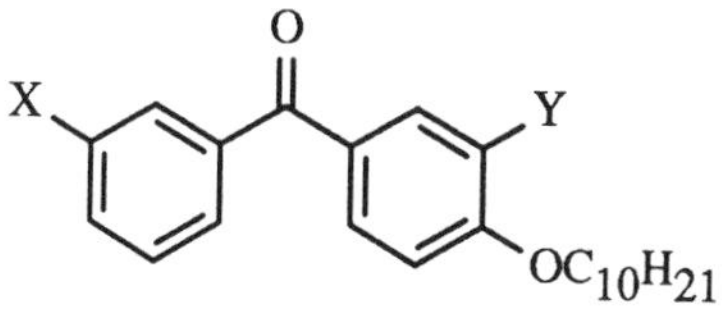

X	Y	% Inhibition^a $10^{-5}M$	$10^{-6}M$
CO$_2$H	CH$_2$-tetrazole	76	26
CO$_2$Et	CH$_2$-tetrazole	−11	14
CN	CH$_2$CN	3	−1
Tetrazole	CH$_2$- tetrazole	81	20
CO$_2$H	CH$_2$CH$_2$CO$_2$H	95	62
CO$_2$H	CH$_2$CH$_2$CH$_2$CO$_2$H	87	52
Tetrazole	CH$_2$CO$_2$H	93	28
CO$_2$H	CH$_2$CH$_2$-tetrazole	96	55
Tetrazole	CH$_2$CH$_2$CO$_2$H	98	71

^{a} Inhibition of [^{3}H]-LTB$_4$ binding by antagonist at each concentration.

Table 18 LTB$_4$ Antagonists: LY-223982 Analogs

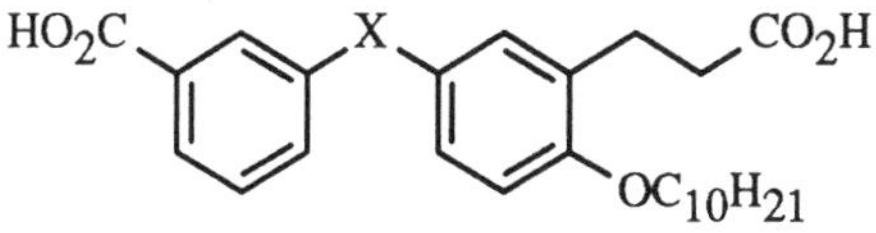

X	% Inhibition^a $10^{-5}M$	$10^{-6}M$	$10^{-7}M$
CO	95	62	17
CHOH	91	55	13
CH$_2$	88	41	—
CNOH	92	61	17
CCH$_2$	71	37	−3
O	88	41	—

^{a} Inhibition of [^{3}H]-LTB$_4$ binding by antagonist at each concentration.

12.13.3.4.3 *Miscellaneous*

Dapsone, 4,4′-diaminodiphenyl sulfone (**168**), is one of the primary agents used in the treatment of chronic skin disorders such as dermatitis herpetiformis.[145] Such conditions are associated with neutrophil and eosinophil accumulation. Good therapeutic results using dapsone have also been reported for subcorneal pustular dermatosis,[146] generalized pustular psoriasis,[147] some cases of rheumatoid arthritis,[148] and Crohn's disease.[149] Several studies have been reported in an effort to elucidate the mechanism of action of dapsone as an antiinflammatory agent.[148,150,151] Recently a study was performed to assess the activity of dapsone with respect to LTB$_4$.[152] The study was designed to monitor the response of dapsone on receptor binding, chemotaxis and *in vivo* activity in an inflammatory model. In the receptor binding assay dapsone inhibits the binding of [^{3}H]-LTB$_4$ to human PMNs at each concentration tested (10–100 µM), exhibiting a dose dependent decrease in specific binding. The data in this test indicate an IC$_{50}$ value of approximately 50 µM. The compound shows no effect on nonspecific binding. Chemotactic response of human PMNs to LTB$_4$ was reduced by dapsone at concentrations found effective in the binding assay. Chemotaxis was reduced by 50% at a dapsone concentration of 100 µM. The compound had no inhibitory effect on chemotaxis induced by FMLP, indicating LTB$_4$ selective activity. The *in vivo* effects were assayed

Table 19 LTB$_4$ Antagonists: LY-223982 Analogs

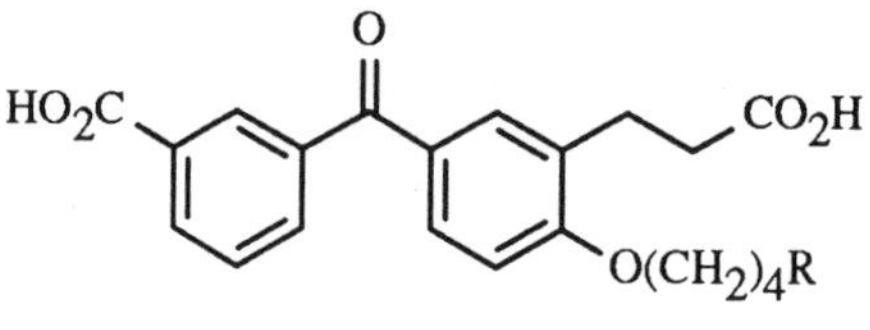

R	% Inhibition[a]		
	$10^{-5} M$	$10^{-6} M$	$10^{-7} M$
—(CH$_2$)$_5$Me	95	62	17
—(CH$_2$)$_2$Ph	97	82	36
 ⟍⟍Ph	96	91	36
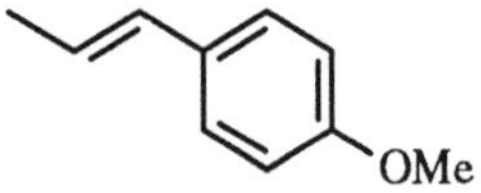 (vinyl–C$_6$H$_4$–OMe, para)	100	97	92
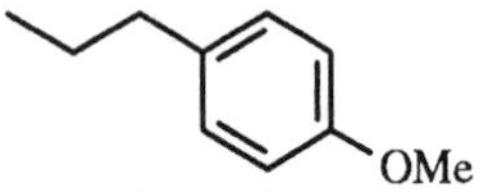 (propyl–C$_6$H$_4$–OMe, para)	105	98	68
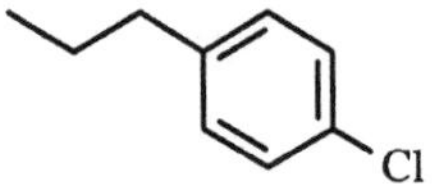 (propyl–C$_6$H$_4$–Cl, para)	106	91	42
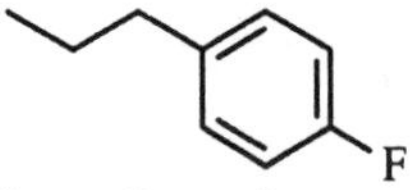 (propyl–C$_6$H$_4$–F, para)	104	81	22
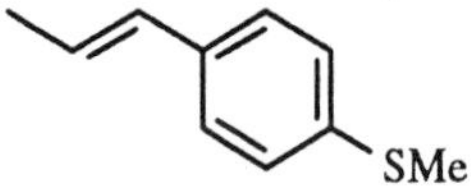 (vinyl–C$_6$H$_4$–SMe, para)	103	79	18
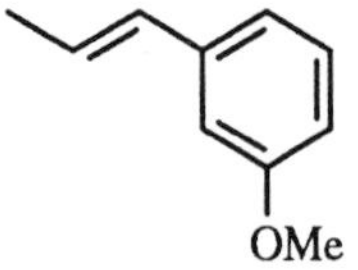 (vinyl–C$_6$H$_4$–OMe, meta)	99	91	49
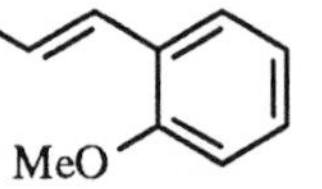 (vinyl–C$_6$H$_4$–OMe, ortho)	101	97	86
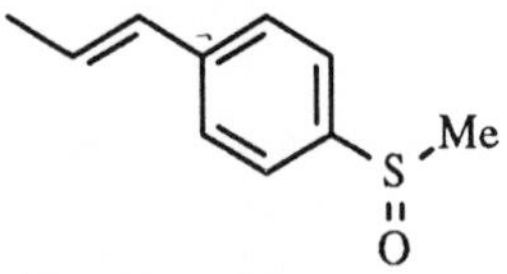 (vinyl–C$_6$H$_4$–S(O)Me, para)	98	96	90
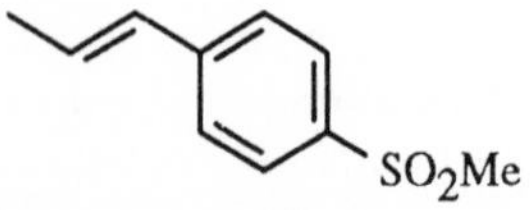 (vinyl–C$_6$H$_4$–SO$_2$Me, para)	98	88	60

[a] Inhibition of [^{3}H]-LTB$_4$ binding by antagonist at each concentration.

using an ear inflammation model in mice. An inflammatory response, which peaked after 4 h, was produced by a local injection of LTB$_4$. Ear biopsies were taken for myeloperoxidase content to measure neutrophil influx. Mice that were treated with dapsone (100 mg kg^{-1}, s.c.) 30 minutes prior to LTB$_4$ injection showed a decrease in MPO activity of about 50%. The authors also found that dapsone did not inhibit 5-lipoxygenase isolated from RBL-1 cells, as measured by the production of

5-HETE. The data suggest that the primary effect of dapsone treatment is the antagonism of the LTB$_4$ receptor, resulting in decreased movement of PMN leukocytes to the site of inflammation. Although the receptor affinity appears to be low, dapsone at therapeutically used concentrations inhibits 50% of the LTB$_4$ binding in human neutrophils.

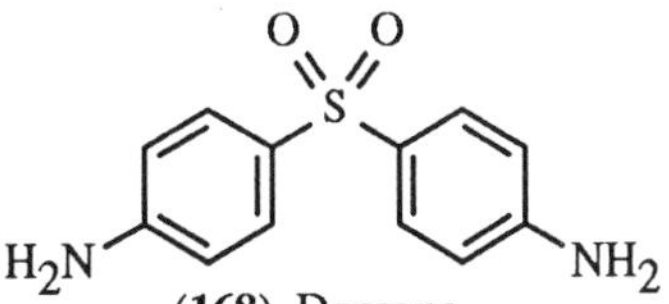

(168) Dapsone 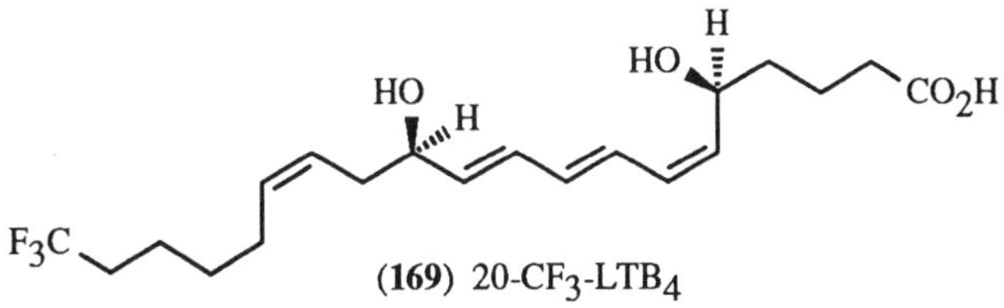   **(169)** 20-CF$_3$-LTB$_4$

Another recent report from G. D. Searle discusses the activity of 20-trifluoromethyl LTB$_4$ (20-CF$_3$ LTB$_4$; **169**) with respect to chemotaxis and degranulation in human neutrophils.[153] In the human PMN binding assay 20-CF$_3$ LTB$_4$ was found to exhibit slightly reduced affinity over that of LTB$_4$. LTB$_4$ had an IC$_{50}$ value of 3 nM, while 20-CF$_3$ LTB$_4$ had an IC$_{50}$ value of 10 nM in displacement of [^{3}H]-LTB$_4$. In the chemotaxis assay 20-CF$_3$ LTB$_4$ was found to be equipotent to LTB$_4$. Both compounds had an EC$_{50}$ of 3 nM, however 20-CF$_3$ LTB$_4$ produced only 55% of the maximal response for that of LTB$_4$. In contrast, 20-CF$_3$ LTB$_4$ shows quite different activity towards neutrophil degranulation as determined by neutrophil MPO release. Whereas LTB$_4$ exhibits maximal and half-maximal degranulation activity at 50 nM and 5–12 nM respectively, 20-CF$_3$ LTB$_4$ shows negligible activity at concentrations ranging from 1 nM to 10 μM. MPO release by 20-CF$_3$ LTB$_4$ was 2–6% of that induced by the maximal effective concentration of LTB$_4$ and was not dose dependent. 20-CF$_3$ LTB$_4$ at 3 nM and 10 nM inhibits the concentration-related degranulation activity of LTB$_4$. This inhibition by 20-CF$_3$ LTB$_4$ (IC$_{50}$ of 1–2 nM) could not be surmounted with higher concentrations of LTB$_4$. Thus 20-CF$_3$ LTB$_4$ appears to be a partial agonist with respect to chemotaxis but an antagonist with respect to degranulation in human neutrophils. Although the lack of hydrogen atoms at C-20 did not result in a marked reduction of potency of LTB$_4$ towards chemotaxis and degranulation, it did affect the ability of LTB$_4$ to maximally induce both of these neutrophil functions. This effect was most dramatic with respect to degranulation. As discussed previously, the high affinity LTB$_4$ receptors are associated with chemotaxis, while the low affinity LTB$_4$ receptors are associated with degranulation. The data suggest that the presence of hydrogen atoms at C-20 is required for low affinity receptor activation.

12.13.3.5 Future Design Perspectives

The design of LTB$_4$ receptor antagonists is currently at a very early stage. Unlike the peptido-leukotriene receptor antagonists which have been under development for over 10 years, the LTB$_4$ receptor has only recently become the focus of major investigation. As a greater understanding is developed of the structural requirements of the LTB$_4$ receptor, as well as an understanding of the features that contribute to partial agonist activity, more potent antagonists will be discovered. These antagonists will provide a means by which to determine the role of LTB$_4$ in various disease states and to establish the therapeutic benefit of LTB$_4$ receptor antagonists.

12.13.4 REFERENCES

1. P. J. Piper, *Physiol. Rev.*, 1984, **64**, 744.
2. P. J. Piper, *Int. Arch. Allergy Appl. Immunol.*, 1985, **76** (suppl. 1), 43.
3. B. Samuelsson, *Science (Washington, D.C.)*, 1983, **220**, 568.
4. C. D. Perchonock, T. J. Torphy and S. Mong, *Drugs of The Future*, 1987, **12**, 9.
5. A. M. Lefer, *Biochem. Pharmacol.*, 1986, **35**, 123.
6. G. Feuerstein, *Prostaglandins*, 1984, **27**, 781.
7. M. B. Forman, J. A. Oates, R. M. Robertson, L. J. Roberts and R. Virmani, *N. Engl. J. Med.*, 1985, **313**, 1138.
8. A. Rosenthal and C. R. Pace-Asciak, *Can. J. Physiol. Pharmacol.*, 1983, **61**, 325.
9. K. F. Badr, C. Baylis, J. M. Pfeffer, M. A. Pfeffer, R. J. Soberman, R. A. Lewis, K. F. Austen, E. J. Corey and B. M. Brenner, *Circ. Res.*, 1984, **54**, 492.
10. R. J. Shaw, P. Fitzharris, O. Cromwell, A. J. Wardlaw and A. B. Kay, *Allergy*, 1985, **40**, 1.
11. A. G. Togias, R. M. Naclerio, S. P. Peters, I. Nimmagaddia, D. Proud, A. Kagey-Sobotka, N. F. Adkinson, P. S. Norman and L. M. Lichenstein, *Am. Rev. Respir. Dis.*, 1986, **133**, 1133.
12. J. T. Zakrzewski, N. C. Barnes, P. J. Piper and J. F. Costello, *Prostaglandins*, 1984, **28**, 641A.

13. D. Keppler, W. Hagmann, S. Rapp, C. Denzlinger and H. K. Koch, *Hepatology*, 1985, **5**, 883.
14. S. T. Crooke, S. Mong, M. Clark, H. Sarau, A. Wong, R. Vegesna, J. D. Winkler, J. Balcarek and C. F. Bennett, in 'Cellular and Molecular Aspects of Inflammation', ed. G. Poste and S. T. Crooke, Plenum Press, New York, 1988.
15. S. Mong, H.-L. Wu, G. K. Hogaboom, M. A. Clark, J. M. Stadel *et al.*, *Eur. J. Pharmacol.*, 1984, **106**, 241.
16. S. Mong, H.-L. Wu, M. A. Clark, J. M. Stadel, J. G. Gleason *et al.*, *Prostaglandins*, 1984, **28**, 805.
17. S. Mong, H.-L. Wu, J. M. Stadel, M. A. Clark and S. T. Crooke, *Pharmacologist*, 1986, **29**, 235.
18. J. H. Fleisch, L. E. Rinkema and S. R. Baker, *Life Sci.*, 1982, **31**, 577.
19. R. D. Krell, B. S. Tsai, A. Berdoulay, M. Barone and R. E. Giles, *Prostaglandins*, 1983, **25**, 171.
20. D. W. Snyder and R. D. Krell, *J. Pharmacol. Exp. Ther.*, 1984, **231**, 616.
21. S. Mong, M. O. Scott, M. A. Lewis, H.-L. Wu, G. K. Hogaboom, M. A. Clark and S. T. Crooke, *Eur. J. Pharmacol.*, 1985, **109**, 183.
22. J. Augstein, J. B. Farmer, J. B. Lee, T. B. Sheard and M. L. Tattersall, *Nature (London)*, 1973, **245**, 215.
23. G. K. Hogaboom, S. Mong, H.-L. Wu and S. T. Crooke, *Biochem. Biophys. Res. Commun.*, 1983, **116**, 1136.
24. S. Mong, H.-L. Wu, M. O. Scott, M. A. Lewis, M. A. Clark *et al.*, *J. Pharmacol. Exp. Ther.*, 1985, **234**, 316.
25. D. W. Snyder and R. D. Krell, *J. Pharmacol. Exp. Ther.*, 1984, **231**, 616.
26. J. G. Gleason, R. F. Hall, C. D. Perchonock, K. F. Erhard, J. S. Frazee, T. W. Ku, K. Kondrad, M. E. McCarthy, S. Mong, S. T. Crooke, G. Chi-Rosso, M. A. Wasserman, T. J. Torphy, R. M. Muccitelli, D. W. Hay, S. S. Tucker and L. Vickery-Clark, *J. Med. Chem.*, 1987, **30**, 959.
27. J. B. Cheng, D. Lang, A. Bewtra and R. G. Townley, *J. Pharmacol. Exp. Ther.*, 1985, **232**, 80.
28. L. Vickery, J. G. Gleason and M. A. Wasserman, *Pharmacologist*, 1986, **28**, 142.
29. D. W. Snyder, R. D. Krell, R. A. Keith, C. K. Buckner, R. E. Giles, Y. K. Yee, P. R. Bernstein, F. J. Brown and B. Hesp, *Pharmacologist*, 1986, **28**, 185.
30. R. C. Murphy, S. Hammerstrom and B. Samuelsson, *Proc. Natl. Acad. Sci. USA*, 1979, **76**, 4275.
31. R. A. Lewis, K. F. Austen, J. M. Drazen, D. A. Clarle, A. Marfat and E. J. Corey, *Proc. Natl. Acad. Sci. USA*, 1980, **77**, 3710.
32. D. W. Snyder, R. E. Giles, R. A. Keith, Y. F. Yee and R. D. Krell, *J. Pharmacol. Exp. Ther.*, 1987, **243**, 548.
33. S. E. Dahlen, P. Hedquist, S. Hammarstrom and B. Samuelsson, *Nature (London)*, 1980, **288**, 484.
34. C. J. Hanna, M. K. Bach, P. D. Pane and R. P. Schellenberg, *Nature (London)*, 1981, **290**, 343.
35. M. A. Lewis, S. Mong, R. L. Vesella, G. K. Hogaboom, H.-L. Wu and S. T. Crooke, *Prostaglandins*, 1984, **27**, 961.
36. B. P. O'Sullivan and S. Mong, *Mol. Pharmacol.*, in press.
37. S.-S. Pong, R. N. DeHaven, F. A. Kuehl and R. W. Egan, *J. Biol. Chem.*, 1983, **258**, 9616.
38. J. B. Cheng, D. Lang, A. Bewtra and R. G. Townley, *J. Pharmacol. Exp. Ther.*, 1985, **232**, 80.
39. R. A. Appleton, J. R. Bantick, T. R. Chamberlain, D. N. Hardern, T. B. Lee and A. D. Pratt, *J. Med. Chem.*, 1977, **20**, 371.
40. N. Chand, *Agents Actions*, 1979, **9** (2), 133.
41. B. Mead, L. H. Patterson and D. A. Smith, *J. Pharm. Pharmacol.*, 1981, **33**, 682.
42. P. Sheard, M. C. Holroyde, A. M. Ghelani, J. R. Bantick and T. B. Lee, 'Leukotrienes and Other Lipoxygenase Products', Raven Press, New York, 1982, p. 229.
43. D. R. Buckle, D. J. Outred, J. W. Ross, H. Smith, R. J. Smith, B. A. Spicer and B. C. Gasson, *J. Med. Chem.*, 1979, **22**, 158.
44. W. S. Marshall, T. Goodson, G. J. Cullinan, D. Swanson-Bean, K. D. Haisch, L. E. Rinkema and J. H. Fleisch, *J. Med. Chem.*, 1987, **30**, 682.
45. D. M. Gapinski, C. R. Roman, L. E. Rinkema and J. H. Fleisch, *J. Med. Chem.*, 1988, **31**, 172.
46. R. D. Dillard, F. P. Carr, D. McCullough, K. D. Haisch, L. E. Rinkema and J. H. Fleisch, *J. Med. Chem.*, 1987, **30**, 911.
47. F. J. Brown, P. R. Bernstein, L. A. Cronk, D. L. Dosset, K. C. Hebbel, T. P. Maduskuie, Jr. H. S. Shapiro, E. P. Vacek, Y. K. Yee, A. K. Willard, R. D. Krell and D. W. Snyder, *J. Med. Chem.*, 1989, **32**, 807.
48. R. A. Lewis, J. M. Drazen, K. F. Austen, M. Toda, F. Brion, A. Marfat and E. J. Corey, *Proc. Natl. Acad. Sci. USA*, 1981, **78**, 4579.
49. J. M. Drazen, R. A. Lewis, K. F. Austen, M. Toda, F. Brion, A. Marfat and E. J. Corey, *Proc. Natl. Acad. Sci. USA*, 1981, **78**, 3195.
50. S. Okuyama, S. Miyamoto, K. Shimoji, Y. Konishi, D. Fukushima, H. Niwa, Y. Arai, M. Toda and M. Hayaski, *Chem. Pharm. Bull.*, 1982, **30**, 2453.
51. J. G. Gleason, T. W. Ku, M. E. McCarthy, B. M. Weichman, D. Holden, R. R. Osborn, B. Zabko-Potapovich, B. Berkowitz and M. A. Wasserman, *Biochem. Biophys. Res. Commun.*, 1983, **117**, 732.
52. B. M. Weichman, M. A. Wasserman, D. A. Holden R. R. Osborn, D. F. Woodward, T. W. Ku and J. G. Gleason, *J. Pharmacol. Exp. Ther.*, 1983, **227**, 700.
53. T. W. Ku, M. E. McCarthy, B. M. Weichman and J. G. Gleason, *J. Med. Chem.*, 1985, **28**, 1847.
54. C. D. Perchonock, I. Uzinskas, T. W. Ku, M. E. McCarthy, W. E. Bondinell, B. W. Volpe and J. G. Gleason, *Prostaglandins*, 1985, **29**, 75.
55. C. D. Perchonock, M. E. McCarthy, K. F. Erhard, J. G. Gleason, M. A. Wasserman, R. M. Mutcitelli, J. F. Devan, S. S. Tucker, L. M. Vickery, T. Kirchner, B. M. Weichman, S. Mong, S. T. Crooke and J. F. Newton, *J. Med. Chem.*, 1985, **28**, 1145.
56. R. D. Eckardt, K. M. Straub, R. H. Dewey, T. B. Leonard, C. D. Perchonock, M. E. McCarthy, J. G. Gleason, R. K. Lynn and J. F. Newton, *Pharmacologist*, 1985, **27**, 249.
57. J. F. Newton, K. M. Straub, R. H. Dewey, C. D. Perchonock, T. B. Leonard, M. E. McCarthy, J. G. Gleason and R. D. Eckardt, *Drug Metab. Dispos.*, 1987, **15**, 161.
58. J. F. Newton, K. M. Straub, G. Y. Kuo, C. D. Perchonock, M. E. McCarthy, J. G. Gleason and R. K. Lynn, *Pharmacologist*, 1985, **27**, 756.
59. M. E. McCarthy, J. G. Gleason and R. K. Lynn, *Drug Metab. Dispos.*, 1987, **15**, 168.
60. R. K. Lynn, K. M. Straub, R. H. Dewey, C. D. Perchonock, M. E. McCarthy, J. G. Gleason and J. F. Newton, *Pharmacologist*, 1985, **27**, 755.
61. C. D. Perchonock, I. Uzinskas, M. E. McCarthy, K. F. Erhard, J. G. Gleason, M. A. Wasserman, R. M. Muccitelli, J. F. DeVan, S. S. Tucker, L. M. Vickery, T. Kirchner, B. M. Weichman, S. Mong, M. O. Scott, G. Chi-Rosso, H.-L. Wu, S. T. Crooke and J. F. Newton, *J. Med. Chem.*, 1986, **29**, 1442.
62. J. G. Gleason, R. F. Hall, C. D. Perchonock, K. F. Erhard, J. S. Frazee, T. W. Ku, K. Konrad, M. E. McCarthy, S. Mong,

S. T. Crooke, G. Chi-Rosso, M. A. Wasserman, T. J. Torphy, R. M. Muccitelli, D. W. Hay, S. S. Tucker and L. Vickery-Clark, *J. Med. Chem.*, 1987, **30**, 959.

63. P. R. Bernstein, E. P. Vacek, E. J. Adams, D. W. Snyder and R. D. Krell, *J. Med. Chem.*, 1988, **31**, 692.

64. A von Sprecher, W. Breltenstein, A. Beck, W. Anderson, M. A. Bray and F. Markl, *Adv. Prostaglandin, Thromboxane, Leukotriene Res.*, 1988, **18**, 647.

65. C. Anagnostopulos, W. Bartmann, G. Beck, P. Below, A. Bergmann, W. Linz, U. Schacht, B. A. Scholkens and G. Wess, *Biomed. Biochim. Acta*, 1988, **47** (10/11), S190.

66. A. Khandwala, S. Coutts, R. Van Inwegen and C. Sutherland, *Agents Actions*, 1985, **16**, 610.

67. R. G. Van Inwegen, G. Nuss, G. Schuessler, S. O'Rourke, J. Travis, D. Sweeney, J. Gricoski, D. Mertz, R. Galemmo, F. C. Hwang and G. Carnathan, *Pharmacologist*, 1988, **A205**, Abstr. 139.8.

68. J. H. Musser, D. M. Kubrak, J. Chang and A. J. Lewis, *J. Med. Chem.*, 1986, **29**, 1429.

69. J. M. Hand, J. H. Musser, A. F. Kreft, S. Schwalm, I. Englebach, M. Aven, M. Skowronele and Y. Chang, *Pharmacologist*, 1987, **29**, 368.

70. J. H. Musser, A. F. Kreft, R. H. Bender, D. M. Kubrak, R. P. Carlson, J. Chang and J. M. Hand, *J. Med. Chem.*, 1989, **32**, 1176.

71. J. H. Musser, *Drug News Perspective*, 1989, 202.

72. J. H. Musser, A. F. Kreft and A. J. Lewis, *Agents Actions*, 1986, **18**, 332.

73. J. H. Musser, D. M. Kubrak, R. H. W. Bender, A. F. Kreft, S. T. Nielsen, A. M. Lefer, J. Chang, A. J. Lewis and J. M. Hand, *J. Med. Chem.*, 1987, **30**, 2087.

74. I. Ahnfelt-Ronne, D. Kirstein and C. Kaergaard-Nielsen, *Eur. J. Pharmacol.*, 1988, **155**, 117.

75. T. Obata, N. Katsube, T. Niyamoto, M. Toda, T. Okegawa, H. Nakai, S. Kosuge, M. Konno, Y. Arai and A. Kawasaki, *Adv. Prostaglandin, Thromboxane, Leukotriene Res.*, 1985, **15**, 229.

76. M. Toda, H. Nakai, S. Kosuge, M. Konno, Y. Arai, T. Miyamoto, T. Obata, N. Katsube and A. Kawasaki, *Adv. Prostaglandin, Thromboxane, Leukotriene Res.*, 1985, **15**, 307.

77. H. Nakai, M. Konno, S. Kosuge, S. Sakuyama, M. Toda, Y. Arai, T. Obata, N. Katsube, T. Miyamoto, T. Okegawa and A. Kawasaki, *J. Med. Chem.*, 1988, **31**, 84.

78. D. W. Snyder, R. E. Giles, R. A. Keith, Y. K. Yee and R. D. Krell, *J. Pharmacol. Exp. Ther.*, 1987, **243**, 548.

79. F. J. Brown, V. G. Matassa, Y. K. Yee and P. R. Bernstein, *Abstr. 21st Natl. Med. Chem. Sym., 1988, Minneapolis, MN.*

80. C. Buckner, J. Fedyna, R. Krell, J. Robertson, R. Keith, V. Matassa, F. Brown, P. Bernstein, Y. Yee, J. Will, R. Fishleder, R. Saban, B. Hesp and R. Giles, *FASEB J.*, 1988, **2**, A1264 (Abstr.).

81. L. Charette, T. R. Jones, E. Champion, P. Masson, A. W. Ford-Hutchinson, R. Dehaven, S. S. Pong, M. Belley, R. Frenette, J. Y. Gauthier, J. Rolrach, H. Williams, R. N. Young and R. Zamboni, *FASEB J.*, 1988, **2**, A1264 (Abstr.).

82. P. Masson, T. R. Jones, L. Charette, E. Champion, C. S. McFarlane, H. Piechuta, A. W. Ford-Hutchinson, M. Belley, R. Dehaven, R. Fernette, J. Y. Gauthier, S. Leger, S. S. Pong, J. Rolkach, H. Williams, R. N. Young and R. Zamboni, *FASEB J.*, 1988, **2**, A1265 (Abstr.).

83. R. N. Young, *Adv. Prostaglandin, Thromboxane, Leukotriene Res.*, 1989, **19**, 643.

84. P. Borgeat and B. Samuelsson, *Proc. Natl. Acad. Sci. USA*, 1979, **76**, 2148.

85. E. J. Corey, A. Marfat, G. Goto and F. Brion, *J. Am. Chem. Soc.*, 1980, **102**, 7984.

86. A. W. Ford-Hutchinson, M. A. Bray, M. V. Doig, M. E. Shipley and M. J. H. Smith, *Nature (London)*, 1980, **286**, 264.

87. A. W. Ford-Hutchinson, M. A. Bray, F. M. Cunningham, E. M. Davidson and M. J. H. Smith, *Prostaglandins*, 1980, **21**, 143.

88. R. M. J. Palmer, R. J. Stepney, G. A. Higgs and K. E. Eakins, *Prostaglandins*, 1980, **20**, 411.

89. E. J. Goetzl and W. C. Pickett, *J. Immunol.*, 1980, **125**, 1789.

90. H. J. Showell, P. H. Naccache, P. Borgeat, S. Picard, P. Vallerand, E. L. Becker and R. I. Sha'afi, *J. Immunol.*, 1982, **128**, 811.

91. E. J. Goetzl, *N. Engl. J. Med.*, 1980, **303**, 822.

92. D. W. Goldman and E. J. Goetzl, *J. Immunol.*, 1982, **129**, 1600.

93. R. A. Kreisle and C. W. Parker, *J. Exp. Med.*, 1983, **157**, 628.

94. D. W. Goldman and E. J. Goetzl, *J. Exp. Med.*, 1984, **159**, 1027.

95. E. J. Goetzl, J. W. Shermann, W. D. Ratnoff, J. P. Harvey, E. Eriksson, W. E. Seaman, L. Baud and C. H. Koo, *Ann. N.Y. Acad. Sci.*, 1988, **524**, 345.

96. D. W. Goldman, L. A. Gifford, D. M. Olson and E. J. Goetzl, *J. Immunol.*, 1985, **135**, 525.

97. J. Palmblad, H. Gyllenhammer, J. A. Lindgren and C. L. Malmsten, *J. Immunol.*, 1984, **132**, 3041.

98. C. H. Koo, J. W. Sherman, L. Baud and E. Goetzl, *Adv. Prostaglandin, Thromboxane, Leukotriene Res.*, 1989, **19**, 191.

99. A. H. Linn, J. Morris, D. G. Wishka and R. R. Gorman, *Ann. N.Y. Acad. Sci.*, 1988, **524**, 196.

100. D. Goldman, D. Olson, L. Gifford and E. Goetzl, *Fed. Proc., Fed. Am. Soc. Exp. Biol.*, 1985, **44**, 736, Abstr. 1898.

101. K. F. Austen and R. J. Soberman, *Ann. N.Y. Acad. Sci.*, 1988, **524**, 11.

102. S. Brain, R. Camp, P. Dowd, A. K. Black and M. Greaves, *J. Invest. Dermatol.*, 1984, **83**, 70.

103. L. B. Klickstein, C. Sharpleigh and E. J. Goetzl, *J. Clin. Invest.*, 1980, **66**, 1166.

104. E. M. Davidson, S. A. Rae and M. J. H. Smith, *Ann. Rheum. Dis.*, 1983, **42**, 677.

105. N. A. Soter, R. A. Lewis, E. J. Corey and K. F. Austen, *J. Invest. Dermatol.*, 1983, **80**, 115.

106. H. Z. Movat, C. Rettl, C. E. Burrowes and M. G. Johnston, *Am. J. Pathol.*, 1984, **115**, 233.

107. M. A. Bray, A. W. Ford-Hutchinson and J. H. Smith, *Prostaglandins*, 1981, **22**, 213.

108. B. R. Allen and S. M. Littlewood, *Br. Med. J.*, 1982, **285**, 1241.

109. V. Kassis, *IRCS Med. Sci.*, 1985, **13**, 182.

110. S. Thorsen, *Scand. J. Rheumatol.*, 1986, **15**, 225.

111. R. M. McMillan and S. J. Foster, *Agents Actions*, 1988, **24**, 114.

112. D. G. Payan, A. Missirian-Bastian and E. J. Goetzl, *Proc. Natl. Acad. Sci. USA*, 1984, **81**, 3501.

113. P. M. O'Bryne, G. D. Leikauf, H. Aizawa, R. A. Bethel, I. F. Ueki, M. J. Holtzman and J. A. Nadel, *J. Appl. Physiol.*, 1985, **59**, 1941.

114. J. Y. Westcott, K. R. Stenmark and R. C. Murphy, *Prostaglandins*, 1986, **31**, 227.

115. S. A. Silbaugh, P. W. Stengel, G. D. Williams, D. K. Herron, P. Gallagher and S. R. Baker, *Am. Rev. Respir. Dis.*, 1987, **136**, 930.

116. N. Taniguchi, G. Mita, H. Saito, Y. Yuo, T. Kajita and T. Shida, *Allergy*, 1985, **40**, 571.
117. R. J. Shaw, D. Cromwell and A. B. Kay, *Clin. Exp. Immunol.*, 1984, **56**, 716.
118. P. Sharon and W. F. Stenson, *Gastroenterology*, 1984, **86**, 453.
119. E. A. Lobos, P. Sharon and W. F. Stenson, *Dig. Dis. Sci.*, 1987, **32**, 1380.
120. S. A. Rae, E. M. Davidson and M. J. H. Smith, *Lancet*, 1982, **2**, 1122.
121. K. M. Mullane, *Adv. Inflam. Res.*, 1988, **12**, 191.
122. S. M. Spaethe and P. Needleman, in 'Cellular and Molecular Aspects of Inflammation', ed. G. Poste and S. T. Crooke, Plenum Press, New York, 1988, p. 153.
123. K. M. Mullane, W. Westlin and R. Kraemer, *Ann. N.Y. Acad. Sci.*, 1988, **524**, 103.
124. M. Sugiura, H. Beierbeck, P. C. Belanger and G. Kotovych, *J. Am. Chem. Soc.*, 1984, **106**, 4021.
125. R. A. Lewis, E. J. Goetzl, J. M. Drazen, N. A. Soter, K. F. Austen and E. J. Corey, *J. Exp. Med.*, 1981, **154**, 1243.
126. S. T. Hoffstein, R. M. Manzi, K. A. Razgaitis, P. E. Bender and J. Gleason, *Prostaglandins*, 1986, **31**, 205.
127. S. Charleson, J. F. Evans, R. J. Zamboni, Y. Leblanc, B. J. Fitzsimmons, C. Leveille, P. D. Dupuis and A. W. Ford-Hutchinson, *Prostaglandins*, 1986, **32**, 503.
128. Y. Leblanc, B. J. Fitzsimmons, S. Charleson, P. Alexander, J. F. Evans and J. Rokach, *Prostaglandins*, 1987, **33**, 617.
129. H. J. Showell, I. G. Otterness, A. Marfat and E. J. Corey, *Biochem. Biophys. Res. Commun.*, 1982, **106**, 741.
130. M. Namiki, Y. Igarashi, K. Sakamoto, T. Nakamura and Y. Koga, *Biochem. Biophys. Res. Commun.*, 1986, **138**, 540.
131. M. Furber, R. J. K. Taylor and S. C. Burford, *J. Chem. Soc., Perkin Trans. 1*, 1987, 1573.
132. J. Morris and D. G. Wishka, *Tetrahedron Lett.*, 1988, **29**, 143.
133. M. M. Morrissey, M. F. Jarvis, C. Angst, A. J. Hutchinson, R. H. Jackson, B. Selgman, J. Wasvary, R. M. Ludewig and C. T. Healy, *FASEB J.*, 1989, **3**, A594, Abstr. 2139.
134. S. W. Djuric, R. I. Shone and S. S. T. Yu, *Eur. Pat.* 292 977 (1987) (*Chem. Abstr.*, 1988, **110**, 173 088c).
135. D. Fretland, S. Levin, B. Tsai, S. Djuric, D. L. Widomski, J. M. Zemaitis, R. L. Shone and R. F. Bauer, *Agents Actions*, 1989, **27**, 395.
136. S. W. Djuric, P. W. Collins, P. H. Jones, R. L. Shone, B. S. Tsai, D. J. Fretland, G. M. Butchko, D. Villani-Price, R. H. Keith, J. M. Zemaitis, L. Metcalf and R. F. Bauer, *J. Med. Chem.*, 1989, **32**, 1147.
137. T. S. Gaginella, A. F. Welton and P. G. Will, *Eur. Pat.* 256 532 (1986) (*Chem. Abstr.*, 1988, **110**, 199 191f).
138. P. Will, W. Allbee, T. Gaginella, A. Welton, L. Iverson, W. Weis, G. Roberts, P. Conzentino and J. Edgcomb, *4th Intl. Conf. Inflammation Res. Assoc.*, 1988, 59.
139. D. M. Gapinski, B. E. Mallet, L. L. Froelich, R. J. Boyd and W. T. Jackson, *FASEB J.*, 1988, **2**, A1110, Abstr. 4728.
140. D. K. Herron, N. G. Bollinger, D. Swanson-Bean, W. T. Jackson, L. L. Froelich and T. Goodson, *FASEB J.*, 1988, **2**, A1110, Abstr. 4729.
141. W. T. Jackson, R. J. Boyd, L. L. Froelich, T. Goodson, N. G. Bollinger, D. K. Herron, B. E. Mallet and D. M. Gapinski, *FASEB J.*, 1988, **2**, A1110, Abstr. 4730.
142. A. Taylor, A. Gasic, T. Kitt, S. Shappell, J. Rui, M. Lenz, C. W. Smith and J. Mitchell, *Clin. Res.*, 1989, **37**, A528 (Abstr.).
143. M. F. Jarvis, R. H. Jackson, C. T. Healy, R. M. Ludewig, A. J. Hutchinson, R. A. Fujimoto and M. M. Morrissey, *FASEB J.*, 1989, **3**, A594, Abstr. 2141.
144. D. M. Gapinski, *Eur. Pat.* 276 064 (1988) (*Chem. Abstr.*, 1988, **110**, 94 687u).
145. T. Cornbleet, *Arch. Dermatol.*, 1951, **64**, 684.
146. I. B. Sneddon and D. S. Wilkinson, *Br. J. Dermatol.*, 1956, **68**, 385.
147. A. L. MacMillan and R. H. Champion, *Br. J. Dermatol.*, 1973, **88**, 183.
148. K. Williams, R. B. Capstick, D. A. Lewis and R. Best, *J. Pharm. Pharmacol.*, 1976, **28**, 555.
149. M. Ward and J. P. A. McManns, *Lancet*, 1975, **1**, 1236.
150. A. J. Lewis, D. K. Gemmell and W. H. Stimson, *Agents Actions*, 1978, **8**, 578.
151. O. Stendahl, L. Molin and C. Dahlgren, *J. Clin. Invest.*, 1978, **62**, 214.
152. B. L. Maloff, D. Fox, E. Bruin and T. M. DiMeo, *Eur. J. Pharmacol.*, 1988, **158**, 85.
153. B. S. Tsai, R. H. Keith, D. Villani-Price, R. A. Haack, R. F. Bauer, R. Leonard, Y. Abe and K. C. Nicolaou, *Prostaglandins*, 1989, **37**, 287.

13.1

Design of Drugs Acting at Peptidergic Receptors

VICTOR J. HRUBY

University of Arizona, Tucson, AZ, USA

13.1.1 INTRODUCTION

It has been increasingly recognized that peptide ligands constitute one of the potentially most useful classes of compounds as selective, nontoxic and potent drugs. There are several reasons for this optimistic outlook. First, and most importantly, it has become evident that peptides and proteins constitute the most numerous and important messengers of intercellular and perhaps even intracellular communication. In highly complex multicellular systems such as animals, including man, rapid, specific and complex intracellular communication is essential for the ability of that system to respond to changes in its environment. Second, in contrast to many of the drugs currently used for the treatment of disease but which are highly or moderately toxic, peptides and peptide analogues are generally much less toxic *per se*. The reasons for this are not clear, but it should be pointed out that many current drugs are based on plant-derived natural products such as terpenes, alkaloids, a variety of heterocycles, *etc.* In general, higher life forms have chosen, with important exceptions, not to use these compounds for intercellular and intracellular communication, though they had ample opportunity in their diet to do so. There perhaps is a good reason for this, namely that these compounds are generally toxic to eukaryotic cells. Third, though many peptide hormones and neurotransmitters are rapidly biodegradeable and designed to be so since they often serve as biological switches, it has become apparent that this is not a necessary property of peptide hormone and neurotransmitter analogues. Indeed it is now clear from our work and that of others that the

797

most promising methods of peptide design using conformational constraints often, perhaps even generally, lead to compounds which are resistant to biodegradation by the proteases found in the circulation, the central nervous system, and even the liver and kidney. Fourth, past design approaches generally utilized structure–biological activity analysis which had several limitations. On the biological side, *in vitro* binding assays and biochemical assays often were not available, making it difficult to examine the early events related to biological activity in quantitative terms and to obtain insights into such important effects as partial agonism which, for example, can often provide leads for the development of antagonists. In addition, most peptide hormones and neurotransmitters interact with multiple receptor subtypes and thus it is necessary to do multiple bioassays to obtain insight into those aspects of structure, conformation and dynamics that are important at each receptor subtype. Such assays have been developed for many peptide hormones and neuropeptides, and continued rapid developments can be expected. On the structural side, most early studies involved simple replacement of one or more amino acid residues with other common amino acid residues. These studies are needed to provide insights into the importance of specific amino acid residues, specific functional groups of a particular amino acid residue and specific stereostructural relationships in the peptide to biological activity. However, in most cases, these studies do not provide critical insights into the conformational requirements for bioactivity because high flexibility is still present. More recently it has become evident that conformational constraints can be introduced which are compatible with general peptide and protein structural properties and which take into account the specific requirements of that peptide's interaction with one or more of its specific receptors. Appropriately constrained analogues can be examined for their conformational and dynamic properties to provide new insights into a proposed 'biologically active' conformation. The validity of such a model can then be tested by specific structural and conformational modifications. In this regard, it has become evident that the overall topographical properties rather than specific conformational properties are the most critical in determining biological properties.

In this discussion we will emphasize the requirement that any rational approach to peptide design for receptors must include an integrated multidisciplinary approach involving organic synthetic and structural chemistry, physical chemistry and biophysics, and detailed quantitative biological activity studies.

13.1.2 BIOLOGICAL CONSIDERATIONS

13.1.2.1 Multiple Receptors

Most peptide hormones and neurotransmitters appear to interact with a variety of receptors on different cell types in complex animals including man. In some cases several of these receptor types or subtypes exist in which the binding interactions of the endogenous peptide ligand with the receptor(s) are within one or two orders of magnitude. Generally it is still unclear whether these different receptors are derived from different genes and hence have completely unrelated protein sequences, or whether they are identical or closely related proteins which differ in ligand specificity due to post-transcriptional modification in the different cell types. If the ligand–receptor interactions are of high affinity and satisfy other criteria, such receptor subtypes are generally considered as 'physiologically significant'. However, many other cases exist in which bioassays have demonstrated biological activities, but only with ligand concentrations 1000 times or greater than those at the high affinity receptors. Often these interactions are ignored and/or said to be of no 'physiological (pharmacological) significance'. In our view this is incorrect thinking. Indeed we believe that such weakly interacting systems can serve as a starting point for the design of receptor selective peptide ligands. In fact, we have found it possible to design somatostatin analogues which interact with μ opioid receptors in the nanomolar range and are highly selective for these receptors both *in vitro* and *in vivo* (5000-fold or greater *versus* δ or κ opioid receptors),[1-3] but which virtually do not interact with the somatostatin receptors. Thus we have converted a somatostatin peptide into a highly selective and potent opioid peptide. We believe this approach has general validity.

It is critically important in the design of peptide receptor ligands that we utilize to the fullest multiple quantitative biological assay systems (for discussions see refs. 4–7).

13.1.2.2 *In Vitro* Bioassays

In vitro bioassays are generally the most useful for ligand design because they can more readily provide specific quantitative data. For example, if one is trying to develop a receptor specific ligand it will be necessary to have a specific assay for the receptor in question, and other specific assays for the other receptors for which one wishes to greatly diminish or eliminate bioactivity. Such bioassays can take a number of specific forms among which the generally most useful are ligand specific binding assays (radiolabeled ligands are needed); biochemically related bioassays, which include measurement of metabolites, metabolic conversion (*e.g.* specific enzymes such as adenylate cyclase), ion fluxes, tissue contractions or relaxations, *etc.* These assays can provide quantitative data for evaluation of either relative affinity or relative activity for both agonists and antagonists. It should be stressed that, often, complete evaluation of ligands which are 1000 or even 100 000 times less potent than the native peptide or some potent analogue is especially needed for good design work. This must be stressed because pharmacologists seem reluctant to perform assays on such 'inactive' ligands. Yet, it is precisely because they differ in binding energy interactions by 5 kcal mol^{-1} (1 kcal = 4.18 kJ) or more from the native peptide ligand that one can reach rational decisions regarding further design. Factors of tenfold or less in potency (unless they can be demonstrated to be due to specific conformational, structural or dynamic changes) often are not useful for further design because changes of 1 to 2 kcal mol^{-1} in interaction energies with a receptor generally cannot be precisely interpreted because of the large number of possible ways to account for the results.

In vitro bioassays generally are essential for the development of peptide receptor antagonists. This is so because the first clues for the development of antagonists usually come from recognizing partial agonist/antagonist activity in analogues, and such analogues generally are full agonists *in vivo*. Full dose–response curves can provide insight into those structural, conformational, or dynamic changes which dissociate the binding elements from those important for transduction.[4, 6, 7]

13.1.2.3 *In Vivo* Bioassays

It is always important to have information on the *in vivo* activity of analogues. For one thing, *in vitro* and *in vivo* bioactivities often are not identical. Several factors can be invoked to explain this including: (i) differences in bioavailability due to differences in tissue distribution *in vivo* that are not seen in *in vitro* assays; (ii) differences in enzymatic degradation—often rates of biodegradation *in vitro* and *in vivo* are quite different and hence local concentrations at receptors can modulate biological potency; (iii) only minor occupation of receptor systems *in vivo* can activate a full biological response because many transduction mechanisms greatly amplify the initial peptide–receptor interaction; and (iv) for reasons not generally explained as yet, compounds which appear to be clean antagonists *in vitro* can sometimes have agonist activity *in vivo*.

Finally, it should be emphasized that frequently one sees large differences in both *in vitro* and *in vivo* biological activity from different animal species. Thus one must be careful to interpret structure–function results in the context of a particular species and compare interspecies results with care.

13.1.3 BIOPHYSICAL CONSIDERATIONS

13.1.3.1 Structural Studies

In general, development of a rational design strategy for peptide hormone and neurotransmitter ligands requires knowledge of the conformational structure and dynamic properties of a ligand, and some model of the relationship(s) of these properties to the biological activities. To obtain insight into conformational and dynamic properties requires application of modern biophysical methods. A book has recently appeared which discusses the most important methods which are currently used for peptides.[8] Here we will briefly outline some of the information that, in principle, is available for examination by these methods.

13.1.3.2 Structural Modifications

Replacement of one amino acid residue by another in most peptide hormones and neurotransmitters can only provide information about the relative importance of the side chain functional groups to receptor interaction since in general the analogue will remain conformationally flexible.

Exceptions to this include proline substitution for any other standard eukaryotic amino acid since N-substituted amino acids such as proline occupy somewhat different conformational space (ϕ, ψ angles). D-Amino acids provide special opportunities because in addition to the change in relationships of the side chain group of this residue to other nearby side chain groups, D-amino acid residues can stabilize β-turn structures. In some cases these effects can be examined by changes in NMR chemical shift parameters due to the anisotropic effects of some side chain groups or by changes in CD curves due to changes in helical or reverse turn content. In other cases, fluorescence, Raman, or ESR spectroscopy can be used to monitor the conformational changes which have resulted. Use of α-substituted amino acids such as α-aminoisobutyric acid (Aib) greatly limits the conformational space available to that amino acid residue in the α-helical (and $^3 10$ helical) region of conformational space. This, of course, can be used to examine whether such a local conformational effect is compatible with potent peptide–receptor interaction. However, the extent to which a local constraint affects more global conformational properties has not been studied in much detail, but could in principle be examined by CD and NMR methods. X-Ray crystallography can provide precise information about the conformational properties in the crystalline state, but the extent to which that will be generally useful is limited because most peptide hormones and neurotransmitters have not been crystallized. In the few cases where crystalline peptides of small linear biologically active peptides have been obtained, such as the enkephalins, it is not clear whether the conformations in the crystalline state are biologically relevant.

Specific amino acid replacements can be made which can increase α-helical, β-sheet, or β-turn structure. If these are done in a structurally conservative manner, it sometimes is possible to demonstrate that such conformational features are of biological significance,[9] and to utilize biophysical measurements such as CD and NMR spectroscopy to obtain corroborating evidence. Alternatively, generalized α-helical sequences can sometimes be utilized to demonstrate their importance in a nonspecific manner for the biological activity of the peptide,[10] and again CD spectroscopy can be utilized to demonstrate that the designed secondary structure is present.

13.1.3.3 Conformational Studies

As discussed above, α-helical structure and also β-sheet structure and to a lesser extent β-turn conformations can be examined by using CD spectroscopy. The most powerful method for examining conformational properties in solution is NMR. The presence of a medium-sized ring (10- to 20-membered) in a peptide structure, with additional constraints, can be particularly useful in providing specific conformational features to a peptide. Use of two-dimensional NMR methods, especially COSY and NOESY experiments in their several variations, can be particularly useful, and other biophysical methods such as IR, Raman, fluorescence and other spectroscopic methods are valuable as well.

13.1.3.4 Topographical Studies

From the standpoint of understanding peptide ligand–receptor interactions, it will be necessary not only to determine and design secondary structural features, but also to define and determine topographical features, that is the three-dimensional relationships of side chain groups. Several methods for examining side chain conformations have been utilized since the earliest days, but only recently have efforts been made to design topographic features by strongly biasing side chain conformations. To determine such conformational features, including dihedral angles, only precise structure determination methods such as X-ray crystallography and NMR spectroscopy will be adequate.

13.1.3.5 Dynamic Considerations

It is now abundantly clear that even constrained peptides, as well as folded proteins with well-defined secondary and tertiary structures, still possess considerable dynamic flexibility. Thus dynamic behavior becomes an important consideration in analogue design. Physical methods for examining dynamic properties include NMR spectroscopy, time-resolved Raman spectroscopy, *etc.* In addition, molecular dynamics simulations and quenched molecular dynamics calculations can be utilized.

13.1.4 DESIGN APPROACHES

13.1.4.1 Structural Modifications

The classical approach to peptide structure–function analysis has involved single or multiple substitution of amino acid residues for other 'normal' amino acid residues. Though there are severe limitations of such studies for rational design, they are generally needed to gain insight into those amino acid residues which are critical for the biological activity, and, in addition, certain systematic studies can provide needed insights.

For a peptide for which little structure–biological activity is available, one can replace each amino acid residue, one at a time, with its D enantiomer: Gly can be replaced with D- and L-alanine and D- and L-phenylalanine to determine whether the pro-*R* or pro-*S* face of the residue might be important for interaction with the receptor(s) under study. Proline can be replaced with *N*-methylglycine. Truncated analogues in which one amino acid residue at a time is deleted from the N terminal or the C terminal end can provide useful insights as to whether partial sequences are sufficient for full biological activity. Often, conversion of C terminal carboxylate groups to carboxamide groups or *vice versa* and/or acetylation of the N terminal residue can provide critical structural insights. If a disulfide bond exists, conversion to carba analogues and/or replacement of each Cys residue with either α-aminobutyric acid (Abu), alanine or *S*-methylcysteine can provide insight into the requirement for the ring structure for bioactivity.

There are a number of simple structural modifications which have proven to be of general use. Pseudoisosteric replacements, though often possessing quite different electronic, acid/base or polar character, are most useful. Examples in this category include norleucine (Nle) for Met or Orn; Val and Thr for each other; Glu for Gln; Asp for Asn and Leu; His for Phe. In many peptide hormone and neurotransmitter analogues it has been found that increased lipophilicity can lead to increased potency. Thus amino acid residues with polar side chain groups are replaced with residues that are isosteric or pseudoisosteric, but lipophilic. Successful approaches have included amino acid residue replacements in which functional groups have been formally replaced by methyl groups, alcohols have been converted to ethers, acid groups to esters and amides, basic groups alkylated, *etc.* When aromatic residues are found to be important for bioactivity, which seems to be the case for most peptide hormones and neurotransmitters, several approaches have proven useful. For Tyr residues *O*-alkylated and *O*-substituted derivatives (OH, Cl, Br, I, F, NO$_2$, *etc.*) and for Phe residues, *p*-substituted analogues (Me, OR, R, Cl, Br, I, F, NO$_2$ and CN) have been the most widely used. Trp can be *N*-formylated and His can be *N*-alkylated. In addition, aromatic residues can be replaced with bulky aliphatic amino acid residues, such as adamantylalanine. Finally, amide bond replacements also can provide important insights into peptide structure–function.[12]

Many other suggestions could be made, but it should be emphasized that most do not provide much insight for rational design of new analogues because the general flexibility of the peptide limits insights into the topographical reason for the change in activity. Hence the need for conformational constraints becomes urgent early in the process of structure–function analysis.

13.1.4.2 Conformational Constraints

The use of conformational constraints to obtain more conformationally defined peptide analogues has led to the most successful rational approach to peptide ligand design thus far.[6, 7, 13–19] Though the approach is still relatively new, there are a number of general principles which are emerging.

Let us first consider peptide hormones or neurotransmitters that already have cyclic structures. Oxytocin is the classical compound here, as it contains a 20-membered disulfide-containing ring (H-Cys-Tyr-Ile-Gln-Asn-Cys-Pro-Leu-Gly-NH$_2$). Early studies demonstrated that efforts to decrease (or increase) ring size led to large decreases in potency.[20] Though it is possible to constrain cyclic peptides further in some cases (for example see somatostatin later[21, 22]), generally it is found that there is an optimal ring size for a peptide's biological potency and large decreases in potency occur if the ring size is increased or decreased by even one carbon atom or one sulfur atom. Thus if one does have a cyclic peptide which is active, the optimum ring size for maximum potency should be sought. From the standpoint of conformational constraint, medium-sized rings (10- to 20-

membered) generally will have the greatest reduction in flexibility, but the degree of remaining flexibility will very much depend on other structural features which may further stabilize conformation, such as intramolecular hydrogen bonding and van der Waal stabilization by side chain–side chain interactions. An example of the former appears to be important in the case of somatostatin analogues,[22] and of the latter in the case of [D-Pen^2,D-Pen^5]enkephalin, the potent δ opioid receptor selective peptide.[23] In medium-sized rings containing a disulfide bridge, the replacement of one or both of the Cys residues with penicillamine (—SCMe$_2$CH(NH)CO—; Pen) often has turned out to be an effective way to help further conformationally constrain the analogue and at the same time accentuate desirable biological activities. Examples where this has proven to be effective include [Pen^1]oxytocin, [Pen$^{7(11)}$]somatostatin analogues, [D-Pen^2, D(L)-Pen^5]enkephalin, and [Pen^1]vasopressin analogues. The conformational constraints involve both local constraints on the disulfide moiety (C—S—S—C angle $\geqslant 110°$) and transannular effects due to the geminal dimethyl effect in medium-sized rings.[24-26]

In the case of somatostatin, it was possible to take a 38-membered disulfide-containing ring and reduce that ring to a 20-membered ring with retention of full biological potency.[21,22] Indeed, eventually it was possible to make a cyclic hexapeptide (18-membered ring) with high potency, though little receptor selectivity. In addition to cyclic disulfide rings, recently considerable success has been obtained making cyclic lactam rings by side chain to side chain cyclizations[15] and by side chain to backbone cyclization.[27] Thus far, examples from the enkephalins,[15] bradykinins[27] and melanotropins[28] among others have appeared. To obtain success in this approach: (i) the new or modified ring must be compatible with the overall conformational and structural features required at the receptor; (ii) key residues and functional groups for ligand–receptor interaction must not be modified greatly; (iii) if the analogue is an agonist, dynamic and conformational features necessary for both receptor recognition and transduction must be maintained. This requires, therefore, a careful analysis of all pertinent structure–function data so that insights into the appropriate locations along the sequence for further conformational constraint can be made. These considerations are particularly important for peptide mimetic design since many standard organic structures are not compatible with peptide and protein conformation.

All of the above considerations, plus others, must be utilized in developing rational approaches to conformational constraints with linear peptide ligands. A major goal in conformational constraints is to segregate information on particular surfaces of the constrained ligand. It has been observed in past successes with conformational constraints that the analogues develop distinct segregation of lipophilic and hydrophilic surfaces much as an amphiphilic helix does in peptide or protein folding. Indeed this segregation of information may be a general feature important to peptide hormone and neurotransmitter ligand–receptor interactions. Thus it is important to look for low energy conformations in which such segregation occurs. This probably will be critical in the design of peptide mimetics as well.

13.1.4.3 Topographical Modifications

Rational design of ligands for peptidergic receptors will inevitably require that, in addition to design of conformational features (helical structures, reverse turn, loops, *etc.*) important for receptor interactions, it will be necessary to develop approaches to design specific topographic structures (the cooperative, three-dimensional relationships of side chain groups) as well. To some extent, conformational constraints which limit topographical structural properties, such as was the case for [Pen1]oxytocin,[24,25] other oxytocin antagonist analogues,[25,26] DPDPE,[23] and μ opioid receptor specific cyclic octapeptides,[29] provided some insights into the topographical requirements for ligand–receptor interaction. However, design requires that specific topographical features can be 'imposed' on the overall conformation by specific biasing of side chain conformations to *gauche*($-$), *gauche*($+$) or *trans* conformations. In fact, we believe that this can be done in ways that are compatible with normal protein structure in general, and potent peptide ligand–receptor interactions in particular. We already have demonstrated, in fact, that specific biasing to one of these side conformations can be accomplished using tetrahydroisoquinolinecarboxylate (Tic) residues[29,30] and β-methyl aromatic amino acid residues.[31] In fact, we anticipate that once a stable conformational template is available which is compatible with strong interactions at a particular receptor or group of receptors, it will be possible to design specific topographical surfaces on to the template to explore the topographical requirement for ligand–receptor interactions adding one more level of rational design of peptide ligand–receptor interactions. Such studies are in progress in our laboratory.

13.1.5 CONCLUSIONS AND FUTURE PERSPECTIVES

Efforts to develop rational approaches to peptide ligand design have begun to reach a level of development where generally successful strategies are possible. In the case of development of potent and receptor selective agonists, careful structure–function analysis, followed by use of conformational constraints, especially *via* stabilization of secondary structure important to bioactivity, and *via* covalent, pseudoisosteric cyclization, have been successful. Generally success will be accelerated by considerations of the likely conformational consequences of specific structural modifications, especially when they lead to large (greater than 100-fold) changes in biological potency and/or selectivity. Hence there is a need for excellent biological assays and for good knowledge of peptide and protein structural chemistry. Once a stable conformational template is obtained that is compatible with the receptor of interest, it is becoming possible to design specific topographical properties into a peptide and thereby further increase the specificity and potency of a ligand.

For the development of potent, receptor selective antagonist analogues, one needs a lead, since, in general, antagonist structure–activity does not parallel agonist structure–activity. This appears to be the case because agonists and antagonists interact with receptors differently and thus use different structural, conformational and topographical properties of the peptide. Though often there is some overlap, the structural regions of overlap can only be defined after the fact. Once a lead is found, however, the general rational design approach to conformation–biological activity relationships are essentially identical for both agonists and antagonists. However, one caveat is very important here, namely that antagonist activity in *in vitro* assays may not carry over to the more complex *in vivo* systems.

Further progress in developing a rational approach to peptide ligand design will depend significantly on developments in synthetic methods for conformationally constrained amino acids and peptides. There is clearly a need for developing peptides or peptidomimetics that 'fix' peptide conformations to specific conformations, and yet are completely compatible with peptide and protein structure. Similarly, the need for special amino acids with two, three or more asymmetric centers that can fix or bias topographical relationships is evident. Finally, and perhaps this is most critical for the synthetic chemist involved in peptide ligand design, there is a need to simultaneously develop a much more interdisciplinary approach to the subject. First, successful design will require interaction with state of the art biology. Thus, close detailed interactions with pharmacologists, physiologists, cell biologists, *etc.* are essential. Second, it appears that many chemists with outstanding synthetic skills are woefully weak in their understanding of peptide and protein conformation and dynamics. Without a proper knowledge and appreciation of protein structural chemistry, progress will be slow and the kind of intuitive insights into conformation–biological activity relationships that are, and will remain, critical will not be obtained. Fortunately, modern molecular-modeling, molecular mechanics and molecular dynamics approaches are available and can greatly accelerate the learning process.

ACKNOWLEDGEMENTS

Work in my laboratory has been supported by grants from the National Science Foundation and the US Public Health Service. The author especially wishes to thank his students and postdoctoral associates whose creativity and hard work have contributed so much to the progress we have made. A special thanks goes to his biological collaborators without whom this work could not have been done.

13.1.6 REFERENCES

1. J. T. Pelton, W. Kazmierski, K. Gulya, H. I. Yamamura and V. J. Hruby, *J. Med. Chem.*, 1986, **29**, 2307.
2. J. T. Pelton, K. Gulya, V. J. Hruby, S. P. Duckles and H. I. Yamamura, *Proc. Natl. Acad. Sci. USA*, 1986, **82**, 236.
3. J. E. Shook, J. T. Pelton, P. F. Lemcke, F. Porreca, V. J. Hruby and T. F. Burks, *J. Pharmacol. Exp. Ther.*, 1987, **242**, 1.
4. J. Rudinger, in 'Drug Design', ed. J. Arians, Academic Press, New York, 1971, vol. 2, p. 319.
5. R. Schwyzer, *Ann. N. Y. Acad. Sci.*, 1977, **297**, 3.
6. V. J. Hruby, *Top. Mol. Pharmacol.*, 1981, 99.
7. V. J. Hruby, in 'Design and Synthesis of Organic Molecules Based on Molecular Recognition', ed. G. van Binst, Springer-Verlag, Berlin, 1986, p. 269.
8. V. J. Hruby (ed.), 'The Peptides. Analysis, Synthesis, Biology', Academic Press, New York, 1985, vol. 7.
9. J. Krsetenansky, D. Trivedi, D. Johnson and V. J. Hruby, *J. Am. Chem. Soc.*, 1986, **108**, 1696.
10. J. W. Taylor, D. G. Osterman, R. J. Miller and E. T. Kaiser, *J. Am. Chem. Soc.*, 1981, **103**, 6965.

11. For a review see V. J. Hruby, in 'Chemistry and Biochemistry of Amino Acids, Peptides and Proteins', ed. B. Weinstein, Dekker, New York, 1974, vol. 3, p. 1.
12. A. F. Spatola, in 'Chemistry and Biochemistry of Amino Acids, Peptides and Proteins', ed. B. Weinstein, Dekker, New York, 1983, vol. 8.
13. G. R. Marshall, F. A. Gorin and M. L. Moore, *Annu. Rep. Med. Chem.*, 1978, **13**, 227.
14. D. Veber, in 'Peptides: Structure and Biological Function', ed. E. Gross and J. Meienhofer, Pierce Chemical Co., Rockford, IL, 1979, p. 409.
15. P. Schiller, in 'Peptides: Structure and Function', ed. V. J. Hruby and D. H. Rich, Pierce Chemical Co., Rockford, IL, 1983, p. 269.
16. V. J. Hruby, *Life Sci.*, 1982, **31**, 189.
17. V. J. Hruby and H. I. Mosberg, *Peptides*, 1982, **3**, 329.
18. V. J. Hruby, *ACS Monograph Ser.*, 1984, **251**, 9.
19. H. Kessler, *Angew. Chem., Int. Ed. Engl.*, 1982, **21**, 512.
20. For a recent comprehensive review of oxytocin structure–function relationships see V. J. Hruby and C. W. Smith, in 'The Peptides: Analysis, Synthesis, Biology', ed. C. W. Smith, Academic Press, New York, 1987, vol. 8, p. 77.
21. D. F. Veber and R. Saperstein, *Annu. Rep. Med. Chem.*, 1979, **14**, 209.
22. R. M. Freidinger and D. F. Veber, *ACS Monograph Ser.*, 1984, **251**, 169.
23. V. J. Hruby, L.-F. Kao, M. Pettitt and M. Karplus, *J. Am. Chem. Soc.*, 1988, **110**, 3351.
24. J.-P. Meraldi, V. J. Hruby and A. I. R. Brewster, *Proc. Natl. Acad. Sci. USA*, 1977, **74**, 1373.
25. V. J. Hruby, K. K. Deb, J. Fox, J. Bjornason and A. T. Tu, *J. Biol. Chem.*, 1979, **253**, 6060.
26. H. I. Mosberg, V. J. Hruby and J.-P. Meraldi, *Biochemistry*, 1981, **20**, 2822.
27. G. I. Chipins, A. J. Krikis and L. K. Polevaya, in 'Biophysical and Biochemical Information Transfer in Recognition,' ed. J. G. Vassileva-Popova and V. Jensen, Plenum Press, New York, 1979, p. 23.
28. F. Al-Obeidi, M. E. Hadley, B. M. Pettitt and V. J. Hruby, *J. Am. Chem. Soc.*, 1989, **111**, 3413.
29. W. Kazmierski and V. J. Hruby, *Tetrahedron*, 1988, **44**, 697.
30. E. E. Sugg, D. Tourwe, W. Kazmierski, V. J. Hruby and G. Van Binst, *Int. J. Pept. Protein Res.*, 1988, **31**, 192.
31. V. J. Hruby, unpublished results.

13.2
Opioid Receptors

DAVID C. REES and JOHN C. HUNTER

Parke-Davis Research Unit, Cambridge, UK

13.2.1   INTRODUCTION

Opium has been extracted from the poppy plant, *Papaver somniferum,* and used to treat pain for thousands of years with little understanding of its mechanism of action. The major active ingredient of opium is the alkaloid morphine (**1**) which is a potent analgesic but its use is limited by undesired side effects (principally physical dependence, respiratory depression and constipation). In the early 1970s biochemical binding experiments with radiolabelled naloxone, which antagonizes the pharmacological effects of morphine, led to the identification of stereospecific opioid receptors in mammalian brain tissue.[1] A further breakthrough came in 1976 when Martin discovered that opioids with different chemical structures exhibit different pharmacological effects in dogs.[2] He found that morphine, ketazocine (**2**) and *N*-allylnormetazocine (SKF 10 047) (**3**) had different effects on respiration, heart rate and locomotor activity. Furthermore, these compounds were unable to substitute for each other to prevent withdrawal symptoms in dogs chronically treated with one of the compounds. On the basis of these pharmacological experiments Martin classified opioid receptors into three subtypes: μ receptors (morphine-like), κ receptors (ketazocine-like) and σ receptors (*N*-allylnormetazocine-like). Subsequent experiments, however, have indicated that the σ site is not an opioid receptor.[3] Martin's hypothesis led to increased interest in separating the desired analgesic activity of morphine from its undesired side effects.

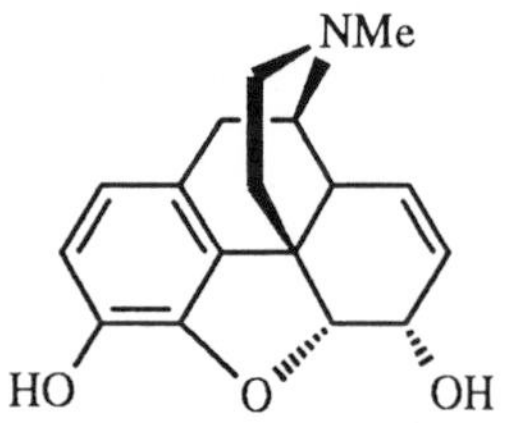

(**1**) Morphine

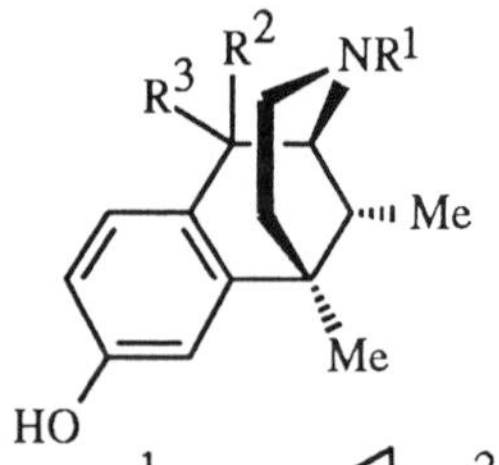

(**2**) Ketazocine; $R^1 = CH_2 \triangleleft$, $R^2 = R^3 = O$

(**3**) *N*-Allylnormetazocine; $R^1 = CH_2CH=CH_2$, $R^2 = R^3 = H$

The characterization of biological receptors in mammalian brain tissue with high selectivity for poppy plant alkaloids led to the search for an 'endogenous opioid'. In 1975 Hughes and Kosterlitz isolated extracts from pig brain which had opioid activity similar to that of the alkaloid. This activity was shown to be due to a mixture of two pentapeptides which they characterized and named Leu-enkephalin (**4**) and Met-enkephalin (**5**) (Figure 1).[4] These, and other opioid peptides produced in the brain, are known collectively as the endorphins.

13.2.2   STRUCTURE, FORMATION, DISTRIBUTION AND METABOLISM OF ENDOGENOUS OPIOID PEPTIDES

13.2.2.1   Nomenclature

The nomenclature used to describe the enkephalins and endorphins in this chapter is that proposed by Snyder and Simantov.[5] The term 'endorphin' (= endogenous morphine) is used to describe any endogenous opioid substance including the two enkephalins, *e.g.* α-, β- or γ-endorphin and dynorphin.

The term 'opioid' is applied to any substance which produces its biological effects through an interaction with any of the three major types of opioid receptor (μ, κ or δ) and whose actions are reversed by naloxone. An opiate is an opioid whose chemical structure and biological properties are similar to morphine (**1**).

13.2.2.2 Structure

The amino acid sequences of the opioid peptides are shown in Figure 1.

The two enkephalins (**4, 5**) are pentapeptides which differ in a single residue at the C terminus. Dynorphin A (**6**) has seventeen residues but due to enzymatic degradation, various biologically active fragments, *e.g.* dynorphin (1–8), (1–11) or (1–13), are frequently used instead of the full (1–17) peptide. Fragments of β-endorphin (**7**) are given different Greek letters to distinguish them.

13.2.2.3 Formation

The opioid peptides are formed in the brain, the pituitary gland and in the adrenal medulla by the proteolytic cleavage of three protein precursors; these are preproopiomelanocortin (POMC) [also known as corticotropin-β-lipotropin precursor (ACTH-β-LPH precursor)]; preproenkephalin A (also known as preproenkephalin), and preproenkephalin B (also known as preprodynorphin).[6] The primary structures of these precursor proteins, each of which has approximately 260 amino acid residues, have been determined by the use of recombinant DNA techniques and are described in reviews by Numa[7] and by Lynch and Snyder.[8] The amino acid sequences of the naturally occurring opioid peptides are contained within these three precursors as shown in Figure 2. For example,

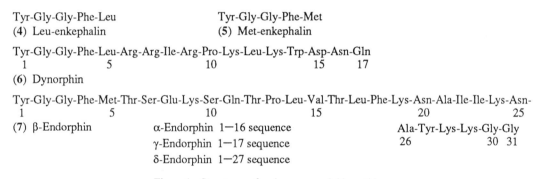

Tyr-Gly-Gly-Phe-Leu
(**4**) Leu-enkephalin

Tyr-Gly-Gly-Phe-Met
(**5**) Met-enkephalin

Tyr-Gly-Gly-Phe-Leu-Arg-Arg-Ile-Arg-Pro-Lys-Leu-Lys-Trp-Asp-Asn-Gln
1   5   10   15   17
(**6**) Dynorphin

Tyr-Gly-Gly-Phe-Met-Thr-Ser-Glu-Lys-Ser-Gln-Thr-Pro-Leu-Val-Thr-Leu-Phe-Lys-Asn-Ala-Ile-Ile-Lys-Asn-
1   5   10   15   20   25
(**7**) β-Endorphin   α-Endorphin 1—16 sequence   Ala-Tyr-Lys-Lys-Gly-Gly
                    γ-Endorphin 1—17 sequence   26   30 31
                    δ-Endorphin 1—27 sequence

Figure 1 Structures of endogenous opioid peptides

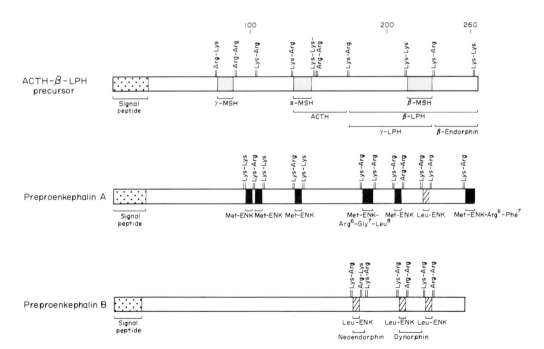

Figure 2 Schematic representation of the opioid peptide precursors. The locations of component peptides bounded by paired basic amino acid residues are indicated (ENK = enkephalin; MSH = melanotropin; LPH = lipotropin)[7]

β-endorphin is a C fragment of β-lipotropin (β-LPH) which is formed from POMC. The constituent opioid peptide fragments are bounded by pairs of basic amino acid residues which are thought to act as signals to the cleaving enzymes.[7]

13.2.2.4   Distribution

The most commonly used techniques for the detection of opioid peptides are: (i) radioimmunoassays (RIAs) which show the distribution of the enkephalins (4, 5), dynorphin (6) and β-endorphin (7); and (ii) binding studies which show the distribution of opioid receptors. A review of the literature describing the use of these techniques for determining the distribution of opioid peptides was published in 1984 by Clement-Jones and Besser.[9]

In human brain and pituitary the highest levels of receptor binding are observed in the amygdala and thalamus with low binding in the cerebral cortex and negligible amounts in the cerebellum (see also Section 13.2.3.1).[10]

Studies with human peripheral tissues show widespread enkephalin immunostaining in the gut,[11] the male reproductive system,[12] the peripheral nervous system,[13] the adrenal medulla,[14] β-endorphin-like material in the pancreas[15] and dynorphin (1–17) in the porcine duodenum.[16]

Elevated levels of immunoreactive β-endorphin and enkephalin have been reported in human plasma after exercise and after surgical stress.[17] The physiological significance of these changes are uncertain.

13.2.2.5   Metabolism

The enkephalins and dynorphin have a much shorter half-life than β-endorphin *in vivo* because of faster hydrolysis by a variety of non-specific metallopeptidases. Consequently, β-endorphin is the only endogenous opioid which causes sustained analgesia after i.v. or i.c.v. administration to mice.[18,19] The two major metabolic processes for the enkephalins are the cleavage of Tyr^1-Gly^2 by membrane bound aminopeptidases, which are inhibited by bestatin (8) or kelatorphan (9), and the hydrolysis of Gly^3-Phe^4 by a variety of metalloendopeptidases including EC 3.4.24.11, termed 'enkephalinase', which is inhibited by thiorphan (10) or kelatorphan (Figure 3).[20]

13.2.2.6   Compounds that Inhibit Metabolism

Roques *et al.* developed thiorphan (10) as an enkephalinase inhibitor.[21] This compound has high selectivity for EC 3.4.24.11 and does not inhibit the closely related angiotensin converting enzyme (ACE). The thiol moiety of thiorphan is thought to chelate to a zinc atom at the active site while the phenyl ring and the alanine methylene groups bind to the S'_1 and S'_2 subsites respectively. Kelatorphan (9) incorporates a hydroxamate moiety which acts as a bidentate chelator to the

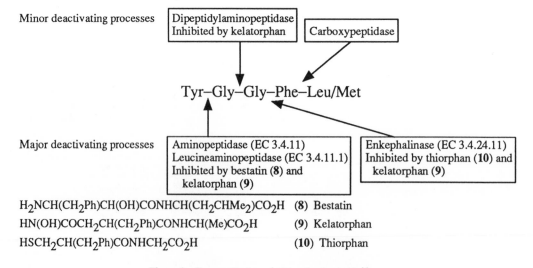

Figure 3   Enzymatic degradation of enkephalin[20]

metal and this has the advantage of inhibiting aminopeptidase EC 3.4.11 (Tyr[1]-Gly[2] cleavage) ($K_i = 3.8 \times 10^{-7}$ M) and the less important dipeptidylaminopeptidase (Gly[2]-Gly[3] cleavage) ($K_i = 0.9 \times 10^{-9}$ M) as well as inhibiting EC 3.4.24.11 ($K_i = 1.7 \times 10^{-9}$ M).[22] Bestatin (**8**) is a non-selective inhibitor of aminopeptidase EC 3.4.11 ($K_i = 5 \times 10^{-7}$ M).[22] It has been claimed that 'enkephalinase inhibitors' might be of use as analgesic drugs but to date there is little clinical data to support this.[23] Schering-Plough are reported to have developed an orally active enkephalinase inhibitor, Sch-34862, (**11**) which is currently in clinical trials.[24]

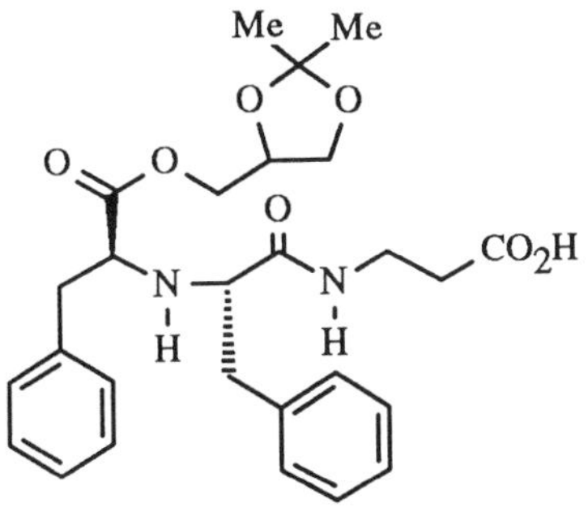

(**11**) Sch-34862

13.2.3 BIOLOGICAL CHARACTERIZATION OF MULTIPLE OPIOID RECEPTORS

The original concept of an opioid receptor was first postulated from the stereoselectivity studies of Beckett and Casy (1954).[25] However, it was several years before Portoghese (1965),[26] based on a correlation between opiate structure and analgesic activity, proposed the possible existence of separate opiate receptors. The stereospecific requirements of these receptors were then subsequently confirmed by both behavioural[27] and biochemical studies.[1]

In behavioural studies in the chronic spinal dog[2,28] it was observed that three distinct syndromes could be elicited following the acute administration of morphine (**1**), ketazocine (**2**) and SKF 10047 (*N*-allylnormetazocine) (**3**). This led to the suggestion that these syndromes resulted from the interaction of each of these prototypic agonists with a separate receptor, namely μ (morphine), κ (ketazocine) and σ (SKF 10047). However, there is now considerable pharmacological and biochemical evidence that indicates that the σ-receptor is not opioid in nature.[29]

Following the discovery of the naturally occurring mammalian opioid peptide family,[4] it was observed that in certain *in vitro* bioassays the pharmacological potency of these compounds was not only much greater than that of morphine and related alkaloids but, in contrast, the effects were much less sensitive to the antagonist, naloxone (**12**).[30] It was concluded that, in addition to interacting with μ and κ receptors, opioid peptides also appeared to be interacting with a third opioid receptor, the δ receptor.[30]

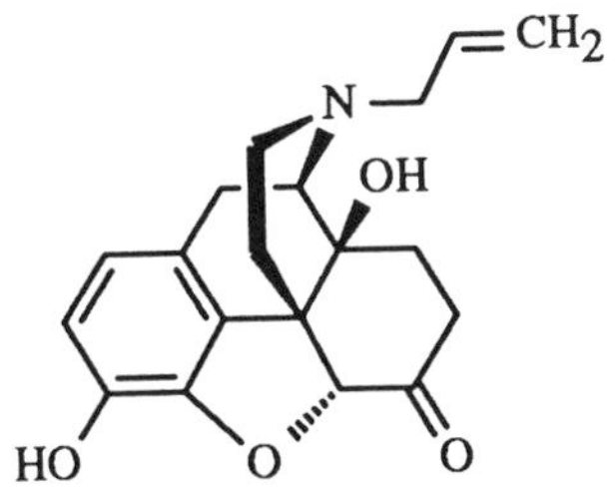

(**12**) Naloxone

In more recent years, through extensive *in vivo* and *in vitro* research, there is now considerable and unequivocal support for the existence of the three major types of opioid receptor, μ, δ and κ.

13.2.3.1 Radioligand Binding Studies

Radioligand binding studies have been primarily responsible for confirming the existence of multiple opioid receptors especially in the mammalian central nervous system (CNS).

This has been achieved through the use of selective compounds which have either been radiolabelled to study a particular opioid receptor directly, or alternatively, have been used unlabelled to investigate the binding of a relatively non-specific radioligand to a single site by suppression of its binding to additional sites.

Characterization of the individual opioid binding sites is then obtained through the analysis of the kinetic properties of the radioligand at, and the rank order of affinities of unlabelled ligands for, each site.

Direct evidence from binding studies to support the classification of three types of opioid binding sites was provided through selective protection of each site, with the appropriate unlabelled ligand, from inactivation by irreversible alkylation with either phenoxybenzamine or *N*-ethylmaleimide (NEM).[31,32]

However, the use of selective radioligands and selective suppression has provided much more detailed information on the characteristics and relative distribution of these receptors. Initially, only the selective labelling of the μ site was possible with the substituted enkephalin analogue [³H][D-Ala²,MePhe⁴,Glyol⁵]enkephalin (DAGO) (13), which had an approximately 200 times higher affinity for the μ site in comparison to the δ site (Table 1).[33]

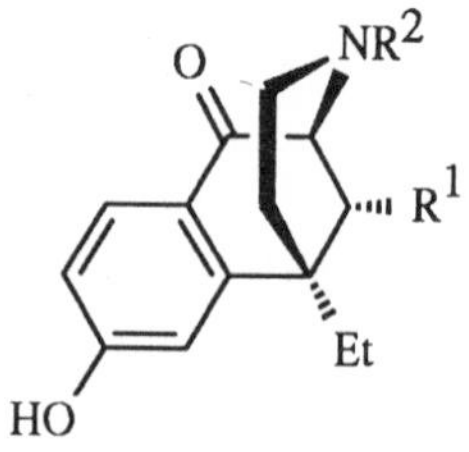

(16) Ethylketazocine (EKC);
R^1 = Me, R^2 = cyclopropylmethyl

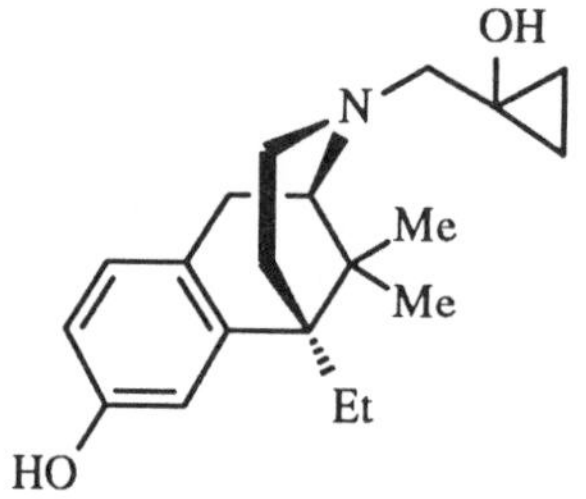

(17) Bremazocine

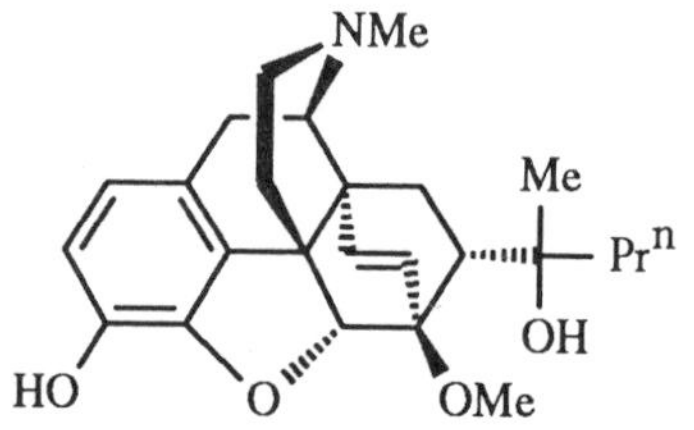

(18) Etorphine

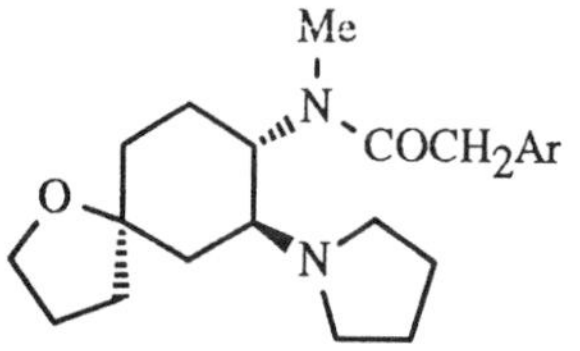

(19) U-69593; Ar = phenyl

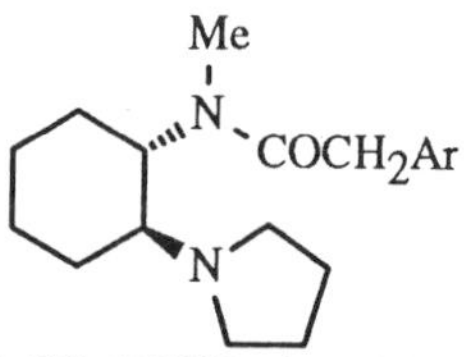

(20) PD-117302; Ar = 4-benzo[*b*]thienyl
(21) U-50488; Ar = 3,4-dichlorophenyl

The most commonly used agent for labelling δ sites was the D-amino acid substituted enkephalin analogue [³H][D-Ala²,D-Leu⁵]enkephalin (DADLE) (14) which had only an approximately tenfold higher affinity for the δ site compared with its affinity at μ sites (Table 1).[39] To ensure binding of [³H]DADLE to a homogeneous population of δ sites, binding to μ sites had to be suppressed by the inclusion in the assay of a saturating concentration of unlabelled DAGO. [³H]DADLE has now been replaced by the much more δ-selective [D-Pen²,D-Pen⁵]-enkephalin (DPDPE) (15, Pen = β, β-dimethylcysteine; see Tables 1 and 4) which, in addition to its high affinity for the δ-binding site, has only minimal affinity at μ and κ sites.[34]

In contrast to μ and δ sites, it has proved much more difficult to obtain a radioligand with high selectivity for the κ receptor. The majority of ligands used to label κ sites have included either the non-peptide benzomorphans [³H]ethylketocyclazocine (EKC) (16)[32,35,36] and [³H]bremazocine (17),[35-37] the oripavine [³H]etorphine (18),[35,36,38] (Table 1) or various radiolabelled dynorphin fragments.[39] However, with all of these ligands there is a considerable degree of cross-reactivity between binding to κ sites and μ or δ sites. Thus, to obtain specific information on the characteristics of the κ-binding site using these radioligands, binding to μ and δ sites has had to be suppressed using saturating concentrations of unlabelled ligands selective for μ (DAGO) and δ (DADLE and DPDPE) sites. Recently, two non-peptide ligands, [³H]U-69593 (19)[40] and [³H]PD-117302 (20)[38] have been synthesized with exceptionally high selectivities for the κ receptor (Table 1). Interaction of both compounds with μ or δ receptors is negligible and has therefore obviated the need for excess concentrations of unlabelled μ- and δ-selective ligands.[38]

Table 1 Relative Binding Potencies of Several Unlabelled Opioids at the Three Major Receptor Sites in either Guinea Pig or Rat Brain

Compound	μ site	δ site	κ site	Ref.
μ ligands				
DAGO (13)	1.0	185	3200	54
Morphine (1)	1.0	50	176	35
Naloxone (12)	1.0	10	2.3	35
δ ligands				
DADLE (14)	7.0	1.0	8000	54
DPDPE (15)	260	1.0	> 5000	54
Leu-enkephalin (4)	21	1.0	> 10 000	32
Met-enkephalin (5)	15	1.0	4800	32
κ ligands				
Bremazocine (17)	1.5	1.8	1.0	53
Etorphine (18)	2.1	1.1	1.0	35
Ethylketocyclazocine (16)	1.9	10	1.0	53
U-69593 (19)	420	> 10 000	1.0	45
PD-117302 (20)	110	> 10 000	1.0	38

The μ-binding site was radiolabelled with either [³H]DAGO or [³H]dihydromorphine. The δ site was radiolabelled with [³H]DADLE in the presence of saturating concentrations of unlabelled DAGO to block binding to the μ site. The κ-binding site was radiolabelled with either [³H]EKC, [³H]bremazocine or [³H]etorphine in the presence of saturating concentrations of unlabelled DAGO or DADLE to block binding to μ and δ sites respectively.

In addition to homogenate-based assays, autoradiographic studies, using frozen tissue sections, have also confirmed the existence of multiple opioid receptors. Using similar radioligand binding techniques to the homogenate-based assays it has now been unequivocally demonstrated that there is a differential distribution of μ-, δ- and κ-binding sites throughout the mammalian CNS.

In the rat and guinea pig the highest density of μ sites is in layers I and IV of the cerebral cortex, dorsomedial and ventral thalamus, hypothalamus, periaqueductal grey, interpeduncular nucleus, inferior colliculus and midbrain median raphe. In the striatum μ sites are found in streaks and clusters rather than distributed diffusely throughout the area.[41,42] δ sites tend to be localized in layers II, III and V of the cerebral cortex, amygdala, nucleus accumbens, olfactory tubercle and the pontine nucleus. In the striatum and hippocampus δ sites are spread diffusely rather than confined to specific areas within these regions.[37,41–43]

In contrast to μ and δ sites, the CNS regions containing the highest density of κ sites differ between the rat and guinea pig. Thus, in the guinea pig, κ-binding sites are localized in layers V and VI of the cerebral cortex, substantia nigra, interpeduncular nucleus, periaqueductal grey, molecular layers of the hippocampus and cerebellum and are spread diffusely throughout the striatum.[38,42–44] In the guinea pig the lowest levels of κ-binding sites are in the granular layers of the cerebellum, thalamus, hypothalamus and cerebral cortex (layers I–IV).[38] In the rat CNS, there are not only considerably fewer κ-binding sites than in the guinea pig,[36] but also, in certain areas, a lack of correlation between species in the relative density of binding sites. Thus, in particular, the thalamus, hypothalamus and amygdala of the rat have a relatively high density of κ sites.[37]

Evidence for separate species of opioid receptors has also been found through the regulation of opioid receptor–ligand interactions by metal ions and guanine nucleotides.

Monovalent cations such as sodium reduce agonist affinity while divalent ions such as magnesium increase agonist affinity.[46,47] In a similar manner to sodium, guanine nucleotides such as GTP, GDP and the non-hydrolyzable analogue Gpp(NH)p, reduce agonist affinity and, when used in association with sodium ions, the effect is synergistic.[47–49]

Initial studies with non-selective ligands suggested that the magnitude of the reduction in affinity due to either sodium ions or guanine nucleotides alone, or in combination, was dependent on the nature of the opioid receptor. Sodium ions and Gpp(NH)p were found to decrease the binding of agonists to μ sites more effectively than to δ sites[47,48,50] with binding to κ sites least affected.[32,47] In addition to the decrease in affinity, the apparent binding capacity of μ and δ sites was also reduced by sodium and Gpp(NH)p while the apparent capacity of κ sites was increased.[47] However, recent studies with the highly selective μ and κ agonists, DAGO (13) and U-50488 (21) respectively, have reported that when used synergistically, sodium ions and Gpp(NH)p have a quantitatively, as well as qualitatively, similar effect on the affinity of these agents at the respective binding sites labelled with the antagonist [³H]diprenorphine (**22**).[49]

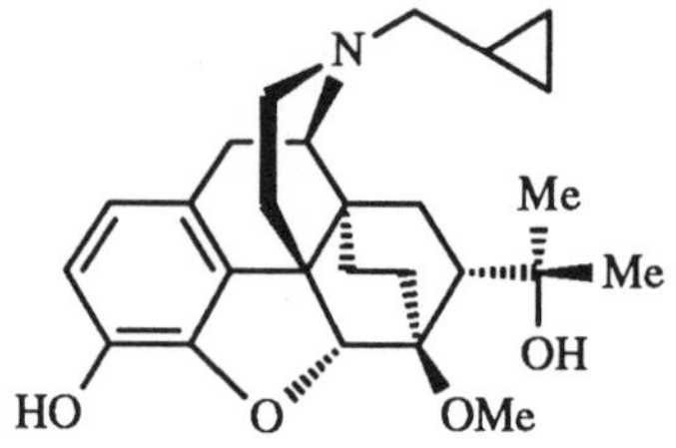

(**22**) Diprenorphine

The binding of radiolabelled opioid antagonists is not affected by sodium ions or guanine nucleotides[47,49] which has led to the suggestion that either agent stabilizes opioid receptors in the ground state or antagonist conformation and therefore prevents the coupling of the agonist form of the receptor with a guanine nucleotide regulatory protein.[49,51] However, the association of an opioid receptor with a second messenger system has only been clearly identified for the δ receptor and adenylate cyclase in the neuroblastoma × glioma hybrid cell line NG108-15.[52]

13.2.3.2 Isolated Tissue Preparations

Radioligand binding assays provide useful information on the affinity of a compound for a receptor but *in vitro* bioassay preparations have been invaluable in determining whether this affinity is translated into either agonist or antagonist physiological activity.

The isolated tissue preparations generally used are the guinea pig ileum (GPI) and either the mouse (MVD), rat (RVD), rabbit (LVD) or hamster vas deferens (HVD). The efficacy of opioid compounds, irrespective of the receptor involved, is measured as an inhibition of the electrically evoked contractions of the smooth muscle.[4,55-57] The guinea pig ileum and mouse vas deferens appear to contain a heterogeneous population of opioid receptors. In the guinea pig ileum the effects of opioid compounds can be mediated through either μ or κ receptors.[30,58,59] In the mouse vas deferens, all three opioid subtypes are present though it has been suggested that there is a predominance of δ over μ sites with only a very small population of κ sites.[30,58]

Despite having a heterogenous population of receptors, both the GPI and MVD can be rendered homogeneous by protecting the appropriate receptor with a selective ligand, and then blocking irreversibly the other two receptors by alkylation with either the non-selective β-chlornaltrexamine (**23**),[60] or β-funaltrexamine (**24**)[61] which is selective for either μ or δ receptors.[59,62,63] Thus, the relative selectivities of opioid compounds at each receptor can be determined (Table 2).[59,63-65]

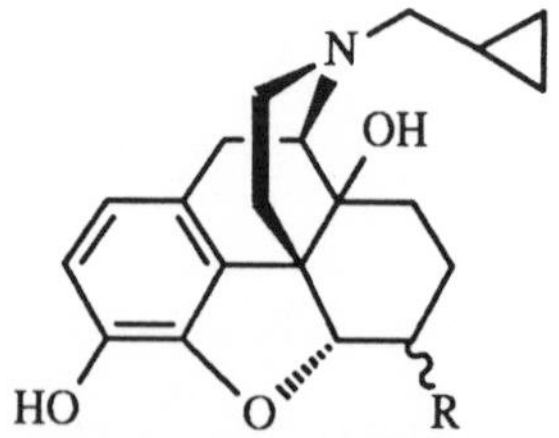

(**23**) β-CNA; R = β-N(CH$_2$CH$_2$Cl)$_2$

(**24**) β-FNA; R = β-NHCOCH$\overset{t}{=}$CHCO$_2$Me

In contrast to the GPI and MVD, certain peripheral tissues have now been reported to contain homogeneous populations of opioid receptors. In the rat vas deferens, it has now been generally accepted that this tissue possesses μ-opioid receptors[68-70] although the presence has also been suggested of either a β-endorphin (**7**) sensitive ε receptor[55,71] or δ receptors.[69] However, most of the evidence in support of the ε receptor can be accommodated on the basis of differences in intrinsic activity at a μ receptor in the RVD.[66,69,70] It has been shown that the potency of naloxone (**12**) against most agonists in the RVD is consistent with an action at μ-opioid receptors.[70] There is also

Table 2 Agonist Potencies (IC_{50}) of a Number of Opioids and Opioid Peptides in Five Isolated Smooth Preparations

Compound	GPI	MVD	RVD IC_{50}	LVD (nM)	HVD	Ref.
μ *selective*						
DAGO (**13**)	5	33	105	0	0	54, 57
Morphine (**1**)	112	298	0	0	0	54, 65, 66
δ *selective*						
DADLE (**14**)	9	0.7	134	0	21	54, 57
DPDPE (**15**)	3000	4	0	0	81	54, 57
Leu-enkephalin (**4**)	36	2	550	0	54	54, 57
Met-enkephalin (**5**)	90	15	—	0	57	56, 57, 65
κ *selective*						
Ketazocine (**2**)	20	166	0	86	—	66
Ethylketazocine (**16**)	0.5	64	0	40	—	38, 66
Bremazocine (**17**)	0.6	7	0	4	—	66
U-50488 (**21**)	4	18	0	370	0	57, 65–67
U-69593 (**19**)	2	—	0	33	0	45
PD-117302 (**20**)	1	—	0	45	0[a]	38

[a] J. C. Hunter, unpublished data. 0 — not active as an agonist. Abbreviations: GPI — guinea pig ileum; MVD — mouse vas deferens; RVD — rat vas deferens; LVD — rabbit vas deferens; HVD — hamster vas deferens.

no evidence to support the existence of δ receptors in the RVD. The highly selective δ agonist [D-Pen^2, D-Pen^5]enkephalin (**15**) is inactive in this tissue[71] (Table 2) and the δ-selective antagonist ICI 174864 (**25**) does not antagonize either DADLE (**14**) or β-endorphin (**7**).[70]

In the rabbit vas deferens (LVD), the selective sensitivity for κ agonists such as bremazocine (**17**), ethylketocyclazocine (**16**), U-69593 (**19**), U-50488 (**21**) and PD-117302 (**20**) and the complete inactivity of μ- (DAGO) and δ-selective (DPDPE, DADLE) agonists was consistent with the presence of a homogeneous population of κ receptors (Table 2).[38,59,67] In the hamster vas deferens, the δ-selective agonists, DPDPE (**15**) and DADLE (**14**), produced a potent inhibition of the electrically evoked contractions of this tissue which was reversed by the δ-selective antagonist, *N,N*-diallyl-Tyr-Gly-Gly-ψ(CH$_2$)-Phe-Leu-OH (ICI 174864) (**25**). In addition, the lack of activity of the μ-selective agonist, DAGO (**13**), and the κ-selective agonist, U-50488 (**21**), was consistent with the presence of a homogeneous population of δ receptors.[57]

13.2.3.3 Second Messenger Systems

Opioid mediated inhibition of transmitter release in various mammalian cells has been reported to involve either a reduction in the influx of Ca^{2+} through activation of κ receptors,[72,73] or an increased outward K^+ conductance through Ca^{2+}-activated K^+ channels following activation of either μ or δ receptors.[74,75]

Opioids have been shown to inhibit either basal[76] or neurotransmitter-stimulated increases in adenylate cyclase activity in several areas of the mammalian CNS.[77] However, the precise relationship between transmembrane signal transduction mechanisms and the functional effects of opioids has not yet been clearly established.

In the cultured neuroblastoma × glioma hybrid cell line, NG108-15, there is a much more definitive interaction between opioids and adenylate cyclase. In NG108-15 cells, stimulation of opioid receptors results in an inhibition of adenylate cyclase and a reduction in the formation of adenosine 3′,5′-cyclic monophosphate (cAMP).[78]

The characteristics of the opioid receptors present in this cell line are consistent with the δ-opioid subtype.[79] The mechanism for opioid inhibition of adenylate cyclase in NG108-15 cells appears to involve stimulation of a high affinity membrane-associated GTPase[80] reflecting an activation of the guanine nucleotide regulatory binding protein, G_i. Pertussis toxin, which reverses receptor mediated inhibition of adenylate cyclase through ADP-ribosylation of the G_i protein,[81] also inhibits enkephalin stimulation of GTPase in NG108-15 cells.[82]

Opioid mediated hyperpolarizations in normal tissue have been reported to be linked to an inhibition of adenylate cyclase through a G_i protein.[83] However, it is still unresolved as to whether this inhibition of adenylate cyclase is directly responsible for the observed electrophysiological responses.

In mammalian brain slices, membrane permeable analogues of cAMP have been shown to be effective in reversing either μ- or δ-mediated hyperpolarizations.[84, 85] However, it is still possible that the cAMP analogues may be depolarizing these neurones through a mechanism unrelated to one mediating the effects of the opioids.[84] Pertussis toxin has also been effective in blocking opioid-induced hyperpolarization of locus coeruleus neurones[84] and in reversing the effects of opioids on afferent transmission in spinal cord–dorsal root ganglion explants.[86] However, in the locus coeruleus, it is possible that the opioid effects may be mediated *via* a Pertussis toxin sensitive cAMP-independent mechanism, possibly through a G_o rather than a G_i protein.[84]

In contrast to μ and δ receptors, occupation of κ receptors results in an inhibition of Ca^{2+} influx due to a decrease in a voltage-dependent calcium conductance.[72]

The effects of κ-selective agonists have been reported to be linked to a Pertussis toxin sensitive low affinity GTPase.[87, 88]

Low concentrations of the κ-selective agonist U-50488 (21) inhibit the GTPase[88] although higher concentrations appear to stimulate the enzyme.[87, 88] However, the significance of these observations with regard to the κ-mediated effects on calcium conductance remains to be determined.

13.2.3.4 Behavioural Studies

Since the original behavioural investigations on the possible existence of multiple opioid receptors,[2, 26, 27] a considerable amount of research has focused on the nature and function of opioid receptors involved in the mediation of antinociception.

Opioid agonists appear to produce antinociception through an interaction at all three major types of opioid receptor, μ, δ and κ.[89] μ and δ receptor agonists produce antinociception when applied at either the level of the spinal cord[2, 90] or at a supraspinal level.[91, 92] In contrast, the level of the neuraxis at which κ agonists produce antinociception is more controversial and is dependent on both the species and type of noxious stimulus used.[93] Peripherally administered μ and κ-receptor agonists are effective antinociceptive agents against chemical, mechanical and electrically induced noxious stimuli with approximately equal efficacy.[92, 94–96] In contrast, in thermal tests, μ-selective compounds are considerably more effective than compounds selective for the κ receptor.[92, 95, 97] Species differences have also been reported within the same test. In the paw pressure test, μ-selective agonists have a similar potency in both the guinea pig and the rat whereas κ-selective compounds have been reported to be significantly more potent in the guinea pig.[97] This observation is probably a reflection of the much higher proportion of κ receptors present in guinea pig brain compared with rat brain.[32, 36]

In mice, the most appropriate test for the initial analysis of a wide variety of opioids for antinociceptive activity is the acetylcholine-induced abdominal constriction test, which appears to be of equal sensitivity to the guinea pig paw pressure test.[97] In comparison, the mouse tail-flick and hot-plate thermal tests are generally less sensitive for both μ- and κ-selective agonists with κ compounds the least effective especially in the hot-plate test, where doses of κ agents that produce antinociception cannot be separated from those that cause either severe sedation or motor impairment.[95, 97]

In addition to antinociception, opioid receptor stimulation also results in sedation which can occur at either similar or higher dose levels than those required to produce an elevation in the nociceptive threshold, depending on the nature of the receptor and the species involved in the study.

In most species the separation between antinociceptive efficacy and sedation is much greater for μ-selective than for κ-selective compounds.[98–100] In rodents and dogs, there is a reasonable separation between doses required to produce antinociception and sedation following the administration of κ-selective agonists.[2, 100, 101] However, in primates these behavioural characteristics appear to be produced at indistinguishable dose levels.[99]

A characteristic of κ, but not μ, receptor occupation is a marked diuresis which has been shown to occur at similar dose levels to those producing antinociception in normally hydrated rats,[100–102] monkeys[99] and also in human volunteers.[103]

A major limitation in the therapeutic use of classical μ-receptor agonists and, in particular, morphine, is that tolerance and dependence liability develops following repeated administration.[104] In contrast, although tolerance also develops to the behavioural effects of κ-selective agonists there is no cross-tolerance to morphine (1).[105, 106] A mild dependence has been shown to occur to the κ-selective agonist U-50488 (21) in rhesus monkeys[105] but not in rats and mice[101, 107] following deprivation or antagonist-induced withdrawal. The withdrawal symptoms in U-50488 dependent monkeys are much less severe than in morphine-dependent monkeys and although U-50488 can suppress the symptoms in U-50488-dependent animals it cannot substitute for morphine in the morphine-dependent animals.[105] The possible involvement of the κ receptor in the production of psychotomimesis has been controversial and would appear to depend on the receptor selectivity and chemical class of the compounds used. κ agonists reported to produce psychotomimesis are all benzomorphans[108,109] and therefore have, in addition to a high κ affinity, significant affinity for the σ receptors.[89] It is still unresolved as to which of the two receptors, if not both, is responsible for the psychotomimetic side effects. The argument for a κ-receptor involvement is supported by the naloxone reversibility of the benzomorphan-induced psychotomimesis[108,109] although a naloxone-sensitive σ-receptor subtype has been proposed.[89] MR2034, a benzomorphan with a high κ affinity but inactive at σ-binding sites, has been reported to produce naloxone-reversible psychotomimesis in man.[108] However, in contrast to the original binding studies, it appears that this compound does have significant affinity at the σ receptor (J. C. Hunter, unpublished observations). Furthermore, a benzacetamide compound with a much higher selectivity for the κ receptor than the benzomorphans, U-62066 (**26**),[103] has been reported to produce only mild subjective effects in man at doses which produce a κ-mediated water diuresis.

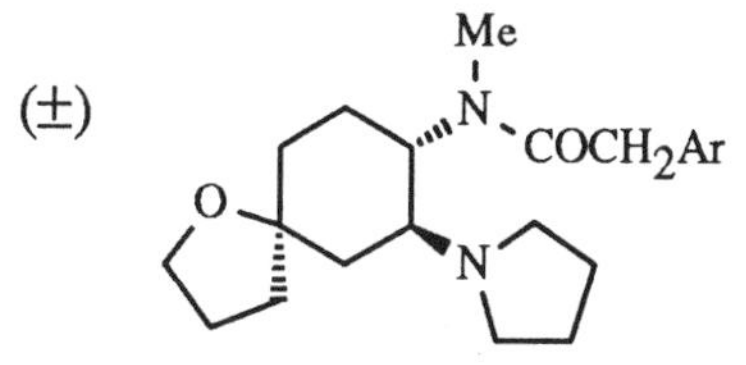

(**26**) U-62066; Ar = 3,4-dichlorophenyl

Opiates and opioid peptides have been shown to cause respiratory depression which is attributed to the stimulation of both μ and δ receptors present in areas of the brain stem associated with the control of respiration (for a review see ref. 89). Thus, μ and δ agonists appear to alter respiratory function by reducing the responsiveness of both central chemoreceptors in the brain stem,[110] and peripheral chemoreceptors in the carotid body,[111] to carbon dioxide.

In contrast to μ and δ, κ receptor occupation has a relatively minor effect on respiratory rate.[2,28,100]

The response of the cardiovascular system to opioids is extremely complex and can be dependent on the species, route of administration, the area of the CNS to which the opioid is applied and the type of anaesthetic used in the study (for a detailed review see ref. 89).

13.2.4 CONFORMATION AND STRUCTURE–ACTIVITY RELATIONSHIPS OF OPIOID PEPTIDES

13.2.4.1 The Conformation of the Enkephalins

13.2.4.1.1 Physical methods

There has been much speculation in the literature concerning the presence of conformations induced by intramolecular hydrogen bonds in enkephalins. The first proposal for the β bend (**27**) in Leu-enkephalin (**4**) was made by Bradbury *et al.*[112] who suggested that this orientates the two aromatic side chains in a similar way to those in the phenethyloripavine, PEO (**30**). Subsequently, a conformational analysis of Met-enkephalin using the Empirical Conformational Energy Programme for Peptides (ECEPP) suggested a low energy conformation (**28**)[113] with a hydrogen bond between the Tyr[1] phenolic proton and the carbonyl oxygen of Gly[3]. A third type of intramolecular hydrogen bond (**29**) was proposed by two groups after early NMR experiments showed low temperature dependence of the chemical shift of the Met[5] amide proton.[114]

An NMR (DMSO) study on a series of enkephalin analogues (Tyr-X-Gly-Phe-Y) indicated the presence of an intramolecular hydrogen bond analogous to (**29**) in opioid active and inactive compounds.[115] This led to the tentative suggestion that the opioid properties under physiological conditions are probably not due to conformation (**29**). This is supported by the observation that the amide proton implicated in this hydrogen bond can be replaced with a methyl group and opioid activity is retained.[116]

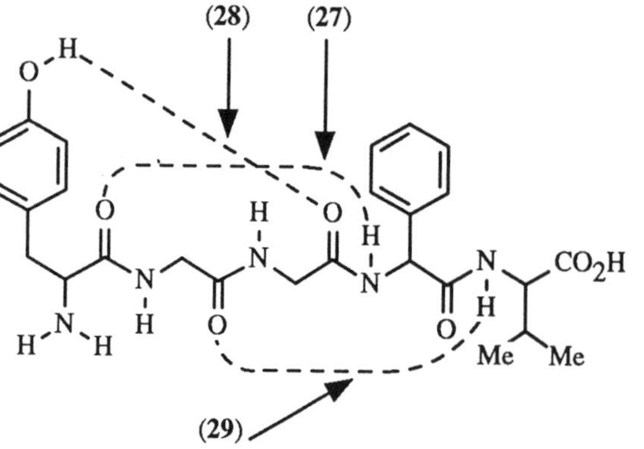

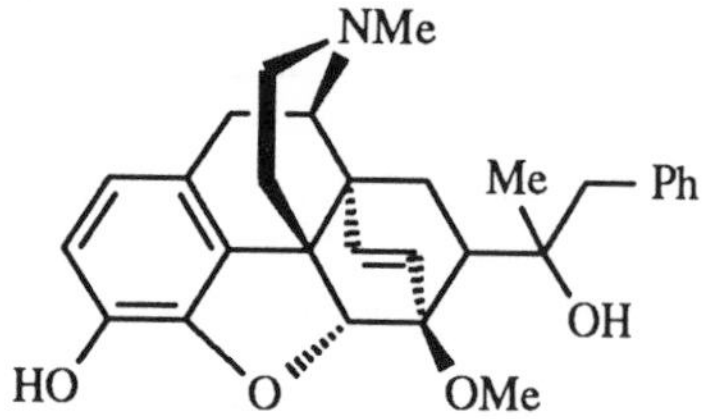

Other physicochemical techniques[116,117] that have been used to study the conformations of the enkephalins lead to the conclusion that the enkephalins are flexible molecules whose conformation depends upon their molecular environment. In aqueous solution at room temperature they may adopt several different conformations.

13.2.4.1.2 Comparison of enkephalins with morphine alkaloids

Several attempts have been made to identify similarities between conformations of the endogenous opioid peptides and rigid morphine derivatives. The literature to 1984 is covered in a review by Schiller.[116] He concluded that there is no agreement regarding the correspondence between structural elements in enkephalin and in morphine (except for the similarity of the Tyr[1] residue and the tyramine fragment in morphine). Portoghese *et al.* have investigated the possibility that morphine alkaloids mimic the amino terminal dipeptide moiety of the endogenous opioid peptides. They prepared compounds (31–38) which have oxymorphone (31) or naltrexone (32) bonded *via* a hydrazone to an enkephalin or dynorphin fragment.[118] The results (Table 3) show that attaching the Phe-Leu fragment of δ-selective Leu-enkephalin increases δ selectivity while the dynorphin fragment Phe-Leu-Arg-Arg-Ile-OMe increases κ selectivity. The changes in affinity obtained by joining the peptides to naltrexone were considerably less than those observed in the oxymorphone series.

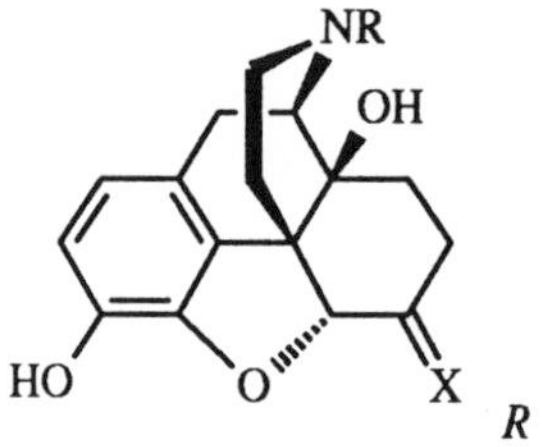

	R	X		R	X
(31)	Me	O (oxymorphone)	(35)	Me	NNHCO-Phe-Leu
(32)	CH₂-◁	O (naltrexone)	(36)	CH₂-◁	NNHCO-Phe-Leu
(33)	Me	NNHCONH₂	(37)	Me	NNHCO-Phe-Leu-Arg-Arg-Ile-OMe
(34)	CH₂-◁	NNHCONH₂	(38)	CH₂-◁	NNHCO-Phe-Leu-Arg-Arg-Ile-OMe

13.2.4.1.3 Conformationally restricted enkephalin analogues

The synthesis and opioid activity of enkephalin analogues with conformational restraints induced by the formation of cyclic structures, the introduction of carbon–carbon double bonds or the replacement of the amide groups with more rigid units have been reviewed by Hruby,[119] Schiller[116] and Casy and Parfitt.[120] Attention has been focused on the synthesis of macrocyclic enkephalin analogues, some of which have high opioid subtype receptor selectivity. For example, the highly δ selective cyclic bis-penicillamine analogue DPDPE (15) (Table 4) is conformationally restricted due to a disulfide bond between the two Cys residues and due to the geminal dimethyl substituents on the ring.

Table 3 Binding of Alkaloid–Peptide Hybrids to Opioid Receptor Types in Guinea Pig Membranes[118]

Compound	Binding: K_i(nM)		
	μ	κ	δ
(31)	15	725	145
(33)	14.5	179	69
(35)	14.8	96	6.5
(37)	15.5	9.8	24
(32)	0.37	4.8	9.4
(34)	0.48	2.6	3.7
(36)	0.76	2.8	3.1
(38)	2.3	2.2	5.7
Leu-enkephalin	380	> 10000	6.0
Dynorphin (1–8)	340	40	50

Table 4 Inhibitory Potencies of Enkephalin Analogues in Guinea Pig Ileum (GPI) and Mouse Vas Deferens (MVD) Assays

Structure	Number	IC_{50}(nM) GPI (μ and κ rich)	IC_{50}(nM) MVD (δ rich)	$\dfrac{IC_{50}(GPI)}{IC_{50}(MVD)}$	Ref.
Leu-enkephalin	**(4)**	246	11.4		
c[D-Cys², L-Pen⁵]-**(4)**		40	0.75	53	34
c[D-Cys², D-Pen⁵]-**(4)**		67	0.13	515	34
c[D-Pen², L-Pen⁵]-**(4)**		2720	2.50	1088	34
c[D-Pen², D-Pen⁵]-**(4)**	**(15)**	6930	2.19	3164	34
DADLE	**(14)**	24.3	0.27	90	34
Tyr-c[Nᵋ-D-Lys-Gly-Phe-Leu]	**(39)**	4.8	141	0.034	121
[Phe(*p*-NO₂)⁴]-**(4)**		9.61	0.266	36	122
Dynorphin (1–13)		0.163	12.7	0.013	122
[Phe(*p*-NO₂)⁴]-dynorphin (1–13)		0.705	15.8	0.045	122

Analogues of the type H-Tyr-D-$\overline{X}$-Phe-$\overline{Y}$-NH$_2$ with an Orn (or Lys) and an Asp (or Glu) residue substituted at X and Y have been cyclized *via* lactam formation between the side chain amino and carboxyl groups.[123] The receptor selectivity of these compounds was found to depend upon the ring size. Thus the 13-membered ring derivative H-Tyr-D-$\overline{Orn}$-Phe-$\overline{Asp}$-NH$_2$ is highly μ selective ($\mu K_i = 10.4$ nM, $\delta/\mu = 213$) while H-Tyr-D-$\overline{Lys}$-Phe-$\overline{Glu}$-NH$_2$, which has a 15-membered ring, is less selective ($\mu K_i = 1.43$ nM, $\delta/\mu = 3.05$). It was concluded that changing the conformational restriction of opioid peptides can produce significant changes in their receptor selectivity profile.[123] The same interpretation can explain the observation that H-Tyr-cyclo[-D-Lys-Gly-Phe-L(or D)-Leu] is μ selective but the conformationally more flexible thiomethylene derivative H-Tyr-cyclo[-D-Lys-Gly-Phe-ψ[CH$_2$S]-L(or D)-Leu] has high affinity for both μ and δ receptors.[124] Other examples where changing the ring size of μ-selective peptides appears to alter receptor selectivity have been cited.[116,119,120]

13.2.4.1.4 Comparison of enkephalin and dynorphin derivatives

The conformation of dynorphin (1–13) has been studied in aqueous solution using 1-D and 2-D NMR spectroscopy at 600 MHz. This indicates that it exists as a flexible polypeptide chain.[125] Analysis of the CD spectra recorded in aqueous solution has led to the same conclusion.[126]

Snell has proposed that it should be possible to deduce the conformations of small peptides at their receptor using the statistical methods of secondary structure prediction for proteins.[127] He has applied the empirical methods of Chou and Fasman[128] to 41 small peptides including dynorphin (1–17) and Met-enkephalin (Figure 4).[127] This predicts that the amino terminal residues in dynorphin adopt a β structure while the corresponding residues in enkephalin form a β bend. If this is the case it may explain the different receptor selectivities of the two peptides.

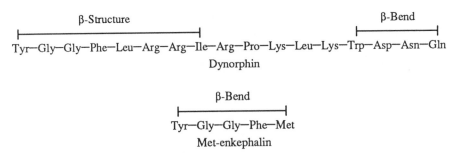

Figure 4 Snell's predicted conformation of dynorphin and enkephalin using Chou and Fasman analysis[127]

Schiller has compared Leu-enkephalin and dynorphin (1–13) derivatives in aqueous solution using fluorescence studies[129] and his results appear to be consistent with Snell's prediction. Thus singlet–singlet energy transfer experiments with [Trp⁴]dynorphin (1–13) and [Trp⁴,Leu⁵]-enkephalin indicate that the distance between the Tyr¹ and Trp⁴ fluorophores is at least 20 Å in the dynorphin derivative but only 10 Å in the corresponding enkephalin.

13.2.4.2 Structure–Activity Relationships of the Enkephalins

Since 1975 when the amino acid sequences of the enkephalins (**4, 5**) were first identified, several hundred analogues have been prepared. Many of these are described in review articles.[130] Most of the work reported up to 1986 is covered by Casy and Parfitt,[120] Morley and Dutta,[131] Morley,[132] Hansen and Morgan[133] and the RSC Specialist Periodical Reports.[134]

The enkephalins themselves are too rapidly metabolized *in vivo* for analgesic testing to provide useful data for structure–activity studies[135,136] and the most commonly reported isolated biological tissues for enkephalin derivatives are the guinea pig ileum (GPI) (rich in μ- and κ-opioid receptors), the mouse vas deferens (MVD) (rich in δ-opioid receptors),[30] and opioid receptor binding studies with brain homogenates (Section 13.2.3).

13.2.4.2.1 *Changes to the amino acid sequence*

*Tyr*¹: This residue is essential for opioid activity of peptides in the guinea pig ileum (GPI), mouse vas deferens (MVD) or receptor binding assays. Both the free phenol and basic amino groups are required. Guanidination of the amino terminus of certain derivatives increases potency in the GPI and MVD assays.[137]

*Gly*²: Substitution of Gly² has produced some highly δ-selective peptides. For example, DADLE (**14**) (Tables 1 and 4) has greatly enhanced potency in the MVD assay (rich in δ-opioid receptors) compared to the GPI assay (rich in μ- and κ-opioid receptors) and is widely used as a δ-selective agonist. The effects of other D-amino acid substitutions has been studied.[138]

The enkephalin derivative DPDPE (**15**) is also highly δ-selective (Tables 1 and 4).

*Gly*³: Structural or conformational changes of Gly³ decrease potency (GPI, MVD, receptor binding assay) with the exception of replacing CH₂ with an NH which increases potency in the GPI assay. Deletion of Gly³ from Met-enkephalin gives Tyr-Gly-Phe-Met which has 0.4% of the potency of Leu-enkephalin in the GPI but it is possible to compensate for this potency loss by introducing a D-Ala² substitution and amidating the CO_2H terminus. Thus Met-enkephalin and Tyr-D-Ala-Phe-Met-NH₂ have almost identical potencies in the GPI.[139,140]

*Phe*⁴: The electron withdrawing *p*-NO₂ group enhances the *in vitro* potency of Leu-enkephalin (**4**) but it reduces the potency of the κ-selective peptide dynorphin (1–13) (GPI, MVD assay, Table 4).[122] This substitution, or a *p*-Cl, enhances the analgesic activity of the δ-selective derivative DADLE (**14**) (Table 5). It has been suggested that the Phe⁴ binding sites of the μ and δ receptors are similar to each other.[122]

*Leu/Met*⁵: Binding assays show Leu-enkephalin (**4**) and Met-enkephalin (**5**) are highly selective for the δ-opioid receptor (μ/δ ratio > 10, κ/δ ratio > 100, Table 1).[144] An aliphatic residue and an unmodified CO_2H terminus are required for binding to δ receptors while complete removal of residue 5 or amidation/esterification of the terminal CO_2H increases resistance to proteases and

Table 5 Effect of Phe^4 (*p*-Substitutions) and Met/Leu^5 Substitutions on Analgesic Potency

Structure	Mouse hot-plate (i.c.v.) ED_{50} (nmol mouse^{-1})	Ref.
DADLE (**14**)	0.83	141
[$Phe(p\text{-}NO_2)^4$]-(**14**)	0.03	141
[$Phe(p\text{-}Cl)^4$]-(**14**)	0.11	141
[$Phe(p\text{-}OMe)^4$]-(**14**)	0.79	141
[$Phe(p\text{-}NH_2)^4$]-(**14**)	8.06	141
[D-Leu-ol^5]-(**14**)	0.18	142
[Pro^5]-(**14**)	0.08	142
[Thr^5]-(**14**)	0.82	142
[$CycloLeu^5$]-(**14**)	0.13	142
	Rat hot-plate (i.v.) *Relative potency*	
Tyr-D-Ala-Gly-Phe-Met-NH_2	1	143
Tyr-D-Ala-Gly-Phe-Met(O)-NH_2	30	143
Morphine	3	143

enhances μ- to δ-receptor selectivity.[145] Modifications to the terminal residue in DADLE and in Met-enkephalin which enhance analgesic potency are shown in Table 5.

[D-Ala^2,Leu^5]Enkephalin-*N*-[(2-nitro-4-azidophenyl)amino]ethylamide (ENAPE) (**40**) is a photo-affinity agent for opioid receptors with a high potency in the GPI ($IC_{50} = 4.4$ nM) and MVD ($IC_{50} = 2.6$ nM).[146]

13.2.4.2.2 Changes to the peptide backbone

The enhanced stability obtained by replacing the amide bonds in Leu-enkephalin with a thiomethylene-bridging group ($-CH_2S-$) is shown in Table 6; the greatest enhancement of stability (26-fold) being obtained by replacing the Phe^4-Leu^5 amide. This enhanced stability may explain the report that when a ketomethylene ($-COCH_2-$) group is used to link both Tyr^1-Gly^2 and Gly^2-Gly^3 the Leu-enkephalin bis(ketomethylene) analogue Tyr-ψ($COCH_2$)Gly-ψ($COCH_2$)Gly-Phe-Leu (**41**) is approximately tenfold more analgesic than Leu-enkephalin (mouse-tail flick assay, i.c.v. administration) despite the opioid receptor binding affinity being reduced by over 1000-fold.[148] Replacement of the Tyr^2-Gly^2 bond with a *trans* ethylene link (**42**) prevents the intramolecular hydrogen bond (**27**) but was thought to preserve the orientation of the amino acid side chains.[149] The opioid receptor binding affinity of (**42**) (4 nM) is almost identical to that of the natural substrate (3 nM), leading to the conclusion that the amide link between Tyr^1-Gly^2 acts primarily as a steric spacer and does not play an essential role in intramolecular hydrogen bonding nor in intramolecular drug receptor interactions.[149]

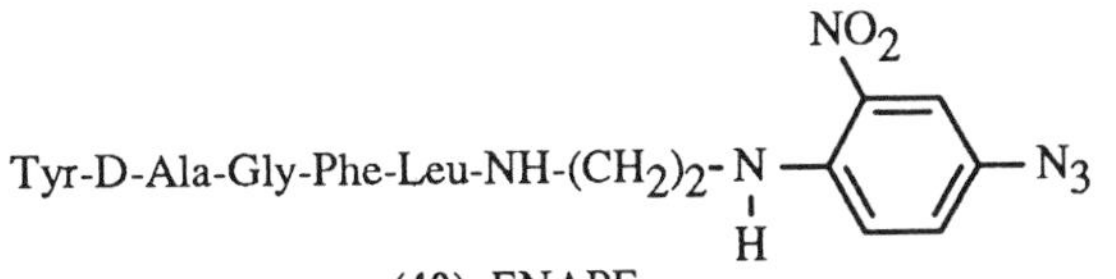

Tyr-D-Ala-Gly-Phe-Leu-NH-$(CH_2)_2$-N(H)- [2-nitro-4-azidophenyl ring, NO_2, N_3]

(40) ENAPE

Tyr-ψ($COCH_2$)Gly-ψ($COCH_2$)Gly-Phe-Leu

(41)

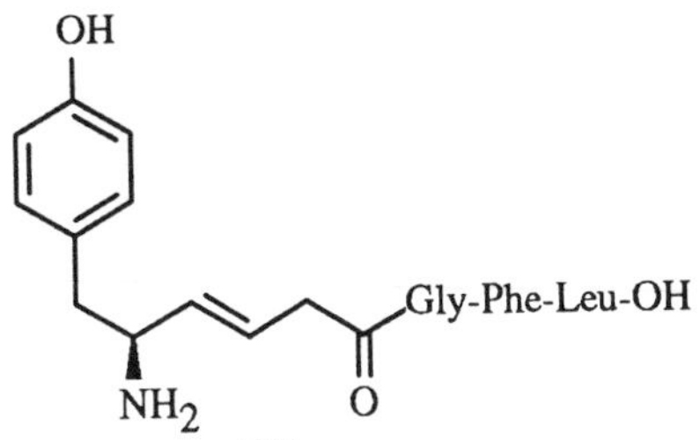

(42)

Table 6 Half-life of Leu-enkephalin Derivatives with a Thiomethylene Linkage[147]

Structure	Amide bond replaced	Half-life (min) in human serum at pH 7.4 (HPLC assay)	Opioid binding (versus etorphine) (nM)
Tyr-Gly-Gly-Phe-Leu	—	12.5	256
Tyr-ψ(CH$_2$S)Gly-Gly-Phe-Leu	1–2	11.8	1060
Tyr-Gly-ψ(CH$_2$S)Gly-Phe-Leu	2–3	85.5	
Tyr-Gly-Gly-ψ(CH$_2$S)Phe-Leu	3–4	134	
Tyr-Gly-Gly-Phe-ψ(CH$_2$S)Leu	4–5	318	480

13.2.4.2.3 Dimeric enkephalins

Dimerization of enkephalin related peptides with bridging groups of different chain lengths has been found to change the selectivity and affinity for the opioid receptor subtypes. The μ-selective ligand DAGO (13) was dimerized *via* ester formation between the terminal alcohol and a series of dicarboxylic acids, HO$_2$C—(CH$_2$)$_n$—CO$_2$H ($n=2$–12).[150] These DAGO dimers with a bridging methylene chain have higher opioid receptor affinities than the monomer and retain μ to δ ratios of 15–50, although as the chain length increases the μ affinity decreases. The δ receptor affinity was maximum when $n=8$ which led to the suggestion that this may represent the optimal distance between the two binding sites, but this has not been corroborated by subsequent studies. Dimerization of the N-terminal tripeptide of DADLE (14) with an alkyl-bridging group produces μ-selective compounds with a short bridging group ($n=2$) and δ-selective ones with longer bridging units ($n=18$).[151]

13.2.4.3 Structure–Activity Relationships of β-Endorphin

Binding studies indicate that β-endorphin (7) has approximately equal affinity for μ and δ receptors but much lower affinity for κ receptors.[152]

Several review articles on the SAR of β-endorphin have been published.[120,134,136,152–154] Many of the electronic and stereochemical activity relationships that have been reported for the Met-enkephalin N-terminal pentapeptide sequence of β-endorphins are the same as those of Met-enkephalin itself.[120] For example, acylation of the Tyr[1] amino group or benzylation of its phenolic oxygen, and substitution of D-Tyr[1] or D-Phe[4] or D-Met[5] residues significantly reduce the opioid properties of β-endorphin.[19]

The *in vitro* opioid activity of β-endorphin fragments with amino acid residues deleted from the carboxy terminus is shown in Table 7. The opioid activity of truncated and extended sequences and of substitution analogues was reviewed in 1984 by Yamashiro and Li.[153] Some substitutions at positions Glu[8], Lys[9], Gln[11] and Tyr[27] are summarized in Table 8. Compound (45) has a basic Arg[11] residue substituted Gln[11] of endorphin (7) and a neutral Gln[9] substituted for the basic Lys[9] of endorphin (7) but still retains high binding affinity for the β-endorphin receptor.

A study on the design of compounds to mimic the biological activity of β-endorphin whilst having minimal structural resemblance, has been reported by Rajashekhar and Kaiser.[156] They viewed

Table 7 Opioid Activity of β-Endorphin (EP) (7) Fragments[155]

Peptide	Guinea Pig Ileum	
	IC$_{50}$(nM)	Relative potency
EP-(1–5)	100	0.25
EP-(1–15)	150	0.17
EP-(1–21)	54	0.46
EP-(1–26)	52	0.48
EP-(1–28)	28	0.89
EP-(1–29)	24	1.04
EP-(1–31)	25	1.00

Table 8 Opioid Activity of β-Endorphin (7) Derivatives

Structure	Number	Opioid binding IC_{50}(nM) versus ^{3}H-(7)	Analgesia mouse tail-flick (relative potency)	Ref.
β-Endorphin (7)	(7)	0.35	100	157
[Gln^8-Trp^{27}]-(7)	(43)	0.045	114	157
[Gln^8-Arg^9-Trp^{27}]-(7)	(44)	0.075	165	157
[Gln^9-Arg^{11}-Trp^{27}]-(7)	(45)	0.078	83	157
[Phe^2-Gly^4]-(7)	(46)	0.47	43	158
[Tyr^5]-(7)	(47)	0.37	30	158
[Trp^5]-(7)	(48)	1.67	4	158

β-endorphin (7) as having three key structural elements, the amino terminal enkephalin fragment (residues 1–5) and a carboxyl terminal helix (residues 14–31) joined by a hydrophobic region. They replaced the terminal helix with the sequence of amino acids in peptide (49) which, they claim, mimic the amphiphilic helical domain of β-endorphin with the hydrophobic face twisting along the axis of the α helix. Peptide (49) (δ IC_{50} = 21 nM, μ IC_{50} = 10 nM) and endorphin (δ IC_{50} = 66 nM, μ IC_{50} = 36 nM) have similar binding affinity and analgesic potency (mice, i.c.v. administration). The endorphin (6–12) fragment which was thought to function as a linking unit was replaced with four units of (S)-4-amino-5-hydroxypentanoic acid linked *via* amide bonds. This was chosen because it was believed to be of similar length to the endogenous heptapeptide spacer and have similar hydrophilicity. The resulting peptide (50), (δ IC_{50} = 32 nM, μ IC_{50} = 9 nM) is homologous to β-endorphin only at residues (1–5), Pro^{13}, Leu^{14}, Leu^{17} and Lys^{28} but has slightly higher binding affinity and exhibits long-lasting naloxone reversible analgesia (mice, i.c.v. administration) of similar potency to the parent β-endorphin.

Tyr-Gly-Gly-Phe-Met-Thr-Ser-Glu-Lys-Ser-Gln-Thr-Pro-Leu-Leu-Lys-Leu-Leu-Gln-Lys-Leu-Leu-Leu-
Lys-Leu-Phe-Lys-Gln-Lys-Gln

(49) Peptide

Tyr-Gly-Gly-Phe-Met-X-X-X-X-Pro-Leu-Leu-Lys-Leu-Leu-Gln-Lys-Leu-Leu-Leu-Gln-Lys-Leu-Phe-
Lys-Gln-Lys-Gln

$$\text{(50) Peptide; X = } \quad \text{HOCH}_2\text{-}\overset{\overset{\displaystyle NH_2}{\big\uparrow}}{\underset{\overset{-}{H}}{C}}\text{-CH}_2\text{CH}_2\text{CO}_2\text{H}$$

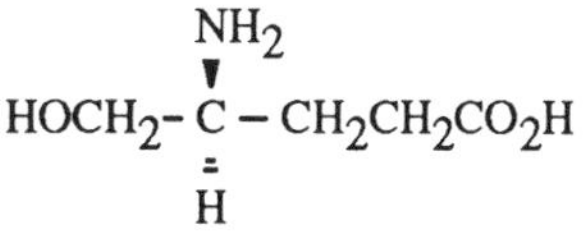

13.2.4.4 Structure–Activity Relationships of Dynorphin

The SAR of dynorphin peptides were reviewed by James[159] in 1986. Dynorphin (1–17) (6) has high affinity and selectivity for the κ-opioid receptor (Table 9). This may be due to a direct κ-receptor binding interaction involving the non-enkephalin fragment of dynorphin [dynorphin (6–17)] or due to a conformational change induced in the 1–5 fragment by the addition of amino acids to the carboxyl terminus of enkephalin (see Section 13.2.4.1.4).

Dynorphin will tolerate the removal of several residues from the carboxyl terminus and still maintain κ receptor affinity[144,160] (Table 9). Dynorphins (1–17) and (1–13) are much more resistant to peptidase degradation and have a correspondingly longer duration of action than the shorter fragments, dynorphins (1–8) and (1–9).[160] Hayes *et al.*[162] have reported that dynorphins (1–17), (1–13) and (1–8) are analgesics in the rat paw-pressure test for analgesia after i.c.v. administration when pressure is the nociceptive stimulus.

The differences between the SAR of the Phe^4 aromatic ring in dynorphin and enkephalin were discussed above (Table 4). A photoaffinity labelling reagent for the κ receptor has been developed by introducing an azide group in the *para* position of the phenyl ring of Phe^4 in dynorphin.[161]

Analogues of dynorphin (1–13) with single Ala residue substitutions at positions 1 through 11 have been evaluated in the guinea pig ileum, mouse vas deferens and κ-opioid receptor binding assays. Residues Tyr^1 and Phe^4 were the most sensitive, with substitution of Ala causing decreases in activity in each of the three assays by greater than 500-fold. The basic groups on the four basic

Table 9 Binding Affinities for Dynorphin Fragments[160]

Structure	Opioid affinity, K_i (nM)		
	μ	δ	κ
Leu-enkephalin	18.8	1.18	8210
Dynorphin (1–8)	3.83	4.99	1.34
Dynorphin (1–9)	3.64	3.24	0.209
Dynorphin (1–13)	0.222	0.485	0.045
Dynorphin (1–17)	0.73	2.38	0.115

residues (Arg^6, Arg^7, Arg^9, Lys^{11}) in dynorphin (1–13) are essential for binding affinity and guinea pig ileum potency.[163] Incorporation of D-Ala^2 (which increases activity in the enkephalins) into dynorphin (1–9) increases stability of the peptide to the binding assay conditions but decreases κ-binding affinity by almost tenfold (κ $K_i = 0.29$ nM to κ $K_i = 2.26$ nM).[164]

13.2.4.5 Structure–Activity Relationships of Miscellaneous Peptides with Opioid Activity

Morphiceptin, Tyr-Pro-Phe-Pro-NH_2 (**51**), is the amidated N-terminal tetrapeptide fragment of β-casomorphin, a natural constituent of the milk protein, β-casein. Morphiceptin behaves as an opioid agonist with high selectivity for the μ receptor (μ $IC_{50} = 63$ nM, δ $IC_{50} = 30\,000$ nM).[165]

The SAR of morphiceptin analogues substituted at positions 2, 3 and 4 were reviewed by Chang in 1986.[165] The analogue Tyr-Pro-MePhe-D-Pro-NH_2 (**52**), formed by methylation of the nitrogen of Phe^3 and replacement of Pro^4 with D-Pro^4, has μ $IC_{50} = 5.5$ nM and when administered i.c.v. in rats it produced potent long-lasting naloxone-reversible analgesia ($ED_{50} = 0.23$ nmoles, morphine $ED_{50} = 8.4$ nmoles).[165]

The addition of a Gly residue to the amino terminus of morphiceptin gives β-casomorphin, Tyr-Pro-Phe-Pro-Gly (**53**), a fragment of bovine β-casein with μ-opioid properties. As with morphiceptin, the substitution of Pro^4 with D-Pro^4 enhances the naloxone reversible analgesic potency (i.c.v. and i.v.). The same change at the Pro^2 position abolished opioid-like actions but when the size of this proline ring was homologated by substituting it with D-pipecolic acid there was a somewhat surprising increase in analgesic activity. The authors suggest that this may involve different subpopulations of the μ receptor.[166]

Dermorphin, Tyr-D-Ala-Phe-Gly-Tyr-Pro-Ser-NH_2 (**54**), is the prototype of a family of opioid peptides isolated from the skin of the Phyllomedusa species of South American frogs. It is a μ-selective opioid exhibiting naloxone reversible analgesia and is effective at alleviating postoperative pain in patients after intrathecal administration.[167] The presence of a D-Ala^2 residue in a natural peptide is surprising but this configuration is essential for the opioid-like biological activity. The presence of Tyr^1 is almost obligatory for an opioid and this residue exhibits the same structural requirements as it does in the enkephalins. Thus N-acetyl Tyr^1, O-methyl Tyr^1 and Phe^1 substitutions all substantially decrease activity in the GPI assay *in vitro* and in the mouse hot-plate analgesia test after intraperitoneal (i.p.) administration (Table 10).[168] Other important features for opioid activity of dermorphin are the 1–3 peptide backbone spacing between the Tyr^1 and Phe^3 aromatic groups, the D-Ala^2 residue which imparts resistance to enzymatic degradation, the C-terminal amide group and the cyclic amino acid residue in the penultimate position.[169] The N-terminal tripeptide,

Table 10 Effect of Substituting Tyr^1 of Dermorphin[168]

Structure	Guinea pig ileum assay (relative potency)	Mouse hot-plate analgesia test (i.p.) ED_{50} (μmol kg^{-1})
Dermorphin (**54**)	1440	0.95
[O-Methyl-Tyr^1]-(**54**)	40.5	60
[N-Acetyl-Tyr^1]-(**54**)	0.0044	>1000
[Phe^1]-(**54**)	0.026	15.5
[D-Phe^1]-(**54**)	0.0042	>1000
Morphine	1	1.7

[D-Arg^2]dermorphin (1–3) was the shortest fragment which retained opioid agonist activity.[169] More details on the SAR of dermorphin can be found in the review in ref. 170 and in subsequent articles.[171]

13.2.5 MORPHINE CONGENERS

13.2.5.1 Introduction

The SAR and chemical synthesis of opiates have been reviewed by Casy and Parfitt.[120] Other reviews have been published by Michne,[172] Johnson and Milne,[173] de Stevens[174] and in the Annual Reports in Medicinal Chemistry.[175] This section describes representative examples from each of the major chemical classes of compounds related to the morphine structure that have been shown to exhibit analgesic effects in whole animal experiments. Much of this biological testing was done before the multiple opioid receptor theory, using tests which do not distinguish between the μ, κ or δ subtypes. Consequently it is frequently not possible to describe the SAR of these compounds in terms of the opioid receptor subtypes. Representative examples from these series which have subsequently been shown to have high selectivity for one of the opioid receptor subtypes are discussed in Section 13.2.6.

13.2.5.2 Morphine Derivatives

Morphine (1) is an alkaloid produced by the poppy plant *Papaver somniferum* whose unripe seed capsule produces a sap which when dried forms opium. The addictive and other undesired side effects of morphine (respiratory depression, constipation) have provided the incentive to search for a 'non-addictive morphine'. Despite the synthesis of several thousand morphine analogues and many false claims, this search continues today. Indeed, in 1898 diacetylmorphine (heroin) (55) was hailed as a compound with reduced dependence liability.[176]

The analgesic properties of morphine are found in the (−)-enantiomer which has the absolute configuration 5(R),6(S),9(R),13(S),14(R).[177] The analgesic potency of some morphine derivatives in the mouse hot-plate test and in man is given in Table 11.[178] Methylation of the phenolic oxygen gives codeine (56) which is a weaker analgesic than morphine but diacetylmorphine (heroin) (55) is more potent despite having a significantly weaker opioid receptor binding affinity.[179] The explanation for this is that heroin is rapidly converted *in vivo* to the active metabolites, 6-acetylmorphine and morphine.[180] Also, heroin, which is more lipophilic than morphine, passes through the blood–brain barrier more effectively than morphine.[181]

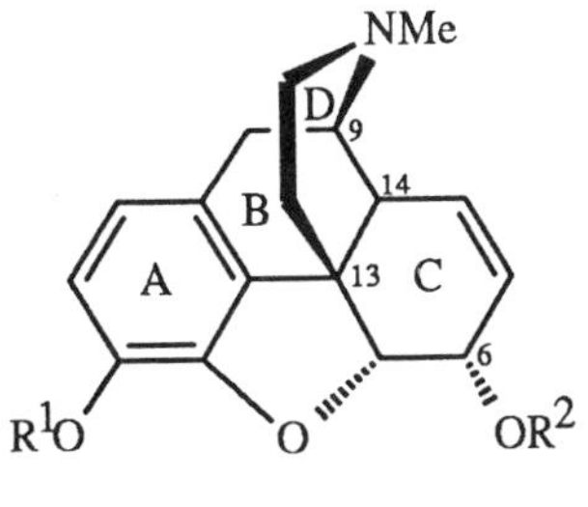

(1) Morphine; R^1 = R^2 = H
(55) Heroin; R^1 = R^2 = COMe
(56) Codeine; R^1 = Me, R^2 = H

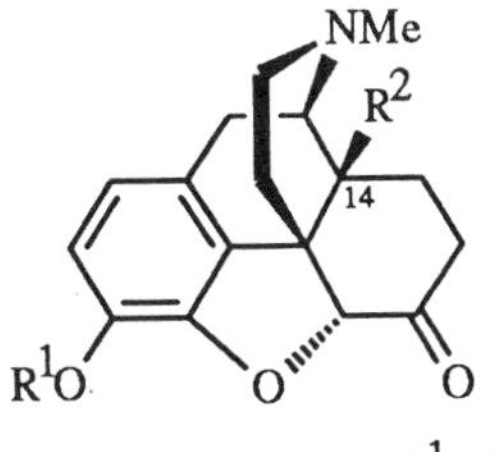

(57) Dihydromorphinone; R^1 = R^2 = H
(58) Dihydrocodeinone; R^1 = Me, R^2 = H
(59) Oxymorphone; R^1 = H, R^2 = OH
(60) Oxycodone; R^1 = Me, R^2 = OH

Portoghese *et al.* have synthesized dimeric morphine derivatives joined *via* the C-6 carbon atom in an attempt to identify bivalent opiate ligands which have two pharmacophores joined through a connecting unit (a similar strategy to that described for the enkephalin dimers in Section 13.2.4.2.3). The dimeric derivatives (61–64) and one monomeric derivative (65) of the antagonist naltrexamine were prepared and evaluated in the guinea pig ileum. The results, shown in Table 12, led to the conclusion that the short spacer (61; *n* = 0) prevents effective interaction of both naltrexamine pharmacophores with vicinal recognition sites but as the spacer is lengthened (63; *n* = 2) it allows

Table 11 Analgesic Activity of Morphine Derivatives[120,178]

Substance	Analgesic action	
	Mouse hot-plate ED_{50} (mg kg^{-1} s.c.)	Man (equivalence to 10 mg of morphine), (mg, parenteral)
Morphine (1)	2.1	10
Heroin (55)	0.9	3–5
Codeine (56)	14.2	60–120
Dihydromorphinone (57)	0.3	2–5
Dihydrocodeinone (58)	3.2	15
Oxymorphone (59)	0.17	1.5
Oxycodone (60)	0.6	15

simultaneous occupation of vicinal recognition sites.[182] The relationship between spacer length and selectivity was also investigated in the series of oxymorphamine dimers (66). Optimal μ-agonist activity occurred with a total of four glycyl units in the bridging moiety ($n = 2$) (selectivity ratio μ:κ:δ = 1:0.03:0.28). In the corresponding series of dimers (67), based on naltrexamine pharmacophores with an N-cyclopropylmethyl group conferring antagonist activity, the shortest spacer results in maximizing the κ-receptor selectivity ($n = 0$) (selectivity ratio μ:κ:δ = 1:1.4:0.14).[183]

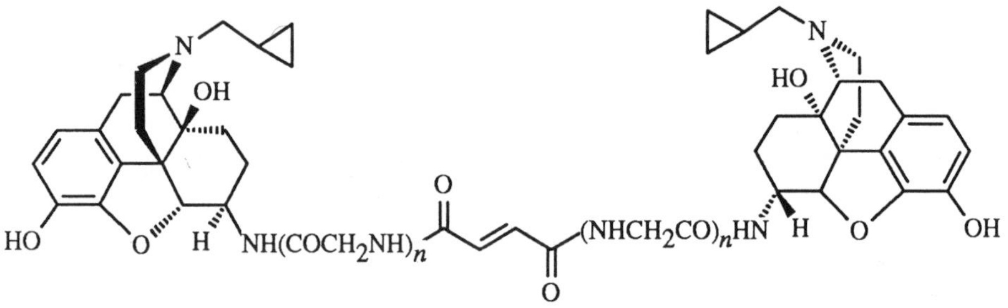

(61) $n = 0$
(62) $n = 1$
(63) $n = 2$
(64) $n = 4$

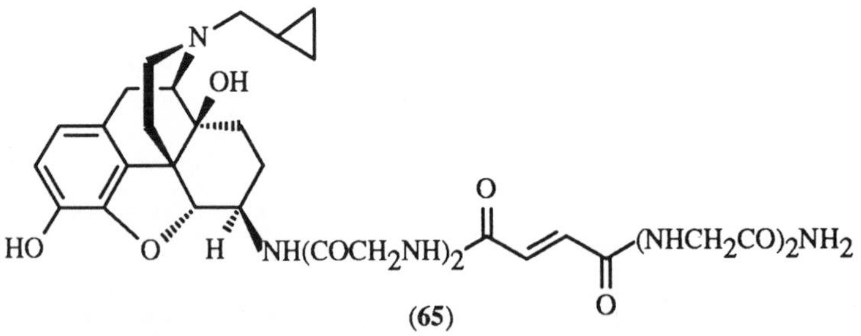

(65)

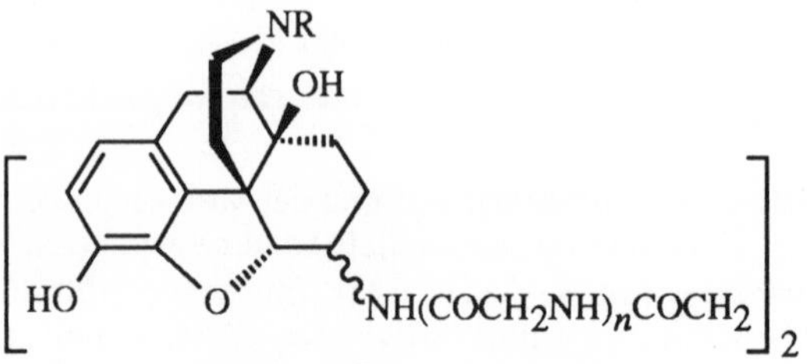

(66) R = Me, $n = 0$-3
(67) R = CH$_2$—◁, $n = 0$-4

Table 12 Antagonist Potencies of Bivalent and Monovalent Ligands on the Electrically Stimulated Guinea Pig Ileum (GPI)

Compound	Morphine IC$_{50}$ ratio[a]	Antagonism relative potency	EKC IC$_{50}$ ratio[a]	Relative potency	Ref.
(61)	4.8	2.1	3.4	2.3	182
(62)	8.2	3.6	6.6	4.4	182
(63)	100	43	19.6	13.1	182
(64)	22.7	9.9	3.3	2.2	182
(65)	2.3	1.0	1.5	1.0	182
(72)	5.4	1.0			185
(73)	181	33.5			185
(74)	7.8	1.4			185

[a] IC$_{50}$ in presence of antagonist (5 nM Ref. 182: 10 nM Ref. 185) divided by control IC$_{50}$ in same tissues.

The potency enhancements of these dimers compared to the monomers may be due to a favourable opioid binding interaction of the second monomer or of the bridging unit or it may be due to bridging between an opioid receptor and a vicinal non-opioid binding site. To investigate these possibilities monomeric analogues (69–71) of the antagonist TENA (68) were prepared.[184] These compounds did not show significant antagonist activity compared with TENA and the results obtained are consistent with the requirement of a second naltrexamine moiety for the antagonist activity of TENA. Further evidence to suggest that these compounds do bridge vicinal opioid receptors has come from the incorporation of an opioid inactive enantiomer into the dimers. Thus the monomeric antagonist (72) was joined to the opioid active (−)-enantiomer of naltrexamine to give (73) and joined to the opioid inactive (+)-enantiomer of naltrexamine to give (74) which exhibits a considerably smaller potency enhancement than (73), supporting the hypothesis that vicinal opioid receptors are the recognition sites involved in the bridging of the bivalent ligand (73) (Table 12).[185]

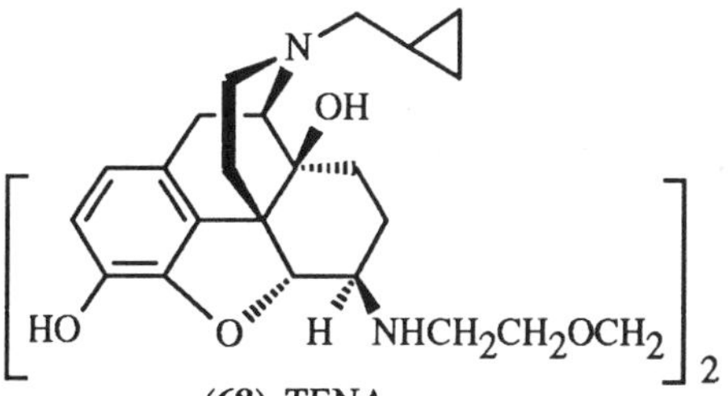

(68) TENA

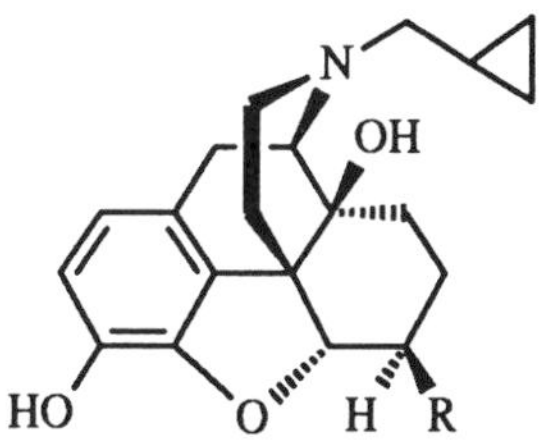

(69) R = NHCH$_2$CH$_2$OCH$_2$CH$_2$OCH$_2$CH$_2$NH$_2$
(70) R = NHCH$_2$CH$_2$OCH$_2$CH$_2$OCH$_2$CH$_2$NH(C=NH)NH$_2$
(71) R = NHCH$_2$CH$_2$OCH$_2$CH$_2$OCH$_2$CH$_2$NHCH$_2$Ph

MeCO-Gly-Gly-R

(72) R = (−)-β-Nal

CH$_2$CO-Gly-Gly-R^1
|
CH$_2$CO-Gly-Gly-R^2

(73) R^1 = R^2 = (−)-β-Nal
(74) R^1 = (−)-β-Nal, R^2 = (+)-β-Nal

β-Nal =

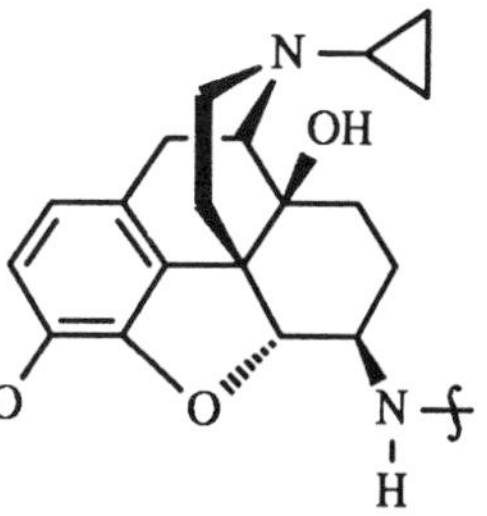

13.2.5.3 Oripavine Derivatives

Diels–Alder adducts of the diene system in thebaine (75) or oripavine (76) are known collectively as the oripavines (77).[186,187] The chemistry of these thebaine Diels–Alder adducts was reviewed by Bently in 1971.[188] The oripavines have a qualitatively similar spectrum of pharmacological actions to morphine but some are much more potent. For example, etorphine (18) is about one thousand times more potent as an analgesic than morphine but because of its side effect profile its use is restricted to veterinary medicine as a sedative for large animals.[189] These compounds provide evidence for a lipophilic binding site in the region of the ethylene bridge. The same lipophilic binding site may also account for the high analgesic potency of the 7-β substituted morphine derivative (78). This compound is 700 times more potent than morphine in the mouse writhing assay (ED_{50} values, $\mu mol\,kg^{-1}$ s.c.; morphine = 2.1, (78) = 0.003) and appears to support the hypothesis that there is an 'oripavine type' lipophilic binding site on the opioid receptor.[190]

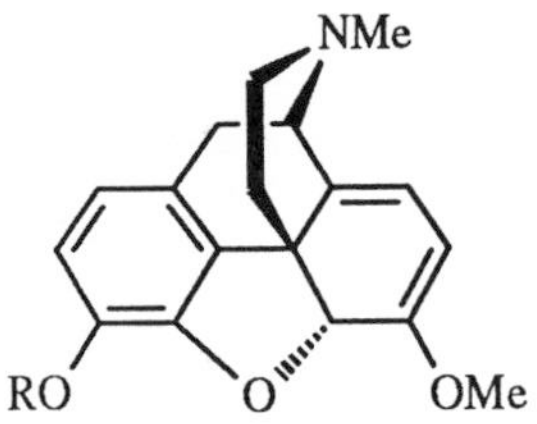

(75) Thebaine; R = Me
(76) Oripavine; R = H

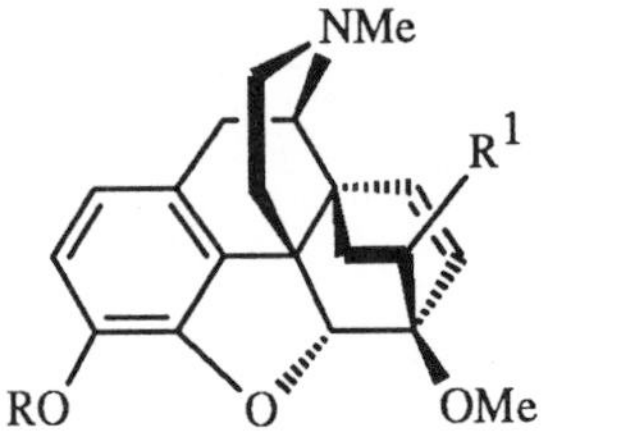

(77) R^1 = CN, CHO, COMe, CO_2Me

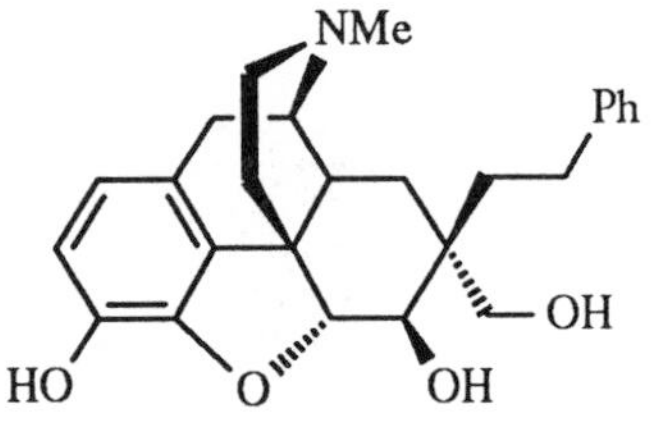

(78)

13.2.5.4 Morphinan and Benzomorphan Derivatives

The oripavine approach attempted to reduce the undesired pharmacological effects of morphine by adding an additional binding group. However, even more work has been done on derivatives which lack one or more of the morphine rings. For example, initial studies aimed at the total synthesis of the morphine skeleton led to the construction of the morphinans, levorphanol (79), analogues (80–83) and the benzomorphans (84–87). These compounds have similar SAR to morphine (Table 13).

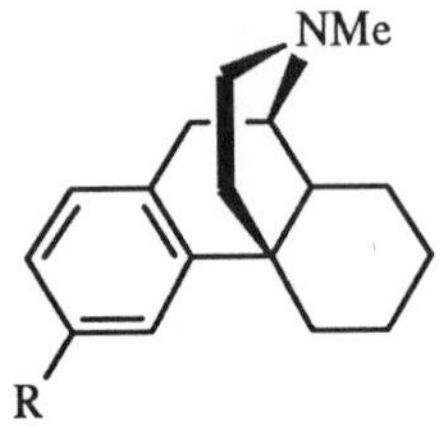

(79) Levorphanol; R = OH
(80) R = OMe
(81) R = H

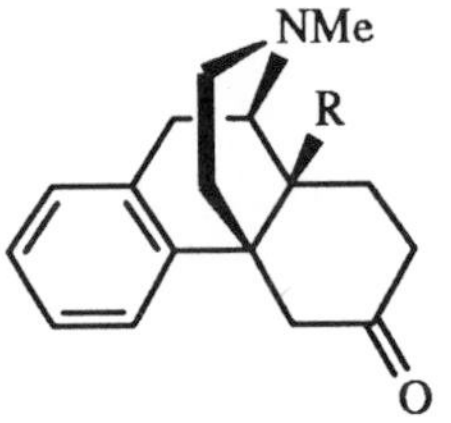

(82) R = OMe
(83) R = OH

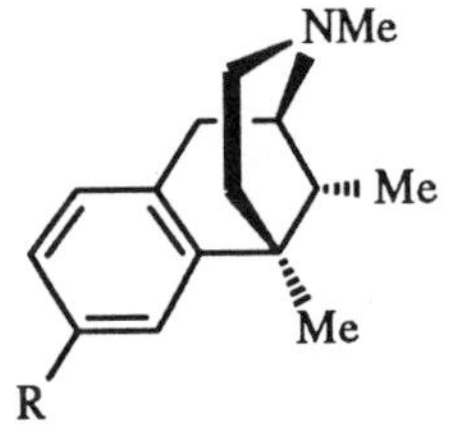

(84) R = H
(85) Metazocine; R = OH
(86) R = OMe
(87) R = OAc

Ketazocine (2) was found to behave as a typical opiate agonist in the guinea pig ileum but it did not support morphine dependence in the monkey. Further study of this unique behaviour in the chronic spinal dog model led Martin to invoke a subset of opioid receptors, the κ receptors, to explain its actions (Section 13.2.3).[89]

Table 13 Analgesic Activity of Morphinans and Benzomorphans[174,191]

Compound	Mouse hot-plate ED_{50} ($mg\,kg^{-1}$, s.c.)
(79)	0.5
(80)	3.0
(81)	11.3
(82)	0.1
(83)	1.8
(84)	27.3
(85)	3.0
(86)	9.8
(87)	1.2
Morphine (1)	2.5

13.2.5.5 Phenylpiperidine and Methadone Derivatives

The opioid analgesic properties of pethidine (meperidine) (**88**) were serendipitously discovered in 1939[192] and since then structural modifications have produced analgesic derivatives of bemidone (**89**), prodine (**90**) and fentanyl (**91**).[120,173]

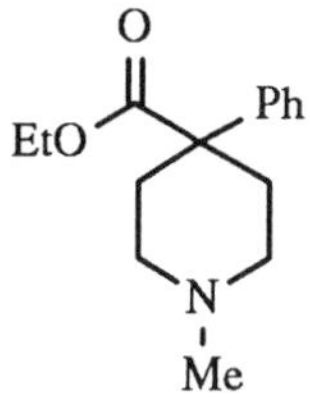

(**88**) Meperidine (pethidine) 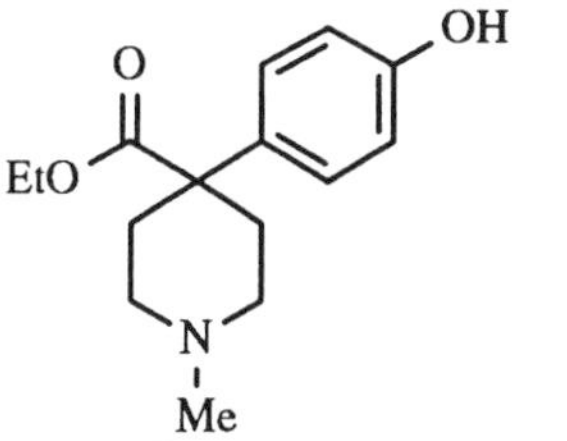   (**89**) Bemidone 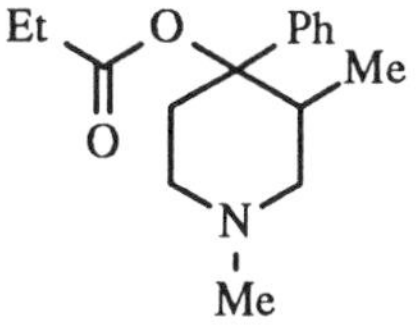   (**90**) Prodine 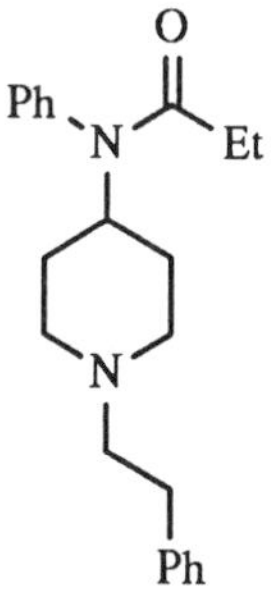   (**91**) Fentanyl

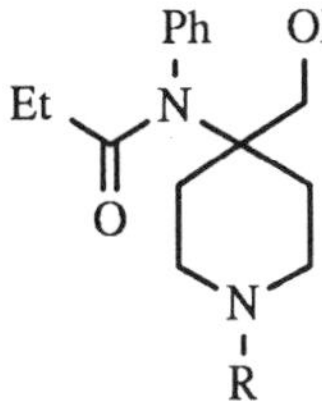

(**92**) Alfentanyl; R = —CH₂CH₂—N   N—Et   (**94**) Carfentanyl 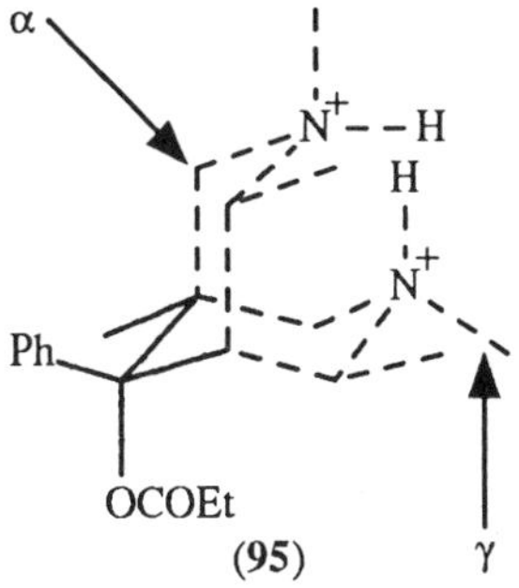   (**95**)   γ

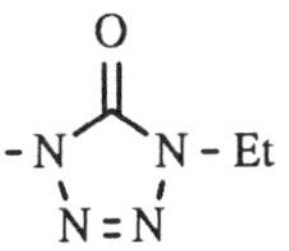

(**93**) Sufentanyl; R = —CH₂CH₂

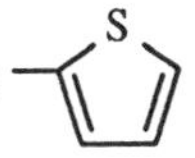

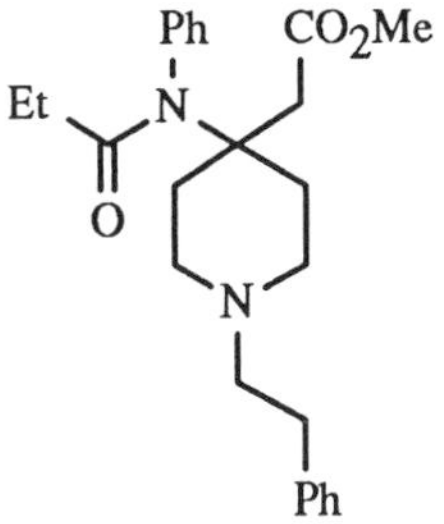

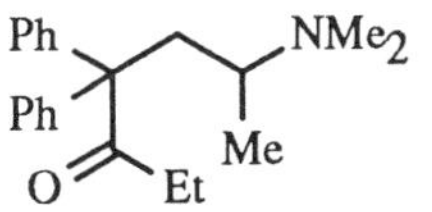

(**96**) Methadone 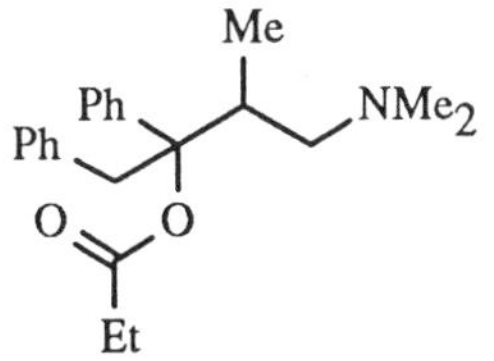   (**97**) Dextropropoxyphene

Janssen pioneered the development of fentanyl and by relatively minor chemical modifications has produced a series of potent analgesics with different pharmacokinetic properties for different clinical applications.[193] Fentanyl itself (**91**) is about 500 times as potent as pethidine (rat, i.v.) and has a significantly improved therapeutic ratio (Table 14). Some of the 4,4-disubstituted piperidines, alfentanyl (**92**), sufentanyl (**93**) and carfentanyl (**94**) are even more potent. The incorporation of an *N*-phenethyl substituent (**91, 94**) may have been made because of the observation that this moiety confers high activity to morphine[194] and enkephalin.[195] In animals the peak analgesic effect of alfentanyl is reached after only 2 min and its duration of action is about 10 min. In contrast sufentanyl and carfentanyl have a much longer duration of analgesia and respiratory depression and indicate a different therapeutic use, *e.g.* anaesthesia.[193]

The 4-phenylpiperidines could mimic morphine by adopting a chair conformation with an axial aromatic group. However, the SAR of the basic nitrogen substituent in some compounds of this series differs from that of the fused-ring morphine series. To account for this an alternative binding mode has been proposed[195a] in which the aromatic ring is equatorial and the amine is orientated towards the same anionic binding site but the position of the nitrogen substituent is very different as shown for the promedol isomers (**95**) (in this structure, the more potent axial phenyl (α) and the less potent equatorial phenyl (γ) promedol diastereoisomers are superimposed upon one another, while the portions that are not superimposed are shown by dashed lines). This hypothesis has been critically reviewed by Casy and Parfitt.[120]

Methadone (**96**) represents a further simplification of the morphine structure. The opioid activity of methadone is abolished by an *N*-phenethyl group and activity does not depend upon the presence of a phenolic OH group.[120] Clinically, methadone has a similar profile to morphine, with the

Table 14   Rat Tail Withdrawal Analgesic Data for Fentanyl Derivatives after I.V. Administration[193]

Compound	ED_{50} (mg kg^{-1}) at time of peak effect	Relative potency	LD_{50} (mg kg^{-1})	Ratio LD_{50}/ED_{50}
Pethidine (**88**)	6.0	1	29.0	4.8
Fentanyl (**91**)	0.011	550	3.1	77
Alfentanyl (**92**)	0.044	137	47.5	1080
Sufentanyl (**93**)	0.00071	8500	17.9	25200
Carfentanyl (**94**)	0.00034	17800	3.4	10000

additional advantage of being orally bioavailable and it is now widely used as a heroin substitute to treat addicts.[196] (+)-Propoxyphene (Darvon, Darvocet) (**97**) is a methadone derivative which currently has a larger market than any other narcotic analgesic drug.

13.2.6   REVERSIBLE AND IRREVERSIBLE LIGANDS WITH SELECTIVITY FOR OPIOID RECEPTORS

13.2.6.1   μ-Selective Ligands

The μ-selective compounds included in Table 15 show the variety of chemical structures that have μ-opioid receptor selectivity. These include the peptide DAGO (**13**); the pentacyclic alkaloids morphine (**1**), normorphine (**98**) and the prototype opiate antagonist naloxone (**12**); the tetracyclic morphinan, levorphanol (**79**); the tricyclic benzomorphan, metazocine (**85**); and the amino ketal valorphin (**99**).

Some exceptionally μ-selective opioid peptides derived from somatostatin, Ala-Gly-Cys-Lys-Asn-Phe-Phe-Trp-Lys-Thr-Phe-Thr-Ser-Cys (**100**), have been prepared by Hruby and co-workers,[197] based on a strategy which involved making structural changes to increase conformational constraints in an attempt to enhance somatostatin's weak affinity for opioid receptors. The precedent for this was that cyclic derivatives had been shown to enhance, selectively, some of the many hormonal properties of somatostatin. For example, the cyclic somatostatin fragment cyclo-[Pro-Phe-D-Trp-Lys-Thr-Phe] is 50–100 times more potent than somatostatin itself at inhibiting

Table 15   Reversible Ligands with Selectivity for Opioid Receptor Subtypes

Compound	Opioid receptor binding K_i (nM)			Relative affinity[a] at			Ref.
	μ	δ	κ	μ	δ	κ	
μ Selective							
Morphine (**1**)	1.8			0.975	0.019	0.006	144
Normorphine (**98**)	4.0			0.962	0.012	0.026	144
DAGO (**13**)	1.9			0.994	0.006	0	144
Valorphin (**99**)	14	200	>10 000	0.93	0.065	—	198
Naloxone (**12**)	1.8			0.85	0.06	0.09	144
Levorphanol (**79**)	0.55			0.86	0.09	0.05	53
Metazocine (**85**)	5.2			0.903	0.043	0.054	53
δ Selective							
Met-enkephalin (**5**)		0.91		0.09	0.91	—	144
Leu-enkephalin (**4**)		1.2		0.06	0.94	—	144
DPDPE (**15**)		2.7		0.004	0.996	—	144, 197
DADLE (**14**)	72	5.0		0.065	0.935	—	120
κ Selective							
Dynorphin (1–17) (**6**)			0.11	0.13	0.04	0.83	144
Dynorphin (1–8)			1.33	0.22	0.16	0.62	144
U-50488 (**21**)			7.7	0.008	0.001	0.991	144, 199
U-69593 (**19**)			9.5	<0.002	<0.002	0.998	40
PD-117302 (**20**)			3.7	0.009	0.002	0.989	200

[a] To give an indication of the relative binding affinities at the μ, δ and κ sites the following equation is used: the relative affinity (K_i^{-1}) for μ, δ or $κ = K_i^{-1}$ for μ, δ or $κ/[(K_i^{-1}$ for μ$)+(K_i^{-1}$ for δ$)+(K_i^{-1}$ for κ$)]$. K_i^{-1} is the reciprocal of the binding affinity constant.

Table 16 Binding of Somatostatin Analogues[197]

Compound	μ-Opioid binding (^{3}H-naloxone) IC_{50}(nM)	δ-Opioid binding (^{3}H-DPDPE) IC_{50}(nM)	Somatostatin binding (^{125}I-CGP996) IC_{50}(nM)	Ratio DPDPE versus naloxone	Ratio CGP versus naloxone
(100)	2000	—	6.0	—	0.0003
(101)	3.7	8400	690	2250	187
(102)	2.8	13500	24330	4600	8700

the release of insulin, glucagon and growth hormone.[201] Furthermore the opioid receptor selectivity of some peptides has been enhanced by cyclization (Section 13.2.4.1.3). Hruby's first success was the identification of the peptide D-Phe-Cys-Tyr-D-Trp-Lys-Thr-Pen-Thr-NH$_2$ (**101**) which has penicilla-mine (Pen, β,β-dimethylcysteine) incorporated to restrict the conformational properties of the cyclic peptide. This compound has significantly higher μ-binding affinity and selectivity than somatostatin (Table 16) and the Tyr^3, Pen^7 and terminal carboxamide residues were particularly important for this. However, (**101**) still retains micromolar affinity for the somatostatin binding site and the next objective, which was to reduce this, was achieved by substitution of Lys^5 by Orn^5 to give D-Phe-Cys-Tyr-D-Trp-Orn-Thr-Pen-Thr-NH$_2$ (**102**) which has very low affinity for somato-statin receptors in the rat brain and a μ/δ ratio greater than 4000 (Table 16).

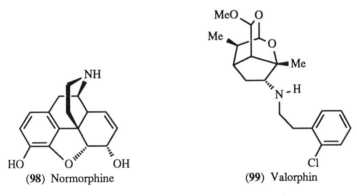

(**98**) Normorphine

(**99**) Valorphin

13.2.6.2 δ-Selective Ligands

The enkephalin peptides (**4, 5**) and the enkephalin analogues (**14, 15**) are amongst the most δ-selective agonists and are included in Table 15. To date, no non-peptide, highly δ-selective agonists have been reported. δ-Selective antagonists are described in Table 19.

13.2.6.3 κ-Selective Ligands

The most selective κ ligands are based on the structure of the non-peptide U-50488 (**21**) which was first reported by the Upjohn company in 1982.[199] Parke-Davis has extensively modified this lead and has reported that the phenoxyacetamide (**103**),[200] naphthyloxyacetamide (**104**)[202] and hetero-aryl acetamide derivatives (**20, 105**)[200] provide κ-selective agonists. The incorporation of a spiro-fused tetrahydrofuran ring in the cyclohexane group also gives highly selective κ ligands with analgesic properties, for example U-69593 (**19**).[40]

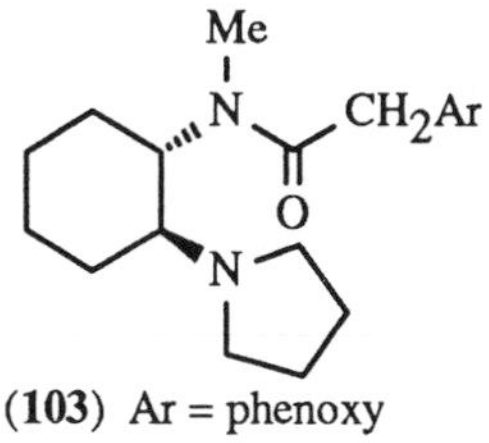

(**103**) Ar = phenoxy

(**104**) Ar = naphthyloxy

(**105**) Ar = 4-benzofuranyl

(106) Tifluadom

(107) MR2266; R^1 = Et, R^2 =

Other structures that have been claimed to be κ selective include the benzodiazepine, tifluadom **(106)** (μ K_i = 6.4 nM, δ K_i = 67 nM, κ K_i = 4.1 nM)[203] and the benzomorphans MR2266 **(107)** (κ K_i = 0.69 nM; μ/κ ratio = 2) and ethylketazocine (EKC) **(16)** (κ K_i = 0.52 nM; μ/κ ratio = 2).[144]

13.2.6.4 Irreversible Ligands

The literature on affinity labels for opioid receptors up to 1984 has been reviewed.[204] Subsequent work[205] includes the design of irreversible ligands based upon the principle of recognition-site-directed covalent association pioneered by Baker.[206] He proposes that high receptor binding selectivity can be obtained *via* a two-step recognition process, a primary recognition process which is reflected by the affinity of the ligand for the receptor (reversible step), followed by the formation of a covalent bond between a functional group on this reversibly bound ligand and a suitably disposed proximal group on the receptor (irreversible step). The starting point was β-naltrexamine **(108)** which was known to possess high opioid selectivity during the primary recognition process. Substituents were attached to the C-6 amino group in an attempt to form a covalent bond to the receptor. This strategy led to the discovery of β-chlornaltrexamine (β-CNA) **(23)** which contains the highly reactive nitrogen mustard group and binds irreversibly to all opioid receptors, probably *via* alkylation of the highly reactive aziridinium ion intermediate **(109)**, to produce opioid antagonism of very long duration *in vivo* and *in vitro*. Decreasing the chemical reactivity of the C-6 substituent as in β-funaltrexamine (β-FNA) **(24)** increases the selectivity of the irreversible opioid binding. Thus β-FNA is an irreversible μ-antagonist and a reversible κ-selective agonist *in vitro* and exhibits antinociceptive actions of short duration *in vivo*.[205] Portoghese suggested that the irreversible μ-binding may be effected by Michael addition of a nucleophile on the μ receptor (*e.g.* a thiol) to the double bond of the fumarate group[205] (Figure 5). This seems to be stereoselective because the C-6 epimer, α-FNA **(110)**, does not bind irreversibly. The difference between the position of the fumarate double bonds in the two epimers has been shown to be greater than 2 Å by comparing their X-ray crystal structures.[207] In an attempt to increase further the binding selectivity of β-FNA, Portoghese's group prepared ester homologues **(111–113)** and found that the aromatic esters **(112)** and **(113)** displayed substantially greater irreversible morphine antagonism than did the aliphatic

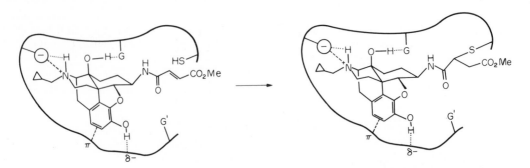

Figure 5 Schematic illustration of the relationship between the electrophilic centre of β-FNA and a proximal nucleophile (SH) attached to the μ-opioid receptor. Other nucleophiles (G′) present on the receptor are either not within bonding distance or are insufficiently reactive to allow alkylation to occur[205]

compounds (111).[208] This is consistent with the proposal of an ancillary oripavine-type lipophilic binding site associated with the μ-receptor (Section 13.2.5.3). Irreversible μ-binding has also been reported for compound (114)[209] which has a potential Michael acceptor group in a similar position to β-FNA.

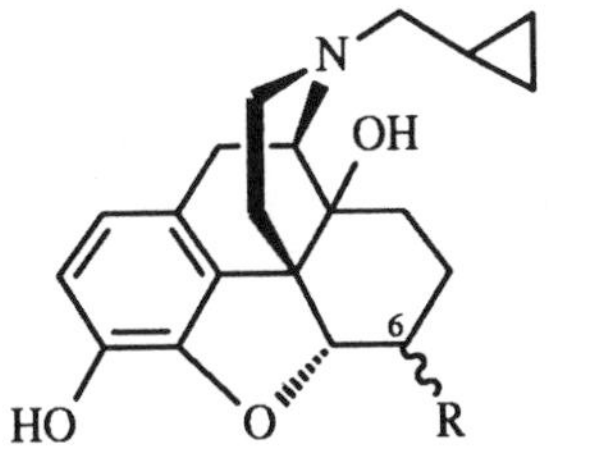

(108) β-Naltrexamine; R = β-NH$_2$

(109) R = β-$\overset{+}{N}$CH$_2$CH$_2$Cl

(110) α-FNA; R = α-NHCOCH$\overset{t}{=}$CHCO$_2$Me

(111) R = β-NHCOCH$\overset{t}{=}$CHCO$_2$(CH$_2$)$_n$Me, $n = 1$-3

(112) R = β-NHCOCH$\overset{t}{=}$CHCO$_2$CH$_2$Ph

(113) R = β-NHCOCH$\overset{t}{=}$CHCO$_2$CH$_2$CH$_2$Ph

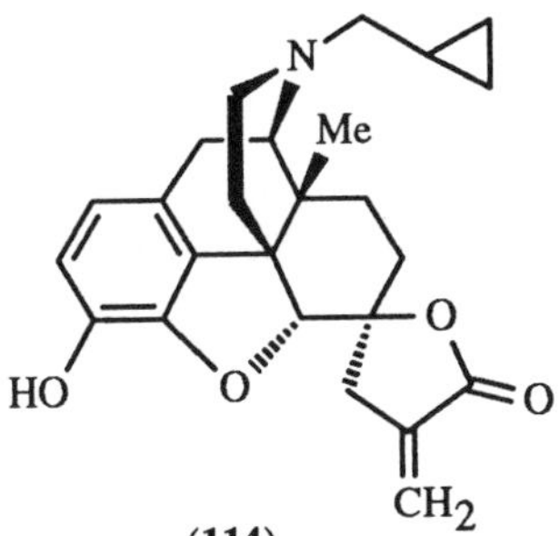

(114)

In the fentanyl series, incorporation of an isothiocyanate group into the phenethyl aromatic ring leads to fentanyl isothiocyanate (FIT) (115) which binds irreversibly to δ receptors.[210] The precedent that a 3-methyl group enhances the analgesic potency of 4-phenylpiperidine[211] and of fentanyl[212] was used to increase the *in vivo* efficacy of FIT. Thus the (+) isomer of *cis*-3-methylfentanyl isothiocyanate (116) is 15 times more potent than FIT in the mouse hot-plate test (s.c. injection) and it irreversibly inactivates δ receptors with five times the potency of FIT. It has been suggested that the electrophilic isothiocyanate group in (116) is located too far from a suitably reactive nucleophile on the μ-receptor for acylation to occur.[213]

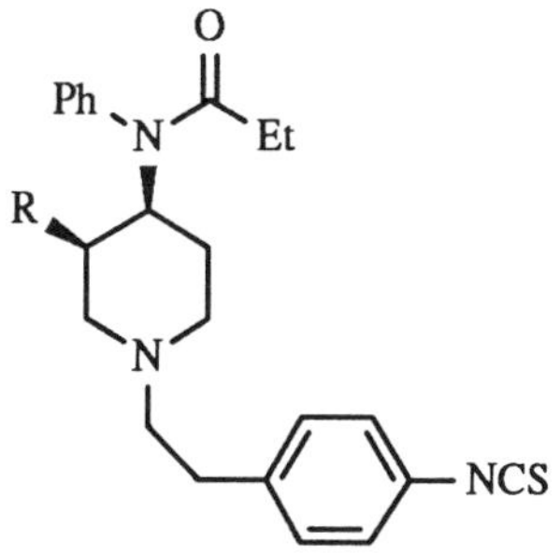

(115) FIT; R = H

(116) R = Me

13.2.7 OPIOID ANTAGONISTS AND PARTIAL AGONISTS

13.2.7.1 Morphine Structures Showing Antagonism

An opioid antagonist is a compound that reverses the pharmacological effects of an opioid agonist. The properties of the prototype antagonist, nalorphine (*N*-allylnormorphine, 117), have been demonstrated in dogs that were highly sedated (narcotized) with morphine. Ninety seconds after an injection of nalorphine they stood up, wagged their tails and appeared quite normal in all respects. Conversely, the administration of nalorphine to dogs that have become morphine tolerant precipitates a characteristic abstinence syndrome.[214] Nalorphine, and more recently naloxone (**12**) and naltrexone (**118**), have been widely used as pharmacological tools to identify and characterize opioid effects. In the clinic they act as an antidote to opioid poisoning and are used to reverse the respiratory depression caused by morphine.[215]

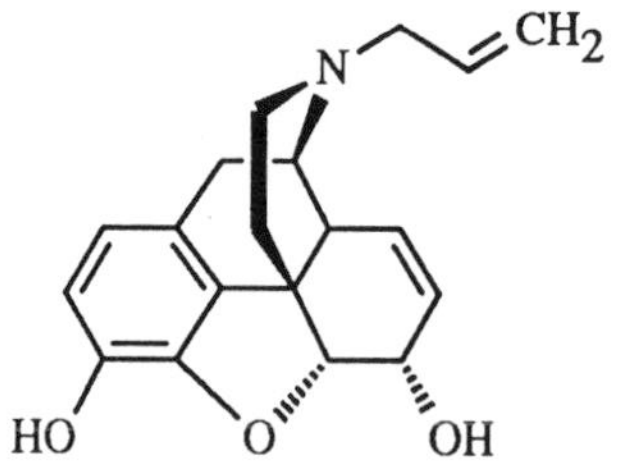

(**117**) Nalorphine

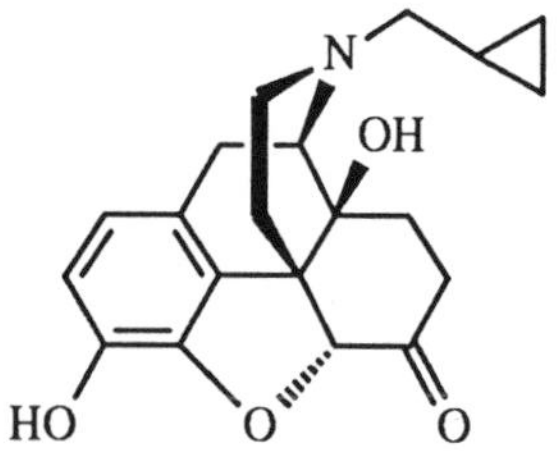

(**118**) Naltrexone

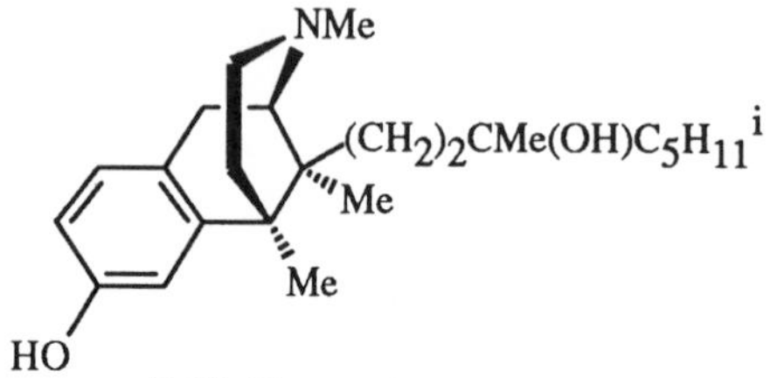

(**119**) Tonazocine

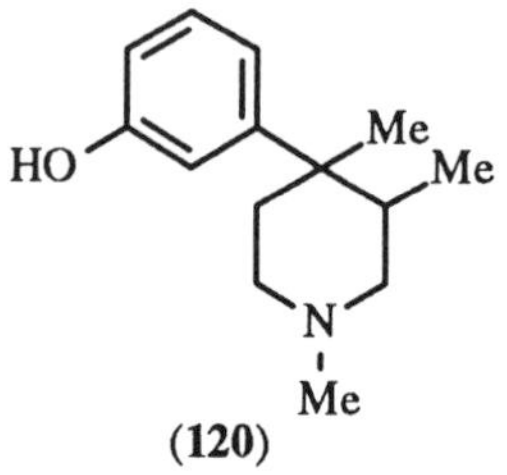

(**120**)

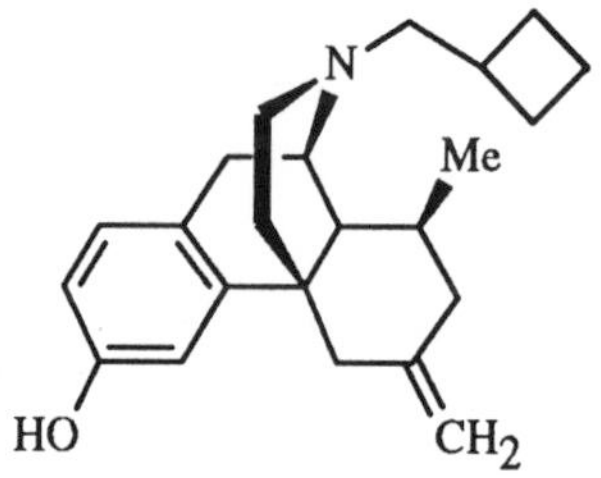

(**121**) Xorphanol

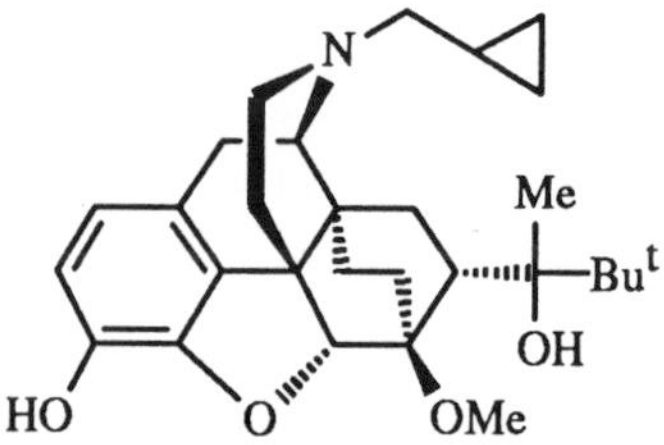

(**122**) Buprenorphine

Agonist activity is frequently associated with an *N*-methyl substituent on the basic nitrogen atom of an opiate while an *N*-allyl or an *N*-cyclopropylmethyl group frequently confers antagonist activity. However, there are numerous exceptions to this; for example tonazocine (**119**) is an antagonist[216] and the 4-phenylpiperidine derivative (**120**) has greater antagonist potency with an *N*-methyl than with an *N*-allyl or *N*-cyclopropylmethyl substituent.[120] Within the morphine skeleton a C-14 hydroxy or alkoxy group and a C-6 ketone are necessary for pure antagonist activity (*e.g.* naloxone).

Some structures possess both agonist and antagonist properties; for example, xorphanol (**121**) is alleged to be a partial agonist at the κ receptor and antagonist at the μ receptor.[217] The oripavine derivative buprenorphine (Temgesic) (**122**) is a partial agonist at the μ receptor and is claimed to have a reduced side-effect profile compared to a full agonist such as morphine. It is currently used clinically as an analgesic by intramuscular injection or sublingual tablets.[218] The mixed agonist/antagonist properties of racemic opiates can sometimes be separated by resolution of enantiomers; for example the separated enantiomers of the 3-methyl-3-(*m*-hydroxyphenyl)piperidines (**123**) have similar μ-receptor binding affinity but the (−)-enantiomers behave as pure agonists while the (+)-enantiomers exhibit both agonist and antagonist activity (Table 17).[219] In this series the effect of the *N*-substituent on the relative agonist and antagonist potency does not mimic the SAR of the fused ring morphine opiates described above and it has been postulated that the observed agonist/antagonist properties could be caused by the receptor binding interactions shown in Figure 6. An overlap of the basic nitrogen with that of morphine leads to agonism (pharmacophore I) while an overlap of the *m*-hydroxyphenyl moieties without an amine overlap is proposed (pharmacophore II) to

Table 17 Agonist Potencies in Mouse Writhing Test and Antagonist Potencies in Mouse Tail-flick Test for Resolved Derivatives of (**123**)[219]

Compound (**123**) R		Agonism ED_{50} (μmol kg^{-1} s.c.)	Antagonism[b] ED_{50} (μmol kg^{-1} s.c.)
Methyl	(−)	26	a
	(+)	41	101
Allyl	(−)	14	a
	(+)	161	112
Cyclopropylmethyl	(−)	12	a
	(+)	>700	139
Phenyl	(−)	18	a
	(+)	12	13

[a] Compounds showed no significant antagonist activity. [b] Antagonism of tail-flick inhibition induced by morphine sulfate (21 μmol kg^{-1} s.c.).

produce antagonism which is independent of the amine substituent. Hence, a single compound could produce both agonist and antagonist activity by binding in this bimodal fashion, or by adopting a piperidine boat conformation (pharmacophore III), such that N–R variations would be expected to modulate the agonism/antagonism as in the ring fused opiates. Separation of the enantiomers of the mixed agonist–antagonist picenadol (**124**) has shown that the (+)-isomer is an opioid agonist at the μ and δ receptors but the (−)-isomer is an antagonist (Table 18).[220] The diastereoisomers of the *N*-tetrahydrofurfurylnoroxymorphones (**125**) (MR2096, MR2097) show agonist and antagonist properties respectively.[221]

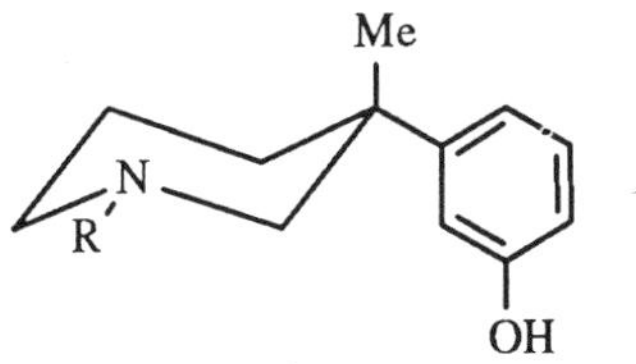

(+) series 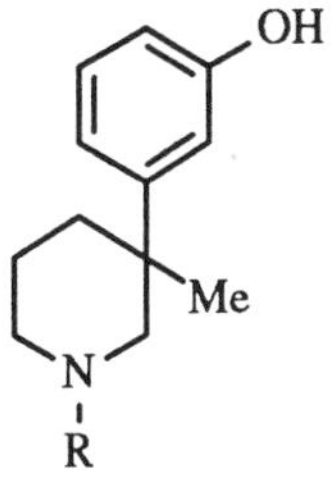   (123) 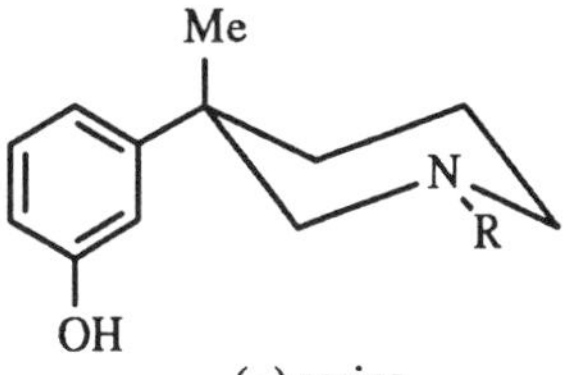   (−) series

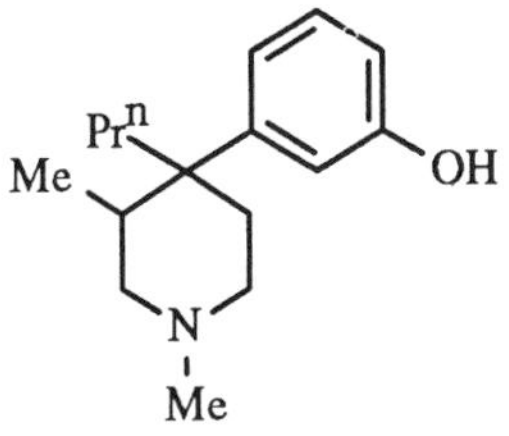

(**124**) Picenadol   (**125**) MR2096, MR2097

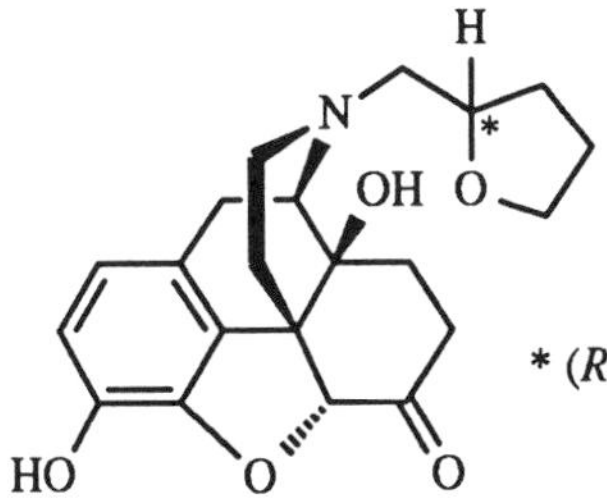

Snyder has suggested that the steric effects of the C-14 hydroxyl group of naloxone makes the *N*-allyl substituent equatorial and this stabilizes the receptor in an antagonist rather than an agonist conformation.[222] However, studies of the axial–equatorial equilibria of opiates using energy calculations,[223] and ^{13}C NMR spectroscopy,[224] do not indicate a significant energy difference

Table 18 Opioid Properties of Picenadol (**124**) and its Enantiomers[220]

	Opioid binding, K_i (nM)			Mouse analgesia (writhing) ED_{50} (mg kg^{-1} s.c.)
	μ	δ	κ	
Picenadol	6.6	10.0	881	1.6
(+)-Isomer	4.0	4.6	>1000	0.76
(−)-Isomer	7.6	15.8	523	8.1

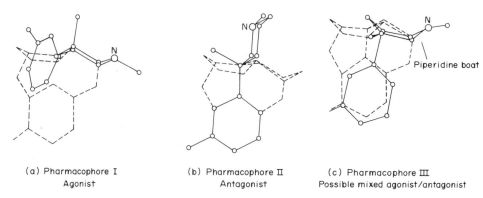

(a) Pharmacophore I   (b) Pharmacophore II   (c) Pharmacophore III
      Agonist   Antagonist   Possible mixed agonist/antagonist

Figure 6 Postulated 3-phenylpiperidine modes of initiating agonist/antagonist activity[219]

between the orientation of the nitrogen substituent in equatorial or axial conformations. These physicochemical methods do not support the hypothesis that the orientation of the lone pair of electrons on the basic nitrogen atom plays a crucial role in determining agonist or antagonist activity.

During the last decade several non-peptide structures with high selectivity for the opioid receptor subtypes have been identified but most of these are agonists not antagonists (Section 13.2.6). Of the antagonists that have been identified as having receptor selectivity, Table 19 shows that naloxone is a μ-selective antagonist, WIN 4444-1 (**126**) has higher κ-affinity than naloxone but is still μ-selective (see also Figure 7). The oripavine derivative 16-methyl cyprenorphine (**128**) is the most selective non-

Table 19 Ke Values of Antagonists at μ, κ and δ Receptors in the MVD[9,225,227]

Compound	$\mu\,Ke$ (nM)	$\kappa\,Ke$ (nM)	$\delta\,Ke$ (nM)
Naloxone (**12**)	1.4	16	9.6
Naltrexone (**118**)	0.44	6.2	5.7
MR2266 (**107**)	2.0	2.3	23
SKF 10047 (**3**)	13	60	150
Xorphanol (**121**)	0.47	0.76	8.7
WIN44441 (**126**)	0.76	1.8	8.6
16-Me-cyprenorphine (**128**)	1.8	60	0.73
Cyprenorphine (**127**)	0.076	0.79	0.68
ICI 154129 (**25**)	10 000	> 50 000	778
ICI 174864 (**130**)	24 700	> 69 000	193

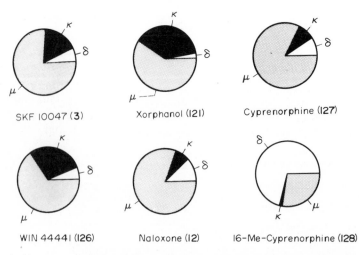

SKF 10047 (**3**)   Xorphanol (**121**)   Cyprenorphine (**127**)

WIN 44441 (**126**)   Naloxone (**12**)   16-Me-Cyprenorphine (**128**)

Figure 7 Pie charts showing % μ, κ and δ receptors occupied by each antagonist in a hypothetical system containing equal numbers of each receptor type (100% = total number of occupied receptors)[225]

peptide δ antagonist. The 16-methyl group is significant because the unsubstituted cyprenorphine (**127**) has a virtually identical antagonist profile to naloxone.[225] A new structural type of opioid antagonist, which to date has not been assayed for *in vitro* receptor subtype selectivity, is represented by the hexahydro-1*H*-1-pyrindines (**129**).[226]

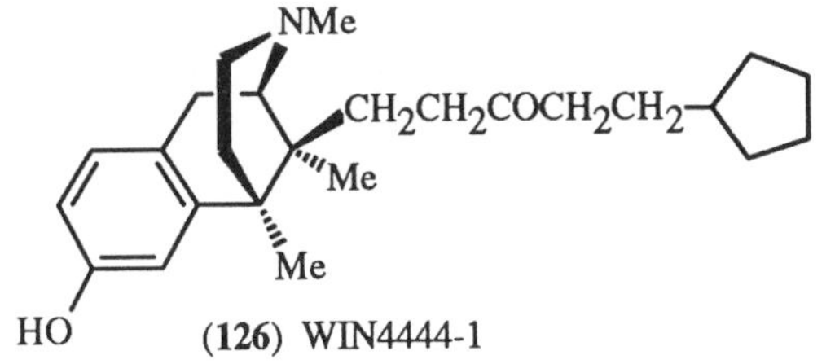

(**126**) WIN4444-1

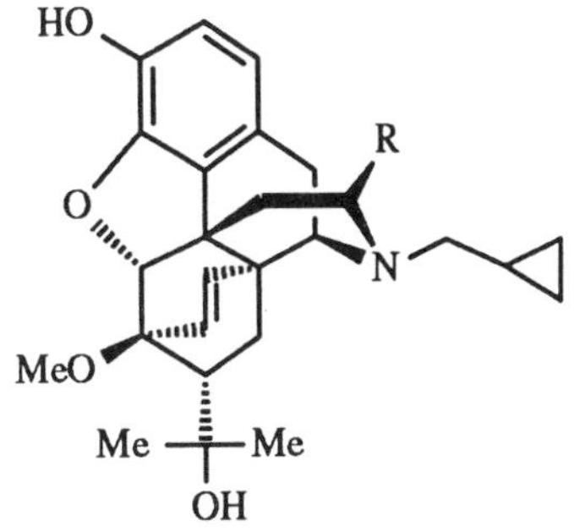

(**129**) R = Me, Et

(**127**) Cyprenorphine; R = H
(**128**) R = Me

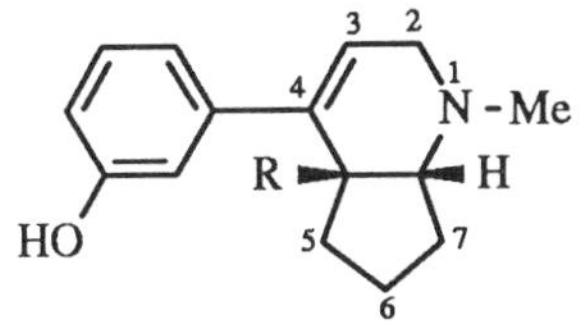

The literature on agonists and antagonists has been reviewed by Casy and Parfitt.[120]

13.2.7.2 Peptide Structures Showing Antagonism

The observation that an *N*-allyl substituent often confers antagonist activity in the non-peptide opiate series has been extended to the Tyr¹ terminal amino group of enkephalins to produce δ-selective antagonists. Two such weakly active compounds, ICI 154129 (**25**) and ICI 174864 (**130**; *N*,*N*-diallyl-Tyr-Aib-Aib-Phe-Leu-OH, where Aib = α-aminoisobutyric acid)[227] are shown in Table 19.

The search for κ-selective antagonists has led to [D-Ala²,Trp⁴]dynorphin (1–13) which appears to have some antagonist properties in the guinea pig ileum assay but only towards dynorphin (1–13) and not to other κ-selective ligands.[54] D-Trp residues have been incorporated into the highly κ-selective agonist [D-Pro¹⁰]dynorphin (1–11)[228] based on the knowledge that D-Trp can impart antagonist properties to LHRH, neurotensin and substance P. The resultant peptides, shown in Table 20,[229] possess competitive κ-antagonist properties against dynorphin in the rabbit vas deferens assay (rich in κ-receptors) but this antagonism is weak with low selectivity.

13.2.8 MODELS OF THE OPIOID RECEPTOR

There have been several reports describing attempts to purify and characterize the opioid receptor which indicate that it has a mass in excess of 10^5 Da and a Stokes radius of about 70 Å.[230] These studies may in future enable the primary structure of the opioid receptor to be characterized but it does not necessarily follow that this will also provide material with identical biological activity to the *in vivo* receptors. Attempts to obtain biologically active models of the opioid receptor have followed

Table 20 Binding of Dynorphin Derivatives[229]

Structure	Opioid receptor binding, K_i (nM)			Rabbit vas deferens Ke (nM)
	μ	δ	κ	
Dynorphin (1–11) (**130**)	2.71	10.66	0.128	—
[D-Pro¹⁰]-(**130**)	2.00	7.47	0.032	—
[D-Trp²,⁸,D-Pro¹⁰]-(**130**)	103	561	153	433
[D-Trp⁵,⁸,D-Pro¹⁰]-(**130**)	20.3	303	20.6	199
[D-Trp²,⁴,⁸,D-Pro¹⁰]-(**130**)	51.5	134	23.8	293

two main strategies. One approach has involved modelling key receptor sites by considering the structural elements of morphine and related opiates based on the assumption that the receptor has complementary binding sites. The other approach has centred around the identification of organic molecules that bind substrates in a similar way to the opioid receptors.

The first approach was pioneered by Beckett and Casy, who in 1954 proposed a model for the active site of the morphine receptor shown in Figure 8.[231] According to this model, the requirements for analgesic activity are: (1) a basic centre which is partially ionized at physiological pH so as to associate with an anionic site on the receptor surface; (2) a planar aromatic structure that has a van der Waals interaction with the receptor; (3) an almost coplanar basic group and aromatic ring; and (4) a hydrocarbon fragment (C-15/C-16 of morphine) projecting out of this plane which binds to a cavity in the receptor.

This model was developed several years before the proposal of the multiple opioid receptor theory and the discovery of the endogenous opioid peptides. It does not specifically accommodate these developments nor does it distinguish between agonists and antagonists. However, it is still a valid model for most of the opiate structures described in Section 13.2.5 and it has stood the test of time remarkably well. Most of the models that have been developed subsequently are more or less based on this original hypothesis and incorporate the same three binding interactions with the most important being a charged nitrogen and an anionic receptor site.

In 1983, Martin[89] proposed a steric theory of opiate agonists and antagonists which extends the original Beckett and Casy hypothesis to include antagonists and μ/κ-selective ligands. Martin's models which are represented in Figure 9 retain the flat aromatic binding site of the Beckett and Casy model and additionally propose that the anionic site on the μ receptor (labelled B in Figure 9) is about 1 Å away from that of the κ receptor (labelled B′ in Figure 9). Furthermore, the κ receptor is proposed to have a site (labelled D) which interacts with the ketonic oxygen of ethylketazocine (16). The F is a site at which covalent bonding can occur to yield irreversible agonists such as chlornaltrexamine. This model accounts for antagonist activity by suggesting that the N-allyl or N-cyclopropylmethyl substituents of μ antagonists have a van der Waals interaction with the receptor which results in moving the nitrogen away from the position required for agonism. Several other groups have suggested that the agonist/antagonist activity of opiates is determined by stereoelectronic interactions of the amino moiety with the receptor and these are discussed in a review by Kolb.[232] There is still no agreement in the literature to explain why changing the amino substituent converts agonists to antagonists.

Snyder et al.[233] have proposed a model which attempts to explain the analgesic potency of opiates on the basis of their receptor conformation. It is suggested that the receptor exists in two interconvertible forms which are allosterically modulated by sodium ions; one has high affinity for antagonists and the other has selective affinity for agonists. These two forms have a common anionic site but different positions for the aromatic group(s). They propose that the high analgesic potency of phenazocine, PET, etonitazene and fentanyl is associated with a common orientation of the two aromatic groups relative to the basic nitrogen atom as shown in Figure 10. According to this model, methadone (96) and dextromoramide are less potent because they cannot adopt the hypothetical 'agonist conformation'. However, this model does not explain the wide range of analgesic potencies of certain 4-phenylpiperidines which are capable of adopting the 'agonist conformation'.[120]

The second approach to modelling the opioid receptor, that of identifying organic molecules which have similar binding characteristics to *in vitro* receptors, started with cerebroside sulfate (CS). This has been proposed as a chemical model of the opioid receptor that fulfills the binding interactions of the Beckett and Casy hypothesis. The postulated binding between CS and a morphinan derivative is shown in Figure 11.[234] The anionic site of the Beckett and Casy model is mimicked by the sulfate group of CS. To test how well this models the binding characteristics of the

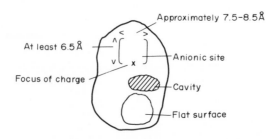

Figure 8   Beckett and Casy's model of the analgesic receptor site[231]

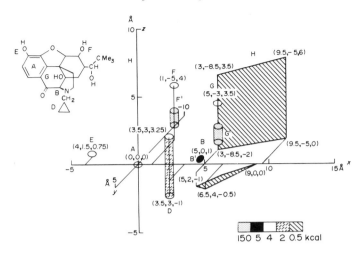

Figure 9 Martin's schematic view of the opioid receptor. The opioid molecule used to construct the receptor is shown with the binding sites designated by letters[89]

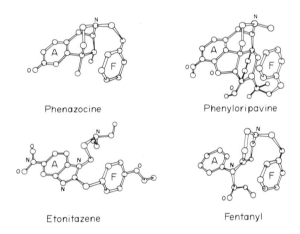

Figure 10 The proposed 'agonist conformation' of phenazocine, phenyloripavine, etonitazene and fentanyl. The two aromatic rings and the basic nitrogen atoms have the same spatial orientation[233]

opioid receptor various opiate agonists and antagonists have been investigated. There appears to be some correlation between their analgesic potency and their ability to inhibit the binding of levorphanol (**79**) to CS in water (ID_{50} values). For example the ID_{50} values (10^{-6} M) and analgesic potencies in man (10^{-6} mol kg^{-1}) are respectively, 1.5 and 5.6 for levorphanol, 5.0 and 26 for morphine (**1**), and 36 and 230 for codeine (**56**).[120] This has led to speculation that CS may be a binding component of the opioid receptor.

Kullmann has designed and synthesized a tetracontapeptide that mimics the binding of endogenous opioid peptides which he calls 'receptor mimetic peptide' (RMP) (Figure 12).[235] According to his rationale RMP provides for the postulated lipophilic binding site *via* the side chains of Ile[3] and Phe[15]. The anionic binding site is represented by the γ carboxylate function of Glu[40], which can form a salt bridge to the positively charged amino group of morphine or the enkephalins. The phenolic hydroxyl group of the enkephalins may hydrogen bond to Glu[17]. The oripavine lipophilic binding site is accommodated by Phe[28] and Phe[36] of RMP. To test the binding characteristics of RMP the affinity of a series of peptides was determined by measuring their ability to displace Leu-enkephalin from RMP: dynorphin (1–8) has $K_i = 1.47 \times 10^{-5}$ M; Met-enkephalin $K_i = 4.95 \times 10^{-5}$ M; naloxone $K_i = 7.46 \times 10^{-3}$ M and neither CCK (1–8) nor the MSH fragment, Tyr-Val-Met-Gly have any effect up to 10^{-2} M. Although this work represents an interesting first step in the design of an opioid receptor mimetic it should be noted that the reported binding affinities for the enkephalins (**4, 5**) and naloxone (**12**) are several orders of magnitude lower than those obtained with *in vitro* opioid receptors.

Neither the CS nor RMP models account for differences between the opioid receptor subtypes.

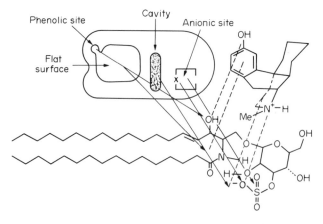

Figure 11 A comparison between CS and Beckett and Casy's model showing possible interactions with a morphinan derivative[234]

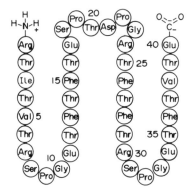

Figure 12 Opioid receptor mimetic peptide (RMP)[235]

13.2.9 CLINICAL USES OF OPIOID DRUGS

13.2.9.1 Introduction

Opium is the dried sap of the poppy plant *Papaver somniferum* and has long been used to treat pain. In 1805 morphine was purified from crude opium[236] and was shown to be a potent analgesic that is still widely used in hospitals today. In the last 50 years many new μ-selective opioid (narcotic) analgesic drugs have been tested in man but they all suffer from clinically limiting side effects. This section describes the opioid effects of agonists (including the first clinical reports on κ-selective and δ-selective ligands), mixed agonist–antagonist and endogenous peptides.

13.2.9.2 Clinical Properties of Opiate Agonists

Morphine is the prototype opiate analgesic. It is still the standard by which most new centrally acting analgesics are measured and its clinical properties are typical of other drugs in this category, some of which are shown in Table 21.[237] Morphine (**1**) still provides effective analgesia to patients with postoperative pain (7–9 mg, s.c.)[238] and to cancer patients.[239] The most commonly reported side effects include respiratory depression caused by a direct effect on the brain stem respiratory centres;[240] constipation, caused by decreasing mobility of the gastrointestinal tract[241] (which can be therapeutically useful in the treatment of diarrhoea or dysentry); nausea and vomiting, caused by direct stimulation of the chemoreceptor trigger zone;[241] and physical dependence (addiction).[242] After chronic administration of morphine is stopped or after administration of an opioid antagonist, for example naloxone (**12**), patients who have become physically dependent develop an abstinence

Table 21 Opiate Agonist Analgesics[237]

Name		Dose (mg)[a]		Duration (h)[b]
Non-proprietary	Trade (US)	Parenteral	Oral	
Alphaprodine	Nisentil	20–60	—	1–2
Anileridine	Leritine	75–100	25–50	2–6
Codeine	—	15–60	15–60	4–6
Dihydrocodine	Paracodine	10–30	10–30	4–6
Ethoheptazine	Zactane	–	75–100	5–6
Fentanyl	Sublimaze	0.05–0.1	–	0.5–1
Heroin	–	–	2–5	3–6
Hydrocodone	Dicodid	–	5–10	4–6
Hydromorphine	Dilaudid	1–4	1–4	4–6
Levorphanol	Levo-dromoran	2–3	2–3	6–8
Meperidine	Demerol	50–100	50–100	3–4
Methadone	Dolophine	2–10	2–10	3–4
Metopon	Metopon	3–6	10–20	3–6
Morphine	–	7–15	–	4–5
Oxycodone	–	–	4–5	5–6
Oxymorphone	Numorphan	1	–	4–6
Pholcodine	Ethnine	–	10–15	4–5
Piminodine	Alvodine	10–20	25–50	4–6
Propoxyphene hydrochloride	Darvon	–	32–65	3–4
Propoxyphene napsylate	Darvon-N	–	50–100	3–4

[a] Usual therapeutic dose range in non-tolerant patients. The treatment of severe pain usually requires administration of doses towards the higher level of the range. [b] Usual duration of the analgesic effect following administration of a therapeutic dose. The duration may vary with the dose administered and intensity of pain.

syndrome characterized by abnormal pain, irritability, cold sweats, diarrhoea, nausea and vomiting. These effects usually last 4–10 weeks.[237, 243]

Morphine is normally administered parenterally because of poor bioavailability[244] but it has been shown to provide effective analgesia to cancer patients p.o.[245] Other routes include buccal administration which has been used to deliver opioid premedication,[246] intrathecal[247] and epidural[248] administration.

A list of clinically used opiate agonist analgesics is shown in Table 21. The most widely used narcotic analgesic in terms of annual sales is propoxyphene (**97**) as distalgesic. The dextro isomer has approximately the same potency as codeine in the treatment of mild to moderate pain.[249] It has a slightly reduced liability to cause physical and psychological dependence[237,250] but other side effects are qualitatively similar to those of morphine. There has been speculation based on animal studies that a selective κ-opioid agonist will produce analgesia without morphine-like dependence liability[251] but to date this has not been confirmed in human clinical studies. In phase I clinical studies the κ-selective non-peptide, U-62066 (spiradoline) (**26**) (κ $K_i = 2.5$ nM, μ/κ ratio = 84),[220] produced a water only diuresis at low doses (2–6 μg kg^{-1}, i.m.)[251] and the benzomorphan κ agonist MR2033 (**132**) caused naloxone reversible dysphoric and psychotomimetic effects.[108] The analgesic doses of these compounds have not been reported.

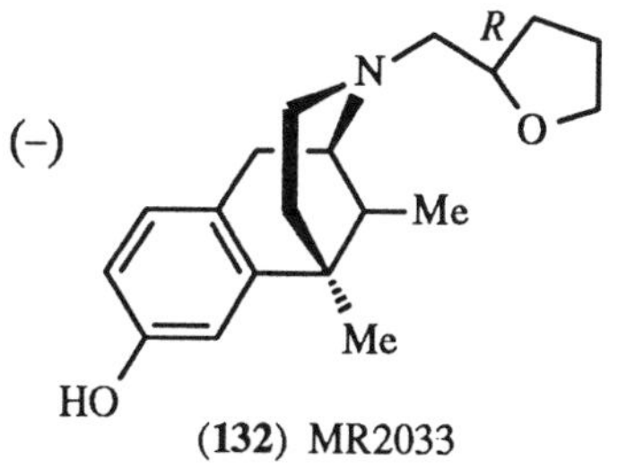

(**132**) MR2033

13.2.9.3 Clinical Properties of Mixed Agonist–Antagonists

Mixed agonist–antagonist opioids are those which have affinity and intrinsic activity at one or more of the opioid receptor subtypes and also have antagonist properties at at least one of the other

Table 22 Mixed Agonist–Antagonist Analgesics[237]

| Name | | Dose (mg)[a] | | Duration (h)[b] |
Non-proprietary	Trade (US)	Parenteral	Oral	
Buprenorphine	Buprenex	0.3–0.6	0.4–0.8[c]	6–8
Butorphanol	Stadol	0.5–4.0	—	3–4
Nalbuphine	Nubain	10–20	—	3–6
Pentazocine	Talwin	30–60	50–100	3–4

[a] Usual therapeutic dose range in non-tolerant patients. The treatment of severe pain usually requires administration of doses towards the higher level of the range. [b] Usual duration of the analgesic effect following administration of a therapeutic dose. The duration may vary with the dose administered and intensity of pain. [c] Sublingual.

receptor subtypes. These compounds are characterized pharmacologically as having a 'ceiling effect' that is lower than the maximum effect of a full agonist. Compounds with this profile, for example those in Table 22, have been developed in the hope that they would have a reduced abuse potential.[252] The prototype agent, pentazocine (133) does not substitute for morphine in morphine-dependent patients[253] and it has been classified as a non-addictive analgesic but in a direct addiction study the abrupt withdrawal of pentazocine resulted in a mild abstinence syndrome.[254] It causes a high incidence of sedation, dizziness and dysphoria which is sometimes more discomforting than the original pain,[255] while an overdose of pentazocine causes respiratory depression and seizures which can be reversed by naloxone (12).[256]

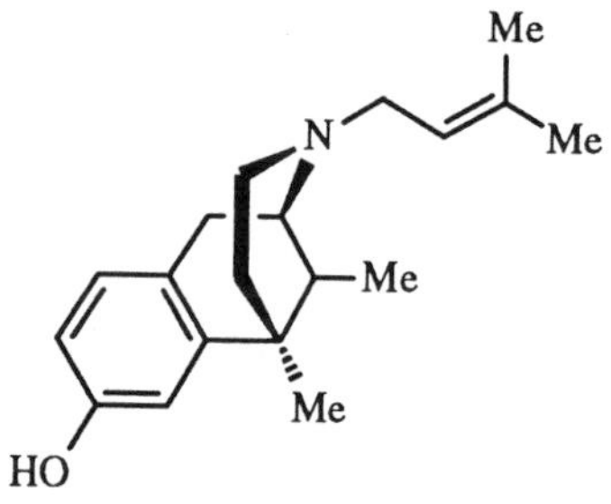

(133) Pentazocine

13.2.9.4 Clinical Properties of Endogenous Opioid Peptides and Derivatives

Both β-endorphin (7)[257] and dynorphin (6)[258] have produced marked analgesia in cancer patients with intractable pain but only when given intrathecally. β-Endorphin does not work i.v. indicating that is does not cross the blood–brain barrier or is rapidly metabolized.[259]

The enkephalins are too labile *in vivo* to be of clinical use but some stabilized derivatives have been tested. Epidurally administered FK 33-824 (Tyr-D-Ala-Gly-NMePhe-Met(O)-OH) had an analgesic effect in patients with postoperative pain but this was not dose related and it induced a feeling of anxiety and heaviness in the muscles.[260] A 70 mg parenteral dose of metkephamid (LY 127623, Tyr-Ala-Gly-Phe-NMeGly-NH₂) was equivalent to 100 mg of meperidine in treating postoperative pain.[261] Side effects included a sensation of heavy limbs, dry mouth, eye redness and nasal stuffiness which are different from μ-selective opiate drugs and may be due to the relatively high affinity of metkephamid for δ-receptors.[262]

The δ-selective peptide DADLE (Tyr-D-Ala-Gly-Phe-D-Leu) (14) has been found to produce effective analgesia after intrathecal administration to cancer patients who had become tolerant to the analgesic effects of morphine.[263]

13.2.10 REFERENCES

1. A. Goldstein, L. I. Lowrey and B. K. Pal, *Proc. Natl. Acad. Sci. USA*, 1971, **68**, 1742; C. B. Pert and S. H. Snyder, *Science (Washington, D.C.)*, 1973, **179**, 1011; L. Terenius, *Acta Pharmacol. Toxicol.*, 1973, **33**, 377.
2. W. R. Martin, G. C. Eades, J. A. Thompson, R. E. Huppler and P. E. Gilbert, *J. Pharmacol. Exp. Ther.*, 1976, **197**, 517.

3. R. S. Zukin and S. R. Zukin, *Mol. Pharmacol.*, 1981, **20**, 246.

4. J. Hughes, T. W. Smith, H. W. Kosterlitz, L. A. Fothergill, B. A. Morgan and H. R. Morris, *Nature (London)*, 1975, **258**, 577.

5. S. H. Snyder and R. Simantov, *J. Neurochem.*, 1977, **28**, 13.

6. V. Hollt, *Annu. Rev. Pharmacol. Toxicol.*, 1986, **26**, 59.

7. S. Numa, in 'The Peptides', ed. S. Udenfriend and J. Meienhofer, Academic Press, New York, 1984, vol. 6, 'Opioid Peptides: Biology, Chemistry and Genetics', p. 1.

8. D. A. Lynch and S. H. Snyder, *Annu. Rev. Biochem.*, 1986, **55**, 733.

9. V. Clement-Jones and G. M. Besser, in 'The Peptides', ed. S. Udenfriend and J. Meinhofer, Academic Press, New York, 1984, vol. 6, 'Opioid Peptides: Biology, Chemistry and Genetics', p. 323.

10. M. J. Kuhar, C. B. Pert and S. H. Snyder, *Nature (London)*, 1973, **245**, 447; J. M. Hiller, J. Pearson and E. J. Simon, *Res. Commun. Chem. Pathol. Pharmacol.*, 1973, **6**, 1052.

11. J. M. Polak, S. N. Sullivan, S. R. Bloom, P. Facer and A. G. E. Pearse, *Lancet*, 1977, **1**, 972.

12. A. Vaalasti, I. Linnoila and A. Hervonen, *Histochemistry*, 1980, **66**, 89.

13. S. P. Hunt, M. N. Rossor, P. C. Emson and V. Clement-Jones, *Lancet*, 1982, **1**, 1023.

14. V. Clement-Jones, P. J. Lowry, L. H. Rees and G. M. Besser, *Nature (London)*, 1980, **283**, 295.

15. J. F. Bruni, W. B. Watkins and S. S. C. Yen, *J. Clin. Endocrinol. Metab.*, 1979, **49**, 649.

16. S. Tachibana, K. Araki, S. Olnya and S. Yoshida, *Nature (London)*, 1982, **295**, 339.

17. E. W. D. Colt, S. L. Wardlaw and A. G. Frantz, *Life Sci.*, 1981, **28**, 1637.

18. L. Graf, A. Z. Ronai, S. Bajusz, G. Cseh and I. Szekely, *Nature (London)*, 1976, **264**, 240; H. H. Loh, L.-F. Tseng, E. Wei and C. H. Li, *Proc. Natl. Acad. Sci. USA*, 1976, **73**, 2895; A. S. Horn and J. R. Rogers, *Nature (London)*, 1976, **206**, 797; L.-F. Tseng, H. H. Loh and C. H. Li, *Nature (London)*, 1976, **263**, 239.

19. B. A. Morgan, C. F. C. Smith, A. A. Waterfield, J. Hughes and H. W. Kosterlitz, *J. Pharm. Pharmacol.*, 1976, **28**, 660; N. J. Birdsall, A. F. Bradbury, A. S. V. Burgen, E. C. Hulme, D. G. Smyth and C. R. Snell, *Br. J. Pharmacol.*, 1976, **58**, 460P; D. Yamashiro, L.-F. Tseng, B. A. Donenn, H. H. Loh and C. H. Li, *Int. J. Pept. Protein Res.*, 1977, **10**, 159; J. F. W. Deakin, J. O. Dostrovsky and D. G. Smyth, *Biochem. J.*, 1980, **189**, 501; E. Weber, C. J. Evans and J. D. Barchas, *Biochem. Biophys. Res. Commun.*, 1981, **103**, 982.

20. N. Marks, M. Benuk and M. J. Berg, *NIDA Res. Monogr. Ser.*, 1986, **70**, 66; Y. Shimohigashi, *NIDA Res. Monogr.*, 1986, **69**, 65; M.-C. Fournie-Zaluski, P. Chaillet, R. Bouboutou, A. Coulaud, P. Cherot, G. Waksman, J. Costentin and B. P. Roques, *Eur. J. Pharmacol.*, 1984, **102**, 525.

21. B. P. Roques and M.-C. Fournie-Zaluski, *NIDA Res. Monogr. Ser.*, 1986, **70**, 128.

22. M.-C. Fournie-Zaluski, A. Couland, R. Bouboutou, P. Chaillet, J. Davin, G. Waksman, J. Costentin and B. P. Roques, *J. Med. Chem.*, 1985, **28**, 1158; P. Cherot, J. Devin, M.-C. Fournie-Zaluski and B. P. Roques, *Mol. Pharmacol.*, 1986, **30**, 338.

23. R. E. Chipkin, *Drugs Future*, 1986, **11**, 593; S. Ehrenpreis, *Prog. Clin. Biol. Res.*, 1985, **192**, 363.

24. *SCRIP Magazine*, 1987, No. 1232, p. 21.

25. A. H. Beckett and A. F. Casy, *J. Pharm. Pharmacol.*, 1954, **6**, 986.

26. P. S. Portoghese, *J. Med. Chem.*, 1965, **8**, 609.

27. W. R. Martin, *Pharmacol. Rev.*, 1967, **19**, 463.

28. P. E. Gilbert and W. R. Martin, *J. Pharmacol. Exp. Ther.*, 1976, **198**, 66.

29. S. G. Holtzmann, *J. Pharmacol. Exp. Ther.*, 1980, **214**, 614; H. E. Shannon, *Eur. J. Pharmacol.*, 1982, **84**, 225; G. T. Shearman and A. Herz, *Psychopharmacology (Berlin)*, 1982, **78**, 63.

30. J. A. H. Lord, A. A. Waterfield, J. Hughes and H. W. Kosterlitz, *Nature (London)*, 1977, **267**, 495.

31. L. E. Robson and H. W. Kosterlitz, *Proc. R. Soc. London, Ser. B*, 1979, **205**, 425; J. R. Smith and E. J. Simon, *Proc. Natl. Acad. Sci. USA*, 1980, **77**, 281.

32. H. W. Kosterlitz, S. J. Paterson and L. E. Robson, *Br. J. Pharmacol.*, 1981, **73**, 939.

33. H. W. Kosterlitz and S. J. Paterson, *Br. J. Pharmacol.*, 1981, **73**, 299P.

34. H. I. Mosberg, R. Hurst, V. J. Hruby, K. Gee, H. I. Yamamura, J. J. Galligan and T. F. Burks, *Life Sci.*, 1983, **33**, Suppl. 1, 447.

35. M. G. C. Gillan, H. W. Kosterlitz and S. J. Paterson, *Br. J. Pharmacol.*, 1980, **70**, 481.

36. M. G. C. Gillan and H. W. Kosterlitz, *Br. J. Pharmacol.*, 1982, **77**, 461.

37. A. Mansour, M. E. Lewis, H. Khachaturian, H. Akil and S. Watson, *Brain Res.*, 1986, **399**, 69.

38. C. R. Clark, B. Birchmore, N. A. Sharif, J. C. Hunter, R. G. Hill and J. Hughes, *Br. J. Pharmacol.*, 1987, **91**, 299P.

39. R. Quirion and C. Pilapil, *Eur. J. Pharmacol.*, 1984, **99**, 361; E. A. Young, J. M. Walker, M. Lewis, R. A. Houghton, J. H. Woods and H. Akil, *Eur. J. Pharmacol.*, 1986, **121**, 355.

40. R. A. Lahti, M. M. Mickelson, J. M. McCall and P. F. Von Voightlander, *Eur. J. Pharmacol.*, 1985, **109**, 281.

41. R. R. Goodman, S. H. Snyder, M. J. Kuher and W. S. Young, *Proc. Natl. Acad. Sci. USA*, 1980, **77**, 6239.

42. R. R. Goodman and S. H. Snyder, *Proc. Natl. Acad. Sci. USA*, 1982, **79**, 5703.

43. R. R. Goodman and S. H. Snyder, *Life Sci.*, 1982, **31**, 1291.

44. R. W. Foote and R. Maurer, *Eur. J. Pharmacol.*, 1982, **85**, 99.

45. A. D. Corbett, M. G. C. Gillan, H. W. Kosterlitz and S. J. Paterson, *Br. J. Pharmacol.*, 1985, **86**, 704P.

46. C. B. Pert and S. H. Snyder, *Mol. Pharmacol.*, 1974, **10**, 868; A. J. Blume, *Proc. Natl. Acad. Sci. USA*, 1978, **75**, 1713.

47. A. Pfeiffer, W. Sadee and A. Herz, *J. Neurosci.*, 1982, **7**, 912.

48. K. J. Chang, A. Hazum, A. Killian and P. Cuatrecasas, *Mol. Pharmacol.*, 1981, **20**, 1.

49. B. Frances, C. Moisand and J. C. Meunier, *Eur. J. Pharmacol.*, 1985, **117**, 223.

50. R. S. Zukin and A. R. Gintzler, *Brain Res.*, 1980, **186**, 486.

51. P. Jauzac, A. Puget and J. C. Meunier, *Life Sci.*, 1983, **33**, 195.

52. A. J. Blume, D. Lichtshtein and G. Boone, *Proc. Natl. Acad. Sci. USA*, 1979, **76**, 5626.

53. J. Magnan, S. J. Paterson, A. Tavani and H. W. Kosterlitz, *Naunyn-Schmiedeberg's Arch. Pharmacol.*, 1982, **319**, 197.

54. S. Lemaire and A. Turcotte, *Can. J. Physiol. Pharmacol.*, 1986, **64**, 673.

55. H. W. Kosterlitz, R. J. Lydon and A. J. Watt, *Br. J. Pharmacol.*, 1970, **39**, 398; S. Lemaire, J. Magnan and D. Regoli, *Br. J. Pharmacol.*, 1978, **64**, 327.

56. T. Oka, K. Negishi, M. Suda, T. Matsumiya, T. Inazu and M. Ueki, *Eur. J. Pharmacol.*, 1981, **73**, 235.

57. A. T. McKnight, A. D. Corbett, M. Marcoli and H. W. Kosterlitz, *Neuropharmacology*, 1985, **24**, 1011.
58. M. Hutchinson, H. W. Kosterlitz, F. M. Leslie and A. A. Waterfield, *Br. J. Pharmacol.*, 1975, **55**, 541; H. W. Kosterlitz, J. A. H. Lord, S. J. Paterson and A. A. Waterfield, *Br. J. Pharmacol.*, 1980, **68**, 333.
59. S. J. Ward, P. S. Portoghese and A. F. Takemori, *Eur. J. Pharmacol.*, 1982, **85**, 163.
60. P. S. Portoghese, D. L. Larson, J. B. Jiang, T. P. Caruso and A. E. Takemori, *J. Med. Chem.*, 1979, **22**, 168.
61. P. S. Portoghese, D. L. Larson, L. M. Sayre, D. S. Fries and A. E. Takemori, *J. Med. Chem.*, 1980, **23**, 233.
62. A. E. Takemori, S. L. Larson and P. S. Portoghese, *Eur. J. Pharmacol.*, 1981, **70**, 445.
63. A. G. Hayes, M. J. Sheehan and M. B. Tyers, *Br. J. Pharmacol.*, 1985, **86**, 899.
64. A. Goldstein and I. F. James, *Mol. Pharmacol.*, 1984, **25**, 343.
65. A. E. Takemori, M. Ikeda and P. S. Portoghese, *Eur. J. Pharmacol.*, 1986, **123**, 357.
66. L. Miller, J. S. Shaw and E. M. Whiting, *Br. J. Pharmacol.*, 1986, **87**, 595.
67. A. G. Hayes and A. J. Kelly, *Eur. J. Pharmacol.*, 1985, **110**, 317.
68. M. G. C. Gillan, H. W. Kosterlitz and J. Magnan, *Br. J. Pharmacol.*, 1981, **72**, 13.
69. C. F. C. Smith and M. J. Rance, *Life Sci.*, 1983, **33**, Suppl. 1, 327.
70. A. G. Hayes and M. J. Sheehan, *Br. J. Pharmacol.*, 1986, **88**, 276P.
71. R. Schulz, E. Faase, M. Wuster and A. Herz, *Life Sci.*, 1979, **24**, 843; A. D. Corbett, M. G. C. Gillan, H. W. Kosterlitz, A. T. McKnight and S. J. Paterson, *Br. J. Pharmacol.*, 1983, **80**, 669P.
72. M. A. Werz and R. L. MacDonald, *Neuroscience*, 1984, **46**, 185.
73. E. Cherubini and R. A. North, *Proc. Natl. Acad. Sci. USA*, 1985, **82**, 1860.
74. C. M. Pepper and G. Henderson, *Science (Washington, D.C.)*, 1980, **209**, 394.
75. J. T. Williams, T. M. Egan and R. A. North, *Nature (London)*, 1982, **299**, 74; K. Morita and R. A. North, *Brain Res.*, 1981, **242**, 145; M. A. Werz and R. L. MacDonald, *J. Pharmacol. Exp. Ther.*, 1983, **227**, 394.
76. P. Y. Law, J. Wu, J. E. Kohler and H. H. Loh, *J. Neurochem.*, 1981, **36**, 1834; D. M. F. Cooper, C. London, D. L. Gill and M. Rodbell, *J. Neurochem.*, 1982, **38**, 1164.
77. D. Tsang, A. T. Tan, J. C. Henry and S. Lal, *Brain Res.*, 1978, **152**, 521; S. A. Walczak, D. Wilkening and M. H. Mokman, *Brain Res.*, 1979, **160**, 105; A. N. M. Schoffelmeer, H. A. Hansen, J. C. Stoof and A. H. Mulder, *Eur. J. Pharmacol.*, 1985, **118**, 363.
78. S. K. Sharma, M. Nirenberg and W. A. Klee, *Proc. Natl. Acad. Sci. USA*, 1975, **72**, 590; W. A. Klee and M. Nirenberg, *Nature (London)*, 1976, **263**, 609.
79. P. Y. Law, D. S. Hom and H. H. Loh, *Mol. Pharmacol.*, 1982, **23**, 26.
80. G. Koski and W. A. Klee, *Proc. Natl. Acad. Sci. USA*, 1981, **78**, 4185.
81. T. Katada and M. Ui, *Proc. Natl. Acad. Sci. USA*, 1982, **79**, 3129.
82. D. L. Burns, E. L. Hewlett, J. Moss and M. Vaughan, *J. Biol. Chem.*, 1983, **258**, 1435.
83. J. F. Tucker, *Br. J. Pharmacol.*, 1984, **83**, 326.
84. G. K. Aghajanian and Y.-Y. Wang, *Neuropharmacology*, 1987, **26**, 793.
85. S. M. Crain, B. Crain and E. R. Petersen, *Brain Res.*, 1986, **370**, 61.
86. S. M. Crain, B. Crain and M. H. Makman, *Brain Res.*, 1987, **400**, 185.
87. M. J. Clark, S. D. Levenson and F. Medzihradsky, *Life Sci.*, 1986, **39**, 1721.
88. H. Ueda, H. Misawa, N. Fukushima and H. Takagi, *Eur. J. Pharmacol.*, 1987, **138**, 129.
89. W. R. Martin, *Pharmacol. Rev.*, 1983, **35**, 283.
90. T. L. Yaksh, *J. Pharmacol. Exp. Ther.*, 1983, **226**, 303; R. E. Rodriguez, G. E. Leighton, R. G. Hill and J. Hughes, *Neuropeptides (Edinburgh)*, 1986, **8**, 221.
91. J. C. Yeung and T. S. Rudy, *J. Pharmacol. Exp. Ther.*, 1980, **215**, 633; K.-J. Chang, P. Cuatrecasas, E. T. Wei and J. K. Chang, *Life Sci.*, 1982, **30**, 1547.
92. S. J. Ward and A. E. Takemori, *J. Pharmacol. Exp. Ther.*, 1983, **224**, 525.
93. M. F. Piercey, R. A. Lahti, L. A. Schroeder, F. J. Einspahr and C. Barsuhn, *Life Sci.*, 1982, **31**, 1197; C. Schmauss, *Eur. J. Pharmacol.*, 1987, **137**, 197; G. E. Leighton, R. E. Rodriguez, R. G. Hill and J. Hughes, *Br. J. Pharmacol.*, 1987, **90**, 281P.
94. M. Skingle and M. B. Tyers, *J. Pharmacol. Methods*, 1979, **2**, 71.
95. M. B. Tyers, *Br. J. Pharmacol.*, 1980, **69**, 503.
96. M. F. Piercey and L. A. Schroeder, *Arch. Int. Pharmacodyn. Ther.*, 1980, **248**, 294; C. Schmauss and T. L. Yaksh, *J. Pharmacol. Exp. Ther.*, 1984, **228**, 1.
97. A. G. Hayes, M. J. Sheehan and M. B. Tyers, *Br. J. Pharmacol.*, 1987, **91**, 823.
98. G. F. Steinfels and L. Cook, *J. Pharmacol. Exp. Ther.*, 1986, **236**, 111.
99. L. A. Dykstra, D. E. Gmerek, G. Winger and J. H. Woods, *J. Pharmacol. Exp. Ther.*, 1987, **242**, 413.
100. G. E. Leighton, M. A. Johnson, K. G. Meecham, R. G. Hill and J. Hughes, *Br. J. Pharmacol.*, 1987, **92**, 915.
101. A. H. Tang and R. J. Collins, *Psychopharmacology (Berlin)*, 1985, **85**, 309.
102. J. D. Leander, *J. Pharmacol. Exp. Ther.*, 1983, **224**, 89.
103. G. R. Peters, N. J. Ward, E. G. Antal, P. Y. Lai and E. W. DeMaar, *J. Pharmacol. Exp. Ther.*, 1987, **240**, 128.
104. W. R. Martin, C. G. Eades, W. O. Thompson, J. A. Thompson and H. G. Flanary, *J. Pharmacol. Exp. Ther.*, 1974, **189**, 759.
105. D. E. Gmerek and J. H. Woods, *Life Sci.*, 1986, **39**, 987.
106. D. E. Gmerek, L. A. Dykstra and J. H. Woods, *J. Pharmacol. Exp. Ther.*, 1987, **242**, 428.
107. P. F. Von Voightlander, R. A. Lahti and J. H. Ludens, *J. Pharmacol. Exp. Ther.*, 1983, **224**, 7.
108. A. Pfeiffer, V. Brantl, A. Herz and H. M. Emrich, *Science (Washington, D.C.)*, 1986, **233**, 774.
109. G. T. Shearman and C. Stenfors, *Pharmacol., Biochem. Behav.*, 1986, **24**, 861; J. M. Moerschbaecher, C. Devia and C. Brooklehurst, *J. Pharmacol. Exp. Ther.*, 1987, **240**, 74.
110. M. Denavit-Saubie, J. Champagnat and W. Zieglgansberger, *Brain Res.*, 1978, **155**, 55; M. Pokorski, P. Grieb and J. Wideman, *Brain Res.*, 1981, **211**, 221.
111. D. S. McQueen and J. A. Ribeiro, *Br. J. Pharmacol.*, 1980, **71**, 297; D. S. McQueen and J. A. Ribeiro, *Q. J. Exp. Physiol.*, 1981, **66**, 273.
112. A. F. Bradbury, D. G. Smyth and C. R. Snell, *Nature (London)*, 1976, **260**, 165.
113. Y. Isogai, G. Nementhy and H. A. Scheraga, *Proc. Natl. Acad. Sci. USA*, 1977, **74**, 414.

114. C. Garbay-Jaureguiberry, B. P. Roques, R. Oberlin, M. Anteunis and A. K. Lala, *Biochem. Biophys. Res. Commun.*, 1976, **71**, 558; C. R. Jones, V. Garsky and W. A. Gibbons, *Biochem. Biophys. Res. Commun.*, 1977, **76**, 619.

115. A. F. Casy, *J. Pharm. Pharmacol.*, 1985, **37**, 421.

116. P. W. Schiller, in 'The Peptides, Analysis, Synthesis, Biology', ed. S. Udenfriend and J. Meienhoffer, Academic Press, New York, 1984, vol. 6.

117. P. W. Schiller, *NIDA Res. Monogr. Ser.*, 1986, **9**, 291; V. J. Hruby, *NIDA Res. Monogr. Ser.*, 1986, **69**, 128; V. Renugopalakrishnan, T. W. Colletter, L. A. Carreira and R. S. Rapaka, *NIDA Res. Monogr. Ser.*, 1986, **69**, 323; A. Camerman and N. Camerman, *NIDA Res. Monogr. Ser.*, 1986, **69**, 351; D. Mastropaolo, A. Camerman, L. Y. Y. Ma and N. Camerman, *Life Sci.*, 1987, **40**, 1995; M. A. Khaled, *NIDA Res. Monogr. Ser.*, 1986, **69**, 266; F. A. Gorin, T. M. Balasubramanian, C. D. Barry and G. R. Marshall, *J. Supramol. Struct.*, 1978, **9**, 27.

118. A. W. Lipowski, S. W. Tam and P. S. Portoghese, *J. Med. Chem.*, 1986, **29**, 1222.

119. V. J. Hruby, *NIDA Res. Monogr. Ser.*, 1986, **69**, 128.

120. A. F. Casy and R. T. Parfitt, 'Opioid Analgesics', Plenum Press, New York, 1986, chap. 10.

121. J. DiMiao, C. Lemieux and P. W. Schiller, *Life Sci.*, 1982, **31**, 2253.

122. P. W. Schiller, T. M.-D. Nguyen, J. DiMaio and C. Lemieux, *Life Sci.*, 1983, **33**, Suppl. 1, 319.

123. P. W. Schiller, T. M. Nguyen, C. Lemieux and L. A. Maziak, *J. Med. Chem.*, 1985, **28**, 1766; P. W. Schiller, T. M. Nguyen, L. Maziak and C. Lemieux, *Biochem. Biophys. Res. Commun.*, 1985, **127**, 558; H. I. Mosberg and P. W. Schiller, *Int. J. Pept. Protein Res.*, 1984, **23**, 462.

124. J. V. Edwards, A. F. Spatola, C. Lemieux and P. W. Schiller, *Biochem. Biophys. Res. Commun.*, 1986, **136**, 730.

125. N. Zhou and W. A. Gibbons, *J. Chem. Soc., Perkin Trans. 2*, 1986, 637.

126. R. Maroun and W. L. Mattice, *Biochem. Biophys. Res. Commun.*, 1981, **103**, 442.

127. C. R. Snell, *Biochim. Biophys. Acta*, 1984, **787**, 53.

128. P. Y. Chou and G. D. Fasman, *Biochemistry*, 1974, **13**, 211 and 222; P. Y. Chou, A. J. Alder and G. D. Fasman, *J. Mol. Biol.*, 1975, **96**, 29.

129. P. W. Schiller, *Int. J. Pept. Protein Res.*, 1983, **21**, 207; P. W. Schiller, B. Eggimann and T. M.-D. Nguyen, *Life Sci.*, 1982, **31**, 1777.

130. C. R. Beddell, R. B. Clark, R. L. Follenfant, L. A. Lowe, F. B. Ubatuba, S. Wilkinson and R. J. Miller, 'Biological Activity and Chemical Structures', Elsevier, Amsterdam, 1977, p. 177; H. W. Kosterlitz, J. A. H. Lord, S. J. Paterson and A. A. Waterfield, *Br. J. Pharmacol.*, 1980, **68**, 333; C. R. Beddell, L. A. Lowe and S. Wilkinson, *Prog. Med. Chem.*, 1980, **17**, 1; R. C. A. Fredrickson, *Life Sci.*, 1977, **21**, 23; M. Gordon and J. A. Vida, *Annu. Rep. Med. Chem.*, 1977, **12**, 20; J. S. Shaw and M. J. Turnbull, *Eur. J. Pharmacol.*, 1978, **49**, 313.

131. J. S. Morley and A. S. Dutta, *NIDA Res. Monogr. Ser.*, 1986, **69**, 42.

132. J. S. Morley, *Annu. Rev. Pharmacol. Toxicol.*, 1980, **20**, 81.

133. P. E. Hansen and B. A. Morgan, in 'The Peptides: Analysis, Synthesis, Biology', ed. S. Udenfriend and J. Meienhoffer, Academic Press, New York, 1984, vol. 6.

134. G. W. Hardy, *Amino-Acids, Pept. Proteins*, 1981, **14**; 1980, **13**; P. W. Schiller, *Amino-Acids, Pept. Proteins*, 1979, **12**; 1978, **11**; B. A. Morgan, *Amino-Acids, Pept. Proteins*, 1977, **10**; B. A. Morgan and G. Metcalf, *Amino-Acids, Pept. Proteins*, 1976, **9**.

135. H. W. Kosterlitz and J. Hughes, *Br. J. Psychiatry*, 1977, **130**, 298.

136. S. R. Childers, in 'Receptors and Recognition', ed. S. J. Enna and H. I. Yamamura, Chapman and Hall, London, 1980, vol. 9, series B.

137. S. Bajusz, A. Z. Ronai, J. I. Szekely, E. Miglecz and I. Berztei, *FEBS Lett.*, 1980, **110**, 85.

138. R. J. Miller and P. Cuatrecasas, *Naturwissenschaften*, 1978, **65**, 507.

139. R. E. Chipkin, D. H. Morris, M. G. English, J. D. Rosamond, C. H. Stammer, E. J. York and J. M. Stewart, *Life Sci.*, 1981, **28**, 1517.

140. R. J. Vavreck, E. J. York and J. M. Stewart, in 'Peptides: Synthesis–Structure Function', Proceedings of the 7th American Peptide Symposium, ed. D. H. Rich and E. Gross, Pierce Chemical Company, 1981, p. 629.

141. Y. Shimohiagashi and C. H. Stammer, *J. Chem. Soc., Perkin Trans. 1*, 1983, 803.

142. T. W. Smith and S. Wilkinson, in 'The Chemical Regulation of Biological Mechanisms', ed. A. M. Creighton and S. Turner, Royal Society of Chemistry, London, 1982, p. 230.

143. J. A. Kiritzy-Roy, S. K. Chan and E. T. Iwamoto, *Life Sci.*, 1983, **32**, 889.

144. H. W. Kosterlitz and S. J. Paterson, *Philos. Trans. R. Soc. London, Ser. B*, 1985, **308**, 291; H. Kosterlitz, *Proc. R. Soc. London, Ser. B*, 1985, **225**, 27.

145. A. Z. Ronai, J. Szekely, I. Berzetei, E. Miglecz and S. Bajusz, *Biochem. Biophys. Res. Commun.*, 1979, **91**, 1239.

146. T. Fiyioka, T. Matsunaga, H. Nakayama, Y. Kanaoka, Y. Hayashi, K. Kangawa and H. Matsuo, *J. Med. Chem.*, 1984, **27**, 836.

147. D. E. Benovitz and A. F. Spatalo, *Peptides (N.Y.)*, 1985, **6**, 257.

148. R. G. Almquist, C. M. Olsen, E. T. Uyeno and L. Toll, *J. Med. Chem.*, 1984, **27**, 115.

149. M. M. Hann, P. G. Sammes, P. D. Kennewell and J. B. Taylor, *J. Chem. Soc., Perkin Trans. 1*, 1982, 307.

150. Y. Shimohigashi, M. Waki, N. Izumia, T. Costa, A. Hertza, M. Kurono and K. Yagi, *Biochem. Int.*, 1986, **13**, 199.

151. R. A. Lutz, R. A. Cruciani, Y. Shimohigashi, T. Costa, S. Kassis, P. J. Munson and D. Rodbard, *Eur. J. Pharmacol.*, 1985, **111**, 257.

152. C. R. Beddell, L. A. Lowe and S. Wilkinson, *Prog. Med. Chem.*, 1980, **17**, 1.

153. D. Yamashiro and C. H. Li, in 'The Peptides: Analysis, Synthesis and Biology', ed. S. Udenfriend and J. Meienhofer, 1984, Academic Press, New York, vol. 6.

154. C. H. Li, *NIDA Res. Monogr. Ser.*, 1986, **70**, 109.

155. H.-Y. Yeung, D. Yamashiro, W.-C. Chang and C. H. Li, *Int. J. Pept. Protein Res.*, 1978, **12**, 42.

156. B. Rajashekhar and E. T. Kaiser, *J. Biol. Chem.*, 1986, **261**, 13617.

157. D. Yamashiro, C. H. Li and M. Westphal, *Int. J. Pept. Protein Res.*, 1984, **24**, 520.

158. D. Yamashiro, M. Westphal and C. H. Li, *Int. J. Pept. Protein Res.*, 1984, **24**, 516.

159. I. F. James, *NIDA Res. Monogr. Ser.*, 1986, **70**, 192.

160. A. D. Corbett, S. J. Paterson, A. T. McKnight, J. Magnan and H. W. Kosterlitz, *Nature (London)*, 1981, **299**, 79;

C. Chavkin and A. Goldstein, *Nature (London)*, 1981, **291**, 591; C. Chavkin, I. F. James and A. Goldstein, *Science (Washington)*, 1982, **215**, 413.

161. K. Okumura, Y. Hatanaka, H. Nakayama and Y. Kanaoka, *Pept. Chem.*, 1985, **22**, 379.
162. A. G. Hayes, M. Skingle and M. B. Tyres, *Life Sci.*, 1983, **33**, Suppl. 1, 657; C. Schmauss, T. L. Yaksh, Y. Shimohigashi, G. Harby, T. Jenson and D. Rodbard, *Life Sci.*, 1983, **33**, Suppl. 1, 653.
163. A. Turcotte, J. M. Lalonde, S. St.-Pierre and S. Lemaire, *Int. J. Pept. Protein Res.*, 1984, **23**, 361.
164. S. J. Paterson, H. W. Kosterlitz, R. J. Vavrek and J. M. Stewart, *Neuropeptides (Edinburgh)*, 1984, **5**, 177.
165. K. J. Chang, E. T. Wei. A. Killian and J. K. Chang, *J. Pharmacol. Exp. Ther.*, 1983, **227**, 403; K. J. Chang, *NIDA Res. Monogr. Ser.*, 1986, **69**, 101.
166. H. Matthies, H. Stark, B. Hartrodt, H. L. Ruethrick, H. T. Spieler, A. Barth and K. Neubert, *Peptides (N.Y.)*, **5**, 463.
167. N. Basso, M. Marcelli, A. Ginaldi and M. De Marco, *Peptides (N.Y.)*, 1985, **6**, Suppl. 3, 177.
168. K. Darlak, Z. Grzonka, P. Janicki, A. Czlonkowski and S. Witold Gumulka, *J. Med. Chem.*, 1983, **26**, 1445.
169. R. de Castiglione and A. C. Rossi, *Peptides (N.Y.)*, 1985, **6**, Suppl. 3, 117.
170. G. Feuerstein, *NIDA Res. Monogr. Ser.*, 1986, **69**, 112.
171. K. Kisara, S. Sakurada, T. Sakurada, Y. Sasaki, T. Sato, K. Suzuki and H. Watanabe, *Br. J. Pharmacol.*, 1986, **87**, 183; S. Salvadori, M. Marastoni, G. Balboni, E. Uberti and R. Tomatis, *Peptides*, 1985, **6**, Suppl. 3, 127; S. Salvadori, M. Marastoni, G. Balboni, G. P. Sarto and R. Tomatis, *J. Med. Chem.*, 1986, **29**, 889; S. Salvadori, M. Marastoni, G. Balboni, G. Marzola and R. Tomatis, *Int. J. Pept. Protein Res.*, 1986, **28**, 262; S. Salvadori, M. Marastoni, G. Balboni, G. Sarto and R. Tomatis, *Int. J. Pept. Protein Res.*, 1985, **25**, 526; S. Salvadori, L. Minozzi and R. Tomatis, *Farmaco, Ed. Sci.*, 1986, **41**, 103.
172. W. F. Michne, in 'Analgesics: Neurochemical, Behavioral and Clinical Perspectives', ed. M. Kuhar and G. Pasternack, Raven Press, New York, 1984, p. 125.
173. M. R. Johnson and G. M. Milne, in 'Burgers Medicinal Chemistry', 4th edn., part III, ed. M. E. Wolff, Wiley, New York, 1981, p. 699.
174. G. de Stevens, 'Analgetics', Academic Press, London, 1965.
175. *Annu. Rep. Med. Chem.*, 1965–1985, **1–20**.
176. H. Dreser, *Dtsch. Med. Wochenschr.*, 1898, **24**, 185.
177. M. Mackay and D. Hodgkin, *J. Chem. Soc.*, 1955, 3261.
178. N. B. Eddy, H. Halbach and O. J. Braenden, *Bull. W. H. O.*, 1957, **17**, 569; E. L. May, in 'Medicinal Chemistry', ed. A. Burger, Wiley (Interscience), New York, 1960, p. 311.
179. C. E. Inturrisi, M. Schultz, S. Shin, J. G. Ulmans, L. Angel and E. J. Simon, *Life Sci.*, 1983, **33**, Suppl. 1, 773.
180. E. L. Way, J. W. Kemp, J. M. Young and D. R. Grasetti, *J. Pharmacol. Exp. Ther.*, 1969, **129**, 144; C. Inturrisi, M. Max, J. Umans, M. Schultz, S. Shin, K. Foley and R. D. Houde, *Clin. Pharmacol. Ther.*, 1982, **31**, 235.
181. W. H. Oldendorf, S. Hyman, L. Braun and S. Z. Oldendorf, *Science (Washington, D.C.)*, 1972, **173**, 985.
182. P. S. Portoghese, G. Ronsisvalle, D. L. Larson and A. E. Takemori, *J. Med. Chem.*, 1986, **29**, 1650.
183. P. S. Portoghese, D. L. Larson, L. M. Sayre, C. B. Yim, G. Ronsisvalle, S. W. Tam and A. E. Takemori, *J. Med. Chem.*, 1986, **29**, 1855.
184. S. Botros, A. W. Lipkowski, A. E. Takemori and P. S. Portoghese, *J. Med. Chem.*, 1986, **29**, 874; P. S. Portoghese and A. E. Takemori, *Life Sci.*, 1985, **36**, 801.
185. P. S. Portoghese, D. L. Larson, C. B. Yim, L. M. Sayre, G. Ronsisvalle, A. W. Lipkowski, A. E. Takemori, K. C. Rice and S. W. Tam, *J. Med. Chem.*, 1985, **28**, 1140.
186. K. W. Bently and D. G. Hardy, *J. Am. Chem. Soc.*, 1967, **89**, 3267.
187. K. W. Bently, A. L. A. Boura, A. E. Fitzgerald, D. G. Hardy, A. McCoubrey, M. L. Aikman and R. E. Lister, *Nature (London)*, 1965, **206**, 102.
188. K. W. Bently, in 'The Alkaloids', ed. R. H. F. Manske, Academic Press, New York, 1971, vol. 13, p. 1.
189. G. F. Blane, A. L. A. Boura, A. E. Fitzgerald and R. E. Lister, *Br. J. Pharmacol.*, 1967, **30**, 11; D. Campbell, R. E. Lister and G. W. McNicol, *Clin. Pharmacol. Ther.*, 1964, **5**, 193; J. D. Wallach, *Vet. Med.*, 1969, **64**, 53; J. M. King and B. Carter, *Afr. Wildlife J.*, 1965, **3**, 19; J. D. Wallach, *J. Am. Vet. Med. Assoc.*, 1966, **149**, 875.
190. M. P. Kotick, D. L. Leland, J. O. Polazzi, J. F. Howes and A. Bousquet, *J. Med. Chem.*, 1983, **26**, 1050.
191. H. Schmidhammer, L. Aeppli, L. Atwell, F. Fritsch, A. E. Jacobson, M. Nebuchla and G. Sperk, *J. Med. Chem.*, 1984, **27**, 1575.
192. O. Eisleb and O. Schaumann, *Dtsch. Med. Wochenschr.*, 1939, **65**, 967.
193. P. A. J. Janssen, *Acta Anaesthesiol. Scand.*, 1982, **26**, 262.
194. E. L. McCawley, E. R. Hart and D. F. Marsh, *J. Am. Chem. Soc.*, 1941, **63**, 314.
195. J. S. Morley and A. S. Dutta, *NIDA Res. Monogr. Ser.*, 1986, **69**, 42.
195a. D. S. Fries and P. S. Portoghese, *J. Med. Chem.*, 1976, **19**, 1155.
196. V. P. Dole and M. E. Nyswander, *JAMA, J. Am. Med. Assoc.*, 1976, **235**, 2117; M. Gossop, *Lancet*, 1978, **1**, 812; R. G. Newman and W. B. Whitehill, *Lancet*, 1979, **2**, 485.
197. J. T. Pelton, W. Kazmierski, K. Gulya, H. I. Yamamura and V. J. Hruby, *J. Med. Chem.*, 1986, **29**, 2370; J. T. Pelton, K. Gulya, V. J. Hruby, S. Duckles and H. I. Yamamura, *Peptides (N.Y.)*, 1985, **6**, Suppl. 1, 159; V. J. Hruby, *NIDA Res. Monogr. Ser.*, 1986, **69**, 128.
198. R. Maurer, D. Romer, H. H. Buscher, B. H. Gahwiler, P. W. Thies and S. David, *Neuropeptides (Edinburgh)*, 1985, **5**, 387.
199. J. Szmuszkovicz and P. F. Von Voigtlander, *J. Med. Chem.*, 1986, **29**, 1087.
200. D. C. Horwell, *US Pat.*, 4 656 182 (1987) (*Chem. Abstr.*, 1987, **106**, 131 727), D. C. Horwell, *US Pat.*, 4 598 087 (1986) (*Chem. Abstr.*, 1986, **104**, 68 752).
201. D. F. Veber, R. Saperstein, R. F. Nutt, R. H. Freidinger, S. F. Brady, P. Curley, D. S. Perlow, W. J. Paleveda, C. D. Colton, A. G. Zacchei, D. J. Tocco, D. R. Hoff, R. L. Vandlen, J. E. Gehrich, L. Hall, L. Mandarino, E. H. Cordes, P. S. Anderson and R. Hirschmann, *Life Sci.*, 1984, **34**, 1371.
202. D. C. Horwell and D. Schofield, *US Pat.*, 4 663 343, (1987) (*Chem. Abstr.*, 1987, **107**, 77 620).
203. P. Petrillo, M. Amato and A. Tavani, *Neuropeptides (Edinburgh)*, 1985, **5**, 403; D. Romer, H. H. Buscher, R. C. Hill, R. Maurer, T. J. Petcher, H. Zeugner, W. Benson, E. Finner, W. Milkowski and P. W. Thies, *Nature (London)*, 1982, **298**, 759.
204. A. E. Takemori and P. S. Portoghese, *Annu. Rev. Pharmacol. Toxicol.*, 1985, **25**, 193.

205. P. S. Portoghese and A. E. Takemori, in 'The Chemical Regulation of Biological Mechanisms', ed. A. M. Creighton and S. Turner, Royal Society of Chemistry, London, 1982, p. 181; S. J. Ward, D. S. Fries, D. L. Larson, P. S. Portoghese and A. E. Takemori, *Eur. J. Pharmacol.*, 1985, **107**, 323.
206. B. R. Baker, 'Design of Active-Site-Directed Irreversible Enzyme Inhibitors', Wiley, New York, 1967.
207. J. F. Griffin, D. L. Larson and P. S. Portoghese, *J. Med. Chem.*, 1986, **29**, 778.
208. J. W. Schoenecker, A. E. Takemori and P. S. Portoghese, *J. Med. Chem.*, 1986, **29**, 1968.
209. G. A. Koolpe, W. L. Nelson, T. L. Gioannini, L. Ange and E. J. Simon, *J. Med. Chem.*, 1984, **27**, 1718.
210. T. R. Burke, Jr., B. S. Bajwa, A. E. Jackobson, K. C. Rice, R. A. Streaty and W. A. Klee, *J. Med. Chem.*, 1984, **27**, 1570.
211. P. S. Portoghese and D. L. Larson, *J. Pharm. Sci.*, 1968, **57**, 711.
212. W. F. M. Van Veber, C. J. E. Niemgeers and P. A. J. Janssen, *J. Med. Chem.*, 1974, **17**, 1047.
213. T. R. Burke, Jr., A. E. Jackobson, K. C. Rice, J. V. Silverton, W. F. Simmonds, R. A. Streaty and W. A. Klee, *J. Med. Chem.*, 1986, **29**, 1087.
214. L. A. Woods, *Pharmacol. Rev.*, 1956, **8**, 175; K. Unna, *J. Pharmacol. Exp. Ther.*, 1943, **79**, 27.
215. R. I. Bodman, *Proc. R. Soc. Med.*, 1953, **46**, 923; C. M. Gruber, Jr., *J. Pharmacol.*, 1954, **111**, 104; 'Martindale, The Extra Pharmacopoeia', 28th edn., ed. J. E. F. Reynolds, The Pharmaceutical Press, London, 1982, pp. 1002–1031.
216. W. F. Michne, R. T. Lewis, S. J. Michalec, A. K. Pierson and F. J. Rosenberg, *J. Med. Chem.*, 1979, **22**, 1158.
217. M. B. Tyres, A. G. Hayes and M. J. Sheehan, *Proc. Int. Narc. Res. Conf.*, 1986, 698.
218. J. W. Lewis, *Drug Alcohol Depend.*, 1985, **14**, 363; H. Adriaensen, B. Mattelaer and H. Vanmeenen, *Acta Anaesthesiol. Belg.*, 1985, **36**, 33; S. L. Wallenstein, R. F. Kaiko, A. G. Rogers and R. W. Honde, *NIDA Res. Monogr. Ser.*, 1982, **41**, 288.
219. A. Cheng, E. Uyeno, W. Polgar, L. Toll, J. A. Lawson, J. I. DeGraw, G. Loew, A. Camerman and N. Camerman, *J. Med. Chem.*, 1986, **29**, 531; G. H. Loew, L. Toll, E. Uyeno, A. Cheng, A. Judd, J. Lawson, C. Keys, P. Amsterdam and W. Pogar, *NIDA Res. Monogr. Ser.*, 1986, **69**, 231.
220. D. M. Zimmerman, S. E. Smits, M. D. Hynes, B. E. Cantrell, J. D. Leander, L. G. Mendelsohn and R. Nickander, *Drug Alcohol Depend.*, 1985, **14**, 381.
221. K. Ramabadran and M. F. Jen, *Arch. Int. Pharmacodyn. Ther.*, 1985, **274**, 180.
222. A. P. Feinberg, I. Creese and S. H. Snyder, *Proc. Natl. Acad. Sci. USA*, 1976, **73**, 4215.
223. M. Froimowitz and S. Matthysse, *J. Med. Chem.*, 1986, **29**, 573.
224. E. L. Eliel, S. Morris-Natschke and V. M. Kolb, *Org. Magn. Reson.*, 1984, **22**, 258.
225. C. F. Smith, *Life Sci.*, 1987, **40**, 267.
226. H. Awaya, E. L. May, M. D. Aceto, L. S. Harris, J. V. Silverton, K. C. Rice, M. V. Mattson and A. E. Jacobson, *J. Med. Chem.*, 1987, **30**, 947.
227. A. D. Corbett, M. G. C. Gillan, H. W. Kosterlitz, A. T. McKnight, S. J. Paterson and L. E. Robson, *Br. J. Pharmacol.*, 1984, **83**, 271.
228. J. E. Gairin, H. Mazarguil, P. Alvinerie, S. Saint-Pierre, J.-C. Meunier and J. Cros, *J. Med. Chem.*, 1986, **29**, 1913.
229. J. E. Gairin, C. Gouarderes, H. Mazarguil, P. Alvinerie and J. Cros, *Eur. J. Pharmacol.*, 1985, **106**, 457.
230. W. F. Simonds, G. Koski, R. A. Streaty, L. M. Hjelmeland and W. A. Klee, *Proc. Natl. Acad. Sci. USA*, 1980, **77**, 4623; J. M. Bidlack, L. G. Abood, P. Osei-Gyimah and S. Archer, *Proc. Natl. Acad. Sci. USA*, 1981, **78**, 636; J. M. Bidlack and L. G. Abood, *Life Sci.*, 1980, **27**, 331; U. T. Ruegg, J. M. Hiller and E. J. Simon, *Eur. J. Pharmacol.*, 1980, **64**, 367.
231. A. H. Beckett and A. F. Casy, *J. Pharm. Pharmacol.*, 1954, **6**, 986; A. H. Beckett, *J. Pharm. Pharmacol.*, 1956, **8**, 848; A. H. Beckett, A. F. Casy, N. J. Harper and P. M. Phillips, *J. Pharm. Pharmacol.*, 1956, **8**, 860.
232. V. M. Kolb, *Adv. Drug Res.*, 1987, **16**, 281.
233. A. P. Feinberg, I. Creese and S. H. Snyder, *Proc. Natl. Acad. Sci. USA*, 1976, **73**, 4215.
234. H. H. Loh, T. C. Cho, Y. C. Wu, R. A. Harris and E. L. Way, *Life Sci.*, 1975, **16**, 1811.
235. W. Kullmann, *J. Med. Chem.*, 1984, **27**, 106.
236. W. A. Serturner, *J. Pharmacol.*, 1805, **13**, 234.
237. C. A. Fredrickson and M. D. Hynes, in 'Drugs in Central Nervous System Disorders', ed. D. C. Horwell, Dekker, New York, 1985.
238. J. E. Denton and H. K. Beecher, *JAMA, J. Am. Med. Assoc.*, 1949, **141**, 1051; L. Lasagna and H. K. Beecher, *JAMA, J. Am. Med. Assoc.*, 1954, **156**, 230.
239. M. N. Levine, D. L. Sackett and H. Bush, *Arch. Intern. Med.*, 1986, **146**, 353.
240. R. D. Dripps and J. H. Comroe, Jr., *Anesthesiology*, 1945, **6**, 462; A. S. Keats and H. J. Beecher, *J. Pharmacol.*, 1952, **105**, 210; H. J. Loeschcke, A. Sweel, R. H. Kough and C. J. Lambertsen, *J. Pharmacol.*, 1953, **108**, 376.
241. J. H. Jaffe and W. R. Martin, in 'The Pharmacological Basis of Therapeutics', ed. A. G. Gilman, L. S. Goodman, T. W. Rall and F. Murad, 7th edn., Macmillan, New York, 1985; K. Budd, *Pharmacol. Ther.*, 1981, **12**, 575.
242. H. F. Fraser, G. D. Van Horn, W. R. Martin, A. B. Wolbach and H. R. Isbell, *J. Pharmacol. Exp. Ther.*, 1961, **133**, 371.
243. H. L. Andrews and C. K. Himmelsbach, *J. Pharmacol. Exp. Ther.*, 1944, **81**, 288.
244. H. K. Beecher, A. S. Keats, F. Mosteller and L. Lasagna, *J. Pharmacol.*, 1953, **109**, 393.
245. T. D. Walsh, *Pain*, 1984, **18**, 1.
246. A. P. Fisher, P. Vine, J. Whitlock and M. Hanna, *Anaesthesia*, 1986, **41**, 1104.
247. A. N. Gonzalez, H. M. M. Zimman, T. A. Molinero, M. J. H. Gonzalez, I. A. Simon, J. M. G. Ortiz and B. F. Ferrero, *Rev. Esp. Oncol.*, 1984, **31**, 639.
248. D. A. Cherry, G. K. Gourlay, M. J. Cousins and B. J. Gannon, *Anaesthesiol. Intensivemed. (Berlin)*, 1985, **13**, 145; S. Arner and B. Arner, *Acta Anaesthesiol. Scand.*, 1985, **29**, 32.
249. C. M. Gruber, Jr., *JAMA, J. Am. Med. Assoc.*, 1977, **237**, 2734; R. E. S. Young, *Curr. Ther. Res.*, 1978, **24**, 495.
250. S. W. Strode, *Am. Fam. Physician*, 1985, **32**, 105.
251. G. R. Peters, N. J. Ward, E. G. Antal, P. Y. Lai and E. W. De Maar, *J. Pharm. Exp. Ther.*, 1987, **240**, 128.
252. W. R. Martin, *Drug Alcohol Depend.*, 1985, **14**, 221.
253. H. E. Fraser and D. E. Rosenberg, *J. Pharmacol. Exp. Ther.*, 1964, **143**, 149.
254. D. R. Janinski, W. R. Martin and R. D. Hoeldthe, *Clin. Pharmacol. Ther.*, 1970, **11**, 385.
255. R. Paddock, G. Beer, J. W. Bellville, B. J. Giliberti, W. H. Forrest and E. V. Miller, *Clin. Pharmacol. Ther.*, 1969, **10**, 355; W. T. Beaver, S. L. Wallenstein, R. W. Houde and A. Rogers, *Clin. Pharmacol. Ther.*, 1966, **7**, 740.
256. L. Roytblat, R. Bear and T. Gesztes, *Isr. J. Med. Sci.*, 1986, **22**, 385.
257. T. Oyama, T. Jin, R. Yamaya, N. Ling and R. Guillemin, *Lancet*, 1976, **1**, 122.

258. H. L. Wen, Z. D. Mehal, B. H. Ong and W. K. K. Ho, *Peptides (N.Y.)*, 1987, **8**, 191.
259. F. E. Bloom, D. Segal, N. Ling and R. Guillemin, *Science (Washington, D.C.)*, 1976, **194**, 630; D. H. Catlin, K. K. Hui, H. H. Loh and C. H. Li, *Commun. Psychopharmacol.*, 1977, **1**, 439.
260. H. B. Andersen, B. C. Jorgenson and A. Engquist, *Acta Anaesthesiol. Scand.*, 1982, **26**, 69.
261. J. F. Calimlim, W. M. Wardell, K. Sriwatanakul, L. Lasagna and C. Cox, *Lancet*, 1982, **1**, 1375.
262. S. S. Bloomfield, T. P. Barden and J. Mitchell, *Clin. Pharmacol. Ther.*, 1983, **34**, 240.
263. D. E. Moulin, M. B. Max, R. F. Kaiko, C. E. Inturrisi, J. Maggard, T. L. Yaksh and K. M. Foley, *Pain*, 1985, **23**, 213; E. S. Krames, D. J. Wilkie and J. Gershow, *Pain*, 1986, **24**, 205.

13.3

Hypothalamic and Adenohypophyseal Hormone Receptors

COIMBATORE B. SRIKANT and MASOOD N. KHAN

McGill University and Royal Victoria Hospital, Montreal, Quebec, Canada

13.3.1 INTRODUCTION

Physiological studies in the mid-20th century laid the foundation for the concept that the hypothalamus might be the central organ unifying neuronal and endocrine systems. Two types of hypothalamic neurons, whose activities are tremendously influenced by input from other parts of the brain, particularly the limbic system, which is involved in emotion and response to stress, communicate directly with the pituitary gland: (i) the larger magnocellular neurons that terminate on and release their neurotransmitters into systemic vessels of the neural lobe (hypothalamo neurohypophyseal system); and (ii) the smaller parvocellular neurons that terminate on the primary plexus of the hypophyseal portal vessels leading to the anterior pituitary (hypothalamo adeno-hypophyseal system). The principal hypothalamic peptide hormones, which regulate the secretion of the different hormones from diverse endocrine cells in the pituitary, include gonadotropin releasing hormone (GnRH), corticotropin releasing hormone (CRH), thyrotropin releasing hormone (TRH), somatostatin (SS) and growth hormone releasing hormone (GRH). The various pituitary hormones [lutinizing hormone (LH), follicle stimulating hormone (FSH), adrenocorticotropin releasing hormone (ACTH), thyroid stimulating hormone (TSH), growth hormone (GH) and prolactin (PRL)] in turn modulate the function of peripheral endocrine organs. The pivotal role of the hypothalamic–pituitary axis in the neuroendocrine regulation of the peripheral endocrine organs is schematically depicted in Figure 1. The exquisite nature of the regulation is evident from the feedback control by a particular pituitary hormone of its hypothalamic regulatory hormone(s) on the one hand and of the pituitary hormone itself by the hormonal product stimulated by it in the target gland on the other hand. Such a regulation is dependent on the interaction of specific cell surface receptors with the respective hormone.

Analysis of the structural and functional characteristics of the receptors has begun to reveal the complexity of the events initiated by the binding of these hormones to their receptors, leading to the ultimate physiological response of the target cells. These processes involve alteration in the concentration of one or more multiple second messengers as the first step in a complex cascade of biochemical changes which lead to a fine-tuned physiological functioning of the responding cell. An understanding of these processes requires the detailed structural characterization of the binding

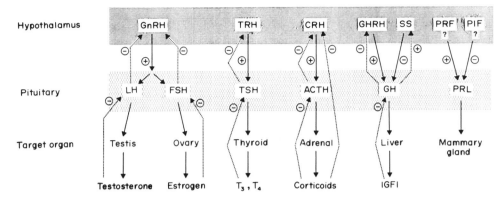

Figure 1 Simplified schematic depiction of neuroendocrine regulation of anterior pituitary hormone secretion. GnRH, TRH, CRH and GHRH exert a stimulatory effect on individual pituitary hormones as shown. SS, on the other hand, exerts inhibitory control on GH secretion. There are several PRL-stimulating factors (PRF) including TRH and vasoactive intestinal peptide. Inhibitory control of PRL secretion is exerted by putative PRL inhibitory factor(s) (PIF) of which dopamine is a prime candidate. The secretory output of the target glands stimulated by the pituitary hormones, in turn, exert feedback inhibition at the level of the pituitary. Corticosteroids can directly inhibit the secretion of CRH from the hypothalamus, in addition to exerting feedback regulation at the level of the pituitary corticotroph. The hypothalamic hormones are carried directly into the pituitary *via* the hypothalamo adenohypophyseal portal circulation. Each hormonal system is characterized by feedback regulatory control, indicated by the plus (stimulatory) or minus (inhibitory) signs

domains of the hormone and its receptor. It is in this context that the importance of manipulating the hormonal action by agents (usually synthetic peptides with structural homology to the native peptide) that elicit cellular response agonistic or antagonistic to the peptide hormone should be emphasized. The development of such compounds has increased our understanding of the molecular mechanism of hormonal action and enabled us to explore receptor function by using specific agonists or antagonists clinically for therapeutic application. This is best illustrated by studies concerning two hormones, SS and GnRH, which, because of their relatively small size, have been the targets of medicinal chemists for manipulating the natural peptide sequence to design antagonists or highly potent agonists with enhanced biological properties. Such an approach is not feasible for larger peptide hormones like CRH and GHRH. Receptors for these two hormones as well as those of TRH have not been completely characterized. In this chapter our current understanding of the anatomical distribution of the hypothalamic hormones (which regulate the endocrine status of the anterior pituitary) and their receptors, structural determinants of receptor binding and activity of these hormones, and the coupling of these receptors to diverse signalling pathways is reviewed. In the case of adenohypophyseal hormones, a very large body of data exists on receptors for GH, PRL, TSH, ACTH, LH and FSH. A detailed review of these receptors will be a formidable task that cannot justifiably be done, given the limitations of space. However, a major breakthrough has recently been made in the case of two of these (GH and PRL) receptors. Therefore only the GH and PRL receptors are reviewed to highlight the complete structural characterization revealed by cloning and sequencing.* Because of the vast amount of literature, the reader is often directed to previous review articles in lieu of most of the early references in this field.

13.3.2 GONADOTROPIN RELEASING HORMONE

Gonadotropin releasing hormone (GnRH), also known as lutinizing hormone releasing hormone (LHRH), is synthesized in neurosecretory cells in preoptic and medial basal regions of the hypothalamus.[1] It is delivered to the pituitary *via* the hypothalamo hypophyseal portal circulation in a pulsatile manner where it stimulates the secretion of LH and FSH.[2] In the male, FSH stimulates spermatogenesis and LH stimulates androgen production in testicular Leydig cells. In the female LH stimulates ovulation and corpus luteum formation, while FSH promotes growth and maturation of ovarian follicles. GnRH thus integrates the neural and endocrine systems. The most important

---

*Since this chapter was written, the LH/HCG receptor has been cloned and shown to contain a seven transmembrane spanning domain similar to other adenylate cyclase coupled receptors (K. C. McFarland *et al.*, *Science (Washington, D.C.)*, 1989, **245**, 494 and H. Loosfelt *et al.*, *Science (Washington, D.C.)*, 1989, **245**, 525).

physiological feature of GnRH release is its pulsatile secretory pattern. Episodic surge in the release of GnRH occurs at intervals of 20–60 min causing, in turn, episodic release of LH and FSH. The episodicity as well as the amplitude of GnRH pulses vary depending on the physiological state of the animal. GnRH has three major actions on pituitary gonadotropes: stimulation of gonadotropin synthesis, secretion and the priming effect. A unique feature of the pituitary gonadotropes is the modulation of their responsiveness to GnRH stimulation under physiological conditions.[3] The secretory response of these cells to GnRH, initiated by the spontaneous preovulatory surge in estradiol-17-β, increases 20- to 50-fold before and during the spontaneous surge of LH. The priming effect of GnRH synchronizes the increasing concentrations of this hormone in portal blood with the increase in pituitary responsiveness resulting in a massive ovulatory surge of LH. This effect of GnRH is unique, possibly because, apart from the oxytocin–uterine contraction system which operates during parturition, the ovulatory surge of LH is the only positive feedback endocrine system that operates under physiological conditions. The ability of GnRH to stimulate reproductive functions at pulsatile low doses in contrast to its ability to inhibit these functions at high doses has been exploited clinically to induce ovulation and spermatogenesis, contraception and in treatment of precocious puberty, endometriosis and steroid dependent tumors, cryptorchidism and other diseases.[4]

13.3.2.1 Structural Features and Biological Activity of GnRH Analogs

GnRH is a decapeptide with the primary structure of pyroGlu-His-Trp-Ser-Tyr-Gly-Leu-Arg-Pro-Gly(amide). Its easily defined structural features have led to the development of an array of very potent and useful agonists and antagonists,[5] which have increased our understanding of the mechanism of GnRH action. A large number of carboxy terminal amidated superagonists have been designed and developed based on Des-Gly^{10}-NH$_2$, proethylamide-GnRH, which is five times more potent on ovulation induction in rat.[6] The potent analogs of GnRH share certain characteristic structural modifications which combine one or more substitutions at amino acid residues 6 and 10, while retaining the Gln^1-Tyr^5 sequence. Gly^6 is adjacent to the site of proteolytic degradation and substitution of D-amino acids at this position yields metabolically stable peptides by strengthening the β turn in the molecule. Substitution of ethylamide for the Gly^{10} amide in analogs containing D-amino acids at position 6 increases the biological potency tenfold. D-Lys^6 derivatization permits, upon introduction of a unique epsilon group, further modification to design more suitable compounds including fluorescent derivatives. Biologically active GnRH analogs exist in a least energy conformation in which the amino and carboxy termini (pyro-Glu^1 and Gly^{10}-amide respectively) are in close proximity and are possibly involved in forming a configuration that is crucial for receptor recognition.[6] The importance of two aromatic residues and two carboxylic groups participating in hormone–receptor complex formation has also been shown.[7,8] Since highly charged polycations (polylysine molecules) can mimic the effect of GnRH on LH release in cultured pituitary cells, it seems that simple charge interaction can evoke LH release.[9] Thus, the Arg^8 residue in GnRH has been implicated to form ionic bonds with the negatively charged carboxy group of the receptor and the complex may be stabilized by π–π interactions between His,Trp and Tyr residues of the ligand and Tyr and Trp moieties of the receptor. D-Amino acid substitutions in the first three residues result in antagonistic properties. Since these analogs bind to the receptor but do not activate the effector system, it is obvious that the biological activity of the GnRH molecule requires the N-terminal residues. Des-His^2 GnRH and Des-His^2,Des-Gly^{10} GnRH ethylamide were the first antagonists identified in *in vitro* and *in vivo* studies respectively.[10,11] More potent antagonists which exhibit up to two orders of magnitude greater affinity for receptor binding than GnRH have since been developed. The common modifications which result in antagonistic behavior include residues 1, 2 and/or 3 as well as at 6 and 10.[6,12] Although GnRH receptors bind the antagonist molecules, the receptor–ligand complexes thus formed do not aggregate into clusters on the cell surface as is normal with GnRH agonist-bound receptors prior to internalization.[13]

13.3.2.2 GnRH Receptors

13.3.2.2.1 Pituitary GnRH receptors

The initial event in the action of GnRH, as in the case of all peptide hormones, is its interaction with specific receptors on target cells, the pituitary gonadotrophs. ^{3}H-Labeled GnRH and

[125]I-labeled GnRH, the first radioligands used in GnRH receptor assays, were susceptible to proteolytic degradation and rapidly dissociated from the receptor. These problems were overcome by the use of high affinity agonists such as buserelin and D-Ala[6]-des-Gly[10]-Pro[9]-NHEt GnRH. Detailed characterization of these receptors using such superagonists of GnRH has shown the presence of a single class of high affinity binding sites that are functional constituents of plasma membrane in the pituitary.[14,15]

13.3.2.2.2 Extrapituitary GnRH receptors

GnRH receptors outside the pituitary have been identified in ovarian, testicular and placental tissues.[1,16] The presence of GnRH-like substances ('gonadocrinins') in placenta[17] and their putative existence in gonads hold out the possibility that the extrapituitary receptors are distinct entities which cross-react with GnRH. This is evidenced by the ability of GnRH to inhibit androgen production and decrease in testicular LH receptors.[18] The low concentration of circulating GnRH and the failure to detect GnRH receptors outside the pituitary in some mammals have resulted in diminished interest in this area.

13.3.2.2.3 Regulation of GnRH receptors

Throughout development and in specific endocrine states the concentration of GnRH receptors changes, without any change in affinity. Such changes are tied in with the dynamically controlled activity of the hypothalamo–pituitary–gonadal axis shown in Figure 1. Receptor number decreases with aging and during lactation, whereas it increases following ovariectomy and on the afternoon of proestrus (the time of LH surge). Alterations in serum gonadotropins are generally predictive of changes in GnRH receptors and the gonadotrope response is modulated, at least in part, by regulation of GnRH receptors. In the female, however, the rapid increase in estradiol causes a large increase in LH secretion to induce ovulation with no apparent change in GnRH receptors. GnRH has been shown to provoke both homologous desensitization and decrease in GnRH receptors. This effect is dependent on both the dose and duration of GnRH challenge as amply documented both *in vivo* and *in vitro*.[19,20] In static pituitary cell cultures preincubation with 1 nM GnRH results, in the first 1–3 h, in a decrease in GnRH binding and later, after 6 h, in augmented binding. In these experiments initial downregulation of GnRH receptors was Ca^{2+} independent, while, in marked contrast, GnRH receptor upregulation occurred only in the presence of extracellular Ca^{2+}.[20] Agents which increase Ca^{2+} entry into the cell, such as veratridine and the calcium ionophore A23187, can promote the increase in the binding of GnRH receptors. GnRH-induced internalization of receptor could reduce the number of cell surface receptors, but this does not appear to be the sole mechanism of GnRH-induced desensitization. Homologous GnRH receptor desensitization was still observed when internalization was blocked.[21] Factors other than receptor number that could dictate GnRH responsiveness, such as altered receptor–effector coupling, have not been fully investigated.

GnRH receptors have been shown to be uniformly distributed on plasma membrane, then to form clusters, which are subsequently internalized. At 37 °C 30% of the cell surface bound labeled hormone is internalized in 15 min. By 45 min, 50% of the receptor bound hormone is intracellularly localized in endosomes, lysosomes, nascent and mature secretory granules as well as in Golgi cisternae. It has been proposed that the receptors in Golgi and secretory granules are recycled.[22] This is supported by the finding that LH release induced by low concentrations of GnRH upregulates the GnRH receptor.[23] This is unique and differs from the classical established concept that receptor recycling is mediated *via* lysosomal compartments in which the ligand is degraded. Evidence for such a conclusion comes from the finding that chloroquine and monensin, agents which prevent a decrease in lysosomal pH, are ineffective in preventing GnRH receptor recycling.[24]

13.3.2.2.4 Structural studies on GnRH receptors

Affinity labeling and ligand immunoblotting of the GnRH receptor indicate the presence of a specifically labeled 60 kDa protein.[25,26] More recently, Conn and Venter have determined the size of the functional GnRH receptor by radiation inactivation (target size analysis) to be 136 ± 8 kDa.[27] The receptor has been shown to be a glycoprotein containing sialic acid residues.[28] This suggests that the functional receptor is either a dimer or a high molecular weight complex in its native active state. Binding of GnRH has been shown to require the presence of lipids and to be dependent on exterior hydrophilic head groups as well as the fatty acid linked to the β carbon of the phospholipid.[29] Detergent-solubilized receptor has been purified by affinity chromatography[30] and used to raise anti-GnRH receptor antibodies.[31] These antibodies do not mimic GnRH action but appear to be capable of inhibiting, in a dose dependent manner, GnRH-stimulated LH secretion, but not K^+-stimulated LH release. Complete characterization of the GnRH receptor protein has not yet been reported.

13.3.2.3 Mechanism of Action of GnRH

13.3.2.3.1 *GnRH actions are* Ca^{2+} *dependent*

Release of LH in response to GnRH stimulation requires the presence of Ca^{2+}. The LH-releasing action of GnRH, but not its priming effect, can be mimicked by K^+ depolarization and Ca^{2+} ionophores. Curtis *et al.* have shown that GnRH priming is associated with the *de novo* synthesis of a 69 kDa protein and is dependent on release of intracellularly sequestered Ca^{2+}.[32] Specific Ca^{2+} channels are activated across the plasma membrane upon GnRH stimulation and intracellular Ca^{2+} increases.[33] Ca^{2+} selective ionophores (*e.g.* A23187, maitotoxin and ionomycin) provoke LH release in the absence of GnRH receptor activation.[34] The association of the Ca^{2+} channel with GnRH receptor is further evidenced by the ability of Ca^{2+} channel blockers (verapamil, methoxyverapamil and ruthenium red) and Ca^{2+}-chelating agents to inhibit the release of LH stimulated by GnRH. Thus GnRH-evoked LH secretion is mediated by receptor-induced changes in intracellular Ca^{2+}, mainly due to the activation of voltage dependent Ca^{2+} channels. Recent studies using Ca^{2+} sensitive fluorophores have demonstrated a transient increase in intracellular Ca^{2+}.[33,35] Calmodulin has been proposed as a mediator of Ca^{2+} signals, based on the finding that it colocalizes with the GnRH receptor patch after GnRH treatment.[36]

13.3.2.3.2 *GnRH alters phospholipid metabolism*

GnRH binding to its receptors causes a rapid turnover of phosphoinositides resulting in increased formation of phosphatidic acid, phosphatidylinositol, phosphatidylinositol 4-phosphate and phosphatidylinositol 4,5-diphosphate.[37] This effect appears to be mediated by phospholipase C (PLC) coupled to the GnRH receptor *via* a guanine nucleotide binding protein (G protein) distinct from the stimulatory and inhibitory G proteins which regulate adenylate cyclase.[38] GnRH-stimulated phosphoinositide turnover results in the formation of diacylglycerol (DAG) and inositol 1,4,5-triphosphate (IP_3), which act as regulators of protein kinase C (PKC) and of intracellular Ca^{2+} respectively. The ability of phorbol myristoyl acetate (PMA) to stimulate LH release further strengthens the concept of the involvement of PKC in GnRH action.[39] However, protein kinase C is not totally responsible for mediating GnRH-induced signals for LH release. This is evidenced by the observation that depletion of protein kinase C by pretreatment with PMA eliminates PKC-mediated LH release and GnRH-stimulated inositol phosphate turnover but the LH secretion due to Ca^{2+}-mobilizing stimuli, including GnRH, is not inhibited.[40] Furthermore PKC-depleted cells exhibit normal homologous desensitization in response to GnRH.[41]

13.3.2.3.3 *GnRH regulates gonadotropin biosynthesis*

GnRH increases the synthesis of both α and β subunits of LH in intact pituitaries. This stimulation has recently been shown to be accompanied by an increase in the mRNAs coding for both α and β LH subunits.[42] Depletion of PKC abolishes this effect without affecting GnRH-induced LH secretion. Thus the regulation and desensitization of the GnRH receptor as well as the action of GnRH on LH mRNA regulation are PKC dependent.[43] In addition to its effects on LH biosynthesis, GnRH has also been shown to induce post-translational modifications such as glycosylation.[44]

13.3.3 CORTICOTROPIN RELEASING HORMONE

The regulation of the secretion of ACTH by the anterior pituitary is under the complex regulation of several hormones including CRH, vasopressin, angiotensin II, α-adrenergic agonists and glucocorticosteroids. Of these, CRH is the key hypothalamic regulator of the secretion of ACTH (and other proopiomelanocorticotropin cleavage products; Figure 1). This 41 amino acid peptide has been isolated and sequenced from ovine hypothalami.[45] Its presence in extrahypothalamic brain regions and in a number of peripheral tissues including the gut, pancreas, adrenal, testis and placenta in several species[46,47] suggests a far wider physiological role for CRH. In particular, CRH appears to play a principal part in the integration of endocrine, autonomic, neuronal and behavioral responses to stress.[48]

13.3.3.1 Structural Features of CRH

The structures of ovine, rat, caprine and bovine CRH have been determined.[49-51] The structure of human CRH has been predicted from the sequence of genomic DNA clones.[52] Rat and human CRHs are identical and differ from ovine CRH by seven residues. Sauvegine, a 40 residue peptide from frog skin, and urotensin, a 41 residue peptide from teleost urophysis, share homologies to CRH.[53] Although it has been determined that the N terminus is not essential for biological activity, removal of the terminal amide reduces activity.[45] α-Helical oCRH and Nleu[21,38] rCRH are more potent than the endogenous ligand in stimulating ACTH release[54] and adenylate cyclase activity in brain.[55] Several C-terminal fragments of CRH, including α-helical oCRH[9–41]NH$_2$, which has been reported to be a weak CRH antagonist,[54] rCRH[1–20], oCRH[1–22], oCRH[7–41]NH$_2$ and oCRH[1–39]NH$_2$ do not possess CRH activity.

13.3.3.2 Actions of CRH *In Vitro*

Ovine CRH stimulates the secretion of proopiomelanocortin-derived peptides from the pituitary. The secretion of ACTH is exquisitely sensitive to the presence of CRH. Maximal response is seen with 1–10 nM CRH, at which concentration range it also stimulates cAMP formation.[56] CRH stimulates adenylate cyclase activity and cAMP formation in neurointermediate lobe cells also, but at higher doses.[56] Continuous exposure of corticotrophs to CRH for 24 h decreases ACTH content which, however, returns to the normal level after eight days of CRH treatment,[57] suggesting a direct stimulatory effect of CRH on ACTH synthesis, evidenced by augmented proopiomelanocortin gene expression and mRNA levels.[58] Stimulation of SS release by CRH from cultured hypothalamic cells has also been reported.[59]

The regulation of ACTH release by CRH is modulated by glucocorticoids, catecholamines and several hypothalamic peptides.[58] Pretreatment of pituitary corticotrophs with dexamethasone for 4 h abolishes their response to subsequent CRH stimulation, whereas addition of dexamethasone at the same time as ovine CRH results only in partial inhibition.[57] Arginine vasopressin and oxytocin potentiate the effect of CRH on ACTH secretion. These two peptides are weak ACTH secretagogues, but each exhibits an additive effect with CRH.[58,60] Catecholamines also additively stimulate ACTH secretion in the presence of CRH.[58]

13.3.3.3 Actions of CRH *In Vivo*

CRH from different species are equipotent and exhibit a similar time course for stimulating ACTH *in vivo* in rodents.[58] In primates and humans, oCRH exerts a longer action and induces a biphasic stimulation of ACTH secretion[61] compared to rCRH and hCRH. This is probably due to low metabolic clearance of oCRH in these species. ACTH response to CRH in the rat is blunted by pretreatment with CRH, an effect which is more pronounced in normal than adrenalectomized animals.[62] This suggests that the diminished response to CRH upon repeated stimulation is due to glucocorticoid feedback regulation. Continuous peripheral CRH infusion in the rat desensitizes the pituitary–adrenal axis, but is still capable of eliciting persistent elevations of both ACTH and glucocorticoid levels. By contrast, chronic administration of ovine CRH results in significant desensitization of the pituitary corticotrophs in man.[63] Vasopressin, oxytocin, angiotensin II and catecholamines potentiate the action of CRH *in vivo*, an effect that is markedly decreased by anti-CRH antiserum, suggesting that these agents primarily act to modulate CRH concentration.[58] Corticosterone inhibits CRH-stimulated ACTH secretion.[57] Although SS inhibits ACTH secretion in pituitary tumor cells, its effect *in vivo* appears not to be significant, requiring concentrations higher than that found in hypophyseal portal circulation. Insulin-induced hypoglycemia, which is used as a provocative test of hypothalamic–pituitary function, is associated with increased ACTH levels. Immunoneutralization of CRH in the rat pretreated with vasopressin antagonist abolishes this ACTH secretory response.[64] Nonetheless, the finding that arginine vasopressin secretion is increased without a concomitant change in CRH or oxytocin levels[64] has led to the proposal that CRH functions in a permissive role by additively maintaining ACTH secretion stimulated by arginine vasopressin. The autoregulation of CRH secretion depicted in Figure 1 may be operative *via* presynaptic inhibition of its release from hypothalamic nerve terminals within the external zone of the median eminence. Microinfusions of CRH into the hypothalamus have been shown to suppress sexual behavior[65] as well as gastric acid secretion.[66] Intracerebroventricular injection of CRH inhibits the release of GH, LH, vasopressin and oxytocin (for a review see ref. 65).

13.3.3.4 CRH Receptors

The presence of high affinity receptors for CRH was first shown in pituitary membranes.[67] Using a radiolabeled agonist [Nleu^{21}, m-^{125}I-Tyr^{32}] oCRH, Perrin *et al.* reported that CRH receptors exist in high or low affinity conformational states, $K_d = 1$ nM and 360 nM respectively, dependent on the presence or absence of divalent cations Mg^{2+}, Mn^{2+} and Ca^{2+}.[68] Furthermore, pituitary CRH binding was shown to be inhibited by guanine nucleotides.[68] High affinity CRH binding sites have been identified in rat CNS[69] and primate peripheral nervous system[70] as well as in peripheral tissues including the adrenal medulla, ventral prostate, spleen, liver, kidney and testis.[71,72] The highest concentration of CRH receptors in the CNS was found in the olfactory bulb followed by progressively lower binding in cerebral cortex cerebellum, hypothalamus, striatum, midbrain, hippocampus and spinal cord. In general, the distribution of CRH binding in the brain corresponded to the distribution of CRH immunoreactive terminals. The existence of CRH receptor subtypes in the brain has been postulated based on the finding that stimulation of adenylate cyclase activity by CRH in the olfactory bulb, despite the twofold greater CRH receptor concentration compared to cerebral cortex, is only about 60% of that observed in cerebral cortex.[65] Both the receptor number and affinity were influenced by the divalent cations and guanine nucleotides in rat brain and pituitary,[68,73] but only the affinity was altered in mouse spleen.[72]

13.3.3.4.1 *Regulation of CRH receptors*

Physiological regulation of CRH receptors by CRH was demonstrated in adrenalectomized rats. Elevated levels of CRH following adrenalectomy results in a marked 80% downregulation of CRH receptors in the pituitary and a concomitant decrease in adenylate cyclase responsiveness.[74] Consistent with these changes CRH-stimulated cAMP production is also reduced in cultured pituitary cells from adrenalectomized rats. This desensitization, which is maximal by 24 h after adrenalectomy, is prevented by dexamethasone treatment.[74] A 30% reduction in CRH binding has also been shown to occur by preincubation of pituitary membranes for 30 min prior to binding and *in vivo* by prolonged CRH infusion. The greater decrease in CRH binding following adrenalectomy suggests that elevated CRH levels alone cannot fully account for the effect of adrenalectomy.[75] It has been shown that vasopressin acts in synergy with CRH to regulate ACTH production and facilitates the desensitization of cultured pituitary cells to CRH after repeated CRH stimulation.[76] Vasopressin levels in the hypophyseal portal blood and the ratio of vasopressin/CRH released into the portal circulation are increased following adrenalectomy.[77] In di/di brattleboro rats, which lack endogenous brain vasopressin, adrenalectomy causes only a slight reduction in pituitary CRH binding, unlike the marked 80% loss of binding in Sprague–Dawley rats. However, marked loss of CRH binding in adrenalectomized brattleboro rats can be evoked by vasopressin infusion. Furthermore coinfusion of vasopressin and CRH in Sprague–Dawley rats mimics the effect of adrenalectomy on pituitary CRH receptors.[75] A low dose of corticosterone, which produces only a transient increase in plasma steroid levels, induces a significant reduction in CRH binding and plasma ACTH concentration.[78] Thus CRH receptor downregulation in the pituitary may be of physiological relevance and may mediate the inhibitory action of glucocorticosteroids on ACTH secretion. Since glucocorticosteroids inhibit the ACTH stimulation by vasopressin, norepinephrine and angiotensin II, it is likely that the steroid effect is mediated not merely through CRH receptor regulation.[75] Adrenalectomy, glucocorticoid administration and stress selectively act on pituitary CRH receptors and appear to exert no downregulatory effect on brain CRH receptors.[78] In Alzheimer's disease and atropine-treated rats, brain CRH receptors appear to be regulated by CRH.[72]

13.3.3.4.2 *Structural studies on CRH receptors*

CRH receptor proteins have recently been identified by chemical crosslinking of radioiodinated analogs of CRH to bovine, rat, porcine and monkey pituitary membranes, and in bovine, porcine, rat, monkey and human brain.[79,80] In all these species a 70–75 kDa protein was identified as the major CRH receptor protein in the pituitary, while the size of the labeled receptor protein in brain was smaller (58 kDa). A 66 kDa labeled protein was identified as the CRH receptor in AtT-20 cells.[81] Purification and further characterization of the CRH receptor have not yet been reported.

13.3.3.5 Mechanism of Action of CRH

13.3.3.5.1 *Stimulation of cAMP*

The binding of CRH with its receptor on a cell membrane activates adenylate cyclase, leading to increased synthesis of cAMP in the pituitary corticotroph.[82] The ED_{50} of CRH for stimulation of cAMP is, however, higher than that for ACTH production. Nonetheless, there is a detectable increase in cAMP at minimal effective doses of CRH for stimulation of ACTH secretion in rat and monkey pituitary cells. Isobutylmethylxanthine (IBMX, a phosphodiesterase inhibitor) potentiates the CRH-induced increase in cAMP production and ACTH secretion. The role of cAMP in mediating the action of CRH is further evidenced by the parallel increase in its concentration and ACTH secretion as well as of cAMP dependent protein kinase activity.[56,58,83]

13.3.3.5.2 *Stimulation of Ca^{2+}*

CRH increases the Ca^{2+} influx. In the absence of extracellular Ca^{2+} the stimulatory effect of CRH on ACTH secretion was partially inhibited.[84] CRH-induced ACTH release declined after the first hour of incubation in the absence of extracellular Ca^{2+} despite a sustained increase in cAMP accumulation, indicating that Ca^{2+} is important at a post-cAMP level. CRH stimulation of ACTH secretion occurs in a biphasic manner: the early phase of rapid increase, which is independent of extracellular Ca^{2+}, and the late phase of constant secretion, which is Ca^{2+} dependent.[85] The early phase of ACTH release stimulated by Ca^{2+} dependent stimuli (*e.g.* vasopressin, norepinephrine and angiotensin II) is also unaffected by removal of extracellular Ca^{2+}. Thus the early phase of ACTH secretion appears to be mediated by inositol triphosphate mediated increase in intracellular free Ca^{2+}, while the later sustained phase is mediated by protein kinase C activation dependent on Ca^{2+} influx.[85]

13.3.3.5.3 *Interactions between CRH and other regulators of ACTH secretion*

A number of hormones such as vasopressin, norepinephrine and angiotensin II, which are by themselves weak secretagogues of ACTH, exert a marked potentiating effect on the stimulatory action of CRH. It is believed that the effects of these agents are mediated *via* PKC.[75] The evidence for this comes from the observations that phorbol esters mimic the action of vasopressin and that the PKC inhibitor retinal blocks the potentiating effect of vasopressin and phorbol esters. Vasopressin can inhibit the low affinity (but not the high affinity) phosphodiesterase, leading to enhanced cAMP production during stimulation by CRH. Other mechanisms involving cAMP independent mediators such as arachidonic acid metabolites have also been postulated.[75] Such interactive regulation of ACTH secretion in the corticotrophs may explain the rapid physiological fluctuation in circulating levels of ACTH, particularly in response to stress.

13.3.4 THYROTROPIN RELEASING HORMONE

Thyrotropin releasing hormone (TRH) was first isolated from porcine hypothalamus and shown to be a weakly basic cyclic tripeptide pyro-Glu-His-Pro-amide.[86] In addition to its principal role in the regulation of thyrotrope function, TRH exerts several other actions on the anterior pituitary. Its wide distribution throughout the extrahypothalamic brain, spinal cord, pancreas and gastro-intestinal tract indicates a greater role for TRH as a neuromodulator in the nervous system and as a paracrine regulator in other tissues. TRH is derived from a precursor which contains three complete and one incomplete copy of the sequence Lys-Arg-Glu-His-Pro-Gly-Lys-Arg-Arg. Proteolytic processing at the Lys-Arg residues and subsequent carboxypeptidase B-like enzymes result in the formation of several Glu-His-Pro molecules which then cyclize into TRH itself.

13.3.4.1 Distribution of TRH

The highest concentration of TRH is found in the median eminence and the paraventricular nucleus in the hypothalamus. Outside the hypothalamus, nucleus acumbens, septum, cranial motor nuclei, medulla oblongata and ventral spinal cord contain significant quantities of TRH.[87] Outside the CNS, TRH is present in the gastrointestinal tract and pancreatic islets. Pancreatic TRH content is high in the early neonatal life and declines steadily to low adult levels. In hypothyroidism, TRH content of the pancreas is increased and in this model TRH has been localized in pancreatic B cells. The presence of TRH has been documented in retina and in reproductive tissues of the male rat as well as in human placenta.[88] Significant quantities of TRH have also been detected in extracts of a number of human tumors.[89]

13.3.4.2 Structural Features of TRH

Since TRH is a small molecule, the structural requirements for its activity are stringent. A cyclized glutamic acid terminus and an intact amide are essential for activity.[90] TRH is rapidly degraded in tissues and serum into diamido-TRH and a stable cyclized metabolite His-Pro-diketopiperazine (His-Pro-DKP). The pyroGlu[1] moiety is susceptible to the proteolytic enzymes since substitution of this residue in analogs such as [Pro[1]]TRH, [*N*-MepyroGlu]TRH and [*N*-formyl-Pro[1]]TRH increases the stability. The rank order potencies of some TRH analogs for receptor binding, correlate well with their biological potencies. The compound cyclopentylcarbonyl–histidine–pyrrolidineamide (cpc-His-pyr) is antagonistic to TRH *in vivo*.

13.3.4.3 Actions of TRH

The main action of TRH, as its name implies, is to stimulate TSH synthesis and secretion in the pituitary. This effect has been shown to occur in the nanomolar concentration range both *in vivo* and *in vitro*. The stimulation of TSH *in vivo* leads, in turn, to the elevation of thyroid hormones with T_3 peaking at 3 h and T_4 by 8 h. Absence of TRH results in decreased TSH output and hypothyroidism ensues the destruction of the hypothalamic–pituitary axis. TRH acts in consonance with hypothalamic dopamine and SS. The stimulation of TSH secretion by TRH is counterbalanced by the thyroid hormones which inhibit TSH secretion. TRH is also capable of stimulating other pituitary hormones, particularly PRL. TRH has been implicated as a PRL-releasing factor in the rat and sheep. Although exogenously administered TRH is a potent stimulator of PRL in both men and women, a physiological role for this hormone in regulating PRL secretion has not been established.[91] Suckling, a major stimulus for PRL secretion, does not stimulate TSH release in humans. TRH stimulates release of ACTH in Cushing's disease and GH secretion in some acromegalic patients.

In the CNS, TRH stimulates increased turnover of norepinephrine and acetylcholine and increases dopamine release in nucleus acumbens. Several pharmacological effects of TRH on behavior, brain–gut actions mediated *via* the vagal cholinergic mechanism and its interactions with other neuropeptides and drugs have been reviewed in detail.[92] In the brain the TRH metabolite His-Pro-DKP causes hypothermia that is antagonized by TRH, while it is more potent than TRH in antagonizing ethanol-induced narcosis.[93] These actions are of considerable interest because His-Pro-DKP may not be derived totally from TRH in the brain.[94]

13.3.4.4 TRH Receptors

The stimulatory effects of TRH on TSH secretion are initiated by its interaction with specific receptors on the cell surface of the pituitary thyrotrope.[95] TRH receptors have also been shown to be present in the brain and other tissues in several species.[93,96,97] The highest concentration of TRH receptors in the rat CNS occurs in the retina, followed by amygdala (301 ± 38 and

$153 \pm 26\,\mathrm{fmol\,mg^{-1}}$ respectively), whereas mouse amygdala, but not retina, is richer in receptor density (222 ± 27 and $65 \pm 3\,\mathrm{fmol\,mg^{-1}}$ respectively). Such heterogeneous distribution of TRH receptors in the CNS has been observed in all species, including man. Detailed characterization of TRH receptors has been carried out in the anterior pituitary and, in particular, in PRL-secreting tumor cell lines GH_3 and GH_4C_1.[95] In general a single high affinity class of noninteracting binding sites has been identified exhibiting a K_d of $\sim 10\,\mathrm{nM}$ for TRH. The pituitary tumor cell lines contain a high TRH receptor concentration ($0.5–1\,\mathrm{pmol\,(mg\,protein)^{-1}}$, equivalent to about 100 000 sites per cell). TRH binding in GH_3 cells is reduced in the presence of lithium ions.[95] The biological potencies of TRH analogs are directly related to their receptor-binding affinity. The differential binding of some TRH analogs to brain and pituitary receptors has been reported,[97] but it is unclear whether such differences arise due to TRH receptor heterogeneity or due to differences in the metabolism of these compounds. The effects of TRH are directly mediated by the plasma membrane receptors and do not appear to depend on receptor internalization.

13.3.4.4.1 *Interaction of benzodiazepines with TRH receptors*

The basic benzodiazepine nucleus has been used as a template for designing drugs targeted against a number of neuropeptide receptors. Sharif and colleagues have shown that some benzodiazepine derivatives bind to TRH receptors. Of these, chlordiazepoxide and midazolam have the highest binding affinity, whereas benzodiazepine derivatives which are potent anxiolytics (*e.g.* flunitrazipam and fluorazipam) are weak TRH agonists.[98] Chlordiazepoxide binds competitively to TRH receptors and shifts the dose–response curve for TRH activity to the right. Furthermore, the ability of these drugs to depress TRH binding appears to be region specific, suggesting the anatomical and functional heterogeneity of the TRH receptors in the brain. In GH_3 cells chlordiazepoxide behaves as a TRH antagonist lacking any intrinsic receptor-stimulating property.

13.3.4.4.2 *Regulation of TRH receptors*

Homologous downregulation of TRH receptors subsequent to prolonged occupation of the receptor by TRH has been demonstrated in both thyrotropes and mammotropes. The time course of TRH receptor downregulation is slow. Prolonged exposure of GH_3 cells to phorbol 12-myristate 13-acetate, an activator of PKC, causes a decrease in the apparent affinity of the receptor for TRH without changing the TRH receptor number.[99] Since sphingosine, which is an inhibitor of PKC, elicits similar changes in TRH binding in these cells, it has been proposed that the loss of affinity of TRH is not secondary to a reduction of PKC activity. Other hormones can exert profound heterologous TRH receptor regulation. The factors regulating TRH receptors have recently been reviewed.[95] The negative feedback control of the pituitary responsiveness to TRH by thyroid hormones is mediated, at least in part, at the level of TRH receptor. Thyroid hormone induced reduction in TRH receptor number has been shown both *in vivo* as well as in cultured pituitary cells and in tumor cells. Estrogens augment TRH receptor binding, thus counterbalancing the downregulatory effect of thyroid hormones. TRH receptor number is decreased by a variety of drugs which stimulate cAMP production, including IBMX, 8-Br-cAMP and cholera toxin. Phorbol esters, which activate PKC, also decrease TRH binding. Since the time course of TRH receptor desensitization is slow, it seems unlikely that changes in TRH binding ensue due to changes in the phosphorylation state of the receptor, a mechanism that is operative in growth factor receptors.

13.3.4.4.3 *Structural studies on TRH receptors*

Structural studies have so far not provided a detailed understanding of the TRH receptors. The requirement of detergents containing a sterol ring for successful solubilization of the native TRH receptor suggests that it belongs to the class of receptors, coupled to G proteins, such as the α and β adrenergic receptors, muscarinic receptors and rhodopsin, which possess multiple membrane-spanning domains as an integral part of the structure. The TRH receptor appears to be glycosylated and contains N-linked sugar residues.[100,101] The properties of the solubilized pituitary and brain TRH receptors appear to be identical. The binding affinity of the solubilized TRH receptors appear to be temperature sensitive, $K_d = 3$ and $> 20\,\mathrm{nM}$ at 0 and $20°C$ respectively. The ability of TRH analogs to inhibit [^{3}H]methyl-TRH binding to both membrane and soluble receptors was identical:

N^3-methyl-His-TRH $\geq$ TRH $>$ pGlu-N^3-methyl-His-Pro(NHCH$_2$)$_6$NH$_2$ $>$ pGlu-His-TyrNH$_2$ $\gg$ TRH free acid.[101]

Recently Wright *et al.* have identified a 64 kDa protein as the TRH receptor in GH$_4$C$_1$ cells by immunoblotting with antibodies to cell surface epitopes as well as by covalent crosslinking of [^{3}H]TRH by UV irradiation.[101] This protein was not present in GH$_1$2C$_1$ cells, a clonal line that lacks TRH receptors. In the only other study describing the molecular properties of the TRH receptor, a 244 kDa receptor–detergent complex has been identified by gel permeation chromatography and density gradient centrifugation in digitonin-solubilized brain membranes.[103] This solubilized receptor preparation was found to exhibit TRH binding properties similar to that of the membrane receptors. The TRH receptor has been expressed recently in frog oocytes and a 3.75 to 4.25 kb species has been identified as the functional TRH receptor mRNA.[104]

13.3.4.5 Mechanism of Action of TRH

13.3.4.5.1 *TRH activates cAMP and inositol phosphate messenger systems*

Thyrotropic and lactotropic cell TRH receptors respond to the binding of TRH by stimulating two enzymes: adenylate cyclase and PLC. The response to TRH requires extracellular Ca^{2+} and oxidative metabolism within the pituitary. TRH receptors are linked to PLC *via* a putative G protein and the activation of this enzyme by receptor-bound TRH results in the phosphatidylinositol 4,5-diphosphate hydrolysis at the cell membrane. This leads to the activation of the phosphoinositide signal pathway. Specifically, IP$_3$ stimulates release of intracellular free Ca^{2+}, causing the initial rapid phase of hormone secretion and the activation of PKC by diacylglycerol contributes to the second phase of hormone release. Activation of PKC has been implicated in the modulation of several aspects of TRH action.[105] Pretreatment of GH$_3$ cells with PMA lowers TRH binding affinity and reduces TRH-stimulated inositol phosphate hydrolysis as well as elevation of Ca$_i^{2+}$. The involvement of a putative G protein in this process is suggested by the lowering of the affinity of TRH receptors by guanine nucleotides and by the stimulation of a low K_m GTPase by TRH.[95] These processes are unaffected by pertussis toxin treatment, suggesting that the G protein associated with the TRH receptor is distinct from G$_i$ and G$_o$. Although this is the currently accepted model for the mechanism of action of TRH, many of the essential components have not been fully characterized.

13.3.5 SOMATOSTATIN

Following its discovery in 1973 as a hypothalamic cyclic tetradecapeptide inhibiting GH release, somatostatin (SS) has been shown to be present in cell bodies throughout extrahypothalamic regions of the brain, notably in the cerebral cortex, hippocampus, thalamus, caudate brain stem nuclei and spinal cord, in D cells in pancreas and gut mucosa, in dorsal root and autonomic ganglia and in the thyroid (for a review see refs. 106, 107). From the wealth of information gathered since its discovery, mammalian SS can now be considered as a member of a phylogenetically ancient, multigene family of peptides with two biologically active hormonal products SS-14 and SS-28. These two peptides, acting as neurotransmitters, neuromodulators, paracrine effectors or true hormones, regulate a variety of processes including multiple endocrine and exocrine secretions, absorption and transport of nutrients, smooth muscle contractility and cell division. Current interest in the field of somatostatin research focuses on the biological roles of SS-14 and SS-28, the mechanisms of their actions mediated by multiple cellular signalling systems, possibly through specific SS receptor subtypes.

13.3.5.1 Biosynthesis and Processing of SS

SS-14 and SS-28 are synthesized as part of a large precursor, preproSS. The structural genes encoding human and rat SS have been cloned and are similar, both having one intron and two exons.[108] While preproSS is structurally identical in the human and rat and is derived from a single SS gene, four preproSS peptides are present in fish, two each in pancreatic islet cells of catfish and anglerfish respectively, derived from distinct SS genes.[109,110] SS-28, which has the entire SS-14 moiety in its carboxy terminus, and SS-14 are the mature biologically active products of preproSS in mammals, whereas two additional structurally distinct peptides, anglerfish SS-28 and catfish SS-22 are present in the fish. The sequence of SS-14 is totally conserved in mammalian hypothalamus and pancreas, frog brain, guinea pig stomach and rat thyroid . The structure of SS-28 does not appear to be conserved in lower species; the avian SS-28 differs in one amino acid from mammalian SS-28, whereas the anglerfish SS-28 differs at nine residues.[111] Processing of proSS generates four additional peptides lacking the SS-14 residue at the C terminus and containing either full or truncated N terminus. The high degree of conservation during evolution suggests a potential biological function for peptides derived from the N-terminal segments of proSS. However, no biological activity has yet been delineated for these peptides. A decapeptide corresponding to preproSS[25–34] with the structure Ala-Pro-Ser-Asp-Pro-Arg-Leu-Arg-Gln-Phe, recently isolated from rat antrum and designated antrin, may be one such potential bioactive product derived from unique monobasic cleavage at Lys^{37}.[112]

13.3.5.2   Tissue Distribution and Molecular Heterogeneity of SS

SS is synthesized in neuronal cells densely distributed throughout the central and peripheral nervous system and in D cells in the endocrine pancreas and gastrointestinal tract. Immunocytochemical evidence for the presence of detectable concentrations of somatostatinergic cells has also been found in such diverse tissues as the thyroid, adrenal, submaxillary gland, urinary tract and placenta (for a review see ref. 106). In the thyroid, SS has been colocalized with calcitonin in a subpopulation of C cells. The gut produces > 60% of total body SS, compared to the brain and pancreas which account for 25 and 5% respectively. The tissue specific processing of ProSS results in considerable variation in the proportions of the two mature hormonal products, SS-14 and SS-28, in different tissues. SS-14 is formed by the proteolytic cleavage at a pair of basic amino acid residues (Arg-Lys), whereas SS-28 is derived from enzymatic processing at a single Arg residue in the proSS molecule. The principal product in hypothalamus, pancreas, antral mucosa and in enteric neurons is SS-14. SS-28 is the preponderant form derived from proSS in the intestinal mucosal cells in the rat and bovine and guinea pig retina.[113] Although SS-28 can be cleaved to generate SS-14, it does not appear to be a mandatory intermediate in the processing of proSS into SS-14. The precursor–product relationship may vary between tissues or even at different stages of development.

Both SS-14 and SS-28 are secreted from tissues and can be quantitated in blood.[114] The circulating SS is mostly derived from the gut and is rapidly metabolized in liver and kidney. The plasma $t_{1/2}$ of SS-14 is 2.3 min, while that of SS-28 is slightly longer. The lability of SS-14 and SS-28 due to plasma enzymes could lead to difficulties in measuring plasma SS concentration. The various radioimmunoassay methodologies and the use of different antibodies used for quantitating SS levels in plasma as well as tissue extracts have been reviewed.[115] The fasting plasma SS concentration range is 8–30 pg mL^{-1} in the human. The plasma SS increases two- to three-fold in response to ingestion of mixed meal. In addition to SS-14 and SS-28, a fragment of SS-14, desAla^{1}SS-14, is detectable in plasma as a biologically active component. SS is also present in other biological fluids, namely cerebrospinal fluid, urine and amniotic fluid.

13.3.5.3   Actions of SS

The role of SS as a regulator of a multitude of physiological functions is now well established. Since most of its actions are directed toward attenuating a vast array of physiological stimulatory processes, SS can be regarded as a universal ubiquitous inhibitory hormone. Its diverse effects on a wide variety of physiological systems have been extensively reviewed.[106,116] In the central nervous system SS acts as a neurotransmitter or neuromodulator, exerting excitatory action on spontaneous electrical activity of many neurons and inhibits TRH, CRH, GHRH and norepinephrine. When intracerebroventricularly administered, it induces profound behavioral changes, which include barrel rotation, motor incoordination and general arousal in rats. Interestingly SS-28, but not SS-14, influences centrally mediated gluco- and thermo-regulations (resulting in hypoglycemia and hyperthermia respectively) as well as hypotension.[116] Peripherally SS influences a number of endocrine and nonendocrine processes.[106] These include inhibition of basal and stimulated GH and TSH secretion in normal conditions, and PRL and ACTH in pathological conditions in the pituitary; inhibition of pancreatic islet cell hormones—insulin, glucagon and pancreatic polypeptide; inhibition of other gastrointestinal hormones including gastrin, secretin, CCK, GIP, VIP and motilin; inhibition of gastric acid, pepsin, salivary amylase and pancreatic bicarbonate and enzymes; inhibition of gastric and biliary motility and splanchnic blood flow; impaired absorption of glucose,

Peptidergic Receptors

xylose, amino acids, triglycerides and ions and inhibition of electrically evoked release of acetyl-choline from myenteric plexuses and firing of myenteric neurons. Although most of these actions are common to SS-14 and SS-28, a comparison of their relative potencies reveals th relative selectivity of SS-28 for some of these actions as schematically depicted in Table 1. A principal issue to be considered in interpreting the effects of SS is to delineate its physiological actions from its pharmacologic effects. Although some of its actions have been regarded as pharmacological due to the requirement of much higher concentrations than encountered in plasma, the multiple routes by which SS can be delivered to the site of its action, illustrated in Figure 2, clearly indicate that the

Table 1 Comparision of Reported Relative Potencies of SS-14 and SS-28 for Inhibition of Hypothalamic CRH Release and of Pituitary, Islet and Digestive Functions (Schematic Depiction)

Biological activity	S-14	S-28
Neuronal		
CRF	−	+
Neuronal K^+ current	↑	↑
Stress-induced hyperglycemia	−	↓
Thermoregulation	−	+
Endocrine		
GH	+	+ +
TSH	+	+ +
Insulin	+	+ + +
Glucagon	+ +	+
Exocrine		
Gastric acid	+ +	+
Pepsin	+ +	+
Pancreatic secretion	+	+ +
Other		
Blood flow		
splanchnic	+	−
portal	+	+ +
Intestinal motility	+	−

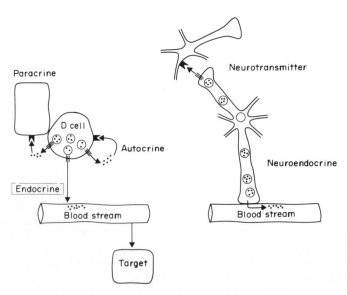

Figure 2 Multiple routes by which SS can be delivered to the site of its action. In the nervous system SS can act as a neurotransmitter or be secreted into circulation as a neuroendocrine hormone. In peripheral tissues it can function as an autocrine regulator of its own secretion, as a paracrine regulator acting on adjacent endocrine cells or as an endocrine hormone, secreted directly into circulation

concentration of SS locally released can be very high and is not necessarily reflected in circulating levels. Therefore most, if not all, of the actions of SS should be considered as of physiological relevance.

13.3.5.4 Structural Determinants of SS Bioactivity

Because of its ubiquitous distribution paralleled by its widespread controlling effects on many facets of cellular function in multiple target organs, considerable attention has been bestowed on the development of structural analogs of SS. The design of such analogs from the beginning has focused on determining the structural requirements of its action and the potential selectivity, metabolic stability and therapeutic applications of such compounds with minimal side effects. The finding that residues 4, 5, 12 and 13 could be deleted with little loss of activity led Rivier *et al.* to conclude that not all of the native hormone was necessary for the full expression of biological activity.[117] Two factors which dictate the structural conformation of the molecule are: (i) peptide backbone conformation generated by the general spatial relationships of individual amino acid side chains; and (ii) specific spatial relation of the side chains due to the rotational angle between the α and β carbons, the x_1 angle.[118,119] The important structural features include: (i) residues 7–11 (Phe-Trp-Lys-Thr-Phe) constitute the biologically active site; (ii) a cyclic structure resulting from an intramolecular disulfide bridge between Cys residues at positions 3 and 13 is essential—substitution of the cyclic structure constituted by disulfide with a dicarba ring structure does not reduce activity; and (iii) the two amino acids, Ala and Gly, at the N-terminal end do not form part of the active sequence. The precise geometric nature of a basic group in position 9 of SS analogs along with a precise distance from the peptide backbone appear to be important factors for high biological activity. From these data an

Table 2 Comparison of the Reported Potencies of Somatostatin Analogs to Inhibit Growth Hormone, Insulin and Glucagon Secretion[a]

Analog	Inhibitory potency		
	GH	Insulin	Glucagon
SS-14:	1[b]	1	1
D-Trp⁸SS-14	8[b]	8.5	6.4
D-Cys¹⁴SS-14	2.7[b]	0.2	3.1
D-Trp⁸,D-Cys¹⁴SS-14	6.5[b]	1.3	10
Des-Asn⁵,D-Trp⁸,D-Ser¹³SS	0.13[b]	17.5	<0.01
SMS 201-997 (sandostatin):	19[b]	4.7	5
D-Phe-Cys-Phe-D-Trp-Lys-Thr-Cys-Thr(ol)	3[c]	3	23
	45[d]	1.3	11
D-Phe-Cys-Phe-D-Trp-Lys-Val-Cys-Thr(NH₂)	11[b]	—[f]	—[f]
	4.2[c]	—[f]	—[f]
D-Phe-Cys-Tyr-D-Trp-Lys-Val-Cys-Thr(NH₂)	79[b]	—[f]	—[f]
	1209[c]		
cyclo(Pro-Phe-D-Trp-Lys-Thr-Phe)	1.7[c]	5.2[b]	8[b]
cyclo(N-Me-Ala-Phe-D-Trp-Lys-Thr-Phe)	3.5[c]	6[b]	16.7[b]
MK-0678:			
cyclo(N-Me-Ala-Tyr-D-Trp-Lys-Val-Phe)	52.3[c]	70[b]	117[b]
CGP-15425:			
cyclo(Asn-Phe-Phe-D-Trp-Lys-Thr-Phe-GABA)			
RC-160:			
D-Phe-Cys-Tyr-D-Trp-Lys-Val-Cys-Trp(NH₂)	113[b]	6.2	10
RC-121:			
D-Phe-Cys-Tyr-D-Trp-Lys-Val-Cys-Thr(NH₂)	117[b]	9	19
Cyclosomatostatin:			
cyclo(aminoheptanoyl-Phe-Phe-D-Trp-Lys-Thr-Phe)	9.3[c]	—[f]	—[f]
Cyclo[7-aminoheptanoyl-Phe-D-Trp-Lys-Thr(Bzl)]	0[e]	—[f]	—[f]

[a] Compiled from refs. 119–123 (and citations therein). In this table the potencies of structurally modified SS analogs to inhibit hormonal secretion in the rat (unless otherwise stated) are expressed relative to that for SS-14 taken as 1. [b] *In vivo.* [c] *In vitro.* [d] *In vivo,* in monkey. [e] This compound did not inhibit GH secretion but was found to block SS inhibition of GH secretion. [f] Data not available.

extended antiparallel β sheet with the residues Trp^8-Lys^9 at the corners of a β turn was predicted to be the most probable conformation of SS-14. Specific rotational relationships between the side chains of Lys and Trp and the two Phe have also been defined, predicting the optimal active site conformation for receptor binding.[120]

On the basis of the above data hundreds of SS analogs have been systematically designed and tested. Compared to the parent tetradecapeptide the following analogs exhibit greater metabolic stability and/or relative selectivity of action. The D-Trp^8 epimer is eight times more potent than SS-14 in inhibiting insulin, glucagon and GH in the rat.[118] D-Trp^8,D-Cys^{14}SS-14 exhibits selective inhibition of glucagon and GH but not of insulin, whereas Des-Asn^5,D-Trp^8,D-Ser^{13}SS selectively inhibits insulin.[121] Differences in tissue selectivity of halogenated derivatives of D-Trp^8SS-14, such as D- and L-fluoro and -bromo-D-Trp^8SS-14, have also been observed. Several compounds designed on the basis of conformational constraints around the active core sequence have turned out to be metabolically stable and capable of longer *in vivo* activity and possessing greater *in vitro*, but not always *in vivo*, potencies.[121-123] The longer *in vivo* activity of some analogs may reflect slower absorption from subcutaneous administration sites. Some of these analogs listed in Table 2 are selective in their actions. However since their efficacies have been assessed in different conditions, a comparison of their selective potencies is difficult. The search for peptides with absolute selectivity for a single target organ has not yet borne fruit. Derivatives of SMS 201-995 such as D-Phe-Cys-Tyr-D-Trp-Lys-Thr-Pen-Thr-NH_2 have been found to be μ opiate agonists.[124] Since opiates stimulate GH secretion, such interactions may be important in dictating the net *in vivo* GH regulatory potencies of these peptides.[125] However, some of the analogs that are potent opiate agonists are very poor SS agonists. Therefore the physiological implications of opiate receptor mediated actions of SS are unclear.

13.3.5.5 SS Receptors

Specific cell surface SS receptors were first documented by Schonbrunn and Tashjian in a growth hormone producing rat pituitary tumor cell line GH_4C_1.[126] The identification and characterization of SS receptors in rat brain synaptosomal membranes was achieved first in our laboratory using [^{125}I-Tyr^{11}]SS-14.[127] We and others have subsequently demonstrated the presence of high affinity SS receptors in rat pituitary,[128,129] adrenal cortex,[130,131] rat and guinea pig exocrine pancreas,[132,133] monkey and human brain[134] as well as in a number of pituitary tumor cells (GH_3, GH_4C_1) and AtT-20,[126,135,136] rat islet cell RINm5f tumor cells,[137] hamster insulinoma,[138] human somatotropic tumors,[139] human meningioma[140] and human lymphocytes.[141] The highest concentration of SS receptor in the rat CNS is found in the cerebral cortex. The regional brain distribution of SS receptors in general parallels the distribution of SS neuronal cell bodies in the CNS in keeping with the postulated interneuronal role of the majority of SS neurons.[127,142,143] SS receptors have been shown to be present on all major endocrine cell types in rat pituitary (somatotrophs, lactotrophs and thyrotrophs) and in pancreatic islets (B, A and D cells, which produce insulin, glucagon and SS respectively).[144,145] Adrenal SS receptors are virtually exclusively localized to the zona glomerulosa of the cortex.[130,143] The existence of soluble cytosolic SS receptors in the stomach, pancreas, kidney and solubilized human placental membranes has been reported.[146-148] The soluble SS binding proteins appear to be of lower affinity than the membrane SS receptor ($K_d = 10^{-6}$ *vs.* 10^{-9} M) and are of unknown physiological significance.

13.3.5.5.1 Regulation of SS receptors

SS, like most other peptide hormones, regulates its own receptors. We have documented that pretreatment with SS causes a marked reduction in SS receptor in AtT-20 cell number, which is also associated with cellular desensitization.[136,149,150] SS-28 was more effective than SS-14 in eliciting these responses. Desensitization of SS receptors in S-49 lymphoma cells has been shown to be associated with translocation of β adrenergic receptor kinase to the cell plasma membrane.[151] In contrast, pretreatment of GH_4C_1 cells and RINm5f insulinoma cells with SS-14 was shown to increase SS receptor binding and had no effect on cellular responsiveness to SS.[152] Downregulation of SS receptors in pancreatic acinar cells by elevated SS levels has been shown to occur in rats with streptozotocin-induced diabetes.[133] Desensitization of SS receptors in normal pituitary has also been reported.[153] In Alzheimer's disease lower than normal levels of SS were found to be associated with reduced receptor binding in frontal cortex (Broadman areas 6, 9 and 10), middle temporal gyrus (Broadman area 21) and in hippocampus.[154] It is not clear whether this is due to a nonspecific degeneration of postsynaptic neurons and/or cortical afferents in this disease or whether excessive release of SS downregulates its receptors and may also account for depletion of endogenous hormone level. It is of interest in this context that parallel changes in both 5-hydroxyindoleacetic acid and SS levels and their receptors in these patients have been documented, suggesting that serotonin receptors may be localized on somatostatinergic neurons.[154] Heterologous regulation of SS receptors has also been reported: estrogen dependent receptor augmentation of SS binding occurs in rat pituitary,[155] whereas glucocorticoids induce a reduction in GH_4C_1 cell SS receptor number.[156]

13.3.5.5.2 *Evidence for SS receptor subtypes*

As in the case of several other neuropeptide hormone receptors the existence of subpopulations of SS receptors is suggested by a considerable body of pharmacological and biochemical evidence, which includes tissue specific ionic dependent ligand binding of the SS receptors,[133,157] differential interaction of SS receptor subtypes in brain with SMS,[158] estrogen sensitive and insensitive SS receptor subtypes in rat pituitary,[155] and human lymphocyte SS receptor subtypes which resemble those in brain.[141] What is unique is that the heterogeneity of SS receptors and the possible distinct functional significance of SS-14 and SS-28 imply the presence of receptor subtypes exhibiting selective specificity for these two peptides. The salient observations supporting this concept have recently been reviewed[157] and include the following: (i) structural analogs of SS-14 exhibit tissue selective binding; (ii) ionic requirements for SS receptor binding differ between tissues; (iii) two receptor subtypes can be distinguished with conformationally restricted SS analogs such as SMS in brain; (iv) amidation of the C-terminal residue of conformationally restricted cyclic octapeptide analogs strikingly alters receptor recognition in brain but not in pituitary; (v) SS-14 and SS-28 bind to SS receptors with tissue specific affinities which reflect their tissue selective effects: SS-28 binds to SS receptors in pituitary more avidly than in brain and within the pituitary itself, estrogen dependent receptor subtypes bind SS-28 with greater affinity than SS-14, while the two peptides bind to estrogen independent SS receptors with reverse order of potencies; (vi) SS-14 and SS-28 preferentially label distinctly discrete regions of brain and pancreatic islet cells as evidenced by *in vivo* and *in vitro* autoradiography; and (vii) nucleotides and ions differentially modulate the binding of SS-14 and SS-28 to cerebrocortical SS receptors.

The properties of SS receptors quantitated using the only available radioiodinated SS-28 analog, $[Leu^8, D-Trp^{22}, ^{125}I-Tyr^{25}]$ SS-28, in direct binding studies were identical to those observed using $[^{125}I-Tyr^{11}]$ SS-14.[143] Nonetheless, autoradiographic studies suggest that certain regions of rat CNS, including median eminence, lateral cingulate body, substantia nigra, superior colliculus, interpenduncular, dentate and fastigial nuclei, are preferentially labeled by this ligand but not by $[^{125}I-Tyr^{11}]$ SS-14.[159,160] Additional evidence for differences in the receptor binding of these two radioligands was seen in their differential sensitivity to GTP and Ca^{2+}: $[^{125}I-Tyr^{11}]$ SS-14 binding to rat brain SS receptors was inhibited by GTP to a greater extent than binding of $[Leu^8, D-Trp^{22}, ^{125}I-Tyr^{25}]$ SS-28 and > 10 mM Ca^{2+} selectively decreased $[Leu^8, D-Trp^{22}, ^{125}I-Tyr^{25}]$ SS-28 binding and increased the affinity of SS-14 but not SS-28 for these sites.[157] These observations suggest that the differential binding of SS-14 and SS-28 may be dictated by the microenvironment of the membrane SS receptor. The failure to distinguish brain receptor subtypes which bind SS-28 with differential affinities in direct binding studies may possibly be due to limitations in achieving an enriched population of the receptor subtypes and the cross-reactivity of the ligands available. In the two clonal anterior pituitary cell lines GH_3 and AtT-20 the SS receptors interact differently with SS-14 and SS-28: AtT-20 cells bind SS-28 more avidly than SS-14 while, in contrast, the GH_3 cells bind SS-14 preferentially compared to SS-28.[136,161] Furthermore SS receptors on AtT-20, but not GH_3 cells, can be desensitized by SS-14 and SS-28 pretreatment. Also, while two pharmacologically distinct SS receptor subtypes in the brain could be inferred from their differential affinities for SMS, *in vitro* autoradiography can demonstrate the uniquely distinct localization of high affinity SMS receptors in layers V and VI, whereas low affinity SMS binding sites measurable with SS-14 and SS-28 ligands are present mainly in the superficial cortical layers I–IV, being particularly enriched in parts of lamina IV.[162]

13.3.5.5.3 *Structural studies on SS receptors*

Basic structural information on SS receptors is not yet available. Several groups have reported size estimates of SS receptor protein on the basis of crosslinking studies. The major proteins identified in these reports correspond to 55–66 kDa[161,163–166] or 82–92 kDa,[155,167] although labeling of proteins ranging in size from 27 to 200 kDa has been observed.[164] The discrepancies in size estimates most likely result from the wide array of ligands, crosslinkers and experimental conditions that have been employed in different laboratories. Detailed evaluation of these procedures in our laboratory has demonstrated that some chemical crosslinking agents such as disuccinimidyl suberate when used at concentrations exceeding 0.5 mM increase labeling of high molecular weight membrane proteins or protein complexes. We have shown that multiple proteins are labeled by SS-14 and SS-28 ligands among which two main proteins could be identified: a 55–60 kDa protein which predominates in peripheral tissues including pituitary, exocrine pancreas and adrenal cortex and a 27 kDa protein which is the main receptor protein in the brain.[164] The presence of an additional minor labeled 32 kDa protein has also been detected in brain but not in other tissues. Neither SS-14 nor SS-28 appear to interact selectively with these proteins, although labeling of the major receptor protein constituents in a given tissue parallels their tissue selective binding affinities. [^{125}I-Tyr^3] SMS labels the same receptor proteins identified with [^{125}I-Tyr^{11}] SS-14 in the brain.[168] In GH$_3$ and AtT-20 cells, however, this ligand preferentially labels the 27 kDa protein in striking contrast to the 58 kDa protein labeled by SS-14 and SS-28 ligands.[163] The observed differences in the ligand binding properties of the receptors in the two cell types may be taken to indicate that the major 58 kDa protein present in AtT-20 cells may possess SS-28 selectivity, while the smaller 27 kDa protein detected in GH$_3$ cells may be SS-14 selective. We have recently developed a *N*-azido derivative of SMS. Photolabeling with this ligand revealed specific labels: a major protein band of 58 kDa and a minor band of 32 kDa in brain, a pattern different from that observed using [^{125}I-Tyr^3] SMS. We have purified the photoaffinity labeled SS receptor proteins from rat brain and AtT-20 cells by electrophoresis on SDS–polyacrylamide gels and subsequent electroelution in our laboratory[169] and this is currently being sequenced to obtain its primary structure.[170] Affinity purification of the native receptor has also been achieved.[165,169] The purification of the principal receptor proteins in brain and AtT-20 cells should lead to cloning of these receptor proteins and their eventual complete characterization.

13.3.5.6 Mechanism of Action of SS

13.3.5.6.1 *Inhibition of adenylate cyclase*

The receptor-mediated actions of SS are amplified by changes in multiple signal transduction systems. First, SS was shown to inhibit stimulated but not basal adenylate cyclase in GH$_4$C$_1$, AtT-20 pituitary tumor cells, normal pituitary cells, pancreatic β cells and the NG108 neuroblastoma cells.[171] Binding of SS to its receptors leads to a reduction of intracellular concentrations of cAMP.[171,172] SS has also been shown to act at a level distal to cAMP formation, as evidenced by its ability to block the hormonal stimulation by 8-bromo-cAMP.[171] The SS receptor is coupled to guanine nucleotide binding protein G$_i$, activation of which results in inhibition of adenylate cyclase.

13.3.5.6.2 *Activation of K$^+$ current*

In GH-secreting adenoma and GH$_4$C$_1$ cells SS increases K$^+$ conductance, thereby hyperpolarizing the cells. The resulting membrane potential is more negative than the threshold, which causes a decrease in the frequency of Ca^{2+} action potential leading to a secondary decrease in Ca$_i^{2+}$.[173,174] Neither the ability of K$^+$ to induce nor the ability of SS to inhibit the secretion of ACTH in AtT-20 cells was dependent on changes in intracellular cAMP levels. Pertussis toxin treatment abolishes both these effects, suggesting that the SS receptor interacts first with G$_i$ and G$_k$ (and possibly other related G proteins) that can be ADP ribosylated by this toxin. In addition to the secondary decrease in Ca^{2+} entry due to increasing K$^+$ conductance, SS has been shown to directly inhibit Ca^{2+} current under a patch clamp.[174] The mechanistic coupling of the SS receptor to one or more G proteins, leading to the inhibition of adenylate cyclase, Ca^{2+} entry, activation of K$^+$ current and exocytosis is schematically depicted in Figure 3.

13.3.5.6.3 *Stimulation of tyrosine phosphoprotein phosphatase*

Conformationally restricted SS analogs (*e.g.* RC-160) have recently been shown to stimulate tyrosine phosphoprotein phosphatase activity in some tumors, a property implicated in the anti-

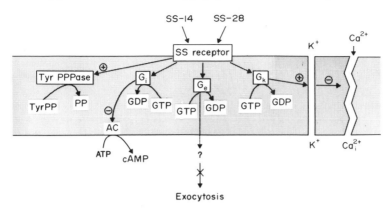

Figure 3 Multiple signal systems involved in the mediation of the action of SS. Activation of the SS receptor by the binding of SS-14 or SS-28 results in: (1) inhibition of stimulated, but not basal, adenylate cyclase (AC) and cAMP production; (2) direct inhibition of exocytosis; and (3) increased K^+ conductance leading to hyperpolarization, thereby decreasing Ca^{2+} influx. All three actions are mediated *via* a family of guanine nucleotide binding proteins (G proteins) that can be ADP ribosylated by pertussis toxin. More recently, certain SS analogs have been reported to activate tyrosine phosphoprotein phosphatase (Tyr PPAse) in tumor cells. It is not known whether this is an intrinsic receptor activity. The Tyr PPAse activity has not been shown to be G protein coupled

tumerogenic action of these peptides.[175] The SS receptor linked phosphatase activity does not appear to be dependent on G protein mediation. The action of SS distal to cAMP formation may involve a direct inhibition of cAMP dependent protein phosphorylation of intracellular proteins, presumably *via* activation of specific phosphatases.[172] Recently, protein phosphorylation stimulated *via* the inositol phosphate second messenger system has also been shown to be inhibited by SS. Lithium is a potent inhibitor of phosphatase involved in cleaving inositol 1-phosphate to inositol, thereby increasing the availability of inositol mono-, di- and tri-phosphates (IP_3). It has been postulated that SS antagonizes this action of lithium. Addition of SS during lithium stimulation decreased both inositol monophosphate and ACTH secretion in AtT-20 cells,[172] suggesting that IP_3 mediated mobilization of intracellular Ca^{2+} as well as the activation of protein phosphorylation by diacylglycerol. Whether SS is capable of regulating the formation of IP_3 from membrane lipid stores directly (*e.g.* by inhibiting PLC) is not known.

13.3.5.6.4 *Direct inhibition of exocytosis*

SS has been shown to inhibit exocytosis of secretory granules by a mechanism that is mediated by a distinct G protein, called G_e. This effect appears to be direct and independent of changes in any of the known signal systems linked to the SS receptor, including adenylate cyclase-cAMP and K^+ channel. Burgoyne has suggested that this as yet uncharacterized G protein may participate in signal transduction through a new putative second messenger that controls exocytosis.[176]

Are the effects of SS on the multiple signal transducing pathways mediated by the same or different receptors? Although the existence of two or more SS receptor subtypes have been documented on the basis of binding data as discussed above, the involvement of such subtypes in mediating the action of SS on one or more of the different signalling systems remains speculative. In AtT-20 cells, SS-14 is more potent than SS-28 in inhibiting cAMP dependent events, whereas SS-28 is more inhibitory than SS-14 on cAMP independent actions.[149] The differential binding of the two peptides in conjunction with their differential modulation of receptor–effector coupling may determine the functional specificities of the two peptides. Whether such differences arise due to differential ligand specificity of SS receptor subtypes and/or their selective coupling to different signalling systems remains to be established. The possibility that the different receptor proteins identified may constitute functionally distinct entities of SS receptors is exciting and waits to be explored. If true, the structural characteristics which dictate either ligand or signalling selectivity should add a new dimension for effective design of very selective and specific agonists and antagonists of SS.

13.3.6 GROWTH HORMONE RELEASING HORMONE

Changes in growth rate occur over relatively long periods of time compared with other neuroendocrine-related events. The first proof that GH secretion is also under neural control came from hypothalamic lesion experiments in animals and from the finding that hypothalamic extracts stimulate GH release. Subsequently this concept was firmly entrenched by the episodicity of GH release followed by a circadian rhythm, its rapid response to stress and electrical stimulation of specific brain regions and its inhibition due to pituitary stalk resection. More than two decades of efforts to characterize the GH-releasing factor succeeded only after the discovery of paraneoplastic syndromes of ectopic secretion of GH-stimulating hormone by pancreatic adenomas in humans. GHRH was first identified and isolated, not from the hypothalamus, but from human pancreatic tumors associated with acromegaly.[177,178] GHRH (also called growth hormone releasing factor, GRF) is a member of the glucagon/secretin/VIP/PHI family[179] and provides the primary stimulus for GH release from the anterior pituitary. The term 'somatocrinin', which has been proposed to replace the term GHRH, has not gained universal acceptance.

13.3.6.1 Tissue Distribution of GHRH

The presence of GHRH in human and monkey brain has been shown using immunohisto-chemical techniques. Immunoreactive cell bodies were found only in the arcuate nucleus, while immunoreactive fibers were detected in the median eminence.[180] Although rodent GHRH is structurally distinct from mammalian GHRH, its distribution is similar. The presence of GHRH in a relatively small number of nuclei is in sharp contrast to the relatively wide distribution of other hypothalamic peptides (SS, CRH and TRH). GHRH has been shown to be detectable in extracts of human pituitary stalk, hypothalamus and optic chiasma.[181] Outside the CNS presence of GHRH, immunoreactivity has been documented in rat and human gut and human placenta.[182] GHRH appears to be colocalized in gastrin in the G cells of the antrum.

13.3.6.2 Structural Features of GHRH

Three molecular forms of GHRH have been identified in the human GHRH-producing tumors: GHRH[1-44]NH_2, GHRH[1-40]OH and GHRH[1-37]OH.[178] In the second tumor extract characterized by Rivier *et al.* the most abundant form was GHRH[1-40]OH, two other fragments GHRH[1-40]NH_2 and GHRH[1-29]NH_2 also being identified.[177] Although these peptides isolated from the pancreatic tumors were designated as hpGRF, in this chapter no distinction is made between the tumor product and the hypothalamic hormone. In contrast to the tumor-derived peptides, hypothalamic GHRH from several species (bovine, caprine, ovine and porcine) contains 44 amino acids and an amidated C terminus. Porcine and bovine GHRH share greater homology with human GHRH, differing only in three (porcine *vs.* human) and five (bovine *vs.* human) amino acids, the alterations primarily located in the C terminus.[182] Rat GHRH, on the other hand, is a 43 amino acid peptide which has only 70% homology with the human GHRH: 13 of 43 amino acids are different.[183] Although the naturally occurring hGHRH[1-40] and hGHRH[1-37] are each flanked by Arg, a potential proteolytic cleavage site, direct conversion of hGHRH[1-44] into the smaller forms has not been shown. This raises the possibility that the different forms of hGHRH may be derived from differential processing of the precursor. The biological activity of GHRH resides in its N-terminal end but a minimum peptide length of 1-29 of the GHRH sequence is essential for activity.[182] GHRH[1-44]NH_2 and GHRH[1-40]OH are equally active, whereas GHRH[1-37]OH is less potent. Ling *et al.* synthesized a series of C termin-ally shortened GHRH peptides and showed that GHRH[1-29] was 23% as active as the native hormone. Further deletion to GHRH[1-19]NH_2 rendered the molecule totally inactive.[184] GHRH[1-44]NH_2 is inactivated rapidly (1 min *in vivo* and within 5 min *in vitro*) with the removal of the amino terminus by an aminopeptidase with the formation of a less hydrophobic metabolite.[185]

Momany *et al.* have synthesized a family of peptides based on the structure of enkephalins that are capable of stimulating GH secretion.[186] The most potent of these, designated as growth hormone releasing peptide (GHRP), has the structure His-D-Trp-Ala-Trp-D-Phe-Lys-NH_2. Although this peptide has no homology to GHRH, it has been suggested that it may be conformationally similar to the active site of GHRH. Others have shown considerable differences in the patterns of GH-stimulating activity of these peptides and GHRH suggesting that they may act by different mechanisms.[187] GHRP-like materials have not been shown to occur naturally.

13.3.6.3 Actions of GHRH

The physiological action of GHRH is very specific and involves direct stimulation of pituitary GH secretion[178] in a dose dependent manner (minimally at 3 pM, half-maximally at 20 pM and maximally above 100 pM).[188] In addition to its stimulation of GH release, GHRH potentiates GH synthesis at the level of gene transcription and increases GH mRNA levels in the pituitary.[189-191] Addition of SS suppressed both basal and GHRH-stimulated GH secretion but did not block GH biosynthesis under either condition. Destruction of hypothalamic GHRH neurons causes a decrease in pituitary GH content as well as plasma GH levels. These actions of GHRH are sensitive to glucocorticoids and thyroid hormone. A glucocorticoid-enhanced effect of GHRH is possibly due to an increased number of pituitary GHRH receptors.[192] T_3 also sensitizes the pituitary somatotrophs to GHRH. The sensitization of pituitary cells *in vitro* by these two hormones was additive.[193] However, dexamethasone blunts the release of GH in response to GHRH in acromegaly and in Cushing's disease.[194] Whether this difference is due to glucocorticoid-mediated changes in the CNS affecting GHRH secretion remains to be established. *In vivo* GHRH studies have shown the feedback inhibition of GH secretion by somatomedin C to stimulate SS release.[195] Intraventricular injection of somatostatin stimulates GHRH release, leading to increased GH output,[196] whereas GHRH administered in a similar manner suppresses GH secretion.[197,198] Clinically a significant proportion of children with idiopathic GH deficiency have a primary defect in GHRH production.[199] The action of GHRH is probably regulated positively by testosterone and negatively by 17-β-estradiol. Furthermore GH secretion is characterized by low basal levels with frequent high amplitude pulses in male rats, whereas low amplitude pulses superimposed on a relatively high baseline defines the GH secretory pattern in female rats. At least three possible factors contribute to greater GH secretion in male than in female rats: a greater proportion of somatotrophs, greater secretory capacity and greater sensitivity to GHRH.[200] Recently intracerebroventricular administration of galanin was shown to increase GH release, while it does not directly stimulate GH secretion in the rat.[201] Coinfusion of galanin with GHRH produced greater GH secretory response than that elicited by GHRH as well as insulin-induced hypoglycemia. These authors have proposed that somatotrophs are under tonic somatostatinergic inhibition after these stimuli, which is diminished or abolished by concomitant galanin administration. Impaired GH response to GHRH is seen in some patients with growth failure, elderly and obese subjects, and in type II diabetic patients.[202,203]

13.3.6.4 GHRH Receptors

Anterior pituitary plasma membranes and dispersed pituitary cells bind GHRH specifically.[204,205] Quantitation of these binding sites with a synthetic C terminally amidated shortened analog with greater biological potency [His^1,Nleu^{27}]GHRH[1–30]NH$_2$ that could be radioiodinated revealed the presence of high affinity receptors with a capacity of 11 fmol per pituitary and a dissociation constant of 0.1 nM. Rat GHRH exhibits fivefold greater binding affinity compared to hGHRH[1–40].[204] Members of the glucagon–secretin family, which are homologous to GHRH, do not interact with these receptors. Pancreatic VIP receptors on the other hand cross-react GHRH with high affinity.[206]

13.3.6.4.1 Regulation of GHRH receptors

Continuous perfusion of somatotrophs with GHRH results in a rapid decrease in GH responsiveness, suggesting homologous receptor downregulation.[207] Homologous regulation of GHRH receptors by GHRH has not been investigated in detail. In the intact animal adrenalectomy results in > 70% loss in GHRH receptor number within one week. The effect of glucocorticoids on GHRH binding to pituitary cells *in vitro* is to enhance receptor number. It thus appears that glucocorticoids are essential for the somatotroph to maintain a normal GHRH receptor number. Glucocorticoids are known to increase GH gene transcription and GH secretion in pituitary tumor cells[208,209] and increase the sensitivity of normal pituitary cells to GHRH both *in vivo* and *in vitro*.[193,210,211] Glucocorticoids possibly amplify this effect by their simultaneous lowering of the sensitivity to somatostatin[192] and decreasing SS binding as has been shown in GH$_4$C$_1$ cells.[156]

13.3.6.5 Mechanisms of GHRH Action

13.3.6.5.1 Stimulation of adenylate cyclase and Ca²⁺ mobilization

GHRH-induced GH secretion is associated with concomitant stimulation of adenylate cyclase, leading to augmented cAMP production, and a rapid dose dependent increase in Ca_i^{2+}. The stimulation of adenylate cyclase by GHRH is dose and GTP dependent.[212] GHRH increases Ca^{2+} influx in rat pituitary cells, a new steady state being established within 30 s. Removal of extracellular Ca^{2+} as well as the addition of Ca^{2+} channel blocker nifedipine abolish GHRH induced Ca_i^{2+} increase.[213] The change in Ca^{2+} concentration occurs at GHRH concentrations about tenfold lower than that required for a measurable increase in cAMP. This, and the observation that a calcium ionophore increases GH secretion without affecting cAMP levels, were interpreted to indicate that Ca^{2+} induces GHRH-induced GH release at a step distal to cAMP.[214] Schettini *et al.*, on the other hand, have reported that calcium ionophores can stimulate both cAMP and GH secretion and that an antagonist of calmodulin reversed the increase in cAMP production and GH secretion.[215] Mougin *et al.* have reported that a different calmodulin antagonist actually increases GHRH-induced cAMP and GH levels.[216] The opposing effects of GHRH and SS on GH secretion suggest that the two peptides exert opposing actions on cAMP and Ca^{2+}. Additional studies are needed to resolve the nature of the interaction between Ca^{2+} and cAMP in the mediation of the action of GHRH.

13.3.6.5.2 Stimulation of arachidonic acid metabolism

GHRH stimulation of GH secretion in pituitary cells is associated with an increase in arachidonic acid levels.[217] Lipoxygenase inhibitors blocked GHRH-induced GH secretion.[218] Prostaglandin E stimulates both adenylate cyclase and GH secretion; both effects are inhibited by SS.[219] These data suggest that an interaction between prostaglandins (and arachidonic acid metabolites) and adenylate cyclase exists in the mediation of GHRH-stimulated GH secretion. The precise mechanism of such an interplay of these second messenger systems remains to be elucidated.

13.3.6.5.3 Activation of the phosphoinositol–PKC system

The stimulation of phosphoinositol turnover by GHRH[220] raises the possibility that the inositol phosphate–PKC system can mediate the stimulatory effect of GHRH. However, a cAMP analog, as well as GHRH, enhanced the effect of maximally stimulatory doses of phorbol esters on GH secretion.[221] Phorbol ester or synthetic diacylglycerol, when added alone, did not alter cAMP levels. Thus the mechanism of action of phorbol esters may be different from that of GHRH.

13.3.7 GROWTH HORMONE

Growth hormone is synthesized in acidophilic somatotropic cells in the lateral wings of the anterior pituitary.[222] GH secretion, as illustrated in Figure 1, is regulated by two hypothalamic hormones—positively by GHRH and negatively by SS. The secretion of GH follows an ultradian rhythm with a peak (20 ng mL⁻¹) frequency of 3–4 h.[223] Several stimuli such as estrogens, opiates, VIP, motilin and bombesin augment GH secretion, while glucocorticosteroids, free fatty acids, neurotensin and substance P decrease GH output.[223] The normal serum concentration of GH in humans is less than 50 ng mL⁻¹.

13.3.7.1 Structural Features and Molecular Heterogeneity of GH

GH is a single-chain polypeptide of 191 amino acids which has a large central disulfide loop between Cys⁵³ and Cys¹⁶⁵ and a short terminal disulfide loop between Cys¹⁸² and Cys¹⁸⁹. GH exhibits significant structural homology to PRL and PL. These three hormones possess growth promoting and lactogenic activities, are of similar size (190–199 amino acids) and protein structure.[223] There is greater homology between human PL and GH than that between human PRL and the other two hormones (92% *vs.* 40%). GH and PRL genes may have evolved from a common ancestral gene.[224] The rat and bovine PL genes are probably derived from PRL gene rather than GH gene.[224,225] The hGH gene is located on chromosome 17. The gene and its mRNA transcript possess five exons separated by four introns. The excision of the second intron could result in alternate splicing with deletion of amino acid residues 32–46 of the translated GH which is smaller (20 kDa) than the normal hGH (22 kDa).[226] The presence of this 20 kDa variant in the pituitary and blood is well documented.[227] A 25 kDa protein called proliferin (produced in proliferating fibroblasts) has also been reported to be homologous to GH and PRL.[228] A placental variant of hGH encoded by an apparently dormant hGH-V gene has been identified.[229]

13.3.7.2 Biological Actions of GH

Human GH exerts a wide variety of effects on somatic growth, development and metabolism.[222] Its effects on carbohydrate and lipid metabolism appear to be direct and initiated by binding to GH receptors on the target cells. In the liver it stimulates the production of insulin-like growth factors (IGF, somatomedin.) Its effect on growth is in fact mediated *via* IGF I and IGF II.[222,230] Although the effect of hGH on carbohydrate metabolism and lypolysis are antagonistic to insulin, hGH exerts acute and transient insulin-like effect *in vivo* and *in vitro* under conditions of suppressed endogenous GH levels.[231] In these situations insulin effect on lipogenesis was much higher than that of hGH and the effect of these two hormones was not additive, suggesting a common metabolic pathway shared by the two hormones.[232] The 20 kDa GH variant has the growth-promoting and lactogenic properties of the native hormone but lacks the diabetogenic activity of GH.[226]

13.3.7.3 GH Receptors

GH receptors have been localized on liver membranes, adipocytes, fibroblasts and lymphocytes and ovary in several mammalian and nonmammalian species[233,234] The high affinity of these receptors ($K_d \leq 1$ nM) is in the physiological concentration range of GH. However, many tissues such as the ovary, thymocytes and lymphocytes which bind GH with high affinity and specificity do not show classical GH responsiveness. On the other hand although hypothalamus is involved in the short-loop feedback inhibition of GH secretion (inhibition of GHRH and stimulation of SS secretion), the presence of GH receptors in this tissue has not been demonstrated.[233] Three distinct subtypes of GH binding sites have been documented: (i) *lactogenic receptors*, where binding of radioiodinated hGH is inhibited only by lactogenic hormones such as hGH, monkey GH, PLs and PRL; (ii) *primate GH receptors*, where binding is inhibited by both nonprimate and primate GH but not by PRL and PLs; (iii) *hGH receptors*, where hGH binding is inhibited only by hGH.[233] It thus appears that nonprimate growth hormones do not stimulate growth and lactation in primates, whereas hGH can stimulate growth and lactation in animals and humans. Species specificity has also been shown for the nonmammalian receptors. For instance teleost growth hormone has very low affinity for mammalian GH receptors, while it binds with high affinity to receptors in fish.[233]

The heterogeneity of GH receptors was first suggested by the identification of two classes of binding sites for rat and rabbit GH in rabbit liver membranes.[233,234] It should be pointed out that these hormones bind only to GH receptor and not to lactogenic receptor. The 20 kDa hGH variant, which has somatogenic activity comparable to that of hGH, binds to hGH binding sites in rabbit liver, but exhibits high affinity for rat GH binding sites on rabbit liver membrane receptors.[233] Thus it appears that the 20 kDa hGH variant binds with high affinity only to a subset of hGH receptors, which perhaps belong to the same subset of receptors which bind rabbit and rat GH with high affinity. Hughes *et al.* have proposed that rabbit liver contains a low capacity, high affinity GH receptor (designated GHR-1) to which rabbit, rat and human GH as well as the 20 kDa hGH variant bind with comparable affinities.[233] The second receptor subset designated GHR-2 binds only to hGH with high affinity and constitutes more than 85% of the GH-binding sites. Prolactin receptors also bind hGH and its 20 kDa variant with high affinity but do not interact with rabbit GH. If labeled rat GH is used in binding studies, the predominant receptor recognized is GHR-1. Since this receptor has comparable affinities for GH from different species, these hormones can effectively displace the binding of rat GH to GHR-1. Such diversity and crossreactivity indicates the need to exercise caution in the interpretation of 'heterologous' binding studies. The physiological significance of these receptor populations is not known.

13.3.7.3.1 *Regulation of GH receptors*

Liver GH receptor binding was decreased following hypophysectomy in rabbits and lambs.[235] Rat GH induces GH as well as prolactin receptors in female rats.[236] Homologous upregulation of GH receptors *in vivo* in rat, swine and bovine livers and in rat adipocytes has been documented.[235–240] On the other hand GH-induced downregulation of its receptors has been reported to occur in lymphoblasts and fibroblasts.[241,242] Moreover in hypophysectomized male rats GH deficiency results in increased hepatic GH binding.[242] GH has been shown to exhibit a concentration dependent effect on GH receptors *in vitro*. GH binding to rat hepatocytes incubated with a low dose of GH ($<250\,\mathrm{ng\,mL^{-1}}$) showed receptor upregulation, while at high concentration ($>1\mu\mathrm{g\,mL^{-1}}$) downregulation was observed.[243] Accordingly two opposing process of receptor production and receptor loss have been postulated to occur following binding of GH. The balance between the two processes dictated by the physiological levels of GH may determine the net change in GH receptor concentration. Since GH receptor mRNA levels are unaffected by hypophysectomy as well as GH treatment, regulation of its receptors by GH is thought to occur at a post-transcriptional level. Heterologous upregulation of GH receptor is induced by thyroxine. Although this effect of thyroxine observed *in vivo* may be indirect due to stimulation of GH release, direct upregulation of GH receptor by thyroxine in rat hepatocytes has been demonstrated.[243]

The ontogeny of GH receptors has been investigated in the rabbit and the rat. A marked increase in hepatic GH receptors occurs at puberty.[233,244] In pregnancy the hepatic GH receptor number doubles in the rabbit. A 10-fold increase in liver GH binding in midgestation that continues throughout pregnancy has been observed in the rat.[233]

13.3.7.3.2 *Biochemical characteristics of GH receptors*

GH receptor in rabbit liver has been estimated to have a relative molecular mass of 50–80 kDa by reduced SDS–gel electrophoresis subsequent to crosslinking of the receptor bound ligand.[233,244,245] GH receptors in rat hepatocytes and adipocytes and human IM-9 lymphocytes have been estimated to be 110 kDa.[233] A GH-binding protein ($M_r = 51$ kDa) has been identified in rabbit and human plasma.[246,247] The GH receptor and the GH-binding protein are immunologically similar as evidenced by their binding to anti-GH receptor monoclonal antibodies.[248] GH receptors in rabbit liver and IM-9 lymphocytes have been purified by detergent solubilization and affinity chromatography using immobilized monoclonal antibodies, hGH as well as lectin columns.[233,245]

13.3.7.3.3 *Cloning and sequencing of GH receptors*

Recently Leung *et al.* made a major breakthrough in this field by sequencing, cloning and expressing the GH receptor and serum binding protein.[249] Amino acid sequence comparison of GH and serum binding protein has shown that the GH binding protein sequence is present in the extracellular hormone binding domain of the GH receptor. Ubiquitin ($M_r = 9$ kDa) has been found

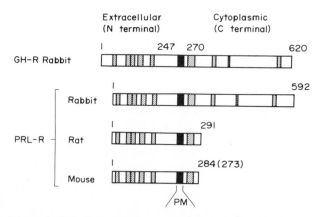

Figure 4 Schematic comparison of rabbit GH, and rabbit, rat and mouse PRL receptor proteins predicted from cDNA sequences. Positions of the first and last amino acid residues in the mature proteins are marked. The proteins are aligned at the 24 amino acid residue stretch constituting the plasma membrane (PM) spanning domain shown in black. Hatched areas indicate regions of conserved homology. The extracellular domain of the GH receptor is longer than that of the PRL receptor (246 *vs.* 210 amino acid residues). The rat PRL receptor containing 294 amino acid residues and two PRL receptors identified in the mouse containing 273 and 284 amino acid residues are smaller than the rabbit PRL receptor which has 592 amino acids. The variations in the size of PRL receptors in these species arise from differing lengths of the cytoplasmic domains

Table 3 Structural Features of Cloned Growth Hormone and Prolactin Receptors

| | GH-R | | PRL-R | | |
	Rabbit	Rabbit	Rat	Mouse	Mouse
Molecular weight (kDa)					
Nonglycosylated	70	66	33	32.7	32.4
Glycosylated	130	80	41	42	42
Amino acids					
Signal sequence	18	19	19	19	19
Mature protein	620	592	291	284	273
Extracellular domain	246	210	210	210	210
Transmembrane domain	24	24	24	24	24
Cytoplasmic domain	350	358	57	50	39
Glycosylation sites (N-linked)	5	3	3	3	3
Ref.	249	297	293	294	294

to be covalently associated with the 130 kDa receptor. The cloned cDNA sequence codes for a 620 amino acid protein with a single centrally located transmembrane-spanning hydrophobic domain of 24 residues, 246 amino acid extracellular domain and a 360 amino acid cytoplasmic domain. The rabbit and human GH receptor clones are very similar, whereas they exhibit lower identity with the rat liver GH receptor.[244]

The expression of GH receptor in rat liver, kidney, heart and muscle is developmentally regulated.[243] The expression of hepatic GH receptor is similar in male and female rats, although pregnant rat liver GH binding is increased. The expression of GH receptor was unaltered by GH treatment or hypophysectomy. The GH receptor is similar to prolactin receptor as depicted schematically in Figure 4 and compared in Table 3. Both these receptors, do not share any homology with other receptors known to act as tyrosine kinases or through guanine nucleotide binding proteins. Recently Husman *et al.* have investigated the biogenesis of the GH receptor in rat liver by ligand affinity crosslinking.[250] Three proteins of 95, 43 and 33 kDa proteins were found to be specifically labeled. Each of these proteins were *N*-glycosylated and the smaller proteins may be derived from the 95 kDa receptor protein. Northern blot analysis and *in vitro* translation studies indicate that the 95 kDa receptor in the mouse liver is encoded by a 3.9 kb mRNA, whereas the 31 kDa truncated GH receptor protein is encoded by a smaller (1.2 kb) mRNA.[250]

13.3.7.4 Mechanism of Action of GH

The mechanism of action of GH is largely unknown. Difficulty in demonstrating direct effects of GH *in vitro* on known target tissues led to the 'somatomedin hypothesis', which states that GH stimulates IGF I production in the liver and that it is IGF I which then regulates longitudinal bone and body growth.[252] This was documented recently by Shoenie *et al.*,[253] who showed that purified IGF I mimics the effect of GH on the growth of epiphyseal width, thymidine incorporation into cartilages and daily body weight gain in hypophysectomized rats. It is believed that IGF I receptor tyrosine kinase may regulate the turnover of putative endogenous proteins phosphorylated at tyrosine residues, which in turn may be involved in GH signal transduction.[254] This concept is, however, not tenable for three reasons: (i) IGF I expression has been detected in virtually all tissues examined;[255,256] (ii) GH receptors are present on a wide variety of nonhepatic cells,[233] including epiphysial chondrocytes;[257] and (iii) GH administered locally in the epiphyseal growth plate stimulates unilateral longitudinal bone growth, an effect that is not dependent on IGF I.[258] Thus it is likely that GH and IGF I are both necessary, with GH inducing differentiation of the progenitor cells and IGF I stimulating their subsequent clonal expansion.[259] The role of IGF I in mediating the effects of GH is complex and not completely understood at the present time. Clearly, the effects mediated by IGF I are delayed effects and therefore may not qualify as biochemical responses that ensue immediately following the binding of GH to its receptor.

GH binding leads to phosphorylation of Tyr residues in the GH receptor,[260] which, however, appears to be devoid of intrinsic tyrosine kinase activity. Recently PKC has been proposed as an intracellular mediator of GH action in adipocytes, based on the observation that downregulation of PKC decreased the lipogenetic effect of insulin and hGH in adipocytes.[261] Direct changes in PKC activity linked to GH receptor binding has, however, not been documented. Similarly GH-induced stimulation of guanylate cyclase activity was reported, but the role of cGMP as a second messenger for GH action has not been proven.[233]

13.3.8 PROLACTIN

Prolactin, one of the principal hormones produced by the pituitary gland, has important physiological functions in diverse species. These include regulation of salt and water balance in fish, promotion of nesting behavior and development of crop sac in birds and regulation of reproductive functions in mammals.[262,263] In mammals PRL affects the prostate and the testis in the male, while it is both luteotropic and luteolytic for the ovary in the female. PRL promotes growth and differentiation of the breast and is the principal hormone that influences the production of milk. PRL shares considerable structural and functional properties with GH and is considered an important member of the GH–PRL–PL (mammosomatotropic) family.[224,225] The synthesis and release of PRL from the pituitary is more active than that of GH. Consequently, the concentration of PRL (150 µg per gland) is 100 times less than that of GH in the pituitary (10 mg per gland).

13.3.8.1 Structural Features and Molecular Heterogeneity of PRL

PRL is an acidic molecule ($pI < 6.5$) with a molecular weight 22 550. It is a single-chain polypeptide containing 198 amino acids. It has a large disulfide loop in the middle (Cys^{58}-Cys^{173}) and two small disulfide loops at the amino and carboxy termini (Cys^4-Cys^{11}) and (Cys^{190}-Cys^{198}) respectively.[264] A 55 kDa PRL-like immunoreactive material has also been identified in pituitary extracts and human plasma, particularly in pregnancy.[265] A glycosylated variant of $M_r = 25$ kDa is present in the pituitary extracts.[266] The PRL gene has five exons and four introns and the exon–intron boundaries are highly conserved amongst the genes for the somatomammotropic hormones.[224,225] There is greater sequence homology between GH and PRL (90%) than between PRL (and GH) and PL (40%). Because of its large size, it is difficult to delineate structural determinants for the activity of PRL by structural modification. Insight into structure–function relationships of PRL was obtained by recombination of different segments of hGH, human PRL and human PL. The 1–134 amino acid segment of PRL was essential for biological activity.[224] Disruption of individual disulfide bridges does not drastically reduce the biological activity of the molecule, but destruction of all three disulfide links renders it totally inactive.[267] The evolutionary aspects of somatomammotropic hormones suggest that PRL, GH and PL are derived by gene duplication from a common ancestral gene.[224,225]

13.3.8.2 PRL Receptors

PRL binding sites of high affinity are present in a number of tissues, including mammary gland, liver, kidney, adrenals, ovaries, testes, prostate, seminal vesicles, hypothalamus, choroid plexus, pancreatic islets and lymphoid tissue, as well as in a number of mammary tumors and in prostatic tumors.[268–270] PRL receptors bind all three lactogenic hormones, GH, PRL and PL.[267] Although the binding affinity of PRL can be directly correlated to its biological potency, for some somatomammotropic hormones such as primate GH and certain PLs the relationship between receptor binding and hormonal potency may be complicated.[268]

High affinity receptors for PRL are present on the cell surface and in various subcellular fractions in a given target tissue. Binding of radioiodinated PRL to PRL receptor initially occurs on the cell membrane but is quickly internalized into the Golgi complex and subsequently into light lysosome-like structures and mature lysosomes.[270,271] The time dependent increase in the concentration of PRL receptors in these subcellular fractions suggests internalization of the cell surface receptor upon PRL binding. The lysosomal compartment is probably involved in receptor degradation and not in mediation of PRL action.[268] Khan *et al.* have shown the presence of distinct endosomes which cosediment with both Golgi complex and lysosomes.[272] The properties of the endosomal PRL receptors are similar to those on plasma membrane. These intracellular receptors consist of a mixed population of internalized and newly synthesized receptors. Cytoplasmic and microsomal PRL receptors have been shown to be immunologically identical.[270,273]

13.3.8.2.1 PRL receptor regulation

The homologous regulation by PRL of its receptors is not simple. Initially PRL receptor binding was shown to be directly dependent on the hormone concentration. First, the loss of PRL binding following hypophysectomy in rats was reversible by pituitary implants under the renal capsule.[274] Second, PRL-secreting tumors were associated with increased hepatic PRL receptor number.[275] Third, the direct stimulatory effect of PRL injections on the receptor level has been reported in rat lung, liver and kidney,[276-279] and golden hamster testes,[280] as well as in rat hepatocytes *in vitro*.[281] On the other hand downregulation of renal PRL receptors by chronic PRL treatment has been reported to occur in bullfrog tadpoles.[282] Heterologous regulation of PRL receptors by other hormones has also been extensively documented. Both lactogenic (human) and nonlactogenic (rat) GH can upregulate PRL receptors.[283,284] The addition of hGH or bGH augmented PRL receptor number in a time and dose dependent manner.[285] Since in rat liver bGH binds exclusively to somatogenic receptors and ovine PRL to lactogenic receptors,[286] it was suggested that in rat hepatocytes each hormone induces PRL receptors *via* its own receptors. Such a dual hormonal control was further evidenced by the additive effect of maximally effective doses of bGH and ovine PRL.[285] Glucocorticoids, sex steroids, thyroxin and insulin also regulate PRL receptor levels.[268-270] The stimulation of PRL binding by estrogen, its fluctuation with estrous cycle and decrease following ovariectomy implies a direct physiological regulation of PRL receptors by estradiol.[286] However, since 17-β-estradiol did not alter PRL receptors on cultured hepatocytes, the *in vivo* regulatory effect of estradiol appears to be indirect, possibly *via* primary effect on GH and PRL secretion.[268,286]

13.3.8.2.2 Biochemical characteristics of PRL receptors

PRL receptors in mammary gland have been characterized in many species and have been described in detail.[268,269] Initial attempts to solubilize membrane PRL receptors were unsuccessful because of detergent-induced aggregation of radiolabeled PRL in the presence of Triton X-100. This difficulty was overcome by using hGH which binds to nonprimate GH receptor as well as PRL receptors and does not aggregate when exposed to Triton X-100,[268] as well as by employing zwitterionic detergents such as 3-[3(3-cholamidopropyl)dimethylammonio]-1-propanesulfonate.[287] The solubilized receptor has been purified by immunoaffinity chromatography using immobilized ovine PRL. The estimated size of the solubilized PRL receptors is influenced by the technique used. Combination of gel filtration and sedimentation velocity determination indicates a size of 73–77.8 kDa.[288] Affinity crosslinking with hGH followed by electrophoresis under reducing conditions has revealed PRL receptor proteins of 30–84 kDa.[289] Several groups have raised PRL receptor antibodies[290-292] Okamura *et al.* isolated large quantities of purified rat liver PRL receptor by immunoaffinity chromatography using immobilized monoclonal PRL receptor antibody.[290] This receptor preparation consisted of a doublet of 40 and 42 kDa. Affinity crosslinking of hGH revealed a 62 kDa hormone–receptor complex in the microsomes and an additional 102 kDa complex in the purified receptor preparation. The higher molecular weight forms of PRL receptors observed in these studies appear to have resulted from spontaneous dimerization of the monomer during storage.[290]

13.3.8.2.3 Cloning and sequencing of PRL receptors

Based on the sequence obtained from the purified PRL receptor, oligonucleotide probes were prepared and used to isolate PRL receptor cDNA from a rat liver library by Boutin *et al.*[293] The primary structure of the PRL receptor was deduced from a single cDNA clone and sequenced to reveal a 19 amino acid signal peptide followed by a 291 amino acid residue mature receptor protein. The extracellular domain consists of 210 residues and the cytoplasmic domain of 57 residues which are connected by a short transmembrane domain of 24 amino acid residues. There are three potential N-linked glycosylation sites in the molecule. PRL receptor thus exhibits similarity to GH receptor (Figure 4, Table 3). In fact, a striking homology between five regions of rat PRL receptor and GH receptor was identified. The region between the first and second Cys and the third and fourth Cys residues have > 67% identity. When conservative amino acid substitutions are considered, the homology in the Cys regions of the two receptors increased to 75–100%. Two additional regions of lower homology (40–60%) have also been identified. In the cytoplasmic domains a segment of 19 highly conserved (68% homology) amino acid residues is present at the same locus in both receptors. Recently expression of multiple forms of PRL receptor in mouse liver has been reported.[294] This is consistent with earlier findings of a 37 kDa PRL receptor with more than one affinity class in mouse liver and marked heterogeneity of PRL receptor in other tissues.[295,296]

Davis and Linzer prepared cDNA clones of the PRL receptor and compared their translation products with the affinity purified receptors.[294] Two forms of PRL receptor of 284 and 273 amino acids were detected which differed markedly in the C-terminal region of the cytoplasmic domains only. A third PRL receptor protein, believed to be truncated, has also been identified. Although this may be secreted, such a form has not been identified under normal conditions.[294] Recently Kelly *et al.* used rat liver PRL receptor cDNA probe to isolate the receptor in rabbit mammary gland and human hepatoma cells.[297,298] These tissues contain a second longer form of the receptor consisting of 592 and 598 amino acids respectively. The size differences arise due to the longer cytoplasmic domains. Unlike other growth factor receptors, neither GH nor PRL receptor contains an intrinsic tyrosine kinase activity in the cytoplasmic domain.

13.3.8.3 Mechanism of Action of PRL

PRL potentiates the growth of mammary tumors in experimental animals. Carcinogen-induced mammary tumors in rodents possess PRL receptors and their growth is sensitive to PRL.[299,300] In human breast cancer cells (T-47D cells) PRL augments glucocorticoid-induced cell rounding, loss of adhesion and, more interestingly, induces synthesis of specific proteins in these cells only in the presence of glucocorticoids.[301] When anti-PRL receptor antibodies were administered in female rats carcinogen-induced mammary tumor development was prevented.[299] Membrane receptors for GnRH, SS and PRL in the Dunning R-3327H rat prostate adenocarcinoma were reduced in number and affinity after *in vivo* treatment with D-Trp[6] GnRH and the SS analog RC-160.[302] The antineoplastic activity of these analogs might be due to abolition of the tumor growth promoting effect of PRL.[303]

The mechanism by which PRL exerts its actions subsequent to receptor binding is still poorly understood. In the mammary gland the cellular events that lead to the induction of casein gene transcription and synthesis do not appear to involve cyclic AMP.[304,305] Prostaglandin, arachidonic acid and polyamines weakly mimic the stimulation of casein synthesis by PRL.[305] PRL stimulates ornithine decarboxylase, the rate-limiting enzyme in polyamine synthesis.[268,306] In other studies cyclic GMP has been implicated in the mitogenic action of PRL.[306] It is not clear whether the role of these mediators in mediating the PRL effect on casein mRNA levels is direct or indirect.[307] Cytoskeletal elements have been implicated in PRL action. For example, colchicine, a microtubule destabilizer, blocks PRL-induced casein gene transcription and mRNA levels.[308] Attempts to identify specific second messenger mediators of PRL have not borne fruit.

PRL and its receptor are readily internalized into endosomal vesicles.[309] This uptake leads to time dependent accumulation of PRL in the 'early' and 'late' endosomes.[310] The internalization and subcellular distribution of [^{125}I]PRL was not affected by the lysosomatotropic agent chloroquine, consistent with its inability to prevent PRL-activated expression of the casein gene.[308] PRL uptake and PRL-induced gene transcription in the mammary gland is inhibited by colchicine essentially by blocking the fusion of endocytotic small vesicles to the lipoprotein-filled endosomal vesicles.[311] It is thus conceivable that internalization of PRL may be an important prerequisite for some, if not all, actions of PRL.[313] Whether PRL acts directly at an intracellular site and/or its effect is mediated by cell surface receptor linked second messenger systems is currently being actively investigated.

The cytoplasmic domains of membrane receptors play a crucial role in initiating integral (*e.g.* tyrosine kinase) or secondary signal transducer (*e.g.* cAMP). The PRL receptor appears to be heterogeneous in terms of its cytoplasmic domain.[294,297] It is thus tempting to speculate that multiple PRL receptors with different cytoplasmic domains may be linked to distinct signal transducing systems. PRL receptors in the rat[292] and mouse[293] livers possess a short cytoplasmic domain (50–57 residues) and resemble the structural arrangement of LDL receptor,[312] which functions as a transporter of low density lipoprotein. Receptor-mediated translocation of PRL in the blood into cerebrospinal fluid by PRL receptor suggests that the short form of PRL receptor may function as a ligand transporter.[313] The PRL receptor with a longer cytoplasmic domain may be involved primarily in gene transcription in the mammary gland.[297] The presence of highly conserved regions in the cytoplasmic domains of GH and PRL receptors suggests that these may be involved in transmembrane signalling.[293,297] Differential expression of the GH, PRL and PL receptors may be responsible for the exquisite control of growth by these hormones during development. Expression of these receptors in suitable cell system and site-directed mutagenesis experiments should help elucidate the structure–function aspects as well as the mechanism of action of GH, PRL and PL.

13.3.9 CONCLUSION

Major advances in neuroendocrinology have been made in the last few years. The knowledge of the structures of the various hypothalamic peptides has led to the understanding of the structural determinants for their receptor binding and bioactivity. The design and development of potent analogs of many of these peptides exhibiting agonistic or antagonistic properties holds great potential for clinical applications. GnRH analogs are currently being used as or being evaluated as therapeutic agents in the treatment of precocious puberty, sterility, endometriosis, and in hormone-related cancers of the breast and prostate. Several conformationally restricted SS analogs have been successfully tested as therapeutic adjuncts in endocrine and digestive diseases, as well as in cancer, either alone or in combination with GnRH analogs. GHRH can be used in the treatment of short stature. Although CRH has not yet been found to be of therapeutic importance, its clinical application in diagnostic testing is clearly useful in many situations. The detailed understanding of the pharmacology and the structure of the receptors of these hormones suggests the possible existence of receptor subtypes that may be selectively coupled to distinct second messenger signalling systems. Further elucidation of the mechanism of action(s) that may be receptor subtype specific should become feasible in the near future with a better understanding of the conformational determinants of ligand specificity of such receptor subtypes. This should enable the design of stable agonists or antagonists with improved target specificity. These advances, coupled with improved target selective delivery of such compounds, hold great potential for clinical applications of these hormones in endocrine and digestive and perhaps psychiatric disorders and, more importantly, in hormone dependent cancers.

13.3.10 REFERENCES

1. A. J. W. Hsueh and B. C. Jones, *Endocrine Rev.*, 1981, **2**, 437.
2. J. Sandow, in 'Neuroendocrine Perspectives', ed. E. E. Muller and R. M. McLeod, Elsevier Biomedical Press, Amsterdam, 1982, vol. 1, p. 339.
3. G. Fink, *Annu. Rev. Physiol.*, 1979, **41**, 571.
4. T. Ziporyn, *J. Am. Med. Assoc.*, 1985, **253**, 469.
5. M. J. Karter and J. E. Rivier, *Endocrine Rev.*, 1986, **7**, 46.
6. D. H. Coy, J. S. Vilchez-Martinez, E. J. Coy and A. V. Schally, *J. Med. Chem. Soc.*, 1976, **190**, 423.
7. E. Hazum, *Methods Enzymol.*, 1986, **124**, 47.
8. D. Keinan and E. Hazum, *Biochemistry*, 1985, **24**, 7728.
9. P. M. Conn, D. C. Rogers, S. G. Seay and D. Staley, *Endocrinology*, 1984, **115**, 1913.
10. W. Vale, G. Grant, J. Rivier, M. Monahan, M. Amoss, R. Blackwell, R. Burgess and R. Guillemin, *Science (Washington, D.C.)*, 1972, **176**, 933.
11. J. A. Vilchez-Martinez, A. V. Schally, D. H. Coy, E. J. Coy, L. Debeljuk and A. Arimura, *Endocrinology*, 1974, **95**, 213.
12. B. H. Vickery, in 'Pharmacology and Clinical Use of Inhibitors of Hormone Secretion and Action', ed. B. J. A. Furr and A. E. Wakeling, Bailliere Tindall, Eastbourne, p. 385.
13. P. M. Conn, D. C. Rogers, J. M. Stewart, J. Neidel and T. Sheffield, *Nature (London)*, 1982, **296**, 653.
14. R. N. Clayton and K. J. Catt, *Endocrine Rev.*, 1981, **2**, 186.
15. J. Marian and P. M. Conn, *Endocrinology*, 1983, **112**, 104.
16. R. Popkin, T. A. Bromley, A. Currie, R. W. Shaw, D. T. Baird and H. M. Fraser, *Biochem. Biophys. Res. Commun.*, 1983, **114**, 750.
17. T. M. Siler-Khodr and G. S. Khodr, *Am. J. Obstet. Gynecol.*, 1978, **130**, 216.
18. A. Hsueh and G. Erickson, *Science (Washington, D.C.)*, 1979, **204**, 854.
19. P. M. Conn, D. C. Rogers and S. G. Seay, *Mol. Pharmacol.*, 1984, **25**, 51.
20. M. Zilberstein, H. Zakut and Z. Naor, *Life Sci.*, 1983, **32**, 663.
21. W. C. Gorospe and P. M. Conn, *Endocrinology*, 1987, **120**, 222.
22. E. Hazum, Y. Koch, M. Liskovitch and A. Amsterdam, *Cell Tissue Res.*, 1985, **293**, 3.
23. E. Loumaye and K. J. Catt, *Science (Washington, D.C.)*, 1982, **215**, 983.
24. I. Schvartz and E. Hazum, *J. Biol. Chem.*, 1987, **262**, 17046.
25. E. Hazum, *Endocrinology*, 1981, **109**, 1281.
26. K. A. Eidne, D. T. Hendricks and R. P. Millar, *Endocrinology*, 1985, **116**, 1792.
27. P. M. Conn and J. C. Venter, *Endocrinology*, 1985, **116**, 1324.
28. E. Hazum, *Mol. Cell. Endocrinol.*, 1982, **26**, 217.
29. E. Hazum, A. Garritson and D. Keinan, *Biochem. Biophys. Res. Commun.*, 1982, **105**, 8.
30. E. Hazum, I. Schvartz, Y. Waksman and D. Keinan, *J. Biol. Chem.*, 1986, **261**, 13043.
31. E. Hazum, I. Schvartz and M. Popliker, *J. Biol. Chem.*, 1987, **262**, 531.
32. A. Curtis, V. Lyons and G. Fink, *J. Endocrinol.*, 1985, **105**, 163.
33. W. R. Huckle and P. M. Conn, *Endocrine Rev.*, 1988, **9**, 387.
34. P. M. Conn, D. D. Staley, T. Yasumoto, W. R. Huckle and J. Janovick, *Mol. Endocrinol.*, 1987, **1**, 154.
35. J. P. Chang, E. E. McCoy, J. Graeter, K. Tasaka and K. J. Catt, *J. Biol. Chem.*, 1986, **261**, 9105.
36. P. M. Conn, D. C. Rogers and T. Sheffield, *Endocrinology*, 1981, **109**, 1122.
37. W. V. Andrews and P. M. Conn, *Endocrinology*, 1986, **118**, 1148.
38. P. M. Conn, W. R. Huckle, W. H. Andrews and C. A. McArdle, *Rec. Prog. Hormone Res.*, 1987, **43**, 29.
39. M. A. Smith and W. W. Vale, *Endocrinology*, 1980, **107**, 1425.

40. C. A. McArdle, W. R. Huckle and P. M. Conn, *J. Biol. Chem.*, 1987, **262**, 5068.
41. C. A. McArdle, W. C. Gorospe, W. R. Huckle and P. M. Conn, *Mol. Endocrinol.*, 1987, **1**, 420.
42. S. S. Papavasiliou, S. Zmeili, S. Khoury, T. D. Landfeld, W. W. Chin and J. C. Marshall, *Proc. Natl. Acad. Sci. USA*, 1986, **83**, 4026.
43. W. V. Andrews, R. A. Maurer and P. M. Conn, *J. Biol. Chem.*, **263**, 13 755.
44. D. L. Vogel, J. A. Magner, R. J. Sherins and B. D. Weintraub, *Endocrinology*, 1986, **119**, 202.
45. W. Vale, J. Speiss, C. Rivier and J. Rivier, *Science (Washington, D.C.)*, 1981, **213**, 1394.
46. L. W. Swanson, P. E. Sawchenko, J. Rivier and W. Vale, *Neuroendocrinology*, 1983, **36**, 165.
47. T. O. Bruhn, W. C. Engeland, E. L. P. Anthony, D. S. Gann and I. M. D. Jackson, *Endocrinology*, 1987, **120**, 25.
48. G. F. Koob, *Perspect. Behav. Med.*, 1985, **2**, 39.
49. J. Rivier, J. Speiss and W. Vale, *Proc. Natl. Acad. Sci. USA*, 1983, **80**, 4851.
50. N. Ling, F. Esch, P. Bohlen, A. Baird and R. Guillemin, *Biochem. Biophys. Res. Commun.*, 1984, **122**, 1218.
51. F. Esch, N. Ling, P. Bohlen, A. Baird, R. Benoit and R. Guillemin, *Biochem. Biophys. Res. Commun.*, 1984, **122**, 899.
52. Y. Furutani, Y. Morimoto, S. Shibahara, M. Noda, T. Takahashi, T. Hirose, M. Asai, S. Inayama, H. Hayashida, T. Miyata and S. Numa, *Nature (London)*, 1983, **301**, 537.
53. P. C. Montecucchi, A. Anastasi, R. de Castiglione and V. Erspamer, *Int. J. Pept. Protein Res.*, 1980, **16**, 19.
54. J. Rivier, C. Rivier and W. Vale, *Science (Washington, D.C.)*, 1984, **224**, 889.
55. F. M. Chen, L. M. Bilezikjian, M. Perrin, J. Rivier and W. Vale, *Brain Res.*, 1986, **381**, 49.
56. V. Giguiere, F. Labrie, J. Cote, D. H. Coy, J. Sueiras Diaz *et al.*, *Proc. Natl. Acad. Sci. USA*, 1982, **79**, 3466.
57. W. Vale, J. Vaughan, M. Smith, G. Yamamoto, J. Rivier *et al.*, *Endocrinology*, 1983, **113**, 657.
58. C. Rivier and P. M. Plotsky, *Annu. Rev. Physiol.*, 1986, **48**, 475.
59. D. M. Gibbs, *Brain Res.*, 1985, **335**, 360.
60. V. Giguere and F. Labrie, *Endocrinology*, 1982, **111**, 1752.
61. D. N. Orth, C. R. De Bold, G. S. DeCherney, R. V. Jackson, W. R. Sheldon *et al.*, *Fed. Proc., Fed. Am. Soc. Exp. Biol.*, 1985, **44**, 197.
62. C. Rivier and W. Vale, *Endocrinology*, 1983, **113**, 1422.
63. H. M. Schuttle, G. P. Chroussos, P. W. Gold, J. D. Booth, E. H. Oldfield *et al.*, *J. Clin. Invest.*, 1985, **750**, 1781.
64. P. M. Plotsky, T. O. Bruhn and W. Vale, *Endocrinology*, 1985, **115**, 1639.
65. E. B. De Souza and G. Battaglia, *Adv. Exp. Biol. Med.*, 1988, **245**, 123.
66. Y. Tache, Y. Goto, M. W. Gunion, W. Vale, J. Rivier and M. Brown, *Science (Washington, D.C.)*, 1983, **222**, 935.
67. P. C. Wynn, G. Aguilera, J. Morell and K. J. Catt, *Biochem. Biophys. Res. Commun.*, 1983, **110**, 602.
68. M. Perrin, Y. Haas, J. Rivier and W. Vale, *Endocrinology*, 1986, **118**, 1171.
69. E. B. De Souza, M. Perrin, J. Rivier, W. Vale and M. J. Kuhar, *Science (Washington, D.C.)*, 1984, **224**, 1449.
70. R. Udelsman, J. P. Harwood, M. A. Milan, G. P. Chrousos, D. S. Goldstein, R. Zimlichman, K. J. Catt and G. Aguilera. *Nature (London)*, 1986, **319**, 147.
71. J. R. Davie, L. Eiden and R. Eskay, *Endocrinology*, 1985, **116**, 2152.
72. E. L. Webster and E. B. De Souza, *Endocrinology*, 1988, **122**, 609.
73. E. B. De Souza, *J. Neurosci.*, 1987, **7**, 88.
74. P. C. Wynn, J. P. Harwood, K. J. Catt and G. Aguilera, *Endocrinology*, 1985, **116**, 1653.
75. G. Aguilera, A.-B. Abou Samra, J. P. Harwood and K. J. Catt, *Adv. Exp. Med. Biol.*, 1988, **245**, 83.
76. A. R. Hoffman, G. Ceda and T. Reisine, *J. Neurosci.*, 1985, **5**, 234.
77. M. C. Holmes, F. A. Antoni, K. J. Catt and G. Aguilera, *Neuroendocrinology*, 1985, **43**, 245.
78. R. L. Hauger, M. A. Millan, K. J. Catt and G. Aguilera, *Endocrinology*, 1987, **120**, 1527.
79. E. Nishimura, N. Billestrup, M. Perrin and W. Vale, *J. Biol. Chem.*, 1987, **262**, 12 893.
80. D. E. Grigoriadis and E. B. De Souza, *J. Biol. Chem.*, 1988, **263**, 10 927.
81. B. E. Rosendale, D. B. Jarret and A. G. Robinson, *Endocrinology*, 1987, **120**, 2357.
82. F. M. Chen, L. M. Bilezikjian, M. Perrin, J. Rivier and W. Vale, *Brain Res.*, 1986, **381**, 49.
83. G. Aguilera, J. P. Harwood, J. X. Wilson, J. Morell, J. H. Brown and K. J. Catt, *J. Biol. Chem.*, 1983, **258**, 8039.
84. V. Giguere, G. Lefevre and F. Labrie, *Life Sci.*, 1982, **31**, 3057.
85. A.-B. Abou Samra, K. J. Catt and G. Aguilera, *Endocrinology*, 1987, **121**, 965.
86. R. Guillemin, *Science (Washington, D.C.)*, 1978, **202**, 390.
87. Y. Koch and E. Okon, *Int. Rev. Exp. Pathol.*, 1979, **19**, 45.
88. I. M. Jackson, *N. Engl. J. Med.*, 1982, **306**, 145.
89. J. F. Wilbur and P. Spinella, *J. Clin. Endocrinol. Metab.*, 1984, **59**, 432.
90. W. Vale, C. Rivier and M. Brown, *Annu. Rev. Physiol.*, 1977, **39**, 473.
91. D. A. Leong, L. S. Frawley and J. D. Neill, *Annu. Rev. Physiol.*, 1983, **45**, 109.
92. E. C. Griffiths and G. W. Bennett (eds.), 'Thyrotropin Releasing Hormone', Raven Press, New York, 1983.
93. C. Prasad, in 'Handbook of Neurochemistry', ed. A. Lajtha, Plenum Press, New York, 1985, p. 175.
94. R. P. Lamberton, R. M. Lechan and I. M. Jackson, *Endocrinology*, 1984, **115**, 2400.
95. P. M. Hinkle, *Ann. N. Y. Acad. Sci.*, 1989, **553**, 176.
96. N. A. Sharif, *Ann. N. Y. Acad. Sci.*, 1989, **553**, 147.
97. N. Ogawa, Y. Yamawaki, H. Kuroda, T. Ofuji, E. Itoga and S. Kito, *Brain Res.*, 1981, **205**, 169.
98. A. H. Drummond, P. J. Hughes, F. Ruiz-Larrea and L. A. Joels, *Ann. N. Y. Acad. Sci.*, 1989, **553**, 197.
99. W. A. Johnson, N. M. Nathanson and A. Horita, *Ann. N. Y. Acad. Sci.*, 1989, **553**, 137.
100. W. J. Philips and P. M. Hinkle, *Mol. Pharmacol.*, 1989, **35**, 533.
101. M. Wright, A. Hogset, P. Alestrom and K. M. Gautvik, *Biochem. Biophys. Res. Commun.*, 1988, **157**, 875.
102. W. A. Johnson, N. M. Nathanson and A. Horita, *Proc. Natl. Acad. Sci. USA*, 1984, **81**, 4227.
103. T. P. Segerson, G. Mandel, R. H. Goodman and P. Brehm, 'Program of the 70th Annual Meeting of the Endocrine Society', New Orleans, USA, 1988, abstract 1014.
104. R. Osborne and A. H. Tashjian, *Cancer Res.*, 1982, **42**, 4375.
105. M. C. Gershengorn, *Annu. Rev. Physiol.*, 1986, **48**, 515.
106. S. Reichlin, *N. Engl. J. Med.*, 1983, **309**, 1495.
107. Y. C. Patel and C. B. Srikant, *Annu. Rev. Physiol.*, 1986, **48**, 551.

108. L. P. Shen and W. J. Rutter, *Science (Washington, D.C.)*, 1984, **224**, 168.
109. M. R. Montminy, R. H. Goodman, S. J. Horovitch and J. F. Habener, *Proc. Natl. Acad. Sci. USA*, 1984, **81**, 3337.
110. J. Dixon and P. C. Andrews, *Adv. Exp. Biol. Med.*, 1985, **188**, 19.
111. J. Spiess and B. Noe, *Proc. Natl. Acad. Sci. USA*, 1985, **82**, 277.
112. R. Benoit, N. Ling and F. Esch, *Science (Washington, D.C.)*, 1987, **238**, 1126.
113. R. Benoit, in 'Somatostatin: Basic and Clinical Status', ed. S. Reichlin, Plenum Press, New York, 1987, p. 33.
114. S. E. Shoelson, K. S. Polonsky, T. Nakabayashi, J. B. Jaspen and H. S. Tager, *Am. J. Physiol.*, 1986, **250**, E428.
115. Y. C. Patel and S. Reichlin, in 'Methods of Hormone Radioimmunoassay', 2nd edn., ed. B. M. Jaffe and H. R. Behrman, Academic Press, New York, 1979, p. 77.
116. M. R. Brown and L. A. Fisher, *Adv. Exp. Med. Biol.*, 1985, **188**, 217.
117. J. Rivier, P. Brazeau, W. Vale and R. Guillemin, *J. Med. Chem.*, 1975, **18**, 123.
118. W. Vale, J. Rivier, N. Ling and M. Brown, *Metabolism*, 1978, **27** (suppl. 1), 1391.
119. D. F. Veber, R. M. Freidinger, D. Schwenk-Perlow, C. Homnick, W. C. Randall, M. S. Glitzer, R. Saperstein and R. Hirschman, *Nature (London)*, 1981, **292**, 55.
120. R. J. Nutt, C. D. Colton, R. Sapperstein and D. F. Veber, in 'Somatostatin: Basic and Clinical Status', ed. S. Reichlin, Plenum Press, New York, 1987, p. 83.
121. W. Vale, J. Rivier, N. Ling and M. Brown, *Metabolism*, 1987, **27** (suppl. 1), 1391.
122. P. Marbach, W. Bauer, U. Briner, W. Dopfner, T. Petcher and J. Pless, *Hormone Res.*, 1988, **29**, 54.
123. R. Z. Cai, B. Szoke, R. Lu, D. Fu, D. T. W. Redding and A. V. Schally, *Proc. Natl. Acad. Sci. USA*, 1986, **83**, 1896.
124. J. T. Pelton, K. Gulya, V. J. Hruby, S. P. Duckles and H. I. Yamamura, *Proc. Natl. Acad. Sci. USA*, 1985, **82**, 236.
125. W. B. Wehrenberg, R. Bloch and N. Ling, *Neuroendocrinology*, 1985, **41**, 13.
126. A. Schonbrunn and A. Tashjian, *J. Biol. Chem.*, 1978, **252**, 6473.
127. C. B. Srikant and Y. C. Patel, *Proc. Natl. Acad. Sci. USA*, 1981, **78**, 3930.
128. C. B. Srikant and Y. C. Patel, *Endocrinology*, 1982, **110**, 2138.
129. G. Aguilera and D. S. Parker, *J. Biol. Chem.*, 1982, **257**, 1134.
130. G. Aguilera, D. S. Parker and K. J. Catt, *Endocrinology*, 1982, **111**, 1376.
131. C. B. Srikant and Y. C. Patel, *Endocrinology*, 1985, **116**, 1717.
132. J. P. Esteve, C. Susini, N. Vaysse, H. Antoniotti, E. Wunch, G. Berthon and A. Ribet, *Am. J. Physiol.*, 1984, **247**, G62.
133. C. B. Srikant and Y. C. Patel, *J. Biol. Chem.*, 1986, **261**, 7690.
134. M. F. Beal, V. T. Tran, M. F. Mazurek, G. Chaltha and J. B. Martin, *J. Neurochem.*, 1986, **46**, 359.
135. U. I. Richardson and A. Schonbrunn, *Endocrinology*, 1981, **108**, 281.
136. C. B. Srikant and S. Heisler, *Endocrinology*, 1985, **117**, 217.
137. S. J. Sullivan and A. Schonbrunn, *Endocrinology*, 1988, **122**, 1137.
138. P. Cotroeno, J. C. Marie and G. Rosselin, *Eur. J. Biochem.*, 1988, **174**, 219.
139. E. Moyse, M. La Dafniet, J. Epelbaum, P. Pagesy, F. Peillon, C. Kordon and A. Enjalbert, *J. Clin. Endocrinol. Metab.*, 1985, **61**, 98.
140. J. C. Reubi, R. Maurer, J. G. M. Klijn, S. Z. Stefanko, J. A. Foekens, G. Blaauw, M. A. Blankenstein and S. W. Lamberts, *J. Clin. Endocrinol. Metab.*, 1986, **63**, 433.
141. S. P. Sreedharan, K. T. Kodama, K. E. Peterson and E. J. Goetzl, *J. Biol. Chem.*, 1989, **264**, 949.
142. R. Elde, O. Johansson and T. Hokfelt, *Adv. Exp. Med. Biol.*, 1985, **188**, 167.
143. C. B. Srikant and Y. C. Patel, *Adv. Exp. Med. Biol.*, 1985, **188**, 291.
144. G. Morel, P. Mesguich, M. P. Dubois and P. M. Dubois, *Endocrinology*, 1985, **116**, 1615.
145. Y. C. Patel, M. Amherdt and L. Orci, *Science (Washington, D.C.)*, 1982, **217**, 1155.
146. F. J. Reyl and M. J. M. Lewin, *Biochem. Biophys. Res. Commun.*, 1982, **109**, 1324.
147. E. Arilla, M. P. Lopez-Ruiz, I. G. Guijarro *et al.*, *Biochim. Biophys. Acta*, 1984, **802**, 203.
148. E. Arilla, B. Colos and J. C. Prieto, *Biosci. Rep.*, 1986, **6**, 283.
149. S. Heisler and C. B. Srikant, *Endocrinology*, 1985, **117**, 271.
150. T. Reisine and J. Axelrod, *Endocrinology*, 1983, **113**, 811.
151. F. Mayor, J. L. Benovic, M. C. Caron and R. J. Lefkovitz, *J. Biol. Chem.*, 1987, **262**, 6468.
152. D. H. Persky and A. Schonbrunn, *J. Biol. Chem.*, 1988, **263**, 714.
153. M. A. Smith, G. Yamamoto and W. Vale, *Mol. Cell. Endocrinol.*, 1984, **37**, 311.
154. M. Beal, M. F. Mazurek, V. T. Tran, G. Chaltha, A. Bird and J. B. Martin, *Science (Washington, D.C.)*, 1985, **229**, 289.
155. N. Kimura, C. Hayafuji and N. Kimura, *J. Biol. Chem.*, 1989, **264**, 7033.
156. A. Schonbrunn, *Endocrinology*, 1982, **110**, 1147.
157. C. B. Srikant and Y. C. Patel, in 'Somatostatin: Basic and Clinical Status', ed. S. Reichlin, Plenum Press, New York, 1987, p. 89.
158. V. Tran, M. F. Beal and J. B. Martin, *Science (Washington, D.C.)*, 1985, **228**, 492.
159. Y. C. Patel, G. Baquiran, C. B. Srikant and B. I. Posner, *Endocrinology*, 1986, **119**, 2262.
160. P. Leroux, R. Quirion and G. Pelletier, *Brain Res.*, 1985, **347**, 74.
161. K. Thermos and T. Reisine, *Mol. Pharmacol.*, 1988, **33**, 370.
162. J. C. Reubi, A. Probst, R. Cortes and J. M. Palcios, *Brain Res.*, 1987, **406**, 391.
163. K. K. Murthy, C. B. Srikant and Y. C. Patel, *Endocrinology*, 1989, **125**, 948.
164. C. B. Srikant, K. K. Murthy and Y. C. Patel, *Endocrinology*, 1989, submitted.
165. H. T. He, K. Johnson, K. Thermos and T. Reisine, *Proc. Natl. Acad. Sci. USA*, 1989, **86**, 1484.
166. J. Bruno and M. Berelowitz, *Endocrinology*, 1989, **124**, 831.
167. J. A. Williams and C. Susini, in 'Somatostatin: Basic and Clinical Status', ed. S. Reichlin, Plenum Press, New York, 1987, p. 103.
168. C. B. Srikant, K. K. Murthy, E. Escher and Y. C. Patel, 'Program of the 71st Annual Meeting of the Endocrine Society', Seattle, USA, 1989, p. 103.
169. K. K. Murthy, C. B. Srikant and Y. C. Patel, 'Program of the 71st Annual Meeting of the Endocrine Society', Seattle, USA, 1989, p. 103.
170. Y. C. Patel, K. K. Murthy, D. Banville, F. Carrier, C. Holmes, A. Bell, J. Spiess and C. B. Srikant, 'Proceedings of International Symposium on Somatostatin', Montreai, Canada, 1989, p. 24.

171. A. Schonbrunn and B. D. Koch, in 'Somatostatin: Basic and Clinical Status', ed. S. Reichlin, Plenum Press, New York, 1987, p. 121.
172. L. C. Mahan and T. Reisine, in 'Somatostatin: Basic and Clinical Status', ed. S. Reichlin, Plenum Press, New York, 1987, p. 121.
173. N. Yamashita, N. Shibuya and E. Ogata, *Proc. Natl. Acad. Sci. USA*, 1986, **83**, 6198.
174. B. D. Koch and A. Schonbrunn, *J. Biol. Chem.*, 1988, **263**, 216.
175. C. Liebow, C. Reilly, M. Serrano and A. V. Schally, *Proc. Natl. Acad. Sci. USA*, 1989, **86**, 2003.
176. R. Burgoyne, *Nature (London)*, 1987, **328**, 112.
177. J. Rivier, J. Spiess, M. Thorner and W. Vale, *Nature (London)*, 1982, **300**, 276.
178. R. Guillemin, P. Brazeau, P. Bohlen, F. Esch, N. Ling and W. B. Wehrenberg, *Science (Washington, D.C.)*, 1982, **218**, 585.
179. D. H. Coy, W. A. Murphy and V. A. Lance, in 'Growth Hormone, Growth Factors and Acromegaly', ed. D. K. Ludecke and G. Tolis, Raven Press, New York, 1987, p. 13.
180. B. Bloch, N. Ling, R. Benoit, W. B. Wehrenberg and R. Guillemin, *Nature (London)*, 1984, **307**, 272.
181. T. Shibasaki, Y. Kiyosawa, A. Masuda, M. Nakahara, N. Hizuka *et al.*, *J. Clin. Endocrinol. Metab.*, 1984, **58**, 215.
182. M. C. Gelato and G. R. Merriam, *Annu. Rev. Physiol.*, 1986, **48**, 569.
183. J. Spiess, J. Rivier and W. Vale, *Nature (London)*, 1983, **303**, 532.
184. N. Ling, A. Baird, W. B. Wehrenberg, H. Ueno, T. Munegumi and P. Brazeau, *Biochem. Biophys. Res. Commun.*, 1984, **123**, 854.
185. L. A. Frohman, T. R. Downs, T. C. Williams, E. P. Heimer, Y.-C. E. Pan and A. Felix, *J. Clin. Invest.*, 1986, **78**, 906.
186. F. A. Momany, C. Y. Bowers, G. A. Reynolds, A. Hong and K. Newlander, *Endocrinology*, 1984, **114**, 1531.
187. T. M. Badger, W. J. Millard, G. F. McCormick, C. Y. Bowers and J. B. Martin, *Endocrinology*, 1984, **115**, 1432.
188. W. Vale, J. Vaughan, M. Smith, G. Yamamoto, J. Rivier and C. Rivier, *Endocrinology*, 1983, **113**, 1121.
189. J. Fukata, D. J. Diamond and J. B. Martin, *Endocrinology*, 1985, **117**, 457.
190. M. Barringa, G. Yamamoto, C. Rivier, W. Vale, R. Evans and M. G. Rosenfeld, *Nature (London)*, 1983, **306**, 84.
191. G. G. Gick, F. N. Zeytin, P. Brazeau, N. Ling, F. Esch and F. C. Bancroft, *Proc. Natl. Acad. Sci. USA*, 1984, **81**, 1553.
192. W. Vale, L. Bilezikjian, N. Billestrup, P. Plotsky, H. Seiferet, M. Perrin, J. Vaughan, J. Spiess and J. Rivier, in 'Neuroendocrine Perspectives', ed. E. E. Muller and R. M. McLeod, Elsevier, Amsterdam, 1986, vol. 5, p. 13.
193. W. Vale, J. Vaughan, G. Yamamoto, J. Spiess and J. Rivier, *Endocrinology*, 1983, **112**, 1553.
194. K. Nakagawa, K. Akikawa, M. Matsubara and M. Kubo, *J. Clin. Endocrinol. Metab.*, 1985, **60**, 306.
195. M. Berelowitz, M. Szabo, L. A. Frohman, S. Firestone, L. Chu and R. L. Hintz, *Science (Washington, D.C.)*, 1981, **212**, 1279.
196. M. D. Lumpkin, A. Negro-Vilar and S. M. McCann, *Science (Washington, D.C.)*, 1981, **211**, 1972.
197. M. D. Lumpkin, W. K. Samson and S. M. McCann, *Endocrinology*, 1985, **116**, 2070.
198. G. S. Tannenbaum, *Science (Washington, D.C.)*, 1984, **226**, 464.
199. M. O. Thorner, J. Reschke, J. Chitwood, A. D. Rogol and R. Furlanetto, *N. Engl. J. Med.*, 1985, **312**, 4.
200. M. O. Thorner, M. L. Vance, W. S. Evans, R. M. Blizzard, A. Rogol, K. Ho, D. A. Leong, J. L. C. Borges, M. J. Cronin, R. M. McLeod, K. Kovacs, S. Asa, E. Horvath, L. Frohman, R. Furlaneto, G. J. Klingensmith, C. Brood, P. Smith, S. Reichlin, J. Rovoer and W. Vale, *Recent Prog. Hormone Res.*, 1986, **42**, 589.
201. A. Ottelecz, W. K. Samson and S. M. McCann, *Peptides*, 1986, **7**, 51.
202. T. Williams, M. Berelowitz, S. N. Joffe, M. O. Thorner, J. Rivier, W. Vale and L. Frohman, *N. Engl. J. Med.*, 1984, **311**, 1403.
203. N. T. Richards, S. M. Wood, N. D. Christofides, S. C. Bhuttacharji and S. R. Bloom, *Diabetologia*, 1984, **27**, 529.
204. H. Seifert, M. Perrin, J. Rivier and W. Vale, *Nature (London)*, 1985, **331**, 487.
205. J. R. Zysk, M. J. Cronin, J. M. Anderson and M. O. Thorner, *J. Biol. Chem.*, 1986, **261**, 16 781.
206. S. J. Pandol, H. Seifert, M. Thomas, J. Rivier and W. Vale, *Science (Washington, D.C.)*, 1984, **225**, 326.
207. Y. Arsenijevic, R. W. Rivest, A. Eshkol, P. C. Sizonenko and M. L. Aubert, *Endocrinology*, 1987, **121**, 1487.
208. R. M. Evans, R. C. Birnbirg and M. G. Rosenfeld, *Proc. Natl. Acad. Sci. USA*, 1982, **79**, 7659.
209. S. R. Spindler, S. H. Mellow and J. D. Baxter, *J. Biol. Chem.*, 1982, **257**, 11 627.
210. B. C. Webb, M. Szabo and L. Frohman, *Endocrinology*, 1983, **113**, 1191.
211. W. B. Wehrenberg, A. Baird and N. Ling, *Science (Washington, D.C.)*, 1983, **221**, 556.
212. A. Spada, L. Vallar and G. Giannatasio, *Endocrinology*, 1984, **115**, 1203.
213. C. Schofl, J. Sandow and W. Knepel, *Am. J. Physiol.*, 1987, **253**, E591.
214. J. Kraicer and J. W. Spence, *Endocrinology*, 1981, **108**, 651.
215. G. Schettini, M. J. Cronin, E. L. Hewlett, M. O. Thorner and A. D. Rogol, *Endocrinology*, 1984, **115**, 1308.
216. C. Mougin, P. Kehrer and R. Gaillard, *Ann. Endocrinol. (Paris)*, 1985, **46**, 61.
217. M. E. Stachura, J. M. Tyler and P. G. Kent, *Endocrinology*, 1987, **120**, 1719.
218. M. J. Cronin, R. M. MacLeod and P. L. Canonico, *Neuroendocrinology*, 1985, **40**, 332.
219. D. Michael, G. Lefevre and F. Labrie, *Mol. Cell. Endocrinol.*, 1983, **33**, 255.
220. L. A. Frohman and J. O. Jansson, *Endocrine Rev.*, 1986, **7**, 223.
221. E. Ohmura and H. G. Friesen, *Endocrinology*, 1985, **116**, 728.
222. O. G. P. Isaksson, S. Eden and J. O. Jansson, *Annu. Rev. Physiol.*, 1985, **47**, 483.
223. R. Collu, in 'Pediatric Endocrinology' ed. R. Collu, J. R. Duscharme and H. J. Guyda, Raven Press, New York, 1989, p. 1.
224. W. L. Miller and N. L. Eberhardt, *Endocrinol. Rev.*, 1983, **4**, 97.
225. C. S. Nicoll, G. L. Mayer and S. M. Russell, *Endocrine Rev.*, 1986, **7**, 169.
226. U. J. Lewis, J. T. Dunn, L. F. Bonewald, B. K. Seavey and W. P. Vanderlaan, *J. Biol. Chem.*, 1979, **253**, 2679.
227. G. Baumann, K. Amburn and M. A. Shaw, *Endocrinology*, 1988, **122**, 976.
228. D. I. H. Linzer and D. Nathan, *Proc. Natl. Acad. Sci. USA*, 1984, **81**, 4255.
229. F. Frankenne, J. Closset, F. Gomez, M. L. Scippa, J. Smal and G. Hennen, *J. Clin. Endocrinol. Metab.*, 1988, **66**, 1171.
230. J. Schwartz, C. M. Foster and M. S. Satin, *Proc. Natl. Acad. Sci. USA*, 1985, **82**, 8724.
231. H. M. Goodman, *Ann. N. Y. Acad. Sci.*, 1968, **148**, 419.
232. J. Smal, J. Closset, G. Hennen and P. DeMeyts, *J. Biol. Chem.*, 1987, **262**, 11 071.

233. J. P. Hughes, H. P. Elsholtz and H. G. Friesen, in 'Polypeptide Hormone Receptors', ed. B. I. Posner, Dekker, New York, 1985, p. 157.
234. L. G. Mendelsohn, *Life Sci.*, 1988, **43**, 1.
235. B. I. Posner, B. Patel, A. Vezinbet and J. Charrier, *Endocrinology*, 1980, **107**, 1954.
236. R. C. Baxter, Z. Zaltsman and J. R. Turtle, *Endocrinology*, 1984, **114**, 1893.
237. R. C. Baxter and Z. Zaltsman, *Endocrinology*, 1984, **115**, 2009.
238. C. H. Hung and W. W. Moore, *Mol. Cell. Endocrinol.*, 1984, **35**, 151.
239. C. S. Chung and T. D. Etherton, *Endocrinology*, 1986, **119**, 780.
240. I. Gause and E. Eden, *Endocrinology*, 1986, **118**, 118.
241. M. A. Lesniak and J. Roth, *J. Biol. Chem.*, 1976, **251**, 3720.
242. L. J. Murphy, E. Vrbovsek and L. Lazarus, *J. Clin. Endocrinol. Metab.*, 1983, **57**, 1117.
243. I. Barash and B. I. Posner, *Mol. Cell. Endocrinol.*, 1989, **62**, 281.
244. L. S. Mathews, B. Enberg and G. Norstedt, *J. Biol. Chem.*, 1989, **264**, 9905.
245. J. P. Hughes and H. G. Friesen, *Annu. Rev. Physiol.*, 1985, **47**, 469.
246. S. I. Ymer and A. C. Harington, *Mol. Cell. Endocrinol.*, 1985, **41**, 153.
247. W. H. Daughaday, B. Trivedi and B. A. Andrews, *J. Clin. Endocrinol. Metab.*, 1987, **65**, 1072.
248. R. Barnard and M. J. Waters, *Biochem. J.*, 1986, **237**, 885.
249. D. W. Leung, S. A. Spencer, G. Cacchianes, R. G. Hammonds, C. Collins, W. G. Henzel, R. Barnard, M. J. Waters and W. I. Wood, *Nature (London)*, 1987, **330**, 537.
250. B. Husman, J. A. Gustafsson and G. Anderson, *J. Biol. Chem.*, 1989, **264**, 690.
251. W. C. Smith, D. I. H. Linzer and F. Talamantes, *Proc. Natl. Acad. Sci. USA*, 1988, **85**, 9576.
252. W. H. Daughaday, H. Hall, M. S. Rabin, W. J. Salmon, Jr., J. L. van der Brande and J. J. Van Wyk, *Nature (London)*, 1972, **235**, 107.
253. E. Shoenie, J. Zapf, R. E. Humbel and E. R. Froesch, *Nature (London)*, 1982, **296**, 252.
254. T. Izumi, M. F. White, T. Kadowaki, F. Takaku, Y. Akanuma and M. Kasugo, *J. Biol. Chem.*, 1987, **262**, 1282.
255. L. S. Mathews, G. Norstedt and R. D. Palmiter, *Proc. Natl. Acad. Sci. USA*, 1986, **83**, 9343.
256. V. K. M. Han, A. J. D'Ercole and P. K. Lund, *Science (Washington, D.C.)*, 1987, **236**, 193.
257. R. Barnard, K. M. Haynes, G. A. Weather and M. J. Waters, *Endocrinology*, 1988, **122**, 2562.
258. O. G. P. Isaksson, J. O. Jansson and I. A. M. Gause, *Science (Washington, D.C.)*, 1982, **216**, 1237.
259. H. Green, M. Morikawa and T. Nixon, *Differentiation*, 1985, **29**, 196.
260. C. M. Foster, J. A. Shafer, F. W. Rozsa, X. Y. Wang, S. D. Lewis, D. A. Renken, J. E. Natale, J. Schwartz and C. Carter-Su, *Biochemistry*, 1988, **27**, 326.
261. J. Small and P. De Myets, *Biochem. Biophys. Res. Commun.*, 1987, **147**, 1232.
262. C. S. Nicoll, in 'Handbook of Physiology', ed. R. O. Greep, Williams & Wilkins, Baltimore, 1974, vol. 4, part 2, p. 253.
263. C. S. Nicoll, *Fed. Proc., Fed. Am. Soc. Exp. Biol.*, 1980, **39**, 2563.
264. M. Wallis, in 'Chemistry and Biochemistry of Amino Acids, Peptides and Proteins: A Survey of Recent Developments', ed. B. Weinstein, Dekker, New York, 1978, vol. 5, p. 213.
265. U. J. Lewis, Y. N. Sinha, E. Markoff and W. P. Vanderlaan, in 'Neuroendocrine Perspectives', ed. E. E. Muller, R. M. Macleod and L. A. Frohman, Elsevier Science Publishers, New York, 1985, vol 4, p. 43.
266. E. Markoff, M. B. Sigel, N. Lacour, B. K. Seavey, H. G. Friesen and U. J. Lewis, *Endocrinology*, 1988, **123**, 1303.
267. A. C. Paladini, C. Pena and E. Poskus, *CRC Crit. Rev. Biochem.*, 1983, **15**, 25.
268. J. R. Hughes, H. P. Elsholtz and H. G. Friesen, in 'Polypeptide Hormone Receptors', ed. B. I. Posner, Dekker, New York, 1985, p. 157.
269. B. I. Posner and M. N. Khan, in 'Prolactin and Prolactinomas', ed. G. Tolis, C. Stefanis, T. Nountokalakis and F. Labrie, Raven Press, New York, 1983, p. 9.
270. P. A. Kelly, M. Katoh, J. Djiane and L. H. Ferland, in 'The Receptors', Academic Press, New York, 1986, vol. 3, p. 355.
271. B. I. Posner, J. J. M. Bergeron, Z. Josefsberg, M. N. Khan, R. J. Khan, B. A. Patel, R. A. Sikstrom and A. K. Verma, *Recent Prog. Hormone Res.*, 1981, **37**, 539.
272. M. N. Khan, B. I. Posner, A. K. Verma, R. J. Khan and J. J. M. Bergeron, *Proc. Natl. Acad. Sci. USA*, 1981, **78**, 4980.
273. M. Emtner, J. Brandt, U. Johansson, B. Jouper, L. Fryklund and P. Roos, *J. Endocrinol.*, 1989, **120**, 401.
274. B. I. Posner, P. A. Kelly and H. G. Friesen, *Science (Washington, D.C.)*, 1975, **188**, 57.
275. B. I. Posner, *Endocrinology*, 1976, **88**, 1168.
276. A. Manni, M. J. Chambers and O. M. Pearson, *Endocrinology*, 1984, **259**, 1398.
277. P. A. Kelly, J. Djiane and A. De Lean, *Prog. Reprod. Biol.*, 1980, **6**, 124.
278. T. Amit, R. J. Barkey, M. Gavish and M. B. H. Voudim, *Mol. Cell. Endocrinol.*, 1985, **39**, 21.
279. I. Barash, Z. Madar and A. Gerter, *Mol. Cell. Endocrinol.*, 1986, **46**, 235.
280. H. G. Klemcke, A. Bartke and K. T. Borer, *Endocrinology*, 1984, **114**, 594.
281. A. A. M. Rosa, L. H. Ferland, J. Djiane, L. M. Houdebine and P. A. Kelly, *Endocrinology*, 1985, **116**, 1288.
282. B. A. White, G. S. Lebovie and C. S. Nicoll, *Gen. Comp. Endocrinol.*, 1981, **43**, 30.
283. R. C. Baxter and Z. Zaltsman, *Endocrinology*, 1984, **115**, 2009.
284. G. Norstedt, G. Andersson and J. A. Gustafsson, *Endocrinology*, 1984, **115**, 672.
285. I. Barash, W. Cromlish and B. I. Posner, *Endocrinology*, 1988, **122**, 1151.
286. P. A. Kelly, B. I. Posner and H. G. Friesen, *Endocrinology*, 1975, **197**, 1408.
287. D. S. Liscia, T. Alhadi and B. K. J. Vonderhaar, *J. Biol. Chem.*, 1982, **257**, 9401.
288. R. C. Jaffe, *Biochemistry*, 1982, **21**, 293.
289. P. A. Kelly, D. Gould, H. Okamura and J. Djiane, in 'Prolactin and Lesions in Breast, Uterus and Prostate', ed. H. Nagasawa, CRC Press, Boca Raton, FL, 1980, p. 61.
290. H. Okamura, S. Raguet, A. Bell, J. Gagnon and P. A. Kelly, *J. Biol. Chem.*, 1989, **264**, 5904.
291. H. Murakami, F. Ike, K. Kohmoto and S. Sakai, *Biochem. J.*, 1988, **256**, 917.
292. H. Okamura, J. Zachwieja, S. Raquet and P. A. Kelly, *Endocrinology*, 1989, **124**, 2499.
293. J.-M. Boutin, C. Jolicoeur, H. Okamura, J. Gagnon, M. Edery, M. Shirota, D. Banville, I. Dusanter-Fourt, J. Djiane and P. A. Kelly, *Cell*, 1988, **53**, 69.
294. J. A. Davis and D. I. H. Linzer, *Mol. Endocrinol.*, 1989, **3**, 674.

295. D. S. Liscia and B. K. Vonderharr, *Proc. Natl. Acad. Sci. USA*, 1982, **79**, 5930.
296. T. Hangaya, W. C. Smith and F. Talamante, *Endocrinology*, 1988, **122**, 1366.
297. M. Edery, C. Jolicouer, C. Lvei-Mevrueis, I. Dusanter-Fourt, B. Petridou, J.-M. Boutin, L. Lesueur, P. A. Kelly and J. Djiane, *Proc. Natl. Acad. Sci. USA*, 1989, **86**, 2112.
298. P. A. Kelly, J.-M. Boutin, C. Jolicoeur, H. Okamura, M. Shirota, M. Edery, I. Dusanter-Fourt and J. Djiane, *Biol. Reprod.*, 1989, **40**, 27.
299. J. F. Sissom, M. L. Eigenbrodt and J. C. Porter, *Am. J. Pathol.*, 1989, **133**, 589.
300. D. W. Gold, N. Bersch, B. A. Solomon, A. Kaplan, D. L. Bimoin and C. H. Li, *N. Engl. J. Med.*, 1980, **303**, 1156.
301. R. P. C. Shiu and B. M. Iwasiow, *J. Biol. Chem.*, 1985, **260**, 11 307.
302. J. Kadar, T. W. Redding, M. Ben-David and A. V. Schally, *Proc. Natl. Acad. Sci. USA*, 1988, **85**, 890.
303. R. P. C. Shiu and H. G. Friesen, *Annu. Rev. Physiol.*, 1980, **42**, 83.
304. J. A. Rillema, *Fed. Proc., Fed. Am. Soc. Exp. Biol.*, 1980, **39**, 2593.
305. T. R. Anderson, G. L. Mayer and C. S. Nicoll, *J. Cyclic Nucleotide Res.*, 1981, **7**, 225.
306. R. J. Matusik and J. M. Rosen, *Endocrinology*, 1980, **106**, 252.
307. L.-M. Houdebine and J. Djiane, *Mol. Cell. Endocrinol.*, 1980, **17**, 1.
308. J. J. M. Bergeron, J. Cruz, M. N. Khan and B. I. Posner, *Annu. Rev. Physiol.*, 1983, **47**, 383.
309. B. I. Posner, M. N. Khan, R. J. Khan, B. A. Patel, S. Savoie and J. J. M. Bergeron, in 'Hormone Receptors in Growth and Reproduction', ed. B. B. Sexana, Raven Press, New York, 1984, p. 103.
310. M. N. Khan, S. Savoie, J. J. M. Bergeron and B. I. Posner, *Biochim. Biophys. Acta*, 1988, **88**, 100.
311. J. M. Molin and E. M. Bogdanove, *Biol. Reprod.*, 1980, **22**, 393.
312. T. Yamamoto, C. G. Davis, M. S. Brown, W. J. Schneider, M. L. Casey, J. L. Goldstein and D. W. Russell, *Cell*, 1984, **39**, 27.
313. R. J. Walsh, P. J. Slaby and B. I. Posner, *Endocrinology*, 1987, **120**, 1846.

13.4

Neurohypophyseal Hormone Receptors

VICTOR J. HRUBY and D. DAVID SMITH
University of Arizona, Tucson, AZ, USA

13.4.1   INTRODUCTION

Oxytocin (**1**; H-Cys^1-Tyr^2-Ile^3-Glu^4-Asn^5-Cys^6-Pro^7-Leu^8-Gly^9-NH$_2$) and arginine vasopressin (**8**; H-Cys^1-Tyr^2-Phe^3-Gln^4-Asn^5-Cys^6-Pro^7-Arg^8-Gly^9-NH$_2$) are members of a class of compounds, found in all mammalian species, called the neurohypophyseal hormones (Table 1). Along with their transport proteins the neurophysins, they are stored in the posterior lobe of the pituitary gland in neurosecretory granules of neuroendocrine transducer cells.[9] Classical biological studies have shown them to possess, to varying degrees, pressor activity, milk ejection activity, antidiuretic activity and uterine contraction activity. More recent work using radioimmunoassay methods and specific antibodies has shown that neurohypophyseal-hormone-like compounds exist within the central nervous system (CNS). This, together with reports that neurohypophyseal hormones possess a wide range of biological activities associated with the CNS, such as maternal and grooming behavior, memory processes, glucagon and insulin metabolism, *etc.*, suggests that there are specific neurohypophyseal hormone receptors within the CNS. These latter findings in the CNS suggest that a new and exciting field of research may result, with many new discoveries and controversies, but will not be the subject of this chapter (those interested should refer to recent reviews[10,11]). Rather in this chapter we will discuss the interaction of these compounds and their analogues with their classical peripheral receptors and their resultant biological activities.

The constitution of a receptor has yet to be clearly defined. Depending on one's perspective, several definitions are available. From a purely biological standpoint, when a tissue in the presence of a hormone (under conditions which are thought to 'physiologically relevant') is stimulated or undergoes a biochemical change, it is said to possess receptors for the hormone. A second approach based on biochemical thinking defines a receptor on the basis of binding experiments, that is, by the ability of the hormone (or analogues) to bind specifically and with high affinity to a pharmacologically or physiologically relevant whole cell preparation or membrane. A more rigorous

Table 1 Biological Activities of Naturally Occurring Neurohypophyseal Hormones

Compound	Rat uterus[a] (units mg^{-1})	V$_1$ receptor[b] (units mg^{-1})	V$_2$ receptor[c] (units mg^{-1})	Ref.
Oxytocin (**1**)	546	3.1	2.7	1.2
Mesotocin (**2**)	289	6.3	1.1	3
Valitocin (**3**)	199	9	0.8	3
Arginine vasotocin (**4**)	127	160	231	4
Aspartocin (**5**)	158	0.12	0.17	5
Isotocin (**6**)	145	0.05	0.75	6
Glumitocin (**7**)	10	0.35	0.40	6
Arginine vasopressin (**8**)	12	487	503	7
Lysine vasopressin (**9**)	4.8	243	203	110
Phenylpressin (**10**)	0.2	122	350	8

[a] In this and subsequent tables the rat uterus assay provides a measure of the effect of the compound on the contraction of the uterus in response to the compound *in vitro*. See refs. 1 and 2 for details. [b] In this and subsequent tables the potency in the V$_1$ receptor is generally the effect of the compound on the blood pressure increase in the rat *in vivo* as a function of the concentration of the compound. See refs. 1, 2 and 3 for details. [c] In this and subsequent tables, the potency in the V$_2$ receptor is the effect of the compound on the antidiuretic response *in vivo* as a function of the concentration of the compound. See refs. 1, 2 and 3 for details.

determination of a receptor for a hormone at a particular cell or tissue involves the isolation of a chemical species in a pure form which binds specifically to the hormone and can be reconstituted in a biologically relevant cell or tissue and display the appropriate biological activity in response to the hormone. To date no neurohypophyseal hormone receptor has been isolated, and thus our knowledge of neurohypophyseal hormone–receptor interactions is largely based on the biological activity obtained from bioassays and binding studies.

A hormone–receptor interaction generally involves at least three different biochemical states.[12] The first is the binding of the hormone to the receptor (recognition; the binding message). For agonist activity, this must be followed by the transduction state of the hormone–receptor complex (usually involving a regulatory protein) leading to activation of the biological response *via* a second messenger such as cAMP. Third, there is the reversal state (generally involving hormone–receptor dissociation or translocation) in which the cell returns in its basal state or to a new basal state. The first two states generally require different structural and conformational properties of the peptide hormone for full agonist activity, and a separation or partial separation of the binding and transduction structure for full competitive antagonist activity or partial agonist and/or antagonist activity, respectively. The idea that receptor-related prolongation of biological activity might be dependent on the conformational and structural properties of the peptide hormone after transduction (for antagonists this would involve a state after the inhibitory complex is formed) is relatively new,[13] but has been substantiated by the synthesis of potent, long lasting α-MSH agonists and oxytocin antagonists.

In this chapter we will make an effort to discuss oxytocin and vasopressin structure–biological activity relationships from the perspective of the above ideas.

13.4.2 OVERVIEW OF NEUROHYPOPHYSEAL HORMONES

Oxytocin (OT) was the first naturally occurring peptide hormone to be synthesized,[14] which then made it possible to prepare new, structurally modified analogues. In the meantime, 10 naturally occurring analogues have been isolated, their primary structure determined, and their biological activity profiles examined (Table 1). They are collectively known as the neurohypophyseal hormones and careful examination of these structures reveals several interesting points about their biological activities. Thus far, five primary assays have evolved to test neurohypophyseal hormones for biological activity. These are: (i) rat uterine contraction; (ii) avian vasodepressor activity; (iii) the milk-ejecting response in the guinea pig, rat or rabbit; (iv) rat antidiuretic activity (V$_2$); and (v) the rat pressor response (V$_1$).

The first three are OT-like activities and the latter two are vasopressin-like activities. However, each of them requires different structural and probably conformational properties of the hormone for hormone–receptor interaction and biological activity. This chapter will cover the actions of neurohypophyseal hormones and their analogues on receptors involved in rat uterine contractions, rat antidiuretic activity (V_2 receptors) and rat pressor activity (V_1 receptors). The other two assays have recently fallen out of favor with experimentalists since their receptors are not relevant to mammalian systems and/or structure–activity work has been unsuccessful in providing potent agonists or antagonists for use in further work.

The natural neurohypophyseal hormones differ from each other by structural changes in positions 2, 3, 4 and 8. They all have biological activity in each of the assay systems (Table 1), but the naturally occurring structural changes are sufficient to modify their potencies by as much as 1000- to 10 000-fold at the different receptors. An exception to this is in the milk ejection assay where a potency change of 100-fold occurs for the natural hormones. This would suggest that the receptor involved in the milk ejection assay is more accommodating to structurally different analogues and therefore is less useful as a tool in the design of specific neurohypophyseal hormone analogues.

Apart from arginine vasotocin (**4**; AVT), when comparing potencies of the hormones at vasopressin-like receptors with OT-like receptors, there is generally a 100- to 1000-fold difference. For example, OT has 546 units mg^{-1} of rat uteronic activity but only 31 units mg^{-1} of rat pressor activity, while phenylpressin (**10**) has 0.2 units mg^{-1} of rat uteronic activity and 122 units mg^{-1} of rat pressor activity. The level of receptor specificity is such that under physiological conditions OT is only active on its smooth muscle receptors and not at vasopressin-like receptors.

The fact that all of the native neurohypophyseal hormones possess some biological activity in all of the assays undoubtedly is due to their structural and topographical similarities. They are all nonapeptides with a C-terminal glycinamide and a 20-membered disulfide bridge. However, the changes made by nature in positions 2, 3, 4 and 8 reveal some interesting properties of the hormone–receptor interactions. Phenylpressin is the only native hormone where Tyr^2 has been replaced. Substitution by a Phe residue leads to a significant decrease in activity in all receptor systems. Replacement of Ile^3 by Phe^3 leads to a hormone with weak OT-like activity, but stronger vasopressin-like activity. Comparison of AVT (**4**) with AVP (**8**; Table 1), where Ile^3 has been replaced by Phe^3 but the structures are otherwise the same, shows a decrease in potency in OT receptor systems. The major difference in compounds with OT-like activity and vasopressin-like activity is the nature of the residue in position 8. OT-like agonist compounds all have a lipophilic side chain in position 8 (Leu, Ile, Val or Glu), whereas vasopressin-like agonist compounds have a basic residue (Arg or Lys). The different aliphatic residue of the OT-like compounds leads to relatively small differences in potencies at OT-like receptors, whereas large differences in potency are seen at vasopressin-like receptors. Similarly, substitution of Glu^4 by Asn or Ser has negligible effect on potencies at OT receptors, but a more extensive effect at vasopressin receptors.

Consideration of the three-dimensional tertiary structure of peptide hormones is essential for a complete picture of the receptor sites and hormone–receptor complexes. Altering the primary structure and then assigning any relevant change in biological activity to changes in the nature of side chain groups only is somewhat naive. Moreover, due to the nature of these peptides and limitations of some experimental techniques, the study of conformational and topological elements has been difficult. However, with the onset of high field NMR (500 MHz, 600 MHz) and improved X-ray crystallography techniques, recently the design of agonists and antagonists of peptide hormones based on three-dimensional properties has become a realistic possibility.[12b–e,13,15,16]

In this chapter the biological activities of agonists and antagonists will be examined from the standpoint of primary structural changes looking at the aforementioned receptors and agonists and antagonists separately, since it is known that agonists and antagonists have different structure–function relationships at these receptors,[17,18] but we also point to conformational implications where possible.[12c,17,19]

13.4.3 THE UTERINE RECEPTOR

13.4.3.1 Agonist Analogues

The rat uterus assay is the most generally accepted and widely used method when examining (testing) a compound for OT-like biological activity. OT was the first peptide hormone extensively examined by structure–function studies, and it still serves to this day as a useful and important peptide for developing rational design methodology.

All of the neurohypophyseal hormones have a 20-membered disulfide bridge and an acyclic tripeptide tail with a C-terminal glycinamide. Early work showed that the acyclic tripeptide Pro-Leu-Gly-NH$_2$(**11**) in the uterine assay system had no biological activity (Table 2) whereas tocinoic acid (OT$_{1-6}$; **12**) is a weakly potent agonist. Interestingly tocinamide, Cys-Tyr-Ile-Gln-Asn-Cys-NH$_2$ (**13**), is a more potent agonist than tocinoic acid (Table 2). The ring-opened (reduced) form of OT (oxytoceine)[23] has very low biological activity and most of it is thought to be derived from OT due to the slow oxidation of the linear peptide to the cyclic form. Interestingly, the pseudoiso-steric analogue of oxytoceine [Ser^1,Ser^6]OT (14; Table 2) is a weak mixed antagonist–agonist. Therefore it would seem that the cyclic moiety of OT is important for receptor recognition and transduction.

Substitution of the N^α-amino functionality by a larger group usually leads to a drop in agonist potency. If amino acids are added, a hormonogen with weak agonistic potency is obtained.[25] Addition of small groups such as the carbamoyl group (15; Table 2) can lead to a 1000-fold drop in potency. Reaction of the α-amino group with acetone[27] (to form the oxazolidenone) or N-isopropyl substitution[28] results in a large decrease in potency. However, replacement of the amino group by a hydrogen gives [1-β-mercaptopropionic acid]OT ([β-Mpa^1]OT; 16), which is almost twice as potent as oxytocin at the rat uterine receptors. Substitution of the amino group by a hydroxyl group gives [α-hydroxy-β-mercaptopropionic acid^1]OT ([α-Hmp^1]OT; 17) an OT analogue with over twice the potency of OT (Table 2). Hence the α-amino group may have a slight repulsive effect on the uterine receptor, and, in addition, there are very stringent steric requirements at the N-terminal group. Furthermore, [D-Cys^1]OT (18; Table 2) has only one thousandth the potency of OT, which demonstrates the stringent stereochemical requirements at the one position. Perturbation of the 20-membered disulfide bridge in other ways usually leads to a drastic drop in potency. Increasing the ring size by one methylene unit ([Hcy^1]OT)[34] leads to nearly a 1000-fold decrease in potency, and other increases in ring size, *e.g.* [5-mercaptovaleric acid^1]OT (19) and [11-mercaptoundecanoic acid^1]OT (20), give inactive analogues (Table 2). Decreasing the ring size by one methylene unit ([Maa^1]OT; 21) leads to about a 20-fold decrease in potency, as does changing the position of the disulfide bridge within the 20-membered ring, *i.e.* [α-mercaptoacetic acid^1,homocysteine^6]OT (22; Table 2). This is interesting because, whereas the changes in ring size revealed the stringent steric requirements for hormone–receptor interaction, the latter analogue also shows the stringent stereoelectronic requirements. Substitution of the disulfide bridge for an amide linkage (cyclo[Asp^1,Dpr^6]OT; 23) leads to a 30-fold decrease in potency, whereas substitution of the disulfide bridge by two methylene units ([1,6-dicarba]OT; 24) leads to a 100-fold decrease in potency. However, when one of the Cys is replaced by a methylene unit (either the carba-1 analogue or the carba-6 analogue), the resulting analogues have increased potencies over the native hormone at the rat uterine receptor (Table 2). Other modifications of the disulfide bridge have included [deamino-1-carba(S$^+$MeI$^-$)]OT (26) and [deamino-1-carba-sulfoxide]OT (27), both of which have low potencies. Replacement of a hydrogen of the β-methylene of Cys^1 by a methyl group to give [β-mercaptobutyric acid^1]OT leads to an analogue with weak agonistic activity.[44] However, substitution of both methylene hydrogens by two methyls (*i.e.* [Pen^1]OT; 75) leads to an antagonist analogue.[45] These results indicate that Cys^1 is directly involved in binding to the receptor, probably in transduction.

The Tyr^2 residue is involved in OT binding and transduction processes at the rat uterine receptor. Its correct stereochemistry, dynamic behavior and conformational properties are critical for both agonist and antagonist activities. [D-Tyr^2]OT (28) does have some partial agonist activity (Table 2), and it has been argued that this is compatible with the 'cooperative model'[46] and the 'dynamic model'[12c,47] of OT activity at the rat uterine receptor.[48] More recently though it has been shown that [cLeu^2]OT (29) is a full agonist, though it cannot have either the conformational or stereoelectronic properties proposed in the 'cooperative model'. Replacement of the phenolic hydroxyl group by a hydrogen results in an analogue [Phe^2]OT (30) with one fifteenth the potency of the native hormone. The hydroxyl group can be replaced with a fluorine [(p-F)Phe^2]OT (31) or an additional hydroxyl group can be added to the aromatic ring [3,4-dihydroxy-Phe^2]OT (32) with maintenance of good potency (Table 2). When a more sterically bulky aromatic residue is substituted for the Tyr^2, *i.e.* [Trp^2]OT (33), the analogue retains agonist activity although somewhat reduced in potency. *O*-Alkylation of the hydroxyl group[54] and *para*-alkyl-substituted Phe^2 analogues have mixed agonist–antagonist or purely antagonist biological activities. Replacement of the Tyr^2 residue by an aliphatic residue generally leads to a drop in potency, with [Leu^2]OT (34), for example, having less than one thousandth the potency. Clearly there are stringent steric, stereochemical and stereoelectronic requirements at position 2 of oxytocin for both binding and transduction in the hormone–receptor interaction.

Position 3 was the subject of much early structure–activity work where the Ile^3 residue was replaced by other aliphatic residues. Generally it was found that full activity was preserved but that potency was reduced in the uterine assay (Table 2). Apparently the [D-Ile^3]OT analogue has not been made. [D-Ala^3]OT (36) has been reported to have inhibitor activity, but [D-cyclohexyl-glycine^3]OT (37), which in some ways is pseudoisosteric to OT, is a weak agonist with no partial antagonist activities. Thus position 3 is not involved in receptor transduction.

Table 2 Biological Activities of Oxytocin Agonist Analogues and Fragments[a]

Compound	*Rat uterus* (units mg^{-1})	*Ref.*
H-Pro-Leu-Gly-NH$_2$ (**11**)	Nil	20
Tocinoic acid (**12**)	0.25	21
Tocinamide (**13**)	3.2	22
[Ser^1,Ser^6]OT (**14**)	Inhib.-agon.	24
N-Carbamoyl-OT (**15**)	0.5	26
[β-Mpa^1]OT (**16**)	803	29
[α-Hmp^1]OT (**17**)	1275	30
[D-Cys^1]OT (**18**)	1.9	31, 32, 33
[5-Mercaptovaleric acid^1]OT (**19**)	0	35
[11-Mercaptoundecanoic acid]OT (**20**)	0	36
[Maa^1]OT (**21**)	25	37
[Maa^1,Hcy^6]OT (**22**)	37	38
Cyclo[Asp^1,Dpr^6]OT (**23**)	16	39
[1,6-Dicarba]OT (**24**)	5	40
[1-Carba]OT (**25**)	734	41
[Deamino-1-carba (S$^+$MeI$^-$)]OT (**26**)	20	42
[Deamino-1-carba-sulfoxide]OT (**27**)	13.1	43
[D-Tyr^2]OT (**28**)	8.4 (p.a.)[b]	48
[cLeu^2]OT (**29**)	4.9	49
[Phe^2]OT (**30**)	30	50
[(*p*-F)Phe^2]OT (**31**)	97	51
[3,4-Dihydroxy-Phe^2]OT (**32**)	26	52
[Trp^2]OT (**33**)	81.2	53
[Leu^2]OT (**34**)	0.45	55, 56
[Leu^3]OT (**35**)	5	57
[D-Ala^3]OT (**36**)	Inhibitor	58
[D-Cyclohexylglycine^3]OT (**37**)	0.03	57
[Ser^4]OT (**38**)	197	58
[Hse^4]OT (**39**)	125	59
[Thr^4]OT (**40**)	900	60
[Val^4]OT (**41**)	139	61
[D-Leu^4]OT (**42**)	Inhibitor	62
[D-Gln^4]OT (**43**)	3.3	21
[Glu^4]OT (**44**)	1.5	62
[Glu(OMe)^4]OT (**45**)	10.5	63
[Orn^4]OT (**46**)	56	64
[Lys^4]OT (**47**)	6	65
[Phe^4]OT (**48**)	0.75	66
[Asp^5]OT (**49**)	20.3	68
[3-Mal^5]OT (**50**)	45.1	69
[Deamino-1-carba]OT (**51**)	1898	71
[Deamino-6-carba]OT (**52**)	929	72
[Sec^6]OT (**53**)	405	73
[Hcy^6]OT (**54**)	12	74
[Δ^{3,4}Pro^7]OT (**55**)	1071	75
[Thi^7]OT (**56**)	1180	76
[Sar^7]OT (**57**)	459	77
[MeAla^7]OT (**58**)	62	77
[Gly^7]OT (**59**)	93	78
[D-Pro^7]OT (**60**)	13	79
[1-Aminocyclopropane-1-carboxylic acid^7]OT (**61**)	9.8	80
[Lys^8]OT (**62**)	100	81
[*t*-Leu^8]OT (**63**)	45	82
[Neo^8]OT (**64**)	61.5	83
[cLeu^8]OT (**65**)	149	83
[Pro^9]OT (**66**)	0.11	85
[Gln^9]OT (**67**)	0.05	85
[GlyNMe$_2$^{9}]OT (**68**)	∼15	86
[Mam^8]OT (**69**)	7.2	87
[α-Hmp^1,Thr^4]OT (**70**)	4179	30
[α-Hmp^1,Δ^{3,4}Pro^7]OT (**71**)	880	75
1,9-Cyclooxytocin (**72**)	Inactive	88
[Phe^3,β-Ala^9]OT (**73**)	0.19	89
[Maa^1,Isa^5]OT (**74**)	0.098	90

[a] The abbreviations and nomenclature for the amino acid residues and the analogues are those recommended by IUPAC–IUB. Additional abbreviations are as follows: OT, oxytocin; α-Hmp, α-hydroxy-β-mercaptopropionic acid; Maa, β-mercaptoacetic acid; cLeu, cycloleucine; Hse, homoserine; Orn, ornithine; Mal, malaimidic acid; Sec, selenocysteine; Hcy, homocysteine; MeAla, *N*-methylalanine; *t*-Leu, L-tertiary-leucine; Neo, L-neopentylglycine; Mam, methylamide; Isa, isoasparagine; Thi, thiazolidinecarboxylic acid. [b] p.a. = partial agonist

Since structure–activity studies began on OT, position 4 has been a popular target for modification. Nature has made a number of changes in position 4 with all of the analogues possessing some agonist activity in the uterine assay (Table 1). The series of analogues Ser⁴, Hse⁴ and Thr⁴ (**38, 39** and **40**; Table 2) stand out among the agonist analogues prepared thus far since it seems the hydrogen bonding donating and/or hydrogen bond accepting properties of the Thr⁴ hydroxyl group is important for hormone–receptor interaction. Interestingly, when the pseudoisosteric, but lipophilic amino acid, Val replaces Thr in position 4, a sevenfold decrease in potency occurs (**41**; Table 2). A report that [D-Leu⁴]OT (**42**) is an antagonist is surprising since [D-Gln⁴]OT (**43**) was found to be a full agonist, with low potency. Replacement of the neutral side chain of Gln⁴ by the acidic side chain of Glu (**44**) results in a drastic 400-fold drop in biological activity which is somewhat reversed by methyl esterification to give [Glu(OMe)⁴]OT (**45**; Table 2). In the latter case greater steric requirements are imposed upon the uterine receptor than with a glutamine residue and this may account for the differences in potency. Position 4 can accommodate a basic residue, *e.g.* [Orn⁴]OT (**46**), to give a fairly potent analogue, although the Lys⁴ analogue (**47**) is considerably less potent (Table 2). However, the uterine receptor is less accommodating to aromatic side chains, since [Phe⁴]OT (**48**) is an agonist with one seven hundredth the potency of OT. The persistent agonist activity shows that position 4 is not involved in transduction.

Limited work has been done on position 5 since it was found early that 5-decarboxamido-oxytocin, [Ala⁵]OT, was a weak partial agonist and therefore it has been assumed that the Asn⁵ residue was vital for transduction.[67] More recent work has found that [Asp⁵]OT (**49**) and the 3-malaimidic acid analogue, [3-Mal⁵]OT (**50**), possess significant potency at the rat uterine receptor (Table 2). A more extensive exploration of structure–function relationships at this residue is needed.

The Cys at position 6 appears to have many of the same structural, stereochemical and topological requirements as the Cys¹ residue. However the Cys⁶ residue is not N terminal, as is the Cys¹ residue, and so some differences do occur. There are stringent stereochemical requirements for Cys⁶ since [D-Cys⁶]OT has only one nine hundredth the potency of OT in the uterine assay system.[70] [Deamino-6-carba]OT (**52**, where the sulfur of Cys⁶ is replaced by a CH₂) is about half as potent as the corresponding [deamino-1-carba]OT (**51**; Table 2), and selenocystine (Sec) analogues (*e.g.* **53**; Table 2) with a selenium replacing a sulfur from either Cys¹ or Cys⁶ are almost equipotent. Substitution of Cys⁶ by Hcy⁶ (**54**) reduces the potency by one forty fifth, in sharp contrast to [Hcy¹]OT whose potency is one eight hundredth that of OT.[34]

Even though nature has retained the Pro residue in position 7 in all neurohypophyseal hormones, Pro⁷ can be replaced by a variety of residues and still maintain high potency. [Δ³,⁴Pro⁷]OT (**55**) and the thiazolidinecarboxylic acid analogue [Thi⁷]OT (**56**) are about twice as potent as oxytocin in the uterine assay (Table 2). [Sar⁷]OT (**57**) is almost equipotent to oxytocin and even the *N*-methylalanine analogue [MeAla⁷]OT (**58**) and the Gly⁷ analogue (**59**; Table 2) retain relatively high potencies. However, fairly stringent stereochemical requirements are still relevant in position 7 since [D-Pro⁷]OT (**60**) is less than one fortieth as potent as OT. Furthermore, use of the highly conformationally constrained residue 1-aminocyclopropane-1-carboxylic acid in position 7 results in an analogue (**61**) with reduced potency (Table 2).

Position 8 can accommodate a large variety of residues and still maintain relatively high potency. Interestingly, substitution for a basic residue as in arginine vasotocin ([Arg⁸]OT; **4**; Table 1) or [Lys⁸]OT (**62**; Table 2) results in compounds with about one fifth the potency of OT. The analogue [*t*-Leu⁸]OT (**63**) has relatively low potency (about one hundredth that of OT), whereas the neopentylglycine analogue [Neo⁸]OT (**64**), in which the *t*-butyl group has been positioned away from the peptide backbone by one methylene unit, has slightly increased activity (Table 2). Moreover, when the conformationally constrained cycloleucine residue is substituted for Leu⁸, the resulting analogue (**65**) retains about 30% uteronic activity and therefore the cycloleucine side chain must be more favorably positioned for peptide–receptor interaction in comparison to the more flexible side chain of the *t*-leucine residue in [*t*-Leu⁸]OT. Of all the positions in OT, position 8 seems to be the least stringent for stereochemical requirements since [D-Leu⁸]OT possesses the highest (20 units mg⁻¹) oxytocic activity.[84]

Since tocinoic acid and tocinamide have modest biological potency, it is surprising that modifications of the C-terminal glycinamide generally leads to more drastic losses in potency. For example, [Pro⁹]OT (**66**) and [Gln⁹]OT (**67**) have one thirtieth and one sixtieth the potency of tocinamide, respectively. Methylation of the carboxamide terminal nitrogen ([GlyNMe₂⁹]OT; **68**), or complete removal of the carboxamide group, *i.e.* with a methylamide group attached to the Leu⁸ residue, [Mam⁸]OT (**69**) results in a large decrease in potency (Table 2).

A large number of agonist analogues have been made with multiple substitutions, but only a few provide new insights into hormone–receptor interactions. Nature has done this with aspartocin, glumitocin and isotocin (Table 1) and the results of the biological activities of these compounds on the rat uterus assay suggest that Gln^4 can be substituted for Asn^4 and Ser^4 without the loss of high potency, but the substitution of Leu^8 by a Gln residue greatly reduces potency. Using multiple substitutions gives the chance to design analogues based on 'additivity rules'. However, this approach to structure–function analysis neglects to consider conformational and topographical effects and as a result often fails. [α-Hmp^1, Thr^4]OT (**70**) is a highly potent agonist (Table 2), much more potent than would be predicted from the potency of [Hmp^1]OT and [Thr^4]OT. On the other hand, [α-Hmp^1, $\Delta^{3,4}Pro^7$]OT (**71**) is less potent than either [α-Hmp^1]OT (**17**) or [$\Delta^{3,4}Pro^7$]OT (**55**). Cyclization of OT by the N^α-amino group of Cys^1 and the C-terminal Gly^9 residue to give a bicyclic compound (S—S bond 1–6, carboxamide bond 1–9) results in an analogue that is inactive (**72**; Table 2). Also, replacement of the C-terminal glycinamide for β-alanine in [Phe^3, β-Ala^9]OT (**73**) leads to low potency, as does the substitution of β-mercaptoacetic acid (Maa) for Mpa^1 in [Maa^1, Isa^5]OT (**74**; Table 2). All of these analogues emphasize stringent steric requirements at the N- and C-terminal positions of OT. The latter analogue also shows the importance of the precise placement of the Asn^5 side chain carboxamide group with respect to the 20-membered disulfide bridge for hormone–uterine receptor interaction by the substitution of Asn^5 for isoasparagine (Isa).

In summary, these studies have provided a number of important insights into oxytocin agonist activity at the rat uterine receptor: (i) The 20-membered disulfide bridge is sufficient for full transduction. (ii) The acyclic tripeptide tail in OT is important for binding but not for transduction in the oxytocin–uterine receptor interaction. (iii) In the intact hormone there is cooperativity between the 20-membered disulfide bridge and the tripeptide side chain that is vital for maximal binding interaction with the uterine receptor and in certain cases this cooperativity can be utilized in the transduction. (iv) The Cys^1, Tyr^2 and Asn^5 residues in the ring appear to be particularly critical for both receptor recognition and especially transduction. (v) The rat uterine receptor for oxytocin appears to have at least three distinct topographical sites for oxytocin–receptor interaction. Positions 1–3 are associated with a lipophilic site which can accommodate a hydrogen or hydroxyl group more readily than an α-amino group at the α-carbon of position 1 and in which the Tyr^2 phenolic hydroxyl is critical. Positions 4 and 5 are encompassed by a more hydrophilic surface possessing hydrogen bond accepting and donating properties. A more lipophilic site is involved with positions 7–9 with the possibility of a positive charge at position 8. (vi) From the point of view of studying the bioactive conformation of oxytocin at the rat uterine receptor, OT is too flexible a molecule and although positions (1, 2 and 5) are intimately involved in transduction, further conformational restriction is necessary to investigate more precisely the topographical relationships that are critical for transduction.

13.4.3.2 Antagonist Analogues

OT antagonists, that is compounds which competitively inhibit the actions of OT at OT receptors, are very important for obtaining an understanding of the nature of a receptor and its interaction with the hormone since they do not transduce the biological message. Successful design of a peptide receptor antagonist requires segregation of the chemical–physical properties of the hormone required for binding to the receptor (the 'Binding Message') from those which are vital for transducing the biological message to give a biological agonist response (the 'Biological Activity Message'). Thus the design and study of antagonists at hormone receptors can lead to information on the conformational and stereostructural properties needed for binding and indirectly (through comparison with agonist analogues) on the differential conformational and stereostructural properties needed for transduction. On the basis of these and other considerations it has been suggested that, in general, therefore, the binding and transduction messages will use different conformational and stereostructural properties of the peptide ligand.[12c,d,13b,91]

Early structure–activity studies on OT at the uterine receptor led to the synthesis of the first partial OT antagonists in du Vigneaud's group and Rudinger's group, which has been extensively reviewed.[17a,54] More recently the design and synthesis of potent OT antagonists has been based on the discovery that [Pen^1]OT (**75**; Table 3) has fairly potent antagonistic activity.[44] Later it has been found that if the methyl groups in the β-position are replaced by bulkier substituents such as two ethyl groups or a cyclopentamethylene unit (**77** and **78**; Table 3) together with the replacement of the α-amino group by a hydrogen, this results in antagonists with increased potency. Other analogues with β,β-dialkyl substitution in position 1 include [Me_2-Maa^1]OT (**79**) and the diastereoisomer [D-Pen^1]OT (**80**), which interestingly possess weak antagonistic activity. From these studies and subsequent studies (for comprehensive reviews see refs. 17a, 96) it can be deduced that the geminal dialkyl substituents should impose conformational constraints upon the hormone which lead to topographical properties of the peptide such that the hormone–receptor interactions prevent transduction. Hruby and coworkers have examined the conformational and topographical properties of this class of antagonists using circular dichroism (CD), NMR and laser Raman spectroscopies.[12d,13a,47,91,97–99] From this work it was found that a β,β-dialkyl substitution imposed conformational restrictions, both local about the disulfide bond and transannular as well. For example, the Tyr[2] side chain conformation was restricted such that one of the rotamers about the χ_1 torsional angle was excluded. That rotamer which was excluded would place the tyrosine over the 20-membered disulfide bridge, and thus it was suggested[12c,91,97] that this restriction was a critical feature of the OT-analogue–receptor interaction which led to the prevention of transduction. Indeed, the conformational studies have suggested that in general [Pen[1]]OT analogues have more restricted overall conformational and topographical properties. A conformational model for one of these analogues is shown in Figure 1. As shown in the figure, intramolecular hydrogen bonds may help stabilize the conformation. In addition, topographical constraints result from the geminal dimethyl groups in the Pen[1] residue, but further work is needed to define these effects more precisely.

Further studies with Pen[1] analogues of OT, however, have supported these conclusions. Replacement of Tyr[2] by other aromatic amino acids with substituents in the 3′, 4′ and/or 5′ positions (**81, 82, 84**; Table 3) generally leads to analogues with antagonistic activity.[96] These latter results suggest also that the fairly potent antagonistic activity of these compounds may result from an improper fit of the aromatic side chain with the receptor such that the hormone–receptor complex assumes a conformation that cannot transduce the message but can competitively compete with OT for binding sites on the receptor. In this regard, a most interesting new class of OT antagonists has recently been obtained in our laboratory by conformational constraint.[174] We found that bicyclization of the very weak OT agonist [β-Mpa[1],Glu[4],Lys[8]]OT *via* a lactam bridge gave bicyclic analogue [β-Mpa[1],Glu[4],Cys[6],Lys[8]]OT (**90**), which was an antagonist with a pA_2 value of 8.2 (Table 3). Single substitutions of the remaining seven positions of the neurohypophyseal hormones generally do not result in compounds with antagonist activity, with the exceptions of the thus far unconfirmed claims for [D-Leu[4]]OT (**42**) and [D-Ala[3]]OT (**36**), which have been reported to be weak antagonists (Table 2).

Potent antagonists of OT have been obtained when penicillamine derivatives are substituted in position 1 together with other substitutions in positions 2, 4 and 8 (**85–87**; Table 3).[96] Interestingly, substitution of a basic amino acid in position 8, such as Orn[8] or Lys[8], leads to antagonist analogues with greater potencies than the Leu[8] derivatives. When considering agonist analogues of OT, we

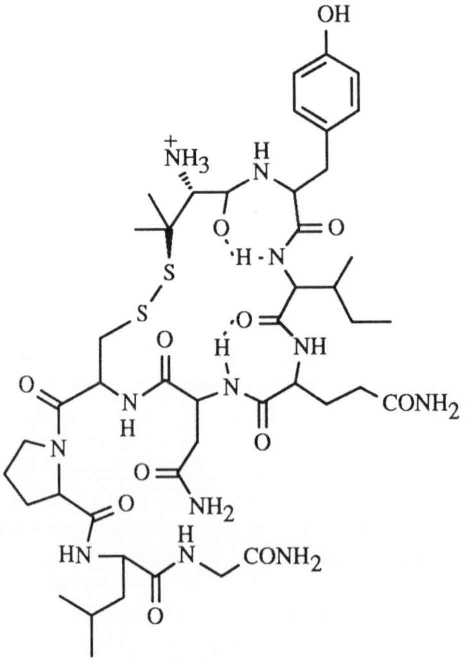

Figure 1   Conformation of [Pen[1]]oxytocin showing the probable hydrogen bonding pattern

Table 3 Antagonist Activities of Oxytocin Analogues[a]

Compound	Rat uterus (pA_2)	Ref.
[Pen^1]OT (**75**)	6.86	92
[dPen^1]OT (**76**)	6.94	93
[Et$_2$-β-Mpa^1]OT (**77**)	6.94	94
[(CH$_2$)$_5$-β-Mpa^1]OT (**78**)	7.43	95
[Me$_2$-Maa^1]OT (**79**)	6.16	94
[D-Pen^1]OT (**80**)	6.32	94
[D-Phe(4-Et)^2]OT (**81**)	8.15	100
[3'-I-Tyr^2]OT (**82**)	7.2	101
[D-Trp^2]OT (**83**)	Weak	102
[β-Mpa^1,Tyr(OEt)^2]OT (**84**)	7.2	103
[β-Mpa^1,Tyr(OEt)^2, Arg^8]OT (**85**)	8.4	104
[Pen^1,Phe^2,Thr^4]OT (**86**)	7.67	105
[Et$_2$-β-Mpa^1,Tyr(OR)^2,Orn^8]OT (**87**)	8.91	106
[Pen^1,Phe^2,Thr^4,Δ^{3,4}Pro^7,Orn^8]OT (**88**)	7.5 (prolonged)	107, 108
[Pen^1,Tyr(OMe)^2,Thr^4,Orn^8]OT (**89**)	> 7.5 (prolonged)	107, 108
[β-Mpa^1,Glu^4,Cys^6,Lys^8]OT (**90**)	8.2	174

[a] Abbreviations as in Table 2. Additional abbreviations include: Pen, β,β-dimethylcysteine; dPen, β,β-dimethyl-β-mercaptopropionic acid, deamino penicillamine; Et$_2$-β-Mpa, β,β-diethyl-β-mercaptopropionic acid; (CH$_2$)$_5$-β-Mpa, β,β-cyclopentamethylene-β-mercaptopropionic acid; Me$_2$-Maa, α,α-dimethyl-α-mercaptoacetic acid.

found previously that substitution of a Leu^8 for a basic amino acid results in a *drop* in potency. These and other results suggested[17b,19,109] that OT antagonists bind in a different manner than agonists when they interact with the uterine receptor. More recent work has shown that appropriately substituted Pen^1 analogues have prolonged antagonistic activity[107,108] (**88, 89**; Table 3) which is not associated with potency or efficacy (transduction). Hence it has been postulated[12e,13a,b] that the prolongation of antagonistic activity is a result of conformational and stereostructural requirements of the hormone for hormone–receptor interaction in the reversal process other than those needed for binding (or transduction when appropriate).

13.4.4 THE V$_1$ RECEPTOR

13.4.4.1 Agonist Analogues

The rat pressor assay is a well-established standard assay for 'vasopressin-like' activities of neurohypophyseal hormones, and the receptor associated with this assay is referred to as the V$_1$ receptor. An examination of these activities (Table 1) suggests that the V$_1$ receptor is the most sensitive to structural changes that occur in the native peptides. High potencies are thought to be associated with a basic residue in position 8, and differences can be as much as 10 000-fold [compare arginine vasopressin (AVP) with isotocin (IT)]. Also important is position 4 since when a Gln residue (as in mesotocin-MT) is replaced by a Ser residue (as in IT) a 100-fold drop in potency occurs. These structure–activity studies demonstrate that the V$_1$ receptor utilizes different structural and conformational requirements for binding than does the uterine receptor.

Unlike OT in the uterine assay, replacement of the α-amino group of AVP and LVP by a hydrogen results in analogues such as [β-Mpa^1]LVP (**91**; Table 4) with reduced potency. Also the 1-carba (and 6-carba) analogues do not have substantial increases in potency over AVP and LVP on the V$_1$ receptor. However, replacement of the Cys^1 α-amino group by a hydroxyl leads to analogues with increased potency. In fact, there does not appear to be any pressor agonist analogue of vasopressin which is substantially (five times) more potent than the native hormone.[96] Interestingly, the acyclic analogues of AVP and LVP, [Ala^1,Ala^6]AVP (**99**) and [Ala^1,Ala^6]LVP (**100**) have weak potency in the pressor assay system (about 1/20 000 the potency of the native hormones).

The stereochemical requirements of position 2 are not very stringent since [D-Tyr^2]AVP (**101**) has about half the potency of AVP on the pressor assay. Also a phenolic hydroxyl group does not seem to be important as both [Phe^2]AVP (**102**) and [Phe^2]LVP (**103**) are quite potent (Table 4). However, the low potencies and sometimes antagonistic properties of AVP and LVP analogues with an alkylated phenol hydroxyl group (*e.g.* **104, 105**; Table 4) suggest that the V$_1$ receptor in its agonist state cannot accommodate bulky aromatic residues.

Table 4 Agonist Activities of Vasopressin Analogues at V_1 and V_2 Receptors[a]

Compound	V_1 receptors	V_2 receptors	Ref.
Arginine vasopressin (AVP) **(8)**	487	503	
Lysine vasopressin (LVP) **(9)**	243	203	
[β-Mpa¹]LVP **(91)**	126	301	110
[β-Mpa¹]AVP **(92)**	395	1400	111
[α-Hmp¹]LVP **(93)**	431	—	112
[α-Hmp¹]AVP **(94)**	549	467	113
[Deamino-1-carba]AVP **(95)**	555	15 000–23 000	114
[Deamino-6-carba]AVP **(96)**	223	1569	115
[Deamino-1,6-dicarba]AVP **(97)**	37.7	1274	116
[Deamino-1,6-dicarba]LVP **(98)**	6.2	208	116
[Ala¹,Ala⁶]AVP **(99)**	0.025	0.08	117
[Ala¹,Ala⁶]LVP **(100)**	0.012	0.05	117
[D-Tyr²]AVP **(101)**	194	207	118
[Phe²]AVP **(102)**	122	350	119
[Phe²]LVP **(103)**	57	21	120
[Tyr(OMe)²]AVP **(104)**	9.7	386	121
[Tyr(OEt)²]LVP **(105)**	5	Inhibitor	122
[Ile³]AVP (AVT) **(4)**	161	236	123
[Tha³]LVP **(106)**	243	332	124
[D-Gln⁴]AVP **(107)**	0.26	0.45	125
[D-Gln⁴]LVP **(108)**	0.38	—	126
[Abu⁴]AVP **(109)**	38	760	127, 128
[Abu⁴]LVP **(110)**	10.2	707	127
[Thr⁴]AVP **(111)**	104	231	129
[Phe⁴]AVP **(112)**	~0.5	17.2	130
[Val⁴]AVP **(113)**	32	738	129
[Asp⁵]AVP **(114)**	6.93	86.5	125
[Asn(Me₂)⁵]LVP **(115)**	5.5	2.55	131
[Ser⁵]LVP **(116)**	<0.1	0.04	132
[Δ³,⁴Pro⁷]AVP **(117)**	255	1260	133
d[Δ³,⁴Pro⁷]AVP **(118)**	240	4134	133
[D-Pro⁷]LVP **(119)**	0.05	20	134
[Gly⁷]LVP **(120)**	0.15	1.0	134
[Sar⁷]AVP **(121)**	3.6	188	135
[trans-4-Hyp⁷]AVP **(122)**	4	712	136
d[trans-4-Hyp⁷]AVP **(123)**	1	780	136
[D-Arg⁸]VP **(124)**	1.08	257	113
d[D-Arg⁸]VP **(125)**	0.5	955	137
d[D-Lys⁸]VP **(126)**	1.1	3.8	138
[D-Dbu⁸]VP **(127)**	3.6	90–150	139
[Dbu⁸]VP **(128)**	149	120	140
[Homolysine⁸]VP **(129)**	267	159	141
[Orn⁸]VP **(130)**	360	88	142
[Gly⁸]VP **(131)**	0.01	—	143
[Ala⁹]AVP **(132)**	<0.4	104	144
[D-Ala⁹]AVP **(133)**	7.6	189	144
[Sar⁹]LVP **(134)**	0.5	—	145
[Gly(Me)₂⁹]LVP **(135)**	0.06	—	146
[DeGly⁹]AVP **(136)**	<0.05	164	147
[DeGly⁹]DDAVP **(137)**	pA_2 6.42	149	148
d[6-Carba,D-Arg⁸]VP **(138)**	2.9	2200	115
d[6-Carba,Orn⁸]VP **(139)**	172	4618	115
[Mpa¹,Phe²,Δ³,⁴Pro⁷]AVP **(140)**	Inactive	13 000	113
d[Asn⁴,D-Arg⁸]AVP **(141)**	Inactive	10 750	149

[a] Abbreviations the same as in Tables 2 and 3. Additional abbreviations include: Asn(Me₂), N',N'-dimethylasparagine; 4-Hyd, 4-hydroxyproline; Abu, α-aminobutyric acid; Dbu, α,γ-diaminobutyric acid; Gly(Me)₂, N',N'-diaminoglycinamide. Compounds with a d prefix are deamino analogues and thus have a β-mercaptopropionic acid residue in position 1.

Structure–activity studies of positions 3 to 6 provide only limited insight into the requirements of the V_1 receptor. Nature's replacement of Phe³ in AVP (or LVP) by Ile³ in AVT **(4)** is consistent with high biological potency in the pressor assay system, as is substitution of 2-thienyl-L-alanine³, ([Tha³]LVP; **106**; Table 4). Position 4 has stringent stereochemical requirements since replacement of Gln⁴ by D-Gln⁴ (**107** and **108**) results in a drastic loss in potency (about 100-fold) for both AVP and LVP. Substitution of the Gln^4 residue by lipophilic amino acids [*e.g.* Thr, Val, Phe or α-aminobutyric acid (Abu)] leads to significant losses in potencies (**109–113**; Table 4). Again position 5 seems to be critical for binding and transduction, since, generally, modifications at this position lead to analogues with less than one thousandth the potency of the native hormone. The exceptions are [Asp^5]AVP (**114**) and [Asn(Me$_2$)^5]LVP (**115**), which are full agonists with reduced potencies (one forty fifth and one seventieth respectively; Table 4). [Deamino-6-carba]AVP (**96**) is fairly potent but the deaminodicarba analogues of AVP and LVP (**97** and **98**) are quite weak, suggesting stringent steric and stereoelectronic requirements imposed by the receptor on the hormone around the disulfide link of the 20-membered ring.

Substitution of Pro^7 by 3,4-dehydroproline (**118**) results in a modest drop in potency, whereas substitution by D-Pro (**119**) leads to a 5000-fold drop in potency. Replacement of Pro^7 by Gly, Sar or Hyp in AVP or LVP also leads to drastic losses in potency (**120–123**; Table 4). Clearly there appears to be stringent steric and stereochemical requirements at position 7 for agonist potency. As mentioned earlier, position 8 is vital for pressor agonist activity. The stereochemical requirements are very stringent since [D-Arg^8]VP (**124**), [D-Lys^8]VP and [D-Dbu^8]VP (**127**) are considerably less potent than all of the L analogues, but virtually any basic residue can be substituted in position 8 with retention of high potency (Table 4).[96] On the other hand, [Gly^8]VP (**131**) is virtually inactive (Table 4). Position 9 has been found to be critical for both binding and transduction at the V$_1$ receptor. Substitution of Gly^9 by structurally similar amino acids such as Sar, D-Ala, Ala and Gly(NHMe) (**132–135**) or by elimination (**136** and **137**) leads to analogues with low or even antagonist activities (Table 4).

The sensitivity of this receptor to structural changes and the stereochemical requirements it imposes on certain positions (4 and 7) of the hormones suggest that it would be an excellent receptor system for examining conformation–activity relationships.

13.4.4.2 Antagonist Analogues

The design and synthesis of antagonists for the V$_1$ receptor closely paralleled the design and synthesis of antagonists at the uterine receptor since many early antagonist analogues were found to be antagonists in both assays. There was not, however, a direct correlation, and, in fact, different structure–activity relationships evolved for antagonist analogues. Early work has been reviewed[25b,150] and more recently Hruby and Mosberg,[17a] Hruby and Smith, and Manning *et al.*[96] have written more extensive reviews of structure–function relationships for V$_1$ receptor antagonists. We will examine those aspects of structure which are critical for preventing transduction and yet maintain binding to the V$_1$ receptor.

Although acylation of the amino group of the Cys^1 residue of vasopressin can lead to analogues with weak antagonistic activity,[17a,25b,150] this has largely been ignored in the more recent design of vasopressin antagonists (Table 5). Just as with OT antagonists at the uterine receptor, the replacement of a Cys^1 residue of vasopressin by the β,β-dialkyl-substituted Cys residue has led invariably to antagonists of pressor activity (**142–146**; Table 5). In general, AVP analogues are more potent than LVP analogues, which in turn are more potent than OT analogues.

Structure–activity studies on position 2 have shown that there is not a high stereochemical requirement for antagonist activity. In fact, usually both diastereoisomers containing the L- or the D-amino acid derivatives are equipotent (**147–152**). Substitution of the tyrosine for other aromatic residues (D or L) usually leads to analogues with moderate to high potency. These include tyrosine derivatives with the phenolic hydroxyl *O*-alkylated (**147**, **149**) or with the hydroxyl group completely removed (**151**). The receptor can apparently accommodate a sterically bulky side chain [such as Tyr(*O*-Pr^i)] or a simple phenyl ring as long as the amino acid is lipophilic. Although it has not been systematically studied, it would seem that in the antagonist series the V$_1$ receptor can either accept an aromatic group (as in the pressin analogues) or an aliphatic group (as in the tocin analogues) in position 3.[96] OT antagonists are usually less potent than vasopressin antagonists, but this could be a result of differences in position 8 rather than position 3.

Single substitutions in position 4 have not led to any insights into the stereostructural sequencements of the antagonist–receptor complex. However, in combination with deamino-β,β-dialkyl-substituted cysteines in position 1, a series of analogues with aliphatic residues in position 4 (**153–160**) have been made and they show that these changes can substantially affect antagonist potency (Table 5). Unfortunately no leads have been obtained for Gln^4 replacement residues that increase antagonist potency. As for positions 5, 6 and 7, very few structure–activity studies on pressor antagonists have been made. Since it is probable that pressor agonists and antagonists bind

Table 5 Biological Activities of Vasopressin Analogues with Antagonist Activity at V_1 and V_2 Receptors[a]

Compound	pA_2 antivasopressor	pA_2 anti-antidiuretic	Ref.
[dPen^1]AVP (**142**)	7.45	w.a.	151
[Et$_2$-β-Mpa^1]AVP (**143**)	8.36	0.38 (agonist)	152
[(CH$_2$)$_5$-β-Mpa^1]AVP (**144**)	8.35	0.033 (agonist)	153
[Et$_2$-β-Mpa^1]LVP (**145**)	7.15	—	154
[Et$_2$-β-Mpa^1]OT (**146**)	6.24	—	154
[N^α-Ac-Cys^1,Tyr(OMe)^2]AVP (**147**)	7.18	0.026 (agonist)	155
[dPen^1,Tyr(OMe)^2]AVP (**148**)	7.98	3.5 (agonist)	151
[(CH$_2$)$_5$-β-Mpa,Tyr(OMe)^2]AVP (**149**)	8.62	0.31 (agonist)	153
[(CH$_2$)$_5$-β-Mpa^1,D-Ile^2]AVP (**150**)	7.79	6.96	156
[(CH$_2$)$_5$-β-Mpa^1,D-Phe^2]AVP (**151**)	8.35	7.21	157
[dPen^1,Phe^2]OT (**152**)	6.57	0.09 (agonist)	158
[dPen^1,Val^4]AVP (**153**)	7.92	312 (agonist)	152
[Et$_2$-β-Mpa^1,Val^4]AVP (**154**)	8.29	1.5 (agonist)	152
[(CH$_2$)$_5$-β-Mpa^1,Val^4]AVP (**155**)	7.92	0.32 (agonist)	152
[Et$_2$-β-Mpa,Thr^4]AVP (**156**)	6.30	—	153
[Et$_2$-β-Mpa^1,Leu^4]AVP (**157**)	6.91	0.05 (agonist)	159
[(CH$_2$)$_5$-β-Mpa^1,D-Ile^2,Ile^4]AVP (**158**)	6.42	8.04	156
[(CH$_2$)$_5$-β-Mpa^1,D-Ile^2,Val^4]AVP (**159**)	6.94	7.98	160
[(CH$_2$)$_5$-β-Mpa^1,D-Phe^2,Ile^4]AVP (**160**)	7.86	8.24	157
[(CH$_2$)$_5$-β-Mpa^1,D-Phe^2,Val^4]AVP (**161**)	8.06	8.07	160
[(CH$_2$)$_5$-β-Mpa^1,D-Phe^2,Val^4,D-Arg^8]VP (**162**)	7.98	7.07	160
[(CH$_2$)$_5$-β-Mpa^1,Tyr(OMe)^2,Val^4]AVP (**163**)	8.22	7.81	161
[(CH$_2$)$_5$-β-Mpa^1,D-Tyr(OMe)^2,Val^4]AVP (**164**)	8.32	7.35	162
[(CH$_2$)$_5$-β-Mpa^1,D-Tyr(OPr^i)^2,Val^4]AVP (**165**)	8.40	7.66	161
[(CH$_2$)$_5$-β-Mpa^1,D-Tyr(OEt)^2,Val^4]AVP (**166**)	8.22	7.81	161
[(CH$_2$)$_5$-β-Mpa^1,D-Tyr(OMe)^2,Val^4,D-Arg^8]AVP (**167**)	8.10	7.19	161
[(CH$_2$)$_5$-β-Mpa^1,D-Tyr(OEt)^2,Val^4,D-Arg^8]VP (**168**)	7.88	7.59	161
[(CH$_2$)$_5$-β-Mpa^1,D-Tyr(OPr^i)^2,Val^4,D-Arg^8]VP (**169**)	8.19	7.51	161
[(CH$_2$)$_5$-β-Mpa^1,D-Arg^8]OT (**170**)	8.52	0.31 (agonist)	152
[dPen^1,Val^4,D-Arg^8]VP (**171**)	7.82	123 (agonist)	163
[DeGly^9][dPen^1,Val^4,D-Arg^8]VP (**172**)	7.25	5.8	164
[DeGlyNH$_2$^{9}][dPen^1,Val^4,D-Arg^8]VP (**173**)	6.92	4.6	164
[DeGly^9][(CH$_2$)$_5$-β-Mpa^1,Tyr(OMe)^2]AVP (**174**)	8.44	6.1	164
[DeGlyNH$_2$^{9}][(CH$_2$)$_5$-β-Mpa^1,Tyr(OMe)^2]AVP (**175**)	8.46	5.38	164
[(CH$_2$)$_5$-β-Mpa(SH)^1,D-Tyr(OEt)^2,Val^4,Cys(SH)^6]AVP (**176**)	7.51	7.05	165
[(CH$_2$)$_5$-β-Mpa(SH)^1,D-Tyr(OEt)^2,Val^4,Abu^6]AVP (**177**)	7.71	7.42	165
[N^α-Propionyl-D-Tyr(OEt)^2,Val^4,Abu^6]AVP (**178**)	6.71	7.74	165

[a] Abbreviations are as in Tables 2, 3 and 4.

differently to the V_1 receptor, such work would undoubtedly provide new insights into the nature of the hormone antagonist–V_1 receptor interaction.

As with position 2, the V_1 receptor does not seem to impose any stringent stereochemical requirements upon position 8 (**162**, **167–171**). Generally, the L amino acid analogues have greater potency, but this may be misleading and the differences at the receptor may actually be greater since it would be expected that analogues containing a D-amino acid in position 8 would be less susceptible to enzymic degradation in *in vivo* assays. Thus it is interesting to note that [(CH$_2$)$_5$-β-Mpa^1,D-Arg^8]OT (**170**) is about twice as potent as [(CH$_2$)$_5$-β-Mpa^1]AVP (**144**) and that the former compound is one of the most potent pressor antagonists known.

Finally it has been shown that position 9 does not affect pressor antagonist potencies (**172–175**; Table 5). For example [(CH$_2$)$_5$-β-Mpa^1,deGly^9]AVP ($pA_2 = 8.38$) has the same potency as [(CH$_2$)$_5$-β-Mpa^1]AVP ($pA_2 = 8.35$). This is surprising since position 9 of neurohypophyseal hormones is very important for binding and transduction of pressor agonists.

Recently Manning and coworkers have found that the fully reduced (linear) form of [(CH$_2$)$_5$-β-Mpa^1,D-Tyr(OEt)^2,Val^4]AVP, a potent V_1 and V_2 antagonist, retains antagonistic activity with fairly high potency (**176**, **177**; Table 5). Furthermore, [(CH$_2$)$_5$-β-Mpa(SH)^1,D-Tyr(OEt)^2,Val^4, Abu^6]AVP (**177**) and [N^α-propionyl-D-Tyr(OEt)^2,Val^4,Abu^6]AVP (**178**) also are quite potent antagonist analogues. These interesting findings show that the disulfide-bridged ring is not necessary for *antagonist* activity, and might not be involved directly in the binding process of the AVP antagonist to the V_1 receptor. Furthermore, replacement of one or both of the SH groups for methyl groups did not diminish the antagonistic activity, and substitution of the sterically bulky cyclopentamethylene group for methyl groups in position 1 gives an analogue with potent antagonistic activity, suggesting that there is no need for a sterically bulky substituent in position 1 in this series of antagonists.

As with OT at the uterine receptor, agonists and antagonists of vasopressin have different structure–function relationships. These differences undoubtedly reflect differences in interaction with the pressor receptor. It can be concluded that agonist and antagonist analogues utilize different properties of the receptor for interaction. Further work on examining the topological and stereo-electronic properties which lead to antagonism is needed.

13.4.5 THE V$_2$ RECEPTOR

13.4.5.1 Agonist Analogues

A second, and more universally accepted, biological activity of vasopressin-like compounds is the antidiuretic response at the V$_2$ receptors in the kidney. In fact, vasopressin itself has been called the antidiuretic hormone (ADH). Since this has been a well-accepted physiological role of vasopressin, work has been done on the binding properties at the V$_2$ receptor using membrane prepara-tions[166,167] as well as the classical antidiuretic assay. Based on these studies and some biophysical work, it has been suggested that the key elements for the agonist binding of vasopressin to the V$_2$ receptor are the side chain groups of Phe^3, Gln^4, Pro^7 and Arg^8 (or Lys^8) and the key elements important in the transduction step are the side chain carboxamide group of the Asn^5 residue and the basic functionality of the side chain of Arg^8 (or Lys^8).[168]

Based on the biological activities of the naturally occurring neurohypophyseal hormones (Table 1), high potency in the antidiuretic assay apparently requires a basic moiety in position 8, but clearly it is not an essential residue. Generally, arginine-containing analogues have a higher potency than lysine-containing analogues. It also appears that an aromatic residue is preferred over an aliphatic residue in position 3.

Replacement of the N^α-amino group of the Cys^1 residue of AVP by a hydrogen results in an analogue (**92**) with almost three times the potency of the native hormone in the antidiuretic assay (Table 4). It is possible that this enhanced potency may be a result of greater stability to enzymic degradation *in vivo* since the antidiuretic assay is an *in vivo* assay. However, binding studies on kidney membranes suggest that the enhanced activity is due to increased binding at the V$_2$ receptors. In contrast to the OT system, substitution of the N^α-amino group by a hydroxyl group leads to an analogue which is slightly less potent than the native hormone. The deaminocarba derivative, [deamino-1-carba]AVP (**95**), has a potency in the antidiuretic assay 30 times that of the native hormone and is the most potent ADH compound known (Table 4). Interestingly, the deamino-dicarba analogue of AVP, (**97**), is significantly less potent and, in the case of LVP (**98**), less potent than the native hormone. Whereas substitution of Cys^1 in neurohypophyseal hormones for deamino-penicillamine (dPen), Et$_2$-β-Mpa and (CH$_2$)$_5$-β-Mpa usually lead to analogues with antagonistic activity on other assays, all of these compounds are agonists in the V$_2$ assay (**142–145**; Table 5).

As in the V$_1$ receptor, position 2 does not seem to be critical for binding and transduction at the V$_2$ receptor. The phenolic hydroxyl group can be replaced by hydrogen and the resulting analogue, [Phe^2]AVP (**102**), still possesses high potency. The phenolic hydroxyl group can be alkylated with a methyl group leading to analogues which are quite potent. Indeed [Tyr(OMe)^2]AVP (**104**) has been reported (Table 4) to be almost as potent as AVP. Moreover, it is worthy to note that [N^α-Ac-Cys^1,Tyr(OMe)^2]AVP (**147**) is a weak agonist (1/20 000 the potency of OT; Table 5), which suggests that the conformational relationships between positions 1 and 2 are critical for binding to the V$_2$ receptor. Many analogues of LVP with large *O*-alkyl substituents on the Tyr^2 residue are apparently mixed agonists–antagonists. Finally, the stereochemical requirements of Tyr^2 do not appear to be important in the antidiuretic assay, since [D-Tyr^2]AVP (**101**) retains over 40% of the potency of AVP.

Substitution of aliphatic amino acids in position 3 of AVP and LVP usually leads to a drastic reduction in potency. Unfortunately, of the many 3-substituted AVP analogues that have been prepared, few have had their biological activities determined on the antidiuretic assay. [D-Gln^4]AVP (**107**) has about one thousandth the potency of AVP, suggesting that there is a fairly stringent stereochemical requirement at position 4. Replacement of the Gln^4 residue for aliphatic amino acids (**109–111, 113**) does not diminish potency. Indeed, [Abu^4]AVP (**109**), [Abu^4]LVP (**110**) and [Val^4]AVP (**113**) are all more potent than the native hormones in the antidiuretic assay (Table 4). However, replacement of Gln^4 by Phe^4 (**112**) results in a significant drop in potency. Since it was suggested that the Asn^5 residue was intimately involved with the transduction step, it is surprising that little structure–function work has been done on this position. Replacement of Asn^5 of AVP for Asp gives an analogue (114) with high potency; however, when Asn^5 of LVP is replaced by Asn(Me)$_2$ (115), a large drop in potency is observed (Table 4). Furthermore, substantial decreases in potencies occur when Asn^5 is replaced by Ala^5 or Ser^5. Clearly, more work is needed on structural alternatives at this position to determine its stereostructural requirements in the hormone–receptor complex.

Replacement of the Cys^6 sulfur in the disulfide bridge by a methylene group slightly increases the potency in the antidiuretic assay. However, the greatly reduced potency of the 1,6-dicarba analogues (97, 98) suggests there is a rather stringent requirement for the correct steric properties in the vicinity of the disulfide bond for maximal potency in the antidiuretic assay.

In contrast to neurohypophyseal hormones at the V$_1$ receptors, the V$_2$ receptor is very accommodating to changes at position 7. [$\Delta^{3,4}$Pro^7]AVP (117) and the corresponding deamino analogue (118) have over twice and eight times the potency of the native hormone in the antidiuretic assay respectively. [*Trans*-4-Hyp^7]AVP (122), d[*trans*-4-Hyp^7]AVP (123) and [*cis*-4-Hyp^7]AVP have higher potencies than the native hormone and [MeAla^7]AVP, [Sar^7]AVP (121) and [oxoazetidine-2-carboxycyclic acid^7]LVP possess significant potency. Even the stereochemical requirements do not seem to be very stringent as [D-Pro^7]LVP (119) has about one tenth the potency of LVP.

As previously mentioned position 8 is thought to be critically involved in the binding and transduction processes of the hormone–V$_2$ receptor complex. It has been found that, usually in conjunction with the β-Mpa residue in position 1, L and D basic amino acids can be accommodated in position 8 without a severe loss in potency. In many cases a basic D-amino acid in position 8 (124–127) results in an analogue more potent than the corresponding L-amino acid analogue (Table 4). Also the biological activities of several analogues with various basic amino acids in position 8 suggest that, although arginine is the residue for maximal potency in the antidiuretic assay, sterically smaller amino acid residues can be accommodated with retention of high potency. Of particular note is the analogue [Mpa^1,D-Arg^8]AVP (125; DDAVP) which has high antidiuretic potency and very low pressor activity. This compound is now widely used as an antidiuretic in human medicine, including treatment of diabetes insipidus.

The C-terminal position 9 is also very flexible with regards to structural requirements for activity in the antidiuretic assay. [Ala^9]AVP (132) and [D-Ala^9]AVP (133) are quite potent and the deamino, deGly and deGlyNH$_2$ derivatives all have significant levels of potency. Further work on structural modifications of this position would prove useful.

Several multiple substituted agonist analogues have been made and are listed in Table 4. Generally, their activities pretty much follow what would be expected from the activities of the monosubstituted analogues and no further major insight has been gained into the nature of hormone–V$_2$ receptor complexes.

13.4.5.2 Antagonist Analogues

The development of antagonists for the V$_1$, uterine and avian depressor receptors occurred roughly at the same time, with the discovery of the 1-penicillamine antagonists. However, the story is different for the development of antidiuretic antagonists, since although they were looked for, no potent antagonists of AVP at the V$_2$ receptor were found until recently. The only early work which showed promise was the report that [Leu^4]OT had weak anti-antidiuretic activity,[169,170] and this compound was also found to be an inhibitor in the toad urinary bladder assay.[171] Efforts to prepare further analogues with antagonist activities for the V$_2$ receptor were unsuccessful,[25,96] though highly potent V$_1$ receptor antagonists were obtained (Table 5). Thus, there was clearly no direct correlation between the structural features which lead to potent V$_1$ antagonists and those for the kidney antidiuretic receptor (V$_2$). Subsequently, it has been shown that analogues with reproducible antagonistic activities can be produced when a combination of structural changes are made, particularly in positions 1, 2, 4 and 8.[162]

The main changes that favor antagonistic activity at the V$_2$ receptor involve the use of highly lipophilic and sterically large β-substituents in position 1 in conjunction with lipophilic aromatic or aliphatic amino acids in positions 2 and/or 4. All antagonists prepared to date with high potencies usually have a (CH$_2$)$_5$-β-Mpa residue or more recently[152,172] an Et$_2$-β-Mpa residue in position 1, a D-amino acid in position 2 and a lipophilic amino acid such as isoleucine or valine in position 4 (Table 5). Examples of some potent antagonists are [(CH$_2$)$_5$-β-Mpa^1,D-Ile^2,Ile^4]AVP (158), [(CH$_2$)$_5$-β-Mpa^1,D-Ile^2,Val^4]AVP (159), [(CH$_2$)$_5$-β-Mpa^1,D-Phe^2,Ile^4]AVP (160) and [(CH$_2$)$_5$-β-

Mpa^1,D-Phe^2,Val^4]AVP (**161**). An important recent discovery has shown that an intact, disulfide-bridged ring is not essential for V$_2$ antagonistic activity. [(CH$_2$)$_5$-β-Mpa^1,D-Tyr(OEt)^2,Val^4]AVP (**166**) is a potent antagonist at the V$_2$ receptor (pA_2 7.81), as is the linear, reduced analogue [(CH$_2$)$_5$-β-Mpa(SH)^1,D-Tyr(OEt)^2,Val^4,Abu^6]AVP (**177**) in which Cys^6 was replaced by α-aminobutyric acid (Abu). Interestingly [N^α-propionyl-D-Tyr(OEt)^2,Val^4,Abu^6]AVP (**178**) was also an antagonist at the V$_2$ (and V$_1$) receptor, which indicated that neither a disulfide bridged ring nor a large sterically bulky substituent is needed in position 1. Generally, multiple substituted analogues containing a D-Arg^8 residue rather than an L-Arg^8 residue have less antagonistic potency in the antidiuretic assay. For example, [(CH$_2$)$_5$-β-Mpa^1,D-Phe^2,Val^4,D-Arg^8]VP (**162**) has pA_2 = 7.07, whereas [(CH$_2$)$_5$-β-Mpa^1,D-Phe^2,Val^4]AVP (**161**) has pA_2 = 8.07. Finally it has been shown that a Gly^9 residue is not essential for binding of the antagonists to the V$_2$ receptor (**172–175**; Table 5).[173]

These studies suggest that there is a fine line between obtaining weak agonist analogues and potent antagonist analogues. For example, [(CH$_2$)$_5$-β-Mpa^1,Val^4,D-Arg^8]VP is a weak agonist, whereas [(CH$_2$)$_5$-β-Mpa^1,Tyr(OMe)^2,Val^4,D-Arg^8]VP is a quite potent antagonist. The simple methyl alkylation of the Tyr^2 phenolic hydroxyl results in an antagonist and this is also the case for the corresponding Tyr(OEt) derivative (Table 5). While it is possible that the methyl alkylation of a weak agonist may result in a radical conformational change which is only compatible with antagonist binding, a more plausible explanation is that the agonist binds to the receptor in such a way that the appropriate side chain groups can 'move' in the transduction process, whereas when the appropriate lipophilic and/or steric surface presents itself, the molecule when bound to the receptor can no longer interact in such a manner that transduction will occur.

The above finding is yet only another example of how the conformational and topographical properties of a hormone must be examined in order to gain an insight into the conformational and structural properties that are critical for antagonist *versus* agonist activity. It would seem that the side chain of residues in positions 1, 2 and 4 are involved in the transduction steps, but it is unclear whether an Asn^5 and Arg^8 interaction is critical for transduction at the kidney antidiuretic receptor as suggested by Walter *et al.*[168] If so, then the antagonist analogues thus far developed must bind to the receptor in such a way as to prevent the appropriate relationship of the Asn^5 and either the D-Arg^8 or L-Arg^8 side chain moieties. Since [Ala^1,Ala^6]AVP (and LVP; Table 4) was found to be a full agonist at the V$_2$ receptor, it was obvious that the disulfide bridge was not necessary for transduction or for binding. Therefore, in hindsight, perhaps it is not surprising that Manning and coworkers have recently found that the disulfide bridge is not essential for binding of antagonists to the V$_2$ receptor. Indeed these latter results would suggest that positions 2, 4 and 8 are more directly involved with antagonist binding to the V$_2$ receptor. Even though the disulfide bridge may not be intimately involved with antagonist binding, it may be indirectly involved in conjunction with a sterically bulky lipophilic residue in position 1 such as (CH$_2$)$_5$-β-Mpa or Et$_2$-β-Mpa to form a conformationally restrained molecule which could present the appropriate binding elements of the molecule more favorably to the receptor in such a manner as to prevent transduction.

13.4.6 CONCLUDING REMARKS

Studies of neurohypophyseal hormone agonist and antagonist structure–biological activity relationships have been of central importance to the development of the entire field of peptide hormone and neurotransmitter ligand–receptor research, and many important lessons have emerged from these studies since these hormones were the first or among the first to be studied. Initially these peptides were viewed almost exclusively as endocrine (*i.e.* hormonal) mediators, and this review has concentrated on these classical biological effects. However, as with many such endocrine peptide hormones, it has become clear in recent years that these peptides also possess a variety of activities in the central nervous system including effects on learning, grooming behavior, maternal behavior, *etc.* The extent to which these biological activities are mediated by receptors that are the same or different to the classical uterine, mammary gland, V$_1$ and V$_2$ receptors remains to be determined. In any case, it is very clear that many challenges to our understanding of the multiple roles of the neurohypophyseal hormones in complex biological animals including human beings remain, and it is equally clear that the development of more potent, receptor selective, and biologically stable analogues will be needed to understand the multiple biological roles of these fascinating hormones, the chemical–physical basis for their biological effects, and the treatment of diseases which result from biological dysfunctions involving these hormones. Thus it is very likely that these hormones will continue to provide an important focus for exciting developments well into the future.

ACKNOWLEDGEMENTS

The work in the Hruby laboratory was supported by grants from the US Public Health Service AM 17420 and the National Science Foundation. We thank Natasha Johnson for typing and helping edit this manuscript.

13.4.7 REFERENCES

1. W. Y. Chan and N. Kelley, *J. Pharmacol. Exp. Ther.*, 1967, **156**, 150.
2. W. Y. Chan and V. du Vigneaud, *Endocrinology (Baltimore)*, 1962, **71**, 977.
3. P. A. Jaquenoud and R. A. Boissonnas, *Helv. Chim. Acta*, 1965, **48**, 1885.
4. M. Manning, E. J. Coy, W. H. Sawyer and M. Acosta, *J. Med. Chem.*, 1973, **16**, 463.
5. A. Twan, M. Manning, J. Maldar and W. H. Sawyer, *J. Med. Chem.*, 1977, **20**, 1169.
6. W. H. Sawyer, T. C. Wuu, T. W. M. Baxter and M. Manning, *Endocrinology (Baltimore)*, 1969, **85**, 385.
7. J. Meienhofer, A. Trzeciak, R. T. Havran and R. Walter, *J. Am. Chem. Soc.*, 1970, **92**, 7199.
8. R. L. Huguenin and R. A. Boissonnas, *Helv. Chim. Acta*, 1962, **45**, 1629.
9. G. L. Robertson, *Recent Prog. Horm. Res.*, 1977, **33**, 333.
10. (a) H. Righter and J. C. Crabbe, *Vitam. Horm. (N.Y.)*, 1979, **37**, 153; (b) R. de Kloet and D. de Wied, in 'Frontiers of Neuroendocrinology', ed. L. Martini and W. F. Ganong, Raven Press, New York, 1980, vol. 6, p. 157; (c) R. Walter, R. F. Ritzman, B. Tabakoff, P. Hoffman and L. B. Flernev, in 'The Role of Peptides in Neuronal Functions', ed. J. L. Barker and T. J. Smith, Jr., Dekker, New York, 1980, p. 653.
11. (a) H. M. Greven and D. de Wied, in 'Perspectives in Peptide Chemistry', ed. A. Eberle, R. Geiger and T. Wieland, Karger, Basel, 1981, p. 356; (b) W. van Nispen, J. A. J. Mannink and H. M. Greven, in 'Peptides: Structure and Function', ed. V. J. Hruby and D. H. Rich, Pierce Chemical Co., Rockford, IL, 1983, p. 421.
12. (a) J.'Rudinger, in 'Drug Design', ed. J. Ariens, Academic Press, New York, 1971, vol. 2, p. 319; (b) R. Schwyzer, *Ann. N. Y. Acad. Sci.*, 1977, **297**, 3; (c) V. J. Hruby, in 'Perspectives in Peptide Chemistry', ed. A. Eberle, R. Geiger and T. Wieland, Karger, Basel, 1981, p. 207; (d) V. J. Hruby, in 'Topics in Molecular Pharmacology', ed. A. S. V. Burgen and G. C. K. Roberts, Elsevier, Amsterdam, 1981, p. 99; (e) V. J. Hruby and M. E. Hadley, in 'Design of Organic Molecules Based on Molecular Recognition', ed. G. van Binst, Springer, Heidelberg, 1986, p. 269.
13. (a) V. J. Hruby, J. J. Knittel, H. I. Mosberg, T. W. Rockway, B. C. Wilkes and M. E. Hadley, in 'Peptides 1982', ed. K. Blaha and P. Malon, de Gruyter, Berlin, 1983, p. 19; (b) V. J. Hruby, *ACS Symp. Ser.*, 1984, **251**, 9.
14. V. du Vigneaud, C. Ressler, J. M. Swan, C. W. Roberts, P. G. Katsoyannis and S. Gordon, *J. Am. Chem. Soc.*, 1953, **75**, 4879.
15. (a) V. J. Hruby and H. I. Mosberg, *Peptides (Fayetteville, N.Y.)*, 1982, **3**, 329; (b) W. Kazmierski and V. J. Hruby, *Tetrahedron*, 1988, **44**, 697; (c) V. J. Hruby, J. L. Krstenansky and W. L. Cody, *Ann. Rep. Med. Chem.*, 1984, **19**, 303; (d) V. J. Hruby, *Trends Pharmacol. Sci.*, 1985, **6**, 259; (e) V. J. Hruby, *Life Sci.*, 1982, **31**, 189.
16. (a) G. R. Marshall, F. A. Gorin and M. L. Moore, *Annu. Rep. Med. Chem.*, 1978, **13**, 227; (b) D. Veber, in 'Peptides: Structure and Biological Function', ed. E. Gross and J. Meienhofer, Pierce Chemical Co., Rockford, IL, 1974, p. 409; (c) G. I. Chipins, A. Krikis and L. K. Polevaja, in 'Biophysical and Biochemical Information Transfer in Recognition', ed. J. G. Vassileva-Popova and E. V. Jensen, Plenum Press, New York, 1979, p. 23; (d) P. Schiller and J. DiMaio, in 'Peptides: Structure and Function', ed. V. J. Hruby and D. H. Rich, Pierce Chemical Co., Rockford, IL, 1983, p. 269; (e) E. T. Kaiser and F. J. Kezdy, *Science (Washington, D.C.)*, 1984, **223**, 249; (f) R. M. Epand, *Mol. Cell. Biochem.*, 1983, **57**, 41.
17. (a) V. J. Hruby and H. I. Mosberg, in 'Hormone Antagonists', ed. M. K. Agarwal, W. de Gruyter, Berlin, 1982, p. 433; (b) V. J. Hruby, *Trends Pharmacol. Sci.*, 1987, **8**, 336.
18. M. Moore, W. Huffman, G. Roberts, S. Rottschaefer, L. Sulat, J. Stefankiewicz and F. Stassen, *Biochem. Biophys. Res. Commun.*, 1984, **121**, 878.
19. See also V. J. Hruby, in 'Biochemical Action of Hormones', ed. G. Litwack, Academic Press, New York, vol. 13, 1988, p. 191.
20. M. E. Hadley and V. J. Hruby, unpublished results.
21. V. J. Hruby, C. W. Smith, D. K. Linn, M. F. Ferger and V. du Vigneaud, *J. Am. Chem. Soc.*, 1972, **94**, 5478.
22. V. J. Hruby, M. F. Ferger and V. du Vigneaud, *J. Am. Chem. Soc.*, 1971, **93**, 5539.
23. D. Yamashiro, D. Gillessen and V. du Vigneaud, *J. Am. Chem. Soc.*, 1966, **88**, 1310.
24. J. Polacek, J. Krejci, M. Nesvadla and J. R. Rudinger, *Eur. J. Pharmacol.*, 1970, **9**, 239.
25. (a) J. Rudinger, V. Pliska and T. Krejci, *Recent Prog. Horm. Res.*, 1972, **28**, 131; (b) B. Berde and R. A. Boissonnas, in 'Handbook of Experimental Pharmacology', ed. B. Berde, Springer, New York, 1968, vol. 23, p. 802; (c) W. H. Sawyer, Z. Grzonka and M. Manning, *Mol. Cell. Endocrinol.*, 1981, **22**, 117; (d) M. Manning, Z. Grzonka and W. H. Sawyer, in 'The Pituitary', ed. C. Beardwell and G. Robertson, Butterworths, London, 1981, p. 265; (e) V. J. Hruby and C. W. Smith, in 'The Peptides: Analysis, Synthesis, Biology', vol. 8, 'Chemistry, Biology and Medicine of Neurohypophyseal Hormones and Analogs', ed. C. W. Smith, Academic Press, New York, 1987, p. 77.
26. D. G. Smyth, *Biochim. Biophys. Acta*, 1970, **200**, 395.
27. V. J. Hruby and V. du Vigneaud, *J. Med. Chem.*, 1969, **12**, 731.
28. V. J. Hruby and V. du Vigneaud, *J. Am. Chem. Soc.*, 1969, **91**, 3624.
29. B. M. Ferrier, D. Jarvis and V. du Vigneaud, *J. Am. Chem. Soc.*, 1966, **88**, 3847.
30. M. Manning, J. Lowbridge, J. Maldar and W. H. Sawyer, *J. Med. Chem.*, 1976, **19**, 376.
31. D. Yamashiro, D. Gillessen and V. du Vigneaud, *Biochemistry*, 1966, **5**, 3711.
32. K. Jost, J. R. Rudinger and F. Sorm, *Collect. Czech. Chem. Commun.*, 1963, **28**, 2021.
33. D. B. Hope, V. V. S. Murti and V. du Vigneaud, *J. Am. Chem. Soc.*, 1963, **85**, 3686.
34. D. Jarvis, M. Bodansky and V. du Vigneaud, *J. Am. Chem. Soc.*, 1961, **83**, 4780.
35. W. Fraefel and V. du Vigneaud, *J. Am. Chem. Soc.*, 1970, **92**, 4426.
36. W. Fraefel and V. du Vigneaud, *J. Am. Chem. Soc.*, 1970, **92**, 1030.

37. D. Jarvis and V. du Vigneaud, *J. Biol. Chem.*, 1967, **242**, 1768.
38. C. W. Smith and M. F. Ferger, *J. Med. Chem.*, 1976, **19**, 250.
39. C. W. Smith, R. Walter, S. Moore, R. C. Makofske and J. Meienhofer, *J. Med. Chem.*, 1978, **21**, 117.
40. O. Keller and J. Rudinger, *Helv. Chim. Acta*, 1974, **57**, 1253.
41. K. Jost, T. Barth, J. Krejci, L. Fruhanfova, Z. Prochazka and F. Sorm, *Collect. Czech. Chem. Commun.*, 1974, **39**, 2835.
42. M. Lebl, T. Barth and K. Jost, *Collect. Czech. Chem. Commun.*, 1979, **44**, 2563.
43. M. Lebl, T. Barth and K. Jost, *Collect. Czech. Chem. Commun.*, 1978, **43**, 1538.
44. H. Schulz and V. du Vigneaud, *J. Am. Chem. Soc.*, 1966, **88**, 5015.
45. H. Schulz and V. du Vigneaud, *J. Med. Chem.*, 1966, **9**, 647.
46. R. Walter, *Fed. Proc., Fed. Am. Soc. Exp. Biol.*, 1977, **36**, 1872.
47. (a) V. J. Hruby and H. I. Mosberg, in 'Neurohypophyseal Hormone and Other Biologically Active Peptides', ed. D. H. Schlesinger, Elsevier/North Holland, New York, 1981, p. 227; (b) V. J. Hruby, in 'Oxytocin: Clinical and Laboratory Studies', ed. J. A. Amico and A. G. Robinson, Elsevier/North Holland, New York, 1985, p. 405.
48. (a) V. J. Hruby, K. K. Deb, A. F. Spatola, D. A. Upson and D. M. Yamamoto, *J. Am. Chem. Soc.*, 1979, **101**, 202; (b) V. J. Hruby, D. A. Upson, D. M. Yamamoto, C. W. Smith and W. Walter, *J. Am. Chem. Soc.*, 1979, **101**, 2717.
49. (a) V. J. Hruby, T. W. Rockway, V. Viswanatha and W. Y. Chan, *Int. J. Pept. Protein Res.*, 1983, **21**, 24; (b) V. J. Hruby, H. I. Mosberg, T. K. Sawyer, J. J. Knittle, T. W. Rockway, J. Ormberg, P. Darman, W. Y. Chan and M. E. Hadley, *Biopolymers*, 1983, **22**, 517.
50. M. Bodansky and V. du Vigneaud, *J. Am. Chem. Soc.*, 1959, **81**, 1258.
51. P. Marbach and J. Rudinger, *Helv. Chim. Acta*, 1974, **57**, 403.
52. B. M. Ferrier and L. A. Branda, *Can. J. Biochem.*, 1976, **54**, 507.
53. B. M. Ferrier and L. A. Branda, *Can. J. Biochem.*, 1976, **54**, 512.
54. J. Rudinger and T. Krejce, in 'Handbook of Experimental Pharmacology', ed. B. Berde, Springer, New York, 1968, p. 748.
55. V. J. Hruby and V. du Vigneaud, *J. Med. Chem.*, 1969, **12**, 731.
56. L. A. Branda, V. J. Hruby and V. du Vigneaud, *Mol. Pharmacol.*, 1967, **3**, 248.
57. K. Eisler, J. Rudinger and F. Sorm, *Collect. Czech. Chem. Commun.*, 1966, **31**, 4563.
58. J. Roy, R. T. Mavran, J. L. Schwartz and R. Walter, *Int. J. Pept. Protein Res.*, 1975, **7**, 171.
59. A. Turan, M. Manning, J. Maldar and W. H. Sawyer, *J. Med. Chem.*, 1977, **20**, 1169.
60. M. Manning, E. J. Coy and W. M. Sawyer, *Biochemistry*, 1970, **9**, 3975.
61. V. du Vigneaud, G. Flouret and R. Walter, *J. Biol. Chem.*, 1966, **241**, 2093.
62. J. Photaki and V. du Vigneaud, *J. Am. Chem. Soc.*, 1965, **87**, 908.
63. J. Photaki, C. Jzougraki and C. Kotsiv-Engonopoulos, *Int. J. Pept. Protein Res.*, 1979, **13**, 426.
64. R. T. Havran, J. L. Schwartz and R. Walter, *J. Am. Chem. Soc.*, 1969, **91**, 1836.
65. O. A. Kamrov, V. F. Martynov and Y. D. Mikhailov, *Zh. Obshch. Khim.*, 1971, **42**, 1654.
66. J. J. Nestor, Jr., M. F. Ferger and V. du Vigneaud, *J. Med. Chem.*, 1975, **18**, 284; J. J. Nestor, Jr., M. F. Ferger and W. Y. Chan, *J. Med. Chem.*, 1975, **18**, 1022.
67. V. du Vigneaud, G. S. Denning, S. Drabarek and W. Y. Chan, *J. Biol. Chem.*, 1964, **239**, 472.
68. R. Walter, G. Skala and C. W. Smith, *J. Am. Chem. Soc.*, 1978, **100**, 972.
69. J. Roy, D. Grazis, R. Shakman and I. L. Schwartz, *Int. J. Pept. Protein Res.*, 1982, **20**, 35.
70. M. Manning and V. du Vigneaud, *J. Am. Chem. Soc.*, 1965, **87**, 3978.
71. T. Barth, J. Krejci, B. Kapkova and K. Jost, *Eur. J. Pharmacol.*, 1973, **24**, 183.
72. K. Jost and F. Sorm, *Collect. Czech. Chem. Commun.*, 1971, **36**, 234.
73. R. Walter and W. Y. Chan, *J. Am. Chem. Soc.*, 1967, **89**, 3892.
74. C. W. Smith and M. F. Ferger, *J. Med. Chem.*, 1976, **19**, 250.
75. S. Moore, A. M. Felix, J. Meienhofer, C. W. Smith and R. Walter, *J. Med. Chem.*, 1977, **20**, 495.
76. J. D. Rosamand and M. F. Ferger, *J. Med. Chem.*, 1976, **19**, 873.
77. Z. Grozonka, B. Lammek, F. Kasprzykowski, D. Gazis and J. L. Schwartz, *J. Med. Chem.*, 1983, **26**, 555.
78. J. Lowbridge, M. Manning, J. Maldar and W. H. Sawyer, *J. Med. Chem.*, 1977, **20**, 120.
79. J. J. Ferraro and V. du Vigneaud, *J. Am. Chem. Soc.*, 1966, **88**, 3847.
80. Z. Prochazka, M. Lebl, T. Barth, J. Hlavacek, A. Trka, M. Budesinsky and K. Jost, *Collect. Czech. Chem. Commun.*, 1984, **49**, 642.
81. C. R. Snell and D. G. Smyth, *Biochem. J.*, 1977, **165**, 43.
82. M. Lebl, J. Popisek, J. Hlavacek, T. Barth, P. Malon, L. Sesrvitova, K. Hauser and K. Jost, *Collect. Czech. Chem. Commun.*, 1982, **47**, 689.
83. J. Hlavacek, J. Pospisek, J. Slaninova, W. Y. Chan and V. J. Hruby, *Collect. Czech. Chem. Commun.*, 1987, **52**, 2317.
84. C. H. Schneider and V. du Vigneaud, *J. Am. Chem. Soc.*, 1962, **84**, 3005.
85. Z. Grozonka, J. D. Glass, T. L. Schwartz and R. Walter, *J. Med. Chem.*, 1974, **17**, 1294.
86. Y. F. Ting, C. W. Smith, G. L. Stahl, R. Walter, P. Cordopatis and D. Theodoropoulos, *J. Med. Chem.*, 1980, **23**, 693.
87. L. A. Branda and V. du Vigneaud, *J. Med. Chem.*, 1966, **9**, 169.
88. M. Zaoral and V. Krchniak, *Collect. Czech. Chem. Commun.*, 1977, **42**, 3500.
89. P. Anagnostaras, P. Cordopatis and D. Theodoropoulos, *Eur. J. Med. Chem.*, 1981, **16**, 171.
90. J. Roy, M. Johnson, S. Dublin, D. Gazis and T. L. Schwartz, *Int. J. Pept. Protein Res.*, 1980, **15**, 279.
91. J.-P. Meraldi, V. J. Hruby and A. I. R. Brewster, *Proc. Natl. Acad. Sci. U.S.A.*, 1977, **77**, 1373.
92. H. Schulz and V. du Vigneaud, *J. Med. Chem.*, 1967, **10**, 1037.
93. W. Y. Chan and N. Kelley, *J. Pharmacol. Exp. Ther.*, 1967, **156**, 150.
94. R. J. Vavrek, M. F. Ferger, G. A. Allen, D. H. Rich, A. T. Blomquist and V. du Vigneaud, *J. Med. Chem.*, 1972, **15**, 123.
95. J. J. Nestor, Jr., M. F. Ferger and V. du Vigneaud, *J. Med. Chem.*, 1975, **18**, 284.
96. For an extensive reference see (a) V. J. Hruby and C. W. Smith, in 'The Peptides: Analysis, Synthesis, Biology', ed. C. W. Smith, Academic Press, New York, 1987, vol. 8, p. 77; see also (b) M. Manning, K. Bankowski and W. H. Sawyer, in 'Vasopressin', ed. D. M. Gash and G. J. Boer, Plenum Press, New York, 1987, p. 335.
97. J.-P. Meraldi, D. Yamamoto, V. J. Hruby and A. I. R. Brewster, in 'Peptides: Chemistry, Structure and Biology', ed. R. Walter and J. Meienhofer, Ann Arbor Science Publishers, Ann Arbor, MI, 1975, p. 803.

98. H. I. Mosberg, V. J. Hruby and J.-P. Meraldi, *Biochemistry*, 1981, **20**, 2822.
99. V. J. Hruby, K. K. Deb, J. Fox, J. Bjarnason and A. T. Tu, *J. Biol. Chem.*, 1978, **253**, 6060.
100. M. Lebl, T. Barth, L. Servitova, J. Slaninova and K. Jost, *Collect. Czech. Chem. Commun.*, 1985, **50**, 132.
101. P. Marbach and J. Rudinger, *Experientia*, 1974, **30**, 696.
102. O. A. Kaurov, V. F. Martynov, Y. D. Mikhailov and Z. P. Auna, *Zh. Obshch. Khim.*, 1972, **42**, 1654.
103. P. Melin, H. Vilhardt, G. Lindeberg, L.-E. Larsson and M. Akerlund, *J. Endocrinol.*, 1981, **88**, 173.
104. P. Melin, J. Trojnar, H. Vilhardt and M. Akerlund, in 'Peptides: Structure and Function', ed. V. J. Hruby and D. H. Rich, Pierce Chemical Co., Rockford, IL, 1983, p. 361.
105. V. J. Hruby, H. I. Mosberg, M. E. Hadley, W. Y. Chan and A. M. Powell, *Int. J. Pept. Protein Res.*, 1980, **16**, 372.
106. K. Bankowski, M. Manning, J. Setes, J. Maldar and W. H. Sawyer, *Int. J. Pept. Protein Res.*, 1980, **16**, 382.
107. W. Y. Chan, V. J. Hruby, T. W. Rockway and J. Hlavacek, *J. Pharmacol. Exp. Ther.*, 1986, **239**, 84.
108. W. Y. Chan, T. W. Rockway and V. J. Hruby, *Proc. Soc. Exp. Biol. Med.*, 1987, **185**, 187.
109. V. J. Hruby, H. I. Mosberg, T. K. Sawyer, J. J. Knittel, T. W. Rockway, J. Ormberg, P. Darman, W. Y. Chan and M. E. Hadley, *Biopolymers*, 1983, **22**, 517.
110. R. D. Kimbrough, W. D. Cash, L. A. Branda, W. Y. Chan and V. du Vigneaud, *J. Biol. Chem.*, 1963, **238**, 1411.
111. R. L. Huguenin, E. Sturmev, R. A. Boissonnas and B. Berde, *Experientia*, 1965, **21**, 68.
112. M. Walti and D. B. Hope, *J. Chem. Soc., Perkin Trans. 1*, 1975, 1691.
113. J. Lowbridge, M. Manning, J. Maldar and W. H. Sawyer, *J. Med. Chem.*, 1977, **20**, 1173.
114. Z. Prochazka, M. Lebl, L. Servitova, T. Barth and K. Jost, *Collect. Czech. Chem. Commun.*, 1981, **46**, 947.
115. K. Jost, Z. Prochazka, J. H. Cort, T. Barth, J. Skopkova, Z. Prusik and F. Sorm, *Collect. Czech. Chem. Commun.*, 1974, **39**, 2840.
116. S. Mase, S. Sakakibara, M. Wahrenburg, M. Kirchberger, I. L. Schwartz and R. Walter, *J. Am. Chem. Soc.*, 1972, **94**, 3590.
117. R. L. Huguenin and St. Guttman, *Helv. Chim. Acta*, 1965, **48**, 1885.
118. V. J. Hruby, D. A. Upson, D. M. Yamamoto, C. W. Smith and R. Walter, *J. Am. Chem. Soc.*, 1979, **101**, 2717.
119. R. L. Huguenin and R. A. Boissonnas, *Helv. Chim. Acta*, 1962, **45**, 1629.
120. B. Berde, H. Weidmann and A. Cerletti, *Helv. Physiol. Pharmacol. Acta*, 1961, **19**, 285.
121. K. Bankowski, M. Manning, J. Maldar and W. M. Sawyer, *J. Med. Chem.*, 1978, **21**, 850.
122. M. Zaoral, *Collect. Czech. Chem. Commun.*, 1965, **30**, 1853.
123. M. Manning, K. Balaspiri, M. Acosta and W. H. Sawyer, *J. Med. Chem.*, 1973, **16**, 376.
124. C. W. Smith, M. F. Ferger and W. Y. Chan, *J. Med. Chem.*, 1974, **18**, 822.
125. C. W. Smith, R. Walter, G. Stavropoulos and D. Theodoropoulos, *J. Med. Chem.*, 1980, **23**, 217.
126. A. S. Dutta, N. Anand and R. C. Srimal, *Indian J. Chem.*, 1969, **7**, 3.
127. D. Gillessen and V. du Vigneaud, *J. Biol. Chem.*, 1967, **242**, 4806.
128. D. Gillessen and V. du Vigneaud, *J. Med. Chem.*, 1970, **13**, 346.
129. W. H. Sawyer, M. Acosta, L. Balaspiri, J. Judd and M. Manning, *Endocrinology (Baltimore)*, 1974, **94**, 1106.
130. F. Brtink, T. Barth, P. Malon, I. Fric, V. E. Khisa and K. Jost, *Collect. Czech. Chem. Commun.*, 1986, **51**, 1532.
131. C. W. Smith, G. Skala and R. Walter, *Int. J. Pept. Protein Res.*, 1980, **16**, 365.
132. R. A. Boissonnas, St. Guttman, R. L. Huguenin, P.-A. Jaquenoud and E. Sandrin, *Helv. Chim. Acta*, 1963, **46**, 2347.
133. C. R. Botos, C. W. Smith, Y.-L. Chan and R. Walter, *J. Med. Chem.*, 1979, **22**, 926.
134. J. Kolc, M. Zaoral and F. Sorm, *Collect. Czech. Chem. Commun.*, 1967, **32**, 2667.
135. Z. Grzonka, B. Lamomaek, F. Kaspozkowski, D. Gazis and I. L. Schwartz, *J. Med. Chem.*, 1983, **26**, 555.
136. A. Buku, J. L. Schwartz, N. Yamin, H. R. Wyssbrod and D. Gazis, *J. Med. Chem.*, 1987, **30**, 1509.
137. M. Manning, L. Balaspiri, H. Acosta and W. H. Sawyer, *J. Med. Chem.*, 1973, **16**, 975.
138. M. Zaoral, J. Kolc and F. Sorm, *Collect. Czech. Chem. Commun.*, 1967, **32**, 1250.
139. M. Zaoral and F. Sorm, *Collect. Czech. Chem. Commun.*, 1966, **31**, 310.
140. M. Zaoral and F. Sorm, *Collect. Czech. Chem. Commun.*, 1966, **31**, 90.
141. G. E. Lindeberg, M. Bodansky, M. Acosta and W. H. Sawyer, *J. Med. Chem.*, 1974, **17**, 781.
142. R. L. Huguenin and R. A. Boissonnas, *Helv. Chim. Acta*, 1963, **46**, 1669.
143. G. S. Papsuevich, A. Y. Kriskis and G. I. Chipens, *Zh. Obshch. Khim.*, 1972, **42**, 244.
144. A. Buku, D. Gazis and J. L. Schwartz, *Int. J. Pept. Protein Res.*, 1984, **23**, 551.
145. J. Meienhofer and V. du Vigneaud, *J. Am. Chem. Soc.*, 1961, **83**, 142.
146. J. D. Glass and V. du Vigneaud, *J. Med. Chem.*, 1972, **15**, 486.
147. M. Manning, A. Olma, W. A. Klis, A. M. Kolodziejczyk, E. Nawrocka, A. Misicka-Kesik, J. Seto and W. H. Sawyer, *Nature (London)*, 1984, **308**, 652.
148. M. Manning, A. Misicka, A. Olma, W. A. Klis, K. Bankowski, E. Nawrocka, M. Kruszynski, A. Kolodziejczyk, I. L. Cheng, J. Seto, N. C. Wo and W. H. Sawyer, *J. Med. Chem.*, 1987, **30**, 2045.
149. M. Zaoral and J. Blaha, *Collect. Czech. Chem. Commun.*, 1977, **42**, 3654.
150. J. Rudinger and I. Krejci, in 'Handbook of Experimental Pharmacology', ed. B. Berde, Springer, New York, 1968, p. 748.
151. K. Bankowski, M. Manning, J. Haldar and W. H. Sawyer, *J. Med. Chem.*, 1978, **21**, 850.
152. M. Manning, B. Lammek, M. Kruszynski, J. Seto and W. H. Sawyer, *J. Med. Chem.*, 1982, **25**, 408.
153. M. Kruszynski, B. Lammek, M. Manning, J. Seto, J. Haldar and W. H. Sawyer, *J. Med. Chem.*, 1980, **23**, 364.
154. D. F. Dyckes, J. J. Nestor, Jr., M. F. Ferger and V. du Vigneaud, *J. Med. Chem.*, 1974, **17**, 250.
155. D. A. Jones and W. H. Sawyer, *J. Med. Chem.*, 1980, **23**, 696.
156. M. Manning, E. Nawrocka, A. Misicka, A. Olma, W. A. Klis, J. Seto and W. H. Sawyer, *J. Med. Chem.*, 1984, **27**, 423.
157. M. Manning, A. Olma, W. A. Klis, J. Seto and W. H. Sawyer, *J. Med. Chem.*, 1983, **26**, 1607.
158. W. H. Sawyer, J. Haldar, D. Gazis, J. Seto, K. Bankowski, J. Lowbridge, A. Turan and M. Manning, *Endocrinology (Baltimore)*, 1980, **106**, 81.
159. D. F. Dyckes, J. J. Nestor, Jr., M. F. Ferger, V. du Vigneaud and W. Y. Chan, *J. Med. Chem.*, 1974, **17**, 969.
160. M. Manning, W. A. Klis, A. Olma, J. Seto and W. H. Sawyer, *J. Med. Chem.*, 1982, **25**, 408.
161. M. Manning, A. Olma, W. A. Klis, M. Kolodziejczyk, J. Seto and W. H. Sawyer, *J. Med. Chem.*, 1982, **25**, 45.
162. W. H. Sawyer, P. K. T. Pang, J. Seto, M. McEnroe, B. Lammek and M. Manning, *Science (Washington, D.C.)*, 1981, **212**, 49.

163. M. Manning, J. Lowbridge, C. T. Stier, Jr., J. Haldar and W. H. Sawyer, *J. Med. Chem.*, 1977, **20**, 1228.
164. M. Manning, A. Misicka, A. Olma, W. A. Klis, K. Bankowski, E. Nawrocka, M. Kruszynski, A. Kolodziejczyk, L.-L. Cheng, J. Seto, N. C. Wo and W. H. Sawyer, *J. Med. Chem.*, 1987, **30**, 2245.
165. M. Manning, J. P. Przybylski, A. Olma, W. A. Klis, M. Kruzynski, N. C. Wo, G. H. Pelton and W. H. Sawyer, *Nature (London)*, 1987, **329**, 839.
166. C. Roy, T. Barth and S. Jard, *J. Biol. Chem.*, 1975, **250**, 3149.
167. O. Hechter, S. Terada, V. Spitzberg, T. Nakahara, S. M. Nakagawaka and G. Flouret, *J. Biol. Chem.*, 1978, **253**, 3230.
168. R. Walter, C. W. Smith, P. K. Mehta, S. Boonjarern, J. A. L. Arruda and N. A. Kurtzman, in 'Disturbances in Body Fluid Osmolality', ed. T. E. Andreoli, J. Gratham and F. C. Rector, American Physiological Society, Bethesda, MD, 1977, p. 1.
169. W. Y. Chan, V. J. Hruby, G. Flouret and V. du Vigneaud, *Science (Washington, D.C.)*, 1968, **161**, 280.
170. V. J. Hruby, G. Flouret and V. du Vigneaud, *J. Biol. Chem.*, 1969, **244**, 3890.
171. R. Walter, M. L. Kirchberger and V. J. Hruby, *Experientia*, 1972, **28**, 959.
172. N. C. F. Yim, M. L. Moore, W. F. Huffman, H. G. Bryan, H.-L. Chang, L. B. Kinter, R. Edwards, F. L. Stassen, D. Schmidt and G. Heckman, *J. Med. Chem.*, 1986, **29**, 2425.
173. F. E.-F. Ali, H.-L. Chang, W. F. Huffman, G. Hechman, L. B. Kinter, E. F. Weedley, R. Edwards, D. Schmidt, D. Ashton-Shue and F. L. Stassen, *J. Med. Chem.*, 1987, **30**, 2291.
174. P. S. Hill, J. Slaninova and V. J. Hruby, in 'Peptides: Chemistry and Biology', ed. G. R. Marshall, ESCOM Science Publishers, Leiden, 1988, p. 468.

13.5

Glucagon and Insulin Receptors

RICHARD M. EPAND and MARIA BRYSZEWSKA
McMaster University, Hamilton, Ontario, Canada

13.5.1 INTRODUCTION

Endocrinologists have long been interested in the peptide hormone insulin because of its effectiveness in alleviating the symptoms of diabetes mellitus. However, insulin cannot be considered in isolation when evaluating hormonal control of carbohydrate and lipid metabolism. A number of hormones have effects on metabolism which are opposite to those of insulin.[1] One of the hormones which is thought to be of prime importance in the counterregulation of insulin-induced hypoglycemia is glucagon.[2] Both insulin and glucagon are produced by the pancreas; a variety of control mechanisms causes the secretion of each of these hormones to be altered in opposite directions as a result of changes in blood glucose concentration.[2] In the diabetic state, one of these control mechanisms is inoperative since there is less insulin suppression of glucagon release.[3] As a result, diabetics are hyperglucagonemic. In diabetes, the elevated glucagon levels as well as the absence of an effective dose of insulin result in hyperglycemia.

Insulin and glucagon research have been very active in recent years and a number of excellent reviews have appeared on various aspects of these hormones. A two-volume 1235-page comprehensive treatise on glucagon appeared in 1983.[4] This review will summarize the current state of knowledge and will give particular emphasis to recent developments in studies of these two hormones.

13.5.2 INSULIN

13.5.2.1 Background

Since its discovery in 1921 by Banting and Best insulin has been studied very intensely, mainly because of its prime importance in the treatment of diabetes mellitus. During this period much information has been gained, especially about hormone biosynthesis, structure and biological function. These areas of investigation are now very well established.

The primary therapeutic use of insulin is in the treatment of type 1 diabetes mellitus. Bovine and porcine insulins have been used for this purpose for over 50 years. Many forms of insulin, including preparations containing zinc or protamine to control the rate of insulin release, have been used therapeutically. Recently, new developments in insulin therapy have included the use of human insulin and new methods of drug delivery. In 1980, human insulin became commercially available for therapy after development of two efficient methods of synthesis. These include enzymatic conversion of porcine insulin to human insulin ('semisynthetic' human insulin) as well as the use of recombinant DNA technology. Insulin can be produced by the enzymatic conversion of cloned preproinsulin or by controlled chemical oxidation of cloned insulin A and B chains ('biosynthetic' human insulin). A review comparing the properties and therapeutic efficacy of highly purified human insulin with bovine and porcine insulin has been presented.[5] The introduction by Pickup *et al.*[6] of insulin administration by continuous subcutaneous infusion (insulin pump) instead of intermittent injections has been another approach used in the treatment of diabetes over the past few years. Critical reviews of this method of insulin administration have recently appeared.[5,7,8] There is also current interest in developing forms of insulin with enhancers to promote transnasal absorption.[9,10]

13.5.2.2 Structure of Insulin

Insulin, synthesized and released from the β cells of the islets of Langerhans of the pancreas, is a small two-chain polypeptide of 6000 Da molecular weight. It is synthesized as preproinsulin, which is converted to proinsulin and then to insulin, the form which is secreted from the β cells together with a connecting 35-residue C-peptide. The two chains of insulin together contain 51 amino acids, the A chain having 21 and the B chain having 30. The A and B chains are held together by two disulfide bridges between cysteine residues B7 and A7 and between B19 and A20. There is another intrachain disulfide bond between residues A6 and A11. The amino acid sequence of bovine insulin was determined by Sanger *et al.*[11] in 1955, and since then many insulins of various species have been described. In mammalian insulins 43 of the 51 amino acids are invariant,[12] with the exception of guinea pig insulin which differs in 17 amino acid residues from porcine insulin.[13] The most variable residues are A8–A10 and B29 and B30;[14] the disulfide bridges and cysteine residues are invariant.[14,15] It is assumed that the tertiary structure of all mammalian insulins is similar to that of porcine insulin.[16,17] There are examples of animals which possess two insulins derived from two nonallelic insulin genes; the mouse, the rat and the toadfish.[18,19] In the presence of zinc most of the insulins crystallize into hexamers; however, insulins from certain hystricomorph rodents, such as the guinea pig and the casiragua, and the primitive cyclostome the hagfish, do not form hexamers.[19] This is attributed to the lack of zinc-binding histidine at position B10 in insulins from these species.

The three-dimensional structure of the porcine insulin molecule in a crystalline state has been established by X-ray analyses.[16–18,20] Each monomer within the crystal has a compact three-dimensional structure which is roughly spherical in shape. Only the amino and carboxyl termini of the B chain extend away from the core of the molecule (Figure 1). The insulin monomer possesses a hydrophobic core and two predominantly hydrophobic surfaces which are important for dimer and, in the presence of zinc, hexamer formation. The hydrophobic core and residues involved in dimer formation are generally maintained invariant in most mammalian insulins. Most of the hydrophilic residues are located on the surface of the hexamer. The rhombohedral unit cell of zinc insulin contains six molecules of the hormone. The hexamer is organized as three equivalent dimers, which,

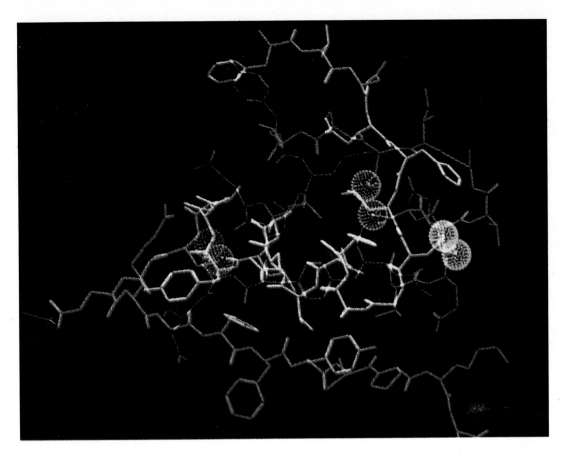

Figure 1 Three-dimensional structure of insulin. The A chain is shown in red and the B chain in blue. Pairs of yellow spheres represent disulfide bonds (reproduced with permission of W. H. Freeman and Co. from L. Stryer, 'Biochemistry', 3rd edn., 1988, p. 996)

in turn, consist of two crystallographically independent molecules only one of which is shown in Figure 1. Each hexamer contains two zinc ions which are situated 16 Å apart and each zinc is coordinated by three equivalent B10 histidines. On the basis of a variety of studies it is believed that the two-zinc hexamer is not the physiologically active form of insulin which is probably monomeric.

The conformation of insulin in solution has been studied mainly by circular dichroism spectroscopy[21-23] and to a lesser extent by NMR spectroscopy.[24-26] It has been established that the structure of insulin in crystals and in solution is very similar. Much less is known about the hormone structure upon binding to its membrane receptor. It has been suggested that in order to express full biological potency insulin has to undergo a conformational adjustment at the receptor during binding.[27,28]

13.5.2.3 Structure–Activity Relationships (SAR)

Extremely useful tools in studies of the relationship between the structure of insulin and its binding, degradation and action are insulin derivatives, especially crosslinked,[28-30] photoreactive[31-34] and radioactively labeled[35,36] molecules. Various analogs of insulin have also been obtained by the use of chemical and enzymatic degradation of the native hormone[37-39] as well as by semisynthesis.[40-43] Modification of insulin may change the biological potency of the molecule either by altering the affinity of the hormone for its receptor or by changing the ability of the receptor–hormone complex formed to cause a biological response. Modified insulins are also of great interest because of their possible use in the treatment of diabetes. Insulin analogs allowed the establishment of a physiological role for many regions of the molecule. The region which includes both A-chain residues A1, A5, A19 and A21 as well as B-chain residues B12, B16, B24, B25 and B26 is thought to be responsible for dimer formation and hormone binding to its receptor.[18,44] Recently, however, involvement of the B-chain residues in insulin binding has been questioned and a new binding region of the molecule has been proposed.[27] It consists of strongly conserved hydrophilic residues of the A-chain, A1, A4, A5, A15, A17, A18, A19 and A21. It has been established that the A1 residue glycine is involved in maintenance of the biological activity of insulin.[18] Very recently, however, it has been reported that the A20–A21 amide bond plays a significant role in expression of the biological activity of the hormone and it was postulated that the binding site and the 'message region' of the molecule are distinguishable.[45] This conclusion is also based on the results of several papers which appeared relatively recently where a discrepancy between insulin potency and its binding activity was found.[30,41,42,46]

Most of the insulin analogs synthesized so far exhibit biological activities equal to or lower than those of the native hormone. Reviews of the properties of synthesized analogs or modified insulins have appeared frequently in the literature.[22,30,38,39,47,48] Recently, Nakagawa *et al.*[49] synthesized an insulin analog Tyr^{B26}-des-(B26–30)-insulin-B25-amide which possessed 330% activity in a fat cell assay, as well as Phe^{B25}-des-(B26–30)-insulin-B25-amide with activity equal to 160% of insulin. Independently, the same analog, Tyr^{B25}-des-(B26–30)-insulin-B25-amide, with a biopotency (biological potency) of 228% and His^{B25}-des-(B26–30)-insulin-B25-amide with a biopotency of 313% were synthesized by another group of researchers.[50].

Structure and structure–function relationship studies of insulin are very far advanced. Less is known about the sequence of molecular events during the hormone action on cells. Despite intensive study, the exact mechanism by which insulin can control such broad and diverse processes remains poorly understood. However, during the past few years much new information has appeared which has significantly enhanced our understanding of insulin action. This is especially so in the area of signal transduction through the plasma membrane. Perhaps most important is the growing evidence for an active role of the insulin receptor in the signaling pathway. This review gives a brief summary of the most recent findings in this field of investigation.

13.5.2.4 Purification and Structure of the Insulin Receptor

The insulin receptor can be solubilized in a form which binds insulin using nonionic detergents.[51] The insulin receptor was first purified by Cuatrecasas from rat liver membranes by affinity chromatography using insulin-Sepharose.[51–53] In order to obtain larger amounts of material from different tissues, the purification procedure was improved by introducing diethylamino-ethyl (DEAE)-cellulose chromatography and affinity chromatography on insulin-agarose and concanavalin A-agarose,[54–57] as well as antiinsulin[58] and antiinsulin receptor antibodies linked to Sepharose.[59] Photoaffinity labeling of the receptor with aryl azide derivatives of insulin,[60,61] affinity crosslinking by using disuccinimidyl suberate[62,63] and immunoprecipitation studies[64,65] have helped to establish the structure of the insulin receptor and the functions of its subunits. Recent cloning of the cDNA for the insulin receptor by two independent groups[66,67] allowed determination of the amino acid sequence of the human insulin receptor protein. The predicted human insulin prorereceptor is composed of 1382[67] or 1370[66] amino acids. This protein is cleaved, starting from the N terminus, into a 27-residue signal peptide, a 735-residue α-subunit and a 620-residue β-subunit. There is an intervening peptide between the subunits which is composed of four basic amino acids (Arg-Lys-Arg-Arg) which is probably a site of a proteolytic cleavage of the precursor.

The mature insulin receptor is an oligomer composed of two α and two β subunits, with approximate molecular weights of 135 kDa and 95 kDa per subunit, respectively. The α and β subunits are linked covalently by disulfide bonds.[63,68,69] On nonreducing gels, the receptor migrates as an oligomer with a molecular mass of about 350 kDa, whereas upon reduction with dithiothreitol only α and β subunits are obtained.[70] This suggests a stoichiometry of $(\alpha\beta)_2$ for the nonreduced form of the insulin receptor.[57,71] This form has been found to possess the highest protein kinase activity (see below).[57]

The α subunit was found to be specifically labeled with photoaffinity insulin analogs[60,61] or affinity crosslinking techniques,[62,63] suggesting that this subunit possesses the insulin binding site. There is some evidence[72] that the insulin receptor is multivalent and binds two insulin molecules. Because the α subunit is iodinated only on right-side-out vesicles from rat adipocytes[73] and is very sensitive to proteolytic cleavage in intact cells,[71] it is considered to be located on the external surface of the plasma membrane.

In contrast to the α subunit, the β subunit is a transmembrane protein which has internal, external and transmembrane domains.[66,67,74] The transmembrane domain consists of 23–26 uncharged nonpolar amino acids, followed immediately by three positively charged residues.[66,67] The β

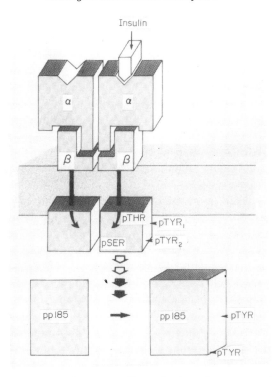

Figure 2 Schematic representation of the insulin receptor, illustrating its action as a protein tyrosine kinase (reproduced from ref. 70 by permission of Academic Press Inc.)

subunit, and more specifically its intracellular domain, is the site of autophosphorylation[70] and of the tyrosine-specific protein kinase activity of the insulin receptor.[75-80]

The insulin receptor is glycosylated. There are 13–15 potential N-linked glycosylation sites in the α subunit and four additional sites on the external portion of the β subunit.

Figure 2 summarizes our current knowledge of the insulin receptor structure and functions of its domains.

13.5.2.5 Biosynthesis and Post-translational Modifications of the Insulin Receptor

Both α and β subunits of the insulin receptor are synthesized from a single chain precursor of a molecular weight of 190 kDa.[71,81-83] The precursor, containing both subunits, is synthesized in the rough endoplasmic reticulum before translocation to the Golgi region of the cell, where it is cleaved to yield pre-α (120 kDa) and pre-β (80 kDa) subunits.[84] The proreceptor is a glycoprotein and contains exclusively asparagine-N-linked high-mannose-type carbohydrate chains, whereas both mature subunits of the insulin receptor contain N-linked high-mannose-type and complex-type carbohydrate chains.[65,81] Thus, in addition to proteolytic cleavage, the proreceptor undergoes some other post-translational changes, such as trimming of some mannose residues from high-mannose side chains, formation of complex carbohydrate side chains by the addition of distal sugars,[65,81] fatty acid acylation[85] and, finally, transportation and insertion of the mature product into the plasma membrane of the cell. The role of glycosylation and the nature of the carbohydrate components of both precursor and the insulin receptor have been intensively studied using inhibitors of glycosylation,[82,86-89] lectins,[90-92] enzymatic digestion of cells or membranes with specific glycosidases[93-95] or, recently, mutant Chinese hamster ovary (CHO) cells with well-defined genetic defects in glycoprotein synthesis and oligosaccharide composition.[92,96-98] It has been found that defects in glycosylation of the insulin receptor at various stages of the process can lead to altered insulin binding, inhibition of some, but not all, actions of the hormone,[86,92,96-98] inhibition of proreceptor processing[82] and receptor recycling.[99]

The structure of the carbohydrate chains attached to the insulin proreceptor as well as of high-mannose chains of the mature α and β subunits of the receptor has recently been analyzed.[100] It has been shown that most oligosaccharides of the insulin proreceptor are of the structure $Man_8GlcNAc_2$

or $Man_9GlcNAc_2$. They constitute approximately 75% of the oligosaccharide core of the pro-receptor. As glycosylation of the insulin prorecptor is believed to occur *via* transfer of an oligosaccharide of type $Glc_3Man_9GlcNAc_2$ from the dolichol intermediate to asparagine residues of protein,[101] further processing of the synthesized prorecptor includes the rapid removal of three glucose residues and also, in some carbohydrate chains, one mannose residue.

Inhibition of glucose removal from core oligosaccharides of the insulin prorecptor by castano-spermine and 1-deoxynojirimycin, inhibitors of glucosidases I and I/II, respectively, resulted in a 50% reduction in cell-surface insulin receptor in cultured IM-9 lymphocytes.[102] It was accompanied by production of an abnormally large prorecptor of approximately 205 kDa molecular weight, which showed a slower rate of processing into the mature insulin receptor. Thus, it has been concluded that an impaired removal of glucose from core oligosaccharides is responsible for a delay of processing of the prorecptor, which in turn may result in a decrease in cell-surface receptors.

After the proteolytic cleavage of the prorecptor at the cationic sequence, Arg-Lys-Arg-Arg,[66,67] further mannose removal occurs. The predominant species of high-mannose chains in the α subunit has been found to be of the $Man_8GlcNAc_2$ type, whereas in the β subunit it is of the $Man_7GlcNAc_2$ type, showing the difference in the degree of mannose trimming in both subunits.[100] Next, before insertion into the plasma membrane, the receptor pre-α and pre-β subunits are further glycosylated and sialated, incorporating galactose, glucosamine, fucose, mannose and sialic acid. This results in the appearance of complex carbohydrate chains[65,81] and yields molecular masses of 135 kDa (α) and 95 kDa (β). However, the structure of these complex-type carbohydrate chains of the mature insulin receptor remains to be elucidated.

Very recently, fatty acid acylation, a new post-translational modification of the insulin receptor, has been identified in human cultured lymphocytes.[85] Two different kinds of fatty acid bonds have been found. The α subunit contained only amide-linked fatty acids, whereas the β subunit possessed amide- and ester-linked fatty acids. Because the prorecptor also contained amide-linked fatty acids, the fatty acylation was postulated to be an early two-step post-translational event. The second step, the esterification of fatty acids to the β subunit, probably occurs after proteolytic cleavage of the insulin prorecptor. Furthermore, the insulin receptor is the first membrane receptor shown to contain a 14-carbon myristic acid. However, the role of covalently bound fatty acids in insulin receptor function is not known.

13.5.2.6 The Insulin Receptor as a Protein Kinase

The insulin receptor belongs to the family of protein kinases which catalyze the transfer of phosphate to the sites of their protein substrates.[103] More specifically, it is a member of protein tyrosine kinases which phosphorylate proteins on their phenolic groups.[103] Protein tyrosine kinases have been divided into two groups, one consisting of the hormone or growth-factor-dependent enzymes and the other of kinases encoded by certain retroviral oncogenes.[103]

As a protein kinase, the insulin receptor undergoes a self-catalyzed autophosphorylation reaction.[104,105] This was first reported by Kasuga *et al.*,[106] who observed phosphorylation of the purified insulin receptor in the presence of insulin. Subsequent studies[54,107-111] have shown that in cell-free systems, immediately after insulin binding, phosphorylation of the highly purified insulin receptor occurs predominantly, if not exclusively, on tyrosine residues and is the result of an intramolecular autophosphorylation reaction.

Using insulin receptors purified from FAO cells, a rat hepatoma cell line, on wheat germ agglutinin agarose[112] and Sepharose-purified receptors from human placenta,[54] it was estimated that up to 2 mol of phosphate are bound per 1 mol of the insulin receptor, *i.e.* two phosphate groups per β subunit.

The kinase activity of the insulin receptor was also reported in various intact cells, such as rat hepatoma cells,[113] IM-9 lymphocytes,[75] cultured 3T3-L1 adipocytes,[77] rat hepatocytes,[76,108,114] adipocytes,[115] skeletal muscle,[116] human erythrocytes,[117,118] fibroblasts[118] and lymphocytes.[113] In the absence of insulin, the insulin receptor phosphorylation in intact cells was found to be entirely on serine and threonine residues.[75,76,108,114] Addition of the hormone led in some cases to a preferential increase of serine phosphorylation[75,76,108] of the β subunit, in contrast to *in vitro* studies. However, in a study using FAO hepatoma cells, Pang *et al.*[119] and White *et al.*[110] were able to show that, although basal receptor phosphorylation was mainly on serine and threonine residues, the exposure of cells to insulin caused a significant increase in tyrosine phosphorylation, reaching a level equal to that of phosphoserine within 20 s. At the same time, only a slight increase in phosphoserine content was observed after longer incubations of FAO cells with the hormone. Very recently, Ballotti *et al.*, using intact rat hepatocytes,[114] have reported that, in contrast to their earlier work,[108] insulin stimulates phosphorylation of its receptor on tyrosine residues. They ascribe this new finding to improved experimental procedures.[114]

In partially purified insulin receptors from rat liver plasma membranes[120] and from placenta,[109] along with tyrosine phosphorylation, there is also a small amount of serine phosphorylation. However, for the highly purified insulin receptor, serine phosphorylation has never been found.[54, 107] These results suggest that the insulin receptor itself is a tyrosine kinase but may also serve as a substrate for serine and threonine kinases present in the intact cells. Indeed, Roth and Beaudoin[121] have recently reported that a highly purified insulin receptor from human placenta is a substrate for the cAMP-dependent protein kinase, which phosphorylates it on residues other than tyrosine. Although this phosphorylation does not affect insulin binding to the receptor, it nevertheless partly inhibits the intrinsic tyrosine kinase activity of the receptor. This may be responsible for changes of the biological responses to insulin in cells with elevated levels of cAMP.[122, 123] In addition, the insulin receptor serves as a substrate for phosphorylation by protein kinase C,[124, 125] which results in a reduction of its protein tyrosine kinase activity. Thus, autophosphorylation on tyrosine residues leads to an increase in the tyrosine kinase activity of the insulin receptor, whereas phosphorylation on serine and threonine residues diminishes this activity and subsequently autophosphorylation.

Activation of the tyrosine-specific protein kinase of the insulin receptor is considered to be part of a cellular signaling mechanism in response to insulin. It has recently been found that inhibition of the insulin receptor kinase by a monoclonal antibody or by replacement of insulin receptor tyrosine residues 1162 and 1163 with phenylalanine blocks insulin action.[126, 127] However, inhibition of autophosphorylation of the solubilized receptor by indomethacin[128] inhibits only some of the actions of insulin. In addition, activation of glucose transport in IM-9 lymphocytes by monoclonal antibodies to the human insulin receptor or activation of glucose transport in rat adipocytes by metformin can occur without activating the kinase activity of the insulin receptor.[129, 130] This indicates a possible heterogeneity in the metabolic control mechanisms of insulin action.

13.5.2.6.1 *Exogenous and endogenous substrates for protein kinase of the insulin receptor*

The discovery of tyrosine-specific protein kinase activity of the insulin receptor has resulted in a search for exogenous and endogenous substrates for this enzyme. It has been found that, in addition to autophosphorylation, the tyrosine protein kinase of the insulin receptor is capable of catalyzing the phosphorylation of a variety of exogenous substrates, among them casein, histones, tubulin, angiotensin II, troponin, actin and tyrosine-containing synthetic peptides.[77, 108, 120, 131−137] However, the physiological significance of these exogenous substrates for tyrosine kinase is unknown.[70] Very recently, however, a number of attempts have led to the discovery of several endogenous substrates for the tyrosine kinase of the insulin receptor. White *et al.*[138] identified a phosphoprotein of a molecular mass of 185 kDa (pp185), which appeared after the stimulation of FAO hepatoma cells by insulin. A similar protein was found in other cell lines such as Madin–Darby canine kidney cells and normal rat kidney cells[139] as well as 3T3-L1 adipocytes.[140] Furthermore, this substrate has been characterized as a (probably) cytoplasmic protein, distinct from the insulin receptor, which contains phosphoserine and phosphothreonine as well as phosphotyrosine. It was suggested that this endogenous substrate could be a member of a multienzyme complex, specifically a serine/threonine kinase or alternatively a component of a serine or threonine phosphatase.[141] Other substrates for the insulin receptor tyrosine kinase have been reported in intact rat adipocytes and it was suggested that their phosphorylation is an early step in insulin signal transmission.[142] These include a 46 kDa membrane protein, not derived from the insulin receptor, distinct from actin and the glucose transporter, as well as at least five cytoplasmic proteins of molecular masses 116 kDa, 62 kDa and between 45 kDa and 50 kDa. Rees-Jones and Taylor[143] have identified a 120 kDa glycoprotein (pp120) in rat liver plasma membranes that is phosphorylated by the insulin receptor in a cell-free system. The phosphorylation of a similar 120 kDa membrane glycoprotein on its tyrosine residues was confirmed in intact H-35 hepatoma cells[144] and its role in mediating the effect of insulin to promote liver cell growth was suggested.

One of the most interesting observations made during the studies on activation of the tyrosine protein kinase of the insulin receptor was that the removal of insulin from the phosphorylated receptor renders it active in the absence of the hormone.[145] Subsequent dephosphorylation of the insulin receptor with alkaline phosphatase results in a loss of phosphate and restores its insulin dependency. Therefore, it has been suggested that not only removal of bound insulin but also the receptor dephosphorylation process may be important in terminating the insulin signal,[146] and that the insulin receptor itself could be a bifunctional enzyme with not only protein kinase but also phosphoprotein phosphatase activities.[147]

13.5.2.6.2 *Sites for autophosphorylation and for tyrosine kinase activity of the insulin receptor—cascade of autophosphorylation*

The insulin receptor contains a number of phosphorylation sites on tyrosine residues, located in the intracellular part of the β subunit.[70] Digestion of the phosphorylated β-subunit with trypsin leads to the separation of several tryptic phosphopeptides[54, 109, 110, 112, 148, 149] named pY1, pY1a, pY2, pY3, pY4 and pY5.[70, 148] Very recently, the exact positions of these phosphopeptides in the β subunit and the possible cascade of tyrosine autophosphorylation events have been reported.[148, 149] Phosphopeptides pY2 and pY3 are located within the 10 kDa C-terminal fragment of the β subunit, which can be removed by mild digestion with a variety of enzymes. The phosphorylation sites are probably Tyr-1316 and Tyr-1322.[148] These sites are independent of the kinase region as their removal does not cause any loss of kinase activity *in vitro*.[148] However, the latter observation remains contrary to the earlier finding by Kathuria *et al.*,[150] who found that the carboxyl-terminal end of the β subunit is critical for manifestation of the tyrosine kinase activity of the insulin receptor, as well as the work by Ellis *et al.*,[127] who showed that a mutant insulin receptor without 112 C-terminal amino acids was not active as a tyrosine kinase.

pY4 and pY5 are derived from the Tyr-1150 domain of the β subunit and contain two phosphotyrosyl residues [2Tyr(P)], one corresponding to Tyr-1146 and the other to Tyr-1150 or -1151.[149] Full activation of the kinase of the insulin receptor *in vitro* results in appearance of pY1 and pY1a, which are also derived from the Tyr-1150 domain but contain three phosphotyrosyl residues [3Tyr(P)], corresponding to Tyr-1146, Tyr-1150 and Tyr-1151.[149] This form is not detected in intact cells.[110] It has been suggested[149] that autophosphorylation of the insulin receptor begins by phosphorylation of Tyr-1146 and either Tyr-1150 or Tyr-1151. Subsequent *in vitro* auto-phosphorylation of the third tyrosyl residue appears immediately, causing full activation of protein kinase. *In vivo*, the 2Tyr(P) form remains predominant, which suggests that regulation of the autophosphorylation cascade may play an important role in transfer of the insulin signal in intact cells.[149]

13.5.2.7 Search for the Second Messenger of Insulin Action

It has been suggested that, during its action, insulin can produce certain molecules which could serve as the second messengers of the hormone action.[151–155] Initially, the messengers were proposed to be of peptide nature, generated by the proteolytic cleavage of membrane proteins at the outer surface of the cell membrane and internalized into the cytoplasm.[156] However, further studies have brought some evidence of a heterogeneity of these mediators; a number of different substances have been suggested as playing the role of insulin's second messenger[157] but none of them appear to have stood the test of time. Very recently, however, Saltiel and Cuatrecasas[158, 159] have reported purification and characterization of two novel mediators generated by insulin in cultured myocytes and hepatic plasma membranes. They appear to be related complex carbohydrate–phosphate substances containing phosphate, inositol, glucosamine and other monosaccharides, negatively charged and of an apparent molecular weight of 1000–2000 Da. Both mediators were able to modulate the activity of cAMP phosphodiesterase[158, 159] as well as pyruvate dehydrogenase and adenylate cyclase.[160] These substances could also be generated from membranes by the addition of a phosphatidylinositol-specific phospholipase C, indicating that they are a result of the insulin-sensitive phosphodiesterase cleavage of a phosphatidylinositol-containing glycolipid precursor in the membrane. This novel glycolipid was identified on silica TLC or high pressure liquid chromato-graphy[161] and was found to be metabolically labeled with radioactive inositol, glucosamine and myristic acid, indicating a phosphatidylinositol (PI) glycan structure. It is believed to have some homology with the glycolipid responsible for the anchoring of several proteins such as cellular alkaline phosphatase or heparan sulfate to plasma membranes.[161, 162] Treatment of this glycolipid with a PI-specific phospholipase C results in the generation of an inositol phosphate glycan, accompanied by the production of myristate-labeled diacylglycerol, which is an endogenous activator of protein kinase C.[162] This also suggests a possible role for diacylglycerol in insulin action, as was previously considered.[158, 163] However, in the case of insulin stimulation, the diacylglycerol arises from the PI glycan rather than from the usual source of PI. The unique species of diacylglycerol generated in response to insulin, labeled with myristic acid, is different from that generated in response to α-adrenergic agonists which contains arachidonic acid.[164] Furthermore, a PI glycan-specific phospholipase C which catalyzes the hydrolysis of PI glycan upon insulin action was purified from liver plasma membranes.[162] The enzyme has an apparent molecular weight of 62 kDa, is calcium independent and specific for glycosylated PI. It does not hydrolyze PI, PI 4,5-bisphosphate or phosphatidylcholine. Thus it is distinct from the other PI-specific phospholipases C.

On the basis of the above findings, a model of insulin action has been proposed[158] in which the binding of insulin to its receptor is linked, perhaps through a coupling protein (*e.g.* a guanine-nucleotide binding protein[165]), to activation of the specific phospholipase C, resulting in the production of an inositol phosphate glycan, which regulates some insulin-sensitive enzymes, and diacylglycerol, which regulates protein kinase C activity. A combination of these two mechanisms would be capable of transducing a variety of insulin-generated signals.

In 1987, the first attempt was made to link the tyrosine-specific protein kinase of the insulin receptor to insulin mediators.[166] The effect of ATP and Mn^{2+} ions on the production of putative insulin mediators from liver plasma membranes was studied. In the presence of both factors which promote autophosphorylation of the insulin receptor, the generation of insulin mediators was significantly enhanced. It is the first demonstration of a possible connection between insulin-stimulated receptor kinase and production of the hormone's mediators. However, further studies are needed to establish the exact role of the insulin receptor kinase in this process.

13.5.2.8 Conclusions

This section summarizes the recent progress on insulin action and structure of the insulin receptor. The unquestionable role of the tyrosine kinase activity of the insulin receptor in mediation of the insulin signal through the plasma membrane has been well established. Findings that the insulin receptor serves as a substrate for cAMP-dependent protein kinase and protein kinase C, as well as the discovery of several endogenous membrane and cytoplasmic substrates for tyrosine kinase of the insulin receptor, possibly members of a multienzyme complex, suggest the existence of a system capable of transduction of a variety of insulin-generated signals. In addition, recent discovery of two novel insulin mediators, inositol phosphate glycan and diacylglycerol, and also an initial attempt to prove the connection between these two pathways of insulin action, seem to support this hypothesis.

13.5.3 GLUCAGON

13.5.3.1 Biosynthesis

Glucagon is synthesized by the α cells of the pancreas as part of a 21 kDa protein preproglucagon. After cleavage of the presequence by a signal peptidase, an 18 kDa protein proglucagon is formed. A variety of peptides are subsequently obtained from proglucagon by proteolytic processing.[167-169] The various cleavage sites and resulting fragments are shown in Figure 3. Glucagon can also be produced by microorganisms with the use of recombinant DNA technology. The glucagon gene was introduced into *Saccharomyces cerevisiae* as a plasmid attached to a modified mating factor α_1 leader sequence. The yeast synthesized and processed a glucagon-containing peptide and secreted significant amounts of glucagon.[170] These results hold promise for future glucagon production as well as site-specific mutagenesis studies.

Regulation of transcription of the glucagon gene was studied in a cloned pancreatic islet cell tumor.[171] It was found that phorbol myristate acetate and diacylglycerols, but not dibutyryl cAMP, increased the steady-state level of glucagon mRNA. The former compounds also stimulated proglucagon biosynthesis. These results suggest that glucagon gene transcription is regulated by a protein kinase C-activated pathway. Glucagon is stored in the secretory granules of the α cells of the pancreas. There is evidence that glucagon is stored as a zinc complex. Glucagon is known to interact with zinc and fold into a more structured conformation.[172] The secretion of glucagon is regulated by a variety of hormonal, nutrient and neuronal stimuli. Activation of either adenylate cyclase or protein kinase C stimulates glucagon secretion from isolated islets of Langerhans.[173].

The human gene for preproglucagon has been sequenced.[174] It is 9.4 kilobases in length and contains six exons and five introns. The human gene has 88% nucleotide sequence homology with the rat glucagon gene for the 130 base pairs on the 5′-flanking region of the glucagon coding region. The coding region for glucagon is identical in both species. The high degree of homology in the

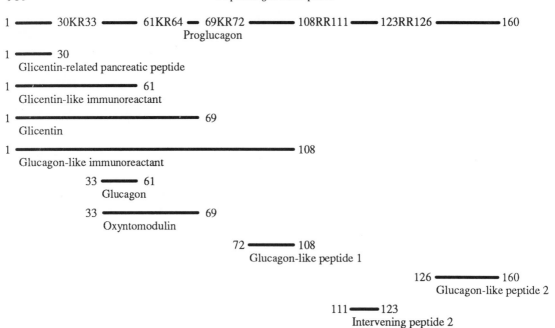

Figure 3 Proglucagon and its proteolytic cleavage products. Only those amino acids which are sites of proteolytic processing are shown. K = Lys, R = Arg

flanking region suggests that it may be involved in the regulation of glucagon gene transcription. The glucagon gene has been shown to be on chromosome 2 of the mouse.[175]

13.5.3.2 Species Variation

Except for guinea pig glucagon, all other mammalian glucagons sequenced, including those of camel, hamster, human, ox, pig, rabbit and rat, are identical and their genes have a similar organization.[176] Guinea pig glucagon differs from other mammalian glucagons at five positions in the carboxyl-terminus region at positions 21, 23, 24, 27 and 29.[177, 178] Guinea pig glucagon is about tenfold less potent than mammalian glucagons in binding to either rat or guinea pig membrane preparations.[179] These results suggest that glucagon receptors in the guinea pig are evolutionarily more conserved than is the hormone itself. Curiously, turkey and chicken glucagon are closer in sequence to most mammalian glucagons, differing only in the substitution of Ser for Asn in position 28, than is guinea pig glucagon. In duck glucagon, there is an additional substitution of Thr for Ser at position 16. The sequences from fish and cartilaginous fish have been determined.[180-182] These differ at three or more positions from mammalian glucagon. Catfish glucagon, which differs at six positions from mammalian glucagon, does not bind to glucagon receptors in rat liver, hypothalamus or pituitary, nor does it stimulate adenylate cyclase in these organs.[182]

13.5.3.3 Glucagon-like Peptides

There is an increasing number of peptide hormones which have been shown to have an amino acid sequence related to that of glucagon. Some of these peptides arise as a result of the proteolytic processing of proglucagon. Those which have been more thoroughly studied are glicentin and oxyntomodulin which contain the glucagon sequence as part of the peptide, as well as glucagon-like peptides 1 and 2 whose sequence has some relationship to that of glucagon (see Figure 3). The amino-terminal extension on glucagon to form glicentin is probably responsible for preventing its binding to hepatic glucagon receptors, since oxyntomodulin which has the same C-terminal extension as glicentin does bind to these receptors.[183] Oxyntomodulin also has glucagon-like effects in the pancreas, stimulating insulin release.[184] Both glicentin and oxyntomodulin inhibit gastric acid secretion.[183] This activity has been ascribed to the common C-terminal eight amino acid residues of these hormones, since an octapeptide corresponding to this sequence also inhibits gastric acid secretion. However, the octapeptide is a hundredfold less potent than oxyntomodulin. Thus, the carboxyl-terminal region of oxyntomodulin probably contributes to this activity but in conjunction with other regions of the molecule.

The other two peptides arising from the processing of proglucagon which are known to be biologically active are glucagon-like peptides 1 and 2. These peptides have no effect on rat liver adenylate cyclase[185] or glycogenolysis[186] although they do cause a small stimulation of gluconeogenesis in piscine hepatocytes.[187] Interestingly, although glucagon-like peptides 1 and 2 do not bind to glucagon receptors in the pituitary or hypothalamus they are potent activators of adenylate cyclase in these organs.[185] This cyclase activation occurs maximally at about 10^{-10} mol dm^{-3} peptide, with marked lowering of the stimulatory effect above 10^{-9} mol dm^{-3}. These results suggest that glucagon-like peptides have separate receptors in the brain and they may function as neurotransmitters and/or neuroendocrine effectors.

A number of polypeptide hormones which are products of other genes have a high sequence homology with glucagon. These hormones include secretin, gastric inhibitory peptide, vasoactive intestinal polypeptide, PHI (a 27 amino acid peptide having an amino-terminal histidine and a carboxy-terminal isoleucine) and growth hormone releasing factor.[188] Secretin has a particularly high homology with glucagon and it acts by stimulating the synthesis of both cAMP and inositol triphosphate[189] as does glucagon (see below). With so many peptides of homologous sequence, one has to be careful when another homologous sequence in a different species is found to decide whether the new peptide represents a newly discovered type of hormone or simply species variation in the sequence of a known hormone. In the case of PHI, porcine PHI differs by one amino acid from bovine PHI but by three amino acids from human PHI.[190] A criterion to determine whether two peptides from different species are different or simply species variants is the measurement and comparison of their biological function and potency. A full discussion of all the biological activities of the glucagon-like peptides is beyond the scope of this review.

13.5.3.4 Conformational Properties

To understand the conformational features of glucagon which are important for biological activity, the receptor-bound conformation as well as the conformation of the hormone in solution should be evaluated. However, receptors are not abundant proteins although they can be cloned and may be reconstituted into a functional system providing that they have the necessary post-translational modifications. An additional problem is that receptors are large integral membrane proteins and are not readily amenable to X-ray crystallographic or NMR techniques although some membrane proteins have been crystallized and developments in saturation transfer or solid-state NMR may make this problem more tractable. Thus, direct determination of the receptor-bound conformation of a peptide hormone is at the borderline of being technologically feasible at present, although one can anticipate future advances in crystallizing membrane systems and in NMR techniques. The conformation of the hormone in solution is also relevant since the receptor affinity will be determined by the free energy difference between the free and receptor-bound states of the hormone. For peptides the size of glucagon, NMR methods are particularly powerful for determining the solution conformation. Unfortunately, peptides of this size have a large degree of conformational flexibility and generally there is not a single conformation which is highly populated. Thus, although glucagon has some structure in free solution, it is not a particularly stable structure and alterations of this structure in analogs is not likely to result in a very large change in receptor affinity. We are therefore left with determining the conformation of glucagon in states where it has more structure, such as the crystal, self-associated in solution, in nonaqueous solvents or bound to detergents or membrane bilayers. These studies can provide a model on which to base the design of new analogs. If predictions made on the basis of such models lead to the successful design of analogs, this can be taken as evidence that the experimentally determined conformation resembles the receptor-bound state.

13.5.3.4.1 X-Ray crystallographic structure

X-Ray diffraction studies of glucagon crystals have given structural information at about 3 Å resolution.[191] With small peptides, the intermolecular forces will make a large contribution to determining the conformational state of the peptide and these forces are unique for each particular crystal form. The conformation of some peptides is altered by differences in crystal packing arrangements or by the addition of heavy atoms or altered pH.[191] The crystal structure of glucagon contains two helical segments which are related by a diad axis of symmetry. Analogous symmetrical features can be proposed for other hormones suggesting that this may be a common feature required for hormone–receptor interactions.[192] Each helical segment is amphipathic, which is also a structural feature of a number of peptide hormones of this size.[193]

13.5.3.4.2 *Solution structure*

A number of lines of evidence indicate that glucagon has a compact folded structure in dilute aqueous solution.[194] However, NMR methods do not provide evidence for a specific tertiary structure.[195] There is NMR evidence for a nonrandom structure involving only residues 22–25 and even this limited structure is populated by only about 20% of the glucagon molecules at ambient temperature.[195] It has also been recognized that the solution conformation of glucagon is very sensitive to conditions. At higher peptide concentrations, glucagon self-associates to conformations with increased helical content.[196] On prolonged standing, glucagon adopts a β-pleated sheet structure.[197] These results confirm that glucagon does not have a stable conformation in aqueous solution and that the conformational features required for receptor binding are formed on a membrane surface or possibly only when bound to the receptor protein.

13.5.3.4.3 *Lipid binding*

Glucagon stimulates cellular responses by binding to cell-surface membrane receptors. Thus, the conformation of glucagon when bound to a membrane surface would be expected to more closely resemble the receptor-bound conformation than any other simple model system. Glucagon binds to lipid and folds into a conformation of higher helical content.[198] Detailed analysis of the lipid-bound structure has been performed using NMR.[199] The structure derived from the NMR studies was compared with the crystallographic structure. There is very close coincidence for the helical region near the carboxyl terminus but the segment of residues 5–15 is more helical in the crystal state.[199]

13.5.3.5 Distribution

Glucagon was first recognized as a 'hyperglycemic factor' contained in insulin preparations from the pancreas. However, studies with depancreatized animals demonstrated that there were other sites of synthesis of this hormone. It has long been recognized that glucagon-like peptides are produced in the gastrointestinal tract.[200] However, because numerous peptide products can be derived from proglucagon (Figure 3), it was not certain how much of this material was identical to the 29 amino acid 'pancreatic glucagon'. Vranic *et al.*[201] were able to isolate a peptide identical to 'pancreatic glucagon' from dog stomach fundus. There is also some glucagon produced in the intestine and colon but the major product of glucagon-producing cells in this part of the gastrointestinal tract is oxyntomodulin.[202] Not only is glucagon present in the gastrointestinal tract but immunohistochemical evidence indicates that it is also produced there.[203]

Glucagon appears to be present and to be synthesized in human salivary glands.[204] Several other organs also appear to contain and produce glucagon including the thymus, adrenals, thyroid and hypophysis, although the level of glucagon is much lower than that in the gastric fundus or pancreas.[205] There is also a high concentration of glucagon in the retina of goldfish, chicken, pigeon and frog and much lower amounts in the retina of cow, pig, rabbit and rat.[206] Care must be taken to confirm these observations since glucagon measurement by radioimmunoassay is prone to artifact. Glucagon is rapidly hydrolyzed by proteolytic enzymes. It has been suggested that [^{125}I]-labeled glucagon is rapidly degraded by salivary gland extracts, resulting in artificially high glucagon levels.[207]

There has been increasing interest in the role of gastrointestinal hormones in brain function. Both glucagon and glucagon-like peptides have been positively identified in the brain with particularly high concentrations in the hypothalamus.[208] Immunohistochemical evidence indicates that glucagon peptides are also produced in the brain.[208] Glucagon peptides were localized in the synaptosomal fraction and are released with high concentrations of potassium, suggesting that these peptides play a role as neurotransmitters.[208] Furthermore, intracerebroventricular administration of glucagon increased the level of glucose more than glucagon given intravenously. This effect was inhibited by atropine, phentomine or hexamethonium, suggesting that it may be mediated by the autonomic nervous system.[208] Glucagon induces the release of somatostatin from the perfused hypothalamus.[209] Glucagon effects in the brain may be related to regulation of the secretion of hypothalamic and/or pituitary hormones. Many of the effects of glucagon on the central nervous system are similar to those that have been described for calcitonin (see Chapter 13.10). Calcitonin is also present in the brain with particularly high concentrations in the hypothalamus. The relationship between the actions of glucagon and calcitonin on the central nervous system should be further investigated.

13.5.3.6 Biological Properties and Methods of Assay

13.5.3.6.1 Secondary messenger systems

(i) cAMP

Glucagon is a potent stimulator of adenylate cyclase. Adenylate cyclase in membranes from a number of different cell types is stimulated by glucagon, but most detailed studies of the mechanism of activation have been carried out with hepatic membranes because they are readily available and show a large effect of glucagon. This effect was studied by Sutherland in his development of the second messenger hypothesis. Rodbell expanded this concept and demonstrated the required role of GTP and GTP-binding membrane proteins. The mechanism of receptor-mediated activation of adenylate cyclase has been reviewed by Rodbell.[210] Since transmission of the signal from an occupied receptor to adenylate cyclase requires interactions between membrane proteins, it is anticipated that the membrane lipid environment will affect the coupling of the receptor with adenylate cyclase. Houslay has extensively studied the dependence of the stimulation of adenylate cyclase activity by glucagon on lipid fluidity[49] and the effect of drugs on these properties.[211,212] Increased bilayer order causes inhibition of hormone-stimulated adenylate cyclase. This factor may account for the observed decrease in glucagon-dependent stimulation of adenylate cyclase activity with age.[213]

There is a rapid desensitization of glucagon-stimulated adenylate cyclase. It has recently been shown that this desensitization results from a cAMP-independent process.[214] In addition to glucagon itself, desensitization is also caused by angiotensin and vasopressin through the stimulation of inositol phosphate metabolism. Phorbol esters also promote desensitization, presumably through stimulation of protein kinase C. It is believed that protein kinase C-catalyzed phosphorylation decouples the glucagon receptor from the stimulatory guanine nucleotide regulatory protein, N_s.

(ii) Calcium

It is now recognized that several hormones can stimulate cellular responses by changes in cAMP and/or changes in Ca^{2+} concentration. The two transducing systems may be mediated by binding to different receptor sites for the same ligand.[215] An analog of glucagon, (1-N-α-trinitrophenylhistidine)glucagon, had been shown to stimulate glycogenolysis by a cAMP-independent pathway.[216] It has recently been shown that a similar analog, (1-N-α-trinitrophenylhistidine,12-homoarginine)glucagon, stimulates the production of inositol phosphates.[217] Using isolated rat hepatocytes, it has been demonstrated that glucagon stimulates both phospholipase C and phosphatidylinositol kinase activity.[218] The resulting production of inositol 1,4,5-trisphosphate leads to the observed release of intracellular Ca^{2+} stores. Intracellular Ca^{2+} levels are critical for the regulation of a variety of cellular activities.

Intracellular Ca^{2+} levels are regulated through a number of mechanisms which involve controlling the flux of Ca^{2+} between extracellular, mitochondrial and endoplasmic reticulum pools of Ca^{2+} which are at high concentrations and the intracellular Ca^{2+} pool at a low concentration. Vasopressin, angiotensin and α-adrenergic agonists are known to affect hepatocytes through changes in intracellular Ca^{2+}. Both glucagon and vasopressin affect release of Ca^{2+} from the same intracellular pool.[219] It is found that low concentrations of glucagon greatly potentiate the effects of the Ca^{2+}-mobilizing hormones both in perfused liver[220] and with isolated rat hepatocytes.[221] This amplification of the calcium signal by glucagon may occur by a cAMP-dependent pathway, since cAMP can replace glucagon for this amplification.[219] Although glucagon can also activate the inositol phosphate pathway, one of the consequences of this is the activation of protein kinase C which results in an attenuation of the glucagon-induced increase in cytoplasmic Ca^{2+}.[222] Protein kinase-catalyzed phosphorylation of specific protein substrates is a mechanism by which both cAMP and phosphatidylinositol Ca^{2+} pathways control cell activity. It has been shown that glucagon and angiotensin/vasopressin stimulate the phosphorylation of distinct protein substrates in intact hepatocytes,[223] and they promote the phosphorylation of different sites on glycogen synthetase.[224]

Another mechanism of glucagon regulation of intracellular Ca^{2+} is through its inhibition of a high affinity $(Ca^{2+}-Mg^{2+})$-ATPase in liver plasma membranes.[225] This enzyme has been shown by reconstitution studies to be a Ca^{2+} pump.[226] Studies of the effects of glucagon analogs suggest that the inhibition is not mediated through adenylate cyclase nor phosphatidylinositol turnover.[225] Curiously, an isolated carboxyl-terminal segment of glucagon, comprising residues 19–29, is a thousandfold more potent than the intact hormone in inhibiting the $(Ca^{2+}-Mg^{2+})$-ATPase.[227] This fragment could arise through proteolytic cleavage of glucagon at the Arg residues at positions 17 and 18.

In summary, glucagon can affect changes in both intracellular cAMP and Ca^{2+} levels. The two transducing systems are mutually interactive with cAMP causing increased intracellular Ca^{2+} and protein kinase C activation leading to inhibition of glucagon-promoted increased Ca^{2+}, possibly through receptor down-regulation. The physiological role of the effects of glucagon on the various mechanisms controlling intracellular Ca^{2+} remains to be fully elucidated.

13.5.3.6.2 *Biological effects*

The most studied biological effect of glucagon is its induction of hyperglycemia. This has been used as the basis for *in vivo* biological assays of hormone potency. Since glucagon also promotes the release of insulin, the resulting elevation of blood glucose levels is not very great. To accentuate the hyperglycemic effect of glucagon, biological assays have been developed using cortisone-primed animals to build up liver glycogen stores prior to glucagon administration.[228]

In the diabetic state with insufficient insulin, glucagon has a major effect in increasing blood glucose levels. Furthermore, the suppression of glucagon release by insulin is diminished in diabetes, leading to diabetic hyperglucagonemia.[229] The response to glucagon is greater in depancreatized humans than in patients with type 1 diabetes, probably as a result of receptor down-regulation in the case of hyperglucagonemic diabetics.[230] In the diabetic state, there is also an abolition of the expression of the inhibitory guanine nucleotide regulatory protein in the liver.[231] Thus, there is no counterregulation of the stimulatory effects of glucagon. Patients with long-standing diabetes develop impaired glucagon response to hypoglycemia as a result of α-cell dysfunction.[232,233] The physiological and pathological role of the E series of prostaglandins in inhibiting the stimulation of hepatic glycogenolysis by glucagon[234,235] requires further investigation.

Glucagon at pharmacological doses lowers plasma calcium and inorganic phosphate. It is not clear if these effects are directly caused by glucagon or are an indirect effect of glucagon-promoted release of calcitonin.[236,237] Curiously, with rats fed on a low phosphate diet, glucagon increases circulating levels of phosphate.[238] The mechanism of this phosphate-mobilizing activity has not been elucidated. Glucagon has other calcitonin-like activities when injected into whole animals. Glucagon reduces food intake,[239] it is useful in the treatment of Paget's disease of the bone[240] and it inhibits gastric acid release.[241] Again these may be direct effects of glucagon or be mediated through glucagon-stimulated release of calcitonin from the thyroid gland.

Glucagon has marked effects on lipid metabolism through its action on both adipose tissue and liver. Glucagon stimulates lipolysis and ketogenesis and decreases circulating levels of triglyceride and cholesterol. Glucagon also inhibits fatty acid biosynthesis. One mechanism of this inhibition is by promoting post-transcriptional processes which lower the mRNA levels for some of the enzymes required for fatty acid synthesis.[242]

Glucagon has inotropic and chronotropic cardiac effects. It has found clinical application in heart failure, cardiogenic shock and β-blocker overdose. Glucagon also relaxes smooth muscle in the lower esophageal sphincter, stomach, small and large intestines, common bile duct and ureters. It is frequently used in endoscopic examination. These and other therapeutic uses of glucagon have been recently reviewed.[243] The only FDA-approved use of glucagon is in the treatment of hypoglycemia.

13.5.3.7 Structure–Activity Relationships (SAR)

It has been shown that in the presence of glucagon antibodies normal blood glucose levels can be maintained with a reduced supply of insulin.[244] This suggests that diabetic hyperglycemia can be alleviated through control of glucagon activity. For this reason, there has been much current interest in SAR of glucagon and in developing a glucagon antagonist which could be used to test the role of glucagon in diabetes and possibly be useful as a therapeutic agent. The groups of Coy, Gurd, Hruby and Merrifield are currently particularly active in this area. Recent reviews have summarized some of the SAR studies on glucagon.[245,246] This chapter will emphasize recent advances.

In designing glucagon analogs, several groups have made amino acid replacements to alter the conformational properties of the hormone. There is evidence that glucagon receptor recognition is, in part, determined by the conformational features of the hormone in the lipid-bound state.[247] In addition to the problem of specific interactions between the hormone and receptor, there is also a difficulty in attempting to predict how amino acid substitutions will affect the conformational features of the peptide. Several groups have used the Chou–Fasman algorithm for these predictions. This is a reasonable first step but it is not clear that this algorithm will accurately predict the conformation of a globular protein[248] much less that of a small peptide on a lipid bilayer surface. Some of the limitations of these predictions have been observed in SAR studies of glucagon analogs.[249] Another general problem is in the method of assay. Most studies have measured adenylate cyclase activation and receptor binding in hepatocyte membranes. These results do not always agree with measurements of glucose production in hepatocytes or whole animals.[216,250] Part of this discrepancy may arise because glucagon can stimulate glycogenolysis by both cAMP-dependent and independent mechanisms.[217] In addition, glucagon analogs, particularly when used at higher concentrations, may begin to cause effects by binding to receptors for glucagon-like hormones. *In vivo* studies are particularly complex to interpret on a mechanistic basis so as to optimize the biological properties of an analog, although these studies are the most relevant for eventual therapeutic application. A particular difficulty arises because of the ability of glucagon to stimulate insulin release. One could imagine an otherwise ideal glucagon antagonist which has hyperglycemic activity *in vivo* as a result of its suppression of glucagon-induced insulin release. Finally, other factors such as the distribution of the peptide, its rate of degradation and the ability of the peptide to down-regulate glucagon receptors can all contribute to apparent changes in potency of a glucagon analog.

The amino acid sequence of glucagon shows little species variation. This fact, along with analog studies,[251,252] suggests that all regions of the peptide contribute to hormone potency. It is therefore not surprising that many glucagon analogs have reduced activity. However, it is also possible to prepare glucagon analogs with enhanced activity. Modifications that enhance potency can be combined with those that decrease maximal activity to make a more potent antagonist.[253] A number of glucagon analogs with enhanced *in vivo* hyperglycemic activity have been described by Coy and co-workers.[254,255] The most potent of these analogs is [D-Phe^4]glucagon.[254] However, when this analog was tested for its activity in binding to glucagon receptors and stimulating adenylate cyclase in rat liver plasma membranes, it was found to be slightly less potent than the native hormone.[256] The increased biological half-life of 7.5 min for [D-Phe^4]glucagon compared with 5.3 min for the native hormone does not seem sufficient to explain the 6.5-fold increase in glycogenolytic activity.[256] [D-Phe^4]glucagon also does not have enhanced stimulatory effects on the metabolism of canine hepatocytes (Hagopian and Tager, personal communication cited in ref. 256). It therefore seems likely that effects of [D-Phe^4]glucagon at some organ other than the liver are responsible for its enhanced activity. Di[δ-(5-nitro-2-pyrimidyl)ornithine^{17,18}]glucagon also has enhanced glycogenolytic activity with no increase in liver adenylate cyclase activation or receptor binding.[257] Further studies are required to elucidate the mechanism of the enhanced hyper-glycogenolytic activity.

It has been proposed that glucagon folds into an amphipathic helix on membrane surfaces.[258] A helical net representation of the glucagon sequence is shown in Figure 4. Glucagon analogs which have been shown to have enhanced activity based on liver membrane receptor binding and adenylate cyclase activation are [Lys^{17,18},Glu^{21}]glucagon and [Phe^{13},Lys^{17,18},Glu^{21}]glucagon. The [Lys^{17,18},Glu^{21}]glucagon is the most potent with a 5.1-fold enhancement in receptor binding and a sevenfold enhancement in adenylate cyclase activation potency.[259,260] These modifications are likely to enhance the helix-forming probability in the lipid-bound state and give strong evidence for the existence of an amphipathic helix in the carboxyl-terminal portion of glucagon in the receptor-bound state.

Several glucagon analogs have been shown to bind to glucagon receptors with tenfold or greater potency than is required for the activation of adenylate cyclase (Table 1). All of these derivatives are potential glucagon antagonists; however, some retain weak agonist or partial weak agonist activity. In addition, the potency of an analog as an antagonist does not always correlate well with its relative receptor binding affinity. For example, des-His^1-[Glu^9]glucagon has fivefold greater membrane

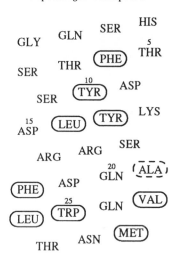

Figure 4 The amino acid sequence of glucagon shown in a helical net diagram; hydrophobic amino acid residues are circled

binding affinity than [Asp^3, Glu^9]glucagon but the former peptide has no greater antagonist activity against glucagon stimulation of adenylate cyclase activity than does the latter peptide.[269] An additional complication is that several analogs are pure antagonists with respect to adenylate cyclase but show agonist activity when assayed *in vivo* for stimulation of hyperglycemia. One analog, des-His^1-[Glu^9]glucagon amide, is a pure adenylate cyclase antagonist. It should be tested for its activity on liver or *in vivo*. Several of the analogs listed, such as [Pro^{11}]glucagon, have lost their ability to activate cyclase but also have greatly reduced receptor binding activity. One approach to making these analogs more potent antagonists is by introducing additional modifications known to increase potency. Four approaches have been used. The first is the introduction of D-Phe at position 4. The modification was thought to stabilize a β bend and [D-Phe^4]glucagon was shown to have enhanced glycogenolytic activity.[255] However, when tested for receptor binding, [D-Phe^4]glucagon was shown to have somewhat less affinity than the native hormone.[256] This therefore now seems to be a poor choice for enhancing antagonist activity since it will not augment receptor binding and may contribute to *in vivo* agonist activity by a cAMP-independent mechanism. The second approach is to introduce Lys^{17,18}, Glu^{21} to enhance the helicity of the carboxy terminus. Although this strategy improved the receptor binding of glucagon,[259, 260] it has not been effective in enhancing the potency of some glucagon antagonists.[269, 270] This appears to be particularly true for analogs with substitution of Glu^9 for the native Asp^9. Since this substitution already increases the helical probability, a further increase in structure with Lys^{17,18}, Glu^{21} may be detrimental to receptor binding because of loss of conformational flexibility in the peptide.[272] However, the incorporation of these three residues in [D-Phe^4, Tyr^5, 3,5-I$_2$-Tyr^{10}, Arg^{12}, Lys^{17,18}, Glu^{21}]glucagon is well tolerated.[267] Thus, this strategy may still be useful to enhance the receptor binding of some less structured analog but not one which already has a greater probability of folding. Another strategy used to enhance potency is iodination.[273] This has proved effective with one analog.[266] The final strategy has been to amidate the carboxyl terminus. This modification would reduce unfavorable electrostatic interactions between the terminal carboxyl group and the helix dipole.[274] Although amidation has no effect on the receptor binding potency of glucagon,[269] it does enhance the binding affinity of some analogs[269] and may be a generally useful approach to enhance the potency of antagonists.

13.5.3.8 Receptor

Reviews on the glucagon receptor have appeared recently.[275-277] These reviews include studies of labeling the receptor and progress toward its isolation and purification. We will discuss only recent evidence concerning the properties of the glucagon receptor.

Most groups find that glucagon binding to its hepatic receptor cannot be described by a simple model of uniform and independent binding sites. A number of explanations of this phenomenon have been proposed including heterogeneity of binding sites, negative cooperativity or differences in binding affinity between the radioligand and unmodified glucagon. Gurd *et al.*[278] have found that,

Table 1 Glucagon Analogs with some Antagonist Activity

Analog[a]	Relative receptor affinity (%)	Relative cyclase potency (%)	Maximal cyclase activation (%)	Antagonist activity[b]	Agonist activity[b]	Ref.
[1-N-α-Trinitrophenylhistidine]G	7	0.1	~0.1	1	1,2c	216, 251
[1-N-α-Trinitrophenylhistidine,12-homoarginine]G	—	0	0	1, 2c, 2v	2c	261–264
[Pro11]G	0.006	0	0	—	—	259, 265
[Pro11,Gly12]G amide	0.014	0	0	—	2v	265
[3-Methyl-His1,Arg12]G	213	22	70	—	—	256
[D-Phe4,Tyr5,Arg12]G	1	0	0	1	—	266
[Asp3,D-Phe4,Ser5,Lys17,18]G	1.3	0	0	1	—	266
I4-[Asp3,D-Phe4,Ser5,Lys17,18]G	5.3	0	0	—	—	266
[des-amino-His1,D-Phe4,Tyr5,Arg12,Lys17,18,Glu21]G	21	0	0	1	2s	250
[Asp3,D-Phe4,Ser5,Lys17,18,Glu21]G	5	0	0	1, 2v	—	267
[D-Phe4,Tyr5,3,5-I2-Tyr10,Arg12,Lys17,18,Glu21]G	50	0	0	1, 2v	2v	267
[Asp3,Glu9]G	1.6	0	0	1	—	268
[Asp3,Glu9,Arg12]G	1.6	0	0	1	—	268
[Asp3,Glu21]G	1.0	0	0	1	—	268
[Asp3,Glu9,D-Phe4]G	2	0.005	0	1	1	269
[Glu9]G	7	0.13	14	—	—	269
[Glu9]G amide	14	0.05	24	—	—	269
des-His1-G	8	0.10	62	—	—	269
des-His1-G-amide	63	0.16	36	—	—	269
des-His1-[Glu9]G	11	0	44	1	—	269
des-His1-[Glu9]G amide	41	0	0	1	—	269
des-His1-[Lys17,18,Glu21]G	15	0.6	0	—	—	269
des-His1-[D-Phe4]G	13	0.1	28	—	—	269
des-His1-[Glu9,Lys17,18,Glu21]G	10	0	48	—	—	269
[Asp3,D-Phe4]G	3.5	0.02	0	1	—	270
des-His1-[Asp3,Glu9,Arg12]G	0.8	0	29	1	—	270
des-His1-[Asp3]G	0.45	0.006	16	1	—	270
des-His1-[Asp3,Glu9,D-Phe4]G	2.4	0	0	1	—	270
des-His1-[Asp3,D-Phe4]G	7.4	0	0	1	—	270
des-His1-[Asp3,D-Phe4,Lys17,18,Glu21]G	2.8	0	0	1	—	270
des-His1-[Tyr22]G	1.6	0	0	1	—	271

[a] G = glucagon. [b] Code for activities: 1, membrane adenylate cyclase; 2, glycogenolysis (c, in hepatocytes; v, *in vivo*; s, in liver slices).

under certain conditions, the binding of glucagon can be represented by binding to an independent homogeneous population of receptors. They suggest that there is a time- and temperature-dependent conversion from a low affinity complex to a high affinity complex. The difference between this model and one in which there is heterogeneity of receptors is subtle. We believe that Gurd's data would also be consistent with preexisting high and low affinity binding sites, provided each class had different kinetics for binding the hormone. Thus, there is no basic disagreement between this model and that of Tager and Hruby *et al.*[279] which describes two classes of binding sites. These latter workers have identified the high affinity sites as those linked to biological response.[279] It is possible that the low and high affinity forms of the glucagon receptor have different functional roles. The low affinity form of the glucagon receptor appears to inhibit cAMP production.[280] Glucagon also inhibits β-adrenergic stimulation of cAMP production.[280] These inhibitory actions of glucagon further complicate the interpretation of *in vivo* assays of agonist and antagonist actions of glucagon analogs, since effects may depend on peptide concentration as well as on the level of epinephrine in the circulation. It is known that glucagon triggers both adenylate cyclase stimulation as well as stimulation of phosphatidylinositol metabolism. It is not yet clear whether these two functions require different receptors. An interesting extension of the two-state receptor hypothesis is its ability to explain partial agonist activity. It has been shown that weak agonists (lower potency) have a reduced affinity for the unoccupied glucagon receptor, while partial agonists (lower maximal activity) show a decreased conversion from the low to the high affinity state.[281] The nucleotide GTP also slows conversion of the low to the high affinity state of the receptor.[282] The effect of GTP on glucagon binding was studied using liver plasma membrane preparations from chicken, rat and rabbit.[283] This study demonstrated that glucagon binding to rabbit membranes was independent of GTP. It was shown that the ratio of N_s to receptor protein was particularly high in rabbit, so that the reaction between the glucagon receptor and N_s could not be reversed by GTP. This interpretation was also consistent with the lack of effect of Mg^{2+} in promoting formation of high affinity receptor sites. In addition to GTP, *N*-ethylmaleimide also causes the loss of high affinity glucagon receptors. Both GTP and *N*-ethylmaleimide reduce the fraction of glucagon receptors that are present as high molecular weight complexes after detergent solubilization.[284] The high molecular weight form of the receptor may represent a complex between the receptor protein and a nucleotide binding protein. Such a complex could be the high affinity form of the glucagon receptor. Thus, binding data demonstrating receptor heterogeneity may result from different states of association of the glucagon receptor with other membrane proteins, rather than from heterogeneity of the receptor protein.

13.5.3.9 Conclusions

It is clear that the action of glucagon, once thought to be a simple classical example of the cAMP secondary messenger hypothesis, is quite complex. Involvement of different classes of receptors and of changes in phosphatidylinositol turnover have been demonstrated. It is not clear which, if any, cAMP-independent mechanism is of physiological importance for glucagon action, but they do demonstrate some of the complexities that will be involved in designing a pharmacologically useful glucagon antagonist. Nevertheless, because of the increased research activity in this direction, we can anticipate further developments in the near future. Additionally, purification of the glucagon receptor and its eventual cloning and reconstitution into model membranes will also help to elucidate the molecular mechanism of the transduction of the glucagon signal and further aid in efforts to control this function.

ACKNOWLEDGEMENTS

Dr Richard M. Epand would like to thank Drs V. J. Hruby, R. B. Merrifield and H. S. Tager for their critical reading of the glucagon section of this manuscript. We are grateful to Ms Lisa Kush for her excellent typing of the manuscript.

13.5.4 REFERENCES

1. P. E. Cryer and J. E. Gerich, *Diabetes Care*, 1983, **6**, 95.
2. R. H. Unger, *Diabetes*, 1983, **32**, 575.
3. A. Starke, T. Imamura and R. H. Unger, *J. Clin. Invest.*, 1987, **79**, 20.
4. P. J. Lefébvre (ed.), 'Glucagon I and II', Springer-Verlag, Berlin, 1983.

5. D. R. Owens, 'Human Insulin', MTP Press, Lancaster, 1986.
6. J. C. Pickup, H. Keen, J. A. Parsons and K. G. M. M. Alberti, *Br. Med. J.*, 1978, **1**, 204.
7. J. C. Pickup (ed.), 'Brittle Diabetes', Blackwell, Oxford, 1985.
8. M. Berger, *Diabetologia*, 1987, **30**, 829.
9. A. C. Moses, G. S. Gordon, M. C. Carey and J. S. Flier, *Diabetes*, 1983, **32**, 1040.
10. A. G. Frauman, M. E. Cooper, B. J. Parsons, G. Jerums and W. J. Louis, *Diabetes Care*, 1987, **10**, 573.
11. A. P. Ryle, F. Sanger, L. F. Smith and R. Kitai, *Biochem. J.*, 1955, **50**, 541.
12. C. C. Yip and M. L. Moule, *Can. J. Biochem.*, 1976, **54**, 866.
13. L. F. Smith, *Am. J. Med.*, 1966, **40**, 662.
14. T. L. Blundell and S. P. Wood, *Nature (London)*, 1975, **257**, 197.
15. M. Bajaj, T. L. Blundell, J. E. Pitts, S. P. Wood, M. A. Tatnell, S. Falkmer, S. O. Emdin, L. K. Gowan, H. Crow, Ch. Schwabe, A. Wollmer and W. Strassburger, *Eur. J. Biochem.*, 1983, **135**, 535.
16. M. J. Adams, T. L. Blundell, E. J. Dodson, G. G. Dodson, M. Vijayan, E. N. Baker, M. M. Harding, D. C. Hodgkin, B. Rimmer and S. Sheat, *Nature (London)*, 1969, **224**, 491.
17. T. L. Blundell, J. E. Cutfield, S. M. Cutfield, E. J. Dodson, G. G. Dodson, D. C. Hodgkin, D. A. Mercola and M. Vijayan, *Nature (London)*, 1971, **231**, 506.
18. T. L. Blundell, G. Dodson, D. Hodgkin and D. Mercola, *Adv. Protein Chem.*, 1972, **26**, 279.
19. T. L. Blundell and R. E. Humbel, *Nature (London)*, 1980, **287**, 781.
20. T. L. Blundell, G. G. Dodson, E. J. Dodson, D. C. Hodgkin and M. Vijayan, *Rec. Prog. Horm. Res.*, 1971, **27**, 1.
21. S. P. Wood, T. L. Blundell, A. Wollmer, N. R. Lazarus and W. J. Neville, *Eur. J. Biochem.*, 1975, **55**, 531.
22. D. Brandenburg and A. Wollmer (eds.), 'Insulin-Chemistry, Structure and Function of Insulin and Related Hormones', de Gruyter, Berlin, 1980.
23. E. H. Strickland and D. Mercola, *Biochemistry*, 1976, **15**, 3875.
24. J. H. Bradbury and L. R. Brown, *Eur. J. Biochem.*, 1977, **76**, 573.
25. K. L. Williamson and R. J. P. Williams, *Biochemistry*, 1979, **18**, 5966.
26. J. H. Bradbury, V. Ramesh and G. Dodson, *J. Mol. Biol.*, 1981, **150**, 609.
27. D. J. Saunders, *Diabetologia*, 1982, **23**, 386.
28. D. Saunders and K. Freude, *Hoppe-Seyler's Z. Physiol. Chem.*, 1982, **363**, 655.
29. J. Cutfield, S. Cutfield, E. Dodson, G. Dodson, D. Hodgkin and C. Reynolds, *Hoppe-Seyler's Z. Physiol. Chem.*, 1981, **362**, 755.
30. A. Schüttler and D. Brandenburg, *Hoppe-Seyler's Z. Physiol. Chem.*, 1982, **363**, 317.
31. D. Brandenburg, C. Diaconescu, D. Saunders and P. Thamm, *Nature (London)*, 1980, **268**, 821.
32. C.-C. Wang, J. A. Hedo, C. R. Kahn, D. T. Saunders, P. Thamm and D. Brandenburg, *Diabetes*, 1982, **31**, 1068.
33. D. Brandenburg, C. Diaconescu, G. Klotz, P. Mucke, J. Neffe, D. Saunders and A. Schüttler, *Biochimie*, 1985, **67**, 1111.
34. G. Klotz, D. J. Saunders and D. Brandenburg, *Hoppe-Seyler's Z. Physiol. Chem.*, 1984, **365**, 493.
35. J. Gliemann, O. Sonne, S. Linde and B. Hansen, *Biochem. Biophys. Res. Commun.*, 1979, **87**, 1183.
36. P. Freychet, R. Kahn, J. Roth and D. M. Neville, Jr., *J. Biol. Chem.*, 1972, **247**, 3953.
37. P. Freychet, D. Brandenburg and A. Wollmer, *Diabetologia*, 1974, **10**, 1.
38. F. H. Carpenter, *Am. J. Med.*, 1966, **40**, 750.
39. J. Gliemann and S. Gammeltoft, *Diabetologia*, 1974, **10**, 105.
40. A. Cosmatos, K. Cheng, Y. Okada and P. G. Katsoyannis, *J. Biol. Chem.*, 1978, **253**, 6586.
41. G. T. Burke, J. D. Chanley, Y. Okada, A. Cosmatos, N. Ferderigos and P. G. Katsoyannis, *Biochemistry*, 1980, **19**, 4547.
42. G. P. Schwartz, T. G. Burke, J. D. Chanley and P. G. Katsoyannis, *Biochemistry*, 1983, **22**, 4561.
43. W. H. Fischer, D. Saunders, D. Brandenburg, A. Wollmer and H. Zahn, *Biol. Chem. Hoppe-Seyler*, 1985, **366**, 521.
44. R. A. Pullen, D. G. Lindsay, S. P. Wood, I. J. Tickle, T. L. Blundell, A. Wollmer, G. Krail, D. Brandenburg, H. Zahn, J. Gliemann and S. Gammeltoft, *Nature (London)*, 1976, **259**, 369.
45. Y.-C. Chu, R.-Y. Wang, G. T. Burke, J. D. Chanley and P. G. Katsoyannis, *Biochemistry*, 1987, **26**, 6966.
46. S. Emdin, O. Sonne and J. Gliemann, *Diabetes*, 1980, **29**, 301.
47. T. Blundell and S. Wood, *Annu. Rev. Biochem.*, 1982, **51**, 123.
48. E. Dafgård, M. Bajaj, A. M. Honnegger, J. Pitts, S. Wood and T. Blundell, *Cell. Sci. Suppl.*, 1985, **3**, 53.
49. S. H. Nakagawa and H. S. Tager, *J. Biol. Chem.*, 1986, **261**, 7332.
50. M. Casaretto, M. Spoden, C. Diaconescu, H.-G. Gattner, H. Zahn, D. Brandenburg and A. Wollmer, *Biol. Chem. Hoppe-Seyler*, 1987, **368**, 709.
51. P. Cuatrecasas, *Proc. Natl. Acad. Sci. U.S.A.*, 1972, **69**, 318.
52. P. Cuatrecasas, *J. Biol. Chem.*, 1972, **247**, 1980.
53. P. Cuatrecasas, *Proc. Natl. Acad. Sci. U.S.A.*, 1972, **69**, 1277.
54. L. Petruzzelli, R. Herrera and O. M. Rosen, *Proc. Natl. Acad. Sci. U.S.A.*, 1984, **81**, 3327.
55. S. Jacobs, K. Schechter, P. Bissell and P. Cuatrecasas, *Biochem. Biophys. Res. Commun.*, 1977, **77**, 981.
56. T. W. Siegel, S. Ganguly, S. Jacobs, O. M. Rosen and C. Rubin, *J. Biol. Chem.*, 1981, **256**, 9266.
57. Y. Fujita-Yamaguchi, *J. Biol. Chem.*, 1984, **259**, 1206.
58. J. Heinrich, P. F. Pilch and M. P. Czech, *J. Biol. Chem.*, 1980, **255**, 1732.
59. L. C. Harrison and A. Itin, *J. Biol. Chem.*, 1980, **255**, 12066.
60. S. Jacobs, E. Hazum, Y. Schechter and P. Cuatrecasas, *Proc. Natl. Acad. Sci. U.S.A.*, 1979, **76**, 4918.
61. C. C. Yip, C. W. T. Yeung and M. L. Moule, *J. Biol. Chem.*, 1978, **253**, 1743.
62. P. F. Pilch and M. P. Czech, *J. Biol. Chem.*, 1979, **254**, 3375.
63. J. Massague, P. F. Pilch and M. P. Czech, *Proc. Natl. Acad. Sci. U.S.A.*, 1980, **77**, 7137.
64. E. Van Obberghen, M. Kasuga, A. LeCam, J. A. Hedo, A. Itin and L. C. Harrison, *Proc. Natl. Acad. Sci. U.S.A.*, 1981, **78**, 1052.
65. J. A. Hedo, M. Kasuga, E. Van Obberghen, J. Roth and C. R. Kahn, *Proc. Natl. Acad. Sci. U.S.A.*, 1981, **78**, 4791.
66. A. Ullrich, J. R. Bell, E. Y. Chen, R. Herrera, L. M. Petruzzelli, T. J. Dull, A. Gray, L. Coussens, Y.-C. Liao, M. Tsubokawa, A. Mason, P. H. Seeburg, C. Grunfeld, O. M. Rosen, and J. Ramachandran, *Nature (London)*, 1985, **313**, 756.

67. Y. Ebina, L. Ellis, K. Jarnagin, M. Edery, L. Graf, E. Clauser, Y.-H. Ou, F. Masiarz, Y. W. Kan, I. D. Goldfine, R. A. Roth and W. J. Rutter, *Cell*, 1985, **40**, 747.
68. P. F. Pilch and M. P. Czech, *J. Biol. Chem.*, 1980, **255**, 1722.
69. S. Jacobs, E. Hazum and P. Cuatrecasas, *J. Biol. Chem.*, 1980, **255**, 6937.
70. M. F. White and C. R. Kahn, in 'The Enzymes', ed. P. Boyer and E. Krebs, Academic Press, New York, 1986, vol. 17, p. 247.
71. M. Kasuga, J. A. Hedo, K. M. Yamada and C. R. Kahn, *J. Biol. Chem.*, 1982, **257**, 10 392.
72. Y. Fujita-Yamaguchi, S. Choi, Y. Sakamoto and K. Itakura, *J. Biol. Chem.*, 1983, **258**, 5045.
73. J. A. Hedo and I. A. Simpson, *J. Biol. Chem.*, 1984, **259**, 11 083.
74. J. A. Hedo, S. W. Cushman and I. A. Simpson, *Diabetes*, 1982, **31** (Suppl. 2), 2A.
75. M. Kasuga, Y. Zick, D. L. Blithe, F. A. Karlsson, H. U. Haring and C. R. Kahn, *J. Biol. Chem.*, 1982, **257**, 9891.
76. E. Van Obberghen and A. Kowalski, *FEBS Lett.*, 1982, **143**, 179.
77. L. M. Petruzzelli, S. Ganguly, C. J. Smith, M. H. Cobb, C. S. Rubin and O. M. Rosen, *Proc. Natl. Acad. Sci. U.S.A.*, 1982, **79**, 6792.
78. R. A. Roth and M. P. Cassell, *Science (Washington, D.C.)*, 1983, **219**, 299.
79. E. Van Obberghen, B. Rossi, A. Kowalski, H. Gazzano and G. Ponzio, *Proc. Natl. Acad. Sci. U.S.A.*, 1983, **80**, 945.
80. M. A. Shia and P. F. Pilch, *Biochemistry*, 1983, **22**, 717.
81. J. A. Hedo, C. R. Kahn, M. Hayoshi, K. M. Yamada and M. Kasuga, *J. Biol. Chem.*, 1983, **258**, 10 020.
82. G. V. Ronnett, V. P. Knutson, R. A. Kohanski, T. I. Simpson and M. D. Lane, *J. Biol. Chem.*, 1984, **259**, 4566.
83. P. J. Deutsch, C. F. Wang, O. M. Rosen and C. S. Rubin, *Proc. Natl. Acad. Sci. U.S.A.*, 1983, **80**, 133.
84. J. A. Hedo and P. Gorden, *Horm. Metab. Res.*, 1985, **17**, 487.
85. J. A. Hedo, E. Collier and A. Watkinson, *J. Biol. Chem.*, 1987, **262**, 954.
86. J. F. Caro, F. Cecchin and M. K. Sinha, *J. Biol. Chem.*, 1984, **259**, 12 810.
87. O. M. Rosen, G. H. Chia, C. Fung and C. S. Rubin, *J. Cell. Physiol.*, 1979, **99**, 37.
88. L. M. Keefer and P. De Meyts, *Biochem. Biophys. Res. Commun.*, 1981, **101**, 22.
89. G. V. Ronnet and M. D. Lane, *J. Biol. Chem.*, 1981, **256**, 4706.
90. P. Cuatrecasas and G. P. E. Tell, *Proc. Natl. Acad. Sci. U.S.A.*, 1973, **70**, 485.
91. J. A. Hedo, L. C. Harrison and J. Roth, *Biochemistry*, 1981, **20**, 3385.
92. D. G. Rouiller, N. Sharon, A. McElduff, J. M. Podskalny and P. Gorden, *Endocrinology (Baltimore)*, 1986, **118**, 1159.
93. P. Cuatrecasas and G. Illiano, *J. Biol. Chem.*, 1971, **246**, 4938.
94. M. Rodbell and A. B. Jones, *J. Biol. Chem.*, 1966, **241**, 140.
95. G. Cherqui, M. Caron, J. Capeau and J. Picard, *Mol. Cell. Endocrinol.*, 1981, **23**, 297.
96. J. M. Podskalny, A. McElduff and P. Gorden, *Biochem. Biophys. Res. Commun.*, 1984, **125**, 70.
97. J. M. Podskalny, D. G. Rouiller, A. McElduff and P. Gorden, *Biochem. Biophys. Res. Commun.*, 1986, **140**, 821.
98. J. M. Podskalny, D. G. Rouiller, G. Grunberger, R. C. Baxter, A. McElduff and P. Gorden, *J. Biol. Chem.*, 1986, **261**, 14 076.
99. R. Kadle, R. E. Fellows and M. K. Raizada, *Exp. Cell Res.*, 1984, **151**, 533.
100. A. McElduff, A. Watkinson, J. A. Hedo and P. Gorden, *Biochem. J.*, 1986, **239**, 679.
101. S. C. Hubbard and R. J. Natt, *Annu. Rev. Biochem.*, 1981, **50**, 555.
102. R. F. Arakaki, J. A. Hedo, E. Collier and P. Gorden, *J. Biol. Chem.*, 1987, **262**, 11 886.
103. E. G. Krebs, in 'The Enzymes', ed. P. D. Boyer and E. G. Krebs, Academic Press, New York, 1986, vol. 17, p. 3.
104. R. Rangel-Aldao and O. M. Rosen, *J. Biol. Chem.*, 1976, **251**, 7526.
105. J. Erlichman, R. Rangel-Aldao and O. M. Rosen, *Methods Enzymol.*, 1983, **99**, 176.
106. M. Kasuga, Y. Zick, D. L. Blithe, M. Crettaz and C. R. Kahn, *Nature (London)*, 1982, **298**, 667.
107. M. Kasuga, Y. Fujita-Yamaguchi, D. L. Blithe and C. R. Kahn, *Proc. Natl. Acad. Sci. U.S.A.*, 1983, **80**, 2137.
108. H. Gazzano, A. Kowalski, M. Fehlmann and E. Van Obberghen, *Biochem. J.*, 1983, **216**, 575.
109. K. T. Yu and M. P. Czech, *J. Biol. Chem.*, 1984, **259**, 5277.
110. M. F. White, S. Takayama and C. R. Kahn, *J. Biol. Chem.*, 1985, **260**, 9470.
111. T. Hunter and J. A. Cooper, *Annu. Rev. Biochem.*, 1985, **54**, 897.
112. M. F. White, H. U. Häring, M. Kasuga and C. R. Kahn, *J. Biol. Chem.*, 1984, **259**, 255.
113. M. Kasuga, F. A. Karlsson and C. R. Kahn, *Science (Washington, D.C.)*, 1982, **215**, 185.
114. R. Ballotti, A. Kowalski, M. F. White, Y. Le Marchand-Brustel and E. Van Obberghen, *Biochem. J.*, 1987, **241**, 99.
115. H. U. Häring, M. Kasuga and C. R. Kahn, *Biochem. Biophys. Res. Commun.*, 1982, **108**, 1538.
116. C. F. Burant, M. K. Treutelaar, G. E. Landreth and M. G. Buse, *Diabetes*, 1984, **33**, 704.
117. F. Grigorescu, M. F. White and C. R. Kahn, *J. Biol. Chem.*, 1983, **258**, 13, 708.
118. F. Grigorescu, J. S. Flier and C. R. Kahn, *J. Biol. Chem.*, 1984, **259**, 15003.
119. D. T. Pang, B. Sharma, J. A. Shafer, M. F. White and C. R. Kahn, *J. Biol. Chem.*, 1985, **260**, 7131.
120. Y. Zick, G. Grunberger, J. M. Podskalny, V. Moncada, S. Taylor, P. Gorden and J. Roth, *Biochem. Biophys. Res. Commun.*, 1983, **116**, 1129.
121. R. A. Roth and J. Beaudoin, *Diabetes*, 1987, **36**, 123.
122. L. Stadtmauer and O. M. Rosen, *J. Biol. Chem.*, 1986, **261**, 3402.
123. H. Häring, D. Kirsch, B. Obermaier, B. Ermel and F. Machicao, *Biochem. J.*, 1986, **234**, 59.
124. S. Takayama, M. F. White, V. Lauris and C. R. Kahn, *Proc. Natl. Acad. Sci. U.S.A.*, 1984, **81**, 7791.
125. G. E. Bollag, R. A. Roth, J. Beaudoin, D. Mochly-Rosen and D. E. Koshland, Jr., *Proc. Natl. Acad. Sci. U.S.A.*, 1986, **83**, 5822.
126. D. O. Morgan, L. Ho, L. J. Korn and R. A. Roth, *Proc. Natl. Acad. Sci. U.S.A.*, 1986, **83**, 328.
127. L. Ellis, E. Clauser, D. O. Morgan, M. Edery, R. A. Roth and W. J. Rutter, *Cell*, 1986, **45**, 721.
128. C. D. Malchoff, J. L. Messina, V. Gordon, S. Tamura and J. Larner, *Mol. Cell. Biochem.*, 1985, **69**, 83.
129. J. R. Forsayeth, J. F. Caro, M. K. Sinha, B. A. Maddux and J. D. Goldfine, *Proc. Natl. Acad. Sci. U.S.A.*, 1987, **84**, 3448.
130. D. B. Jacobs, G. R. Hayes, J. A. Truglia and D. H. Lockwood, *Diabetologia*, 1986, **29**, 798.
131. L. A. Stadtmauer and O. M. Rosen, *J. Biol. Chem.*, 1983, **258**, 6682.
132. F. Machicao, T. Urumow and O. H. Wieland, *FEBS Lett.*, 1983, **163**, 76.

133. Y. Zick, R. W. Rees-Jones, G. Grunberger, S. I. Taylor, V. Moncada, P. Gorden and J. Roth, *Eur. J. Biochem.*, 1983, **137**, 631.
134. M. Kasuga, Y. Fujita-Yamaguchi, D. L. Blithe, M. F. White and C. R. Kahn, *J. Biol. Chem.*, 1983, **258**, 10 973.
135. S. Braun, W. E. Raymond and E. Racker, *J. Biol. Chem.*, 1984, **259**, 2051.
136. Y. Zick, J. Whittaker and J. Roth, *J. Biol. Chem.*, 1983, **258**, 3431.
137. J. E. Casnellie, M. L. Harrison, L. J. Pike, K. E. Hellström and E. G. Krebs, *Proc. Natl. Acad. Sci. U.S.A.*, 1982, **79**, 282.
138. M. F. White, R. Maron and C. R. Kahn, *Nature (London)*, 1985, **318**, 183.
139. T. Izumi, M. F. White, T. Kadowaki, F. Takaku, Y. Akanuma and M. Kasuga, *J. Biol. Chem.*, 1987, **262**, 1282.
140. E. M. Gibbs, W. J. Allard and G. E. Lienhard, *J. Biol. Chem.*, 1986, **261**, 16597.
141. M. F. White, E. W. Stegmann, T. J. Dull, A. Ullrich and C. R. Kahn, *J. Biol. Chem.*, 1987, **262**, 9769.
142. H. U. Häring, M. F. White, F. Machicao, B. Ermel, E. Schleicher and B. Obermaier, *Proc. Natl. Acad. Sci. U.S.A.*, 1987, **84**, 113.
143. R. W. Rees-Jones and S. I. Taylor, *J. Biol. Chem.*, 1985, **260**, 4461.
144. N. Perrotti, D. Accili, B. Marcus-Samuels, R. W. Rees-Jones and S. I. Taylor, *Proc. Natl. Acad. Sci. U.S.A.*, 1987, **84**, 3137.
145. O. M. Rosen, R. Herrera, Y. Olowe, L. M. Petruzzelli and M. H. Cobb, *Proc. Natl. Acad. Sci. U.S.A.*, 1983, **80**, 3237.
146. M. H. Cobb and O. M. Rosen, *Biochim. Biophys. Acta*, 1984, **738**, 1.
147. F. Machicao, T. Urumow and O. H. Wieland, *FEBS Lett.*, 1982, **149**, 96.
148. H. J. Goren, M. F. White and C. R. Kahn, *Biochemistry*, 1987, **26**, 2374.
149. M. F. White, S. E. Shoelson, H. Keutmann and C. R. Kahn, *J. Biol. Chem.*, 1988, **263**, 2969.
150. S. Kathuria, S. Hartman, C. Grunfeld, J. Ramachandran and Y. Fujita-Yamaguchi, *Proc. Natl. Acad. Sci. U.S.A.*, 1986, **83**, 8570.
151. J. Larner, G. Galasko, K. Cheng, A. A. De Paoli-Roach, L. Huang, P. Daggy and J. Kellogg, *Science (Washington, D.C.)*, 1979, **206**, 1408.
152. K. Cheng, G. Galasko, L. Huang, J. Kellogg and J. Larner, *Diabetes*, 1980, **29**, 659.
153. J. R. Seals and M. P. Czech, *J. Biol. Chem.*, 1981, **256**, 6529.
154. M. P. Czech, *Am. J. Med.*, 1981, **70**, 142. ˙
155. J. Larner, *J. Cyclic Nucleotide Res.*, 1982, **8**, 289.
156. J. Larner, *Am. J. Med.*, 1983, **74**, 38.
157. C. R. Kahn, *Annu. Rev. Med.*, 1985, **36**, 429.
158. A. R. Saltiel, J. A. Fox, P. Sherline and P. Cuatrecasas, *Science (Washington, D.C.)*, 1986, **233**, 967.
159. A. R. Saltiel and P. Cuatrecasas, *Proc. Natl. Acad. Sci. U.S.A.*, 1986, **83**, 5793.
160. A. R. Saltiel, *Endocrinology (Baltimore)*, 1987, **120**, 967.
161. A. R. Saltiel, P. Sherline and J. A. Fox, *J. Biol. Chem.*, 1987, **262**, 1116.
162. J. A. Fox, N. M. Soliz and A. R. Saltiel, *Proc. Natl. Acad. Sci. U.S.A.*, 1987, **84**, 2663.
163. R. V. Farese, M. L. Strandaert, D. E. Barnes, J. S. Davis and R. J. Pollet, *Endocrinology (Baltimore)*, 1985, **116**, 2650.
164. R. V. Farese, J. S. Davis, D. E. Barnes, M. L. Standaert, J. S. Babischkin, R. Hock, N. K. Rosic and R. J. Pollet, *Biochem. J.*, 1985, **231**, 269.
165. M. D. Houslay, M. J. O. Wakelam and N. J. Pyne, *TIBS*, 1986, **11**, 393.
166. S. Suzuki, T. Toyota, S. Tamura, K. Kikuchi, S. Tsuiki, L. Huang, C. Villar-Palasi, J. Larner and Y. Goto, *J. Biol. Chem.*, 1987, **262**, 3199.
167. G. I. Bell, R. F. Santerre and G. T. Mullenbach, *Nature (London)*, 1983, **302**, 716.
168. L. C. Lopez, M. L. Frazier, C.-J. Su, A. Kumar and G. F. Saunders, *Proc. Natl. Acad. Sci. U.S.A.*, 1983, **80**, 5485.
169. C. Patzelt and E. Schiltz, *Proc. Natl. Acad. Sci. U.S.A.*, 1984, **81**, 5007.
170. A. J. Moody, F. Norris, K. Norris, M. T. Hansen and L. Thim, *FEBS Lett.*, 1987, **212**, 302.
171. J. Philippe, D. J. Drucker and J. F. Habener, *J. Biol. Chem.*, 1987, **262**, 1823.
172. R. M. Epand, *Mol. Pharmacol.*, 1982, **22**, 105.
173. C. S. Hii and S. L. Howell, *Mol. Cell Endocrinol.*, 1987, **50**, 37.
174. J. W. White and G. F. Saunders, *Nucleic Acids Res.*, 1986, **14**, 4719.
175. P. A. Lalley, A. Y. Sakaguchi, R. L. Eddy, N. H. Honey, G. I. Bell, L.-P. Shen, W. J. Rutter, J. W. Jacobs, G. Heinrich, W. W. Chin and S. L. Naylor, *Cytogenet. Cell Genet.*, 1987, **44**, 92.
176. G. I. Bell, *Peptides (N.Y.)*, 1986, **7**, 27.
177. J. M. Conlon, H. F. Hansen and T. W. Schwartz, *Regul. Pept.*, 1985, **11**, 309.
178. S. Seino, W. Welsh, G. I. Bell, S. J. Chan and D. F. Steiner, *FEBS Lett.*, 1986, **203**, 25.
179. C.-G. Huang, J. Eng, Y.-C. E. Pan, J. D. Hulmes and R. S. Yalow, *Diabetes*, 1986, **35**, 508.
180. J. M. Conlon, M. S. Davis and L. Thim, *Gen. Comp. Endocrinol.*, 1987, **66**, 203.
181. J. M. Conlon, L. O'Toole and L. Thim, *FEBS Lett.*, 1987, **214**, 50.
182. N. M. Hoosein, A. M. Mahrenholz, P. C. Andrews and R. S. Gurd, *Biochem. Biophys. Res. Commun.*, 1987, **143**, 87.
183. D. Bataille, C. Jarrousse, C. Kervran, C. Depigny and M. Dubrasquet, *Peptides (N.Y.)*, 1986, **7**, 37.
184. C. Jarrousse, D. Bataille and B. Jeanrenaud, *Endocrinology*, 1984, **115**, 102.
185. N. M. Hoosein and R. S. Gurd, *FEBS Lett.*, 1984, **178**, 83.
186. I. Shimizu, M. Hirota, C. Ohboshi and K. Shima, *Biomed. Res.*, 1986, **7**, 431.
187. T. P. Mommsen, P. C. Andrews and E. M. Plisetskaya, *FEBS Lett.*, 1987, **219**, 227.
188. R. J. Miller, *Med. Biol.*, 1984, **61**, 159.
189. E. R. Trimble, R. Bruzzone, T. J. Binden, C. J. Meehan, D. Andreu and R. B. Merrifield, *Proc. Natl. Acad. Sci. U.S.A.*, 1987, **84**, 3146.
190. M. Carlquist, R. Kaiser, K. Tatemoto, H. Jörnvall and V. Mutt, *Eur. J. Biochem.*, 1984, **144**, 243.
191. K. Sasaki, S. Dockerill, D. A. Adamiak, I. J. Tickle and T. Blundell, *Nature (London)*, 1975, **257**, 751.
192. C. R. Beddell, G. C. Sheppey, T. L. Blundell, K. Sasaki, S. Dockerill and P. J. Goodford, *Int. J. Pept. Protein Res.*, 1987, **9**, 161.
193. R. M. Epand, *Mol. Cell Biochem.*, 1983, **57**, 41.
194. A. P. Korn and F. P. Ottensmeyer, *J. Theor. Biol.*, 1983, **105**, 403.

195. C. Boesch, A. Bundi, M. Oppliger and K. Wüthrich, *Eur. J. Biochem.*, 1978, **91**, 209.
196. S. Formisano, M. L. Johnson and H. Edelhoch, *Proc. Natl. Acad. Sci. U.S.A.*, 1977, **74**, 3340.
197. E. C. Moran, P. Y. Chou and G. D. Fasman, *Biochem. Biophys. Res. Commun.*, 1977, **77**, 1300.
198. J. R. Ernandes, R. M. Epand and S. Schreier, *Biochem. Biophys. Acta*, 1983, **733**, 75.
199. W. Braun, G. Wider, K. H. Lee and K. Wüthrich, *J. Mol. Biol.*, 1983, **169**, 921.
200. E. W. Sutherland and C. de Duve, *J. Biol. Chem.*, 1948, **175**, 663.
201. K. Doi, M. Prentki, C. Yip, W. A. Müller, B. Jeanrenaud and M. Vranic, *J. Clin. Invest.*, 1979, **63**, 525.
202. A. Munck, A. Kervran, J.-C. Marie, D. Bataille and G. Rosselin, *Peptides (N.Y.)*, 1984, **5**, 553.
203. M. Ravazzola, R. H. Unger and L. Orci, *Diabetes*, 1981, **30**, 879.
204. A. Perez-Castillo and E. Blazquez, *Diabetologia*, 1980, **19**, 123.
205. A. Perez-Castillo and E. Blazquez, *Diabetologia*, 1980, **238**, E258.
206. R. Ekman and K. Tornqvist, *Invest. Ophthalmol. Vis. Sci.*, 1985, **26**, 1405.
207. M. Tominaga, K. Yamatani, S. Marubashi, H. Kaneda, H. Manaka, T. Kamimura, T. Katagiri and H. Sasaki, *Diabetologia*, 1984, **27**, 392.
208. H. Sasaki, M. Tominaga, S. Marubashi and T. Katagiri, *Biomed. Res.*, 1985, **6**, 91.
209. A. Shimatsu, Y. Kato, N. Matsushita, H. Katakami, N. Yanaihara and H. Imura, *Endocrinology (Baltimore)*, 1982, **110**, 2113.
210. M. Rodbell, in 'Receptors, Antibodies and Disease', ed. D. Evered and J. Whelan, Ciba Foundation Symposium 90, Pitman, London, 1982, p. 3.
211. M. D. Houslay and L. M. Gordon, *Curr. Top. Membr. Transp.*, 1983, **188**, 179.
212. L. Needham, N. J. F. Dodd and M. D. Houslay, *Biochim. Biophys. Acta*, 1987, **899**, 44.
213. G. Poli, M. Cassader, E. Chiarpotto, F. Biasi, G. Cecchini and G. Pagano, *Int. J. Tissue React.*, 1986, **8**, 367.
214. G. J. Murphy, V. J. Hruby, D. Trivedi, M. J. O. Wakelam and M. D. Houslay, *Biochem. J.*, 1987, **243**, 39.
215. O. H. Petersen and C. Bear, *Nature (London)*, 1986, **323**, 18.
216. T. E. Cote and R. M. Epand, *Biochim. Biophys. Acta*, 1979, **582**, 295.
217. M. J. O. Wakelam, G. J. Murphy, V. J. Hruby and M. D. Houslay, *Nature (London)*, 1986, **323**, 68.
218. D. E. Whipps, A. E. Armston, H. J. Pryor and A. P. Halestrap, *Biochem. J.*, 1987, **214**, 835.
219. N. Kraus-Friedmann, *Proc. Natl. Acad. Sci. U.S.A.*, 1986, **83**, 8943.
220. J. G. Altin and F. L. Bygrave, *Biochem. J.*, 1986, **238**, 653.
221. L. Combettes, B. Berthon, A. Binet and M. Claret, *Biochem. J.*, 1986, **237**, 675.
222. J. M. Staddon and R. G. Hansford, *Biochem. J.*, 1986, **238**, 737.
223. J. C. Garrison and J. D. Wagner, *J. Biol. Chem.*, 1982, **257**, 13135.
224. C. Ciudad, M. Camici, Z. Ahmad, Y. Wang, A. A. De Paoli-Roach and P. J. Roach, *Eur. J. Biochem.*, 1984, **142**, 511.
225. S. Lotersztajn, R. M. Epand, A. Mallat and F. Pecker, *J. Biol. Chem.*, 1984, **259**, 8195.
226. C. Pavoine, S. Lotersztajn, A. Mallat and F. Pecker, *J. Biol. Chem.*, 1987, **262**, 5113.
227. A. Mallat, C. Pavoine, M. Dufour, S. Lotersztajn, D. Bataille and F. Pecker, *Nature (London)*, 1987, **325**, 620.
228. F. Tarding, P. Nielsen, B. Keiser-Nielsen and A. V. Nielsen, *Diabetologia*, 1969, **5**, 146.
229. R. H. Unger, *Diabetologia*, 1985, **28**, 574.
230. D. R. Bajorunas, J. G. Fortner, J. Jaspan and R. S. Sherwin, *J. Clin. Endocrinol. Metab.*, 1986, **63**, 439.
231. D. Gawler, G. Milligan, A. M. Spiegel, C. G. Unson and M. D. Houslay, *Nature (London)*, 1987, **327**, 229.
232. G. Bolli, P. de Feo, P. Compagnucci, M. G. Cartechini, G. Angeletti, F. Santeusanio, P. Brunetti and J. E. Gerich, *Diabetes*, 1983, **32**, 134.
233. D. G. Patel, *Diabetes*, 1983, **32**, 55.
234. G. E. Wheeler and R. M. Epand, *Mol. Pharmacol.*, 1975, **11**, 335.
235. E. P. Brass, M. J. Garrity and R. P. Robertson, *FEBS Lett.*, 1984, **169**, 293.
236. P. H. Stern and N. H. Bell, *Endocrinology (Baltimore)*, 1970, **87**, 111.
237. K. E. W. Melvin, A. H. Tashjian and E. F. Voelkel, in 'Calcitonin', ed. S. Taylor, Heinemann, London, 1979, p. 487.
238. R. C. Mühlbauer, J.-P. Bonjour and H. Fleisch, *Miner. Electrolyte Metab.*, 1987, **13**, 45.
239. S. P. Grossman, *Neurosci. Biobehav. Rev.*, 1986, **10**, 295.
240. J. R. London, J. Surtees and V. Robinson, *Postgrad. Med. J.*, 1981, **57**, 84.
241. S. J. Konturek, J. Biernat, N. Kwecien and J. Olesky, *Gastroenterology*, 1975, **68**, 448.
242. D. W. Back, S. B. Wilson, S. M. Morris, Jr. and A. G. Goodridge, *J. Biol. Chem.*, 1986, **261**, 12555.
243. K. Hall-Boyer, G. P. Zaloga and B. Chernow, *Critical Care Medicine*, 1984, **12**, 584.
244. R. M. Epand and R. J. Douglas, *Biochim. Biophys. Acta*, 1973, **320**, 741.
245. V. J. Hruby, J. L. Krstenansky, T. McKee and J. T. Pelton, in 'Hormonal Control of Gluconeogenesis', ed. N. Kraus-Friedman, CRC Press, Boca Raton, FL, 1986, vol. 2, p. 3.
246. R. M. Epand, *Mol. Cell Biochem.*, 1983, **57**, 41.
247. G. V. Shah, R. M. Epand and R. C. Orlowski, *Mol. Cell Endocrinol.*, 1987, **49**, 203.
248. P. Argos and J. K. MohanaRao, in 'Methods in Enzymology', ed. C. H. Wittirs and S. N. Timasheff, Academic Press, Orlando, FL, 1986, vol. 130, p. 185.
249. J. Murphy, W. Zhang, W. Macaulay, G. Fasman and R. B. Merrifield, *J. Biol. Chem.*, 1987, **262**, 17304.
250. R. L. McKee, D. Trivedi, C. Zechel, D. Johnson, K. Brendel and V. J. Hruby, in 'Peptides: Chemistry and Biology', ed. G. R. Marshall, Escom, Leiden, 1988, p. 341.
251. R. M. Epand, G. Rosselin, D. H. B. Hoa, T. E. Cote and M. Laburthe, *J. Biol. Chem.*, 1981, **256**, 1128.
252. E. K. Frandsen, F. C. Grønvald, L. G. Heding, N. L. Johansen, B. F. Lundt, A. J. Moody, J. Markussen and A. Vølund, *Hoppe-Seyler's Z. Physiol. Chem.*, 1981, **362**, 665.
253. M. Rosenblatt, G. H. Mahaffey and G. T. Potts, Jr., in 'Peptides', ed. M. Goodman and J. Meienhofer, Wiley, New York, 1977, p. 581.
254. J. Sueiras-Diaz, V. A. Lance, W. A. Murphy and D. H. Coy, *J. Med. Chem.*, 1984, **27**, 310.
255. W. A. Murphy, D. H. Coy and V. A. Lance, *Peptides (N.Y.)*, 1986, **7**, 69.
256. R. L. McKee, J. T. Pelton, D. Trivedi, D. G. Johnson, D. H. Coy, J. Sueiras-Diaz and V. J. Hruby, *Biochemistry*, 1986, **25**, 1650.
257. R. M. Epand and J. J. Liepnieks, *J. Biol. Chem.*, 1983, **258**, 203.

258. R. M. Epand, *Trends Biochem. Sci. (Pers. Ed.)*, 1983, **8**, 205.
259. V. J. Hruby, J. Krstenansky, B. Gysin, J. T. Pelton, D. Trivedi and R. L. McKee, *Biopolymers*, 1986, **25**, S135.
260. J. L. Krstenansky, D. Trivedi, D. Johnson and V. J. Hruby, *J. Am. Chem. Soc.*, 1986, **108**, 1696.
261. M. D. Bregman, D. Trivedi and V. J. Hruby, *J. Biol. Chem.*, 1980, **255**, 11 725.
262. S. Corvera, J. Huerta-Bahena, J. T. Pelton, V. J. Hruby, D. Trivedi and J. A. Garcia-Sáinz, *Biochim. Biophys. Acta*, 1984, **804**, 434.
263. J. A. Garcia-Sáinz, L.Sánchez-Sevilla, J. T. Pelton, D. Trivedi and V. J. Hruby, *Biochim. Biophys. Acta*, 1986, **886**, 310.
264. V. J. Hruby, M. D. Bregman and D. Trivedi, *Science (Washington, D.C.)*, 1982, **215**, 1115.
265. J. L. Krstenansky, D. Trivedi and V. J. Hruby, *Biochemistry*, 1986, **25**, 3833.
266. B. Gysin, D. Trivedi, D. G. Johnson and V. J. Hruby, *Biochemistry*, 1986, **25**, 8278.
267. B. Gysin, D. G. Johnson, D. Trivedi and V. J. Hruby, *J. Med. Chem.*, 1987, **30**, 1409.
268. D. Andreu and R. B. Merrifield, *Eur. J. Biochem.*, 1987, **164**, 585.
269. C. G. Unson, D. Andreu, E. M. Gurzenda and R. B. Merrifield, *Proc. Natl. Acad. Sci. U.S.A.*, 1987, **84**, 4083.
270. R. B. Merrifield, C. Unson, E. M. Gurzenda and D. Andreu, in 'Peptides 1986', ed. D. Theodoropoulos, de Gruyter, Berlin, 1987, p. 517.
271. G.-S. Lu, S. Mojsov and R. B. Merrifield, *Int. J. Pept. Protein Res.*, 1987, **29**, 545.
272. R. M. Epand, in 'Protides of the Biological Fluids', ed. H. Peeters, Pergamon Press, Oxford, 1987, p. 481.
273. M. C. Lin, S. Nicosia and M. Rodbell, *Biochemistry*, 1976, **15**, 4537.
274. D. E. Bladgon and M. Goodman, *Biopolymers*, 1975, **14**, 241.
275. S. K. Beckner, R. Horuk, F. J. Darfler and M. C. Lin, in 'Control of Animal Cell Proliferation', ed. A. L. Boynton and H. L. Leffert, Academic Press, New York, 1985, vol. 1, p. 251.
276. B. Desbuquois, in 'Polypeptide Hormone Receptors', ed. B. I. Posner, Dekker, New York, 1985, p. 345.
277. R. T. Premont and R. Iyengar, in 'Peptide Hormone Receptors', ed. M. Y. Kalimi and J. R. Hubbard, de Gruyter, Berlin, 1987, p. 129.
278. E. M. Horwitz, W. T. Jenkins, N. M. Hoosein and R. S. Gurd, *J. Biol. Chem.*, 1985, **260**, 9307.
279. W. A. Hagopian, H. S. Tager, B. Gysin, D. Trivedi and V. J. Hruby, *J. Biol. Chem.*, 1987, **262**, 15 506.
280. T. Grady, M. Fickova, H. S. Tager, D. Trivedi and V. J. Hruby, *J. Biol. Chem.*, 1987, **262**, 15 514.
281. E. M. Horwitz, R. J. Wyborski and R. S. Gurd, *J. Biol. Chem.*, 1986, **261**, 13 670.
282. R. J. Wyborski, E. M. Horwitz, W. T. Jenkins, J. S. Mormol and R. S. Gurd, *Arch. Biochem. Biophys.*, 1988, **262**, 532.
283. E. Padrell, J. T. Herberg, B. Monsatirsky, G. Floyd, R. T. Premont and R. Iyenger, *Endocrinology (Baltimore)*, 1987, **120**, 2316.
284. K. E. Lipson, A. A. Kolhatker, A. Dorato and D. B. Donner, *Biochemistry*, 1986, **25**, 5678.

13.6

Gastrointestinal Regulatory Peptide Receptors

JEAN MARTINEZ

CNRS-INSERM, Montpellier, France

13.6.1 INTRODUCTION

Since the discovery of a blood-borne factor, named secretin, by Bayliss and Starling in 1902, introducing the new concept of 'chemical messengers', several other polypeptide hormones have been isolated from the gastrointestinal tract. Most, if not all, of these polypeptides have been further identified in the central nervous system, leading to their designation as brain–gut peptides. Many of these peptides have strong structural similarities which divide them into three main families: (i) the glucagon–secretin family, which includes vasoactive intestinal peptide (VIP), gastric inhibitory peptide (GIP) and the peptide having N-terminal histidine and C-terminal isoleucine (PHI); (ii) the gastrin–cholecystokinin family; and (iii) the bombesin–gastrin-releasing peptide family. Studies on the gastrointestinal hormone receptors have been extensively reviewed.[1] In the following discussion, the author will try to emphasize the structural requirements of brain–gut peptides related to receptor occupancy and biological activities.

13.6.2 BOMBESIN

13.6.2.1 Introduction

Bombesin (BB) is a natural tetradecapeptide, which was first isolated from the skin of the European frogs *Bombina bombina* and *Bombina variegata variegata* by Anastasi *et al.*[2a] Several other bombesin-like peptides have been isolated from the skin of amphibians, including alytesin[2a] from *Alytes obstetricans*, ranatensin[3] from *Rana pipiens* and litorin[2b] from *Litoria (Hyla) aurea*. All of these peptides have in common the C-terminal octapeptide, with the only difference being that in the bombesin–alytesin family, the penultimate amino acid is leucine, and in the litorin–ranatensin family it is phenylalanine (Figure 1). Other peptides belonging to the litorin family have been isolated

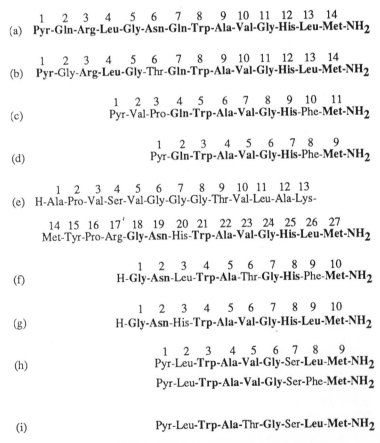

Figure 1 Amino acid sequences for: (a) bombesin; (b) alytesin; (c) ranatensin; (d) litorin; (e) porcine gastrin-releasing peptide (GRP); (f) neuromedin B; (g) neuromedin C; (h) peptides isolated from *Phyllomedusa sauvagei*; and (i) rohdei litorin. Identical amino acid residues with bombesin are indicated in bold letters

recently, including two phyllolitorins from the skin of the South American frog *Phyllomedusa sauvagei* characterized by the occurrence of a leucine residue in position 2 and by a serine residue in position 7, in place of histidine;[4] and rohdei litorin from *Phyllomedusa rohdei* (Figure 1).

The mammalian counterpart of bombesin (gastrin releasing peptide; GRP) has been isolated from porcine gut and identified as a 27 amino acid peptide.[5] It shares the C-terminal sequence with bombesin. Two other molecular forms were identified in mammalian peripheral and central nervous systems, the C-terminal decapeptide of GRP (neuromedin C) and a structurally related decapeptide, named neuromedin B (Figure 1).[6]

Bombesin/GRP-like immunoreactivity has been found in the mammalian brain, pituitary, adrenal gland, spinal cord, lung and gastrointestinal tract,[7] and also in avian and amphibian brain. Most, if not all, of the mammalian bombesin appears to be associated with neurons.

13.6.2.2 Biological Activities

Bombesin and GRP-like peptides exhibit a wide range of similar biological activities,[8] with different potencies.

Bombesin has been shown to stimulate intestinal, uterine and urinary tract smooth muscle contractions and the release of gut hormones (*e.g.* gastrin, cholecystokinin, growth hormone, gastric inhibitory polypeptide, pancreatic polypeptide, motilin, pancreatic glucagon, enteroglucagon and insulin). Bombesin also stimulates, directly or indirectly, *via* the release of gastrin or cholecystokinin, gastric[9] and pancreatic[10] secretions.

More recently, bombesin has been found to stimulate mitogenesis, growth of various cells such as 3T3 mouse fibroblasts,[11] and normal bronchial epithelial cells.[12] Bombesin-like peptides, which are present in high concentrations in small cell lung cancer (SCLC), also function as autocrine growth factors for these cells.[13]

Central administration of bombesin has been shown to cause pronounced analgesia,[14] hypothermia,[15] hyperglycemia,[16] excessive grooming,[17] increases in sympathetic activity[16b] and changes in gastrointestinal functions, including inhibition of gastric secretion (both volume and acidity), and of pancreatic secretion.[18] In addition, bombesin increases growth hormone and prolactin secretion from the anterior pituitary after injection into the rat.[19]

Both central and peripheral administration of bombesin induces satiety in rats.[20]

13.6.2.3 Bombesin Receptors

Receptors for bombesin and bombesin-like peptides are widely distributed throughout the peripheral and central nervous system. $[^{125}I]$-(Tyr-4)-bombesin has been used as a ligand to identify high affinity bombesin-binding sites. Specific bombesin-binding sites were found in pancreatic acinar cells,[21] in the gastrointestinal tract from various species,[22] and particularly on endocrine cells in the antral mucosa. High affinity bombesin-binding sites were also identified in membrane preparations from two cell lines in which bombesin potently stimulates hormone secretion: GH4C1 rat pituitary cells, which secrete prolactin, and HIT hamster pancreatic cells, which secrete insulin,[23] as well as on smooth muscles and neurons. Bombesin and related peptides also interact with high affinity receptors in Swiss mouse 3T3 cells,[24] and spare receptors of bombesin have been identified in small cell lung cancer cells.

Most, if not all, of the actions of bombesin and related peptides were found to be associated with an increase in cytosolic Ca^{2+} from intracellular stores,[25] most likely mediated by phosphatidylinositol turnover and the generation of inositol triphosphate. Specific bombesin-binding sites have also been identified in rat pituitary cell lines[26] and in rat brain, where binding sites were high in the amygdala, hippocampus and hypothalamus, intermediate in the striatum as well as the thalamus, and low in the cerebellum.[27] As in the peripheral system, binding sites detected in the nervous system were associated with phosphatidylinositol turnover.

13.6.2.4 Structure–Activity Relationships

In the majority, if not all, of the bioassays, bombesin is the most potent peptide of the family. GRP was found to be less potent than bombesin in inducing hypothermia and eliciting grooming, as well as in reducing body temperature, following intracerebroventricular injections in the rat. Furthermore, the effects of bombesin appeared to be more persistent than those of related peptides, suggesting possible differences in the catabolism, affinity, intrinsic activity and/or access to the sites of action. Surprisingly, when neuromedin C (GRP-10), with a histidine substitution in position 7 (when referred to bombesin), was compared with bombesin on CNS-mediated changes in thermoregulation and glucose metabolism,[28] or as a mediator of gastrin release *in vivo*,[29] it showed only little biological activity. However, recent results on canine antral muscle indicate full potency of neuromedin C.[30] On the other hand, neuromedin B, in which leucine replaces glutamine-7 and phenylalanine replaces leucine-13 (when referred to bombesin), was found to be less potent than bombesin in various bioassays. Litorin, having the same C-terminal octapeptide as bombesin, except for having phenylalanine replacing leucine-13, showed almost equal potency as bombesin in the endocrine and exocrine pancreas.[10a,31]

The intrinsic biological central and peripheral activities of bombesin and structurally related peptides are a property of the C-terminal portion of the molecule. In most, if not all, central and peripheral bioassays, it was demonstrated that the C-terminal octapeptide of bombesin was sufficient for biological activity.[32] Some bombesin-like effects began to appear in the C-terminal heptapeptide in some peripheral tests,[33] *i.e.* on smooth muscle, gastric acid secretion in dogs, blood pressure in various species, and myoelectric activity of the dog duodenum, whereas the C-terminal hexapeptide was inactive, indicating the significance of the tryptophan residue for the appearance of bombesin-like activities. Protection of the N-terminal tryptophan residue in the heptapeptide, with a Boc group, led to a derivative as potent as the C-terminal octapeptide.[34] In fact, the C-terminal nonapeptide of bombesin has the same potency and efficacy as does the native tetradecapeptide,[10a,35] indicating that the asparagine residue in position 6 is critical for full potency of bombesin. Removing the C-terminal amide group (*e.g.* BB-1–14-OH) resulted in an almost completely inactive analog, although it retained some ability in stimulating insulin secretion.[36] According to Girard *et al.*,[37] at high concentrations, the C-terminal tetrapeptide of bombesin, BB-11–14, was found to exhibit bombesin-like effects in the rat stomach strip, but with decreased efficacy. On the other hand, bombesin N-terminal fragments, such as BB-1–12-OH, exhibited bombesin-like activity on rat stomach strip with full efficacy and low potency, while BB-1–11-OH, BB-1–10 and BB-1–9 displayed only reduced intrinsic activity, with even lower potency.[37] These results suggest an important role for the C-terminal tripeptide, His-Leu-Met, in optimal stimulation for bombesin receptors, since reduced efficacy ($\sim 50\%$) and potency occurred when these amino acids were deleted.

As in the case of many other peptides, Met-14 can be replaced by Leu without significantly affecting biological activity. Most bombesin analogs, in which one amino acid has been replaced by its corresponding D isomer, were found to be much less active and even inactive. Interestingly, (D-Gln-7)-bombesin was as potent and efficacious as bombesin on thermoregulation, whereas (D-His-12)-bombesin was found to be completely inactive,[38] confirming previous statements on the important role of His-12 for full biological activity.[33,39] His-12 and Trp-8 were also found to play a relatively critical role in the hypothermic and hyperglycemic effects of synthetic bombesin derivatives,[40] their replacement by alanine-producing analogs of markedly reduced potency. In the peripheral system, the crucial role of an intact histidine residue for bombesin-like activity was clearly demonstrated.[33] The described behavior of bombesin in the presence of lipid membranes can explain why Trp-8 and His-12 are essential for biological activity. It is reported that in contact with flat phospholipid bilayer membranes, bombesin adopts a membrane structure in which the C-terminal message segment is inserted into a relatively hydrophobic membrane compartment as an α-helical domain, while the N-terminal peptide segment remains in the aqueous compartment as a random coil. The residues Trp-8 and His-9 show a unique arrangement in the lipid-induced α helix, the two side chains being oriented in order to obtain a hydrogen bond between the indole NH group and the basic imidazole nitrogen thus stabilizing the typical bombesin membrane structure.[41]

Pharmacological studies conducted with the naturally occurring Ser-containing bombesin-like peptides, isolated from *Phyllomedusa* skin, in which serine replaces histidine in position 12, revealed that these peptides were more potent agonists than litorin or bombesin in inducing intense scratching in rats and in stimulating the rat urinary bladder. Conversely, these peptides were much less active than bombesin and litorin on the bombesin receptor involved in the central regulation of feeding, body temperature and gastric secretion. It was concluded from these last structure–activity relationships that two types of bombesin receptors may exist. The first type of bombesin receptor has been named BB_1 receptor, and appears to be sensitive to C-terminal modifications of the bombesin sequence. The second type of receptor, named BB_2 receptor, responsible for the stimulation of the urinary bladder, for grooming and scratching, appears to be less sensitive to C-terminal modifications and more specific for the N-terminal sequence of bombesin.[42]

A summary of the structural requirements of bombesin for biological activity is shown in Figure 2.

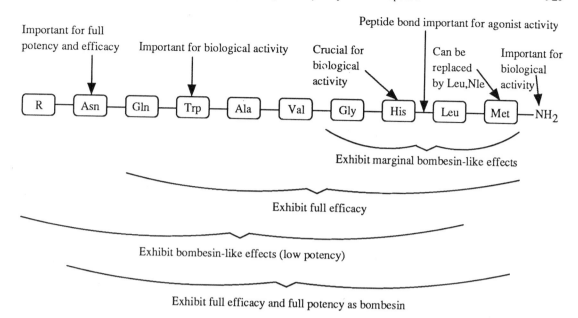

Figure 2 Structural requirements for biological activity of bombesin

13.6.2.5 Bombesin Antagonists

Attempts to develop analogs of bombesin-related peptides that function as specific bombesin antagonists are in progress. The first proposed bombesin antagonists were substance P (SP) analogs, including spantide (D-Arg-1, D-Trp-7, D-Trp-9, Leu-11)-SP; (D-Arg-1, D-Pro-2, D-Trp-7, D-Trp-9, Leu-11)-SP;[43] and (D-Arg-1, D-Phe-5, D-Trp-7, D-Trp-9, Leu-11)-SP;[44] but they lacked specificity for bombesin receptors. Recently, Heinz-Erian *et al.*[45] proposed a new class of specific bombesin-receptor antagonists, (D-Phe-12)-bombesin analogs, including (D-Phe-12)-bombesin, (D-Phe-12, Leu-14)-bombesin and (Tyr-4, D-Phe-12)-bombesin. These analogs showed pronounced selectivity for the bombesin receptor on rat pancreatic acini, although with approximately 2000-fold lower affinity than bombesin itself, and were able to antagonize the action of bombesin. At the International Symposium on Bombesin-like Peptides in Health and Disease, in Italy, using the strategy which led to gastrin antagonists,[177] Coy introduced the much-awaited specific competitive bombesin antagonist, *e.g.* Pyr-Gln-Arg-Leu-Gly-Asn-Gln-Trp-Ala-Val-Gly-His-Leu-ψ(CH₂NH)-Leu-NH₂, [Leu-13-ψ(CH₂NH)-Leu-14]-bombesin. This pseudopeptide exhibited little agonist activity in terms of stimulating amylase secretion from isolated pancreatic acini from various species, and was able to inhibit binding of labeled (Tyr-4)-bombesin on isolated pancreatic acini, as well as the secretory action of bombesin. On the other hand, this pseudopeptide showed selectivity for the bombesin receptor, and was potent in antagonizing Swiss mouse 3T3 cell growth (in culture) in response to bombesin.[46]

13.6.3 CHOLECYSTOKININ (CCK)

13.6.3.1 Introduction

A gastrointestinal agent which stimulates the contraction of the gall bladder was discovered by Ivy and Oldberg in 1928,[47] and was named 'cholecystokinin' (CCK). Fifteen years later, a factor causing the release of digestive enzymes from the pancreas was detected by Harper and Raper in the intestinal mucosa of the hog.[48] They named this substance 'pancreozymin'. After isolation and purification from hog upper small intestine, it was demonstrated that a single compound, which proved to be a peptide of 33 amino acid residues (Figure 3), was responsible for both kinds of activities,[49] its C-terminal pentapeptide being identical to that of gastrin. As the first described action of this peptide was gall bladder contraction, it was named cholecystokinin (CCK, CCK-33). Although the sequence of CCK is identical within species, in guinea pig CCK showed an amino acid variance, a valine replacing methionine in position 28.[50]

CCK appeared to be produced from a single 115 (rat, human or mouse) or 114 (porcine) amino acid residue precursor, prepro-CCK, in which there is only one single copy of the largest known biologically active form of CCK (CCK-58).[51] Removal of the N-terminal hydrophobic signal or

$$\begin{array}{c} 1 \qquad\qquad\qquad 10 \\ \text{(a) Lys-Ala-Pro-Ser-Gly-Arg-Val-Ser-Met-Ile-Lys-Asn-Leu-Gln-Ser-Leu-Asp-Pro-Ser-} \end{array}$$

$$\begin{array}{c} 20 \qquad\qquad\qquad 26\ 27 \qquad 28\ 29\ 30\ 31\ 32\ 33 \\ \text{His-Arg-Ile-Ser-Asp-Arg-} \textbf{Asp-Tyr(SO}_3\textbf{H)-Met-Gly-Trp-Met-Asp-Phe-NH}_2 \end{array}$$

(b)   Pyr-Gln-**Asp-Tyr(SO$_3$H)-**Thr-**Gly-Trp-Met-Asp-Phe-NH$_2$**

(c)   **Asp-Tyr(SO$_3$H)-Met-Gly-Trp-Met-Asp-Phe-NH$_2$**

(d)   **Trp-Met-Asp-Phe-NH$_2$**

Figure 3   Primary structures of: (a) porcine cholecystokinin-33 (CCK-33); (b) caerulein; (c) CCK-8; and (d) CCK-4 (identical to G-4; tetragastrin). Homologous sequences are indicated in bold letters.

leader sequence, which is a characteristic of the precursor form of all secretory peptides, and which probably occurs early in biosyntheses, would generate a pro-CCK of 95 amino acid residues. The main forms of CCK, *i.e.* CCK-8, CCK-33, CCK-39 and CCK-58, correspond to peptides produced by cleavage at a single arginine residue. In addition, CCK-22 had been isolated from rat and guinea pig gut, and would be produced by cleavage at a single lysine residue. Several other molecular forms of CCK, which have in common the C-terminal sequence, have been identified, including the shorter C-terminal fragments, CCK-5, CCK-4 (identical to tetragastrin, G-4), and probably CCK-21 and CCK-12. Later on, a shorter peptide, caerulein, with very similar biological activities and having a sequence sharing seven of the eight C-terminal amino acid residues with the C-terminal octapeptide of cholecystokinin (Figure 3), was isolated from the skin of the Australian Hylid frog *Hyla caerulea* by Anastasi and coworkers.[52]

The major naturally occurring molecular forms of CCK are CCK-8 and, to a lesser extent, CCK-33 and CCK-4. CCK (CCK-33, CCK-8 and CCK-4 in particular) is present throughout the digestive tract, in the small intestine, with high concentrations in the duodenum and particularly in the jejunum. Intestinal cholecystokinin is released into the blood under the influence of alimentary stimuli. CCK is also widely distributed throughout both the central and peripheral nervous system. High concentrations of the cholecystokinin C-terminal octapeptide (CCK-26–33; CCK-8) have been found in the brain,[53] in significant amounts in all regions, except in the pineal body, the pituitary and the cerebellum, with the highest concentrations in the cerebral cortex. In fact, CCK is the most abundant peptide in the brain and there is a controversy concerning the major natural forms of CCK, although CCK-8 and CCK-33 seem to be predominant.[54] In the peripheral nervous system, CCK was found in the colon and ileum nerves, as well as in the nerves of the muscle wall of the urinary bladder and the distal part of the uterus. According to some investigators, CCK-4 (G-4) is the major molecular form in nerve terminals of the endocrine pancreas.

13.6.3.2 Biological Activities

Cholecystokinin displays biological activities both in the peripheral and in the central nervous system.[55]

In the peripheral system, the two major physiological actions of cholecystokinin are stimulation of gall bladder contraction and of pancreatic enzyme secretion.[56] In addition to its ability to cause stimulation of pancreatic enzyme secretion, CCK also causes desensitization, as well as residual stimulation, of enzyme secretion.[57] Beside the two major effects mentioned above, cholecystokinin stimulates glucose and amino acid transport, protein and DNA syntheses, energy metabolism and growth in the exocrine pancreas, and also affects secretion, absorption and motility in the stomach and intestine. It also stimulates pancreatic hormone secretion such as insulin, glucagon, somatostatin and pancreatic polypeptide, both *in vivo* and *in vitro*.[58] At least in two mammalian species, the rat and cat, CCK and related peptides are full agonists of gastric acid secretion, producing a maximal response similar to that of gastrin but with less potency. In contrast, in dogs and humans, CCK is a weak stimulant of acid secretion, and this has been explained by a stimulated secretion of somatostatin which acts as an inhibitor of acid secretion by the parietal cell.

In the central nervous system, CCK induces hypothermia, analgesia, hyperglycemia, stimulation of pituitary hormone release and decrease in exploratory behavior. CCK has also been found to induce satiety, either following central administration or even after peripheral administration, probably *via* activation of vagal afferent nerve endings. However, the mechanism by which CCK exerts its satiety effect is uncertain and appears to differ within species. Cholecystokinin was demonstrated to behave as a neuromodulator or neurotransmitter: (i) it is synthesized and stored by specific neurons in the brain; (ii) it is released under physiological conditions from nerve endings and can be inactivated after release; (iii) there are specific CCK receptors located in regions where the peptide is present; (iv) it can alter the firing rates of neurons when applied iontophoretically; and (v) it modifies the release and turnover of other neurotransmitters. Particularly, it has been demonstrated that CCK and dopamine (DA) coexist within mesolimbic and mesocortical dopaminergic neurons. Experiments concerning functional interaction between CCK and dopamine indicate that CCK reduces or increases dopamine release depending on the brain region. In addition, CCK appears to increase dopamine-receptor affinity and reduce receptor density in the striatum. Behavioral studies showed that CCK can increase, decrease or have no effect upon DA-mediated behavior such as stereotypy and locomotor activity. In other studies, CCK has been reported to increase, decrease or have little effect on the $[^3H]DA$ release from striatal slices *in vitro*. However, despite the increasing number of studies, the consequence of CCK–DA interaction within the brain has still not been elucidated, and there seems to be a great deal of inconsistency within the literature regarding the interaction of CCK and DA.

13.6.3.3 CCK Receptors

Specific CCK-binding sites have been identified in the pancreas (dispersed acini, acinar cells, purified plasma membrane preparations), pyloric sphincter, gall bladder, vagus nerve and in multiple brain areas of different mammalian species. Highly specific biologically active ligands, *e.g.* $[^{125}I]BH$-CCK-33, $[^{125}I]BH$-CCK-8 (BH = Bolton–Hunter reagent), as well as tritiated CCK derivatives have been used to characterize CCK receptors in these different tissues.

In the exocrine pancreas, CCK receptors are probably restricted to acinar cells, which have been extensively studied. In rat pancreatic membranes, surprisingly, a single class of cholecystokinin-binding sites has been identified by Scatchard analysis of the competitive inhibition curve produced by unlabeled ligand. In isolated rat, mouse or guinea pig pancreatic acini, two types of binding sites have been described,[59] namely a high affinity binding site and a low affinity binding site described in the earlier studies, the affinities and capacities of which have not been defined unambiguously. Two classes of CCK-binding sites have also been defined in normal and cancerous pancreatic membranes from humans. Most of the binding characteristics of CCK to pancreatic acini (cells or membranes) from different animal species, however, have been reported to be similar by various groups of workers. An excellent correlation has been found between the binding and biological potency on amylase secretion of CCK.

A feature of CCK in stimulating amylase from pancreatic acini is that the response is biphasic. As the peptide concentration increases, amylase secretion increases, becomes maximal, and then decreases with supramaximal peptide concentrations. A plausible explanation for this effect is that both the high and low CCK-binding sites regulate amylase release, the high affinity site stimulates the release, while the role of the low affinity site is to inactivate the effects of the high affinity receptor. It has also been postulated that the low affinity binding site could regulate glucose uptake and amino acid transport function, as well as mediate the inhibition of the synthesis of pancreatic protein.[59c] The 'peripheral' CCK-receptor type, termed 'CCK-A',[60] exhibits a higher degree of specificity for the sulfated forms of CCK than for desulfated CCK (dCCK) or shorter C-terminal fragments (*e.g.* CCK-6, CCK-5 and CCK-4).[61] A number of recent studies suggested that pancreatic acini might also possess a gastrin-type receptor, for which CCK and gastrin have a high affinity, that is distinct from the CCK-A-type receptor. This 'gastrin-type' receptor was found in dogs,[62] and recently it was characterized in guinea pig pancreatic acini.[63] It does not stimulate enzyme secretion, and, although its functions are not well established, it might be involved in the mediation of Na^+–H^+ exchange.[64] In the CNS, a 'gastrin-type' receptor, referred to as 'CCK-B' 'central-type', demonstrating a relatively high affinity for CCK-8, desulfated CCK-8 (dCCK), gastrin and CCK-4, has been evidenced.

Specific myogenic and neural CCK receptors have also been demonstrated on cat gall bladder and sphincter of Oddi,[65] where three distinct sets of CCK receptors were found on postganglionic cholinergic neurons (CCK-A), smooth muscle cells (resembling CCK-B) and postganglionic non-cholinergic, nonadrenergic inhibitory neurons (CCK-C-type, which are not discriminative and not critically dependent on the sulfate group, but which are stimulated by fragments as short as CCK-3 or CCK-2).[66] In the guinea pig gall bladder, two types of CCK receptors have been described, dbc-GMP sensitive muscular receptors (CCK-A) and dbc-GMP insensitive neural receptors which are believed to be of the 'gastrin-type' (CCK-B). In the cat lower esophageal sphincter, two types of CCK receptors resembling CCK-A and CCK-B receptors[67] were also described. Specific CCK receptors have been demonstrated on membranes[68] and on cell membranes prepared from the muscularis layer of bovine gall bladder,[69] where only one sulfate sensitive binding site was described which seems to be different from the pancreatic CCK receptor. On the other hand, the presence of two classes of CCK-binding sites were found on rabbit gall bladder membranes prepared from either the total or only the muscular layer.[70]

In the pig endocrine pancreas, the CCK receptor that mediates secretion may still be of another type (CCK-D), as this receptor appears to be more sensitive to activation by CCK-4 than by larger molecular forms.[67] In fact, CCK-4, which is the predominant form of CCK in nerve terminals in the pancreatic islets, was more potent as a releaser of insulin and other islet hormones than CCK-8 or gastrin.[67a]

CCK has also been shown to stimulate pepsinogen release from isolated gastric glands.[71] The responses to the peptides appeared to be a direct action on the chief cells, and the CCK receptors involved in this biological process seem to be of type A, but characterization of these receptors and of their interactions should lead to a firmer understanding of the cellular control of pepsinogen secretion.

CCK receptors are also present in the central nervous system.[72] Although peripheral (CCK-A) and central (CCK-B) CCK receptors share many similar binding characteristics (*e.g.* affinity, acidic optimum pH and a Mg^{2+} dependence), they differ markedly in selectivity. Homogenate-binding studies have demonstrated that brain CCK receptors do not differentiate between CCK and gastrin, and between sulfated and desulfated CCK-8 forms to the degree shown by peripheral pancreatic and gastric receptors. These binding sites are widespread, diffusely distributed in the brain and relatively 'nonspecific'. It was rapidly demonstrated that CCK receptors displaying relatively low affinity for desulfated CCK, resembling peripheral receptors (CCK-A-type), were present in discrete areas of the brain, namely in the area postrema, the nucleus tractus solitaris and the interpeduncular nucleus.[60] These results were recently confirmed by the use of nonpeptidic selective CCK-receptor antagonists.[73]

13.6.3.4 Intracellular Events

Intracellular events involved in the action of cholecystokinin[74] on pancreatic acini include mobilization of intracellular calcium, increased cGMP production and enhanced membrane permeability for Na^+, Cl^- and K^+. In pancreatic acini, cholecystokinin stimulates the enzymatic breakdown of phosphatidylinositol 4,5-diphosphate (PIP_2), a key step in the action of calcium-mobilizing agonists, yielding inositol 1,4,5-triphosphate (1,4,5-IP_3) and diacylglycerol (DG). Both of these compounds are known to possess important second messenger functions: 1,4,5-IP_3 is responsible for the release of calcium from intracellular stores, and diacylglycerol can activate the Ca^{2+}/phospholipid dependent protein kinase C. Recently, it has been suggested that protein kinase C exerts a negative feedback regulation of pancreatic enzyme secretion.[75] It was demonstrated that CCK activates adenylate cyclase in broken-cell preparations from pancreatic acini, and also causes a small but significant increase in cellular cAMP when pancreatic acinar cells were incubated in the presence of an inhibitor of cyclic nucleotide phosphodiesterase. CCK is unique in that it possesses the ability to increase cAMP and cGMP in the same cell system. Although it is suggested that the low affinity CCK receptor in pancreatic acinar cells mediates the CCK induced increase in cellular cAMP, there are, however, still unanswered questions regarding its role in acinar cell function.[76] CCK also causes smooth muscle contraction by Ca^{2+} mobilization, although, in some cases, this effect might be mediated by acetylcholine or substance P released from neurons.

13.6.3.5 Structure–Activity Relationships

13.6.3.5.1 Partial sequences of cholecystokinin

There are two characteristic features of the action of CCK on its target tissues, gall bladder and pancreas: the dose–response curve is broad, and has a biphasic contour. Low doses of the agonist increase the biological response, and high doses progressively reduce the stimulated levels almost to basal in some species. Extensive structure–activity relationships have been performed on CCK and related peptides, particularly on pancreatic acini. It rapidly appeared that the C-terminal octapeptide (CCK-8) and its N-terminal extension (CCK-10), which possess the whole range of biological activities, were slightly more potent than CCK-33 or CCK-16. However, it has recently been reported that CCK-8 is not more potent than its longer analogs, CCK-33 or CCK-39.[77]

It was recognized early on that the minimal structure required for full biological activity resides in the desulfated C-terminal heptapeptide, which is, however, less potent than CCK-8. C-terminal fragments having four to six amino acid residues were shown to possess only part of the total activity.[61] They were able to cause the same maximal increase in amylase secretion as CCK, with lower potency, but the inhibition in the response at supramaximal concentrations was not so pronounced: in guinea pig pancreatic acini, the decrease in enzyme secretion was about 30% for the C-terminal hexapeptide and about 10% for the C-terminal tetrapeptide.

In terms of the peptide concentration that causes maximal stimulation of enzyme secretion, the relative potencies of the CCK fragments are CCK-10 ≈ CCK-8 > CCK-7 > CCK-6 > CCK-5 = CCK-4,[61] CCK-10 and CCK-8 being as potent as CCK-33 or CCK-39. Each of these peptides caused desensitization of amylase release measured during a subsequent incubation, and the relative potencies by which the peptides induced desensitization were the same as those which stimulated amylase release.[78] The structural requirements for cholecystokinin-induced residual stimulation differ markedly, since both the C-terminal pentapeptide and tetrapeptide do not cause residual stimulation of amylase release. These studies indicate that fragments of seven or more amino acids of the C-terminal sequence of CCK may act as full agonists at both high and low affinity binding sites, while shorter fragments act as full agonists of the binding site related to enzyme secretion and as partial agonists of the binding site controlling inhibition of secretion.

The significance of the sulfate ester on tyrosine has been clearly established: for all molecular forms of CCK, sulfation of tyrosine in position 7 increases potency for gall bladder contraction and pancreatic enzyme secretion 200-fold or more. Desulfated CCK-7 (dCCK-7) gives the same maximal response as sulfated CCK-8 but with lower potency. The importance of the location of the sulfate ester has been pointed out. High activity is associated with the presence of a tyrosine sulfate residue separated from the tryptophan residue by two other amino acid residues, *e.g.* -Tyr(SO$_3$H)-Xxx-Xxx-Trp-Met-Asp-Phe-NH$_2$. When the sulfate group is nearer the tetrapeptide moiety (*e.g.* in gastrin-II-like peptides), activity is considerably less and there is little difference between the activities of sulfated and desulfated forms. This marked effect of sulfation is a characteristic feature of CCK-like peptides, and suggests the significant role that the tyrosine sulfate residue must play in the binding of CCK peptides to the receptors concerned in their characteristic actions.

There is a close correlation between the relative potencies of the CCK fragments for stimulating amylase release and their relative potencies for inhibiting binding of labeled CCK to its receptors, as well as for stimulating calcium outflux, and increasing cGMP concentration. It rapidly appeared that the N-terminal amino acid, Asp-26, could be replaced by an amino-protecting group (benzyloxycarbonyl (Z), *t*-butyloxycarbonyl (Boc), acetyl (Ac), *etc.* without significant loss of activity. In fact, Boc-CCK-7, Z-CCK-7 and Ac-CCK-7 derivatives were almost as potent as CCK-8, Boc- and acetyl-protecting groups leading to the most potent compounds.[79] The N-terminal amino group (either free or acylated) plays a minor role: it may be omitted or its configuration can be changed without considerable loss of activity.[80]

Although no extensive studies were performed by ligand-binding techniques on gall bladder CCK receptors, their chemical specificity appears to be closely similar to that of the exocrine pancreatic receptor. Thus the C-terminal octapeptide (CCK-8) was found to be fully active, and the sulfate ester on tyrosine remained crucial for the potency of the peptide, whereas the C-terminal tetrapeptide retained the whole activity but was only 1% as potent as CCK-8. On isolated smooth muscle cells from gastric antrum of the rabbit, CCK and gastrin gave the same specific contractile response (39% decrease in cell length, ED$_{50}$ ≈ 10^{-11} M), whereas CCK-4 showed lower potency (1000-fold).[94] On the endocrine pancreas, CCK-4 was reported to be more potent than larger CCK forms in the pig, while in the rat and in the dog the effects of CCK-8 significantly surpassed those of CCK-8.[81] The effects of CCK-4 and CCK-8 as pancreatic D cell secretagogs were similar only in the perfused dog pancreas.[82] Studies performed on the endocrine rat pancreas showed that the C-terminal amino acid residues appeared to be important for the activity of CCK peptides, as well as the amide group of the C-terminal phenylalanine residue: deamidated CCK-8 was found to be quite potent on amylase secretion[81,87] and less on insulin release.[87] In fact, the structural requirements for CCK-induced stimulation of pancreatic juice and amylase secretion were found to be identical to those required for CCK-induced insulin secretion, except for minor variations, but species differences do exist.

Recently, it was described that C-terminal tripeptide of CCK acts as a weak antagonist of the actions of CCK on pancreas, while the C-terminal dipeptide may have some minimal effect and the C-terminal phenylalanine amide has no effect at all.[83] Again, adding an amino-protecting group, *e.g.* Boc, increased the potency by which the C-terminal tri- and di-peptides act as CCK antagonists.

Interestingly, removal of the C-terminal phenylalanine residue, *e.g.* Z-Tyr(SO$_3$H)-Met-Gly-Trp-Met-Asp-NH$_2$ (Z-CCK-27–32-NH$_2$), leads to a potent specific CCK-receptor antagonist on guinea pig pancreatic acini,[84] while it behaves as a partial agonist in the rat and mouse.[85] However, removal of the phenylalanine residue induced a loss of 1000-fold in the apparent affinity for the peripheral CCK receptor. These results clearly demonstrated that the C-terminal phenylalanine residue is essential for the whole intrinsic CCK-like activity, but is not essential for binding of the peptide to CCK receptors. Conversely, a pentapeptide analog of the C-terminal heptapeptide of CCK, Suc-CCK-27–31-NH$_2$, lacking both Asp-32 and Phe-33, was found to be as efficacious as CCK-8 in rat pancreatic acini,[86] a supramaximal concentration causing a submaximal stimulation of amylase secretion. On the other hand, it has been shown that Z-CCK-27–32-NH$_2$ has no relaxing action in hog duodenal circular muscle but shows a potent CCK-induced relaxation antagonist activity.[87] Z-CCK-27–32-NH$_2$ was also able to antagonize gastrin-induced acid secretion in the rat,[88] indicating that this compound is also able to interact with the gastrin receptor.

Recently, the role of the amide group of CCK has been pointed out. Various analogs of CCK-7 and CCK-8, in which the C-terminal primary amide was deleted, have been synthesized.[89] On rat pancreatic acini, these compounds, acting at the CCK receptors, were able to cause full stimulation of amylase secretion without a decrease in the response at supramaximal concentrations.[90] It was clearly demonstrated, however, that these analogs were unable to induce significant inositol phosphate (IP) accumulation, while they were able to dose dependently antagonize the CCK-7-induced IP accumulation.[91] From these results, it was hypothesized that these analogs are full agonists at the high affinity binding site and may act as antagonists at the low affinity binding site, which may be related to phosphatidylinositol (PI) hydrolysis.[92] When tested on the guinea pig gall bladder, ileum and stomach muscle strips,[93] as well as on isolated smooth muscle cells from rabbit antrum,[94] CCK analogs lacking the C-terminal primary amide group were able to antagonize the contractile activity induced by CCK-7 or CCK-8.

From these studies, it clearly appeared that the aromatic ring of phenylalanine is important for the binding to CCK receptors, whereas the C-terminal amide group is crucial for full biological activity. Interestingly, the same kind of modifications applied to the C-terminal tetrapeptide of CCK, producing potent gastrin antagonists[95] (*e.g.* Boc-Trp-Leu-Asp-2-phenylethylamide, Boc-Trp-Leu-Asp-2-phenylethyl ester), without significant activity on amylase release and which behave as weak CCK antagonists.[92] These CCK-4 analogs did not induce IP accumulation (unpublished results).

In the central nervous system, cholecystokinin receptors showed much less selectivity in their ability to discriminate between sulfated and shorter desulfated forms of CCK. The tripeptide Met-Asp-Phe-NH$_2$ had the lowest affinity and the dipeptide Asp-Phe-NH$_2$ failed to show binding.[96] dCCK-8, dCCK-7 (desulfated forms of CCK-8 and CCK-7) and shorter forms up to CCK-4 have much greater affinity for the brain than for the pancreatic receptors, but there is some difference in the relative affinity for desulfated CCK forms and their shorter C-terminal fragments among brain tissues and mammalian species.[97] They interact with the CCK receptor with approximately 5–500 times less potency than CCK-8. The disparity between the biological actions and behavioral pharmacology of CCK-related peptides in the central nervous system, probably due to differences in experimental procedures and the experimental animal tested, makes the presentation of rational structure–activity relationships difficult. For instance, some studies found that CCK increased the turnover of dopamine in the striatum, while others found a reduction or no change.[98]

There are also many discrepancies in the effects of CCK-8, desulfated forms of CCK and their shorter fragments on behavioral studies.[99] An attempt to summarize the structural requirements of CCK and CCK-derived peptides related to neuropharmacological effects and behavior was recently described.[100]

On the other hand, it was shown that Z-CCK-27–32-NH$_2$ has almost the same affinity for the peripheral and brain CCK receptors.[101] This compound is able to antagonize some central effects of CCK, particularly dopamine-like effects in the striatum,[102] as well as CCK-induced inhibition of synaptic transmission in the hippocampus.[103]

13.6.3.5.2 *Significance of residues and of peptide bonds*

Numerous analogs of CCK-8 and CCK-7 have been synthesized and the role of each residue and of the peptide bonds has been studied, particularly in relation to enzyme secretion from pancreatic acini and gall bladder contraction. Chemical modifications and amino acid substitutions generally produced analogs exhibiting decreased affinity and biological potency.

The distance of the sulfate ester to the peptide backbone was found to be significant for the potency,[104a] while the aromatic ring of Tyr-27 was less crucial.[104b] Replacement of Tyr(SO$_3$H) by Ser(SO$_3$H) decreased potency by ~1000-fold, whereas its replacement by ε-hydroxynorleucine sulfate decreased potency by only 10-fold, as compared to CCK-8. Variations in the tyrosyl *O*-sulfated residue generally led to less active compounds.[80b] However, in order to enhance the chemical stability of CCK-containing tryrosine-*O*-sulfated analogues, Marseigner *et al.*[105a] replaced the —O—SO$_3$H by an —CH$_2$—SO$_3$H group. The resulting CCK analogues displayed high affinity for peripheral and central CCK-receptors ($K_i \approx 10^{-9}$ M), and proved to be full agonists in the stimulation of enzyme secretion from pancreatic acini and on inducing guinea pig ileum contractions.[105b] Both Met-28 and -31 can be substituted by norleucine (or even by leucine) without significant loss of activity,[80b] the peptide Boc-(Nle-28, 31)-CCK-7 being almost as potent as CCK-8. Oxidation of methionine residues leads to compounds of reduced potency, while substitution of Met-31 by its oxygen analog, *e.g.* methoxinine, produced active derivatives.[106] Any change made at the tryptophan residue affected the potency, indicating that the ability of the indole ring to donate electrons and to be involved in hydrogen bonding is important for binding.[107] Similarly, any change made at Asp-32 resulted in less active compounds, and, in particular, it was demonstrated that the side chain carboxyl group was necessary. Unexpectedly, its substitution by threonyl *O*-sulfated, seryl *O*-sulfated or hydroxyprolyl *O*-sulfated residues led to highly potent analogs with increased contractile activity as compared to CCK-8, and different selective potencies on acid secretion and on anticonvulsive activity,[108] indicating the importance of an acidic group. Interestingly, substitution of Gly-29 by D-tryptophan or by D-alanine led to analogs which stimulated pancreatic exocrine secretion with the same potency as CCK-8, whereas they were almost devoid of contractile activity.[109] These results pointed out the role that glycine may play in the backbone flexibility of CCK, the selectivity in activity of such molecules probably being the result of increased rigidity, which influences binding to a preferential receptor. The same kind of separation in the peripheral activities was encountered by replacing Asp-32 by β-Asp, but with less pronounced effects and decreased potency.[110]

According to conformational studies,[111] a number of rigid CCK analogs have been synthesized. Some of them, *e.g.* (1a), were more potent on the central nervous system receptor than on the peripheral CCK receptor.[112a,b] More recently, specific CCK-receptor antagonists were synthesized by constraining the C-terminal tetrapeptide moiety[113] through a succinyl bridge (*e.g.* 1c). Cyclic CCK-8 analogs, obtained by cyclization through amide bond formation between side chains of Asp-26 and D-Lys-29 (replacing Gly) (*e.g.* 1b), were found to be efficient in differentiating peripheral CCK receptors, being agonists in stimulating amylase release from rat pancreatic acini and exhibiting a weak, albeit significant, antagonist activity on CCK-induced contractions in the guinea pig ileum.[112c]

Recently, the role of the peptide bonds of the C-terminal heptapeptide of CCK has been studied. Their replacement, one at a time, by a 'reduced bond', *e.g.* CH$_2$NH, produced analogs whose activity on stimulation of amylase secretion and ability to bind to central and peripheral receptors were reduced. Only the bond between Nle-28 and Gly-29 could be modified without significant loss of potency. However, the peripheral receptors turned out to be more affected by the modification of the bond between Gly-29 and Trp-30 than the central receptors.[114]

The same structure–activity relationship considerations may also apply to caerulein-derived peptides. A summary of the structural requirements for the binding and biological activities of CCK-like peptides is given in Figure 4.

Boc-γ-D-Glu–Tyr(SO$_3$H)–Nle–D-Lys–Trp–Nle–Asp–PheNH$_2$

(1a)

Boc-D-Asp–Tyr(SO$_3$H)–Nle–D-Lys–Trp–Nle–Asp–PheNH$_2$

(1b)

Ac–Tyr(SO$_3$H)–Lys–Gly–Trp–Lys–Asp–PheNH$_2$
       | |
    CO-CH$_2$-CH$_2$-CO   (1c)

(2) Dibutyryl cyclic GMP

13.6.3.6 CCK-receptor Antagonists

A number of recent reviews have dealt with cholecystokinin-receptor antagonists.[115] It has been proposed by different authors that cholecystokinin antagonists may be classified into four groups: (i)

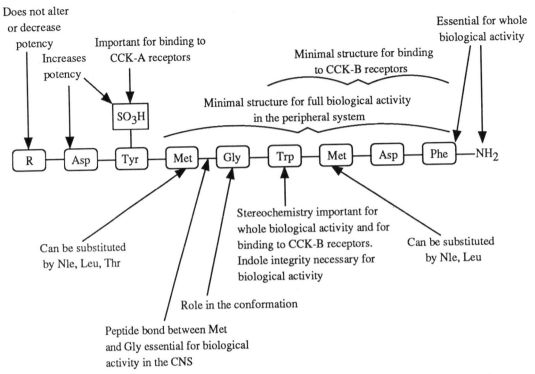

Figure 4 Structural requirements for biological activity of cholecystokinin peptides

derivatives of cyclic nucleotides; (ii) derivatives of amino acids; (iii) partial sequences of the C-terminal region of CCK; and (iv) nonpeptidic compounds.

13.6.3.6.1 *Derivatives of cyclic nucleotides*

More than a decade ago, it was recognized that dibutyryl cyclic GMP (Bt_2cGMP; **2**) was able to competitively antagonize the action of CCK on pancreatic acini, by acting at the CCK receptor and being specific for those agonists that act at the CCK receptor. Bt_2cGMP was demonstrated to be a specific CCK antagonist on a number of other CCK target tissues, including the gall bladder, gastric and ileal muscles, gastric chief and parietal cells and myenteric plexus. However, Bt_2cGMP is considered to be a weak CCK antagonist ($IC_{50} \approx 100$ mM on pancreatic acini), and its usefulness is limited, particularly in *in vivo* systems. Structure–activity relationship studies concerning cyclic nucleotides revealed that a hydrophobic moiety (*e.g.* butyrate) at the O-2′-position may be an important determinant of CCK antagonism. Although hydrophobicity could not fully explain the situation, structural factors affecting the purine ring appeared to be significant for CCK-antagonist potency. Interestingly, native cyclic nucleotides (cAMP, cGMP and cIMP) did not alter the actions of CCK even when tested at concentration as high as 3 mM.

13.6.3.6.2 *Derivatives of amino acids*

The second class of CCK-receptor antagonists is composed of amino acid derivatives, including proglumide (a glutamic acid derivative, DL-4-benzamido-*N*,*N*-dipropylglutaramic acid; **3**) and benzotript (a tryptophan derivative, *N*-*p*-chlorobenzoyl-L-tryptophan; **4**), two derivatives formerly recognized as gastrin-receptor antagonists. These two compounds are slightly more potent than Bt_2cGMP (four to six times) and were similarly found to competitively antagonize CCK actions by acting at the CCK receptor. Numerous studies were carried out with proglumide, which had been shown to antagonize most of the CCK actions, in both the peripheral and central nervous systems.

An intriguing feature concerning the pharmacological studies of proglumide is the questionable use of a mixture of D and L compounds.

In order to elucidate the structural requirements for CCK-antagonist activity, various structural modifications were applied to proglumide.[116] Two derivatives were designated as very potent peripheral CCK antagonists,[117] namely CR1409, lorglumide (*i.e.* DL-4-(3,4-dichlorobenzoylamino)-5-(di-*n*-pentylamino)-5-oxopentanoic acid; **5**), and CR1505, loxyglumide (*i.e.* DL-4-(3,4-dichlorobenzoylamino)-5-(*N*-3-methoxypropyl-*N*-pentylamino)-5-oxopentanoic acid; **6**). These compounds are competitive and reversible CCK antagonists, selective for the peripheral CCK receptor (type A), and were found to be approximately 4000 to 6000 times more potent than proglumide. Their potency and their simple and chemically stable nonpeptidic structure suggest a promising therapeutic utility,[118] although pharmacological evaluations would probably have to be performed on the pure L and D compounds. Preliminary recent results showed that the D isomer is more potent than the L isomer.[119]

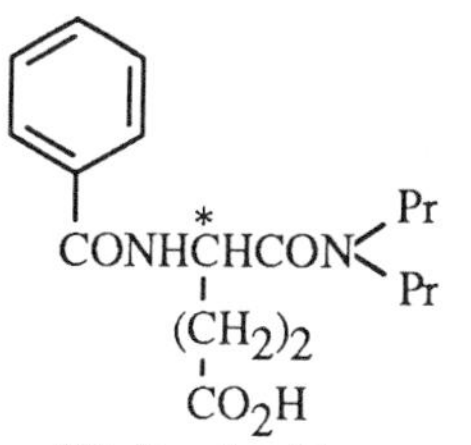

(3) Proglumide

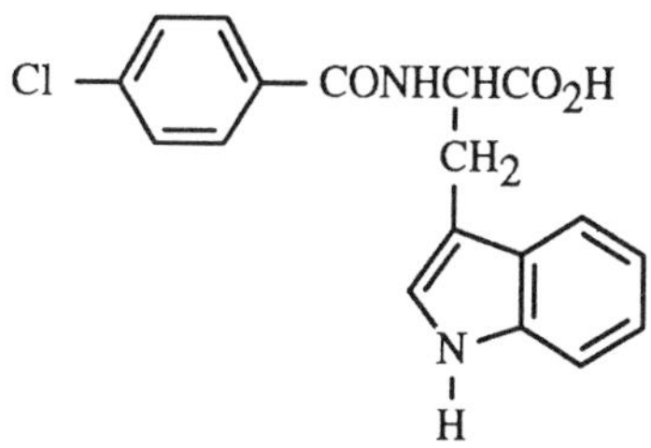

(4) Benzotript

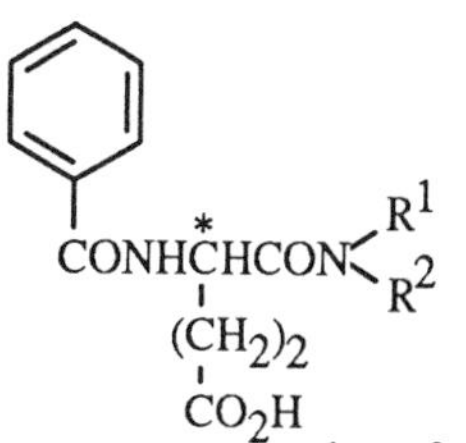

(5) Lorglumide; CR 1409; $R^1 = R^2 = (CH_2)_4Me$
(6) Loxyglumide; CR 1505; $R^1 = (CH_2)_4Me$, $R^2 = (CH_2)_3OMe$

* DL compounds

Subsequent studies were undertaken to assess the role of tryptophan and of its amino-protecting group for antagonism of CCK by comparing the effects of a variety of other *N*-acyltryptophan and *N*-acyl amino acid derivatives with benzotript. The results indicate that both the *N*-acyl substitution and the amino acid side chain hydrophobicities are of major importance for CCK-antagonist activity. Tryptophan itself is a poor CCK antagonist, but adding hydrophobic N-protecting groups increased its antagonist potency.[120] Replacing tryptophan by various amino acids showed that, in addition to structural features like the presence of an aromatic group, antagonist potency was related to the hydrophobicity of the amino acid side chain.[121]

13.6.3.6.3 *Partial sequences derived from the C terminus of CCK*

As mentioned previously, the C-terminal tripeptide of CCK and its *N*-acylated derivatives act as weak CCK antagonists, whereas the C-terminal dipeptide has some minimal antagonist effect.[83] Once again, hydrophobic features seem to be the major determinants in the CCK-antagonist potency of small C-terminal fragments of CCK.

N-terminal fragments of CCK have also been examined for their CCK-antagonistic properties. Z-CCK-27–32-NH$_2$ (Figure 5) was the most potent CCK antagonist of the series, being about 30 times more potent than Bt$_2$cGMP in the guinea pig (IC$_{50}$ ≈ 3 mM),[84] but behaving as a partial agonist on rat or mouse pancreatic acini.[85] Interestingly, this compound did not discriminate between the central and the peripheral CCK receptor and was able to antagonize some effects of CCK in the brain.[101,102]

Replacing the L-tryptophan by a D-tryptophan in the peptide lacking the C-terminal amide function led to potent competitive CCK-receptor antagonists.[122] The most potent compound in this series was Boc-Tyr(SO$_3$H)-Nle-Gly-D-Trp-Nle-Asp-2-phenylethyl ester giving half-maximal inhibition of labeled CCK to rat or guinea pig pancreatic acini at approximately 7 nM. Although this compound was devoid of agonist activity in rat, mouse or guinea pig pancreatic acini, it was able to antagonize the action of CCK, giving half-maximal inhibition at approximately 0.1 mM.[92] This CCK antagonist did not induce IP accumulation, but was able to dose dependently antagonize the CCK-induced IP accumulation.[92] As it has been previously hypothesized, CCK derivatives without the C-terminal primary amide group might be inefficient at the low affinity binding site, therefore one can deduce that changes in the stereochemistry of tryptophan may also affect the functions of the high affinity binding site on pancreatic acini. Interestingly, compounds in this series were

(a) Z-Tyr(SO$_3$H)-Met-Gly-Trp-Met-Asp-NH$_2$ Z-CCK-27-32-NH$_2$

(b) Boc-Tyr(SO$_3$H)-Nle-Gly-D-Trp-Nle-Asp-2-phenylethyl ester

(c) Boc-Tyr(SO$_3$H)-Nle-ψ(COCH$_2$)-Gly-Trp-Nle-Asp-Phe-NH$_2$

Figure 5   Peptide and pseudopeptide derivatives and antagonists of CCK: (a) CCK antagonist in both the peripheral and the central nervous systems; (b) preferential peripheral CCK antagonist; and (c) selective central CCK antagonist

approximately 100 times less potent in inhibiting the binding of labeled CCK to the brain than to pancreatic CCK receptors,[92,122] suggesting some selective affinity for the peripheral *versus* the central CCK receptor. These results seem to indicate that the whole antagonist CCK activity is related not only to the C-terminal part of the CCK molecule, *i.e.* the phenylalanine residue, or, more precisely, the primary amide function, but also depends on the stereochemistry of tryptophan. However, the spatial orientation of the tryptophan side chain appears to be more crucial for binding to central than to peripheral CCK receptors. Compounds in this series also appeared to antagonize the effects of gastrin and CCK on isolated smooth muscle cells from rabbit antrum,[94,123] as well as gastrin-induced acid secretion in the anesthetized rat (unpublished results).

Recently, a pseudopeptide analog of the C-terminal heptapeptide of CCK, in which the peptide bond between Nle-28 and Gly-29 was replaced by a 'COCH$_2$' bond (*e.g.* Boc-Tyr(SO$_3$H)-Nle-ψ(COCH$_2$)-Gly-Trp-Nle-Asp-Phe-NH$_2$; Figure 5) was proposed as a potent and full agonist of CCK in the peripheral system, although it was able to antagonize central effects of CCK. This pseudopeptide was as potent as CCK-8 in inhibiting the binding of labeled CCK-8 to rat and guinea pig pancreatic acini and to guinea pig and mouse brain membranes. It induced full stimulation of enzyme secretion from the pancreatic acini of different species with the same potency as CCK-8. However, this compound was devoid of activity following intrastriatal injection into mice, but was able to antagonize the dopaminomimetic effects of CCK with great potency.[124,125] Replacement of the CONH peptide bond between Nle-28 and Gly-29 by a NHCO bond, or Gly-29 by Sar, leads to analogs of weaker potency but exhibiting the same pharmacological profile. Surprisingly, replacement of the peptide bond between Nle-28 and Gly-29 by a CH$_2$CH$_2$ or a CH$_2$NH group, or replacement of Gly-29 by D-Ala,[125] produced CCK-agonist compounds of varying potencies in both the peripheral and central nervous systems.[125,126] These discrepancies may probably be attributed to different conformational changes, or may reflect some unknown linkage, if any, between this behavioral response and occupation of brain CCK receptors.[126]

13.6.3.6.4   *Nonpeptidic compounds*

The use of the radioreceptor assay technique as a screening tool to search for naturally occurring novel peptide antagonists led to the recent discovery of 'asperlicin' (7), a substance isolated from a strain of *Aspergillus alliaceus*, showing strong affinity for different peripheral CCK receptors (IC$_{50}$ for rat pancreatic acini $\approx$ 1.4 mM, 300 to 400 times that of proglumide).[127] This substance did not have any CCK-like effects but was able to antagonize CCK actions competitively on various peripheral tissues. In fact, asperlicin showed a high degree of selectivity for the peripheral CCK receptor.[128] This discovery is quite significant since it represents the first example of a nonpeptide antagonist of a peptide hormone isolated from natural sources. These very promising results were tempered by asperlicin's apparent lack of useful oral activity and a receptor affinity which was markedly less than that of CCK. It was noted early in these studies that asperlicin contained an indolinylmethyl group, which is biosynthetically derived from L-tryptophan, a key amino acid in the CCK sequence, as well as the 1,4-benzodiazepine substructure.[129]

Recent reports have suggested that the 5-phenyl-1,4-benzodiazepine ring is a very effective peptide-receptor ligand, and this has been adopted as the basis for the design of improved CCK antagonists. These very attractive structure–activity relationship studies led to the synthesis of a potent nonpeptide CCK antagonist, *i.e.* (3S)-(−)-N-(2,3-dihydro-1-methyl-2-oxo-5-phenyl-1H-1,4-benzodiazepin-3-yl)-1H-indole-2-carboxamide (L-364 718; 8).[130] This compound showed a very high affinity for both pancreatic (IC$_{50}$ = 81 pM) and gall bladder (IC$_{50}$ = 45 pM) receptors in radioligand-binding assays, similar to that of CCK itself, and greatly exceeding that of other reported CCK antagonists.[131] Functional studies revealed that L-364 718 is a powerful competitive antagonist of CCK, which lacks agonist activity and exhibits a very high selectivity for peripheral

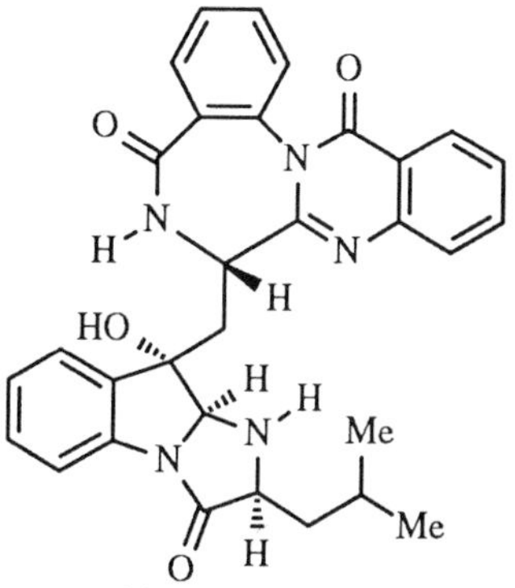

(7) Asperlicin

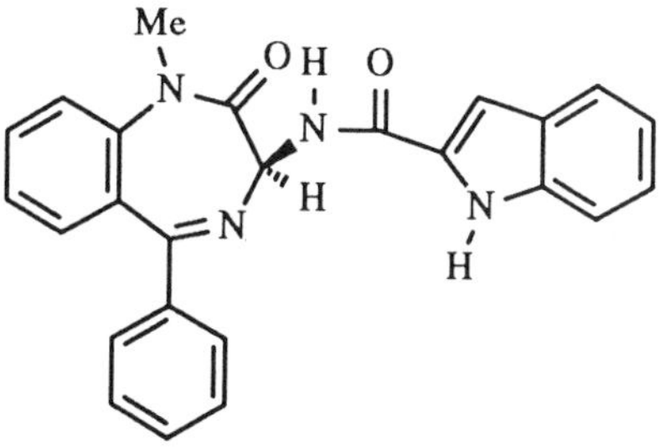

(8) L-364,718

CCK receptors relative to brain CCK, gastrin and various other peptide and nonpeptide receptors, in both *in vivo* and *in vitro* assays. Interestingly, L-364 718 was highly effective when orally administered with long-lasting *in vivo* efficacy. It appeared that CCK-antagonist potencies critically depend on the nature of the group attached to the 3-position of the benzodiazepine ring, and also on the linkage forming the attachment.[133] Recently, it has been demonstrated that 3-substituted 1,4-benzodiazepin-2-amines are as potent as their 3-substituted 1,4-benzodiazepin-2-one counterpart (*e.g.* L-364 718), but display a marked enhancement in aqueous solubility, which might be an important feature for optimization of CCK antagonists as potential therapeutic agents.[132] Similarly, the same group of investigators showed that triazolobenzodiazepines can be used with the same success as 1,4-benzodiazepines to design CCK antagonists.[133]

13.6.4 GASTRIN

13.6.4.1 Introduction

The existence of gastrin was first suggested in 1905, after the observation of Edkins, who found that antral mucosa extracts were able to stimulate acid secretion in anesthetized rats.[134] In 1964, Gregory and Tracy isolated and purified, from hog antral mucosa, a heptadecapeptide named little gastrin (G-17), responsible for this activity.[135] Full characterization of gastrin showed that it exists in both sulfated (gastrin II) and desulfated (gastrin I) forms.[136] Chemical synthesis of G-17 I confirmed the structure of the natural active compound.[137] Subsequently, several molecular forms of gastrin have been isolated and identified, including big gastrin[138] (G-34), minigastrin[139] (G-14) in both sulfated and desulfated forms, and the C-terminal tetrapeptide, tetragastrin, G-4 (identical to CCK-4; Figure 6). Larger forms of gastrin, big big gastrin[140] and Rehfeld component I[141] have been identified by chromatography and RIA, but have not been chemically characterized. There are four

(a)
```
        1                                    10
   Pyr-Leu-Gly-Pro-Gln-Gly-Pro-Pro-His-Leu-Val-Ala-Asp-Pro-Ser-Lys-Lys-Gln-
```
```
            20                              29  30  31  32  33  34
   Pro-Gly-Trp-Leu-Glu-Glu-Glu-Glu-Glu-Ala-Tyr*-Gly-Trp-Met-Asp-Phe-NH₂
```

(b)
```
    1                                    12  13  14  15  16  17
   Pyr-Pro-Gly-Trp-Leu-Glu-Glu-Glu-Glu-Glu-Ala-Tyr*-Gly-Trp-Met-Asp-Phe-NH₂
```

(c)
```
    1                            9   10  11  12  13  14
   Trp-Leu-Glu-Glu-Glu-Glu-Glu-Ala-Tyr*-Gly-Trp-Met-Asp-Phe-NH₂
```

(d)
                                                    Trp-Met-Asp-Phe-NH₂

Figure 6 Primary structures of human gastrin. (a) Big gastrin, G-34 II; *tyrosine *O*-sulfated, G-34 I. (b) Little gastrin, G-17 II; *tyrosine *O*-sulfated, G-17 I. (c) Minigastrin, G-14 II; *tyrosine *O*-sulfated, G-14 I. (d) Tetragastrin, G-4 (= CCK-4). *Tyrosine is either *O*-sulfated, type I, or desulfated, type II

domains in the gastrin precursor, in addition to a signal sequence.[51] Cleavage at pairs of basic amino acid residues generates an extreme C-terminal tryptic fragment, G-17, extended at the C terminus by Gly-Arg (which is further amidated by specific enzymes and converted into G-17), and two N-terminal fragments.

Immunochemical studies revealed that the principal site of gastrin is the antrapyloric mucosa, but gastrin is also found in the proximal duodenum, in the gastric fundus, jejunum and ileum, exocrine and endocrine pancreas, the pituitary and the vagal nerves. In many mammals, G-34 and G-17 are the predominant forms, sulfated and desulfated, existing in about equal amounts in both the tissues and blood. G-4 has been identified throughout the stomach and the small intestine, as well as minute quantities in the brain.

Gastrin is released into blood under the influence of neural (cholinergic) or alimentary stimuli. Gastrin and cholecystokinin share the same C-terminal pentapeptide of sequence Gly-Trp-Met-Asp-Phe-NH$_2$.

13.6.4.2 Biological Activities

Gastrin exerts a variety of secretory, motor and trophic actions in the gastrointestinal tract, and also has some behavioral effects in the central nervous system.

The major effect of gastrin is to stimulate gastric acid secretion from the stomach, by at least four separate paths: (i) direct action on the parietal cell; (ii) potentiating histamine action; (iii) stimulating the release of histamine; and (iv) eliciting brain stimulation, probably *via* a vagus dependent mechanism.[142] The mechanisms by which gastrin stimulates acid secretion are still poorly understood. Although it has recently been clearly demonstrated that gastrin has an independent acid secretory effect, which is much reduced in the absence of histamine, interactions among gastrin, histamine and acetylcholine are important in determining the overall gastric acid secretory response to gastrin.[143] Interestingly, it has been recognized that gastrin may exert an auto inhibitory effect at large doses.[144] The role of cAMP as a mediator of gastrin stimulated acid secretion is considered as controversial, and there is no clearly defined second messenger for the action of gastrin as a stimulant of acid secretion.

In addition, it has been clearly established that gastrin is a physiological trophic hormone for gastric, fundic and intestinal mucosa and for the pancreas,[145] and there is a strong possibility that this effect is mediated by gastrin receptors.

Subsequently, gastrin had been shown to stimulate pepsin secretion and to increase gastric mucosal blood flow, causing electrolyte and water secretion by the stomach, pancreas, liver and Brunner's glands. Gastrin also stimulates smooth muscle contraction, especially the lower esophageal sphincter and the antrum. The gall bladder, especially from mammals, is much less responsive to gastrin than to CCK.

In the central nervous system, besides its possible role in the control of acid secretion, tetragastrin injected i.c.v. affects behavior in rats, increasing locomotion and rearing,[146] exhibiting opposite effects to those elicited by CCK-8. More detailed information concerning G-4 (CCK-4) effects have been reviewed in the previous section dealing with CCK.

13.6.4.3 Gastrin Receptors

Preparations used as sources of gastrin receptors have included crude membrane fractions and isolated cells, none of them responding to gastrin by specific biological effects. High affinity gastrin-binding sites have been identified in rat oxyntic membranes,[147] in mucosa from the stomach, and the duodenum and colon of rats,[148] dogs[149] and rabbits.[150] Recently, gastrin receptors were found on canine parietal cells and on a nonparietal cell population containing somatostatin cells of the gastric mucosa.[151]

Although gastrin and cholecystokinin appear to bind to the same sites in guinea pig fundic gastric glands, their different binding characteristics may indicate the presence of more than one single binding site.[152] In fact, the existence of two binding sites for gastrin and cholecystokinin in rabbit gastric mucosa has been postulated.[153] Specific binding sites for gastrin have also been demonstrated in dog gastric antral smooth muscles.[154]

Attempts to define molecular properties and chemical characterization of the gastrin receptor are actually under study.[155] Interestingly, high affinity gastrin receptors have been found on a number of gastrointestinal cancer cell lines and in human cancers.

13.6.4.4 Structure–Activity Relationships

Studies with different molecular forms of gastrin have shown that most of the molecular properties required for binding to the gastrin receptor and eliciting biological activity reside in the C-terminal region of the molecule. Potencies of G-34 and G-17 are not significantly different, whereas the C-terminal tridecapeptide, G-13, is nearly as potent as G-17 in its ability to bind to the gastrin receptor in rabbit gastric mucosal cells and in eliciting acid secretion from the rat stomach.[156] In rat oxyntic gland mucosa, even the C-terminal heptapeptide, G-7, showed almost the same potency as G-17 in inhibiting the binding of labeled gastrin to gastrin receptors.[157] However, the results of Göhring *et al.*, who showed that increasing the peptide length of tetragastrin at the N terminus led to an enhancement of potency, suggest that the pentaglutamic sequence bears specific information for a pronounced amplification of the hormonal activity.[158] Tracy and Gregory discovered that the C-terminal tetrapeptide of gastrin, H-Trp-Met-Asp-Phe-NH$_2$ (G-4), possessed the full range of biological effects of G-17, although it was less potent on a molar basis.[159] There is usually a close correlation between the ability of the gastrin fragments to bind to the gastrin receptors in gastric membranes and to stimulate acid secretion *in vivo*.

Acylation of the N terminus of tetragastrin or larger C-terminal fragments, which increases resistance to enzymatic hydrolysis, usually leads to compounds of preserved or enhanced potency. In particular, *N* acylation with saccharides resulted in more potent compounds.[160] In contrast to cholecystokinin, the few comparative studies reported so far seem to indicate that sulfated and desulfated forms of gastrin have approximately equal potency in stimulating acid secretion. However, the lack of synthetic material has hampered, for years, detailed investigations on the physiological and pharmacological significance of sulfated forms of gastrin. In fact, sulfation of short gastrin-related peptides was found to enhance their potency in the cat, both *in vivo* and *in vitro*.[161] Recent results clearly confirmed the role of sulfation,[162] using an active analog of minigastrin II,[163] and suggested that sulfated forms of gastrin might play a significant biological role. Subsequently, it has been shown that the C-terminal tripeptide retains a small amount of activity,[164] and even the C-terminal dipeptide, at high concentrations, displays some activity on acid secretion.[165]

Replacement of Met-15 in little gastrin by leucine, norleucine or methoxinine resulted in analog with activities that were practically indistinguishable from that of the parent hormone.[166] Replacement of the C-terminal primary amide group by a carboxylate group led to almost completely inactive compounds, retaining less than 1% of the potency and failing to inhibit the binding of labeled gastrin by more than 20% at maximally effective concentrations. The finding that the whole range of activities was associated with the C-terminal tetrapeptide of gastrin resulted in a structure–activity relationship study on an unprecedented scale. Acylation of the N terminus of G-4 usually resulted in more potent compounds, one of the most active derivatives being the pentapeptide Boc-β-Ala-Trp-Met-Asp-Phe-NH$_2$ named 'pentagastrin'.[167a] Some minor modifications can be made at the tryptophan residue, the indole moiety appearing to be important for the conservation of both significant binding and biological activity.[168] Many changes may be made at the methionine position without a resulting loss of activity. In particular, it can be substituted by norleucine or leucine, the length of the side chain being the main feature for retaining full activity. It was clearly demonstrated that any replacement at the aspartic acid residue by natural amino acids always led to inactive derivatives. The only substitution which resulted in active compounds was its replacement by an unnatural residue (having a tetrazol-5-yl as the side chain), which predictably maintains the electronic character and location of the carboxyl group.[167b] Conversely, it was reported that C-terminal tripeptide derivatives lacking the carboxyl group of aspartic acid were able to stimulate, to some extent, acid secretion in dogs.[169] Modifications affecting the phenylalanine residue are permitted. Highly active derivatives were obtained by modifying the phenyl ring, *i.e.* substitution by groups of differing electronic effects and replacement by a cyclohexyl group. The parent acid or the methyl ester were found to be inactive, whereas limited substitution on the nitrogen of the terminal amide group is permitted.

Recently, the significance of phenylalanine, more particularly of its phenyl ring and of the primary amide function, were investigated. As in the case of cholecystokinin, suppression of the phenylalanine moiety resulted in analogs that were able to bind to the gastrin receptor, but were devoid of secretory activity.[170a] Z-CCK-27–32-NH$_2$,[171] a CCK-receptor antagonist, and its corresponding analogs of the gastrin series behave as potent gastrin antagonists.[172] It was shown that deletion of the C-terminal phenylalanyl residue in the C-terminal fragments of gastrin led also to gastrin antagonists,[170b] acting at the gastrin receptor. The peptide Boc-Trp-Leu-Asp-NH$_2$ was described as the smallest fragment presenting selective antigastrin activity.[173]

Conversely, it was reported that the N-terminal tridecapeptide fragment (G-1–13) of G-17, an endogeneous peptide, was able to inhibit the acid secretory response to feeding and to exogenous

G-34 and G-17,[174] but these results could not be confirmed by other investigators.[175] Morley reported that suppression of the C-terminal amide group (*e.g.* Boc-Trp-Leu-Asp-2-phenylethylamide) produced inactive derivatives. It has been further demonstrated that these compounds were able to potently antagonize *in vivo* gastrin activity on acid secretion.[95b] In fact, the depsipeptide Boc-β-Ala-Trp-Leu-Asp-2-phenylethyl ester was among the most potent compounds in the series, being as potent as pentagastrin in antagonizing the binding of gastrin to its receptors but inhibiting the gastrin-stimulated acid secretion in the rat with great potency ($ED_{50} \approx 0.04$ mg kg^{-1}).[95a] These results clearly showed that one can attribute a functional rather than a binding role for the phenylalanine residue, although suppression of this residue resulted in a significant loss in the affinity of the peptide for gastrin receptors ($\sim$100-fold). In fact, the entire binding potency of phenylalanine appeared to reside in its benzyl moiety, since 2-phenylethylamide and 2-phenylethyl ester derivatives were as potent as the parent peptidic compound in inhibiting the binding of gastrin to its receptors. A functional role can be attributed to the C-terminal amide group since its suppression leads to derivatives devoid of biological activity, but able to bind to the gastrin receptor with the same potency as the parent peptide. Similarly, these derivatives were able to bind to the central receptor with approximately the same affinity as tetragastrin.[176]

The significance of the peptide bonds was pointed out, particularly the importance of the bond between leucine and aspartic acid. The pseudopeptide Boc-Trp-Leu-ψ(CH$_2$NH)-Asp-Phe-NH$_2$, in which the peptide bond between leucine and aspartic acid has been replaced by a 'reduced peptide bond', *e.g.* CH$_2$NH, had the same apparent affinity for the gastrin receptor on isolated gastric mucosal cells as the parent peptide, but was devoid of secretory activity. It was able to antagonize *in vivo* gastrin-stimulated acid secretion from anesthetized[177] and conscious rats[178] and cats[179] with chronic gastric fistula, with high potency ($ED_{50} \approx 0.3$–0.5 mg kg^{-1}). This derivative also exhibited high potency in binding to guinea pig or rat brain membranes.[180] These results clearly demonstrated the importance of the peptide bond between leucine and aspartic acid, which is not significant for binding to gastrin receptors but is crucial for the biological activity. A series of retro inverso analogs of the C-terminal tetrapeptide of gastrin, in which the peptide bond between Leu and Asp has been modified, were synthesized and demonstrated to behave as potent gastrin antagonists,[181] confirming the significance of this peptide bond. In contrast, when the bond between tryptophan and leucine was modified to a CH$_2$NH bond, the resulting pseudopeptide behaved as a full agonist, as potent as the peptide of natural sequence. The bond between aspartic acid and phenylalanine was of lesser importance and its replacement by a 'reduced peptide bond' resulted in less active compounds. Recently, it was reported that replacement of the peptide linkage in G-4 by a *trans* double bond (CH=CH) at either the Trp-Leu, Leu-Asp or Asp-Phe sites resulted in a major loss of binding affinity for guinea pig cortical CCK receptors. On the other hand the same kind of modification of Boc-G-5 at the Gly-Trp bond resulted in a two- to three-fold enhancement of potency.[182]

From the structure–function studies, Morley concluded that two distinct 'sites' had been distinguished in tetragastrin: binding 'sites' (Trp, Met, Asp and the C-terminal amide) and a 'functional

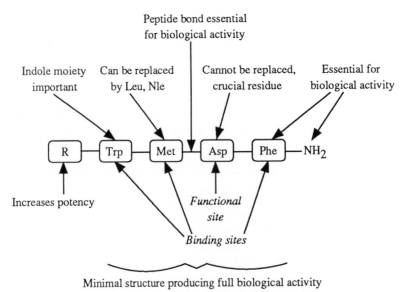

Figure 7   Structural requirements for biological activity of gastrin-like peptides

site' (Asp) which directly participates in the chemical event associated with the action of the hormone. Recent results reported in the literature somewhat confirmed this hypothesis and pointed out the role of both the peptide bond between leucine and aspartic acid and of the C-terminal primary amide group, which are crucial for the biological activity and unimportant for binding to the gastrin receptor. It is tempting to assume that for exhibiting biological activity, the bond between leucine (or methionine) and aspartic acid has to be a peptide bond, an enzymatically cleavable bond, and the C-terminal amide has to be present. Recently, it was reported that a membrane fraction from rat gastric mucosa,[183a] and even rabbit gastric mucosal cells possessing gastrin receptors,[183b, c] were able to specifically cleave Boc-tetragastrin and its leucine analog, Boc-Trp-Leu-Asp-Phe-NH_2, between leucine and aspartic acid and that this cleavage could result from the action of angiotensin converting enzyme.[183d] Whether or not this enzymatic cleavage is related to the biological activity remains to be determined. A summary of the structural requirements for the binding and biological activities of gastrin-like peptides is given in Figure 7.

13.6.4.5 Gastrin Antagonists

Most of the CCK-receptor antagonists (*e.g* Bt_2cGMP, benzotript, proglumide) behave as gastrin antagonists, although, in some cases, with much less potency on the gastrin receptor. One of the most studied gastrin antagonist is proglumide, resembling the C-terminal tripeptide of gastrin. It has been shown to inhibit gastrin-stimulated acid secretion,[184] the trophic action of pentagastrin[185] and central effects of tetragastrin. This derivative demonstrated significant efficacy in patients with duodenal ulcers. Recently, proglumide was found to inhibit the growth of colon cancer and to enhance survival in mice.[186] As in the case of CCK, benzotript as well as tryptophan derivatives were also shown to antagonize the actions of gastrin.[187]

Partial C-terminal sequences of CCK, or of gastrin lacking the phenylalanine residue, were found to be effective in antagonizing the action of gastrin on acid secretion, Z-CCK-27–32-NH_2 being approximately 150 times more potent than proglumide.[88] Other peptidic gastrin antagonists were proposed, including NPS-pentagastrin,[188] pentagastrin derivatives in which histamine had been coupled to the β-carboxylate of aspartic acid,[189] Boc-Gly-Trp-Met-Gly-NH_2 and Boc-Trp-Met-Asp-D-Ala-NH_2.[144] As mentioned before (see Section 13.6.3.5.1), Boc-Trp-Leu-Asp-2-phenylethylamide or Boc-Trp-Leu-Asp-2-phenylethyl ester are potent gastrin antagonists ($\sim$1000-fold more potent than proglumide), and behaved as CCK antagonists on rat pancreatic acini.[92] Unexpectedly, the pseudopeptide, Boc-Trp-Leu-ψ(CH_2NH)-Asp-Phe-NH_2, which was also found to be a potent gastrin antagonist, behaves as an agonist on amylase secretion from rat pancreatic acini, showing the same pattern and with the same potency as the parent peptide,[180] suggesting a difference in the receptors for both CCK and gastrin on pancreatic acini or a different mechanism of action.

Recently, two potent antigastrin compounds were described, namely CR1718 and CR1719 (whose chemical structure has not been communicated), being approximately 15 times more potent than proglumide in reducing the acid output induced by an i.v. infusion of pentagastrin in the rat and in inhibiting the binding of labeled gastrin to guinea pig stomach glands.[192]

On the basis of the chemical structure of their potent CCK antagonists, and using the same concepts, the researchers of the Merck Sharp and Dohme group presented a nonpeptidic, specific and potent gastrin antagonist, namely compound L-365260 (9). This compound was found to be orally active on gastrin-stimulated acid secretion in the mouse, rat and guinea pig ($ED_{50} \approx 0.03$ mg kg^{-1} in mouse).[193a,b] This molecule will probably be of great interest and much help for investigating the role of gastrin and CCK-B receptors in physiology and disease. However, this new molecule confirms the concept of the Merck Sharp and Dohme researchers on the possibilities of obtaining nonpeptidic active molecules on peptidergic receptors, by coupling the 'active organic group' of the peptide to a nonpeptidic molecule used in therapy (*e.g.* benzodiazepines).

(9) L-365,260

13.6.5 NEUROTENSIN (NT)

13.6.5.1 Introduction

During purification of substance P from bovine hypothalamus, a peptidic by-product was isolated by Carraway and Leeman and named neurotensin (NT).[194] Later, the same authors established that neurotensin was a tridecapeptide of sequence Pyr-Leu-Tyr-Glu-Asn-Lys-Pro-Arg-Arg-Pro-Tyr-Ile-Leu-OH.[195,200] Neurotensin, subsequently isolated from bovine,[196] and human intestine,[197] has the same sequence as neurotensin from bovine hypothalamus.

Nucleotide sequence analysis of cloned cDNA, encoding neurotensin isolated from a cDNA library derived from primary cultures of canine enteric mucosal cells, has revealed the primary structure of a 170 amino acid precursor protein that encodes both neurotensin and the neurotensin-like peptide, neuromedin N.[198]

Neurotensin is classified as a gut brain peptide, widely distributed in the central nervous system[199] and also found in high concentration in the hypothalamus, amygdala, nucleus accumbens and septum, but over 90% occurs in the peripheral system, mainly in the small intestine, in the small bowel, with the greatest amounts in the ileum and somewhat less in the jejunum.[200] Neurotensin is stored in large granules concentrated in the basal portion of N cells (NT cells), which have been identified in the small intestine of humans and animals. Neurotensin is chemically and biologically related to an octapeptide isolated from the skin of the frog *Xenopus laevis*, which was named xenopsin,[201] sharing four out of the five amino acid residues of the C-terminal pentapeptide (Figure 8). Recently, neuromedin N, a novel hexapeptide having a remarkable sequential homology to the C-terminal region of neurotensin, has been isolated from procine spinal cord,[202] and the hexapeptide, Lys-8, Asn-9, NT-8–13 (LANT-6), has been isolated from chicken intestine[203] and brain.[204] Both share with neurotensin the C-terminal tetrapeptide of sequence Pro-Tyr-Ile-Leu-OH (Figure 8). More recently, using a radioimmunoassay towards the C-terminal region of neurotensin, an immunoreactive and biologically active neurotensin-related peptide (NRP), having the same C-terminal hexapeptide as NT, has been isolated from pepsin treated fractions of bovine, canine, human and rat plasma (Figure 8).[205]

13.6.5.2 Biological Activities

Neurotensin has been shown to possess an extensive pharmacological profile, including actions on both the peripheral and central nervous systems where it may act as a neuromodulator or neurotransmitter. At pharmacological concentrations, peripheral administration of NT[206] induces hypotension, stimulates gut contraction, increases vascular permeability, hypotension, hyperglycemia, hyperglucagonemia and hypercholesterolemia. At physiological doses, neurotensin has been found to increase the concentration of plasma pancreatic polypeptide, inhibit gastric acid secretion, delay gastric emptying, and reduce lower esophageal sphincter pressure. Neurotensin has also been reported to modulate pancreatic exocrine function.[207,208] In addition, NT was found to be a potent mast cell secretagog, both *in vitro* and *in vivo*.

Central administration of NT produces a variety of behavioral effects,[209] including antinociception and hypothermia, locomotor activity and trial-conditioned active avoidance behavior, as well

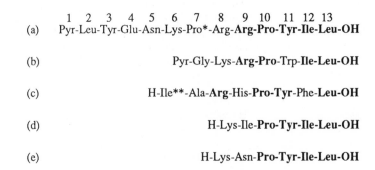

<pre>
            1   2   3   4   5   6   7   8   9   10 11 12 13
(a)   Pyr-Leu-Tyr-Glu-Asn-Lys-Pro*-Arg-**Arg-Pro-Tyr-Ile-Leu**-OH

(b)   Pyr-Gly-Lys-**Arg-Pro**-Trp-**Ile-Leu**-OH

(c)   H-Ile**-Ala-**Arg**-His-**Pro-Tyr**-Phe-**Leu**-OH

(d)   H-Lys-Ile-**Pro-Tyr-Ile-Leu**-OH

(e)   H-Lys-Asn-**Pro-Tyr-Ile-Leu**-OH
</pre>

Figure 8 Amino acid composition of: (a) neurotensin (*Ser in guinea pig); (b) xenopsin; (c) neurotensin-related peptide (NRP) (**Val in rat); (d) neuromedin N; (e) Lys-8, Asn-9, NT-8–13 (LANT-6). Amino acid homologies with neurotensin are indicated in bold letters

as maintenance of gastric mucosal integrity.[210] A large body of evidence indicates that NT modulates nigrostriatal and mesolimbic dopaminergic systems.[211]

In addition, NT has a significant effect in accentuating the action of barbiturates, mediating pituitary growth hormone and prolactin release, increasing the plasma concentration of ACTH, LH and FSH.

The neuronal cell type (neuroblastoma clone N1E-115) has been used as a model to investigate the transduction mechanisms that are involved in the interaction of NT with its target cells. Three different intracellular events were affected. Neurotensin has been found to stimulate the formation of intracellular cyclic GMP, whereas a 20–30% decrease of cAMP basal levels was observed. On the other hand, NT produces a rapid and transient stimulation of inositol phospholipid hydrolysis. It was suggested that these three biochemical events are mediated by the same receptor.[212]

13.6.5.3 Neurotensin Receptors

Specific neurotensin receptors have been identified by radioligand binding and autoradiographic studies in central and peripheral systems, on both neuronal and nonneuronal structures. NT-specific binding sites have been identified in synaptic membranes, particulate fractions from mammalian brains, smooth muscle membranes from different species, in a cell line (HT29) derived from a human colon carcinoma, and in mast cells and macrophages. Two different classes of binding sites were recognized in the brain membranes of various mammalian species,[213] in smooth muscle plasma membranes from rat fundus or dog ileum and in rat liver plasma membranes.[214] NT receptors resemble the low affinity type in HT29 cells and the high affinity type in the neuronal cell type N1E-115.[215]

13.6.5.4 Structure–Activity Relationships

Structure–activity relationships of neurotensin-like peptides are complicated by the fact that results from *in vivo* and *in vitro* studies often differ markedly. Rather than differences in neurotensin receptors, these discrepancies may reflect *in vivo* peptidase inactivation of neurotensin-like peptides. Nevertheless, it rapidly became clear that the biological activities and binding properties obtained from biological assays, typically employing whole animals, intact organs or tissues dissected from rodent heart, stomach or intestine, reside in the C-terminal portion of the molecule.[216] The shortest sequence which can bind to NT receptors, and still be able to promote the whole biological response, although with lower potency, is the C-terminal pentapeptide NT-9–13.[217] Adding one residue to the N-terminal pentapeptide generally produces a more potent agonist, NT-8–13, although this result is controversial.[217,218] The N-terminal part of the molecule appeared to be unimportant for the expression of biological activities, but may play a role in conformation and/or a protective role against exopeptidases. In fact, *N* acetylation of the C-terminal hexapeptide led to a derivative, Ac-NT-8–13, whose effects mimic those of the complete structure of NT.[217a] Results obtained with xenopsin confirmed these findings, which were consistent with the existence of an aminopeptidase activity shortening the fully efficient NT sequence into derivatives with low activities. Interestingly, N-terminal fragments of NT exhibited some remarkable biological activities. NT-1–8 and NT-1–10, which are naturally occurring metabolites of NT, were able to significantly prevent development of cold-restraint-stress (CRS)-induced gastric ulcers in rats after intracisternal (i.c.) injection.[210b] Similarly, it was found that NT-1–8 and NT-1–11, the chief fragments that accumulate in the plasma in physiological conditions and that have a longer half-life than NT, stimulate amylase secretion from dispersed pancreatic acini at concentrations that occur in peripheral plasma (10^{-11} M).[208] It was further demonstrated that suppression of the Leu-13 C-terminal residue,[219] its amidation[220] or its *N* methylation[221] led to almost completely inactive analogs.

Side chains of C-terminal Leu-13 and of penultimate Ile-12 residues are necessary requirements for expression of full biological activities, probably because they are part of a hydrophobic C-terminal area and/or because of specific requirements for aliphatic branched side chains.

The tyrosine residue in position 11 plays an important role in the process of receptor activation. Its replacement by various amino acids and amino acid derivatives indicated that the aromatic group should be at a proper distance from the peptidic backbone, the hydroxyl function is suggested to be involved by hydrogen bonding with NT receptors,[222] and the L configuration is necessary to optimize both binding to NT receptors and biological activities. Replacement of Tyr-11 by Trp led to an analog of equivalent potency to NT, whereas its replacement by D-Phe produced a derivative,

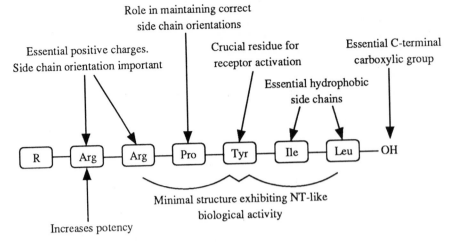

Figure 9 Structural requirements for biological activity of neurotensin peptides

(D-Phe-11)-NT, as active as NT on behavioral effects in an open field situation,[223] and even more active than NT in hypothermia, although it has a relatively low affinity for rat brain NT receptors.[221]

Replacement of Pro-10 by D-Pro or by Gly greatly lowers the activity. As observed in many other biologically active peptides, the proline residue is probably deeply involved in maintaining a correct conformation of the whole NT molecule, providing the critical orientation of the amino acid residues of the C-terminal region involved in the receptor interaction.[224].

Systematic substitution and modifications of the arginine residues in positions 8 and 9 revealed that both arginine residues are required for optimal NT-receptor recognition and full expression of biological activities, their spatial configuration and their positive charges being particularly significant. However, it has been recognized that Arg-9 plays a greater role than Arg-8 in the binding to NT receptors, according to the criterion of configuration.[225] On the other hand, Arg-8 seems to be more crucially involved than Arg-9 in the binding to mast cell receptor sites.[226]

A summary of the structural requirements of neurotensin-like peptides is given in Figure 9.

13.6.5.5 Neurotensin Antagonists

There are not too many potent neurotensin antagonists. (D-Trp-11)-NT has been proposed as a specific and competitive NT antagonist, inhibiting the vasoconstrictor and pressor effects of NT, as well as the rise of plasma glucagon, glucose and histamine levels evoked by NT in rats. Unfortunately, this compound still retained some NT activity when used in high concentrations.[227,228] Surprisingly, [Tyr(Me)-11]-NT was also found to specifically antagonize the actions of NT in the isolated, perfused rat heart, when used in concentrations lower than 10^{-6} M. Again, this analog behaved as a relatively weak agonist when tested in concentrations above 10^{-6} M, and was found without effect in inhibiting the NT actions on rat stomach strips and guinea pig atria,[217c] suggesting some differences in the NT receptor of these tissues.

13.6.6 SECRETIN

13.6.6.1 Introduction

Secretin is a linear peptide of 27 amino acid residues (Figure 10),[229] first isolated in purified form by Jorpes and Mutt, from the hog small intestine.[230] Bodanszky *et al.* synthesized the secretin molecule and confirmed the structure of the natural isolated compound.[231]

Later on, secretin was isolated from various sources, and it appeared that the hormone sequence differed significantly from different species. More recently, a larger form of secretin, having 30 amino acid residues, has been isolated from porcine upper intestine tissue, and found to be as potent as secretin.[232]

(a) His-Ser-Asp-Gly-Thr-**Phe-Thr**-Ser-Glu-Leu-Ser-**Arg-Leu-Arg**-
 1 5 10

 15 20 25 27
 Asp-Ser-Ala-Arg-Leu-Gln-Arg-Leu-**Leu**-Gln-Gly-Leu-Val-NH$_2$

(b) His-Ser-Asp-Ala-Val-**Phe-Thr**-Asp-Asn-Tyr-Thr-**Arg-Leu-Arg**-
 1 5 10

 15 20 25 28
 Lys-Gln-Met-Ala-Val-Lys-Lys-Tyr-**Leu**-Asn-Ser-Ile-Leu-Asn-NH$_2$

(c) His-Ser-Gln-Gly-**Thr-Phe-Thr**-Ser-Asp-**Tyr**-Ser-Lys-Tyr-Leu-
 1 5 10

 15 20 25 28 29
 Asp-Ser-**Arg-Arg**-Ala-**Gln**-Asp-Phe-Val-**Gln**-Trp-**Leu**-Met-**Asn**-Thr-OH

(d) Tyr-Ala-Glu-**Gly-Thr-Phe**-Ile-Ser-Asp-**Tyr**-Ser-Ile-Ala-Met-
 1 5 10

 15 20 25 28
 Asp-Lys-Ile-**Arg**-Gln-**Gln**-Asp-Phe-Val-**Asn**-Trp-**Leu-Leu**-Ala-Gln- - -

(e) His-Ala-**Asp-Gly-Val-Phe-Thr**-Ser-Asp-Phe-**Ser-Arg-Leu**-Leu-
 1 5 10

 15 20 25 27
 Gly-Gln-Leu-Ser-Ala-**Lys-Lys-Tyr-Leu**-Glu-**Ser-Leu**-Ile-NH$_2$

Figure 10 Amino acid sequence of peptides of the secretin family (porcine sequences). (a) Secretin (Glu-15, Gly-16 in human and Leu-5, Tyr-10, Lys-12, Met-13, Gly-15, Asn-16, Gln-18, Val-19, Lys-21, Phe-22, Ile-23, Asn-25, Met-27 in chicken); (b) vasoactive intestinal peptide (VIP) of porcine, rat and human sequences (Leu-5, Thr-9, Met-19, Val-26 in guinea pig and Ser-11, Phe-13, Val-26, Thr-28 in chicken); (c) glucagon; (d) gastrin-inhibiting polypeptide (GIP), only the N-terminal part of the sequence is shown; (e) peptide having N-terminal histidine and C-terminal isoleucine amide (PHI). Homologies in amino acids with secretin and VIP are indicated in bold letters

Most of the immunoreactive secretin has been localized in the S cells of the small intestine, particularly in duodenum and jejunum, with some differences among species.[233] Outside the alimentary tract, secretin-containing cells were found in endocrine monolayer cultures of the rat pancreas[234] and, by mean of immunocytochemistry, secretin cells were also detected in antral mucosa of humans, dogs and rats.[235] Endogenous secretin-like bioactivity has been detected in extracts of porcine brain.[236] Immunoreactive secretin has recently been found in rat and porcine brain extracts,[237] with the highest concentrations being found in the pineal and pituitary glands, followed by the thalamus and hypothalamus in the rat.[238]

To the best of our knowledge, the structure of prepro-secretin is unknown, because of the scarcity of secretin-producing cells in the gut and the apparent absence of 'secretinomas' in human pathology.

13.6.6.2 Biological Activities

Secretin is biologically active in the mammalian peripheral and central nervous systems. In addition to its action at physiological doses, secretin exhibits a wide variety of pharmacological activities.[239]

The main effect of secretin is to stimulate secretion of water and bicarbonate in the duct cells of the pancreas, this action being brought about by physiological concentrations. In addition, secretin stimulates secretion of pancreatic enzymes, growth of the pancreas, and increases plasma levels of serum parathormone. At pharmacological concentrations it stimulates insulin release and induces colonic mucin secretion in dogs. In the stomach, secretin increases pepsinogen secretion by chief cells and exhibits a cytoprotective effect, whereas it stimulates gastric luminal bicarbonate and mucus glycoprotein secretions and has an inhibitory action of gastric acid secretion in response to various stimuli. In addition to its role as an enterogastrone,[240] secretin exerts a direct action on oxyntic and pyloric glands of the stomach.[241] Secretin also stimulates cardiac output and has a lipolytic effect on fat cells. The actions of secretin appear to be mediated by cAMP.

In the central nervous system, intracerebroventricular injection of secretin into the rat produces metabolic, physiological and behavioral alterations. Secretin stimulates hypothalamic tyrosine hydroxylase activity[242] and dopamine metabolism.[243] In addition, secretin induces a reduction in prolactin and luteinizing hormone secretion,[237,242,243] as well as in open-field activity and novel item approach.[244] Secretin also alters respiration. As with the peripheral system, these actions are mediated by cAMP.

13.6.6.3 Secretin Receptors

Few data are available on the binding site of secretin due to difficulties in obtaining a highly potent labeled derivative. Conjugation of a preiodinated Bolton–Hunter group to the free α-amino group of histidine at the N terminus resulted in an analog displaying significant biological activity but of no value for receptor-binding studies. Secretin contains no tyrosine and direct iodination results in radioligand derivatives in which the N-terminal histidine is iodinated. Such compounds may be less competitive with secretin[245] and are biologically less active by several orders of magnitude.[247] However, they have been used to characterize secretin-binding sites. [³H]secretin, although much more biologically potent, has not been routinely utilized as a radiolabeled ligand. Specific binding sites for secretin[248] have been observed in plasma membranes of rat fat cells,[249] cell and membrane preparations of rat, guinea pig and cat pancreas, rat gastric glands,[241] canine gastric antral smooth muscle,[250] and mouse glial cells,[251] and are coupled to cAMP production. Both low and high affinity binding sites were demonstrated in pancreatic acini from different species, in gastric chief cells prepared from guinea pig stomach and in membranes of rat gastric epithelial glands. In pancreatic acinar cells, secretin increases cAMP by interacting with a high affinity binding site,[252] whereas it seems highly probable that a low affinity binding site is linked to phospholipase C activation.[253]

High affinity secretin-binding sites have also been detected in mammalian brain extracts,[254] coupled with adenylate cyclase.[255] As in the peripheral system, both high and low affinity binding sites were identified.

13.6.6.4 Structure–Activity Relationships

Secretin analogs and partial secretin sequences are usually less potent and/or less efficient than secretin in exhibiting its various biological actions. It has been demonstrated that the N-terminal part of the molecule is important for eliciting full biological activity and for stabilizing the interaction of secretin with its receptor. Secretin-1–14 fragment has some effect in isolated pancreatic acinar cells,[256] and fat cells,[257] although with less potency than secretin. Shorter N-terminal fragments, such as secretin-1–6, were found to be inactive, as well as C-terminal fragments such as secretin-23–27, 14–27, 9–27 and 5–27. Although it has been reported that secretin-5–27 retains the capacity to stimulate pancreatic secretion in the rat and guinea pig, but with reduced efficacy and potency,[258] it has been further reported that secretin-5–27 caused no increase in the cellular cyclic AMP in guinea pig pancreatic acinar cells and had no agonistic properties in isolated guinea pig pancreatic acini.[245] More recently, it has been shown that secretin-5–27 has no intrinsic secretin-like activity in rat gastric glands,[241] in accordance with the data of Makhlouf *et al.* who found that this fragment has no enterogastrone activity on pentagastrin-stimulated gastric acid secretion in conscious dogs.[259] Secretin-5–27 neither alters pepsinogen release from isolated guinea pig gastric chief cells, nor alters cellular cyclic AMP.[260] However, secretin-5–27 interacts with the secretin receptor, and is able to antagonize the action of secretin on pancreatic acini of various species, on guinea pig gastric chief cells and on rat gastric glands.[241,260,261b] Longer C-terminal fragments, such as secretin-7–27, also inhibit the secretin-stimulated enzyme activity in rat pancreatic membranes.[261] C-terminal fragments, secretin-5–27 and 7–27, competitively and specifically inhibit secretin action through 'secretin-preferring receptors'. These selective secretin antagonists can thus be used as tools to distinguish between 'VIP-preferring' and 'secretin-preferring' binding sites.[262] Similarly, secretin-5–27 was demonstrated to function as a central secretin-receptor antagonist.[255]

The importance of the first amino acids of the N-terminal region of secretin was further illustrated by the data obtained with analogs in which the N-terminal residues have been deleted or replaced. Deletion of the N-terminal histidine residue, *i.e.* (de-His-1)-secretin, its modification, *i.e.* [¹²⁵I](His-1)-secretin,[263] (*N*-π-methyl-His-1)-secretin or (*N*-τ-methyl-His-1)-secretin,[264] or its substitution by Ala, Phe, Tyr,[264] or by D residues, *etc.*,[265,267] always leads to compounds of significantly reduced biological potency. In contrast, elongation at the N-terminus [*i.e.* (*N*-α-Tyr)-secretin or (deamino-Tyr-β-Ala)-secretin] causes only a moderate reduction in the biological activity.[266] Suppression of the *N*-α-amino function (*i.e.* (deamino-His-1)-secretin), as well as its protection (*i.e.* benzyloxycarbonyl-secretin), lead to compounds of weaker potency but still retaining significant activity, exhibiting, respectively, 25 and 36% of the biological activity of secretin in the ferret, cat and dog, indicating that the α-amino group is not essential but is important for full biological activity.[267] However, it has been reported recently that a free α-amino group at the N terminus is required for a sustained interaction with the secretin receptor on rat pancreatic acinar cells.[268] In position 3, the aspartic acid is of great importance and its substitution by glutamic acid, glutamine or asparagine, causes a sharp drop in biological activity.[269] Forming the peptide bond with the β-carboxylic function of aspartic acid (*i.e.* (β-Asp-3)-secretin) or cyclizing the aspartic acid in position 3 into succinimide (*i.e.* (aspartoyl-3)-secretin) also produced analogs exhibiting lower secretin activity.[270] Only its substitution by a cysteic acid, which mimics the charge and the shape of aspartic acid, leads to an analog of high potency.[271] Similarly, phenylalanine in position 6 was found to be significant, since an amino acid with an aromatic side chain is required for full biological activity.[272] Replacement of threonine in position 5 by valine resulted in an analog exhibiting the same activity as secretin in rat pancreatic acini.[272] Leucine in position 13 and alanine in position 17 are also important for biological activity, since their replacement leads to analogs of weaker potency.[267]

In conclusion, one can say that the whole sequence of secretin seems to be necessary for full biological potency and efficacy and that the N-terminal part is important for biological activity, particularly histidine in position 1, aspartic acid in position 3 and phenylalanine in position 6. In addition, all the amino acids of the N-terminal hexapeptide should have an L configuration. Leucine in position 13 and alanine in position 17 are also important for secretin-like activity.

Recently, the significance of leucine residues in positions 10 and 13 was pointed out. Their substitution by tyrosine residues was sufficient to practically eliminate secretin-induced changes in both inositol triphosphate and intracellular calcium, probably coupled to the low affinity secretin receptor in pancreatic tissues, although they have almost no effect on cAMP formation. These results suggested that the mechanism by which secretin stimulates adenylate cyclase and activates phospholipase C in acinar tissues is completely independent, and that the middle portion of the secretin molecule is important for binding to the low affinity receptor and/or activation of phospholipase C.[253]

On the endocrine pancreas, it has been demonstrated that the C-terminal hexapeptide of secretin, Leu-Leu-Gln-Gly-Leu-Val-NH$_2$, potentiates insulin release in mouse islets, mimicking the activity of secretin, although with less potency.[273] Interestingly, the N-terminal part of secretin, *i.e.* secretin-1–6 and secretin-2–6, were found to affect only glucose-induced insulin release.[274] These activities, even though much lower than that of secretin on a molar basis, were correlated to a hypothetical secretin receptor in the β-cell plasma membrane that might be activated by a particular conformational structure of secretin.

13.6.7 VASOACTIVE INTESTINAL PEPTIDE (VIP)

13.6.7.1 Introduction

Vasoactive intestinal peptide (VIP) was first isolated by Said and Mutt from hog upper intestinal tissue.[275] Its amino acid sequence was determined by the same group of investigators (Figure 10).[276] VIP consists of a single chain of 28 amino acid residues, with basic properties due to the predominance of arginine and lysine residues, and terminating in a carboxamide group. It became immediately obvious that this peptide, from its structural resemblance, belongs to the secretin family of gastrointestinal peptides, which also includes glucagon, gastric inhibitory polypeptide (GIP) and a peptide having N-terminal histidine and C-terminal isoleucine amide (PHI) (Figure 10).

VIP is processed from an approximately 20 kDa prepro-VIP, which also contains PHM-27 (peptide histidine methionine).[277]

As shown by radioimmunoassay and immunofluorescence, VIP immunoreactive neurons are found all over the central nervous system where VIP is a major component of the 'peptidergic' system of nerves, and are widely distributed in many organ systems, including the gastrointestinal, genitourinary, respiratory and cardiovascular systems.[278] VIP has also been localized in circulating platelets, mast cells[279] and neutrophils.[280]

Within mammals, VIP is generally well conserved, and sequences obtained from pig, rat, cow, dog and goat are identical. Guinea pig and chicken VIP differ from the porcine sequence, each having four amino acid substitutions (in positions 11, 13, 26 and 28 in the chicken, and in positions 5, 9, 19 and 26 in the guinea pig). The limited data available suggest, however, that these substitutions do not greatly affect biological activity.[281]

13.6.7.2 Biological Activities

VIP affects a variety of motor, secretory and metabolic processes in peripheral tissues. The effects of VIP include actions on vascular, respiratory and gastrointestinal smooth muscle, blood sugar, hormone release, gastrointestinal secretion, metabolism of liver and fat cells.[282] VIP is a potent vasodilator in most vascular beds, including the peripheral systemic vessels, as well as the splanchnic, coronary, cerebral, extracranial, salivary gland and pulmonary vessels (*vide infra*). In addition to its relaxant effect on pulmonary vascular smooth muscle, physiological studies have revealed that VIP can act as a potent bronchodilator in humans. In the gastrointestinal tract, VIP inhibits both acid and pepsin secretions stimulated by food, histamine and pentagastrin, although with less potency than secretin. VIP was demonstrated to be a potent stimulant of water and electrolyte secretion in intestinal epithelium, with greater potency than glucagon and secretin. In the pancreas, VIP stimulates enzyme and bicarbonate secretion. VIP also increases gall bladder secretion, particularly bicarbonate secretion. VIP stimulates both liver lipolysis and glycogenolysis, as well as endocrine secretion in the anterior pituitary, pancreas and adrenal cortex. An action of VIP on renal tubular reabsorption has been recently suggested.[283]

In the immune system, VIP appears to modulate lymphocyte migration,[284] mast cell mediator release[285] and natural killer cell activity.[286]

In the central nervous system, VIP causes neuronal depolarization and excitation. Recently, a neurotrophic action of VIP has been demonstrated in dissociated spinal cord cultures where VIP was shown to increase survival of spinal cord neurons.[287] Most, if not all, effects of VIP appear to be mediated by an increase in the production of cAMP.

13.6.7.3 VIP Receptors

Specific VIP-binding sites and/or VIP sensitive adenylate cyclase cAMP systems have been localized in the gastrointestinal tract, including the salivary gland, gastric smooth muscle, gastric cells, intestinal epithelial cells, pancreatic acini and islets, gall bladder, liver, adrenal gland, anterior pituitary, the blood vessels, the retina, the uterine smooth muscle, the adipocytes, myometrium, heart and lung from various species.[288] When comparing the ability of VIP and related peptides to interact with receptors and the coupled adenylate cyclase system in pancreatic acinar cells from rat or guinea pig,[289] and in gastric chief cells from guinea pig,[260] a first distinction between 'VIP-preferring' and 'secretin-preferring' binding sites can be established. Two classes of 'VIP-preferring' binding sites were generally demonstrated, a high affinity and a low affinity binding site.

Brain receptors for VIP were characterized in the cortex, hippocampus, striatum and thalamus, where both high affinity and low affinity binding sites were observed. Recent autoradiographic studies revealed that VIP receptors in the brain are mainly concentrated on the luminar surface of superficial blood vessels, in the first layer of the cortex and in the supraoptic, medial geniculate, cochlear, facial and thalamic nuclei, as well as in the limbic system.

The VIP receptor has also been characterized in human peripheral blood lymphocytes. Both high affinity and low affinity VIP-binding sites were observed in mononuclear leucocytes, whereas a single class of high affinity binding sites was observed in monocyte-depleted, lymphocyte-enriched populations. The putative lymphocyte receptor appears to be specific for VIP.

Heterogeneity of VIP receptors has been demonstrated by biochemical analysis of putative receptor proteins, after crosslinking $[^{125}I]$-VIP to membrane proteins by using bifunctional reagents. Both a high affinity receptor protein form ($M = 73\,000$–$86\,000$) and a low affinity receptor protein form ($M = 30\,000$–$36\,000$) have been detected in the liver and intestine. In addition, in rat liver, a third high affinity VIP-receptor protein has been identified ($M = 48\,000$), similar to that found in lymphocytes. Finally, recent studies have identified a 55 000 Da form of the VIP receptor in rat lung membranes.[290]

Taken together, the kinetic binding studies, the biochemical crosslinking experiments, and the functional tests of adenylate cyclase activation support the concept of at least two subclasses of high affinity VIP-binding sites, and a distinct molecular entity corresponding to the low affinity VIP receptor.

Based on kinetic studies, VIP receptors in the brain, intestine and immune cells appear to be very similar, with each tissue exhibiting both high affinity (1–10 nM) and low affinity (46–285 nM) binding sites. The high affinity binding site displays specificity for the entire 28 amino acid sequence, in preference to the C-terminal VIP fragment (VIP-10–28) or peptides of the secretin family. On the other hand, it was clearly demonstrated that VIP stimulates adenylate cyclase activity in the tissues that possess high affinity binding sites.

13.6.7.4 Structure–Activity Relationships

Systematic structure–activity studies, in which the contribution of the primary structure is evaluated by successive replacement of each residue, are possible with small peptides, but are rather tedious for polypeptides such as VIP. A few studies have documented the structural requirements for VIP-receptor recognition and ensuing adenylate cyclase activation and biological response, using VIP fragments, parent peptides of VIP and secretin analogs. Initial studies clearly indicated the structural importance of the whole VIP sequence for full biological activity.[291] However, the structural requirements of VIP receptors vary significantly from tissue to tissue.

No partial sequence of VIP satisfies the structural requirements for the full biological potency and effectiveness of the peptide, in contrast with other peptides such as cholecystokinin, gastrin and neurotensin, for which the full biological activity is retained in a small fragment. It was clearly demonstrated that neither the N-terminal sequences up to 1–14, nor the C-terminal sequences up to 20–28 were able to interact significantly with VIP receptors in rat and human intestine. Only VIP-2–28, VIP-14–28 and VIP-15–28 were able to inhibit binding of labeled VIP to human and rat intestinal membranes competitively, although with lower potency than VIP (respectively, 88, 8300 and 25 000 times less potent in rat and 70, 7900 and 13 000 times less potent in humans). The ability of these various VIP sequences in stimulating adenylate cyclase activity was in accordance with their binding data, whereas their efficacy was lower than that of VIP. These sequences, however, did not show any effect when tested *in vivo* on the rat blood pressure,[292] or *in vitro*, on the rabbit perfused heart.[293] Interaction of VIP-15–28 with VIP receptors was tentatively related to its ability to adopt an α-helical structure.[293]

The role of the N-terminal histidine residue of VIP has been studied. Various VIP analogs, *e.g.* (D-His-1)-VIP, (3-Me-His-1)-VIP, (Ac-His-1)-VIP and (D-Phe-1)-VIP, were compared to VIP in stimulating adenylate cyclase activity from various tissues. The integrity of the imidazole ring, in a well-defined orientation, appeared to be important, considering the weak potency and/or efficacy of (D-His-1)-VIP, (3-Me-His-1)-VIP and (D-Phe-1)-VIP. Similarly, the α-NH$_2$ group of histidine in position 1 appeared to be essential, since its acetylation led to an analog, (Ac-His-1)-VIP, of weaker potency and efficacy. However, some differences could be found in the responses of mammalian tissues to these VIP analogs. VIP and VIP analogs displayed almost the same intrinsic activity in lung and liver membrances from rats, the analogs being characterized by their reduced potency. In these two tissues, the α-amino group of histidine did not appear to be greatly significant. However, VIP analogs modified on the histidine residue in position 1 act as partial VIP agonists in rat brain, pituitary and pancreatic membranes, and as full VIP agonists, although with reduced potency, in rat liver and pulmonary membranes. These differences in activity were reported by the authors, not to necessarily reflect basic receptor difference, but probably a different coupling of VIP receptors to adenylate cyclase activity.[294] In other words, the same VIP analog might act as a full VIP agonist in a highly coupled system and as a partial VIP agonist in a poorly coupled system. Suppression of the histidine residue in position 1 led to a VIP fragment (*e.g.* VIP-2–28) with a markedly reduced affinity for the VIP receptor on intestinal epithelial cells,[295] and an even greater reduced activity in adenylate cyclase activation. However, VIP-2–28 is a partial VIP agonist in rat intestinal epithelial membranes and a full VIP agonist in similar human membranes, although with much lower potency.[295]

When the N-terminal and the C-terminal parts of the VIP sequence were joined together by a peptide bond, such as in VIP-1–6; 20–28 or VIP-1–9; 21–28, no activity at all was detected in terms of binding to VIP receptors and adenylate cyclase activation in human and rat intestinal membranes, or contraction of the isolated guinea pig *Taenia coli*,[296] supporting a major role also for the middle sequence.

When amino acid substitutions were applied in the 2-, 3- or 4-position of VIP, *e.g.* replacement of L isomers by their D isomers, less active analogs than VIP on rat pancreatic, hepatic and pituitary membranes, and on rat pancreatic acini,[297] were usually obtained. Their potency decreased gradually when D substitutions were closer to the N terminus: (D-Ala-4)-VIP > (D-Asp-3)-VIP > (D-Ser-2)-VIP > (D -His-1)-VIP. However, the efficacy of analogs substituted in the 2-position was different according to the tissue tested, probably reflecting a tissue dependent VIP-receptor/effector coupling. Coy *et al.* suggested that VIP (and secretin) may have a β-bend structure in the 1–4 region,[298] which could explain the importance of the L configuration of the first four amino acids of VIP for binding to VIP receptors and in resulting adenylate cyclase activation.

It has also been clearly established that the amino acid residues from positions 11 to 22 play a significant role in the recognition of VIP receptors on synaptosomes from the rat cerebral cortex.[299] In particular, the basic amino acids, Arg-12, Lys-20 and Lys-21, seem to be important for VIP-receptor recognition, whereas Arg-14 appeared to be less crucial.[300] Amino acid residues Asp-3, Phe-6, Thr-7 and Leu-23, which are common in VIP, secretin, PHI and GRF, may also be important for VIP-receptor binding. Oxidation of the methionine residue in position 17, or iodination of the tyrosine residue in position 10, does not significantly modify the biological activity of VIP.[301] Interestingly, iodination of Tyr-22, located in the apolar helical C-terminal region of VIP, increases the effectiveness of VIP interaction with its receptors.[299,302]

Conversely, it appeared that the interaction of VIP with NK cells requires a smaller portion of the molecule than its vasoactive effects. Such a short fragment as VIP-15–28, which was found to adopt a highly helical structure,[292] exhibits the activity of the entire VIP molecule.[286]

In conclusion, one can say that results collected in the literature reveal a complex structure–activity relationship in the VIP molecule. However, one main feature of VIP seems to be the structural integrity of the entire sequence for retaining biological activity. The α-helical structure of the middle portion of the molecule seems to be crucial for recognition of VIP receptors, but the N- and C-terminal parts are necessary for full potency of VIP binding. An organized molecular conformation seems to be important for biological activity of VIP and for its interaction with its binding sites.

13.6.7.5 VIP Antagonists

Structure–activity relationships in VIP and related peptides indicated that His-1 plays an important role not only for the recognition by VIP receptors, but also more crucially, for generating the biological responses, *e.g.* stimulation of adenylate cyclase activity, suggesting that further substitutions or modifications in this area could lead to the design of VIP antagonists. In this connection, substituted human growth hormone-releasing factors (hGRF), which have a Tyr-1 instead of His-1 in VIP, were tested for their ability to compete with labeled-VIP binding and to stimulate adenylate cyclase activity in rat and human intestinal epithelial plasma membranes. One of the hGRF analogs, *e.g.* (Ac-Tyr-1)-hGRF, was found to competitively antagonize VIP actions in the rat.[303] VIP-10–28, which was suggested as a VIP antagonist in rat pancreatic acini,[304] was proposed as an antagonist of VIP in the colon carcinoma cell line, HT29.[305] More recently, (4-Cl-D-Phe-6, Leu-17)-VIP was found to selectively antagonize the action of peptides that interact with the VIP receptor,[306] in exocrine pancreas and in a colon tumor cell line (T84 cells), but exhibited partial agonist activity at high concentrations. However, there is still a need for specific, potent VIP antagonists.

13.6.8 REFERENCES

1. B. Desbuquois, *Recept. Ligands in Intracell. Commun.*, 1985, **4**, 419 and references cited therein.
2. (a) A. Anastasi, V. Erspamer and M. Bucci. *Experientia*, 1971, **27**, 166; (b) A. Anastasi, V. Erspamer and R. Endean, *Experientia*, 1975, **31**, 510.
3. T. Nakajima, T. Tanimura and J. J. Pisano, *Fed. Proc., Fed. Am. Soc. Exp. Biol.*, 1970, **23**, 282.
4. T. Yasuhara, T. Nakajima, K. Nikihara, C. H. Yanaihara, N. Yanaihara, V. Erspamer and G. Falconieri-Erspamer, *Biomed. Res.*, 1983, **4**, 407.
5. T. J. McDonald, H. Jornvall, G. Nilsson, M. Vagne, M. Ghatei, S. R. Bloom and V. Mutt, *Biochem. Biophys. Res. Commun.*, 1979, **90**, 227.
6. (a) N. Minamino, K. Kangawa and H. Matsuo, *Biochem. Biophys. Res. Commun.*, 1983, **114**, 541; (b) J. R. Reeve, J. H. Walsh, P. Chew, B. Clark, D. Hawke and J. E. Shively, *J. Biol. Chem.*, 1983, **258**, 5582; (c) N. Minamino, K. Kangawa and H. Matsuo, *Biochem. Biophys. Res. Commun.*, 1984, **119**, 14.
7. P. Melchiorri, in 'Comprehensive Endocrinology', ed. G. B. J. Glass, Raven Press, New York, 1980, p. 717.
8. G. H. Greeley, Jr. and J. Newman, in 'Gastrointestinal Endocrinology', ed. J. C. Thompson, G. H. Greeley, P. L. Rayford and C. M. Townsend, Jr., McGraw-Hill, New York, 1987, vol. 25, p. 322.
9. (a) M. Miyata, P. L. Rayford and J. C. Thompson, *Surgery (St. Louis)*, 1980, **87**, 209; (b) A. Ayalon, R. Yazigi, P. G. Devitt, P. L. Rayford and J. C. Thompson, *Biochem. Biophys. Res. Commun.*, 1981, **99**, 1390; (c) N. W. Bunnett, B. Clark,

H. T. Debas, R. C. Del Milton, T. O. G. Kovacs, M. S. Orloff, T. N. Pappas, J. R. Reeve, J. E. Rivier and J. H. Walsh, *J. Physiol. (London)*, 1985, **365**, 121; (d) Y. Tache, W. Marki, J. Rivier, W. Vale and M. Brown, *Gastroenterology*, 1981, **81**, 298.

10. (a) M. Deschodt-Lanckman, P. Robberecht, P. De Neef, M. Lammens and J. Christophe, *J. Clin. Invest.*, 1976, **58**, 891; (b) H. R. Fender, P. J. Curtis, P. L. Rayford and J. C. Thompson, *Surg. Forum*, 1976, **27**, 414.

11. (a) A. N. Corps, L. H. Rees and K. D. Brown, *Biochem. J.*, 1985, **231**, 781; (b) I. Zachary and E. Rozengurt, *Proc. Natl. Acad. Sci. USA*, 1985, **82**, 7616.

12. J. C. Willey, J. F. Lechner and C. C. Harris, *Exp. Cell Res.*, 1984, **153**, 245.

13. (a) F. Cuttitta, D. N. Carney, J. Mulshine, T. W. Moody, J. Fedorko, A. Fischler and J. D. Minna, *Nature (London)*, 1985, **316**, 823; (b) M. B. Sporn and A. B. Roberts, *Nature (London)*, 1985, **313**, 745.

14. A. Pert, T. Moody, C. Pert, L. DeWald and J. Rivier, *Brain Res.*, 1980, **193**, 209;

15. (a) D. D. Avery, M. F. Hawkins and B. A. Wunder, *Neuropharmacology*, 1980, **20**, 23; (b) M. Brown, J. Rivier and W. Vale, *Science (Washington, D.C.)*, 1977, **196**, 998; (c) J. E. Rivier and M. R. Brown, *Biochemistry*, 1978, **17**, 1766; (d) Y. Tache, Q. Pittman and M. Brown, *Brain Res.*, 1980, **188**, 525.

16. (a) M. R. Brown, J. E. Rivier and W. W. Vale, *Life Sci.*, 1977, **21**, 1729; (b) M. Brown, Y. Tache and D. Fisher, *Endocrinology (Baltimore)*, 1979, **105**, 660.

17. (a) G. De Caro, M. Mariotti, M. Massi and L. G. Micossi, *Pharmacol. Biochem. Behav.*, 1980, **13**, 229; (b) P. J. Kulkosky, J. Gibbs and G. P. Smith, *Physiol. Behav.*, 1982, **28**, 505.

18. M. Dubrasquet, C. Roze, N. Ling and H. Florencio, *Regul. Pept.*, 1982, **3**, 105.

19. C. Rivier, J. Rivier and W. Vale, *Endocrinology (Baltimore)*, 1978, **102**, 519.

20. (a) C. B. Nemeroff, D. Luttinger and A. J. Prange, Jr., in 'The Handbook of Psychopharmacology', ed. L. L. Iversen, S. D. Iversen and S. H. Snyder, Plenum Press, New York, 1983, p. 363; (b) L. J. Stein and S. C. Woods, *Peptides (N.Y.)*, 1981, **2**, 431; (c) J. Gibbs, D. J. Fauser, E. A. Rowe, B. J. Rolls, E. T. Rolls and S. J. Madison, *Nature (London)*, 1979, **281**, 208.

21. (a) R. T. Jensen, T. Moody, C. Pert, J. E. Rivier and J. D. Gardner, *Proc. Natl. Acad. Sci. USA*, 1978, **75**, 5372; (b) R. T. Jensen and J. D. Gardner, *Regul. Pept.*, 1987, **19**, 116.

22. (a) P. W. Mantyh, C. R. Mantyh, A. S. Giraud, A. H. Soll, J. H. Walsh and S. R. Vigna, *Regul. Pept.*, 1987, **19**, 125; (b) P. Singh, H. Singh, J. Marks and J. C. Thompson, *Can. J. Physiol. Pharmacol. (abstract)*, 1986, 175; (c) S. R. Vigna, A. Giraud, A. H. Soll and J. H. Walsh, *Can. J. Physiol. Pharmacol. (abstract)*, 1986, 4.

23. J. B. Fischer and A. Schonbrunn, *Regul. Pept.*, 1987, **19**, 108.

24. I. Zachary and E. Rozengurt, *Proc. Natl. Acad. Sci. USA*, 1985, **82**, 7616.

25. (a) S. A. Mendoza, J. A. Schneider, A. Lopez-Rivas, J. W. Sinnet-Smith and E. Rozengurt, *J. Cell. Biol.*, 1986, **102**, 2223; (b) T. W. Moody, A. Murphy, S. Mahmoud and G. Fiskum, *Biochem. Biophys. Res. Commun.*, 1987, **147**, 189; (c) R. Heikkila, J. B. Trepel, F. Cuttitta, L. M. Neckers and E. A. Sausville, *J. Biol. Chem.*, 1987, **262**, 16 456.

26. J. M. Westendorf and A. J. Schonbrunn, *J. Biol. Chem.*, 1983, **258**, 7527.

27. (a) A. Pert, T. W. Moody, C. Pert, L. A. Dewald and J. Rivier, *Brain Res.*, 1980, **193**, 209; (b) M. A. Zarbin, M. J. Kuhar, T. L. O'Donohue, S. S. Wolf and T. W. Moody, *J. Neurosci.*, 1985, **5**, 429; (c) S. S. Wolf and T.W. Moody, *Peptides (N.Y.)*, 1985, **6**, suppl. 1, 111; (d) T. W. Moody, R. L. Getz, C. A. Merchant and J. M. Rosenstein, *Regul. Pept.*, 1987, **19**, 99.

28. W. Marki, M. Brown and J. E. Rivier, *Peptides (N.Y.)*, 1981, **2**, 169.

29. G. H. Greeley, Jr., A. Spannagel, F. L. C. Hill and J. C. Thompson, *Proc. Soc. Exp. Biol. Med.*, 1986, **183**, 136.

30. E. A. Mayer, J. R. Reeve, Jr., S. Khawaja, P. Chew, J. Elashoff, B. Clark and J. H. Walsh, *Am. J. Physiol.*, 1986, **250**, G581.

31. S. L. Swope and A. Schonbrunn, *Proc. Natl. Acad. Sci. USA*, 1986, **81**, 1822.

32. (a) Y. Taché, M. Brown and R. Collu, in 'Brain Neurotransmitters and Hormones', ed. R. Collu, J. R. Ducharme, G. Tolis and A. Barbeau, Raven Press, New York, 1982, p. 183; (b) F. Girard, C. Aubé, S. St. Pierre and F. Jolicoeur, *Neuropeptides (Edinburgh)*, 1983, **3**, 443.

33. M. Broccardo, G. Falconier, G. Erspamer, P. Melchiorri and L. Negri, *Br. J. Pharmacol.*, 1975, **55**, 221.

34. V. Erspamer and P. Melchiorri, *Pure Appl. Chem.*, 1973, **35**, 463.

35. (a) V. Erspamer and P. Melchiorri, in 'Gastrointestinal Hormones', ed. J. C. Thompson, University of Texas Press, Austin, Texas, 1975, p. 575; (b) R. T. Jensen, J. E. Rivier and J. D. Gardner, *Gastroenterology*, 1979, **76**, 1160 (abstract); (c) J. Rivier and M. Brown, *Biochemistry*, 1978, **17**, 1766.

36. H. Mukai, K. Kawai, Y. Suzuki, K. Yamashita and E. Munekata, *Am. J. Physiol.*, 1987, **252**, E765.

37. F. Girard, H. Bachelard, S. St.Pierre and F. Rioux, *Eur. J. Pharmacol.*, 1984, **102**, 489.

38. J. E. Rivier and M. R. Brown, *Biochemistry*, 1978, **7**, 1766.

39. T. W. Moody, J. N. Crawley and R. T. Jensen, *Peptides (N.Y.)*, 1982, **3**, 559.

40. W. Märki, M. Brown and J. E. Rivier, *Peptides (N.Y.)*, 1981, **2**, suppl. 2, 169.

41. D. Erne and R. Schwyzer, *Biochemistry*, 1987, **26**, 6316.

42. L. Negri, *Eur. J. Pharmacol.*, 1986, **132**, 207.

43. R. T. Jensen, S. W. Jones, K. Folkers and J. D. Gardner, *Nature (London)*, 1984, **309**, 61.

44. P. J. Woll and E. Rozengurt, *Proc. Natl. Acad. Sci. USA*, 1988, **85**, 1859.

45. P. Heinz-Erian, D. H. Coy, M. Tamura, S. W. Jones, J. D. Gardner and R. T. Jensen, *Am. J. Physiol.*, 1987, **252**, G439.

46. D. H. Coy, P. Heinz-Erian, N. Y. Jiang, J. Taylor, J. P. Moreau, W. T. Wolfrey, J. D. Gardner and R. T. Jensen, *J. Biol. Chem.*, 188, **263**, 5056.

47. A. C. Ivy and E. Oldberg, *Am. Physiol.*, 1928, **86**, 599.

48. A. A. Harper and M. S. Raper, *J. Physiol. (London)*, 1942, **102**, 115.

49. J. E. Jorpes, *Gastroenterology*, 1968, **55**, 157.

50. Z. Z. Zhou, J. Eng. Y. C. E. Pan, P. M. Chang, J. D. Hulmes, J. P. Ruafman and R. S. Yallow, *Peptides (N.Y.)*, 1985, **6**, 337.

51. G. J. Dockray, R. Dimaline, S. Pauwels and A. Varro, in 'Peptide Hormones, Prohormones and their Fragments: Processing, Biological Activity and Pharmacology', ed. J. Martinez, Horwood, Chichester, 1989, p. 244.

52. A. Anastasi, V. Erspamer and R. Endean, *Experientia*, 1967, **23**, 699.

53. (a) G. J. Dockray, R. A. Gregory, J. B. Hutchinson, J. I. Harris and M. J. Runswick, *Nature (London)*, 1977, **270**, 359; (b) J. F. Rehfeld, *J. Biol. Chem.*, 1978, **253**, 4022; (c) P. Robberecht, M. Deschodt-Lanckman and J. J. Vanderhaeghen, *Proc. Natl. Acad. Sci. USA*, 1978, **75**, 524.

54. J. E. Morley, *Life Sci.*, 1982, **30**, 479.

55. For a general review see: 'Neuronal Cholecystokinin', eds. J. J. Vanderhaeghen and J. N. Crawley, *Ann. N.Y. Acad. Sci.*, 1985, **448**, 1.
56. V. Mutt, in 'Gastrointestinal Hormones', ed. G. B. J. Glass, Raven Press, New York, 1980, p. 169; M. I. Grossman, in 'Endocrinology of the Gut', ed. W. Y. Chey and F. P. Brooks, C. B. Slack, Inc., Thorofare, NJ, 1974, p. 65.
57. (a) M. L. Villanueva, J. Martinez, M. Bodanszky, S. M. Collins, R. T. Jensen and J. D. Gardner, *Am. J. Physiol.*, 1982, **243**, G214; (b) M. Younes, R. T. Jensen and J. D. Gardner, *Biochim. Biophys. Acta*, 1987, **930**, 410.
58. M. Marx, G. Gomez, J. Lonovics and J. C. Thompson, in 'Gastrointestinal Endocrinology', ed. J. C. Thompson, G. H. Greeley, Jr., P. L. Rayford and C. M. Townsend, Jr., McGraw-Hill, New York, 1987, vol. 15, p. 213.
59. (a) H. Sankaran, I. D. Goldfine, C. W. Deveney, K. Y. Wong and J. A. Williams, *J. Biol. Chem.*, 1980, **255**, 1849; (b) R. T. Jensen, G. F. Lemp and J. D. Gardner, *Proc. Natl. Acad. Sci. USA*, 1980, **77**, 2079; (c) H. Sankaran, I. D. Goldfine, A. Bailey, V. Licko and J. A. Williams, *Am. J. Physiol.*, 1982, **250**, G242.
60. T. H. Moran, P. H. Robinson, M. S. Goldrich and P. R. McHugh, *Brain Res.*, 1986, **362**, 175.
61. R. T. Jensen, G. F. Lemp and J. D. Gardner, *J. Biol. Chem.*, 1982, **257**, 5554.
62. D. Fourmy, A. Zahidi, L. Pradayrol, J. Vaysette and A. Ribet, *Regul. Pept.*, 1984, **10**, 57.
63. D. H. Yu, M. Noguchi, Z. C. Zhou, M. L. Villanueva, J. D. Gardner and R. T. Jensen, *Am. J. Physiol.*, 1987, **253**, G793.
64. (a) M. Delvaux, M. J. Bastie, M. Dufresne, N. Vaysse and A. Ribet, in 'Gastrin and Cholecystokinin, Chemistry, Physiology and Pharmacology', ed. J. P. Bali and J. Martinez, Elsevier, Amsterdam, 1987, p. 65; (b) M. J. Bastie, M. Delvaux, M. Dufresne, J. S. Saunier-Blache, N. Vaysse and A. Ribet, *Am. J. Physiol.*, 1988, **254**, G25.
65. J. Behar and P. Biancani, *J. Clin. Invest.*, 1980, **66**, 1231.
66. J. Behar and P. Biancani, *Gastroenterology*, 1987, **92**, 764.
67. (a) J. F. Rehfeld, L. I. Larsson, N. R. Goltermann, T. W. Schwartz, J. J. Holst, S. L. Jensen and J. S. Morley, *Nature (London)*, 1980, **284**, 33; (b) S. Rattan and R. K. Goyal, *Gastroenterology*, 1986, **90**, 94.
68. R. W. Steigerwalt, I. D. Goldfine and J. A. Williams, *Am. J. Physiol.*, 1984, **247**, G709.
69. M. J. Shaw, E. M. Hadac and L. J. Miller, *J. Biol. Chem.*, 1987, **262**, 14 313.
70. P. Singh and J. C. Thompson, in 'Gastrointestinal Endocrinology', ed. J. C. Thompson, G. H. Greeley, Jr., P. L. Rayford and C. M. Townsend, Jr., McGraw-Hill, New York, 1987, vol. 7, p. 69.
71. (a) S. J. Hersey, D. May and D. Schyberg, *Am. J. Physiol.*, 1983, **244**, G192; (b) D. K. Kasbekar, R. T. Jensen and J. D. Gardner, *Am. J. Physiol.*, 1983, **244**, G392.
72. (a) A. Saito, H. Sankaran, I. D. Goldfine and J. A. Williams, *Science (Washington, D.C.)*, 1980, **208**, 1155; (b) R. B. Innis and S. H. Snyder, *Proc. Natl. Acad. Sci. USA*, 1980, **77**, 6917; (c) S. E. Hays, M. C. Beinfeld, R. T. Jensen, F. K. Goodwin and S. M. Paul, *Neuropeptides (Edinburgh)*, 1980, **1**, 53.
73. D. R. Hill, N. J. Campbell, T. M. Shaw and G. N. Woodruff, *J. Neurosci.* 1987, **7**, 2967.
74. J. D. Gardner and R. T. Jensen, *Recent Prog. Horm. Res.*, 1983, **39**, 211.
75. P. H. G.M. Willems, I. G. P. van Nooij, H. E. M. G. Haenen and J. J. H. H. M. de Pont, *Biochim. Biophys. Acta*, 1987, **930**, 230.
76. T. V. Schrenck, R. T. Jensen and J. D. Gardner, in 'Gastrin and Cholecystokinin, Chemistry, Physiology and Pharmacology', ed. J. P. Bali and J. Martinez, Elsevier, Amsterdam, 1987, p. 49.
77. T. E. Solomon, T. Yamada, J. Elashoff, J. Wood and C. Beglinger, *Am. J. Physiol.*, 1984, **247**, G105.
78. M. L. Villanueva, S. M. Collins, R. T. Jensen and J. D. Gardner, *Am. J. Physiol.*, 1982, **242**, G416.
79. (a) G. Z. Pan, J. Martinez, M. Bodanszky, R. T. Jensen and J. D. Gardner, *Biochim. Biophys. Acta*, 1981, **678**, 352; (b) M. Bodanszky, J. C. Tolle, J. D. Gardner, M. D. Walker and V. Mutt, *Int. J. Pept. Protein Res.*, 1980, **16**, 402.
80. (a) M. Bodanszky, J. Martinez, M. D. Walker and J. D. Gardner, *J. Med. Chem.*, 1980, **23**, 82; (b) R. de Castiglione, in 'First International Symposium on Hormonal Receptors in Digestive Tract Physiology', ed. S. Bonfils, P. Fromageot and G. Rosselin, Elsevier, Amsterdam, 1977, p. 33.
81. Y. Okabayashi, M. Otsuki, A. Ohki, C. Sakamoto and S. Baba, *Endocrinology (Baltimore)*, 1983, **113**, 2210.
82. K. Hermansen, *Endocrinology (Baltimore)*, 1984, **114**, 1770.
83. R. T. Jensen, S. W. Jones and J. D. Gardner, *Biochim. Biophys. Acta*, 1983, **761**, 269.
84. M. Spanarkel, J. Martinez, C. Briet, R. T. Jensen and J. D. Gardner, *J. Biol. Chem.*, 1983, **258**, 6746.
85. J. M. Howard, M. Knight, R. T. Jensen and J. D. Gardner, *Am. J. Physiol.*, 1984, **247**, G261.
86. M. Otsuki, Y. Okabayashi, A. Ohki, T. Oka, M. Fujii, T. Nakamura, N. Sugiura, N. Yanaihara and S. Baba, *Am. J. Physiol.*, 1986, **250**, G405.
87. M. Kimura, I. Kimura, T. Kondoh and M. Kimura, *Eur. J. Pharmacol.*, 1986, **132**, 245.
88. J. Martinez and J. P. Bali, *Regul. Pept.*, 1984, **9**, 259.
89. M. Rodriguez, M. F. Lignon, M. C. Galas, C. Mendre and J. Martinez, in 'Peptides 1986, Proc. 19th Eur. Peptide Symp.', ed. D. Theodoropoulos, de Gruiter, Berlin, 1987, p. 455.
90. M. C. Galas, M. F. Lignon, M. Rodriguez, C. Mendre, P. Fulcrand, J. Laur and J. Martinez, *Am. J. Physiol.*, 1988, **254**, G176.
91. M. F. Lignon, M. C. Galas, M. Rodriguez, G. Guillon, S. Jard and J. Martinez, in 'Gastrin and Cholecystokinin, Chemistry, Physiology and Pharmacology', ed. J. P. Bali and J. Martinez, Elsevier, Amsterdam, 1987, p. 57.
92. J. Martinez, M. Rodriguez, M. F. Lignon and M. C. Galas, in 'CCK-receptors Antagonists, Cold Spring Harbor Seminars', ed. R. Wang and R. Schoenfeld, Liss, New York, 1988, vol. 47, p. 29.
93. A. Rakovska, P. Henklein, K. Milenov, K. Nieber and P. Oehme, *Methods Find. Exp. Clin. Pharmacol.*, 1987, **9**, 429.
94. C. Moummi, R. Magous, M. Rodriguez, J. Martinez and J. P. Bali, in 'Gastrin and Cholecystokinin, Chemistry, Physiology and Pharmacology', Le Cap d'Agde, France, 7–11 September 1987, abstract; *Gastroent. Clin. Biol.*, 1987, **11**, 737.
95. (a) J. Martinez, M. Rodriguez, J. P. Bali and J. Laur, *J. Med. Chem.*, 1986, **29**, 2201; (b) J. Martinez, M. Rodriguez, J. P. Bali and J. Laur, *Int. J. Pept. Protein Res.*, 1986, **28**, 529.
96. M. Knight, C. A. Tamminga, L. Steardo, M. E. Beck, P. Barone and T. N. Chase, *Eur. J. Pharmacol.*, 1984, **105**, 49.
97. J. A. Williams, K. A. Gryson and D. J. McChesney, *Peptides (N.Y.)*, 1986, **7**, 293.
98. A. Dumbrille-Ross and P. Seeman, *Peptides (N.Y.)*, 1984, **5**, 1207.
99. T. Moroji and Y. Hagino, *Neuropeptides (Edinburgh)*, 1986, **8**, 273.
100. G. Zetler, in 'Neuronal Cholecystokinin', ed. J. J. Vanderhaeghen and J. N. Crawley, *Ann. N.Y. Acad. Sci.*, 1985, **448**, 448.

101. S. R. Vigna, J. Szecowka and J. A. Williams, *Brain Res.*, 1985, **343**, 394.
102. P. Worms, J. Martinez, C. Briet, B. Castro and K. Bizière, *Eur. J. Pharmacol.*, 1986, **121**, 395.
103. B. A. MacVicar, J. P. Kerrin and J. S. Davidson, *Brain Res.*, 1987, **406**, 130.
104. (a) M. Bodanszky, S. Natarajan, W. Hahne and J. D. Gardner, *J. Med. Chem.*, 1977, **20**, 1047; (b) M. Bodanszky, J. Martinez, G. P. Priestly, J. D. Gardner and V. Mutt, *J. Med. Chem.*, 1978, **21**, 1030.
105. (a) I. Marseigne and B. Roques, *J Org. Chem.*, 1988, **53**, 3621; (b) I. Marseigne, P. Roy, A. Dor, C. Durieux, D. Pelaprat, M. Reibaud, J. C. Blanchard and B. P. Roques, *J. Med. Chem.*, 1989, **32**, 445.
106. D. Gillissen, A. Trzeciak, R. K. M. Muller and R. O. Studer, *Int. J. Pept. Protein Chem.*, 1979, **13**, 130.
107. H. M. Rajh, M. J. Smyth, B. A. M. Renckens, J. W. C. M. Jansen, J. J. H. H. M. Depont, S. L. Bonting, G. I. Tesser and R. J. V. Nivard, *Biochim. Biophys. Acta*, 1980, **632**, 386.
108. B. Penke, F. Hajnal, L. Lonovics, G. Holzinger, T. Kadar, G. Telegdy and J. Rivier, *J. Med. Chem.*, 1984, **27**, 845.
109. C. Yanaihara, N. Sugiura, K. Kashimoto, M. Kondo, M. Kawamura, S. Naruse, A. Yasui and N. Yanaihara, *Biomed. Res.*, 1985, **6**, 111.
110. J. Martinez, F. Winternitz, M. Bodanszky, J. D. Gardner, M. D. Walker and V. Mutt, *J. Med. Chem.*, 1982, **25**, 589.
111. C. Durieux, J. Belleney, J. Y. Lallemand, B. P. Roques and M. C. Fournier-Zaluski, *Biochem. Biophys. Res. Commun.*, 1983, **114**, 705.
112. (a) B. Charpentier, I. Marseigne, A. Dor, D. Begue, C. Durieux, D. Pelaprat, M. Reibaud, J. L. Zundel, J. C. Blanchard and B. P. Roques, in 'Peptides, Chemistry and Biology, Proc. Tenth Am. Peptide Symp. ', ed. G. R. Marshall, Escom, Leiden, 1988, p. 608; (b) B. Charpentier, D. Pelaprat, C. Durieux, A. Dor, M. Reibaud, J. C. Blanchard and B. P. Roques, *Proc. Natl. Acad. Sci. USA*, 1988, **85**, 1968; (c) B. Charpentier, C. Durieux, I. Menant and B. P. Roques, *J. Med. Chem.*, 1987, **30**, 962.
113. M. Rodriguez, M. F. Lignon, M. C. Galas and J. Martinez, 'Proc. 11th American Reptide Symposium', ed. J. Rivier, Escom, Leiden, 1989, in press.
114. M. Rodriguez, M. F. Lignon, M. C. Galas, P. Fulcrand, C. Mendre, A. Aumelas, J. Laur and J. Martinez, *J. Med. Chem.*, 1987, **30**, 1366.
115. (a) J. D. Gardner and R. T. Jensen, *Am. J. Physiol.*, 1984, **246**, G471; (b) P. N. Maton, R. T. Jensen and J. D. Gardner, *Horm. Metab. Res.*, 1986, **18**, 2; (c) M. A. Silverman, R. E. Greenberg and S. Bank, *Am. J. Gastroenterol.*, 1987, **82**, 703.
116. (a) R. T. Jensen, R. B. Murphy, M. Trampota, L. H. Schneider, S. W. Jones, J. M. Howard and J. D. Gardner, *Am. J. Physiol.*, 1985, **249**, G214; (b) F. Makovec, R. Chisté, M. Bani, L. Revel, I. Setnikar and L. A. Rovati, *Eur. J. Med. Chem.*, 1986, **21**, 9; (c) R. T. Jensen, Z. C. Zhou, R. B. Murphy, S. W. Jones, I. Setnikar, L. A. Rovati and J. D. Gardner, *Am. J. Physiol.*, 1986, **251**, G839.
117. (a) F. Makovec, R. Chisté, M. Bani, M. A. Pacini, I. Setnikar and L.A. Rovati, *Arzneim-Forsch. Drug Res.*, 1985, **35**, 1048; (b) F. Makovec, M. Bani, R. Chiste, L. Revel, L. C. Rovati and L. A. Rovati, *Arzneim-Forsch. Drug Res.*, 1986, **36**, 98; (c) I. Setnikar, M. Bani, R. Cereda, R. Chiste, F. Makovec, M. A. Pacini, L. Revel, L. C. Rovati and L. A. Rovati, *Arzneim-Forsch. Drug Res.*, 1987, **37**, 703; (d) L. C. Rovati, M. Bani, F. Makovec, L. Revel and I. Setnikar, in 'Gastrin and Cholecystokinin, Chemistry, Physiology and Pharmacology', ed. J. P. Bali and J. Martinez, Elsevier, Amsterdam, 1987, p. 45.
118. (a) F. Makovec, M. Bani, R. Cereda, R. Chiste, L. Revel, L. C. Rovati, I. Setnikar and L. A. Rovati, *Peptides (N.Y.)*, 1986, **7**, 1159; (b) L. A. Rovati, in 'Gastrin and Cholecystokinin, Chemistry, Physiology and Pharmacology', ed. J. P. Bali and J. Martinez, Elsevier, Amsterdam, 1987, p. 255.
119. (a) F. Makovec, R. Chisté, L. C. Rovati and I. Setnikar, *Regul. Pept.*, 1987, **11**, 725; (b) M. F. Lignon, M. C. Galas, M. Rodriguez and J. Martinez, in '2éme Forum Peptides', Nancy, France, 2–6 May 1988, abstract.
120. R. T. Jensen, R. W. Jones and J. D. Gardner, *Biochim. Biophys. Acta*, 1983, **761**, 269.
121. P. N. Maton, V. E. Sutliff, R. T. Jensen and J. D. Gardner, *Am. J. Physiol.*, 1985, **248**, G479.
122. M. F. Lignon, M. C. Galas, M. Rodriguez, A. Aumelas, J. Laur and J. Martinez, *J. Biol. Chem.*, 1987, **262**, 7226.
123. C. Moummi, Ph.D. Dissertation, Universite de Montpellier I, Sciences Pharmaceutiques et Biologiques, Montpellier, France, 1987.
124. C. Mendre, M. Rodriguez, C. Guedet, M. F. Lignon, M. C. Galas, J. Laur, P. Worms and J. Martinez, *J. Biol. Chem.*, 1988, **263**, 10641.
125. C. Mendre, M. Rodriguez, J. Laur, A. Aumelas and J. Martinez, *Tetrahedron*, 1988, **44**, 4415.
126. C. Mendre, Ph.D. Dissertation, Universite des Sciences et Techniques du Languedoc, Montpellier, France, 1987.
127. M. A. Goetz, M. Lopez, R. L. Monaghan, R. S. L. Chang, V. J. Lotti and T. B. Chen. *J. Antibiot.*, 1985, **38**, 1633.
128. R. S. L. Chang, V. J. Lotti, R. L. Monaghan, J. Birnbaum, E. O. Stapley, M. A. Goetz, G. Albers-Schönberg, A. A. Patchett, J. M. Liesch, O. D. Hensens and J. P. Springer, *Science (Washington, D.C.)*, 1985, **230**, 177.
129. P. S. Anderson, R. M. Freidinger, B. E. Evans, M. G. Bock, K. E. Rittle, R. M. DiPardo, W. L. Whitter, D. F. Veber, R. S. L. Chang and V. J. Lotti, in 'Gastrin and Cholecystokinin, Chemistry, Physiology and Pharmacology', ed. J. P. Bali and J. Martinez, Elsevier, Amsterdam, 1987, p. 235.
130. B. E. Evans, M. G. Bock, K. E. Rittle, R. M. DiPardo, W. L. Whitter, D. F. Veber, R. P. S. Anderson and R. M. Freidinger, *Proc. Natl. Acad. Sci. USA*, 1986, **83**, 4918.
131. R. L. Chang and V. J. Lotti, *Proc. Natl. Acad. Sci. USA*, 1986, **83**, 4923.
132. M. G. Bock, R. M. DiPardo, B. E. Evans, K. E. Rittle, R. M. Friedinger, R. S. L. Chang and V. J. Lotti, *J. Med. Chem.*, 1988, **31**, 264.
133. M. G. Bock, R. M. Dipardo, B. E. Evans, K. E. Rittle, D. F. Veber, R. M. Freidinger, R. S. L. Chang and V. J. Lotti, *J. Med. Chem.*, 1988, **31**, 176.
134. J. S. Edkins, *Proc. R. Soc. London, Ser. B*, 1905, **76**, 376.
135. R. A. Gregory and H. J. Tracy, *Gut*, 1964, **5**, 103.
136. H. Gregory, P. M. Hardy, D. S. Jones, G. W. Kenner and R. C. Sheppard, *Nature (London)*, 1964, **204**, 931.
137. J. C. Anderson, M. A. Barton, R. A. Gregory, P. M. Hardy, G. W. Kenner, J. K. MacLeod, J. Preston and R. C. Sheppard, *Nature (London)*, 1964, **204**, 934.
138. R. A. Gregory and H. J. Tracy, *Lancet*, 1972, **2**, 797.
139. R. A. Gregory and H. J. Tracy, *Gut*, 1974, **15**, 683.
140. R. A. Yallow and S. A. Berson, *Biochem. Biophys. Res. Commun.*, 1972, **48**, 391.

141. J. F. Rehfeld, F. Stadil and J. Vikelsoe, *Gut*, 1974, **15**, 102.
142. M. Feldman and C. T. Richardson, in 'Physiology of the Gastrointestinal Tract', ed. L. R. Johnson, Raven Press, New York, 1981, vol. 1, p. 693.
143. A. H. Soll and J. H. Walsh, *Annu. Rev. Physiol.*, 1979, **41**, 35.
144. J. S. Morley, in 'Gut Peptides and Ulcer', ed. A. Miyoshi, Biomedial Research Foundation, Tokyo, 1983, p. 1.
145. L. R. Johnson, *Gastroenterology*, 1976, **70**, 278.
146. S. Hsiao, G. Katsuura and S. Itoh, *Life Sci.*, 1984, **34**, 2165.
147. (a) J. Brown and N. D. Gallagher, *Biochim. Biophys. Acta.* 1978, **42**, 538; (b) P. M. Kleveland and H. L. Waldum, *Scand. J. Gastroenterol.*, 1986, **21**, 547.
148. (a) M. Lewin, A. Soumarmon, J. P. Bali and S. Bonfils, *FEBS Lett.*, 1976, **66**, 166; (b) K. Takeuchi, G. R. Speir and L. R. Johnson, *Am. J. Physiol.*, 1979, **237**, E295; (c) M. Nakamura, M. Oda, K. Kaneko, Y. Yonei, N. Tsukada, H. Komatsu, M. Tsugu and M. Tsuchiya, *Peptides (N.Y.)*, 1987, **8**, 391.
149. M. J. Rutten and A. H. Soll, *Ann. N.Y. Acad. Sci.*, 1981, **372**, 637.
150. R. Magous and J. P. Bali, *Eur. J. Pharmacol.*, 1982, **82**, 47.
151. (a) A. H. Soll, D. A. Amirian, L. P. Thomas, J. Park, J. D. Elashoff, M. A. Beaven and T. Yamada, *Am. J. Physiol*, 1984, **247**, G715; (b) A. H. Soll, D. A. Amirian, L. P. Thomas, J. Park, J. D. Elashoff, M. A. Beaven and T. Yamada, *J. Clin. Invest.*, 1984, **73**, 1434; (c) A. H. Soll, in 'Gastrin and Cholecystokinin, Chemistry, Physiology and Pharmacology', ed. J. P. Bali and J. Martinez, Elsevier, Amsterdam, 1987, p. 141.
152. M. Praissman and M. Walden, *Biochem. Biophys. Res. Commun.*, 1984, **123**, 641.
153. R. Magous, J. C. Galleyrand, B. Baudiere, A. Leonard, A. Choquet and J. P. Bali, in 'Gastrin and Cholecystokinin, Chemistry, Physiology and Pharmacology', ed. J. P. Bali and J. Martinez, Elsevier, Amsterdam, 1987, p. 153.
154. S. Baur and V. C. Bacon, *Biochem. Biophys. Res. Commun.*, 1973, **73**, 928.
155. (a) G. S. Balwin, R. Chandler, D. B. Scanlon and J. Weinstock, *J. Biol. Chem*, 1986, **261**, 12 252; (b) M. Matsumoto, J. Park and T. Yamada, *Am. J. Physiol.*, 1987, **252**, G143.
156. (a) L. Moroder, G. Borin, A. Lobbia, J. P. Bali and E. Wünsch, in 'Chemistry of Peptides and Proteins', ed. W. Voelter, E. Bayer, Y. A. Ovchinnikov and E. Wünsch, de Gruiter, Berlin, 1984, p. 255; (b) L. Moroder and E. Wünsch, in 'Gastrin and Cholecystokinin, Chemistry, Physiology and Pharmacology', ed. J. P. Bali and J. Martinez, Elsevier, Amsterdam, 1987, p. 21.
157. K. Takeuchi, G. R. Speir and L. R. Johnson, *Am. J. Physiol*, 1980, **239**, G395.
158. W. Göhring, L. Moroder, G. Borin, A. Lobbia, J. P. Bali and E. Wünsch, *Hoppe-Seyler's Z. Physiol. Chem.*, 1984, **365**, 83.
159. H. J. Tracy and R. A. Gregory, *Nature (London)*, 1964, **204**, 935.
160. A. Previero, G. Mourier, J. P. Bali, M. F. Lignon and L. Moroder, *Hoppe-Seyler's Z. Physiol. Chem.*, 1982, **363**, 813.
161. B. H. Hirst, J. Holland, A. P. Maar, M. E. Parsons and D. J. Sanders, *J. Physiol. (London)*, 1984, **357**, 441.
162. E. Wünsch, L. Moroder, W. Göhring, G. Borin, A. Calderan and J. P. Bali, *FEBS Lett.*, 1986, **206**, 203.
163. G. Borin, A. Calderan, P. Ruzza, L. Moroder, W. Göhring, G. Bovermann and E. Wünsch, *Biol. Chem. Hoppe Seyler*, 1987, **368**, 1363.
164. T. M. Lin, G. L. Southard and G. F. Spray, *Gastroenterology*, 1976, **70**, 733.
165. G. Bertaccini, *Pharmacol. Future Man. Proc. Int. Congr. Pharmacol., 5th*, 1972, **5**, 336.
166. E. Wünsch, D. Gillissen, U. B. Soerensen and J. P. Bali, *Hoppe-Seyler's Z. Physiol. Chem.*, 1982, **363**, 665.
167. (a) J. S. Morley, *Proc. R. Soc. London, Ser. B*, 1968, **170**, 97; (b) J. S. Morley, *Fed. Proc., Fed. Am. Soc. Exp. Biol.*, 1968, **27**, 1314.
168. R. Magous, J. P. Bali, L. Moroder and A. Previero, *Eur. J. Pharmacol.*, 1982, **77**, 11.
169. T. M. Lin, G. F. Spray and G. L. Southard, *Gastroenterology*, 1977, **72**, 566.
170. (a) J. Martinez, R. Magous, M. F. Lignon, J. Laur, B. Castro and J. P. Bali, *J. Med. Chem.*, 1984, **27**, 1597; (b) J. Martinez, J. P. Bali, R. Magous, J. Laur, M. F. Lignon, C. Briet, D. Nisato and B. Castro, *J. Med. Chem.*, 1985, **28**, 273.
171. C. Briet, A. Aumelas and J. Martinez, *Int. J. Pept. Protein Res.*, 1985, **26**, 294.
172. J. Laur, M. Rodriguez, A. Aumelas, J. P. Bali and J. Martinez, *Int. J. Pept. Protein Res.*, 1986, **27**, 386.
173. A. Lavezzo, J. P. Bali, R. Magous, M. F. Lignon, D. Nisato, J. Laur, B. Castro and J. Martinez, *Regul. Pept.*, 1986, **15**, 111.
174. B. Petersen, J. Christiansen and J. F. Rehfeld, *Regul. Pept.*, 1983, **7**, 323.
175. S. Pauwels, G. J. Dockray, R. Walker and S. Marcus, *Gastroenterology*, 1985, **89**, 49.
176. M. C. Galas, M. F. Lignon, M. Rodriguez and J. Martinez, unpublished results.
177. (a) J. Martinez, J. P. Bali, R. Magous, J. Laur, M. F. Lignon, M. Rodriguez and B. Castro, *CR Hebd. Seances Acad. Sci., Ser. B*, 1985, **300**, 437; (b) J. Martinez, J. P. Bali, R. Magous, J. Laur, M. F. Lignon, M. Rodriguez and B. Castro, *J. Med. Chem.*, 1985, **28**, 1874.
178. C. Jarrousse, J. Martinez and D. Bataille, unpublished results.
179. M. Dubrasquet and J. Martinez, unpublished results.
180. M. C. Galas, M. F. Lignon, M. Rodriguez and J. Martinez, unpublished results.
181. M. Rodriguez, Ph. Dubreuil, J. P. Bali and J. Martinez, *J. Med. Chem.*, 1987, **30**, 758.
182. Y. K. Shue, J. M. Carrera, Jr., A. M. Nazdan, J. F. Kerwin, H. Kopecka and C. W. Lin, in 'Peptides, Chemistry and Biology', ed. G. Marshall, ESCOM, Leiden, 1988, p. 112.
183. (a) Ph. Dubreuil, M. F. Lignon, R. Magous, M. Rodriguez, J. P. Bali and J. Martinez, *Drug Des. Delivery*, 1987, **2**, 49; (b) Ph. Dubreuil, M. C. Galas, M. F. Lignon, M. Rodriguez, J. P. Bali and J. Martinez, in '2éme Forum Peptides', Nancy, France, May 2–6, 1988, abstract.
184. (a) P. Seez and F. Hagemuller, in 'Proglumide and Other Gastrin-receptor Antagonists', ed. J. Weiss and S. E. Miederer, 1979, p. 23; (b) R. Magous and J. P. Bali, *Regul. Pept.*, 1983, **7**, 233.
185. L. R. Johnson and P. D. Guthrie, *Am. J. Physiol.*, 1984, **246**, G62.
186. R. D. Beauchamp, C. M. Townsend, Jr., M. D. P. Singh, E. J. Glass and J. C. Thompson, *Ann. Surg.*, 1985, 303.
187. R. Magous, J. Martinez, M. F. Lignon, D. Nisato, B. Castro and J. P. Bali, *Biochim. Biophys. Acta*, 1985, **845**, 158.
188. A. Soumarmon, M. Lewin, M. Dubrasquet, S. Bonfils, J. P. Girma, J. L. Morgat and P. Fromageot, in 'Hormonal Receptors in Digestive Tract Physiology', ed. S. Bonfils, P. Fromageot and G. Rosselin, Elsevier, Amsterdam, 1979, p. 404.

189. M. H. Charon. P. Pham Van Chuong and M. Dubrasquet, *CR Hebd. Seances Acad. Sci.*, *Ser. B*, 1983, **296**, 895.
190. P. Dubreuil, M. Rodriguez, P. Fulcrand, J. Laur and J. Martinez, 'Proc. 11th American Reptide Symposium', ed. J. Rivier, Escom, Leiden, 1989, in press.
191. P. Dubreuil, P. Fulcrand, M. Rodriguez, H. Fulcrand, J. Laur and J. Martinez, *Biochem. J.*, 1989, **262**, 125.
192. L. A. Rovati, in 'Gastrin and Cholecystokinin, Chemistry, Physiology and Pharmacology', ed. J. P. Bali and J. Martinez, Elsevier, Amsterdam, 1987, p. 225.
193. (a) M. G. Bock, R. M. Dipardo, B. E. Evans, K. E. Rittle, W. L. Whitter, D. F. Veber, P. S. Anderson and R. M. Freidinger, *J. Med. Chem.*, 1989, **32**, 13; (b) V. J. Lotti and R. S. L. Chang, *Eur. J. Pharmacol.*, 1989, **162**, 273.
194. R. E. Carraway and S. E. Leeman, *J. Biol. Chem.*, 1973, **248**, 6854.
195. R. E. Carraway and S. E. Leeman, *J. Biol. Chem.*, 1975, **250**, 1912.
196. P. Kitabji, R. Carraway and S. E. Leeman, *J. Biol. Chem.*, 1976, **251**, 7053.
197. R. A. Hammer, S. E. Leeman, R. Carraway and R. H. Williams, *J. Biol. Chem.*, 1980, **255**, 2476.
198. P. R. Dobner, D. L. Barber, L. Villa-Komaroff and C. McKiernan, *Proc. Natl. Acad. Sci. USA*, 1987, **84**, 3516.
199. C. B. Nemeroff, D. Luttinger and A. J. Prange, Jr., in 'Handbook of Psychopharmacology', Plenum Press, New York, 1982, vol. 16, p. 609.
200. R. E. Carraway and S. E. Leeman, *J. Biol. Chem.*, 1976, **251**, 7045.
201. K. Araki, S. Tachibana, M. Uchiyama, T. Nakajima and T. Yusuhara, *Chem. Pharm. Bull.*, 1975, **23**, 3132.
202. N. Minamino, K. Kangawa and H. Matsuo, *Biochem. Biophys. Res. Commun.*, 1984, **122**, 542.
203. R. E. Carraway and C. F. Ferris, *J. Biol. Chem.*, 1983, **258**, 2475.
204. R. E. Carraway, S. E. Ruane and R. S. Ritsema, *Peptides (N.Y.)*, 1983, **4**, 111.
205. R. E. Carraway, S. P. Mitra and D. E. Cochrane, *J. Biol. Chem.*, 1987, **262**, 5968.
206. (a) M. H. Fernstrom, R. E. Carraway and S. E. Leeman, in 'Frontiers in Neuroendocrinology', ed. L. Martini and W. F. Ganong, Raven Press, New York, 1980, vol. 6, p. 103; (b) L. Peric-Golia, C. F. Gardner and M. Peric-Goria, *Eur. J. Pharmacol.*, 1979, **55**, 407.
207. M. Singh and M. S. Bandisode, *Dig. Dis. Sci.*, 1987, **32**, 65.
208. E. R. Trimble, C. Shaw, R. Bruzzone, A. Gjinovci and K. D. Buchanan, *Gastroenterology*, 1987, **92**, 699.
209. G. Bissette, C. B. Manberg, C. B. Nemeroff and A. J. Pranje, *Life Sci.*, 1978, **23**, 2173.
210. (a) C. B. Nemeroff, D. E. Hernandez, R. C. Orlando and A. J. Pranje, Jr., *Am. J. Physiol.*, 1982, **242**, G342; (b) D. E. Hernandez, C. M. Richardson, C. B. Nemeroff, R. C. Orlando, S. St. Pierre, F. Rioux and A. J. Prange, Jr., *Brain Res.*, 1984, **301**, 153.
211. R. Quirion, *Peptides (N.Y.)*, 1983, **4**, 609.
212. (a) J. A. Gilbert, C. J. Moses, M. A. Pfenning and R. Richelson, *Biochem. Pharmacol.*, 1986, **35**, 391; (b) K. S. Kanba and E. Richelson, *Biochem. Pharmacol.*, 1986, **36**, 869.
213. J. Mazella, S. Amar, J. C. Bozou, P. Kitabgi and J. P. Vincent, *J. Recept. Res.*, 1987, **7**, 157.
214. K. Muraki, Y. Nishi, M. Arai, K. Ueda, H. Shikata, Y. Nakata, T. Segawa, N. Yanaihara and H. Yajima, *Biochem. Biophys. Res. Commun.*, 1987, **145**, 1071.
215. C. Poustis, J. Mazella, P. Kitabgi and J. P. Vincent, *J. Neurochem.*, 1984, **42**, 1094.
216. R. Carraway and S. E. Leeman, in 'Peptides: Chemistry, Structure and Biology', Proceedings of the Fourth American Peptide Symposium', ed. R. Walter and J. Meienhofer, Ann Arbor Sci., Ann Arbor, Michigan, 1975, p. 679.
217. (a) C. Granier, J. Van Riestchoten, P. Kitabgi, C. Poustis and P. Freychet, *Eur. J. Biochem.*, 1982, **124**, 117; (b) R. Quirion, D. Regoli, F. Rioux and S. St. Pierre, *Br. J. Pharmacol.*, 1980, **68**, 83; (c) R. Quirion, F. Rioux, D. Regoli and S. St. Pierre, *Eur. J. Pharmacol.*, 1980, **66**, 257; (d) F. Rioux, R. Quirion, D. Regoli, M. A. Leblanc and S. St. Pierre, *Br. J. Pharmacol.*, 1980, **68**, 273.
218. L. H. Lazarus, M. R. Brown and M. H. Perrin, *Neuropharmacology*, 1977, **16**, 625.
219. P. Kitabgi, R. Carraway, J. Van Riestchoten, C. Granier, J. L. Morgat, A. Menez, S. E. Leeman and P. Freychet, *Proc. Natl. Acad. Sci. USA*, 1977, **74**, 1846.
220. K. Folkers, D. Chang, J. Humphries, R. Carraway, S. E. Leeman and C. Y. Bowers, *Proc. Natl. Acad. Sci. USA*, 1979, **76**, 3833.
221. J. Rivier, L. H. Lazarus, M. H. Perrin and M. R. Brown, *J. Med. Chem.*, 1977, **20**, 1409.
222. R. Quirion, D. Regoli, F. Rioux and S. St. Pierre, *Br. J. Pharmacol.*, 1980, **69**, 689.
223. P. J. Elliot, J. Chan, Y. M. Parker and C. B. Nemeroff, *Brain Res.*, 1986, **381**, 259.
224. S. St. Pierre, J. M. Lalonde, M. Gendreau, R. Quirion, D. Regoli and F. Rioux, *J. Med. Chem.*, 1981, **24**, 370.
225. P. Kitabgi, C. Poustis, C. Granier, J. Van Riestchoten, J. Rivier, J. L. Morgat and P. Freychet, *Mol. Pharmacol.*, 1980, **18**, 11.
226. L. H. Lazarus, M. H. Perrin, M. R. Brown and J. Rivier, *J. Biol. Chem.*, 1977, **252**, 7180.
227. R. Quirion, D. Regoli, F. Rioux and S. St. Pierre, *Eur. J. Pharmacol.*, 1980, **61**, 309.
228. F. Rioux, R. Kérouac and S. St. Pierre, *Neuropeptides (Edinburgh)* 1983, **3**, 354.
229. J. E. Jorpes and V. Mutt, *Biochem. Biophys. Res. Commun.*, 1962, **9**, 275.
230. V. Mutt, S. Magnusson, J. E. Jorpes and E. Dahl, *Biochemistry*, 1965, **4**, 2358.
231. M. Bodanszky, M. A. Ondetti, S. D. Levine, V. L. Narayanan, M. Von Saltza, J. T. Sheehan, N. J. Williams and E. F. Sabo, *Chem. Ind. (London)*, 1962, **42**, 1757.
232. G. Gafvelin, M. Carlqvist and V. Mutt, *FEBS Lett.*, 1985, **184**, 347.
233. (a) G. Bussolati, C. Capella, E. Solcia, G. Vassallo and P. Vezzadini, *Histochemie*, 1971, **26**, 218; (b) J. M. Polak, I. Coulling, S. Bloom and A. G. E. Pearse, *Scand. J. Gastroenterol.*, 1971, **6**, 739.
234. C. Rufener, M. Amherdt, D. Baetens, N. Yanaihara, and L. Orci, *Histochemistry*, 1976, **47**, 171.
235. (a) W. Y. Chey, T. A. Chang, H. J. Park, K. Y. Lee and R. Escoffery, *Endocrinology (Baltimore)*, 1983, **113**, 651; (b) W. Y. Chey and R. Escoffery, *Endocrinology (Baltimore)*, 1976, **98**, 1390.
236. V. Mutt, M. Carlqvist and K. Tatemoto, *Life Sci.*, 1979, **25**, 1703.
237. W. K. Samson, M. D. Lumpkin and S. M. McCann, *Life Sci.*, 1984, **34**, 155.
238. T. L. O'Donohue, C. G. Charlton, R. L. Miller, G. Boden and D. M. Jacobowitz, *Proc. Natl. Acad. Sci. USA*, 1981, **78**, 5221.
239. (a) K. A. Hubel, *Gastroenterology*, 1972, **62**, 318; (b) J. H. Walsh, in 'Physiology of the Gastrointestinal Tract', ed. R. L.

Johnson, Raven Press, New York, 1982, vol. 1, p. 59; (c) H. R. Doyle, F. Lluis and P. L. Rayford, in 'Gastrointestinal Endocrinology', ed. J. C. Thompson, J. H. Greeley, Jr., P. L. Rayford and C. M. Townsend, McGraw-Hill, New York, 1987, vol. 5, p. 223.

240. C. H. You and W. Y. Chey, *Dig. Dis. Sci.*, 1987, **32**, 466.
241. C. Gespach, D. Bataille, N. Vauclin, L. Moroder, E. Wünsch and G. Rosselin, *Peptides (N.Y.)*, 1986, **7**, suppl. 1, 155.
242. G. Babu and E. Vijayan, *Brain Res. Bull.*, 1983, **11**, 25.
243. K. Fuxe, K. Anderson, T. Hökfelt, V. Mutt, L. Ferland, L. F. Agnati, D. Ganten, S. Said, P. Eneroth and J. A. Gustafsson, *Fed. Proc., Fed. Am. Soc. Exp. Biol.*, 1979, **38**, 2333.
244. C. G. Charlton, T. L. O'Donohue, R. L. Miller and D. M. Jacobowitz, *Peptides (N.Y.)*, 1982, **3**, 565.
245. R. T. Jensen, C. G. Charlton, H. Adachi, S. W. Jones, T. L. O'Donohue and J. D. Gardner, *Am. J. Physiol.*, 1983, **245**, G186.
246. (a) S. Milutinovic, I. Schulz and G. Rosselin, *Biochim. Biophys. Acta*, 1976, **436**, 113; (b) B. Desbuquois, *Eur. J. Biochem.*, 1974, **46**, 439.
247. J. T. Lin, S. Milutinovic and F. Farenholz, *Anal. Biochem.*, 1978, **88**, 587.
248. G. Rosselin, *Peptides (N.Y.,)* 1986, **7**, suppl. 1, 89.
249. D. Bataille, P. Freychet and G. Rosselin, *Endocrinology (Baltimore)*, 1974, **95**, 713.
250. S. Baur, B. Grant and R. K. Spaulding, *Biochim. Biophys. Acta*, 1979, **584**, 365.
251. D. V. Van Claker. M. Müller and B. Hamprecht, *Proc. Natl. Acad. Sci. USA*, 1980, **77**, 6907.
252. P. Robberecht, T. P. Conlon and J. D. Gardner, *J. Biol. Chem.*, 1972, **251**, 4635.
253. E. R. Trimble. R. Bruzzone, T. J. Biden, C. J. Meehan, D. Andreu and R. B. Merrifield, *Proc. Natl. Acad. Sci. USA*, 1987, **84**, 3146.
254. R. T. Fremeau, R. T. Jensen, G. C. Charlton, R. L. Miller, T. L. O'Donohue and T. W. Moody, *J. Neurosci.*, 1983, **3**, 1620.
255. R. T. Fremeau, Jr., L. Y. Korman and T. W. Moody, *J. Neurochem.*, 1986, **46**, 1947.
256. (a) J. D. Gardner, T. P. Conlon, M. L. Fink and M. Bodanszky, *Gastroenterology*, 1976, **71**, 965; (b) P. Robberecht, T. P. Conlon and J. D. Gardner, *J. Biol. Chem.*, 1976, **251**, 5635.
257. D. Rudman and A. E. Del Rio, *Endocrinology (Baltimore)*, 1969, **85**, 610.
258. G. M. Makhlouf, M. Bodanszky, M. L. Fink and M. Schebalin, *Gastroenterology*, 1978, **75**,̧ 244.
259. G. M. Makhlouf, A. M. Zfass, S. I. Said and M. Schebalin, *Proc. Soc. Exp. Biol. Med.*, 1978, **157**, 565.
260. V. E. Sutliff, J. P. Raufman, R. T. Jensen and J. D. Gardner, *Am. J. Physiol.*, 1986, **251**, G96.
261. (a) P. Robberecht, M. Waelbroeck, M. Noyer, P. Chatelain, P. De, Neef, W. König and J. Christophe, *Digestion*, 1982, **23**, 201; (b) P. Robberecht, D. H. Coy, P. De Neff, J. C. Camus, A. Cauvin, M. Waelbroeck and J. Christophe, *Eur. J. Biochem.*, 1987, **165**, 243.
262. J. Christophe, M. Svoboda, M. Lambert, M. Waelbroeck, J. Winand, J. P. Dehaye, M. C. Vandersmeers-Piret, A. Vandersmeers and P. Robberecht, *Peptides (N.Y)*, 1986, **7**, suppl. 1, 101.
263. S. Mulitinovic, I. Schultz and G. Rosselin, *Biochim. Biophys. Acta*, 1976, **36**, 113.
264. N. Yanaihara, M. Sakagami, H. Sato, K. Yamamoto, T. Hashimoto, C. Yanaihara, Z. Ito, K. Yamaguchi and K. Abe, *Gastroenterology*, 1977, **72**, 803.
265. (a) W. König, M. Bickel, H. Wissmann, R. Uhmann and R. Geiger, in 'Hormone Receptors in Digestion and Nutrition' ed. G. Rosselin, P. Fromageot and S. Bonfils, Elsevier, Amsterdam, 1979, 137; (b) P. Chatelain, P. Robberecht, P. De Neef, M. Deschodt-Lanckman, W. König and J. Christophe, *Pfluegers Arch.*, 1980, **389**, 21.
266. (a) N. Yanaihara, M. Kubota, M. Sakagami, H. Sato, T. Mochizuki, N. Sakura, T. Hasimoto and C. Yanaihara, *J. Med. Chem.*, 1977, **20**, 648; (b) L. Moroder, E. Jaeger, F. Drees, M. Gemeiner, S. Knof, H. Stelzel, P. Thamm, D. Bataille, S. Domschke, W. Schlegel, I. Schulz and E. Wünsch, *Bioorg. Chem.*, 1980, **9**, 27.
267. W König, M. Bickel, K. Karch, W. Teetz and R. Uhmann, *Peptides (N.Y)*, 1984, **5**, 189.
268. R. S. Izzo and M. Praissman, *Int. J. Pept. Protein Res.*, 1984, **23**, 292.
269. (a) W. König, R. Geiger, H. Wissmann, M. Bickel, R. Obermeier, W. Teetz and R. Uhmann, *Gastroenterology*, 1977, **72**, 797; (b) E. Wünsch, E. Jaeger and L. Moroder, in 'Hormonal Receptors in Digestive Tract Physiology', ed. S. Bonfils, P. Fromageot and G. Rosselin, North-Holland, Amsterdam, 1977, p. 30.
270. D. Voskamp and H. C. Beyerman, *Int. J. Pept. Protein Res.*, 1981, **18**, 284.
271. W. König, M. Bickel, H. Wissmann and J. Sandow, *Peptides (N.Y.)*, 1986, **7**, suppl. 1, 61.
272. P. Robberecht, P. Chatelain, J. Waelbroeck and J. Christophe, in 'Vasoactive Intestinal Peptide', ed. S. I. Said, Raven Press, New York, 1982, p. 323.
273. H. Kofod, B. Hansen. A. Lernmark and C. J. Hedeskov, *Am. J. Physiol.*, 1986, **250**, E107.
274. H. Kofod, *Regul. Pept.*, 1986, **15**, 229.
275. S. I. Said and V. Mutt, *Eur. J. Biochem.*, 1972, **28**, 199.
276. V. Mutt and S. I. Said, *Eur. J. Biochem.*, 1974, **42**, 581.
277. J. Christophe, M. Svoboda, J. P. Dehaye, J. Winand. M. C. Vandermeers-Piret, A. Vandermeers, A. Cauvin, P. Courlet and P. Robberecht, in 'Peptide Hormones, Prohormones and Their Fragments: Processing, Biological Activity and Pharmacology', ed. J. Martinez, Horwood, Chichester, 1989, p. 211.
278. (a) M. R. Pandian, A. Horvath and S. I. Said, in 'Vasoactive Intestinal Peptide', ed. S. I. Said, Raven Press, New York, 1982, p. 35; (b) L. I. Larsson, in 'Vasoactive Intestinal Peptide', ed. S. I. Said, Raven Press, New York, 1982, p. 51; (c) T. Hökfelt, M. Schultzberg, J. M. Lundberg, K. Fuxe, V. Mutt, J. Fahrenkrug and S. I. Said, in 'Vasoactive Intestinal Peptide', ed. S. I. Said, Raven Press, New York, 1982, p. 65; (d) W. K. Samson, in 'Vasoactive Intestinal Peptide', ed. S. I. Said, Raven Press, New York, 1982, p. 91; (e) J. M. Polak and S. R. Bloom, in 'Vasoactive Intestinal Peptide', ed. S. I. Said, Raven Press, New York, 1982, p. 107; (f) R. Hakanson, F. Sundler and R. Uddman, in 'Vasoactive Intestinal Peptide', ed. S. I. Said, Raven Press, New York, 1982, p. 121.
279. A. Giachetti, A. Goth and S. I. Said, *Fed. Proc., Fed. Am. Soc. Exp. Biol.*, 1978, **37**, 657.
280. M. S. O'Dorisio. T. M. O'Dorisio, S. Cataland and S. P. Balcerzak, *J. Lab. Clin. Med.*, 1980, **96**, 666.
281. (a) A. Nilson, *FEBS Lett.*, 1975, **60**, 322; (b) B. H. Du, J. Eng, J. D. Hulmes, M. Chang. Y. C. E. Pan and R. S. Yallow, *Biochem. Biophys. Res Commun.*, 1985, **128**, 1093; (c) J. P. Raufman, J. Eng, B. H. Du, E. Straus and R. Yallow, *Regul. Pept.*, 1986, **14**, 93.
282. (a) T. Khalil, G. Alinder and P. L. Rayford, in 'Gastrointestinal Endocrinology', ed. J. C. Thompson, G. H. Greeley, P. L. Rayford and C. M. Townsend, Jr., McGraw-Hill, New York, 1987, vol. 19, p. 260; (b) J. H. Walsh, in 'Physiology of the

Gastrointestinal Tract', ed. L. R. Johnson, Raven Press, New York, 1983, vol. 1, p. 86; (c) General review: 'Vasoactive Intestinal Peptide', ed. S. I. Said, Raven Press, New York, 1982.

283. R. M. Rosa, P. Silva, J. S. Stoff and F. H. Epstein, *Am. J. Physiol.*, 1985, **249**, E494.
284. C. A. Ottoway, *J. Exp. Med.*, 1984, **160**, 1054.
285. J. C. Foreman and W. Piotrowski, *J. Allergy Clin Immunol.*, 1984, **74**, 127.
286. M. Rola-Plesczynski, D. Bolduc and S. St. Pierre, *J. Immunol.*, 1985, **135**, 2569.
287. D. E. Brenneman and G. A. Foster, *Peptides (N.Y.)*, 1987, **8**, 687.
288. S. I. Said, *Peptides (N.Y.)*, 1984, **5**, 143.
289. (a) P. Robberecht, P. Chatelain, M. Waelbroeck and J. Christophe, in 'Vasoactive Intestinal Peptide', ed. S. I. Said, Raven Press, New York, 1982, p. 323; (b) P. Robberecht, T. P. Colon and J. D. Gardner, *J. Biol. Chem.*, 1976, **251**, 4635; (c) J. Christophe, T. P. Conlon and J. D. Gardner, *J. Biol. Chem.*, 1976, **251**, 4629.
290. S. Provow and G. Velicelebi, *Endocrinology (Baltimore)*, 1987, **120**, 2442.
291. M. Bodanszky, Y. S. Klausner and A. Bodanszky, *Proc. Natl. Acad. Sci. USA*, 1973, **70**, 382.
292. A Fournier, J. K. Saunders and S. St. Pierre, *Peptides (N.Y.)*, 1984, **5**, 169.
293. A. Fournier, J. K. Saunders and S. St. Pierre, *Regul. Pept.*, 1982, **6**, 302.
294. P. Robberecht, M. Waelbroeck, J. C. Camus, P. de Neef, D. Coy and J. Christophe, *Peptides (N.Y.)*, 1984, **5**, 877.
295. A. Couvineau. C. Rouyer-Fessard, A. Fournier, S. St. Pierre, R. Pipkorn and M. Laburthe, *Biochem. Biophys. Res. Commun.*, 1984, **121**, 493.
296. R. Pipkorn and R. Hakanson, *Peptides (N.Y.)*, 1984, **5**, 267.
297. P. Robberecht, D. H. Coy, P. De Neef, J. C. Camus, A. Cauvin, M. Waelbroeck and J. Christophe, *Eur. J. Biochem.*, 1987, **165**, 243.
298. D. H. Coy, W. A. Murphy, J. Sueiras-Diaz, E. J. Coy and V. A. Lance, *J. Med. Chem.*, 1985, **28**, 181.
299. P. Staun-Olsen, B. Ottesen, S. Gammeltoft and J. Fahrenkrug, *Peptides (N.Y.)*, 1986, **7**, suppl. 1, 181.
300. A. Robichon and J. C. Marie, *Biochim. Biophys. Acta*, 1987, **923**, 250.
301. Y. Suzuki, D. McMaster, K. Lederis and O. P. Rorstad, *Brain Res.*, 1984, **322**, 9.
302. J. C. Marie, D. Hui Bon Hoa, R. Jackson, G. Hejblum and G. Rosselin, *Regul. Pept.*, 1985, **12**, 113.
303. M. Laburthe, A. Couvineau and C. Rouyer-Fessard, *Mol. Pharmacol.*, 1986, **29**, 23.
304. B. M. Bissonette, M. J. Collen, H. Adachi, R. T. Jensen and J. D. Gardner, *Am. J. Physiol.*, 1984, **246**, G710.
305. J. T. Turner, S. B. Jones and D. B. Bylund, *Peptides (N.Y.)*, 1986, **7**, 849.
306. S. J. Pandol, K. Dharmsathaphorn, M. S. Schoeffield, W. Vale and J. Rivier, *Am. J. Physiol.*, 1986, **250**, G553.

13.7
Angiotensin and Bradykinin Receptors

GRAHAM J. MOORE

University of Calgary, Alberta, Canada

13.7.1 INTRODUCTION

The octapeptide angiotensin II, Asp-Arg-Val-Tyr-Ile-His-Pro-Phe (ANG II), is the principal mediator of the renin–angiotensin system producing an increase in blood volume and blood pressure *via* its actions at receptors in numerous target tissues.[1] ANG II is produced in the blood stream by the action of the enzyme renin on the glycoprotein angiotensinogen. As ANG II has not been shown to be produced directly by glandular secretion or by neurosecretory mechanisms, it is not an endocrine hormone in the strictest classical sense. However, since ANG II is a potent mediator of the secretion[2,3] of numerous hormones from endocrine glands (*e.g.* aldosterone, adrenocorticotropin, vasopressin, growth hormone, noradrenaline) by paracrine as well as blood-borne mechanisms, it may be justifiably classified as a paracrine/exocrine hormone or releasing hormone.

Similar considerations apply to the nonapeptide bradykinin, Arg-Pro-Pro-Gly-Phe-Ser-Pro-Phe-Arg, which is produced in the bloodstream by the action of the kalikrein enzymes on kininogen.

The actions of bradykinin include mediation of inflammatory and pain responses, these effects being due to a modulatory function on neurotransmission and cellular function. Bradykinin does not demonstrate the broad-based hormone-releasing properties of angiotensin. Bradykinin can either contract or relax vascular smooth muscle, depending on the blood vessel in question, and the overall depressor effects of this peptide are attributed to its dilatory actions on small blood vessels, particularly the arterioles. In contrast to the dual actions of bradykinin on vascular tissues, ANG II is exclusively a vasoconstrictor.

Despite the fact that bradykinin is (i) destroyed by the same converting enzyme which generates ANG II, and (ii) produces the opposite effects on blood pressure, bradykinin is not generally considered to be the natural counterpart to ANG II. Rather the direct actions of atrial natriuretic peptide causing vasodilation, inhibition of aldosterone release, natriuresis and diuresis would seem to make this peptide a better candidate for the role of ANG II counterpart.

13.7.2 ANGIOTENSINS II AND III

13.7.2.1 Biosynthesis and Metabolism

Angiotensins II and III are derived from angiotensinogen, a large glycoprotein (M 58 000) which is present in many tissues and which is secreted in physiologically significant amounts by the liver.[1] ANG II forms the N-terminal octapeptide of angiotensinogen (renin substrate; **1**) and is released from this protein in the form of a decapeptide precursor by the action of an acid protease, namely renin. Renin is also found in numerous body tissues but the physiologically relevant plasma level of this enzyme is due to its secretion by the kidney.[1] The action of renin on angiotensinogen results in the release of a decapeptide called angiotensin I (ANG I), which, generally speaking, has very low biological activity (early findings of bioactivity for this peptide were due to the presence of converting enzymes in target tissues) and which therefore acts as a precursor for the biologically active peptides angiotensins II and III. Circulating ANG I is acted on by a dipeptidyl carboxy-peptidase called angiotensin converting enzyme (ACE), which is present in significant amounts in membrane-bound form in the lung.[4] ACE yields the most potent component of the renin–angiotensin system, namely the octapeptide ANG II.

The action of angiotensinase A, an aminopeptidase which removes the N-terminal aspartic acid residue from ANG II (or ANG I), gives rise to the heptapeptide angiotensin III (ANG III), which retains most of the biological activity of the octapeptide ANG II. Although ANG III appears to be equipotent with ANG II at certain receptors, it is generally less potent than the octapeptide at the vast majority of receptors which have been investigated, so that its physiological role, if any, has been the subject of much controversy.[4]

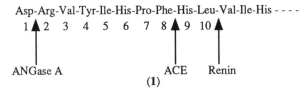

Human angiotensin (renin substrate)

Asp-Arg-Val-Tyr-Ile-His-Pro-Phe-His-Leu-Val-Ile-His - - - -

ANGase A   ACE   Renin

(1)

Both of the biologically·active angiotensins, *i.e.* ANG II and III, are deactivated by enzymes present in the circulation and also in target tissues. One major route of degradation is by the action of a carboxypeptidase which removes the C-terminal Phe residue;[14] this enzyme is a somewhat unusual carboxypeptidase since it is not inhibited by the presence of the penultimate Pro residue. Other suspected avenues of degradation of ANG II and III include trypsin-like cleavage at the Arg residue (which severely reduces, but does not abolish, biological activity) and chymotrypsin-like cleavage at the Tyr residue (which eradicates biological activity). Precise details of the pathways of catabolism of ANG II and III in specific target tissues are not very well worked out at the present time; this area of research has not received a great deal of attention in recent years.

13.7.2.2 Classification and Localization of Receptors

Angiotensin acts at specific receptors in numerous target tissues to produce a variety of myotropic and secretory responses. The number of identified receptors or known sites of action of this 'fight or flight' peptide probably exceeds that of any other hormone. The main physiological effects of angiotensin are to increase blood pressure and heart rate and cause retention of salt and water.[1,4] These effects derive from (i) a direct vasoconstrictor and myocardial actions of angiotensin; (ii) its ability to release other vasoconstrictors from endocrine and neuroendocrine tissues; and (iii) its ability to release sodium- and water-retaining hormones, primarily aldosterone and vasopressin. It is presently believed that physiological control of angiotensin levels is exerted primarily at the level of the kidney (renin release), as a direct consequence of pressor receptors and sympathetic outflow in that organ. However, the levels of angiotensinogen (primarily from the liver) and ACE (primarily from the lung) could well be significant determinants of angiotensin bioavailability.

Possibly the two most important actions of angiotensin for the elevation of blood pressure occur as the result of specific receptors on vascular smooth muscle cells leading to vasoconstriction, and as a consequence of specific receptors on the adrenal glomerulosa cells of the adrenal cortex which mediate the release of aldosterone. The vasoconstrictor action of angiotensin is an immediate or 'short loop' pressor action of this peptide, whereas the salt-retaining (and thereby water-retaining) actions of aldosterone on the kidney can be considered as a 'long loop' volume-expanding action of angiotensin. Either or both of these mechanisms, if not adequately regulated, can lead to hypertension.[1] Angiotensin is apparently involved in most forms of hypertension known in man, including not only those in which renin–angiotensin levels are elevated, but also in essential hypertension where the levels of renin and angiotensin are normal or low. The latter became apparent when it was found that ACE inhibitors, which reduce plasma angiotensin levels, caused lowering of blood pressure in patients with essential hypertension.[1]

In addition to its direct action on specific receptors in smooth muscle to cause contraction, angiotensin is also capable of causing the secretion of agents which directly act at their own receptors on smooth muscle to cause contraction. Foremost of these agents are the catecholamines, which are produced by the action of angiotensin at specific receptors in the adrenal medulla. In addition, angiotensin has specific receptors on the magnocellular neurons of the supraoptic region of the hypothalamus which mediate the release of vasopressin from the neurohypophysis;[2] this antidiuretic hormone, in addition to causing water retention by its action at kidney receptors, also induces contraction of vascular smooth muscle. There is also evidence to suggest that angiotensin can act on sympathetic nerve terminals. Facilitating the release of norepinephrine, thereby increasing vascular tone.[3] Angiotensin is also known to act centrally to cause the release of ACTH from the anterior pituitary.[4]

Although the renin–angiotensin system (RAS) is believed to exist in a number of tissues including the kidney, the brain RAS has received a great deal of attention in the past decade. There is very good evidence to suggest that the brain RAS is quite distinct from the RAS of the periphery,[5] and that it may represent a significant factor in central control of blood pressure. Angiotensin receptors in the brain occupy a number of different regions and have a number of different functions. The dipsogenic receptors for angiotensin were localized to a single region of the brain (subfornical organ) after i.c.v. injections of angiotensin were found to induce drinking behavior.[6] In addition to the receptors mediating the neuroendocrine events (vasopressin and ACTH section), it is believed that central angiotensin receptors mediating sympathetic nervous system activity may be of paramount importance in determining not only vascular tone, but also renal renin release. One of the more important actions of β blockers such as propranolol in treating hypertension is believed to result from its action as an inhibitor of renin release.

Although angiotensin receptors are localized in numerous tissues, the problem of classifying angiotensin receptors into groups or subtypes has proved facile. Initially efforts were made to classify angiotensin receptors on the basis of rank orders of potency of agonists, although it has long been recognized that agonists do not give reliable indices of receptor subtypes. Since agonist potency is determined by two independent variables, namely affinity and efficacy, and the latter is determined by receptor and effector number, agonists cannot be used for classifying receptors. Receptor subtyping in intact tissues depends on the availability of specific antagonists which can be used to measure a single parameter, namely receptor affinity. Using antagonists, it becomes possible to classify receptors according to antagonist binding affinity, or using rank orders of potency of antagonists. However, an antagonist with a high binding affinity for the resting state of the receptor in question is required (see Section 13.7.2.8 for details); the significance of low affinity binding is questionable and it is important not to place too much emphasis on receptor blockade which requires very large doses of an antagonist (*i.e.* $pA_2 < 6$).

Receptors can also be classified according to the rank order of affinities of agonists or antagonists from membrane-binding studies with a given tissue, although it is always difficult to know if the conditions of a binding assay really represent the physiological situation of interest. Agonist affinities can also be determined by irreversibly labeling a fraction of the receptors in a responding intact tissue, although this approach requires the availability of a specific affinity label for the receptors being examined. The importance of the irreversible labeling approach in receptor characterization cannot be overstated, since it is presently the only method for determining agonist affinities in responding tissues.

Although many claims concerning differences in angiotensin receptors from different tissues have been made, virtually none of these has stood the test of time. In the first instance, many of these claims were based on rank orders of agonist potencies, which is an invalid approach due to the composite nature of agonist potency. Other differences have been based on rank orders of binding affinities of ligands in binding assays, which are suspect for the reasons outlined above concerning assay conditions. The importance of faithfully reproducing physiologically relevant binding assay conditions is exemplified by a study involving photoaffinity labeling of intact tissues, which suggested that the rank order of affinities of ANG II and III varied between the smooth muscle tissues investigated.[7] However, it was later found that a tissue (rat portal vein) which had a higher affinity for ANG III than ANG II probably displayed these properties because the levels of calcium and magnesium used in the bioassays were subphysiological; when these divalent cations were raised to physiological levels, the receptors preferred ANG II over ANG III.[8]

Two types of angiotensin antagonist have been identified by structure–activity studies: type I antagonists modified at position 8, *e.g.* [Sar^1,Ala^8]ANG II (saralasin) and [Sar^1,Ile^8]ANG II,[9] and type II antagonists modified at position 4, *e.g.* [Sar^1,Tyr(Me)^4]ANG II (sarmesin) and [Sar^1,Phe^4]ANG II (Sar; sarcosine).[10] Both classes of antagonist are effective in blocking all angiotensin receptors which have been examined thus far, although a rank ordering of these antagonists has not yet been studied in sufficient detail to permit conclusions concerning possible receptor subtypes. Suffice it to say that there is at present no clear-cut evidence which would suggest that any of the numerous tissue receptors for angiotensin are significantly different from one another. This does not mean that it is not possible to classify angiotensin receptors into subtypes; rather it reflects the fact that sufficiently discriminating experimentation either has not been done or has not succeeded in differentiating angiotensin receptors into subclasses. The single exception to this conclusion rests with some very recent evidence that suggests that hypothalamic receptors may be specific for ANG III rather than ANG II.[11] [Tables 5 and 6 in Section 13.7.2.8 list the affinities and efficacies, respectively, of some angiotensin analogs at several smooth muscle receptors; taking into account the different assay conditions utilized in different laboratories, the data in Table 5 do not illustrate obvious differences in angiotensin receptors, although the data in Table 6 appear to illustrate differences based on agonist efficacy (see Section 13.7.2.8 for details).]

13.7.2.3 Bioassays *In Vitro* and *In Vivo*

Traditionally the most popular methods for measuring angiotensin responses have been by myotropic and pressor assays. *In vitro* myotropic assays have usually involved contraction of uterine or vascular smooth muscles. *In vivo* pressor assays have generally been done on anesthetized rats with varying degrees of sympathetic and parasympathetic blockade, or on conscious rats. Myotropic assays have to be conducted with a certain amount of care because tachyphylaxis to angiotensin can be very prevalent if conditions such as divalent cation concentration and pH are depressed. One of the most reproducible and reliable smooth muscle assays for angiotensin is the rat isolated uterus assay, and this assay has been used extensively in many different laboratories to obtain a considerable amount of biological activity data on angiotensin analogs. Vascular smooth muscle assays have also been very prevalent in the analysis of angiotensin analogs, although there is a great deal of variability in the reproducibility and ease of management of certain vascular tissues. However the fact that it has been possible to carry out photoaffinity labeling experiments on isolated tissues[7] provides some insight into the hardiness and reliability which can be achieved with these *in vitro* smooth muscle bioassays. Pressor assays represent a more complex situation which is difficult to interpret, although the obvious relevance of these assays in relation to hypertension has maintained their popularity.

Bioassays have also been carried out on dispersed adrenal glomerulosa cells, with measurement of release of aldosterone being a convenient and relatively reliable index of biological responsiveness. More recently, dispersed smooth muscle cells have been investigated, and second messenger characteristics such as inositide turnover and calcium mobilization have been shown to provide an index of bioactivity.[12] Ionophoretic techniques coupled with single-cell recordings have been used to measure neuroresponsiveness to angiotensin.[11] Numerous binding assays on a variety of tissues have also been conducted.

13.7.2.4 Chemical Properties of Angiotensins

ANG II and III, like most other peptides, are hydrophilic substances which are relatively soluble in water (up to about 20 mg mL^{-1}). In contrast to peptides of a similar size, such as vasopressin and oxytocin, ANG II is also sparingly soluble in alcohol and acetone. Paradoxically, the overall hydrophobicity of angiotensin, as measured by HPLC elution times from reversed-phase columns, is not significantly different from the neurohypophysial hormones and therefore does not explain its solubility characteristics. Angiotensin, like most other peptides, retains bioactivity for prolonged periods of time (years) in the lyophilized state (lyophilized from dilute acetic acid) at $-20\,°C$. Solutions of angiotensin (1 mg mL^{-1}), when stored at acid pH (0.25% acetic acid) at $4\,°C$, retain 100% bioactivity for periods of several days (up to one week). Very dilute solutions of angiotensin may not maintain full biological activity for more than one day, and samples obtained by lyophilization from aprotic solvents such as dimethyl sulfoxide show variability in recovery of biological activity.

13.7.2.5 Structure–Activity Relationships of Agonists

A very large number of angiotensin analogs have been synthesized over the years and no attempt will be made to review these in detail here. The majority of these analogs have been tabulated in extensive reviews on the subject.[13,14] The aim of the present treatise will be to highlight important aspects of the accumulated findings from structure–activity studies, and to try to crystallize perspectives on the roles of individual amino acids (Table 1).

13.7.2.5.1 Position 1

Undoubtedly the residue in ANG II most tolerant to change without loss of biological activity is the aspartic acid residue occupying position 1. Almost any modification (substitution) or elongation (acylation) is permitted; even deletion of this residue does not severely disrupt the biological activity of most agonists (*e.g.* ANG III) or antagonists (*e.g.* [Ile^7]ANG III), the only exception being type II antagonists such as sarmesin.[15] The positive charge at the N terminus of ANG II is important for full binding affinity, whereas the negative charge on the Asp side chain appears to be of little consequence for binding. Thus it has been possible to substitute a variety of functional groups in position 1, *i.e.* charged, uncharged, branched, extended hydrophobic, affinity labels, photolabile groups, *etc.*, without drastic loss of activity. The positive charge at the N terminus of angiotensin, besides contributing to binding affinity, is also important for the tachyphylactic effects of this peptide on isolated smooth muscle tissues.[16]

Substitution of Sar into position 1 of angiotensin analogs results in increased activity for both agonists and antagonists. Initially this was thought to be due to protection against aminopeptidase activity, although more recent studies suggest that substitution of Sar has more far-reaching consequences. [Sar^1]ANG II produces tachyphylaxis in isolated organs more readily than the native peptide,[16] and Sar^1 analogs of angiotensin show higher binding affinities in membrane-binding studies on a variety of different target tissues. The effect of sarcosine in these peptides is not well understood at the present time, although it seems likely that it is modifying the conformation of the molecule with consecutive biological activity alteration. NMR studies have shown that the NMe group of sarcosine in these peptides is subjected to a very strong shielding influence, pointing to an interaction with other groups of the molecule.[17] Elucidating the exact nature of this

Table 1 Effects on Activity of Amino Acid Substitutions at Each Position of Angiotensin II[a]

Position	1	2	3	4	5	6	7	8
Natural amino acid	Asp	Arg	Val	Tyr	Ile	His	Pro	Phe
Acceptable amino acid	(All)[b]	Lys,Orn	Pro,Ala	Phe(4-NH$_2$)	Tyr,Pro	Pza,3-Me-His[c]	Sar,MeAla	Tyr,Trp[d]
Unacceptable amino acid		Sar	Gly	Ala	Ala	Ala,1-Me-His	Gly,Hyp	Lys,Glu
Antagonist substitution				Tyr(Me),Phe				Ala,Ile[e]

[a] The D isomer of the naturally occurring amino acid is unacceptable at all positions in ANG II except D-Asp^1 (150% activity) and D-Arg^2 (10% activity). [b] A large variety of substitutions are permitted; substitutions which increase agonist activity (up to twofold) include Sar, β-D-Asp, Pyr, Aib. [c] Pza; pyrazolylalanine. [d] Many other substituents retain significant agonist activity, *e.g.* α-C-Me-Phe, Phe(4-NH$_2$), Phe(4-Br), Phe(4-OMe), Phe(4-F). [e] Many other substitutions provide antagonists, *e.g.* Leu, Val, Gly, Thr, Thr(Me), Cha (cyclohexylalanine), Val(F$_6$), Phe(F$_5$), Phe(Br$_5$), MePhe, D-Phe, D-Tyr, D-Trp, D-Phg (D-phenylglycine), D-Val, D-Ile.

interaction would represent an important step in understanding the mechanism of action of angiotensin at its receptors.

13.7.2.5.2 *Position 2*

The positively charged guanidinium group on the side chain of Arg in position 2 has an important role in determining the binding affinity of angiotensin peptides, but does not appear to have a functional role in the response-producing mechanism. Thus replacement of Arg with Gly decreases the activities of both agonists and antagonists to about 10%. Similarly replacement with Nle (norleucine), which retains the long side chain of Arg but removes the guanidino group, also reduces the activity to about 10%, indicating that the long carbon side chain of Arg does not contribute to binding.[18] The positive charge on the side chain of the Arg residue in angiotensin seems to contribute more to the binding affinity of the peptide than the positive charge at the N terminus.[18] A special circumstance is seen for heptapeptide ANG III analogs where the Arg residue is the N-terminal amino acid; substitution of the Arg residue in [Ile[7]]ANG III with Sar increases the binding affinity of the peptide at smooth muscle receptors, whereas substitution of Sar for Arg in [Sar[1],Ile[8]]ANG II severely disrupts the binding affinity of this octapeptide antagonist.[18]

13.7.2.5.3 *Position 3*

The role of the Val residue occupying position 3 in angiotensin appears to be that of conformation director. The bulky side chain probably creates steric hindrance in relation to neighboring side chains and forces these groups into the correct orientation in space. This is demonstrated by the fact that the role of the Val residue can be served by both Ala and Pro (81% and 53% pressor activity, respectively) but not Gly (0.5% pressor activity). The permissible substitution of Pro is a good indication that the role of the side chain at position 3 is a steric one.

13.7.2.5.4 *Position 4*

The Tyr residue occupying position 4 of ANG II plays a very important functional role in receptor activation. Replacement of the Tyr residue with Ala, Gly or Ile produces peptides with less than 1% of the pressor activity of ANG II. Methylation or deletion of the phenolic hydroxyl group produces antagonists, with the latter retaining significant agonist activity. When the Tyr hydroxyl is methylated, high affinity binding to smooth muscle receptors only occurs when there is concomitant substitution of Sar in position 1.[15] In pressor assays, [Sar[1],Phe[4]]ANG II is a considerably more potent antagonist than [Sar[1],Tyr(Me)[4]]ANG II.[19] It has been suggested that the phenolic hydroxyl group participates in hydrogen bonding to the receptor.[20] It has also been suggested that the phenolic hydroxyl group may participate initially in a hydrogen bond with the imidazole group of ANG II and, subsequently, in a covalent bond with the receptor (Figure 1).[15,29]

Substitution of a variety of groups in the 3-position of the phenyl ring, *i.e.* adjacent to the Tyr hydroxyl group, is permitted. Among these, amino, chloro, iodo, azido and nitro are accommodated with only minor changes in receptor-binding affinity and biological activity.[21] Even 3,5-disubstitution with dichloro, diiodo or dinitro maintains 10–20% of the biological activity, suggesting that steric hindrance in the vicinity of the hydroxyl group and accompanying decreases in the pK_a of the hydroxyl group can be tolerated. In the case of dinitro-Tyr, the pK_a would be reduced from about 10 to about 4; this may explain why 4-amino-Phe substitution for the Tyr residue in ANG II occurs with retention of about 15% biological activity (the pK_a of aniline is about 4.6). It has been suggested that the most important characteristic associated with the Tyr residue in ANG II derives not from aromaticity, lipophilicity or pK_a, but from the electronegativity of the side chain,[21] although clearly the phenoxyl proton has a critical role.

13.7.2.5.5 *Position 5*

Removal of the isobutyl side chain of Ile causes a serious loss of biological activity, but many aliphatic groups that retain β branching, such as isopropyl and cyclohexyl, can be substituted without serious loss of activity. The isosteric residue *O*-methylthreonine retains full biological activity, and the substitution of Thr or Pro produces peptides with 10% of the pressor activity of ANG II. The Ile residue occupying position 5 appears to have a steric role not unlike that for the Val residue occupying position 3, except that β branching is more important at position 5. A good deal of steric hindrance seems to be required at position 5, perhaps to force the neighboring side chains into the correct orientation; the Ile[5] residue may have a critical role in directing the C-terminal domain of ANG II into its biologically active conformation.

13.7.2.5.6 Position 6

The His residue occupying position 6 of ANG II appears to have a critical functional role. Removal of the imidazole ring results in drastic loss of biological activity; activity is partially restored by the presence of a phenyl ring, suggesting that a heterocyclic ring is important at position 6. The pK_a of imidazole is such that histidine can exist in its neutral or cationic form at physiological pH. The histidine ring (4-methylimidazole, pK_a 7.6) can be replaced by 3-methylpyrazole (pK_a 3.6)[61] but not by 2-methylimidazole (pK_a 7.9),[62] indicating that only one of the two nitrogens may be adjacent to the γ carbon atom, and that the receptor can interact productively with the neutral form of the heterocyclic ring. Methylation of His at N^1 (1,5-dimethylimidazole, pK_a 7.7) drastically reduces activity, whereas methylation of N^3 (1,4-dimethylimidazole, pK_a 7:2) has somewhat less severe consequences,[63] perhaps illustrating steric constraints in the region of N^1 which are less severe for (methylation of) N^3.

13.7.2.5.7 Position 7

The presence of a secondary amino acid in position 7 is necessary for receptor binding; substitution with Gly, Ala or hydroxyproline causes a drastic reduction in biological activity. A number of secondary amino acids are tolerated at position 7 in the octapeptide ANG II, but these same substitutions in ANG III analogs cause substantial reductions in binding affinity.[22] It appears that a bend produced by the presence of a secondary amino acid in position 7 is a very important aspect. Substitution of D-Pro in angiotensin analogs destroys receptor-binding activity, illustrating the definitive nature of the role of the penultimate Pro residue in directing the conformation of the C-terminal portion of the molecule. It has been suggested that the presence of the Pro residue creates a γ turn at the C terminus of ANG II, which permits the C-terminal carboxylate to interact with the imidazole ring,[23] although others have not been able to demonstrate an interaction between these two functional groups.[24] There is no doubt, however, that the bend caused by the Pro residue in position 7 is mandatory for receptor recognition and binding. The His—Pro bond in ANG II exists primarily in the *trans* configuration in solution.[24]

13.7.2.5.8 Position 8

The Phe residue occupying position 8 of ANG II has received more attention than any other residue in the molecule. This was the direct result of an intense search for a therapeutically useful analog after it was discovered that the substitution of Ala for Phe produced an antagonist. Although [Sar¹,Ala⁸]ANG II (saralasin) has been the most popular antagonist over the years, it is not the most potent antagonist available and it retains significant agonist activity. The antagonist of choice is [Sar¹,Ile⁸]ANG II due to its high potency and lack of agonist activity in myotropic and adrenal assays; however, this analog, like all other antagonist analogs, retains significant (1%) intrinsic activity in blood pressure assays.

Antagonists are produced by substituting the phenyl ring of Phe⁸ by almost any aliphatic group of similar or smaller size than the ring. However, when the phenyl ring is replaced by a cyclohexyl, indole or thiophene ring, the resulting antagonist analogs retain significant intrinsic agonist activity. Thus the steric requirements for the side chain in position 8 for receptor binding do not appear to be very conservative. Antagonists are also produced when position 8 is replaced by a D amino acid (including D-Phe) or N-methyl amino acid, e.g. N-methyl-Phe. Antagonists with remarkably protracted activity have been obtained by increasing the hydrophobicity with multiple halogen substitution, e.g. pentabromo-Phe[25] and hexafluoro-Val.[26] Different considerations apply to pentafluoro-Phe, which can also serve as a useful NMR probe for conformational studies (unpublished work).

Whereas receptor binding seems to be largely unaffected by the nature of the side chain at position 8, the stimulation of the receptor response requires the presence of the Phe side chain. Aromaticity, size and particularly orientation are important factors contributing to biological activity; exact placement of the phenyl ring is critical and there appears to be very little leeway for an induced fit. The negative charge on the C-terminal carboxyl group of ANG II is essential for biological activity.[50]

13.7.2.6 Structure–Activity Relationships of Antagonists

It is to be expected that a flexible ligand such as a peptide will change shape when it binds to its receptor, and that there will be an 'induced fit' between peptide and receptor. Because physico-chemical techniques only provide information on solution conformation, the importance of structure–activity studies in dissecting the biologically active conformation of a ligand cannot be overstated. Until X-ray analysis of ligand–receptor complexes becomes feasible, competitive *antagonists* remain the only reliable tools for mapping the receptor-binding domain and delineating the triggering mechanism. The multifactorial nature of the activity of agonists (comprising affinity and efficacy terms) precludes their use as pharmacological tools for evaluating receptor binding.

Two different classes of angiotensin antagonists have been identified by structure–activity studies (Table 2). Type I antagonists are those modified at position 8 (and often concomitantly modified at position 1), such as [Sar^1,Ile^8]ANG II and [Sar1,Ala^8]ANG II (saralasin). Type II antagonists are obtained by modification of position 4 and position 1, *e.g.* [Sar^1,Phe^4]ANG II and [Sar^1,Tyr(Me)^4]ANG II (sarmesin). The properties of sarmesin-like antagonists differ from sara-lasin-like antagonists in several respects. Firstly, sarmesin is readily reversible and surmountable, whereas the blockade induced by [Sar^1,Ile^8]ANG II is non-surmountable and slow to reverse.[10] Secondly, there is an absolute requirement for Sar at position 1 in sarmesin but not in [Sar^1,Ile^8]ANG II (Table 3).[15] Thirdly, sarmesin is a much weaker pressor antagonist than [Sar^1,Ile^8]ANG II, although [Sar^1,Phe^4]ANG II is a potent antagonist *in vivo* (Table 2).[19]

As mentioned above, type I antagonists appear to illustrate that the phenyl ring at position 8 of ANG II is required for triggering of angiotensin receptors but does not influence binding affinity. However, recent findings[55,57] have suggested that type I antagonists produce their effects primarily by binding to an allosteric site on the angiotensin receptor, and therefore the Phe^8 residue could in fact be required for true receptor binding and may not be directly involved in the expression of ligand efficacy. Correct orientation of the phenolic hydroxyl group at position 4 is necessary for triggering angiotensin receptors and, since there is also a requirement for Sar at position 1 in Type II antagonists, it probably follows that correct orientation of the side chain in position 4 is also required for receptor binding. When both position 4 and position 8 are substituted simultaneously to produce a type I/II hybrid, *e.g.* [Sar^1,Phe^4,Ile^8]ANG II, the resulting peptide has lower antagonist potency in rat isolated uterus (Table 2) than either of the single-substituted peptides,[27] suggesting that the 'additivity rule' does not necessarily apply to antagonists (the additivity rule, which implies that multiple substituent effects should be additive, is probably more applicable to the efficacy component than the affinity component of peptide analogs). [Sar^1,Phe^4,Ile^8]ANG II is a reversible competitive antagonist, illustrating that the slow reversal properties of [Sar^1,Ile^8]ANG II depend on the presence of a free phenolic hydroxyl group.[27]

The low intrinsic pressor activity associated with type I/II hybrid antagonists (Table 2) is a therapeutically desirable property, which makes this class of antagonist worthy of further pursuit. More recent investigations have suggested that type I/II hybrid antagonists, unlike both type I or type II antagonists, do not necessarily benefit from the presence of an *N*-methyl amino acid at the N terminus.[56] Thus [Aib^1,Tyr(Me)^4,Ile^8]ANG II (pA_2 7.1, rat uterus) is considerably more potent than [MeAib^1,Tyr(Me)^4,Ile^8]ANG II (pA_2 5.1, rat uterus) and more potent than [Sar^1,Tyr(Me)^4,Ile^8]ANG II (pA_2 6.6, Table 2; Aib; aminoisobutyric acid). This information may provide a new avenue of exploration in the search for potent antagonists with low intrinsic pressor activity which have potential therapeutic utility.

For studies *in vitro*, where competitive antagonism and the derivation of pA_2 values are required, the type II antagonist sarmesin is presently the analog of choice for studying angiotensin receptors.[41] For *in vivo* studies such as pressor assays, where the level and duration of the receptor blockade are the most important considerations, [Sar^1,Ile^8]ANG II is presently the antagonist of choice.

The synthesis of cyclic analogs is another approach which is expected to provide antagonists with improved therapeutic properties. Cyclization increases resistance to enzyme degradation and should

Table 2 Biological Activities of Some Angiotensin II Antagonists

Peptide	Antagonist classification	Rat uterus assay		Rat pressor assay		
		Agonist activity (%)	Antagonist activity (pA_2)	Agonist activity (%)	Antagonist activity (folds)	Therapeutic quotient[a] (folds %$^{-1}$)
[Sar^1,Ile^8]ANG II	Type I	<0.1	8.1	1.6	500	300
[Sar^1,Tyr(Me)^4]ANG II	Type II	<0.1	7.5	2.5	2	1
[Sar^1,Phe^4]ANG II	Type II	22	7.9	9	270	30
[Sar^1,Phe^4,Ile^8]ANG II	I/II hybrid	<0.1	6.7	0.2	7	35
[Sar^1,Tyr(Me)^4,Ile^8]ANG II	I/II hybrid	<0.1	6.6	0.04	0	0

[a] Therapeutic quotient = antagonist activity (number of folds of shift to the right of dose–response curve to ANG II when the antagonist is infused at a rate of 500 ng kg^{-1} min^{-1})/agonist activity (% of ANG II).

Table 3   The Importance of the Sar¹ Residue of Sarmesin ([Sar¹,Tyr(Me)⁴]ANG II) for
Receptor Blockade

Residue at position 1	pA₂ (rat uterus)	Residue at position 1	pA₂ (rat uterus)
Sar	7.7	Acp	<6
Asp	<6	Aib	<6
Ala	<6	MeAib	6
Pro	<6	Me₂Gly	6
Oxm	<6	Etgly	6.9

increase the plasma half-life of angiotensin antagonists. It is also possible that this type of modification may improve the bioavailability of the peptide; both gastrointestinal and nasal routes of absorption of peptides seem to be prone to a high level of unpredictability, which has deterred many from pursuing peptides as drugs. Thus far only one cyclic angiotensin antagonist has been reported, namely the disulfide-linked analog [Cys¹,⁸]ANG II.[49] The antagonist activity (pA₂ 6.1, rat uterus) of this cyclic peptide was not sufficient to warrant an *in vivo* investigation in blood pressure assays, but provided the first indication that cyclic angiotensin antagonists could be prepared. Further efforts to synthesize cyclic analogs in this laboratory using cross-linking agents such as phenyl diisothiocyanate with hexa-, hepta- and octa-peptides have proved disappointing both chemically and pharmacologically (unpublished work).

The problem of bioavailability associated with peptide drugs, together with the advent of advanced computer graphics and design technology, have perpetrated the view that the only role for peptides is to provide the receptor conformation upon which non-peptide drugs can be modeled. Realistically speaking, the main deterrent to this approach is the enormous difficulty in obtaining a reliable receptor conformation, as evidenced by the still unsolved problems encountered with angiotensin after 30 years and hundreds of analogs (see below). Furthermore, synthesis of non-peptide 'designer' molecules will probably not be a simple matter. Although cloning of receptors and X-ray analysis of receptor–peptide complexes will eventually provide the information required for 'designer' synthesis, in the meantime the main priority must continue to be the search for ways to administer peptide drugs in a reliable and reproducible manner.

13.7.2.7   Angiotensin II Conformation and Receptor Recognition

Because of its established role in blood pressure regulation and hypertension, ANG II has been the subject of many conformational studies. From the beginning it was generally agreed by most investigators that ANG II exists in a folded conformation, although there has been little agreement about any of the details. Indeed the contradictory interpretations of the various spectral techniques applied to study the conformation of ANG II serve to illustrate that we have entered an era where technology is far ahead of theory.

Titrations of the functional groups in ANG II, either by spectroscopic methods or by direct methods, have shown that the pK_a values of the Tyr hydroxyl and α-carboxyl groups lean on the high side, whereas the pK_a of the α-amino group tends towards the low side.[24] The remaining ionizable groups appear normal, and it has been suggested that an electrostatic interaction between the N and C termini may exist.[28] Other studies based on CD spectra[24] and chemical reactivity[29] have suggested an interaction between the His and Tyr rings, in one case involving the α-carboxylate also.[29] Based on proton NMR and ESR studies, ion–dipole formation between the α-carboxylate and the imidazole ring has also been proposed,[23] although ¹³C-NMR studies have not supported this concept.[24]

Chemical reactivity studies on ANG II have also given conflicting results. In one study only the α-amino group was found to have elevated nucleophilicity,[30] whereas in another study both the His and Tyr residues were found to be superreactive at physiological pH.[29] Based on the latter study, it was suggested that the α-carboxylate might interact with the imidazole, which might in turn interact with the phenolic hydroxyl group, thereby forming a Tyr charge relay system analogous to the Ser charge relay system present at the catalytic site of serine proteases (Figure 1).[29] Whereas the ANG II molecule may exhibit a limited tendency towards formation of the 'charge relay' conformer in solution situations, it might be the dominant conformation at the receptor. Taking this notion a step

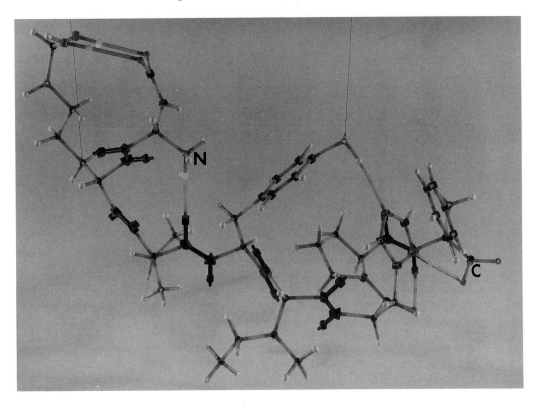

Figure 1 The proposed 'scorpion' conformation for angiotensin II showing the triad of interacting groups which form the charge transfer system (net free energy gain $\sim$ 20 kcal mol^{-1}; 1 kcal = 4.18 kJ).[31] The TyrOH–His–carboxylate interaction could lead to transfer of the negative charge from the α-carboxylate to the His ring . Very recent *ab initio* calculations suggest that electrostatic interaction between His$^-$ (imidazole anion) and the Phe ring (benzene quadrupole) will have perpendicular-plate geometry (energy gain $\sim$ 3 kcal mol^{-1})[54] rather than the traditional parallel-plate 'stacking' geometry shown here. The conformation illustrated was deduced on the basis of the available structure–activity relationships, NMR data and chemical reactivities of the functional groups.[37] Whilst the intramolecular interactions illustrated provide a convenient explanation for much of the accumulated data on ANG II, elements of the proposed receptor conformation require substantiation by alternative physicochemical techniques (see Addendum, Section 13.7.4)

further by applying semi-empirical calculations, it was suggested that a charge transfer system in ANG II might lead to receptor acylation of the Tyr or His as an intermediate in the receptor-binding and -triggering mechanism.[31] The possibility that a covalent bond may be formed when a ligand interacts with its receptor, whilst conceptually novel, is of particular interest in a pharmaceutical setting since it provides the opportunity of synthesizing 'suicide hormones'. The incorporation of a charge transfer system into the ANG II molecule gives rise to a 'scorpion-like' receptor conformation (Figure 1),[37] and also provides an explanation for the structure–activity data on sarmesin. Thus, because of hydrogen bonding between the Tyr hydroxyl proton and His imidazole nitrogen, the Tyr–His interaction in ANG II would be stabilized, whereas in sarmesin no such influence would be present to cause the Tyr ring to lean over towards the His ring. This could explain why the presence of Sar^1 in sarmesin is an absolute requirement for receptor binding, *i.e.* the steric hindrance associated with the *N*-methyl group of Sar may act to repel the Tyr ring towards the His ring and allow the peptide to correctly access the receptor-binding site.[15]

The role of the C-terminal Phe side chain in receptor activation remains unsolved. NMR studies have suggested an interaction between the Phe ring and the His ring, which might involve π–π* interaction.[32] Stacking interactions between aromatic rings are present in the DNA helix and predicted to exist in a number of peptides. However, recent *ab initio* calculations suggest that the interactions between pairs of small aromatic rings in peptides and proteins prefer perpendicular-plate geometry (rather than traditional parallel-plate geometry), and that the attraction will be increased when one ring is charged.[54]

13.7.2.8 Signal Transduction by Angiotensin Receptors

It has been proposed that the ANG II molecule may harness electrical potential (Figure 1), and release this energy upon contacting a receptor which has an appropriate recognition and transduction mechanism.[33] In other words, the ANG II molecule can be viewed to exist in a high energy conformation, which upon contact with the receptor (possibly acylation by the receptor) adopts a relaxed conformation and gives up its free energy to the receptor.[33] This has formed the basis for an 'excited state' receptor theory which has the potential for quantile analysis (Figure 2).[34] Evidence has been obtained to indicate that the excited state of the receptor (produced as a result of interaction with the agonist) has a higher affinity than the resting ground state of the receptor, so that in binding studies an agonist is seen to interact with two binding sites (resting state and excited state respectively), whereas the antagonist [Sar^1,Ile^8]ANG II (which cannot excite the receptor) interacts only with the resting ground state of the receptor.[35] Furthermore data from bioassays, particularly photoaffinity labelling studies,[37] appear to support this concept. Table 4 summarizes the kinetic constants which were obtained from bioassays and binding assays on a single tissue. These values indicate that the antagonist [Sar^1,Ile^8]ANG II has higher affinity than ANG II for the resting state of the receptor, but that ANG II has even higher affinity for the excited state of the receptor.

It appears that excitation of the receptor involves interaction of the receptor with a guanine nucleotide binding (G) protein.[36] Present findings suggest that interaction of the agonist with the resting ground state of the receptor induces the receptor to sequester a G protein (or subunit thereof) which inhibits adenylate cyclase (Figure 2). Although the series of events leading to angiotensin-induced contraction or secretion is not well understood, excitation of the receptor and sequestration of G_i in turn brings about phosphoinositide turnover and mobilization of intracellular stores of calcium.[37] It is not yet clear if in fact the receptor interacts with another G protein which mediates

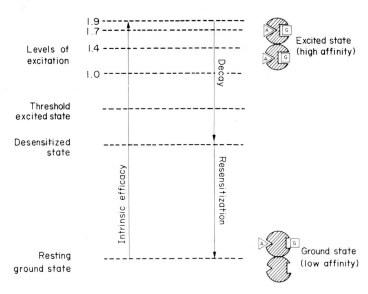

Figure 2 Receptor excitation by angiotensin II. A quantum ladder of possible receptor transition states induced by agonists are shown together with corresponding molecular interactions of the receptor. The molecular interaction illustrated forms the basis for a *homotropic hexamer model* of receptor function (see text). Agonist-induced homotropic cooperativity between the two subunits of the symmetrical receptor dimer engenders an increase in the heterotropic cooperativity between receptor and G protein. Heterotropic binding reciprocity between agonist (A) and G protein (G) occurs, so that the influence A has on the receptor-binding affinity of G is equivalent to the effect that G has on the receptor-binding affinity of A. Thus A can demonstrate at least two receptor-binding affinities: (i) a low affinity interaction with the resting state of the receptor; and (ii) a high affinity interaction with the G-protein-coupled excited state. The ratio of binding affinities at the two states is a measure of homotropic efficacy (Table 6),[55] and can be determined in binding studies from the GTP shift[52] (the change in affinity induced by dissociation of G protein from the receptor by GTPγS). The importance of this knowledge rests on its potential utility for receptor classification; it appears that we now have a method for measuring both the affinity (resting state, in the presence of GTPγS) and the efficacy (GTP shift) of an agonist in binding studies, which can be used for a detailed examination, and comparison, of different tissue receptors for a single ligand. The agonist Hill coefficient determined in bioassays also offers a means for determining agonist efficacy and for comparing tissue receptors *in vitro*; recent studies in this laboratory have demonstrated kinetic differences between smooth muscle receptors for ANG II based on differences in Hill coefficient.[55] There is actually quite good agreement between the values for homotropic efficacies obtained for ANG II and ANG III from bioassays (β_H) and binding assays (β_G) in rat uterus (Table 6). Furthermore, the relative efficacies of ANG II and ANG III in three smooth muscle tissues determined from Hill slopes, on the one hand, and by irreversible labeling methods, on the other hand, are quite similar (Table 6)

Table 4 Binding Affinities of Angiotensin II For Receptors in Rat Uterus Determined by Pharmacological and Biochemical Methods[a]

	Angiotensin II	*[Sar^1,Ile^8]ANG II*
Bioassay		
pD_2 (EC_{50})	9.3	—
pK_D (photolabeling)	7.5	—
pA_2 (Schild plot)	—	8.6
Binding assay		
pK_D	9.3 and 7.5[b]	8.7

[a] Binding affinities are given as $-$ log molar and are in all cases theoretically equivalent to the equilibrium dissociation constant.[37] [b] Low affinity sites are not always observed in binding studies; however, addition of GTPγS (10^{-4} M) produces a population of binding sites which resembles the low affinity/resting state of the receptor.[52]

calcium mobilization, or whether different subunits of the same G_i may elicit two different events. Analysis of dose–response curves supports the hypothesis that the angiotensin receptor operates as a dimer; Hill plots of dose–response data from smooth muscle bioassays have slopes greater than unity and less than two, suggesting that homotropic two-site cooperativity is involved in the ANG II-induced contraction of smooth muscle.[37,55]

Table 5 lists available data taken from the literature and interpreted according to the excited state receptor theory. Although there is some tissue variability observed for agonists, the data for antagonists are remarkably consistent. These data may exemplify minor kinetic differences in smooth muscle receptors or differences in bioassays among laboratories, but do not illustrate the presence of receptor 'subtypes', *i.e.* receptors which differ as a result of different receptor proteins or coupling mechanisms. Rather Table 5 may exemplify 'isoreceptors' for angiotensin, which display relatively subtle kinetic differences, perhaps based on differences in agonist efficacy (Table 6). Pharmacological data, even for antagonists, should be applied to receptor classification with caution because of the occurrence of multiple states of each receptor induced by the agonist during bioassay; thus it is necessary to first classify each antagonist according to the receptor state(s) with which it interacts (see legend to Table 5).

Tachyphylaxis to ANG II is very prevalent, particularly in vascular smooth muscle tissues. Depending on the magnitude of the original stimulus, responsiveness to a second challenge of agonist can be greatly decreased. This may be because a certain portion of the excited receptor reverts to a 'desensitized' state rather than immediately returning to the resting ground state (Figure 2).[37] The possibility has been entertained that the receptor may acylate a small percentage of

Table 5 Comparison of Angiotensin Receptors in Target Tissues: Apparent Binding Affinities of Agonists and Antagonists for Resting Ground State (G) and Excited State (E) of Receptor[a]

		Rat uterus[b]	*Rabbit aorta*[c]	*Rat stomach*[c]	*Rat heart*[d]	*Bovine adrenal cortex*[e]
Angiotensin II	(G)	7.5[g,h]			8.2[h,i]	7.6[h],7.8[i]
	(E)	9.3[f,h]	8.9[f]	7.7[f]	9.2[h]	8.8[h]
Angiotensin III	(G)	6.5[g,h]				7.6[h]
	(E)	8.3[f,h]	7.6[f]	7.5[f]		9.2[h]
[Sar^1]ANG II	(G)					8.5[h]
	(E)	9.5[f]	9.1[f]	8.2[f]		9.6[h]
[Sar^1,Ile^8]ANG II	(G)[j]	8.6[f],8.7[h]	9.3[f]			8.9[h]
[Sar^1,Leu^8]ANG II	(G)[j]		9.1[f]	9.2[f]	9.2[h]	9.1[h]

[a] Values are given as the negative logarithm of molar concentration. The interpretation of published data in terms of dual states of the receptor does not necessarily reflect the conclusions reached in the cited references. [b] Data from refs. 35 and 48. [c] Data from refs. 44 and 46. [d] Data from ref. 47. [e] Data from ref. 36. [f] Value obtained by bioassay of intact tissue: pD_2 for agonists and pA_2 for antagonists. [g] Value obtained by irreversible labeling of intact tissues. [h] Value obtained from membrane-binding assay. [i] Value obtained from membrane-binding assay in the presence of GTPγS. [j] Classified as a 'ground state' antagonist because it does not appear to interact significantly with the excited state of the receptor[37]

Table 6 Homotropic Efficacies Estimated for Angiotensins II and III in Several Smooth Muscle
Tissues[d]

	Aorta		Portal vein		Uterus		
	$n_H^{obs\,a}$	β_H	$n_H^{obs\,a}$	β_H	$n_H^{obs\,a}$	β_H	$\beta_G{}^b$
Angiotensin II	1.95	390	1.75	70	1.35	21	20
Angiotensin III	1.43	25	1.02	10	1.28	18	24
ANG II/ANG III β_H ratio	—	15.6	—	7	—	1.2	0.8
ANG II/III efficacy ratio[c]		(14)		(11)		(0.9)	

[a] The Hill coefficient (n_H^{obs}) was determined from Hill plots of dose–response data obtained at low agonist concentrations,[37] and homotropic efficacy (β_H) was calculated[55] from $\beta_H = 10\,[(n_H^{max}/n_H^{obs})^{-1}]$ where $n_H^{max} = 2$ for angiotensin receptor dimers. [b] In uterine binding studies, homotropic efficacy (β_G) was determined[55] from the GTP shift (the ratio of agonist binding affinities in the absence and presence of 10^{-4} M GTPγS). [c] ANG II/ANG III efficacy ratio determined by photoaffinity labeling of intact tissues.[37] [d] These data serve to illustrate that each tissue receptor has its own intrinsic *avidity* for a given ligand, thereby defining the existence of a new receptor-based kinetic parameter which complements intrinsic agonist efficacy. Based on β_H values, the aortic receptor has about 6 times the avidity of the portal vein receptor for ANG II and about 20 times the avidity of the uterine angiotensin receptor for ANG II, whereas the relative avidities of the three receptors for ANG III are similar.

the ANG II molecules at the Tyr hydroxyl and that this more slowly reversing intermediate could effectively inactivate some of the receptors temporarily.[34] Such considerations can explain the importance of the Tyr hydroxyl group in the slow rates of dissociation of certain antagonists[10,27] but are clearly speculative in relation to tachyphylaxis to agonists where the mechanism is unknown. However, [Sar[1]]ANG II and [Sar[1],Ile[8]]ANG II both display unusually slow receptor dissociation rates,[36] perhaps indicating that similar receptor inactivation mechanisms exist for both agonists and antagonists. Recent findings suggest that receptor desensitization might involve binding of the desensitizing ligand to an allosteric site on the receptor.[55,57]

13.7.2.8.1 Homotropic hexamer model

The presently available data suggest that angiotensin receptors, and possibly other receptors coupled to G protein, can be described by a homotropic hexamer model (Scheme 1).[57] In this scheme the affinity constants, K_1 and K_2, and the reciprocal heterotropic cooperativity, α, denote equilibria involving agonist (A) and G protein (G) with the resting ground state of the receptor (R—R). Likewise K_3 and K_4 and β are the equivalent parameters for the excited state of the receptor (R*—R*). The homotropic hexamer model predicts that the Hill coefficient and the percentage spare receptors determined in bioassays (see legend to Figure 2), and also the ratio of affinity constants

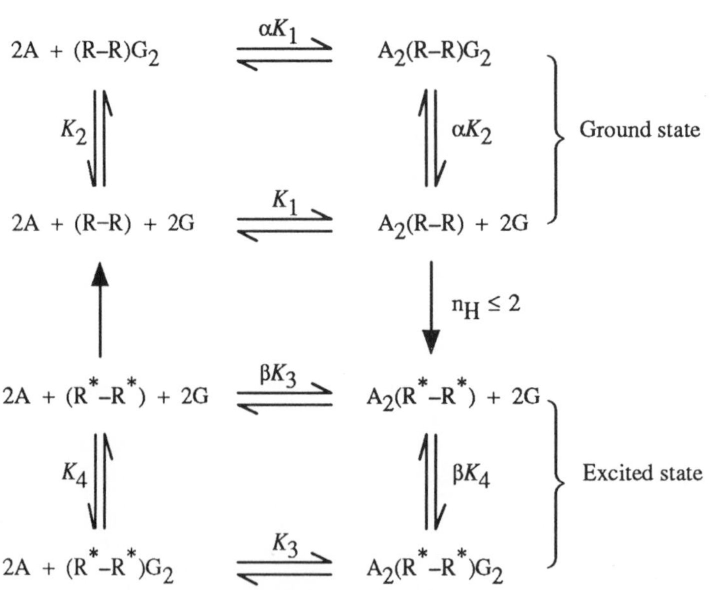

Scheme 1

determined in binding assays in the absence and presence of GTPγS (GTP shift), reflect the homotropic efficacy of an agonist (Table 6).[55] Absolute intrinsic efficacy is given by $\beta + \alpha$, and when $\beta \gg \alpha$ (strong agonist), homotropic efficacy becomes equivalent to intrinsic efficacy (*NB*: Stephenson's classical efficacy term[58] is equal to the product of intrinsic efficacy *and* receptor concentration[37]). Variations on Scheme 1 should also be considered.[57]

13.7.2.9 Isolation and Purification of Receptors

Using irreversible labeling techniques, angiotensin receptors have been isolated from several tissues including smooth muscle,[38] liver[39] and adrenal cortex.[36] In each case the denatured reduced receptor species behaved as a protein with a molecular weight 60–70 kD.[37] In the absence of denaturing and reducing agents, larger molecular species (105–130 kD) were observed. In liver and adrenal the size of the native receptor was dependent on the nature of the attached radioligand, with agonist-associated receptor being significantly larger than antagonist-associated receptor.[36,39] The size difference between agonist- and antagonist-associated receptors has been difficult to assess,[36] although more recent estimates[40] have suggested the size difference is about 40 kD (equivalent to the α or the β subunit of a G protein). Thus present data could illustrate that the excited state of the angiotensin receptor exists in a dimeric form made up of two subunits of molecular weight 60–70 kD which may be held together by a disulfide bond. Apparently when the receptor is excited by an agonist, G_i^{α} or $G_i^{\beta\gamma}$ is sequestered, and consequent interactions lead to adenylate cyclase inhibition and calcium mobilization.

13.7.2.10 Biological Properties of Selected Analogs in Animals and Man

For many years the antagonist most used in studies on both animals and man was saralasin ([Sar^1,Ala^8]ANG II). In fact during the 1970s saralasin was used quite extensively in the diagnosis of different forms of hypertension: a decrease in blood pressure resulting from saralasin infusion was used to diagnose renovascular hypertension, although the success rate was only about 60%. Saralasin infusion was superseded by renal-vein renin assay, where the diagnosis success rate was closer to 80%. In animal studies, the use of saralasin has been largely superseded by [Sar^1,Ile^8]ANG II, which is a more potent antagonist with less intrinsic agonist activity than saralasin. More recently, the reversible competitive antagonist sarmesin has become the antagonist of choice for *in vitro* assays.[41] No one has yet discovered an angiotensin analog which has no agonist activity *in vivo*. The most popular inhibitors of the renin–angiotensin system at present are the ACE inhibitors and renin inhibitors. The former have been widely used to treat hypertension in man, whereas the latter are still in experimental stages and further developments can be expected in the not too distant future.

13.7.2.11 Key Drugs Used in Therapy

The only angiotensin-related drugs currently used in man are the ACE inhibitors captopril (Squibb) and enalapril (Merck). The use of these drugs is indicated for the diseases of hypertension and congestive heart failure. They may one day find use in the treatment of other edematous disease states, *e.g.* pulmonary edema not related to congestive heart failure. ACE inhibitors are fast becoming the drug of choice for treating hypertension, and are replacing combinations of a β-blocker and a diuretic as first line treatment. The use of ACE inhibitors in congestive heart failure is a rapidly expanding field with much potential. Limitations and side effects of ACE inhibitors are largely idiosyncratic; captopril causes a rash in a small percentage of individuals. Enalapril is devoid of this side effect, apparently because of the absence of a sulfur atom in the chemical structure, and lower doses of enalapril can be used because it has a higher affinity for the converting enzyme. More serious side effects of ACE inhibitors, *i.e.* proteinuria (caused by glomerulonephritis) and reversible neutropenia, occur in less than 1% of patients.

ACE inhibitors represent a classical example of successful rational drug design. Basically they are dipeptidic structures (containing a single peptide bond), which dispels the myth that peptides cannot be used as drugs. ACE inhibitors perhaps may herald a new epoch in drug therapy, namely the emergence of a new generation of peptide drugs whose vast potential has yet to be realized. It will be interesting to see if the renin inhibitors, which are currently being actively pursued in different quarters, will also turn out to be therapeutically useful antiangiotensin agents.[53] It is not yet clear if blocking angiotensin production will turn out to be a more useful therapeutic approach than blocking angiotensin effects. The former avenue has been championed by the ACE inhibitors, although the latter would seem to be the more direct approach. The main critique against biosynthesis inhibitors is that the further back along the biosynthesis pathway that an inhibitor acts, the greater the likelihood of interfering with other important biochemical pathways. In the case of ACE inhibitors, the additional effect of elevating bradykinin seems to be advantageous, but this will not always be the case. For reasons of specificity, wisdom would suggest therapeutic intervention at a point as close as possible to the last step, which in the case of angiotensin would be blockade of the receptor itself. Time will tell which route is preferred, particularly now that cyclic angiotensin antagonists have been pioneered.[49] However, identifying a potent receptor antagonist with negligible agonist activity *in vivo* remains an elusive goal. Furthermore, the bioavailability characteristics of peptides continue to hamper pharmaceutical development and, until a suitable general method of administration, which is reproducible and of reasonable duration, is developed for peptides, the main emphasis will continue to be on the modeling and design of non-peptide mimetics based on the peptide blueprint. The first non-peptide angiotensin receptor inhibitors have already been reported.[66]

13.7.3 BRADYKININS

13.7.3.1 Biosynthesis and Metabolism

The kinin system is somewhat analogous to the renin–angiotensin system in that the production of the biologically active species does not involve direct endocrine secretion, but rather secretion of enzymes of the kallikrein family which have a function similar to that of renin. The kallikreins act on the kininogens, which are kinin precursor proteins present in plasma. In the same way that the renin–angiotensin system produces ANG I, II and III, the kallikrein–kininogen system produces kallidin ([Lys^0]bradykinin), bradykinin itself, and [desArg^9]bradykinin. Bradykinin (BK) is a nonapeptide with the sequence Arg-Pro-Pro-Gly-Phe-Ser-Pro-Phe-Arg. The family of kinins have important actions on the cardiovascular system,[64] generally causing dilation of peripheral small blood vessels resulting in hypotension, *i.e.* the opposite effect to angiotensin. The role of BK in blood pressure regulation and different forms of hypertension is not well understood. The peptide also has a role in inflammation; it increases capillary permeability, leukocyte migration rates and pain.

The kinins are broken down by a host of proteolytic enzymes present in plasma which, as is the case for angiotensin, have not yet been characterized in any detail. Interestingly the angiotensin converting enzyme (ACE) degrades BK, and it has been suggested that one of the actions of ACE inhibitors, in addition to decreasing the circulating level of angiotensin, might be to increase the circulating level of the vasodepressor BK. However, the therapeutic importance of the effect of ACE inhibitors on BK in relation to their antihypertensive effects requires substantiation experimentally.

13.7.3.2 Bioassays, Receptors and Structure–Activity Relationships

Although BK exerts effects on the inflammatory response and on exocrine function, the most convenient and direct methods for measuring BK biological activity are bioassays on isolated vascular (or non-vascular) smooth muscles. BK effects are bimodal, with low doses causing prostaglandin-mediated relaxation and higher doses acting directly on smooth muscle to cause contraction.[59] Thus although BK is a hypotensive agent, it contracts a number of vascular smooth muscles, *e.g.* rabbit aorta, rabbit jugular vein, dog carotid artery and rat mesenteric vein.

It is perhaps unfortunate for the kinin field that early studies[42] demonstrated the presence in rabbit aorta of a low potency BK receptor (pD_2 6.2), which was selectively blocked by the octapeptide analog [Leu^8,desArg^9]BK (pA_2 6.7). Since other vascular receptors were not inhibited by [Leu^8,desArg^9]BK the aorta receptor was, rather surprisingly, designated as B$_1$, and subjected to an intense structure–activity study,[42] whilst physiologically relevant high potency BK receptors present in all other tissues [*e.g.* dog carotid artery (pD_2 8.6)] were designated B$_2$ and largely ignored. Later it was noted that the 'B$_1$ receptor' increased in amount during bioassays, suggesting that it emerged as the result of tissue injury inflicted during the setting up of the bioassay.[43] It therefore appears that the so-called B$_1$ receptor subtype may be a stress-induced artifact of the tissue bioassay

Table 7 Effects of Amino Acid Substitutions at Each Position of Bradykinin and Kallidin (Lys-BK)

Position	0	1	2	3	4	5	6	7	8	9
Natural amino acid	Lys	Arg	Pro	Pro	Gly	Phe	Ser	Pro	Phe	Arg
Acceptable amino acid	Gly,Tyr	Aib,Ala	Ala,Aib	Ala,Hyp	Ala,Phe	Cha,Thi	Ala,D-Phe	Aib	Cha,Trp	Lys,Nle
Unacceptable amino acid				D-Pro		Ala,Tyr	Phe	Ala,D-Pro	Ala,Leu	
Antagonist substitution								D-Phe		

procedure, and that the most relevant biological actions of the kinins are mediated by a single receptor (which unfortunately has been labeled B_2). Apparently the latent appearance of the stress-induced receptor in rabbit aorta assays is blocked by cycloheximide,[42] suggesting that it may be of pathophysiological significance if it is induced by the presence of BK or its primary metabolite [desArg⁹]BK.

The bradykinin field owes much to the rational efforts of Stewart and his colleagues to find physiologically relevant antagonists. True classical kinin receptors in normal tissues have high potency, displaying pD_2 values of 7–7.5 for the octapeptide, 8.5–9 for the nonapeptide BK, and ≥ 9 for the decapeptide kallidin.[51] The octapeptide analog [Leu⁸,desArg⁹]BK does not bind to these receptors; Stewart's group found that they are blocked[43] by the nonapeptide [Thi⁵,⁸,D-Phe⁷]BK (pA_2 6.4, dog carotid artery) and the corresponding decapeptide [Lys⁰,Thi⁵,⁸,D-Phe⁷]BK (pA_2 6.9). The most potent *in vivo* antagonist reported thus far is [D-Arg⁰,Hyp³,Thi⁵,⁸,D-Phe⁷]BK (Hyp: hydroxyproline, Thi: thienylalanine).[44] There is a large discrepancy between the apparent affinity (pA_2) in bioassays and the affinity observed in binding assays, which may reflect the rapid breakdown of BK, and perhaps BK receptors, in bioassays.

With the exception of the low potency 'pathological' receptor observed in rabbit aorta assays, there does not appear to be very much difference in normal physiological BK receptors amongst the various smooth muscle tissues which have been investigated. Table 7 lists some of the acceptable and unacceptable amino acid substitutions for BK and kallidin acting on classical receptors. It is probably safer to assume for the present that a single physiologically relevant receptor for the kinin family of peptides has been identified. Since decapeptide analogs are often the most potent, there is a case for using the term kallidin 'K' receptor, at least until the 'B_1 and B_2 receptor' controversy is cleared up. The situation for kinin receptors seems to be similar to that observed at present for peripheral angiotensin receptors. Whereas the angiotensin receptor demonstrates the following potency order: ANG II (octapeptide) > ANG III (heptapeptide) $\gg$ ANG I (decapeptide), the order of potency for the kinin receptor is: kallidin (decapeptide) $\geq$ BK (nonapeptide) $\gg$ [desArg⁹]BK (octapeptide).

It is quite probable that receptor subtypes do exist for both angiotensins and kinins, perhaps in relatively understudied tissues such as resistance vessels and brain. It is interesting to note that vasopressin has receptor subtypes, V_1 (pressor) and V_2 (antidiuretic), which differ not only in location and structure–activity profile but also in terms of their second messenger systems. Past attempts at categorizing angiotensin and kinin receptors illustrate that caution should prevail, and that classifications based on differences in second messenger systems may be a safer and wiser approach. However, this has not proved necessary for the classification of opiate receptors. Very recently, two different BK receptors were found to mediate prostaglandin synthesis in rat fibroblasts and bovine endothelial cells, respectively, *via* different phospholipases.[65]

Although a number of photolabile analogs of BK have been prepared,[45] there is not yet a report of the successful isolation of the kinin receptor.

13.7.3.3 Potential Therapeutic Applications of Kinin Analogs

The antiinflammatory actions of BK antagonists pose interesting possibilities for the application of these analogs in situations where antihistamines are used, *e.g.* the common cold. Since the actions of BK antagonists would be 'upstream' of histamine production, none of the undesirable effects of massive histamine production would be observed. The potential applicability of these antagonist analogs to other inflammatory situations has not been adequately assessed. The involvement of BK in mediating pain also poses interesting possibilities for the application of BK antagonists as analgesics.[60]

13.7.4 ADDENDUM

Recently, several relevant advances have been made in the angiotensin field which deserve mention.

(1) *Biologically active conformation of angiotensin II.* The presence of a Tyr charge relay system in ANG II has recently been confirmed by nanosecond time-resolved fluorescence decay studies on a number of angiotensin analogues in receptor-simulating environments (Turner *et al.*, 1989). 2D-ROESY proton NMR studies have also provided insight concerning the biologically active conformation of ANG II, particularly with regard to the relative positioning in space of the

attendant groups surrounding the charge relay network (Matsoukas *et al.*, 1989). Two amendments to the 'scorpion' conformation shown in Figure 1 are suggested by these studies. Firstly, the Phe ring should probably be placed on the back side of the His ring, rather than on the front side as shown in Figure 1. Secondly, the N-terminal portion of the molecule probably folds along the front of the peptide backbone, rather than over the top of the peptide backbone as shown in Figure 1.

(2) *Therapeutic update.* The currently available ACE inhibitors, captopril and enalapril (which will soon be joined by several new 'me too' drugs), apparently have a number of potential clinical applications in addition to their use in hypertension and congestive heart failure. These include myocardial infarction, stroke, cardiac arrhythmia, diabetic nephropathy and impaired cognition; the scientific bases for some of these effects are not obvious. There is a continuously expanding list of therapeutic benefits supposedly associated with blockade of angiotensin production or action, and, since the *mas* oncogene encodes an angiotensin receptor, one wonders if anticancer effects might be next. It has turned out that the smallest effective renin inhibitors are tetra/pentapeptides, which have poor bioavailability, so that the clinical future of renin inhibitors looks uncertain at present. On the other hand, the future of *N*-benzylimidazole compounds, which are angiotensin receptor antagonists (with all the attendant possibilities for receptor selectivity), looks promising; interestingly, studies with these antagonists tend to suggest that the blood pressure lowering effect of ACE inhibitors has no bradykinin component.

ACKNOWLEDGEMENTS

Grant support from the Alberta Heart Foundation and the Alberta Heritage Foundation for Medical Research are duly acknowledged. Thanks are due to Tammara Cross for typing this manuscript and members of my laboratory, past and present, for their contributions.

13.7.5 REFERENCES

1. J. M. Sullivan, *Annu. Rev. Med.*, 1984, **34**, 169.
2. T. Akaishi, H. Negoro and S. Kobayasi, *Brain Res.*, 1980, **188**, 499.
3. K. Starke, *Rev. Physiol. Biochem. Pharmacol.*, 1977, **77**, 1.
4. W. F. Ganong, *Annu. Rev. Physiol.*, 1984, **46**, 17.
5. V. G. Dzau, *Hypertension*, 1986, **8**, 553.
6. M. Nakamaru, R. Takayanagi and T. Inagami, *Peptides*, 1986, **7**, 373.
7. Y. C. Kwok and G. J. Moore, *J. Pharmacol. Exp. Ther.*, 1984, **231**, 137.
8. M. N. Scanlon and G. J. Moore, *Proc. West. Pharmacol. Soc.*, 1986, **29**, 455.
9. R. K. Turker, M. N. Hall, N. Yamamoto, C. S. Sweet and F. M. Bumpus, *Science (Washington, D.C.)*, 1972, **177**, 1203.
10. J. M. Matsoukas, M. H. Goghari, M. N. Scanlon, K. J. Franklin and G. J. Moore, *J. Med. Chem.*, 1985, **28**, 780.
11. J. W. Harding, D. Felix, J. B. Erickson, M. J. Sullivan, C. A. Camara, J. W. Wright, R. F. Abhold and I. Rogulja, *Proc. West. Pharmacol. Soc.*, 1987, **30**, 11.
12. J. B. Smith, L. Smith, E. R. Brown, D. Barnes, M. A. Sabir, J. Davis and R. V. Farese, *Cell Biol.*, 1984, **81**, 7812.
13. M. C. Khosla, R. R. Smeby and F. M. Bumpus, in 'Handbook of Experimental Pharmacology', ed. I. H. Page and F. M. Bumpus, Springer-Verlag, Berlin, 1974, vol. 37, p. 126.
14. F. M. Bumpus and M. C. Khosla, in 'Hypertension: Physiopathology and Treatment', ed. J. Genest, E. Koiw and O. Kuchel, McGraw-Hill, New York, 1978, p. 183.
15. M. H. Goghari, K. J. Franklin and G. J. Moore, *J. Med. Chem.*, 1986, **29**, 1121.
16. N. Miasiro, M. E. M. Oshiro, T. B. Paiva and A. C. M. Paiva, *Eur. J. Pharmacol.*, 1983, **87**, 397.
17. J. M. Matsoukas and G. J. Moore, *Arch. Biochem. Biophys.*, 1986, **248**, 419.
18. G. J. Moore, R. C. Ganter, M. H. Goghari and K. J. Franklin, 1989, submitted for publication.
19. K. J. Franklin and G. J. Moore, *Proc. West. Pharmacol. Soc.*, 1987, **30**, 313.
20. K. Hsieh, I. C. Kiraly-Olah and E. C. Jorgensen, *J. Med. Chem.*, 1979, **22**, 1044.
21. G. Guillemette, M. Bernier, P. Parent, R. Leduc and E. Escher, *J. Med. Chem.*, 1984, **27**, 315.
22. G. J. Moore, in 'Peptides: Synthesis–Structure–Function', ed. D. H. Rich and E. Gross, Pierce Chemical Co., Rockford, IL, 1981, p. 245.
23. R. J. Weinkam and E. C. Jorgensen, *J. Am. Chem. Soc.*, 1971, **93**, 7033, 7038.
24. R. R. Smeby and S. Fermandjian, in 'Chemistry and Biochemistry of Amino Acids, Peptides and Proteins', ed. B. Weinstein, Dekker, New York, 1978, vol. 5, p. 117.
25. R. Leduc, M. Bernier and E. Escher, *Helv. Chim. Acta*, 1983, **66**, 960.
26. K. H. Hsieh, P. Needleman and G. R. Marshall, *J. Med. Chem.*, 1987, **30**, 1097.
27. G. J. Moore, K. J. Franklin, D. M. Nystrom and M. H. Goghari, *Can. J. Physiol. Pharmacol.*, 1985, **63**, 966.
28. L. Juliano and A. C. M. Paiva, *Biochemistry*, 1974, **13**, 2445.
29. G. J. Moore, *Int. J. Pept. Protein Res.*, 1985, **26**, 469.
30. L. Juliano, P. Boschcov and A. C. M. Paiva, *Biochemistry*, 1974, **13**, 4263.
31. A. Rauk, G. Hamilton and G. J. Moore, *Biochem. Biophys. Res. Commun.*, 1987, **145**, 1349.
32. J. M. Matsoukas and G. J. Moore, *Biochem. Biophys. Res. Commun.*, 1984, **122**, 434.
33. G. J. Moore and J. M. Matsoukas, *Biosci. Rep.*, 1985, **4**, 407.

34. G. J. Moore, *Proc. West. Pharmacol. Soc.*, 1987, **30**, 377.
35. G. J. Moore and Y. C. Kwok, *Life Sci.*, 1987, **41**, 505.
36. A. De Lean, M. Ong, J. Gutkowska, P. W. Schiller and N. McNicoll, *Mol. Pharmacol.*, 1984, **26**, 498.
37. G. J. Moore, *Pharmacol. Ther.*, 1987, **33**, 349.
38. A. M. Capponi and K. J. Catt, *J. Biochem.*, 1980, **255**, 12081.
39. G. Guillemette, G. Guillon, J. Marie, C. Pantaloni, M. N. Bolestre, E. Escher and S. Jard, *J. Recept. Res.*, 1984, **4**, 267.
40. E. Escher, *Pharmacol. Ther.*, 1988, **37**, 37.
41. M. N. Scanlon and G. J. Moore, *Pharmacol. Ther.*, 1988, **37**, 137.
42. D. Regoli and J. Barabe, *Pharmacol. Rev.*, 1980. **32**, 1.
43. R. J. Vavrek and J. M. Stewart, *Peptides*, 1985, **6**, 161.
44. W. H. Beierwaltes, O. A. Carretero, A. G. Scicle, R. J. Vavrek and J. M. Stewart, *Proc. Soc. Exp. Biol. Med.*, 1986, **186**, 79.
45. E. Escher, E. Laczko, G. Guillemette and D. Regoli, *J. Med. Chem.*, 1981, **24**, 1409.
46. D. Regoli, W. K. Park and F. Rioux, *Pharmacol. Rev.*, 1974, **26**, 69.
47. T. B. Rogers, *J. Biochem.*, 1984, **259**, 8106.
48. Y. C. Kwok and G. J. Moore, *Eur. J. Pharmacol.*, 1985, **14**, 6.
49. J. M. Matsoukas, M. N. Scanlon and G. J. Moore, *J. Med. Chem.*, 1984, **27**, 404.
50. K. H. Hsieh and G. R. Marshall, *J. Med. Chem.*, 1986, **29**, 1968.
51. J. M. Stewart, *Handbook Exp. Pharmacol.*, 1978, **25**, Suppl., 227.
52. M. N. Scanlon and G. J. Moore, *Proc. West. Pharmacol. Soc.*, 1987, **30**, 71.
53. J. J. Plattner and H. D. Kleinert, *Annu. Rep. Med. Chem.*, 1987, **22**, 63.
54. P. W. Fowler and G. J. Moore, *Biochem. Biophys. Res. Commun.*, 1988, **153**, 1296.
55. G. J. Moore and M. N. Scanlan, *Gen. Pharmacol.*, 1988, **20**, 193.
56. J. Matsoukas, P. Cordopatis, U. Belte, M. H. Goghari, R. C. Ganter, K. J. Franklin and G. J. Moore, *J. Med. Chem.*, 1989, in press.
57. M. N. Scanlon, P. Koziarz and G. J. Moore, *Gen. Pharmacol.*, 1989, in press.
58. R. P. Stephenson, *Br. J. Pharmacol.*, 1956, **11**, 177.
59. P. Boschcov, A. C. M. Paiva, T. B. Paiva and S. I. Shimuta, *Br. J. Pharmacol.*, 1984, **83**, 591.
60. L. R. Steranka, C. J. DeHaas, R. J. Vavrek, J. M. Stewart, S. J. Enne and S. H. Synder, *Eur. J. Pharmacol.*, 1987, **136**, 261.
61. R. Andreatta and K. J. Hofmann, *Am. Chem. Soc.*, 1986, **90**, 7334.
62. K. Hsieh and E. C. Jorgensen, *J. Med. Chem.*, 1979, **22**, 1199.
63. P. Needleman, G. R. Marshall and J. Rivier, *J. Med. Chem.*, 1973, **16**, 968.
64. J. N. Sharma, *Gen. Pharmacol.*, 1988, **19**, 177.
65. B. R. Conklin, R. M. Burch, L. R. Steranka and J. Axelrod, *J. Pharmacol. Exp. Ther.*, 1988, **244**, 646.
66. A. T. Chiu, D. J. Carini, A. L. Johnson, D. E. McCall, W. A. Price, M. J. Thoolen, P. C. Wong, R. I. Taber and P. B. Timmermans, *Eur. J. Pharmacol.*, 1988, **157**, 13.

13.8
Atrial Natriuretic Factor Receptors

RAYMOND J. WINQUIST and GEORGE P. VLASUK

Merck Sharp & Dohme Research Laboratories, West Point, PA, USA

13.8.1 INTRODUCTION

The discovery of atrial natriuretic factor (ANF) by de Bold *et al.* in 1981[1] launched an intensive effort to characterize the significance of this peptide in the regulation of cardiovascular homeostasis.

Several groups played key roles in the isolation and purification of ANF,[2-5] which led to the documentation that the synthetic peptide is a potent vasodilator and natriuretic agent.[4-7] ANF effectively relaxes vascular smooth muscle both *in vitro* and *in vivo* and promotes the urinary excretion of sodium and water both from isolated preparations and intact animals.[8] Atrial stretch, such as would occur during volume expansion, has been shown to be the primary stimulus for release of ANF,[9] which qualifies ANF as a candidate for the humoral substance mediating natriuresis during volume expansion as originally postulated by deWardener *et al.*[10] ANF also effectively inhibits aldosterone secretion and renin release, which may be important for the overall actions of the peptide on cardiovascular homeostasis.[8] Localization of this peptide to the cardiac atria seemingly provides a hormonal secretory pathway in a tissue ideally suited as an endogenous sensor for increases in extracellular volume. In addition, ANF appears to have effects in the central nervous system as intraventricular administration results in an inhibition of vasopressin release and an antagonism of angiotensin II-induced thirst.[8] ANF has also been observed to lower intraocular pressure after topical application or intraocular injection.[11]

Thus ANF exhibits an extensive pharmacological profile with demonstrable biological effects in several diverse tissues. Administration of ANF antiserum to anesthetized rats causes an increase in blood pressure and a decrease in renal excretion of electrolytes, which suggest an important physiological role for circulating ANF.[12] The discovery of this hormonal system has also generated tremendous enthusiasm from a drug discovery point of view with the prospect of developing improved therapeutic agents for such diseases as hypertension, cardiac failure (*e.g.* producing a balanced vasodilator that would maintain renal function) and possibly glaucoma.

The research compiled on ANF has documented that this substance fulfills the criteria required for that of a peptide hormone: *i.e.* biosynthesis, secretion into the bloodstream and, importantly, an interaction with specific receptor sites in target tissues to elicit a biological response. High affinity receptors for ANF have been demonstrated in all of the tissues responsive to the peptide, such as vascular smooth muscle, kidney, adrenal gland, eye and central nervous system.[13] However, the presence of high affinity receptors on tissues for which a functional response is at present obscure (*e.g.* vascular endothelial cells, platelets and placenta) reflects the need for further investigation of this hormonal system. Moreover, radioligand binding studies on ANF receptors have unveiled an intriguing hypothesis unparalleled in hormone–receptor interaction: the presence of silent or 'uncoupled' high affinity receptors (not linked to a second messenger system) on many tissue types which may be important for clearance of circulating peptide.[14] This chapter will review the progression of the studies instrumental in characterizing the high affinity receptors for ANF. In addition, special attention will be devoted to the dual receptor hypothesis (*i.e.* coupled and uncoupled receptors) in how it may underlie some of the clinical data accrued to date for ANF. This approach requires, as a preamble, a survey of the chemical and biological properties of this interesting peptide.

13.8.2 STRUCTURE OF THE ATRIAL PEPTIDES

The discovery of ANF by deBold *et al.*[1] crystallized many indications in the literature that the cardiac atria played an important role in the regulation of extracellular fluid volume and hence blood pressure. Henry *et al.* showed that distension of the left atrium in anesthetized dogs led to a diuresis.[15] Atria were known to contain secretory-type granules[16] whose granularity changed depending on whether an animal underwent either a water load (increased granularity) or salt load (decreased granularity).[17] deBold's report triggered studies from several laboratories showing that both high (20–40 kDa) and low (3000–5000 Da) molecular weight substances, partially purified by extraction of rat atria with acetic acid, followed by Sephadex G-75 column fractionation, exhibited natriuretic and vasorelaxant activity.[18,19] Subsequent analysis of the low molecular weight fraction by reverse phase HPLC led to the amino acid sequence of atrial peptides (see Table 1) which were collectively referred to as ANF.

The amino acid sequences reported for the atrial peptides showed a common 17-membered ring structure containing a disulfide bridge and various C- and N-terminal extensions. The different lengths of peptides amongst laboratories probably resulted from varying degrees of proteolysis due to the different protocols utilized.[21] That the atrial peptides originated from a common precursor (high molecular weight substance) was suggested by the isolation of several biologically active polypeptides containing an identical C-terminal sequence[22] and the identification, in both rats[23] and man,[20] of a 126 residue prohormone as the major storage form. Sequencing of the prohormone precursor revealed a potential 24 (rat) or 25 (man) amino acid signal peptide followed by a 128 amino

Table 1 Amino Acid Sequences of Several Atrial Peptides Purified From Atrial Tissue[a]

Designation	NH₂ ——— 100 —————————— 110 —————————— 120 ——— CO₂H	Ref.
α-hANP	S L R R S S C F G G R M D R I G A Q S G L G C N S F R Y	3
Atriopeptin I	S S I N S	2
Atriopeptin II	S S N S F R	2
Atriopeptin III	S S N S F R Y	2
ANF (1–33)	L A G P R S L R R S S N S F R Y	4
ANF (3–33)	G P R S L R R S S N S F R Y	4
ANF (8–33)	R R S S N S F R Y	4
Cardionatrin I	S L R R S S N S F R Y	5
Auriculin A	R S N S F R	6
Auriculin B	R S N S F R Y	6
β-hANP	S L R R S S C F G G R M D R I G A Q S G L G C N S F R Y	20
	Y R F S N C G L G S Q A G I R D M R G G F C S S R R L S	

[a] The disulfide-bridged core structure is common to all peptides, thus only amino or carboxy terminal differences are shown.

acid propeptide containing the N-terminal connecting fragment and a highly conserved (across species) C-terminal portion containing the sequence of the atrial peptides initially purified.[23-29] The final two C-terminal residues are presumed to be removed prior to storage of the prohormone in the secretory granules.

It is now widely accepted that the circulating form of ANF in both animals and man is the final 28 amino acid peptide from the C terminus.[30,31] Based on the sequence and numbering of the prohormone, one nomenclature refers to this fragment as ANF.[99-126] The rat (isoleucine) and human (methionine) circulating peptides differ only at position 110. Amongst the animal kingdom ANF from rabbit, mouse and rat are identical while that from other species studied (*e.g.* dog, cow, pig) are similar to human.[32] Another numbering convention refers to the secreted form as ANF,[1-28] a nomenclature used by some laboratories active in structure–activity studies around the native peptide.

The near simultaneous purification and sequencing of the atrial peptides by several laboratories spawned individualized terminology including cardionatrin 1, α-hANP (h referring to human sequence), ANF, auriculin and atriopeptin (Table 1). Upon determination of the peptidic nature of ANF, it has also been common to use atrial natriuretic peptide (ANP). Atriopeptin is preferred by many, as the term does not connote limitations on the pharmacological effects of the peptide. ANF has been routinely used as an abbreviation and will be used throughout the rest of this chapter.

The cyclic structure formed by the disulfide bond is critically important for biological activity.[33] The C-terminal sequence, except for the terminal tyrosine, is required for maximal vasorelaxant and natriuretic activity.[33] Conversely, the amino terminus of ANF[99-126] can survive significant truncation without affecting the biological responses to ANF.[33] To date, no biological function has been ascribed to the N-terminal domain (*i.e.* residues 1–98), which is proteolytically processed from the prohormone at some point during the secretion process.

Two atrial peptides of low molecular weight have been isolated from human atria, the 28 amino acid fragment (designated as α-hANP) and an antiparallel dimer of hANP designated β-hANP.[3,20] β-hANP is linked by two intermolecular disulfide bonds, has been found to circulate and may be elevated in certain disease states.[10,34]

13.8.3 CHEMICAL PROPERTIES OF ATRIAL NATRIURETIC FACTOR

13.8.3.1 Synthesis and Metabolism

The purification of ANF led to the production of synthetic peptide which was a key step in documenting the biological effects of the putative sequence. Chemical synthesis also allowed development of a radioimmunoassay for in-depth analysis of tissue levels of peptide. As mentioned above, biochemical purification of ANF from atrial tissue resulted in both high and low molecular weight substances, each of which exhibited biological activity (*e.g.* relaxation of smooth muscle). A precursor–product relationship between the substances was suggested by enhanced activity in the high molecular weight fraction by proteolytic treatment.[35] The active species released by trypsin gave a similar chromatographic profile as the purified low molecular fraction.

The relationship between precursor and product was also examined using techniques in molecular biology to clone the complementary DNA (cDNA) sequences and structural genes encoding pro-ANF.[23-29] Proteolytic processing of peptide hormones typically occurs at dibasic residues preceding the active sequence. This is not the case for both rat and human pro-ANF as an Arg—Ser bond is cleaved to result in the 28 amino acid fragment believed to be the principal circulating form. The mechanisms underlying processing of pro-ANF resulting in the release of the 28 amino acid ANF remain obscure. The intact prohormone is stable when incubated in whole blood or plasma but is usually present at extremely low levels in the circulation.[36] An appropriate stimulus for ANF release appears to result in processing of pro-ANF to ANF immediately before or during the exocytosis of storage granules. An atrial dipeptidyl carboxyhydrolase, distinct from angiotensin converting enzyme, has been shown to cleave Phe^{124}-Arg^{125} from ANF,[103-123] using atrial tissue homogenates.[37] The importance of this membrane-bound, metalloenzyme remains questionable, since the circulating form of the peptide is $ANF.^{99-126}$

Synthesis of $ANF^{101-126}$ (rat sequence) as an acetate salt exhibits a single spot, R_f 0.33, on TLC (45:20:6:24 butanol–pyridine–HOAc–H_2O) and a retention time of 49 min on HPLC (Vydac C-18, 5 μm, 300 Å, 15 × 0.4 cm column).[38] Gas chromatography analysis has shown 6.9% acetic acid and 8.1% water and the purified material has a specific rotation $[\alpha]_D^{26}$ of +47.3°. The crystalline structure of ANF has not been determined.

13.8.3.2 Inactivation

The elimination and degradation of circulating ANF is rapid and may occur through binding, with subsequent internalization, to a 'clearance' receptor (see Section 13.8.6) or through peptidase activity. Incubation of ANF with kidney membrane preparations results in hydrolysis at three possible sites, Cys^{105}-Phe^{106}, Arg^{112}-Ile^{113} and Gly^{114}-Ala^{115}, with Cys^{105}-Phe^{106} being the preferred site of cleavage.[39-41] The protease activity is inhibited by the metalloendoprotease inhibitors thiorphan, phosphoramidon and zincov,[39,41] and coelutes with (and is therefore identified as) protease 3.4.24.11 (enkephalinase) during each chromatographic step during purification.[41] The degradation product (hydrolysis at Cys^{105}-Phe^{106}) has been found to be biologically inactive.[42,43] Interestingly, ANF analogs with mercapto-acetic, -propionic or -butyric acid substituted for Cys^{105} all showed enhanced biological activity *in vivo*, which may be related to resistance to enzymatic degradation.[44] However, the physiological significance of kidney enkephalinase in the degradation of ANF remains to be determined since the half-life of circulating native peptide is unaltered in nephrectomized rats.[45]

13.8.4 BIOLOGICAL EFFECTS OF ATRIAL NATRIURETIC FACTOR

13.8.4.1 Cardiovascular

13.8.4.1.1 In vitro

The initial report on ANF by deBold *et al.* documented that injection of an atrial extract caused a hypotensive response in bioassay rats.[1] It was subsequently published that both atrial extracts and synthetic peptide could effectively relax precontracted aortic segments studied *in vitro*.[7] The relaxation to ANF has been shown to be independent of an intact endothelial layer and to be associated with elevations in cGMP, but not cAMP, in vascular smooth muscle.[46] ANF is distinguished as being an activator of the particulate (ostensibly the membrane-bound form) isozyme of guanylate cyclase, the enzyme responsible for the production of cGMP, as compared to the nitrovasodilators which activate primarily the soluble (or cytosolic) isozyme.[46] The possible consequence of two vasodilators elevating cGMP by activating the different isozymes of guanylate cyclase is shown in Figure 1, where the vasodilator effect of ANF and a nitrovasodilator appear additive.

Elevation of cGMP has been traditionally considered as an effective means for effecting relaxation of vascular smooth muscle by one of several hypothesized mechanisms.[48] Rapoport has found that cGMP elevated by ANF (and by nitrovasodilators) may antagonize vasoconstriction by inhibition of phosphatidylinositol hydrolysis.[49] Moreover, calcium mobilization by vasoconstrictors (*e.g.* angiotensin II) can decrease the ANF-induced accumulation of cGMP possibly by activation of

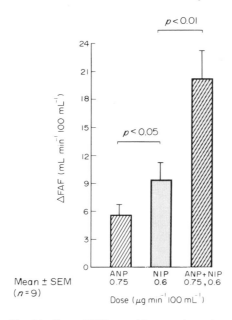

Figure 1 The increase in forearm blood (ordinate, FAF) caused by a maximum intraarterial dose of either ANF (α-hANP, 0.75 μg min^{-1} per 100 ml forearm blood volume), sodium nitroprusside (NIP, 0.6 μg min^{-1} per 100 ml) or the two drugs combined in nine normotensive subjects. Forearm blood flow was measured by venous occlusion plethysmography. The combined infusion protocol causes an additive increase in FAF that is significantly greater than that observed with either drug alone (reproduced from ref. 47 by permission of the American Heart Association Inc.)

a calcium dependent phosphodiesterase.[50] The data on the effects of ANF on basal levels of intracellular calcium in vascular smooth muscle have been conflicting, with both a decrease (cultured rat aortic cells)[51] and no change (rabbit aortic segments) reported.[52] Interestingly, Takuwa and Rasmussen reported that ANF inhibited contractile responses but had variable effects on the calcium transients (or plateau levels) generated by agonists in rabbit aorta.[52] These authors speculated that ANF must act at a site distal to agonist-induced increases in intracellular calcium.

Unlike the nitrovasodilators, ANF exhibits regional differences in its ability to relax isolated vascular preparations. Large conduit arteries from rabbits[53] or rats[54] are differentially sensitive to ANF with the aorta and renal artery among the most effectively relaxed. In canine vessels, the pulmonary artery presents the most impressive relaxation response to ANF.[55] Venous preparations are typically unresponsive to administered peptide. Small renal (resistance) arteries, but not similar caliber vessels from the heart, mesenteric or skeletal muscle bed, relax to ANF.[56,57] Small cerebral vessels have been reported to be both refractory (rat posterior cerebral branch)[57] and sensitive (feline cortical pial vessels)[58] to the relaxant effects of ANF, which may reflect either species or regional cerebral vascular differences.

13.8.4.1.2 In vivo

The potent vasorelaxant effects on arteries *in vitro* contrast with the hemodynamic pattern observed with infusion of ANF in the whole animal where the fall in blood pressure is often associated with a decrease in cardiac output and not total peripheral resistance.[59] Resistance in some vascular beds actually increases during ANF infusion, which appears to be a function of reflex increases in sympathetic outflow.[60] Interestingly, the hypotensive response is typically associated with a bradycardia, which implies regional differences in the reflex changes of sympathetic efferent traffic. The ANF-induced fall in blood pressure in some animal species[61] and man (Section 13.8.10) is often sustained beyond the cessation of infusion. Since the plasma half-life of ANF is of the order of minutes, the prolonged biological half-life may reflect sequestration of peptide into target tissues or prolonged production of second messenger.

ANF appears to cause arteriolar dilation when vascular resistance (afterload) is elevated by pressor agents[62] or in experimental models of hypertension.[63] Bolus injections of peptide can dilate peripheral beds with the renal vasculature being especially sensitive.[64,65] Thus both the route of administration as well as the underlying state of vascular tone are important determinants of the hemodynamic profile obtained with ANF.

When observed, the ANF-induced fall in cardiac output does not appear to result from a negative inotropic action,[53] although extraordinarily high concentrations of ANF may, in a buffer-perfused cardiac preparation, cause decreases in coronary flow and cardiac contractility.[66] The significance of this latter observation is questionable, since ANF has been shown to effect coronary vasodilation both *in vitro*[67] and *in vivo*.[8,68] The decrease in cardiac output probably results, indirectly, from diminished venous return due to venodilation[59] or, paradoxically, from localized venoconstriction causing an increased resistance to venous return.[69] ANF has also been reported to stimulate cardiac vagal afferents,[70] which may result in a fall in cardiac output due to a withdrawal of sympathetic tone to the heart.

In laboratory animals the effective dose range for ANF-induced decreases in arterial blood pressure is $0.03–20\,\text{nmol}\,\text{kg}^{-1}$ $(0.1–60\,\mu\text{g}\,\text{kg}^{-1})$ for bolus administration and $0.01–2\,\text{nmol}$ $\text{kg}^{-1}\,\text{min}^{-1}$ $(0.03–6\,\mu\text{g}\,\text{kg}^{-1}\,\text{min}^{-1})$ for intravenous infusion.[8] There have been studies documenting that long-term administration of ANF in dogs[71] and, at low level infusion with osmotic minipumps, in hypertensive rats[72] can result in cardiovascular (*i.e.* depressor) effects without natriuretic effects. These data suggest that, under certain circumstances, the cardiovascular actions can be either more sustained or sensitive compared to the renal responses. The low level infusion studies $(35–350\,\text{pmol}\,\text{h}^{-1})$[72] also raise an important clinical issue of whether efficacy could be obtained in particular indications with sustained, low dose ANF.

A consistent observation, originally noted by deBold *et al.*,[1] has been an increase in hematocrit (approximately 10%) following infusion of ANF in animals[73] and man.[74] The increase occurs in nephrectomized animals,[73] is independent of changes in red cell mass[73] and is associated with a decrease in plasma volume.[75] This apparent fluid shift from vascular to extravascular space may, in part, account for the decreased venous return precipitating the fall in cardiac output described above. In a survey of some 20 tissues dissected from bioassay rats, the ANF-induced hemoconcentration was found to be associated with enhanced albumin permeability in skeletal muscle and cardiac ventricle.[76] Therefore ANF may elicit changes in capillary permeability or hydrostatic pressure in some tissues.[77] There are data demonstrating that the ANF-induced rise in cGMP is associated with stimulation of the Na^+,K^+,Cl^- cotransport system in vascular tissue.[78] Activation of this cotransport system may play a role in fluid shifts accompanying intracellular accumulation of these ions during ANF infusion.

13.8.4.2 Renal

ANF is a potent natriuretic agent in rats with a ceiling lower than furosemide but comparable to that obtained with hydrochlorothiazide.[79] The diuresis and natriuresis are typically observed with similar or even slightly lower doses of ANF than those found to elicit depressor responses.[8] The renal effects are dose dependent[79,80] but diminish with higher doses of peptide, probably as a consequence of depressed renal perfusion pressure due to the concomitant depressor response.[81]

The mechanisms underlying the natriuretic response to ANF are complex and likely to involve several sites of action. An increase in glomerular filtration rate (GFR) has been observed both *in vitro*[82] and *in vivo*[83] and has been advanced as being the primary, if not sole mechanism, by which ANF effects natriuresis. The increase in GFR may involve an actual constrictor action, possibly by release of an autocoid, on the efferent arteriole combined with dilation of the afferent arteriole.[84] ANF may also increase GFR by increasing the capillary hydrostatic pressure across the glomerulus and/or by increasing the glomerular ultrafiltration coefficient.[85] The increase in GFR is impressive, considering concomitant decreases in renal perfusion pressure and, at times, renal plasma flow. This profile results in an increase in the filtration fraction which is a unique attribute amongst natriuretic agents. However, several groups have failed to record statistically significant increases in GFR and have therefore postulated that hyperfiltration may not be required for the natriuretic effect of ANF.[86,87] ANF has been shown to decrease medullary hypertonicity (medullary washout), secondary to either enhanced vasa recta blood flow, increased permeability to sodium in the distal nephron or an increase in GFR, which could act to magnify or account for the increased sodium excretion.[88] Inhibition of sodium reabsorption in proximal tubules has been deduced from renal clearance experiments[89] but these data are controversial, since micropuncture studies have failed to demonstrate any effect of ANF, under basal conditions, in superficial proximal tubules.[82] However, fluid reabsorption stimulated by angiotensin II appears to be antagonized by ANF in the proximal tubule.[90] ANF has no effect on epithelial NaCl transport in experimental models of distal nephron transport.[88] However, a more distal site of action has been reported by Sonnenberg *et al.*[91] in that ANF increases the delivery of fluid and electrolytes to the papillary collecting ducts. In addition, ANF inhibits oxygen consumption stimulated by the sodium pump in papillary collecting duct cells, which is an effect shared by amiloride,[92] and antagonizes the vasopressin-induced increase in hydraulic conductivity in collecting tubules.[93] These data show that ANF has demonstrable effects in the distal areas of the nephron.

In acute experiments, ANF can elicit a natriuretic response in hypertensive rats that is comparable to or greater than that recorded in normotensive counterparts.[8] Variable effects have been observed with ANF in experimental models of heart failure. Dogs with coronary artery embolization[94] exhibit a natriuresis in response to ANF but low-output models are poorly responsive to administered peptide.[95] These latter data seem consistent with the diminished efficacy of ANF during conditions of limited renal perfusion (*e.g.* renal artery clamp).[81, 83]

13.8.4.3 Effects on Humoral Factors and Hormones

13.8.4.3.1 Steroidogenesis

ANF has been documented to effectively inhibit aldosterone biosynthesis *in vitro*[96-98] and decrease plasma levels of circulating aldosterone in the whole animal.[95,97] The IC_{50} value for inhibition of aldosterone biosynthesis is approximately 1 nM. Interestingly, the inhibitor effect of ANF in adrenal tissue does not appear to be critically dependent on an elevation in levels of cGMP.[99] De Lean has found that the efficacy of ANF in the inhibition of aldosterone secretion is enhanced by amiloride,[100] an effect which may be reflective of an interaction between amiloride and the ANF receptor (see Section 13.8.8). *In vitro*, ANF has a more profound inhibitory effect on stimulated, as compared to basal, levels of aldosterone release from zona glomerulosa cells. These data are consistent with the observations *in vivo* where ANF has been more efficacious in decreasing plasma levels of aldosterone when the concentration of this hormone is elevated above normal. The ability of ANF to decrease circulating levels of aldosterone appears independent of any concomitant inhibitory action on the release of renin.[95]

ANF stimulates the production of testosterone in isolated mouse interstitial cells[101] or Leydig cells.[102] The reported stimulation of testosterone may reflect the pronounced activation of guanylate cyclase and large increases in cGMP upon exposure to ANF in testes.[103] In addition, ANF increases steroidogenesis (progesterone release) in female gonadal tissue (cultured human granulosa–lutein cells).[104]

13.8.4.3.2 Renin

Administration of ANF to anesthetized dogs is associated with a fall in blood pressure and an inhibition of the renin secretory rate.[88,105] As discussed with the inhibitory effect on circulating aldosterone, the inhibition of enhanced renin secretory rate or plasma renin activity is more easily demonstrated. The inhibition of renin secretion could be an indirect result of an increased delivery of NaCl to the macula densa, which would effectively shut down secretion. Very high concentrations (10^{-7} M) of ANF can inhibit renin release from isolated kidney tissue;[106] however, other investigators have failed to corroborate this effect with lower concentrations.[107] ANF can exert a sustained, inhibitory effect on renin release since plasma renin activity typically remains suppressed, although a fall in blood pressure is maintained with infusions of peptide.[88,105]

13.8.4.3.3 Vasopressin

Dose dependent peripheral administration of ANF inhibits the stimulated (*i.e.* water deprivation or hemorrhage) secretion of vasopressin in rats.[108] Injection of ANF into the third ventricle results in an inhibition of basal levels of vasopressin.[109] Obana *et al.* reported that ANF can inhibit vasopressin release *in vitro*.[110] ANF also inhibits the physiological effect of vasopressin in the collecting duct, which may be an important mechanism for the renal actions of ANF.[93]

13.8.4.4 Ocular Effects of ANF

Topical (0.5% solution), intracameral (10 μg) or intravitreal (10 μg) administration of ANF lowers intraocular pressure in rabbits with no apparent peripheral effect.[11] The ocular effect appears to be associated with stimulation of guanylate cyclase and elevation of cGMP levels, which may regulate aqueous humor formation by the ciliary process.[111]

13.8.4.5 Effects in the Central Nervous System

Central administration of ANF depresses single neuron firing rates in the septum and preoptic areas in rats,[109] suggesting a possible neuromodulator role. Intraventricular infusion of rather high concentrations of ANF are required to see relatively minimal changes in renal function in dogs (78 pmol kg^{-1} over 30 min)[112] or rats (30–60 pmol).[113] These doses typically have no effect on blood pressure but can cause antagonism of the pressor response to centrally administered angiotensin II.[114]

The inhibitory effects of ANF on vasopressin have already been mentioned (Section 13.8.4.3.3). Central administration of ANF also antagonizes the increased water intake promoted by either dehydration or administration of angiotensin II.[115] Moreover, intracerebroventricular injection of ANF (0.2–2 nmol) reduces the salt appetite in salt-depleted rats.[109] The inhibitory effects on water and salt intake complement the renal effects (*i.e.* natriuresis and diuresis) of peripherally administered ANF.

ANF acts to decrease the production of cerebrospinal fluid in anesthetized rabbits and activates guanylate cyclase in a purified preparation of choroid epithelial cells.[116] ANF is also effective in stimulating enzyme activity in cerebral microvessels.[116] These data implicate ANF as an important modulator of intracranial water and electrolyte regulation.

13.8.5 LOCALIZATION OF RECEPTORS FOR ATRIAL NATRIURETIC FACTOR

The characterization of receptor sites for ANF using radioreceptor assays followed the development of optimal conditions for radioiodination of synthetic peptides to a high specific activity.[117] Cold iodinated peptide retains comparable vasorelaxant and natriuretic activity. In general, the binding is associated with the sarcolemma fraction in tissues, is time dependent, specific and is of high affinity with K_d values in the sub- to low-nanomolar range (Figure 2). This calculated affinity approximates the appropriate range in considering the physiological importance for circulating ANF.

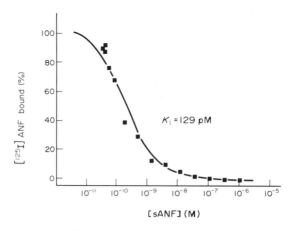

Figure 2 Competitive displacement of [^{125}I]ANF by unlabeled ANF (referred to as sANF, abscissa) in membranes prepared from rabbit aorta. Scatchard analysis reveals a single high affinity population of receptors ($K_d = 129$ pM, 96 fmol per mg protein). Binding of the peptide was linear over a protein range of 6–100 μg with the plotted data performed with 100 μg protein at 0° C (reproduced from ref. 117 by permission of the US National Academy of Sciences)

13.8.5.1 Cardiovascular System

High affinity, specific receptors for ANF are located in plasma membranes prepared from vascular ring segments[117,118] as well as from rat and bovine aortic cells maintained in culture.[119,120] The number of ANF receptors on the cell surface is relatively high (compared to other peptide hormone systems) with smooth muscle cells containing approximately 10^6 sites per cell. The distribution of receptors amongst large conduit (rabbit) arteries is partially correlated with the ability of the vessels to relax to exogenously applied ANF *in vitro*.[118] Autoradiographic studies in the whole animal (rat) show that receptors exist in the vasculature of kidney, adrenal gland, lung and liver.[121]

Whole tissue studies are somewhat compromised by the existence of receptors on the vascular endothelium (as demonstrated using cultured endothelial cells).[120,122] These endothelial cells contain approximately 10^5 binding sites per cell. The presence of these receptors is puzzling, since the endothelium is not important for the relaxant effects (at least *in vitro*) of ANF.[46] The receptors may be instrumental for shuttling peptide to a target tissue. In addition, ANF binding to the vascular endothelium may be involved in the hemoconcentration observed with intravenous ANF (Section 13.8.4.1.2).[76,122]

In cardiac tissue, receptors for ANF have only been described in cultured mesenchymal non-myocardial cells.[123] Platelets have also been found to contain high affinity binding sites for ANF, although platelet function is not altered by exposure to the peptide.[124]

13.8.5.2 Renal

Napier *et al.* demonstrated that high affinity receptors for ANF were located on plasma membranes prepared from rat and rabbit renal cortex.[117] These authors also detected binding sites in a cell line derived from porcine kidney (LLC-PK) which are used as a model system for proximal tubular function. Basolateral membranes from kidney cortex, which exhibit some of the transport functions of proximal tubules, also contain receptors for ANF.[125] However, analysis of micro-dissected rat and rabbit nephrons fails to detect any binding in the proximal tubule.[126] These data are of interest concerning the controversy regarding effects of ANF on proximal tubular function noted above (Section 13.8.4.2).

Most investigators, using both *in vitro* and *in vivo* techniques, have localized the ANF binding sites to the glomerulus.[13,88] This is consistent with the hypothesis that increases in GFR are important for the renal effects of ANF. Along these lines Suzuki *et al.* have found an excellent correlation of ANF binding in the kidney cortex and renal function in the isolated, perfused kidney (Figure 3).[127] Both positive[121] and negative[128] results have been reported for the localization of receptors on efferent (or afferent) arterioles, which leaves in question the role of this vessel in the hyperfiltration response to ANF. A controversy also exists with the relative presence[129] or absence[130] of binding sites on renal mesangial cells, although functional responses have been reported.[131] ANF binding sites on mesangial cells may be important in regulating glomerular blood flow and/or filtration coefficient, thereby influencing GFR.

In vitro autoradiographic experiments have shown binding sites associated with bundles of vasa recta in the outer medulla,[132] which could be consistent with the medullary washout hypothesis discussed in Section 13.8.4.2. ANF binding sites in the rat renal papillae were reported by Murphy *et al.*,[133] which may correlate with the functional studies of Zeidel *et al.*[92]

13.8.5.3 Glandular Tissues

The adrenal cortex contains high affinity receptors for ANF, which correlates well with the potent effects of ANF in the inhibition of aldosterone release.[121,128,134] Appropriately, autoradiographic analysis[121] localizes the majority of binding sites to the zona glomerulosa cells which, when isolated, exhibit the expected high affinity binding to ANF.[134] Functional receptors for ANF have been reported in human pheochromocytoma,[135] a catecholamine-secreting adrenomedullary tumor. ANF has been observed to inhibit the secretion of norepinephrine from cultured pheochromocytoma cells.[136]

The functional effects of ANF in gonadal preparations (Section 13.8.4.3.4) prompted investigators to determine if receptors existed in these tissues. Cultured murine[137] and rat[138] Leydig tumor cells contain high affinity binding sites for ANF. Human ovarian granulosa-lutein cells in culture also possess binding sites for ANF.[104] The functional and radioligand binding data suggest a role for

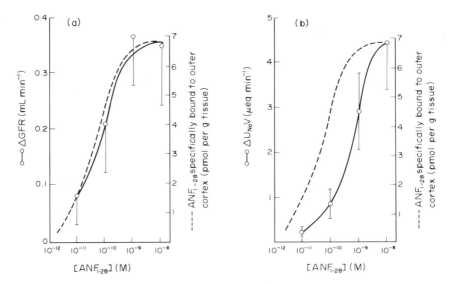

Figure 3 The relationship between specific binding in the renal (outer) cortex and the renal physiological effects of ANF in isolated, perfused rat kidneys. The specific binding experiments (perfusion with [^{125}I]ANF as well as nonlabeled peptide) were performed in nonfiltering kidneys to circumvent possible problems with peptide degradation and nonspecific binding (both aspects being a function of metabolism and/or accumulation *via* the filtration–luminal route). Administration of ANF causes progressive increases in glomerular filtration rate (GFR, a) and natriuresis ($U_{Na}V$, b), which are well correlated with the specific binding curve in the cortex. The binding and renal functional effects occur at near-physiological concentrations of ANF (reproduced from ref. 127 by permission of the American Physiology Society)

ANF in gonadal steroidogenesis. Receptors have also been localized in human placenta;[139] however, no apparent functional link has been described.

13.8.5.4   Ocular Tissue

In vivo autoradiography combined with radioligand binding experiments in rats has localized ANF binding sites on the pigmented epithelium of the ciliary process.[140] Isolated ciliary processes exhibit marked increases in cGMP upon exposure to ANF,[111] which may underline the effects of ANF on intraocular pressure (Section 13.8.4.4).

13.8.5.5   Central Nervous System

High densities of ANF binding sites have been visualized in guinea pig olfactory bulb, subfornical organ, thalamic nuclei, medial geniculate nucleus and cerebellum.[141,142] A different distribution is observed in rat (subfornical organ, area postrema and ventricles) and monkey (cerebellum) brain tissue. Interestingly, in rats, the subfornical organ contains high densities of both ANF and angiotensin II binding sites. Central binding sites are correlated with areas important for fluid and electrolyte balance and ion exchange, but also exist in areas (*e.g.* cerebellum) which have no defined analogous role.

Quantitative autoradiography has also pointed out the existence of ANF binding sites in the anterior and posterior pituitary.[143] These sites may be involved in the inhibitory effects of ANF on vasopressin release. High affinity binding of ANF has been documented in isolated choroid plexus, which correlates with the effects of ANF on cerebrospinal fluid production. The presence of ANF receptors on cerebral capillary endothelium suggests that ANF may be an important modulator of the blood–brain barrier.[116]

13.8.5.6   Other Sites

Kuno *et al.*[144] utilized rat lung for their work on the isolation of the ANF receptor. ANF has modest relaxant effects on tracheal, but not parenchymal, tissue *in vitro and* fails to significantly alter pulmonary function *in vivo*.[145] Leitman *et al.* demonstrated ANF receptors on lung fibroblasts, which may account for some, if not all, of the receptors in whole lung.[146] It is tempting to speculate that the lung binding sites may be important for the processing of prohormone or regulation of circulating peptide levels.

An autoradiography analysis detected ANF binding sites in the rat small intestine.[147] The authors included some functional data showing that ANF increases salt and water absorption in the small intestine *in vivo*. Atrial peptides have been found to effectively relax chick rectum[19] but not mammalian intestinal smooth muscle preparations.[148] Specific, high affinity sites for ANF occur in cultured normal and malignant osteoblasts.[149] ANF induces tremendous increases in cGMP in these cells; however, the importance of this for the major processes in bone is at present unknown. As in many other tissues, ANF has no effect on the levels of cAMP in these cells.

13.8.6 RECEPTOR CLASSIFICATION FOR ATRIAL NATRIURETIC FACTOR

The widespread localization of receptors for ANF underlies the marked diversity of pharmacological effects observed with this peptide and leads to questions regarding the existence of multiple receptor subtypes. Radioligand crosslinking methodologies have been utilized to examine the receptor subunit composition in various target tissues.[13] These experiments have incorporated bifunctional crosslinking reagents, photolabile analogs of ANF and photoaffinity labeling with direct UV crosslinking of native peptide. In combination with SDS-PAGE analysis, these studies have provided evidence that more than one form of ANF receptor may exist in different target tissues.

In general, the crosslinking experiments have concluded that target tissues contain a disulfide-linked dimer composed of polypeptides having an estimated M_r of 60 000 to 70 000, as well as a single 120 000 to 130 000 M_r polypeptide, as determined from SDS-PAGE analysis. In addition, some investigators have noted the existence of both lower ($M_r = 60 000$)[150] and higher ($M_r = 180 000$)[122] polypeptides which appear distinct from the above subunits or complexes due to their electrophoretic behavior in nonreducing and reducing SDS-PAGE gels. The low M_r disulfide-linked dimer and higher M_r monomer subunits exist in vascular (both smooth muscle and endothelial cells), adrenal and renal tissue.[13, 122, 150-152] Cultured vascular smooth muscle cells and either cultured kidney cells or preparations enriched in glomerular or collecting duct tissue appear to have the lower M_r monomer species (*i.e.* 60 000),[153-155] while endothelial cells have been reported to contain the higher 180 000 M_r monomer.[122]

The discovery of these multiple components of the ANF binding sites was of interest in the light of studies attempting to correlate radioligand binding with function. In both cultured endothelial[156] and smooth muscle cells[159] a dissociation was observed between binding and elevation of cGMP using selective analogs of ANF (Figure 4). In these studies selective analogs were shown to bind with comparable high affinity (approximately 0.3 nM) as compared to native ANF, but differed over several orders of magnitude of concentration in their ability to elevate tissue levels of cGMP (see Section 13.8.7). In addition, it was clearly shown that these analogs were not acting as classical competitive antagonists of native ANF (Figure 4). Crosslinking data utilizing these selective ANF analogs have implicated the 120 000 to 130 000 monomer polypeptide as the species associated with activation of guanylate cyclase, while the disulfide-linked dimer appears to constitute the major ANF binding component and is not linked to cGMP elevation.[13, 158, 159] Interestingly, the majority of binding studies have typically disclosed a single class of high affinity binding sites (*i.e.* Figure 2) in cells that have shown a dissociation of binding and cGMP elevation. The comparable affinity amongst analogs in the binding assays mentioned above imply that in the cultured endothelial and vascular smooth muscle cells (i) the majority of binding sites are attributed to the disulfide-linked dimer and (ii) this receptor species is relatively nonselective in structural requirements for recognition. These concepts will be developed below. Therefore the crosslinking data were instrumental in the development of the hypothesis that the dissociation between binding and function could be explained by a molecular heterogeneity of ANF receptor polypeptides.[156, 157]

Building on these developments, classification of these receptor subtypes according to function has been advanced by Maack *et al.*[14] Administration of an ANF analog which displaced ^{125}I-labeled ANF but had no effect on guanylate cyclase caused an increase in circulating levels of ANF as well as a concomitant natriuretic and hypotensive response (Figure 5). The authors concluded that the aforementioned 'silent' receptor actually is important in sequestration and metabolic clearance of the circulating native ANF. Analogs selective for this 'C' receptor subtype (equivalent to the disulfide-linked dimer mentioned above) could displace or compete with native peptide resulting in

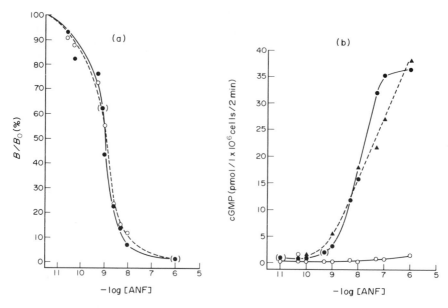

Figure 4   The dissociation between receptor binding (a) and the ability to elevate cGMP (b) with a linear analog of ANF (Arg^{101}–Tyr^{126} with Phe substituted for Cys at positions 105 and 121). In (a), both the linear analog (○) and native (●) peptide are similarly effective in displacing [^{125}I]ANF (competitive binding) from cultured bovine aortic endothelial cells. However, in (b), the linear peptide (○) fails to cause any appreciable increase in cGMP in this same cell line. Native peptide causes large increases in cGMP either alone (●) or in the presence (▲) of saturating concentrations of linear peptide. This latter observation renders unlikely the possibility that the linear analog is a receptor antagonist (reproduced from ref. 122 by permission of the National Research Council of Canada)

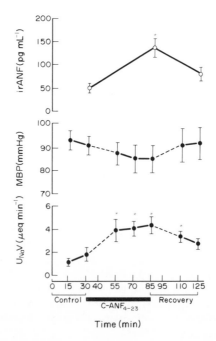

Figure 5   The effects of an ANF analog (Arg^{102}–Cys^{121}, $deGln^{116}$, Ser^{117}, Gly^{118}, Leu^{119}, Gly^{120}, designated C-ANF$_{4-23}$), which binds with high affinity but has no agonist or antagonist activity *in vitro*, on plasma concentrations of immunoreactive ANF (irANF), mean arterial blood pressure (MBP) and sodium excretion ($U_{Na}V$) in anesthetized rats ($n = 8$). C-ANF$_{4-23}$ was administered as a bolus injection (10 μg kg^{-1}) followed by a constant infusion (1 μg kg^{-1} min^{-1}). C-ANF$_{4-23}$ causes an increase in circulating ANF as well as having physiological effects on blood pressure (lowering) and renal function (increased natriuresis). The inactive C-ANF analog may act to decrease the binding of endogenous ANF to silent or clearance receptors, which results in increased levels of circulating ANF and thus the physiological responses (reproduced from ref. 14 by permission of the American Association for the Advancement of Science)

its decreased clearance and in increased functional response. This classification of ANF receptor subtype may help explain some of the data in pathological situations where circulating levels of ANF are extraordinarily high yet the subject remains very responsive to administered synthetic peptide (see Section 13.8.10).

13.8.7 STRUCTURE–ACTIVITY RELATIONSHIPS OF ATRIAL NATRIURETIC FACTOR ANALOGS

13.8.7.1 Structure–Biological Activity Relationships

The first two residues of the amino terminus (*i.e.* Ser^{99}-Leu^{100}) can be removed without an effect on biological activity.[160] Removal of the next four amino acids (Arg^{101}-Arg^{102}-Ser^{103}-Ser^{104}) causes a gradual loss of efficacy in vasorelaxation and binding assays (down to 10% of native) but reportedly not in natriuresis or in relaxation of nonmammalian gut muscle (*i.e.* chick rectum).[33,161,162] Some of these data are difficult to interpret due to species differences (Section 13.8.9).

Deletions at the C terminus have a more profound effect on biological potency. An exception may be the terminal tyrosine which, when deleted, has been shown to slightly enhance potency in some reports.[157] Removal of the next two amino acids (Phe^{124}-Arg^{125}) can drop the relative potency of the peptide to below 1% of native.[157,162] Again, there are some exceptions (*i.e.* atriopeptin I, Ser^{103}–Ser^{123}), which appear to be a function of species differences.

The disulfide ring structure alone has activity (3–15%) in some (*i.e.* vasorelaxation, natriuresis, inhibition of aldosterone) but not all assays (binding, cGMP).[33,157] Species differences and the diverse array of functional (and binding) assays complicate strict comparative analysis. Nonetheless, the disulfide ring as well as linear fragments[33,122,163] can elicit functional responses leading to the qualitative conclusion that the ring is important but not essential for biological activity. These data bear importantly on the exciting development of the 'C' receptor hypothesis based on selective analogs; such analogs require rigorous analysis in several functional assays prior to evaluation in whole animal models.

Point substitutions in the peptide chain have identified certain residues as key components in SAR. Arg^{125} has been described as a primary contributor to biological activity,[164] but this appears to be the case only in the presence of concomitant deletion of cationic sites in the N terminus.[165] These results suggest that a charged moiety, supplied from either terminus, is important for biological activity. Substitution of hydrophobic residues individually by alanine at Phe^{106}, Ile^{113} and Leu^{119} reduces biological activity to approximately 1% of native, while substitution of hydrophilic residues by alanine (*i.e.* Arg^{109} and Gln^{116}) has only a modest effect.[33,165] Substitution of mercapto derivatives for Cys^{105} enhances activity which may be due to resistance to proteolysis (Section 13.8.3.2).

13.8.7.2 Structure–Receptor Binding Activity

Analysis of ANF analogs in receptor binding assays has played an important role in the attempts to classify receptor subtypes (Section 13.8.6). Several groups disclosed analogs which showed a dissociation between receptor binding (comparable affinity to native) and an ability to elevate cGMP (poorly active compared to native) in cultured endothelial and vascular smooth muscle cells (*i.e.* Figure 4). These analogs include atriopeptin I (Ser^{103}–Ser^{123}),[156] several C- and N-terminal deleted analogs[157] and a linear fragment (Arg^{101}–Tyr^{126} with Phe substituted for Cys at positions 105 and 121).[122] These data led to the concept of 'silent' receptors being present on the cultured cells. As discussed above, Maack *et al.* have shown that an analog selective for the silent receptor subtype (Arg^{102}–Cys^{121} with several deletions, Figure 5), which binds with high affinity (but has no intrinsic efficacy with respect to cGMP elevation), causes natriuresis and hypotension in bioassay rats.[14] The physiological response is thought to be mediated ostensibly by displacement and/or blockade of native peptide from the silent or clearance receptor. This provocative development casts a new light on SAR studies of ANF analogs when one considers *in vitro versus in vivo* activity.

It should be pointed out that an excellent correlation between radioligand binding experiments and functional (*i.e.* vasorelaxation, natriuresis, inhibition of aldosterone) assays can be obtained when the former is conducted with membranes prepared from freshly dissected tissue (*i.e.* vascular)[117] or dispersed cells (*i.e.* zona glomerulosa) cultured for short periods of time (*i.e.* 3 d).[161] The reason for this apparent discrepancy between binding in cultured cells and in freshly isolated tissue is not at present clear, especially since the studies in cultured cells led to the multiple receptor hypothesis, which has been seemingly corroborated *in vivo*.[14] It remains possible that tissues important for clearance in the whole animal (for example some areas in the kidney) contain predominantly the C receptor, but that commonly used target tissues (*i.e.* vascular, adrenal, renal cortex) contain predominantly the receptor subtype linked to guanylate cyclase. Maintenance of even target tissues in culture could result in a predilection of C receptor expression.

13.8.8   ISOLATION AND PURIFICATION OF RECEPTORS

An important component of the multiple receptor hypothesis has been the isolation and purification of receptor polypeptides. Schenk *et al.* have purified an ANF receptor to apparent homogeneity from cultured (bovine) aortic smooth muscle cells.[166] The native protein has an estimated M_r of 125 000, which is composed of two ($M_r = 60\,000$) subunits. The purified receptor binds ANF with high affinity but exhibits no guanylate cyclase activity, a profile expected from a silent or C receptor subtype. Uchida *et al.* have reported that the subunits of the low M_r receptor arise as primary translation products of 58 000 M_r and, subsequent to glycosylation, undergo disulfide linkage and, presumably, insertion into the plasma membrane.[167] Kuno *et al.* have reported a partially purified, single 120 000 M_r polypeptide from rat lung which both binds ANF and shows guanylate cyclase activity (basal but not ANF-stimulated).[144] A key difference between the Schenk *et al.* and Kuno *et al.* studies may have been the use of a GTP-affinity column by the latter group in the isolation procedure. Takayanagi *et al.* took these observations a step further and, using both an ANF- and a GTP-affinity column, isolated two ANF binding proteins to near homogeneity from bovine adrenal gland (Figure 6).[168] One of the isolated proteins has an estimated M_r of 135 000, is composed of two (62 500) subunits, and binds ANF but fails to have any guanylate cyclase activity. The second peptide is a monomer having an M_r of 135 000 which binds ANF and has demonstrable guanylate cyclase activity. The two peptides appear structurally distinct on the basis of peptide mapping. Therefore the study by Takayanagi *et al.* may be the first demonstration of the isolation of both the silent and coupled form of the ANF receptor, respectively.

Another interpretation for the functional heterogeneity of the ANF receptor has been provided by Meloche *et al.*[169] Using membranes prepared from zona glomerulosa cells, these investigators found only a single band in crosslinking experiments ($M_r = 130\,000$) and an excellent correlation amongst analogs between displacement of labeled native peptide and inhibition of aldosterone secretion. However, analysis of the binding data reveals both high and low affinity binding sites suggesting heterogeneity. Further evidence for this heterogeneity is provided by subjecting membranes prelabeled with [^{125}I]ANF to steric exclusion chromatography, where two protein peaks of ANF binding activity eluted with Stokes radii of 50 and 70 Å (Figure 7). Interestingly, the diuretic amiloride enhances the surface of the 70 Å peak while decreasing that of the 50 Å peak. The ability of amiloride to enhance the inhibitory efficacy of ANF on aldosterone secretion (see Section 13.8.4.3.1) led these authors to conclude that the protein resident in the high molecular weight (*i.e.* 70 Å) peak represents a ternary (*i.e.* ANF, ANF binding protein, effector protein sensitive to amiloride) molecular form of the ANF receptor. Whether the effector protein which is stabilized or enhanced by amiloride exhibits guanylate cyclase is not known, but the inhibitory effect of ANF in zona glomerulosa does not appear to be critically linked to an elevation in cGMP (Section 13.8.4.3.1).

13.8.9   SPECIES DIFFERENCES IN STRUCTURE–ACTIVITY RELATIONSHIPS OF ATRIAL NATRIURETIC FACTOR ANALOGS

An early analysis of atrial peptide pharmacology included the finding that atriopeptin I (Ser[103]–Ser[123]) contained natriuretic activity (using bioassay rats) but not vasorelaxant activity (using isolated rabbit aortic strips).[2] Subsequent analysis showed that atriopeptin I is capable of relaxing rabbit aortic strips although at much higher concentrations (250 times) than that required by the native peptide.[170] Of greater significance was the finding that rat aortic strips are equisensitive to atriopeptin I and native peptide.[170] Consistent with these data is the observation that atriopeptin I is both natriuretic and vasorelaxant in rat but not other species as dog.[171]

Another example of species differences concerns the putative oxidation product of human sequence ANF (Ser[99]–Tyr[126], methionine sulfoxide at position 110). This analog was found to have approximately 3% activity when compared to unoxidized peptide in rat binding and cGMP

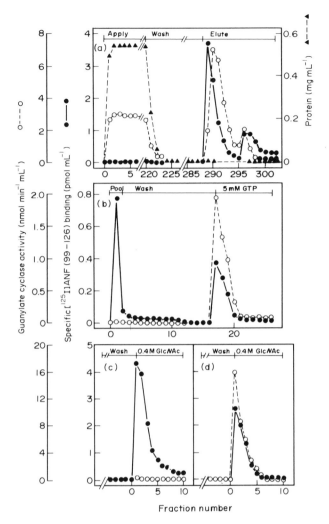

Figure 6 Purification of solubilized ANF receptors, with and without guanylate cyclase activity, from bovine adrenal cortex. Protein concentration (▲), ANF binding activity (●) and guanylate cyclase activity (○) were followed in the eluates from an ANF–agarose affinity column (a), a GTP–agarose affinity column (b) and wheat germ agglutinin–Sepharose columns (c and d). Crude Triton X-100 extract (2.3 g of adrenocortical membranes) was loaded onto (a) and material eluted with a sodium acetate buffer. Pooled (peak) fractions were loaded onto (b), which was eluted with 5 mM GTP. In the elution profile from (b), two peaks of ANF binding are observed but only one of these peaks is associated with cyclase activity. Both peaks from (b) are also recovered from the wheat germ agglutinin columns (eluted with *N*-acetylglucosamine), demonstrating that both binding proteins are glycosylated. Therefore two populations of ANF binding proteins exist in bovine adrenal gland, one coupled to guanylate cyclase and one not associated with cyclase activity (reproduced from ref. 168 by permission of the American Society of Biological Chemists)

assays.[172] Surprisingly, the methionine sulfoxide analog is equieffective with the native peptide in vascular assays from rabbit, dog and monkey.[173] Whether this finding represents a species specific reduction of the methionine sulfoxide has not been determined.

Wangler *et al.* have reported that atriopeptin II (Ser[103]–Arg[125]) causes coronary vasoconstriction in a buffer-perfused guinea pig heart preparation (see Section 13.8.4.1.2).[66] This response was obtained with extraordinarily high concentrations of peptide (approximately 10^{-5} M to 10^{-4} M) and has not been observed in isolated cardiac preparations[45] nor in dogs *in vivo*.[8,68] Nonetheless, the finding in the guinea pig heart could be a (qualitative) species difference in the effects of ANF on the coronary circulation.

As mentioned above (Section 13.8.4.1.1), infusion of ANF in laboratory animals is often associated with a fall in cardiac output rather than total peripheral resistance.[59] Some of the clinical data accrued with ANF have revealed signs of afterload reduction including tachycardia, flushing and an elevated skin blood flow (Section 13.8.10.1). In addition, ANF causes an increase in forearm blood flow when injected intraarterially (Figure 1). Therefore, ANF appears to be more effective as an arteriolar vasodilator in conscious man *versus* conscious laboratory animals.

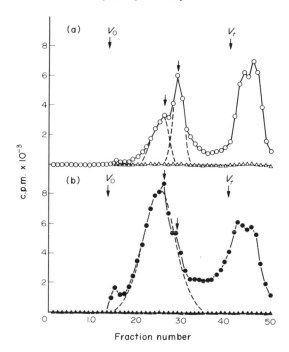

Figure 7 The effect of amiloride on the steric exclusion HPLC elution profile of solubilized [^{125}I]ANF-labeled adrenal zona glomerulosa cell membranes. Labeled membranes were incubated in the absence (top panel) or presence (bottom panel) of 10^{-4} M amiloride, solubilized and injected onto a Superose 6 steric exclusion column. V_0 and V_t correspond to the void and total volumes of the column, respectively. The arrows designate positions of ANF binding activity with mean Stokes radii of 70 Å (first peak) and 50 Å (second peak). The dashed line represents a computerized fit of the peaks as modeled by a Gaussian distribution. Amiloride causes an increase in the 70 Å peak (2–3 times) while nearly abolishing the surface of the 50 Å peak. The results suggest that the ANF receptor in these cells exists in two forms, the relative distribution of which is modulated by amiloride (reproduced from ref. 169 by permission of the American Society of Biological Chemists)

13.8.10 SUMMARY OF THE CLINICAL PHARMACOLOGY OF ATRIAL NATRIURETIC FACTOR

13.8.10.1 Cardiovascular

Both bolus[174,175] and infusion[74,176] of ANF (rat or human sequence, Ser[99]–Tyr[126] or Arg[101]–Tyr[126] peptide) decrease blood pressure (by approximately 10–15 mmHg) and cause small increases in heart rate in normotensive volunteers. This decrease in blood pressure is typically associated with indices of arteriolar dilation and can be sustained during recovery periods, although the plasma half-life of ANF is of the order of minutes.[47,74,174–177] The role of clearance receptors in this prolonged biological effect (*e.g.* slow dissociation) remains to be examined.

Profound hypotensive episodes often associated with bradycardia have been recorded with infusion protocols.[175,176] The severe hypotension has been likened to a vasovagal response, which is of interest concerning the preclinical literature suggesting an activation of cardiac vagal afferents.[70] An unusual attribute of the ANF-induced profound hypotension has been its occurrence subsequent to cessation of the infusion, which is suggestive of an accumulation and sudden release of peptide. There have been no reports of hypotensive episodes with bolus administration.

ANF administration lowers blood pressure in both hypertensive[175,178] and heart failure[175,179–181] patients (10–15%) at similar or lower doses (approximately 0.01 μg kg^{-1} min^{-1}) than those required to lower pressure in normotensive volunteers. Rather dramatic increases in cardiac output with calculated decreases in total peripheral resistance have been observed by several groups infusing ANF in patients with heart failure. Such findings have been intriguing since these pathologies are associated with elevated plasma levels of circulating, endogenous ANF.[175] The lack of apparent down-regulation of the coupled receptor is therefore surprising but may involve a buffering or protecting role of the clearance receptors. If a tentative equilibrium is in effect between the high, circulating levels of peptide and the clearance receptors, further administration of peptide could result in an impressive hemodynamic response. Hypotensive emergencies have also been observed in hypertensive and heart failure patients.

13.8.10.2 Renal

Administration of ANF can result in natriuresis and diuresis at doses which are subthreshold for hemodynamic effects.[175, 182] As mentioned for the blood pressure response, the renal effects of ANF can be sustained after a bolus injection or cessation of infusion. The natriuresis and diuresis response to ANF typically subsides at higher doses due to a concomitant fall in renal perfusion pressure.

The renal effects of ANF appear to be enhanced in hypertensive patients[175, 178, 183] but only modest effects have been observed in heart failure patients.[181] The latter finding may be associated with depressed renal perfusion in severe failure since preclinical data demonstrated diminished efficacy in renal clamp experiments (Section 13.8.4.2). The renal response to ANF in patients with cirrhosis or nephrotic syndrome is also minimal, possibly due to similar problems with renal perfusion.[184]

The clinical development of an agent which has vasodilatory effects as well as promoting natriuresis/diuresis has strong appeal. The clinical data accrued to date with ANF have been disappointing, particularly with the profound hypotension observed in some patients. However, most of the data have been from rather high dose infusion studies; low dose, sustained infusion protocols may prove to be better tolerated and efficacious in some of the pathologies targeted for ANF. In addition, the clinical profile of ANF antagonists, selective for either the silent or coupled receptor, will be of interest, especially in the disease states where plasma levels of ANF rise dramatically.

13.8.11 REFERENCES

1. A. J. deBold, H. B. Borenstein, A. T. Veress and H. Sonnenberg, *Life Sci.*, 1981, **28**, 89.
2. M. G. Currie, D. M. Geller, B. R. Cole, N. R. Siegel, K. F. Fuk, S. P. Adams, S. R. Eubanks, G. R. Gallupe and P. Needleman, *Science (Washington, D.C.)*, 1984, **223**, 67.
3. K. Kangawa and H. Matsuo, *Biochem. Biophys. Res. Commun.*, 1984, **118**, 131.
4. N. G. Seidah, C. Lazure, M. Chretien, G. Thibault, R. Garcia, M. Cantin, J. Genest, R. F. Nutt, S. F. Brady, T. A. Lyle, W. J. Palaveda, C. D. Colton, T. M. Ciccarone and D. F. Veber, *Proc. Natl. Acad. Sci. U.S.A.*, 1984, **81**, 2640.
5. T. G. Flynn, M. L. deBold and A. J. deBold, *Biochem. Biophys. Res. Commun.*, 1983, **117**, 859.
6. S. A. Atlas, H. D. Kleinert, M. J. Camargo, A. Januszewicz, J. E. Sealey, J. H. Laragh, J W. Schilling, J. A. Lewicki, C. K. Johnson and T. Maack, *Nature (London)*, 1984, **309**, 717.
7. R. J. Winquist, E. P. Faison and R. F. Nutt, *Eur. J. Pharmacol.*, 1984, **102**, 169.
8. R. J. Winquist, *Endocrinol. Metab. Clinics North Am.*, 1987, **16**, 163.
9. J. Dietz, *Am. J. Physiol.*, 1984, **247**, R1093.
10. H. E. deWardener, I. H. Mills, W. F. Clapham and C. J. Hayter, *Clin. Sci.*, 1961, **21**, 249.
11. M. F. Sugrue and M.-P. Viader, *Eur. J. Pharmacol.*, 1986, **130**, 349.
12. C. Hirth, J.-P. Stasch, A. John, S. Kazda, F. Morich, D. Neuser and S. Wohlfeil, *J. Cardiovasc. Pharmacol.*, 1986, **8**, 268.
13. J. W. Jacobs, G. P. Vlasuk and M. Rosenblatt, *Endocrinol. Metab. Clinics North Am.*, 1987, **16**, 63.
14. T. Maack, M. Suzuki, F. A. Almeida, D. Nussenzveig, R. M. Scarborough, G. A. McEnroe and J. A. Lewicki, *Science (Washington, D.C.)*, 1987, **238**, 675.
15. J. P. Henry, O. H. Gauer and J. L. Reeves, *Circ. Res.*, 1956, **4**, 85.
16. J. D. Jamieson and G. E. Palade, *J. Cell Biol.*, 1964, **23**, 151.
17. A. J. deBold, *Proc. Soc. Exp. Biol. Med.*, 1979, **161**, 508.
18. N. C. Trippodo, A. A. MacPhee, F. E. Cole and H. L. Blakesley, *Proc. Soc. Exp. Biol. Med.*, 1982, **170**, 502.
19. M. G. Currie, D. M. Geller, B. R. Cole, S. G. Boylan, W. Husheng, S. W. Holmberg and P. Needleman, *Science (Washington, D.C.)*, 1983, **221**, 71.
20. K. Kangawa, A. Fukuda and H. Matsuo, *Nature (London)*, 1985, **313**, 397.
21. K. Kangawa, A. Fukuda, I. Kubota, Y. Hayashi and H. Matsuo, *Biochem. Biophys. Res. Commun.*, 1984, **121**, 585.
22. D. M. Geller, M. G. Currie, N. R. Siegel, K. F. Fok, S. P. Adams and P. Needleman, *Biochem. Biophys. Res. Commun.*, 1984, **121**, 802.
23. K. Kangawa, Y. Tawaragi, S. Oikawa, A. Mizuno, Y. Sakuragawa, H. Nakazato, A. Fukuda, N. Minamino and H. Matsuo, *Nature (London)*, 1984, **312**, 152.
24. M. Yamanaka, B. Greenberg, L. Johnson, J. Seilhamer, M. Brewer, T. Friedmann, J. Miller, S. Atlas, J. Laragh, J. Lewicki and J. Fiddes, *Nature (London)*, 1984, **309**, 722.
25. S. Oikawa, M. Imai, A. Ueno, S. Tanaka, T. Noguchi, H. Nakazato, K. Kangawa, A. Fukuda and H. Matsuo, *Nature (London)*, 1984, **309**, 724.
26. C. E. Seidman, K. D. Bloch, K. A. Klein, J. A. Smith and J. G. Seidman, *Science (Washington, D.C.)*, 1984, **226**, 1206.
27. B. D. Greenburg, G. H. Bencen, J. J. Seilhamer, J. A. Lewicki and J. C. Fiddes, *Nature (London)*, 1984, **312**, 656.
28. S. Argentin, M. Nemer, J. Drouin, G. K. Scott, B. P. Kennedy and P. L. Davies, *Nature (London)*, 1985, **260**, 4568.
29. G. P. Vlasuk, J. Miller, G. H. Bencen and J. A. Lewicki, *Biochem. Biophys. Res. Commun.*, 1986, **136**, 396.
30. D. Schwartz, D. M. Geller, P. T. Manning, N. R. Siegel, K. Y. Fok, C. E. Smith and P. Needleman, *Science (Washington, D.C.)*, 1985, **229**, 397.
31. A. Miyata, T. Toshimori, T. Hashiguchi, K. Kangawa and H. Matsuo, *Biochem. Biophys. Res. Commun.*, 1987, **142**, 461.
32. S. P. Adams, *Endocrinol. Metab. Clinics North Am.*, 1987, **16**, 1.
33. R. F. Nutt and D. F. Veber, *Endocrinol. Metab. Clinics North Am.*, 1987, **16**, 19.

34. A. Sugawara, K. Nakao, N. Morii, T. Yamada, H. Itoh, S. Shino, Y. Saito, M. Mukoyama, H. Arai, K. Nishimura, K. Obata, H. Yasue, T. Ban and H. Imura, *Biochem. Biophys. Res. Commun.*, 1988, **150**, 60.
35. M. G. Currie, D. M. Geller, B. R. Cole and P. Needleman, *Proc. Natl. Àcad. Sci. U.S.A.*, 1984, **81**, 1230.
36. M. L. Michener, J. K. Gierse, R. Seetharam, K. F. Fok, P. O. Olins, M. S. Mai and P. Needleman, *Mol. Pharmacol.*, 1986, **30**, 552.
37. R. B. Harris and I. B. Wilson, *Peptides (Fayetteville, N.Y.)*, 1985, **6**, 393.
38. T. A. Lyle, S. F. Brady, T. M. Ciccarone, C. D. Colton, W. J. Paleveda, D. F. Veber and R. F. Nutt, *J. Org. Chem.*, 1987, **52**, 3752.
39. S. R. Stephenson and A. J. Kenny, *Biochem. J.*, 1987, **243**, 183.
40. G. M. Olins, K. L. Spear, N. R. Siegel and H. A. Zurcher-Neely, *Biochim. Biophys. Acta*, 1987, **901**, 97.
41. J. L. Sonnenberg, Y. Sakane, A. Y. Jeng, J. A. Koehn, J. A. Ansell, L. P. Wennogle and R. D. Ghai, *Peptides (Fayetteville, N.Y.)*, 1988, **8**, 173.
42. G. M. Olins, K. L. Spear, N. R. Siegel, E. J. Reinhard and H. A. Zurcher-Neely, *Eur. J. Biochem.*, 1987, **170**, 431.
43. A. A. Seymour, N. G. Delaney, J. N. Swerdel, S. A. Fennell, R. Neubeck, S. P. Druckman, D. W. Cushman and J. M. DeForrest, *FASEB J.*, 1988, **2**, A936.
44. P. W. Schiller, L. A. Maziak, T. M.-D. Nguyen, J. Godin, R. Garcia, A. De Lean and M. Cantin, *Biochem. Biophys. Res. Commun.*, 1987, **143**, 499.
45. N. Katsube, D. Schwartz and P. Needleman, *J. Pharmacol. Exp. Ther.*, 1986, **239**, 474.
46. R. J. Winquist, E. P. Faison, S. A. Waldman, K. Schwartz, F. Murad and R. Rapoport, *Proc. Natl. Acad. Sci. U.S.A.*, 1984, **81**, 7661.
47. P. Bolli, F. B. Muller, L. Linder, A. E. Raine, T. J. Resink, P. Erne, W. Kiowski, R. Ritz and F. R. Buhler, *Circulation*, 1987, **75**, 221.
48. F. Murad, D. C. Leitman, B. M. Bennett, C. Molina and S. A. Waldman, *Am. J. Med. Sci.*, 1987, **294**, 139.
49. R. M. Rapoport, *Circ. Res.*, 1986, **58**, 407.
50. J. B. Smith and T. M. Lincoln, *Am. J. Physiol.*, 1987, **253**, C147.
51. A. Hassid, *Am. J. Physiol.*, 1986, **251**, C681.
52. Y. Takuwa and H. Rasmussen, *J. Clin. Invest.*, 1987, **80**, 248.
53. E. P. Faison, P. K. S. Siegl, G. Morgan and R. J. Winquist, *Life Sci.*, 1985, **37**, 1073.
54. M. L. Cohen and K. W. Schenck, *Eur. J. Pharmacol.*, 1985, **108**, 103.
55. N. Ishikawa, A. Hayakawa, T. Uematsu and M. Nakashima, *Jpn. J. Pharmacol.*, 1987, **44**, 515.
56. C. Aalkjaer, M. J. Mulvany and N. C. B. Nyborg, *Br. J. Pharmacol.*, 1985, **86**, 447.
57. G. Osol, W. Halpern, B. Tesfamariam, K. Nakayama and D. Weinberg, *Hypertension (Dallas)*, 1986, **8**, 606.
58. I. M. Macrae, D. I. Graham and J. McCulloch, *Brain Res.*, 1987, **435**, 195.
59. R. W. Lappe, J. F. M. Smits, J. A. Todt, J. J. M. Debets and R. L. Wendt, *Circ. Res.*, 1985, **56**, 606.
60. R. W. Lappe, J. A. Todt and R. L. Wendt, *Am. J. Physiol.*, 1985, **249**, R781.
61. P. Bie, B. C. Wang, R. J. Leadley, Jr. and K. L. Goetz, *Am. J. Physiol.*, 1988, **254**, R161.
62. M. Yasujima, K. Abe, M. Kohzuki, M. Tanno, Y. Kasai, M. Sato, K. Omata, K. Kudo, K. Tsunoda, K. Takeuchi, K. Yoshinaga and T. Inagami, *Circ. Res.*, 1985, **57**, 470.
63. M. Volpe, R. E. Sosa, F. B. Muller, M. J. F. Camargo, N. Glorioso, J. H. Laragh, T. Maack and S. A. Atlas, *Am. J. Physiol.*, 1986, **250**, H871.
64. H. Koike, T. Sada, M. Miyamoto, K. Oizumi, M. Sugiyama and T. Inagami, *Eur. J. Pharmacol.*, 1984, **104**, 391.
65. T. H. Hintze, M. G. Currie and P. Needleman, *Am. J. Physiol.*, 1985, **248**, H587.
66. R. D. Wangler, B. A. Breuhaus, H. O. Otero, D. A. Hastings, M. D. Holzman, H. H. Saneii, H. V. Sparks, Jr. and J. E. Chimoskey, *Science (Washington, D.C.)*, 1985, **230**, 558.
67. A. Yanagisawa, J. A. Osborne, G. L. Stahl and A. M. Lefer, *J. Cardiovasc. Pharmacol.*, 1987, **10**, 320.
68. A. Chu and F. R Cobb, *Circ. Res.*, 1987, **61**, 485.
69. Y. W. Chien, E. D. Frohlich and N. C. Trippodo, *Am. J. Physiol.*, 1987, **252**, H894.
70. P. Thoren, A. L. Mark, D. A. Morgan, T. P. O'Neill, P. Needleman and M. J. Brody, *Am. J. Physiol.*, 1986, **251**, H1252.
71. J. P. Granger, T. J. Opgenorth, J. Salazar, J. C. Romero and J. C. Burnett, Jr., *Hypertension (Dallas)*, 1986, **8**, II-112.
72. R. Garcia, G. Thibault, J. Gutkowska, K. Horky, P. Hamet, M. Cantin and J. Genest, *Proc. Soc. Exp. Biol. Med.*, 1985, **179**, 396.
73. J. P. Fluckinger, B. Waeber, G. Matsueda, B. Delaloye, J. Nussberger and H. R. Brunner, *Am. J. Physiol.*, 1986, **251**, H880.
74. P. Weidmann, L. Hasler, M. P. Gnadinger, R. E. Lang, D. E. Uehlinger, S. Shaw, W. Rascher and F. C. Reubi, *J. Clin. Invest.*, 1986, **77**, 734.
75. F. A. Almeida, M. Suzuki and T. Maack, *Life Sci.*, 1986, **39**, 1193.
76. R. J. Winquist, E. P. Baskin, E. P. Faison, J. Clair and R. Gould, in 'Resistance Arteries', ed. W. Halpern, M. Mulvany and G. Osol, Perinatology Press, New York, 1988, p. 435.
77. N. C. Trippodo and R. W. Barbee, *Am. J. Physiol.*, 1987, **252**, R915.
78. M. E. O'Donnell and N. E. Owen, *J. Biol. Chem.*, 1986, **261**, 15461.
79. A. A. Seymour, E. H. Blaine, E. K. Mazack, S. G. Smith, I. I. Stabilito, A. B. Haley, M. A. Napier, M. A. Whinnery and R. F. Nutt, *Life Sci.*, 1985, **36**, 33.
80. K. Goetz, *Am. J. Physiol.*, 1988, **254**, E1.
81. A. A. Seymour, S. G. Smith and E. K. Mazack, *Am. J. Physiol.*, 1987, **253**, F234.
82. C. L. Huang, J. Lewicki, L. K. Johnson and M. G. Cogan, *J. Clin. Invest.*, 1985, **75**, 769.
83. R. E. Sosa, M. Volpe, D. N. Marion, S. A. Atlas, J. H. Laragh, E. D. Vaughan, Jr. and T. Maack, *Am. J. Physiol.*, 1986, **250**, F520.
84. M. J. F. Camargo, H. D. Kleinert, S. A. Atlas, J. E. Sealey, J. H. Laragh and T. Maack, *Am. J. Physiol.*, 1984, **246**, F447.
85. T. A. Fried, R. N. McCoy, R. W. Osgood and J. H. Stein, *Am. J. Physiol.*, 1986, **250**, F1119.
86. A. A. Seymour, S. G. Smith, E. K. Mazack and E. H. Blaine, *Hypertension (Dallas)*, 1986, **8**, 211.
87. D. M. Pollock and W. J. Arendshorst, *Am. J. Physiol.*, 1986, **251**, F795.
88. S. A. Atlas and T. Maack, *Endocrinol. Metab. Clinics North Am.*, 1987, **16**, 107.
89. T. G. Hammond, A. Haramati and F. G. Knox, *Am. J. Physiol.*, 1985, **249**, F315.

90. P. J. Harris, D. Thomas and T. O. Morgan, *Nature (London)*, 1987, **326**, 697.
91. H. Sonnenberg, U. Honrath, C. K. Chong and D. R. Wilson, *Am. J. Physiol.*, 1986, **250**, F963.
92. M. L. Zeidel, J. L. Seifter, S. Lear, B. M. Brenner and P. Silva, *Am. J. Physiol.*, 1986, **251**, F379.
93. M. A. Dillingham and R. J. Anderson, *Science (Washington, D.C.)*, 1986, **231**, 1572.
94. C. S. Sweet, C. T. Ludden, C. M. Frederick, L. G. T. Ribeiro, J. Nussberger, E. E. Slater and E. H. Blaine, *Eur. J. Pharmacol.*, 1985, **115**, 267.
95. R. H. Freeman, J. O. Davis and R. C. Vari, *Am. J. Physiol.*, 1985, **248**, R495.
96. K. Atarashi, P. J. Mulrow and R. Franco-Saenz, *J. Clin. Invest.*, 1985, **76**, 1807.
97. L. Chartier, E. Schiffrin, G. Thibault and R. Garcia, *Endocrinology (Baltimore)*, 1984, **115**, 2026.
98. T. L. Goodfriend, M. Elliott and S. A. Atlas, *Life Sci.*, 1984, **35**, 1675.
99. H. Matsuoka, M. Ishii, Y. Hirata, K. Atarashi, T. Sugimoto, K. Kangawa and H. Matsuo, *Am. J. Physiol.*, 1987, **252**, E643.
100. A. De Lean, *Life Sci.*, 1986, **39**, 1109.
101. F. Bex and A. Corbin, *Eur. J. Pharmacol.*, 1985, **115**, 125.
102. K. N. Pandey, S. N. Pavlou, W. J. Kovacs and T. Inagami, *Biochem. Biophys. Res. Commun.*, 1986, **138**, 399.
103. S. A. Waldman, R. M. Rapoport and F. M. Murad, *J. Biol. Chem.*, 1984, **259**, 14 332.
104. K. N. Pandey, K. G. Osteen and T. Inagami, *Endocrinology (Baltimore)*, 1987, **121**, 1195.
105. J. C. Burnett, Jr., J. P. Granger and T. S. Opgenorth, *Am. J. Physiol.*, 1984, **247**, F863.
106. K. Obana, M. Naruse, K. Naruse, H. Sakurai, H. Demura, T. Inagami and K. Shizume, *Endocrinology (Baltimore)*, 1985, **117**, 1282.
107. D. Rodriguez-Puyol, G. Arriba, A. Blanchart, J. C. Santos, C. Caramelo, A. Fernandez-Cruz, L. Hernando and J. M. Lopez-Novoa, *Biochem. Biophys. Res. Commun.*, 1986, **138**, 496.
108. W. K. Samson, *Neuroendocrinology*, 1985, **40**, 277.
109. W. K. Samson, *Endocrinol. Metab. Clinics North Am.*, 1987, **16**, 145.
110. K. Obana, M. Naruse, T. Inagami, A. B. Brown, K. Naruse, K. Kurimoto, H. Sakurai, H. Demura and K. Shizume, *Biochem. Biophys. Res. Commun.*, 1985, **132**, 1088.
111. T. W. Mittag, A. Tormay, M. Ortega and C. Severin, *Curr. Eye Res.*, 1987, **6**, 1189.
112. M. Shoji, T. Kimura, K. Matsui, K. Ota, K. Iitake, M. Inoue, M. Yasujima, K. Abe and K. Yoshinaga, *Acta Endocrinol. (Copenhagen)*, 1987, **115**, 433.
113. D. A. Fitts, R. L. Thunhorst and J. B. Simpson, *Brain Res.*, 1985, **348**, 118.
114. H. Itoh, K. Nakao, N. Morii, T. Yamada, S. Shiono, M. Sakamoto, A. Sugawara, Y. Saito, G. Katsuura, T. Shiomi, M. Eigyo, A. Matsushita and H. Imura, *Brain Res. Bull.*, 1986, **16**, 745.
115. J. Antunes-Rodrigues, S. M. McCann, L. C. Rogers and W. K. Samson, *Proc. Natl. Acad. Sci. U.S.A.*, 1985, **82**, 8720.
116. L. Steardo and J. A. Nathanson, *Science (Washington, D.C.)*, 1987, **235**, 470.
117. M. A. Napier, R. L. Vandlen, G. Albers-Schonberg, R. F. Nutt, S. Brady, T. Lyle, R. Winquist, E. P. Faison, L. A. Heinel and E. H. Blaine, *Proc. Natl. Acad. Sci. U.S.A.*, 1984, **81**, 5946.
118. R. J. Winquist, M. A. Napier, R. L. Vandlen, K. Arcuri, M. E. Keegan, E. P. Faison and E. P. Baskin, *Clin. Exp. Hypertens.*, 1985, **A7**, 869.
119. Y. Hirata, M. Tomita, H. Yoshimi and M. Ikeda, *Biochem. Biophys. Res. Commun.*, 1984, **125**, 562.
120. D. B. Schenk, L. K. Johnson, K. Schwartz, H. Sista, R. M. Scarborough and J. A. Lewicki, *Biochem. Biophys. Res. Commun.*, 1985, **127**, 433.
121. C. Bianchi, J. Gutkowska, G. Thibault, R. Garcia, J. Genest and M. Cantin, *Histochemistry*, 1985, **82**, 441.
122. G. Vlasuk, R. W. Babilon, R. F. Nutt, T. M. Ciccarone and R. J. Winquist, *Can. J. Physiol. Pharmacol.*, 1987, **65**, 1684.
123. Y. Hirata, M. Tomita, S. Takata and I. Inoue, *Biochem. Biophys. Res. Commun.*, 1985, **131**, 222.
124. E. Schiffrin, M. Deslongchamps and G. Thibault, *Hypertension (Dallas)*, 1986, **8**, II-6.
125. R. Hori, K.-I. Inui, H. Saito, Y. Matsukawa, K. Okumura, K. Nakao, N. Morii and H. Imura, *Biochem. Biophys. Res. Commun.*, 1985, **129**, 773.
126. D. Butlen, M. Mistaoui and F. Morel, *Pfluegers Arch.*, 1987, **408**, 356.
127. M. Suzuki, F. A. Almeida, D. R. Nussenzveig, D. Sawyer and T. Maack, *Am. J. Physiol.*, 1987, **253**, F917.
128. C. Koseki, Y. Hayashi, S. Torikai, M. Furuya, N. Ohnuma and M. Imai, *Am. J. Physiol.*, 1986, **250**, F210.
129. B. J. Ballermann, R. L. Hoover, M. J. Karnovsky and B. M. Brenner, *J. Clin. Invest.*, 1985, **76**, 2049.
130. C. Bianchi, J. Gutkowska, G. Thibault, R. Garcia, J. Genest and M. Cantin, *Am. J. Physiol.*, 1986, **251**, F594.
131. R. G. Appel, J. Wang, M. S. Simonson and M. J. Dunn, *Am. J. Physiol.*, 1986, **251**, F1036.
132. S. Y. Chai, P. M. Sexton, A. M. Allen, R. Figdor and F. A. O. Mendelsohn, *Am. J. Physiol.*, 1986, **250**, F753.
133. K. M. M. Murphy, L. L. McLaughlin, M. L. Michener and P. Needleman, *Eur. J. Pharmacol.*, 1985, **111**, 291.
134. A. De Lean, J. Gutkowska, N. McNicoll, P. W. Schiller, M. Cantin and J. Genest, *Life Sci.*, 1984, **35**, 2311.
135. H. Shionoiri, N. Hirawa, I. Takasaki, Y. Ishikawa, K. Minamisawa, E. Miyajima, Y. Kinoshita, K. Shimoyama, M. Shimonaka, M. Ishido and S. Hirose, *Biochem. Biophys. Res. Commun.*, 1987, **148**, 286.
136. K. Racz, O. Kuchel, N. T. Buu, W. Debinski, M. Cantin and J. Genest, *N. Engl. J. Med.*, 1986, **314**, 321.
137. K. N. Pandey, T. Inagami and K. S. Misono, *Biochemistry*, 1986, **25**, 8467.
138. G. P. Vlasuk, K. E. Arcuri, T. M. Ciccarone and R. F. Nutt, *FEBS Lett.*, 1988, **228**, 290.
139. I. Sen, *Biochem. Biophys. Res. Commun.*, 1986, **135**, 480.
140. C. Bianchi, M. B. Anand-Srivastava, A. De Lean, J. Gutkowska, D. Forthomme, J. Genest and M. Cantin, *Curr. Eye Res.*, 1986, **5**, 283.
141. R. Quirion, M. Dalpe and T.-V. Dam, *Proc. Natl. Acad. Sci. U.S.A.*, 1986, **83**, 174.
142. C. R. Mantyh, L. Kruger, N. C. Brecha and P. W. Mantyh, *Brain. Res.*, 1987, **412**, 329.
143. J. M. Saavedra, *Cell. Mol. Neurobiol.*, 1987, **7**, 151.
144. T. Kuno, J. W. Andresen, Y. Kamisaki, S. A. Waldman, L. Y. Chang, S. Saheki, D. C. Leitman, M. Nakane and F. Murad, *J. Biol. Chem.*, 1986, **261**, 5817.
145. R. Hamel and A. W. Ford-Hutchinson, *Eur. J. Pharmacol.*, 1986, **121**, 151.
146. D. C. Leitman, V. L. Agnost, J. J. Tuan, J. W. Andresen and F. Murad, *Biochem. J.*, 1987, **244**, 69.
147. Y. Kanai, N. Ohnuma and H. Matsuo, *Jpn. J. Pharmacol.*, 1987, **45**, 7.
148. R. Winquist, *Fed. Proc., Fed. Am. Soc. Exp. Biol.*, 1986, **45**, 2371.

149. A. E. Fletcher, E. H. Allan, D. J. Casley and T. J. Martin, *FEBS Lett.*, 1986, **208**, 263.
150. R. L. Vandlen, K. E. Arcuri and M. A. Napier, *J. Biol. Chem.*, 1985, **260**, 10 889.
151. S. Hirose, F. Akiyama, M. Shinjo, H. Ohno and K. Murakami, *Biochem. Biophys. Res. Commun.*, 1985, **130**, 574.
152. M. Shinjo, Y. Hirata, H. Hagiwara, F. Akiyama, K. Murakami, S. Kojima, M. Shimonaka, Y. Inada and S. Hirose, *Biomed. Res.*, 1986, **1**, 35.
153. D. B. Schenk, M. N. Phelps, J. G. Porter, R. M. Scarborough, G. A. McEnroe and J. A. Lewicki, *J. Biol. Chem.*, 1985, **260**, 14 887.
154. M. A. Napier, K. E. Arcuri and R. L. Vandlen, *Arch. Biochem. Biophys.*, 1986, **248**, 516.
155. C. Koseki, Y. Hayashi, N. Ohnuma and M. Imai, *Biochem. Biophys. Res. Commun.*, 1986, **136**, 200.
156. D. C. Leitman and F. Murad, *Biochem. Biophys. Acta*, 1986, **885**, 74.
157. R. Scarborough, D. B. Schenk, G. A. McEnroe, A. Arfsten, L.-L. Kang, K. Schwartz and J. A. Lewicki, *J. Biol. Chem.*, 1986, **261**, 12 960.
158. K. S. Misono, R. T. Grammer, J. W. Rigby and T. Inagami, *Biochem. Biophys. Res. Commun.*, 1985, **130**, 994.
159. D. C. Leitman, J. W. Andresen, T. Kuno, Y. Kamisaki, J.-K. Chang and F. Murad, *J. Biol. Chem.*, 1986, **261**, 11 650.
160. N. Katsube, K. Wakitani, K. F. Fok, F. S. Tjoeng, M. E. Zupec, S. R. Eubanks, S. P. Adams and P. Needleman, *Biochem. Biophys. Res. Commun.*, 1985, **128**, 325.
161. A. De Lean, G. Thibault, N. G. Seidah, C. Lazure, J. Gutowska, M. Chretien, J. Genest and M. Cantin, *Biochem. Biophys. Res. Commun.*, 1985, **132**, 360.
162. G. Thibault, R. Garcia, F. Carrier, N. G. Seidah, C. Lazure, M. Chretien, M. Cantin and J. Genest, *Biochem. Biophys. Res. Commun.*, 1984, **125**, 938.
163. P. W. Schiller, L. Maziak, T. M.-D. Nguyen, J. Godin, R. Garcia, A. De Lean and M. Cantin, *Biochem. Biophys. Res. Commun.*, 1985, **131**, 1056.
164. P. Needleman, S. P. Adams, B. R. Cole, M. G. Currie, D. M. Geller, M. L. Michener, C. B. Saper, D. Schwartz and D. G. Standaert, *Hypertension (Dallas)*, 1985, **7**, 469.
165. R. F. Nutt, T. M. Ciccarone, S. F. Brady, C. D. Colton, W. J. Paleveda, T. A. Lyle, T. M. Williams, D. F. Veber, A. Wallace and R. J. Winquist, in 'Peptides', ed. G. R. Marshall, Escom, New York, 1988, p. 444.
166. D. B. Schenk, M. N. Phelps, J. G. Porter, F. Fuller, B. Cordell and J. Lewicki, *Proc. Natl. Acad. Sci. U.S.A.*, 1987, **84**, 1521.
167. K. Uchida, M. Shimonaka, T. Saheki, T. Ito and S. Hirose, *J. Biol. Chem.*, 1987, **262**, 12 401.
168. R. Takayanagi, T. Inagami, R. M. Snajdar, T. Imada, M. Tamura and K. S. Misono, *J. Biol. Chem.*, 1987, **262**, 12 104.
169. S. Meloche, H. Ong and A. De Lean, *J. Biol. Chem.*, 1987, **262**, 10 252.
170. R. Rapoport, R. J. Winquist, E. P. Baskin, E. P. Faison, S. A. Waldman and F. Murad, *Eur. J. Pharmacol.*, 1986, **120**, 123.
171. K. Wakitani, T. Oshima, A. D. Loewy, S. W. Holmberg, B. R. Cole, S. P. Adams, K. F. Fok, M. G. Currie and P. Needleman, *Circ. Res.*, 1985, **56**, 621.
172. T. Hirata, T. Tomita, S. Takata and H. Yoshimi, *Biochem. Biophys. Res. Commum.*, 1985, **128**, 538.
173. R. Winquist, *Blood Vessels*, 1987, **24**, 128.
174. A. M. Richards, M. G. Nicholls, H. Ikram, M. W. I. Webster, T. G. Yandle and E. A. Espiner, *Lancet*, 1985, **1**, 545.
175. M. G. Nicholls and A. M. Richards, *Endocrinol. Metab. Clinics North Am.*, 1987, **16**, 199.
176. J. P. Bussien, J. Biollaz, B. Waeber, J. Nussberger, G. A. Turini, H. R. Brunner, F. Brunner-Ferber, H. J. Gomez and E. S. Otterbein, *J. Cardiovasc. Pharmacol.*, 1986, **8**, 216.
177. T. G. Yandle, A. M. Richards, M. G. Nicholls, R. Cuneo, E. A. Espiner and J. H. Livesey, *Life Sci.*, 1986, **38**, 1827.
178. J. R. Cusson, P. Hamet, J. Gutkowska, O. Kuchel, E. Schiffrin, T. DuSouich, J. Genest, M. Cantin and P. arochelle, *J. Cardiovasc. Pharmacol.*, 1986, **8**, 1293.
179. I. G. Crozier, H. Ikram, H. J. Gomez, M. G. Nicholls, E. A. Espiner and N. J. Warner, *Lancet*, 1986, **2**, 1242.
180. G. A. J. Riegger, E. P. Kromer and K. Kochsiek, *J. Cardiovasc. Pharmacol.*, 1986, **8**, 1107.
181. R. J. Cody, S. A. Atlas, J. H. Laragh, S. H. Kubo, A. B. Covit, K. S. Ryman, A. Shaknovich, K. Pondolfino, M. Clark, M. J. F. Camargo, R. M. Scarborough and J. A. Lewicki, *J. Clin. Invest.*, 1986, **78**, 1362.
182. J. J. Freitag, B. R. Walker and H. K. Marder, *Kidney Int.*, 1987, **31**, 270.
183. A. M. Richards, M. G. Nicholls, E. A. Espiner, H. Ikram, T. G. Yandle, S. L. Joyce and M. M. Cullens, *Hypertension (Dallas)*, 1985, **7**, 812.
184. D. R. Hricik, R. Appel, J. Green, R. D. Smith and M. J. Dunn, *Kidney Int.*, 1987, **31**, 273.

13.9
Tachykinin Receptors

ANAND S DUTTA

ICI Pharmaceuticals, Alderley Park, UK

13.9.1 INTRODUCTION

Tachykinins are a family of deca-, undeca- and dodeca-peptides which share a common C-terminal sequence, Phe-X-Gly-Leu-Met-NH$_2$ (X = Phe, Tyr, Ile or Val). In addition to the chemical similarities the biological profiles of these peptides are also very similar. All of these lower blood pressure, stimulate isolated preparations of intestinal smooth muscle and cause salivary secretion.[1]

The first member of the tachykinin family, eledoisin (ELE), was isolated from the Mediterranean octopod *Eledone moschata*. Later members, *e.g.* physalaemin (PHY), phyllomedusin, uperolein and kassinin (KAS), were isolated from amphibian skin. The mammalian tachykinins, substance P (SP), neurokinin α (also known as substance K, neuromedin L or neurokinin A; NKA) and neurokinin β (also called neuromedin K or neurokinin B; NKB) were the last to be discovered.[2,3] The amino acid sequences of these tachykinins are shown in Table 1.

Table 1 Chemical Structures of Tachykinins

Tachykinin	Sequence
Substance P (SP)	Arg-Pro-Lys-Pro-Gln-Gln-Phe-Phe-Gly-Leu-Met-NH$_2$
Physalaemin (PHY)	⌐Glu-Ala-Asp-Pro-Asn-Lys-Phe-Tyr-Gly-Leu-Met-NH$_2$
Phyllomedusin	⌐Glu-Asn-Pro-Asn-Arg-Phe-Ile-Gly-Leu-Met-NH$_2$
Uperolein	⌐Glu-Pro-Asp-Pro-Asn-Ala-Phe-Tyr-Gly-Leu-Met-NH$_2$
Eledoisin (ELE)	⌐Glu-Pro-Ser-Lys-Asp-Ala-Phe-Ile-Gly-Leu-Met-NH$_2$
Kassinin (KAS)	Asp-Val-Pro-Lys-Ser-Asp-Gln-Phe-Val-Gly-Leu-Met-NH$_2$
Neurokinin A (NKA)	His-Lys-Thr-Asp-Ser-Phe-Val-Gly-Leu-Met-NH$_2$
Neurokinin B (NKB)	Asp-Met-His-Asp-Phe-Phe-Val-Gly-Leu-Met-NH$_2$

In recent years (since 1972) most of the chemical and biological work has centred around substance P. Work on the other mammalian tachykinins, isolated and sequenced in 1983–84, is just beginning to emerge. This article is, therefore, primarily directed towards mammalian tachykinins (SP, NKA and NKB), and nonmammalian tachykinins are discussed mainly in the section dealing with the classification of the receptors. A limited amount of structure–activity relationship data (SAR) on these other tachykinins have been included to highlight the main similarities to or differences from SP.

Although the occurrence of SP was widely known for a long time, its amino acid sequence was first published in 1971 from bovine hypothalamus,[4] and two years later from horse intestine.[5] SP has been shown to be widely distributed in the body. Its presence in the nervous system, gastrointestinal tract, blood and blood vessels *etc.* has been well documented. Along with its wide distribution, SP has also been associated with a large number of biological effects, the most important of these being on gastrointestinal, cardiovascular, respiratory and nervous systems. Some of these aspects have recently been reviewed.[6–10]

13.9.2   DISTRIBUTION AND METABOLISM OF TACHYKININS

Since NKA and NKB have only been isolated recently, very little has been reported so far on their distribution and metabolism. Most of the distribution and inactivation studies have centered around SP and are summarized in recent reviews.[7,8]

Extensive radioimmunological and immunohistochemical studies have shown the presence of SP in the nervous system, gastrointestinal tract, respiratory tract and circulation. High concentrations of SP in the central nervous system are present in olfactory tubercle, amygdala, nucleus caudatus, globus pallidus, hypothalamus, posterior pituitary, substantia nigra (particularly zona reticularis) and dorsal horn of the spinal cord. In the peripheral nervous system SP is localized to primary sensory neurones and neurones intrinsic to the gastrointestinal tract. In the circulatory system SP immunoreactive fibres are present in heart and various other blood vessels. SP is also present in the plasma of humans, dog, rat, calf and cat. This indicates that in addition to its local function SP may also be transported like a hormone to act on distant organs. In the respiratory tract SP nerve fibres are found within the respiratory epithelium and around blood vessels of the nasal mucosa.

The distribution of NKA and NKB has recently been studied in rat brain and spinal cord using autoradiographic receptor-binding and radioimmunoassay techniques.[11–14] All three mammalian tachykinins (NKA, NKB, SP) were present in various areas of the brain but their relative concentrations were different. High concentrations of these tachykinins were found in the dorsal horn of spinal cord and in hypothalamus, medulla-pons and midbrain-thalamus. Striatum, hippo-campus and olfactory bulb had somewhat lower concentrations but the lowest concentrations of the three tachykinins were recorded in cerebellum.[14] The amount of SP was higher than NKA and NKB in all parts of the rat brain and spinal cord. The ratio of SP to NKA was around 2–2.5 and of SP to NKB between 3.5 (cerebral cortex) and 11.7 (medulla-pons) in various parts of the rat brain and spinal cord. The concentrations of the three tachykinins were about five times higher in the dorsal half than in the ventral half of the spinal cord.[14]

Inactivation of the neurotransmitter substances is known to occur either by extracellular metabolism or by reuptake followed by intracellular metabolism. In the case of SP there is no information suggesting the reuptake process to be the main inactivation pathway.[15] Only one report indicating the existence of an active uptake process for the C-terminal (5–11)-heptapeptide of SP into rat brain and rabbit spinal cord slices has been published.[16] On the other hand a number of crude or purified enzyme preparations and also mixtures of enzymes present in tissue homogenates have been shown to inactivate SP. The relevance of this kind of inactivation to the actual metabolism at or near the receptor sites remains unclear.

A comparison of the inactivation of SP by crude homogenates of rat kidney, small intestine, liver, lung, heart and whole brain showed the kidney homogenate to be 5–20 times more effective than the other homogenates in metabolizing SP.[17] The rat plasma also rapidly degraded SP and the C-terminal (4–11)-octa- and (6–11)-hexa-peptide derivatives. This degradation was inhibited by captopril, an inhibitor of the angiotensin converting enzyme.[18] *In vivo* metabolism of SP by various organs was studied by infusing it into various vascular beds and then measuring the salivary response in rats. Liver, hind limbs and kidney were most effective and lungs and cerebral blood vessels were least effective in inactivating SP.[19]

Calcium dependent cysteine proteinases, Calpain I and II, were shown to cleave the C-terminal amide of SP and PHY. These enzymes were specific for the C-terminal amide and left the side chain amide groups of the two glutamine residues in SP intact. The deamidation reaction was inhibited by leupeptin, antipain and calpastatin.[20]

Angiotensin converting enzyme from lung and corpus striatum also degraded SP. Two patterns of SP degradation with purified lung angiotensin converting enzyme were observed.[21] One pattern involved an initial cleavage between Phe^8-Gly^9, which led to the C-terminal tripeptide, Gly-Leu-Met-NH_2, and the N-terminal octapeptide, which was further cleaved by sequential removal of dipeptides (Phe-Phe, Gln-Gln, Lys-Pro and Arg-Pro). In the second pattern the C-terminal dipeptide, Leu-Met-NH_2, was first liberated and the N-terminal nonapeptide was then cleaved to give Phe-Gly, Gln-Phe and Arg-Pro-Lys-Pro-Gln. The presence of a penultimate Pro residue in the pentapeptide rendered it resistant to further cleavage.[21] The inability of the angiotensin converting enzyme to cleave the C-terminal Pro-X dipeptides was first demonstrated in the case of bradykinin-potentiating peptides. The initial cleavage between Phe^8-Gly^9 was favoured (3:1) by the lung enzyme but the striatal enzyme favoured (1.4:1) the Gly^9-Leu^{10} cleavage. SP and NKA were degraded to approximately the same extent by the lung enzyme but the striatal enzyme only cleaved SP. Neurokinin A was stable to the striatal converting enzyme even after incubations at 37 °C for 15 h.[21]

The inactivation of SP and PHY was also studied with endopeptidase-24.11 (enkephalinase) isolated from pig kidney or caudate synaptic membranes. This enzyme cleaves the peptide bonds formed by the amino groups of the hydrophobic amino acid residues. Three peptide bonds in SP (Gln^6-Phe^7, Phe^7-Phe^8, Gly^9-Leu^{10}) and PHY (Lys^6-Phe^7, Phe^7-Tyr^8 and Gly^9-Leu^{10}) were cleaved by the enzyme.[22,23] The cleavage pattern was identified by characterizing seven peptide fragments Arg-Pro-Lys-Pro-Gln-Gln (1–6), Arg-Pro-Lys-Pro-Gln-Gln-Phe (1–7), Arg-Pro-Lys-Pro-Gln-Gln-Phe-Phe-Gly (1–9), Phe-Phe-Gly-Leu-Met-NH_2 (7–11), Phe-Phe-Gly (7–9), Phe-Gly (8–9) and Leu-Met-NH_2 (10–11), obtained by treating SP with the kidney enzyme.

Effects of various peptidase inhibitors on the outflow of the endogenous SP (K^+-evoked) from slices of rat substantia nigra have been investigated in order to assess the significance of some of the above-mentioned enzymes in the *in vivo* degradation of SP. The two enkephalinase inhibitors (thiorphan and phosphoramidon), the aminopeptidase inhibitor (bestatin) and the calpain inhibitor (leupeptin) enhanced the K^+-induced overflow of the SP-like immunoreactive material from slices of substantia nigra.[24] All of the above information suggests that the metabolism of SP may be the result of a number of different degradation pathways.

Additional information on the metabolism of SP which has been used in the design of analogues stable to enzymic degradation is presented in Section 13.9.6.3.

13.9.3 PHARMACOLOGICAL ASSAYS

Due to the large number of pharmacological actions associated with SP and other tachykinins, the list of *in vitro* and *in vivo* tests used for the assessment of the agonist and antagonist properties of the analogues is very long and it is not possible to describe all of these in this section.

Guinea pig ileum is the most widely used *in vitro* test preparation. Nearly all of the analogues have been tested on the ileum and we have mainly used these data for SAR discussions. Details of this test are described below. The procedures used for the other *in vitro* and *in vivo* tests can be found in the publications cited in the SAR section.

In the guinea pig assay guinea pigs (300–350 g) of both sexes were sacrificed by stunning and exsanguination and the distal ileum rapidly dissected out and suspended in a 5 or 10 mL organ bath containing oxygenated (95% O_2:5% CO_2) Kreb's solution at 37°C. The tissues are maintained under a resting tension of 0.5 g and the contractile responses were recorded using an isotonic transducer connected to a chart recorder.

Concentration–response curves of the agonist analogues are measured by consecutive additions of the peptide solutions after an initial equilibration period of 30 to 60 min. The concentration of the compound causing half of the maximal response was taken as EC_{50}. Although EC_{50} values have been recorded in some publications, in a number of others the analogue EC_{50} value was compared with the EC_{50} value of SP and the agonist potency of the compound was reported as percent of SP.

The antagonist activities of the compounds were tested by constructing concentration–response curves in the absence and presence of the putative antagonist (contact time 15–30 min). The antagonist activities are recorded either as dose ratios (ratio of the EC_{50} value of the agonist in the presence of the antagonist to the EC_{50} value of the agonist alone) or as pA_2 values.

13.9.4 RECEPTOR CLASSIFICATION

Even before the discovery of the two recent mammalian tachykinins (neurokinins A and B) the potencies of the other tachykinins were compared in various *in vitro* and *in vivo* test preparations. The significant potency differences observed in these tests pointed to the possibility of multiple tachykinin receptors.[1,25,26] Present evidence suggests the existence of at least three receptor subtypes: substance P-preferring (SP-P, NK-P or NK-1), neurokinin A-preferring (SP-K, NK-A or NK-2), and/or neurokinin B-preferring (SP-N, NK-B or NK-3). Since in most of the publications cited in this article P-, K- or N-type of nomenclature has been used, it has been retained here as well.

The receptor classification has been based on the biological effects (*in vitro* and *in vivo*) of various tachykinins, tachykinin fragments and other agonist and antagonist analogues. All of these approaches (discussed below) suffer from a number of problems,[26] two of the main ones being the enzymic stability and receptor accessibility of the peptides. In addition, a large number of different *in vitro* tissue preparations have been used by various investigators and most of these contain more than one receptor subtype. This leads to difficulties in the interpretation of the results. The present generation of the antagonists are also not very potent or selective. Because of these problems the receptor classification of the tachykinins has not yet been finalized. More and more evidence which may help to clarify the situation is presently being accumulated and some of this is summarized in the following sections. Of the various approaches discussed below, the receptor classification based on naturally occurring tachykinins and their more selective synthetic analogues (see Section 13.9.4.1) is most advanced at this stage.

13.9.4.1 Classification Based on Tachykinins

The potency rank order of SP, PHY, ELE and KAS in various test systems is shown in Table 2. Although the absolute potencies quoted in different publications may vary somewhat, the overall rank order still remains the same for all the test preparations except guinea pig ileum. As shown in Table 2, in one test[9] ELE was 2.7 times more potent than SP, whereas in another test ELE and SP were nearly equipotent.[28] Since the difference between the least potent and the most potent tachykinin in any set of results is less than threefold, it may just be due to some subtle variation in the test system or biological variation.

On the basis of these results, Iversen *et al.* suggested that on SP-P systems, *e.g.* guinea pig ileum and vas deferens and guinea pig and rat bladder, various tachykinins possess similar potencies, while on SP-E systems, *e.g.* rat vas deferens and duodenum and mouse and hamster bladder, ELE and KAS are 100–400 times more potent than SP and PHY.[29] On the basis of this criterion some of the other tissue preparations listed in Table 2, *e.g.* guinea pig trachea, rat colon, dog, monkey and human urinary bladders, frog spinal motoneurones and neonatal spinal cord, may be classified as belonging to the SP-E system. On the other hand, the receptors involved in *in vivo* blood pressure lowering and coronary blood flow[31] and in the isolated carotid artery, rabbit ear artery[32] and pig coronary artery[33] appear to be SP-P type. In the anaesthetized pig coronary blood flow test mentioned above, SP was about 10 times more potent than NKA in eliciting coronary dilation but NKB was inactive.[31] On the isolated pig coronary artery the order of potency was SP = PHY > ELE > KAS > NKA > NKB. The most potent tachykinin (SP) was about 100 times more potent than the least potent tachykinin (NKB). The receptor appears to be located on the endothelium because when it was removed none of the tachykinins induced vasodilation.[33]

Table 2 Rank Order Potencies of Tachykinins

Test	Rank order	Ref.
Dog, rabbit and rat blood pressure	SP > PHY > ELE > KAS	1
Dog hepatic arterial blood flow	SP > PHY > ELE	1
Dog carotid artery	SP = PHY > ELE > KAS	9, 27
Rabbit mesenteric vein	ELE > SP = PHY	9
Guinea pig ileum	ELE > PHY > SP	9
	(2.7) (1.8) (1.0)	
	PHY > KAS ≈ SP ≈ ELE	28
	(1.6) (1.1) (1.0) (0.9)	
	PHY ≈ ELE > SP > KAS	1
	(1) (0.3–1.2) (0.2–0.6) (0.1–0.4)	
Guinea pig vas deferens	SP ≈ PHY > ELE > KAS	29
Guinea pig bladder	PHY ≈ SP ≈ ELE ≈ KAS	29
Rat bladder	PHY > SP ≈ ELE ≈ KAS	29
Guinea pig trachea	KAS > ELE > PHY ≈ SP	27
Rat colon	ELE ≈ KAS > PHY > SP	1, 9
Rat duodenum	ELE ≈ KAS > PHY > SP	1, 29
Hamster, mouse, dog, monkey and human urinary bladder	ELE ≈ KAS > PHY > SP	1, 29
Rat vas deferens	ELE > PHY	1
	KAS > ELE > SP ≈ PHY	28, 29
Frog spinal motorneurones	ELE > PHY > SP	1
Rat neonatal spinal cord	ELE > PHY > SP	30
Rat antidipsogenic effect	ELE > PHY > SP	1
Pigeon dipsogenic effect	ELE > PHY > SP	1

The recent discoveries of NKA and NKB and the comparisons of their biological profiles with other tachykinins have led to the possibility of not just two but three tachykinin receptor subtypes. In addition to the P and E receptor subtypes mentioned above, Buck *et al.* have suggested a third receptor subtype, SP-K, based on the binding studies using [^{125}I]-Bolton–Hunter-labelled-NKA, -ELE and -SP and crude membrane preparations.[34-36] The regional distribution *via* autoradiography was also studied. The P sites, for which SP is the probable endogenous ligand, were found in the CNS and other peripheral tissues identified earlier. The E sites were found in the rat cortex but not in the rat duodenum, the mouse bladder or in the rat submaxillary gland. The K sites were found throughout the rat gastrointestinal tract and in the guinea pig small and large intestine and the mouse bladder. Further studies on the urinary bladders of hamster, rat and guinea pig showed that the hamster bladder contained large numbers of K sites and very few P sites, the rat bladder contained both P and K sites in nearly equal numbers, and the guinea pig bladder contained almost exclusively P sites.[36] Maggi *et al.* have suggested the existence of P and E sites on the rat bladder and P and K sites on the rat duodenum.[37,38] Osakada *et al.* also reported NKA and NKB to be respectively 400 and 210 times more potent than SP on the rat duodenum. On the rat vas deferens NKA and NKB were respectively 252 and 32 times more potent than SP.[39]

Three receptor subtypes were also suggested by Laufer *et al.* by comparing potencies of various agonists on the guinea pig ileum and hamster and mouse urinary bladders. On the isolated guinea pig ileum muscular receptors (SP-P type) the rank order of potencies was PHY > SP ≈ NKB ≈ KAS > ELE > NKA but on the neuronal receptors the rank order was NKB > ELE > KAS > PHY > NKA ≈ SP. This rank order of potencies on the neuronal receptors was different to that obtained on the hamster and mouse urinary bladders (tissues previously claimed to have SP-E type receptors). NKA and NKB were similar in potency to ELE and about 100 times more potent than SP on the bladder preparations. The above neuronal receptor on which NKB was the most potent tachykinin was termed SP-N by these workers.[40] The SP-N receptor subsites, different from P and E sites, were also shown to be present in the rat brain.[41]

Mizrahi *et al.* have also investigated the effects of SP, PHY, ELE, KAS and NKA on eight *in vitro* tissue preparations and divided these into three groups.[42] On the dog carotid artery and the guinea pig ileum and urinary bladder, PHY and SP were three to six times more potent than the other tachykinins. NKA was the most potent tachykinin on the rabbit mesenteric vein, the rat duodenum and the guinea pig trachea and KAS was more potent than the rest of the tachykinins on the hamster and the dog urinary bladders.

Some of the tissue preparations (mentioned above) in which various tachykinins show minor differences in potency, *e.g.* guinea pig ileum, are poorly selective, but a number of other tissue preparations, *e.g.* rat duodenum, rat vas deferens, hamster urinary bladder, appear to be much more selective, the differences between the least and the most potent tachykinin being 50–400 times. Efforts have recently been made to identify tissue preparations which are much more selective for one of the mammalian tachykinins (SP, NKA or NKB).[43] The receptor subtypes on the dog carotid artery were most sensitive to SP which was four times more potent than NKA and 12 times more potent than NKB on this preparation. The other SP-P/NK-P preparation, the guinea pig ileum, was much less discriminatory. The three SP-E/NK-A preparations, guinea pig trachea, rat duodenum and rabbit pulmonary artery, showed preferences for NKA. On the most sensitive of these preparations, the rabbit pulmonary artery, NKA was about six times more potent than NKB and about 120 times more potent than SP. A fragment of NKA, NKA (4–10)-heptapeptide, was about 250 times more potent than SP on this preparation. The preparation most sensitive to NKB was the rat portal vein on which it was about 17 times more potent than NKA and about 72 times more potent than SP. On the basis of these results Regoli *et al.* have defined the three tachykinin receptor subtypes in the following manner: (i) SP-P/NK-P type on which the rank order of potency was SP > NKA > NKB and the three tachykinins were more potent than any of the fragments; (ii) SP-E/NK-A type where NKA or some of its fragments were at least 10 times more potent than NKB and 100 times more potent than SP; and (iii) NK-B type on which the order of potency was NKB > NKA > SP. The potency of the nonmammalian tachykinin, KAS, was in between NKB and NKA on this receptor subtype.[43]

In addition to the selective tissue preparations, selective agonists for these receptor subtypes have also been reported. One of these, [MePhe^7]-NKB (4–10) (Asp-Phe-Phe-MePhe-Gly-Leu-Met-NH$_2$) was nearly as potent as NKB on the rat portal vein (NK-B type) but was inactive on the rabbit pulmonary artery (NK-A/SP-E type) and only weakly active (1.5% NKB) on the dog carotid artery (SP-P/NK-P type).[44] Two other SP analogues, succinyl-[Asp^6,MePhe^8]-SP(6–11)- and [^{L}Glu^6,MePhe^8]-SP(6–11)-hexapeptide were also selective NKB receptor agonists.[45,46] Both of these were equipotent in stimulating the SP-N receptor type on the guinea pig ileum and the potency ratio (SP-N/SP-P) for the more selective succinyl analogue was 70 000. Conformationally restricted analogues of SP hexapeptide, ^{L}Glu-Phe-X-Gly-Leu-Met-NH$_2$ (X = Phe, Ile or Val) in which the α carbon atom of the Gly residue and the nitrogen atom of the Leu residue were joined together by an ethylene bridge to give a lactam, were selective ELE receptor agonists.[47] These analogues were 500–1500 times more potent as inhibitors of [^{125}I]-Bolton–Hunter-labelled ELE ([^{125}I]-BHELE) than similarly labelled SP for binding to rat brain cortex membranes. The most selective agonists for the SP-P/NK-P type of receptor were [Sar^9,Met(O$_2$)^{11}]-SP and [β-Ala^4,Sar^9,Met(O$_2$)^{11}]-SP(4–11)-octapeptide. Both of these analogues were at least twice as potent as SP on the dog carotid artery. On the rabbit pulmonary artery and the rat portal vein the undecapeptide analogue was inactive and the octapeptide analogue was very weakly active (0.1% SP).[48]

In summary, all of the above information, based on naturally occurring tachykinins and more selective synthetic analogues, suggests at least three receptor subtypes. These have been termed as follows (suggested natural ligands in brackets): SP-P (SP), SP-K (NKA) and SP-E (NKB) by Buck *et al.*,[34] SP-P (SP, NKB), SP-E (NKA, NKB) and SP-N (NKB) by Laufer *et al.*,[40] and NK-P (SP), NK-A (NKA) and NK-B (NKB) by Regoli *et al.*[43] In the light of all this recent information (summarized in Table 3) it can be seen that most of the *in vitro* tissue preparations contain more than one receptor subtype. Only a few, *e.g.* dog carotid artery, rabbit pulmonary artery, rat and rabbit vas deferens, human urinary bladder and rat portal vein, contain predominantly one receptor subtype. Of these the dog carotid artery, rabbit pulmonary artery and the rat portal vein were suggested to contain homogeneous receptor populations of NK-P, NK-A and NK-B subtypes, respectively.[49,52]

13.9.4.2 Classification Based on Substance P and Fragments

Piercey *et al.* studied the effects of the C- and N-terminal fragments of SP in a number of *in vitro* (guinea pig ileum and single cat dorsal horn neurones) and *in vivo* (salivation in rats and scratching in mice) test systems.[53,54] The C-terminal fragments as small as the heptapeptide were equipotent to SP as agonists in all the tests. The N-terminal fragments, SP(1–10)-NH$_2$, SP(1–9)-NH$_2$ and SP(1–8)-NH$_2$, were inactive on the guinea pig ileum but were weak agonists in the rat salivation and the CNS tests. On this basis the receptors were subdivided into those present in the guinea pig ileum and the rat colon (SP$_1$, insensitive to the N-terminal fragments) and those present in the mouse spinal cord and the rat salivary gland (SP$_2$, sensitive to N-terminal fragments). Confirmation of these two receptor subtypes was also obtained by studying the effects of [D-Pro^9]-SP(6–11)- and [L-Pro^9]-SP(6–11)-hexapeptide in some of the above tests. The D-Pro analogue was five times more potent than the L-Pro analogue on the guinea pig ileum. On the rat colon the D-Pro hexapeptide was

Table 3 Receptor Subtypes in Various Tissue Preparations Identified by Using Potent/Selective Agonists

Tissue	Receptor subtype	Potent/selective agonist	Ref.
Dog carotid artery	NK-P	SP > NKA > NKB	43
	NK-P	$[Sar^9,Met(O_2)^{11}]$-SP ≈ $[\beta\text{-}Ala^4,Sar^9,Met(O_2)^{11}]$-SP(4–11) > SP > $[^LGlu^6,Pro^9]$-SP(6–11) > NKA > NKB	48, 49
Dog urinary bladder	NK-P, NK-A	NKA(4–10) ≈ NKB > NKA > SP ≈ $[Sar^9,Met(O_2)^{11}]$-SP > $[MePhe^7]$-NKB	49
Guinea pig ileum	SP-P	SP ≈ PHY ≈ ELE	30
	SP-P, SP-E	SP > NKB > NKA	39
	NK-P, NK-A, NK-B	$[Sar^9,Met(O_2)^{11}]$-SP ≈ $[Succ\text{-}Asp^6,MePhe^8]$-SP(6–11) > SP ≈ $[MePhe^7]$-NKB > NKB > NKA	49
Guinea pig ileum (atropine, indomethacin and diphenhydramine treated)	NK-P, NK-A	$[^LGlu^6,Pro^9]$-SP(6–11) > $[Sar^9,Met(O_2)^{11}]$-SP ≈ SP ≈ SP-OMe > NKB ≈ NKA	49
Guinea pig ileum (muscular receptors)	SP-P	PHY > SP ≈ NKB ≈ KAS > ELE > NKA	40
	SP-P	$[^LGlu^6,Pro^9]$-SP(6–11) ≈ SP ≈ NKB > $[Succ\text{-}Asp^6,MePhe^8]$-SP(6–11)	45
Guinea pig ileum (neuronal receptors)	SP-N	NKB > ELE > KAS > PHY > NKA ≈ SP	40
	SP-N	$[^LGlu^6,MePhe^8]$-SP(6–11) ≈ $[Succ\text{-}Asp^6,MePhe^8]$-SP(6–11) ≈ NKB > SP > $[^LGlu^6,Pro^9]$-SP(6–11)	45
Guinea pig urinary bladder	SP-P	SP > NKA > NKB	36
	SP-P, NKA	$[^LGlu^6,Pro^9]$-SP(6–11) ≈ SP > NKB > NKA > $[MePhe^7]$-NKB ≈ $[Succ\text{-}Asp^6,MePhe^8]$-SP(6–11)	49
Guinea pig trachea	NK-P, NK-A	NKA(4–10) > NKA > $[^LGlu^6,Pro^9]$-SP(6–10) > NKB > SP > $[Succ\text{-}Asp^6,MePhe^8]$-SP(6–11)	49
Guinea pig small intestine	SP-K	NKA > KAS > ELE > NKB > SP > PHY	35
Hamster urinary bladder	SP-E	NKA ≈ NKB ≈ ELE > SP ≈ PHY	40
	SP-K	NKA > KAS > ELE > NKB > SP > PHY	36
	SP-P	SP > NKA > NKB	36
	NK-A, NK-B	NKA(4–10) > NKA > NKB > SP > $[^LGlu^6,Pro^9]$-SP(6–11) > SP-OMe	49

Table 3 *(Contd.)*

Tissue	Receptor subtype	Potent/selective agonist	Ref.
Human urinary bladder	NK-A	NKA > NKB > [Sar^9,Met(O$_2$)^{11}]-SP	49
Mouse urinary bladder	SP-E	NKA ≈ NKB ≈ ELE > SP ≈ PHY	40
Pig isolated carotid artery	NK-P	SP ≈ PHY > ELE > KAS > NKA > NKB	33
Rabbit mesenteric vein	NK-P, NK-A	[Sar^9,Met(O$_2$)^{11}]-SP > NKA > [Glu^6,Pro^9]-SP(6–11) > SP > NKB > [MePhe^7]-NKB(4–10) ≈ [Succ-Asp^6,MePhe^8]-SP(6–11)	49
Rabbit pulmonary artery	NK-A	NKA(4–10) > NKA > KAS > NKB > SP > [Sar^9,Met(O$_2$)^{11}]-SP	43, 48, 49
Rabbit vas deferens	NK-A	NKA(4–10) ≈ NKA > NKB > SP > [MePhe^7]-NKB(4–10) > [Sar^9,Met(O$_2$)^{11}]-SP	49
Rat duodenum	SP-K	NKA > KAS > ELE > NKB > SP > PHY	35
	SP-P	KAS ≈ NKA ≈ SP	38
	NK-A	NKA > NKB > SP	39
	NK-P, NK-A, NK-B	[MePhe^7]-NKB > NKA > NKB > [Sar^9,Met(O$_2$)^{11}]-SP > SP > [Glu^6,Pro^9]-SP(6–11)	49
Rat portal vein	NK-B	NKB > NKA > SP	50
	NK-B	[MePhe^7]-NKB > NKB > [Succ-Asp^6,MePhe^8]-SP(6–11) > KAS > NKA > SP > [Sar^9,Met(O$_2$)^{11}]-SP	43, 44 48, 49
Rat urinary bladder	NK-P, NK-A	[Sar^9,Met(O$_2$)^{11}]-SP > NKA > SP > NKB > [MePhe^7]-NKB	49
Rat vas deferens	NK-A	NKA > NKB > SP	39
Rat vas deferens (prostatic part)	NK-A	NKA(4–10) ≈ KAS > NKA ≈ ELE > NKB ≈ SP ≈ PHY	49, 51
Rat vas deferens (epididymal part)	NK-A	NKA(4–10) > NKA ≈ KAS > NKA ≈ ELE > NKB ≈ SP ≈ PHY ≈ [MePhe^7]-NKB(4–10)	49, 51

equipotent to SP whereas the L-Pro analogue was inactive. An opposite effect was seen in the rat salivation and the mouse scratching assays. The L-Pro analogue and SP were equipotent but the D-Pro analogue was inactive.

The existence of multiple receptor subtypes on the guinea pig ileum, rat ileum, cow pupillary sphincter and the guinea pig urinary bladder was also suggested by Teichberg *et al.*[55] SP and the C-terminal hepta- and octa-peptides were equipotent in the guinea pig ileum but in the rat ileum SP and the octapeptide were more potent than the C-terminal heptapeptide. In contrast, on the cow pupillary sphincter and the guinea pig urinary bladder, SP was markedly less potent than the C-terminal octa-, hepta- and hexa-peptides.[55]

13.9.4.3 Classification Based on Substance P Antagonists

The existence of multiple tachykinin receptors, using various weak antagonists, was initially suggested by a number of investigators on the basis of (i) potency differences and (ii) agonist or antagonist profiles of the analogues in various tissue preparations. One of the first antagonists to be discovered, [D-Pro^2,D-Phe^7,D-Trp^9]-SP, was a weak antagonist of SP on the guinea pig ileum smooth muscle receptor but was an agonist on the guinea pig ileum (*via* neuronal receptors), the rabbit external jugular vein and the rat superior cervical ganglion cells. This agonist response, mediated *via* release of acetylcholine, suggested that the smooth muscle receptors may be different to those of neuronal receptors.[56] The above antagonist and [D-Trp^{7,9}]-SP were also partial agonists on the rat colon.[57] Four other similar analogues, [D-Pro^2,D-Phe^7,D-Trp^9]-SP, [D-Pro^2,D-Trp^{7,9}]-SP, [D-Arg^1,D-Pro^2,D-Phe^7,D-Trp^9]-SP and [D-Arg^1,D-Pro^2,DTrp^{7,9}]-SP, were weak antagonists of SP in the guinea pig ileum (pA_2 4.6–5.4) and the most potent of these, [D-Pro^2,D-Trp^{7,9}]-SP, antagonized SP, PHY and ELE on the ileum and also inhibited SP- and PHY-stimulated salivary secretion in the rat, but none of these analogues blocked the blood pressure lowering effects of SP.[58] [D-Arg^1,D-Pro^2,D-Trp^{7,9},Leu^{11}]-SP antagonized SP and ELE in the guinea pig ileum, bladder and vas deferens (SP-P type) and the rat duodenum and vas deferens (SP-E type), but failed to antagonize either SP or ELE in the hamster bladder.[59] A number of other SP antagonists showed selectivity between the guinea pig ileum and the rat spinal cord preparations.[60,61] Some of these, *e.g.* [N^α-Z-Arg^1,N^ε-Z-Lys^3,D-Trp^{7,9},D-Met^{11}]-SP-OMe, [D-Trp^{7,8,9}]-SP-OMe and [D-Pro^2,D-Trp^{7,9}]-SP, antagonized SP and SP(6–11)-hexapeptide in the guinea pig ileum but only antagonized the hexapeptide in the rat spinal cord preparation. In contrast, some other antagonists, *e.g.* [D-Phe^{7,8},D-Met^{11}]-SP-OMe, [N^α-Z-Arg^1,N^ε-Z-Lys^3,D-Pro^{9,10}]-SP-OMe and [D-Pro^2,Asn^5,Lys^6, D-Phe^7,D-Trp^9]-SP-OMe were inactive on the guinea pig ileum but still antagonized the hexa-peptide on the rat spinal cord. On the guinea pig ileum alone some compounds, *e.g.* [N^α-Z-Arg^1, N^ε-Z-Lys^3,D-Trp^{7,8},D-Met^{11}]-SP-OMe, were more potent against the hexapeptide than SP, whereas some other antagonists, *e.g.* [N^α-Z-Arg^1,D-Pro^2,N^ε-Z-Lys^3,Asn^5,Arg^6,D-Phe^7,D-Trp^9]-SP-OMe and the corresponding amide, were more potent against SP than the hexapeptide.[60,61]

Some other work using undecapeptide and octapeptide antagonists has also indicated the existence of three receptor subtypes. [D-Arg^1,D-Pro^2,D-Trp^{7,9},Leu^{11}]-SP and [D-Pro^4,D-Trp^{7,9,10}]-SP(4–11)-octapeptide antagonized SP, PHY, ELE and KAS in a range of smooth muscle preparations (guinea pig ileum, rat colon and duodenum *etc.*). Both of the antagonists were nearly equipotent on all of these tissue preparations (pA_2 5.8–6.2) but on the guinea pig bladder the octapeptide was inactive, whereas the potency of the undecapeptide antagonist was comparable to its potency on the other tissue preparations.[62] Against SP and NKA the undecapeptide antagonist was equipotent on the guinea pig ileum and field-stimulated rat vas deferens (suggesting a single population of receptors) but it was significantly more potent against NKA than SP on the guinea pig urinary bladder (two receptor subtypes). On the hamster urinary bladder the undecapeptide antagonist did not change the response to NKA (third receptor subtype).[63] The coexistence of three receptor subtypes on the rabbit iris sphincter smooth muscle, using the above antagonist, was indicated by Hosoki *et al.*[64]

As in the case of agonists (mentioned above), efforts to find more selective antagonists for various receptors subtypes have continued.[65-67] Some of the initial octapeptide antagonists, *e.g.* [D-Pro^4, D-Trp^{7,9}]-SP(4–11)- and [D-Pro^4,D-Trp^{7,9,10}]-SP(4–11)-octapeptide, were potent antagonists of SP on the SP-P (dog common carotid artery and guinea pig ileum) and SP-E receptor subtypes, but were much weaker antagonists of SP on the rabbit mesenteric vein.[65,66] When position 11 of these antagonists was also modified, the resulting compounds [D-Pro^4,D-Trp^{7,9},X^{11}]-SP(4–11)- and [D-Pro^4,D-Trp^{7,9,10},X^{11}]-SP(4–11)-octapeptide (X = Met, Leu, Nle, Nva or Phe) were also potent antagonists of SP on the guinea pig ileum, guinea pig trachea and the dog common carotid artery but the analogues without the D-Trp^{10} residue were more potent than the D-Trp^{10} analogues on the rabbit mesenteric vein. In the D-Trp^{10} series of analogues, [D-Pro^4,D-Trp^{7,9,10},Nle^{11}]-SP(4–11)- and [D-Pro^4,D-Trp^{7,9,10},Phe^{11}]-SP(4–11)-octapeptide were more selective than the other analogues. The Nle^{11} analogue was more potent than the Phe^{11} analogue in the guinea pig ileum and the dog carotid artery (SP-P type) but was less potent than the Phe^{11} analogue in the guinea pig trachea (SP-E type).[65,66] The Phe^{11} analogue was only a weak antagonist of SP in the rat duodenum and had no effect against SP on the hamster bladder. In contrast, a closely related analogue, [D-Pro^4,Lys^6,D-Trp^{7,9,10},Phe^{11}]-SP(4–11)-octapeptide, was a full agonist on the dog carotid artery, was a weaker antagonist than [D-Pro^4,D-Trp^{7,9,10},Phe^{11}]-SP(4–11)-octapeptide on the guinea pig ileum and the guinea pig trachea, but was also an antagonist of SP, KAS and NKA on the hamster urinary bladder. The most potent antagonist of these three tachykinins on the hamster and dog urinary bladders was [D-Tyr^4,D-Trp^{7,9},Nle^{11}]-SP(4–11)-octapeptide.[40]

Some of these more selective antagonists, [D-Pro^4,D-Trp^{7,9,10},Phe^{11}]-SP(4–11)-, [D-Tyr^4, D-Trp^{7,9},Nle^{11}]-SP(4–11)- and [D-Pro^4,Lys^6,D-Trp^{7,9,10},Phe^{11}]-SP(4–11)-octapeptide, were also studied against SP, NKA, and NKB on the dog carotid artery (SP-P/NK-P type), rabbit pulmonary artery (SP-E/NK-A type) and the rat portal vein (NK-B/SP-K type).[43] Except for the Lys^6 analogue which was a full agonist on the dog carotid artery, the two other compounds were potent antagonists of SP (pA_2 6.7–7.0) on this tissue preparation. Against NKA on the rabbit pulmonary vein the three antagonists were somewhat weaker (pA_2 5.2–6.2) but all of these were even less potent against NKB on the rat portal vein.

13.9.5 CONFORMATIONS AND CONFORMATIONALLY RESTRICTED ANALOGUES OF TACHYKININS

Conformation studies using conformational energy calculations on SP and its fragments have pointed to a number of low energy conformers.[69–72] These differ not only in the peptide backbone conformations but also in the positions of the various amino acid side chains. The lowest energy structure (-76.4 kcal mol^{-1}; 1 kcal = 4.18 kJ), obtained by Manavalan and Momany, appears to be stabilized by hydrogen bonding between the amide group of the Gln^6 side chain and the carbonyl oxygen of Met^{11}. The side chains of Pro^2, Lys^3 and Gln^5 were on one side of the molecule and of Arg^1 and Pro^4 were on the other side. Because of a bend in the C-terminal region the Phe^7 and Leu^{10} residues were near to each other.[68] In another low energy conformer (-70 kcal mol^{-1}) the N-terminal residues (Arg^1 to Phe^8) had an almost extended structure but the residues between Phe^8 and Met^{11} were part of a bend. In this structure the C-terminal amide group was hydrogen bonded to the carbonyl oxygens of Phe^7 and Phe^8 residues.[68] Extended structures for the N-terminal tetrapeptide, Arg-Pro-Lys-Pro, were also suggested to be the most stable conformations on the basis of semiempirical calculations on a model peptide, Ac-Arg-Pro-Lys-Pro-NHMe. These studies also pointed to the existence of Arg and Lys side chains in opposite directions.[69] Nikiforovich *et al.* suggested the presence of an approximately 90° bend in the peptide backbone in the vicinity of Phe^7 and a less marked bend near Leu^{10}. The side chains of Gln^6 and Met^{11} were closely spaced in this structure.[71] Cotrait and Hospital have suggested that the C-terminal 5–11 residues of SP, PHY and ELE exist as helical structures.[72]

The conformations of various tachykinins in solution (water, methanol and dimethyl sulfoxide) have been studied by NMR and circular dichroism (CD) techniques.[73–75] Although CD spectra of SP and its C-terminal fragments did not show any evidence for ordered structures in aqueous solutions,[73] there was evidence for preferred conformations in various other solvents. In dimethyl sulfoxide and pyridine, SP adopted an extended structure. In methanol, the N-terminal tripeptide region, Arg-Pro-Lys, was flexible, but the middle part of SP, -Pro-Gln-Gln-Phe-Phe-, showed evidence for an α-helical conformation.[74] The C-terminal amide was hydrogen bonded to the side chain amide groups of Gln^5 and Gln^6. The NMR evidence in water did point to the existence of a few hydrogen bonds but no clear conclusions could be drawn. When sodium dodecyl sulfate, lysophosphatidylglycerol or lysophosphatidylcholine were added to the aqueous solution the conformations similar to those mentioned above in methanol were observed.[74,75]

NMR studies (350, 500 MHz) on PHY in dimethyl sulfoxide and methanol have suggested the existence of preferred conformations.[76,77] The middle region of PHY, -Pro-Asn-Lys-Phe-Tyr-, was folded into a helical conformation and in this aspect the PHY conformation was similar to that proposed above for SP in methanol. In addition, a salt bridge between the Asp^3 and Lys^6 side chains of the N-terminal region of the peptide (⁻Glu-Ala-Asp-Pro-Asn-Lys-) was also observed which helped to stabilize the helical conformation.[77] Because of the differences in the N-terminal region, such a salt bridge was not possible in SP. In comparison to the N-terminal tripeptide of SP, which was flexible, the N-terminal tripeptide of PHY existed in an extended conformation.[77]

The existence of an intramolecular salt bridge in the N-terminal region of NKA (His-Lys-Thr-Asp-Ser-Phe-Val-Gly-Leu-Met-NH$_2$) was also indicated by NMR studies in water, methanol and dimethyl sulfoxide.[78] This salt bridge between the side chain of His^1 or Lys^2 and Asp^4 was present in all the three solvents. Unlike SP and PHY the middle region of NKA was not helical but appeared to exist as a β-pleated sheet structure.[78]

Conformationally restricted analogues of SP have been made in the hope of improving the potency, selectivity and duration of action. The conformational freedom of the analogues has been restricted either by incorporating N-methyl amino acid residues or by making cyclic analogues. A few hexapeptide analogues with a five-membered lactam ring between positions 9 and 10 have also been synthesized. A number of cyclic hexa- or hepta-peptides incorporating a disulfide bridge between residues 5 and 6, 5 and 11, and 6 and 11 were nearly inactive.[79,80] Only one such analogue, [Cys^5,Cys^6]-SP(5–11)-heptapeptide, was somewhat more potent (4.5% SP) on the guinea pig ileum.[80] Two cyclic analogues in which amino acid side chains in the N-terminal region were linked by an amide bond, Boc-Lys-Phe-Ile-Glu-Phe-Phe-Gly-Leu-Met-NH$_2$ and Boc-Lys-Phe-Ile-Glu-Gln-Phe-Phe-Gly-Leu-Met-NH$_2$, had respectively 25 and 110% of the potency of SP on the guinea pig ileum.[81] Since these more potent analogues were not tested on other tissue preparations, their selectivity for various receptor subtypes remains unknown. Another cyclic analogue with a disulfide bridge (instead of an amide bond) in the N-terminal region of SP, [Cys^3,Cys^6,Tyr^8]-SP, was equipotent to SP on the ileum.[82] In a rat brain synaptosome binding assay the cyclic peptide inhibited the binding of [^{125}I]-BHSP (1.5 times SP) and [^{3}H]-NKB (32 times SP). A similar analogue of NKB, [Cys^2,Cys^5]-NKB, was also equipotent to NKB and SP on the ileum, but in the binding assay it was much more selective. It inhibited the binding of [^{3}H]-NKB (70% NKB) but was very poor in inhibiting the binding of [^{125}I]-BHSP (0.02% SP).[82]

In terms of receptor selectivity the N-methyl amino acid substitutions have given more promising results. Most of these substitutions have been attempted in the partial sequences of SP,[28,45] NKA[83] and NKB.[44] In a series of heptapeptide analogues, [^{L}Glu^5]-SP(5–11) and [^{L}Glu^5,Sar^9]-SP(5–11) were nearly equipotent on the guinea pig ileum and in a rat brain membrane-binding assay. When the Sar^9 change was combined with MePhe^8 replacement the resulting analogue, [^{L}Glu^5, MePhe^8,Sar^9]-SP(5–11), in comparison to [^{L}Glu^5]-SP(5–11), was 50% as potent as in the receptor-binding assay and about 30 times less potent on the guinea pig ileum.[28]

In a series of hexapeptide analogues, [^{L}Glu^6]-SP(6–11), [^{L}Glu^6,Sar^9]-SP(6–11) and [^{L}Glu^6,MeLeu^{10}]-SP(6–11) were nearly equipotent as agonists on the guinea pig ileum muscular (SP-P) and neuronal (SP-N) receptors. Although the presence of an N-methylglycine (Sar) residue in position 9 did not have much effect on selectivity, when proline was substituted in this position the resulting analogue, [^{L}Glu^6,Pro^9]-SP(6–11) (Septide), was as potent as [^{L}Glu^6]-SP(6–11) on the muscular receptors and about 100 times less potent on the neuronal receptors. The N-methylation of Phe^7 also gave a SP-P selective analogue but [^{L}Glu^6,MePhe^7]-SP(6–11) was a much weaker agonist (∼5% as potent as the parent peptide). A much more selective analogue was obtained by the N-methylation of the Phe^8 residue. Compared to [^{L}Glu^6]-SP(6–11), the MePhe^8 analogue [^{L}Glu^6,MePhe^8]-SP(6–11)-hexapeptide, was about 100 times less potent on the muscular receptors but was about 10 times more potent on the neuronal receptors.[45]

N-Methylations in NKB(4–10)-heptapeptide (Asp-Phe-Phe-Val-Gly-Leu-Met-NH$_2$) also resulted in changes in potency and selectivity.[44] [Sar^8]-NKB(4–10) was about four times more potent than NKB(4–10) on the dog carotid artery (SP-P type) but was about 16 times less potent than the parent peptide on the rabbit pulmonary artery (NK-A type). The difference on the rat portal vein (NK-B type) was only twofold. In contrast, [MePhe^7]-NKB(4–10) was about 10 times more potent than NKB(4–10) on the rat portal vein but only about 2.5% as potent as the parent peptide on the dog carotid artery. It was inactive on the rabbit pulmonary artery.[44]

N-Methyl analogues of NKA(4–10)-heptapeptide also displayed some selectivity on various tissue preparations. [MeSer^5]-NKA(4–10) and [Sar^8]-NKA(4–10) were about five times less potent than NKA(4–10) on the rat vas deferens (NK-A type) but were nearly equipotent to the parent peptide on the guinea pig ileum and the rat portal vein preparations. The most selective analogue of the series, [MeVal^7]-NKA(4–10),was about 12–13 times more potent than NKA(4–10) on the guinea pig ileum but two times and 12 times less potent than NKA(4–10) on the rat portal vein (NK-B) and the rat vas deferens (NK-A) preparations, respectively. [MePhe^6]-NKA(4–10) was less potent than NKA(4–10) in the three tissue preparations.[83]

Four analogues of SP(6–11)-hexapeptide containing a lactam residue between positions 9 and 10 were synthesized and three of these were shown to be selective agonists for SP-E receptor types.[47]

Three of the analogues, ⌐Glu-Phe-X-Gly[ANC-2]Leu-Met-NH$_2$ (ANC-2 describes a 2-carbon bridge between the α carbon of the glycine residue and the α nitrogen of the leucine residue), with X = Phe, Ile or Val in position 8 and an *R* configuration at the lactam α carbon, displaced [^{125}I]-BHELE from rat brain cortex membranes as effectively as ELE. The analogues were more than 2000 times less effective than SP in displacing [^{125}I]-BHSP from the same membranes. These three analogues were also potent agonists on the guinea pig ileum and the rat vas deferens but were at least 500 times less potent than SP in stimulating salivation in rats. The fourth analogue (X = Phe and with an *S* configuration at the lactam α carbon), was inactive in all the above tests.[47]

13.9.6   STRUCTURE–ACTIVITY RELATIONSHIPS OF TACHYKININ AGONISTS

Most of the structure–activity relationship (SAR) data discussed below are based on SP analogues. Only a limited number of analogues of the two other mammalian tachykinins, NKA and NKB, have so far been reported. These SAR data have also been included. A large majority of the tachykinin analogues were only tested on the guinea pig ileum, therefore the ileum results form a major part of the SAR discussions. The available results in other *in vivo* and *in vitro* test systems have been included only when relevant.

13.9.6.1   SAR of Tachykinin Fragments

Even before the discovery of the mammalian tachykinins, it had been established that the C-terminal fragments of PHY and ELE show full agonist activity. Just like these nonmammalian tachykinins, the C-terminal fragments of SP, NKA and NKB have also proved to be full agonists. Some of these have also been useful in the receptor classification studies.

Although there is some dispute about the relative potencies of the C-terminal (5–11)-hepta- and the (4–11)-octa-peptides of SP, both of these appear to be slightly more potent (1.2 to four times) than SP. The C-terminal (6–11)-hexa- and (3–11)-nona-peptides are equipotent to SP, but the other smaller peptides are much less potent.[6]

A more detailed investigation of the C-terminal hexa-, hepta- and octa-peptides on tissue preparations more selective for SP-P, NK-A or NK-B receptor types indicated significant potency differences.[27,42-44] On the guinea pig ileum SP and the C-terminal hexa- and hepta-peptides were nearly equipotent but the octapeptide was 2.4 times more potent. On another SP-P preparation (dog carotid artery) SP was respectively two, five and 25 times more potent than the C-terminal octa-, hepta- and hexa-peptides. On two of the SP-E/NK-A tissue preparations (guinea pig trachea and rat duodenum) the hexapeptide was two to five times more potent than SP, while on the third SP-E preparation (rabbit pulmonary artery) the heptapeptide was the most active fragment. On one of the NK-B receptor preparations (dog urinary bladder) the fragments were two to 10 times less potent than SP but on the other NK-B preparation (rat portal vein) the hexapeptide was about three times more potent than SP.[43]

NKA and NKA(2–10)-nonapeptide were nearly equipotent on the above SP-P preparations (five times less potent than SP) but the C-terminal octa-, hepta- and hexa-peptides were less potent. In contrast, on each of the SP-E/NK-A and NK-B preparations one of the fragments of NKA was always more potent than NKA. The NKA(4–10)-heptapeptide was the most active fragment on the guinea pig trachea and the rat portal vein (two times NKA, 75–250 times SP), while NKA(2–10)-nonapeptide was the most potent fragment on the rat duodenum (two times NKA, 20 times SP). The NKA(4–10)-heptapeptide and the NKA(2–10)-nonapeptide were also respectively the most potent fragments on the two NKB receptor preparations, the dog urinary bladder (two times NKA, 20 times SP) and the rat portal vein (six times NKA, 26 times SP).

The C-terminal hexa-, hepta- and octa-peptide fragments of NKB were less potent than NKB on all the above tissue preparations except the rat portal vein where the NKB(3–10)-octapeptide was two times more potent than NKB and about 66 times more potent than SP.[43]

13.9.6.2   SAR of Tachykinins—Effects of Amino Acid Substitutions

Starting from the C terminal amide group the changes in each amino acid position of various tachykinins are discussed below. Unless mentioned otherwise, all the biological results are those obtained on the guinea pig ileum.

The C-terminal amide group of SP appears to be important for the biological activity. The analogues with a free carboxyl group, a methyl ester or a substituted amide or hydrazide group at the C terminus, *e.g.* —NHMe, —NMe$_2$, —NHNH$_2$ or —NHNMe$_2$, were much less potent.[60,84] SP methyl ester had only 16% of the potency of SP on the guinea pig ileum, but on the rat spinal cord preparation the two compounds were equipotent.[60] The loss of the methionine residue from position 11 resulted in an inactive compound ($<0.03\%$ SP),[85] but its replacement with Ala or Leu residues led only to about a fivefold reduction in potency.[85,86] Some other analogues with L amino acid residues in position 11, [Eth^{11}]-SP (Eth = 2-amino-4-(ethylthio)butyric acid) and [Nle^{11}]-SP, were nearly as potent as SP, but [D-Met^{11}]-SP was much less potent (3% SP).[87–89] Oxidation of the methionine residue gave compounds which were slightly more potent than SP on the dog carotid artery (SP-P/NK-P type) but were much less potent on the rabbit pulmonary artery (NK-A type).[48] On guinea pig ileum as well [Met(O)^{11}]-SP was only half as potent as SP.[89] [Met(O)^{11}]-SP was more selective than [Met(O$_2$)^{11}]-SP. In the SP(5–11)-heptapeptide series, the replacement of Met^{11} by Arg, Nle, Hse(OMe), Ser(Et), Cys(Et), Cys(Bzl) and Cys(Me) led to much less potent compounds ($<5\%$ SP).[90,91] The replacement of Leu^{10} by an alanine residue resulted in a 50% reduction in potency.[86] The Gly residue in position 9 could be replaced by a β-Ala, Pro, Met or a sarcosine residue without any loss in potency.[48,86,92] [D-Ala^9]-SP was about 10 times less potent than SP, but other analogues with more bulky D amino acid residues in position 9, *e.g.* [D-Phe^9]-SP and [D-Leu^9]-SP, were much less potent (0.5 to 2.7% SP).[88,93,94] [Pro^9]-SP and [Sar^9]-SP were respectively 1.5 and 2.4 times more potent than SP on the dog carotid artery but on the rabbit pulmonary artery the Pro^9 analogue was four times less potent than SP. The Sar^9 analogue was nearly inactive (0.1% SP) on the latter tissue preparation. On the rat portal vein the Sar^9 analogue was as potent as SP but the Pro^9 analogue was inactive. When Sar^9 and Pro^9 changes were combined with Met(O$_2$)^{11} substitution, the resulting analogues, [Sar^9,Met(O$_2$)^{11}]-SP, [Pro^9,Met(O$_2$)^{11}]-SP and [β-Ala^4,Sar^9,Met(O$_2$)^{11}]-SP(4–11)-octapeptide, were about 1.6 to 2.8 times more potent than SP on the dog carotid artery, but were inactive on the rabbit pulmonary artery and the rat portal vein.[48]

The two Phe residues in positions 7 and 8 were quite different to each other in their response to amino acid substitutions. [Phe(*p*-F)^7]-SP, [Phe(*p*-F)^8]-SP, [Phe(*p*-F)^{7,8}]-SP, [Tyr^7]-SP and [Tyr^8]-SP were nearly equipotent to SP[88,92,95] (Kitagawa *et al.* have reported [Tyr^8]-SP to be 1.73 times more potent than SP),[96] but all other replacements in position 7 led to a greater loss in potency than in position 8.

[Ala^8]-SP (22.3% SP) was 100 times more potent than [Ala^7]-SP (0.23% SP),[86][Ile^8]-SP (180% SP)[93] was 1200 times more potent than [Ile^7]-SP (0.15% SP),[85] and similarly [Met^8]-SP, [Leu^8]-SP, [Tyr(Me)^8]-SP and [Cha^8]-SP were respectively 50, 30, three and five times more potent than the corresponding position 7 analogues.[87]

In the Nle^{11} series of analogues, [Phe(*p*-NO$_2$)^8,Nle^{11}]-SP was about 10 times more potent than [Phe(*p*-NO$_2$)^7,Nle^{11}]-SP, but [Phe(*p*-NH$_2$)^8,Nle^{11}]-SP, [Phe(*p*-N$_3$)^8,Nle^{11}]-SP, [Phe(*p*-NH$_2$)^7,Nle^{11}]-SP and [Phe(*p*-N$_3$)^7,Nle^{11}]-SP were almost equipotent (25–35% SP).[97] In the SP(6–11)-hexapeptide series of analogues, Phe(*p*-NO$_2$)^8, Phe(*p*-Cl)^8 and Phe(*p*-NH$_2$)^8 analogues were of very similar potency (60–100% SP-hexapeptide) and were only slightly more potent than the corresponding position 7 modified analogues. All six of these hexapeptides showed comparable activities on the rat spinal cord preparation but in sialogogic assay in rats, [Phe(*p*-NH$_2$)^7]-SP(6–11)- and [Phe(*p*-NH$_2$)^8]-SP(6–11)-hexapeptide were inactive, whereas the other four analogues were potent sialogogic agents (44–100% SP-hexapeptide).[98]

The amino acid residues in the N-terminal hexapeptide of SP can be replaced by a number of other residues with retention of biological activity. [Met^5]- and [Met^6]-SP were equipotent to SP.[89] When the two glutamine residues in positions 5 and 6 were replaced individually or together with homoglutamine, the resulting analogues, [Hgn^5]-, [Hgn^6]- and [Hgn^{5,6}]-SP, were reported to be more potent than SP. The most potent of these analogues, [Hgn^{5,6}]-SP, was 3.4 times more potent than SP on the ileum and two times more potent than SP on the guinea pig trachea. The C-terminal octapeptides containing homoglutamine residues in positions 5 and 6 were also more potent than SP. [Hgn^5]-SP(4–11)-octapeptide was respectively 3.4 and 4.4 times more potent than SP on the ileum and the guinea pig trachea.[99] The undecapeptide and octapeptide analogues of SP containing D-homoglutamine in positions 5 and 6 were much less potent than SP on the guinea pig ileum and trachea.[100] A number of other heptapeptide analogues containing an L- or D-homoglutamine residue in position 6 and an L- or D-pyrohomoglutamic acid residue at the N terminus also showed agonist activity.[100–102] The most potent of these on the ileum (2.6 times SP), [D-Hgu^5,Hgn^6]-SP(5–11)-heptapeptide, was about 10 times less potent on the trachea. One of the octapeptides, [D-Hgn^{5,6}]-SP(4–11), was a very weak agonist ($<0.04\%$ SP) but was claimed to be an antagonist.[100] Some antagonist activity was also reported in [N^5-dimethyl-Gln^5]-SP(5–11)-heptapeptide but this compound and another similar analogue, [N^5-dimethyl-Gln^6]-SP(5–11)-heptapeptide, also showed good agonist activity (25–37% SP).[103,104] The elimination of the side chain carboxamide group, by replacing Gln^6 in the hexapeptide series of analogues with Val, Thr, Thr(OMe) or Orn, did not have much effect on the potency of these analogues on the rat colon muscularis mucosae, but the agonist activity on the ileum was reduced (five to 10 times). Only [Orn^6]-SP(6–11)-hexapeptide displayed agonist activity comparable to the parent peptide on the ileum and about a fivefold increase in potency on the rat colon preparation.[105] Other replacements of Gln^5 and Gln^6 residues with Gly, 4-aminobutyric acid, 5-aminovaleric acid, 6-aminocaproic acid and D-Val gave moderately potent agonists.[60,91] [Asn^5]-SP was about two times more potent than SP.[96]

The amino acid residues in positions 1 to 4 were also not very sensitive to changes. [D-Arg^1]-, [Lys^1]-, [$^-$Glu^1]- and [de-NH$_2$-Arg^1]-SP were as potent as SP, and the replacement of the two proline residues with D-Pro also gave a moderately active compound.[60,85,89] [Gly^4]-SP was equipotent to SP but [Asp^3]-SP was only 40% as potent as the parent peptide.[89] The replacement of these four amino acid residues with some nonpeptide residues, *e.g.* N^α-[1-(9-hypoxanthyl)-β-D-ribofuranuronosyl], N^α-[1-(9-adenyl)-β-D-ribofuranuronosyl], gave heptapeptide derivatives which were almost 10 times more potent than SP on the guinea pig ileum.[106] SP could also be extended at the N terminus and two such dodecapeptides containing a Lys or a Tyr residue at the N terminus were as potent as SP.[89]

Unlike SP, in NKA (His-Lys-Thr-Asp-Ser-Phe-Val-Gly-Leu-Met-NH$_2$) replacement of the C-terminal Met^{10} with Met(O), Met(O$_2$) and Nle^{10} resulted in less potent analogues.[48] Only [Nle^{10}]-NKA showed some selectivity for the NKA receptor system. It retained good activity on the rabbit pulmonary artery (62% NKA) and rat portal vein (100% NKA) but was about 20 times less potent than NKA on the dog carotid artery. [Ala^{10}]-NKA was only weakly active in the three tissue preparations.[48]

All of the NKB analogues modified in position 10, [Met(O)^{10}]-,[Met(O$_2$)^{10}]-, [Nle^{10}]- and [Ala^{10}]-NKB, were at least 10 times less potent than NKB on the rat portal vein and the rabbit pulmonary artery. On the dog carotid artery only [Nle^{10}]-NKB was as potent as NKB.[48] One of the position 7 modified analogues, [MePhe^7]-NKB, was at least four times more potent than NKB on the rat portal vein but was 150 and 250 times less potent than NKB respectively on the dog carotid artery and the rabbit pulmonary artery.[48] This appears to be one of the most potent and selective analogues for NK-B receptor subtype. As in the case of NKB itself, the replacement of Val^7 with MeVal or MePhe^7 in the NKB(4–10)-octapeptide also led to NKB receptor selective agonists. Both these analogues were nearly equipotent to NKB on the rat portal vein but were much less potent on the dog carotid artery and the rabbit pulmonary artery (1–5% NKB).[48]

The replacement of Phe^6 and Val^7 by Gly residues in the octapeptide led to inactive compounds but the analogues with Asp^4 or Phe^5 replaced with glycine residues retained agonist activity. The more potent of these analogues, [Gly^5]-NKB (3–10)-octapeptide, was respectively two and 1.6 times more potent than NKB on the guinea pig ileum and the rat vas deferens.[107] A number of other NKB(3–10)-octapeptide and NKB(2–10)-nonapeptide analogues, [Arg^3,Sar^6]-NKB(3–10), [Arg^3,D-Phe^6]-NKB(3–10), [Arg^3,D-Phg^6]-NKB(3–10), [Arg^2,D-Arg^6]-NKB(2–10), [Arg^2,D-Pro^6]-NKB(2–10) and [Arg^2,D-Hgu^6]-NKB(2–10), were inactive on the ileum.[108] Two other analogues, [Gly^6]-NKB(3–10)- and [Arg^3,D-Ala^6]-NKB(3–10)-octapeptide were antagonists of NKB on the ileum (pA_2 5.8).[108] The C-terminal heptapeptides of NKA and NKB were less potent than the parent peptides on the guinea pig ileum and the rat duodenum. Further replacements in positions 4 (Asp to Gln) and 7 (Val to Phe) of these heptapeptides led to even less potent analogues.[109]

13.9.6.3 Enzyme Resistant Agonists of Substance P

Like most of the other peptides, SP and its analogues are also rapidly degraded *in vivo*. A number of attempts to identify the most susceptible peptide bonds and also to synthesize more stable analogues have been made and these have recently been summarized.[6]

Early studies using rat brain homogenate indicated that endopeptidases present in the homogenate cleaved peptide bonds between Gln^6-Phe^7 or Phe^7-Phe^8 and Gly^9-Leu^{10} very rapidly. The N-terminal residues were degraded much more slowly.[110] Later work using purified enzymes showed several other cleavage points.[111–114] A membrane-bound neutral metallo-endopeptidase, purified from human brain, cleaved SP between Gln^6-Phe^7, Phe^7-Phe^8 and Phe^8-Gly^9 residues.[111] Two of the cleavage points were similar to those observed with the enzymes present in the rat brain homogenate. Liver dipeptidyl aminopeptidase was shown to cleave SP from the N-terminal end releasing Arg-Pro and Lys-Pro dipeptides.[112,113] A postproline cleaving enzyme from bovine brain was shown to cleave SP between Pro^4-Gln^5 residues, liberating the N-terminal tetrapeptide, Arg-Pro-Lys-Pro, and the C-terminal heptapeptide, Gln-Gln-Phe-Phe-Gly-Leu-Met-NH_2.[114]

Based on the human metallo-endopeptidase cleavage results mentioned above, several N-methyl amino acid residues were incorporated in the C-terminal region of SP to stabilize this peptide. [Sar^9]-SP showed no increase in stability but [$MePhe^8$,Sar^9]-SP and [$^{\llcorner}Glu^5$,$MePhe^8$,Sar^9]-SP(5-11)-heptapeptide were stable to the human enzyme for up to three and five hours, respectively.[92] In the [$^{\llcorner}Glu^6$]-SP(6-11)-hexapeptide series of analogues, $MePhe^7$ replacement alone did not confer metabolic stability to the enzymes present in rat parotid slices, but the [$^{\llcorner}Glu^6$,$MePhe^7$,$MeLeu^{10}$] analogue was much more stable.[112] This analogue also was stable to pepsin, chymotrypsin, papain and thermolysin. Although this N-methyl amino acid substitution approach was successful in preventing enzymic degradation, it did not enhance the potency. All of these stable analogues were about 20 times less potent than SP on the guinea pig ileum. In comparison a glycosylated analogue, [N^{α}-Boc-β-D-Glc-p(Cl → 5)Gln^5]-SP(5-11)-heptapeptide, was much more potent on the ileum (35% SP) and was also stable to the enzymes present in rat hypothalamic slices (20% degradation in 2 h), but it did not bind to the [^{125}I]-BHSP specific binding sites on rat brain synaptosomes.[116]

13.9.7 DISCOVERY AND STRUCTURE–ACTIVITY RELATIONSHIPS OF ANTAGONISTS OF SUBSTANCE P

Although a few analogues containing L-amino acid residues, *e.g.* [N^5-dimethyl-Gln^5]-SP(5-11)-heptapeptide, have been claimed to show a weak antagonist activity,[103] most of the moderately potent antagonists have been obtained by D amino acid substitutions in SP or its C-terminal octapeptide.

13.9.7.1 Undecapeptide Antagonists

[De-NH_2-Arg^1]-SP and some analogues of SP containing one or two D amino acid residues, *e.g.* [D-Phe^7]-, [D-Arg^1]- and [D-Leu^8,D-Phe^9]-SP, were originally claimed to be antagonists of SP,[85,94] but one of these, [D-Phe^7]-SP, was later shown to be an agonist ($\sim$5% SP) and the antagonist activity of this analogue was attributed to a specific desensitization of the tissue to the effect of SP.[117] The agonist activity of [D-Phe^7]-SP was considerably reduced ($\sim$0.005% SP) when more D amino acid residues were introduced into the sequence. Two such analogues, [D-Pro^2,D-$Trp^{7,9}$]-SP and [D-Pro^2,D-Phe(p-Cl)^7,D-Trp^9]-SP, were weak antagonists and were required at 0.1 mM concentration to show any significant antagonism.[118] Further improvement in potency was obtained by modifying positions 1 and 11 in the above analogues. One such analogue, [D-Arg^1,D-Pro^2,D-$Trp^{7,9}$,Leu^{11}]-SP, at a concentration of 0.1 mM, required a 100 times increase in SP concentration to give a 50% maximal response. Other similar analogues with Met, Thr, D-Ala and D-Leu residues in position 11 were much less potent.[119] The D-proline residue in position 2 was not important for the antagonist activity. [D-Arg^1,D-Pro^2,D-$Trp^{7,9}$,Leu^{11}]-SP and [D-Arg^1,D-$Trp^{7,9}$,Leu^{11}]-SP (Spantide) were equiactive on guinea pig taenia coli (pA_2 values 7.1-7.2).[120] The antagonist potency of Spantide was further enhanced by modifications in positions 5, 8 and 11. [D-Arg^1,D-Phe^5,D-$Trp^{7,9}$,Nle^{11}]-SP, [D-Arg^1,D-Phe(Cl_2)^5,D-$Trp^{7,9}$,Nle^{11}]-SP and [D-Arg^1,D-Nal^5,D-$Trp^{7,9}$,Nle^{11}]-SP were considerably more potent than Spantide.[121] The D-Nal^5 analogue, most potent of the series, was about five times more potent than Spantide.

Another approach to undecapeptide antagonists involved modifications either in positions 7, 8 and 9 or in positions 9 and 10 along with some other changes at the C- or N-terminal part of the molecule.[60,61] Two such analogues, [N^{α}-Z-Arg^1,N^{ε}-Z-Lys^3,D-$Trp^{7,8}$,D-Met^{11}]-SP and [N^{α}-Z-Arg^1,N^{ε}-Z-Lys^3,D-$Trp^{7,8}$,D-Met^{11}]-SP-OMe, were potent antagonists of SP (dose ratio 14.6 and 10.5 respectively) and the SP(6-11)-hexapeptide (dose ratio 18 and 90 respectively). Both these analogues were more potent antagonists than [D-Pro^2,D-$Trp^{7,9}$]-SP (dose ratio 5.3 against SP and 4.3 against the hexapeptide).[60] The benzyloxycarbonyl (Z) groups were very important for the antagonist activity. When these groups were removed the resulting analogues, [D-$Trp^{7,8}$,D-Met^{11}]-SP and [D-$Trp^{7,8}$,D-Met^{11}]-SP-OMe, were inactive as antagonists of SP and the hexapeptide on the guinea pig ileum. The benzyloxycarbonyl analogues with D-$Phe^{7,8}$, D-$Val^{7,8}$ or D-$Pro^{7,8}$ in place of D-$Trp^{7,8}$ were inactive. Further replacements in a position 7, 8 and 11 modified analogue, [N^{α}-Z-Arg^1,N^{ε}-Z-Lys^3,D-$Pro^{2,4}$,D-$Phe^{7,8}$,D-Met^{11}]-SP-OMe, by Sar^9, Sar^9-$MeLeu^{10}$, $Gly^9\psi(CH_2S)$-

Leu[10] or Gly[9]ψ(CH$_2$S)D-Leu[10] residues gave potent antagonists of SP and the hexapeptide.[61] Analogues modified in positions 9 and 10, e.g. [N$^\alpha$-Z-Arg[1],N$^\epsilon$-Z-Lys[3],D-Pro[9,10]]-SP-OMe and the corresponding D-Phe[9,10],D-Trp[9,10] or D-Val[9,10] analogues, were inactive on the ileum but some of these were antagonists of SP and the hexapeptide on the rat spinal cord.[61]

13.9.7.2 Heptapeptide and Octapeptide Antagonists

In addition to the undecapeptide antagonists mentioned above, some C-terminal (5–11)-hepta- and (4–11)-octa-peptides have also been shown to antagonize SP.[61,65,120,122–124] In general the SAR pattern in the octapeptide antagonists has been very similar to that of undecapeptide antagonists. Like [D-Pro[2],D-Trp[7,9]]-SP (mentioned above), [D-Pro[4],D-Trp[7,9]]-SP(4–11)-octa-peptide was also a weak antagonist of SP (pA_2 5.65), but the analogue with four D amino acid residues, [D-Pro[4],D-Trp[7,9,10]]-SP(4–11)-octapeptide, was relatively more potent (pA_2 6.3). Further modifications in position 11 gave even more potent antagonists in the D-Trp[7,9] and D-Trp[7,9,10] series of analogues. [D-Pro[4],D-Trp[7,9],Nle[11]]-SP(4–11)-, [D-Pro[4],D-Trp[7,9],Phe[11]]-SP(4–11)-, [D-Pro[4],D-Trp[7,9,10],Nle[11]]-SP(4–11)- and [D-Pro[4],D-Trp[7,9,10],Phe[11]]-SP(4–11)-octapeptide were equipotent as antagonists of SP on the ileum (pA_2 7–7.2), but the corresponding Met[11], Leu[11] and Nva[11] analogues were somewhat less potent. When the D-Trp[7,9] residues in one of the above analogues were replaced by D-naphthylalanine residues, the resulting compound, [D-Pro[4],D-Nal[7,9], Phe[11]]-SP(4–11)-octapeptide, was also a potent antagonist of SP, being equipotent to [D-Pro[4],D-Trp[7,9],Phe[11]]-SP(4–11) on the guinea pig ileum and urinary bladder. On the dog carotid artery, the rat duodenum and the guinea pig trachea the D-Trp[7,9] analogue was more potent than the D-Nal[7,9] analogue but on the hamster urinary bladder the D-Nal[7,9] analogue was more potent.[125]

Only a few weak antagonists based on the NKB sequence have so far been reported. Two octapeptides, [Gly[6]]-NKB(3–10) and [Arg[3],D-Ala[6]]-NKB(3–10), and a decapeptide, [D-Pro[2], D-Trp[6,8], Nle[10]]-NKB, were weak antagonists of NKB (pA_2 5.5–5.8).[108,126] The decapeptide analogue did not antagonise SP and NKA.[126]

13.9.8 BIOLOGICAL PROPERTIES AND POTENTIAL USES OF SUBSTANCE P AGONISTS AND ANTAGONISTS

The neurotransmitter or modulator role of SP has been reviewed in detail in two of the recent reviews.[7,8] This section here deals with some of the recent studies using antagonist analogues of SP.

13.9.8.1 SP Antagonists as Analgesics

Substance P has been shown to be concentrated in the dorsal horn of the spinal cord where a large number of the primary afferent fibres terminate and form synapses.[8,127] It is synthesized in spinal ganglia and transported through the dorsal root to the nerve terminal in the cord. When applied in low concentrations, SP induced depolarization of motoneurones in isolated spinal cord.[127] The depolarizing potency of SP was 1000 to 9000 times higher than that of L-glutamate on the isolated rat spinal cord preparation.

In addition to its presence in the spinal cord, SP-like immunoreactive material has also been shown to be released in response to noxious stimuli at central and peripheral ends of the primary afferents.[128,129] This release was inhibited by opiates.[128–131] Morphine inhibited the release of immunoreactive SP-like material (evoked by electrical stimulation) from peripheral endings of primary afferent neurones in anaesthetized cats[131] and [D-Ala[2],Met[5]]-enkephalinamide and morphine both blocked the release of this material from subnucleus caudalis of the brain-stem trigeminal sensory nuclear complex of rabbits.[132] In a rat spinal cord preparation, K$^+$- or veratridine-induced release of SP-like material was enhanced by two μ-receptor selective agonists, Tyr-D-Ala-Gly-MePhe-Gly-Ol (DAGO) and Tyr-D-Ala-Gly-MePhe-Met(O), and inhibited by δ-selective agonists (Tyr-D-Thr-Gly-Phe-Leu-Thr and Tyr-D-Pen-Gly-Phe-D-Pen), indicating that δ-opiate receptors may be involved in blocking SP release.[133] All of the above information led to a hypothesis that SP may be an excitatory transmitter of primary sensory neurones and, therefore, SP antagonists may be novel types of analgesics.

A number of SP antagonists have been tested in various analgesic tests but the results so far have been inconclusive and contradictory. In the earlier studies intraspinal injections of [D-Pro^2, D-Phe^7,D-Trp^9]-SP and [D-Pro^2,D-Trp^{7,9}]-SP in male mice were shown to be analgesic as judged from the tail withdrawal time from hot water (50 °C).[134] Both of these analogues and [D-Pro^4, D-Trp^{7,9,10}]-SP(4–11)-octapeptide also depressed the scratching and biting behaviours elicited by intrathecal injections of SP,[135,136] but in the mouse tail-flick, hotplate and tail-pinch assays only one of the above compounds, [D-Pro^2,D-Trp^{7,9}]-SP, showed antinociceptive activity (50 times less potent than morphine).[136] Naloxone, at a dose that completely blocked morphine-induced antinociception, had no effect on the SP antagonist-induced antinociception.[136] Higher doses of [D-Pro^2, D-Phe^7,D-Trp^9]-SP and [D-Pro^2,D-Trp^{7,9}]-SP caused hindlimb paralysis.[135,137] The licking, biting and scratching response induced by an intradermal hypertonic saline injection was also blocked by an intrathecal injection of [D-Pro^2,D-Trp^{7,9}]-SP at a lower dose but again at a slightly higher dose paralysis of both hindpaws lasting up to 4 d was observed.[138] The flaccid hindlimb paralysis induced by [D-Pro^2,D-Trp^{7,9}]-SP was not blocked by the prior administration of naloxone. SP coadministered with the antagonist also failed to prevent the hindlimb paralysis.[139]

Like [D-Pro^2,D-Trp^{7,9}]-SP, another slightly more potent antagonist, [D-Arg^1,D-Trp^{7,9},Leu^{11}]-SP, at a dose of 0.2 to 2 μg per rat (intrathecal) elicited antinociception in rats in hotplate and tail-flick tests, but at a dose of 2 μg per rat all the animals showed a profound motor impairment of the hindlimbs which persisted for three days after the injection. The histopathological examination showed extensive necrosis of the neuronal bodies in both the ventral and dorsal horns.[140] On the basis of a comparison between [D-β-Nal^{7,9,10}]-SP and [D-Pro^4,Lys^6,D-Trp^{7,9,10}, Phe^{11}]-SP(4–11)-octapeptide in rats, Regoli *et al.* suggested that part of the spinal toxicity may be due to the D-Trp residues.[141]

Some of the recent results using mice instead of rats in the analgesic tests have been more encouraging.[142–144] A number of analogues, *e.g.* [D-Pro^2,D-Phe^7,D-Trp^9]-, [D-Pro^2,D-Trp^{7,9}]-, [D-Arg^1,D-Trp^{7,9},Leu^{11}]-, [D-Arg^1,D-Pro^{2,4},D-Phe^7,D-His^9]-, [D-Arg^1,D-Pro^{2,4},D-Trp^{7,9},Leu^{11}]-SP and [D-Trp^{7,9},Leu^{11}]-SP(6–11)-hexapeptide, prevented SP-induced biting and scratching responses and some of these were also analgesic in the hotplate and tail-flick tests. Intrathecal administration of some of the antagonists (up to 20 μg per rat) showed no hindlimb paralysis.[142–144] The results in the guinea pig and rabbits were similar to those seen above in mice.[130] The antinociceptive effect of [D-Trp^{7,9},Leu^{11}]-SP in mice was inhibited by pretreatment with naloxone.[142]

A number of other analogues, *e.g.* [Boc-Asn^5,Arg^6,D-Phe^7,D-Trp^9]-SP(5–11)-OMe, [$N^α$-Z-Arg^1,D-Pro^{2,4},$N^ε$-Z-Lys^3,D-Phe^{7,8},Gly^{9}ψ(CH$_2$S)Leu^{10},D-Met^{11}]-SP-OMe and [D-Trp^{1,3,9}, D-Phe^7]-SP-OMe, were also tested in mouse acetylcholine abdominal constriction and rat acetic acid abdominal constriction, paw pressure and paw plasma extravasation tests. The analgesic activity of all these analogues was always associated with side effects such as motor impairment in the rotorod test and hindlimb paralysis.[145]

Some piperazinone derivations of the SP C-terminal hexapeptide (Figure 1) were also shown to antagonize the scratching induced by an intraspinal injection of SP or by topical application of capsaicin.[146] These analogues were also analgesic in the hotplate test when injected intraspinally, and unlike [D-Pro^2,D-Phe^7,D-Trp^9]-SP, caused little or no hindlimb paralysis. These analogues were inactive in the tail-flick test and did not prevent somatostatin-induced scratching.[146]

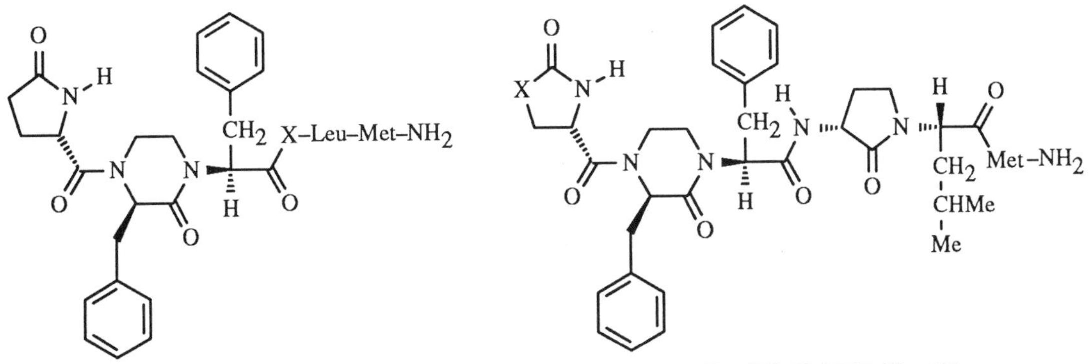

U-62713, X = Gly; U-65823, X = D-Pro U-66739, X = NH; U-67202, X = CH$_2$

Figure 1 Structures of piperazinone derivatives

13.9.8.2 SP Antagonists in Neurogenic Inflammation

The vasodilation and plasma extravasation following antidromic stimulation of sensory nerves is thought to be mediated by peripheral release of SP from chemosensitive pain fibres. Along with the direct effects of SP, the release of histamine induced by SP may also be partly responsible for this phenomenon. Various reports on the vasodilation induced concomitantly with the release of SP in the skin, dental pulp and the eye have been summarized in the earlier reviews.[6,7]

Electrical and mechanical stimulation of the trigeminal nerve released SP-like immunoreactive material into the aqueous humour of the eye.[147] Intracameral injections of SP into the anterior chamber was also shown to produce miosis.[147] These and some other similar studies have led to the hypothesis that the inflammatory response to trauma in the eye may be due to the release of SP and, therefore, antagonists of SP may be clinically useful in alleviating these inflammatory responses. A number of reports assessing the potential of different antagonists have already appeared in the literature.

Intravitreal or topical application of [D-Pro^2,D-Trp^{7,9}]-SP inhibited the irritant effects of exogenous SP and also the inflammatory response to IR irradiation of the iris.[148] At higher doses the antagonist itself produced miosis in the rabbit eye. [D-Pro^2,D-Trp^{7,9}]-SP, [D-Arg^1,D-Trp^{7,9}, Leu^{11}]-SP and [Arg^5,D-Trp^{7,9}]-SP-(5–11)-heptapeptide blocked the bradykinin- and capsaicin-induced contraction of the isolated rabbit sphincter pupillae muscle and also the miosis and breakdown of the blood–aqueous barrier caused by these agents.[149,150] A long-term treatment with [D-Pro^2,D-Trp^{7,9}]-SP (2–3 months) blocked the aqueous flare response up to 2 d after stopping the treatment without any adverse reactions.[151] The pupillary response to intravitreal SP during the treatment period was also abolished.[152]

In contrast to the antagonistic effects of [D-Pro^2,D-Trp^{7,9}]-SP mentioned above, Mandahl and Bill have reported this compound to be an agonist. The analogue at a dose of 100 μg caused miosis, breakdown of the blood–aqueous barrier and a rise in intraocular pressure in the rabbit eye. At a lower dose (10 μg) the antagonist caused slight miosis and did not inhibit the miotic response caused by SP or capsaicin but significantly reduced the miotic response to PGE$_1$ or electrical intracranial antidromic trigeminal nerve stimulation.[153] Unlike [D-Pro^2,D-Trp^{7,9}]-SP, another antagonist, [D-Arg^1,D-Pro^2,D-Trp^{7,9},Leu^{11}]-SP, was found to have no miotic effect but it did cause a breakdown of the blood–aqueous barrier.[154] Miosis caused by SP, trigeminal stimulation, capsaicin, PGE$_1$, compound 48/80, histamine and echothiophate iodide was blocked by this antagonist.[154,155]

13.9.8.3 SP Antagonists in Neurogenic Bronchoconstriction

The antidromic activation of sensory neurones induces changes in the respiratory tract and, as in the case of the neurogenic inflammation of the eye, the mediator here also appears to be a tachykinin.[6]

Previous studies (immunohistochemical) had shown that SP immunoreactive afferent neurones innervate the epithelium, blood vessels and bronchial smooth muscle of the respiratory tract and the activation of these neurones induced bronchoconstriction and an increase in vascular permeability in the tracheobronchial mucosa. Recently, immunoreactive material corresponding to NKA was also identified in human bronchial extracts.[156]

In a human isolated bronchial preparation NKA was about 100 times more potent than SP. NKB was inactive in this *in vitro* preparation, suggesting that NKA receptors may be involved in bronchoconstriction.[157] In other plasma extravasation and bronchoconstriction studies in the guinea pig SP, NKA, PHY, ELE and KAS were all shown to increase insufflation pressure (indicator of tracheobronchial resistance to air) in a dose dependent manner. NKA, which had a significantly longer insufflation pressure increasing effect than the other tachykinins, along with ELE and KAS was more potent than SP and PHY.[158] The bronchoconstrictor potency of NKA was several hundred times greater than SP, and its effect was unchanged by atropine, mepyramine and cimetidine treatment.[156] In contrast to the direct bronchoconstrictory effect, NKA and SP were less potent than PHY and ELE in increasing plasma extravasation.[158] Taken together, the above results indicate that more than one tachykinin may be released from sensory nerves upon mucosal irritation and may then be responsible for protective reflexes in the airways. SP may be more important for the increase in vascular permeability, while bronchoconstriction may be induced by NKA.

The involvement of more than one tachykinin in the airways was also indicated by the use of antagonists.[159] PHY (about five times), ELE (about five times) and eledoisin-related peptide (ERP, about 1.8 times) were more potent than SP in increasing the airways resistance and dynamic thoracic elastance in the guinea pigs. [D-Pro^2,D-Trp^{7,9}]-SP had no effect on the SP-induced increases but significantly reduced the ERP-induced increases. On the other hand, [D-Arg^1,D-Pro^2, D-Trp^{7,9},Leu^{11}]-SP reduced SP- and PHY-induced increases but did not effect ERP-induced increases.[159]

The tachykinins may also be involved in the nicotine-induced vasoconstriction of the airways. [D-Arg^1,D-Pro^2,D-Trp^{7,9},Leu^{11}]-SP abolished the nicotine-induced contraction of the isolated guinea pig bronchial preparation.[160] This antagonist also abolished the cigarette-smoke-induced increase in vascular permeability and local oedema in the rat.[161]

13.9.8.4 Tachykinins and Gastrointestinal Motility

Time- and dose-dependent effects of SP and NKA on gastric emptying and gastrointestinal transit in rats have recently been reported.[162] Three minutes after the test meal, SP and NKA both inhibited gastric emptying and gastrointestinal transit. NKA was at least 10 times less potent than SP. Pretreatment with atropine changed this inhibitory effect to a stimulant effect. Fifteen minutes after the test meal only a stimulant effect was seen with SP and NKA and only the effect of NKA was abolished by atropine treatment. Intraperitoneal injections of [D-Pro^2,D-Trp^{7,9}]-SP and [D-Arg^1,D-Trp^{7,9},Leu^{11}]-SP inhibited the gastric emptying and gastrointestinal transit in a dose-dependent manner.[163]

13.9.8.5 Tachykinins and Histamine Release

The histamine-releasing effect of tachykinins may be involved (at least in part) in some of the biological effects, *e.g.* smooth muscle contraction, peripheral vasodilation and plasma extravasation, associated with these peptides. In addition, the histamine-releasing property of the antagonists may be responsible for some of the side effects seen with these compounds.

Except SP, which induced a dose dependent release of histamine from rat peritoneal mast cells, all the other tachykinins (ELE, PHY, KAS, NKA and NKB) were either inactive or very weakly active.[6,164] In the rat isolated hindquarter preparation, only SP significantly increased the release of histamine, while ELE, KAS and NKA were inactive.[165] The fragments of SP, SP(1–9), SP(1–7), SP(1–4) and SP(4–11), were 10 to 70 times less potent than SP in releasing histamine from the rat mast cells, but the undecapeptide antagonists of SP were much more potent than the parent peptide.[164] One such compound, [D-Trp^{7,9,10}]-SP, was about 70 times more potent than SP in releasing histamine.[164] When the N^α amino group of Arg^1 and N^ε amino group of Lys^3 were protected with benzyloxycarbonyl groups the analogues were much less potent. Thus, [N^α-Z-Arg^1,D-Pro^{2,4},N^ε-Z-Lys^3,D-Phe^{7,9},Sar^9,D-Met^{11}]-SP-OMe and a number of related analogues were about 10 times less potent than [D-Pro^2,D-Trp^{7,9}]-SP.[61]

SP also produced dose dependent flare and wheal responses when injected intradermally into the volar surface of the human forearm.[166] PHY was two times more potent than SP in inducing the wheal response. Two of the SP antagonists, [D-Trp^{7,9}]-SP and [D-Pro^2,D-Phe^7,D-Trp^9]-SP, were two times more potent than SP in inducing the flare reaction but ELE, PHY and SP(4–11)-octapeptide were inactive.[164] One of the SP antagonists, [D-Pro^4,D-Trp^{7,9,10}]-SP(4–11)-octapeptide, antagonized the histamine-releasing activity of SP in the rat peritoneal mast cells and also the flare response induced by SP in the human skin.[167]

13.9.9 SIDE EFFECTS ASSOCIATED WITH SUBSTANCE P ANTAGONISTS

In addition to the histamine-releasing activity, a number of SP antagonists have also been shown to have neurotoxic, cardiovascular and local anaesthetic effects. A marked decrease in SP-like and tyrosine hydroxylase immunoreactivity was seen in the zona reticulata of substantia nigra when [D-Pro^2,D-Trp^{7,9}]-SP was injected directly into the rat brain.[168] SP itself did not induce any of these changes even at 10 times higher concentrations. Intrathecal injections of [D-Pro^2,D-Phe^7,D-Trp^9]-SP, [D-Pro^2,D-Trp^{7,9}]-SP and [D-Arg^1,D-Pro^2,D-Trp^{7,9},Leu^{11}]-SP produced loss of responsiveness to thermal and tactile stimuli and flaccid paralysis of the hindquarters, which persisted for 48 hours.[169] Examination of the spinal cord revealed local destruction of the grey matter. Widespread neuronal necrosis in the lumbar region of the spinal cord was seen after an intrathecal injection of

[D-Arg[1],D-Trp[7,9],Leu[11]]-SP.[140] The necrotic changes induced by the antagonist were prevented by injecting (i.v.) several doses of thyrotropin releasing hormone before and after the antagonist injection.[170]

A number of analogues containing D-Trp in positions 7, 9 and 10 also affected mean arterial pressure and heart rate.[171] Intrathecal injections of [D-Trp[7,9,10]]-SP, [D-Trp[7,9,10],Trp[11]]-SP, [D-Pro[4],D-Trp[7,9,10],Phe[11]]-SP(4–11)- and a number of other related octapeptides induced a long-lived hypotension which lasted for at least 90 min. The heart rate was also drastically decreased 10 to 15 min after the injection. Some other analogues with D-naphthylalanine residues in place of D-Trp, *e.g.* [D-α-Npa[7,9,10]]-SP or [D-Pro[4],D-α-Npa[7,9,10]]-SP(4–11)-octapeptide, only caused a slight short-lived fall in mean arterial pressure without significant change in heart rate. None of the above analogues had any effect on mean arterial pressure and heart rate when administered intravenously.[171] [D-Pro[2],D-Trp[7,9]]-SP and [Arg[5],D-Trp[7,9]]-SP(5–11)-heptapeptide also showed potent local anaesthetic actions.[172] Both of these analogues suppressed the compound action potential of the frog isolated sciatic nerve and were four times more potent than lidocaine. Similarly in the rat isolated sciatic nerve [D-Pro[2],D-Trp[7,9]]-SP suppressed the compound action potentials. It was more potent in the A_α than in the C-fibres. SP itself did not affect conduction in any of the above preparations.

13.9.10 REFERENCES

1. V. Erspamer, *Trends Neurosci.*, 1981, **4**, 267.
2. N. Minamino, K. Kangawa, A. Fukuda and H. Matsuo, *Neuropeptides (Edinburgh)*, 1984, **4**, 157.
3. J. E. Maggio, *Peptides (Fayetteville, N.Y.)*, 1985, **6** (Suppl. 3), 237.
4. M. M. Chang, S. E. Leeman and H. D. Niall, *Nature, New Biol., 1971*, **232**, 86.
5. R. O. Studer, H. Trzeciak and W. Lergier, *Helv. Chim. Acta*, 1973, **56**, 860.
6. A. S. Dutta, *Drugs of the Future*, 1987, 781.
7. B. Pernow, *Pharmacol. Rev.*, 1983, **35**, 85.
8. R. A. Nicoll, C. Schenker and S. E. Leeman, *Annu. Rev. Neurosci.*, 1980, **3**, 227.
9. R. Couture and D. Regoli, *Pharmacology*, 1982, **24**, 1.
10. B. E. B. Sandberg and L. L. Iversen, *J. Med. Chem.*, 1982, **25**, 1009.
11. N. Lindefors, E. Brodin and U. Ungerstedt, *Neuropeptides (Edinburgh)*, 1986, **8**, 127.
12. N. Lindefors, E. Brodin, E. Theodorsson-Norheim and U. Ungerstedt, *Regul. Pept.*, 1985, **10**, 217.
13. P. W. Mantyh, J. E. Maggio and S. P. Hunt, *Eur. J. Pharmacol.*, 1984, **102**, 361.
14. N. Minamino, H. Masuda, K. Kangawa and H. Matsuo, *Biochem. Biophys. Res. Commun.*, 1984, **124**, 731.
15. H. Berger, K. Fechner, E. Albrecht and H. Niedrich, *Biochem. Pharmacol.*, 1979, **28**, 3173.
16. Y. Nakata, Y. Kusaka, H. Yajima and T. Segawa, *J. Neurochem.*, 1981, **37**, 1529.
17. P. E. Ward and A. R. Johnson, *Biochem. J.*, 1978, **171**, 143.
18. R. Couture and D. Regoli, *Can. J. Physiol. Pharmacol.*, 1981, **59**, 621.
19. F. Lembeck, P. Holzer, M. Schweditsch and R. Gamse, *Naunyn-Schmiedeberg's Arch. Pharmacol.*, 1979, **305**, 9.
20. M. Hatanaka, T. Sasaki, T. Kikuchi and T. Murachi, *Arch. Biochem. Biophys.*, 1985, **242**, 557.
21. E. A. Thiele, S. M. Strittmatter and S. H. Snyder, *Biochem. Biophys. Res. Commun.*, 1985, **128**, 317.
22. R. Matsas, I. S. Fulcher, A. J. Kenny and A. J. Turner, *Proc. Natl. Acad. Sci. USA*, 1983, **80**, 3111.
23. R. Matsas, A. J. Kenny and A. J. Turner, *Biochem. J.*, 1984, **223**, 433.
24. A. Mauborgne, S. Bourgoin, J. Benoliel, M. Hirsch, J. Berthier, M. Hamon and F. Cesselin, *J. Pharmacol. Exp. Ther.*, 1987, **243**, 674.
25. S. H. Buck and E. Burcher, *Trends Pharmacol. Sci.*, 1986, 65.
26. S. P. Watson, *Life Sci.*, 1984, **35**, 797.
27. D. Regoli, J. Mizrahi, P. D'Orleans-Juste and E. Escher, *Eur. J. Pharmacol.*, 1984, **97**, 171.
28. C.-M. Lee, L. L. Iversen, M. R. Hanley and B. E. B. Sandberg, *Naunyn-Schmiedeberg's Arch. Pharmacol.*, 1982, **318**, 281.
29. S. P. Watson, B. E. B. Sandberg, M. R. Hanley and L. L. Iversen, *Eur. J. Pharmacol.*, 1983, **87**, 77.
30. J. W. Growcott, A. Jamieson, A. V. Tarpey and L. D. Topham, *Eur. J. Pharmacol.*, 1983, **86**, 59.
31. D. Ezra, F. R. M. Laurindo, J. Eimerl, R. E. Goldstein, C. C. Peck and G. Feuerstein, *Eur. J. Pharmacol.*, 1986, **122**, 135.
32. P. Illes and S. V. Falkenhausen, *Naunyn-Schmiedeberg's Arch. Pharmacol.*, 1986, **333**, 52.
33. N. Gulati, R. Mathison, H. Huggel, D. Regoli and J.-L. Beny, *Eur. J. Pharmacol.*, 1987, **137**, 149.
34. S. H. Buck, E. Burcher, C. W. Shults, W. Lovenberg and T. L. O'Donohue, *Science (Washington, D.C.)*, 1984, **226**, 987.
35. E. Burcher, S. H. Buck, W. Lovenberg and T. L. O'Donohue, *J. Pharmacol. Exp. Ther.*, 1986, **236**, 819.
36. E. Burcher and S. H. Buck, *Eur. J. Pharmacol.*, 1986, **128**, 165.
37. C. A. Maggi, P. Santicioli, S. Giuliani, D. Regoli and A. Meli, *J. Pharmacol. Exp. Ther.*, 1986, **238**, 259.
38. C. A. Maggi, S. Giuliani, S. Manzini, P. Santicioli and A. Meli, *J. Pharmacol. Exp. Ther.*, 1986, **238**, 341.
39. F. Osakada, K. Kubo, K. Goto, I. Kanazawa and E. Munekata, *Eur. J. Pharmacol.*, 1986, **120**, 201.
40. R. Laufer, U. Wormer, Z. Y. Friedman, C. Gilon, M. Chorev and Z. Selinger, *Proc. Natl. Acad. Sci. USA*, 1985, **82**, 7444.
41. R. Laufer, C. Gilon, M. Chorev and Z. Selinger, *J. Biol. Chem.*, 1986, **261**, 10 257.
42. J. Mizrahi, S. Dion, P. D'Orleans-Juste, E. Escher, G. Drapeau and D. Regoli, *Eur. J. Pharmacol.*, 1985, **118**, 25.
43. D. Regoli, G. Drapeau, S. Dion and P. D'Orleans-Juste, *Life Sci.*, 1987, **40**, 109.
44. G. Drapeau, P. D'Orleans-Juste, S. Dion, N. E. Rhaleb and D. Regoli, *Eur. J. Pharmacol.*, 1987, **136**, 401.
45. U. Wormer, R. Laufer, Y. Hart, M. Chorev, C. Gilon and Z. Selinger, *EMBO J.*, 1986, **5**, 2805.
46. R. Laufer, C. Gilon, M. Chorev and Z. Selinger, *J. Med. Chem.*, 1986, **29**, 1284.

47. M. A. Cascieri, G. G. Chicchi, R. M. Freidinger, C. D. Colton, D. S. Perlow, B. Williams, N. R. Curtis, A. T. McKnight, J. J. Maguire, D. F. Veber and T. Liang, *Mol. Pharmacol.*, 1986, **29**, 34.
48. G. Drapeau, P. D'Orleans-Juste, S. Dion, N. E. Rhaleb, N. Rouissi and D. Regoli, *Neuropeptides (Edinburgh)*, 1987, **10**, 43.
49. S. Dion, P. D'Orleans-Juste, G. Drapeau, N. E. Rhaleb, N. Rouissi, C. Tousignant and D. Regoli, *Life Sci.*, 1987, **41**, 2269.
50. D. Mastrangelo, R. Mathison, H. J. Huggel, S. Dion, P. D'Orleans-Juste, N. E. Rhaleb, G. Drapeau, P. Rovero and D. Regoli, *Eur. J. Pharmacol.*, 1986, **134**, 321.
51. C. Tousignant, S. Dion, G. Drapeau and D. Regoli, *Neuropeptides (Edinburgh)*, 1987, **9**, 333.
52. S. Dion, G. Drapeau, N. E. Rhaleb, P. D'Orleans-Juste and D. Regoli, *Eur. J. Pharmacol.*, 1987, **138**, 125.
53. M. F. Piercey, P. J. K. Dobry, F. J. Einspahr, L. A. Schroeder and N. Masiques, *Regul. Pept.*, 1982, **3**, 337.
54. M. F. Piercey, P. J. K. Dobry-Schreur, N. Masiques and L. A. Schroeder, *Life Sci.*, 1985, **36**, 777.
55. V. I. Teichberg, S. Cohen and S. Blumberg, *Regul. Pept.*, 1981, **1**, 327.
56. A. B. Hawcock, A. G. Hayes and M. B. Tyers, *Eur. J. Pharmacol.*, 1982, **80**, 135.
57. S. J. Bailey and C. C. Jordan, *Br. J. Pharmacol.*, 1984, **82**, 441.
58. U. Bjorkroth, S. Rosell, J.-C. Xu and K. Folkers, *Acta Physiol. Scand.*, 1982, **116**, 167.
59. S. P. Watson, *Br. J. Pharmacol.*, 1983, **80**, 205.
60. A. S. Dutta, J. J. Gormley, A. S. Graham, I. Briggs, J. W. Growcott and A. Jamieson, *J. Med. Chem.*, 1986, **29**, 1163.
61. A. S. Dutta, J. J. Gormley, A. S. Graham, I. Briggs, J. W. Growcott and A. Jamieson, *J. Med. Chem.*, 1986, **29**, 1171.
62. S. J. Bailey, R. L. Featherstone, C. C. Jordan and I. K. M. Morton, *Br. J. Pharmacol.*, 1986, **87**, 79.
63. J. C. Hunter and J. E. Maggio, *Eur. J. Pharmacol.*, 1984, **105**, 149.
64. R. Hosoki, T. Hisayama and I. Takayanagi, *Naunyn-Schmiedeberg's Arch. Pharmacol.*, 1987, **335**, 290.
65. D. Regoli, E. Escher and J. Mizrahi, *Pharmacology*, 1984, **28**, 301.
66. D. Regoli, E. Escher, G. Drapeau, P. D'Orleans-Juste and J. Mizrahi, *Eur. J. Pharmacol.*, 1984, **97**, 179.
67. D. Regoli, J. Mizrahi, P. D'Orleans-Juste, S. Dion, G. Drapeau and E. Escher, *Eur. J. Pharmacol.*, 1984, **109**, 121.
68. P. Manavalan and F. A. Momany, *Int. J. Pept. Protein Res.*, 1982, **20**, 351.
69. M. Cotrait, *Int. J. Pept. Protein Res.*, 1983, **22**, 110.
70. M. Cotrait and M. Hospital, *Biochem. Biophys. Res. Commun.*, 1982, **109**, 1123.
71. G. V. Nikiforovich, Y. Y. Balodis and G. I. Chipens, *Pept. Proc. Eur. Pept. Symp. 16th*, 1981, 631.
72. M. Cotrait and M. Hospital, *Int. J. Pept. Protein Res.*, 1986, **28**, 450.
73. B. Mehlis, M. Rueger, M. Becker, M. Bienert, H. Niedrich and P. Oehme, *Int. J. Pept. Protein Res.*, 1980, **15**, 20.
74. G. Chassaing, O. Convert and S. Lavielle, *Eur. J. Biochem.*, 1986, **154**, 77.
75. G. A. Woolley and C. M. Deber, *Pept. Proc. Eur. Pept. Symp. 19th*, 1987, 439.
76. J.-L. Bernier, J.-P. Henichart and N. Helbecque, *Eur. J. Biochem.*, 1984, **142**, 371.
77. G. Chassaing, O. Convert and S. Lavielle, *Biochim. Biophys. Acta*, 1986, **873**, 397.
78. G. Chassaing, O. Convert and S. Lavielle, *Pept. Proc. Eur. Pept. Symp.*, 19th, 1987, 303.
79. P. S. Darman, G. C. Landis, J. R. Smits, L. D. Hirning, K. Gulya, H. I. Yamamura, T. F. Burks and V. J. Hruby, *Biochem. Biophys. Res. Commun.*, 1985, **127**, 656.
80. D. Theodoropoulos, C. Poulos, D. Gatos, P. Cordopatis, E. Escher, J. Mizrahi, D. Regoli, D. Dalietos, A. Furst and T. D. Lee, *J. Med. Chem.*, 1985, **28**, 1536.
81. K. Neubert, H. W. Mansfeld, B. Hartrodt, E. Bergeg, H. D. Jakubke, J. Bergmann and B. Mehlis, *Pept. Proc. Eur. Pept. Symp. 15th*, 1979, 455.
82. S. Lavielle, G. Chassaing, J. Besseyre, A. Marquet, L. Bergstrom, J.-C. Beaujouan, Y. Torrens and J. Glowinski, *Eur. J. Pharmacol.*, 1986, **128**, 283.
83. P. Rovero, V. Pestellini, R. Patacchini, P. Santicioli, C. A. Maggi and A. Meli, *Neuropeptides (Edinburgh)*, 1987, **10**, 355.
84. E. Escher, R. Couture, C. Poulos, N. Pinas, J. Mizrahi, D. Theodoropoulos and D. Regoli, *J. Med. Chem.*, 1982, **25**, 1317.
85. J. Leban, G. Rackur, I. Yamaguchi, K. Folkers, V. Bjorkroth, S. Rosell, N. Yanaihara and C. Yanaihara, *Acta Chem. Scand., Ser. B, 1979,* **33**, 664.
86. R. Couture, A. Fournier, J. Magnan, S. St. Pierre and D. Regoli, *Can. J. Physiol. Pharmacol.*, 1979, **57**, 1427.
87. A. Fournier, R. Couture, D. Regoli, M. Gendreau and S. St. Pierre, *J. Med. Chem.*, 1982, **25**, 64.
88. R. E. Chipkin, J. M. Stewart, V. E. Sweeney, K. Harris and R. Williams, *Arch. Int. Pharmacodyn. Ther.*, 1979, **240**, 193.
89. S. Lavielle, G. Chassaing, S. Julien, J. Besseyre, A. Marquet, J. C. Beaujouan, Y. Torrens and J. Glowinski, *Neuropeptides (Edinburgh)*, 1986, **7**, 191.
90. D. Theodoropoulos, C. Poulos, D. Gatos and P. Cordopatis, *Pept. Proc. Eur. Pept. Symp. 17th*, 1983, 521.
91. K. Torigoe, S. Sofuku, H. Sato and I. Muramatsu, in 'Peptide Chemistry', ed. T. Shioiri, Protein Research Foundation, Osaka, 1981, p. 71.
92. B. E. B. Sandberg, C.-M. Lee, M. R. Hanley and L. L. Iversen, *Eur. J. Biochem.*, 1981, **114**, 329.
93. G. Rackur, I. Yamaguchi, J. Leban, U. Bjorkroth, S. Rosell and K. Folkers, *Acta Chem. Scand., Ser. B*, 1979, **33**, 375.
94. I. Yamaguchi, G. Rackur, J. Leban, U. Bjorkroth, S. Rosell and K. Folkers, *Acta Chem. Scand., Ser. B*, 1979, **33**, 63.
95. H. Tanaka, F. Osakada, S. Ohashi, M. Shiraki and E. Munckata, *Chem. Lett.*, 1986, 391.
96. K. Kitagawa, Y. Ban, K. Ujita, T. Akita, T. Segawa, Y. Nakata and H. Yajima, *Chem. Pharm. Bull.*, 1978, **26**, 2899.
97. E. Escher, R. Couture, G. Champagne, J. Mizrahi and D. Regoli, *J. Med. Chem.*, 1982, **25**, 470.
98. E. Munekata and I. Kanazawa, *Pept. Proc. Eur. Pept. Symp. 17th*, 1983, 527.
99. Y. Uchida, M. Nishijima, T. Moro, N. Sakura, K. Hirose, H. Kontani and T. Hashimoto, *Bull. Chem. Soc. Jpn.*, 1986, **59**, 4003.
100. T. Hashimoto, Y. Uchida, M. Nishijima, T. Moro, N. Sakura and K. Hirose, *Bull. Chem. Soc. Jpn.*, 1986, **59**, 4009.
101. T. Hashimoto, N. Sakura, K. Hirose, Y. Uchida, M. Nishijima and T. Moro, *Bull. Chem. Soc. Jpn.*, 1987, **60**, 827.
102. T. Hashimoto, Y. Uchida, M. Nishijima, N. Sakura and K. Hirose, *Bull. Chem. Soc. Jpn.*, 1987, **60**, 1207.
103. N. Pinas, C. P. Poulos and D. Theodoropoulos, *FEBS Lett.*, 1979, **108**, 45.
104. C. P. Poulos, N. Pinas and D. Theodoropoulos, *FEBS Lett.*, 1980, **136**, 1104.
105. C. P. Poulos, J. R. Brown and C. C. Jordan, *J. Med. Chem.*, 1986, **29**, 1281.
106. M. Hirohashi, Y. Yamamoto, T. Nishida, N. Yanaihara, Y. Hioki, H. Watari and M. Otsuka, in 'Peptide Chemistry', ed. T. Shioiri, Protein Research Foundation, Osaka, 1981, p. 71.

107. T. Hashimoto, T. Moro and Y. Uchida, *Bull. Chem. Soc. Jpn.*, 1986, **59**, 4006.
108. Y. Uchida, K. Okimura, K. Kurosawa, N. Sakura, K. Hirose and T. Hashimoto, *Bull. Chem. Soc. Jpn.*, 1987, **60**, 1561.
109. E. Munekata, K. Kubo, H. Tanaka and F. Osakada, *Peptides (Fayetteville, N.Y.)*, 1987, **8**, 169.
110. M. Benuck and N. Marks, *Biochem. Biophys. Res. Commun.*, 1975, **65**, 153.
111. C.-M. Lee, B. E. B. Sandberg, M. R. Hanley and L. L. Iversen, *Eur. J. Biochem.*, 1981, **114**, 315.
112. E. Heymann and R. Mentlein, *FEBS Lett.*, 1978, **91**, 360.
113. T. Kato, T. Nagatsu, K. Fukasawa, M. Harada, I. Nagatsu and S. Sakakibara, *Biochim. Biophys. Acta*, 1978, **525**, 417.
114. S. Blumberg, V. I. Teichberg, J. L. Charli, L. B. Hersch and J. F. McKelvy, *Brain Res.*, 1980, **192**, 477.
115. R. Laufer, M. Chorev, C. Gilon, Z. Y. Friedman, U. Wormser and Z. Selinger, *FEBS Lett.*, 1981, **123**, 291.
116. C. Poujade, S. Lavielle, Y. Torrens, J.-C. Beaujouan, J. Glowinski and A. Marquet, *Neuropeptides (Edinburgh)*, 1984, **4**, 361.
117. J. W. Growcott and N. N. Petter, *J. Pharm. Pharmacol.*, 1980, **32**, 376.
118. K. Folkers, J. Horig, G. Rampold, P. Lane, S. Rosell and U. Bjorkroth, *Acta Chem. Scand., Ser. B*, 1982, **36**, 389.
119. K. Folkers, S. Rosell, X. Jie-Cheng, U. Bjorkroth, L. Yi-An and L. Yin-Zeng, *Acta Chem. Scand., Ser. B*, 1983, **37**, 623.
120. K. Folkers, R. Hakanson, J. Horig, X. Jie-Cheng and S. Leander, *Br. J. Pharmacol.*, 1984, **83**, 449.
121. K. Folkers, S. Rosell, J. Chu, L. Lu, P. L. Tang and A. Ljungqvist, *Acta Chem. Scand., Ser. B*, 1986, **40**, 295.
122. S. Caranikas, J. Mizrahi, P. D'Orleans-Juste and D. Regoli, *Eur. J. Pharmacol.*, 1982, **77**, 205.
123. J. Mizrahi, E. Escher, S. Caranikas, P. D'Orleans-Juste and D. Regoli, *Eur. J. Pharmacol.*, 1982, **82**, 101.
124. J. Horig and H. Schultheiss, *Eur. J. Pharmacol.*, 1984, **105**, 65.
125. E. Escher, P. D'Orleans-Juste, S. Dion, G. Drapeau, J. Mizrahi and D. Regoli, *Eur. J. Pharmacol.*, 1984, **105**, 375.
126. H. I. Jacoby, I. Lopez, D. Wright and J. L. Vaught, *Life Sci.*, 1986, **39**, 1995.
127. M. Otsuka and T. Takahashi, *Annu. Rev. Pharmacol. Toxicol.*, 1977, **17**, 425.
128. T. L. Yaksh, T. M. Jessell, R. Gamse, A. V. Mudge and S. E. Leeman, *Nature (London)*, 1980, **286**, 155.
129. L. Olgart, B. Gazelius, E. Brodin and G. Nilsson, *Acta Physiol. Scand.*, 1977, **101**, 510.
130. T. M. Jessell and L. L. Iversen, *Nature (London)*, 1977, **268**, 549.
131. E. Brodin, B. Gazelius, P. Panopoulos and L. Olgart, *Acta Physiol. Scand.*, 1983, **117**, 567.
132. N. Yonehara, T. Shibutani, H.-Y. Tsai and R. Inoki, *Eur. J. Pharmacol.*, 1986, **129**, 209.
133. A. Mauborgne, O. Lutz, J.-C. Legrand, M. Hamon and F. Cesselin, *J. Neurochem.*, 1987, **48**, 529.
134. F. Lembeck, K. Folkers and J. Donnerer, *Biochem. Biophys. Res. Commun.*, 1981, **103**, 1318.
135. M. F. Piercey, L. A. Schroeder, K. Folkers, J.-C. Xu and J. Horig, *Science (Washington, D.C.)*, 1981, **214**, 1361.
136. J. L. Vaught and L. J. Post, *Adv. Pain Res. Ther.*, 1985, **9**, 47.
137. B. Akerman, S. Rosell and K. Folkers, *Acta Physiol. Scand.*, 1982, **114**, 631.
138. A. S. Hwang and G. L. Wilcox, *Life Sci.*, 1986, **38**, 2389.
139. H. Matsumura, T. Sakurada, A. Hara, H. Kuwahara, R. Ando, S. Sakurada and K. Kisara, *Neuropharmacology*, 1985, **24**, 811.
140. C. Post and I. Paulsson, *Neurosci. Lett.*, 1985, **57**, 159.
141. R. Couture, E. Escher and D. Regoli, *Eur. J. Pharmacol.*, 1987, **134**, 355.
142. C. Post and K. Folkers, *Eur. J. Pharmacol.*, 1985, **113**, 335.
143. J. L. Vaught and R. Scott, *Life Sci.*, 1987, **40**, 175.
144. T. Sakurada, H. Kuwahara, S. Sakurada, K. Kisara, M. Ohba and E. Munekata, *Neuropeptides (Edinburgh)*, 1987, **9**, 197.
145. J. W. Growcott, I. Briggs, A. Jamieson, A. S. Dutta and J. J. Gormley, in 'Tachykinin Antagonists', ed. R. Hakanson and F. Sundler, Elsevier, Amsterdam, 1985, p. 345.
146. M. F. Piercey, M. W. Moon, J. R. Blinn and P. J. K. Dobry-Schreur, *Brain Res.*, 1986, **385**, 74.
147. A. Bill, J. Stjernschantz, A. Mandahl, E. Brodin and G. Nilsson, *Acta Physiol. Scand.*, 1979, **106**, 371.
148. G. Holmdahl, R. Hakanson, S. Leander, S. Rosell, K. Folkers and F. Sundler, *Science (Washington, D.C.)*, 1981, **214**, 1029.
149. G. Bynke, R. Hakanson, J. Horig and S. Leander, *Eur. J. Pharmacol.*, 1983, **91**, 469.
150. C. Wahlestedt, G. Bynke and R. Hakanson, *Eur. J. Pharmacol.*, 1984, **106**, 577.
151. G. Bynke, R. Hakanson, J. Horig and K. Folkers, *Experientia*, 1984, **40**, 368.
152. G. Bynke, C. Wahlestedt, B. Beding and R. Hakanson, *Eur. J. Pharmacol.*, 1985, **108**, 217.
153. A. Mandahl and A. Bill, *Acta Physiol. Scand.*, 1983, **117**, 139.
154. A. Mandahl and A. Bill, *Acta Physiol. Scand.*, 1984, **120**, 27.
155. A. Mandahl, *Eur. J. Pharmacol.*, 1985, **114**, 121.
156. C.-R. Martling, E. Theodorsson-Norheim and J. M. Lundberg, *Life Sci.*, 1987, **40**, 1633.
157. C. Advenier, E. Naline, G. Drapeau and D. Regoli, *Eur. J. Pharmacol.*, 1987, **139**, 133.
158. X. Hua, J. M. Lundberg, E. Theodorsson-Norheim and E. Brodin, *Naunyn-Schmiedeberg's Arch. Pharmacol.*, 1984, **328**, 196.
159. V. Goel and D. F. Biggs, *Life Sci.*, 1987, **40**, 1007.
160. Y. Kizawa and I. Takayanagi, *Eur. J. Pharmacol.*, 1985, **113**, 319.
161. J. M. Lundberg, L. Lundblad, A. Saria and A. Anggard, *Naunyn-Schmiedeberg's Arch. Pharmacol.*, 1984, **326**, 181.
162. P. Holzer, *Br. J. Pharmacol.*, 1985, **86**, 305.
163. P. Holzer, U. Holzer-Petsche and S. Leander, *Br. J. Pharmacol.*, 1986, **89**, 453.
164. P. Devillier, M. Renoux, J.-P. Giroud and D. Regoli, *Eur. J. Pharmacol.*, 1985, **117**, 89.
165. U. Holzer-Petsche, E. Schimek, R. Amann and F. Lembeck, *Naunyn-Schmiedeberg's Arch. Pharmacol.*, 1985, **330**, 130.
166. J. C. Foreman, C. C. Jordan, P. Oehme and H. Renner, *J. Physiol.*, 1983, **335**, 449.
167. J. C. Foreman, C. C. Jordan and W. Piotrowski, *Br. J. Pharmacol.*, 1982, **77**, 531.
168. T. Hokfelt, S. Vincent, L. Hellsten, S. Rosell, K. Folkers, K. Markey, M. Goldstein and C. Cuello, *Acta Physiol. Scand.*, 1981, **113**, 571.
169. B. F. Cox, R. L. Shelper, F. M. Faraci, A. H. Werber and M. J. Brody, *Fed. Proc. Fed. Am. Soc. Exp. Biol.*, 1985, **44**, 427.
170. J. Freedman, T. Hokfelt, G. Jonsson and C. Post, *Exp. Brain Res.*, 1986, **62**, 175.
171. R. Couture, A. Gupta, R. Kerouac, E. Escher and D. Regoli, *Can. J. Physiol. Pharmacol.*, 1987, **56**, 412.
172. C. Post, J. F. Butterworth, G. R. Strichartz, J. A. Karlsson and C. G. A. Persson, *Eur. J. Pharmacol.*, 1985, **117**, 347.

13.10

Calcitonin and Parathyroid Hormone Receptors

RICHARD M. EPAND

McMaster University, Hamilton, Ontario, Canada

and

MICHAEL P. CAULFIELD

Merck Sharp & Dohme Research Laboratories, West Point, PA, USA

13.10.1 INTRODUCTION

The calcium concentration in blood is normally maintained within narrow limits at about 2.5 mmol L^{-1}. This occurs despite wide fluctuations in dietary calcium, excreted calcium and calcium exchange between blood and bone. Calcium homeostasis is regulated by the coordinated actions of parathyroid hormone (PTH), calcitonin (CT) and vitamin D. This review will concentrate on the properties of CT and PTH. CT is produced by the C cells of the thyroid gland in higher organisms. It is a 32 amino acid peptide hormone which acts to lower blood calcium levels. Parathyroid hormone is a single polypeptide chain of 84 amino acid residues. It is synthesized in the parathyroid glands which are located close to the posterior surface of the thyroid gland. Parathyroid hormone causes a rise in blood calcium levels, an action opposite to that of calcitonin. There is feedback regulation by calcium on the secretion of CT and PTH. Elevated blood calcium increases CT release and decreases PTH release. The opposite occurs in hypocalcemia.

13.10.2 CALCITONIN

13.10.2.1 Biosynthesis

As with most smaller peptide hormones, CT is biosynthesized in a precursor form which is processed by proteolytic enzymes. In addition, enzymes amidate the carboxyl terminus to give the final 32 amino acid form of CT which is found in the circulation and is biologically active. CT biosynthesis also provides an example of alternative processing of the primary RNA transcript.[1] In the thyroid, the RNA is processed to give a mRNA which codes for CT, while in the brain the same gene gives rise after splicing to a mRNA which codes for calcitonin gene-related peptide (CGRP). The pathways for the biosynthesis of these hormones are shown (Figure 1). The sequence of steps in this RNA processing has recently been elucidated.[2] In addition, a second CT gene exists in man which gives rise to mRNA which only codes for a second CGRP and not CT.[3] Both CT and CGRP lower blood calcium and inhibit bone resorption in the rat, but a peptide which arises as a result of proteolytic cleavage of the carboxyl terminal portion of procalcitonin is devoid of these activities.[4] Our review will center on studies of CT.

13.10.2.2 Chemical Structure

Calcitonin is synthesized in the ultimobranchial gland of lower vertebrates as well as by the thyroid gland of higher organisms. The amino acid sequence of chicken CT has recently been determined by cDNA sequencing.[5] Its sequence compared to that of some other known forms of CT is given below:

Species	Sequence
Human	CGNLSTCMLGTYTQDFNKFHTFPQTAIGVGAP-amide
Porcine	CSNLSTCVLSAYWRDLNNFHRFSGMGFGPETP-amide
Chicken	CASLSTCVLGKLSQELHKLQTYPRTDVGAGTP-amide
Salmon	CSNLSTCVLGKLSQELHKLQTYPRTNTGSGTP-amide

Several structural features of CT are common to all forms of CT. There are two cysteine residues at positions 1 and 7 linked by a disulfide bond. In addition, identical amino acids occur at positions 4, 5, 6, 9, 28 and 32 and the terminal carboxyl group is always amidated.

Calcitonin may also exist in higher molecular weight forms as a result of binding to serum albumin.[6]

13.10.2.3 Conformational Properties

Circular dichroism (CD) studies indicate that neither salmon, human nor porcine CT has much secondary structure in aqueous solution.[7] Recent NMR evidence confirms the lack of structure of salmon CT (sCT) in solution.[8] However, when residues 8–22 of CT are displayed on a helical wheel, the tendency of this segment to form an amphipathic helix is illustrated.[7,9] Furthermore, statistical mechanical theory predicts that residues 11–19 of sCT will have a high probability of helix formation in the presence of lipids, particularly anionic lipids.[10] This has been demonstrated experimentally by CD.[7]

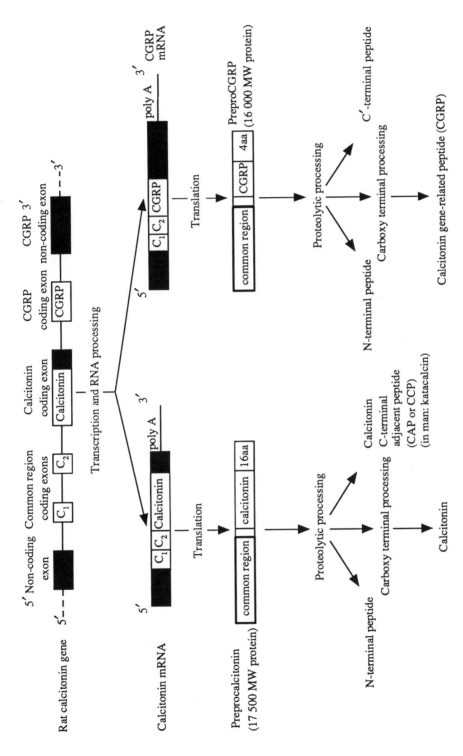

Figure 1 Schematic representation of the biosynthesis of rat CT and related peptides resulting from alternative RNA splicing and post-translational processing

13.10.2.4 Distribution

The distribution of CT in mammals is complex as this hormone has been found to be present in numerous organs. Human calcitonin (hCT), in addition to the thyroid, is found in the human brain principally in the posterior hypothalamus, the median eminence and the pituitary.[11] In addition to hCT, peptides with sCT-like immunoreactivity and chromatographic properties have been demonstrated in the human thyroid and brain suggesting that humans synthesize more than one type of CT-like peptide.[12]

Calcitonin-like peptides are also produced in certain cancers. Medullary thyroid carcinomas in man produce an sCT-like peptide[13] and a chicken CT-like peptide[14] in addition to hCT. Calcitonin is also produced in a number of non-thyroid tumours.[15] In particular, breast and bronchogenic carcinomas which produce CT are often associated with hypercalcemia and bony metastases.[15]

13.10.2.5 Biological Properties and Methods of Assay

13.10.2.5.1 In vitro

Regulation of adenylate cyclase activity is recognized as one of the mechanisms for controlling cellular activity. There has been considerable interest in the effects of CT on the adenylate cyclase activity of two of the recognized target organs of this hormone, kidney and bone. Stimulation of adenylate cyclase activity in renal membrane preparations by calcitonin has been used as an assay for the activity of CT and its analogues.[16] Kidney membranes are more readily obtained than are membranes from bone cells. However, the relationship of adenylate cyclase stimulation to the biological activity of CT has been controversial. Both CT as well as PTH stimulate this enzyme, yet these two hormones have opposite effects on bone resorption. It is believed that PTH and CT act on different cells in bone. PTH stimulates adenylate cyclase in osteoblasts while CT acts on the cyclase of osteoclasts.[17] There is a cloned bone cell line whose adenylate cyclase is stimulated by both of these hormones.[18] Calcitonin also stimulates adenylate cyclase activity in a human breast cancer cell line.[19] Curiously, CT inhibits adenylate cyclase activity in the brain, although this effect has been demonstrated only at very high hormone concentrations.[20]

Another important mechanism of membrane receptor-mediated regulation of cell activity is through changes in phosphatidylinositol metabolism. It has been recently shown that sCT inhibits the incorporation of inositol into phosphatidylinositol.[21] One of the consequences of phosphatidylinositol turnover is the production of diacylglycerols which are potent activators of protein kinase C. It has been shown that the phosphorylation of one of the substrates of protein kinase C in the brain is stimulated by CT.[22] This is opposite to the effect predicted on the basis of the inhibitory activity of sCT on phosphatidylinositol turnover. Calcitonin, however, does inhibit the phosphorylation of other brain proteins, but this is thought to be *via* a calcium–calmodulin dependent protein kinase.[22] Protein kinase C activation leads to increased intracellular calcium concentrations. Calcitonin affects the distribution of calcium in a number of cells. Calcitonin inhibits the motility of human sperm by a mechanism that is thought to involve a stimulation of the release of calcium from intracellular stores.[23] Calcitonin also increases the duration of a calcium-dependent potential in parasympathetic ganglia.[24] Calcitonin increases the calcium content in liver cells both by stimulating calcium influx and by inhibiting calcium efflux.[25] However, CT may also be able to lower cytoplasmic calcium through the stimulation of microsomal[26] and mitochondrial[27] calcium uptake in liver or by inhibition of calcium influx across the plasma membrane of the hypothalamus.[28] Thus, the effects of CT on calcium fluxes and distribution at the cellular level appear dependent on the cell type and involve changes in flux across both the plasma membrane as well as intracellular organelles. Many cell functions are dependent on the concentration of free calcium in the cytoplasm. The effect of CT on this calcium pool deserves further study.

Calcium is not the only ion whose distribution is regulated by CT. Calcitonin also lowers plasma phosphorus levels, in part, by inhibiting bone resorption but also through a small phosphaturic effect. Calcitonin inhibits Na^+–P_i cotransport in isolated brush border membrane vesicles.[29]

Thus, CT has effects on the two major secondary messenger systems: cAMP and inositol triphosphate/diacylglycerol. In addition, CT affects ion flux across membranes either as a result of changes in secondary messenger concentration or by direct effects on ion transport proteins. These regulatory mechanisms are influenced by CT in several organs, the most well-studied ones being bone and kidney. Effects of CT on nerve and liver have also been demonstrated. In addition, there are an increasing number of examples of CT inhibition of hormone release from endocrine cells.

Calcitonin inhibits the release of insulin from isolated rat pancreatic islets[30] and prolactin from isolated rat pituitary cells.[31] This would suggest a CT-stimulated lowering of cytoplasmic calcium.

Transforming growth factors (TGF) stimulate the growth of cells. Primary cultures of fetal bone (calvariae) produce TGF-β. The production of this growth factor is inhibited by CT.[32]

13.10.2.5.2 *In vivo*

The most studied activity of CT *in vivo* is its stimulation of reduced calcium levels in plasma. This effect is thought to be due primarily to a net inhibition of the transfer of calcium from bone to blood.[33,34] Concomitant with the decrease in plasma calcium, there is also a decrease in the circulating levels of phosphate. In addition to reduced bone resorption, CT promotes loss of calcium and phosphate in urinary excretion[35] and in bile[36] as well as inhibiting intestinal absorption of these ions.[37]

Many other biological effects of CT have been reported. In general, it is not well established which, if any, of these effects have physiological relevance. Nevertheless they may have pharmacological applications. In particular, there is increasing interest in the role of peptide hormones in the brain. It has been demonstrated that there is immunoreactive CT in the brain as well as receptors for CT (see below). Direct effects of CT on the electrical excitability of neurons in the rat forebrain has been demonstrated.[38] Calcitonin has antinociceptive activity, increasing the pain latency in the hot-plate test[39] as well as anorectic activity.[40,41] Another action of CT that is believed to be mediated through the central nervous system is the inhibition of gastric acid secretion.[42]

Calcitonin appears to act on endocrine organs by inhibiting hormone release, in a manner very similar to that of somatostatin, although the activity of the latter hormone has received much more attention to date. Calcitonin inhibits the release of thyroid-stimulating hormone,[43] prolactin,[44] growth hormone,[45] gastrin[46] and insulin[47] when injected systematically.

Because of the inhibitory action of CT on insulin release, there has been interest in the possible role of CT as a diabetogenic hormone.[48] However, recent evidence suggests that the effect of CT is transient and only occurs if administered at the time of a meal.[49] The response of CT release to calcium infusion is not altered in type I diabetes, suggesting that changes in CT levels do not play a role in diabetes-related bone loss.[50] An animal model related to obesity and diabetes is the Zucker rat. Obese Zucker rats have higher circulating levels of CT[51] without down regulation of renal CT receptors.[52]

Calcitonin is also vasoactive but its effects seem complex and have not been extensively studied. Calcitonin causes coronary vasoconstriction, but hepatic vasodilation. In both organs CT augments PTH-induced vasodilation.[53]

13.10.2.6 Structure–Activity Relationships (SAR)

13.10.2.6.1 *Interspecies differences*

Most studies of SAR have been done in mammals or using mammalian tissue, cells or membranes. It is therefore surprising that ultimobranchial CT has a much higher hypocalcemic activity in these systems than do mammalian forms of this hormone.[54] Central nervous system effects of CT, as measured by inhibition of gastric acid secretion, are also more sensitive to ultimobranchial than to mammalian CT.[55] This phenomenon has been ascribed to a greater resistance of ultimobranchial CT to degradation[56] or to a greater receptor binding affinity of these forms of CT.[57] We have noted that in the presence of lipid, sCT adopts a more helical conformation than do mammalian forms of CT. This suggests that a conformational difference in the membrane-bound forms of different CT may be responsible for their different biological activities.[7]

13.10.2.6.2 *Role of an amphipathic helix*

Segrest *et al.*[58] proposed that serum apolipoproteins could form helical segments in which hydrophobic and hydrophilic residues were on opposite faces of the helix. It was proposed that such helical segments, termed amphipathic helices, could interact with phospholipids. We subsequently demonstrated that this concept could be applied to several peptide hormones[59] including CT which solubilizes lipid.[60] The importance of an amphipathic helical segment for the biological activity of

CT was dramatically demonstrated by Moe and Kaiser.[61] These workers substituted several amino acids in the amphipathic helical region of CT for other amino acids with similar polarity, without loss of biological activity. The region of the sCT molecule predicted to form an amphipathic helix comprises approximately residues 11 to 19.[10] We demonstrated that the hypocalcemic potency of human and salmon CT as well as several analogs of CT generally correlated with their extent of lipid solubilization and lipid-induced helix formation.[62] In addition, the stimulation of adenylate cyclase and receptor binding in a human breast cancer cell line was markedly reduced when a hydrophobic residue in the center of the amphipathic helix was omitted.[63] However, neither the extent of separation of hydrophilic and hydrophobic groups on opposite faces of the helix as measured by the calculated hydrophobic moment nor the extent of helix formation is well correlated with biological activity.[64] In addition, a number of analogs of sCT have markedly reduced helicity in the presence of lipid but greater hypocalcemic potency than unmodified sCT (Table 1). The least structured of these analogs, [Gly^8]sCT, also has equal cyclase-activating ability and receptor-binding potency in breast cancer cells[69] and has anorectic activity when administered intracerebroventricularly but not when administered peripherally.[70] The effect of Gly at position 8 on biological potency is opposite for human and salmon CT. In the former case, replacement of Met with Gly decreases the activity[62, 69] while sCT replacement of Val with Gly increases the activity. This can be rationalized since hCT has less structure than sCT so that a further increase in flexibility results in a decrease in receptor binding. In contrast, sCT requires increased flexibility to adapt to the receptor-bound conformation. This argument is reinforced by the findings that when Met at position 8 in hCT is replaced by the more conformationally restricted Val, the hypocalcemic activity increases about fivefold.[71] Recently, Kaiser *et al.* have shown that introduction of a Glu at position 15 on the hydrophobic face of the amphipathic helix of his analog MCT H improves the activity.[72] This result is difficult to interpret in terms of increased conformational flexibility. The Glu introduced at position 15 is present at that position in the sequence of unmodified sCT. Therefore, the new analog might have additional specific interactions with the receptor as a result of a negative charge at that position. Furthermore, introduction of the Glu allows for an additional ionic interaction between residues 15 and 18 which can stabilize a helical conformation. Because these analogs differ in several respects from the sequence of sCT, it is difficult to ascribe enhanced activity to any single factor. However, the finding that substitution or deletion of a single amino acid residue from various positions of the putative amphipathic helical sequence of sCT can both decrease structure and increase hypocalcemic activity (Table 1) can most easily be interpreted in terms of increased conformational flexibility. Conformational flexibility has also been suggested to play a role in the binding of oxytocin to its receptor.[73] From these and other studies, we can conclude that the amphipathic helix contributes to hormone potency but biological activity is also influenced by conformational features such as helix-forming potential, conformational flexibility and long-range interactions.[74]

13.10.2.6.3 *Role of the disulfide ring structure*

As indicated above, although there is considerable sequence variation among CT from different species, there are a few invariant residues. These invariant residues include the two Cys residues at position 1 and 7 as well as the disulfide bond between them. Of the eight invariant residues, five are

Table 1 Potent Analogs of sCT with Reduced Helicity

Peptide	$-[\Theta]_{222}$ ($°\,cm^2\,dmol^{-1}$)^a	Hypocalcemic activity (IU mg^{-1})^b	Ref.
sCT	12 350	4500	64, 65
Des-Ser^{13}-sCT	10 300	4650	64
Des-Thr^{21}-sCT	11 390	5200	66
Des-Tyr^{22}-sCT	7715	5200	66
[Met^8]sCT	10 900	5500	10
[Ala^{19}]sCT	10 450	5500	67
[Ala^{16}]sCT	7940	6200	10
[Gly^8]sCT	5400	6500	10
[Ala$^{16, 19}$]sCT	9200	7200	68
Des-Leu^{19}-sCT	7905	8000	64

^{a} Mean residue ellipticity at 222 nm, $[\Theta]_{222}$ measured from CD of a 100 µmol L^{-1} peptide solution with 1 mmol L^{-1} DMPG, 20 mmol L^{-1} Pipes, 1 mmol L^{-1} EDTA, 0.15 M NaCl and 0.02 mg mL^{-1} NaN$_3$, pH 7.40, 25 °C. ^{b} *In vivo* assay of calcitonin-induced blood hypocalcemia in rats.

within the ring structure formed by the disulfide bridge. Nevertheless, Ser residue 2,[75] Asn residue 3[76] and Leu residue 4[77] can all be removed as single deletions without loss of biological activity. Even the double deletion analog [Des-Ser², Ans³]-sCT[78] is fully active. The free amino terminus of hCT can be acetylated[79] with a resulting 50% increase in biological activity. Acetylation of sCT or sCT analogs results in only a slight increase in activity.[80] Analogs of human[81] and rat[82] CT not containing a disulfide bond have virtually no activity. The disulfide bond and α-amino groups can be replaced by an ethylene linkage yielding a fully active and more stable form of eel CT.[83] More surprisingly, Cys at positions 1 and 7 can be replaced by Ala or by S-acetamido-methylcysteine to yield open chain analogs with full hypocalcemic potency.[65]

13.10.2.6.4 *Other sequences*

The amino terminal segment of sCT, sCT(1-23)-peptide amide, has equal maximal hypocalcemic activity but only 0.25% of the potency of the native hormone while the carboxyl terminal segment of sCT comprising residues 12–32 amide is devoid of hypocalcemic activity.[84] This suggests that the former segment has all of the amino acid residues required for receptor activation. However, a peptide containing residues 11–32 of eel CT has about 2% of the renal cyclase activation and receptor binding compared with the intact hormone.[85] It is difficult to compare these two results as there are several differences in the sequence of these two peptides and different biological activities were assessed. Yamamoto *et al.*[85] from studies of this and smaller segments, suggested that the carboxyl terminal portion is more important for receptor binding than for cyclase activation. This is an important finding for the design of CT antagonists. Slightly shortening hCT with [Pro²⁹]-hCT-(1-29)amide and hCT-(1-31)amide results in a marked reduction in hypocalcemic activity to 2 or 12%, respectively compared with the native hormone.[79] Simple hydrolysis of the carboxyl terminal amide or its replacement by a methyl ester also markedly reduces the hypocalcemic activity to 6 or 13%, respectively.[79] Changes in the sequence of the carboxyl terminal region can also affect biological activity, particularly in the case of hCT. If Val²⁹ and Ala³¹ of hCT are exchanged, the hypocalcemic activity drops to 6% that of the native sequence.[86] If these residues are replaced by the amino acids occurring in these positions in sCT to give [Ser²⁹, Thr³¹]-hCT, the hypocalcemic activity is fivefold greater than hCT.[86] If positions 29 and 31 of sCT are replaced by the residues found in hCT, the activity drops by half.[87] Further studies of the conformational properties and role in receptor binding are required to define the features of the carboxyl terminal portion of CT which are important for biological activity.

13.10.2.7 Receptor

The most documented biological effect of CT is its inhibition of bone resorption. Autoradiographic studies have demonstrated that CT binding sites in bone are present in osteoclasts.[88] The characteristics of the CT receptor in isolated rat osteoclasts have recently been studied.[89] The dissociation constant of sCT and osteoclast receptors is $1-6 \times 10^{-10}$ M. The receptor sites are most prevalent on multinucleated cells (80%). After covalent crosslinking, the receptor was shown to have $M_r = 80-90$ kDa. Chicken osteoclasts, in contrast, do not respond to CT and do not have CT receptors.[90]

Kidney is another target organ of CT. Autoradiographic studies demonstrate that CT binding sites are located on the superficial layer of the cortex and the outer medulla.[91] These sites are down-regulated by high concentrations of sCT.[91] The characteristics of these receptors are similar to those of osteoclasts. They have a dissociation constant of 7.6×10^{-10} M for sCT.[92] Crosslinking studies have identified a protein component of similar size ($M_r = 70$ kDa) as well as two additional components with $M_r = 33$ and 40 kDa. There is a kidney cell line which expresses CT receptors.[93]

As with many peptide hormones, CT has receptor sites in the brain. Calcitonin-like immunoreactivity has been detected in various regions of the brain[94] although the synthesis of CT in the brain has not been demonstrated. Binding of sCT to preparations from different regions of the brain show a number of regions that can bind sCT. Particularly high specific binding occurs in the hypothalamus.[95] The hypothalamic receptors are high affinity with an estimated $K_D = 3.7 \times 10^{-11}$ M.[96] Autoradiographic studies confirm the binding of CT to the hypothalamus and several other regions of the brain (see refs. 96 and 97 and references therein). The effects of CT on pituitary hormone release may also be mediated through hypothalamic receptors by regulating the production of releasing factors.

Human breast cancer cells also have CT receptors. These receptors have a component of similar size, $M_r = 85$ kDa, to other CT receptors.[98] This receptor is glycosylated[99] and the hormone–receptor complex is processed by endocytosis.[100]

Calcitonin receptors have also been demonstrated on lymphocytes,[101] lung,[102] Leydig cells[103] and liver.[104] Most of the studies of CT receptors have used [^{125}I]-labelled sCT with hCT having little affinity for these receptors. The study of hepatic receptors[104] used [^{125}I]-labelled hCT. In this work, [Asu^{1,7}]eel CT had only a weak potency in displacing the hCT. This is opposite to the more common observation of ultimobranchial CT having a higher potency than mammalian CT. The biological function, if any, of CT receptors in some of these tissues has not been established.

A recent review discussing the calcitonin receptor has appeared.[105]

13.10.2.8 Therapeutic Applications

The only established clinical use of CT is in the treatment of Paget's disease of bone. It is used for this condition to relieve bone pain, prevent development of bone deformity, reduce the incidence of fractures, produce a reconstructive action on the osteolytic lesion, and decrease hypercalciuria. Three forms of CT are currently in clinical use. These are the carba-type analog of eel CT (Elcatonin, Toyojozo Company), sCT (Armour Pharmaceutical Company and Sandoz Company) and hCT (Ciba-Geigy). There is current interest in new forms of drug delivery for CT. Parenteral administration of sCT or hCT entrapped in liposomes enhances the hypocalcemic potency of the hormone.[106] Salmon CT administered by nasal spray or by suppository showed renal activity. Although these routes of administration were less effective than the parenteral route, both new modes of administration improved the focal bone balance of osteolytic lesions of Paget's disease and were free of systemic side effects.[107]

Administration of sCT over a twelve-month period has been shown to result in increased bone mass in women with postmenopausal osteoporosis.[108] It has also been suggested that CT treatment of postmenopausal osteoporosis is only effective over a long period of time if other hormones are intermittently administered. A model of bone remodeling occurring in discrete packets has led to the adoption of coherence therapy consisting of the stages: activate, depress, free, repeat. Coherence treatment with growth hormone and sCT has given promising results.[109]

Calcitonin levels are elevated in preterm infants compared with term infants. This has led to the suggestion that CT has a pathogenic role in neonatal hypocalcemia.[110] A CT antagonist could be useful in the treatment of this condition.

Calcitonin also has effects on the central nervous system. Salmon CT has been found effective in treating intractable pain from advanced malignancy.[111,112] It has also been successfully applied in migraine prophylaxis.[113]

13.10.3 PARATHYROID HORMONE

13.10.3.1 Biosynthesis

A single gene, localized to chromosome 11, encodes PTH. Regulation of transcription of the PTH gene has been investigated recently. Sherwood and co-workers[114] were able to show by an analysis of PTH mRNA levels that treatment of cells with 1,25-dihydroxy vitamin D_3 (1,25(OH)$_2$D$_3$) decreased the levels of PTH mRNA. This decrease was slow to manifest itself taking up to 24 hours after treatment, reflecting the relatively long half-life of PTH mRNA. Sherwood and co-workers[115] and also Heinrich *et al.*[116] found that PTH mRNA levels did not increase in response to decreasing extracellular calcium levels, but that PTH mRNA decreased with increased extracellular calcium. These data suggest that the PTH gene is normally transcribed at a maximal rate and that under certain conditions, like hypercalcemia or increased 1,25(OH)$_2$D$_3$ levels, transcription is decreased. The amount of PTH secreted is also controlled post-transcriptionally.

Transcriptional control of PTH synthesis has recently been investigated directly using a reporter gene, chloramphenicol acetyl transferase (CAT), fused to the 5′-untranslated region of the PTH gene.[117] A comparison of the effect on transcription of two different lengths of the 5′-untranslated region, 468 and 4600 bases, indicated that a silencer element was located within this region. Transcription of the 4600 base fusion containing the silencer element resulted in fivefold lower levels of CAT activity than transcription of the 468 base fusion. The availability of cloned parathyroid cell lines[118] and further studies with the CAT fusion system will allow direct examination of the transcriptional control by calcium and vitamin D metabolites.

The structure of the gene encoding PTH was obtained from the nucleotide sequence of the cloned gene. Like many other eukaryotic genes, the PTH gene contains introns. The larger intron, intron A, occurs in the 5'-untranslated region of the mRNA. Comparison of the bovine gene with the human and rat PTH genes shows that intron A varies significantly in size, 1714, 3400 and 1600 nucleotides, respectively.[119-121] The other intron, intron B, occurs within the region coding for the pro segment of preproPTH. This intron also varies in length but is much shorter, 119, 103 and 111 nucleotides in the bovine, human and rat genes, respectively.[119-121] After transcription, splicing removes the two introns to yield the intact mRNA which is transported from the nucleus to the cytoplasm where it is translated by ribosomes associated with the rough endoplasmic reticular membrane (RER).

The route of biosynthesis, transport and processing through the cell are outlined in Figure 2.

The PTH mRNA encodes a larger precursor protein preproPTH. The pre region is a structurally typical signal or leader sequence with a positively charged N terminus, a hydrophobic core and a region of small neutral amino acids at the cleavage site. The signal sequence is involved in the attachment of the ribosome to the RER *via* the signal recognition particle, docking protein pathway.[122] After attachment of the ribosome to the RER and the initiation of secretion the vectorial transfer of preproPTH across the RER membrane occurs. During this transfer the signal sequence is removed by an enzyme, signal peptidase, located on the lumenal side of the RER. ProPTH is subsequently released into the lumen of the RER and from there is transferred to the Golgi apparatus.

In the Golgi stack the proPTH is further processed by a trypsin-like activity, removing the hexapeptide pro region which is then rapidly degraded to yield the full length mature PTH.[123-125] After processing in the Golgi PTH is sequestered within secretory granules (formed by budding of the Golgi stack) where it remains until a suitable signal, such as low serum calcium, causes the cell to release PTH by exocytosis.

13.10.3.2 Metabolism

There is evidence that PTH can undergo further proteolytic cleavage while stored in the parathyroid cell, by a parathyroid cathepsin B.[123] This protease cleaves intact PTH between Ala-(36) and Leu-(37) to yield both N-terminal and C-terminal fragments. The C-terminal fragment is stable to further proteolytic action while N-terminal fragments are degraded further by the cathepsin to yield inactive fragments.[123] The rate of proteolysis appears to be related, although possibly indirectly, to the levels of serum calcium. In hypocalcemia, when stimulation of secretion is maximal, the rate of cleavage is decreased due to the minimal length of time PTH remains stored in granules.[123] N-terminal and C-terminal fragments are released into the circulation together with intact hormone.

PTH secretion is primarily controlled by the level of calcium in the blood. Secretion is stimulated by a decrease in serum calcium. Under high levels of calcium PTH secretion is suppressed. The mechanism by which the calcium levels are relayed to the cell is not known. Alterations in extracellular calcium levels cause changes in the intracellular calcium levels which have an effect on PTH secretion. Calcium is not the only second messenger to affect PTH secretion as cAMP has also been found to cause PTH release.[126]

Other secretagogues, such as vitamin D metabolites, magnesium and agents that raise or lower intracellular cAMP, are known to have effects on PTH secretion.[126,127] However, these are not considered to be the major factors influencing PTH secretion and will not be described further.

PTH circulates as a mixture of fragments. These include the full length hormone, C-terminal fragments and N-terminal fragments. As mentioned previously PTH may undergo proteolytic processing in the parathyroid cell prior to its release, resulting in a stable C-terminal fragment and N-terminal fragments of various lengths which are most likely inactive. However, the major portion of fragments circulating in the blood are generated by peripheral proteolytic processing in both the kidney and the liver.[128]

The possible routes of metabolism and clearance are illustrated in Figure 3.

The liver can only take up intact hormone which is then cleaved into a C-terminal fragment and an N-terminal fragment. The N-terminal fragment is not released back into the circulation from the liver and probably undergoes further degradation. The C-terminal fragment is released from the liver.[128]

The kidney also takes up the intact hormone and cleaves it to form N-terminal and C-terminal fragments both of which are returned to the circulation. In addition, the kidney takes up N- and C-terminal fragments and is responsible for the clearance of approximately 45% of the N-terminal

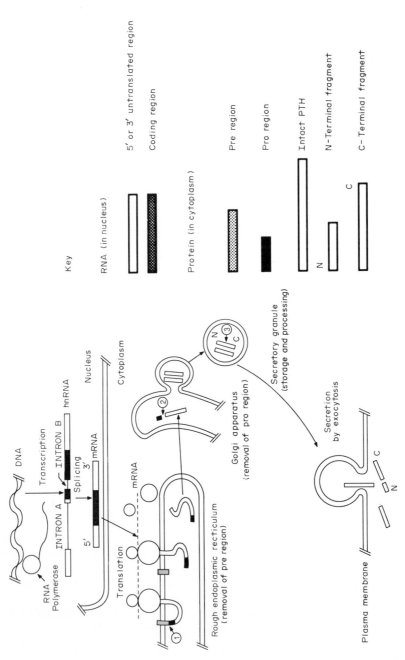

Figure 2   Pathway of biosynthesis and secretion of PTH, with representations of proteolytic cleavages by the following enzymes: ① signal peptidase, ② trypsin-like protease, ③ cathepsin B

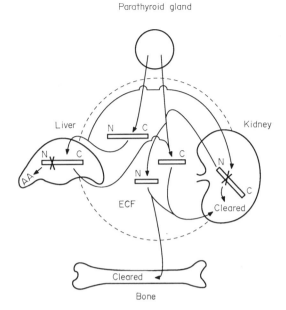

Figure 3 Routes of metabolism and clearance of PTH. Intact and N- and C-terminal fragments are released from the parathyroid gland into the extracellular fluid (ECF). Arrows leading from PTH or its fragment to a tissue indicate its involvement in metabolism or clearance (AA; amino acids)

fragments from the circulation.[128] Bone also plays a role in the clearance of the N-terminal fragments. Martin *et al.* have shown in an isolated perfused bone system that bone can remove bPTH(1-34), up to 36% as measured by arterovenous difference. Unlike kidney and liver, bone does not apparently take up the intact peptide or its C-terminal fragment.[128]

The major cleavage sites in PTH which yield the N-terminal and C-terminal fragments have been shown to be between residues 33–34 and 36–37.[128,129] Cleavage of intact PTH by the parathyroid cathepsin B occurs only between residues 36–37.[123] Since the full spectrum of bioactivity of PTH resides in the N-terminal 1-to-34 region[130] (see Section 13.10.3.3) these cleavages could result in release of biologically active N-terminal fragments. Indeed, this processing may be of profound physiological relevance since there have been reports that PTH(1–84) does not exert effects on bone.[128,131]

13.10.3.3 Bioactivity

The principal target tissues for PTH are bone, kidney and indirectly the gut. This is illustrated in Figure 4. As mentioned above the bioactive component of PTH has been localized to the N-terminal 1-to-34 fragment while the C-terminal fragment is apparently inactive. In addition, the N-terminal fragment generated *in vivo*, 1-to-34-like in size, may be the biologically important hormone in bone; a number of *in vivo* assays have suggested that the intact 1-to-84 hormone is biologically inactive unless it has passed through the circulation.[132a,b] This suggests processing at some peripheral site.[128,131]

PTH, like other peptide hormones, exerts effects on its target tissues by interacting with a PTH-specific receptor (see Section 13.10.3.7). PTH receptors coupled to adenylate cyclase are present at a number of sites in the renal tissue[133] and are also present in bone cells. PTH receptors have been localized to bone cells by autoradiography of chick calvaria after labeling with iodinated [^{125}I]-bPTH(1-34). Receptors were shown to reside specifically on osteoblasts and their progenitor cells but not osteoclasts.[134]

The receptor response is relayed to the cell *via* a second messenger. In the case of PTH this second messenger is known to be cAMP, although other second messengers may contribute to the PTH response. The PTH receptor is coupled to the adenylate cyclase through the guanine nucleotide-binding protein. Upon interaction of PTH with its receptor the hormone–receptor complex interacts with the stimulatory guanine nucleotide-binding protein which exchanges bound GDP for GTP. The guanine nucleotide-binding protein then stimulates the catalytic subunit of adenylate cyclase

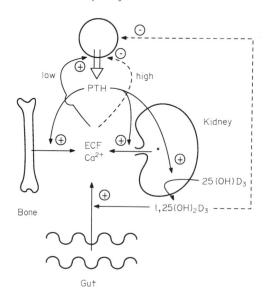

Figure 4   Sites of action of PTH. PTH is secreted from the parathyroid gland in response to a decrease in the calcium levels in blood. Solid arrows leading from PTH, calcium in the extracellular fluid (ECF) and 1,25(OH)$_2$ vitamin D$_3$ represent a positive effect on the respective tissues. Broken lines leading from 1,25(OH)$_2$ vitamin D$_3$ and ECF calcium indicate negative feedback on PTH secretion

causing the hydrolysis of the bound GTP and an increase in cAMP production. This pathway of hormone stimulation of adenylate cyclase has been previously described.[135]

PTH elicits its response in kidney by immediately increasing levels of cAMP in renal tissue and urine. The cellular response to the increased levels of cAMP results in increased reabsorption of calcium and decreased reabsorption of phosphate in the renal tubules. In addition to these responses, PTH also increases the activity of the vitamin D 1-α hydroxylase which results in an increase in the production of 1,25(OH)$_2$D$_3$. Elevated levels of active vitamin D cause an increase in the absorption of calcium, from the diet, through the intestine.

Localization of PTH receptors in bone cells is somewhat paradoxical. It has not been possible to demonstrate PTH receptors on osteoclasts. Osteoblasts, on the other hand, which are responsible for bone formation do have PTH receptors. It has been suggested that after stimulation by PTH the osteoblasts decrease their rate of matrix production and release a cytokine which is involved in osteoclast recruitment and activation.[136] Other possible mechanisms have been proposed to account for the involvement of osteoblasts in bone resorption. These include a possible direct involvement of osteoblasts in bone resorption by the synthesis and release of collagenase after stimulation by PTH.[137] Rodan and Martin[138] proposed that osteoblasts normally line the bone surface and prevent osteoclast access to bone. After stimulation by PTH the osteoblast changes shape permitting bone resorption by osteoclasts which now have access to the bone surface.[138] PTH may also have an effect on osteocytes and be able to mobilize calcium release from pools localized close to the osteocyte. This release of calcium by osteocytes might be important in the short-term regulation of calcium homeostasis.[139]

PTH has also been shown to have a vasodilatory effect on vascular smooth muscle with an EC$_{50}$ of 10^{-9} M. This response does not appear to be mediated by cAMP.[140,141] This suggests that at least some responses to PTH may be transmitted by a second messenger other than cAMP. Likely candidates for alternate second messengers are calcium fluxes, protein phosphorylation by protein kinase C and increased phosphatidylinositol breakdown. Increased calcium fluxes and stimulation of phosphoinositol triphosphate production have been reported[142,143] in UMR-106 cells after treatment with PTH.

The precedent for hormone action being mediated by more than one second messenger is glucagon which had been assumed to act solely through the adenylate cyclase system. However, recently it was shown to also work through the phosphoinositol pathway[144] (see also Chapter 13.5). This was determined when analogs that were able to favor one of the two pathways became available.

13.10.3.4 Structure

The primary structure of preproPTH from human, bovine and rat is shown in Figure 5. PTH is a single chain polypeptide of 84 amino acids. It does not contain any disulfide bonds and is therefore relatively free to alter its conformation in response to its environment. As can be seen from Figure 5, PTH sequences from different species have high degrees of homology with one another. The limited differences between the sequences, in the N terminus, are of especial interest in studies relating structure to activity and might explain the different potencies displayed by the various forms in certain *in vivo* and *in vitro* assays.[126,145]

PTH has not been crystallized and therefore its tertiary structure is not known. The structure of PTH has been examined using standard biophysical techniques such as proton nuclear magnetic resonance spectroscopy (NMR) and circular dichroism (CD).

Based on NMR studies, Zull and Lev[146] proposed a theoretical model for the structure of the intact PTH molecule. This model has structured regions at both the N and C terminus connected by a short string of amino acids. Zull and Lev postulate that the structure at the N terminus depends upon a hydrophobic interaction between certain amino acids in the 1-to-34 region.

In addition the structure of the PTH molecule has also been examined by high-resolution dark-field electron microscopy. The predicted structure from a Chou and Fasman analysis was fitted to the observed structure seen. Chou and Fasman predictions of the structure of PTH indicate regions of α helix, β sheet and β turns.[123,147] The structure, proposed by Fiskin *et al.*,[148] is described in a review by Cohn and MacGregor.[123]

13.10.3.4.1 *Conformational properties*

Circular dichroism has been used to investigate the structure of PTH in both aqueous and non-aqueous environments. The results of this type of study are discussed in the review by Cohn and MacGregor.[123] In general PTH has less α-helical content in aqueous solution than predicted but this increases in a hydrophobic environment, almost reaching predicted values. Similar results have recently been obtained with hPTH(1-34)[149] and with a number of bPTH and hPTH 1-to-34 analogs.[147]

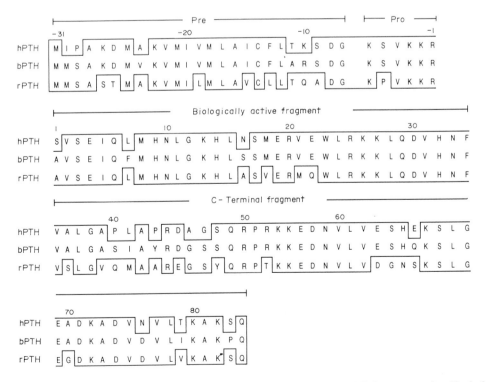

Figure 5 Comparison of the primary amino acid sequences of human, bovine and rat PTH. Sequences enclosed in the boxed area indicate homology (sequences were taken from refs. 109–111)

Bundi *et al.*, using a pentapeptide of the 20-to-24 region, demonstrated by NMR that the side groups of the Val-(21) and Trp-(23) interact and support a structural motif similar to a γ turn.[150] This observation has been confirmed by Zull and co-workers in studies with the 1-to-34 region. In addition, a des-Lys-(13) sequence of this fragment destabilizes the interaction of the Val-(21) and Trp-(23).[151] These workers have also demonstrated that the three His residues are exposed differently to the solvent environment. His-(9) and His-(32) have less access to solvent than His-(14); this agrees with the structural model in which the former two His residues are involved in the hydrophobic core.[152] Zull and co-workers have also shown that the two methionines in positions 8 and 18 have different labilities with respect to oxidation. In agreement with their model the Met-(8) is more protected than Met-(18), again indicating its possible involvement in a hydrophobic core.[153]

The shift to a somewhat more ordered structure in a non-aqueous environment may be critical for the interaction of PTH with its receptor. PTH could circulate in a relatively flexible structure and upon interaction with the phospholipid bilayer of the cell it could become a more rigid structure. Possibly PTH could form an amphipathic helix in the membrane,[154] a structure proposed to be important in the interaction of peptide ligands with their receptors[155] (see Section 13.10.2.6.2). Construction of helical wheels for PTH to examine this possibility does indeed suggest that PTH could form an amphipathic helix at its N terminus, specifically between residues 1-to-8 and 15-to-25.[146] The possibility of a change in structure may be an important consideration to take into account when designing potential antagonists.

13.10.3.5 Assays for Structure–Activity Studies

Table 2 lists *in vitro* and *in vivo* assays that have been and are presently being used for structure–function studies. To describe each assay in detail is beyond the scope of this review and more details of each can be obtained from the relevant reference given in the table. Additional information on assays is available in the review by Cohn and MacGregor[123] which also describes relative differences in the respective units of measure of PTH activity.

It should be stressed that the majority of structure–function studies have been done *in vitro* and this is particularly true for antagonist studies. The reason for this is simply that to obtain significant data *in vivo*, prohibitive amounts of antagonists are consumed. Nevertheless, [Tyr[34]]-bPTH(7-34)NH$_2$[172] has been shown to be a true antagonist in a number of different *in vivo* assays.[156,158]

Table 2 Bioassays Used for Structure–Activity Relationships for PTH

Assay	Response	Ref.
Whole animals		
Rat (TPTX)[a]	Urinary cAMP, P$_i$	156
Rat-acute (TPTX, NX)[b]	Serum calcium	157
Rat (TPTX)	Serum calcium	158
Canine (TPTX)	Serum calcium, urinary cAMP, P$_i$	159
Chick	Serum calcium	160
Tissue		
Perfused bone	cAMP, calcium release	132, 161
Isolated bone	Calcium release	162
Cells		
Osteoblastic		
UMR-106	cAMP	163
MC3T3	cAMP	164
ROS 17/2.8	cAMP	165
Renal		
Oppossum kidney (OK)	cAMP	166
Others		
Human bone giant cells	cAMP	167
Human forskin fibroblast	cAMP	167
Rabbit costal chondrocytes	cAMP	168
Membranes		
Renal cortex (rat/bovine/canine)	cAMP/binding	169–171

[a] TPTX = thyroparathyroidectomy. [b] NX = nephrectomy.

At present there is not a good *in vitro* assay that reliably predicts partial agonism *in vivo*. It is worthwhile stating that an antagonist *in vitro* should be judged to be an antagonist only when it has been shown to be an antagonist *in vivo*, as was demonstrated by studies with [Nle[8,18], Tyr[34]]bPTH(3-34)NH$_2$[156] (see Section 13.10.3.6.1).

13.10.3.6 Structure–Activity Relationships

13.10.3.6.1 *Agonists*

Studies covered in previous reviews[126,173,174] for both agonists and antagonists will only briefly be discussed here. The knowledge that the biological function resided in the N-terminal 1-to-34 fragment indicated that structure–function analysis could be performed on the 1-to-34 bPTH sequence. Removal of the first amino acid decreases the bioactivity by 95% and removal of the second effectively abolished agonist activity[126] and resulted in a compound with antagonist activity. Thus it appeared that the 3-to-34 region was a potential antagonist. The sulfur-free analog of the 1-to-34 region, [Nle[8,18], Tyr[34]]bPTH-(3-34)NH$_2$, which is a potent antagonist *in vitro* (for example see Table 4), when assayed *in vivo* in both a canine[159] and rat[175] model was found to be a weak agonist. In the canine assay it had 1% of the activity of bPTH-(1-34) and, in addition, had no antagonist activity.[159] In the rat assay [Nle[8,18], Tyr[34]]bPTH-(3-34)NH$_2$ was 50-fold less potent than bPTH-(1-34) and was not assayed for antagonist properties.[175] However, the [Nle[8,18], Tyr[34]]bPTH-(3-34)NH$_2$ peptide is still used as an *in vitro* antagonist due to its high affinity for the PTH receptor but in light of the results obtained *in vivo* studies using this peptide have to be evaluated with this in mind. Subsequently, further truncation at the amino terminus to residue 7 has revealed a true antagonist (see Section 13.10.3.6.2).

In addition other structure–function studies have been reported in which the C-terminus of the 1-to-34 region has been truncated. Fragment 1-to-31 was found to have lost 85% of the activity and further truncation decreased this value. It was also shown that the 1-to-34 sequence had to be contiguous since a mixture of the 1-to-12 and 13-to-34 fragments was inactive. Replacement of the C-terminal Phe-(34) by Tyr-(34) amide was found to increase the activity of the 1-to-34 fragment up to threefold perhaps by generating a more biologically stable peptide. Finally, replacement of the Met residues at 8 and 18 by the almost isosteric norleucine increased the activity of the 1-to-34 fragment up to twofold.[126] This fragment has proved invaluable as a tool for studying the PTH receptor (see Section 13.10.3.7).

Chou and Fasman predictions indicate the possibility of a β turn around position 12 in the PTH sequence.[145] Recently this possibility has been investigated[176] in the hPTH 1-to-34 fragment by either increasing or decreasing the propensity for a β turn. A residue such as proline substituted for glycine results in a stronger β turn, while substitutions such as L-Ala and D-Ala favor a helix conformation, although not totally eliminating the chance of a β turn. Analogs were synthesized with the above substitutions and assayed in bovine renal cortical membrane binding and adenylate cyclase assays.[171] As can be seen in Table 3 the Pro-(12) substitution effectively eliminated the bioactivity of the fragment while both the L-Ala and D-Ala substitutions were well tolerated. This

Table 3 Biological Activity of Bovine and Human N-terminal PTH Agonist Analogs in Bovine Renal Cortical Membrane Assays

Analog	Biological activity	
	Binding K_i (nmol L^{-1})	Adenylate cyclase K_m (nmol L^{-1})
Reference compounds		
[Tyr[34]]bPTH(1-34)NH$_2$	1.1 ± 0.3	1.1 ± 0.4
[Tyr[34]]hPTH(1-34)NH$_2$	0.7 ± 0.3	0.7 ± 0.1
Position 12 substitutions		
[Ala[12],Tyr[34]]hPTH(1-34)NH$_2$	1.0 ± 0.1	1.5 ± 0.2
[D-Ala[12],Tyr[34]]hPTH(1-34)NH$_2$	0.8 ± 0.1	1.4 ± 0.1
[Pro[12],Tyr[34]]hPTH(1-34)NH$_2$	590 ± 200	2500 ± 800
C-terminal extension		
[Tyr[34]]hPTH(1-38)NH$_2$	1.3 ± 0.3	2.3 ± 1.1

(Taken from refs. 171 and 176).

strongly suggests that the preferred conformation of the 1-to-34 fragment around residue 12 is helical and not a β turn.

One other structure–function issue was examined. The C terminus was extended to see if this resulted in an increase in potency as has been suggested.[177a] The bPTH(1-38)NH$_2$ peptide was found to be equipotent to the 1-to-34 peptide (Table 3).

13.10.3.6.2 *Antagonists*

As mentioned above the 3-to-34 region of PTH, [Nle^{8,18},Tyr^{34}]bPTH(3-34)NH$_2$, appeared to be an antagonist *in vitro* but in canine and rat *in vivo* assays it was found to have weak agonist properties. Further truncation of the amino terminus to 7 yielded a full antagonist. This antagonist has a low binding affinity for the PTH receptor and when assayed *in vivo* required a 200-fold molar excess to cause an inhibition of the PTH action on kidney[156] and bone.[158]

The kinds of structure–function studies described above for the 1-to-34 region have also been performed on the 7-to-34 region (Table 4).

As with the 1-to-34 the presence of an amino acid that stabilizes a β turn, sarcosine (Sar) or Pro, caused a decrease in potency suggesting that an α helical confirmation is the preferred structure around residue 12 in the antagonist as well as the agonist.

Recently a more potent antagonist of PTH has been reported[177b] which incorporates a non-natural amino acid, D-Trp, substituted for Gly at position 12. *In vitro* in a bone-based (rat osteosarcoma, ROS 17/2.8, cells) and a kidney-based (bovine renal cortical plasma membranes) assay [D-Trp^{12}, Tyr^{34}]bPTH(7-34)NH$_2$ was 10- to 30-fold more potent than [Tyr^{34}]bPTH-(7-34)NH$_2$ in inhibiting both PTH binding and PTH-stimulated adenylate cyclase.[177b] The rationale for the incorporation of the D-Trp at position 12 was based upon the results shown in Table 4 where substitutions that did not introduce a helix breaking residue were well tolerated. The increased potency was specific to the D-Trp substitution as substitution of L-Trp did not result in increased antagonist potency.[177b] Future work will determine whether this new antagonist is as effective *in vivo* as it is *in vitro*.

As mentioned above, NMR studies focusing on residues 20-to-24 have indicated a possible γ turn in that region. To investigate this possibility a similar approach to that described above for Gly-(12)

Table 4 Biological Activity of Human and Bovine N-terminal PTH Antagonist Analogs in Bovine Renal Cortical Membrane Assays

Analog	Biological activity	
	Binding K_i (nmol L^{-1})	Adenylate cyclase K_i (nmol L^{-1})
Reference compounds		
[Tyr^{34}]hPTH(7-34)NH$_2$	260 ± 40	840 ± 180
[Tyr^{34}]bPTH(7-34)NH$_2$	76 ± 9	840 ± 70
[Nle^{8,18}, Tyr^{34}]bPTH(7-34)NH$_2$	150 ± 10	1600 ± 300
Position 12 substitutions		
[Ala^{12}, Tyr^{34}]hPTH(7-34)NH$_2$	110 ± 30	410 ± 70
[D-Ala^{12}, Tyr^{34}]hPTH(7-34)NH$_2$	120 ± 10	610 ± 120
[Pro^{12}, Tyr^{34}]hPTH(7-34)NH$_2$	470 ± 40	6300
[Sar^{12}, Tyr^{34}]bPTH(7-34)NH$_2$	500 ± 90	2500 ± 700
Position 22/23 substitutions		
[D-Trp^{23}, Tyr^{34}]bPTH(7-34)NH$_2$	76 000 ± 15 000	96 000 ± 16 000
[Phe^{23}, Tyr^{34}]bPTH(7-34)NH$_2$	480 ± 30	2300 ± 800
[Nle^{8,18}, Leu^{23}, Tyr^{34}]bPTH(7-34)NH$_2$	2300 ± 900	7100
[Nle^{8,18}, N-MePhe^{23}, Tyr^{34}]bPTH(7-34)NH$_2$	> 30 000	
[Nle^{8,18}, N-MeGlu^{22}, Tyr^{34}]bPTH(7-34)NH$_2$	8000 ± 1500	40 000
C-terminal and N-terminal extension		
[Tyr^{34}]bPTH(7-38)NH$_2$	520 ± 110	2100 ± 1100
[Tyr^{34}]hPTH(7-38)NH$_2$	640 ± 160	4800 ± 800
[Tyr^{34}]bPTH(5-34)NH$_2$	120 ± 20	1600 ± 300
[Tyr^{34}]bPTH(5-38)NH$_2$	530 ± 180	1300 ± 200
[Nle^{8,18}, Tyr^{34}]bPTH(3-34)NH$_2$	2.9 ± 0.3	32 ± 4

(Taken from refs. 171 and 176).

Figure 6 Comparison of hPTH(1-34) with the 1-to-34 sequence of the human hypercalcemia of malignancy factor.[179] Sequence homology of hHCF with hPTH is indicated by inclusion in the boxed area

was taken. As Table 4 shows, substitution of D-Trp-(23) or Leu-(23) for L-Trp-(23) was not well tolerated which suggests that the side group of the L-Trp is involved in the interaction with Val-(21). However, substitution of *N*-MeGlu-(22) for Glu-(22) or *N*-MePhe-(23) for Trp-(23), both of which should stabilize a γ turn, resulted in a loss of activity. This could be explained by a steric effect of the *N*-methyl group rather than the absence of a γ turn, so it is still uncertain that a γ turn is present in this region and further work is required to answer this question.

Extensions of the N terminus and C terminus were also examined. The 7-to-38 analog was less potent than the 7-to-34 peptide while extension to residue 5 had little if any effect on activity. Further extension to residue 3 caused an increase in potency but, as mentioned before, the 3-to-34 analog displays agonism *in vivo*.

Future structure–function studies will be made possible by the recent purification and cloning of the hypercalcemia of malignancy factor (HCF).[178,179] The existence of this factor, exerting its effect through the PTH receptor, was proposed over 40 years ago. The human tumor factor, isolated from a squameous carcinoma of the lung cell line, has a high degree of homology with PTH at the N terminus (8 of the first 13 are identical), see Figure 6. The C-terminal regions from residue 14 vary substantially. HCF is longer than PTH, containing a total of 141 amino acids in the intact molecule.[179] In addition a similar protein has been cloned from a human renal carcinoma.[180] This protein is identical to that isolated from the lung cells except that it is two amino acids shorter at the C terminus.

Like PTH, HCF has a biologically active N-terminal fragment. The 1-to-34 sequence of HCF (Figure 6) was synthesized in our laboratory and was found to display similar bioactivities to PTH in all systems examined.[157] These results and results by others[181] confirm that the hypercalcemia factor does work through the PTH receptor. Furthermore [Nle^{8,18},Tyr^{34}]bPTH(3-34)NH$_2$ can block effects of the hypercalcemia of malignancy factor *in vitro*.[182]

13.10.3.7 Receptor

The PTH receptor has been under study for a number of years and a substantial body of information relating to it has been accumulated. The major advance in studying the receptor was the synthesis of the sulfur-free analog of bPTH(1-34), [Nle^{8,18},Tyr^{34}]bPTH(1-34)NH$_2$. This peptide permitted the isolation of biologically active iodinated peptide and the development of a photoaffinity labelling reagent.[183,184] A number of groups have used this reagent or the iodinated [Nle^{8,18},Tyr^{34}]bPTH(1-34)NH$_2$ with an affinity crosslinking approach to identify the PTH receptor.[185,186] The molecular weights reported for the PTH receptor are 70 to 85 kDa.[183,185-188] The differences in size could be the result of proteolysis of the 85 kDa protein,[185] and would depend on the techniques used to isolate the receptor and the precautions taken therein to protect against proteolysis. Although different sizes for the PTH receptor have been reported, as mentioned above, one investigation showed only a single size for the PTH receptor, 70 kDa, present in different tissues and in different species.[187]

In addition to the principally labeled 70–85 kDa protein other molecular forms have been reported. Proteins of 95 and 28 kDa have been shown to competitively label in the osteogenic osteosarcoma cell line, ROS 17/2.8.[185] Others have reported 130, 55 and 14 kDa species in canine renal membranes.[186,189] A 55 kDa PTH-binding protein has also been observed in bovine renal membrane preparations.[190]

The relationship between all these different PTH-binding proteins is not clear. However, Karpf *et al.*[189] have been able to demonstrate that the 55 and the 85 kDa proteins from canine renal membranes are cleaved into similar proteolytic fragments after treatment with Staph V8 or elastase. They were also able to show that the 14 kDa species was only seen on sodium dodecylsulfate polyacrylamide gel electrophoresis when samples had been reduced with dithiothreitol, suggesting that the 14 kDa species is normally associated with the higher molecular weight species *via* a disulfide bridge.[189]

The 70–85 kDa PTH receptor has been shown to contain complex N-linked glycans. The glycosylated PTH receptor binds to wheat germ agglutinin, succinylated wheat germ agglutinin and ricin suggesting the presence of terminal sialic acid.[191a,b] Karpf and co-workers have shown that after deglycosidation with Endoglycosidase F the 85 kDa PTH receptor has a molecular weight of 58 kDa. They have shown that lectins bound to the PTH receptor can inhibit binding of ligand suggesting that part of the glycan is close to the PTH-binding site on the receptor.[191a]

As mentioned earlier the PTH receptor is coupled to the adenylate cyclase *via* a guanidine nucleotide-binding protein, G_s. Nissenson *et al.* have shown that iodinated PTH bound to canine renal membranes which are then solubilized with CHAPS is associated with a protein complex. Upon incubation of this complex with GTP or its analogs, PTH was released. ATP was ineffective in this process. This is in good agreement with the predicted behavior of the receptor bound to a G_s protein. They found that the PTH–protein complex migrated at a molecular mass of 180 kDa on gel filtration and proposed that this represented the 70 kDa PTH-binding protein complexed with the G_s protein.[192]

The purification of the PTH receptor to homogeneity has been elusive. The major stumbling block has been the absence of PTH binding to solubilized receptors.[192] However, a number of different approaches have been used to try to obtain purified receptor; these are briefly described below.

Wright *et al.* utilized the finding that PTH crosslinked to the PTH receptor is still recognized by an N-terminal specific antiPTH antibody.[185]

Karpf *et al.* have reported a similar approach with the additional step of a wheat germ agglutinin column. They report a 200-fold purification with a combination of these two steps.[191]

Brennan and Levine have used biotin–avidin chemistry to try to purify the receptor. They have been able to demonstrate that biotin-labeled PTH is still competitively bound to the PTH receptor and that after crosslinking of the biotin–PTH a protein of molecular weight 68–70 kDa can be isolated by binding to streptavidin. In addition they report conditions for binding of PTH to solubilized receptor.[188]

Zull and co-workers were able to identify a 50 kDa protein on two-dimensional SDS polyacrylamide gel electrophoresis that bound PTH. They used solubilized porcine renal membranes run directly on this gel system to purify this PTH-binding protein.[190]

As yet there is no published sequence for the PTH receptor but progress with the different approaches that have been taken indicates that this will shortly be forthcoming. This will ultimately lead to cloning of the PTH receptor cDNA and its expression in a mammalian cell line to demonstrate functionality.

It will be interesting, once the PTH receptor has been cloned, to compare its structure with other adenylate cyclase coupled receptors such as the β-adrenergic receptor. The β-adrenergic receptor has recently been cloned[193] and shown to contain an N-terminal extracellular domain, seven membrane-spanning regions and a C-terminal cytoplasmic domain.[194] Rhodopsin bears homology to the β-adrenergic receptor;[193] it is coupled to transducin and is known to have seven membrane-spanning regions.[195] This could conceivably be the gross structure of the PTH receptor and other G protein-linked signal transducers.

13.10.3.8 Therapeutic Applications

The possible therapeutic applications for a potent PTH antagonist have been well documented elsewhere.[196,197] Table 5 gives a list of the possible uses of an antagonist of PTH. It is beyond the scope of this article to expand on the medical rationale for these proposed treatments.

In addition to the disease states listed in Table 5, the recent demonstration that the hypercalcemia of malignancy factor binds to the PTH receptor indicates that potential antagonists of PTH may also be antagonists of this new factor. *In vitro* [Nle[8,18], Tyr[34]]bPTH(3-34)NH$_2$ has been shown to be able to compete with the hypercalcemic factor for the PTH receptor.[182] This may suggest a new therapy for the hypercalcemia of malignancy associated with a number of cancers.

13.10.4 CONCLUSIONS

Calcitonin has long been recognized for its role in the regulation of the exchange of calcium between plasma and bone. Recent studies have demonstrated additional biological effects of CT on the central nervous system and on hormone release from endocrine cells. SAR studies have

Table 5 Potential Uses of PTH Antagonists[196]

Short-term treatment of hypercalcemic crisis ('parathyroid storm' due to parathyroid adenoma, hyperplasia or carcinoma);
    for preoperative optimization of blood calcium levels
Long-term treatment of hyperparathyroidism
    In high-risk surgical candidates
    In patients who have undergone unsuccessful surgery
    In parathyroid carcinoma (inoperable)
    For general medical management of hyperparathyroidism (?)
Adjunct treatment
    After renal transplantation, when there is persistent 'secondary' parathyroidism
    In osteoporosis (?)

---

elucidated some of the structural features required for the hypocalcemic activity of the hormone. Further studies are required to determine if these same structural features affect the other biological activities of CT. There are likely to be new therapeutic applications of CT and its analogs to other bone diseases such as osteoporosis, in addition to its use as an analgesic agent or as an inhibitor of the release of specific hormones.

Parathyroid hormone plays the opposite role to CT in calcium regulation and is recognized as the principal hormone responsible for increasing serum calcium by its action on bone, kidney and gut. At present PTH antagonists are not used as therapeutic agents due to the following reasons: very weak antagonism *in vivo* and lack of oral activity, *i.e.* the active peptide fails to reach the circulation due to proteolysis in the gut. The major problem of PTH antagonists at present is their weakness, since delivery could be accomplished by continuous intravenous administration or by an implanted pump. However, the cost to produce sufficient amounts of the best antagonist available, $[Tyr^{34}]bPTH(7-34)NH_2$, would be prohibitive. The ideal candidate for a PTH antagonist for therapeutic use would either be very potent and/or orally active. At present neither of these traits has been fulfilled. This may change as information obtained from the recent sequencing of the hypercalcemic factor is assimilated and new structure–function studies are initiated.

ACKNOWLEDGEMENT

Richard M. Epand is grateful for the collaboration of Dr. R. C. Orlowski with whom our studies of calcitonin have been undertaken. Michael P. Caulfield would like to thank Drs M. E. Goldman and M. Chorev for communication of their results prior to publication and to Dr J. Heath and J. E. Fisher for critically reading the manuscript.

13.10.5 REFERENCES

1. M. G. Rosenfeld, J.-J. Mermod, S. G. Amara, L. W. Swanson, P. E. Sawchenko, J. Rivier, W. W. Vale and R. M. Evans, *Nature (London)*, 1983, **304**, 129.
2. R. A. Bovenberg, W. P. van-de-Merendonk, P. D. Baas, P. H. Steenbergh, C. J. Lips and H. S. Jansz, *Nucleic Acids Res.*, 1986, **14**, 8785.
3. P. H. Steenbergh, J. W. Hoppener, J. Zandberg, A. Visser, C. J. Lips and H. S. Jansz, *FEBS Lett.*, 1986, **209**, 97.
4. B. A. Roos, J. A. Fischer, W. Pignat, C. B. Alander and L. G. Raisz, *Endocrinology (Baltimore)*, 1986, **118**, 46.
5. F. Lasmoles, A. Jullienne, C. Desplan, G. Milhaud and M. S. Moukhtar, *FEBS Lett.*, 1985, **180**, 113.
6. Y. Saito, M. Yasuhara, K. Okumura and R. Hori, *Biochem. Pharmacol.*, 1985, **34**, 3543.
7. R. M. Epand, R. F. Epand, R. C. Orlowski, R. J. Schleuter, L. T. Boni and S. W. Hui, *Biochemistry*, 1983, **22**, 5074.
8. A. Motta, M. A. Castiglione-Morelli, T. Tancredi, E. Trivellone, G. Borin, N. Goud and P. A. Temussi, *Abstracts, Am. Pept. Symp., 10th,* 1987, P-198.
9. G. R. Moe, R. J. Miller and E. T. Kaiser, *J. Am. Chem. Soc.*, 1983, **105**, 4100.
10. R. M. Epand, R. F. Epand, R. C. Orlowski, J. K. Seyler and R. L. Colescott, *Biochemistry*, 1986, **25**, 1964.
11. J. A. Fischer, P. H. Tobler, M. Kaufmann, W. Born, H. Henke, P. E. Cooper, S. M. Sagar and J. B. Martin, *Proc. Natl. Acad. Sci. USA*, 1981, **78**, 7801.
12. J. A. Fischer, P. H. Tobler, H. Henke and F. A. Tschopp, *Clin. Endocrinol. Metab.*, 1983, **57**, 1314.
13. P. H. Tobler, F. A. Tschopp, M. A. Dambacher and J. A. Fischer, *Clin. Endocrinol. (Oxford)*, 1984, **20**, 253.
14. F. Lasmoles, A. Jullienne, C. Desplan, G. Milhaud and M. S. Moukhtar, *FEBS Lett.*, 1985, **180**, 113.
15. T. J. Martin, J. M. Moseley, D. M. Findlay and V. P. Michelangeli, in 'Hormones in Normal and Abnormal Human Tissues', ed. K. Fotherby, Walter de Gruyter, Berlin, 1981, p. 429.
16. W. F. Neuman and N. Schneider, *Endocrinology (Baltimore)*, 1980, **107**, 2082.
17. R. A. Luben, G. L. Wong and D. V. Cohn, *Endocrinology (Baltimore)*, 1976, **99**, 526.
18. G. E. Gutierrez, G. R. Mundy and M. S. Katz, *Endocrinology (Baltimore)*, 1984, **115**, 2342.

19. V. P. Michelangeli, S. A. Livesey and T. J. Martin, *Biochem. J.*, 1984, **224**, 371.
20. S. Nicosia, F. Guidobono, M. Musanti and A. Pecile, *Life Sci.*, 1986, **39**, 2253.
21. M. S. Rappaport and P. H. Stern, *J. Bone Miner. Res.*, 1986, **1**, 173.
22. J. Patel, A. Fabbti, C. Pert, L. Gnessi, F. Fraioli and R. McDevitt, *Biochem. Biophys. Res. Commun.*, 1985, **130**, 669.
23. L. Gnessi, L. Silvestroni, A. Fabbri, C. Moretti, A. E. Panerai, V. Bonifacio and F. Fraioli, *Biochem. Biophys. Res. Commun.*, 1984, **125**, 199.
24. M. Nohmi, P. Shinnick-Gallagher, P.-W. Gean, J. P. Gallagher and C. W. Cooper, *Brain Res.*, 1986, **367**, 346.
25. M. Yamaguchi and J. R. Williamson, *Horm. Metab. Res.*, 1983, **15**, 176.
26. M. Yamaguchi and K. Momose, *Acta Endocrinol. (Copenhagen)*, 1983, **102**, 572.
27. M. J. de la Cruz, J. Alemany and A. de Cos, *Biochim. Biophys. Acta*, 1986, **852**, 169.
28. M. Koida, Y. Yamamoto, H. Nakamuta, J. Matsuo, M. Okamoto, T. Morimoto, J. K. Seyler and R. C. Orlowski, *Jpn. J. Pharmacol.*, 1982, **32**, 981.
29. A. N. Yusufi, T. J. Berndt, N. Murayama, F. G. Knox and T. P. Dousa, *Am. J. Physiol.*, 1987, **252**, F598.
30. A. Alwmark, M. W. Stavinoha, C. W. Cooper, G. H. Greeley, Jr. and J. C. Thompson, *Diabetes*, 1986, **35**, 58.
31. G. V. Shah, R. M. Epand and R. C. Orlowski, *J. Endocrinol.*, 1988, **116**, 279.
32. J. Pfeilschifter and G. R. Mundy, *Proc. Natl. Acad. Sci. USA*, 1987, **84**, 2024.
33. R. V. Talmage, S. A. Grubb, H. Norimatsu and C. J. Vanderwiel, *Proc. Natl. Acad. Sci. USA*, 19080, **77**, 609.
34. G. G. Jaros, P. C. Belonje, R. van Hoorn-Hickman and E. Newman, *Am. J. Physiol.*, 1984, **246**, R693.
35. J. P. Barlet, *J. Endocrinol.*, 1972, **55**, 153.
36. M. Yamaguchi and K. Katayama, *Endocrinol. Jpn.*, 1982, **29**, 401.
37. T. Matsui, N. Kuramitsu, H. Yano and R. Kawashima, *Endocrinol. Jpn.*, 1983, **30**, 485.
38. M. J. Twery and R. L. Moss, *Peptides (N.Y.)*, 1985, **6**, 373.
39. F. Guidobono, C. Netti, V. Sibilia, I. Villa, A. Zamboni and A. Pecile, *Peptides (N.Y.)*, 1986, **7**, 315.
40. W. J. Freed, M. J. Perlow and R. J. Wyatt, *Science (Washington, D.C.)*, 1979, **206**, 850.
41. S. A. Wager-Srdar, J. E. Morley and A. S. Levine, *Peptides (N.Y.)*, 1986, **7**, 729.
42. J. E. Morley, A. S. Levine and S. E. Silvis, *Science (Washington, D.C.)*, 1981, **214**, 671.
43. T. Mitsuma, T. Nogimori and M. Chaya, *Eur. J. Pharmacol.*, 1984, **102**, 123.
44. V. Olgiati, C. Netti, F. Guidobono and A. Pecile, *Endocrinology (Baltimore)*, 1982, **111**, 641.
45. A.-M. J. Lengyel and G. S. Tannenbaum, *Endocrinology (Baltimore)*, 1987, **120**, 1377.
46. R. M. Bolman, III, C. W. Copper, S. C. Garner, P. L. Munson and S. A. Wells, Jr., *Endocrinology (Baltimore)*, 1977, **100**, 1014.
47. A. Petralito, M. Lunetta, A. Liuzzo, C. E. Fiore and G. Heynen, *J. Endocrinol. Invest.*, 1979, **2**, 209.
48. N. Passariello, D. Giugliano, S. Sgambato, R. Torella and F. D'Onofrio, *J. Clin. Endocrinol. Metab.*, 1981, **53**, 318.
49. R. Candrina, B. Cerudelli, A. Cimino, A. Coppini, C. Figosa and G. Giustina, in 'Endocrinology 85', ed. G. M. Molinatti and L. Martini, Elsevier, Amsterdam, 1986, p. 225.
50. O. Schmitz, C. K. Christensen, S. E. Christensen and K. Emmertsen, *Horm. Metab. Res.*, 1984, **16**, 100.
51. J. J. Flynn, D. L. Margules, T.-C. Peng and C. W. Cooper, *Physiol. Behav.*, 1983, **31**, 79.
52. P. K. Seitz and C. W. Cooper, *Bone Miner.*, 1987, **2**, 53.
53. P. L. Moore, M. L. Strickland and M. F. Crass, III, *J. Hypertens.*, 1986, **4**, S186.
54. J. T. Potts, Jr. and G. D. Aurbach, in 'Handbook Physiology', section 7, Endocrinology 7, Williams and Wilkins, Baltimore, 1976, p. 423.
55. Y. Okimura, K. Chihara, H. Abe, H. Kaji, T. Kita, Y. Kashio and T. Fujita, *Endocrinol. Jpn.*, 1986, **33**, 273.
56. J. F. Habener, F. R. Singer, L. J. Deftos, R. M. Neer and J. T. Potts, Jr., *Nature (London)*, 1971, **232**, 91.
57. S. J. Marx, C. J. Woodward and G. D. Aurbach, *Science (Washington, D.C.)*, 1972, **178**, 999.
58. J. P. Segrest, R. L. Jackson, J. D. Morrisett and A. M. Gotto, Jr., *FEBS Lett.*, 1974, **38**, 247.
59. R. M. Epand, *Mol. Cell. Biochem.*, 1983,·**57**, 41.
60. S. W. Hui, R. M. Epand, K. R. Dell, R. F. Epand and R. C. Orlowski, *Biochim. Biophys. Acta*, 1984, **772**, 264.
61. G. R. Moe and E. T. Kaiser, *Biochemistry*, 1985, **24**, 1971.
62. R. M. Epand, R. F. Epand and R. C. Orlowski, *Int. J. Pept. Protein Res.*, 1985, **25**, 105.
63. D. M. Findlay, V. P. Michelangeli, R. C. Orlowski and T. J. Martin, *Endocrinology (Baltimore)*, 1983, **112**, 1288.
64. R. M. Epand, J. K. Seyler and R. C. Orlowski, *Eur. J. Biochem.*, 1986, **159**, 125.
65. R. C. Orlowski, R. M. Epand and A. R. Stafford, *Eur. J. Biochem.*, 1987, **162**, 399.
66. R. M. Epand, R. F. Epand, A. R. Stafford and R. C. Orlowski, *J. Med. Chem.*, 1988, **31**, 1595.
67. R. C. Orlowski and R. L. Colescott (Rorer Inc.), Serial No. 047 798 (Filing date May 6, 1987).
68. R. C. Orlowski, G. L. Stahl and R. L. Colescott (Rorer Inc.), *U.S. Pat.* 4 639 509 (1987) (*Chem. Abstr.*, 1987, **106**, 196 800).
69. D. M. Findlay, V. P. Michelangeli, T. J. Martin, R. C. Orlowski and J. K. Seyler, *Endocrinology (Baltimore)*, 1985, **117**, 801.
70. H. Nakamuta, M. Koida, Y. Ogawa and R. C. Orlowski, *Folia Pharmacol. Jpn.*, 1987, **89**, 191.
71. R. Maier, B. Kamber, B. Riniker and W. Rittel, *Horm. Metab. Res.*, 1975, **7**, 511.
72. F. R. Green, III, B. Lynch and E. T. Kaiser, *Proc. Natl. Acad. Sci. USA*, 1987, **84**, 8340.
73. S. P. Wood, I. J. Tickle, A. M. Treharne, J. E. Pitts, Y. Mascarenhas, J. Y. Li, J. Husain, S. Cooper, T. L. Blundell, V. J. Hruby, A. Buku, A. J. Fischman and H. R. Wyssbrod, *Science (Washington, D.C.)*, 1986, **232**, 633.
74. R. M. Epand and R. C. Orlowski, in 'Protides of the Biological Fluids', vol. 35, ed. H. Peeters, Pergamon Press, Oxford, 1987, p. 481.
75. K. E. Schwartz, R. C. Orlowski and R. Marcus, *Endocrinology (Baltimore)*, 1981, **108**, 831.
76. R. C. Orlowski and J. K. Seyler (Rorer Inc.), *US Pat.* 4 391 747 (1983) (*Chem. Abstr.*, 1983, **99**, 140 412).
77. R. C. Orlowski and J. K. Seyler (Rorer Inc.), *US Pat.* 4 605 514 (1986) (*Chem. Abstr.*, 1986, **105**, 209 401).
78. R. C. Orlowski and J. K. Seyler (Rorer Inc.), *US Pat.* 4 622 388 (1986) (*Chem. Abstr.*, 1987, **107**, 7614).
79. W. Rittel, R. Maier, M. Brugger, B. Kamber, B. Riniker and P. Sieber, *Experientia*, 1976, **32**, 246.
80. R. C. Orlowski and J. K. Seyler (Rorer Inc.), Serial No. 830, 785 (Filing date February 9, 1986).
81. D. Goltzman, *Endocrinology (Baltimore)*, 1980, **106**, 510.
82. H. J. Lenz, J. E. Rivier and M. R. Brown, *Regul. Pept.*, 1985, **12**, 81.

83. T. Morikawa, E. Munekata, S. Sakakibara, T. Noda and M. Otani, *Experientia*, 1976, **32**, 1104.
84. R. M. Epand, G. L. Stahl and R. C. Orlowski, *Int. J. Pept. Protein Res.*, 1986, **27**, 501.
85. I. Yamamoto, R. Morita, M. Fukunaga, S. Kohoh, C. Shigeno, K. Torizuka and T. Noda, *Endocrinology (Baltimore)*, 1981, **108**, 698.
86. R. Maier, B. Riniker and W. Rittel, *FEBS Lett.*, 1974, **48**, 68.
87. J. Pless, W. Bauer, H. Bossert, K. Zehnder and S. Guttmann, in 'Endocrinology 1971', Proceedings of the Third International Symposium, 1972, Heinemann Medical Books, London, p. 67.
88. H. Warshawsky, D. Goltzman, M. F. Rouleau and J. M. Bergeron, *J. Cell Biol.*, 1980, **85**, 682.
89. G. C. Nicholson, J. M. Moseley, P. M. Sexton, F. A. O. Mendelsohn and T. J. Martin, *J. Clin. Invest.*, 1986, **78**, 355.
90. G. C. Nicholson, J. M. Moseley, P. M. Sexton and T. J. Martin, *J. Bone Miner. Res.*, 1987, **2**, 53.
91. Z. Bouizar, W. H. Rostène and G. Milhaud, *Proc. Natl. Acad. Sci. USA*, 1987, **84**, 5125.
92. Z. Bouizar, M. Fouchereau-Peron, J. Taboulet, M. S. Moukhtar and G. Milhaud, *Eur. J. Biochem.*, 1986, **155**, 141.
93. A. Wohlwend, K. Malmström, H. Henke, H. Murer, J.-D. Vassalli and J. A. Fischer, *Biochem. Biophys. Res. Commun.*, 1985, **131**, 537.
94. J. A. Fishcer, P. H. Tobler, M. Kaufmann, W. Born, H. Henke, P. E. Cooper, S. M. Sagar and J. B. Martin, *Proc. Natl. Acad. Sci. USA*, 1981, **78**, 7801.
95. D. Goltzman and J. Mitchell, *Science (Washington, D.C.)*, 1985, **227**, 1343.
96. F. Guidobono, C. Netti, F. Pagani, P. Bettica, I. Villa and A. Pecile, *Neurosci. Lett.*, 1987, **79**, 91.
97. H. Henke, F. A. Tschopp and J. A. Fischer, *Brain Res.*, 1985, **360**, 165.
98. J. M. Moseley, D. M. Findlay, T. J. Martin and J. J. Gorman, *J. Biol. Chem.*, 1982, **257**, 5846.
99. J. M. Moseley, D. M. Findlay, J. J. Gorman, V. P. Michelangeli and T. J. Martin, *Biochem. J.*, 1983, **212**, 609.
100. D. M. Findlay, K. W. Ng, M. Niall and T. J. Martin, *Biochem. J.*, 1982, **206**, 343.
101. S. J. Marx, G. D. Aurbach, J. R. Gavin, III and D. W. Buell, *J. Biol. Chem.*, 1974, **249**, 6812.
102. M. Fouchereau-Peron, M. S. Moukhtar, A. A. Benson and G. Milhaud, *Proc. Natl. Acad. Sci. USA*, 1981, **78**, 3973.
103. A. Chausmer, M. D. Stevens and C. Severn, *Science (Washington, D.C.)*, 1982, **216**, 735.
104. M. Yamaguchi and M. Ito, *Endocrinol. Jpn.*, 1984, **31**, 327.
105. R. W. Downs, Jr., in 'Peptide Hormone Receptors', ed. M. Y. Kalimi and J. R. Hubbard, Walter de Gruyter & Co., 1987, p. 639.
106. M. Fukunaga, M. M. Miller, K. Y. Hostetler and L. J. Deftos, *Endocrinology (Baltimore)*, 1984, **115**, 757.
107. C. Nagant de Deuxchaisnes, J. P. Devogelaer, J. P. Huaux, J. P. Dufour, W. Esselinckx, J. P. Engelbeen, P. Stasse, P. Hermans and J. P. de Buisseret, *Clin. Orthop. Relat. Res.*, 1987, **217**, 56.
108. G. F. Mazzuoli, M. Passeri, C. Gennari, S. Minisola, R. Antonelli, C. Valtorta, E. Palummeri, G. F. Cervellin, S. Gonnelli and G. Francini, *Calcif. Tissue Int.*, 1986, **38**, 3.
109. J. F. Aloia, A. Vaswani, P. J. Meunier, C. M. Edouard, M E. Arlot, J. K. Yeh and S. H. Cohn, *Calcif. Tissue Int.*, 1987, **40**, 253.
110. P. S. Venkataraman, R. C. Tsang, I.-W. Chen and M. A. Sperling, *J. Pediatr. (St. Louis)*, 1987, **110**, 599.
111. J. Chrubasik, K. F. Falke, M. Zindler, B. Volk, S. Blond and J. Meynadier, *Pain*, 1986, **27**, 273.
112. G. F. Schiraldi, E. Soresi, S. Locicero, S. Harari and S. Scoccia, *Int. J. Clin. Pharmacol. Ther. Toxicol.*, 1987, **25**, 229.
113. C. Gennari, M. S. Chierichetti, S. Gonneli, C. Vibelli, M. Montagnani and M. Piolini, *Headache*, 1986, **26**, 13.
114. J. Russell, D. Lettieri and L. M. Sherwood, *Endocrinology (Baltimore)*, 1986, **119**, 2864.
115. J. Russell, D. Lettieri and L. M. Sherwood, *J. Clin. Invest.*, 1983, **72**, 1851.
116. G. Heinrich, H. M. Kronenberg, J. T. Potts, Jr. and J. F. Habener, *Endocrinology (Baltimore)*, 1983, **112**, 449.
117. J. D. Zajac, T. Okazaki, S. A. Goodart, M. L. Brandi, K. Sakaguchi, G. Aurbach and H. M. Kronenberg, *J. Bone Miner. Res.*, 1987, **2**, 245 (Abstract).
118. K. Sakaguchi, A. Santora, M. Zimering, F. Curcio, G. D. Aurbach and M. L. Brandi, *Proc. Natl. Acad. Sci. USA*, 1987, **84**, 3269.
119. C. A. Weaver, D. F. Gordon, M. S. Kissil, D. A. Mead and B. Kemper, *Gene*, 1984, **28**, 319.
120. T. J. Vasicek, B. E. McDevitt, M. W. Freeman, B. J. Fennick, G. N. Hendy, J. T. Potts, Jr., A. Rich and H. M. Kronenberg, *Proc. Natl. Acad. Sci. USA*, 1983, **80**, 2127.
121. G. Heinrich, H. M. Kronenberg, J. T. Potts, Jr. and J. F. Habener, *J. Biol. Chem.*, 1984, **259**, 3320.
122. P. Walter and G. Blobel, *J. Cell Biol.*, 1981, **91**, 557.
123. D. V. Cohn and R. R. MacGregor, *Endocr. Rev.*, 1981, **2**, 1.
124. B. Kemper, in 'Cell Biology of the Secretory Process', ed. M. Cantin, Karger Press, Basel, 1984, p. 443.
125. M. Rosenblatt, *Miner. Electrolyte Metab.*, 1982, **8**, 118.
126. J. F. Habener, M. Rosenblatt and J. T. Potts, Jr., *Physiol. Rev.*, 1984, **64**, 985.
127. L. H. Caporale and M. Rosenblatt, *Contr. Nephrol.*, 1986, **50**, 73.
128. K. J. Martin, K. A. Hruska, J. J. Freitag, S. Klahr and E. Slatopolsky, *N. Engl. J. Med.*, 1979, **301**, 1092.
129. J. E. Zull and J. Chuang, *J. Biol. Chem.*, 1985, **260**, 1608.
130. J. T. Potts, Jr., G. W. Tregear, H. T. Keutmann, H. D. Niall, R. Sauer, L. J. Deftos, B. F. Dawson, M. L. Hogan and G. D. Aurbach, *Proc. Natl. Acad. Sci. USA*, 1971, **68**, 63.
131. T. Galceran, E. Slatopolsky and K. J. Martin, *Calcif. Tissue Int.*, 1987, **41**, 290.
132. (a) J. A. Parsons and C. J. Robinson, in 'Parathyroid Hormone and Thyrocalcitonin', ed. R. V. Talmage and L. F. Belanser, 1967, Excerpta Medica, Amsterdam, p. 329. (b) J. Fisher, unpublished results.
133. R. Ardaillou, 'Endocrinology of Calcium Metabolism', ed. J. A. Parsons, Raven Press, New York, 1982, p. 41.
134. C. M. Silve, G. T. Hradek, A. L. Jones and C. D. Arnaud, *J. Cell Biol.*, 1982, **94**, 379.
135. J. D. Baxter and J. W. Funder, *N. Engl. J. Med.*, 1979, **301**, 1149.
136. P. M. J. McSheehy and T. J. Chambers, *Endocrinology (Baltimore)*, 1986, **119**, 1654.
137. J. K. Heath, S. J. Atkinson, M. C. Meikle and J. J. Reynolds, *Biochim. Biophys. Acta*, 1984, **802**, 151.
138. G. A. Rodan and T. J. Martin, *Calcif. Tissue Int.*, 1981, **33**, 349.
139. J. Reeve and J. M. Zanelli, *Clin. Sci.*, 1986, **71**, 231.
140. R. J. Winquist, E. P. Baskin and G. P. Vlasuk, *Biochem. Biophys. Res. Commun.*, 1987, **149**, 227.
141. R. D. Wright, J. R. Blair-West, J. F. Nelson, G. W. Tregear and M. Rosenblatt, *J. Endocrinol.*, 1984, **102**, 375.

142. R. Civitelli, L. R. Reid, V. Dobre, V. Shen, L. Halstead, L. V. Avioli and K. Hruska, *J. Bone Miner. Res.*, 1987, **2**, 233 (Abstract).
143. I. R. Reid, R. Civitelli, L. R. Halstead, L. V. Avioli and K. A. Hruska, *Am. J. Physiol.*, 1987, **252**, E45.
144. M. J. O. Wakelam, G. J. Murphy, V. J. Hruby and M. D. Houslay, *Nature (London)*, 1986, **323**, 68.
145. H. T. Keutman, A. W. Griscom, S. R. Nussbaum, B. F. Reiner, A. N. Goud, J. T. Potts, Jr. and M. Rosenblatt, *Endocrinology (Baltimore)*, 1985, **117**, 1230.
146. J. E. Zull and N. B. Lev, *Proc. Natl. Acad. Sci. USA*, 1980, **77**, 3791.
147. S. R. Nussbaum, N. V. Beaudette, G. D. Fasman, J. T. Potts, Jr. and M. Rosenblatt, *J. Protein Chem.*, 1985, **4**, 391.
148. A. M. Fiskin, D. V. Cohn and G. S. Peterson, *J. Biol. Chem.*, 1977, **252**, 8261.
149. G. V. Shah, R. M. Epand and R. C. Orlowski, *Mol. Cell Endocrinol.*, 1987, **49**, 203.
150. A. Bundi, R. H. Andreatta and K. Wuthrich, *Eur. J. Biochem.*, 1978, **91**, 201.
151. J. E. Zull, L. M. Smith, J. Chuang and J. Jentoft, *Mol. Cell Endocrinol.*, 1987, **51**, 267.
152. L. M. Smith, J. Jentoft and J. E. Zull, *Arch. Biochem. Biophys.*, 1987, **253**, 81.
153. A. L. Frelinger, III and J. E. Zull, *Arch. Biochem. Biophys.*, 1986, **244**, 641.
154. R. M. Epand, R. F. Epand, S. W. Hui, N. B. He and M. Rosenblatt, *Int. J. Pept. Protein Res.*, 1985, **25**, 594.
155. E. T. Kaiser and F. J. Kezdy, *Science (Washington, D.C.)*, 1984, **223**, 249.
156. N. Horiuchi, M. F. Holick, J. T. Potts, Jr. and M. Rosenblatt, *Science (Washington, D.C.)*, 1983, **220**, 1053.
157. N. Horiuchi, M. P. Caulfield, J. E. Fisher, M. E. Goldman, R. L. McKee, J. E. Reagan, J. J. Levy, R. F. Nutt, S. B. Rodan, T. L. Schofield, T. L. Clemens and M. Rosenblatt, *Science (Washington, D.C.)*, 1987, **238**, 1566.
158. S. H. Doppelt, R. M. Neer, S. R. Nussbaum, P. Federico, J. T. Potts, Jr. and M. Rosenblatt, *Proc. Natl. Acad. Sci. USA*, 1986, **83**, 7557.
159. G. V. Segre, M. Rosenblatt, G. L. Tully III, J. Lahgharn, B. Reit and J. T. Potts, Jr., *Endocrinology (Baltimore)*, 1985, **116**, 1024.
160. J. A. Parsons, B. Reit and C. J. Robinson, *Endocrinology (Baltimore)*, 1973, **92**, 454.
161. T. Galceran, E. Slatopolsky and K. J. Martin, *Calcif. Tissue Int.*, 1987, **41**, 290.
162. L. G. Raisz, *J. Clin. Invest.*, 1965, **44**, 103.
163. S. M. Forrest, K. W. Ng, D. M. Findlay, V. P. Michelangeli, S. A. Livesey, N. C. Partridge, J. D. Zajac and T. J. Martin, *Calcif. Tissue Int.*, 1985, **37**, 51.
164. Y. Nakatani, M. Tsunoi, Y. Hakeda, N. Kurihara, K. Fujita and M. Kumegawa, *Biochem. Biophys. Res. Commun.*, 1984, **123**, 894.
165. R. J. Majeska, S. B. Rodan and G. A. Rodan, *Endocrinology (Baltimore)*, 1980, **107**, 1494.
166. A. P. Teitelbaum and G. J. Strewler, *Endocrinology (Baltimore)*, 1984, **114**, 980.
167. S. R. Goldring, J. E. Mahaffey, M. Rosenblatt, J.-M. Dayer, J. T. Potts, Jr. and S. M. Krane, *J. Clin. Endocrinol. Metab.*, 1979, **48**, 655.
168. T. Takano, M. Takigawa, E. Shirai, F. Suzuki and M. Rosenblatt, *Endocrinology (Baltimore)*, 1985, **116**, 2536.
169. R. Marcus and G. D. Aurbach, *Endocrinology (Baltimore)*, 1969, **85**, 801.
170. R. A. Nissenson, S. R. Abbott, A. P. Teitelbaum, O. H. Clark and C. D. Arnaud, *J. Clin. Endocrinol. Metab.*, 1981, **52**, 840.
171. M. E. Goldman, M. Chorev, J. E. Reagan, R. F. Nutt, J. J. Levy and M. Rosenblatt, *Endocrinology (Baltimore)*, 1988, **123**, 1468.
172. M. Rosenblatt and J. T. Potts, Jr. (Massachusetts General Hospital Corp.), *US Pat.* 4 423 037 (1983) (*Chem. Abstr.*, 1984, **100**, 97 414).
173. M. Rosenblatt, in 'Comprehensive Endocrinology', ed. J. A. Parsons, Raven Press, New York, 1982, p. 103.
174. J. T. Potts, Jr., H. M. Kronenberg and M. Rosenblatt, *Adv. Protein Chem.*, 1982, **35**, 323.
175. N. Horiuchi, M. Rosenblatt, H. T. Keutmann, J. T. Potts, Jr. and M. F. Holick, *Am. J. Physiol.*, 1983, **244**, E589.
176. M. Chorev, M. E. Goldman, L. H. Caporale, J. J. Levy, J. E. Reagan, P. DeHaven, C. T. Gay, R. F. Nutt and M. Rosenblatt, in 'Peptide Chemistry, 1987', ed. T. Shiba and S. Sakakibara, Protein Research Foundation, Japan, 1987, p. 621.
177. (a) R.-D. Hesch, J. Heck, B. Auf'mKolk, T. Schettler and M. J. Atkinson, *Horm. Metabol. Res.*, 1984, **16**, 559. (b) M. E. Goldman, R. L. McKee, M. P. Caulfield, J. E. Reagan, J. J. Levy, C. T. Gay, P. A. DeHaven, M. Rosenblatt and M. Chorev, *Endocrinology (Baltimore)*, 1988, **123**, 2597.
178. J. M. Moseley, M. Kubota, H. Diefenbach-Jagger, R. E. H. Wettenhall, B. E. Kemp, L. J. Suva, C. P. Rodda, P. R. Ebeling, P. J. Hudson, J. D. Zajac and T. J. Martin, *Proc. Natl. Acad. Sci. USA*, 1987, **84**, 5048.
179. L. J. Suva, G. A. Winslow, R. E. H. Wettenhall, R. G. Hammonds, J. M. Moseley, H. Diefenbach-Jagger, C. P. Rodda, B. E. Kemp, H. Rodriguez, E. Y. Chen, P. J. Hudson, T. J. Martin and W. I. Wood, *Science (Washington, D.C.)*, 1987, **237**, 893.
180. M. A. Thiede, G. J. Strewler, R. A. Nissenson, M. Rosenblatt and G. A. Rodan, *Proc. Natl. Acad. Sci. USA*, 1988, **85**, 4065.
181. B. E. Kemp, J. M. Moseley, C. P. Rodda, P. R. Ebeling, R. E. H. Wettenhall, D. Stapleton, H. Diefenbach-Jagger, F. Ure, V. P. Michelangeli, H. A. Simmons, L. G. Raisz and T. J. Martin, *Science (Washington, D.C.)*, 1987, **238**, 1568.
182. G. J. Strewler, R. D. Williams and R. A. Nissenson, *J. Clin. Invest.*, 1983, **71**, 769.
183. M. D. Coltrera, J. T. Potts, Jr. and M. Rosenblatt, *J. Biol. Chem.*, 1981, **256**, 10555.
184. M. W. Draper, R. A. Nissenson, J. Winer, J. Ramachandran and C. D. Arnaud, *J. Biol. Chem.*, 1982, **257**, 3714.
185. B. S. Wright, G. A. Tyler, R. O'Brien, L. H. Caporale and M. Rosenblatt, *Proc. Natl. Acad. Sci. USA*, 1987, **84**, 26.
186. R. A. Nissenson, D. Karpf, T. Bambino, J. Winer, M. Canga, K. Nyiredy and C. D. Arnaud, *Biochemistry*, 1987, **26**, 1874.
187. S. R. Goldring, G. A. Tyler, S. M. Krane, J. T. Potts, Jr. and M. Rosenblatt, *Biochemistry*, 1984, **23**, 498.
188. D. P. Brennan and M. A. Levine, *J. Biol. Chem.*, 1987, **262**, 14 795.
189. D. B. Karpf, D. Duffy, K. L. King, T. Bambino, C. D. Arnaud and R. A. Nissenson, *J. Bone Miner. Res.*, 1987, **2**, 111 (Abstract).
190. J. Chuang, I. Yike, J. H. Reese, R. Laethem and J. E. Zull, *J. Biol. Chem.*, 1987, **262**, 10760.
191. (a) D. B. Karpf, C. D. Arnaud, K. King, T. Bambino, J. Winer, K. Nyiredy and R. A. Nissenson, *Biochemistry*, 1987, **26**, 7825. (b) B. S. Wright, G. A. Tyler and M. Rosenblatt, personal communication.
192. R. A. Nissenson, E. Mann, J. Winer, A. P. Teitelbaum and C. D. Arnaud, *Endocrinology (Baltimore)*, 1986, **118**, 932.

193. R. A. F. Dixon, B. K. Kobilka, D. J. Strader, J. L. Benovic, H. G. Dohlman, T. Frielle, M. A. Bolanowski, C. D. Bennett, E. Rands, R. E. Diehl, R. A. Mumford, E. E. Slater, I. S. Sigal, M. G. Caron, R. J. Lefkowitz and C. D. Strader, *Nature (London)*, 1986, **321**, 75.

194. Y. Yarden, H. Rodriguez, S. K.-F. Wong, D. R. Brandt, D. C. May, J. Burnier, R. N. Harkins, E. Y. Chen, J. Ramachandran, A. Ullrich and E. M. Ross, *Proc. Natl. Acad. Sci. USA*, 1986, **83**, 6795.

195. D. M. Engelman, A. Goldman and T. A. Steitz, *Methods Enzymol.*, 1982, **88**, 81.

196. M. Rosenblatt, *N. Engl. J. Med.*, 1986, **315**, 1004.

197. A. B. Schneider and L. M. Sherwood, *Metab. Clin. Exp.*, 1974, **23**, 975.

14.1

Drugs Acting on Ion Channels and Membranes

DAVID J. TRIGGLE

State University of New York at Buffalo, NY, USA

14.1.1 INTRODUCTION

The excitable cell maintains an asymmetric distribution of ions across both the plasma membrane that defines the extracellular and intracellular environments, and across the membranes of the internal organelles that define the several intracellular environments. This maintained and regulated asymmetric distribution serves two principal objectives: it contributes to the generation and maintenance of a potential gradient and the subsequent generation of electrical currents following appropriate stimulation, and it permits the ions themselves to serve as cellular messengers to link membrane excitation and cellular response. In some instances the flow of current itself may be the end response as, for example, in the electric organ of electric fishes. In most instances, however, the current serves to initiate or modulate another cellular response, including propagation of impulses in nerve fibers, alteration of the sensitivity of membranes to other stimuli or coupling to cellular responses such as contraction and secretion. In the latter examples, a role for Ca^{2+} is particularly prominent since it can serve as both a current-carrying and a messenger species.[1,2]

The asymmetric distribution of ions is maintained through the selectively permeable properties (barriers) of cell membranes and by the existence of ion pumps which maintain ionic gradients in the face of leaks and restore the ionic gradients subsequent to stimulated ion movements. Prominent examples of such processes are the Na^+, K^+-ATPase and Ca^{2+}-ATPase proteins of the plasma membrane.[3,4] Ion channels traverse cellular membranes, respond to chemical, electrical or other physical stimuli (including pressure) and permit the rapid movements of ions in directions dictated by electrical and chemical gradients.[1,5,6] Ion channels (or their equivalent) are a necessary consequence of the lipid bilayer construction of cell membranes. The bilayer is essentially impermeable to ions, exerting an energy barrier of some $100\,kT$ to a monovalent ion moving from a bulk aqueous medium to a low dielectric lipid medium. It is clear that a fixed channel or open pore or pathway through which ions may freely traverse serves little cellular function and may, in fact, constitute a lethal cell device. This is probably the case with the colicins, bacterial toxins which incorporate into cells to form K^+ channels where they can achieve 'single hit' cell killing.[7] Similarly, the uncontrolled movement of Ca^{2+} into cells following damage by ischemia or a toxic chemical probably contributes significantly to the death of the cell.[8]

The general properties of ion channels indicate that they must be regulated species. In principle, it is possible to consider several different modes of regulation (Figure 1). Channels may be regulated exclusively by electrical or chemical signals corresponding to purely potential-dependent or receptor-operated channels, respectively. However, receptor activation may alter the operation of a potential-dependent channel, for example by phosphorylation processes (Figure 1b), and many ligand-sensitive ion channel processes show limited dependence on membrane potential because of the influence of electric field on the dipoles and orientations of membrane proteins or on the ligands themselves. Receptor processes may alter ion channel activity directly or indirectly. Thus, the nicotinic acetylcholine receptor consists of five subunits, $\alpha_2\beta\gamma\delta$, two of which comprise the acetylcholine binding sites and all of which comprise the ion channel;[9] this constitutes a direct linkage (Figure 1a). In many instances, however, the link is indirect, *via* a second messenger such as cAMP or cGMP derived from stimulation of adenylate and guanylate cyclases or inositol polyphosphates—derived from phospholipase C-stimulated hydrolysis of inositol phospholipids.[10-15]

Functional analogies between ion channels and other effectors of excitable membranes, including adenylate cyclase, phospholipase C and vision, have been strengthened by observations that guanine nucleotide binding proteins (G proteins) couple some ion channels and membrane receptors (Figure 1c).[16,17] G proteins (dissociable heterotrimers)[17,18] are involved in several channel types including the acetylcholine-activated K^+ channel[19,20] and neurotransmitter-inhibited Ca^{2+} chan-

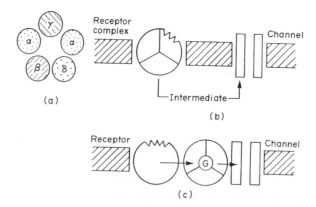

Figure 1 Schematic representation of receptor-mediated regulation of ion channels. (a) Organization of pentameric acetylcholine receptor (nicotinic) where the subunit arrangement generates the central ion channel. In this scheme the receptor is the channel and the channel is the receptor. (b) Organization whereby channel activity is regulated by a discrete diffusible biochemical intermediate (cAMP, inositol triphosphate (IP_3), *etc.*). (c) Organization of receptor-mediated channel regulation in which receptor and channel are linked by a guanine nucleotide binding (G) protein

nels.[21,22] Challenging questions of excitable molecule structure and organization are raised, since in multiply sensitive cells it will be necessary to ensure that the coupling functions of G proteins which mediate different events are maintained in discrete fashion. In cardiac cells, G proteins couple both β-adrenoceptor-mediated increases in Ca^{2+} current and muscarinic-receptor-mediated increases in K^+ current which promote cardiac acceleration and slowing respectively. The maintenance of physically distinct systems is one obvious resolution to these questions, perhaps achieved through membrane constraints. Alternatively, different components of the G protein complex may serve to couple different functions.[17,20]

Regardless of regulatory mechanism, ion channels may be regarded as allosteric enzymes; their function is to accelerate the transit of ions across an essentially impermeable barrier and to be responsive to a variety of heterotropic signals. Ion channels which are directly activated (integral sensor) will be differentiated from channels with remote sensors and messenger intermediaries by several criteria, including more rapid response (Table 1). Although the preceding types of chemical regulation are critical to both the physiological and pharmacological understanding of ion channel function, they will not form the focus of discussion of this chapter. Rather, the emphasis will be placed on drug regulation of ion channel activities at sites that are not defined in terms of classical receptors for neurotransmitters or hormones. These sites, at which a number of pharmacologically and therapeutically active agents function, including antiarrhythmics, local anesthetics, Ca^{2+} channel antagonists and neurotoxins, are components of the subunits from which ion channels are constituted. The relationship of these sites to the physiological control of ion channel function remains to be defined and it is entirely possible that they represent one or more receptors for endogenous ligands that await discovery. Thus, although this division of sites of drug action may be artificial it is still a useful distinction at this present stage of our knowledge. Additionally, the actions of general anesthetics that may regulate ion channel activity by less well-defined or global cellular interactions will be included. Traditionally, the general anesthetics have been considered to act by partitioning into the lipid component of the membrane, but more recent developments indicate a protein site of action and thus raise the question of whether receptor sites for general anesthetics may exist.

Recent developments in both electrophysiological and biochemical techniques have greatly enhanced our understanding of ion channel function and structure. The advent of the patch clamp technique in its several forms has made accessible the study of single ion channel events and the consequences of activation and modification of single molecules[23,24] including those in reconstituted systems.[25] Additionally, the techniques of molecular biology have made possible the determination of the structures of four ion channels, the nicotinic acetylcholine receptor channel,[9] the Na^+ channel,[26,27] the K^+ channel[28,29] and the Ca^{2+} channel,[30,31] and have revealed the existence of subclasses of ion channel types. Determination of these structures will facilitate greatly the task of ascertaining how channels permeate, how they are electrically and chemically gated and how these functions are regulated by drugs.[32]

14.1.2 PROPERTIES, ORGANIZATION AND REGULATION OF ION CHANNELS

Ion channels represent one of several pathways through which ions cross cellular membranes; other major pathways include carriers, of which the vectorial enzymes Na^+,K^+-ATPase and Ca^{2+}-ATPase are prominent examples. Channels and carriers have at least one property in common, namely ionic discrimination. Such discrimination indicates, consistent with the previously discussed concepts of regulation, that channels are not to be regarded simply as aqueous pores discriminating solely on the basis of ion size. Ionic discrimination exerted at the levels both of cation/anion selection and selection within ion series indicates that interactions occur between ions and specific sites both on channels and carriers.[33-36]

Table 1 Differentiation Between Directly Activated and Messenger-activated Ion Channels

	Directly activated	*Messenger mediated*
Speed of response	Very rapid	Slower
Second messengers	No effect	Have effect
Response in patch	Maintained	May be lost
Response reconstituted	Maintained	Lost

Channels are usually distinguished from carriers on the basis of their high conductance and ion transport rates. Thus ion channels with conductances (resistance^{-1}) in the picosiemen (pS) range can permeate ions at rates of between 10^6 and 10^8 ions s^{-1} and generate currents of several picoamperes.[33] These rates approach the theoretical limits of ion mobility; no carriers and only a few enzymes, including catalase, carbonic anhydrase and acetylcholinesterase, approach such turnover rates. High permeation rates appear to be a distinctive feature of ion channels; however, it is possible that there exists a continuum of rates, with slow channels and fast carriers occupying the middle ground between the limiting situations.[37]

The high efficiency of ion channels underscores observations derived from biophysical and biochemical techniques that these channels are relatively rare molecular entities in most cell membranes. Many membrane proteins, including the carriers Na$^+$,K$^+$-ATPase and Ca^{2+}-ATPase and the nicotinic acetylcholine receptor, are found at surface densities of 10^2–10^4 molecules per square micrometer; in contrast, ion channel density is frequently two to four orders of magnitude less.[24, 34, 38] However, to charge a membrane with a capacity of 1 μF cm^{-2} by 100 mV requires the transfer of some 6000 ions per square micrometer and a channel of 20 pS conductance can execute this activity in only 0.5 ms.[38] Thus, large cellular signals can be generated by very few channels with exceedingly small ionic fluxes. In large cells, such as axons, channel activity will exert negligible effect on ionic levels, but in very small cells significant perturbation can occur.

Despite very high permeation rates, ion channels demonstrate ion selectivity at levels according to channel category. Thus, the cation-selective channel in axons and muscles responsible for the fast inward current of the action potential exhibits the permeation sequence Na$^+$ > Li$^+$ > K$^+$ > Rb$^+$ > Cs$^+$ and discriminates against K$^+$ relative to Na$^+$ by an approximately twelvefold factor. K$^+$ channels discriminate against Na$^+$ relative to K$^+$ by a similar factor. These ionic selectivities form the basis of one mode of ion channel classification—according to the major permeant species.[34, 39] In contrast, the ion channel associated with the nicotinic acetylcholine receptor is far less discriminating and, whilst cation selective, permeates both inorganic and organic species.[39, 40]

Clearly ionic selectivity is not based on size alone and interactions of ions with channel components must occur. These interactions, controlled by ion charge, size, hydration energy and ligand substitution rates, determine selectivity and permeation rates.[33, 34] A formalism frequently employed to describe ion permeability and selectivity of membrane channels is the Goldman–Hodgkin–Katz constant field theory[39–42] which assumes ionic independence and constant electric field across a homogeneous membrane. Accordingly, the potential of a cell at which no current flows, E_{rev}, is given by equation (1). The reversal potential permits determination of permeability ratios and of the ions involved in permeability changes. If a single ion only is considered, the formalism becomes equivalent to the Nernst equation (equation 2), where E_X is the equilibrium potential for ion X$^+$ and is the potential at which there will be no net ion flux. Thus, for a K$^+$-selective channel, current flow is given by equation (3) and is determined by the channel conductance, g_{K^+}, and the net driving force, given by the difference in membrane potential E_m and the equilibrium potential for K$^+$. A more detailed description of these relationships and of the derived current–voltage forms is given by Hille.[39]

$$E_{rev} = RT/F \ln \left(\frac{P_{K^+}[K^+]_o + P_{Na^+}[Na^+]_o + P_{Cl^-}[Cl^-]_i}{P_{K^+}[K^+]_i + P_{Na^+}[Na^+]_i + P_{Cl^-}[Cl^-]_o} \right) \tag{1}$$

$$E_X = RT/F \ln \left(\frac{[X]_o}{[X]_i} \right) \tag{2}$$

$$I_{K^+} = g_{K^+}(E_m - E_{K^+}) \tag{3}$$

Despite the success of approaches based on ionic independence, it is quite clear that ion permeation is a more complex process than indicated by the Goldman–Hodgkin–Katz formalism. In particular, ions do interact with sites within the channel during the permeation process and an ionic presence within the channel may affect, often significantly, the passage of other solutes including ions.[34, 43]

Failure of the independence principle is seen clearly in the saturation of ion fluxes through channels. Accordingly, currents can be described with Michaelis–Menten formalism (equation 4). Thus, the saturation of the Ca^{2+} currents shown in Figure 2 probably represents saturation of specific binding sites within the Ca^{2+} channel. One ion occupying a channel 2 Å wide by 28 Å in length is in a volume of 3.52×10^{-22} mL and at an effective concentration of approximately 0.5 mol dm^{-3}. Since mono- and di-valent ions may be concentrated in channels by factors of 10 and

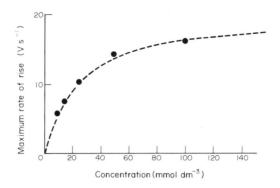

Figure 2 Relationship between Ca^{2+} concentration and the rate of rise of action potential carried by Ca^{2+} in barnacle muscle (reproduced from ref. 44 by permission of Rockefeller University Press)

100, the saturating concentrations in the bulk phase will approximate 10^{-1}–1 mol dm^{-3} and 10^{-2}–10^{-1} mol dm^{-3}, respectively.[34]

$$I_S = \frac{I_{max}}{1 + K_S/[S]} \tag{4}$$

Deviations from ionic independence are also observed because channels can accommodate simultaneously a number of permeating ions whose movements are linked. Such flux coupling means that unidirectional movements will differ from those predicted, according to concentration and electrical gradients on the basis of independent behavior. Furthermore, in such multiion channels, ionic permeabilities will be dependent both upon ionic concentrations and the nature of the ion present. Thus, in some Ca^{2+} channels Ba^{2+} is actually more permeant than Ca^{2+}.[45] However, when both ions are present the conductance shows a minimum rather than a simple linear dependence upon ionic concentration (Figure 3). This anomalous mole-fraction effect probably indicates that ions bind to at least two sites at which they mutually interact.[34, 43, 46–48] These interactions may be of considerable importance to the control of rates of ion permeation through the channel, permeation being assisted by repulsion between mutually occupied sites. This phenomenon probably also underlies the remarkable selectivity exhibited by the Ca^{2+} channel in the face of much higher concentrations of monovalent cations. It is assumed that the channel contains two binding sites for Ca^{2+}, with an affinity of approximately 10^{-6} mol dm^{-3}, but that with double occupancy the affinity is greatly reduced, due to negatively cooperative interactions, and one Ca^{2+} ion is ejected to generate the Ca^{2+} current. Under physiological conditions, one site is always occupied by Ca^{2+} and the channel is Ca^{2+} selective because Na^+, or other monovalent cation, does not cause this mutual repulsion, and current does not flow.[46] This hypothesis also suggests that a high affinity Ca^{2+}-binding protein may be a component of the ion translocating machinery of this channel.

Ion channels are characterized according to their chemical, electrical or other sensing process and according to their ion selectivity. Other criteria may also be employed. Voltage-dependent channels may be classified according to the voltage ranges over which they open and close, and the kinetics of the opening and closing processes serve as further criteria for classification.

In the squid axon, the dominant currents of the action potentials are carried by the inward and outward movements of Na^+ and K^+, respectively.[49–53] These currents can be distinguished by a number of criteria including their different time courses (Figure 4). The Na^+ channel activates rapidly and inactivates at a constant membrane potential. In contrast, the K^+ channel opens more slowly, hence it is termed a 'delayed rectifier', and maintains its open state for some time. Inactivation is a slower process than activation and channel recycling to the resting or activatable state requires a period of repolarization. Channels must exist, therefore, in a minimum of three states or families of states: closed and activatable, open and activated, and closed and inactivated (Figure 5).

Transitions between the several states of ion channels involve voltage-dependent rate constants which reflect the influence of the membrane electric field on the charges and dipoles of the membrane proteins.[53] These voltage-dependent interconversions between channel conformations are of considerable importance to any consideration of modes of drug action. Drugs may have differential affinity and access according to the dominant channel state—resting, open or inactivated. Accordingly, pharmacological activities and tissue selectivities of channel-directed drugs may depend upon the equilibria existing between these channel states (Section 14.1.3).

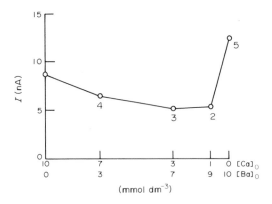

Figure 3 Mole-fraction dependence of Ca^{2+} channel current through cardiac Ca^{2+} channel as a function of divalent cation concentrations. A channel with a single binding site would generate a monotonic dependence of current upon ion concentration (reproduced from ref. 46 by permission of Macmillan Journals Ltd)

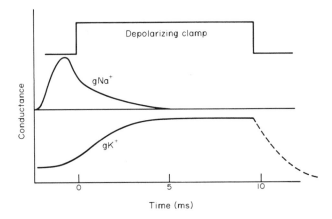

Figure 4 Schematic representation of Na^+ and K^+ conductance changes in axons. A step depolarization evokes the rapid and transient Na^+ conductance and the delayed and ongoing K^+ current. When repolarization is initiated the K^+ current falls (dashed line) (modified from refs. 50–52)

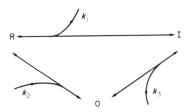

Figure 5 Ion channel cycling amongst the resting (R), open (O) and inactivated (I) states. The rate constants k_1, k_2 and k_3 refer to the association of ligands with the resting, open and inactivated states, respectively

The Hodgkin–Huxley formalism employed to define axonal Na^+ and K^+ currents describes the voltage-dependent activation and inactivation processes in terms of charged particles moved by the electric field during the necessary conformational changes undergone by channels in their several transitions. The gating currents accompanying these charge movements can be measured and used to determine the gating charges associated with each channel.[53-55] Axonal Na^+ channels have approximately six unitary charges (or their summed fractional equivalent) per channel which serve as the corresponding voltage sensors.

These elementary considerations of channel properties permit a general view of channel organization (Figure 6). At this level of organization, ion channels may be regarded as being composed of a pore organized by the subunit(s) of the channel which provides the permeant pathway and, by a combination of steric and chemical interactions, serves as a selectivity filter to define the ionic pathway. Some calculated dimensions for selectivity filters for different ion channels are shown in

Figure 7. The Ca^{2+} channel, though very selective for Ca^{2+} ions, is actually a large pore through which ions as large as tetramethylammonium (diameter 6 Å) can pass;[57] this reinforces the previously expressed view that the selectivity of the Ca^{2+} channel is dictated more by specific binding interactions than by size exclusion criteria. The prototypical channel must also possess gates that serve to open and close the channels and sensors that respond to chemical, electrical and other stimuli. Chemical sensors for physiological stimuli will be surface components, but voltage sensors will lie within the membrane core where they respond to alterations in electric field. This depiction of ion channel organization is useful in order to indicate that, in addition to any specific chemical sensor component of the channel (for neurotransmitter or neurohormone reception), there will be a number of other sites including the gates, voltage sensors and the channel pore itself that can provide binding sites for effectors active as modifiers of one or other ion channel processes including activation, inactivation, permeation and voltage sensitivity.

The gross representation of an ion channel depicted in Figure 6 has been substantially refined in recent years by the determination of the structures of the nicotinic receptor ion channel complex,[9,58-60] the Na^+ channel of electric eel and brain[26,61] and the gap junction channel of liver[62] amongst others. There may exist significant organizational similarities despite the very different functions of these channels. All three channels have close to cyclic symmetry and the pore size increases with increasing number of organizational units comprising the total channel structure (Figure 9).[63] The nicotinic receptor has five subunits, $\alpha_2\beta\gamma\delta$, and each of the subunits possesses four hydrophobic membrane spanning sequences and one amphipathic sequence.[64] The association of the five amphipathic sequences (from the five subunits) constitutes the pore of the channel. The Na^+ channel is composed of a major polypeptide of mass 260 kDa with a core polypeptide of approximately 210 kDa constituting the functional channel. This single peptide has four homologous domains each of which consists of five dominantly hydrophobic segments and one segment (S4) that contains repeating positively charged residues.[26,61] These domains probably define the Na^+ channel pore, with the positively charged residues of S4 constituting the voltage sensor. Graded movement of these charges under the influence of changing electric field will represent the conformational transitions between the multiple states of the channel (Figure 8). Residue movements of some 5–10 Å

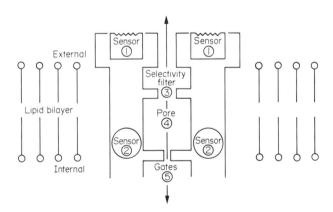

Figure 6 Schematic representation of ion channel organization showing the channel as an integral membrane protein consisting of a pore (4), selectivity filter (3), gates (5) and electrical and chemical sensors (1 and 2)

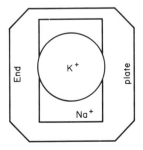

Figure 7 Representation of minimum pore size of ion channel selectivity filters. The total area of the K^+ channel is 8.6 Å^2, of the Na^+ channel 15.8 Å^2 and of the end-plate channel 40.3 Å^2 (modified from refs. 5 and 56)

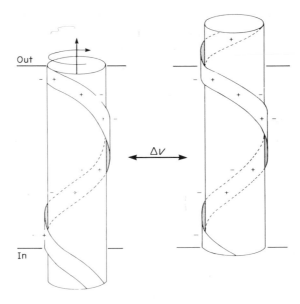

Figure 8 Schematic representation of Na$^+$ channel conformational change during depolarization. At the left the S4 helix is shown in the polarized state where there is pairing of positive and negative charges. During depolarization the helix screws through approximately 60° and outwards by some 5 Å because the forces holding the positive charges in an inward position are reduced (reproduced from ref. 65 by permission of Elsevier Scientific Publishing Co.)

probably define these transitions, conformational changes which are not inconsistent with those measured in other proteins.[27,65,66]

14.1.3   DRUG INTERACTIONS AT ION CHANNELS

According to the general description of ion channel structure and function outlined previously, a number of binding sites and routes of access of drugs will, in principle, be available. These several interactions will differ, according to site and channel state, in their mechanisms and access pathways and in the subtlety of their effects on ion channel function. An agent may function simply by physically occluding a pore and thus prevent ion permeation. Interactions with gating components may similarly block channel function or, by facilitating gate opening, cause persistent channel activation. At a more sophisticated level, drug interactions with voltage sensor components may shift activation and inactivation curves along the voltage axis and produce enhanced blockade or facilitated activation. Binding sites for drugs may be available only by extracellular or intracellular access and sites may become available only during certain channel states. Furthermore, drugs may become trapped or locked into a particular site as channel proteins undergo the conformational changes associated with their activation–inactivation cycle.

Access to binding sites may thus be an important determinant of drug action. The conformational changes that occur in channel proteins during ion permeation indicate that drug affinities may differ according to channel state. Furthermore, for drugs that interact with an internal component of the channel, the rate constants for drug association and dissociation may be voltage dependent since the drug moves through the electric field of the membrane to interact with the binding site.[67]

These preliminary views of drug–channel interactions indicate the many subtleties that are likely to occur and the potential complexities of interpretation of mechanisms of action. Ion channels are moving targets for drug action and the interpretation of structure–activity relationships for these systems must be particularly cognizant of this mobility. Prior to any discussion of specific channel systems some general examples of drug–channel interactions will be analyzed briefly.

Quaternary ammonium ion antagonism of K$^+$ channels provides an example of vectorial access to a binding site, occupancy of which is also dependent on channel function and state. Tetraethylammonium and related ions, including the more hydrophobic nonyltriethylammonium and related species, block the delayed rectifier class of K$^+$ channels. An important set of investigations by Armstrong and co-workers[68–70] showed that these ions blocked outward K$^+$ current more readily than they blocked inward K$^+$ current, that external K$^+$ ions accelerated the relief of block particularly during the open channel state and that channel blockade developed during the activation phase and not during the resting state. Collectively, these observations suggest that quaternary ammonium ions block K^+ channels with access from the cytoplasmic surface when the channel is open; because of this directional access, the blocking agent is displaced by inwardly moving K^+ ions and the channel then behaves as an inward rectifier. Additionally, the channel can close and occlude the quaternary ammonium ion at its internal binding site. Thus, a resting block can be achieved but only because it was initiated during the open channel state. A summary representation of these actions of quaternary ammonium ions at K^+ channels is provided in Figure 9.

The preceding observations are of fundamental import to an understanding of drug–channel interactions, including those of therapeutically useful agents, because they demonstrate that drug access to and interaction with ion channels is dependent upon channel state, that the properties of the drug–channel complex depend upon ion movements through the channel and that these interactions offer information concerning the architecture of the channel.[71]

Blockade of K^+ channels by internally applied quaternary ammonium ions demonstrates voltage dependence because access of drug and interaction with permeating ions are voltage-dependent processes. Blockade of Na^+ channels by protons illustrates a different principle, where the decreased peak conductance and slow relief of blockade during depolarization have been interpreted[71,72] with the assumption that the group protonated, $pK_a = 5.6$, is within the channel and hence subject to the channel field. Changes in membrane potential alter the association and dissociation rate constants whereby, for proton binding, the pK_a is given by equation (5), where δ is the binding site distance from the outside $(+)$ or the inside $(-)$ respectively of the membrane.

$$pK_a = -\log(k_{-1}/k_1)$$
$$= pK_a(0\,\text{mV}) \pm \left(\frac{2.303\,zFE\delta}{RT}\right) \tag{5}$$

Additional considerations of drug–channel interactions derive from the many studies of local anesthetics which block propagated action potentials by their actions at Na^+ channels.[71,73–75] Quaternary ammonium derivatives of local anesthetics behave at Na^+ channels analogously to tetraethylammonium analogs at K^+ channels; blockade develops from intracellularly applied drug, requires open channels and is enhanced by use-dependent processes during repetitive stimulation. The rate of block is proportional to the number of channels opened and the extent of block increases with increasing depolarization from a polarized level. Accordingly, frequency-dependent inhibition arises from a faster rate of binding (or access) to open channels ($k_2 \gg k_1, k_3$; Figure 5) and inhibition increases since drug remains bound when channels inactivate or return to the resting state. Equilibrium is achieved when the amount of drug dissociating between pulses equals the amount of drug binding during the pulse. Nonquaternary and neutral local anesthetics can access channels through states other than the resting state and it is therefore apparent that two major pathways exist for drug access to binding sites.[71,76] A hydrophilic pathway, through the cytoplasmic side of the open Na^+ channel, is available to quaternary ammonium derivatives, protonated local anesthetics and to other sufficiently hydrophilic species, and a hydrophobic pathway, accessing the channel even in its closed state, is available to bind hydrophobic drug species (Figure 10).

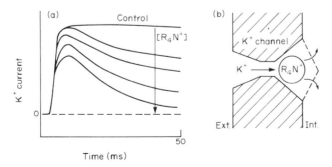

Figure 9 Interaction of K^+ channels with quaternary ammonium ions. (a) Time course of block of squid axon, internally perfused with quaternary ammonium ion (QA) in increasing concentrations ($\downarrow$) as a function of time (ms). (b) Incorporation of QA into the channel showing that inward flow of K^+ relieves blockade (for further details, ref. 5 may be consulted)

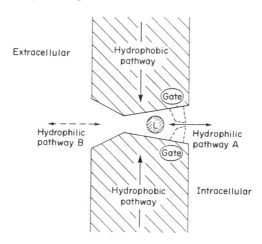

Figure 10 Organization of ion channel depicting hydrophobic pathways and two hydrophilic pathways available from extracellular and intracellular faces, respectively, governing ligand access to channel binding sites (modified from ref. 76)

Channel state and membrane potential determine the interactions of local anesthetics with the Na^+ channel. In turn, the interactions of local anesthetics alter the gating kinetics of the Na^+ channel. In the presence of local anesthetics, Na^+ channel inactivation is intensified, the voltage dependence of inactivation is shifted in the hyperpolarizing direction and recovery from inactivation is slowed. The data suggest that local anesthetics bind preferentially to the inactivated state of the Na^+ channel, that according to their structure they can access this site *via* hydrophilic or hydrophobic pathways, that they stabilize the inactivated state and that experimental conditions which favor access of drug to the inactivated state of the channel will increase the apparent affinity of the agent.

The concept that channel gating determines drug affinity and that bound drug modifies channel gating is expressed as the modulated receptor hypothesis.[71,76-78] The formalism of this hypothesis is identical to that advanced by Monod and co-workers[79] for allosteric enzymes where ligand affinity and conformation are reciprocally linked. There are several important implications to this concept of state-dependent binding: (i) different channel states may have different affinities for a drug; (ii) drugs may exhibit qualitatively and quantitatively different structure–activity relationships according to the channel state with which they interact or access; (iii) drugs stabilize different channel states; and (iv) drugs alter the kinetics and voltage dependence of channel state interconversion processes.

Alternative formalisms are available to accommodate many of the experimental observations previously discussed. In particular, the hypothesis has been advanced of the 'guarded receptor' whereby gate activity controls ligand access to channel binding sites.[80-82] When gate behavior is voltage dependent, access to receptors will be similarly voltage dependent as will the resultant channel blockade. It should be noted that the fundamental postulate of the guarded receptor hypothesis is quite distinct from that of the modulated receptor hypothesis since they predict, respectively, binding sites of constant and variable affinity for channel-modulating ligands. The guarded receptor hypothesis is able to account for both local anesthetic blockade of Na^+ channels and 1,4-dihydropyridine blockade of Ca^{2+} channels (Sections 14.1.4.3.5 and 14.1.5.2). It is clearly possible to envisage intermediate situations in which both constant access and guarded access of a ligand underlie channel blocking mechanisms.

The mechanisms of ligand interaction at ion channels present a richly complex picture with many of the details awaiting experimental resolution. However, the modulated receptor hypothesis, discussed originally in terms of local anesthetic action at Na^+ channels, has proved to be a powerful tool for the interpretation of drug action at many channel classes. For medicinal chemistry it is particularly important to realize that different structure–activity relationships may exist according to channel state and hence according to the experimental methods employed for drug evaluation.

14.1.4 DRUGS ACTIVE AT Na^+ CHANNELS

14.1.4.1 Introduction

A remarkably diverse group of agents, natural and synthetic, simple and complex, exert effects at the Na^+ channel. These compounds range from naturally occurring toxins, including tetrodotoxin and scorpion toxins, to local anesthetics and natural and synthetic insecticides. Collectively, these agents have proved to be remarkably useful as molecular probes of the Na^+ channel and as indices of Na^+ channel function. Several comprehensive reviews are available that detail the characteristics of action of these ligands at Na^+ channels.[5,83-89] Naturally occurring toxins, including α-bungarotoxin, played a critical role in defining the nicotinic acetylcholine receptor; several distinct groups of toxins have played a similarly important role for the definition, localization and isolation of the Na^+ channel.

Perhaps paradoxically, it is the very subtleties of channel function that these agents have uncovered which has made delineation of structure–activity relationships difficult and ambiguous. Virtually all of the drug classes active at Na^+ channels show state-dependent behavior, according to which their activity, both quantitative and qualitative, depends upon channel state (Section 14.1.3). Measured activities are therefore frequently apparent and, unless identical methodologies have been used, not strictly comparable. This can be demonstrated very easily with, for example, local anesthetics where affinity and stereoselectivity can change significantly according to the mode of stimulation and the state of the channel.

14.1.4.2 Sites and Mechanisms of Action

Early progress on the characterization of Na^+ channels was achieved with the guanidinium toxins, tetrodotoxin (**1**; TTX) and saxitoxin (**2**; STX). Because they are amongst the most poisonous nonpeptide agents known, TTX and STX must have been long, if unpleasantly, familiar to man.[90,91] Tetrodotoxin, found in fish of the order *Tetraodontiformes* and including fugu or puffer fish, is also found in many other species including amphibians, goby fish and cephalopod and gastropod molluscs, suggesting a bacterial rather than an endogenous production.[92] Saxitoxin, the ingestion of which causes paralytic shellfish poisoning, is also an exogenous product, being derived from dinoflagellates ingested by shellfish.[91]

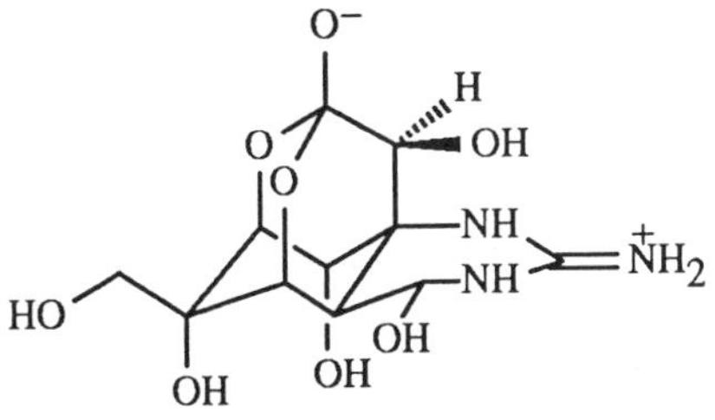

(**1**) 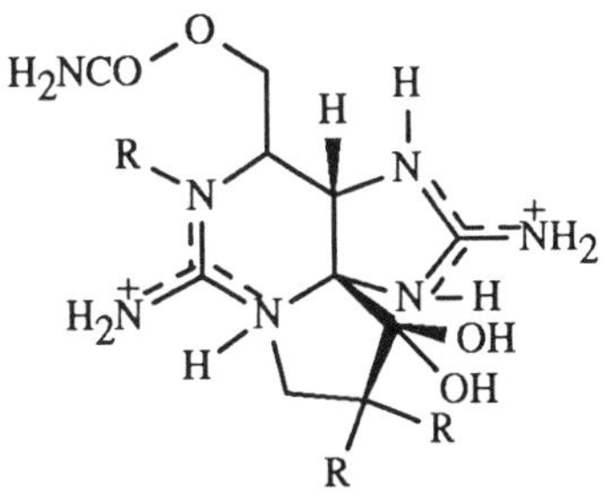   (**2**)

The presence of the guanidine group in both TTX and STX suggested, because guanidine itself is Na^+ channel permeant, that the toxins might enter and subsequently block the channel pore to reduce channel availability.[93] This is not the case and both TTX and STX are believed to bind adjacent to the external surface of the channel pore, in a voltage-dependent manner, to interact with the binding sites for other classes of channel ligands.[89,94,95] Thus, these toxins enhance the fraction of Na^+ channels in the slow inactivated state that results from prolonged depolarization[85] and the affinity of both TTX and STX is postulated to be lower for the ion-associated channel than for the ion-free channel.[94]

Several discrete groups of peptide neurotoxins are also powerful modulators of Na^+ channels. These include scorpion α-, β- and γ-toxins,[85,89,96-99] the sea anemone toxins, homologous save for *Anemonia sulcata* toxin III (ATX 3),[85,89,97,100,101] and the μ-conotoxins, one of the several groups of ion-channel-selective toxins isolated from the fish-hunting cone snails.[85,89,102,103] Some sequences are shown in Figure 11; all of the toxins contain between three and four disulfide bridges which render them as a species both relatively compact and rigid.

Scorpion α-toxins (from North American and North African scorpions including *Androctonis australis*, *Buthus occitanus*, *Leirus quinquestriatus* and *Centruroidas sculpturatus*) block Na^+ channel inactivation and prolong the current and duration of the action potential. Interaction of the α toxin is a voltage-dependent process, being weakest at depolarized levels which favor generation of the inactivated state. Accordingly, binding is strongest to the resting and open channel states.[89,104] Sea anemone toxins, though not homologous to the scorpion toxins, behave similarly. They act only from the external membrane surface, they slow channel inactivation and show

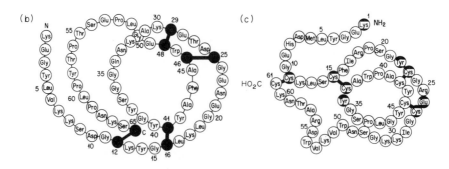

Figure 11 Structures of Na$^+$ channel toxins: (a) μ-conotoxin; (b) variant 3 toxin from *Centruroides sculpturatus Ewing* (reproduced from ref. 132 by permission of Academic Press); (c) structure of Tityus γ-toxin[97]

voltage-dependent interactions, though less dramatically so than the scorpion α-toxins. A complete identification of the sites of action of these two toxin classes has not been established.

Scorpion β-toxins (North American scorpions including *C. sculpturatus* and *C. suffus suffus*) also facilitate an open state of the Na$^+$ channel by accelerating activation and slowing deactivation (conversion of open to resting channels) and inducing repetitive firing. These effects of β toxins are exerted at sites distinct from those at which the α toxin effects are mediated.

Scorpion γ-toxin (Tityus toxin) appears to compete with β toxins for a common binding site, but functions to shift the activation curve in a hyperpolarizing direction, thus generating open channels at membrane potentials where channels are normally closed.

The lipid-soluble toxins are composed of at least three major groups, the alkaloids (including aconitines, batrachotoxin, grayanotoxin and veratridine), the pyrethroids and the brevetoxins. Other categories are quite likely to exist. The alkaloid toxins (Figure 12) possess, despite their chemical heterogeneity, the common ability to activate Na$^+$ channels in persistent fashion but do so by different mechanisms. Thus batrachotoxin (BTX) interacts with very high affinity with open Na$^+$ channels to produce a noninactivating state with reduced ion selectivity.[89,105,106] In contrast, veratridine causes Na$^+$ channels to remain open both at rest and at more depolarized potentials whereby inactivation is greatly reduced.[89,107,108] The brevetoxins are derived from a dinoflagellate, *Ptychodiscus brevis*, responsible for red tides and subsequent fish kills in the Mexican Gulf. The actions of the brevetoxins (Figure 13) are similar to those induced by batrachotoxin and veratridine, namely a hyperpolarizing shift of the Na$^+$ channel activation curve, depolarization, inhibition of inactivation and a reduction in ion selectivity.[89,109]

A summary of the actions of the major toxin groups on the Na$^+$ channel is provided in Table 2.[86,87,89] The identification of specific receptors for the various toxin classes as components of the Na$^+$ channel has permitted the use of these agents as probes of the channel topography and to identify subtypes of Na$^+$ channels with different pharmacological and functional characteristics.

Fluorescent probes based on channel-active toxins derivatized with a variety of sensitive groups including 7-dimethylaminocoumarin, *N*-methylanthranilate, dinitrophenyl and nitrobenzoxadiazolyl have permitted energy transfer measurements and distance determinations between the several toxin receptors.[110] Accordingly, the distance between the TTX and the scorpion α-toxin site was determined as 35 Å, but at 42 Å in the presence of BTX, consistent with a conformational change occurring in the channel protein and being propagated over a long distance. Similarly, the distance between the scorpion α- and β-toxin sites, representing inactivation and activation gates, respectively, was determined as 22 Å.

The fact that TTX sensitivity of Na$^+$ channels varies substantially according to tissues has long been recognized. Mammalian cardiac cells are resistant to TTX and blocked only at high concentra-

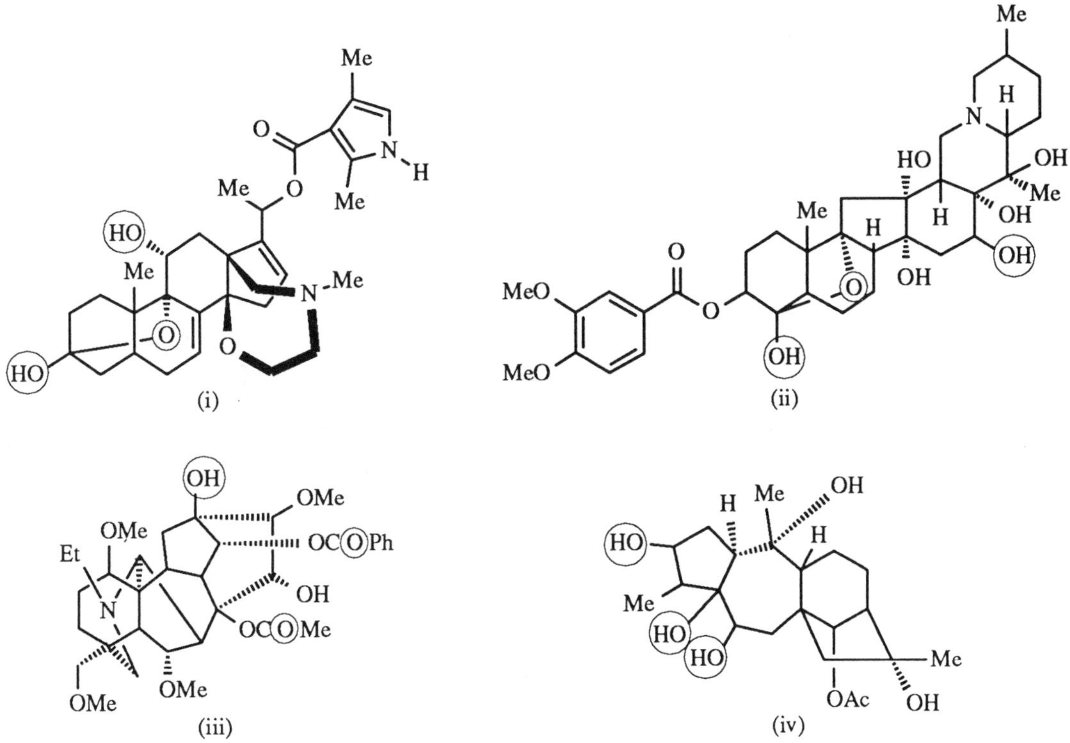

Figure 12 Structural formulae of batrachotoxin (i), veratridine (ii), aconitine (iii) and grayanotoxin (iv). Circled atoms represent common constellations of oxygen atoms proposed to be involved in receptor binding

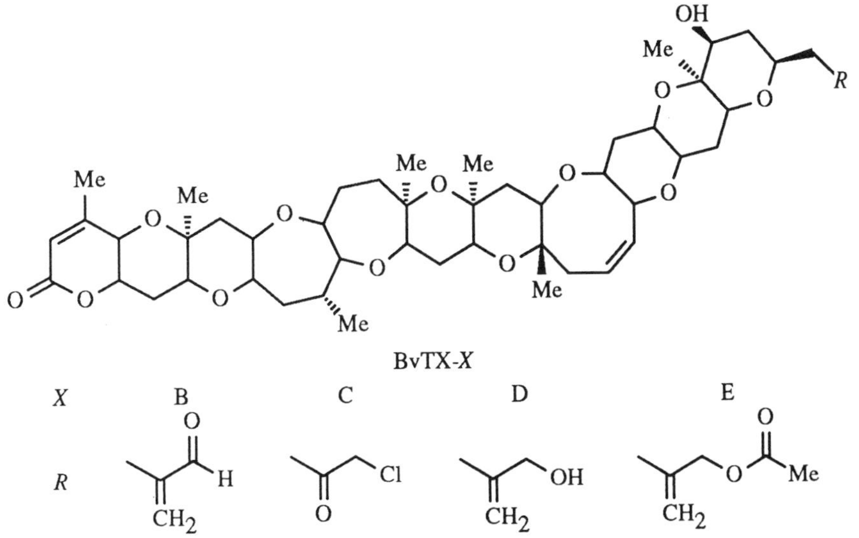

Figure 13 Structure of brevetoxins

tions, 10^{-6} to 10^{-5} mol dm^{-3}; muscle and nerve channels are very sensitive being blocked at 10^{-9}–10^{-8} mol dm^{-3} TTX. Similarly, high and low affinity binding sites for TTX and STX have been identified in excitable cells.[93,101,111-114] An additional classification can be provided by the selective actions of other toxins. Thus the μ-conotoxin GIIIA behaves very similarly to TTX and STX as a Na$^+$ channel blocker in skeletal muscle, but the TTX/STX-sensitive channel in neurons is insensitive to the μ-conotoxins as are the cardiac TTX/STX-insensitive channels.[113] Considerable effort is needed to complete this pharmacological classification of Na$^+$ channels, but determination of the tissue distribution, ontogeny, regulation and functions of the channel subclasses is critical to an understanding of ligand pharmacology.

Table 2 Classification of Toxin Actions on Na^+ Channels[83,84,89]

Site	Toxin	Effect
1	Tetrodotoxin Saxitoxin	Block Na^+ movement
2	Aconitine Batrachotoxin Grayanotoxin Veratridine	Cause persistent activation
3	Scorpion α-toxins (North American, North African) Sea anemone toxin	Slow inactivation
4	Scorpion β-toxins (Central and South American)	Enhance activation

The existence of distinct channel types is reinforced by the discovery of messenger RNAs in rat brain coding for at least two distinct proteins.[115] Such structural studies will permit determination of the binding sites for the various drug categories. The major peptide, $M_r = 260$ kDa, represents the functional channel and two smaller β_1 and β_2 subunits are associated with the major protein isolated from brain and skeletal muscle and confer TTX/STX sensitivity.[116,117]

14.1.4.3 Structure–Activity Relationships of Drugs Active at Na^+ Channels

14.1.4.3.1 *Tetrodotoxin and saxitoxin*

The chemistry of TTX and STX has not encouraged the synthesis of large numbers of analogs.[91,118] Accordingly, structure–activity relationship studies are correspondingly limited. In the study of TTX and its analogs the most successful work has focussed attention on the C-6 and C-11 positions, with substitution at the guanidinium nucleus leading to greatly reduced activity.[110,119–124] Thus, direct esterification of the C-11 hydroxyl group has yielded a potent photoactivatable derivative (Figure 14)[121] and Lazdunski and co-workers[122–124] have made analogs from the C-11 aldehyde derivative of TTX and the 6-ketonortetrodotoxin.

Saxitoxin has yielded a more extensive series of derivatives, both naturally occurring and synthetic. The data of Table 3 show that good agreement exists between the abilities of natural STX analogs to block Na^+ channel responses and [^{3}H]STX binding. Most substituents reduce activity; however, oxygenation at N-1 produces an approximately fourfold increase in activity. A number of synthetic analogs (as racemates) modified at the carbamyl (C-6) and the gem diol substituent (C-12) have also been examined; none was more active than STX itself.[125]

The C-12 gem diol function of STX exists in equilibrium with the keto form, increasing pH favoring the latter form. Neosaxitoxin (Table 3) is significantly more potent than STX itself and exists to a greater extent as the keto form. It is suggested that STX binds to its receptor by a two-step process in which the positively charged guanidinium group initially binds and facilitates dehydration of the gem diol and subsequent formation of a weak covalent bond to the receptor (Figure 15).[126]

14.1.4.3.2 *Peptide toxins*

The venoms of the marine snail of the *Conus* genera have proved to be a rich source of neuroactive toxins.[127] The μ toxins from *Conus geographus L.* constitute a family of 22 amino acid peptides of which GIIIA (Figure 11) is a major constituent.[128] Other toxins from *Conus* include the ω toxins which block some types of Ca^{2+} channels and the α toxins which block postsynaptic acetylcholine receptors. The μ toxin GIIIA distinguishes subclasses of Na^+ channels since it blocks those in skeletal muscle but does not act on neuronal Na^+ channels.[114,128,129] Interaction of GIIIA with Na^+ channels is similar to that of TTX and STX in certain respects: block is achieved only at the extracellular face of the channel and binding increases with hyperpolarization. A partial identity of binding sites of the μ toxins and the guanidinium toxins has been proposed.[128]

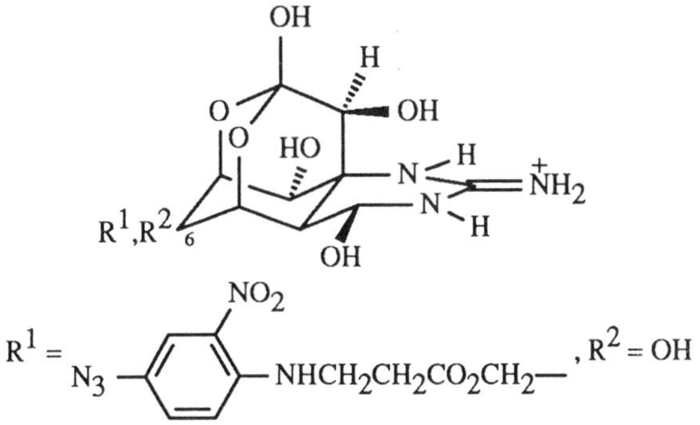

Figure 14 Structures of tetrodotoxin derivatives used in photolabeling experiments on the Na^+ channel

Table 3 Pharmacological and Radioligand Binding Activities of Saxitoxin Derivatives at Na^+ Channels[125,126]

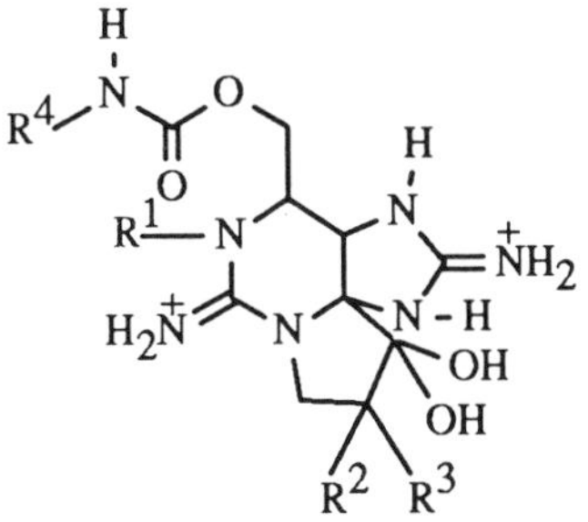

Compound	R^1	R^2	R^3	R^4	Channel block (K_D/K_{STX})	Binding (K_I/K_{STX})
Saxitoxin	H	H	H	H	1.0	1.0
GTX 1	OH	H	OSO_3^-	H	3.5	2.5
GTX 2	H	H	OSO_3^-	H	6.5	2.9
GTX 3	H	OSO_3^-	H	H	1.0	0.5
GTX 4	OH	OSO_3^-	H	H	—	0.3
Neosaxitoxin	OH	H	H	H	0.28	0.2
Cl	H	H	OSO_3^-	SO_3^-	581	800
Bl	H	H	H	SO_3^-	42	40

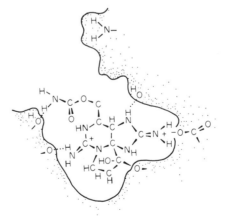

Figure 15 Representation of saxitoxin binding to Na^+ channel in which a labile covalent bond is formed to binding site (reproduced from ref. 125 by permission of New York Academy of Sciences)

The scorpion neurotoxins represent a large protein family, homologous despite differences in specificities and actions,[130,131] and possessing 60–70 amino acids (long chain toxins) or less than 40 amino acids (short chain toxins) with four intrachain disulfide bridges (Figure 11). The presence of the disulfide bridges confers stability and a compact structure. The solid state structure of the toxin from *C. sculpturatus* reveals a further feature of particular interest, a hydrophobic patch containing the majority of the aromatic amino acid residues, together with leucines 17 and 19, alanine 43 and prolines 59 and 61, and associated with many of the conserved residues.[132] This hydrophobic arrangement is probably critical for channel site interaction, since the binding of toxin III from *C. suffus suffus* is a hydrophobically-determined reaction, characterized as an entropy-driven process with a large negative heat-capacity change.[133]

14.1.4.3.3   Alkaloid toxins

In the alkaloid toxin group some structure–activity data are available, notably for the grayano-toxins (Figure 12).[134] From an extensive series of analogs, several functional groups appear to be particularly important for activity: these include the 3-hydroxy or 2,3-epoxy group, β-hydroxy groups at the C-5 and C-6 positions and the β-methyl group at C-10 (Table 4). However, other factors are obviously important, since activity decreases with substituent changes which alter the hydrophobic:hydrophilic balance from that seen in grayanotoxin and its active analogs. Despite the chemical heterogeneity of the alkaloid group of Na$^+$ channel activators, there have been suggestions that they function by interacting at a common site, presenting a common constellation of three oxygen atoms in a triangular arrangement (Figure 12; Table 4).[134–136] This must be an oversimpli-fied view and other groups, notably the amine functions of veratridine, batrachotoxin and aconitine and a presumed equivalent group in grayanotoxin, must also be involved.

14.1.4.3.4   Insecticides

The Na$^+$ channel represents a major site of action for insecticides, including those of the pyrethroid and DDT classes.[89,137–140] These agents probably function in qualitatively similar fashion to prolong Na$^+$ currents. Thus a pyrethroid-modified open Na$^+$ channel closes very slowly, relative to unmodified channels, during prolonged depolarization or when repolarized. Pyrethroids are frequently divided into major groups, characterized by the presence and absence of a cyano function respectively (Figure 16). This classification, originally based on differences in poisoning symptoms and the ability of type I and type II pyrethroids to produce repetitive and prolonged depolarization respectively, is now regarded as representing simply two extremes of pyrethroid behavior at the Na$^+$ channel, characterized by very rapid (type I) and very slow (type II) decay of modified Na$^+$ currents following depolarization. The existence of specific sites of action for the pyrethroids is suggested by the existence of stereoselectivity of action[141] and further supported by the demonstration of specific saturable binding.[142] Many of the pyrethroids contain centers of asymmetry and are geometrical isomers also. Complex relationships may exist in the interaction of these compounds with Na$^+$ channels. Thus the (+)-*cis* and -*trans* isomers of tetramethrin are active whilst the corresponding (−) isomers are inactive. However, the (−) isomers do interact with the channel to block the effects of the active (+) isomers in both a competitive and noncompetitive manner.[142] This suggests that there may exist at least two distinct pyrethroid binding sites associated with the Na$^+$ channel, one of high affinity concerned with modification of channel properties and at which (+)-*cis*-, (+)-*trans*- and (−)-*cis*-tetramethrin bind, and a high affinity allosteric site at which the (−)-*trans* isomer interacts.

14.1.4.3.5   Local anesthetics

Local anesthetics are exceedingly widely used agents, employed therapeutically for their effects in many acute and chronic pain-generating situations and for their antiarrhythmic properties. Local anesthetics are employed pharmacologically for their ability to serve as functional probes of the Na$^+$ channel, a primary, but not exclusive, target.

Determination of the structural features controlling local anesthetic activity is particularly difficult, since this is an activity possessed by many molecules including alcohols, antidepressants, β-adrenoceptor antagonists and anticonvulsants. For many of these compounds local anesthesia is secondary to other pharmacological activities and is exhibited only at higher concentrations. An additional complexity to the interpretation of structure–activity relationships is the exhibition of state-dependent interactions (Section 14.1.3). This is seen very clearly in the action of lidocaine on cardiac Na$^+$ channels.[143] The measured affinity of lidocaine is strongly voltage-dependent with a

Table 4 Arrangement of Proposed Essential Groups for Common Binding of Na$^+$ Channel Toxins[132-136]

Toxin	Important functional groups		
	A	B	C
Grayanotoxin	3-β-OH (or 2-β,3-β-epoxide)	5-β-OH	6-β-OH
Batrachotoxin	3-α-OH	3-α,9-α-oxide	11-α-OH
Veratridine	17-α-OH	12-α-OH	14-α-OH
Aconitine	16-β-OMe	15-α-OH	8-β-CO$_2$Me

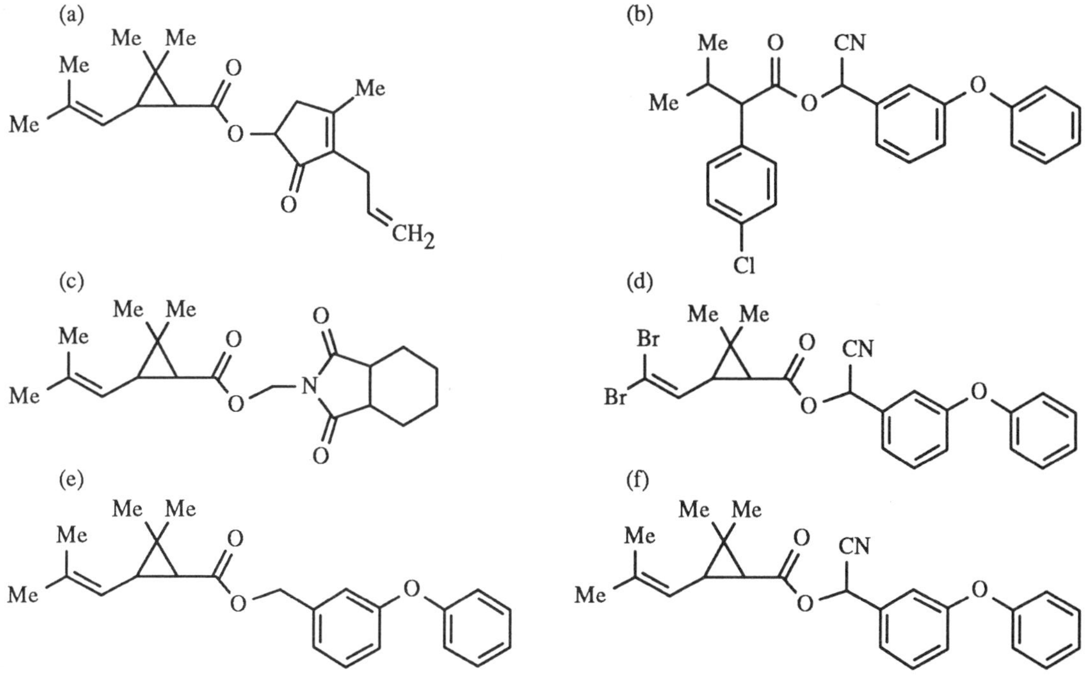

Figure 16 Structure of pyrethroid molecules

K_D of 4×10^{-4} mol dm^{-3} measured from negative holding potentials and of 10^{-5} mol dm^{-3} at a depolarized potential. The activity of lidocaine is strongly use-dependent, increasing with increasing frequency of depolarizing pulses, and interpulse recovery of channel activity progressively slows with increasing lidocaine concentration. These actions are interpretable according to the modulated receptor hypothesis whereby lidocaine binds preferentially to a state or states of the Na$^+$ channel, activated or inactivated, accessed by maintained or frequency-dependent depolarization (Figure 17). Accordingly, the apparent (measured) affinity of lidocaine will depend upon the equilibrium between the resting and inactivated states, as shown in equation (6) where h and $1 - h$ are the channel fractions in the resting and inactivated states, respectively.[143] A listing of estimated dissociation constants according to channel state for several Na$^+$ channel blocking drugs is given in Table 5.[78]

$$1/K_{app} = h/K_r + (1 - h)/K_I \qquad (6)$$

General reviews of local anesthetics are available[144-145] and a representative selection of local anesthetic structures is given in Figure 18. Interpretation of structure–activity relationships within the framework of the preceding considerations and the modulated receptor hypothesis (Section 14.1.3)[146] indicates that molecular features determining resting state block (tonic block) and frequency-dependent block (phasic block) and the kinetics of onset and offset to these states must be separately factored. Consideration of both kinetic and equilibrium factors is thus important. Thus, for an effective antiarrhythmic agent, a fast onset of frequency-dependent block may be very desirable, whereas for nerve block activity the level of resting equilibrium blockade is likely to be more important in the choice of therapeutic agent. Several efforts to accomplish a separation of

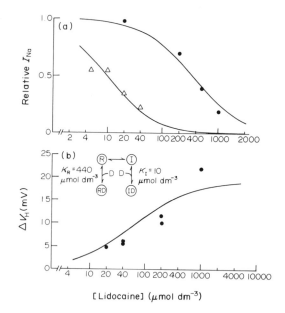

Figure 17 (a) Dose–response curve of lidocaine block of cardiac Na⁺ channels at holding potentials (V_H) of -120 (●) and -65 (△) mV with test pulses to -40 mV. (b) Shift in the midpoint of the Na⁺ channel availability curve as a function of lidocaine concentration. Inset: dissociation constant values for modulated receptor.model (reproduced from ref. 143 by permission of Rockefeller University Press)

Table 5 Estimated Dissociation Constants For Drug Interaction at Discrete Na⁺ Channel States[78]

Drug	K_D ($\times 10^{-6}$ mol dm⁻³)		
	Resting	*Open*	*Inactivated*
Amiodarone	100 000	1000	20
Lidocaine	440	High	10
Procainamide	1 850 000	37 000	370
Propafenone	300 000	1.0	0.5
Quinidine	Very high	100	0.5

structural and steric features determining equilibria and kinetics of resting and frequency-dependent Na⁺ channel block have been made.[146-156]

Development of and relief from resting and frequency-dependent block in a nerve preparation by a series of 12 local anesthetics has been shown to involve different molecular properties (Table 6).[147-149] Tonic activity, adjusted for pK_a differences, correlates well with partition coefficients for the amide series, though the remaining structures are anomalously active (Figure 19). In particular, tetracaine and procaine are significantly more active as tonic blockers than are the amide-linked structures. Cyclic amide and ureide anticonvulsants, including phenytoin, phenobarbital, phensuximide and carbamazepine, are also less active in producing resting state block than predicted from partition coefficient considerations alone.[152] The correlation depicted is consistent with hydrophobic processes that may dominate channel binding site interactions or that dominate channel access, *via* the membrane lipid bilayer, to the binding site. In contrast, frequency-dependent or phasic block decreases with increasing molecular size and with increasing partition coefficient (Table 6; Figure 20), consistent with the necessity for a hydrophilic pathway of access to the open state or with the existence of a relatively more polar binding site in open channel than in resting channel block.

Recovery from the blocked channel state is an important consideration for the selectivity that a drug may possess for aberrant over regular rhythms in cardiac tissue.[150] Rates of unblocking of closed channels by a series of local anesthetics correlate well with molecular size, smaller drugs showing faster recovery rates (Figure 21).[149,153] However, an extension to a greater number of structures suggests that channel recovery rate from local anesthetic block correlates best with a combination of molecular size and hydrophobicity (Figure 22).[147,156]

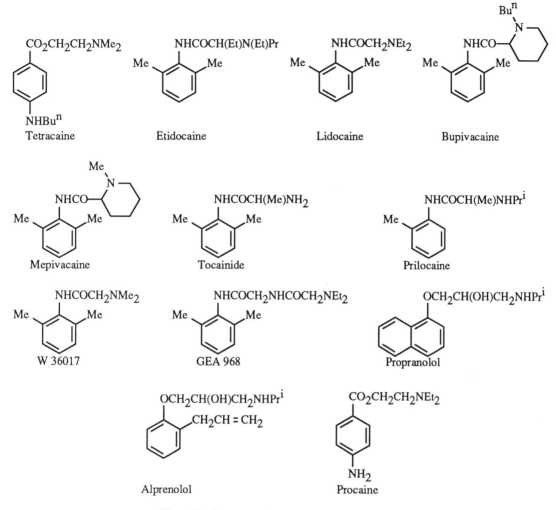

Figure 18 Structures of local anesthetic molecules

Homologous series that provide a more coherent structural base have also been examined.[154,155] In a series of lidocaine derivatives where the size of the *N*-alkyl substituent varies (**3**), tonic block in nerve fibers correlates with the octanol–water partition coefficient (Figure 23). However, frequency-dependent block does not depend simply on hydrophobicity, suggesting that the molecular features governing access to or interaction with the corresponding channel states are different.[154] In the disopyramide (Norpace) series (**4**) both molecular size and octanol–water partition coefficient are determinants of Na$^+$ channel blocking activity in a nerve preparation.[155] As with the local anesthetic series, the structural requirements for resting and frequency-dependent block differ and a good correlation between potency and molecular weight is found only for the latter component of block (Figure 24).

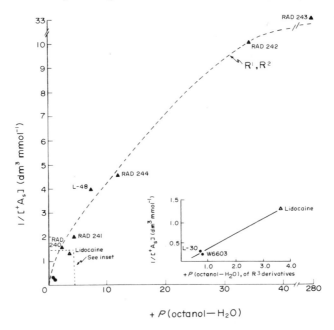

Figure 19 The activity of lidocaine and its homologs to reduce frog nerve action potentials evoked by low frequency stimulation as a function of the calculated partition coefficient of the charged form. The drugs refer to structure (**3**): (**3a**) RAD 240; (**3b**) RAD 241; (**3c**) RAD 244; (**3d**) RAD 242; (**3e**) RAD 243; (**3f**) L-48; (**3g**) lidocaine (reproduced from ref. 154 by permission of Williams & Wilkins Co.)

Table 6 Local Anesthetic Activities in Sciatic Nerve[149]

Drug	Concentration ($\times 10^{-6}$ mol dm^{-3})	Molecular weight	pK_a	log P^a	Block (resting) (%)	Onset rate (frequency dependent)^b (pulses^{-1})	Offset rate (s^{-1})
Tocainamide	500	192	7.8	1.08	44	0.22	0.10
W36017	500	208	7.4	1.68	54	0.76	0.47
Prilocaine	250	220	7.8	1.78	31	0.90	0.90
Procaine	130	236	9.0	2.00	64	0.65	0.31
Alprenolol	40	249	~9	2.8	43	0.22	0.10
(+)-Propranolol	20	259	9.5	2.8	42	0.12	0.07
GEA 968	600	291	7.7	0.71	41	0.05	0.02
Mepivacaine	250	246	7.6	2.04	63	0.19	0.06
Lidocaine	250	234	7.9	2.76	64	0.84	0.18
Bupivacaine	50	302	8.1	4.33	62	0.17	0.01
Etidocaine	15	276	7.7	4.38	68	0.10	0.04
Tetracaine	0.7	264	8.5	3.40	69	0.09	0.04

^{a} Calculated for octanol–water (base form). ^{b} 2 Hz stimulation rate.

In principle, the differences in structural requirements exhibited by local anesthetics for the production of resting and frequency-dependent block may be due to differences in the conformations of channel states, to differences in access pathways to the binding sites or to some combination of both. Local anesthetics exhibit stereoselectivity,[147,157-160] evidence in favor of a specific rather than a nonspecific mode of action. With the enantiomeric pairs RAC 109-I and RAC 109-II and the corresponding quaternary derivatives (Figure 25), virtually no stereoselectivity of resting block was observed. However, significant stereoselectivity, by an approximately tenfold factor, was observed following repetitive stimulation (Table 7), clearly consistent with the previously discussed hypothesis that different structural requirements exist for Na$^+$ channel blockade according to channel state. Of particular interest are observations that the properties of enantiomers of 4-[3-(4-diphenylmethyl-1-piperazinyl)-2-hydroxypropoxy]-1H-indolo-2-carbonitrile (**5**; DPI 201-106) are qualitatively and quantitatively distinct, the (*R*) enantiomers block Na$^+$ channels while the (*S*) enantiomers enhance Na$^+$ current and slow inactivation.[161]

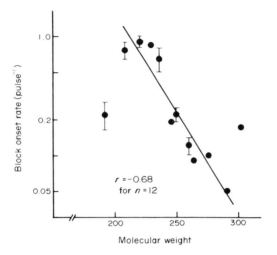

Figure 20 Rate of onset of block of nerve action potentials by local anesthetics (Table 6)[149] at 2 Hz stimulation rate as a function of molecular weight. The deviations are tocainide (left) and bupivacaine (right) (reproduced from ref. 149 by permission of Williams & Wilkins Co.)

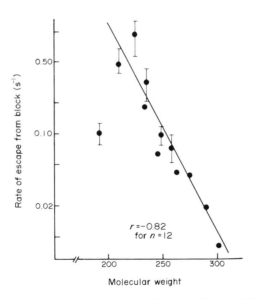

Figure 21 Rate of escape from block of nerve action potentials (stimulation frequency 2 Hz) by a series of local anesthetics (Table 6)[149] as a function of molecular weight (reproduced from ref. 149 by permission of Williams & Wilkins Co.)

Local anesthetic potency varies considerably between tissues and according to experimental conditions.[147,162] In part this may reflect fundamentally different sensitivities between tissues: skeletal muscle may be intrinsically more sensitive than nerve preparations to local anesthetics.[163] However, it is also clear that a significant difference in activity occurs because of tissue-dependent differences in the gating behavior of Na^+ channels. Such differences are reflected in different ratios of

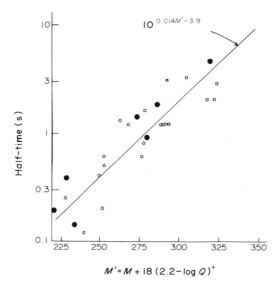

Figure 22   The unblocking of Na^+ channels by local anesthetic molecules as a function of size (molecular weight, M) and lipid distribution coefficient (Q) (reproduced from ref. 147 by permission of Springer-Verlag)

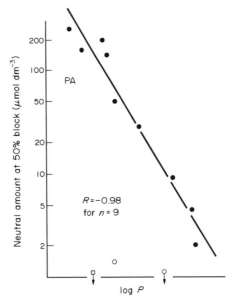

Figure 23   Correlation between the activity of amide-based local anesthetics (Table 6 and procainamide, PA)[149] in neutral form as a function of partition coefficient ($\log P$). Ester structures (○) and β-blockers (□) deviate significantly (reproduced from ref. 149 by permission of Williams & Wilkins Co.)

channel states under resting conditions and hence different apparent affinities of local anesthetics (Section 14.1.3). Thus, preparations which physiologically or pathologically show partial activation or inactivation of Na^+ channels at resting potential will show an enhanced degree of resting (tonic) block according to the state populations. In nerve and skeletal muscle a significant fraction of Na^+ channels are inactivated at the resting potential and the typically brief action potential adds little to the fractional inactivated state occupancy. In contrast, in cardiac muscle there is little resting inactivation but a considerable increase in this component occurs during the sustained action potential. Consequently, little resting block is seen with cardiac Na^+ channels and most block occurs during each cardiac action potential.

    The extent of use-dependent block depends upon the association and dissociation rates of the drug molecule. Rapidly dissociating molecules will show less use-dependent block than slowly dissociating molecules. Cardiac rate will thus be an important determinant of drug potency.

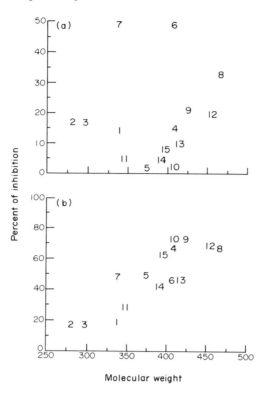

Figure 24 Relationship between Na^+ channel blocking activity by disopyramide (**4**; Norpace) and 14 derivatives as a function of molecular weight: (a) resting block, (b) use-dependence block (reproduced from ref. 155 by permission of Rockefeller University Press)

Table 7 Stereoselectivity of Local Anesthetic Activity in Squid Axon[160]

Local anesthetic	ED_{50} (mmol dm^{-3})		
	Initial block	Conditioned block[a]	
		0 mV	+80 mV
RAC 109-I	1.40	0.14	0.034
RAC 109-II	1.45	0.79	0.49
RAC 421-I	1.99	0.10	0.042
RAC 421-II	2.35	0.98	0.42

[a] Following 30 conditioning pulses to 0 or +80 mV.

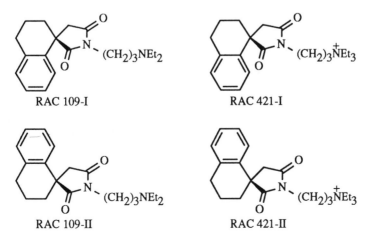

Figure 25 Structural formulae of stereoisomeric pairs of local anesthetics

Lidocaine, which dissociates rapidly, will be selectively antiarrhythmic during rapid cardiac rhythms or premature beats. Indeed, antiarrhythmic agents of class I can be classified according to such kinetic considerations (Table 8). Optimally, antiarrhythmic drugs will effectively limit abnormal rhythms and propagations with minimal effect on normal tissue.

Essentially similar explanations underlie the efficacy of some anticonvulsants, including phenytoin (6) and carbamazepine (7), which show voltage- and frequency-dependent block of Na^+ channels and interact preferentially with the inactivated state of the channel.[165-167] This behavior underlies the selective actions of these agents on neurons undergoing epileptic discharges which increase the population of Na^+ channels in the inactivated state.[168]

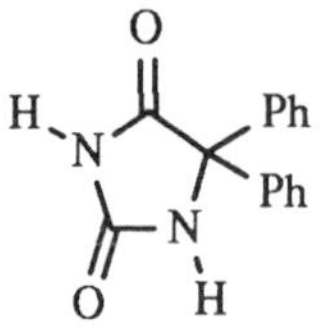

(6) 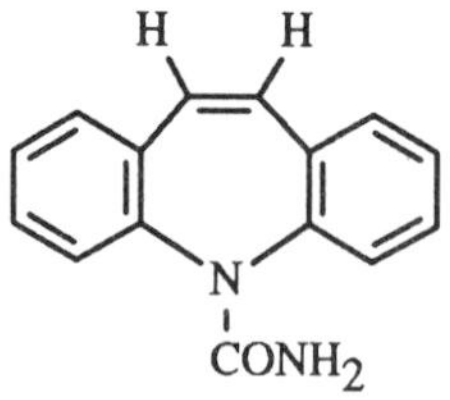   (7)

14.1.5 DRUGS ACTIVE AT Ca^{2+} CHANNELS

14.1.5.1 Introduction to Cellular Ca^{2+} Regulation

There are many similarities between drug action at Ca^{2+} and Na^+ channels. In both instances a heterogeneous group of compounds can serve both to block or to activate the channel. Although the primary target of these agents is the voltage-dependent Ca^{2+} or Na^+ channel, the modulation achieved reflects interaction at different sites and by different mechanisms. This similarity of behavior of drug action at Na^+ and Ca^{2+} channels reflects the underlying homologies in structure and similarities of organization.[26,27,30,31]

The group of compounds variously described as Ca^{2+} antagonists, Ca^{2+} channel antagonists (blockers) and Ca^{2+} entry blockers was introduced into clinical medicine over the past 15 years.[169-171] This group of agents, which includes the clinically available verapamil, nifedipine and diltiazem (Figure 26), is used very successfully in a number of cardiovascular disorders including angina in its several forms, hypertension and peripheral cardiovascular disorders and some cardiac arrhythmias (Table 9). Additionally, these agents are being employed experimentally in a variety of disorders ranging from achalasia to vertigo.[172] The recent classification introduced by the World Health Organization described verapamil (phenylalkylamine), nifedipine (1,4-dihydropyridines) and diltiazem (benzothiazepine) as representatives of group I, II and III specific Ca^{2+} antagonists respectively (Table 9). A number of studies ranging from early observations that their effects on cardiac function resembled those of Ca^{2+} withdrawal (and that their effects could be overcome by addition of excess Ca^{2+}) to later electrophysiological studies, including action potential and patch clamp measurements, have amply confirmed that the primary actions of the Ca^{2+} channel antagonists are exerted at one category of membrane channels, the voltage-dependent Ca^{2+} channel. Despite the known significance of voltage-dependent Ca^{2+} channels to neuronal function it

Table 8 Effects of Local Anesthetic Antiarrhythmic Agents[162,166]

Drug	Class[a]	Recovery kinetics, phasic block	Action potential duration	Effective refractory period
Lidocaine	IA[b]	Fast	Abbreviated	Abbreviated
Tocainide	IA	Fast	Abbreviated	Abbreviated
Phenytoin	IA	Fast	Abbreviated	Abbreviated
Quinidine	IB[c]	Slow	Prolonged	Prolonged
Disopyramide	IB	Slow	Prolonged	Prolonged
Procainamide	IB	Slow	Prolonged	Prolonged

[a] Based on action potential duration; class IC not listed here (flecainide) have no effect on action potential duration. [b] Newer agents = ajmaline, cibenzoline, ORG 6001. [c] Newer agents = droxicainide, ethacizin.

Table 9 Therapeutic Uses of Ca^{2+} Channel Antagonists[a]

Use	Verapamil (I)[b]	Antagonist Nifedipine (II)[b]	Diltiazem (III)[b]
Angina			
exertional	+++	+++	+++
Prinzmetal's	+++	+++	+++
variant	+++	+++	+++
Paroxysmal supraventricular tachyarrhythmias	+++	—	+++
Atrial fibrillation and flutter	++	—	++
Hypertension	++	+++	+
Hypertrophic cardiomyopathy	+	—	—
Raynaud's phenomenon	++	++	++
Cardioplegia	+	+	+
Cerebral vasospasm (post-hemorrhage)	—	+	—

[a] Number of plus signs indicates extent of use, +++ being very common; —, not used. [b] Classes I, II and III as defined by the World Health Organization.[172]

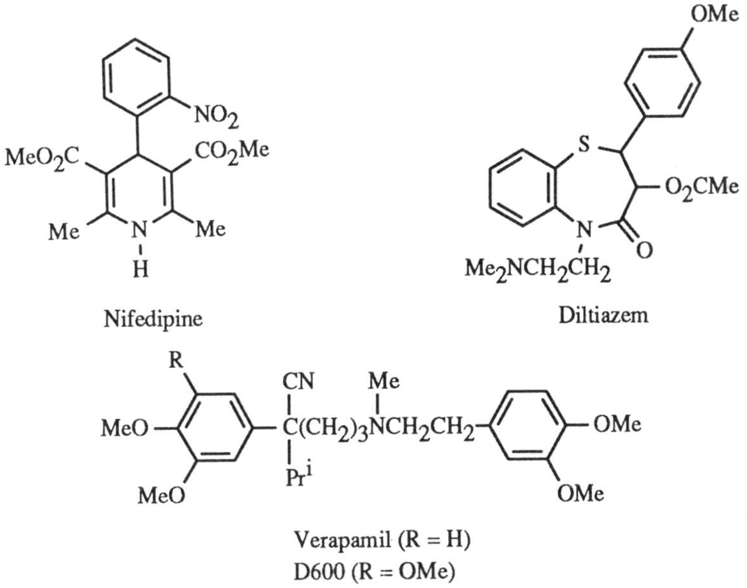

Figure 26 Structural formulae of three major categories of Ca^{2+} channel antagonists

is noteworthy that the currently available Ca^{2+} channel antagonists commonly do not exert major effects, experimentally or therapeutically, in nervous tissue.

The clinically available Ca^{2+} channel antagonists are a chemically heterogeneous collection of molecules. Consistent with this, these agents do not exhibit an identical spectrum of pharmacological and therapeutic effects. The major difference is that nifedipine and other 1,4-dihydropyridines are dominantly vasodilator species, whilst verapamil and diltiazem share both vasodilator and cardiodepressant properties. The antihypertensive effect of nifedipine and the antiarrhythmic activity of verapamil are particularly obvious differences. These differences are due, at least in part, not to different receptors in cardiac and smooth muscle but rather to the subtleties of state-dependent interactions. The differential effects of the Ca^{2+} channel antagonists on hemodynamic properties are listed in Table 10.

Therapeutic utility of these agents may not be limited to the uses listed in Table 9. They are employed or have been considered for use in aortic and mitral valvular insufficiency, cardioplegia, cerebral insufficiency, congestive heart failure, migraine and cluster headache, intermittent claudication, stroke, subarachnoid hemorrhage and ventricular tachycardia in the cardiovascular system, in nonvascular smooth muscle spasm, including achalasia, asthma, dysmenorrhea, chronic obstructive lung disease and urinary incontinence, and for a variety of other diseases, including primary

Table 10 Hemodynamic Effects of Ca^{2+} Channel Antagonists[a]

	Verapamil	*Nifedipine*	*Diltiazem*
Coronary blood flow	↑↑	↑↑↑	↑↑
Peripheral vasodilation	↑↑	↑↑↑	↑
Heart rate	↑↓	0	0, ↓
Contractility	↓	0, ↑	0, ↓
Preload	0	0, ↓	0
AV node conduction	↓↓	0	↓
AV node effective refractory period	↑↓	0	↑↓
PR interval	↑	0	↑
AH interval	↑	0	↓

[a] ↑ = increase, ↓ = decrease, ↓↑ = variable effect, 0 = no effect.

aldosteronism, epilepsy, manic depression, motion sickness, antitumor drug resistance, schizophrenia, Tourette's syndrome, vertigo and immunosuppressive therapy. The Ca^{2+} channel antagonists will certainly not become drugs of first choice in all of these disorders. Thus, the presently available agents have little apparent effectiveness in asthma. A review by Janis *et al.*[173] is available. The side effects of the Ca^{2+} channel antagonists are, in general, related to their principal actions on the cardiovascular system and include headache, facial flushing, dizziness and gastrointestinal symptoms including constipation (verapamil) and edema (nifedipine).

Plasmalemmal Ca^{2+} channels represent one of the important pathways through which the Ca^{2+} demands of the excited cell are met. A schematic representation of cellular Ca^{2+} metabolism is depicted in Figure 27. General reviews of cellular Ca^{2+} metabolism are available.[173,174] Present within the cell are several distinct categories of Ca^{2+} channel. Plasmalemmal Ca^{2+} channels are often classified as potential dependent and receptor operated, a terminology used to indicate with some imprecision a distinction between electrically and chemically gated channels, respectively. However, it is clear that potential-dependent channels are, in fact, also chemically regulated species.[12,175] Thus, cardiac Ca^{2+} channels are activated by phosphorylation, mediated through β-adrenoceptor-associated adenylate cyclase, a process which enhances the probability of channel opening.[175,176] A variety of models may be advanced to describe plasmalemmal receptor-operated Ca^{2+} channels (Section 14.1.2).[173] Most recently, an association has been proposed with the receptor-initiated G protein-linked phospholipase C-mediated hydrolysis of polyphosphatidylinositol, which yields inositol 1,4,5-triphosphate (IP_3) and 1,3,4,5-tetraphosphate (Figure 27).[177-179] The latter species is proposed to activate receptor-operated channels in the plasma membrane. Of particular interest are well-documented observations that inositol triphosphate mediates intracellular release of Ca^{2+} through activation of Ca^{2+} channels present in the endoplasmic reticulum.[180,181] The definition of receptor-operated Ca^{2+} channels and their chemical sensitivity will be an important area of investigation for drug action.[182]

Ca^{2+} channels, in common with other cellular transducing systems, probably use G proteins as coupling devices. Inhibition of neuronal Ca^{2+} currents by the neurotransmitters norepinephrine, GABA and opiates is sensitive to guanine nucleotides, blocked by pertussis toxin and restored by the addition of G_0.[22]

14.1.5.2 Drugs Active at Ca^{2+} Channels

The analysis of drug action at voltage-dependent Ca^{2+} channels presents a number of interesting contrasts to the situation with Na^+ channels. For the latter, very prominent roles have been assumed by the naturally occurring toxins that have constituted a key factor in channel characterization and isolation. For Ca^{2+} channels, synthetic molecules have constituted the driving force for channel characterization. Moreover, Ca^{2+} channels have revealed, relatively early in their development, a multiple character which will permit faster interpretation and exploitation of their pharmacology.

The primary focus of the Ca^{2+} channel drugs has been on the verapamil, nifedipine and diltiazem structures (Figure 26). There are, however, many other structures that possess Ca^{2+} channel blocking properties, either associated with other properties or as a secondary component of other and better defined pharamcological activities. Prenylamine, perhexiline, fendiline, terodiline,

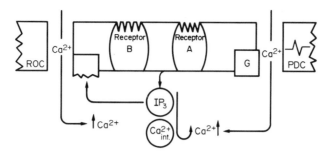

Figure 27 Schematic representation of plasmalemmal Ca^{2+} regulation. Depicted are potential-dependent Ca^{2+} channels (PDC) and receptor-activated (receptors A and B) Ca^{2+} mobilization through the intermediacy of inositol triphosphate (IP_3) which serves both to mobilize Ca^{2+} from intracellular and through receptor-operated channels (see text for further details)

lidoflazine and caroverine (Figure 28) fall into the former category, as do cinnarizine and flunarizine, but a very broad spectrum of agents including the α-adrenoceptor antagonists phenoxybenzamine and yohimbine, antischizophrenic drugs including the diphenylbutylpiperidines and phenothiazines, barbiturates, benzodiazepines and other agents, both natural and synthetic, probably fall into the second category.[173,174] The specificity of action of many of these agents is in doubt since in many instances, despite assignment of title, there is little direct evidence to support the claim of specific Ca^{2+} channel antagonism.

Although major emphasis has been placed on the development of Ca^{2+} channel antagonists, the 1,4-dihydropyridine series also contains structures that, whilst closely resembling nifedipine, possess the opposing property of Ca^{2+} channel activation. These agents, including Bay K 8644, CGP 28 392 and PN 202 791 (Figure 29), serve to induce Ca^{2+} currents by stabilizing the open channel state to initiate positive inotropic responses, vasoconstriction, hormone secretion and neurotransmitter release.[173] The subtle structural differentiation between activator and antagonist 1,4-dihydropyridines is underscored by the enantiomeric selectivity displayed by Bay K 8644, PN 202 791

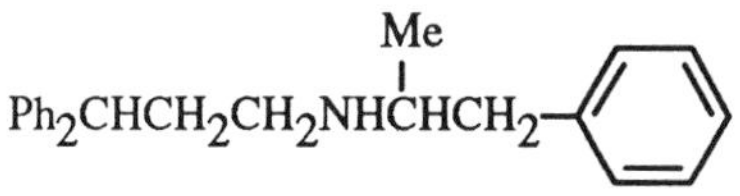

Prenylamine $Ph_2CHCH_2CH_2NHCHCH_2-$ (with Me)

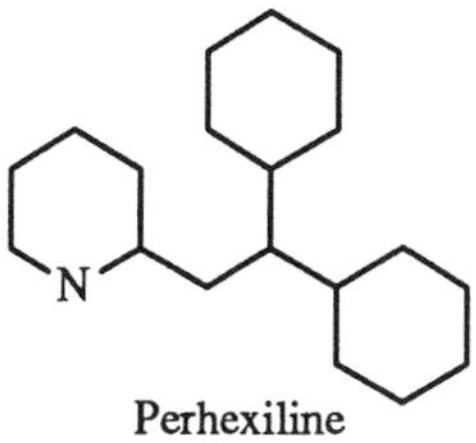

Perhexiline

Fendiline $Ph_2CHCH_2CH_2NHCH-$ (with Me)

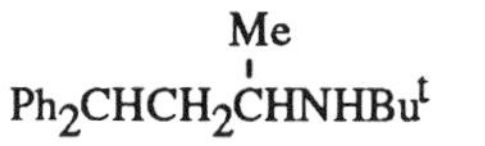

Terodiline $Ph_2CHCH_2CHNHBu^t$ (with Me)

Lidoflazine $(4\text{-}FC_6H_4)_2CH(CH_2)_3-N\qquad N-CH_2CONH-$ (with Me, Me)

Caroverine (with $CH_2CH_2NEt_2$, O, OMe, N, H)

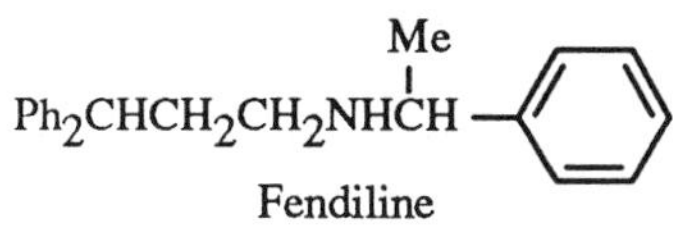

Cinnarizine $Ph_2CH-N\qquad N-CH_2CH=CHPh$

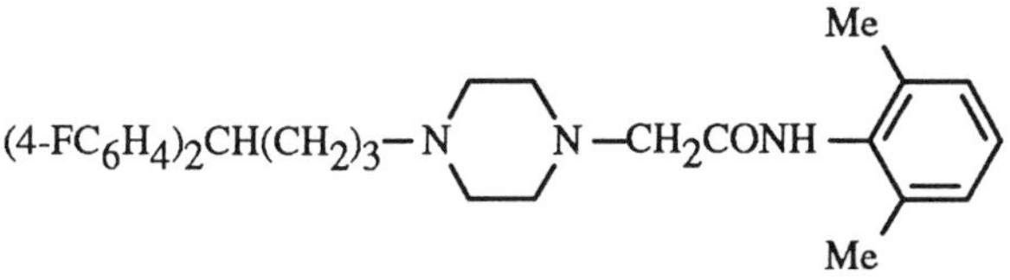

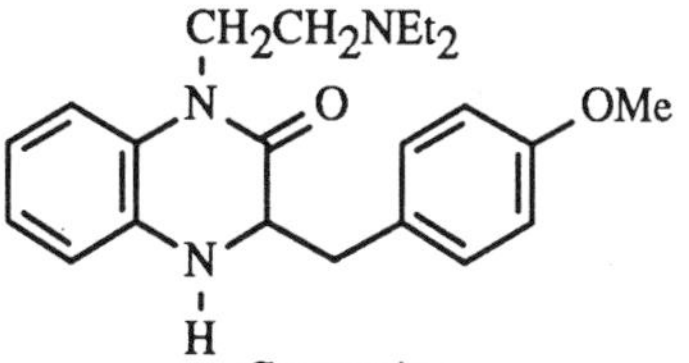

Flunarizine $(4\text{-}FC_6H_4)_2CH-N\qquad N-CH_2CH=CHPh$

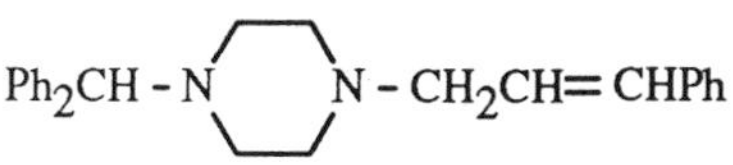

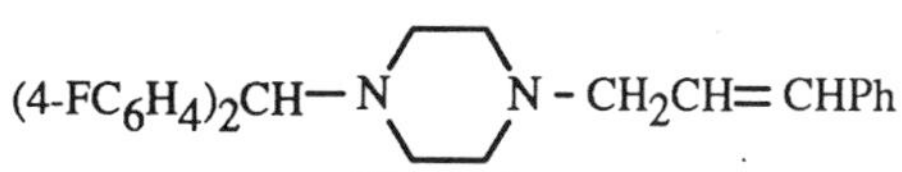

Figure 28 Structural formulae of 'nonspecific' Ca^{2+} channel antagonists

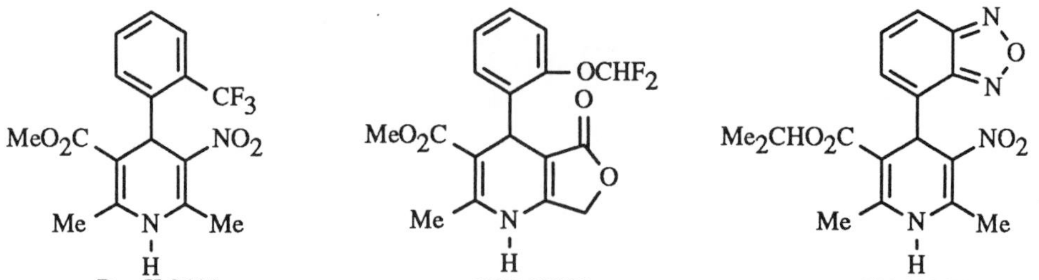

Figure 29　Structural formulae of Ca^{2+} channel activators

and related compounds, where the (S) and (R) enantiomers are activator and antagonist, respectively.[183,184]

Ca^{2+} channel activators have not been reported in the phenylalkylamine or benzothiazepine series, but fewer members of these series, particularly of the benzothiazepines, have been available. However, Ca^{2+} channel activator properties have been described for the anthelmintic agent praziquantel (**8**),[185,186] but these are far weaker than those described for the 1,4-dihydropyridines and the site of action of praziquantel remains to be defined.

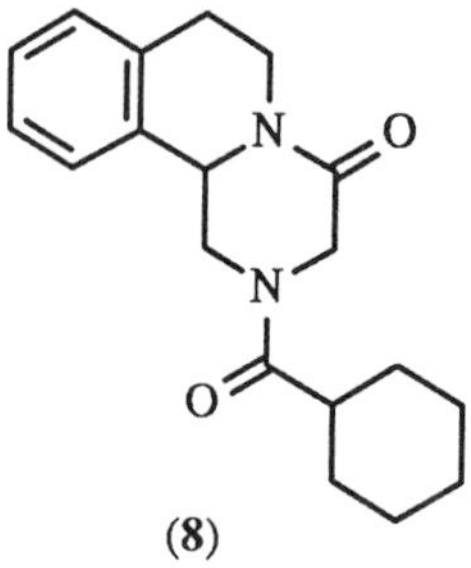

(**8**)

Of the three major structural categories of Ca^{2+} channel ligands, the greatest number of analogs is available in the 1,4-dihydropyridine series. Structural requirements for antagonism in this series have been quite well established from both *in vivo* and *in vitro* pharmacological and radioligand binding measurements.[173,187−192]

(a) In a series of 2,6-dimethyl-3,5-di(alkoxycarbonyl)-1,4-dihydropyridines, activity increases with substitution in the 4-position in the sequence H < methyl < cycloalkyl < phenyl and substituted phenyl.

(b) Optimum activity occurs when the phenyl ring substituents are in the *ortho* or *meta* positions and are electron withdrawing. Regardless of substituent character, *para*-substituted compounds are greatly reduced in activity suggesting a steric hindrance to interaction.

(c) The 1,4-dihydropyridine ring is essential, the NH proton is critical to activity and conversion to oxidized (pyridine) or reduced (piperidine) products abolishes activity.

(d) Ester groups are optimum in the C-3 and C-5 positions for antagonist activity. Other electron-withdrawing groups, such as acetyl and cyano, are less effective and the nitro group is associated with activator activity.

(e) When the C-3 and C-5 ester groups differ, C-4 becomes chiral and stereoselectivity of action is observed. There is substantial tolerance to the size of the ester groups permitted ('bulk tolerance') and some evidence that such asymmetrically substituted esters, including nimodipine, nisoldipine and nitrendipine (Figure 30), may have enhanced selectivity for cerebral, coronary and peripheral blood vessels, respectively.[193] Most active 1,4-dihydropyridines contain methyl groups at C-2 and C-6; however, agents such as amlodipine (Figure 30) are potent antagonists, indicating larger binding site sizes at these positions than previously suspected.[194]

Several attempts have been made to quantify the structure–activity relationships of the 1,4-dihydropyridine antagonists.[173,188,189,195] The major limitations to these studies have been the small numbers of compounds studied and the narrow activity range frequently expressed. For a series of 2,6-dimethyl-3,5-di(methoxycarbonyl)-4-substituted (*ortho, meta, para*) phenyl-1,4-dihydropyridines, radioligand binding in intestinal smooth muscle was described by equation (7),[195] where B_1 and L are the Verloop steric constants. There are a number of

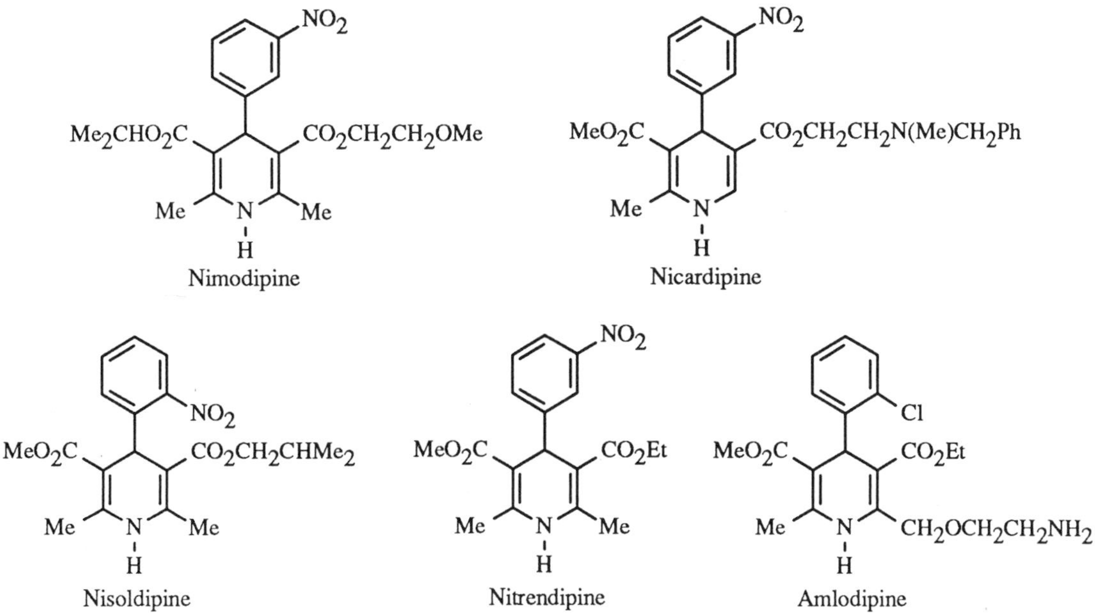

Figure 30 Structural formulae of 1,4-dihydropyridine Ca^{2+} channel antagonists

inconsistencies with this analysis[196] and the equation should more properly be written as equation (8).

$$\log(1/IC_{50}) = 2.4B_1(o,m) - 0.47L(m) - 0.67L(p) + 1.93(m) + 7.43 \qquad (7)$$

$$n = 18, \quad r = 0.93, \quad s = 0.43$$

$$\log(1/IC_{50}) = 5.05 + 2.4[B_1(o) + B_1(m)] - 0.47L(m) - 0.67L(p) + 1.93(m) \qquad (8)$$

A larger set of compounds, derived from the nonchiral 2,6-dimethyl-3,5-di(methoxycarbonyl)-4-substituted phenyl-1,4-dihydropyridines, and including *ortho*-, *meta*-, *para*- and multiply-substituted compounds, has been analyzed for their activity against tension responses of intestinal smooth muscle.[190,196] For a series of compounds covering an approximately 10^5-fold range of activity, equation (9) can be derived, where o and o' and m and m' represent orientations of the *ortho* and *meta* substituents over and away from the plane of the 1,4-dihydropyridine ring, respectively. Several features of the ligand–receptor interaction are described in equation (9). Steric interactions are most unfavorable at the *para* position of the 4-phenyl ring and more unfavorable at the *ortho'* and *meta'* positions than at the *ortho* and *meta* positions. Solid state structural studies of *ortho*- and *meta*-substituted compounds show that the preferred conformer has, with rare exception, the substituent oriented away from the 1,4-dihydropyridine ring. The use of σ_m as the electronic term irrespective of substituent position is of interest and may indicate that the global phenyl ring electronic density, rather than positional density, is important.

$$\log(1/IC_{50}) = 15.24 + 0.62\pi + 1.79\sigma_m - 0.13L(o) - 0.50L(m) - 1.70L(p) - 1.12L(m') - 0.46L(o') \qquad (9)$$

$$n = 47, \quad r = 0.913, \quad s = 0.63$$

The effects of phenyl ring and ester substitution are expressed independently, since in several series with different ester groups, including 3,5-di(methoxycarbonyl), 3-ethoxycarbonyl-5-methoxycarbonyl, 3-methoxycarbonyl-5-(2-N-benzyl)-N-methylaminomethoxycarbonyl and 3-methoxycarbonyl-5-isobutoxycarbonyl, the same rank order of phenyl ring substituent activity is expressed.[197] This is seen quite clearly in Figure 31 which correlates the activities of phenyl-ring-substituted compounds of the nifedipine [3,5-di(methoxycarbonyl)] and nisoldipine (3-methoxy-carbonyl-5-isobutoxycarbonyl) series.[197] It remains to be determined whether this same situation is true for substituent variations at other positions.

The role of aromatic substituents in determining activity is probably due to a combination of electronic and steric effects. Solid state structures of 1,4-dihydropyridines reveal an approximately perpendicular projection of the phenyl and 1,4-dihydropyridine rings (Figure 32a).[198–200] The importance of this conformation is confirmed by the activities of a series of rigid analogs (9)[201] with

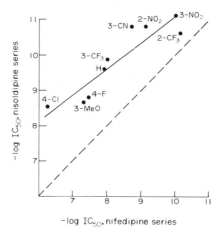

Figure 31 Correlation between the pharmacological activities of phenyl ring substituted nifedipine [3,5-di(methoxy-carbonyl)] and nisoldipine (3-methoxycarbonyl-5-isobutoxycarbonyl) 1,4-dihydropyridine derivatives against the tonic component of K^+ depolarization-induced tension responses in intestinal smooth muscle. The solid line is the regression and the dashed line is unit slope (data from ref. 197)

increasing lactone bridge (X) size and increasing interring angle. Similarly, the importance of the conformation in which the 4-phenyl ring is in a pseudoaxial orientation approximately bisecting the flattened boat 1,4-dihydropyridine ring is reinforced by the activity of rigid 1,3-benzothiazocine analogs (**10**) where the β diastereomers are more potent than the α diastereomers.[202] The activity of phenyl-ring-substituted derivatives increases with increasing planarity of the 1,4-dihydropyridine ring; quite possibly this reflects an increased ability of a planar 1,4-dihydropyridine ring to interact with a binding site (Figure 32b).[198–200]

The role of the C-3 and C-5 substituents in the 1,4-dihydropyridine ring has also received attention.[199,203] Antagonist activity is optimum with ester substituents and is reduced in their absence or by their replacement with other electron withdrawing groups, including cyano and acetyl. However, quite large variations of ester group size can be tolerated with maintenance or enhancement of activity and even the apparent demonstration of modest degrees of vascular bed selectivity.[173,191] Thus, nimodipine and nisoldipine are reportedly selective for cerebral and cor-

The majority of the antagonist 1,4-dihydropyridines whose solid state structures have been determined[198–200,203] are found to have both a *cis* and *trans* ester group orientation, whereby the carbonyl bond of one ester group is oriented *cis* to one of the 1,4-dihydropyridine double bonds and

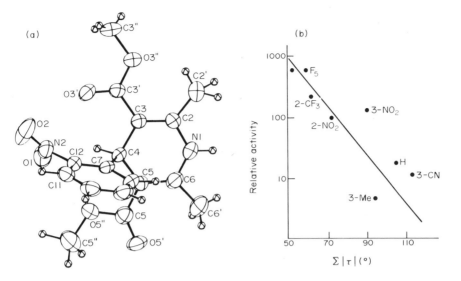

Figure 32 (a) Solid state structure of nifedipine (reproduced from ref. 198 by permission of the American Chemical Society); (b) correlation between planarity of the 1,4-dihydropyridine ring (sum of torsion angles) and Ca^{2+} channel blocking activities of a series of 1,4-dihydropyridines (reproduced from ref. 199 by permission of the American Chemical Society)

onary beds, respectively. Bis(1,4-dihydropyridine)s linked at the ester group by a polymethylene chain (**11**) show high activity but no evidence for bridging of adjacent receptor sites,[203] and it is likely that the second 1,4-dihydropyridine ring bridges to a local hydrophobic area.

(11)

the other is oriented *trans*. Such an arrangement (Figure 33a) places the *cis* ester group adjacent to the aryl ring face and the *trans* ester group at a distance from the 1,4-dihydropyridine ring. A few examples of *cis,cis* geometry are known (Figure 33b), but no examples of *trans,trans* geometry (Figure 33c). The full significance of ester group orientation to pharmacological activity remains to be determined, although the importance of an asymmetric disposition of ester group binding sites is clearly suggested. The activities of the α and β diastereomers of the 1,3-benzothiazocines (**10**), where the highest activity is associated with the β isomers, indicates the importance of the pseudoaxial 4-aryl ring, the synperiplanar orientation of the phenyl substituent and the C-4 hydrogen and the near coplanarity of the 3,5-di(alkoxycarbonyl) groups.

Steric factors alone do not determine pharmacological activity, since inactive molecules also share some of these conformational features, and activator and antagonist 1,4-dihydropyridines enjoy very similar solid state conformations. Additionally, Berntsson and Wold[204] have argued that, despite the correlations between solid state structure and pharmacological activity in the 1,4-dihydropyridines, ordinary physicochemical parameters are better and more effective descriptors of activity.

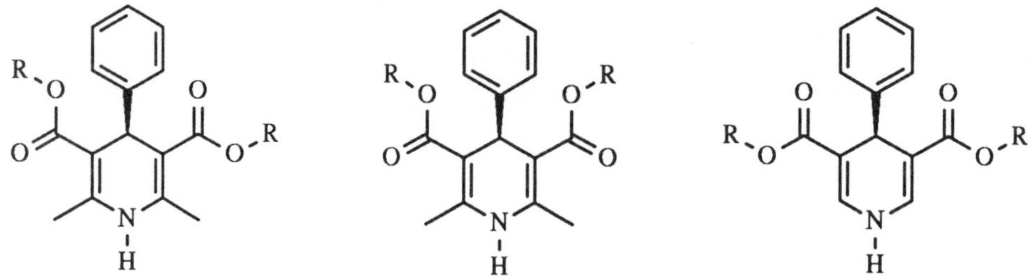

Figure 33 Conformational arrangements of 3,5 ester groups in 1,4-dihydropyridines: (a) *cis,trans*; (b) *cis,cis*; (c) *trans,trans*

Although the ester functions or the corresponding substituents at the C-3 and C-5 positions of the 1,4-dihydropyridine ring and the 4-phenyl ring substituents have received the greatest attention, the effects of substitutions at other positions have not been ignored. 2-Amino-substituted derivatives have antihypertensive activity, as do the 2-dialkylamino-3,4-dihydropyridines.[205] A series of 2-aminoalkoxymethyl derivatives, including 2-aminoethoxymethyl-6-methyl-3-ethoxycarbonyl-5-methoxycarbonyl-4-(2-chlorophenyl)-1,4-dihydropyridine (amlodipine), have potent activity.[206] Significant stereoselectivity is observed in this series, together with very prolonged duration of action and slow onset times. These characteristics are observed *in vivo* and *in vitro* and thus are not simply due to reduced metabolic degradation.

Fewer structure–activity relationships are available for the phenylalkylamine series and almost none for the benzothiazepines.[173] The antagonist activities of verapamil and D600 have been shown to be stereoselective in a variety of preparations in both pharmacological and radioligand binding assays. Although the ratios vary considerably between tissues, the (S) enantiomers are always the more potent.[173] The phenylalkylamine studies[189,207-209] describe relationships for both cardiac and smooth muscle activities but the interpretation is limited because of the small number of structures and the narrow activity range expressed. However, a correlation in a series of 13 analogs of verapamil substituted in both phenyl rings was noted (equation 10), suggesting that interactions of the substituted benzene rings of verapamil with the receptor are increased by electron-withdrawing substituents as measured by the inductive constant F. The same structural features that control the negative inotropic potency of verapamil and its ring-substituted analogs also control the binding affinities to cardiac membranes (equations 11 and 12).[210] However, there is an approximately hundredfold discrepancy between binding and pharmacological activities (equation 13), suggestive of state-dependent binding processes.

$$\log(1/IC_{50}) = 0.93F - 0.59MR \tag{10}$$

$$n = 13, \quad r = 0.82, \quad s = 0.35$$

$$\log(1/EC_{50}) = 0.72F + 4.23 \tag{11}$$

$$n = 12, \quad r = 0.82, \quad s = 0.3$$

$$\log(1/K_1) = 0.50F + 6.59 \tag{12}$$

$$n = 12, \quad r = 0.85, \quad s = 0.2$$

$$\log(1/EC_{50}) = 1.28\log(1/K_1) - 4.05 \tag{13}$$

Hybrid molecules **(12)** sharing structural features of both the 1,4-dihydropyridines and the 1,5-benzothiazepines have been synthesized.[211] These agents share the properties of both parents, interacting competitively at both the 1,4-dihydropyridine and diltiazem binding sites.

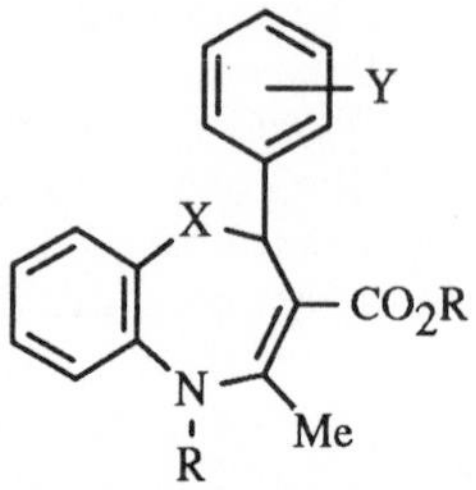

(12)   X = S or NH
R = H or $CH_2CH_2NMe_2$

The three major structural classes of Ca^{2+} channel antagonist occupy separate sites at the channel and, as judged by the inactivity of extracellularly applied quaternary ammonium derivatives of verapamil and nifedipine, act at plasmalemmal sites accessible only from the intracellular surface.[212,213] Radioligand binding studies[173,190,214-218] indicate a relative stoichiometry of verapamil:nifedipine:diltiazem = 1:1:1 and indicate that these sites are on a single major polypeptide component, $M_r = 170$ kDa, of the channel. However, these studies do not indicate the specific sites on the channel protein. Such information will eventually come from the sequence studies now under way. The binding sites occupied by the major classes of drugs active at the Ca^{2+} channel are linked allosterically one to the other, so that occupancy at one site modulates the interaction of drugs at the other binding sites. Thus, drug interaction at these sites represents a set of temperature-dependent heterotropic interactions (Figure 34),[173;190,218,219] whereby the 1,4-dihydropyridine and benzothiazepine sites are positively heterotropic one to the other and both of these sites are negatively heterotropic to the phenylalkylamine site.

Several attempts have been made to define the structural differences between Ca^{2+} channel antagonists and activators.[173,220] However, structure–activity relationships for 1,4-dihydropyridine activators remain to be defined and the enantiomeric discrimination, whereby the (R) enantiomers of Bay K 8644 and PN 202 791 are antagonists and the (S) enantiomers are activators or antagonists depending upon membrane potential,[183,184,221,222] also serves to underscore the complexity of the situation. Solid state structural studies of several activators, including Bay K 8644 (2,6-dimethyl-3-methoxycarbonyl-5-nitro-4-(2-trifluoromethyl)phenyl-1,4-dihydropyridine) and the corresponding 3-nitrophenyl, 3-trifluoromethyl and 4-nitrophenyl analogs, all show similar features including the flattened 1,4-dihydropyridine ring and bond shortening of the N(1)–C(6) and C(5)–N(5) bonds of the 1,4-dihydropyridine ring, consistent with electron delocalization from N-1 to N-5.[220,223] Pharmacological and radioligand binding studies for a series of activators show very good agreement between the two sets of data (Table 11), suggesting, as in the case of the 1,4-dihydropyridine antagonists, that the sites of interaction are fundamentally similar in different excitable tissues. The effects of the phenyl ring substitution pattern in the activators parallel those in the antagonist series, *ortho > meta > para*. However, the activity enhancing effects of *ortho* and *meta* substitution may be less than in the antagonist series.

Several suggestions have been advanced to provide a molecular distinction between 1,4-dihydropyridine activators and antagonists. Mahmoudian and Richards[224] suggest that differences in the hydrogen-bonding characteristics of ester and nitro groups cause the induction of different receptor conformations (Figure 35). Force field and quantum calculations indicate[225] that specific differences are associated with the molecular electrostatic fields of activators and antagonists in the areas associated with activator/antagonist differences (Figure 36) and that the molecular potential of tryptophan, simulating a receptor site, was decreased and increased by activators and antagonists respectively. A differential hydrogen-bonding model has also been advanced by Fossheim,[226] who suggests that activators form an *ap* hydrogen bond, whereas antagonists form an *sp* hydrogen bond in the critical region (left-hand side of Figure 36). It is possible that such differential interactions underlie the finding that the activator species become antagonists under depolarizing conditions that permit greater accessibility of the high affinity antagonist binding inactivated state.

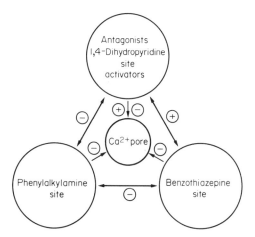

Figure 34 Representation of heterotropic interactions between ligand binding sites and permeation machinery of the Ca^{2+} channel. The + and − symbols denote positive and negative heterotropic interactions, respectively

Table 11 Comparative Pharmacological and Radioligand Binding Activities of 1,4-Dihydropyridine Activators[a]

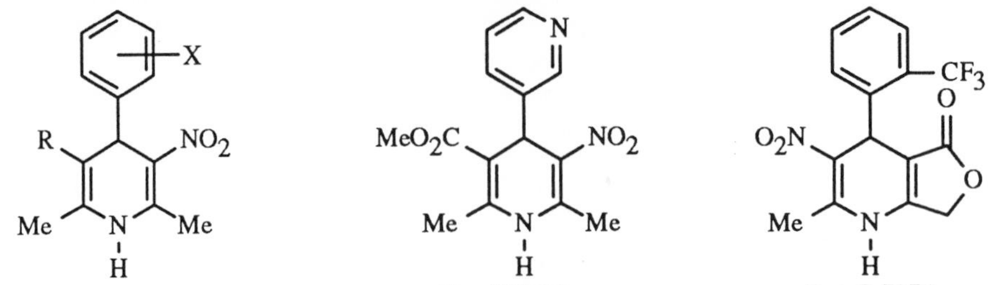

Bay K 9383

Bay Q 7274

	Compound	Pharmacology, $-\log EC_{50}$ (mol dm^{-3})			Binding, $-\log K_I$ (mol dm^{-3})		
X	R	Gut[b]	Atria[b]	Brain[c]	Gut	Heart	Brain
2-CF$_3$	CO$_2$Me	8.65(1.0)	7.12(1.0)	—	8.25	8.56	8.89
3-NO$_2$	CO$_2$Me	7.06(0.66)	6.27(0.64)	—	8.11	8.31	8.53
3-CF$_3$	CO$_2$Me	7.02(0.36)	6.34(0.64)	—	7.51	7.86	7.90
2-NO$_2$	CO$_2$Me	6.68(0.45)	6.32(0.30)	—	7.29	7.68	7.94
4-NO$_2$	CO$_2$Me	6.35(0.57)	5.61(0.56)	—	6.45	6.82	6.82
2-CF$_3$	H	6.12(0.30)	5.95(0.36)	—	6.21	6.10	6.28
Bay K 9383		5.76(0.66)	c	—	5.81	6.07	6.27
Bay Q 7274		c	c	—	5.71	5.85	6.06

[a] Data from Kwon, Joslyn, Luchowski, Frankowiak and Triggle (unpublished). [b] Parentheses indicate relative maximum response. [c] No activator pharmacology observed.

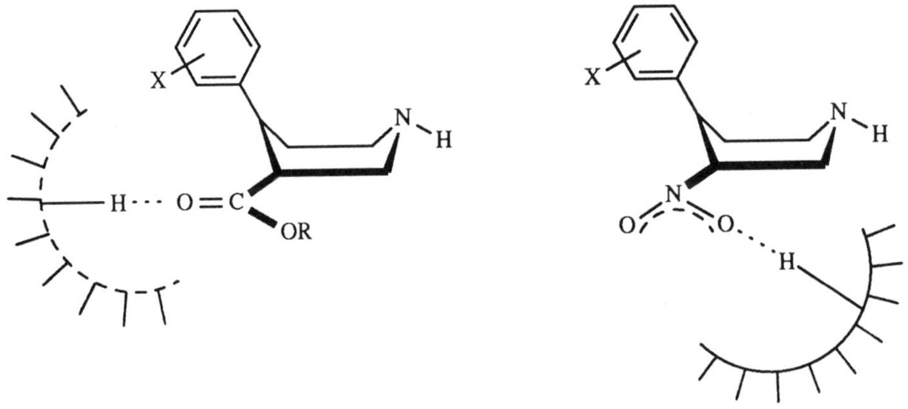

Antagonist H-bonding

Activator H-bonding

Figure 35 Model of binding site discrimination between 1,4-dihydropyridine activators and antagonists showing differential hydrogen-bonding characteristics in the two molecules (after ref. 224)

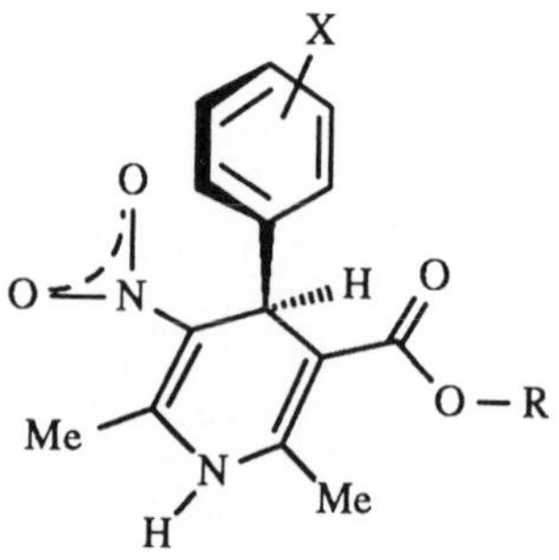

Figure 36 1,4-Dihydropyridine molecule capable of exerting both activator and antagonist effects. In the configuration shown where the nitro group is to the left, activation is the consequence at polarized membrane potentials. In the opposite configuration antagonism is exerted. It is thus assumed (see Figure 35) that the left-hand quadrant of the interaction is critical to the distinction between activation and antagonism

Structure–activity relationships for Ca^{2+} channel antagonists and, to a significantly lesser extent, for Ca^{2+} channel activators have been determined under a variety of experimental conditions. The results have been of value to the interpretation of mechanisms of action and have revealed substantial similarities to the actions of local anesthetics and antiarrhythmic agents at the Na^{+} channel (Section 14.1.4.3.5). Correlations between the abilities of series of 1,4-dihydropyridines to bind to the high affinity sites in plasma membranes and to inhibit pharmacological response (Figure 37) indicate that the same rank order of activity is expressed in smooth muscle, cardiac muscle and neuronal preparations, and that similar high affinity binding is observed in all preparations,[173] but that high affinity pharmacology is expressed in depolarized smooth muscle, low affinity pharmacology in paced cardiac muscle and that Ca^{2+} channel antagonists frequently appear to be inactive in neuronal tissue.[227,228] Similar quantitative discrepancies of activity, but with identical rank order of expression, are noted when the sensitivities of the phasic (fast) and tonic (slow) components of response of smooth muscle to K^{+} depolarization are compared (Figure 38). These data, too, indicate the variable expression of a common structure–activity relationship according to experimental conditions. Similar discrepancies between binding and pharmacological activities have been observed in the phenylalkylamine series.[210]

Whether the binding representation depicted in Figure 34 can accommodate all ligand classes remains to be established. It is possible that the 1,4-dihydropyridine site consists of two separate sites which initiate activator and antagonist activity, respectively.[230-232] It is also possible that other discrete binding sites exist to accommodate other ligand classes. Of particular interest are the diphenylbutylpiperidine neuroleptics, including pimozide, clopimozide, fluspirilene and penfluridol (Figure 39). These agents appear to interact with Ca^{2+} channels with high potency at sites distinct

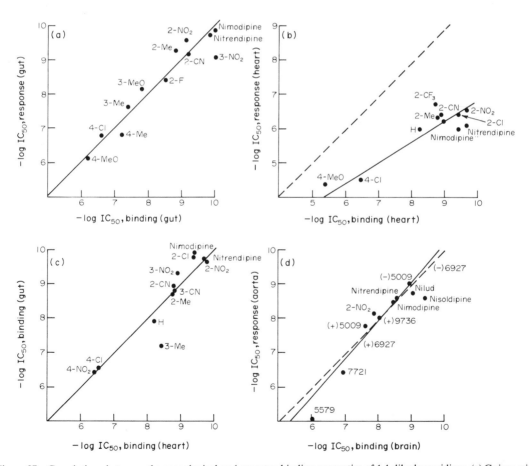

Figure 37 Correlations between pharmacological and receptor binding properties of 1,4-dihydropyridines. (a) Guinea pig ileal longitudinal smooth muscle. Binding, displacement of [³H]nitrendipine: pharmacology, inhibition of K^{+} depolarization-induced response (tonic phase) (data from ref. 190). (b) Rat heart. Binding, displacement of [³H]nitrendipine: pharmacology, cat papillary muscle (data from ref. 188). (c) Binding, displacement of [³H]nitrendipine: rat heart and guinea pig gut (data from refs. 190 and 352). (d) Binding, displacement of [³H]nimodipine in rat brain: pharmacology, inhibition of K^{+} depolarization-induced tension responses in rabbit aorta (data from ref. 227). The solid lines are the regressions and the dashed lines are 1:1 equivalency

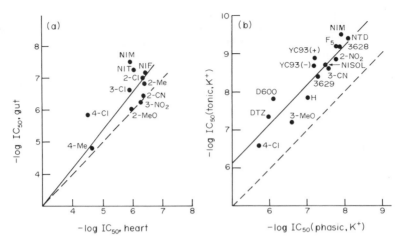

Figure 38 (a) Correlation between the abilities of a series of nifedipine (NIF) (X = phenyl substituent), nimodipine (NIM) and nitrendipine (NIT) to block phasic (fast) component of K^+ depolarization-induced response in guinea pig ileum and paced cat papillary muscle (data from refs. 188 and 190). The solid line is the regression and the dashed line is unit slope. (b) Correlation between the abilities of a series of calcium channel antagonists (DTZ, diltiazem; NIM, nimodipine; NTD, nitrendipine; NISOL, nisoldipine; 4-Cl, 3-MeO, H, 3-CN, 2-NO$_2$, F$_5$ phenyl substituents in nifedipine derivatives) to block phasic (fast) and tonic (slow) components of response in bladder smooth muscle (data from ref. 353). The solid line is the regression and the dashed line is unit slope

from those occupied by the other major structural classes.[233-235] These agents bind with potencies of $10^{-8} - 10^{-7}$ mol dm^{-3} in brain, cardiac and smooth muscle but with substantially higher affinity, approximately hundredfold, to skeletal muscle. The excellent correlation between the abilities of the diphenylbutylpiperidine series to interact with [^{3}H]fluspirilene and [^{3}H]verapamil binding sites suggests that the site at which the neuroleptics exert their activating and antianxiety effects may be a component of the Ca^{2+} channel.[233-235]

The ligand binding site arrangement depicted in Figure 34 is also associated with inorganic cation interactions. Thus, high affinity 1,4-dihydropyridine binding is dependent upon the availability of divalent cations, including Ca^{2+} and Mg^{2+} [236-238] These high affinity interactions of divalent cations are, however, distinct from the affinity sequences determining calmodulin activation, although calmodulin antagonists block 1,4-dihydropyridine interactions with the same activity sequence that blocks calmodulin-dependent processes.[237] It is likely that these cation binding sites may reflect the high affinity intrachannel binding sites that are believed to be associated with the permeation process of the Ca^{2+} channel.[239]

Electrophysiological studies indicate directly the importance of state-dependent interactions for Ca^{2+} channel ligands.[173,240,241] Thus the actions of verapamil, D600 and diltiazem are frequency and voltage dependent, inhibition of Ca^{2+} channel function increasing with increasing frequency of

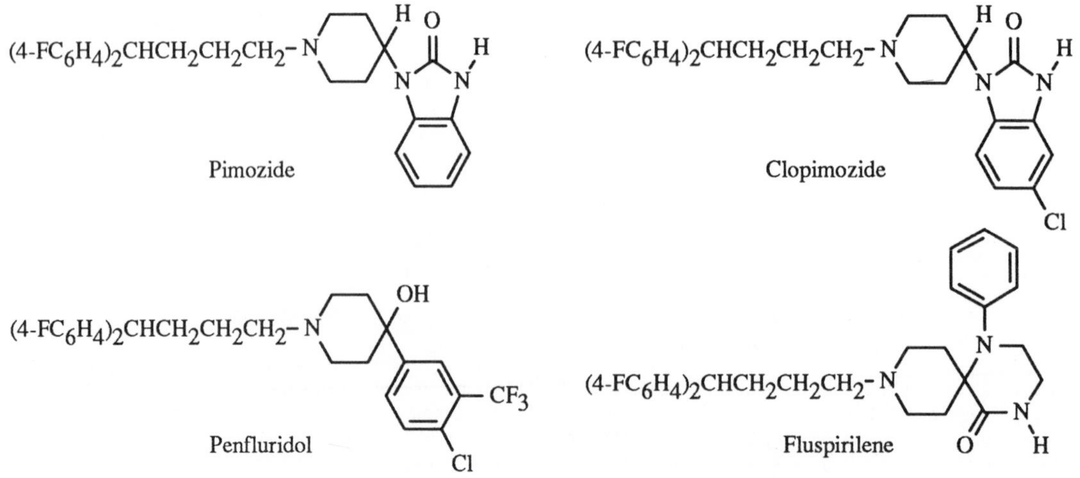

Figure 39 Structural formulae of neuroleptic molecules with Ca^{2+} channel blocking properties

depolarization and with depolarizing and hyperpolarizing stimuli favoring block and unblock, respectively, of the channel.[241-246] These properties are clearly very similar to those exhibited by local anesthetics at the Na^+ channel (Section 14.1.4.3.5).

1,4-Dihydropyridine activity, both antagonist and activator, shows both voltage- and frequency-dependent behavior.[173,240,246] Block of cardiac Ca^{2+} channels by nifedipine or nisoldipine is strongly enhanced by depolarization with an affinity increase of 2–4 orders of magnitude from the 10^{-6}–10^{-7} mol dm^{-3} of the polarized preparation to 10^{-9}–10^{-10} mol dm^{-3} in the depolarized preparation,[247,248] suggesting a preferential interaction with the inactivated state of the channel (Table 12). The high affinity interactions seen in depolarized preparations[213,247,248] are very similar to the values observed in radioligand binding in membrane preparations[78,173,240,251] where the channels are presumably in an inactivated state. Voltage-dependent interactions are also revealed in radioligand binding protocols in whole cells which show that binding affinity increases with depolarization.[230,256] The 1,4-dihydropyridines also show frequency-dependent interactions under the appropriate conditions of high frequency of stimulation or the presence of a hydrophilic side chain as in nicardipine (Figure 30).[247]

These considerations of state-dependent interactions of Ca^{2+} channel antagonists clearly underlie, at least in part, the observed tissue selectivity of these agents. Selective interactions with and access to resting, open and inactivated states of the channel will determine selectivity in cardiac and vascular muscle, tissues regulated by repetitive and tonic depolarization respectively. Additionally these considerations may also underlie the general neuronal insensitivity of most Ca^{2+} channel antagonists; the typically brief and pulsatile firing events of neurons will not allow adequate time for drug equilibration to the favored high affinity state(s). Only during sustained or repetitive depolarization will Ca^{2+} channel antagonists be active and this may occur in disease states or during channel activation by the 1,4-dihydropyridine activators.

Considerations of state dependence of interactions are also critical to the interpretation of activator–antagonist activities in the 1,4-dihydropyridines and possibly also in other ligand series. Ca^{2+} channels have been suggested to possess three basic gating modes, 0, 1 and 2, characterized by zero openings, brief openings and rare long openings respectively (Figure 40).[257] This model suggests that 1,4-dihydropyridine antagonists favor mode 0 and that the activators favor mode 2. Accordingly, the ratio of affinities of ligands for modes 0 and 2 will determine the balance of activator:antagonist properties. This balance will be voltage dependent since channel state equilibria are voltage dependent; consistent with this postulate, activator 1,4-dihydropyridines exhibit antagonist properties at depolarized membrane potentials (Table 13).[184,255,258] Thus, a further and subtle determinant of tissue selectivity in the 1,4-dihydropyridines stems from the selection of agonist–partial agonist–antagonist properties according to membrane potential. The voltage dependence of Ca^{2+} channel activation by 1,4-dihydropyridines is seen very clearly in Figure 41 depicting the dual effect of Bay K 8644 on Ca^{2+} channel availability.[259] Since the conformations of the open and inactivated states must differ, it is possible that 1,4-dihydropyridines can bind to each of these states with affinities that depend upon ligand structure. The data shown in Figure 41 may also be interpreted according to interaction at a single site with reduction of a single rate constant,

Table 12 State-dependent Interactions of 1,4-Dihydropyridines

1,4-Dihydropyridine	Preparation	K_I or IC_{50} ($\times 10^{-9}$ mol dm^{-3})	Proposed binding site	Ref.
Nitrendipine	Cardiac ventricle	0.4	Inactivated	248
		700	Resting	
	Mesenteric artery	0.5	Inactivated	252
		2220	Resting	
Nifedipine	Cardiac atrial	30	Inactivated	213
		300	Resting	
	Cardiac ventricle	40	Inactivated	253
		450	Resting	
	GH_4C_1 cells	0.5	Open	254
		7000	Resting	
(R) PN 202 791	Cardiac myocytes	9	Inactivated	255
		200	Resting	
(+) PN 200 110	Skeletal muscle	0.15	Inactivated	250
		13	Resting	

$$R \underset{k_{21}}{\overset{k_{12}}{\rightleftharpoons}} O \underset{k_{32}}{\overset{k_{23}}{\rightleftharpoons}} I$$

Scheme 1

Table 13   Activator and Antagonist Potencies of 1,4-Dihydropyridines[184]

Compound	Rat tail artery		Guinea pig intestine	
	EC_{50} (mol dm^{-3})	IC_{50}^a (mol dm^{-3})	EC_{50} (mol dm^{-3})	IC_{50}^a (mol dm^{-3})
(S) Bay K 8644	2.0×10^{-9}	5.3×10^{-7}	1.1×10^{-8}	2.6×10^{-6}
(S) PN 202 791	3.2×10^{-8}	4.1×10^{-6}	7.1×10^{-8}	—

^{a} Inhibitory activity measured against responses to K$^+$ depolarization.

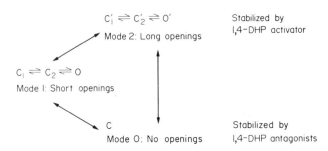

Figure 40   Postulated modes of Ca^{2+} channel gating. In the absence of drug it is assumed that transitions between modes are much slower than transitions within modes (modified from ref. 257)

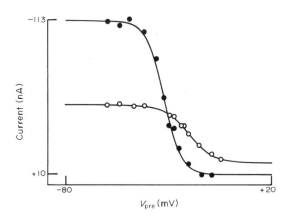

Figure 41   The shift of Ca^{2+} channel availability in Purkinje fibers by Bay K 8644. The abcissa denotes conditioning voltage (V_{pre}) and the ordinate denotes current to test pulse after conditioning. ○, control; ●, Bay K 8644, 2×10^{-7} mol dm^{-3} (reproduced from ref. 259 by permission of Rockefeller University Press)

k_{21}, as shown in Scheme 1. It will be predicted that for channels which do not inactivate, $k_{23} < 0$, Ca^{2+} channel activators will not show antagonist properties. This has been indicated in pituitary cells.[260]

14.1.5.3   Multiple Classes of Ca^{2+} Channels

The phenylalkylamine, 1,4-dihydropyridine and benzothiazepine structures are ligands for one major class of voltage-dependent plasmalemmal Ca^{2+} channels, the L type, which inactivate slowly and produce Ca^{2+} currents of relatively prolonged duration. It is this type of Ca^{2+} channel which has been a major focus of attention for many years. At least two other classes of voltage-sensitive Ca^{2+} channels exist, referred to as T type, which inactivate rapidly and produce a transient current, and the N type, which are intermediate in behavior between L and T types. These different channel types are widely distributed in excitable cells, including neurons, cardiac and smooth muscle and secretory cells,[77,261,262] but N-type channels appear to be neuron selective. It is likely that L channels function to supply both electrical and chemical signals as in the cardiac action potential and secretory responses, respectively, whilst T channels may function in the generation of rhythmic responses and N channels are involved in neurotransmitter release in some, but not all, neurons. These channel types differ in a number of characteristics (Table 14) and, of particular importance, differ in their pharmacological sensitivity. Only the L-type channels are sensitive to the currently available Ca^{2+} channel ligands. However, ω-conotoxin-GVIA (13), a 27 amino acid peptide from fish-eating molluscs of the *Conus* genus,[263-266] appears to discriminate other channel types since it is a potent blocker of neuronal N- and L-type channels, but does not block non-neuronal L-type channels.[229,265,266] It is probable that each of these major classes of plasmalemmal voltage-dependent Ca^{2+} channels is composed of a number of subclasses.

$$\text{Cys-Lys-Ser-Hyp-Gly-Ser-Ser-Cys-Ser-Hyp-Thr-Ser-Tyr-Asn-Cys-Cys-Arg-Ser}$$
$$|$$
$$\text{Tyr-Cys-Arg-Lys-Thr-Tyr-Hyp-Asn-Cys}$$
$$(\mathbf{13})$$

Plasmalemmal Ca^{2+} channels have been the major focus of attention, but Ca^{2+} channels are important in intracellular organelles, notably the endoplasmic and sarcoplasmic reticulum of secretory and contractile cells, respectively. Relatively little is known of the pharmacology of these intracellular channels, but the IP_3-activated Ca^{2+} release mechanism has been noted previously. Ca^{2+} release from sarcoplasmic reticulum is important for excitation–contraction coupling in cardiac and skeletal muscle and this process is sensitive to a variety of stimuli including adenine nucleotides, dantrolene, ruthenium red and ryanodine.[267-269] At least two types of sarcoplasmic reticulum Ca^{2+} channels, of low and high conductance, have been reported.[270-273] The pharmacological behavior of these channels and their complete insensitivity to verapamil, nifedipine and diltiazem distinguishes them clearly from plasmalemmal Ca^{2+} channels.

14.1.6 DRUGS ACTIVE AT K$^+$ CHANNELS

14.1.6.1 Introduction

In marked contrast to the two preceding categories of cation-selective channels, those for Na^+ and Ca^{2+}, K^+-selective channels are far less well-characterized in terms of specific drug action. However, there is a considerable interest in selective ligands as representatives of class III antiarrhythmic agents (Section 14.1.8).

Although the first reference to the selective K^+ permeability of the plasma membrane was probably made by Bernstein in 1902,[274] definition of the K^+ channel awaited characterization of the axonal action potential by Hodgkin and Huxley.[49,50] Subsequently, it has been realized that several categories of K^+ channels exist that may be distinguished by both electrophysiological and pharmacological criteria.[275,276] A major function of K^+ channel activation is that of maintaining or

Table 14 Properties of Plasmalemmal Ca^{2+} Channels[a]

Property	L	T	N
Activation range (mV)	> -10	> -70	> -30
Inactivation range (mV)	-60 to -10	-100 to -60	-120 to -30
Inactivation rate	Very slow	Rapid	Moderate
Conductance (pS)	25	8	13
Kinetics	Little inactivation	Brief burst, inactivation	Long burst, inaction
Permeation	$Ba^{2+} > Ca^{2+}$	$Ba^{2+} = Ca^{2+}$	$Ba^{2+} > Ca^{2+}$
Cd^{2+} sensitivity	Sensitive	Insensitive	Sensitive
1,4-Dihydropyridine sensitivity	Sensitive	Insensitive	Insensitive
ω-Conotoxin sensitivity	Sensitive (neurons) Insensitive (muscle)	Insensitive	Sensitive

[a] Data computed from a variety of sources.

restoring membrane potential by bringing the potential closer to that for K^+. Conversely, K^+ channel antagonism will serve to reduce membrane potential and, in general, to increase membrane excitability. Although K^+ channels may differ substantially in their kinetic and pharmacological characteristics, they appear to show very similar ionic discrimination.[49]

14.1.6.2 Sites and Mechanisms of Action

The K^+ channel mediating the major repolarizing current of the axon action potential is referred to as the 'delayed rectifier', because its activation is delayed after a voltage step. There are probably several different subclasses of delayed rectifier K^+ channels.[276,277] Thus, tetraethylammonium (TEA) blocks axonal K^+ channels only internally, but blocks nodal channels when applied either internally or externally. It has been indicated that there may exist three or more subtypes of the delayed rectifier K^+ channel.[278,279] In contrast to the slowly inactivating delayed rectifier K^+ channel, a transient current, I_A, flows through A channels which are activated when a cell is depolarized following a period of hyperpolarization.[275,280-282] These transient channels serve to regulate repetitive firing patterns and appear to be less sensitive to TEA and more sensitive to 4-aminopyridine than the delayed rectifier channels.[275] A third major category of K^+ channel, the inward rectifier, differs from other categories of channel since its conductance increases and decreases with hyperpolarization and depolarization respectively.[1,275] Such channels probably contribute to ionic economy in spontaneously active tissues and can aid in the generation of long-lasting depolarizing responses.[275] There exist several types of Ca^{2+}-dependent K^+ channel which are activated by elevated intracellular Ca^{2+}.[1,275,276,283-285] The two major classes of K^+-selective Ca^{2+}- and voltage-activated channels may be distinguished by their very different conductances—a large channel with conductance 150–300 pS and a small channel with conductance 20–50 pS. These may represent more than one channel type. Additionally, a Ca^{2+}-activated nonselective cation channel has also been identified. The current carried by Ca^{2+}-activated K^+ channels, $I_{K+(Ca^{2+})}$, is clearly associated with cell hyperpolarization and reduction of inward Ca^{2+} current, but is also an important component of K^+ secretion in secretory cells[285,286] and serves to maintain rhythmic firing in neurons.[1,275]

Additional to these categories of voltage-dependent K^+ channels there exist classes of chemically mediated K^+ channels that are modulated by signals initiated at specific receptors. Thus, the slow excitatory postsynaptic potential mediated through acetylcholine activation of muscarinic receptors in ganglia represents the closing of a K^+ conductance in M channels.[286-288] Several different receptors are probably coupled to such channels.

For at least some K^+ channels, coupling to receptors is probably achieved through guanine nucleotide binding proteins. This has been demonstrated for the muscarinic-receptor-activated K^+ channel in cardiac muscle[289,290] and it is probably also true for the K^+ channels in *Aplysia* ganglia that are multiply activated by acetylcholine, histamine and dopamine.[291] Moreover, this coupling is probably direct rather than through any intermediary messenger.[292] Similar coupling processes may be components of other categories of chemically sensitive K^+ channels including the S-type K^+ channels closed by 5-hydroxytryptamine[293] and ATP-sensitive channels in secretory cells.[285]

K^+ channels pose major problems of classification. Currently, there are literature descriptions of as many as 12 putatively different K^+ channels. Definition of channel-specific drug action is proving to be correspondingly difficult, but some differentiation is possible.

14.1.6.3 Drugs Active at K^+ Channels

The classic pharmacological tools employed to define K^+ channels include tetraethylammonium (TEA) and related quaternary ammonium ions, and quinidine and 4-aminopyridine. These agents are generally neither very potent nor very discriminatory. Thus, TEA appears to block all types of K^+ channel, either intracellularly or extracellularly, but does reveal a number of potency and vectorial differences. The inward rectifier K^+ channel is more sensitive to extracellularly applied quaternary ammonium ions and the high conductance $K^+(Ca^{2+})$ channel is more sensitive to extracellular TEA than is the low conductance channel. More recent developments in the classification of K^+ channels have employed apamin and charybdotoxin.

Apamin, a polypeptide of 18 amino acids from bee venom (**14**), appears to be potently selective for the low conductance Ca^{2+}-activated K^+ channel.[294,295] Interaction with [^{125}I]apamin permits characterization of this channel type (Figure 42).[296-298] Charybdotoxin, from scorpion venom, is reported to block the high conductance Ca^{2+}-activated K^+ channel.[299]

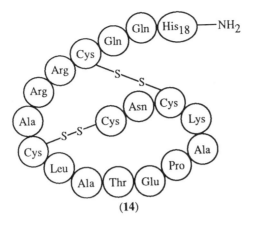

(14)

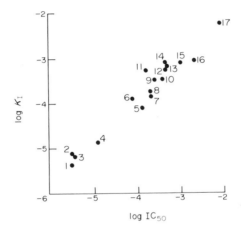

$\log IC_{50}$

Figure 42 Correlation between affinities of drugs to block [^{125}I]apamin binding and to inhibit Ca^{2+}-induced K^+ efflux from guinea pig hepatocytes. 1, atracurium; 2, tubocurarine; 3, pancuronium; 4, gallamine; 5, 9-aminoacridine; 6, quinacrine; 7, chloroquine; 8, strychnine; 9, quinidine; 10, cinchonine; 11, quinine; 12, 16, hexamethonium; 17, tetraethylammonium (reproduced from ref. 298 by permission of Cambridge University Press)

Few studies are available describing structure–activity relationships of drugs active at K^+ channels. Such studies[300–302] detail primarily the actions of quaternary ammonium analogs of TEA. In squid axon the delayed rectifier K^+ channel possesses two distinct quaternary ammonium ion receptors, available from the intracellular and extracellular surfaces respectively. Binding to the internal receptor is voltage dependent, consistent with the positive charge of the ligand being approximately 20% of the way through the membrane field. The data of Table 15 indicate that in alkyltriethylammonium derivatives activity increases with increasing alkyl chain length and, at a constant chain length, decreases with size or increasing hydrophilic character of the N substituents. Similarly, in a series of symmetrically substituted tetraalkylammonium ions, R_4N^+, where R = Me to C_5H_{11}, activity increases generally with increasing size. These data suggest a large and relatively nonpolar binding site available at the internal channel entrance.

A similar structure–activity relationship probably underlies the actions of quaternary ammonium agents including and related to clofilium (**15**). In a series of phenylbutyltrialkylammonium deriva-'tives, $Ph(CH_2)_4N^+R_3$, prolongation of Purkinje fiber duration (an index of K^+ channel activity),

Table 15 Activity of Quaternary Ammonium Derivatives in Squid Axon[300–302]

Structure	$K_D{}^a(\times 10^{-6}\,mol\,dm^{-3})$	Structure	$K_D{}^a(\times 10^{-6}\,mol\,dm^{-3})$
$C_7H_{15}\overset{+}{N}Et_3$	17.6	$C_{10}H_{21}\overset{+}{N}Et_3$	3.7
$C_8H_{17}\overset{+}{N}Et_3$	7.3	$C_{10}H_{21}\overset{+}{N}Pr_3$	92.0
$C_9H_{19}\overset{+}{N}Et_3$	4.1	$C_8H_{17}\overset{+}{N}(CH_2CH_2OH)_3$	1120.0

^{a} Measured at +100 mV.

increases with increasing size of the R substituent. Clofilium itself and the corresponding 4-nitro derivative and its tertiary analog (**16** and **17**) are rather more potent with EC_{20} values of between 2×10^{-8} mol dm^{-3} and 2.5×10^{-9} mol dm^{-3}.[302]

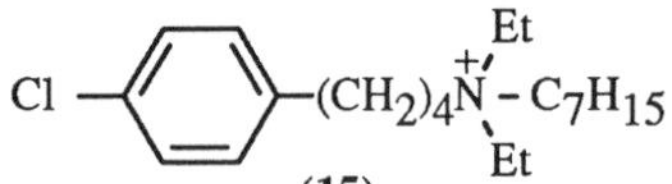

In principle, K^+ channel activators should, by opening K^+ channels, hyperpolarize membranes and decrease excitability. Such compounds should be vasorelaxants and antihypertensive. The benzo[*b*]pyran BRL 34915 (**18**) may represent such an agent[303] and this category of compounds is under intensive investigation as a new group of potential antihypertensive agents. However, their mechanism of action remains to be established and it is not currently clear whether they act directly at the K^+ channel or indirectly *via* a messenger species. Their actions thus form an interesting parallel to the Ca^{2+} channel antagonists and the K^+ channel activators may well form an important new class of therapeutic agent.[305]

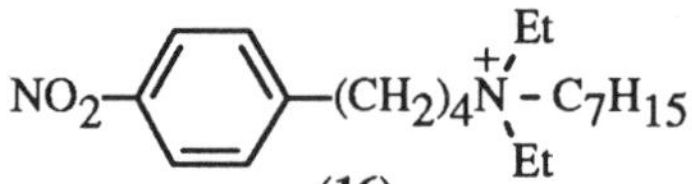

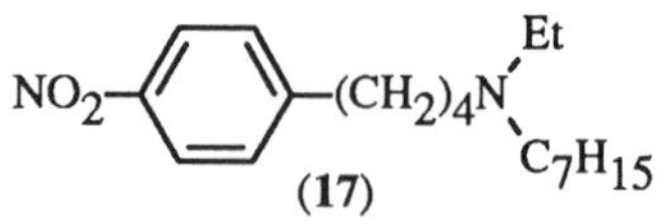

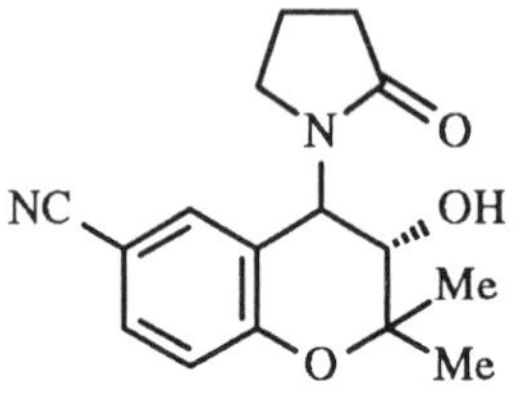

(18)

Considerable scope exists for the determination of structure–activity studies of drugs active at K^+ channels. A limiting factor is, however, the need for systems in which channel activity, of a distinct type, can be measured conveniently. One such preparation may be the synaptosome where four distinct categories of K^+ channels have been reported. Of particular interest, phencyclidine (**19**) and its analogs appear to block very potently the voltage-dependent noninactivating categories of K^+ channels in synaptosomes, and the ability of these analogs to inhibit K^+ channels parallels both behavioral potency and the ability to bind specifically to plasmalemmal phencyclidine binding sites.[304]

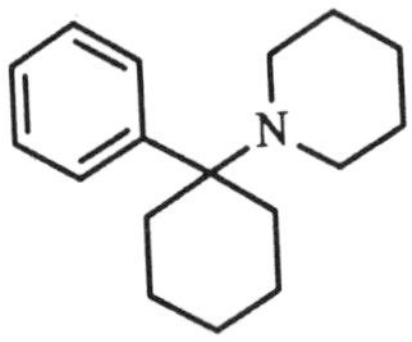

(19)

Recent advances in the analysis of K^+ channel structure and function through molecular biology techniques suggest that the observed pharmacological and electrophysiological complexity of K^+ channels may have its origin in the production and subsequent assembly of multiple K^+ channel components by alternative gene splicing.[306]

14.1.7 GENERAL ANESTHETICS

14.1.7.1 Introduction

The general anesthetics comprise a chemically diverse group of agents, both volatile and nonvolatile, generally active at high concentrations at which they may be assumed to be widely distributed throughout the body. These agents have, however, a common pharmacological end-point, namely the production of general anesthesia. Despite this commonality of action, it remains to be defined at what sites and by what mechanisms general anesthesia is produced.[307-310] Progress to such definition has been slow for several reasons, including the apparent nonspecificity of action of general anesthetics and the corresponding lack of specific antagonists that have proved so critical to the definition of receptor function in other areas of pharmacology. Additionally, the difficulties of disentangling from the many actions anticipated from the high concentrations of these agents those that are responsible for general anesthesia should be noted. It is generally assumed that proteins are the ultimate targets of anesthetic action but it remains to be determined whether these are direct targets or indirectly modulated through primary actions of the general anesthetics on membrane lipids.

14.1.7.2 General Anesthetic Action

The multiplicity of structures with the ability to induce general anesthesia ranges from the inert gases to hydrocarbons, halocarbons and alcohols to more sophisticated organic molecules including barbiturates and steroids (Figure 43) and raises important questions concerning both the specificity of general anesthetic action and the number of sites and mechanisms by which general anesthesia occurs. It is generally assumed that general anesthetics function to alter central neuronal excitability either by depressing excitatory responses or by amplifying inhibitory responses. Thus, depression of Na^+ conductance or facilitation of K^+ conductance would both be associated with a reduction in neuronal excitability.[309,311,314] A considerable amount of evidence is available to document the modulatory actions of general anesthetics on transmitter release and postsynaptic sensitivity, but this has contributed relatively little to mechanistic interpretation of general anesthetic action. There is no agreement as to whether unitary or multiple mechanisms of action exist for general anesthesia.

14.1.7.3 Sites of General Anesthetic Action

Despite difficulties in assigning specific sites to general anesthetic action, more progress has been made in determining the nature of the sites at which general anesthetics may act. Overton and Meyer[315,316] both drew attention to the fact that all general anesthetic molecules are lipid soluble and that anesthetic potency is related to this solubility. These observations, using olive oil as the lipid phase, have been repeated with other bulk nonaqueous media including octanol, phospholipids and plasma membranes (Figure 44). Early attention was thus drawn to the lipids as sites of action and to the idea that general anesthetics functioned by dissolving in the phospholipids of cellular membranes from which apparently nonspecific site they depressed cellular excitability. These observations indicate, however, only that an amphiphilic site is probably involved in general anesthesia and this could be lipid, protein or both. To distinguish between these possibilities with the available molecules has proved to be difficult, but an increasing amount of evidence suggests a direct action of anesthetics at protein sites.[317-320]

14.1.7.3.1 Lipid sites of action

The solubility theory of general anesthesia was generalized over 50 years ago by Ferguson[321] who suggested that general anesthetic potency (and other 'nonspecific' biological indices) correlated with thermodynamic activity. For volatile anesthetics, equation (14) can be derived, where a_{50} is the thermodynamic activity, P_{50} is the partial pressure for 50% anesthesia and P_0 is the vapor pressure of the pure anesthetic; activities are in the range 0.01–0.05.[309,322-324] Given the availability of empirical rules to generate both partition coefficients and vapor pressures, the solubility approach has clear predictive value. For nonvolatile anesthetics (and which are not too freely soluble) the thermodynamic activity approximates the relative saturation of the system. Limitations to

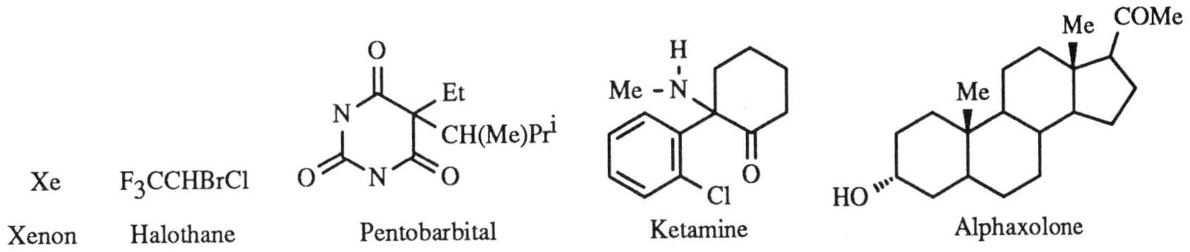

Figure 43 Structural formulae of molecules serving as general anesthetics

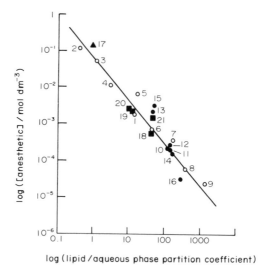

Figure 44 Anesthetic potency as a function of partition coefficient for water:phosphatidylcholine bilayer system. 1, benzyl alcohol; 2, ethanol; 3, propanol; 4, butanol; 5, pentanol; 6, hexanol; 7, heptanol; 8, octanol; 9, nonanol; 10, halothane; 11, methoxyflurane; 12, isuflurane; 13, fluroxene; 14, pentobarbital; 15, phenobarbital; 16, thiopental; 17, acetone; 18, cyclopropane; 19, xenon; 20, carbon tetrafluoride; 21, sulfur hexafluoride (reproduced from ref. 309 by permission of Academic Press)

Ferguson's approach have been noted:[309, 324] P_0 is dependent solely upon the structure of the anesthetic and only the derived quantity a contains information about the anesthetic site. In contrast, the Meyer–Overton treatment substitutes for the ideal solubility ($1/P_0$) solubility in a solvent that approximates the site of action of the general anesthetic. Thus, the predictive value of the Ferguson approach depends upon the congruent behavior of intermolecular and molecule–site interactions. This relationship will be of the highest accuracy in homologous series and will break down when atypical molecules, notably fluorinated hydrocarbons, are included (Figure 45).

$$a_{50} = P_{50}/P_0 \qquad (14)$$

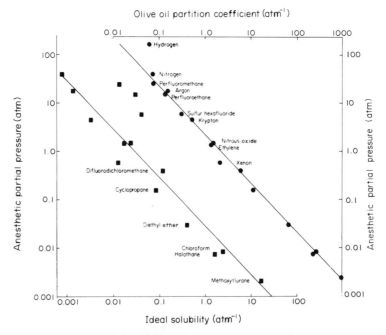

Figure 45 Correlations of anesthetic potency with ideal solubility (■) and solubility in olive oil (●), 1 atm = 101 325 Pa (reproduced from ref. 324 by permission of Wiley-Interscience)

It is to be anticipated that the dissolution of general anesthetics into the lipid phase of membranes will effect changes in both physical and excitability parameters of specific membrane proteins.[309,319,324] Such changes, including enhanced lipid bilayer fluidity,[317,325-328] alterations of phase transitions,[329-331] increased membrane dimensions[307,332,333] and increased and decreased permeability[334,335] have been observed. In principle, each of the preceding phenomena could form the basis for an attractive theory of general anesthesia; in practice, none of the changes seems able to accommodate completely anesthetic effects.[319] Thus, increased membrane fluidity generally requires very high anesthetic concentrations. Although it can be argued that microviscosity changes in lipid annuli of integral proteins critical to membrane excitability would be experimentally very small and might occur at lower anesthetic concentrations, elevated temperature alone does not induce anesthesia and, in fact, decreases anesthetic potency.[319,327] Similar arguments have been advanced against the significance to general anesthesia of other physical changes in lipid structure and organization.[312,319,333]

Although the well-documented reversal by pressure of anesthetic action[336-340] accords with a solubility theory in which anesthesia is a consequence of the expansion of a nonpolar region beyond a critical point by solution of inert molecules,[338,339] it is not uniquely consistent with lipids as the target nor is it critically distinguishable from a binding model where the equilibrium constant for binding varies with pressure.[319]

A further apparent limitation to solubility hypotheses is anesthetic 'cut off', whereby ascent of a homologous series is accompanied by a very sharp decrease and abolition of anesthetic potency.[307,309,321,323,336,337,340,341] Thus, in the 1-alkanol series 1-tetradecanol (C_{14}) is completely inactive but 1-dodecanol (C_{12}) is the most potent of the series. The abrupt loss of activity in this and other homologous series has been attributed to a progressive inability to achieve critical membrane concentrations because the rate of decrement of aqueous solubility exceeds the rate of increase of partition coefficient (C_{mem}/C_{aq}). Thus, a_{50} increases from 0.01 for 1-octanol to 0.04 for 1-decanol and to 0.53 for 1-tridecanol and is > 1.0 for 1-tetradecanol.[323] However, 1-alkanols do show a linear dependence of lipid–water partition coefficient on chain length at least to C_{15} and membrane concentrations of 10–30 mmol dm^{-3}, judged necessary for anesthesia, are achieved by these agents.[342]

14.1.7.3.2 *Protein sites of action*

Powerful evidence that proteins may serve as effector sites for general anesthetics has been obtained using the light-generating enzyme luciferase as a model system.[320,343,344] The pure protein is competitively inhibited by general anesthetics with activities that correlate very well with those producing anesthesia (Figure 46). The binding site is of defined proportions and two molecules of 1-hexanol are accommodated but only one of 1-octanol. Hence the binding volume approximates 250 mL mol^{-1}, probably the size of the luciferin substrate pocket (Figure 47). If anesthetic action

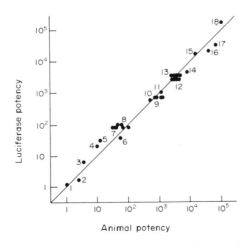

Figure 46 Correlation between the abilities of a series of general anesthetics to produce general anesthesia and to inhibit luciferase activity. 1, methanol; 2, ethanol; 3, acetone; 4, propanol; 5, butanone; 6, paraldehyde; 7, diethyl ether; 8, butanol; 9, benzyl alcohol; 10, chloroform; 11, hexanol; 12, halothane; 13, methoxyflurane; 14, octanol; 15, pentane; 16, nonanol; 17, hexane; 18, decanol (reproduced from ref. 320 by permission of Macmillan Journals Ltd)

involves binding to a similarly defined pocket in proteins controlling cellular excitability then the 'cut off' phenomenon is immediately explained. Indeed, a comparison of the abilities of the 1-alkanols to inhibit luciferase and to produce general anesthesia shows substantial molecular similarity (Figure 46).

Luciferase appears to be a useful protein for modeling anesthetic interactions. However, there is ample literature documenting the specific interactions of inert gases and nonpolar agents with proteins, including β-lactoglobulin and bovine serum albumin.[309] It remains to be determined whether proteins of relevance to cellular excitability, for example receptor and channel proteins, also bind anesthetics, whether a single protein or multiple proteins are involved and how an anesthetic molecule binding to such proteins modifies cellular excitability. These are not trivial questions, but some answers may be forthcoming in the future.

Although the search for a unitary mechanism capable of accommodating the presumed non-specificity of action of general anesthetics has taken substantial effort, it should not be forgotten that some general anesthetics will probably fall into categories characterized by specific actions at defined proteins.[314] Thus, barbiturates act to potentiate GABA inhibition[345] and the dissociative anesthetics ketamine and phencyclidine inhibit the excitatory actions of *N*-methyl-D-aspartate.[346] Similarly, a number of agents show a very respectable correlation between anesthetic potency and an ability to increase neuronal K^+ conductance (Figure 48). Finally, the recent demonstration by ^{19}F NMR of

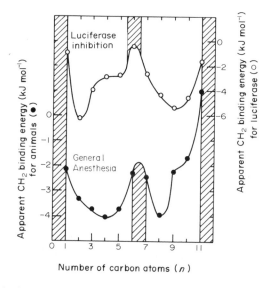

Figure 47   Similarity of molecular features required to produce general anesthesia and to inhibit luciferase (reproduced from ref. 343 by permission of Macmillan Journals Ltd)

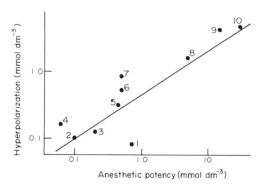

Figure 48   Correlation between anesthetic activity and hyperpolarizing activity in spinal motoneurons of a series of general anesthetics. 1, α-Chloralose; 2, pentobarbital; 3, halothane; 4, methoxyflurane; 5, chloroform; 6, phenobarbital; 7, enflurane; 8, chloral hydrate; 9, ether; 10, urethane (reproduced from ref. 313 by permission of the American Association for the Advancement of Science)

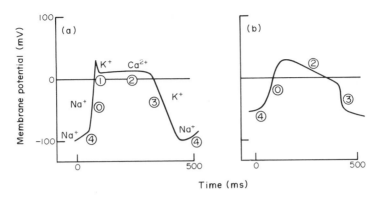

Figure 49 Cardiac action potentials and the underlying ionic currents in (a) conducting regions and (b) nodal regions

specific binding sites for halothane in rat brain indicates that progress continues to be made towards the definition of the molecular basis of general anesthesia.[347]

14.1.8 SUMMARY

The preceding sections of this chapter have endeavored to discuss general aspects of drug action at ion channels. Emphasis has been placed on the mechanisms involved in drug action and this has primarily focussed discussion on three categories of cation-selective channel—those permeating Na^+, Ca^{2+} and K^+ ions. The drugs involved lend themselves to a variety of uses as therapeutic, pharmacological and biochemical agents. A common theme, however, is their application as antiarrhythmic agents.[348-351] Na^+, Ca^{2+} and K^+ currents all contribute to the cardiac action potential either initiating, maintaining or terminating the linked components of this response (Figure 49).

Arrhythmias may arise as a consequence of changes in impulse generation or impulse conduction. Antiarrhythmic agents may accordingly function through several discrete mechanisms and are frequently classified accordingly. Thus class I agents act primarily at Na^+ channels, class II agents interfere with β-adrenoceptor mechanisms, class III agents interact at K^+ channels (and other sites) and class IV agents constitute the specific Ca^{2+} channel antagonists. Such a scheme of classification is very helpful, but it is important to realize that the categories are not totally separate and that some drugs belong to more than one class. This is not entirely unexpected, and as the structures of more ion channels are determined and the evolutionary relationships deciphered it will almost certainly be found that there is much in common with respect to both the organization and the mechanisms of drug action even at apparently discrete channel types.

14.1.9 REFERENCES

1. S. Hagiwara, 'Membrane Potential-dependent Ion Channels in Cell Membrane, Phylogenetic and Developmental Approaches', Raven Press, New York, 1983.
2. A. K. Campbell, 'Intracellular Calcium. Its Universal Role as Regulator', Wiley, New York, 1984.
3. W. D. Stein, 'Transport and Diffusion Across Cell Membranes', Academic Press, New York, 1986, p. 477.
4. G. Inesi, *Annu. Rev. Physiol.*, 1985, **47**, 573.
5. B. Hille, 'Ionic Channels of Excitable Membranes', Sinauer, Sunderland, MA, 1984.
6. W. D. Stein, 'Transport and Diffusion Across Cell Membranes', Academic Press, New York, 1986.
7. S. J. Schein, B. L. Kagen and A. Finkelstein, *Nature (London)*, 1978, **276**, 159.
8. J. Y. Cheung, J. V. Bonventre, C. D. Malis and A. Leaf, *N. Engl. J. Med.*, 1986, **314**, 1670.
9. M. P. McCarthy, J. P. Earnest, E. F. Young, S. Choe and R. M. Stroud, *Annu. Rev. Neurosci.*, 1986, **9**, 383.
10. D. A. Mathers and J. L. Barker, *Int. Rev. Neurobiol.*, 1982, **23**, 1.
11. S. A. Siegelbaum and R. W. Tsien, *Trends NeuroSci. (Pers. Ed.)*, 1983, **6**, 307.
12. H. Reuter, *Nature (London)*, 1983, **301**, 569.
13. M. J. Berridge, *ISI Atlas of Pharmacology*, 1987, **1**, 91.
14. L. Stryer, *Annu. Rev. Neurosci.*, 1986, **9**, 87.
15. M. J. Berridge, *Annu. Rev. Biochem.*, 1987, **56**, 159.
16. C. F. Stevens, *Nature (London)*, 1986, **319**, 622.
17. H. R. Bourne, *Nature (London)*, 1987, **325**, 296.
18. A. M. Spiegel, *Mol. Cell. Endocrinol.*, 1987, **49**, 1.

19. J. M. Martin, D. D. Hunter and N. M. Nathanson, *Biochemistry*, 1985, **24**, 7521.
20. D. E. Logothetis, Y. Kurachi, J. Galper, E. J. Neer and D. E. Clapham, *Nature (London)*, 1987, **325**, 321.
21. G. G. Holz, S. G. Rane and K. Dunlap, *Nature (London)*, 1986, **319**, 676.
22. J. Hescheler, W. Rosenthal, W. Trautwein and G. Schultz, *Nature (London)*, 1987, **325**, 445.
23. B. Sakmann and E. Neher (eds.), 'Single Channel Recording', Pergamon Press, New York, 1983.
24. A. Auerbach and F. Sachs, *Annu. Rev. Biophys. Bioeng.*, 1984, **13**, 269.
25. C. Miller, 'Ion Channel Reconstitution', Plenum Press, New York, 1986.
26. M. Noda, S. Shimizu, T. Tanabe, T. Takai, T. Kayano, T. Ikeda, H. Takahashi, H. Nakayama, Y. Kanaoka, N. Minamino, K. Kangawa, H. Matsuo, M. A. Raftery, T. Hirose, S. Inayama, H. Hayashida, T. Miyata and S. Numa, *Nature (London)*, 1984, **312**, 121.
27. C. F. Stevens, in 'Proteins of Excitable Membranes', ed. B. Hille and D. M. Fambrough, Wiley-Interscience, New York, 1986.
28. B. Tempel, D. M. Papazian, T. L. Schwarz, Y. N. Jan and L. Y. Jan, *Science (Washington, D.C.)*, 1987, **237**, 720.
29. D. M. Papazian, T. L. Schwarz, B. L. Tempel, Y. N. Jan and L. Y. Jan, *Science (Washington, D.C.)*, 1987, **237**, 749.
30. T. Tanabe, H. Takeshima, A. Mikami, Y. Flockerzi, H. Takahashi, K. Kangawu, M. Kojima, H. Matsuo, T. Herose and S. Numa, *Nature (London)*, 1987, **328**, 313.
31. N. Nakayama, T. L. Kirley, P. L. Vaghy, E. McKenna and A. Schwartz, *J. Biol. Chem.*, 1987, **262**, 6572.
32. B. Hille and D. M. Fambrough (eds.), 'Proteins of Excitable Membranes', Wiley-Interscience, New York, 1986.
33. B. Hille, 'Ionic Channels of Excitable Membranes', Sinauer, Sunderland, MA, 1984, chaps. 7 and 8.
34. W. D. Stein, 'Transport and Diffusion Across Cell Membranes', Academic Press, New York, 1986, chap. 3.
35. J. Diamond and E. M. Wright, *Annu. Rev. Physiol.*, 1969, **31**, 581.
36. G. Eisenman and R. Horn, *J. Membr. Biol.*, 1983, **76**, 197.
37. K. Cooper, E. Jakobsson and P. Wolynes, *Prog. Biophys. Mol. Biol.*, 1985, **46**, 51.
38. B. Hille, 'Ionic Channels of Excitable Membranes', Sinauer, Sunderland, MA, 1984, chaps. 8 and 9.
39. B. Hille, 'Ionic Channels of Excitable Membranes', Sinauer, Sunderland, MA, 1984, chap. 10.
40. P. H. Barry and P. W. Gage, *Curr. Top. Membr. Transp.*, 1984, **21**, 1.
41. D. E. Goldman, *J. Gen. Physiol.*, 1943, **27**, 37.
42. A. L. Hodgkin and B. Katz, *J. Physiol. (London)*, 1949, **108**, 87.
43. B. Hille, 'Ionic Channels of Excitable Membranes', Sinauer, Sunderland, MA, 1984, chap. 11.
44. S. Hagiwara and K. Takahashi, *J. Gen. Physiol.*, 1967, **50**, 583.
45. R. W. Tsien, *Annu. Rev. Physiol.*, 1983, **45**, 341.
46. P. Hess and R. W. Tsien, *Nature (London)*, 1984, **309**, 453.
47. W. Almers, E. W. McCleskey and P. T. Palade, *J. Physiol. (London)*, 1984, **353**, 565.
48. W. Almers and E. W. McCleskey, *J. Physiol. (London)*, 1984, **353**, 585.
49. B. Hille, 'Ionic Channels of Excitable Membranes', Sinauer, Sunderland, MA, 1984, chap. 3.
50. A. L. Hodgkin and A. F. Huxley, *J. Physiol. (London)*, 1952, **116**, 449.
51. A. L. Hodgkin and A. F. Huxley, *J. Physiol. (London)*, 1952, **116**, 473.
52. A. L. Hodgkin and A. F. Huxley, *J. Physiol. (London)*, 1952, **117**, 500.
53. B. Hille, 'Ionic Channels of Excitable Membranes', Sinauer, Sunderland, MA, 1984, chaps. 13 and 14.
54. W. Almers, *Rev. Physiol., Biochem. Pharmacol.*, 1978, **82**, 96.
55. C. M. Armstrong, *Physiol. Rev.*, 1981, **61**, 644.
56. T. M. Dwyer, D. J. Adams and B. Hille, *J. Gen. Physiol.*, 1980, **75**, 469.
57. E. W. McCleskey and W. Almers, *Proc. Natl. Acad. Sci. U.S.A.*, 1985, **82**, 7149.
58. M. Noda, H. Takahashi, T. Tanabe, M. Toyosoto, Y. Furutani *et al.*, *Nature (London)*, 1982, **299**, 793.
59. M. Noda, H. Takahashi, T. Tanabe, M. Toyosato, S. Kikyotani *et al.*, *Nature (London)*, 1983, **302**, 528.
60. M. Mishina, T. Tobimatsu, K. Imoto, K. Tanaka, Y. Fujita, K. Fukuda, M. Kurasaki, H. Takahashi, Y. Morimoto, T. Hirose, S. Inayama, T. Takahashi, M. Kuno and S. Numa, *Nature (London)*, 1985, **313**, 364.
61. M. Noda, T. Ikeda, T. Kayano, H. Suzuki, H. Takeshima, M. Kurasaki, H. Takahashi and S. Numa, *Nature (London)*, 1986, **320**, 188.
62. D. L. Paul, *J. Cell Biol.*, 1986, **103**, 123.
63. N. Unwin, *Nature (London)*, 1986, **323**, 12.
64. E. T. Kaiser and F. J. Kezdy, *Science (Washington, D.C.)*, 1984, **223**, 249.
65. W. A. Catterall, *Trends NeuroSci. (Pers. Ed.)*, 1986, **9**, 7.
66. H. R. Guy and P. Seetharamulo, *Proc. Natl. Acad. Sci. U.S.A.*, 1986, **83**, 508.
67. A. M. Woodhull, *J. Gen. Physiol.*, 1973, **61**, 687.
68. C. M. Armstrong, *Q. Rev. Biophys.*, 1975, **7**, 179.
69. P. R. Stanfield, *Rev. Physiol., Biochem. Pharmacol.*, 1983, **97**, 1.
70. C. M. Armstrong and L. Binstock, *J. Gen. Physiol.*, 1965, **48**, 859.
71. B. Hille, 'Ionic Channels of Excitable Membranes', Sinauer, Sunderland, MA, 1984, chap. 12.
72. A. M. Woodhull, *J. Gen. Physiol.*, 1973, **61**, 687.
73. S. Weidmann, *J. Physiol. (London)*, 1955, **129**, 568.
74. G. R. Strichartz, *J. Gen. Physiol.*, 1973, **62**, 37.
75. K. R. Courtney, *J. Pharmacol. Exp. Ther.*, 1975, **195**, 225.
76. B. Hille, *J. Gen. Physiol.*, 1977, **69**, 497.
77. L. M. Hondeghem and B. G. Katzung, *Biochim. Biophys. Acta*, 1977, **472**, 373.
78. L. M. Hondeghem and B. G. Katzung, *Annu. Rev. Pharmacol. Toxicol.*, 1984, **24**, 387.
79. J. Monod, J. P. Changeux and F. Jacob, *J. Mol. Biol.*, 1963, **6**, 306.
80. C. F. Starmer, A. O. Grant and H. C. Strauss, *Biophys. J.*, 1984, **46**, 15.
81. C. F. Starmer and A. O. Grant, *Mol. Pharmacol.*, 1985, **28**, 348.
82. C. F. Starmer, D. L. Packer and A. O. Grant, *J. Theor. Biol.*, 1987, **124**, 335.
83. W. A. Catterall, *Annu. Rev. Pharmacol. Toxicol.*, 1980, **20**, 15.
84. W. A. Catterall, in 'Cell Membranes, Methods and Reviews', ed. R. Elson, S. Frazier and B. Glaser, Plenum Press, New York, 1983, p. 151.
85. P. Honerjager, *Rev. Physiol., Biochem. Pharmacol.*, 1982, **92**, 1.

86. W. A. Catterall, *Science (Washington, D.C.)*, 1984, **223**, 653.
87. W. A. Catterall, in 'New Insights into Cell and Membrane Transport Processes', ed. G. Poste and S. T. Crooke, Plenum Press, New York, 1986, p. 3.
88. C. Y. Kao and S. R. Levinson (eds.), *Ann. N.Y. Acad. Sci.*, 1986, **479**, 1.
89. G. Strichartz, T. Rando and G. K. Wang, *Annu. Rev. Neurosci.*, 1987, **10**, 237.
90. F. A. Fuhrman, *Ann. N.Y. Acad. Sci.*, 1986, **479**, 1.
91. E. J. Schantz, *Ann. N.Y. Acad. Sci.*, 1986, **479**, 15.
92. T. Yasumoto, H. Nagai, D. Yasumura, T. Mishishita, A. Endo, M. Yotsu and T. Kotaki, *Ann. N.Y. Acad. Sci.*, 1986, **479**, 44.
93. J. M. Ritchie and R. B. Rogart, *Rev. Physiol., Biochem. Pharmacol.*, 1977, **79**, 1.
94. V. L. Salgado, J. Z. Neh and T. Narahashi, *Ann. N.Y. Acad. Sci.*, 1986, **47**, 84.
95. B. K. Krueger, J. F. Worley, III and R. J. French, *Ann. N.Y. Acad. Sci.*, 1986, **479**, 257.
96. H. Rochat, P. Bernard and F. Couraud, *Adv. Cytopharmacol.*, 1979, **3**, 325.
97. M. Lazdunski, C. Frelin, J. Barhanin, A. Lombet, H. Merri, D. Pauron, G. Romey, A. Schmid, H. Schweitz, P. Vigne and H. P. M. Vijverberg, *Ann. N.Y. Acad. Sci.*, 1986, **479**, 204.
98. D. D. Watt and J. M. Simard, *J. Toxicol. Toxin Rev.*, 1984, **3**, 181.
99. H. Meaves, J. M. Simard and D. D. Watt, *Ann. N.Y. Acad. Sci.*, 1986, **479**, 113.
100. L. Beress, in 'Chemistry of Peptides and Protein', ed. W. Voelter, E. Wunsch, J. Ovchinnikov and V. Ivanov, deGruyter, Berlin/New York, 1982, vol. 1, p. 121.
101. J. Barhanin, M. Hugus, H. Schweitz, J. P. Vincent and M. Lazdunski, *J. Biol. Chem.*, 1981, **256**, 5764.
102. B. M. Olivera, W. R. Gray, R. Zeikus, J. McIntosh and J. Varga, *Science (Washington, D.C.)*, 1985, **230**, 1338.
103. K. Hashimoto, S. Uchida, H. Yoshida, Y. Nishiuchi, S. Sakakibara and K. Yukari, *Eur. J. Pharmacol.*, 1985, **118**, 351.
104. G. R. Strichartz and G. K. Wang, *J. Gen. Physiol.*, 1986, **88**, 413.
105. B. I. Khodorov, in 'Membrane Transport Processes', ed. D.C. Tosteson, Y.A. Orchinnikov and R. Latorre, Raven Press, New York, 1978, p. 153.
106. Y. M. L. Huang, N. Moran and G. Ehrenstein, *Biophys. J.*, 1984, **45**, 313.
107. T. Rando, quoted in ref. 89.
108. T. Rando, quoted in ref. 89.
109. J. M. C. Huang, C. H. Wu and D. G. Baden, *J. Pharmacol. Exp. Ther.*, 1984, **229**, 615.
110. K. Angelides, S. Terawaka and G. B. Brown, *Ann. N.Y. Acad. Sci.*, 1986, **479**, 221.
111. J. C. Lawrence and J. Coopersmith, *Mol. Pharmacol.*, 1981, **20**, 533.
112. C. Frelin, P. Vigne, H. Schweitz and M. Lazdunski, *Mol. Pharmacol.*, 1984, **26**, 70.
113. E. Moczydlowski, B. M. Olivera, W. R. Gray and G. R. Strichartz, *Proc. Natl. Acad. Sci. U.S.A.*, 1986, **83**, 5321.
114. R. Rogart, *Ann. N.Y. Acad. Sci.*, 1986, **479**, 402.
115. M. Noda, T. Ikeda, T. Hayano, H. Suzuki, H. Takeshima, M. Kurasaki, H. Takahashi and S. Numa, *Nature (London)*, 1986, **320**, 188.
116. D. J. Messner and W. A. Catterall, *J. Biol. Chem.*, 1986, **261**, 211.
117. A. L. Goldin, T. Snutch, H. Lubbert, A. Dowsett, J. Marshall, V. Avid, W. Downey, L. C. Fritz, H. A. Lester, R. Dunn, W. A. Catterall and N. Davidson, *Proc. Natl. Acad. Sci. U.S.A.*, 1986, **83**, 7503.
118. Y. Shimizu, *Ann. N.Y. Acad. Sci.*, 1986, **479**, 24.
119. H. S. Mosher, *Ann. N.Y. Acad. Sci.*, 1986, **479**, 32.
120. R. Y. Tsien, D. P. L. Green, S. R. Levinson, B. Rudy and J. K. M. Sanders, *Proc. R. Soc. London, Ser. B*, 1975, **191**, 555.
121. R. J. Guillory, M. D. Rayner and J. S. D'Arrigo, *Science (Washington, D.C.)*, 1977, **196**, 883.
122. R. Chicheportiche, M. Balerna, A. Lombet, G. Romey and M. Lazdunski, *J. Biol. Chem.*, 1979, **254**, 1552.
123. R. Chicheportiche, M. Balerna, A. Lombet, G. Romey and M. Lazdunski, *Eur. J. Biochem.*, 1980, **104**, 617.
124. K. J. Angelides, *Biochemistry*, 1981, **20**, 4107.
125. G. Strichartz, T. Rando, S. Hall, J. Gitschier, L. Hall, B. Magani and C. H. Bay, *Ann. N.Y. Acad. Sci.*, 1986, **479**, 90.
126. G. Strichartz, *J. Gen. Physiol.*, 1986, **84**, 281.
127. L. J. Cruz, W. R. Gray, D. Yoshikami and B. M. Olivera, *J. Toxicol. Toxin Rev.*, 1985, **4** (2), 107.
128. L. J. Cruz, W. R. Gray, B. M. Olivera, R. D. Zeikus, L. Kerr, D. Yoshikami and E. Moczydlowski, *J. Biol. Chem.*, 1985, **260**, 9280.
129. E. Moczydlowski, B. M. Olivera, W. R. Gray and G. R. Strichartz, *Proc. Natl. Acad. Sci. U.S.A.*, 1986, **83**, 5321.
130. M. J. Dufton and H. Rochat, *J. Mol. Evol.*, 1984, **5**, 120.
131. D. D. Watt and J. M. Simard, *J. Toxicol. Toxin Rev.*, 1984, **3** (2 & 3), 181.
132. R. J. Almassy, J. C. Fontecilla-Camps, F. L. Suddath and C. E. Bugg, *J. Mol. Biol.*, 1983, **170**, 497.
133. E. Jover, J. Bablito and F. Couraud, *Biochemistry*, 1984, **23**, 1147.
134. T. Masutani, I. Seyama, T. Narahashi and J. Iwasa, *J. Pharmacol. Exp. Ther.*, 1981, **217**, 812.
135. P. W. Codding, *J. Am. Chem. Soc.*, 1983, **105**, 3172.
136. P. W. Codding, *J. Am. Chem. Soc.*, 1983, **105**, 3177.
137. K. Nishimura and T. Narahashi, *Pestic. Biochem. Physiol.*, 1978, **8**, 53.
138. A. E. Lund and T. Narahashi, *Pestic. Biochem. Physiol.*, 1983, **20**, 203.
139. T. Narahashi, in 'Cellular and Molecular Neurotoxicology', ed. T. Narahashi, Raven Press, New York, 1984, p. 85.
140. T. Narahashi, *Neurotoxicology*, 1985, **6** (2), 3.
141. A. E. Lind and T. Narahashi, *Neurotoxicology*, 1982, **3**, 11.
142. D. M. Soderland, S. M. Ghiasuddin and D. W. Helmuth, *Life Sci.*, 1983, **33**, 261.
143. B. P. Bean, C. J. Cohen and R. W. Tsien, *J. Gen. Physiol.*, 1983, **81**, 613.
144. P. Lechat (ed.), 'International Encyclopedia of Pharmacology and Therapeutics', Pergamon Press, New York, 1971, vol. I, sect. 8.
145. G. R. Strichartz (ed.), 'Handbook of Experimental Pharmacology', Springer, Berlin, 1986, vol. 81.
146. G. R. Strichartz and J. M. Ritchie, in 'Handbook of Experimental Pharmacology', ed. G. R. Strichartz, Springer, Berlin, 1986, vol. 81, p. 21.
147. K. R. Courtney and G. R. Strichartz, in 'Handbook of Experimental Pharmacology', ed. G. R. Strichartz, Springer, Berlin, 1986, vol. 81, p. 53.
148. K. R. Courtney, J. J. Kindig and E. N. Cohen, *J. Pharmacol. Exp. Ther.*, 1978, **207**, 594.

149. K. R. Courtney, *J. Pharmacol. Exp. Ther.*, 1980, **213**, 114.
150. K. R. Courtney, *J. Mol. Cell. Cardiol.*, 1980, **12**, 1273.
151. K. R. Courtney, in 'Progress in Anesthesiology', ed. B. R. Fink, Raven Press, New York, 1980, vol. 2, p. 111.
152. K. R. Courtney and E. F. Etter, *Eur. J. Pharmacol.*, 1983, **8**, 1.
153. T. J. Campbell, *Br. J. Pharmacol.*, 1983, **80**, 33.
154. P. M. Bokesch, C. Post and G. Strichartz, *J. Pharmacol. Exp. Ther.*, 1986, **237**, 773.
155. J. Z. Yeh and R. E. TenEick, *Biophys. J.*, 1987, **51**, 123.
156. K. R. Courtney, *J. Mol. Cell. Cardiol.*, 1987, **19**, 319.
157. S. B. A. Akerman, G. Camougis and R. V. Sandberg, *Eur. J. Pharmacol.*, 1969, **8**, 337.
158. S. B. A. Akerman, *Acta Pharmacol. Toxicol.*, 1973, **32**, 97.
159. H. G. Mautner, C. Lorenc, P. Quain and J. K. Marquis, *J. Med. Chem.*, 1980, **23**, 282.
160. J. Z. Yeh, in 'Progress in Anesthesiology', ed. B. R. Fink, Raven Press, New York, 1980, vol. 2, p. 35.
161. G. Romey, U. Quast, D. Pauron, C. Frelin, J. F. Renaud and M. Lazdunski, *Proc. Natl. Acad. Sci. U.S.A.*, 1987, **84**, 890.
162. G. A. Gintant and B. F. Hoffman, in 'Handbook of Experimental Pharmacology', ed. G. Strichartz, Springer, Berlin, 1986, vol. 81, p. 213.
163. K. R. Courtney, *Eur. J. Pharmacol.*, 1981, **74**, 9.
164. H. J. Reiser and M. E. Sullivan, *Fed. Proc., Fed. Am. Soc. Exp. Biol.*, 1986, **45**, 2206.
165. W. A. Catterall, *Mol. Pharmacol.*, 1981, **20**, 356.
166. M. Willow, E. A. Kuenzel and W. A. Catterall, *Mol. Pharmacol.*, 1984, **25**, 228.
167. M. Willow, T. Gonoi and W. A. Catterall, *Mol. Pharmacol.*, 1985, **27**, 549.
168. W. A. Catterall, *Trends Pharmacol. Sci.*, 1987, **8**, 57.
169. A. Fleckenstein, *Annu. Rev. Pharmacol. Toxicol.*, 1977, **17**, 149.
170. A. Fleckenstein, *Circ. Res.*, 1983, **52** (suppl. I), 3.
171. A. Fleckenstein, 'Calcium Antagonism in Heart and Smooth Muscle. Experimental Facts and Therapeutic Products', Wiley, New York, 1983.
172. P. M. Vanhoutte, *Am. J. Cardiol.*, 1987, **59**, 3A.
173. R. A. Janis, P. Silver and D. J. Triggle, *Adv. Drug Res.*, 1987, **16**, 309.
174. T. Godfraind and R. Miller, *Pharmacol. Rev.*, 1986, **38**, 321.
175. R. W. Tsien, B. P. Bean, P. Hess, J. B. Lansman, B. Nilius and M. C. Nowycky, *J. Mol. Cell. Cardiol.*, 1986, **18**, 691.
176. M. Kameyama, J. Hescheler, F. Hofman and W. Trautwein, *Pfluegers Arch.*, 1986, **407**, 123.
177. M. F. Berridge and R. F. Irvine, *Nature (London)*, 1984, **312**, 315.
178. R. F. Irvine and R. M. Moor, *Biochem. J.*, 1986, **240**, 917.
179. J. W. Putney, *Cell Calcium*, 1986, **7**, 1.
180. H. Streb, R. F. Irvine, M. J. Berridge and I. Schulz, *Nature (London)*, 1983, **306**, 67.
181. R. F. Irvine, A. J. Letcher, D. J. Lander and M. J. Berridge, *Biochem. J.*, 1986, **240**, 301.
182. D. J. Triggle, in 'Proceedings of Chemrawn V. Conference, Heidelberg, 1986', ed. H. Machleidt, VCH Verlagsgesellschaft, Weinheim, 1987.
183. P. R. Hof, U. T. Ruegg, A. Hof and A. Vogel, *J. Cardiovasc. Pharmacol.*, 1985, **7**, 689.
184. X. Y. Wei, E. M. Luchowski, A. Rutledge, C. M. Su and D. J. Triggle, *J. Pharmacol. Exp. Ther.*, 1986, **239**, 144.
185. J. M. Chubb, J. L. Bennett, T. Akera and T. M. Brody, *J. Pharmacol. Exp. Ther.*, 1978, **207**, 284.
186. K. Jim and D. J. Triggle, *Can. J. Physiol. Pharmacol.*, 1979, **57**, 1460.
187. B. Loev, M. M. Goodman, K. M. Snader, R. Tedeschi and E. Macko, *J. Med. Chem.*, 1974, **17**, 956.
188. R. Rodenkirchen, R. Bayer, R. Steiner, F. Bossert, H. Meyer and E. Moller, *Naunyn-Schmiedeberg's Arch. Pharmacol.*, 1979, **310**, 69.
189. R. Mannhold, R. Rodenkirchen and R. Bayer, *Prog. Pharmacol.*, 1982, **5**, 25.
190. G. T. Bolger, P. J. Gengo, R. Klockowski, E. Luchowski, H. Siegel, R. A. Janis, A. M. Triggle and D. J. Triggle, *J. Pharmacol. Exp. Ther.*, 1983, **225**, 291.
191. C. M. Su, F. B. Yousif, D. J. Triggle and R. A. Janis, in 'Cardiovascular Effects of Dihydropyridine-type Calcium Antagonists and Agonists', ed. A. Fleckenstein, C. van Breemen, R. Gross and F. Hofmeister, Springer, Berlin, 1985, p. 104.
192. F. B. Yousif and D. J. Triggle, *Can. J. Physiol. Pharmacol.*, 1986, **64**, 273.
193. A. Fleckenstein, C. van Breemen, R. Gross and F. Hofmeister (eds.), 'Cardiovascular Effects of Dihydropyridine-type Calcium Antagonists and Agonists', Springer, Berlin, 1985.
194. R. A. Burges, D. G. Gardiner, M. Gwilt, A. J. Higgins, K. J. Blackburn, S. F. Campbell, P. E. Cross and J. F. Stubbs, *J. Cardiovasc. Pharmacol.*, 1987, **9**, 110.
195. M. Mahmoudian and W. G. Richards, *J. Pharm. Pharmacol.*, 1986, **38**, 272.
196. R. A. Coburn, M. Wierzba, M. J. Suto, A. J. Solo, A. M. Triggle and D. J. Triggle, *J. Med. Chem.*, 1988, **31**, 2103.
197. R. Fossheim, A. Joslyn, A. J. Solo, E. Luchowski, A. Rutledge and D. J. Triggle, *J. Med. Chem.*, 1988, **31**, 300.
198. A. M. Triggle, E. Shefter and D. J. Triggle, *J. Med. Chem.*, 1980, **23**, 1442.
199. R. Fossheim, K. Svarteng, A. Mostad, C. Romming, E. Shefter and D. J. Triggle, *J. Med. Chem.*, 1982, **25**, 126.
200. R. Fossheim, A. Joslyn, A. J. Solo, E. Luchowski, A. Rutledge and D. J. Triggle, ref. 197 and unpublished observations.
201. W. Seidel, H. Meyer, L. Born, S. Kazda and W. Dompert, 'American Chemical Society, 187th National Meeting, St. Louis, MO, April 8–14, Medicinal Chemistry Abstracts', 1984, abstr. 14.
202. J. J. Baldwin, D. A. Claremon, P. K. Lumma, D. E. McClure, S. A. Rosenthal, R. J. Winquist, E. P. Faison, G. J. Kaczorowski, M. J. Trimble and G. M. Smith, *J. Med. Chem.*, 1987, **30**, 690.
203. D. J. Triggle, R. Fossheim, M. Hawthorn, A. Joslyn, A. M. Triggle and X. Y. Wei, in 'Proceedings of the 6th Camerino-Noordwijkerhout Symposium, Camerino, 1987', Elsevier, Amsterdam, 1988, p. 123.
204. P. Berntsson and S. Wold, *Quant. Struct.-Act. Relat.*, 1986, **5**, 45.
205. H. Meyer, E. Wehinger, F. Bossert, K. Stoepel and W. Vater, *Arzneim.-Forsch.*, 1981, **31**, 407.
206. J. E. Arrowsmith, S. F. Campbell, P. E. Cross, J. K. Stubbs, R. A. Burges, D. G. Gardiner and K. J. Blackburn, *J. Med. Chem.*, 1986, **29**, 1696.
207. R. Mannhold, R. Steiner, W. Haas and W. Kaufmann, *Naunyn-Schmiedeberg's Arch. Pharmacol.*, 1978, **302**, 217.
208. R. Mannhold, P. Zierden, R. Bayer, R. Rodenkirchen and R. Steiner, *Arzneim.-Forsch.*, 1981, **31**, 773.

209. R. Mannhold, R. Bayer, M. Ronsdorf and L. Martens, *Arzneim.-Forsch.*, 1987, **37**, 419.
210. A. Goll, H. Glossmann and R. Mannhold, *Naunyn-Schmiedeberg's Arch. Pharmacol.*, 1986, **334**, 303.
211. K. S. Atwal, J. L. Bergey, A. Hedberg and S. Moreland, *J. Med. Chem.*, 1987, **30**, 635.
212. J. D. Hescheler, D. Pelzer and W. Trautwein, *Pfluegers Arch.*, 1982, **303**, 287.
213. A. Uehera and J. R. Hume, *J. Gen. Physiol.*, 1985, **85**, 621.
214. M. L. Garcia, M. J. Trumble, J. P. Reuben and G. J. Kaczorowski, *J. Biol. Chem.*, 1984, **259**, 15013.
215. J. P. Galizzi, M. Borsotto, J. Barhanin, M. Fosset and M. Lazdunski, *J. Biol. Chem.*, 1986, **261**, 1393.
216. M. Takahashi and W. A. Catterall, *Science (Washington, D.C.)*, 1987, **236**, 88.
217. A. T. Leung, T. Imagawa and K. P. Campbell, *J. Biol. Chem.*, 1987, **262**, 7943.
218. H. Glossmann and D. R. Ferry, *Methods Enzymol.*, 1985, **109**, 513.
219. H. Glossmann, D. R. Ferry, F. Lubbecke, R. Mewes and F. Hofmann, *Trends Pharmacol. Sci.*, 1982, **3**, 431.
220. D. A. Langs and D. J. Triggle, *Mol. Pharmacol.*, 1985, **27**, 544.
221. X. Y. Wei and D. J. Triggle, *J. Pharmacol. Exp. Ther.*, 1986, **239**, 144.
222. R. Kass, *Circ. Res.*, 1987, **61** (suppl. 1).
223. D. A. Langs, G. Frankowiak, P. D. Strong, Y. W. Kwon and D. J. Triggle, submitted for publication.
224. M. Mahmoudian and W. G. Richards, *J. Chem. Soc., Chem. Commun.*, 1986, 739.
225. H.-D. Holtje and S. Marrer, *J. Comput. Aided Mol. Des.*, 1987, **1**, 23.
226. R. Fossheim, *Acta Chem. Scand., Ser. B*, 1987, **41**, 581.
227. P. Bellemann, A. Schade and R. Towart, *Proc. Natl. Acad. Sci. U.S.A.*, 1983, **80**, 2356.
228. R. J. Miller, in 'Structure and Physiology of the Slow Inward Calcium Channel', ed. D. J. Triggle and J. C. Venter, Liss, New York, 1987.
229. R. J. Miller, *Science (Washington, D.C.)*, 1986, **235**, 46.
230. S. Kokubun, B. Prod'hom, C. Becker, H. Porzig and H. Reuter, *Mol. Pharmacol.*, 1986, **30**, 571.
231. G. P. Dube, Y. H. Bait and A. Schwartz, *J. Cardiovasc. Pharmacol.*, 1985, **7**, 377.
232. K. Miwa and A. Schwartz, *Biochem. Biophys. Res. Commun.*, 1987, **148**, 1.
233. R. J. Gould, K. M. M. Murphy, I. J. Reynolds and S. H. Snyder, *Proc. Natl. Acad. Sci. U.S.A.*, 1983, **80**, 5122.
234. J.-P. Galizzi, M. Fosset, G. Romen, P. Laduron and M. Lazdunski, *Proc. Natl. Acad. Sci. U.S.A.*, 1986, **83**, 7513.
235. J. Qar, J.-P. Galizzi, M. Fossett and M. Lazdunski, *Eur. J. Pharmacol.*, 1987, **141**, 261.
236. J. Gould, K. M. M. Murphy and S. H. Snyder, *Proc. Natl. Acad. Sci. U.S.A.*, 1982, **79**, 3656.
237. E. M. Luchowski, F. Yousif, D. J. Triggle, S. C. Maurer, J. G. Sarmiento and R. A. Janis, *J. Pharmacol. Exp. Ther.*, 1984, **230**, 607.
238. A. C. Maan, J. Ptasienski and M. M. Hosey, *J. Pharmacol. Exp. Ther.*, 1986, **237**, 768.
239. R. Tsien, P. Hess, E. W. McCleskey and R. L. Rosenberg, *Annu. Rev. Biophys. Chem.*, 1987, **16**, 265.
240. D. J. Triggle and R. A. Janis, *Annu. Rev. Pharmacol. Toxicol.*, 1987, **27**, 347.
241. R. Bayer, R. Hennekes, R. Kaufmann and R. Mannhold, *Naunyn-Schmiedeberg's Arch. Pharmacol.*, 1975, **290**, 49.
242. T. Ehara and R. Kaufmann, *J. Pharmacol. Exp. Ther.*, 1978, **207**, 49.
243. D. Pelzer, W. Trautwein and T. F. McDonald, *Pfluegers Arch.*, 1982, **394**, 97.
244. T. F. McDonald, D. Pelzer and W. Trautwein, *J. Physiol. (London)*, 1984, **352**, 203.
245. T. F. McDonald, D. Pelzer and W. Trautwein, *J. Physiol. (London)*, 1984, **352**, 217.
246. J. H. Chin, *Biochem. Pharmacol.*, 1986, **35**, 4115.
247. M. C. Sanguinetti and R. S. Kass, *Circ. Res.*, 1984, **55**, 336.
248. B. P. Bean, *Proc. Natl. Acad. Sci. U.S.A.*, 1984, **81**, 6388.
249. K. S. Lee and R. W. Tsien, *Nature (London)*, 1983, **302**, 790.
250. C. Cognard, M. Lazdunski and G. Romey, *Proc. Natl. Acad. Sci. U.S.A.*, 1986, **83**, 517.
251. R. W. Tsien, *Annu. Rev. Physiol.*, 1983, **45**, 341.
252. B. P. Bean, M. Sturek, A. Puga and K. Hermsmeyer, *Circ. Res.*, 1986, **59**, 229.
253. A. M. Gurney, J. M. Nerbonne and H. A. Lester, *J. Gen. Physiol.*, 1985, **86**, 353.
254. C. J. Cohen and R. T. McCarthy, *J. Physiol. (London)*, 1987, **387**, 195.
255. A. Yatani, S. L. Hamilton and A. M. Brown, *Circ. Res.*, 1986, **9**, 356.
256. W. P. Schilling and J. A. Drews, *J. Biol. Chem.*, 1986, **261**, 2750.
257. P. Hess, J. B. Lansman and R. W. Tsien, *Nature (London)*, 1984, **311**, 538.
258. M. C. Sanguinetti and R. S. Kass, *J. Mol. Cell. Cardiol.*, 1984, **16**, 667.
259. M. C. Sanguinetti, D. S. Krafte and R. S. Kass, *J. Gen. Physiol.*, 1986, **88**, 369.
260. R. T. McCarthy and C. J. Cohen, *Biophys. J.*, 1986, **49**, 432 abs.
261. M. C. Nowycky, A. P. Fox and R. W. Tsien, *Nature (London)*, 1985, **316**, 440.
262. E. W. McCleskey, A. P. Fox, D. Feldman and R. W. Tsien, *J. Exp. Biol.*, 1986, **124**, 177.
263. B. M. Olivera, J. M. McIntosh, R. Zeikus, W. R. Gray, J. Varga, J. Rivier, V. deSantos and L. J. Cruz, *Science (Washington, D.C.)*, 1985, **230**, 1338.
264. T. M. Perney, L. D. Hirning, S. E. Leeman and R. J. Miller, *Proc. Natl. Acad. Sci. U.S.A.*, 1986, **83**, 6656.
265. J. River, R. Galyean, W. R. Gray, A. Azimi-Zonooz, J. M. McIntosh, L. J. Cruz and B. M. Olivera, *J. Biol. Chem.*, 1987, **262**, 1194.
266. I. J. Reynolds, J. A. Wagner, S. H. Snyder, S. A. Thayer, B. M. Olivera and R. J. Miller, *Proc. Natl. Acad. Sci. U.S.A.*, 1986, **83**, 8804.
267. G. Meissner, *J. Biol. Chem.*, 1984, **259**, 2365.
268. G. Meissner, *J. Biol. Chem.*, 1986, **261**, 6300.
269. I. N. Pessah, A. O. Francini, D. J. Scales, A. L. Waterhouse and J. E. Casida, *J. Biol. Chem.*, 1986, **261**, 8643.
270. B. A. Suarez-Isla, C. Orozco, P. F. Heller and J. P. Froehlich, *Proc. Natl. Acad. Sci. U.S.A.*, 1986, **83**, 7741.
271. E. Rousseau, J. S. Smith, J. S. Henderson and G. Meissner, *Biophys. J.*, 1986, **50**, 1009.
272. J. S. Smith, R. Coronado and G. Meissner, *Biophys. J.*, 1986, **50**, 921.
273. B. K. Chamberlain, P. Volpe and S. Fleischer, *J. Biol. Chem.*, 1984, **259**, 7547.
274. J. Bernstein, *Pfluegers Arch.*, 1902, **82**, 521.
275. B. Hille, 'Ionic Channels of Excitable Membranes', Sinauer, Sunderland, MA, 1984, chap. 5.
276. P. Latorre and C. Miller, *J. Membr. Biol.*, 1983, **71**, 11.

277. P. R. Stanfield, *Rev. Physiol., Biochem. Pharmacol.*, 1983, **97**, 1.
278. J. M. Dubois, *J. Physiol. (London)*, 1981, **318**, 297.
279. J. M. Dubois, *Prog. Biophys. Mol. Biol.*, 1983, **42**, 1.
280. J. A. Connor and C. F. Stevens, *J. Physiol. (London)*, 1971, **213**, 1.
281. J. A. Connor and C. F. Stevens, *J. Physiol. (London)*, 1971, **213**, 31.
282. J. A. Connor, *Fed. Proc., Fed. Am. Soc. Exp. Biol.*, 1978, **37**, 2139.
283. O. H. Petersen and Y. Maruyama, *Nature (London)*, 1984, **307**, 693.
284. O. H. Petersen, *Am. J. Physiol.*, 1986, **251**, 91.
285. O. H. Petersen, I. Findlay, K. Suzuki and M. J. Dunne, *J. Exp. Biol.*, 1986, **124**, 33.
286. P. R. Adams, D. A. Brown and A. Constantini, *J. Physiol. (London)*, 1982, **330**, 537.
287. P. R. Adams, D. A. Brown and A. Constantini, *J. Physiol. (London)*, 1982, **332**, 223.
288. D. A. Brown, *Trends NeuroSci. (Pers. Ed.)*, 1983, **6**, 302.
289. S. Sorota, Y. Tsuji, T. Tajima and A. J. Pappano, *Circ. Res.*, 1985, **57**, 748.
290. P. J. Pfaffinger, J. M. Martin, D. D. Hunter, N. M. Nathanson and B. Hille, *Nature (London)*, 1985, **317**, 536.
291. K. Sasaki and M. Sato, *Nature (London)*, 1987, **325**, 259.
292. A. Yatani, J. Codina, A. M. Brown and L. Birnbaumer, *Science (Washington, D.C.)*, 1987, **235**, 207.
293. M. J. Shuster, J. S. Camardo, S. A. Siegelbaum and E. R. Kander, *Nature (London)*, 1985, **313**, 392.
294. M. Lazdunski, *Cell Calcium*, 1983, **4**, 421.
295. G. Romey, M. Hugues, H. Schmid-Antomarchi and M. Lazdunski, *J. Physiol. (Paris)*, 1984, **79**, 259.
296. M. Hughes, D. Duval, P. Katabgi, M. Lazdunski and J. P. Vincent, *J. Biol. Chem.*, 1982, **257**, 2762.
297. H. Schmid-Antomarchi, M. Hugues, R. Norman, C. Ellory, M. Borsotto and M. Lazdunski, *Eur. J. Biochem.*, 1984, **142**, 1.
298. N. S. Cooke and D. G. Haylett, *J. Physiol. (London)*, 1985, **358**, 373.
299. C. Miller, E. Moczydlowski, R. Latorre and M. Phillips, *Nature (London)*, 1985, **313**, 316.
300. R. P. Swenson, Jr., *J. Gen. Physiol.*, 1981, **77**, 255.
301. R. J. French and J. J. Shoukimas, *Biophys. J.*, 1981, **34**, 271.
302. M. I. Steinberg and E. L. Michelson, in 'Mechanisms and Treatment of Cardiac Arrhythmias; Relevance of Basic Studies to Clinical Management', ed. H. J. Reiser and L. N. Horowitz, Urban and Schwarzenberg, Baltimore, 1985.
303. T. C. Hamilton, S. W. Weir and A. H. Weston, *Br. J. Pharmacol.*, 1986, **8**, 103.
304. D. K. Bartschat and M. P. Blaustein, *Proc. Natl. Acad. Sci. U.S.A.*, 1986, **83**, 189.
305. M. C. Coldwell and D. R. Howlett, *Biochem. Pharmacol.*, 1987, **36**, 3663.
306. T. L. Schwarz, B. L. Tempel, D. M. Papazian, Y. N. Jan and L. Y. Jan, *Nature (London)*, 1988, **331**, 137.
307. P. Seeman, *Pharmacol. Rev.*, 1972, **24**, 583.
308. A. S. Janoff and K. W. Miller, in 'Biological Membranes', ed. D. Chapman, Academic Press, London, 1982, p. 417.
309. K. W. Miller, *Int. Rev. Neurobiol.*, 1985, **27**, 1.
310. S. H. Roth and K. W. Miller (eds.), 'Molecular and Cellular Mechanisms of Anesthetics', Plenum Press, New York, 1986.
311. C. D. Richards, *Gen. Pharmacol.*, 1978, **9**, 287.
312. C. D. Richards, *Trends NeuroSci. (Pers. Ed.)*, 1980, **3**, 9.
313. R. A. Nicoll and D. V. Madison, *Science (Washington, D.C.)*, 1982, **217**, 1055.
314. K. Krnjevic, in 'Molecular and Cellular Mechanisms of Anesthetics', ed. S. H. Roth and K. W. Miller, Plenum Press, New York, 1986, p. 3.
315. E. Overton, 'Studien uber die Narkose', Fisher, Jena, 1901.
316. H. H. Meyer, *Harvey Lect.*, 1906, 11.
317. C. D. Richards, K. Martin, S. Gregory, C. A. Keightley, T. R. Hesketh, G. A. Smith, G. B. Warren and J. C. Metcalf, *Nature (London)*, 1978, **276**, 775.
318. N. P. Franks and W. R. Lieb, *Nature (London)*, 1978, **274**, 339.
319. N. P. Franks and W. R. Lieb, *Nature (London)*, 1982, **300**, 482.
320. N. P. Franks and W. R. Lieb, *Nature (London)*, 1984, **310**, 599.
321. J. Ferguson, *Proc. R. Soc. London, Ser. B*, 1939, **127**, 387.
322. K. W. Miller, W. D. M. Paton, R. A. Smith and E. B. Smith, *Anesthesiology*, 1971, **36**, 339.
323. M. J. Pringle, K. B. Brown and K. W. Miller, *Mol. Pharmacol.*, 1981, **19**, 49.
324. K. W. Miller, 'Burger's Medicinal Chemistry', 4th edn., ed. M. E. Woiff, Wiley-Interscience, New York, 1981, vol. III, p. 623.
325. J. C. Metcalf, P. Seeman and A. S. V. Burgen, *Mol. Pharmacol.*, 1968, **4**, 87.
326. N. P. Franks and W. R. Lieb, *J. Mol. Biol.*, 1979, **133**, 469.
327. K. W. Miller and K. Y. Pang, *Nature (London)*, 1976, **263**, 253.
328. W. R. Lieb, M. Kovaycsik and R. Mendelsohn, *Biochim. Biophys. Acta*, 1982, **688**, 388.
329. M. W. Hill, *Biochim. Biophys. Acta*, 1974, **356**, 117.
330. D. B. Mountcastle, R. Biltonen and M. J. Halsey, *Proc. Natl. Acad. Sci. U.S.A.*, 1978, **75**, 4906.
331. A. G. Lee, *Biochemistry*, 1976, **15**, 2448.
332. P. Seeman and S. Roth, *Biochim. Biophys. Acta*, 1972, **255**, 171.
333. N. P. Franks and W. R. Lieb, *Nature (London)*, 1982, **292**, 248.
334. S. M. Johnson, K. W. Miller and A. D. Bangham, *Biochim. Biophys. Acta*, 1973, **307**, 42.
335. K. Pang, T. Chang and K. W. Miller, *Mol. Pharmacol.*, 1979, **15**, 729.
336. F. H. Johnson and E. A. Flagler, *Science (Washington, D.C.)*, 1952, **112**, 91.
337. M. J. Lever, K. W. Miller, W. D. M. Paton and E. B. Smith, *Nature (London)*, 1971, **231**, 368.
338. K. W. Miller, W. D. M. Paton, R. A. Smith and E. B. Smith, *Mol. Pharmacol.*, 1973, **9**, 131.
339. L. J. Mullins, *Chem. Rev.*, 1954, **54**, 289.
340. A. S. Janoff, M. J. Pringle and K. W. Miller, *Biochim. Biophys. Acta*, 1981, **649**, 125.
341. A. S. Janoff and K. W. Miller, in 'Biological Membranes', ed. D. Chapman, Academic Press, London, 1982, vol. 4, p. 417.
342. N. P. Franks and W. R. Lieb, *Proc. Natl. Acad. Sci. U.S.A.*, 1986, **83**, 5116.
343. N. P. Franks and W. R. Lieb, *Nature (London)*, 1985, **316**, 349.
344. K. W. Miller, *Trends NeuroSci. (Pers. Ed.)*, 1986, **9**, 49.

345. S. H. Roth, K.-S. Tan and M. B. MacIver, in 'Molecular and Cellular Mechanisms of Anesthesia', ed. S. H. Roth and K. W. Miller, Plenum Press, New York, 1986, p. 43.
346. N. A. Anis, S. C. Berry, N. R. Burton and D. Lodge, *Br. J. Pharmacol.*, 1983, **79**, 565.
347. A. S. Evers, B. A. Berkowitz and D. A. d'Avignon, *Nature (London)*, 1987, **328**, 157.
348. E. M. Vaughn Williams, *J. Clin. Pharmacol.*, 1984, **24**, 129.
349. J. T. Bigger and B. F. Hoffman, in 'The Pharmacological Basis of Therapeutics', 7th edn., ed. A. G. Gilman, L. S. Goodman, T. W. Rall and F. Murad, Macmillan, New York, 1985.
350. P. J. Podrid, *Annu. Rev. Med.*, 1987, **38**, 1.
351. D. P. Zipes, *Circulation*, 1985, **72**, 949.
352. R. A. Janis, J. G. Sarmiento, S. C. Maurer, G. T. Bolger and D. J. Triggle, *J. Pharmacol. Exp. Ther.*, 1984, **231**, 8.
353. F. Yousif, G. T. Bolger, A. L. Ruzycky and D. J. Triggle, *Can. J. Physiol. Pharmacol.*, 1985, **63**, 453.

15.1

Lymphokines and Cytokines of the Immune System

WENDELL WIERENGA and JUDITH A. NICHOLAS

The Upjohn Company, Kalamazoo, MI, USA

15.1.1   INTRODUCTION

The classification of agents that modify the immune response of the host has been inconsistent, based on either functional descriptors or structural descriptors. The term biological response modifiers (BRM) has been coined to encompass the diversity of terminology used to describe agents which elicit responses from the host, which in turn are believed to have some beneficial effect on the pathogenesis of the disease in the host. Various synonyms for BRMs which appear in the literature include immunomodulators, immunotherapeutics, immunorestoration, disease-modifying agents, host defense, adoptive transfer, differentiation regulators, growth/maturation factors, chemoprevention, antigenic modulation, angiogenesis modulation, and finally various 'biologicals', which include cytokines, lymphokines, antibodies, antigens and immunological effector cells. The first part of this chapter deals with the very large group of BRMs known as cytokines and lymphokines, their source, their properties, their biochemical, cellular and physiological effects, and their therapeutic potential. The second half of this chapter will continue the theme of immunomodulators, but will focus on natural and synthetic agents which, when given to the host, induce various immunological responses, including the induction of the cytokines and lymphokines.

The discussion of the cytokines and lymphokines of the immune system and other BRMs presented below is provided as a general and broad-based, rather than comprehensive, overview of the field of soluble mediators which may have a significant impact on prevention or control of cancer or infectious diseases. Wherever reasonable, the discussion has been restricted to properties associated with the human, rather than the murine, system. Although these lymphokines and cytokines are discussed individually, it should be kept in mind that a vast array of soluble mediators are released from activated mononuclear cells during the course of the immune response, not all of which are covered here, and that these combinations of interleukins, interferons, tumor necrosis factors, colony-stimulating factors, B cell stimulatory factors and other mediators may synergize to increase the proliferative or functional responsiveness of their respective target cells, or they may act antagonistically.

Most of the cytokines and lymphokines of the following discussion are released only after 'activation' of the appropriate immunological cells. Activation of macrophages is poorly understood at the biochemical level. However, following encounter with antigen, activated macrophages become highly phagocytic and vacuolated, they exhibit increased expression of membrane proteins which are intricately involved in generation of the immune response (class II antigens of the major histocompatibility complex, MHC) and secrete the soluble mediators discussed in more detail below. The biochemical events leading to T cell activation are initiated by crosslinking of the T cell receptor with antigen (T_i/CD_3 complex) when the antigen is presented by an appropriate accessory cell, typically a macrophage. Stimulation of the T_i/CD_3 complex is followed by hydrolysis of a membrane inositol phospholipid to two second messengers, diacylglycerol and inositol-1,4,5-triphosphate, which in turn activate protein kinase C and increase cytosolic Ca^{2+}. These events of signal transduction culminate in *de novo* protein, RNA and DNA synthesis and lead to the release of soluble immune response regulatory proteins, generally referred to as lymphokines. Direct cell to cell interaction and production and release of soluble mediators establish a complex but precisely regulated interrelationship between macrophages and lymphocytes within the reticuloendothelial system and their precursor cells in the bone marrow.

15.1.2   CELLULAR SOURCES, BIOSYNTHESIS, LOCALIZATION, DISTRIBUTION AND SITES OF ACTION

15.1.2.1   Interleukin 1

Soluble factors which mediate a variety of different biological activities were previously reported in the literature by names which described their bioactivity (Table 1). One of the best-characterized soluble factors released from macrophages is now known as interleukin 1 (IL1), and the cDNAs for two forms of IL1, IL1-α and IL1-β,[1] have been cloned. Human peripheral blood monocytes appear to make both forms of IL1, but the β form predominates over α by a ratio of approximately 10:1 at the level of mRNA induction,[2] although the reverse is the case for the murine system. These two forms of IL1 differ in their physicochemical properties (below), but have indistinguishable biological activities. Many cell types have been documented to produce IL1 activity (Table 2). Normal cells produce IL1 only in response to a stimulus, and bacterial lipopolysaccharide or phorbol esters are the most widely used stimuli for *in vitro* induction of IL1. *In vivo* induction of IL1 probably

Table 1 Common Synonyms and Abbreviations for Cytokines and Lymphokines

Current nomenclature	Previous/alternate nomenclature
Interleukin 1 (IL1)	Lymphocyte-activating factor (LAF), endogenous pyrogen (EP), leukocyte endogenous mediator
Interleukin 2 (IL2)	T cell growth factor (TCGF)
Interleukin 3 (IL3)	Multicolony-stimulating factor, mast cell growth factor, hematopoietic growth factor, P-cell-stimulating factor (PSF), burst-promoting activity (BPA)
Interleukin 4 (IL4)	B cell stimulatory factor 1 (BSF-1), B cell growth factor (BCGF)
B cell stimulatory factor 2 (BSF-2)[a]	Interferon beta 2 (IFN-β2), B cell differentiation factor (BCDF), T-cell-replacing factor[b] (TRF), IgG-inducing factor[b]
Tumor necrosis factor alpha (TNF-α)	Cachectin
Tumor necrosis factor beta (TNF-β)	Lymphotoxin
Interferon alpha (IFN-α)	Acid stable IFN, type I IFN, leukocyte IFN
Interferon beta (IFN-β)	Acid stable IFN, type I IFN, fibroblast IFN
Interferon gamma (IFN-γ)	Acid labile IFN, type II IFN, immune IFN, macrophage-activating factor (MAF)
Granulocyte/macrophage	Neutrophil migration inhibition factor
Colony-stimulating factor (GM-CSF)	Pluripoietin alpha (PPO-α)
Myeloid colony-stimulating factor (M-CSF)[b]	Colony-stimulating factor 1 (CSF-1)[b]
Granulocyte colony-stimulating factor (G-CSF)	Pluripoietin (PPO)

[a] Terminology for human factors. [b] Terminology for murine factors.

Table 2 Cell Types Which Produce or Respond to Interleukin 1

	Immunological	Nonimmunological
IL1-producing cells	Macrophages/monocytes, B lymphocyte cell lines, T lymphocyte cell lines, large granular lymphocytes (NK cells)	Endothelial cells, epithelial cells, astrocytes, microglial cells
IL1 responsive cells	Macrophages/monocytes, B lymphocytes, large granular lymphocytes, T lymphocytes	Fibroblasts, osteoclasts, chondrocytes, muscle cells, epithelial cells, endothelial cells, synovial cells

occurs *via* phagocytosis of microorganisms or exposure to microbial breakdown products, antigen–antibody complexes, microbial toxins or physical trauma to tissues.

IL1 receptors[3] are found on a multitude of distinct cell types throughout the body, many of which are listed in Table 2. The human IL1 receptor is a transmembrane protein with $M = 80\,000$; however, a 41 kDa protein was identified as the IL1 receptor on the human leukemic cell line K562. Receptor density ranges from as few as 10 receptors per cell for resting T lymphocytes, a few hundred receptors per cell for other various T cell populations, a few thousand receptors on fibroblast cells, to as many as 20 000 per cell using a subline of the EL4 thymoma. Matsushima *et al.*[4] determined an autoregulatory role for IL1 and IL1-receptor expression, such that exposure to IL1 down-regulates receptor expression at the cell surface by internalization of the receptor–ligand complex, which may account for the high variability in receptor expression by various cell types. Several laboratories have detected a single type of affinity receptor for IL1 with $K_d \sim 10^{-10}$ M, but others have detected both high affinity and low affinity ($K_d = 10^{-12}$ M and 10^{-10} M, respectively) receptors for IL1 and have shown that only the high affinity receptor is biologically active due to its ability to internalize its ligand.[5] The high affinity receptor comprises only 1–2% of the total number of receptors per cell, and the ratio of high to low affinity receptors remains constant for a variety of different T cell types. IL1-α and IL1-β bind to the same receptor.

At a local site of infection, injury or immunization, macrophages or other cells produce IL1 which chemically attracts polymorphonuclear and mononuclear phagocytes. This local reaction is quickly followed by systemic symptoms, which result from the action of IL1 on multiple target tissues, including endothelial cells, hepatocytes, the hypothalamus or cells within the central nervous system. In arthritic inflammation, IL1, which is produced locally, acts on synovial cells, osteoclasts and chondrocytes. One of the most significant roles of IL1 is in immunoregulation, and promotion of the specific immune response by its action on T lymphocytes.

15.1.2.2 Tumor Necrosis Factors

Tumor necrosis factor (TNF) was originally described as a cytotoxic agent in the sera of mice and rabbits injected with *Mycobacterium bovis* or another immunostimulatory agent, followed by injection with endotoxin.[6] Thus, induction of TNF requires two signals, priming and elicitation, and the eliciting agents, both *in vitro* and sometimes *in vivo*, are the bacterial breakdown products, the most notable being lipopolysaccharides. TNF has tumor-necrotizing activity *in vivo* and *in vitro* and is cytotoxic or cytostatic for a variety of tumor cell targets. There are two forms of TNF, which are about 30% homologous at the level of DNA, *i.e.* α and β (see Table 1). TNF-α is a product of macrophages, both *in vitro* and *in vivo*, while TNF-β is a product of T lymphocytes. TNF travels through the circulation to target cells within the liver, skin, kidney, lung and gastrointestinal (GI) tract.[7]

The receptor for TNF has not been characterized but two polypeptide chains of 75 kDa and 95 kDa have been implicated.[8] TNF-α and TNF-β share the same receptor, which appears on the surface of both TNF sensitive and TNF resistant cells. Thus the basis of TNF selectivity in the mechanism of killing target cells is not known.[9]

15.1.2.3 Interferons α and β

Interferons (IFNs) are a diverse family of proteins which are secreted by virtually every cell type within the body in response to a variety of inducers, both viral and nonviral. IFN is produced locally upon viral infection. Much of the IFN activity remains at the sites of virus induction but, upon widespread infection with extensive tissue damage or viremia, high titers of IFN are also found in the serum. There are three major species of IFN, α, β and γ, respectively, induced from leucocytes, from fibroblasts (or other nonleucocyte cells) or from lymphocytes which have been stimulated with antigen or mitogen. IFN is primarily species specific in its spectrum of bioactivity, although some exceptions are apparent. This discussion focuses on IFN-α, and to some degree IFN-β, leaving IFN-γ to the lymphokines section (below) because of significant differences in the biological activities of the three species of IFN, and because IFN-γ binds to a unique receptor, which is different from the receptor for IFN-α and IFN-β.

Human IFN-α refers to a group of at least 14 structurally related polypeptides which are transcribed from a multigene family.[10,11] Human IFN-β refers to two IFN subtypes, which are structurally related to IFN-α, and IFN-β1 is the major subtype. Induction of either IFN requires *de novo* RNA and protein synthesis. A single, high affinity ($K_d = 10^{-9}–10^{-12}$ M) IFN receptor binds both IFN-α and IFN-β on various cell types, and the molecular weight of the receptor for IFN-α/β has been estimated to be about 130 kDa by gel electrophoresis.[12] The number of receptors per cell, depending on the cell type under investigation, lies between 300 and 20 000, but receptor expression is down-regulated by ligand binding and internalization.[13]

15.1.2.4 Interleukin 2

Interleukin 2 (IL2) is the product of a subset of T lymphocytes, T-helper cells, and was originally described in 1976 as a factor which promoted, for the first time, extended growth of T lymphocytes *in vitro* (Table 1).[14] The *de novo* synthesis and secretion of IL2 is triggered by interaction of the T-cell receptor complex with the appropriate antigen and antigen-presenting cells, but also requires a second signal provided by IL1.[15] The best-characterized target sites for IL2 are T lymphocytes, including the T lymphocytes which produce IL2, where IL2 regulates expression of the IL2 receptor at the cell surface.[16] IL2 receptor expression, and hence IL2-mediated regulation of the immune response, also occurs on activated B lymphocytes and on natural killer (NK) cells.

The IL2 receptor was originally described as a glycosylated membrane protein of $M \sim 58$ kDa. It was identified by the monoclonal antibody (anti-TAC), which bound to a surface protein found on activated T cells (TAC), but not on resting T cells, and was further defined by studies which revealed that anti-TAC competed with IL2 for binding to its receptor. Activated T lymphocytes express about 10 000 anti-TAC-binding sites per cell. Low affinity ($K_d = 10^{-8}$ M) and high affinity ($K_d = 10^{-12}$ M) receptors for IL2 have been described. Receptors of both affinities bind anti-TAC, but only the high affinity receptor mediates the biological activity of IL2. The high affinity receptor comprises only 5–10% of the total anti-TAC-binding sites and consists of two transmembrane polypeptide chains, α and β, of 75 kDa and 55 kDa, respectively.[17] The noncovalent association of both chains is required for binding IL2, which occurs at sites on each chain, whereas anti-TAC binds solely to the β chain.

Recently, a soluble form of the IL2 receptor was described in the sera of normal and leukemic individuals. This soluble receptor is approximately 10 kDa smaller than its membrane-associated counterpart, and binds IL2 efficiently.[18]

15.1.2.5 Interferon γ

In addition to IL2, activation of T lymphocytes results in the *de novo* synthesis and secretion of a variety of factors which enhance the immunological response at multiple cellular targets; one of these is interferon gamma (IFN-γ). IFN-γ is the product of a single gene, unlike the multigene family which encodes IFN-α and IFN-β. IFN-γ acts on monocytes/macrophages to induce *de novo* gene expression and to enhance expression of membrane proteins. Of primary significance in the immune response, IFN-γ activates macrophages and increases the expression of the class II molecules required for effective antigen presentation.[19] Other targets for IFN-γ action within the immune system include T lymphocytes, NK cells and B lymphocytes, while targets outside of the immune system include endothelial cells and, in *in vitro* studies, various carcinoma and melanoma cell lines. The receptor for IFN-γ was studied on malignant cells having high receptor density. It is of high affinity, with $K_d = 2 \times 10^{-11}$ M, and, while the receptor on normal lymphoid and myeloid cells appeared to be similar, substantially fewer receptors were expressed on the nonmalignant cells.[20]

15.1.2.6 B Cell Growth and Differentiation Factors

Activated T lymphocytes also secrete factors which promote the growth and differentiation of resting B lymphocytes into cells which secrete antibody. Aside from IL2 and IFN-γ, the two best characterized of these molecules in the human system are interleukin 4 (IL4) and B cell stimulatory factor 2 (BSF-2), which are produced by two structurally unrelated genes. The range of target cells for IL4 is not limited to B lymphocytes, and in the murine system receptors for IL4 are found on T lymphocytes, mast cells, undifferentiated hematopoietic cells and macrophages.[21] A single high affinity receptor was identified ($K_d \sim 1 - 3 \times 10^{-10}$ M), of $M \sim 60$ kDa, by crosslinking studies.[21] Receptor expression on resting cells is in the range of a few hundred molecules per cell.

15.1.2.7 Colony-stimulating Factors

Factors which promote the growth and differentiation of hematopoietic stem cells in the bone marrow and the activity of mature monocytes and granulocytes may be grouped into two broad categories: (i) those produced by activated T cells, which include interleukin 3 (IL3) and granulocyte-macrophage colony-stimulating factor (GM-CSF); and (ii) those of non-T cell origin, which include colony-stimulating factor 1 (CSF-1 or M-CSF), erythropoietin (EPO) and granulocyte colony-stimulating factor (G-CSF).[22] The primary difference between these two broad groupings is that the factors of non-T cell origin are produced constitutively, whereas production of the T-cell-derived factors is a part of the regulated immune response of T cell activation.

In addition to T cells, one or more of the CSFs is synthesized by macrophages, endothelial cells, epithelial cells or fibroblasts. CSFs are produced and act locally at sites of inflammation following exposure to endotoxin or other bacterial products. If high levels of endotoxin occur, CSF activity may be found in the circulation and in virtually every tissue. A unique receptor is present at the cell surface for each of the four CSFs and cells may simultaneously exhibit more than one type of receptor. Table 3 further characterizes these factors and their receptors.

15.1.3 CHEMICAL AND PHYSICAL PROPERTIES

15.1.3.1 Interleukin 1

IL1 exists in two distinct forms, acidic and basic, with approximate p*I* values of 5 and 7, representing the α and β forms, respectively.[1] The secreted form of IL1 is processed from a unique precursor, of $M = 35$ kDa by gel electrophoresis or 31 kDa by cDNA sequencing, which has no clear

Table 3 Factors Which Promote Growth and Differentiation of Hematopoietic Stem Cells

Factor	Origin	Mol. wt. of glycoprotein (kDa)	Mol. wt. of receptor $(mu)^b$ (kDa)	Lineage stimulated	Other biological effects
M-CSF (CSF-1)	Many cell types	45 (hu), 70 (mu), homodimeric	165	Myeloid	Growth/differentiation of monocytes and macrophages
G-CSF	Unknown	20 (hu), 24 (mu)	150	Granulocytic, erythroid	Neutrophil proliferation
Erythropoietin	Hepatocytes, kidney	36 (mu), 34 (mu)	—	Erythroid	Increase circulating red blood cells
IL3	T cells	14.6 (hu),^{a} 28 (mu)	50–70^a	Granulocytic, lymphoid, myeloid, erythroid	Growth/differentiation of mast cells, induces CSF-1 receptors, increases histamine levels, augments natural cytotoxicity activity, stimulates superoxide production and lysozyme secretion, may promote early differentiation of T cells, augments inflammation
GM-CSF	T cells	22 (hu), 25 (mu)	50	Granulocytic, myeloid	Activates eosinophils, recruits neutrophils, increases neutrophil phagocytosis and cytotoxicity

^{a} Molecular weight based on amino acid composition deduced from cloned DNA. ^{b} Human counterparts for these receptors have not yet been identified. (hu) = human; (mu) = murine.

signal sequence for cleavage. The two mature forms of IL1 each have $M = 17$ kDa. By comparing the sequences of mature IL1-α and IL1-β, two regions of homology are found, which may represent the active site of the molecule, while two additional regions of homology are found in the precursor.

15.1.3.2 Tumor Necrosis Factors

TNF-α is a nonglycosylated protein which forms mono-, di-, tri- or penta-meric oligomers.[23] Gel filtration reveals a 45 kDa protein, while gel electrophoresis detects the 17 kDa monomer.[24] Four exons encode a TNF-α precursor of 233 amino acids, 76 amino acids of which are the leader sequence. The leader sequence is cleaved in at least eight sites to yield the mature 157 amino acid product.

TNF-β is a glycosylated protein which also forms oligomeric structures. Gel filtration reveals a 60–70 kDa oligomer, while monomeric TNF-β is 25 kDa.[25] The TNF-β gene has three introns. The mature TNF-β product of 171 amino acids becomes glycosylated with N-linked carbohydrate, but glycosylation does not appear to be required for biological activity.

15.1.3.3 Interferons α and β

The group of IFN-α comprises mildly hydrophobic proteins of 165–166 amino acids in length, some subtypes of which have O-linked glycosylation but none having N-linked carbohydrate;[26] two disulfide bonds are found in most α subtypes.[27] IFN-α is acid stable at pH $= 2.0$, but recently an acid labile IFN-α was described in the sera of patients with Kaposi's sarcoma[28] or systemic lupus erythematosis (SLE).[29] IFN-α resists denaturation in SDS but is heat labile. IFN-β is an acid stable, hydrophobic glycoprotein of 166 amino acids with a single N-linked carbohydrate moiety and a single disulfide bond.[30]

15.1.3.4 Interleukin 2

IL2 has been purified from a variety of different T cell sources, including T cell lines or peripheral blood T cells, and exhibits molecular heterogeneity owing to glycosylation. Glycosylation is not essential for bioactivity. The various human IL2 glycoproteins range in molecular weight from 14 500 to 17 000 with a predominant species at 15 500, determined by gel electrophoresis, and isoelectric points vary between 6.8 and 8.2. The human IL2 cDNA was originally prepared by Taniguchi *et al.*,[31] and was shown to encode a 153 amino acid chain containing a signal sequence of 20 residues.

15.1.3.5 Interferon γ

IFN-γ is an acid and heat labile, hydrophilic protein of 143 amino acids which undergoes C-terminal processing to create heterogeneous subspecies.[32] Further heterogeneity is obtained by variable glycosylation, at one or both of the glycosylation sites within the protein, creating multiple species of $M = 17.5$ kDa, 21 kDa and 25 kDa, shown by gel electrophoresis.

15.1.3.6 B Cell Growth and Differentiation Factors

The cDNA for human IL4 contains a single, open reading frame, encoding a 153 amino acid protein with a 24 amino acid leader sequence, which is cleaved to yield a 15 kDa protein having two N-glycosylation sites.[33]

Human BSF-2 is a 184 amino acid protein that is derived from a 212 amino acid precursor by cleavage of a hydrophobic signal peptide.[34] The protein has $M = 21$ kDa, and has two potential glycosylation sites, although glycosylation has not yet been confirmed. The equivalent molecule in the murine system is 133 amino acids with three potential glycosylation sites, at least one of which is N-glycosylated.[35]

15.1.3.7 Colony-stimulating Factors

Each of the colony-stimulating factors are glycoproteins of heterogeneous molecular weight and pertinent chemical and physical properties are summarized in Table 3. Some additional information is contained below.

The open reading frame for M-CSF predicts a 224 amino acid structure with a 32 residue putative leader sequence. The protein undergoes extensive posttranslational processing to yield a mature glycoprotein of 45–60 kDa (human) or 60–80 kDa (murine). M-CSF is found as a secreted homodimer.

IL3 is species specific in both its activity and its sequence. Analysis of cDNA encoding murine IL3 suggests a putative transmembrane form although this has not been confirmed by other means.[200] Processing of the glycoprotein results in extensive heterogeneity at the amino terminus.

The RNA encoding G-CSF exists in two forms, one encoding three extra residues which may be a splicing artifact. The mature glycoprotein contains a free SH group at its amino terminus and carbohydrate residues are not required for bioactivity. Homology between human and murine G-CSF is approximately 75%.

The mature GM-CSF glycoprotein results from processing of a precursor, pro-GM-CSF, and a putative prepro-GM-CSF,[200] the latter of which is suggestive of a transmembrane form. Limited truncation of the amino terminus of GM-CSF does not reduce bioactivity but the receptor-binding site of the molecule is not known. Murine and human GM-CSF are 56% homologous.

15.1.4 MECHANISM OF ACTION AND BIOLOGICAL EFFECTS

15.1.4.1 Interleukin 1

15.1.4.1.1 Interleukin 1 in lymphocyte activation and immune regulation

Following crosslinking of the T-cell–receptor complex, IL1 has been shown by many investigators to be required for activation and proliferation of T lymphocytes. Macrophages and competent antigen-presenting cells provide both signals for transition of resting T cells from the G0 phase to the G1 phase of the cell cycle. However, it is not yet clear whether a soluble, released form of IL1 or the membrane-bound form of IL1[36] is required for T cell activation. Little is known of the biochemical events which follow IL1 binding and internalization. The calcium ionophone, A23187, synergizes with IL1 to promote thymocyte proliferation,[37] suggesting that calcium channel formation is required for its biological effects. Resch and Martin, et al.[38,39] have suggested that the IL1 receptor possesses tyrosine-specific protein kinase activity, which results in autophosphorylation of the receptor at an ATP-binding and -cleavage site in human myelogenous K562 cells, although demonstrating receptor kinase activity in other cell types has been difficult. IL1 has both direct and indirect effects on B lymphocyte proliferation and differentiation into immunoglobulin-secreting cells. IL1 will directly induce immature B cell lines to synthesize immunoglobulin light chains, and indirectly stimulates immunoglobulin production by B cells *via* activation of T cells. IL1 is a prerequisite for induction of the synthesis and secretion of a multitude of lymphokines by T cells, and thus plays a critical role in regulation of the immune response.

15.1.4.1.2 Interleukin 1 effects on cells other than the immune system

IL1 produces multiple effects by action on cells other than immunocompetent B and T lymphocytes (Table 1). During the acute-phase response, IL1 induces hepatocytes to synthesize a battery of acute-phase proteins, which include serum amyloid A and serum amyloid P, C-reactive protein, fibrinogen, haptoglobin and α1-antitrypsin,[40,41a] many of which appear to be regulated at the mRNA level. IL1 plays a central role in inflammation by inducing changes in endothelial cells, which are directly related to lesion formation, including production of prostaglandins I_2 and E_2, and promoting adherence of neutrophils, monocytes and lymphocytes.[41a] IL1 is strongly chemically attracted to neutrophils, inducing them to migrate from the bone marrow and activating them to release lysosomal enzymes.[1] Additional effects on endothelial cells influence blood clotting in that IL1 increases procoagulant activity and induces plasminogen activator inhibitor.[41b] IL1 stimulates endothelial cell proliferation and production of granulocyte-macrophage colony-stimulating activity. IL1 acts on muscle, fibroblasts and synovial cells to induce prostaglandin E_2 and collagenase; on chondrocytes, to release collagenase, neutral proteases and plasminogen activator; on osteoclasts to release collagenase and resorb bone; on epithelial cells to produce collagen type IV; on the hypothalamus to induce fever; and on other ill-defined cellular targets in the CNS to produce anorexia and drowsiness.[1,40,41a,41b] IL1 therefore stimulates the proliferation of multiple cell types including fibroblasts, endothelial cells, synovial cells and epithelial cells, in addition to B and T lymphocytes. Cytocidal activity is induced in natural killer cells and in macrophages upon treatment of target tumor cells with IL1.

Recently, a nonapeptide of the human IL1 molecule, representing residues 163–171, was shown to have T cell immunostimulatory activity but was devoid of prostaglandin-inducing and pyrogenic activity.[42] Systematic dissection of the multiple activities of IL1 may lead to increasingly useful clinical therapeutics.

15.1.4.2 Tumor Necrosis Factors

TNF was originally described for its cytotoxic and cytostatic activity on a variety of tumor cell targets.[23,24,43] The mechanism by which this occurs is poorly understood, but TNF has been shown to suppress transcription of specific mRNA[23] and TNF-β induces DNA fragmentation in target cells.[44a] Tumor cells exposed to TNF-β are growth arrested in the G0/G1 phase of the cell cycle. Recently, the spectrum of activity of TNF has been expanded, and TNF is now known to play a significant role in proliferation and differentiation of myelomonocytic cells.[65a,65b] TNF activates polymorphonuclear cell function,[44b,44c] including adherence to vascular endothelium, degranulation and phagocytosis. Other effects of TNF on vascular endothelium produce clotting abnormalities by inhibition of thrombomodulin and stimulation of procoagulant activity.[23] TNF induces fever by a direct effect on the hypothalamus and by induction of IL1 and also increases prostaglandin E_2 and collagenase production by a variety of cell types.[23] TNF increases expression of class I gene products of the MHC and, in combination with IFN-γ, enhances both class I and class II gene product expression on tumor cell targets.[44d]

15.1.4.3 Interferons α and β

Pretreatment of cells with IFN induces resistance to virus infection. IFN inhibits virus production at any of several stages in the virus replication cycle depending upon the virus, the cell and the type of IFN. Thus, virus penetration into the cell and release of virus nucleic acid may be prevented by IFN pretreatment, as can be transcription or translation of virus nucleic acids or assembly of the structural components of new virus particles. Three enzymes, which are induced by IFN, operate to inhibit virus replication. A 2′-5′-oligoadenylate synthetase (2,5A) polymerizes ATP into $ppp(A2'p)A/n$ ($n = 2$–15) which activates a ribonuclease (RNAse F) to degrade ribosomal RNA and disrupt translation.[45] A protein kinase phosphorylates the small subunit of initiation factor, eIF-2, which prevents binding of GTP and reduces the rate of initiation of translation at the ribosome.[46] A 2′-phosphodiesterase has a dual role in regulating 2,5A by degradation of the oligomers and by cleaving the terminal trinucleotide, CCA, of transfer RNA, to reduce protein synthesis.[47] Induction of the phosphodiesterase requires extremely high levels of IFN. Altogether, a total of 15–20 different genes are activated by IFN.[48]

In addition to its antiviral properties, IFN has antiproliferative activity; IFN treatment prolongs the amount of time cells spend in all phases of the cell cycle, with particular inhibitory activity in the G1 and G2 phases.[49] Induction of 2,5A probably plays a role in the inhibitory activity of IFN on cellular proliferation, but IFN may also inhibit cellular proliferation by blocking normal induction of certain 'growth-associated' genes. IFN, and the induction of 2,5A, has been shown to enhance differentiation of human skeletal muscle, promyelocytic leukemia and melanoma cells, thus providing a hypothesis for the *in vivo* mechanism of tumor inhibition by IFN.

15.1.4.4 Interleukin 2

The T-helper lymphocyte has been accorded the central role in promoting the immune response because of its ability to regulate the function of virtually every cell involved in the immune response *via* soluble mediators. The primary function ascribed to IL2 is the up-regulation of the immune response and induction of proliferation in lymphocytes. IL2 enhances the expression of its own receptor on T lymphocytes[16] and the receptor for the growth factor, transferrin. IL2 enhances the production of at least two other lymphokines, GM-CSF and IFN-γ, which, respectively, promote hematopoiesis and stimulate macrophages to process and present antigen. In the murine system, IL2 also enhances the production of IL4 and BSF-2, which stimulate the proliferation and differentiation of B lymphocytes into immunoglobulin-secreting cells,[50] or IL2 may induce these functions directly in B cells. Similar actions for IL2 in the human system are likely to be determined in the near future. The biological effects of IL2 are dependent upon binding of IL2 to the high affinity receptor and internalization of the ligand *via* receptor-mediated endocytosis,[51] although the exact role of this process in signal transduction remains unclear. In the murine system, internalization of IL2 results in phosphorylation of multiple membrane proteins, including the IL2 receptor, and translocation of protein kinase C.[52] Phosphorylation of cytoplasmic proteins does not occur, and together these data suggest that IL2:IL2-receptor interactions may share a common pathway with other polypeptide growth factors that stimulate protein kinases. The membrane phosphorylation events are believed to play a significant role in regulation of lymphocyte proliferation during the immune response.

15.1.4.5 Interferon γ

Many of the same genes which are activated by IFN-α/β are also activated by treatment of cells with IFN-γ.[48] However, the main functions of IFN-γ appear to be immunoregulatory rather than antiviral, although indirect antiviral and antitumor effects are a frequent consequence of IFN-γ treatment. The multiple biological effects of IFN-γ have been reviewed.[53] IFN-γ increases class I molecules of the MHC on all types of cells, potentially rendering virus-infected cells or neoplastic cells more susceptible to immune effector mechanisms which depend on class I interaction with their target cell.[48] IFN-γ directly potentiates the ability of immune effector cells to kill virus-infected cells, and induction of the release of cytotoxins by monocytes is probably a major mechanism by which target cells are eliminated. IFN-γ potentiates the production of TNF and IL1 in macrophages and increases expression of class II MHC-encoded molecules, and, in some cases, induces *de novo* expression of these molecules. This latter activity is believed to increase the ability of antigen-presenting cells to trigger the immune response.

Other immunoregulatory roles for IFN-γ include the increased expression of IL2 receptors on human peripheral blood mononuclear cells, increased expression of receptors for TNF on a variety of human tumor cells, enhanced production of IL1 by human endothelial cells and sensitization of B lymphocytes to mitogenic stimulation. It was recently shown that, in the mouse, IFN-γ induced expression of a differentiation antigen, unique to endothelial cells, which regulates extravasation of lymphocytes from the blood to tissues,[54] suggesting a role for locally produced IFN-γ in lymphocyte trafficking.

15.1.4.6 B Cell Growth and Differentiation Factors

Our understanding of the role of B cell growth and differentiation factors in induction of antibody secretion is provided primarily by murine model systems where, unfortunately, the naming of many of the factors is different from nomenclature used in the human system. IL4 is terminology used in both systems; BSF-2 is terminology unique to the human system, and alternate terminology is shown in Table 1. (BSF-2 may be renamed using the interleukin terminology.) The activation of B cells requires crosslinking of immunoglobulin (antigen receptor) expressed at the cell membrane and the sequential action of stimulatory factors which lead to proliferation and differentiation of B lymphocytes into cells which secrete antibody. *In vivo*, initial crosslinking occurs by binding of antigen to membrane immunoglobulin, which primes the cell for clonal expansion and secretion of antigen-specific immunoglobulin following exposure to soluble mediators secreted by activated T cells. *In vitro*, B cell activation is studied by crosslinking the cell's surface immunoglobulin with antibody (anti-IgM) in the presence of soluble factors. Binding of antigen or anti-IgM by resting B cells in the G0 phase of the cell cycle induces progression to the G1 phase and an increase in cell volume and RNA synthesis. Subsequent binding of IL4 drives B cells into the S phase of the cell cycle and is followed by secretion of immunoglobulin. Signal transduction mediated by IL4 in B lymphocytes is poorly understood. Phosphorylation of a membrane protein occurs following binding of IL4 but, unlike many other receptor–ligand interactions, hydrolysis of phosphatidyl-inositol, calcium mobilization, and protein kinase translocation do not occur.[55] Binding of BSF-2 induces further differentiation of activated B cells into cells that secrete immunoglobulin, and influences the type of antibody which is secreted, generally promoting secretion of subtypes of immunoglobulin G. Differentiation and final maturation of B cells, induced by BSF-2, are regulated at the level of mRNA.[56] Besides induction of growth and differentiation of B lymphocytes, IL4 induces the expression of class II molecules of the MHC on B lymphocytes, regulates generation of cytolytic T lymphocytes and promotes growth of T lymphocytes and mast cells.

15.1.4.7 Colony-stimulating Factors

CSFs regulate the growth and differentiation of precursor phagocytic cells in the bone marrow and stimulate the functional and metabolic activities of mature phagocytes (Table 3). The biochemical events which occur following binding of CSFs are poorly understood. Changes in the rate of protein synthesis may occur, and, in some instances, regulatory binding of CSF is followed by protein phosphorylation.[57] The four different CSFs are believed to influence stem cell maturation at different stages of cell differentiation.[58] M-CSF directly, and perhaps exclusively, stimulates cells of the monocyte/macrophage lineage, but may indirectly stimulate cells of other lineages by augmenting production of other CSFs. M-CSF action on macrophages stimulates their production of prostaglandins, IFN, IL1 and TNF and increases their cytotoxic activity for tumor cells.[59] The action of G-CSF is not limited to cells of a single lineage (Table 3) and thus probably acts at an earlier stage of cell differentiation than M-CSF. Binding of G-CSF to mature neutrophils promotes their phagocytic and cytotoxic activities for tumor cell targets, and increases the expression of receptor number or affinity for the bacterial peptide, fMLP.[60] GM-CSF stimulates cells of at least two lineages, suggesting that it acts at an earlier stage of differentiation than G-CSF or M-CSF. The concentration of GM-CSF influences the commitment of precursor cells to a given pathway of differentiation, *i.e.* granulocytic *versus* macrophage.[58] GM-CSF activity on neutrophils stimulates phagocytosis, cytolytic activity and the release of lysozyme and oxygen radicals. Other activities of GM-CSF are listed in Table 3. Recently, GM-CSF was shown to induce leucocytosis and reticulocytosis *in vivo* upon infusion into primates,[61] suggesting potential clinical utility for CSFs (see Section 15.1.6). The biological effects of IL3 are numerous, suggesting that it acts at a very early stage of stem cell differentiation, and these effects have been extensively reviewed by Ihle and Weinstein.[22] In addition to the effects listed in Table 3, IL3 induces expression of the T cell enzyme, 20α-hydroxysteroid dehydrogenase (20α-SDH), and of a T cell marker protein, Thy-1, in normal bone marrow cells, suggesting that IL3 may influence the early differentiation of cells into the T cell pathway. Other effects on T cells showed that IL3, directly or indirectly, augments cytotoxic T lymphocyte activity for virus-infected cells.

15.1.5 ASSAY METHODS

15.1.5.1 Interleukin 1

There are three major *in vitro* assays for IL1 which depend on measurement of T lymphocyte proliferation. None of these assays measure IL1 directly but each depends on IL1-induced production of IL2.[62] There has not yet been a good standardization of the assays for IL1, and the specific activity of any preparation may vary by several orders of magnitude depending on which assay is being employed and whether the α or β form of IL1 predominates in the biological sample. The most commonly used assay for IL1, and probably the most sensitive assay, is the 'thymocyte costimulator assay'. Suboptimal concentrations of T cell mitogen (typically concanavalin A or phytohemagglutinin), which do not alone stimulate T cell proliferation, are mixed with the sample being tested for IL1 activity and incubated for 72 h with murine thymocytes. Samples which contain IL1 synergize with mitogen to stimulate IL2 dependent thymocyte proliferation, as measured by pulse labeling with [^{3}H]thymidine for the final 5 h of incubation. In the 'direct mitogenesis' assay for IL1, the suboptimal concentration of T cell mitogen is omitted. The IL1 'conversion assay' is performed on cell lines which produce IL2 in response to IL1, typically the LBRM-33-1A5 or EL4-6.1 T lymphoma cell lines. Quantitation of IL2 is then used to determine IL1 activity.

Alternatively, IL1 has been determined from assays of biological activity other than T cell activation. The 'B cell activation assay' measures the ability of IL1 to stimulate IgM antibody production by spleen cells from mice deficient in T cells and immunized with sheep red blood cells,[63] or by measurement of antibody production from human peripheral blood B lymphocytes cultured with the B cell mitogen, pokeweed mitogen. IL1 activity has also been measured by induction of prostaglandin E$_2$ from human chondrocytes or from porcine or human synovial cells, or by *in vivo* fever induction in rabbits.

15.1.5.2 Tumor Necrosis Factors

TNF-α and TNF-β are indistinguishable in their spectrum of biological activity, although quantitative differences have been reported. An assay of TNF is dependent upon cytostatic or cytotoxic, antiproliferative activity of transformed cells *in vitro*.[64,65a] A variety of variations of the bioassay have been reported, some of which include addition of inhibitors of RNA or protein synthesis to potentiate the effects of TNF. TNF is not species specific, therefore mouse L929, B16 melanoma or WI38 cells are each suitable target cells. Antiproliferative effects are measured by direct cell count or by staining target cells with vital dyes and measuring the optical density.

15.1.5.3 Interferons

IFN is assayed primarily by its antiviral activity, keeping in mind the species specificity of IFN, and a detailed assay procedure for human IFN has been reported recently.[66] Cells are pretreated with IFN, one to several hours before infection with a cytolytic virus; usually the vesicular stomatitis or encephalomyocarditis virus is used (VSV, EMC). At the end of the assay, cells are stained with a vital dye and the absorbance is monitored. The titer of IFN is the reciprocal of the dilution which inhibits by 50% the cytolytic activity of the virus. When this is compared to a reference standard prepared by the National Institutes of Health (NIH), IFN activity is reported as international units (IU). Determination of the subtype of IFN (α, β, or γ) is carried out using reference antisera which neutralize the antiviral activity of each respective subtype of IFN.[67] Radioimmunoassays for human IFN have also been described.

15.1.5.4 Interleukin 2

The most widely used assays for human IL2 are those based on the original description by Gillis *et al*.[68] Log 2 dilutions of IL2-containing fluids are applied to a murine T cell line which is dependent upon IL2 for growth, typically the CTLL1 or HT2 cell lines. Growth is measured by incorporation of [^{3}H]thymidine into DNA after pulse labeling cells for 4 h in a 24 h assay, and a typical sigmoidal dose–response curve is shown in Figure 1. The murine cell lines, rather than human cell lines, are used because they are 5–10 times more sensitive to IL2-mediated growth promotion. One unit of IL2 is defined as the quantity of IL2 which induces 50% maximal growth following linear regression analysis. A reference standard IL2 preparation is available from the Biological Response Modifiers Program of the NIH.

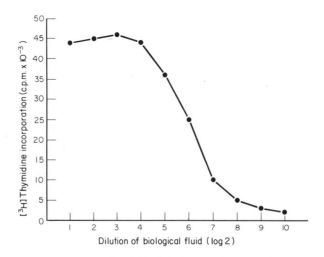

Figure 1   Titration of interleukin 2 activity in biological fluids. The curve is representative of titration of IL2 activity in the supernatant fluid of rat splenocytes stimulated with an optimum concentration of the T cell mitogen, concanavalin A. Incorporation of [^{3}H]thymidine in the absence of IL2 is typically less than 300 c.p.m.

15.1.5.5 B Cell Growth and Differentiation Factors

There are two assays for factors which stimulate growth/differentiation of B cells. In the preactivation assay, purified human tonsilar or peripheral blood B cells are preincubated with SAC (*Staphylococcus aureus* strain Cowan I bacteria) for three days, before addition of varying concentrations of growth factors; after another three days incubation, proliferation is measured by pulse labeling cultures with [^{3}H]thymidine.[69] In the costimulation assay, a submitogenic dose of anti-IgM antibody is added to purified B cells simultaneously with varying concentrations of growth factor, and proliferation is measured by [^{3}H]thymidine incorporation at three days.[70] In either assay, differentiation of B cells is determined by measuring secretion of IgM or IgG antibody into the culture fluids by standard ELISA (enzyme-linked immunosorbent assay). In some cases, T or B cell lines may substitute for primary blood or tonsilar B cells.

15.1.5.6 Colony-stimulating Factors

The most commonly used assay for factors which promote hematopoietic stem cell growth and differentiation is the formation of colonies in soft agar. Cells derived from bone marrow are incubated with the specified factor and the stem cell specificity is determined morphologically.[71] For factors such as erythropoietin, a two-week assay is typical, whereas a one-week assay may be employed for most of the other CSF activities. However, outgrowth of the different lineages of stem cells occurs at different times in the assay period for factors which stimulate more than one progenitor type. Alternatively, certain cell lines, which are dependent upon a single one of these growth factors, may be used to quantitate activity in biological fluids in a standard two- or three-day assay based upon [^{3}H]thymidine incorporation. A common but laborious assay for IL3 is derived from its ability to induce 20α-SDH activity in T cells.[22]

15.1.6 CLINICAL TRIALS

The evaluation of cytokines and lymphokines in the treatment of various diseases has expanded rapidly in the 1980s with the advent of genetic engineering and capability of producing these recombinant proteins readily and reproducibly. Although many of the early clinical trials with IFNs were conducted with material isolated from leucocytes or fibroblasts, most of our clinical knowledge of IFNs and other BRMs today results from evaluation of recombinantly produced material. Since IFNs are produced from a multigenic family, one might anticipate some claims of differences between isolated natural IFNs and recombinantly derived material. However, by and large, there have been modestly few differences between the so-called natural lymphokines and the recombinantly prepared lymphokines.

To date, there is very little information in the primary literature on clinical evaluation of the cytokines and lymphokines discussed in this chapter, except for IFN-α.[72] Several recombinant IL1 preparations are just now proceeding into phase I (tolerance) clinical evaluations. Speculations on the efficacy of IL1 include anticancer, since IL1 inhibits proliferation of some tumor cell lines and augments NK cell activity.[73] Additional potential uses could include adjuvant use with vaccines and bone marrow protection and/or regeneration. Since IL1 plays a pivotal role in the initiation of lymphocyte activation and in the development of acute-phase reactions, one might anticipate side effects of IL1 to be similar to those seen with adjuvants, such as polyinosinic/polycytidylic acid (poly I:C) and muramyl dipeptide (MDP), as well as with IFNs.

TNF is presently in transition from phase I clinical trials to phase II studies in the USA as well as in Japan. Without the advantage of citations in the primary literature on clinical trial results, one can only speculate on the future role for TNF. Certainly, various solid tumors and leukemias will be targeted with this agent for phase II (efficacy) clinical studies, as well as combination trials with other cytokines such as IFN-γ. Preliminary results on phase I studies presented at recent meetings suggest that TNF is not without side effects at the current doses and schedules being employed including significant incidences of hypotension, chills, fatigue, headache, confusion and vomiting.

B cell growth and differentiation factors and CSFs are just beginning clinical evaluations. While speculation for potential efficacies of these agents is even more premature than those described above with the previous lymphokines, it is anticipated that these growth and differentiating factors will have a positive effect on the regeneration and differentiation of bone marrow stem cells, along with increases in monocytes/lymphocytes in peripheral blood.[58] Therefore, CSFs could be effective in combination therapies for marrow preservation from chemotherapy or radiotherapy, or as an adjunct to chemotherapy, correction of other induced hematopoietic dysfunctions (such as AIDS), and in the treatment of anemias. In fact, a very recent report on a phase I/II trial in AIDS patients, involving the administration of a recombinant GM-CSF, disclosed a dose dependent increase in circulating leucocytes.[199]

Clinical evaluation of IL2 has advanced substantially into phase II trials on two fronts: (i) the use of IL2 as a single agent modality and (ii) the use of IL2-activated killer cells (LAK cells) in adoptive immunotherapy. Adoptive immunotherapy with LAK cells involves the transfer of cells with antitumor activity to a patient's tumor, back to that patient after *ex vivo* expansion and activation by treatment with IL2. While the administration of LAK cells to humans could be achieved with minimal toxicity, the coadministration of IL2 during this therapy resulted in substantial toxicity, presumably due to a capillary permeability syndrome, resulting in significant fluid retention.[74] Preliminary results from phase I/II studies indicated encouraging objective response rates in renal cell carcinoma and melanoma. Therapy with IL2 alone is just entering phase II clinical evaluation. Phase I results at relatively low doses ($< 10^6 \, U \, m^{-2}$ per day) included minimal side effects, transient increases in circulating monocytes, no antitumor responses in cancer patients[75] and no beneficial reversal of various immunological deficits in AIDS patients.[76] While higher doses ($1–10 \times 10^6 \, U \, m^{-2}$ per day) may have greater immunomodulatory effects, preliminary results suggest significant morbidity analogous to IL2/LAK cell adoptive immunotherapy.[77] Targeted indications for IL2 include various cancers and AIDS.

By far, the most advanced of the lymphokines in clinical evaluation is IFN-α. To date, IFN-α is approved in a number of countries for treatment of Kaposi's sarcoma, hairy cell leukemia, multiple myeloma and condylomata acuminatum (venereal warts). Many of the immunomodulatory effects noted in cell culture, as well as in animal models, have been seen, to one extent or another, in humans, including enhanced antigen expression, differentiation and immunomodulation, principally seen with NK cells and macrophage activation.[78] However, the dose–response relationship in anticancer trials with IFN suggests that its antiproliferative action is important for its efficacy.[79] In terms of clinical results, it is clear that the initial, historical enthusiasm for IFN was out of proportion relative to its current clinical usefulness. On the other hand, after substantial clinical investigation, it is clear that IFN-α represents a successful beginning in the fourth arm of cancer therapy called immunotherapy, the other three arms being surgery, radiotherapy and chemotherapy. Recent reviews summarize the clinical efficacy of high dose IFN-α, in advanced disease, as a single agent.[80,81] The results, measured as objective response in terms of tumor shrinkage, include 80–90% response rates against hairy cell leukemia and chronic myelogenous leukemia, 50% response rates against nodular lymphoma and 20–30% response rates against multiple myeloma. Against solid tumors, the response rate of IFN-α is much lower, with the highest response rates being seen in Kaposi's sarcoma (50%), and 20–30% response rates against melanoma and renal cell carcinoma. Although several trials have established the efficacy of IFN-α in recurrent laryngeal papillomas, the response rates and disease-free intervals have varied significantly.

It is arguable that clinical results with IFN-α are owing to immunomodulation rather than cytotoxicity, since it is known, for example, that low doses of IFN-α achieve maximal NK cell activity, whereas high doses suppress NK cell activity. Therefore, there are many trials in progress evaluating the activity of low dose IFN as a possible immune stimulant, as well as promoting tumor antigen expression. In addition, trials in adjuvant use, as well as combination studies with chemotherapy, are in progress and the efficacy of local IFN therapy is also being explored. For example, intravesicular treatment of bladder neoplasms, intraperitoneal treatment of ovarian carcinoma and intranodular injections in certain solid tumor lesions are under investigation. Interestingly in this regard, a recent report describes the effective use in a pilot phase II study of intralesional IFN-α in basal cell carcinoma.[82]

There has been significant clinical evaluation of IFN-α in the treatment of a number of viral diseases. Areas of some clinical success have included the prophylactic intranasal treatment of rhinovirus colds,[83,84] the modulation of hepatitis B virus infections, the intralesional treatment of refractory venereal warts,[85] the reduction of cutaneous dissemination of herpes zoster, and the reduction in cytomegalovirus infection in transplant recipients.[86] While it appears that IFN-α is not effective in the topical treatment of genital herpes, there is some evidence that altered formulations may be effective.[87]

IFN-γ is now well along in phase II evaluation in a variety of tumor types, as well as rheumatoid arthritis. It is speculated that IFN-γ will have an overlapping antitumor profile with that of IFN-α including efficacy in renal cell carcinoma, Kaposi's sarcoma and lymphoma. Additional potential indications include uses as an antiinfective in selective settings, as an immunological adjuvant to surgery or radiotherapy in cancer and as a treatment for lepromatous leprosy.[88] Indeed, positive benefit with intradermal injection of IFN-γ in patients with leprosy was recently reported.[89] IFN-γ appears to share some of the side effects seen with IFN-α including a flu-like syndrome with high fevers and shaking chills. Immunomodulatory properties of IFN-γ in humans include activation of blood monocytes isolated from cancer patients treated intramuscularly with low doses, whereas high doses were suppressive to monocyte activation,[90] and activation of 2,5A and β2 microglobulin in peripheral blood lymphocytes in patients treated with continuous intravenous infusion.[91]

15.1.7 OTHER BIOLOGICAL RESPONSE MODIFIERS

Classification of immunomodulators has often been structurally based and has included materials of biological origin, such as extracts of microorganisms, and natural products from various sources including microorganisms, plant and marine sources, wherein structures have been elucidated. Other subclasses include products of the immune system, such as the lymphokines and cytokines, described earlier in this chapter, and synthetic materials, both high molecular weight and low molecular weight. Table 4 serves to illustrate some of the agents classed as synthetics and natural products which have received extensive study in terms of their immunology and therapeutic activity. This is by no means an exhaustive list. It is organized to exemplify the diversity of materials described as immunomodulators and, where known, the immunological profile of these agents based on effects on cell-mediated and humoral immunity. In the 1980s, there has been an increasing emphasis on low molecular weight, defined synthetic substances which act as immunomodulators.[92,93,193,194] One reason for this level of interest is that these agents can be reproducibly manufactured in an economic fashion analogous to most therapeutic drugs. In addition, they appear to offer more selective immunomodulatory activities, relative to the pleiotropic effects noted with extracts of bacterial or viral origin or high molecular weight chemical agents or biopolymers.

To explore these types of immunomodulators in some depth, we will focus on six specific substances which have achieved the stage of clinical evaluation and represent both natural products and synthetic immunomodulators. These six substances include thymosin α1, muramyl dipeptide (MDP), levamisole, poly I:C, OK-432 (picibanil) and pyrimidinones (bropirimine).

Table 4 Synthetic and Natural Product BRM/Immunomodulators[a]

Immunomodulators	Monocytes/Mφ	Induction/activation T cells[b]			B cells	NK	IFN	IL
		T diff	T s	CTL				
Synthetics								
Polynucleotides (I:C, A:U)	X			X	X	X	X	
Pyrans (MVE-2)	X			X			X	
Levamisole (WY-18251)		X						
Isoprinosine (NPT-16416)		X	(X)		X			
Azimexon		X		X	X			
Tilorone	X			X			X	
Pyrimidinones	X				X	X	X	X
Quinoline-3-carboxamide (LS2616)						X		X
Tuftsin	X				X			
MDP analogs	X				X			
Lipoidal amines (CP-20,961)	X						X	
HEDS/ADA 202-718				X	X			X
Cimetidine		X		X				
CL-259,763	X		X		X			X
Natural products								
BCG	X	X		X	X	X	X	
Picibanil (OK-432)	X	X	X	X		X		
Thymosin α1 (5)		X	X					
Bestatin	X							
Imreg 1,2	X							X
Lentinan	X	X		X	X	X		
S.a. protein A				X	X	X	X	
Cyclosporine			X					
PSK (Krestin)	X					X		

[a] X, modulation is seen. [b] Induction of: T cell differentiation, T-suppressor cells, cytolytic T cells.

15.1.7.1   Thymosins

It is well known that the thymus plays a critical role in the genesis and maturation of cellular immunity in the body. Indeed, impairment of lymphoid elements, including the thymus, with noxious agents, or simply advancing age, leads to immunological deficiencies and a variety of diseases. The thymus has been shown to be the source of a number of factors or hormones, of which the thymosin fraction has been studied the most.[94,95] While it is yet to be demonstrated that a deficiency in thymosin production from the thymus is a cause of disease relating to immune deficiencies, it is clear that various thymosins have significant immunopotentiating effects.

Homogenization of calf thymus followed by a series of precipitation and chromatographic steps leads to a material termed fraction 5 (F5) containing a series of low molecular weight polypeptides.[96] While significant *in vitro* and *in vivo* immunomodulatory effects have been demonstrated with thymosin F5, further fractionation employing various chromatographic procedures has yielded several pure polypeptides, of which thymosin α1 is the most studied.[97] Thymosin α1 (**1**) is an N-terminal-acylated 28 amino acid polypeptide with significantly enhanced immunostimulatory potency relative to thymosin F5. It appears to be highly conserved amongst species, including human, pigs, sheep and mice, and has been prepared synthetically using solid phase amino acid synthesis procedures, as well as recombinantly in *E. coli*.[98,99] Numerous other pure thymosins have been isolated from thymosin F5 including β4 and α7.

Ac-Ser-Asp-Ala-Ala-Val-Asp-Thr-Ser-Ser-Glu-Ilu-Thr-Thr-Lys-Asp-Leu-Lys-

Glu-Lys-Lys-Glu-Val-Val-Glu-Glu-Ala-Glu-Asn-OH

(**1**) Thymosin α1

The immunological profile of thymosin α1 includes mainly a T cell repertoire of functional modulation. The main activity appears to be directed towards amplification of T-helper cell function. It has been reported that thymosin α1 also stimulates *in vitro* T cell dependent, specific antibody production, in addition to a pan-T cell response (Thy-1.2$^+$ and Lyt-1,2,3$^+$). At high concentrations, it appears to enhance the number of bone marrow and spleen cells expressing terminal deoxynucleotidal transferase, whereas at low concentrations there is a suppression of this same activity in murine thymocytes. Administration of thymosin α1 to mice has resulted in the stimulation of IFN, IL2, corticosterone and TNF-β. Thymosin is active in the mixed lymphocyte reaction (MLR) and enhances the response of lymphoid cells to mitogens. Therapeutic responses, as measured by an increase in survival, have been demonstrated in tumor-bearing mice and immuno-suppressed mice with an experimental *Candida* infection.[100] Recently, it has been reported that there is significant homology between thymosin α1 and the gag-encoded sequence for the gp120 structural protein of the AIDS virus, HIV-1.[101] In addition, significant levels of thymosin α1, elevated above background, are seen in AIDS or AIDS related complex (ARC) patients. This has led to the interesting speculation that epitopes on gag proteins having the thymosin α1 homology could serve as the basis for a crossprotective vaccine.

Early clinical evaluation of thymosin F5 involved patients with autoimmune disorders or immunodeficiencies. Since these were uncontrolled clinical trials, there is no statistical significance to clinical response. However, there were positive effects noted on T cell function and numbers, as determined by the MLR assay and the E-rosette assay.[102] It has been reported that clinical trials for evaluating efficacy in rheumatoid arthritis and SLE are in progress with thymosin F5. More recently, studies have been initiated with synthetic thymosin α1, principally through the Biological Response Modifier Program (BRMP) of the National Cancer Institute. The interest in using thymosin α1 in cancer patients stemmed from earlier studies of thymosin F5 in small cell lung cancer.[103] Given as adjunctive therapy to chemotherapy, thymosin F5 was reported to enhance survival in the subset of patients who exhibited the best response to primary chemotherapy, and who had exhibited diminished levels of total T cells prior to therapy. However, more recent trials in small cell and nonsmall cell lung cancer, combining thymosin F5 with chemotherapy or radiotherapy, failed to confirm the earlier findings.[104]

In a phase I/II study in nonsmall cell lung cancer, thymosin α1 was administered on two schedules after radiation therapy to the primary lesion and mediastinum. This was a randomized, placebo-controlled trial, wherein patients were given therapy twice a week, with and without a loading dose regimen at the beginning of therapy, for up to one year or until relapse.[105] Thymosin α1 was well tolerated, and significant improvement or normalization of T cell function (as measured by the MLR assay) was noted only in those patients receiving the loading dose regimen. Interestingly, patients treated with either schedule of thymosin α1 exhibited a significant improvement in disease-free survival over the placebo ($p = 0.04$) and in overall survival ($p = 0.009$). These early results in this adjuvant trial in nonsmall cell lung cancer are encouraging, and other phase I/II trials are in progress. Thymosin α1 is also being evaluated clinically as a potential adjuvant for influenza and hepatitis vaccines. Lastly, thymosin F5 and α1 are being examined in patients with pre-AIDS.[106] While there were some positive responses in these patients, as determined by the MLR assay at one dose of thymosin F5, no effects were observed on other immunological parameters such as T-helper cell levels, NK activity or on HIV antibody titer.

15.1.7.2 Levamisole

In 1966, a new broad-spectrum anthelmintic named tetramisole was disclosed.[107] One of the optical isomers of this phenyl-substituted tetrahydroimidazothiazole was determined to be the active isomer and called levamisole (**2**). Several years later, it was determined that levamisole had immunomodulatory properties by virtue of potentiating the protection of *Brucella* vaccines in a *B. abortus* challenge model in mice.[108] Extensive subsequent work has shown that the principal immunomodulatory effects are on cell-mediated immunity, particularly T cells, and with some of the phagocytic cell populations, such as monocytes and polymorphonuclear neutrophils.[109]

(2) Levamisole

This low molecular weight compound exhibits many properties in common with thymosin α_1. Functional effects noted on T cells include restoration of spontaneous or mitogen-induced proliferation, antibody plaque cell formation, IL2 production and suppressor activity.[110,111] Little effect is noted on B cell immunology or on normal T cells. Functional effects noted with phagocytic cells include chemotaxis, complement/antibody-mediated receptor activities, peroxidase activities and, of course, phagocytosis. At the biochemical level, it has been shown that levamisole increases cyclic GMP levels in thymocytes, and increases adenosine deaminase, and enzyme normally low in certain immunodeficiency syndromes. These types of findings lead to studies exploring the modulation of the arachidonic acid cascade, including inhibition of thromboxane and prostaglandin biosynthesis, and the generalized finding of inhibition of peroxidation of a variety of cellular substrates. Thus, it appears that levamisole has an antioxidant effect which may play a role in its inhibition of inflammatory mechanisms.

Levamisole has been examined in a variety of models of infection, inflammation, autoimmune disorders and cancer. For example, levamisole suppresses the oxazolone challenge reaction, as well as picryl chloride-induced hypersensitivity, in a fashion similar to penicillamine.[112] Similar responses are noted in models of chronic rheumatoid arthritis. In models of autoimmune syndromes, such as SLE and experimental allergic encephalomyelitis (EAE), levamisole exhibits minimal activity. In autochthonous tumor models, levamisole exhibits some growth inhibition properties when therapy is initiated early in tumor development. It is ineffective at high tumor burden, either in transplantation tumor models or spontaneous tumor models. As with many immunomodulators, the dose and schedule were quite important in exhibiting optimal activity. Often, high doses of levamisole led to immunosuppressive effects, while intermediate to low doses exhibited significant tumor reduction. Levamisole also showed activity in combination modality experiments employing either chemotherapy, radiation or pretreatment surgery.

Clinically, levamisole has been used in treating polyarthritis, chronic infections and as an adjuvant with acute chemotherapy in cancer patients. The principal clinical evaluation of levamisole in chronic inflammatory diseases has been rheumatoid arthritis. Several clinical trials have demonstrated that levamisole has a positive effect on a number of clinical endpoints such as phagocytic activity, suppression of B cell function and reduction in immunoglobulin and autoantibody levels.[113] In addition, there seemed to be an increase in T-helper cell levels and, while there was an immunorestoration of monocyte activities, there was no effect on NK cells. Improvement in certain autoimmune syndromes has been seen such as Behcet's disease, and mild SLE (no effect on active

SLE); on the other hand, it is inactive in Crohn's disease and erythema multiforme. Further work is ongoing in multiple sclerosis. Beneficial effects in chronic infections have been very limited; however, improvements were noted in the severity of febrile episodes in children with upper respiratory tract infections and in tuberculosis.[114]

Numerous studies have been conducted with levamisole in cancer patients where the drug has been given orally on a chronic or intermittent chronic basis.[115] Endpoints such as disease-free survival, overall survival, reduction of postoperative metastases, and various immunological endpoints, such as cutaneous hypersensitivity, circulating α2-globulin, α-fetoprotein levels, and motility/chemotaxis/activation of monocytes and lymphocytes were measured. In a number of these scenarios, there were positive changes in the immunological profile; however, there was no statistically significant enhancement of disease-free survival or overall survival in a prospectively randomized clinical trial, or significant objective tumor responses. Recently, however, in the treatment of colorectal carcinoma, a prospectively randomized trial of 5-fluorouracil (5-FU) *versus* 5-FU + levamisole in an adjuvant setting showed a statistically significant enhancement of disease-free survival and overall survival.[116] This trial is now being replicated and, if the results are again affirmative, this could represent a significant advance in adjuvant chemotherapy of colorectal carcinoma.[117] Lastly, a number of trials have been conducted in various chronic infections, both bacterial and viral infections, such as herpes simplex, herpetic keratitis and herpes zoster.[118] In summary, positive responses have been limited, although brucellosis, meloidosis tuberculosis and leprosy have exhibited modest improvement with levamisole. However, it is clear that overall clinical benefit has been minimal and, in all likelihood, combination therapy is indicated if significant clinical benefit is to be obtained.

While a number of analogs of levamisole have been investigated, a series of thiazolobenzimidazole acetic acid analogs have been studied in some detail because of their effective immunomodulatory properties. Specifically, WY-18,251 (**3**; tilomisole) has exhibited antimetastatic activity in several animal models and, in addition, exhibited positive effects on cellular immune reactions, including delayed-type hypersensitivity, lymphocyte response to mitogens and IL2 production.[119] In addition, WY-18,251 suppressed the symptoms of EAE in rats and also suppressed *in vivo* generation of plaque-forming cells in mice immunized with sheep red blood cells (SRBC). However, this agent is not an IFN inducer, and does not appear to affect NK cells. Overall, it appears to be very similar to levamisole, except in some cases it is less potent.[120]

Another recently disclosed structural relative is PR-879-317A (**4**). This agent is reported to enhance the splenic lymphocyte proliferative response to mitogens and augments a polyclonal B cell response. In addition to exhibiting antiviral activities in a schedule dependent manner in murine hepatitis virus-infected mice (comparable to levamisole), it also increased the levels of IL1, IL2, and ADCC from spleen isolates from the infected mice.[195]

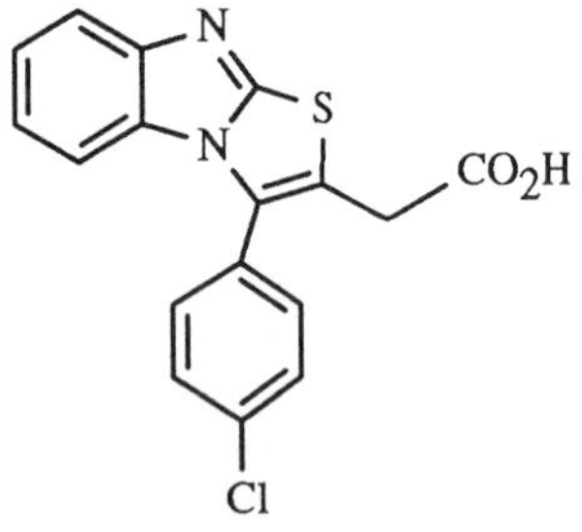

(**3**) WY-18,251

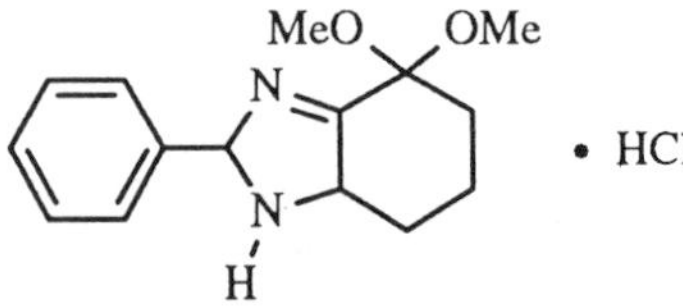

(**4**) PR-879-317A

15.1.7.3 Muramyl Dipeptides (MDP)

MDP (**5**) represents the minimally defined, essential moiety in the mycobacterium that is responsible for the immunoadjuvant properties of killed mycobacteria in oil/water emulsion, often referred to as Freund's adjuvant. The ubiquitous nature of the MDP moiety in bacterial cell walls, coupled with its immune-stimulating properties, prompted studies of the potential of MDP to increase host resistance to both extracellular and intracellular pathogens. While MDP was shown to be devoid of certain side effects produced by mycobacteria, such as tuberculin skin sensitization or adjuvant arthritis, it does produce a number of immunomodulating effects.[121]

Like Freund's adjuvant, MDP has been shown to enhance antibody response to an antigen.[122] Well over 100 analogs of MDP have been synthesized to attempt to improve on MDP's adjuvant properties.[123] Murabutide (6) represents a nonpyrogenic analog of MDP which is under clinical evaluation as a vaccine adjuvant and in combination therapy for a variety of bacterial infections and cancers. The typical studies with the T cell dependent antigen, SRBC, demonstrated that MDP potentiates the primary response. However, there are some conflicting data as to whether the T cell or the B cell is the primary target for MDP, since similar responses are seen in T cell deficient nude mice. The present data suggest that MDP interacts with B cells, perhaps mimicking a T-helper cell signal.[124] In addition to the data on B cell stimulation of MDP, there are data supporting the role of MDP in activation of the macrophage. Parenteral administration of MDP enhances clearance of colloidal carbon, and pretreatment of spleen cells with specific antimacrophage serum completely suppresses the response to SRBC.[125] However, since water-soluble MDP is so rapidly cleared from the body, other analogs, including more lipophilic analogs and liposome-encapsulated MDP, have been explored to enhance the immunomodulating properties of the agent. Recently, it has been suggested that MDP may share a receptor with serotonin on macrophages.[127] A photoaffinity analog was made to label the receptor and work is ongoing.[198]

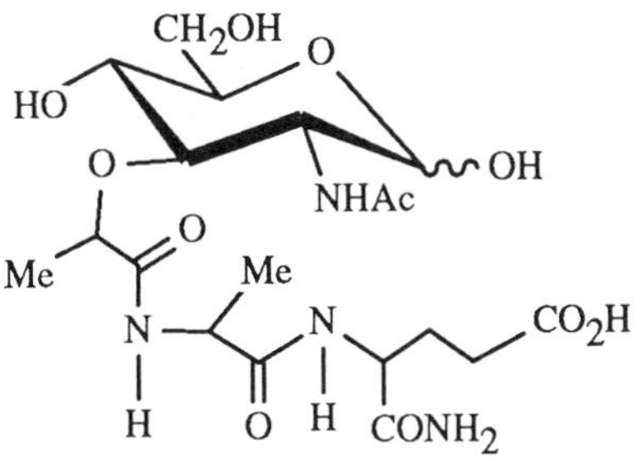

(5) MDP 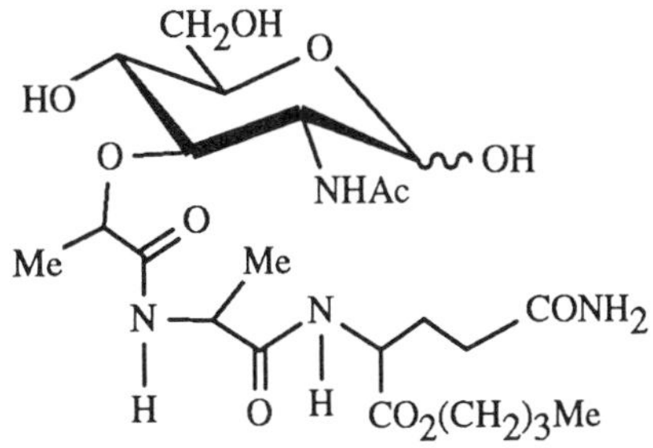   (6) Murabutide

MDP also has effects on down-regulating the immune response, as shown by prolongation of graft survival, suppression of delayed-type hypersensitivity to *Bacillus Calmette Guerin* (BCG) or *Listeria monocytogenes* and the suppression of cytotoxic T lymphocyte responses of splenocytes stimulated by mastocytoma cells. Evidence suggests that MDP induces T-suppressor cells and inhibits IL2 production.[126] As is seen with many other activators of phagocytes, MDP affects a variety of biological activities associated with macrophage activation, such as increases in intracellular cAMP and cGMP, oxygen-generating capacity, secretory products such as collagenase, prostaglandin E_2 and various activating factors, and stimulation of glucosamine incorporation.[127]

Numerous studies have been undertaken to understand the role of MDP in resistance to infection in animal models, autoimmune disorders and tumor therapy. MDP has exhibited efficacy in protecting the host against such experimental infections as *Klebsiella pneumonia*, *Staphylococcus typhimurium*, *Streptococcus pneumonia*, *Staphylococcus aeruginosa* and *Listeria monocytogenes*. In addition, synergism between MDP and antibiotics against bacterial infections has been demonstrated in both normal and immunocompromised hosts. Derivatives of MDP have also been exploited as adjuvants in many of these systems. For example, MDP can be coupled to natural peptide carriers, such as tetanus toxoid or, indeed, epitopes of the specific antigen against which one is attempting to achieve protection, such as with influenza subunits. One of the derivatives of MDP called MTP-PE, which represents a phosphatidylethanolamine analog of MDP, exhibits prophylactic and therapeutic antiviral activity in animals against both RNA and DNA viral infections.[128]

MDP analogs exhibit very little direct antitumor activity on their own; however, various acylated/lipophilic analogs clearly potentiate endotoxin-induced necrosis and regression of tumors. The mechanism is most likely due to activation of macrophages together with stimulation of TNF-α and TNF-β.[129] Similarly, the use of liposomes as carriers for MDP, designed to potentiate the activity of MDP *in vivo*, have led to an enhanced antitumor response.[130] Intravenous injection of liposome-encapsulated MDP leads to the complete regression of established pulmonary and lymph node metastases.

While MDP analogs have side effects such as fever, inflammation, uveitis, and several have somnogenic activity (perhaps related to induction of GM-CSF), it is clear that several MDP analogs will be explored clinically for use as adjuvants for vaccines, in combination chemotherapy for chronic bacterial infections and cancer, and possibly as encapsulated liposome entities for the treatment of cancers directly. Further work is ongoing exploring other routes of delivery of MDP analogs, including intranasal and intraperitoneal, to induce a localized immune response.[131]

15.1.7.4   OK-432 (Picibanil)

OK-432 is a lyophilized powder of *Streptococcus pyogenes*, isolated after incubation and treatment with penicillin G. The majority of the preclinical and clinical research on this BRM has been done in Japan, where the agent has been on the market for over 11 years for the treatment of several types of cancer.[132] Although OK-432 exhibits a direct antitumor effect (cytostasis) in murine tumor cells in culture,[133] further work has shown that the *in vivo* antitumor activity of this material is principally due to its immunomodulatory effects in the host. Intraperitoneal administration of OK-432 induces a significant population of neutrophils in the peritoneal exudate cell population followed, later on, by an increase in the number of activated macrophages. Intravenous administration results in an increase in number and activation of circulating NK cells, in addition to the production of IFNs-α, -β and -γ, and IL1 and IL2.[134] NK cell elevation was noted for up to seven days; however, multiple treatments resulted in a hyporesponsiveness to the drug. The agent also appears to induce the production of CSFs and stimulates a cytolytic T cell response against an allogeneic murine tumor system.[135]

OK-432 has been examined, both as a single agent and in combination therapies, in a variety of rodent tumor models. Intraperitoneal administration of OK-432 in subcutaneously transplanted syngeneic bladder carcinoma tumors in rats results in a substantial increase in life span, to the extent of cures in a number of the animals. Antitumor effects have also been noted in other syngeneic mouse tumor systems such as the methylcholanthrene-induced fibrosarcoma.[136] Furthermore, a significant reduction in metastases in several animal tumor models has been reported, including the reduction of pulmonary metastases in the difficult to treat Lewis lung tumor model.[137] Synergistic efficacy of OK-432 in combination with antitumor agents such as mitomycin C, 5-FU, cyclophosphamide and adriamycin has been noted. However, there was significant schedule dependency in the demonstration of synergism, with maximum effects being noted when OK-432 was given after chemotherapy on a multiple dose regimen.[138]

OK-432 has enjoyed significant clinical experience (to date, principally in Japan). It has been given *via* several routes of administration including intravenous, intramuscular, intradermal, intraperitoneal and intralesional. Intramuscular administration results in increased peripheral blood lymphocytes (PBL) with normal T cell ratios and an increased blastogenic response to mitogens. NK cell augmentation was also noted in PBLs, with the maximum being observed using intravenous administration. Intrapleural injection of OK-432 resulted in an augmentation of NK cell activity in the pleural effusions, which the authors correlated with a reduction in tumor cells in the pleural effusion, and clinical improvement.[139] The only significant side effects to OK-432 at the doses presently employed in the clinic have been transient fever and some pain at the site of injection. Clinically, OK-432 has been used as a single agent and in combination with chemotherapeutics, such as 5-FU, in a number of tumor histiotypes. Early controlled studies showed some increase in disease-free survival in advanced adenocarcinoma of the stomach and the lung.[140] Follow-up studies have demonstrated that the optimum effect of OK-432 immunotherapy is in chronic or adjuvant administration in resected gastric cancer patients after chemotherapy (intradermal injection). Additional reports of efficacy in adjuvant settings have been noted for small cell carcinoma of the lung, and surgically resected malignant glioma, with the minimal effect noted in Hodgkin's disease and ovarian carcinoma. Lastly, in a randomized postoperative adjuvant therapy trial in nonsmall cell lung cancer, randomized between no treatment and chronic OK-432 therapy, a statistically significant improvement in survival rate was noted.[141]

15.1.7.5   Polyribonucleotides

The combination of the early findings that nucleic acids exhibited nonspecific immunomodulating effects, together with the discovery of a virus-induced substance, termed IFN, led to the preparation and evaluation of synthetic polynucleotides as immunoaugmenting IFN-inducing agents.[142] Subsequent work focused on polyribonucleotides and, specifically, poly I:C double-stranded RNA complexes.[143] The pioneering studies concentrated on poly I:C as an IFN inducer. However, further investigations demonstrated that poly I:C exhibited BRM properties beyond simply IFN induction.[144] Thus, while the earlier work was driven by the desire to utilize poly I:C as an inducer of host IFN, rather than using exogenous IFN, the rationale for more recent studies on poly I:C and related analogs has been guided by its broader BRM properties.[145]

Poly I:C has exhibited effects on both humoral and cellular immunity. While poly I:C is similar to other BRMs, in that it often exhibits a bell-shaped dose–response curve, it is unique in the sense that it is a very potent agent relative to other, nonbiological BRMs. For example, doses as low as 10 µg per mouse, administered i.p. or i.v., result in an enhancement of antibody response after antigen challenge, whereas a dose of 1000 µg results in a suppression.[146] Usually somewhat higher doses are required to stimulate cell-mediated immunity. Poly I:C has been shown to enhance macrophage activity[147] and NK cell activity in animals and humans in a dose dependent fashion.[148] Poly I:C is a potent mitogen at very low concentrations, and at higher concentrations it has demonstrated an antiproliferative effect. It appears that the antiproliferative effect is, in part, due to IFN; however, it cannot be totally ascribed thereto based on studies with anti-IFN antibody. Mitogenic effects have been noted on T and B cells, spleen cells and fibroblasts, whereas antiproliferative effects have been noted on the latter, in addition to epithelial cells and tumor cells.[149] While similar inhibitory effects have been observed on the hematopoietic system (for example, lymphopenia and thrombocytopenia have been observed in animals and humans), poly I:C also appears to induce the stimulation of cell differentiation and the proliferation of pluripotent stem cells.

In view of the IFN-inducing properties of poly I:C, some of the biochemistry induced by this agent is not surprising. For example, it activates protein kinase and 2,5-oligoadenylate synthetase, in addition to depressing cytochrome *P*-450.[150] Moreover, it has recently been reported that an analog of poly I:C (poly ICLC, *vide infra*) induced CSF in peritoneal macrophages and bone marrow cells at low doses, in a dose and time dependent fashion *in vitro* and *in vivo*. At high doses, for example >4 mg kg^{-1}, poly ICLC was myelosuppressive.[151] These findings are consistent with the previously reported effects on hematopoiesis and myelomonocytic differentiation.

With the demonstration that the biological responses of polyribonucleotides were very dependent on the nucleic acid composition of the double-stranded RNA,[152] together with the substantial toxicity of poly I:C (pyrogenicity and significant immunopathology, reminiscent of that associated with bacterial endotoxins), came a significant research effort to synthesize and evaluate analogs. One of the early polyribonucleotides studied was poly A:U. Poly A:U exhibited similar adjuvant-type properties to poly I:C; however, it was a much poorer IFN inducer and much less toxic.[153] The rationale for analogs of poly I:C seems to be divided along attempts to stabilize the double-stranded nature of the molecule and, in the opposite sense, to enhance its susceptibility to RNAse. Two analogs which have been the most widely studied are poly ICLC, a complex of poly-L-lysine and carboxymethylcellulose with poly I:C,[154] and poly I:C$_{12}$U, a so-called mismatched poly I:C analog involving a uridine substitution for a cytidine in a ratio of 1:12.[155] Basically, these analogs of poly I:C exhibit a similar immunomodulatory profile to poly I:C. For example, *in vitro* and *in vivo* augmentation of macrophage and NK cell activation were seen with both poly ICLC[156] and poly I:C$_{12}$U.[157] The stabilized analog, poly ICLC, did exhibit a much more sustained IFN induction in animals and humans relative to poly I:C. In contrast, poly I:C$_{12}$U, similar to poly A:U, is a rather weak IFN inducer, but shares with poly A:U the common absence of significant toxicity associated with poly I:C and poly ICLC. However, it should be noted that low doses (nontoxic) of poly ICLC have been shown to have immunomodulatory activity in the absence of detection of circulating IFN in humans.[158] This exemplifies the difficulty in establishing optimum immunomodulatory doses and schedules, since different doses result in amplification or diminution of various components of the immune response. Ultimately, of course, this must be correlated with various clinical parameters measuring therapeutic efficacy.[159]

Evaluation of the efficacy of polyribonucleotides in animal model studies has been principally limited to viral diseases and cancers. Poly I:C is a broad-spectrum antiviral agent demonstrating efficacy in a variety of disease models including influenza, vaccinia, several herpes viruses and Semliki Forest virus. While efficacy is not exclusive to prophylactic administration, generally only modest therapeutic efficacy was demonstrated.[160] Its antiviral profile is basically very similar to IFN-α. *In vivo* antitumor studies have involved principally poly I:C and poly ICLC. These BRMs induce increases in life span and/or a decrease in tumor size in several spontaneous, as well as transplantable, tumors in mice. In contrast to the antiviral profile, there are several examples of antitumor responses to poly I:C which could not be duplicated with exogenous IFN.[161] For example, an IFN resistant cell population of the human HT1080 fibrosarcoma remained sensitive to poly I:C.[162] Overall, the antitumor activity in transplantable tumor models was moderate and very much a function of tumor burden. Poly I:C also exhibited activity in chemically induced tumors, employing intermittent chronic therapy, in the inhibition of experimental and spontaneous pulmonary metastases, and in synergistic antitumor efficacy in rapidly growing transplantable tumors in combination with chemotherapy.[163]

Clinical evaluation of polyribonucleotides has included poly I:C, poly ICLC, poly I:C$_{12}$U and poly A:U. While most of these studies have involved the treatment of various types of cancer, early studies were conducted with poly I:C in herpes keratitis administered as eyedrops, and in rhinovirus and influenza virus infections administered as an intranasal spray. While efficacy was noted in ocular keratitis, it was equivocal in the upper respiratory infections. Systemic administration has been employed in treating other types of viral diseases such as varicella zoster, herpes simplex, polio, rubella and laryngeal papillomatosis. While some side effects were noted, compared to the local administration in keratitis and upper respiratory infections, efficacy was not evident in most of these studies except papillomatosis.[159]

The efficacy of polynucleotides in the treatment of human malignancies has not yet been fully evaluated; however there have been some positive results, both in terms of biological responses and in clinical endpoints. As mentioned previously, these agents appear to be pleiotropic in modulating an immune response, including augmentation of NK cell activity, stimulation of macrophage-mediated cytotoxicity, stimulation of production of CSF and direct antitumor effects. In addition, certain results raise the question as to whether the antitumor effects of the polyribonucleotides are attributed to IFN production, or whether other effects, not mediated by IFN, are important.[164] In phase I/II trials with poly I:C or poly ICLC, therapeutic effects have been observed, but overall, a rather small proportion of the patients have responded. There have been some responses in adult leukemia,[165] multiple myeloma,[166] and renal carcinoma.[167] In a phase I/II clinical trial with poly I:C$_{12}$U, significantly less toxicity was noted than with the poly I:C or poly ICLC and several objective responses were noted. Further studies are in progress.[168] Poly A:U has been evaluated in a prospectively randomized clinical trial in breast cancer, with and without radiation after surgery.[169] Patients were treated with 30 mg of poly A:U i.v. once a week for six weeks. With four year follow-up treatment, disease-free survival was 72% in the poly A:U-treated group *vs.* 56% in the radiation only group. The beneficial effects were noted both in the complete treatment group and in the node positive patients.[170] Overall, clinical results to date with the polynucleotides, while encouraging, are too immature to evaluate efficacy and correlation with biological response in comparison to IFN therapy. If additional positive results are forthcoming, future clinical trials should include combination chemotherapy to evaluate the beneficial effect of polyribonucleotides with cytoreductive therapy.

15.1.7.6 Pyrimidinones

The increasing interest in the early 1970s in the properties and use of IFN, together with the difficulty in producing useful amounts of IFN, led to the search for agents that would induce IFN in the host. Precedence at that time for IFN inducers included viruses and bacterial wall constituents and entities of large molecular weight such as the polynucleotides. There were also several examples of low molecular weight substances, such as certain antibiotics and the antiviral agent, tilorone.[93,171,172] In 1976, it was reported that a 6-methylpyrimidinone (2-amino-5-bromo-6-methyl-4-(3*H*)pyrimidinone, ABMP) induced circulating levels of IFN in several animal species upon oral or intraperitoneal administration.[173] Subsequent structure–activity studies yielded a more potent and less toxic 6-phenyl analog called ABPP or bropirimine (2-amino-5-bromo-6-phenyl-4-(3*H*)pyrimidinone) (Figure 2 and Table 5).[174,175] Bropirimine and related 6-aryl analogs were examined extensively for efficacy in virus and tumor models, along with their immunomodulatory properties and overall pharmacological effects.[176]

Bropirimine (ABPP) induces significant levels of circulating IFN in mice, which peak in the 4–12 h range irrespective of the route of administration. IFN has also been induced in a number of other species of animals, as well as in cancer patients where the drug was administered orally. Interestingly, a closely related analog, the 5-iodopyrimidinone (AIPP), induces undetectable serum levels of IFN when given orally to mice, yet exhibited significant antiviral and antitumor activity. These early data, together with studies with other analogs,[177] suggested that the efficacy and biological activities of these pyrimidinones cannot be quantitatively correlated with the levels of circulating IFN that were induced. Like most agents that induce IFN, bropirimine exhibited an IFN hyporesponsiveness on multiple administration; however, this hyporesponsiveness could be diminished or abrogated by either employing an initial priming dose of IFN or stretching the bropirimine administration to every three days. The advantages to this approach were demonstrated in a transplanted murine neuroblastoma model, wherein bropirimine exhibited synergistic therapeutic effects with IFN.[178]

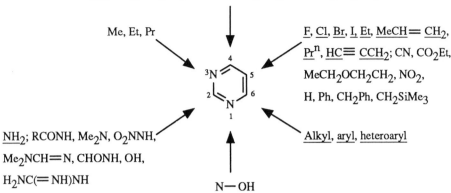

Figure 2 Preliminary SAR of antiviral activity of pyrimidinones (underlined substituents were active)

Table 5 Antiviral Activity of 5-Halogeno-6-arylpyrimidinones

	Antiviral activity[a]		
	Monosubstituted	Disubstituted	'Heterocyclic'
Active	2-F, OMe, Me	3,5-OMe	1-Naphthyl
	3-F, OMe, Cl, NO$_2$,	2,5-Cl$_2$	2-Pyrazyl
	Me, CF$_3$, MeCH$_2$CH$_2$O,	3,5-OMe	2,3-Pyridyl
	Br, I	3,4-Cl$_2$	2-Furyl
	4-F, Cl	3,5-Cl$_2$	
Inactive	4-Me, CN, Bu^t,	2,3-OMe	2-Naphthyl
	OH, OCH$_2$Ph, OMe		1-Furyl
			4-Pyridyl
			2-Quinoline

[a] Listed in approximate order of decreasing activity, as determined by i.p. administration of compound.

Further studies with bropirimine and other pyrimidinones demonstrated that these agents augment levels of antibody-forming cells to SRBC with significant elevation of IgG levels in the serum.[179] In addition to this B cell response, bropirimine, upon i.p. administration to mice, augmented bone marrow colony-forming units which may be IFN driven *via* CSF induction. Bropirimine is generally not directly mitogenic in murine tissue culture or cell culture or human PBLs. Analysis of induction of lymphocyte cell populations in bropirimine-treated mice suggested a mixed response. This is consistent with the demonstration that bropirimine down-regulates delayed hypersensitivity, and behaves as an inhibitor in several models of inflammation and polyarthritis.[180] Interestingly, in addition to IFN induction, bropirimine is a potent inducer of IL1 both *in vitro* and *in vivo*.[181] A recent study examined the role of bropirimine as a potential immunorestorative agent by examining its effect on suppressed T cell responses and IL2 responses. Murine cytomegalovirus (CMV) infection in mice results in a suppression of IL2 responses in spleen cells and a reduction in the ratio of T-helper to T-suppressor cells. Bropirimine was able to restore the T-helper to T-suppressor ratio and significantly augmented the number of cells inducible for expression of IL2 receptors.[182] There is substantial evidence that the efficacy of pyrimidinone is also dependent on augmentation of NK cell activity and macrophage activity. Interestingly, NK cell cytotoxicity did not parallel IFN-inducing activity.[183] Systemic administration of bropirimine resulted in augmentation of NK cell cytotoxicity in the peritoneal exudate, the peripheral blood, lung, liver and spleen but not in the bone marrow.

As with the polynucleotides, the pyrimidinones exhibited significant activity against IFN sensitive viruses such as Semliki Forest virus *in vivo*. However, in addition, they exhibited prophylactic and therapeutic activity upon either local or systemic administration to rodents infected with a variety of DNA viruses, such as the herpes viruses (HSV-1, HSV-2, CMV and pseudorabies), and when administered intranasally for upper respiratory infections, such as infectious bovine rhinotracheitis, influenza A and parainfluenza-3. Particularly interesting activity was noted with bropirimine on intravaginal administration in protection against HSV-2 intravaginal infection in guinea pigs, an important model for genital herpes in humans.[184] Bropirimine also exhibited activity when given either intraperitoneally or orally to mice infected with *Listeria monocytogenes*. The efficacy in this model (which was similar to poly I:C) was not abrogated by the addition of anti-IFN antibody.[185]

Bropirimine exhibited single agent activity in several transplantable tumor models. However, the activity was very dependent on initial tumor burden.[186] Efficacy was also noted against several artificial and spontaneous pulmonary metastasis models in animals, wherein the agent was given postoperatively. The antimetastatic activity appeared to be mediated through host resistance mechanisms, involving macrophages and NK cells rather than T cells, since efficacy was also noted in T cell deficient mice.[187] Interesting activity was also demonstrated in several carcinogen-induced tumor models, wherein bropirimine was administered in an adjuvant setting with chronic intermittent therapy for up to three months. Oral administration resulted in a significant diminution of the number and size of tumors in the bladder carcinoma and mammary carcinoma models.[188,189] Synergistic activity with a number of chemotherapeutic agents in several transplantable tumor models has been demonstrated with the pyrimidinones. Optimum activity was noted with pyrimidinone administration every four days after tumor inoculum and cytoreductive therapy. Synergistic combinations included cyclophosphamide and cisplatin, wherein NK cell augmentation was demonstrable, but not synergistic with vincristine, mitomycin C, doxorubicin and actinomycin D, wherein inhibition of NK cell augmentation was seen.[190,191]

The lead candidate, bropirimine (ABPP), is presently undergoing clinical evaluation administered orally to patients with both cancer and certain viral diseases such as AIDS, as well as topically for the treatment of genital infections. Oral phase I studies in cancer patients have demonstrated that the agent is well tolerated and induces circulating IFN-α, elevated 2,5A synthetase in circulating PBLs, and a febrile response not unlike that noted with moderate doses of IFN.[192] Phase I topical trials have also been completed with no adverse effects. Phase II trials with oral drug are in progress in renal cell carcinoma, bladder carcinoma, hepatoma and lymphoma. A recently completed study in Kaposi's sarcoma/AIDS patients yielded a drug-related increase in peripheral T cell proliferative responses, adenosine deaminase levels and circulating IFN.[196]

15.1.8 REFERENCES

1. J. J. Oppenheim, E. J. Kovacs, K. Matsushima and S. K. Durum, *Immunol. Today*, 1986, **7**, 45.
2. C. J. March, B. Moseley, A. Larsen, D. P. Cerretti, G. Braedt, V. Price, S. Gillis, C. Henney, S. R. Kronheim, K. Grabstein, P. J. Conlon, T. P. Hopp and D. Cosman, *Nature (London)*, 1985, **315**, 644.
3. S. K. Dower and D. L. Urdal, *Immunol. Today*, 1987, **8**, 46.
4. K. Matsushima, J. Yodoi, Y. Tagaya and J. J. Oppenheim, *J. Immunol.*, 1986, **137**, 3183.
5. J. W. Lowenthal and H. R. MacDonald, *J. Exp. Med.*, 1986, **164**, 1060.
6. E. A. Carswell, L. J. Old, R. L. Kassel, S. Green, N. Fiore and B. Williamson, *Proc. Natl. Acad. Sci. USA*, 1975, **72**, 3666.
7. B. Beutler, I. W. Milsark and A. Cerami, *J. Immunol.*, 1985, **135**, 3972.
8. F. C. Kull, S. Jacobs and P. Cuatrecasas, *Proc. Natl. Acad. Sci. USA*, 1985, **82**, 5756.
9. B. Y. Rubin, S. L. Anderson, C. A. Sullivan, B. D. Williamson, E. A. Carswell and L. J. Old, *J. Exp. Med.*, 1985, **162**, 1099.
10. D. V. Goeddel, D. W. Leung, T. J. Dull, M. Gross, R. M. Lawn, P. H. McCandless, A. Seeburg, A. Ullrich, E. Yelverton and P. W. Gray, *Nature (London)*, 1981, **290**, 20.
11. M. Rubinstein, W. P. Levy, J. A. Moschera, C. Y. Lai, R. D. Hershberg, R. T. Bartlett and S. Pestka, *Arch. Biochem. Biophys.*, 1981, **210**, 307.
12. C. R. Faltynek, A. A. Branca, S. McCandless and C. Baglioni, *Proc. Natl. Acad. Sci. USA*, 1983, **80**, 3269.
13. A. A. Branca and C. Baglioni, *J. Biol. Chem.*, 1982, **257**, 13 197.
14. D. A. Morgan, F. W. Ruscetti and R. C. Gallo, *Science (Washington, D.C.)*, 1976, **193**, 1007.
15. B. Manger, A. Weiss, C. Weyand, J. Goronzy and J. D. Stobo, *J. Immunol.*, 1985, **135**, 3669.
16. G. H. Reem and N. H. Yeh, *Science (Washington, D.C.)*, 1984, **225**, 429.
17. K. Teshigawara, H.-M. Wang, K. Kato and K. A. Smith, *J. Exp. Med.*, 1987, **165**, 223.
18. L. A. Rubin, G. Jay and D. L. Nelson, *J. Immunol.*, 1986, **137**, 3841.
19. R. M. Schultz and W. J. Kleinschmidt, *Nature (London)*, 1983, **305**, 239.
20. D. Berkovic, H. H. Bartsch, P. Scheurich, U. Ucer and K. Pfizenmaier, *Immunobiology*, 1986, **172**, 243.
21. J. Ohara and W. E. Paul, *Nature (London)*, 1987, **325**, 537.
22. J. N. Ihle and Y. Weinstein, *Adv. Immunol.*, 1986, **39**, 1.
23. B. Beutler and A. Cerami, *Nature (London)*, 1986, **320**, 584.
24. L. J. Old, *Science (Washington, D.C.)*, 1985, **230**, 630.
25. P. W. Gray, B. B. Aggarwal, C. V. Benton, T. S. Bringman, W. J. Henzel, J. A. Jarrett, D. W. Leung, B. Moffat, P. Ng, L. P. Svedersky, M. A. Palladino and G. E. Nedwin, *Nature (London)*, 1984, **312**, 721.
26. J. E. Labdon, K. D. Gibson, S. Sun and S. Pestka, *Arch. Biochem. Biophys.*, 1984, **232**, 422.
27. R. Wetzel, *Nature (London)*, 1981, **289**, 606.
28. J. DeMaeyer-Guignard and E. DeMaeyer, in 'Interferon', ed. I. Gresser, Academic Press, New York, 1985, vol. 6, p. 69.
29. O. T. Preble, R. J. Black, R. M. Friedman, J. H. Klippel and J. Vilcek, *Science (Washington, D.C.)*, 1982, **216**, 429.

30. T. Taniguchi, S. Ohno, Y. Fujii-Kuriyama and M. Muramatsu, *Gene*, 1980, **10**, 11.
31. T. Taniguchi, H. Matsui, T. Fujita, C. Takaoka, N. Kashima, R. Yoshimoto and J. Hamuro, *Nature (London)*, 1983, **302**, 305.
32. E. Rinderknecht, B. H. O'Connor and H. Rodriguez, *J. Biol. Chem.*, 1984, **259**, 6790.
33. T. Yokota, T. Otsuka, T. Mosmann, J. Banchereau, T. DeFrance, D. Blanchard, J. E. DeVries, F. Lee and K. Arai, *Proc. Natl. Acad. Sci. USA*, 1986, **83**, 5894.
34. T. Hirano, K. Yasukawa, H. Harada, T. Taga, Y. Watanabe, T. Matsuda, S. Kashiwamura, K. Nakajima, K. Koyama, A. Iwamatsu, S. Tsunasawa, F. Sakiyama, H. Matsui, Y. Takahara, T. Taniguchi and T. Kishimoto, *Nature (London)*, 1986, **324**, 73.
35. T. Kinashi, N. Harada, E. Severinson, T. Tanabe, P. Sideras, M. Konishi, C. Azuma, A. Tominaga, S. Bergstedt-Lindqvist, M. Takahashi, F. Matsuda, Y. Yaoita, K. Takatsu and T. Honjo, *Nature (London)*, 1986, **324**, 70.
36. E. A. Kurt-Jones, D. I. Beller, S. B. Mizel and E. R. Unanue, *Proc. Natl. Acad. Sci. USA*, 1985, **82**, 1204.
37. K. Matsushima and J. J. Oppenheim, *Cell. Immunol.*, 1985, **90**, 226.
38. M. Martin, D. H. Lovett and K. Resch, *Immunobiology*, 1986, **171**, 165.
39. K. Resch, M. Martin, D. H. Lovett, U. Kyas and D. Gemsa, *Immunobiology*, 1986, **172**, 336.
40. C. A. Dinarello, *Rev. Infect. Dis.*, 1984, **6**, 51.
41. (a) C. A. Dinarello, *Immunobiology*, 1986, **172**, 301; (b) C. A. Dinarello, *J. Clin. Immunol.*, 1985, **5**, 287.
42. G. Antoni, R. Presentini, F. Perin, A. Tagliabue, P. Ghiara, S. Censini, G. Volpini, L. Villa and D. Boraschi, *J. Immunol.*, 1986, **137**, 3201.
43. B. Beutler and A. Cerami, *New Engl. J. Med.*, 1987, **316**, 379.
44. (a) D. S. Schmid, J. P. Tite and N. H. Ruddle, *Proc. Natl. Acad. Sci. USA*, 1986, **83**, 1881; (b) M. R. Shalaby, B. B. Aggarwal, E. Rinderknecht, L. P. Svedersky, B. S. Finkle and M. A. Palladino, *J. Immunol.*, 1985, **135**, 2069; (c) J. R. Gamble, J. M. Harlan, S. J. Klebenoff, A. F. Lopez and M. A. Vadas, *Proc. Natl. Acad. Sci. USA*, 1986, **82**, 8667; (d) R. J. Chang and S. H. Lee, *J. Immunol.*, 1986, **137**, 2853.
45. M. Revel, in 'Interferon', ed. I. Gresser, Academic Press, New York, 1979, vol. 1, p. 101.
46. M. J. Clemens, V. M. Pain, S. T. Wong and E. C. Henshaw, *Nature (London)*, 1982, **296**, 93.
47. A. Schmidt, A. Zilberstein, L. Shulman, P. Federman, H. Berissi and M. Revel, *FEBS Lett.*, 1978, **95**, 257.
48. M. Revel and J. Chebath, *Trends Biochem. Sci. (Pers. Ed.)*, 1986, **11**, 166.
49. A. B. Pardee, R. Dubrow, J. L. Hamlin and R. F. Kletzien, *Annu. Rev. Biochem.*, 1978, **47**, 715.
50. M. Howard, L. Matis, T. R. Malek, E. Shevach, W. Kell, D. Cohen, K. Nakanishi and W. E. Paul, *J. Exp. Med.*, 1983, **158**, 2024.
51. A. M. Weissman, J. B. Harford, P. B. Svetlik, W. L. Leonard, J. M. Depper, T. A. Waldman, W. C. Greene and R. D. Klausner, *Proc. Natl. Acad. Sci. USA*, 1986, **83**, 1463.
52. W. L. Farrar and M. Taguchi, *Lymphokine Res.*, 1985, **4**, 87.
53. G. R. Adolf, *Oncology*, 1985, **42** (suppl. 1), 33.
54. A. M. Duijvestijn, A. B. Schreiber and E. C. Butcher, *Proc. Natl. Acad. Sci. USA*, 1986, **83**, 9114.
55. L. Justement, Z. Chen, L. Harris, J. Ransom, V. Sandoval, C. Smith, D. Rennick, N. Roehm and J. Cambier, *J. Immunol.*, 1986, **137**, 3664.
56. T. Hirano, T. Taga, K. Yasukawa, K. Nakajima, N. Nakano, F. Takatsuki, M. Shimizu, A. Murashima, S. Tsunasawa, F. Sakiyama and T. Kishimoto, *Proc. Natl. Acad. Sci. USA*, 1987, **84**, 228.
57. D. Metcalf, *Science (Washington, D.C.)*, 1985, **229**, 16.
58. S. C. Clark and R. Kramer, *Science (Washington, D. C.)*, 1987, **236**, 1229.
59. P. Ralph, M. K. Warren, I. Nakoinz, M.-T. Lee, L. Brindley, A. Sampson-Johannes, E. S. Kawasaki, M. B. Ladner, J. E. Strickler, A. Boosman, J. Csejtey and T. J. White, *Immunobiology*, 1986, **172**, 194.
60. E. Platzer and J. R. Kalden, *Blut*, 1987, **54**, 129.
61. R. E. Donahue, E. A. Wang, D. K. Stone, R. Kamen, G. G. Wong, P. K. Sehgal, D. G. Nathan, and S. C. Clark, *Nature (London)*, 1986, **321**, 872.
62. K. A. Smith, K. J. Gilbride and M. F. Favata, *Nature (London)*, 1980, **287**, 853.
63. D. D. Wood and P. M. Cameron, *Cell. Immunol.*, 1976, **21**, 133.
64. S. H. Lee, B. B. Aggarwal, E. Rinderknecht, F. Assissi and H. Chiu, *J. Immunol.*, 1984, **133**, 1083.
65. (a) G. Trinchieri, M. Kobayashi, M. Rosen, R. Loudon, M. Murphy and B. Perussia, *J. Exp. Med.*, 1986, **164**, 1206; (b) K. Takeda, S. Iwamoto, H. Sugimoto, T. Takuma, N. Kawatani, M. Noda, A. Masaki, H. Morise, H. Arimura and K. Kono, *Nature (London)*, 1986, **323**, 338.
66. R. L. Foreti, S. S. Schuffman, H. A. Davies and W. M. Mitchell, *Methods Enzymol.*, 1986, **119**, 533.
67. Y. Kawade, *Methods Enzymol.*, 1986, **119**, 558.
68. S. Gillis, M. M. Ferm, W. Ou and K. A. Smith, *J. Immunol.*, 1978, **120**, 2027.
69. A. Muraguchi and A. S. Fauci, *J. Immunol.*, 1982, **129**, 1104.
70. K. Yoshizaki, T. Nakagawa, T. Kaieda, A. Muraguchi, Y. Yamamura and T. Kishimoto, *J. Immunol.*, 1982, **128**, 1296.
71. A. W. Burgess, C. G. Begley, G. R. Johnson, A. F. Lopez, D. J. Williamson, J. J. Mermod, R. J. Simpson, A. Schmitz and J. F. DeLamarter, *Blood*, 1987, **69**, 43.
72. A. S. Fauci, *Ann. Intern. Med.*, 1987, **106**, 421.
73. Y. Endo, K. Matsushima and J. J. Oppenheim, *Immunobiology*, 1986, **172**, 316.
74. S. A. Rosenberg, M. T. Lotze, L. M. Muul, S. Leitman, A. E. Chang, S. E. Ettinghausen, Y. L. Matory, J. M. Skibber, E. Shiloni, J. T. Vetto *et al.*, *New Engl. J. Med.*, 1985, **313**, 1485.
75. M. T. Lotze, R. J. Robb, S. A. Sharrow, L. W. Frana and S. A. Rosenberg, *J. Biol. Response Modif.*, 1984, **3**, 475.
76. R. Mertelsmann, K. Welte, I. Sternberg, R. O'Reilly, M. A. S. Moore, B. D. Clarkson and H. F. Oettgen, *J. Biol. Response Modif.*, 1984, **3**, 483.
77. S. A. Rosenberg, M. T. Lotze, L. M. Muul, A. E. Chang, F. P. Avis, S. Leitman, W. M. Linehan, C. N. Robertson, R. E. Lee, J. T. Rubin *et al.*, *New Engl. J. Med.*, 1987, **316**, 889.
78. W. E. Stewart and D. K. Blanchard, in 'Immunity to Cancer', ed. A. W. Reif, Academic Press, New York, 1984, p. 295.
79. I. Gresser (ed.), in 'Interferon', Academic Press, New York, 1985, vol. 6.
80. D. Goldstein and J. Laszlow, *Cancer Res.*, 1986, **46**, 4315.
81. E. M. Bonmem, *Invest. New Drugs*, 1987, **5**, suppl. 65.

82. H. T. Greenway, R. C. Cornell, D. J. Tanner, E. Peets, G. M. Bordin and C. Nagi, *J. Am. Acad. Dermatol.*, 1986, **15**, 437.
83. R. M. Douglas, B. W. Moore, H. B. Miles, L. M. Davies, N. M. Graham, P. Ryan, D. A. Worswick and J. K. Albrecht, *New Engl. J. Med.*, 1986, **314**, 65.
84. F. G. Hayden, D. L. Kaiser and J. M. Gwaltney, Jr., *New Engl. J. Med.*, 1986, **314**, 71.
85. J. C. Vance, B. J. Bart, R. C. Hansen, R. Reichman, C. McEwan and K. D. Hatch, *Arch. Dermatol.*, 1986, **122**, 272.
86. S. Levin, *Isr. J. Med. Sci.*, 1983, **19**, 955.
87. F. Rapp and H. Wrzos, *Antimicrob. Agents Chemother.*, 1985, **28**, 449.
88. S. A. Sherwin, *Ann. Intern. Med.*, 1987, **106**, 425.
89. C. F. Nathan, G. Kaplan, W. R. Levis, A. Nusrat, M. D. Witmer, J. A. Shermwin, C. K. Job, C. R. Horowitz, R. M. Steinman and Z. A. Cohn, *New Engl. J. Med.*, 1986, **315**, 6.
90. E. S. Kleinerman, R. Kurzrock, D. Wyatt, J. R. Quesada, J. U. Gutterman and I. J. Fidler, *Cancer Res.*, 1986, **46**, 5401.
91. M. G. Rosenblum, A. Riso and J. U. Gutterman, *Cancer Chemother. Pharmacol.*, 1986, **16**, 273.
92. R. L. Fenichel and M. A. Chirigos, 'Immune Modulation Agents and Their Mechanism', Dekker, New York, 1984.
93. W. Wierenga, in 'Annual Reports of Medicinal Chemistry', ed. H.-J. Hess, Academic Press, New York, 1982, vol. 17, p. 151.
94. T. L. K. Low and A. L. Goldstein, in 'Thymic Hormones and Lymphokines', ed. A. L. Goldstein, Plenum Press, New York, 1984, p. 21.
95. T. L. K. Low and A. L. Goldstein, in 'Immune Modulation Agents and Their Mechanisms', ed. R. L. Fenichel and M. A. Chirigos, Dekker, New York, 1984, p. 135.
96. J. A. Hooper, M. C. McDaniel, G. B. Thurmann, G. H. Cohen, R. S. Schuloff and A. L. Goldstein, *Ann. N. Y. Acad. Sci.*, 1974, **249**, 125.
97. T. L. K. Low, G. B. Thurmann, M. McAdoo, J. E. McClure, J. L. Rossio, P. H. Neiler and A. L. Goldstein, *J. Biol. Chem.*, 1979, **254**, 981.
98. T. W. Wong and R. B. Merrifield, *Biochemistry*, 1980, **19**, 3233.
99. R. Wetzel, H. L. Heyneker, D. V. Goeddel, P. Jhurani, J. Shapiro, R. Crea, T. L. K. Low, J. E. McClure and A. L. Goldstein, *Biochemistry*, 1980, **19**, 6096.
100. M. M. Zats, M. Glaser, C. M. Seals and A. L. Goldstein, in 'Lymphokines and Thymic Hormones: Their Potential Utilization in Cancer Therapeutics', ed. A. L. Goldstein and M. Chirigos, Raven Press, New York, 1981.
101. P. S. Sarin, D. K. Sun, A. H. Thornton, P. H. Naylor and A. L. Goldstein, *Science (Washington, D.C.)*, 1986, **232**, 1135.
102. D. J. Barrett, D. J. Warra, D. J. Ammann and M. J. Cowan, *J. Pediatr. (St. Louis)*, 1980, **97**, 66.
103. M. H. Cohen, P. B. Chretien, D. C. Ihde, B. E. Fossicek, R. Makuch, P. A. Bunn, A. V. Johnston, S. E. Shackney, M. J. Mathews, S. O. Lipson, D. E. Kennady and J. D. Minna, *JAMA, J. Am. Med. Assoc.*, 1979, **241**, 1813.
104. R. S. Schulof, M. J. Lloyd, P. A. Cleary, S. R. Palaszynski, D. A. Mai, J. W. Cox, O. Alabaster and A. L. Goldstein, *J. Biol. Response Modif.*, 1985, **4**, 147.
105. A. L. Goldstein and R. S. Schulof, 'Immunity to Cancer', Academic Press, New York, 1985, p. 469.
106. R. S. Schulof, G. L. Simon, M. B. Sztein, D. M. Parenti, R. A. DiGioia, J. W. Courtless, J. M. Orenstein, C. M. Kessler, P. D. Kind, S. Schlesselman *et al.*, *J. Biol. Resp. Modif.*, 1986, **5**, 429.
107. D. Thienpont, O. F. J. Van Parons, A. H. M. Raeymaekers, J. VanderBerk, P. J. A. Demoen, F. T. N. Allewun, R. P. H. Marsboom, C. J. E. Neimegeers, K. H. L. Schellenkens and P. A. J. Janssen, *Nature (London)*, 1966, **209**, 1084.
108. G. Renoux and M. Renoux, *C. R. Hebd. Seances Acad. Sci., Ser. D*, 1971, **272**, 349.
109. W. K. Amery and C. Horig, in 'Immune Modulation Agents and Their Mechanisms', ed. R. L. Fenichel and M. A. Chirigos, Dekker, New York, 1984, p. 383.
110. G. Renoux, *Trends Pharmacol. Sci.*, 1981, **2**, 248.
111. W. K. Amery, *J. Reticuloendothel. Soc.*, 1978, **24**, 187.
112. J. P. Tareyren and H. Leuressergues, *J. Pharm. Pharmacol.*, 1980, **32**, 584.
113. E. M. Vays, H. Mielants, G. VerBruggen, E. Dhondt, L. Goethals, L. Cherouthre and H. Buelens, *J. Rheumatol.*, 1981, **8**, 44.
114. M. Singh, P. Kumar, A. N. Malaviya and R. Kumar, *Am. Rev. Respir. Dis.*, 1981, **123**, 277.
115. R. K. Oldham and R. V. Smalley, in 'Cancer: Principles and Practices of Oncology', ed. V. T. DeVita, Jr., S. Hellman and S. A. Rosenberg, Lippincott, Scranton, PA, 1985, vol. 2, p. 2223.
116. E. C. Borden, T. E. Davis, J. J. Crowley, *et al.*, in 'Immunotherapy of Human Cancer', ed. W. D. Terry and S. A. Rosenberg, Elsevier, New York, 1982, p. 225.
117. H. Miwa, T. Kawai, H. Nakahara and K. Ortia, *Int. J. Immunopharmacol.*, 1980, **2**, 31.
118. J. Symones, W. F. DeCree, M. VonBever and P. A. J. Janssen, in 'Pharmacological and Biochemical Properties in Drug Substances', ed. M. Goldberg, American Pharmaceutical Association, Washington, D.C., 1979, vol. 2, p. 407.
119. F. J. Gregory, in 'Immune Modulation Agents and Their Mechanisms', ed. R. L. Fenichel and M. A. Chirigos, Dekker, New York, 1984, p. 21.
120. S. C. Gilman, R. P. Carlson and A. J. Lewis, *J. Immunopharmacol.*, 1985, **7**, 79.
121. F. Audibert, C. LeClercq and L. Schedid, in 'Biological Response Modifiers', ed. P. F. Torrence, Academic Press, New York, 1985, p. 307.
122. F. Audibert, L. Schedid, P. LeFrancier and J. Choay, *Cell. Immunol.*, 1976, **21**, 243.
123. P. LeFrancier and E. Lederer, in 'Progress in the Chemistry of Organic Natural Products', ed. W. Herz, H. Greisbach and G. W. Kerby, Springer-Verlag, Heidelberg, 1981, vol. 40, p. 1 (see also H. S. Warren, F. R. Vogel and L. A. Chedid, *Annu. Rev. Immunol.*, 1986, **4**, 369).
124. C. LeClercq, E. Bourgeois and L. Schedid, *Immunol. Commun.*, 1979, **8**, 55.
125. M. Fevrier, J. L. Birrien, C. LeClercq, L. Schedid and P. Liacopoulous, *Eur. J. Immunol.*, 1978, **8**, 558.
126. C. LeClercq, A. Morin and L. Schedid, in 'Recent Advances in Clinical Immunology', ed. R. A. Thompson and N. R. Rose, Livingstone, Edinburgh, 1983, vol. 3, p. 187.
127. W. E. Fogler and I. J. Fidler, in 'Immune Modulation Agents and Their Mechanisms', ed. R. L. Fenichel and M. A. Chirigos, Dekker, New York, 1984, p. 499.
128. B. Lukas, K. H. Schmidt-Ruppin and F. M. Detrich, in 'Proceedings International Symposium Immunomodulation Chemically Defined Adjuvants', Sapporo, Japan, 1983, p. 42.
129. N. Bloksma, F. M. A. Hofhuis and J. M. N. Willers, *Cancer Immunol. Immunother.*, 1985, **19**, 205.
130. E. S. Kleinerman, K. L. Erickson, A. J. Schroit, W. E. Fogler and I. J. Fidler, *Cancer Res.*, 1983, **43**, 210.

131. E. Lederer, in 'Experimental Cancer Therapy and Present Status of Nontoxic Concepts in Cancer', ed. K. F. Klippel and E. Macher, Karger, Basel, 1987, p. 119.
132. N. Ishida and T. Hoshino, 'OK-432, A Streptococcal Preparation as a Potent Biological Response Modifier', 2nd edn., Excerpta Medica, Tokyo, 1985.
133. Y. Sakurai, S. Tsukagoshi, H. Sato, T. Akiba, S. Suzuki and Y. Takagaki, *Cancer Treat. Rep.*, 1972, **56**, 9.
134. M. A. Chirigos, T. Saito and J. E. Talmadge, in 'Clinical and Experimental Studies in Immunotherapy', ed. T. Hoshinl and A. Uchida, Excerpta Medica, Amsterdam, 1984, p. 20.
135. S. Kai, J. Tanaka, K. Nomoto and M. Torisu, *Clin. Exp. Immunol.*, 1979, **37**, 98.
136. H. Yamagishi *et al.*, *Cancer Immunol. Immunother.*, 1980, **9**, 63.
137. M. Micksche, O. Kokran and A. Uchida, in 'Current Concepts in Human Immunology and Cancer Immunomodulation', ed. B. Serrou, C. Rosenfeld, J. C. Daniels and J. P. Saunders, Elsevier, New York, 1982, p. 31.
138. S. Koshimura and K. Ryoyama, *Cancer Treat. Rep.*, 1977, **61**, 17.
139. A. Uchida and M. Mickshe, *Int. J. Cancer*, 1983, **31**, 1.
140. A. Uchida and T. Hoshino, *Cancer (Philadelphia)*, 1980, **45**, 476.
141. Y. Watanabe and T. Iwa, *J. Biol. Response Modif.*, 1987, **6**, 169.
142. A. G. Johnson, in 'Biological Response Modifiers', ed. P. F. Torrence, Academic Press, New York, 1985, p. 107.
143. W. A. Carter, P. M. Pitha, L. W. Marshall, I. Tazawa, S. Tazawa and P. O. P. Ts'o, *J. Mol. Biol.*, 1972, **70**, 567.
144. I. M. Kerr, R. E. Brown, M. J. Clemens and C. W. Gilbert, *Eur. J. Biochem.*, 1976, **69**, 551.
145. J. J. Green and P. O. P. Ts'o, in 'Clinical Applications of Interferons and Their Inducers', 2nd edn., Dekker, New York, 1986.
146. T. J. Chester, E. DeClercq and T. C. Merigan, *Infect. Immun.*, 1972, **3**, 516.
147. R. M. Schultz, J. D. Papamatheakis and M. A. Chirigos, *Cell. Immunol.*, 1977, **29**, 403.
148. R. B. Herberman, J. Ortaldo and G. Bonnard, *Nature (London)*, 1979, **277**, 221.
149. J. A. O'Malley, S. S. Leong, J. S. Horoszewicz, W. A. Carter, J. L. Alderer and P. O. P. Ts'o, *Mol. Pharmacol.*, 1979, **15**, 165.
150. P. F. Torrence, *Mol. Aspects Med.*, 1982, **5**, 129.
151. E. Schlick, F. Bettens, R. Ruffmann, M. A. Chirigos and P. Hewetson, *J. Biol. Response Modif.*, 1985, **4**, 628.
152. E. DeClercq, *Antibiot. Chemother.*, 1980, **27**, 251.
153. A. G. Johnson, *Springer Semin. Immunopathol.*, 1979, **2**, 149.
154. H. B. Levey, E. Lvousky, F. Riley, D. Harrington, A. Anderson, J. Moe, J. Hilfenhaus and E. Stephen, *Ann. N. Y. Acad. Sci.*, 1980, **350**, 33.
155. W. A. Carter, P. M. Pitha, L. W. Marshall, I. Tazawa, S. Tazawa and P. O. P. Ts'o, *J. Mol. Biol.*, 1972, **70**, 567.
156. J. E. Talmadge, J. Adams, H. Phillips, M. Collins, B. Lenz, M. Schnieder, E. Schlick, R. Ruffmann, R. H. Wiltrout and M. A. Chirigos, *Cancer Res.*, 1985, **45**, 4774.
157. D. Nolibe, E. Aumaitre and M. N. Thang, *Cancer Res.*, 1985, **45**, 4774.
158. A. E. Maluish, J. W. Reid, E. A. Crisp, W. R. Overton, H. Levy, K. A. Foon and R. B. Herbermann, *J. Biol. Response Modif.*, 1985, **4**, 656.
159. R. B. Herbermann, *Cancer Treat. Rep.*, 1985, **69**, 1161.
160. A. I. Freeman, N. Al-Bussman, J. A. O'Malley, L. Stutzman, S. Bjornsson and W. A. Carter, *J. Med. Virol.*, 1977, **1**, 79.
161. E. DeClercq, *Cancer Res.*, 1977, **37**, 1502.
162. S. L. Lin, J. J. Greene, P. O. P. Ts'o and W. A. Carter, *Nature (London)*, 1982, **297**, 417.
163. J. E. Talmadge, J. Adams, H. Phillips, M. Collins, B. Lenz and M. Chirigos, *Cancer Res.*, 1985, **45**, 1066.
164. M. Ligo, M. S. Chapeker and R. I. Glazer, *Cancer Res.*, 1985, **45**, 439.
165. A. S. Levine, M. Sivulich, P. H. Wiernik and H. B. Levy, *Cancer Res.*, 1979, **39**, 1645.
166. B. G. M. Durie, H. B. Levy, J. Voakes, J. R. Jett and A. S. Levine, *J. Biol. Response Modif.*, 1985, **4**, 518.
167. S. E. Krown, D. Kerr, W. E. Stewart, II, A. F. Field and H. F. Oettgen, *J. Biol. Response Modif.*, 1985, **4**, 640.
168. I. Brodsky, D. R. Strayer, L. J. Krueger and W. A. Carter, *J. Biol. Response Modif.*, 1985, **4**, 669.
169. J. Lacour, F. Lacour, A. Spira, M. Michelson, J. Y. Petit, G. Delage, D. Sarrazin, G. Contesso and J. Viguier, *Lancet*, 1980, **2**, 162.
170. J. Lacour, *J. Biol. Response Modif.*, 1985, **4**, 538.
171. D. A. Stringfellow (ed.), in 'Interferon and Interferon Inducers: Clinical Applications', Dekker, New York, 1980.
172. G. D. Mayer, *Pharmacol. Ther.*, 1980, **8**, 173.
173. F. R. Nicholas, S. D. Weed and G. E. Underwood, *Antimicrob. Agents Chemother.*, 1976, **9**, 433.
174. D. A. Stringfellow, H. C. Vanderberg and S. D. Weed, *J. Interferon Res.*, 1980, **1**, 1.
175. W. Wierenga, H. I. Skulnick, D. A. Stringfellow, S. D. Weed, H. E. Renis and E. E. Eidson, *J. Med. Chem.*, 1980, **23**, 237.
176. W. Wierenga, *Pharmacol. Ther.*, 1985, **30**, 67.
177. H. I. Skulnick, S. D. Weed, E. E. Eidson, H. E. Renis, D. A. Stringfellow and W. Wierenga, *J. Med. Chem.*, 1985, **28**, 1864.
178. T. Oku, J. Imanishi and T. Kishida, *Gann*, 1984, **75**, 631.
179. P. E. Fast, C. A. Hatfield, E. L. Sun and D. A. Stringfellow, *J. Biol. Response Modif.*, 1982, **1**, 199.
180. H. I. Skulnick, J. H. Ludens, M. G. Wendling, E. M. Glenn, N. A. Rohloff, R. J. Smith and W. Wierenga, *J. Med. Chem.*, 1986, **29**, 1499.
181. K. A. Richard and D. E. Tracey, *J. Leukocyte Biol.*, 1985, **37**, 733.
182. R. J. Brideau and J. A. (Wolcott) Nicholas, *Clin. Exp. Immunol.*, 1987, **68**, 613.
183. E. Lotzova, C. A. Savary and D. A. Stringfellow, *J. Immunol.*, 1983, **130**, 965.
184. H. E. Renis, E. E. Eidson, B. A. Court and J. E. Gray, '22nd Interscience Conference on Antimicrobial Agents and Chemotherapy, October 4–6, 1982', Abstract No. 435.
185. H. R. Anthony, M. M. Stevenson and E. Skamene, *Int. J. Immunopharmacol.*, 1982, **4**, 260 (see also *Clin. Invest. Med.*, 1984, **7**, 343).
186. D. A. Stringfellow, *Prog. Cancer Res. Ther.*, 1981, **16**, 215.
187. L. Milas, N. Hunter, H. Ito, E. Lotzova and D. A. Stringfellow, *Clin. Exp. Metastasis*, 1983, **1**, 213.
188. A. Y.-C. Chang, K. J. Pandya, C. Chuang and W. Wierenga, *J. Biol. Response Modif.*, 1986, **5**, 112.
189. Y. A. Sidky, E. C. Borden, W. Wierenga, D. S. Groveman and G. T. Bryan, *Cancer Res.*, 1986, **46**, 3798.
190. L. H. Li, T. L. Wallace, K. A. Richard and D. E. Tracey, *Cancer Res.*, 1985, **45**, 532.

191. L. H. Li, T. F. DeKoning and T. L. Wallace, *Proc. Am. Assoc. Cancer Res.*, 1987, **28**, 1368.
192. R. H. Earhart, R. D. Hamilton, C. S. Henry, C. K. Hanover, M. H. Maile, B. L. Agarwal and W. M. Todd, *Proc. Am. Assoc. Cancer Res.*, 1985, **26**, 629.
193. V. St. Georgiev, in 'Annual Reports of Medicinal Chemistry', Academic Press, New York, 1987, vol. 22, p. 127.
194. A. J. Lewis, J. Chang and S. C. Gilman, in 'Trends in Medicinal Chemistry', ed. E. Mutschler and E. Winterfeldt, VCH Verlagsgesellschaft, Weinheim, 1987, p. 517.
195. R. W. Sidwell, J. H. Huffman, E. W. Call, R. P. Warren, L. A. Radov and R. J. Murray, *Antimicrob. Agents Chemother.*, 1987, **31**, 1130.
196. A. Chachoua, H. Hochster, C. Ward, G. Gutknecht, A. Chuang-Stein, J. Nicholas and J. Merritt, *Proc. Am. Soc. Clin. Oncol.*, 1989, in press.
197. J.-P. Tenu, A. Adam, V. Souvannavong, G. Barratt, A. Yapo, J.-F. Petit, M. Level, M. Clemance and K. Douglas, *FEBS Lett.*, 1987, **220**, 93.
198. J. E. Groopman, R. T. Mitsuyasu, M. J. DeLeo, D. H. Oette and D. W. Golde, *New Engl. J. Med.*, 1987, **317**, 593.
199. G. Morstyn and A. W. Burgess, *Cancer Res.*, 1988, **48**, 5624.

16.1

Molecular Mechanism of the Action of 1,25-Dihydroxyvitamin D₃

HECTOR F. DELUCA, JAMES BURMESTER, HISHAM DARWISH and
JOHANN KRISINGER
University of Wisconsin-Madison, WI, USA

16.1.1 THE CLASSICAL ACTIONS OF 1,25-DIHYDROXYVITAMIN D₃

Vitamin D was discovered as being essential for the mineralization of the skeleton and thus for the prevention of the diseases rickets and osteomalacia.[1,2] It was apparent even at that time that the animal in the vitamin D deficient state is able to synthesize organic matrix of the skeleton, but is unable to deposit calcium and phosphorus in the form of hydroxyapatite on the collagen fibrils to bring about mineralization of the skeleton.[3] Although classic experiments provided strong evidence that vitamin D was not involved in the direct mineralization process, clinical evidence suggested that vitamin D may well be required for the synthesis of organic matrix of bone and for the mineralization process *per se*.[4,5]

Recently, however, very clear evidence has been presented that vitamin D is not required for either the synthesis of organic matrix of bone or the mineralization process as such.[6-8] In short, the function of vitamin D is to raise blood calcium and phosphorus to levels that are required for the mineralization process.[3,8-10] To do this, vitamin D stimulates the enterocyte of the small intestine to absorb calcium and phosphorus from dietary components.[10] It stimulates bone cells to transport calcium from the bone fluid compartment to the plasma compartment,[10] and finally it stimulates the distal renal tubules to reabsorb the remaining calcium in the forming urine.[11] These then represent the classical actions of vitamin D that prevent the disease rickets, and the adult counterpart osteomalacia.

For almost 50 years it was believed that vitamin D must act directly to bring about its functions in calcium and phosphorus transport. In 1960 and in 1967, two prominent investigators in the field concluded that vitamin D functions directly without metabolic alteration in the target tissues.[12, 13] However, the synthesis of radiolabeled vitamin D of high enough specific activity permitted experiments with truly physiologic doses. With these doses it could be demonstrated that vitamin D rapidly disappears and becomes transformed into polar metabolites.[14] Thus, it was demonstrated that vitamin D must be processed first in the liver and subsequently in the kidney before it could stimulate the classical target organs.[15] Isolation and identification of these metabolites were carried out in 1968 and in 1971. Furthermore, their structures, which were deduced by mass spectrometry, specific chemical reactions, UV absorption spectrophotometry and NMR spectrometry, were confirmed by chemical synthesis.[15] Thus, it became clear that vitamin D, whether absorbed in the diet or manufactured in skin, is first 25-hydroxylated in the microsomes of the hepatocytes to form the circulating form of vitamin D, 25-hydroxyvitamin D_3 (25-OH-D_3). This compound is then converted in the mitochondria of the kidney to the final vitamin D hormone, 1,25-dihydroxyvitamin D_3 (1,25-$(OH)_2D_3$; Figure 1). The actions reported here will be those of 1,25-$(OH)_2D_3$.

1,25-Dihydroxyvitamin D_3 is a true steroid hormone[10] whose biogenesis is strongly feedback regulated by the need for calcium and phosphorus. This hormone in turn plays an important role in the mobilization of these two important mineral elements from diet and, when required, from bone. It is on these classical actions that this review will focus. It will also call the attention of readers to important new functions of the vitamin D hormone at previously unappreciated sites of action.

16.1.1.1 Intestinal Calcium and Phosphorus Transport

The enterocyte of the small intestine transports calcium against an electrochemical potential gradient.[16, 17] It also transports phosphorus against an electrochemical potential gradient in an independent manner.[16, 18] Sodium is required for the expulsion of calcium on the serosal surface,[19] whereas sodium is required for phosphate transport on the mucosal surface.[18–20] Both processes are energy dependent, and the response to 1,25-$(OH)_2D_3$ requires hours and not minutes.[21] A typical time course of intestinal calcium transport response is shown in Figure 2.[22] In this experiment a single injection of 1,25-$(OH)_2D_3$ had no effect on calcium transport until approximately 3–4 h post-injection, reaching a maximum at 6 h, followed by a minimum at 12 h, only to return to a maximum at 24 h and remain there for several days. This curious biphasic response has been reproduced many times.[23, 24] A second injection after 24 h brings about a superinduction of the initial response but does not bring about a comparable increase in transport by the second mechanism. Thus, it appears that there may be two mechanisms of intestinal calcium transport in response to 1,25-$(OH)_2D_3$. One most certainly appears to be direct action on the enterocyte and the second may be an action on the crypt cells causing their differentiation into calcium-transporting cells as they appear in the villus. Thus, the response to the vitamin D hormone *in vivo* is a complex one.

There has been considerable controversy as to whether the intestinal calcium transport response is blocked by transcription and translation inhibitors.[25, 26] Experiments *in vivo* have been equivocal and perhaps uninterpretable. However, in chick intestinal organ cultures, it is quite clear that transcription and protein synthesis inhibitors specifically and reversibly block the intestinal calcium transport response to 1,25-$(OH)_2D_3$.[27] It therefore appears that this function of vitamin D is at least in part nuclear mediated. More recently, reports from a single laboratory[28] have appeared, claiming rapid intestinal calcium transport responses of the order of 10–14 min post-injection to 1,25-$(OH)_2D_3$. Thus far, confirmation of this phenomenon is lacking and has not been seen in the rat in our laboratory.

The mechanism of intestinal calcium transport remains largely unknown. An intestinal membrane calcium-binding complex has been reported to be formed in response to 1,25-$(OH)_2D_3$.[29] However, most certainly a cytoplasmic calcium-binding protein is specifically synthesized in response to 1,25-$(OH)_2D_3$.[30] This calcium-binding protein is 28 000 Da in the case of the chick, and 9000 in the case of mammals.[30] Exactly how and if it functions in calcium transport remains largely unknown.

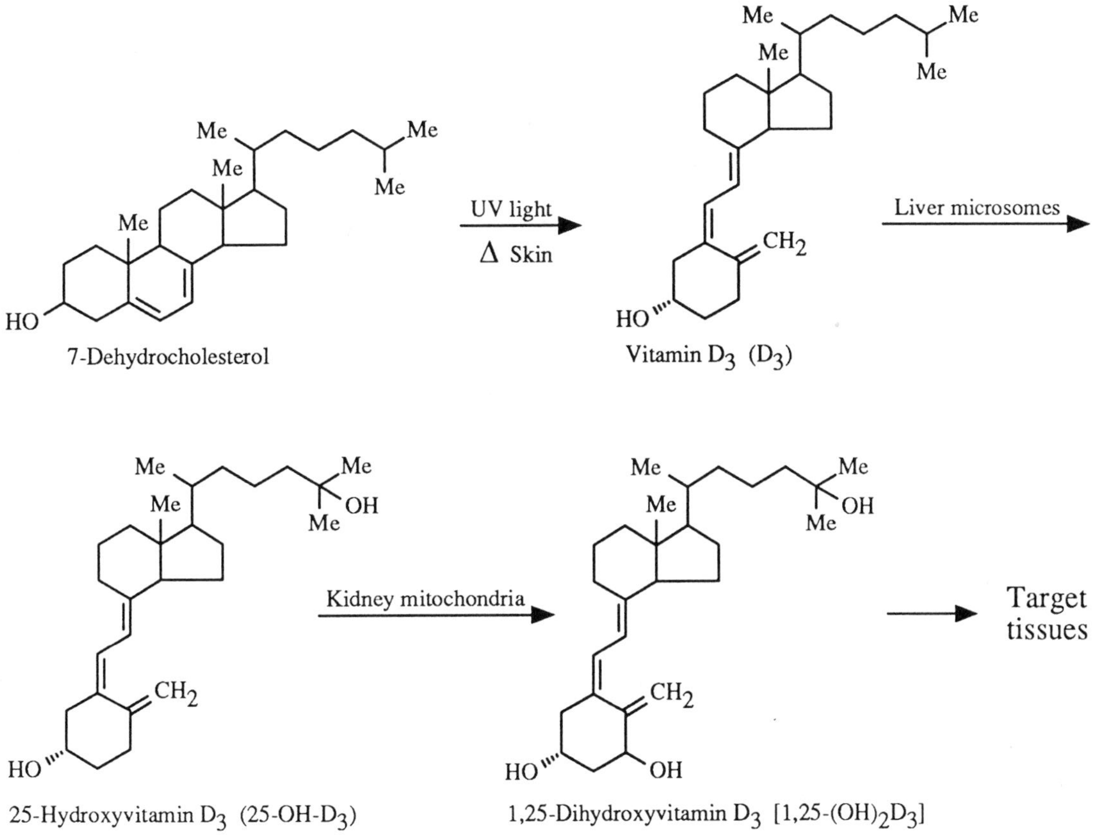

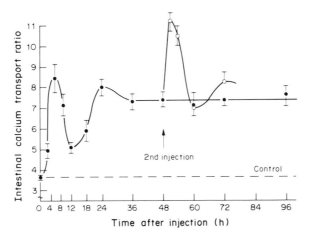

Figure 1   Biogenesis and functional metabolism of vitamin D₃

Figure 2   Time course of response of intestinal calcium transport to intravenous administration of 1,25-(OH)₂D₃. Vitamin D deficient rats were injected with either vehicle or *via* vehicle containing 650 pmol of 1,25-(OH)₂D₃. At various times indicated, groups of six animals were killed and their intestinal calcium transport determined by the everted sac method. At 48 h, a second injection of 1,25-(OH)₂D₃ was administered. Vertical bars represent standard errors of the mean for six animals

16.1.1.2   Functions of 1,25-Dihydroxyvitamin D₃ in Bone

1,25-Dihydroxyvitamin D₃ has profound actions on bone. As pointed out previously, these actions are not on the mineralization process, although it has been reported that 1,25-(OH)₂D₃ in culture may stimulate collagen synthesis.[31] However, no evidence for this phenomenon is found *in vivo*. The actions of 1,25-(OH)₂D₃ in bone are twofold. 1,25-Dihydroxyvitamin D₃ given to vitamin

D deficient rats on a low calcium diet will induce the mobilization of calcium from the skeleton to the plasma compartment.[32, 33] This is a rapid response which can be measured within 6 h after injection and which disappears after about 12 h post-injection.[34] This mobilization of calcium requires the presence of parathyroid hormone.[32] In a reverse fashion, the mobilization of calcium by parathyroid hormone from bone also requires the presence of the vitamin D hormone *in vivo*.[35] The molecular mechanism of this mobilization remains largely unknown.

1,25-Dihydroxyvitamin D_3 added to cultures of embryonic bone brings about osteoclastic-mediated bone resorption.[36, 37] This process does not require the presence of the parathyroid hormone in clear contrast to the *in vivo* experiments.[38] In fact, both 1,25-$(OH)_2D_3$ and parathyroid hormone cause identical bone resorptive activity. How this can be interpreted *in vivo* is unknown at the present time. Osteoclastic-mediated bone resorption is the first event in the bone remodeling system.[39] Thus, these two hormones may activate osteoclastic-mediated bone resorption that is required for bone formation in the remodeling systems.

16.1.1.3   1,25-Dihydroxyvitamin D_3 and Kidney Function

1,25-Dihydroxyvitamin D_3 has an important role in the distal renal tubule, where it stimulates renal reabsorption of calcium.[11] Recent work has provided convincing demonstration of this important function of 1,25-$(OH)_2D_3$. As with the bone calcium mobilization system, 1,25-$(OH)_2D_3$ requires the presence of parathyroid hormone for this function to occur.

The time course of response of all systems is consistent with a nuclear-mediated action of 1,25-$(OH)_2D_3$. The major question is how does 1,25-$(OH)_2D_3$, a steroid hormone, mediate these classical actions of vitamin D?

16.1.2   RECEPTORS FOR 1,25-DIHYDROXYVITAMIN D_3

Following an intravenous injection of 1,25-$(OH)_2$-$[^3H]D_3$, it localizes in the nuclei of the enterocyte and crypt cells of the small intestine. This has been clearly demonstrated by frozen section autoradiography done in an extremely careful manner.[40,41] Similar nuclear localization of 1,25-$(OH)_2D_3$ can be found in osteoblasts, in bone lining cells and in the distal renal tubules.[42] This localization is saturable and can be competed away by excess nonradioctive 1,25-$(OH)_2D_3$. It is not competed away by 25-OH-D_3 given in physiological amounts. Thus, prior to the first measurable intestinal response to 1,25-$(OH)_2D_3$, this hormone localizes in the nuclei and not in any other cell component such as the basolateral membrane, the brush border or the Golgi apparatus. Thus, 1,25-$(OH)_2D_3$, which is regarded as a steroid, is found in the nuclei of the target cells, and its actions are blocked by transcription and translation inhibitors. A mechanism similar to that postulated for other steroid hormones can, therefore, be expected.

Consistent with this hypothesis was the demonstration of the existence of specific receptors for 1,25-$(OH)_2D_3$. Specific binding of 1,25-$(OH)_2D_3$ to nuclear chromatin was demonstrated by Brumbaugh and Haussler.[43] The preparation of soluble cell extracts containing a macromolecule sedimenting at 3.7S and which specifically binds 1,25-$(OH)_2D_3$ with high affinity and low capacity was provided by Kream *et al.*[44] This receptor was found largely in the nuclei in low salt extracts with very little appearing in the cytoplasm.[45] Thus, by classical cell fractionation, it has been demonstrated in two laboratories that less than 10% of the specific 1,25-$(OH)_2D_3$ binding protein is found in the cytosol and 90% found in the nuclei. The receptor for 1,25-$(OH)_2D_3$ appears likely to be a nucleoprotein. However, true frozen section autoradiography experiments which delineate where the receptor might be prior to interaction with the hormone have not yet been satisfactorily carried out despite recent reports.[46] It is unknown, therefore, whether the receptor to 1,25-$(OH)_2D_3$ is initially found in the cytosol, becoming transformed following interaction with the hormone, then translocating to the nucleus and carrying out the functions of the vitamin D hormone. It is equally possible that 1,25-$(OH)_2D_3$ appears in the nucleus, then interacts with the receptor, initiating the sequence of events resulting in intestinal calcium transport. As will be pointed out subsequently, the receptor for 1,25-$(OH)_2D_3$ has now been demonstrated in a variety of cells and tissues. The meaning of this distribution is not fully known at the present time.

Of considerable importance are experiments which provide evidence that the interaction of the receptor with the ligand is required for expression of vitamin D activity. Two lines of evidence have been provided. The first comes from experiments in which a vitamin D resistant rachitic condition has been described where there is a target organ resistance to the vitamin D hormone.[47, 48] A subgroup of these vitamin D resistant subjects suffers from a defective receptor in that it does not bind ligand.[49] Thus, the intestine of these subjects is unable to respond to the hormone, illustrating the requirement of a functional receptor for 1,25-$(OH)_2D_3$ for the intestinal calcium transport response.

Another line of evidence is that the developing intestine of neonatal rats does not respond to 1,25-$(OH)_2D_3$ until approximately 16–18 days post-partum.[50] Prior to that time there is an absence of receptor for 1,25-$(OH)_2D_3$ and the receptor appears at precisely the time when the intestinal calcium transport response to 1,25-$(OH)_2D_3$ makes its appearance.[51] Adrenalectomy delays this response, whereas injection of hydrocortisone stimulates the response.[51] Thus, in the case of the neonatal rat, its intestine is not responsive to vitamin D until the receptor for 1,25-$(OH)_2D_3$ is found in the target cells.

More recently, cell cultures lacking receptor for 1,25-$(OH)_2D_3$ show a lack of responsiveness to the hormone, whereas other cells of the same line retaining receptor retain their responsiveness as well.[52] Thus, it is abundantly clear that the receptor is required for the hormone to carry out its function.

16.1.3 BIOCHEMICAL CHARACTERIZATION OF THE 1,25-DIHYDROXYVITAMIN D_3 RECEPTOR

Scatchard plot analysis has revealed the receptor from a variety of sources to have a k_D of the order of 5×10^{-11} to approximately 1×10^{-10} M.[53] Furthermore, the receptor is rather selective for the vitamin D hormone, showing diminished binding to various metabolites of vitamin D.[53] For example, the precursor of 1,25-$(OH)_2D_3$ binds at least one and possibly two orders of magnitude less tightly to the receptor than does the final vitamin D hormone.[54] 1,24,25-Trihydroxyvitamin D_3 is about one-tenth as active as 1,25-$(OH)_2D_3$ in binding to the receptor. In short, the biological activity of vitamin D metabolites correlates well with their affinity for the receptor. In fact, it is believed that the reason 25-OH-D_3 acts *in vivo* in anephric patients is because it is given at high enough concentration to serve as an analog of 1,25-$(OH)_2D_3$ for the intestinal receptor.[10, 53] Nevertheless, the receptor shows high selectivity for 1,25-$(OH)_2D_3$.

There are exceptions to the rule among analogs of 1,25-$(OH)_2D_3$. For example, 26,27-hexafluoro-1,25-$(OH)_2D_3$ and 24,24-difluoro-1,25-$(OH)_2D_3$ are actually more biologically active *in vivo* than 1,25-$(OH)_2D_3$, but they either bind equally well or not quite as well as 1,25-$(OH)_2D_3$ to the receptor.[55, 56] The increased activity may be that the fluoro derivatives are less rapidly degraded metabolically than 1,25-$(OH)_2D_3$. Alternatively, the more lipophilic nature of the fluoro-substituted compounds may also play a role in increased biological activity.

It has been suggested that the molecular weight of the 1,25-$(OH)_2D_3$ receptor is as high as 100 000.[57] However, it is quite clear now by means of immunoblotting with monoclonal antibodies that the receptor for 1,25-$(OH)_2D_3$ in mammals has a molecular weight of approximately 55 000[58, 59] and in birds two receptor bands are seen, one having a molecular weight of 61 000 and the other a molecular weight of 63 000.[60] These conclusions are further supported by the size of the coding region of the cDNA for the receptor.[61, 62]

The isoelectric point of the receptor appears to be somewhere around 6.1, although charge heterogeneity appears to be evident as will be described below.[63] A pI of 5.9 is also noted as well as a form of the receptor which does not enter the electrofocusing gel.[64]

16.1.4 PURIFICATION OF RECEPTOR AND DEVELOPMENT OF IMMUNOLOGICAL PROBES

The 1,25-$(OH)_2D_3$ receptor is a very low abundance nuclear protein.[65] It has been estimated that to reach homogeneity from whole tissue extracts would require approximately 80 000-fold purification.[65, 66] This discouraging idea did not, however, prevent attempts by primarily two laboratories to purify the receptor.[65–68] Purification has been carried out primarily from chick and pig intestinal sources. So far, ligand affinity chromatography has not proved useful, while DNA and immunoaffinity purification has been successfully applied, as will be described below.

The first important determination for purification is obtaining a tissue source with the highest concentration of receptor. So far the richest natural source of the 1,25-$(OH)_2D_3$ receptor is the intestine. The chick intestine possesses approximately 500 fmol of binding activity per mg protein[67] and the pig intestine, when taken from 60-lb pigs, has a concentration of as high as 2000 fmol per mg protein.[65] An additional preliminary purification could be obtained by isolating the nuclei and eliminating the cytoplasmic proteins. Furthermore, it is important to wash the intestinal mucosa as free of proteolytic enzymes as possible prior to extraction.[44]

An important purification resulted from the nucleotide-binding properties of the receptor. Thus, receptor for 1,25-$(OH)_2D_3$ will bind to nonspecific DNA sufficiently tightly to perform chromatography. Thus, DNA immobilized on cellulose or Sephadex can be used for purification. The receptor can be eluted with increasing salt concentrations. Approximately 0.22 M potassium chloride will elute the receptor from immobilized DNA. This results in a substantial purification with approximately a 50% yield. Ammonium sulfate fractionation will also bring about significant purification, but gel exclusion chromatography either by high performance liquid chromatography (HPLC) or by gravity flow chromatography will also give a substantial purification. Final purification is obtained by means of ion exchange chromatography, the best preparations being approximately 24% pure with the best preparation reported being of 50% purity following these four steps in purification.[65] Electrofocusing columns have been used as have electrophoretic separations, both of which give low yields but considerable purity.[63] It is unclear as to whether homogeneous preparations can be obtained by classical purification, although by Coomassie Blue staining of gels, a homogeneous preparation of chick intestinal receptor appeared to be obtained at 60 000-fold purification.[63] On the other hand, it is likely that if these gels had been stained with a more sensitive stain, such as silver nitrate, additional bands would have been detected. In any case, purification of sizable quantities of the receptor by classical protein fractionation was not possible. At 50% purity, it was possible to demonstrate by renaturing the protein bands from SDS gels that the 55 000 molecular weight band represented the true porcine receptor, which was then confirmed by immunoblotting using monoclonal antibodies generated from the partially purified receptor.[65]

By means of immunization with the impure porcine preparations, a titer of antibodies could be detected in the plasma of mice.[69] Fusion of spleen cells taken from these mice with myeloma cells resulted in the successful generation of 24 monoclonal antibodies directed to the 1,25-$(OH)_2D_3$ receptor. Of these, 17 were well characterized. Monoclonal antibodies using spleen from immunized rats have also been obtained by both Pike *et al.*[70] and by Dame *et al.*[69] These, however, proved to be less useful in the authors' laboratory than the mouse antibodies. The cross-reactivity of the 17 monoclonal antibodies obtained is shown in Table 1. Furthermore, those that react in immunoblotting on SDS gel preparations are illustrated. Thus, eight of the antibodies could be used to detect receptor protein on SDS gels using Western blotting.

The antibodies could be segregated into four distinct epitope groups.[69] By means of competition experiments, it was possible to demonstrate that one group recognized only the pig receptor and

Table 1   Monoclonal Antibodies to the Porcine Intestinal Receptor

	Cross-reactivity, intestinal receptor					
Clone designation	Pig	Monkey	Human	Rat	Chicken	Immunoblot
Mouse: NS-1						
IVA7E7	+	+	+	+	+	+
IVB12G12[a]	+	+	+	+	+	+
IVG8C11	+	+	+	+	+	+
VA3C12	+	+	+	+	+	−
VB3F12	+	+	+	+	+	−
VD2F12	+	+	+	+	+	+
VIIA1E9A7	+	+	+	+	+	−
VIIIB8B2A9	+	+	+	+	+	−
VIIID8C12	+	+	+	+	+	+
VIIIF7E12	+	+	+	+	+	−
IXD5F10	+	+	+	+	+	−
XA9E8	+	+	+	+	+	−
XH12G11	+	+	+	+	+	+
XIID9G5D6	+	+	+	+	+	−
XVA9A7B6	+	+	+	+	+	−
XVIE6E6G10[b]	+	−	−	−	−	+
XVIE10B6A5	+	−	−	−	−	+
Rat: NS-1						
IXC1H5	+	+	nd[c]	−	+	+

[a] IgA; all other mouse hybridomas IgG.   [b] Protein A binding antibody.   [c] Not done.

three other groups of antibodies were found distinct from each other. One group of antibodies prevented binding of the receptor to DNA cellulose, indicating that this epitope fell very near or on the DNA-binding site of the receptor. These distinct epitope groups proved to be useful in subsequent work, not only in cloning but also in immunoblotting. Pike *et al.* retained two monoclonal antibodies to the same epitope site on the chick receptor.[71] These antibodies, however, cross-reacted with receptor from other sources.

The monoclonal antibodies have been extremely useful in studying the structure, chemistry and biology of the 1,25-$(OH)_2D_3$ receptor. Two reports of successful immunoaffinity chromatography for the receptor have appeared.[71, 72] In the latest report, a monoclonal antibody specific for the pig intestinal receptor was immobilized on a Sepharose-CL4B resin. The resin bound the specific ligand-binding activity quantitatively from a pig intestinal extract. Elution with high salt and high pH successfully brought off the receptor in almost homogeneous form.[73] The final purification of the receptor was carried out on sodium dodecyl sulfate gels to yield a single band of pure material, which was then subjected to amino acid sequence analysis. The receptor is amino terminal blocked *in vivo* and hence did not enter the amino acid sequencing system. However, the immunoaffinity purified receptor could be digested with a protease directly in the stacking gel and then developed to yield four bands which were then sequenced. This led to two segments of amino acid sequence being determined for the hog intestinal nuclear receptor. This immunoaffinity purification system is now being utilized to purify receptor for specific binding to nucleotide sequences in the promoter region of the calcium-binding protein gene as will be described below.

Another important question was to determine whether in rat intestinal tissue all the specific binding for 1,25-$(OH)_2D_3$ is due to the 1,25-$(OH)_2D_3$ receptor.[59] To carry out this study, biotinylated monoclonal antibody was used to form a complex with the receptor–ligand complex and the entire complex was precipitated by means of avidin coupled to Sepharose beads. This resulted in 100% precipitation of the specific binding activity in whole rat and hog intestinal mucosal extracts.[59] Thus, it appears that receptor and receptor-related peptides are responsible for all of the specific binding of 1,25-$(OH)_2D_3$ found in the intestine.

The battery of monoclonal antibodies has also been used for immunoblotting experiments. Thus, both from the laboratories of Pike[74, 75] and of DeLuca[59, 65] has come the clear evidence that the highest molecular weight receptor protein in mammals is 55 000 and the highest molecular weight protein from the chick is 63 000. In whole tissue extracts of small intestine, bands of immunoreactive material can be detected at 43 000 Da and 28 000 Da. These probably represent proteolytic cleavage products of the receptor.

Of considerable importance is the immunoblotting of fresh tissue and nuclear extracts from rat and pig on two-dimensional gel electrophoresis.[59] These results confirmed sodium dodecyl sulfate tube gel studies in which the highest molecular weight protein that blots with the various monoclonal antibodies is 55 000 in the case of the pig and rat. However, the electrofocusing portion of the two-dimensional gel system separates that receptor band into three distinct spots. One has an isoelectric point of 6.1, another has an isoelectric point of 5.9 and still another spot does not enter the electrofocusing gel either from the acid or base side. Thus, there appear to be three forms of the receptor, the major form being the protein with a molecular weight of 55 000 and an isoelectric point of about 6.1. A minor form has an isoelectric point at 5.9 and it could be that these represent either phosphorylated or dephosphorylated forms of the receptor. Other possibilities exist as well. No evidence of glycosylation of the receptor was found.

It is of some interest that a portion of the receptor did not enter the electrofocusing gel. It is apparent that in 8 M guanidine some complex form of the receptor still exists, which prevents its entrance into the gel. This would, therefore, represent an interesting form of the receptor. It is not clear which of the three forms of the receptor is the active form, and it is not clear at this stage whether all three forms of the receptor are capable of binding ligand. Certainly one of these forms represents the functional form of the 1,25-$(OH)_2D_3$ receptor, and certainly microheterogeneity is apparent for the 1,25-$(OH)_2D_3$ receptor.

By far the most important application of the monoclonal antibodies to the receptor is in screening cDNA expression libraries in order to clone the receptor. This has been successfully carried out by two groups, that of O'Malley and Pike and that of DeLuca. This will be described in the next section.

Two other applications of the monoclonal antibody for the receptor have been developed. One is an immunoassay for total receptor peptide concentration. Throughout the course of 1,25-$(OH)_2D_3$ receptor studies, there has been a great interest in determining occupied and unoccupied forms of the receptor. There is also the possibility that there are forms of the receptor which are no longer capable of binding ligand, or alternatively precursor forms of the receptor which are incapable of binding ligand. The estimates of occupied and unoccupied receptor concentrations are at best highly suspect and thus are not worthy of discussion here. Both kinetic analysis[76] and pleotropic agent released ligand have been used as methods of determining occupied receptor.[77] In other studies, regulation of receptor has been deduced primarily on the basis of ligand binding,[78-80] conclusions from which are suspect. For these reasons, an immunoaffinity assay for the receptor is highly desirable. Standard immunoassays require a standard protein that can be radiolabeled and used for competition with unlabeled protein. This has been a major problem, since the receptor is difficult to obtain in quantity and in the iodinated form it is quite unstable. Instead, Sandgren and DeLuca[81] have developed a sandwich assay in which one monoclonal antibody is used to bind the receptor and a monoclonal antibody that reacts to a different site is iodinated and used to measure the amount of receptor immobilized by the first monoclonal antibody. Using this method, it has been determined that in pig and rat intestine, total receptor peptide is approximately 1.5 times the level determined by ligand-binding activity. Thus, it appears that 30% of the $1,25\text{-}(OH)_2D_3$ receptor protein is either incapable of binding ligand or is occupied under normal circumstances. This assay will find great usefulness in determining receptor regulation and quantitating receptor in a variety of tissues.

An important new development has been the discovery of a new method of assaying for $1,25\text{-}(OH)_2D_3$ using the monoclonal antibodies directed to the receptor (DeLuca, Prahl, Dame and Pierce, unpublished results). In this assay, just saturating amounts of radioligand are added to a sample of receptor. To this is added the sample of serum or plasma containing the vitamin D transport protein and the $1,25\text{-}(OH)_2D_3$ to be measured. The receptor, because of its high affinity for ligand, will take $1,25\text{-}(OH)_2D_3$ from the blood transport protein. This unlabeled $1,25\text{-}(OH)_2D_3$ in the serum will complete with the radiolabeled $1,25\text{-}(OH)_2D_3$ for the binding site on the receptor. The receptor then is quantitatively precipitated using a tight binding monoclonal antibody that has been biotinylated. Immunoprecipitation is completed with avidin bound to Sepharose beads. The radioligand in the precipitate is counted. The displacement curve is then used to determine the amount of unlabeled $1,25\text{-}(OH)_2D_3$ in the blood sample. The vitamin D transport protein binds all other metabolites of vitamin D, so they are unable to interfere. The specific immunoprecipitation eliminates the need for extraction and chromatography and thus allows for a very sensitive and rapid assay in which large numbers of samples can be processed in a single day. Undoubtedly, other applications of the antibodies will be found.

16.1.5   CLONING OF THE 1,25-DIHYDROXYVITAMIN D₃ RECEPTORS: STRUCTURE OF THE cDNA AND PROTEIN

A total of four papers have now appeared on cloning of the $1,25\text{-}(OH)_2D_3$ receptor.[61, 62, 82, 83] A λGT-11 cDNA expression library from chick intestine was used in the first report in which a partial amino acid sequence for the receptor was reported.[82] That this cDNA represented the receptor protein depended largely on the selectivity of the monoclonal antibody, on the homology of the determined sequence with the sequence of other steroid hormone receptors, and on hybrid select translation experiments.[82] A λGT-11 cDNA expression library prepared from rat kidney mRNA was used by the DeLuca group.[83] A mixture of three monoclonal antibodies each directed to different epitope groups on the receptor was used to screen this expression library. A clone was isolated which produced a protein in *E. coli* containing all three of the regions detected by the three different monoclonal antibodies. Of considerable interest is that the monoclonal antibodies that are specific for pig receptor did not recognize the recombinant protein nor was it recognized by an irrelevant antibody.[83] Furthermore, an irrelevant sequence in the λGT-11 expression vector did not produce a material recognized by the antibodies. The recombinant fusion protein when produced in *E. coli* was fully capable of binding $1,25\text{-}(OH)_2D_3$ with the expected affinity and capacity. Finally, the partial sequence of the receptor deduced from this clone exactly correlated with a sequence in the chick cDNA clone and most important is that the sequence had in it a section that exactly agreed with the partial sequence obtained directly on the isolated porcine receptor. The receptor cDNA for rat kidney has been isolated and sequenced. The chick cDNA probe has been used to isolate a full length cDNA, representing the human receptor, by O'Malley's group.[62] At the same time, a full length cDNA sequence for the rat receptor has also been obtained by the DeLuca group.[61] The homology between human and rat cDNA is high. The two receptors are 100% homologous in the DNA-binding region, while the steroid-binding domain is greater than 93% conserved. The lowest homology is found in the hinge region in which four amino acids are deleted in the rat sequence. The structure of the rat receptor cDNA is presented in Figure 3. The structure of the receptor is very much like that of the other steroid hormone receptors. It has a DNA-binding domain, a hinge area

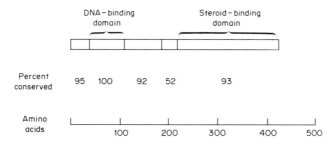

Figure 3 Diagrammatic representation of the 1,25-(OH)₂D₃ receptor protein cloned from a λGT-11 library made from rat kidney mRNA. The percent conserved indicates the percent of homology between the rat *versus* human sequences. The amino acid number is indicated on the lowest bar

and a ligand-binding domain. Exactly how these receptors bind to DNA and the steroid remains unknown at the present time. The full three-dimensional structure of the receptor will be of considerable interest in determining how the ligand is bound and how, in binding the ligand, the receptor is altered in order to bind to specific DNA sequences which in turn may be responsible for selectively turning on the expression of specific structural genes.

16.1.6 RECEPTOR REGULATION

It is currently believed that, in the vitamin D deficient state, receptor is constitutively present, suggesting that 1,25-(OH)₂D₃ is not required for expression of the receptor gene.[44] However, there have been reports that 1,25-(OH)₂D₃ added to cells in culture increases ligand-binding capacity.[84] It has been speculated that receptor concentration is increased by 1,25-(OH)₂D₃. Support for this idea has been obtained by immunoblotting, although it is not clear how quantitative the immunoblotting experiments are.[82] In 3T6 cells, 1,25-(OH)₂D₃ increases mRNA levels for the receptor according to Northern analysis.[82] It therefore appears that 1,25-(OH)₂D₃ may up-regulate receptor concentration by a transcriptional means, which would suggest that the ligand plus receptor must in some way interact with the receptor gene. However, true quantitative experiments have not yet been carried out, and thus a firm conclusion as to the nature of the up-regulation is not available.

The most interesting stage of the regulation of receptor levels is during development. 1,25-Dihydroxyvitamin D₃ receptor appears in chick intestine at about 14 days of incubation and may appear as early as 12 days.[85] The same is true for the chorioallantoic membrane.[85] In mammals, developmental studies have been carried out in the rat in which it appears that receptors are found in intestine only after 16 days post-partum.[51,86] Thus, the small intestine is not responsive to 1,25-(OH)₂D₃ until this period. At this time, the intestine begins to transport calcium actively and becomes responsive to 1,25-(OH)₂D₃.[50] This is now clearly a receptor regulation. Adrenalectomy delays the appearance of receptor and hydrocortisone will cause precocious appearance of the receptor.[51] Furthermore, incubation of intestinal tissue with hydrocortisone *in vitro* brings about an increase in 1,25-(OH)₂D₃ binding.[87] It may well be, therefore, that glucocorticoids may regulate expression of the 1,25-(OH)₂D₃ receptor gene, at least in the neonatal state. This area requires considerable investigation and may provide important new information on vitamin D responsiveness.

One of the most interesting areas of investigation is into the disease vitamin D dependency rickets Type II. This disease was discovered when children were found with high blood levels of 1,25-(OH)₂D₃ but having severe rickets.[47,48] This autosomal recessive disorder is a defect in target organ responsiveness to the receptor. Liberman *et al.* have taken fibroblasts from such patients and in comparison with normal human fibroblasts have found that unlike normal fibroblasts, a subset of these subjects possess a receptor unable to bind ligand.[88] Still another group possesses a ligand-binding receptor that is unable to bind to DNA.[88] This series of subjects should provide important information on the molecular mechanism of action of vitamin D as well as understanding the genetic defect involved.

Phosphorylation of steroid hormone receptors is well known.[89,90] Apparently, the 1,25-(OH)₂D₃ receptor is also phosphorylated.[91] Pike and his colleagues have demonstrated that receptor as studied on sodium dodecyl sulfate gels accumulates ³²P derived from ATP.[91] This ³²P can be removed by phosphatase and appears to be a serine phosphorylation. It is not clear which protein kinase is involved in the phosphorylation nor is it clear whether the phosphorylation activates or deactivates the receptor. It is also possible that phosphorylation plays no role in receptor activity. Nevertheless, it is apparent that chick receptor does, in fact, become phosphorylated by a protein kinase. Only when the appropriate molecular system has been isolated will it be possible to determine whether phosphorylation or dephosphorylation is involved in receptor activation or deactivation.

16.1.7 GENE EXPRESSION IN RESPONSE TO 1,25-DIHYDROXYVITAMIN D_3 AND ITS RECEPTOR

Unlike other steroid hormone receptors, the proteins made in response to $1,25\text{-}(OH)_2D_3$ remain largely unknown. A notable exception is the calcium-binding protein originally reported by Wasserman and Taylor.[92,93] In the intestine, chicks synthesize a calcium-binding protein having a molecular weight of 28 000.[92] It possesses two high affinity calcium-binding sites. In mammals the intestinal vitamin D induced calcium-binding protein has a molecular weight of 9000.[94] These proteins are absent in vitamin D deficiency and are initiated in response to the vitamin D hormone.[30] There has been considerable debate as to whether the calcium-binding protein made in response to $1,25\text{-}(OH)_2D_3$ is, in fact, responsible for calcium transport.[95-97] It seems almost certain that other proteins must be induced by $1,25\text{-}(OH)_2D_3$ to carry out the calcium transport process. So far these have not yet been defined, although in the intestine there have been reports that ornithine decarboxylase,[98] alkaline phosphatase[99] and a calcium dependent ATPase[100] may be induced by $1,25\text{-}(OH)_2D_3$. In addition, there is a large molecular weight calcium-binding protein found in the membranes that has been reported to be induced by $1,25\text{-}(OH)_2D_3$.[100] So far these have been largely unstudied and their relationship to the vitamin D response is not clear. In the case of ornithine decarboxylase, it is unlikely that this enzyme is specifically induced by $1,25\text{-}(OH)_2D_3$, since many other agents appear to increase ornithine decarboxylase.

Only the calcium-binding proteins of the small intestine are available as clear products of $1,25\text{-}(OH)_2D_3$ action. For this reason, considerable effort has been placed on the biochemistry of these calcium-binding proteins, especially for the possible role they may play in calcium transport. A full length cDNA has been obtained for the rat intestinal calcium-binding protein and the entire structure of the calcium-binding protein mRNA and hence protein is known.[101,102] This structure agrees exactly with an amino acid structure determined by classical sequence analysis except for two amino acids which were uncertain in the case of the protein sequence analysis.[103] The cDNA has been used to clone the calcium-binding protein gene.[104,105] The structure of the calcium-binding protein gene as deduced is shown in Figure 4. An imperfect palindrome at the end of the first exon and the beginning of the first intron of the gene is found. This imperfect palindrome has considerable homology with the glucocorticoid and estrogen responsive elements as shown in Figure 5, and has been postulated as being the D responsive element. The chick intestinal calcium-binding protein cDNA and its corresponding gene have also been cloned.[106,107] Besides a GC rich region and several other putative regulatory signals in the promoter region, a glucocorticoid-like responsive element at -410 was noticed; however, the relevance of these sequences to the regulation of this gene is not known at the present time.

There are other genes whose expression is stimulated by $1,25\text{-}(OH)_2D_3$. In particular, in culture, osteocalcin synthesis is stimulated by $1,25\text{-}(OH)_2D_3$.[108-110] More recently, osteonectin[111] and osteopontin[112] have also been reported to be stimulated by $1,25\text{-}(OH)_2D_3$. Furthermore, $1,25\text{-}(OH)_2D_3$ has been shown to modulate the activity of other genes, such as the parathyroid hormone gene,[113] c-myc gene[114] and metallothionein.[115] Therefore, unlike the other steroid hormones, the D responsive element has not yet been clearly defined but it is likely that this definition will take place in the next year.

One of the important new developments in the vitamin D field has been the recognition that $1,25\text{-}(OH)_2D_3$ suppresses growth and stimulates differentiation of several malignant cell lines to non-proliferating differentiated cells. This has been found true of breast carcinoma[116] and melanoma cells,[117] but most dramatically in the promyelocyte cell. Thus, Suda and his colleagues were the first to demonstrate that $1,25\text{-}(OH)_2D_3$ causes mouse promyelocyte cell line M1 to differentiate into what was believed to be granulocytes but later revised to monocytes.[118] Similarly, the human promyelocyte HL-60 line differentiates readily in response to $1,25\text{-}(OH)_2D_3$.[119] These responses require the presence of receptor, since cell lines without the receptor do not respond. The molecular mechanism of the differentiation remains largely unknown. Furthermore, the physiological significance of the differentiation phenomenon has not been determined. The monocytes are known to be precursors of the giant bone resorption cells — osteoclasts — and thus considerable effort is being

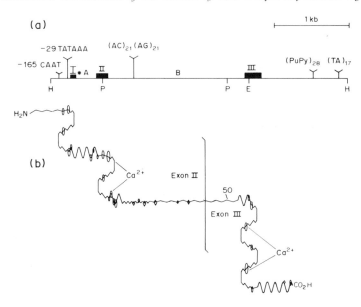

Figure 4 Structure of the rat intestinal 9000 Da calcium-binding protein gene (a) and its protein product (b). Exons 1, 2 and 3 are represented. The site of the TATAA box is indicated as are other repetitive sequences. The asterisk represents a possible D responsive element (see Figure 5). Exon 2 codes for one of the calcium-binding sites, whereas exon 3 codes for the C-terminal calcium-binding site

ICaBP gene		A	G	G	T	C	A	G	G	G	T	G	A	T	C	T
ERE consensus	(35)		G	G	T	C	A	C	N	$\frac{A}{G}$	T	G	$\frac{A}{T}$	C	C	T
ERE consensus	(36)	A	G	G	T	C	A	C	A	G	T	G	A	C	C	T
GRE consensus	(37)		G	G	T	A	C	A	N	N	N	T	G	T	T	C	T

Figure 5 Base sequence of putative D responsive element located at the end of the first exon and beginning of the first intron of the calcium-binding protein gene. It is compared with the ERE (estrogen) consensus sequence or the glucocorticoid (GRE) consensus sequence

spent on the idea that 1,25-$(OH)_2D_3$ may stimulate osteoclast activity by stimulating differentiation of promyelocytes into the precursor of the osteoclast.[120] This has not been clearly determined and thus remains an active area of investigation.

16.1.8 POSSIBLE NEW SITES OF ACTION OF 1,25-DIHYDROXYVITAMIN D₃

Perhaps one of the most surprising findings in the area of 1,25-$(OH)_2D_3$ action is its specific nuclear localization in tissues not previously appreciated as target organs of vitamin D. In particular, Stumpf and his colleagues demonstrated that specific nuclear localization of 1,25-$(OH)_2D_3$ takes place not only in the enterocyte of the small intestine, the osteoblasts and cells of bone, and the distal renal tubule cells, but also in unexpected sites such as the islet cells of the pancreas,[121] the parathyroid cells,[122] certain cells of the brain,[123] the mammary epithelium,[124] placenta,[42] sertoli cells of the male reproductive organs,[125] and keratinocytes of skin.[126] No specific localization was found in liver, smooth muscle, skeletal muscle, spleen, neural tissue and osteoclasts. When receptor technology became widely available, 1,25-$(OH)_2D_3$ specific receptors were found in these tissues with the possible exception of brain. Thus, receptor for 1,25-$(OH)_2D_3$ could readily be demonstrated in both fibroblasts and keratinocytes of skin,[127,128] in the parathyroid cells,[129] the islet cells of the pancreas,[129] heart muscle,[130] and placenta.[129] Furthermore, 60% of all malignant cells contain significant amounts of receptor.[131] Based on the presence of receptor to 1,25-$(OH)_2D_3$, functions for 1,25-$(OH)_2D_3$ have been looked for in some of these target tissues. Most prominent has been in the parathyroid glands. It is now clear that the preproparathyroid hormone gene is suppressed by 1,25-$(OH)_2D_3$ and its receptor.[113] In fact, suppression elements have been postulated for the promoter region of this gene that are activated in some way by 1,25-$(OH)_2D_3$. In the islet cells of the pancreas there have been reports that 1,25-$(OH)_2D_3$ is required for insulin secretion.[132]

Keratinocytes differentiate in response to 1,25-$(OH)_2D_3$ and have been the basis for postulating the use of vitamin D and its metabolites for the treatment of skin disorders such as psoriasis.[133-135] Probably, functions of 1,25-$(OH)_2D_3$ will be found to be wide-spread and thus this substance, originally thought to be a calcium-regulating hormone, may find wide application.

16.1.9 OTHER REPORTED RECEPTORS FOR VITAMIN D COMPOUNDS AND OTHER REPORTED MECHANISMS OF ACTION OF 1,25-DIHYDROXYVITAMIN D_3 NOT RELATED TO RECEPTORS

Most prominent among the vitamin D metabolites that have been studied is 24,25-dihydroxy-vitamin D_3 (24,25-$(OH)_2D_3$). This abundant metabolite of vitamin D was discovered by Holick *et al.*,[136] and this metabolite is formed when production of 1,25-$(OH)_2D_3$ is suppressed.[10] For many years a function for this metabolite has been a subject of considerable investigation. It has been reported to be a hatching hormone in birds,[137] a requirement for calcium homeostasis,[138] and for the mineralization of the skeleton.[139] These have been largely disproved.[140, 141] Reports have appeared claiming that 24,25-$(OH)_2D_3$ has a specific receptor.[142] Unfortunately, these reports are not convincing and, in fact, they can easily represent the 1,25-$(OH)_2D_3$ receptor, which will bind 24,25-$(OH)_2D_3$ if present in sufficient quantities. Convincing evidence for a receptor for this metabolite is lacking.

There have been reports that 1,25-$(OH)_2D_3$ functions by a nonreceptor, nonnuclear mechanism. For example, it has been suggested that vitamin D functions in a liponomic mechanism.[143] It has been reported that 1,25-$(OH)_2D_3$ changes the ratio of cholesterol esters to cholesterol in intestinal membrane and has been reported to change phospholipid concentrations in the membrane. These reports have never been adequately confirmed and, if so, it is difficult to see how this might account for the function of vitamin D.

More recently, Nemere *et al.* have reported that intestinal calcium transport can be turned on within minutes after injection of 1,25-$(OH)_2D_3$ into perfused chicken intestine.[28] These surprising results must be confirmed elsewhere before they can be accepted as fact. In the rat, our group has never observed a change in calcium transport in the small intestine before 2–3 h post-injection of the metabolite. Thus, there is no compelling evidence to suspect that 1,25-$(OH)_2D_3$ functions by any mechanism other than a receptor nuclear-mediated sequence of events.

16.1.10 SUMMARY

The vitamin D system is a recently discovered steroid endocrine system. The hormonal form is 1,25-$(OH)_2D_3$, produced by a mixed function monooxygenase in the kidney. This hormone acts by means of a receptor mechanism to stimulate classical target organs of intestine, bone and kidney. In the case of the intestine, this appears to be a nuclear-mediated mechanism involving a 55 000 molecular weight receptor whose structure is now known and which is believed to bind to specific elements in the promoter region of genes that are expressed and whose protein products are involved in calcium and phosphorus transport. Similar mechanisms are suspected for the actions of this compound on bone and on distal renal tubule cells. Evidence exists that 1,25-$(OH)_2D_3$ stimulates production of important bone proteins, one of which is osteocalcin. The vitamin D dependent calcium-binding protein gene expressed in response to 1,25-$(OH)_2D_3$ has been cloned and its genomic structure determined. It is likely that this gene will serve as a model for understanding the molecular events involved in the action of 1,25-$(OH)_2D_3$. Furthermore, new and unexpected actions of 1,25-$(OH)_2D_3$ are now known that involve interaction of the hormone with the 1,25-$(OH)_2D_3$ receptor found in those tissues. This includes the parathyroid gland, the islet cells of the pancreas and keratinocytes of skin.

16.1.11 REFERENCES

1. A. Hess (ed.), in 'Rickets, Including Osteomalacia and Tetany', Lea and Febiger, Philadelphia, 1929, p. 22.
2. W. H. Sebrell, Jr. and R. S. Harris (eds.), in 'The Vitamins', Academic Press, New York, 1954, vol. II, p. 131.
3. H. F. DeLuca, *Vitam. Horm. (N.Y.)*, 1967, **25**, 315.
4. J. B. Eastwood, E. Harris, T. C. B. Stamp and H. E. De Wardener, *Lancet*, 1976, **2**, 1209.
5. H. Ramussen and P. Bordier, *Metab. Bone Dis. Relat. Res.*, 1978, **1**, 7.
6. J. L. Underwood and H. F. DeLuca, *Am. J. Physiol.*, 1984, **246**, E493.

7. R. S. Weinstein, J. L. Underwood, M. S. Hutson and H. F. DeLuca, *Am. J. Physiol.*, 1984, **246**, E499.
8. M. E. Holtrop, K. A. Cox, D. L. Carnes and M. F. Holick, *Am. J. Physiol.*, 1986, **251**, E234.
9. M. Lamm and W. F. Neuman, *Arch. Pathol.*, 1958, **66**, 204.
10. H. F. DeLuca, in 'The Harvey Lectures', Academic Press, New York, 1981, p. 333.
11. M. Yamamoto, Y. Kawanobe, H. Takahashi, E. Shimazawa, S. Kimura and E. Ogata, *J. Clin. Invest.*, 1984, **74**, 507.
12. E. Kodicek, in 'Ciba Foundation Symposium on Bone Structure and Metabolism', ed. G. W. E. Wolstenholme and C. M. O'Connor, Little, Brown, Boston, 1956, p. 161.
13. M. R. Haussler and A. W. Norman, *Arch. Biochem. Biophys.*, 1967, **118**, 145.
14. J. Lund and H. F. DeLuca, *J. Lipid Res.*, 1966, **7**, 739.
15. H. F. DeLuca, *Fed. Proc., Fed. Am. Soc. Exp. Biol.*, 1974, **33**, 2211.
16. H. F. DeLuca, *Ann. N.Y. Acad. Sci.*, 1982, **355**, 1.
17. R. H. Wasserman, F. A. Kallfelz and C. L. Comar, *Science (Washington, D.C.)*, 1961, **133**, 883.
18. R. H. Wasserman and A. N. Taylor, *J. Nutr.*, 1973, **103**, 586.
19. D. L. Martin and H. F. DeLuca, *Am. J. Physiol.*, 1969, **216**, 1351.
20. R. H. Wasserman, *J. Nutr.*, 1962, **77**, 69.
21. T. C. Chen, L. Castillo, M. Korycka-Dahl and H. F. DeLuca, *J. Nutr.*, 1974, **104**, 1056.
22. B. P. Halloran and H. F. DeLuca, *Arch. Biochem. Biophys.*, 1981, **208**, 477.
23. N. C. Kendrick, B. Kabakoff and H. F. DeLuca, *Biochem. J.*, 1981, **194**, 178.
24. B. Kabakoff, N. C. Kendrick and H. F. DeLuca, *Am. J. Physiol.*, 1982, **6**, E470.
25. D. D. Bikle, D. T. Zolock, R. L. Morrissey and R. H. Herman, *J. Biol. Chem.*, 1978, **253**, 484.
26. D. D. Bikle, R. L. Morrissey and D. T. Zolock, *Am. J. Clin. Nutr.*, 1979, **32**, 2322.
27. R. T. Franceschi and H. F. DeLuca, *J. Biol. Chem.*, 1981, **256**, 3848.
28. I. Nemere, Y. Yoshimoto and A. W. Norman, *Endocrinology*, 1984, **115**, 1476.
29. D. Schachter and S. Kowarski, *Fed. Proc., Fed. Am. Soc. Exp. Biol.*, 1982, **41**, 84.
30. R. H. Wasserman and J. J. Feher, in 'Calcium Binding Proteins and Calcium Function', ed. R. H. Wasserman, R. A. Corradino, E. Carafoli, R. H. Kretsinger, D. H. MacLennan and S. L. Siegel, Elsevier, Amsterdam, 1977, p. 292.
31. D. W. Rowe and B. E. Kream, *J. Biol. Chem.*, 1982, **257**, 8009.
32. M. Garabedian, Y. Tanaka, M. F. Holick and H. F. DeLuca, *Endocrinology*, 1974, **94**, 1022.
33. Y. Tanaka, H. Frank and H. F. DeLuca, *Endocrinology*, 1973, **92**, 417.
34. Y. Tanaka and H. F. DeLuca, *Arch. Biochem. Biophys.*, 1971, **146**, 574.
35. H. Rasmussen, H. DeLuca, C. Arnaud, C. Hawker and M. von Stedingk, *J. Clin. Invest.*, 1963, **42**, 1940.
36. L. G. Raisz, C. L. Trummel, M. F. Holick and H. F. DeLuca, *Science (Washington, D.C.)*, 1972, **175**, 768.
37. J. J. Reynolds, M. F. Holick and H. F. DeLuca, *Calcif. Tissue Res.*, 1973, **12**, 295.
38. P. H. Stern, B. P. Halloran, H. F. DeLuca and T. J. Hefley, *Am. J. Physiol.*, 1983, **244**, E421.
39. H. M. Frost, in 'Bone Dynamics in Osteoporosis and Osteomalacia', Henry Ford Hospital Surgical Monograph Series, Thomas, Springfield, IL, 1966.
40. W. E. Stumpf, M. Sar, F. A. Reid, Y. Tanaka and H. F. DeLuca, *Science (Washington, D.C.)*, 1979, **206**, 1188.
41. M. Zile, E. C. Bunge, L. Barsness, S. Yamada, H. K. Schnoes and H. F. DeLuca, *Arch. Biochem. Biophys.*, 1978, **186**, 15.
42. W. E. Stumpf, M. Sar and H. F. DeLuca, in 'Hormonal Control of Calcium Metabolism', ed. D. V. Cohn, R. V. Talmage and J. L. Matthews, Excerpta Medica, Amsterdam, 1981, p. 222.
43. P. F. Brumbaugh and M. R. Haussler, *Life Sci.*, 1975, **16**, 353.
44. B. E. Kream, R. D. Reynolds, J. C. Knutson, J. A. Eisman and H. F. DeLuca, *Arch. Biochem. Biophys.*, 1976, **176**, 779.
45. M. Nakada, R. U. Simpson and H. F. DeLuca, *Proc. Natl. Acad. Sci. USA*, 1984, **81**, 6711.
46. U. Berger, P. Wilson, R. A. McClelland, K. Colston, M. R. Haussler, J. W. Pike and R. C. Coombes, *J. Clin. Endocrinol. Metab.*, 1988, **67**, 607.
47. M. H. Brooks, N. H. Bell, L. Love, P. H. Stern, E. Orfei, S. F. Queener, A. J. Hamstra and H. F. DeLuca, *New Engl. J. Med.*, 1978, **298**, 996.
48. J. F. Rosen, A. R. Fleischman, L. Finberg, A. Hamstra and H. F. DeLuca, *J. Pediatr. (St. Louis)*, 1979, **94**, 729.
49. C. Eil, U. A. Liberman and S. J. Marx, in 'Steroid Hormone Resistance', ed. G. P. Chrousos, D. L. Loriaus and M. B. Lipsett, Plenum Press, New York, 1986, p. 407.
50. B. P. Halloran and H. F. DeLuca, *Am. J. Physiol.*, 1980, **239**, E64.
51. B. P. Halloran and H. F. DeLuca, *J. Biol. Chem.*, 1981, **256**, 7338.
52. S. Dokoh, C. A. Donaldson and M. R. Haussler, *Cancer Res.*, 1984, **44**, 2103
53. R. Link and H. F. DeLuca, in 'The Receptors', ed. P. M. Conn, Academic Press, New York, 1985, vol. II, p. 1.
54. R. P. Link and H. F. DeLuca, *Steroids*, 1988, **51**, 583.
55. S. Okamoto, Y. Tanaka, H. F. DeLuca, Y. Kobayashi and N. Ikekawa, *Am. J. Physiol.*, 1983, **7**, E159.
56. M. Inaba, S. Okuno, A. Inoue, Y. Nishizawa, H. Morii and H. F. DeLuca, *Arch. Biochem. Biophys.*, 1989, **268**, 35.
57. J. E. Bishop, W. Hunziker and A. W. Norman, *Biochem. Biophys. Res. Commun.*, 1982, **108**, 140.
58. M. C. Dame, E. A. Pierce and H. F. DeLuca, *Proc. Natl. Acad. Sci. USA*, 1985, **82**, 7825.
59. E. A. Pierce, M. C. Dame and H. F. DeLuca, *J. Biol. Chem.*, 1988, **262**, 17092.
60. J. W. Pike, N. M. Sleator and M. R. Haussler, *J. Biol. Chem.*, 1987, **262**, 1305.
61. J. K. Burmester, R. J. Wiese, N. Maeda and H. F. DeLuca, *Proc. Natl. Acad. Sci. USA*, 1988, **85**, 9499.
62. A. R. Baker, D. P. McDonnell, H. Hughes, T. M. Crisp, D. J. Mangelsdorf, M. R. Haussler, J. W. Pike, J. Shine and B. W. O'Malley, *Proc. Natl. Acad. Sci. USA*, 1988, **85**, 3294.
63. R. U. Simpson, A. Hamstra, N. C. Kendrick and H. F. DeLuca, *Biochemistry*, 1983, **22**, 2586.
64. E. A. Pierce, M. C. Dame and H. F. DeLuca, *J. Biol. Chem.*, 1987, **262**, 17092.
65. M. C. Dame, E. A. Pierce and H. F. DeLuca, *Proc. Natl. Acad. Sci. USA*, 1985, **82**, 7825.
66. P. Brumbaugh and M. R. Haussler, *J. Biol. Chem.*, 1974, **249**, 1251.
67. R. U. Simpson and H. F. DeLuca, *Proc. Natl. Acad. Sci. USA*, 1982, **79**, 16.
68. J. W. Pike and M. R. Haussler, *Proc. Natl. Acad. Sci. USA*, 1979, **76**, 5485.
69. M. C. Dame, E. A. Pierce, J. M. Prahl, C. E. Hayes and H. F. DeLuca, *Biochemistry*, 1986, **25**, 4523.
70. J. W. Pike, S. L. Marion, C. A. Donaldson and M. R. Haussler, *J. Biol. Chem.*, 1983, **258**, 1289.
71. J. W. Pike, *J. Biol. Chem.*, 1984, **259**, 1167.

72. J. W. Pike, N. M. Sleator and M. R. Haussler, *J. Biol. Chem.*, 1987, **262**, 1305.
73. T. A. Brown, J. M. Prahl and H. F. DeLuca, *Proc. Natl. Acad. Sci. USA*, 1988, **85**, 2454.
74. D. J. Mangelsdorf, J. W. Pike and M. R. Haussler, *Proc. Natl. Acad. Sci. USA*, 1987, **84**, 354.
75. J. W. Pike, N. M. Sleator and M. R. Haussler, *J. Biol. Chem.*, 1987, **262**, 1305.
76. W. R. Wecksler and A. W. Norman, *J. Biol. Chem.*, 1980, **255**, 3571.
77. E. R. Massaro, R. U. Simpson and H. F. DeLuca, *Proc. Natl. Acad. Sci. USA*, 1983, **80**, 2549.
78. T. L. Chen, C. M. Cone, C. M. Holton and D. Feldman, *J. Biol. Chem.*, 1982, **257**, 13564.
79. T. L. Chen and D. Feldman, *J. Biol. Chem.*, 1981, **256**, 5561.
80. T. L. Chen, C. M. Cone, E. Morey-Holton and D. Feldman, *J. Biol. Chem.*, 1983, **258**, 4350.
81. M. Sandgren and H. F. DeLuca, *FASEB J.*, 1988, **2**, A1098 (Abst. no. 4659).
82. D. P. McDonnell, D. J. Mangelsdorf, J. W. Pike, M. R. Haussler and B. W. O'Malley, *Science (Washington, D.C.)*, 1987, **235**, 1214.
83. J. K. Burmester, N. Maeda and H. F. DeLuca, *Proc. Natl. Acad. Sci. USA*, 1988, **85**, 1005.
84. E. M. Costa, M. A. Hirst and D. Feldman, *Endocrinology*, 1985, **117**, 2203.
85. M. Nakada and H. F. DeLuca, *Arch. Biochem. Biophys.*, 1985, **238**, 129.
86. E. A. Pierce and H. F. DeLuca, *Arch. Biochem. Biophys.*, 1988, **261**, 241.
87. E. R. Massaro, R. U. Simpson and H. F. DeLuca, *Am. J. Physiol.*, 1983, **244**, E230.
88. U. A. Liberman, C. Eil and S. J. Marx, *J. Clin. Invest.*, 1983, **71**, 192.
89. J. J. Dougherty, R. K. Puri and D. O. Toft, *J. Biol. Chem.*, 1982, **257**, 14226.
90. A. Miller-Diener, T. J. Schmidt and G. Litwack, *Proc. Natl. Acad. Sci. USA*, 1985, **82**, 4003.
91. J. W. Pike and N. M. Sleator, *Biochem. Biophys. Res. Commun.*, 1985, **131**, 378.
92. R. H. Wasserman and A. N. Taylor, *Science (Washington, D.C.)*, 1966, **152**, 791.
93. R. H. Wasserman, C. S. Fullmer and A. N. Taylor, in 'Vitamin D', ed. D. E. M. Lawson, Academic Press, New York, 1978, p. 133.
94. R. H. Wasserman and C. S. Fullmer, *Annu. Rev. Physiol.*, 1983, **45**, 375.
95. H. F. DeLuca, R. T. Franceschi, B. P. Halloran and E. R. Massaro, *Fed. Proc., Fed. Am. Soc. Exp. Biol.*, 1982, **41**, 66.
96. R. Spencer, M. Charman, P. Wilson and E. Lawson, *Nature (London)*, 1976, **263**, 161.
97. C. Roche, C. Bellaton, D. Pausu, A. Miller, III and F. Bronner, *Am. J. Physiol.*, 1986, **251**, G314.
98. N. Takahashi, T. Shinki, N. Kawate, K. Samejima, Y. Nishii and T. Suda, *Endocrinology*, 1982, **111**, 1539.
99. M. A. Mulkins and H. H. Sussman, *Endocrinology*, 1987, **120**, 416.
100. S. Kowarski and D. Schachter, *J. Biol. Chem.*, 1980, **255**, 10834.
101. H. M. Darwish, J. Krisinger, M. Strom and H. F. DeLuca, *Proc. Natl. Acad. Sci. USA*, 1987, **84**. 6108.
102. C. Desplan, M. Thomassett and M. Moukhtar, *J. Biol. Chem.*, 1983, **258**, 2762.
103. J. P. MacManis, D. C. Watson and M. Yaguchi, *Biochem. J.*, 1986, **235**, 585.
104. J. Krisinger, H. M. Darwish, N. Maeda and H. F. DeLuca, *Proc. Natl. Acad. Sci. USA*, 1988, **85**, 8988.
105. C. Perret, N. Lomri, N. Gouhier, C. Auffray and M. Thomasset, *Eur. J. Biochem.*, 1988, **172**, 43.
106. W. Hunziker, *Proc. Natl. Acad. Sci. USA*, 1986, **83**, 7578.
107. P. P. Minghetti, L. Lancela, Y. Frigisawa, G. Theofan and A. W. Norman, *Mol. Endocrinol.*, 1988, **2**, 355.
108. P. A. Price and S. A. Banikol, *J. Biol. Chem.*, 1980, **255**, 11660.
109. J. D. Faraser, Y. Otawara and P. A. Price, *J. Biol. Chem.*, 1988, **263**, 911.
110. J. B. Lian and C. M. Gundberg, *Clin. Orthop. Relat. Res.*, 1988, **226**, 267.
111. R. Gehron, D. M. Findlay, M. F. Young, J. N. Baresford, J. Stubbs, L. W. Fischer and J. D. Termine, *J. Bone Miner. Res.*, 1986, **1**, 288.
112. C. W. Prince and W. T. Butler, *Collagen Relat. Res.*, 1987, **7**, 305.
113. J. Silver, J. Russell and L. M. Sherwood, *Proc. Natl. Acad. Sci. USA*, 1985, **82**, 4270.
114. D. W. Rowe and B. E. Kream, *J. Biol. Chem.*, 1982, **257**, 8009.
115. M. Karasawa, J. Hsoi, H. Hashiba, K. Nose, C. Tohyaja, E. Abe, T. Suda and T. Kuroki, *Proc. Natl. Acad. Sci. USA*, 1987, **84**, 8810.
116. R. J. Frampton, S. A. Omond and J. A. Eisman, *Cancer Res.*, 1983, **43**, 4443.
117. J. A. Eisman and R. J. Frampton, in 'Endocrine Control of Bone and Calcium Metabolism', ed. C. V. Colin, J. T. Potts, Jr. and T. Fujita, Elsevier, Amsterdam, 1984, p. 237.
118. E. Abe, C. Miyaura, H. Sakagami, M. Takeda, K. Konno, T. Yamazaki, S. Yoshiki and T. Suda, *Proc. Natl. Acad. Sci. USA*, 1981, **78**, 4990.
119. H. Tanaka, E. Abe, C. Miyaura, T. Kuribayashi, K. Konno, Y. Nishii and T. Suda, *Biochem. J.*, 1982, **204**, 713.
120. H. Tanaka, T. Hayashi, Y. Shiina, C. Miyaura, E. Abe and T. Suda, *FEBS Lett.*, 1984, **174**, 61.
121. S. A. Clark, W. E. Stumpf, M. Sar, H. F. DeLuca and Y. Tanaka, *Cell Tissue Res.*, 1980, **209**, 515.
122. W. E. Stumpf, M. Sar, F. A. Reid, S. Huang, R. Narbaitz and H. F. DeLuca, *Cell Tissue Res.*, 1981, **221**, 333.
123. W. E. Stumpf, M. Sar, S. A. Clark and H. F. DeLuca, *Science (Washington, D.C.)*, 1982, **215**, 1403.
124. R. Narbaitz, M. Sar, W. E. Stumpf, S. Huang and H. F. DeLuca, *Horm. Res.*, 1981, **15**, 263.
125. W. E. Stumpf, M. Sar, K. Chen, J. Morin and H. F. DeLuca, *Cell Tissue Res.*, 1987, **247**, 453.
126. W. E. Stumpf, S. A. Clark, M. Sar and H. F. DeLuca, *Cell Tissue Res.*, 1984, **238**, 489.
127. R. U. Simpson and H. F. DeLuca, *Proc. Natl. Acad. Sci. USA*, 1980, **77**, 5822.
128. D. Feldman, T. Chen, M. Hirst, K. Colston, M. Karasek and C. Cone, *J. Clin. Endocrinol. Metab.*, 1980, **51**, 1463.
129. J. W. Pike, L. L. Gooze and M. R. Haussler, *Life Sci.*, 1980, **26**, 407.
130. R. E. Weishaar and R. U. Simpson, *J. Clin. Invest.*, 1987, **79**, 1706.
131. R. J. Frampton, L. J. Suva, J. A. Eisman, D. M. Findlay, G. E. Moore, J. M. Moseley and T. J. Martin, *Cancer Res.*, 1982, **42**, 1116.
132. B. S. Chertow, W. I. Sivitz, N. G. Baranetsky, S. A. Clark, A. Waite and H. F. DeLuca, *Endocrinology*, 1983, **113**, 1511.
133. E. L. Smith, N. C. Walworth and M. F. Holick, *J. Invest. Dermatol.*, 1986, **86**, 709.
134. S. Morimoto, S. Onishi, S. Imanaka, H. Yukawa, T. Kozuka, Y. Kitano, K. Yoshikawa and Y. Kumahara, *Calcif. Tissue Int.*, 1986, **38**, 119.
135. S. Takamoto, S. Onishi, S. Morimoto, S. Imanaka, S. Yukawa, T. Kozuka, Y. Kitano, Y. Seino and Y. Kumahara, *Calcif. Tissue Int.*, 1986, **39**, 360.

136. M. F. Holick, H. K. Schnoes, H. F. DeLuca, R. W. Gray, I. T. Boyle and T. Suda, *Biochemistry*, 1972, **11**, 4251.
137. H. L. Henry and A. W. Norman, *Science (Washington, D.C)*, 1978, **201**, 835.
138. A. W. Norman, H. L. Henry and H. H. Malluche, *Life Sci.*, 1980, **27**, 229.
139. A. Ornoy, D. Goodwin, D. Noff and S. Edelstein, *Nature (London)*, 1978, **276**, 517.
140. B. R. Brommage and H. F. DeLuca, *Endocr. Rev.*, 1985, **6**, 491.
141. L. E. Hart, H. F. DeLuca, S. Yamada and H. Takayama, *J. Nutr.*, 1984, **114**, 2059.
142. J. Merke and A. W. Norman, *Biochem. Biophys. Res. Commun.*, 1981, **100**, 551.
143. H. Rasmussen, O. Fontaine and T. Matsumoto, *Ann. N.Y. Acad. Sci.*, 1981, **372**, 518.

16.2

Thyroid Hormone Receptors

PAUL D. LEESON

Merck, Sharp & Dohme Research Laboratories, Harlow, UK

and

ANTHONY H. UNDERWOOD

Smith, Kline & French Research Ltd., Welwyn, UK

16.2.1 INTRODUCTION

16.2.1.1 Historical Perspective

The thyroid is a bilobed, highly vascular organ positioned on both sides of the trachea and filled with a collagenous substance. These characteristics undoubtedly accounted for earlier hypotheses concerning its function, when it was variously thought of as serving as a vascular shunt to prevent 'too violent access of the blood to the brain', as part of the vocal apparatus, or as providing a lubricant for the trachea. However, towards the end of the 19th century, the endocrine nature of its function was established when it was noticed that the spontaneous diseases of myxoedema and cretinism were associated with thyroid atrophy, and that surgical removal of the thyroid resulted in similar conditions. The dramatic improvement in the symptoms of these diseases, which was seen when thyroid extract was given to patients, confirmed the endocrine function of the organ, and initiated a search for the hormonal constituent. This was facilitated by the observation that administration of thyroid extract enhanced whole body oxygen consumption and increased nitrogen excretion since these measurements provided assay procedures for the active constituent.[1]

16.2.1.2 Chemical Structures of Thyroid Hormones

In 1896 Bauman isolated a fraction from the thyroid which contained up to 10% iodine, and which relieved the symptoms of hypothyroidism. Later, Kendall isolated crystals from thyroidal extracts which contained up to 64% iodine and had an empirical formula corresponding to $C_{11}H_{10}O_3NI_3$. Kendall thought that his 'Thyroxin' was trihydrotriiodo-α-oxyindolepropionic acid, but Harington was to show in 1933 that Kendall's empirical formula was wrong and that thyroxine was in fact 3,5,3',5'-tetraiodo-L-thyronine (T_4; **2**). His approach was to reductively deiodinate T_4, characterize the resulting amino acid as thyronine, and then identify the positions of the iodines. It was commonly recognized at this time that the T_4 content of the thyroid gland was inadequate to explain its hormonal activity, and Harington himself thought that T_4 circulated as part of a more active peptide. It was not until much later that Gross and Pitt-Rivers showed that the thyroid and plasma contained a second iodinated component 3,5,3'-triiodo-L-thyronine (T_3; **1**), which was more active than T_4.[2] Nowadays, it is thought that T_4 acts mainly through its conversion to T_3.

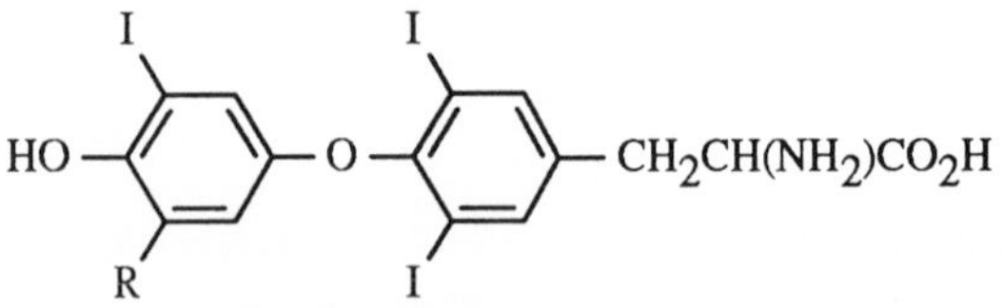

(**1**) R = H, T_3
(**2**) R = I, thyroxine, T_4

16.2.1.3 Physiological Role of Thyroid Hormones

Since the latter part of the last century, it has been recognized that the thyroid hormones, while not absolutely essential for life, have a wide variety of actions in most organs, both on their development and function. Some of these effects are direct, in that they are mediated by thyroid hormone receptors in the individual cells, whilst others are indirect, as a consequence of changes distal to the organ, such as a modification of the level of another hormone. It is beyond the scope of this review to document all of the innumerable effects of these hormones, so only the most important, either clinically or therapeutically, will be briefly described.

16.2.1.3.1 *Energy metabolism*

The stimulating actions of thyroid hormones on whole body oxygen consumption, first observed almost a century ago, are reflected in their actions on the oxygen consumption of some tissues (*e.g.* liver, kidney, heart, skeletal muscle) but not others (*e.g.* brain, gonads, spleen). The mechanism for this effect is still unclear. Thyroid hormones *in vitro* are known to uncouple oxidative phosphorylation in isolated mitochondria but these effects only occur at very high concentrations compared to those needed to raise oxygen consumption *in vivo*. Furthermore, mitochondria isolated from hyperthyroid animals are still highly coupled.[3] In most physiological circumstances oxygen consumption is controlled by energy utilization so it seems more appropriate to look for energy-utilizing processes which are stimulated by thyroid hormones. Ismail-Beigi and Edelman[4] have proposed that the primary effect of thyroid hormones is to increase the amount of energy expended in translocating cations across cell membranes, probably as a response to an increased passive leak of sodium into, and potassium out of, cells. However, the energy required for this is only a small proportion of the total oxygen consumption of the cell.[5] It may be that there is no single effect of thyroid hormones responsible for the enhancement of energy utilization, but rather that this represents the sum of a large number of separate actions.

16.2.1.3.2 *Cardiovascular system*

Hyperthyroidism is frequently accompanied by profound effects on the heart. Rate of beating and cardiac output are increased dramatically and often accompanied by arrhythmias and angina. In hypothyroid patients the opposite effects occur. These cardiac effects are either due to direct effects of thyroid hormones on the myocardium, or indirect consequences of other peripheral changes. For instance, hyperthyroidism induces a reduction in peripheral resistance (presumably due, at least in part, to increased tissue oxygen consumption), which could lead to the increases in rate or output. In animals, both direct and indirect effects are seen. Both the rate of beating and contractility are increased in hearts isolated from rats treated with thyroid hormones.[6] In the dog, however, the increased heart rate seems to be due to a diminished vagal drive.[7] Changes in contractility in rat hearts caused by changes in thyroid status are accompanied by changes in the myosin isozyme profile, but it is not clear that this mechanism operates in larger species. Thyroid hormones also have electrophysiological effects. Thus, hyperthyroidism enhances conduction velocity and shortens the refractory period in atrial cells. These effects are probably direct actions of the hormones.[6]

16.2.1.3.3 *Lipid metabolism*

In hyperthyroidism plasma cholesterol levels are diminished. Conversely, hypothyroidism is accompanied by hypercholesterolaemia and also hypertriglyceridaemia. The mechanisms underlying these changes are complex. In hypothyroidism both fatty acid oxidation and (surprisingly) fatty acid synthesis are increased. Despite a decrease in glycerol 3-phosphate concentration in hyperthyroid livers, very low density lipoprotein (VLDL)-triglyceride secretion *in vivo* may not be reduced, because the level of free fatty acids is increased. However, the clearance of VLDL and its metabolite, low density lipoprotein (LDL), are increased by hyperthyroidism, probably because thyroid hormones enhance hepatic LDL-receptor concentrations, and this leads to the reduction in total- and LDL-cholesterol concentrations.[8] Probably because of their elevated plasma cholesterol concentrations, hypothyroid patients often suffer from severe atherosclerosis which, however, does not manifest itself in an increased frequency of angina or myocardial infarction. This is presumably because the decreased cardiac oxygen consumption and contractility, and also the decreased workload associated with hypothyroidism, protects the myocardium against the consequences of atherosclerosis. The patient can experience difficulties such as angina, unstable angina, infarction or even death when thyroid replacement therapy is initiated, and these may necessitate coronary revascularization before treatment for hypothyroidism.[9]

16.2.1.3.4 *Brain*

Although the brain does not respond to changes in thyroid status with changes in oxygen consumption, there are clear effects of these hormones on brain function. The hyperthyroid patient, for instance, may show increases in motor activity, restlessness, insomnia and even frank deliriums. Normal subjects treated with T_3 exhibit similar changes, becoming unfriendly and agitated.[10] The hypothyroid patient, on the other hand, is often characterized by slowness of thought and lethargy.[11] The development of the brain is also affected by thyroid hormones. Cretinism is a condition caused by severe hypothyroidism in early life and is characterized, among other things, by severe mental retardation. Many of the symptoms of cretinism can be avoided if replacement therapy is instituted within the first four weeks of life.[12] In the Third World, cretinism is most frequently a consequence of simple iodine deficiency, and is thus by far the most important, preventable cause of intellectual and physical impairment.[13]

16.2.2 FORMATION, DISTRIBUTION AND METABOLISM OF THYROID HORMONES

16.2.2.1 Biosynthesis

The functional units of the thyroid are the acini or thyroid follicles, which are spherical structures consisting of a lumen surrounded by an epithelium of follicular cells. These cells elaborate and secrete into the lumen an iodinated protein, thyroglobulin (Tg), which contains within its primary sequence both T_4 and T_3 residues. Upon stimulation by thyroid stimulating hormone (TSH) the acini hydrolyze Tg to its constituent amino acids, and the hormones thereby generated are released into the blood system.

Noniodinated Tg, as synthesized in the follicular cells, has a molecular weight of about 300 000. It is then dimerized and glycosylated before being secreted into the follicular lumen with a molecular weight of about 660 000. The iodination of Tg then takes place at the border of the lumen, utilizing iodide concentrated within the follicle by an active transport system which can be blocked by inorganic ions such as perchlorate. The thyroid peroxidase, which is responsible for this iodination, also catalyzes the transfer of an iodophenol moiety from one iodotyrosine residue to another to generate iodothyronines within the Tg. The Tg thus formed contains 3-mono- and 3,5-di-iodinated tyrosine (MIT and DIT) as well as T_3 and T_4. Even when the iodine content of Tg is 70 mol (mol Tg)$^{-1}$, the T_4 content does not exceed 3 mol (mol Tg)$^{-1}$. This emphasizes the role of Tg as a store for iodine as well as a precursor for thyroid hormones.[14]

TSH binds to receptors on the follicular cells and promotes an increase in intracellular cAMP and calcium concentrations. In some way, as yet incompletely defined, these changes result in endo-cytosis of lumenal Tg. The resulting endocytotic vacuoles in the follicular cells then fuse with lysosymes which contain the enzymes necessary to promote degradation of Tg to its constituent amino acids. The MIT, DIT, T_3 and T_4 are subsequently deiodinated to varying extents: MIT and DIT completely, T_3 mainly and T_4 very little. The result is that the effluent from the gland contains mainly T_4 with a little T_3, although this is dependent upon physiological conditions such as the supply of iodide and the consequent composition of the Tg.[14]

16.2.2.2 Control of Thyroid Function

The plasma concentrations of thyroid hormones are kept constant by a negative feedback control system. As documented above, TSH stimulates the thyroid to release its hormones. These, in turn, inhibit the release (and synthesis) of TSH by the pituitary. This effect appears to be mediated by the classical, nuclear, thyroid hormone receptors (see Section 16.2.3) and probably involves the synthesis of a specific TSH-release inhibitory protein. Although T_3 is usually regarded as the active hormone, with T_4 being relegated to the role of a prohormone, plasma TSH concentration usually correlates better with plasma T_4 than T_3. This is because the majority of the T_3 which occupies pituitary receptors is derived by intrapituitary deiodination of T_4.[15]

Superimposed on this simple system is a series of more complex control mechanisms. Principal among these is the tonic stimulation of pituitary TSH release by thyrotropin stimulating hormone (TRH) secreted by the hypothalamus. Thyroid hormones inhibit the effect of TRH on the pituitary, and also probably decrease the release of TRH from the hypothalamus. In addition, somatostatin, neurotensin, noradrenaline and dopamine are all known to modulate TSH release and may play physiologically significant roles.[15]

Finally, the thyroid itself is known to be innervated by adrenergic, cholinergic and peptidergic nerves, all of which may affect its function.[16]

16.2.2.3 Transport in Blood

In normal, euthyroid man, the total plasma concentration of T_4 is about 100 nM and of T_3 1 to 2 nM. The majority of both hormones is reversibly bound to plasma proteins, only 0.03% of T_4 and 0.3% of T_3 being free.[14] Three binding proteins are involved; thyroxine-binding globulin (TBG), prealbumin (PA) and albumin (Alb). The affinities of these for both T_4 and T_3 are in the order TBG > PA > Alb, and they each bind T_4 better than T_3. The concentrations of the binding proteins are such that two-thirds of the T_4 is carried on TBG with about 10% bound to PA and 20% to Alb. T_3 is probably more evenly distributed.[17]

The concentrations of the binding proteins and their affinities for the hormones can be affected by physiological state (*e.g.* pregnancy), inherited molecular variations, or the presence of competing drugs. However, while these factors can lead to large variations in total plasma hormone concentrations, in the absence of any other thyroidal disease the patient remains euthyroid; this is because it is the free level of the hormones which determines thyroid status and which is maintained by the homeostatic mechanisms described in Section 16.2.2.3.[17]

The reason for this large reservoir of bound thyroid hormone is presently uncertain, although it could clearly act as a buffer to attenuate rapid fluctuations in free hormone levels. Ekins has recently suggested that the level of *bound* hormone can determine the relative delivery of hormone to the different organs.[18] Thus, the increase in TBG observed in pregnancy may serve to enhance hormonal delivery to the foetus.[18]

16.2.2.4 Tissue Uptake of Thyroid Hormone

Thyroid hormones were formerly thought to enter cells by simple diffusion. However, recently evidence for an active process mediated by specific carrier systems has been obtained.[19] Two binding sites with high affinities (K_d in the nM range) for T_3 and T_4 have been found in plasma membranes from rat liver and kidney. Although both hormones bind to both sites, it seems that they represent separate entities. These binding sites appear to mediate hormone transport into cells. Such uptake systems with high affinities for T_3, T_4 and 3,3',5'-triiodo-L-thyronine (rT_3) have been demonstrated using isolated cell systems. The rates of uptake are dependent upon temperature and intracellular ATP concentrations, and are inhibited by amiodarone, radiocontrast agents, and inhibitors of Na^+/K^+-ATPase. Despite this there is no evidence that thyroid hormones accumulate within cells against a concentration gradient.[20]

These cellular uptake systems appear to be a control point for the metabolism of thyroid hormones. Thus the so-called 'low T_3 syndrome', which is characterized by a normal plasma total T_4 concentration, an increased free T_4 concentration, and a diminished T_3 concentration, is accompanied by reduced hepatic uptake of T_4. This is presumed to lead to a reduced availability of T_4 for conversion to T_3 in the liver which is the principal source of plasma T_3.[19]

16.2.2.5 Metabolism of Thyroid Hormones

The principal route of degradation of T_4 is deiodination. Removal of the 5'-iodine (outer ring deiodination; ORD) produces T_3, and is thus an activation step. About 40% of T_4 is metabolized in this way, and the T_3 produced represents 90% of that formed in the body. Inactivation of T_4 by deiodination at the 5-position (inner ring deiodination; IRD) produces rT_3. Both T_3 and rT_3 can undergo further deiodinations leading to the isomeric diiodothyronines, monoiodothyronines, and ultimately thyronine. Iodothyronines can also be conjugated with glucuronic and sulfuric acids to yield conjugates which can be excreted as such or which may themselves undergo deiodination. Other pathways of metabolism are deamination, possibly decarboxylation, and ether ring cleavage.[21]

Three types of deiodinase are currently known, and are distinguished from each other on the basis of their location, substrate preference, mechanism, susceptibility to inhibitors, and response to changes in thyroid status. All are microsomal and require thiol cofactors, although the nature of the endogenous stimulators is currently unknown.[22] The type I deiodinase is found in liver and kidney, catalyzes both IRD and ORD, and is thought to be principally responsible for the generation of T_3 and the removal of rT_3. Type II deiodinase catalyzes ORD, and is found in brain, brown adipose tissue and the pituitary. The brain also contains the type III enzyme as does skin and placenta. This enzyme is probably the principal source of circulating rT_3.[23]

16.2.3   THE IDENTIFICATION OF THYROID HORMONE RECEPTORS AND THEIR MECHANISM OF ACTION

Although there are certain exceptions (see Section 16.2.3.4), the majority of physiological responses to thyroid hormones do not occur immediately after their administration, but rather after a delay lasting from several hours to days. Any hypothesis concerning the mechanism of action of these hormones must account for this singular and prolonged latent period. Currently, it is believed that cytoplasmic T_3, derived either from plasma or intracellularly by deiodination of T_4 enters the nucleus and binds to a specific receptor-protein on the genome. This binding modifies transcription so as to alter the types of mRNA molecules produced. These different mRNA molecules direct the synthesis of new proteins, and it is the appearance of these which causes the characteristic changes in the biochemistry and physiology of the responsive organ. It is believed that the time taken for this series of events constitutes, in part, the reason for the latent period.

16.2.3.1   The Nuclear T_3 Receptor

Nuclei isolated from cells responsive to thyroid hormones contain a chromatin-bound, non-histone protein which can be extracted with 0.4 M KCl. Both the nuclei and extracted protein can be shown to bind T_3 with an affinity of about 10^9 M^{-1}. Several lines of evidence lead to the conclusion that this T_3-binding protein is the receptor for thyroid hormones.[24] (i) For a large number of thyronines, thyromimetic activities are proportional to their affinities for isolated nuclear receptors (measured by competition with $[^{125}I]$-T_3), particularly when account is taken of their known metabolism or distribution. (ii) The location of these T_3-binding sites within the genome accords well with the known effects of thyroid hormones on transcription. (iii) At physiological plasma concentrations of T_3 the receptor is only partially occupied. Furthermore, although the relationship between receptor occupation and response is not always linear, maximal agonist response always coincides with receptor saturation.

Despite the fact that only a single class of T_3-binding site has been detected, two T_3-binding proteins of relative molecular masses of 47 000 and 57 000 Da have been detected. The receptor proteins seem to be preferentially associated with transcriptionally active DNA, which constitutes further evidence for their role as obligatory mediators of thyroid hormone activity.[25]

So far, purification of these receptors by conventional means has not been achieved. However, using genetic engineering techniques, it has been shown that the protein coded for by the c-erb-A gene (the cellular counterpart of the viral oncogene, v-erb-A) from both human[26] and chick[27] tissues, binds thyromimetics with high affinity, and with an SAR very similar to that of the T_3-binding proteins in cell nuclei. Furthermore, the relative molecular masses of these proteins are very similar to that of the endogenous thyroid hormone receptor, suggesting that the c-erb-A protein does indeed correspond to the receptor. There is considerable homology between the genes coding for c-erb-A protein and various steroid receptors, implying that both they and the v-erb-A gene have common ancestry and may be part of a superfamily of genes coding for regulatory proteins.

Recently a gene has been identified in rat brain which also encodes a thyroid hormone binding protein.[28] This is more closely related to that encoded by the chick c-erb-A protein than the human variant, and has a somewhat different SAR to both of them. The rat brain protein is not expressed in rat liver. DNA hybridization studies suggest that there may be as many as five different, related genes coding for thyroid hormone receptors, although no evidence for them has yet been found by more conventional techniques (see Section 16.2.5).

16.2.3.2   Access of T_3 to its Receptor

The affinity of T_3 for isolated nuclei is about 10^9 M^{-1}. Since the receptor is about 50% occupied in euthyroid animals, this would imply that the nuclear free T_3 concentration is about 10^{-9} M.

However, as has been emphasized in Section 16.2.2.4, the calculated free T_3 concentrations in cytoplasm are very little different from those in plasma which are about 10^{-11} M. Since cytoplasmic free T_3 is assumed to be the precursor of nuclear free T_3, Schwartz *et al.* have proposed a 'nuclear pump' which is operative *in vivo* but not *in vitro*, and which concentrates T_3 within the nucleus.[20] So far, no concrete evidence for this pump has yet been adduced. Alternative explanations are that the assumptions inherent in calculating the free cytoplasmic concentration from measurements in inevitably diluted cytoplasmic samples are invalid, that cytoplasmic T_3 is not the precursor of nuclear T_3, or that receptor affinity is modified during isolation of nuclei.

16.2.3.3 Postreceptor Events

The T_3-stimulated synthesis of certain specific proteins is preceded by, and therefore presumably due to, an increase in the concentrations of their corresponding mRNA. Thus, T_3 increased the concentrations of mRNA for growth hormone (GH), malic enzyme and the α-subunit of myosin ATPase. Conversely the disappearance of other proteins, such as TSH and the β-subunit of myosin ATPase correlated with a reduction in their mRNA concentrations.[29] In a study in rats to quantify the effects of T_3 on hepatic mRNA species the concentrations of about one-twelfth of over 200 separate mRNAs were altered, some were increased and others decreased.[25] About one-third of the T_3-responsive molecules were probably not affected directly by T_3 but by growth hormone (GH) whose production was stimulated by the thyroid hormone. One of the most rapid effects of T_3 in rat liver was to increase the concentration of the mRNA coding for a protein termed 'spot 14' (S14). This mRNA started to appear after a latent period of only 20 min and its nuclear precursor appeared even before this. The function of S14 is unknown, although it may be involved in lipogenesis.

The mechanisms of these changes in specific mRNA concentrations are varied. Changes in the rates of transcription were adequate to account for the alterations in the concentrations of mRNA for GH and TSH.[29] Barlow *et al.*[30] have recently shown that the promoter region of the GH gene contained regions which bound the endogenous thyroid hormone receptor, but only in the presence of T_3. This suggests that T_3 renders its receptor capable of recognizing specific regions within genes and regulating their expression, either directly or by release of a repressor mechanism. While some actions of T_3 on specific mRNA concentrations could be explained by transcriptional effects, these were too small to account for the increase in mRNA for malic enzyme and S14. Narayan and Towle have speculated that the occupied T_3 receptor in some way stabilizes the nuclear precursor of the mRNA for spot 14, possibly by inhibiting an endonuclease, leading to an enhanced production of the mature mRNA.[31] Whether this hypothesis is more generally applicable is unknown.

16.2.3.4. Alternative Thyroid Hormone Receptors

Despite the fact that the nuclear T_3 receptor is currently universally regarded as an important and obligatory step in most actions of thyroid hormones, there is evidence that receptors do exist in other organelles, and mediate some hormonal responses. In general this evidence consists of a demonstration that the organelles contain binding sites for thyromimetics, and that they can also respond to their presence with a change in function. This subject has recently been reviewed by Segal and Ingbar,[32] and will only be briefly reiterated here.

According to some authors the inner membranes of mitochondria contain a thyroid hormone binding protein which has a high affinity for T_3 (10^{11} M^{-1}), and binds other thyromimetics with affinities which parallel their thyromimetic potencies by conventional tests. However, other workers have failed to confirm the existence of this binding site. Although after *in vivo* administration of thyroid hormones there is a considerable delay before any increase in total body oxygen consumption is observed (see Section 16.2.1.3), there have been a number of reports of very rapid effects of thyroid hormones on mitochondrial ATP synthesis, oxygen uptake, ion translocation and protein synthesis. Some of these only occurred at very high concentrations of hormone, but others were apparent at levels closer to physiological.

As has been documented in Section 16.2.2.4, plasma membranes possess thyroid hormone binding sites. These may represent transport systems but could also be mediators of the various effects of thyroid hormones on plasma membrane functions which have been documented. In isolated-cell systems various thyromimetics have been shown to promote the intracellular accumulation of nonmetabolizable amino acids. Furthermore, these actions could also be demonstrated after *in vivo* administration of T_3 and did not require concomitant protein and RNA synthesis. The transport of nonmetabolizable sugars into cells has also been shown to be stimulated by thyroid hormones both *in vivo* and *in vitro*. This action was biphasic in that protein synthesis was not required to achieve the initial effect but the later response was dependent on protein synthesis.

The relationship between these relatively rapid effects on mitochondrial and plasma membrane function and the more conventional physiological measures of thyroid hormone actions which generally only occur after a relatively prolonged latent period is currently unclear. It may be that occupation of nuclear, mitochondrial and plasma membrane receptors is necessary to achieve conventional thyromimetic action, although there is no evidence for this. On the other hand each receptor may mediate independent effects.

16.2.4 BIOASSAY OF THYROMIMETICS

As outlined above, there is a multitude of actions of thyroid hormones, each of which could be (and often has been) used as the basis of a bioassay system. However, it is not the purpose of this section to provide an exhaustive summary of these techniques as this has been done elsewhere.[14] Rather, a strategy will be outlined based upon current understanding of the mechanism of action of these hormones and their properties. By analogy with other hormonal systems one might anticipate that novel drugs based on thyroid hormones would be either tissue-selective agonists or antagonists. The first step in the definition of a strategy, therefore, is to decide which tissues' functions should be modified, and, just as importantly, which should not. For instance, it is known that in man T_3 and T_4, either produced endogenously or administered exogenously, can reduce circulating plasma cholesterol concentrations, probably *via* action on the liver. However, the natural hormones have other effects in man. They increase heart rate and contractility, and frequently precipitate angina and arrhythmias. Clearly then the natural hormones cannot be used as hypocholesterolaemic agents since the therapeutic utility of these is mainly to protect the heart. A solution to this problem, therefore, is to devise a thyromimetic which decreases plasma cholesterol but has no cardiac effects. A strategy to devise such compounds could be to compare the activity of novel thyronines on plasma cholesterol and on (say) heart rate. However, both these measurements involve complicated and time-consuming experiments. It is more economical to refine further the definition of the objective as a thyromimetic which is active on the liver but not on the heart. This then allows the selection of simple and hopefully unambiguous assay procedures based on the fundamental biology of thyroid hormones.

Highly active agonists or antagonists must bind to the relevant receptor with high affinity. It is, therefore, reasonable to measure the affinity of novel compounds for T_3 receptors either in isolated nuclei[33] or nuclear extracts[34] from tissues being compared. However, it is clear that many factors can modulate the capacity of a compound to occupy receptors *in vivo*, in addition to its basic affinity measured *in vitro*. Thus the compound may be bound more or less avidly to plasma proteins, may or may not accumulate within cells, or may be metabolically converted to a more or less active form intracellularly. It is, therefore, also important to measure the capacity of novel compounds to occupy receptors *in vivo*. This can be done by determining their ability to prevent the nuclear binding of $[^{125}I]$-T_3 administered concurrently.[33] A comparison of receptor affinity measured *in vitro* with receptor occupation measured *in vivo* allows some quantification of the various processes, outlined above, which modify basic affinity *in vivo*. Despite ignorance of the fundamental nature of these processes, useful and productive structure–activity relationships (SAR) can be defined. Measurement of affinity, either *in vivo* or *in vitro*, cannot predict activity, and such measurements must be complemented with a determination of thyromimetic or indeed antagonist potency. Until recently this was complicated by the long latent period characteristic of thyroid hormones. This meant that any potency assessments had to be made *in vivo* over a prolonged period of time. We have used the induction of mitochondrial α-glycerophosphate dehydrogenase (GPDH) as a specific and highly sensitive measure of tissue thyroid status in the rat. This measurement allows accurate and relatively easy quantification of peripheral thyromimetic potency after a period of only 48 h.[35]

Although they have not yet been used to assess potency quantitatively, some of the techniques of molecular biology may offer advantages over GPDH induction in that measurements could be made over much smaller time periods and even presumably *in vitro* in tissue or cell culture. Thus, the measurement of changes in specific mRNAs such as those for S14 or other defined proteins could be used. It should be borne in mind that not all effects of thyroid hormones are a direct consequence of their interaction with their receptor in that tissue. The induction of α_2-macroglobulin mRNA for instance appears to be a consequence of the release of GH from the pituitary by thyroid hormones.[29] Such an assay would therefore be useless in determining hepatic thyromimetic activity. The detection of thyroid hormone antagonists presents special problems when conducted *in vivo* using classical measures of thyroid hormone activity. The necessity to do these studies over long periods of time means that for any activity to be detected the potential antagonist must not only be reasonably potent but also have a duration of action comparable to that of the natural agonist T_3. Even in the rat this is very long. The newer techniques of molecular biology should allow the circumvention of these problems, especially if used in cell culture systems.

Finally, it should be recognized that viable alternatives to nuclear receptor antagonism do exist. In those tissues which generate their own T_3 from T_4, inhibitors of ORD might be effective hormonal antagonists. Although transport of thyroid hormones into cells is not normally thought of as rate limiting in the overall activity, specific transport systems do appear to exist and potent inhibitors of these systems may demonstrate functional hormone antagonism. Furthermore there is the possibility (see Section 16.2.6) that these transport systems differ from tissue to tissue so that organ selectivity may be achievable.

16.2.5 STRUCTURE–ACTIVITY RELATIONSHIPS OF THYROID HORMONE ANALOGUES

16.2.5.1 Introduction

Structure–activity relationships of thyroid hormone analogues have been summarized in several review articles[14,36-39] and in key publications in the primary literature.[40-44] The intensive structure–activity studies[36,37] which followed Harington's elegant characterization and synthesis of T_4 in 1927[45] were given fresh impetus by the introduction of receptor-binding assays in the 1970s.[14,38,39] However, despite the developments in understanding of the mechanisms of thyroid hormone action over the past decade,[46] studies of structure–activity relationships have not attracted the attention of medicinal chemists to the same extent as many other hormones and transmitters. This may be ascribed to the failure, to date, to identify receptor subtypes and the lack of an armoury of agonists and antagonists possessing tissue or functional selectivity. In addition, one of the principal objectives of considerable medicinal and synthetic chemistry, namely the design of plasma cholesterol lowering thyromimetics lacking adverse cardiac activity, seemed to be undermined by the results of the Coronary Drug Project using D-T_4, where increased mortality in the drug-treated group was found.[47] It is now known that D-T_4 is not selective, and the first convincing examples of tissue selective thyromimetics have recently been reported.[44,48] These findings, together with the identification and sequencing of multiple thyroid hormone receptors,[28] indicate that tissue and functional selectivity by means of receptor differentiation has become a realistic objective. The structure–activity studies presented in this review focus on biological activity data obtained from assays which gave affinities for the physiologically relevant nuclear receptor,[46] and for subsequent receptor-mediated events *in vivo*. The nuclear receptor is characterized by having tenfold greater affinity for T_3 than for T_4, which parallels the *in vivo* activity of the hormones. A nuclear extract which binds T_4 more avidly than T_3 has been used in structure–activity studies,[49] but this binding site appears to be of doubtful physiological relevance.[50] Structure–activity relationships have been reported in several other systems, of which the most significant is rat liver iodothyronine deiodinase.[51,52] Studies of structure–activity relationships in thymocytes,[53] Ca^{2+}-ATPase[54] and binding to serum albumin and thyroxine-binding globulin[38,39] will not be reviewed here. The determination of the three-dimensional structure of the plasma protein thyroxine-binding prealbumin[55] (TBPA) has stimulated studies of ligand binding and molecular modelling of iodothyronine–protein interactions, which will be discussed. Physical properties of thyroid hormones, and syntheses of analogues, have been reviewed previously.[56] Applications have been reported of the principal routes of hormone analogue synthesis, namely phenol–dinitrophenol condensation,[57] diaryliodonium salt–phenol coupling[58] and phenol oxidative coupling[59] for the preparation of 3'-arylmethyl-substituted thyromimetics.

16.2.5.2 Conformational Properties of Thyroid Hormones and Analogues

Iodo substitution at the 3,5-positions in thyroid hormones and analogues causes the diphenyl ether to adopt conformations where the aromatic rings are mutually perpendicular (see Figure 1). The importance of diphenyl ether conformation for biological activity was first proposed by Jorgensen and Zenker in 1959[60] and it is now widely accepted that the orthogonal arrangement of the aromatic rings is critical for high receptor affinity and thyromimetic activity. Evidence supporting the mutually perpendicular conformation includes a large number of structures derived from

X-ray crystallography,[61,62] ^{1}H NMR[63] and ^{13}C NMR[64] studies in solution, and theoretical calculations.[41] The preferred diphenyl ether conformation results in two possible orientations for the 3'-substituent, either *distal* or *proximal* to the alanine-bearing ring (Figure 1). Distal and proximal conformers of the natural hormones are of near equal energy and a barrier to rotation of 8–9 kcal mol^{-1} (1 kcal = 4.18 kJ) has been observed in 3,5-diiododiphenyl ethers.[63] Substitution at the 2'-position results in a single low energy conformation where the 2'-methyl group is distally fixed.[63] Comparisons of the biological activities of 2',3'- and 2',5'-dimethyl analogues[14,60] have shown that it is a distally oriented 3'-substituent that is required for both receptor recognition and thyromimetic activity (Figure 1). The 4'-phenolic hydroxyl group can adopt conformations *cis* or *trans* to the 3'-substituent (Figure 2). Theoretical calculations[41] and structure–activity studies[40] suggested a model for receptor binding where the nonionized 4'-hydroxyl donates a hydrogen bond to a basic acceptor group. In support of this model, it has been shown that 3'-acyl-substituted analogues, which possess intramolecular 4'-hydroxyl–3'-substituent hydrogen bonds with energies of 6–8 kcal mol^{-1}, have free energy of binding to the T$_3$ receptor reduced by 1.1–1.9 kcal mol^{-1} [43] This loss of binding energy, which is the same as that found upon removal of the 4'-hydroxyl,[42,65] suggests that the receptor cannot break the intramolecular hydrogen bond in the 3'-acyl derivatives. Analyses of intermolecular hydrogen bonding in the crystals of hormone analogues[66] and model phenols[67] are in agreement with theoretical studies[41,68] and show that the hydrogen bond may deviate from the plane of the aromatic ring by up to 40°.

The bioactive conformation of the alanine side chain in thyroid hormone analogues has not yet been defined. In principle this could be approached by the synthesis of conformationally fixed cyclic or unsaturated derivatives. However, in order to provide an unequivocal answer to the question of which overall *cisoid* or *transoid* hormone conformation (Figure 3) is biologically important, the diphenyl ether would also have to be conformationally restrained. The *cisoid* and *transoid* conformations result from the methine group in the alanine side chain being *cis* or *trans* respectively to the phenolic ring (Figure 3). These conformations appear to be of similar energy, since both are found in thyroactive structures determined by X-ray crystallography.[61,62] In addition, each of the staggered low energy PhCH$_2$CHN rotamers has been observed in the solid state.

16.2.5.3 Effects of Substituent Modifications on Thyromimetic Activity

16.2.5.3.1 Scope

Structure–activity data on several hundred thyroid hormone analogues have been tabulated.[14,36-44] The key findings from early studies are summarized in Table 1. More recent investigations have focussed on 3'-substituted analogues (Tables 2 and 3) and on liver selective

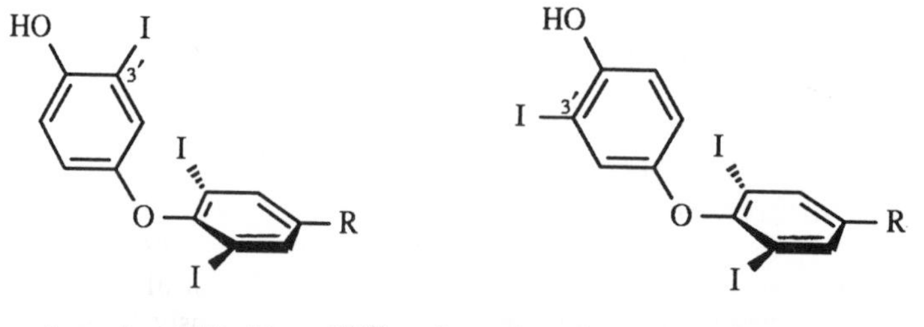

Figure 1 Alternative conformations of T$_3$. Skewed[61,62] conformations of T$_3$ (R = L-Ala) which place the 3'-iodo substituent distal (right) or proximal (left) to the tyrosyl ring. The distal conformation is postulated to be required for receptor binding

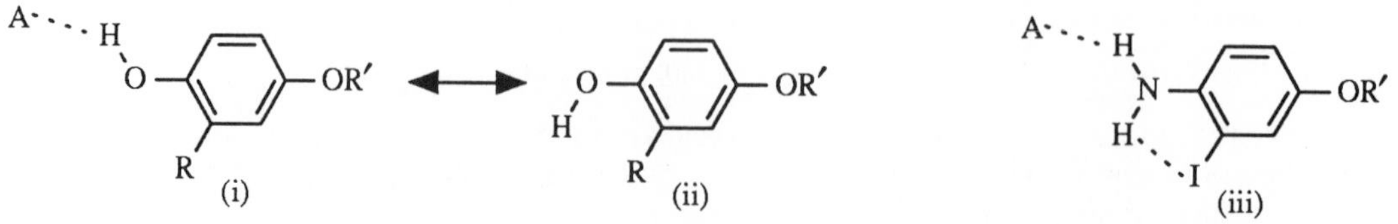

Figure 2 Conformations of 4'-hydroxyl (i) and (ii) and 4'-amino (iii) groups. The *trans* conformation (i)[41] and the intramolecularly hydrogen-bonded conformation (iii)[14] are believed to be required for ligand hydrogen bond donation to a receptor electron donor (A)[65]

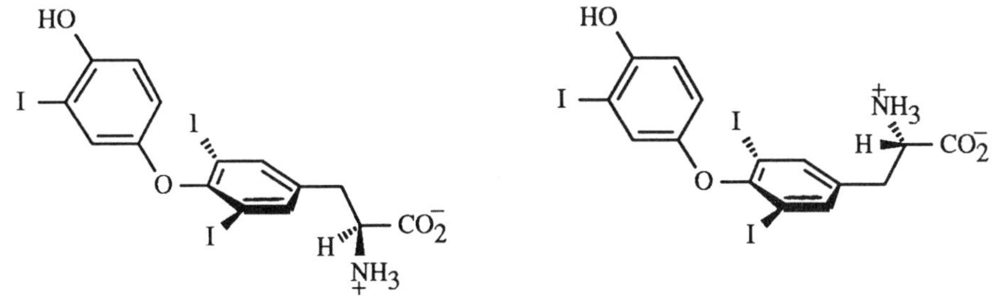

Figure 3 Distal conformations of T_3 having *transoid* (left) and *cisoid* (right) overall conformations. The thyroactive conformation has not been established

Table 1 Thyromimetic Activities of Thyroxine Derivatives[14,38,42]

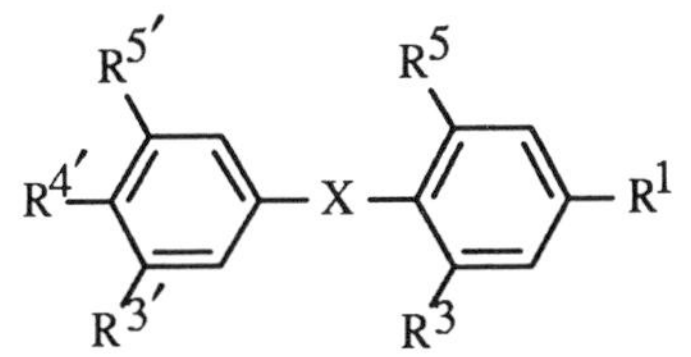

Compound	$R^{4'}$	$R^{3'}$	$R^{5'}$	X	R^3	R^5	R^1	In vivo activity[a]		In vitro nuclear binding[b]	
								Antigoitre	GPDH	Intact	Solubilized
(1; T_3)	OH	I	H	O	I	I	L-Ala	100	100	100	100
(2; T_4)	OH	I	I	O	I	I	L-Ala	18.1			14.4
(3)	NH₂	I	H	O	I	I	L-Ala	>0.27	9.9	12	
(4)	H	I	H	O	I	I	DL-Ala	>27	116	0.8	4.6
(5)	OMe	I	H	O	I	I	L-Ala	11			1.3
(6)	OMe	Pr^i	H	O	I	I	L-Ala	19	111	1.8	6.8
(7)	OH	Pr^i	H	O	I	I	L-Ala	142	290	87	92.5
(8)	OH	Pr^i	Cl	O	I	I	L-Ala				57
(9)	OH	Pr^i	Br	O	I	I	L-Ala				23.8
(10)	OH	Pr^i	I	O	I	I	L-Ala				13.5
(11)	OH	I	H	—	I	I	DL-Ala	0	LM	0.9	
(12)	OH	I	H	CH₂	I	I	DL-Ala	54	F	183	
(13)	OH	I	H	S	I	I	L-Ala	14	4.5	185	
(14)	OH	Pr^i	H	S	I	I	L-Ala		639	291	
(15)	OH	H	H	O	I	I	L-Ala	0.8	1.1	0.08	0.012
(16)	OH	H	H	S	I	I	L-Ala		0.2	7.4	
(17)	OH	Pr^i	H	O	Br	Br	DL-Ala	30		36	
(18)	OH	Pr^i	H	O	Me	Me	L-Ala	3.6	16	0.4	0.47
(19)	OH	Pr^i	H	O	Pr^i	Pr^i	DL-Ala		LM	0.2	
(20)	OH	I	H	O	I	H	DL-Ala	0.06	0	0.35	0.75
(21)	OH	I	H	O	I	Me	DL-Ala	3.6			
(22)	OH	I	H	O	I	Br	DL-Ala	41			
(23)	OH	I	H	O	I	I	D-Ala	7.5	44	36	62.8
(24)	OH	I	H	O	I	I	CO₂H	0.05			85
(25)	OH	I	H	O	I	I	CH₂CO₂H	6.5	F	421	282
(26)	OH	Pr^i	H	O	I	I	CH₂CO₂H		58	154	
(27)	OH	I	H	O	I	I	(CH₂)₂CO₂H	4.5	1.9	624	234
(28)	OH	I	H	O	I	I	(CH₂)₃CO₂H	1		14	
(29)	OH	Pr^i	H	O	I	I	(CH₂)₂NH₂		21	0.3	

[a] *In vivo* activity in rats relative to T_3 = 100% for goitre prevention and induction of liver GPDH (mitochondrial cytochrome *c* 3-phosphoglycerate oxidoreductase). F = full agonist, LM = low maximum response. [b] Nuclear receptor affinity, relative to T_3 = 100%, for binding to intact nuclei and solubilized receptors.

thyromimetics (Table 4). The principal biological assays used to estimate thyromimetic activity *in vivo* are goitre prevention[38] and induction of mitochondrial *sn*-glycerol-1-phosphate cytochrome *c* oxidoreductase (GPDH).[5] Affinity for nuclear receptors both *in vivo* and *in vitro* using radioligand binding techniques is now routinely used.[14,44] *In vitro* receptor binding is particularly useful for defining the ligand structural properties required for receptor recognition, without the complicating

Table 2 Thyromimetic Activities of 3′-Substituted-3,5-Diiodothyronines[43]

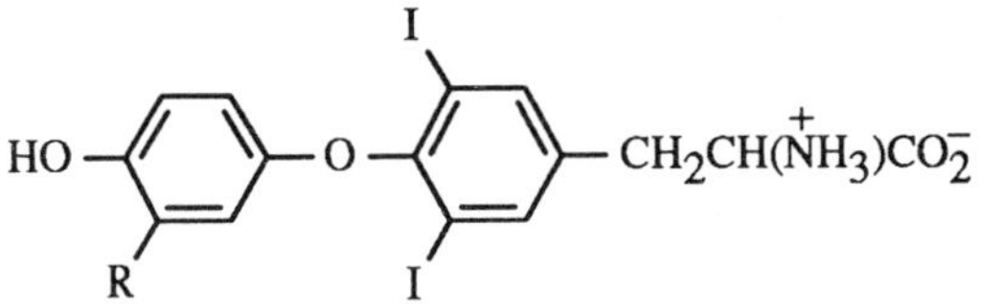

Compound[a]	R	Liver		Heart	
		Rel. IC_{50}[d]	Rel. ED_{50}[e]	Rel. IC_{50}[d]	Rel. ED_{50}[e]
(15)	H	0.08	1.1	0.40	0.45
(30)[b]	Me	0.6	7.5	3.9	3.2
(31)	Et	56.0	139.0	44.1	108.0
(32)[c]	$CH{=}CH_2$	17.0	10.7	15.3	12.5
(33)	Pr^n	45.2	88.9	24.5	32.8
(7)	Pr^i	87.0	290.0	119.2	348.0
(34)[c]	$CH_2CH{=}CH_2$	32.1	33.7	37.5	15.4
(35)[c]	Bu^n	43.6	120.0	88.4	F
(36)	CH(Me)Et	72.1	F	60.4	F
(37)	CH_2CHMe_2	20.5	F	18.7	F
(38)[b]	Bu^t	25.0	25.6	30.0	18.1
(39)[b]	$(CH_2)_4Me$	32.2	7.5	24.6	9.7
(40)	$(CH_2)_5Me$	60.0	4.92	40.0	LM (62)
(41)	$c\text{-}C_6H_{11}$	9.83	F		LM (48)
(42)[c]	$(CH_2)_6Me$	8.74	LM (51)	8.7	LM (16)
(43)	$CH_2\text{-}c\text{-}C_6H_{11}$	36.4	F	27.5	F
(44)[b]	Ph	7.3	6.6	4.85	4.4
(45)	CH_2Ph	21.7	2.16	13.0	1.43
(46)	$(CH_2)_2Ph$	1.8	LM (61)	3.61	LM (21)
(47)	F	0.76	F		F
(48)	Cl	5.1	2.79	12.0	1.92
(49)	Br	13.0	20.2	49.1	10.0
(1)	I	100.0	100.0	100.0	100.0
(50)	OH	0.04	LM (47)	0.05	LM (55)
(51)	CH_2OH	0.39	LM (75)	0.59	0.07
(52)	$(CH_2)_2OH$	0.45	LM (30)	0.68	LM (36)
(53)	$(CH_2)_4OH$	1.61	LM (27)		LM (40)
(54)	$(CH_2)_5OH$	5.34	LM (20)	2.33	LM (42)
(55)	$p\text{-}C_6H_4OH$	0.76	LM (81)	0.50	LM (22)
(56)	CH_2OMe	2.55	25.0	1.42	F
(57)	CH_2OPr^n	5.07	F	2.45	F
(58)[c]	$(CH_2)_3OEt$	1.45	F	0.96	LM (55)
(59)[c]	$(CH_2)_4OMe$	10.89	0.78	5.1	F
(60)[c]	$t\text{-}CH{=}CH(CH_2)_2OMe$	2.24		0.81	
(61)	CH_2SBu^n	19.0	F	6.3	LM (54)
(62)	$CH_2NHCOPr^n$	0.016	I	0.013	I
(63)	$(CH_2)_2NHCOEt$	0.12	LM (42)	0.061	I
(64)	$(CH_2)_3NHCOMe$	0.14	LM (37)	0.22	I
(65)	CO_2H	0.004	I	0.01	I
(66)	CH_2CO_2H	0.03	LM (25)	0.10	LM (22)
(67)	CH_2NH_2	0.01	I	0.03	I
(68)	$(CH_2)_2NH_2$	0.005	LM (37)	0.006	I
(69)	CHO	0.18	LM (50)	0.20	F
(70)	COMe	0.37	121.0	0.54	58.0
(71)	COEt	0.31	F	1.4	1.6
(72)	COPh	0.37	LM (13)	0.41	LM (40)
(73)	NO_2	0.13	0.32	1.0	F

[a] All compounds are L-thyronines, except where indicated. [b] DL-derivatives. [c] Partially racemized. [d] *In vitro* affinity for intact nuclei, relative to $T_3 = 100\%$; IC_{50} values for T_3: liver, 0.2–0.5 nM; heart, 0.2–0.5 nM. [e] Potency for induction of GPDH (mitochondrial cytochrome *c* 3-phosphoglycerate oxidoreductase) 48 h after single intramuscular injection relative to $T_3 = 100\%$; ED_{50} values for T_3: liver 160 nM kg^{-1}; heart 70 nM kg^{-1}. LM: low maximum response after two daily intramuscular injections of 50 mg kg^{-1}; percentage of the T_3 maximum response given in brackets. F = full agonist, potency not determined. I = inactive.

Table 3 Thyromimetic Activities of 3'-Arylmethyl-3,5-diiodo-L-thyronines[44]

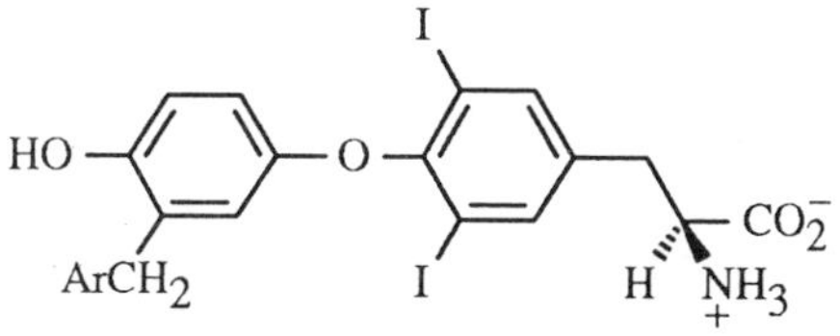

Compound	Ar	Liver[a]			Heart[a]			S[e]
		Rel. IC_{50}[b]	Rel. ID_{50}[c]	Rel. ED_{50}[d]	Rel. IC_{50}[b]	Rel. ID_{50}[c]	Rel. ED_{50}[d]	
(45)	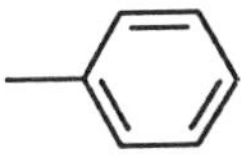 phenyl	15	5.1	2.2	13	0.30	0.50	17.0
(74)	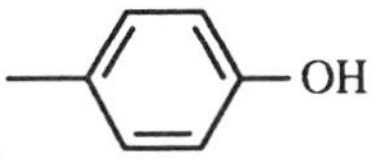 4-OH-phenyl	17	19	2.2	56	0.70	<0.10	27.1
(75)	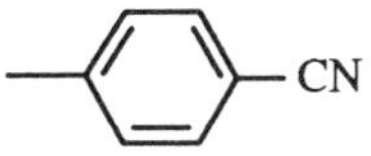 4-CN-phenyl	13	6.1	LM	6.5	0.22	1	27.7
(76)	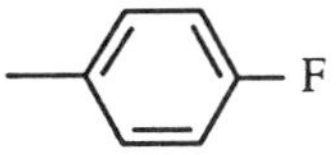 4-F-phenyl	60	98	5.7	43	8.6	3.7	11.4
(77)	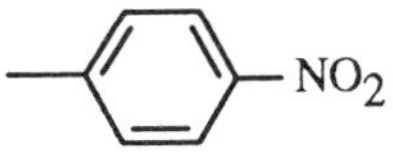 4-NO_2-phenyl	20	9.8	LM	64	0.71	0.90	13.8
(78)	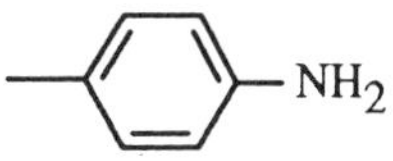 4-NH_2-phenyl	0.63	0.21	I	1.1	0.023	I	9.13
(79)	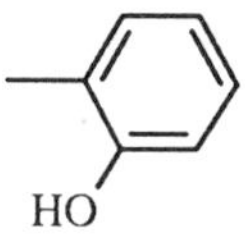 2-HO-phenyl	0.81	0.024	LM	2.2	0.024	LM	1.00
(80)	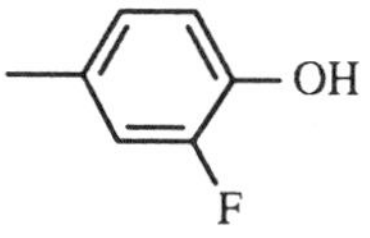 4-OH-3-F-phenyl	31	0.60	LM	31	0.37	I	1.62
(81)	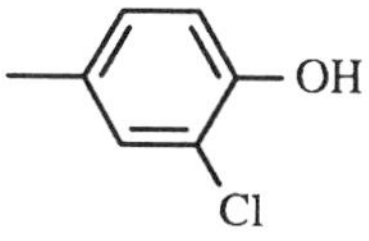 4-OH-3-Cl-phenyl	5.9	0.07	LM	15	0.07	I	1.00
(82)	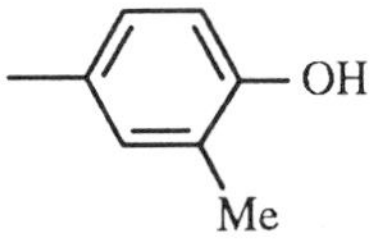 4-OH-3-Me-phenyl	7.4	0.35	LM	9.7	0.10	I	3.50
(83)	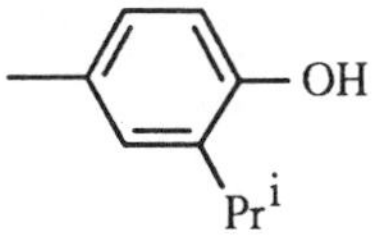 4-OH-3-Pr^i-phenyl	0.67	0.11	LM	4.4	0.11	LM	1.00
(84)	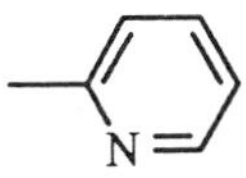 2-pyridyl	0.96	2.4	F	3.5	0.54	LM	4.44

Table 3 (*Contd.*)

Compound	Ar	Liver[a]			Heart[a]			S^e
		$Rel.\,IC_{50}{}^{b}$	$Rel.\,ID_{50}{}^{c}$	$Rel.\,ED_{50}{}^{d}$	$Rel.\,IC_{50}{}^{b}$	$Rel.\,ID_{50}{}^{c}$	$Rel.\,ED_{50}{}^{d}$	
(85)	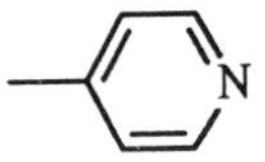 pyridin-4-yl	8.5	7.0	LM	15	1.6	LM	4.38
(86)	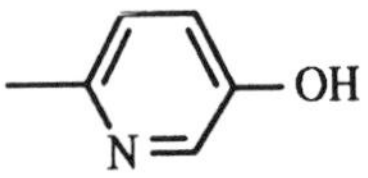 6-hydroxypyridin-3-yl	20	31	1.7	15	2.5	LM	12.4
(87)	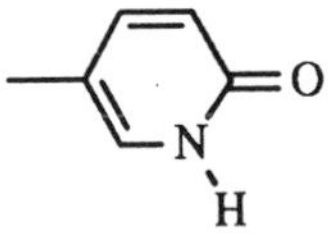 2-oxo-1,2-dihydropyridin-4-yl (NH)	2.3	10	1.7	2.7	0.20	I	50.0
(88)	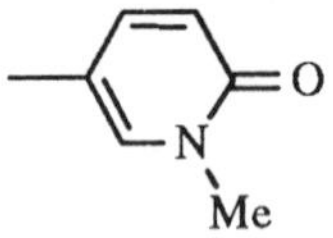 1-methyl-2-oxo-1,2-dihydropyridin-4-yl (NMe)	0.76	4.3	LM	0.58	0.058	I	74.1
(89)	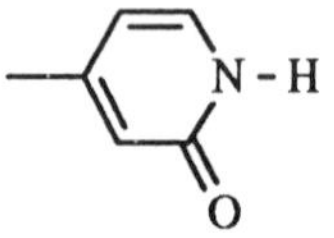 2-oxo-1,2-dihydropyridin-5-yl (N–H)	0.042	0.070	LM	0.045	0.0035	I	20.0
(90)	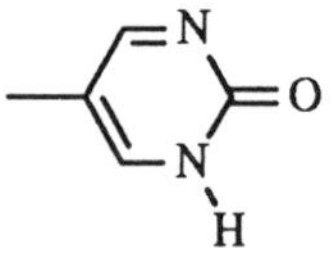 2-oxopyrimidinyl (N, NH)	0.15	0.28	I	0.58	0.0062	I	45.2
(91)	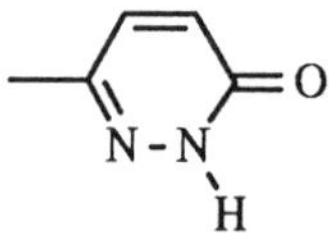 pyridazinonyl (N–NH)	2.0	38	2.4	4.0	0.40	<0.10	95.0
(92)	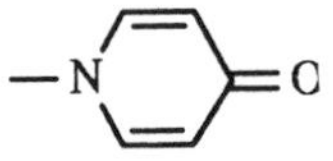 2-oxopyridin-1-yl (N)	0.25	2.7	1.4	0.40	0.013	I	208

[a] Determined in rats using the methods described in refs. 35 and 48. All activities are quoted relative to $T_3 = 100\%$. [b] *In vitro* binding to isolated nuclei; IC_{50} values for T_3: liver, 0.2–0.5 nM; heart, 0.2–0.5 nM. [c] *In vivo* binding to nuclei determined 1 h after intravenous administration of test compounds; ID_{50} values for T_3: liver, 2.4 nM kg^{-1}; heart, 2.4 nM kg^{-1}. [d] Potency for induction of GPDH (mitochondrial cytochrome *c* 3-phosphoglycerate oxidoreductase) 48 h after single intramuscular injection; ED_{50} values for T_3: liver, 160 nM kg^{-1}; heart, 70 nM kg^{-1}. LM: low maximum response after two daily doses of 50 mg kg^{-1}; F: full agonist, potency not determined; I: inactive after two daily doses of 50 mg kg^{-1}. [e] Selectivity, defined as the ratio (rel. ID_{50})$_{liver}$/(rel. ID_{50})$_{heart}$.

metabolic and pharmacokinetic effects present in *in vivo* assays.[43] Correlations between *in vivo* receptor binding and *in vivo* thyromimetic activity have been found for several series of thyroid hormone analogues.[38,43,69] These correlations provide good support for the nuclear receptor hypothesis of thyroid hormone action,[46] and additionally suggest that *in vivo* penetration to receptors depends on specific hormonal structural properties.[43,44]

16.2.5.3.2 The 4'-substituent

A nonionized 4'-hydroxyl group at the 4'-position is essential for high hormonal activity. Removal of the 4'-hydroxyl to give 4'-unsubstituted compounds (*e.g.* **4**, Table 1) results in reduction of

Table 4 Thyromimetic Activities of 1,3,5- and Ether Link Analogues of the Selective Thyromimetics (**87**) and (**91**)[44]

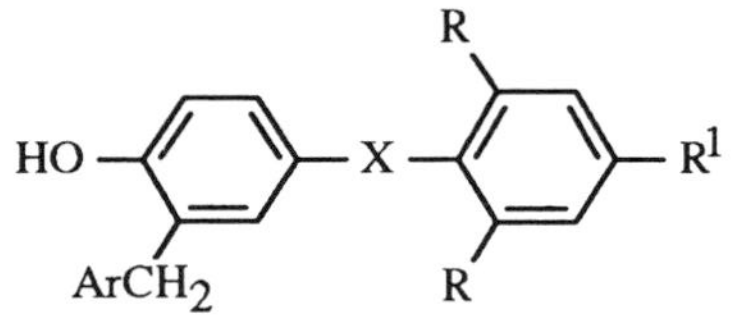

General structure:

HO–C6H2(R)(R)–X–C6H3(R¹)–, with ArCH2 substituent (Ar as shown).

Compound	Ar	R	X	R'	Liver[a] Rel.IC_{50}[b]	Liver[a] Rel.ID_{50}[c]	Liver[a] Rel.ED_{50}[d]	Heart[a] Rel.IC_{50}[b]	Heart[a] Rel.ID_{50}[c]	Heart[a] Rel.ED_{50}[d]	% increase O_2 consumption (dose mg kg^{-1})[e] IM	% increase O_2 consumption (dose mg kg^{-1})[e] PO
(87)	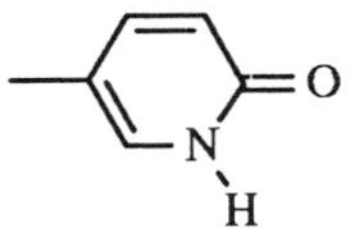 5-methyl-2(1H)-pyridinone	I	O	L-$CH_2CH(NH_2)CO_2H$	2.3	10	1.7	2.7	0.20	I	19 (3.3)	I (50)
(93)	"	Br	O	L-$CH_2CH(NH_2)CO_2H$	2.0	23	6.9	1.8	0.30	I	32 (3.3)	31 (5)
(94)	"	Cl	O	L-$CH_2CH(NH_2)CO_2H$	0.49	13	1.2	0.53	0.5	LM	26 (3.3)	31 (5)
(95)	"	Me	O	DL-$CH_2CH(NH_2)CO_2H$	0.083		1.1	0.14		I	28 (10)	18 (5)
(96)	"	I	S	L-$CH_2CH(NH_2)CO_2H$	14.8		16.6	19.4		I	26 (3.3)	I (50)
(97)	"	Br	S	L-$CH_2CH(NH_2)CO_2H$	9.8		14.5	10.2		LM		16 (5.3)
(98)	"	I	O	D-$CH_2CH(NH_2)CO_2H$	1.1		1.0	1.9		I		I (50)
(99)	"	Br	O	CH_2CO_2H	3.0	4.9	2.0	7.2	0.05	I	21 (20)	I (50)
(100)	"	Br	O	$(CH_2)_2CO_2H$	31.6	13.8	2.0	33.2	4.2	0.04		
(101)	"	Br	O	$(CH_2)_3CO_2H$	21.7	3.3	0.69	21.7	0.26	I		19 (5)
(91)	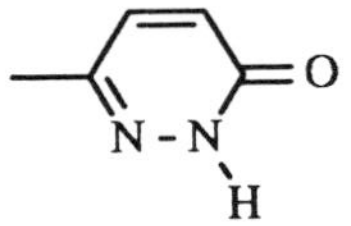 6-methyl-3(2H)-pyridazinone	I	O	L-$CH_2CH(NH_2)CO_2H$	2.0	38	2.4	4.0	0.40	<0.1	19 (3.3)	20 (10)
(102)	"	Br	O	L-$CH_2CH(NH_2)CO_2H$	0.9	50	18	2.0	1.3	<0.1	20 (0.1)	20 (0.1)
(103)	"	Cl	O	L-$CH_2CH(NH_2)CO_2H$	0.48		25	0.8		LM		15 (0.04)

[a-d] See Table 3. [e] % increase in oxygen consumption after seven daily doses of test compound, given intramuscularly (IM) or orally (PO) to euthyroid rats (see ref. 48 for details of method used). I = inactive. These compounds produce characteristic submaximal increases in oxygen consumption relative to T_3 (see ref. 48).

receptor affinity by two orders of magnitude.[42,65] In some instances, 4'-unsubstituted compounds retain activity *in vivo* as a consequence of metabolic hydroxylation.[70] 4'-Methyl ethers of active thyromimetics (*e.g.* **5**) also retain *in vivo* activity because of demethylation to the active 4'-hydroxyl analogues. All other attempts to find bioactive replacements for the 4'-hydroxyl have been fruitless to date, with the exception of the 4'-amino derivative of T$_3$ (**3**), which, uniquely amongst 4'-amino derivatives,[14] has 10% of the activity of T$_3$ both *in vitro* and *in vivo*. The available structure–activity relationships in 4'-substituted derivatives show that the effect of 3'-substituents on activity is strongly dependent on the nature of the 4'-substituent. The high activity of (**3**) has been postulated to be a result of a specific intramolecular hydrogen bond between iodo and amino groups, resulting in donation of the second NH to an H-bond acceptor group on the receptor, in agreement with the proposed model[41] for 4'-hydroxyl–receptor interaction (Figure 2). 3'-Alkyl-4'-amino compounds, in which repulsive interactions between 3'- and 4'-substituents lead to a different orientation of the N—H bond, have reduced receptor affinity relative to the corresponding 4'-hydroxyl analogues.[14]

16.2.5.3.3 The 3'-substituent

Replacement of the 3'-iodo group in T$_3$ by a variety of alternative substituents has been shown to retain affinity for the nuclear receptor. Studies of the 3'-substituent gained impetus following the key finding that isopropyl is a highly effective bioisosteric replacement for iodo at the 3'-position in T$_3$ and other analogues.[38] Studies utilizing a wide range of 3'-substituted T$_3$ analogues[40,43,44] (Tables 2 and 3) have provided comprehensive structure–activity relationships using both receptor-binding (*in vitro* and *in vivo*) and *in vivo* thyromimetic activity. The 3'-halo, -alkyl, -substituted alkyl and -acyl compounds in Table 2 have provided a basis for extensive quantitative structure–affinity studies,[40,43] which have been used to generate a model of 3',4'-substituent–receptor interactions.[41,43] The 3'-arylmethyl compounds in Table 3 are representative of a series of thyromimetics, some of which posses liver selective, cardiac sparing activity.[44,48,57]

Amongst nonpolar hydrocarbon and halogen 3'-substituents (Table 2, **1**, **7**, **15** and **30–49**) receptor affinity *in vitro* increases sharply with increasing substituent volume or length,[40,43] up to that of iodo or isopropyl (Table 2). The retention of high receptor affinity with certain bulky 3'-substituents, for example *n*-hexyl (**40**), cyclohexylmethyl (**43**) and benzyl (**45**) shows that the 3'-iodo binding pocket on the T$_3$ nuclear receptor is considerably larger than the natural iodo substituent. In comparison with the other bulky hydrocarbon 3'-substituents, 3'-phenyl (**44**), -cyclohexyl (**41**), -phenethyl (**46**) and -heptyl (**42**) compounds possess reduced affinity. These compounds were used[43] in a conformational study designed to identify the optimal 3'-substituent shape required for receptor recognition. The relative affinities could be explained by steric interaction with the receptor in 3'-substituents, which extend beyond a van der Waals envelope defined by superimposition of the high-binding cyclohexylmethyl (**43**) and benzyl (**45**) compounds.

Introduction of hydrophilic hydroxyl groups (**50–55**) into the 3'-substituent reduces receptor binding. In addition, replacement of methylene groups with polar functionality in the optimally sized high-binding hexyl analogue (**40**) yielded ethers (**57–61**) and amides (**62–64**) with clearly lowered binding. Highly polar charged 3'-substituents (**65–68**) have the weakest affinity in this series. 3'-Acyl and -nitro analogues (**69–73**) have reduced affinity as a consequence of both lowered lipophilicity and intramolecular hydrogen bonding with the 4'-hydroxyl.[43] Based on the overall effects of substituent size and hydrophobicity, a quantitative structure–affinity relationship was developed,[43] using all of the analogues in Table 2

$$\log(\text{rel. IC}_{50})_{\text{liver}} = -0.671\lambda - 1.23 L < I - 0.360D - 1.38H + 1.58 \tag{1}$$

$$n = 47, \quad r = 0.962, \quad s = 0.349, \quad F = 131.4$$

In equation (1), λ is an estimate of substituent hydrophilicity, calculated from substituent surface area and hydrophobicity (π); $L < I$ is substituent length, in Å, less than iodo, along the axis of the C—3'-R bond; D is the length, in Å, that substituents protrude from the optimal van der Waals envelope defined by the union of compounds (**43**) and (**45**); and H is an indicator variable, equal to unity for 3'-acyl and nitro analogues (**69–73**) which form acceptor intramolecular hydrogen bonds with the 4'-hydroxyl. The relative affinities of the 3'-arylmethyl compounds (Table 3) can be described by a similar equation[44]

$$\log(\text{rel. IC}_{50})_{\text{liver}} = -0.625\lambda - 0.551D_{o,m} - 2.66Q\text{-}p + 0.794p\text{-}OH + 1.53 \tag{2}$$

$$n = 20, \quad r = 0.965, \quad s = 0.239, \quad F = 51.2$$

In equation (2), $D_{o,m}$ is the substituent length, in Å, greater than hydrogen, of *ortho* and *meta* groups on the aryl ring; *Q-p* is the partial charge on the *para* substituent, derived from *ab initio* molecular orbital calculations; and *p*-OH is an indicator variable equal to unity for compounds (**74**), (**80–83**) and (**86**) (Table 3) having a hydroxyl group at the *para* position. Equation (2) shows that receptor affinity can be enhanced by electronegative and hydroxyl groups at the *para* position of the arylmethyl group.[44,57] The similar coefficients for the bulk and hydrophobicity terms in these equations suggest that the compounds in Tables 1 and 2 interact with the same size-limited, hydrophobic 3'-substituent binding site. Similar equations were obtained for binding to heart nuclei and the excellent correlations between *in vitro* affinities in heart and liver suggest that the receptors from these tissues may be structurally similar.[43,44]

The essential features of the 3'-substituent recognition site as deduced from these studies can be summarized as follows. The depth of the binding site is limited to the length of the natural iodo substituent (4.2 Å) and alternative 3'-substituents which do not extend fully into the site have affinity reduced in proportion to the decrease in substituent length relative to iodine, reflecting reduced van der Waals or hydrophobic binding. Substituents of greater bulk than iodine can be tolerated, provided that conformations are available where the additional bulk is confined to the volume encompassed by the union of the optimally sized benzyl and cyclohexylmethyl substituents. The binding site is hydrophobic but polar groups present at the *para* position of arylmethyl substituents can enhance affinity, suggesting that the receptor contains a specifically located dipolar element, which can participate in charge–charge or hydrogen-bonding interactions with suitable ligands. Intramolecular acceptor hydrogen bonds between 3'-substituents and the 4'-hydroxyl reduce binding affinity, showing that a free 4'-hydroxyl is required for receptor recognition.

Significant correlations between *in vitro* receptor affinity and thyromimetic activity have been found for the compounds in Table 2[43]

$$\log(\text{rel. ED}_{50})_{\text{liver}} = 0.948\log(\text{rel. IC}_{50})_{\text{liver}} - 0.591\text{MR} + 1.03 \tag{3}$$

$$n = 19, \quad r = 0.854, \quad s = 0.457, \quad F = 21.5$$

$$\log(\text{rel. ED}_{50})_{\text{heart}} = 1.14\log(\text{rel. IC}_{50})_{\text{heart}} - 0.379 \tag{4}$$

$$n = 16, \quad r = 0.894, \quad s = 0.437, \quad F = 55.7$$

These correlations, together with similar correlations linking receptor binding and antigoitre activity,[69] provide excellent support for the nuclear receptor hypothesis of thyroid hormone action. The requirements for a 3'-substituent property (MR, molar refractivity) to obtain a significant correlation in the liver (equation 3), but not in the heart (equation 4), suggest differences in tissue responsiveness. The 3'-acetyl derivative (**44**) was omitted in the derivation of equations (3) and (4) since it proved to be an outlier, having potent thyromimetic activity *in vivo* but weak affinity *in vitro*. This apparent discrepancy was resolved by measurement[35] of the receptor affinity of (**44**) *in vivo*, which was found to be fully consistent with *in vivo* activity. Generally, *in vivo* receptor binding provides a superior correlation with activity than does *in vitro* binding, and all discrepancies between analogue *in vitro* affinity and *in vivo* activity have been resolved by measurement of *in vivo* receptor affinities.[14] Reasons for the variance between *in vitro* and *in vivo* receptor affinities are not known, but could result from a variety of pharmacokinetic phenomena which control the concentration of hormone analogue penetrating to the nucleus *in vivo*.[48,71] The requirements for 3'-substituent MR in equation (3), but not in equation (4) may reflect tissue differences in structurally selective processes governing access to receptors *in vivo*.[43,44,48]

Specific 3'-arylmethyl substitution[44] (Table 3) results in compounds (*e.g.* **87** and **91**) possessing little or no cardiac activity, whilst maintaining (in rats) potent liver and hypocholesterolemic activities.[48] Selectivity is not due to differences in receptor recognition, since *in vitro* affinities in the two tissues are well correlated. The observed selectivity is explicable by difference in *in vivo* binding seen with this group of compounds (Table 2 and Figure 4). Quantitative structure–selectivity studies[44] have shown that liver/heart selectivity, *S*, defined as the ratio of *in vivo* relative affinities in the two tissues, increases with increasing 3'-substituent hydrophilicity and is reduced by substitution at *ortho* and *meta* positions on the aryl ring.

$$\log S = 0.350\lambda - 0.559D_{o,m} + 0.586 \tag{5}$$

$$n = 20, \quad r = 0.819, \quad s = 0.416, \quad F = 17.3$$

The mechanism underlying *in vivo* selectivity is as yet not firmly established. As indicated above in the analysis of equations (3) and (4), differential tissue penetration to receptors, or 'selective access'[48] would be one possible explanation. The intriguing possibility exists that these compounds may be

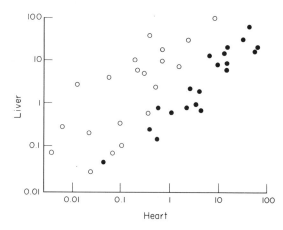

Figure 4 Relationship between liver and heart receptor binding (relative to $T_3 = 100\%$) for the 3′-arylmethyl derivatives in Table 3. There is a significant correlation both *in vitro* ($r = 0.938$) and *in vivo* ($r = 0.758$) but liver selectivity is present for many compounds *in vivo*. ● rel. IC_{50}; ○ rel. ID_{50}

exposing differences in obligatory hormonal transport mechanisms present in heart and liver, which in principle could operate at the plasma membrane[72] and/or the nucleus.[71]

16.2.5.3.4 The 5′-substituent

Structure–activity studies with 5′-substituted compounds have not been explored systematically beyond simple alkyl and halogen substitution.[38,42] In all cases of 3′,5′-disubstitution, addition of the 5′-substituent results in loss of activity and receptor affinity, as seen with the 5′-substituted 3′-isopropyl series (**7–10**; Table 1). The reduction in affinity has been correlated with 5′-substituent lipophilicity or bulk, and interpreted as either direct steric inhibition of binding, or inhibition of 4′-hydroxyl–receptor hydrogen bonding.[40,41]

16.2.5.3.5 The 3,5-substituents

Unlike the 3′-substituent, replacement of the 3,5-iodo groups by alkyl (*e.g.* **19**) results in substantial loss of activity and receptor affinity.[14,38,39] The halogen free analogue 3′-isopropyl-3,5-dimethyl-L-thyronine[73] (DIMIT; **18**), however, retains appreciable thyromimetic activity, and, unlike T_3, has the capacity to cross the placental membrane. Replacement of one of the 3,5-iodo groups by methyl or halogen results in increasingly reduced activity as the size of the substituent group diminishes (compare **1**, **20–22**). Certain 3,5-dibromo and dichloro analogues with liver selective thyromimetic activity have shown enhanced activity *in vivo* relative to diiodo derivatives (Table 4; see Section 16.2.5.3.8). Replacement of the 3,5-iodo groups by cyano, nitro, amino, ethylthio and phenylthio gives analogues devoid of activity *in vivo*.[38]

There are insufficient data available to establish firmly the 3,5-substituent physicochemical properties which are necessary for receptor recognition, since substituent variation at these positions is at present too limited to enable unambiguous quantitative structure–affinity relationships to be established.[42] Theoretical studies[41] have indicated that reducing 3,5-substituent size results in increased energy being required to 'lock' the conformation into the mutually perpendicular arrangements of the aromatic rings that are postulated to be essential for receptor interaction. This has led to the proposal[41,74] that there is a dual role for the 3,5-substituents in receptor recognition, namely a direct dipolar attraction, coupled with maintenance of the appropriate overall molecular conformation. On the basis of NMR studies of hormones and analogues in the presence of aromatic hydrocarbons,[75] it has been suggested that a π–π interaction between the tyrosyl ring and a receptor aromatic residue may contribute to hormonal affinity. The energy of this interaction was found to correlate with binding affinity for a series of 1-substituted analogues, all containing 3,5-diiodo substitution. Interestingly, the π–π interaction energy for L-T_3 was found to be 0.9 kcal mol⁻¹ greater than that found for D-T_3,[75] which is in qualitative agreement with the observed differences in receptor affinity (Table 1) and *in vivo* activity of the enantiomers.[20]

16.2.5.3.6 The ether link

Removal of the ether oxygen to give biphenyl derivatives (*e.g.* **11**), or its extension to methyleneoxy, results in complete loss of thyromimetic activity.[38] Replacement of the oxygen by linking groups such as sulfur (**13** and **14**) and methylene (**12**)[14,39] leads to retention of activity. These results are consistent with the requirement of the specific conformation found in the diphenyl ether (Figure 1) being essential for receptor recognition. In some diphenyl sulfide derivatives, for example the T_2 derivative (**16**)[14] and the selective thyromimetics (**96**) and (**97**)[44] (Table 4), receptor binding is greater than the corresponding ethers. This may be a consequence of the change in geometry, which results in lengthened aryl—X bonds and a reduction in the aryl—X—aryl angle as X changes from O to S.[76]

16.2.5.3.7 The L-alanine substituent

The L-alanine side chain is not essential for thyromimetic activity of T_3 and hormone analogues.[14,38,39] The D-enantiomer of T_3 (**22**) retains activity, possessing up to one-half of the activity of the L-isomer (Table 1).[14,20] The lack of marked enantioselectivity is emphasized by the absence of an absolute requirement for the amino group; thus deaminoalanine (propionic acid) derivatives (*e.g.* **27**) are bound up to six times more tightly to nuclear receptors than the corresponding L-alanines.[14,42] Acetic acid analogues (**25**) and (**26**) also have enhanced affinity, but those of formic (**24**) and butyric (**28**) acids are less active.[42] Despite their high affinities *in vitro*, the carboxylic acid analogues possess weak thyromimetic activity *in vivo*. This has been explained by the short half lives and duration of receptor occupation[14,77] found *in vivo* with the acid derivatives. The liver/heart selective thyromimetic activity found with the 3′-arylmethyl analogues (Table 3) appears to be dependent in part on side chain structure (see Table 4 and Section 16.2.5.3.8).[44]

16.2.5.3.8 Selective thyromimetics

The most active of the 3′-substituted T_3 derivatives possessing liver selective activity, the heteroarylmethyl derivatives (**87**) and (**91**) (Table 3), have relatively weak liver activity and are not orally active. A series of modifications to the 1,3,5- and ether link substituents were made (Table 4) in order to improve potency and bioavailability.[44] The trends in *in vitro* receptor binding follow those seen with other analogues possessing nonselective 3′-iodo and -isopropyl groups (Table 1), with the selective 3′-arylmethyl series having approximately tenfold weaker receptor binding. Thus, alternative halogen or methyl at the 3,5-positions reduce binding, acidic side chains and sulfides have increased affinity, and there is little alanine enantioselectivity (Table 4). Consequently, both selectivity conferring and nonselective 3′-substituents bind to the same recognition site on the T_3 receptor, *distal*[44] to the tyrosyl ring binding site.

All the analogues in Table 4 retain *in vivo* liver/heart selective activity and selective *in vivo* nuclear binding, with the exception of the propionic acid analogue (**100**). This suggests that the amino groups in the D- and L-alanine derivatives are essential for selectivity *in vivo*. An additionally surprising finding is the enhanced activity *in vivo* of the 3,5-dibromo analogues (**93**) and (**102**) relative to the corresponding iodo derivatives (**87**) and (**91**) respectively. The dibromo analogues, unlike the diiodo derivatives, possess oral activity, as shown by comparisons of the relative increases in whole body oxygen consumption found following oral or intramuscular administration (Table 4). Despite having potent selective activity, the sulfides (**96**) and (**97**) are less orally active than the corresponding ethers. The pyridazinone (**102**; SK & F L-94 901) was investigated in more detail, and was shown to be equiactive with T_3 as a liver thyromimetic and hypocholesterolaemic after chronic dosing, while possessing minimal cardiac activity.[48] This series of compounds represents the first convincing examples of cardiac-sparing thyromimetics with potential therapeutic utility as hypolipidaemic agents. Previous attempts to obtain selective thyromimetics[78] gave compounds which are now recognized not to be selective, *e.g.* D-T_4.[48]

16.2.5.4 Thyroxine-binding Prealbumin (TBPA)

The determination of the three-dimensional structure of human thyroxine-binding prealbumin[55,79] (TBPA) has permitted detailed structural studies of protein–thyroid hormone interactions. Although there are clear differences in structure–affinity trends, the topology of the hormonal binding site in TBPA has been suggested to serve as a model for the T_3 nuclear receptor,[14,55] and also for deiodinase[51] and the dioxin (Ah) receptor.[80]

16.2.5.4.1 *Hormone–protein interactions*

TBPA exists as a tetramer of identical subunits, forming two identical T_4-binding channels which display negative cooperativity of ligand binding; the affinities of T_4 for the two sites are approximately 10^{-8} and 10^{-6} M. The T_4 binding site in TBPA has been examined in detail.[55,83] The binding channel forms three pairs of symmetry-related pockets, four being filled by the T_4 iodine atoms, one by a crystallographically identifiable water molecule, and the sixth, in the vicinity of the 2'-substituent, is empty.[83] The 4'-hydroxyl, which is probably ionized, is hydrogen bonded to the water molecule, which interacts with serine and threonine hydroxyls located near the centre of the binding channel. The alanine ammonium and carboxylate groups are ion paired with lysine and glutamate residues at the opening of the channel. Because of the symmetry of the binding channel, the 3',5'-iodines bind to structurally different sites with some hydrophilic character, whereas the 3,5-iodines interact with identical hydrophobic binding pockets. The proximal 5'-iodo group of T_4 forms a close contact with the carbonyl oxygen of Ala-109A, the geometry of the interaction (I–O, 2.960 Å; C—I—O 161°) being within the distribution of such interactions found from an analysis of the Cambridge crystallographic data base.[84] Experimentally determined modes of binding of closely related hormone analogues, using X-ray difference density maps, have revealed striking differences.[85,86] Removal of the phenolic ring 3',5'-iodines or replacement by isopropyl groups results in analogues penetrating deeper into the binding channel than does T_4 itself. Remarkably, the analogues lacking one (rT_3) or both (3',5'-T_2) of the tyrosyl ring iodines appear to bind in a 'reverse' mode, with the alanine moiety inserted into the channel and the phenolic ring at the mouth of the channel. These findings suggest that a cautious interpretation is warranted of the results of molecular modelling[87] and QSAR[88,89] studies of TBPA binding, which necessarily make use of a common mode of binding for a structurally diverse group of ligands. However, molecular mechanics calculations[90] and modelling studies[83] using the T_4 mode of binding have permitted successful predictions of the binding affinities of alanine-modified[90] and 2',3'-substituted analogues.[83] Each of the ligands in these reports possesses 3,5-iodo substitution, and a common mode of binding might be predicted.

16.2.5.4.2 *TBPA as a model for the nuclear receptor*

TBPA binds T_4 more effectively than T_3, in contrast with the nuclear receptor where T_3 is more tightly bound. In addition, the specificity of ligand recognition by TBPA is markedly less than the nuclear receptor; for example, the tyrosyl ring in T_4 is not necessary for binding to TBPA, and a variety of simple halogenated phenols possess greater affinity for TBPA than does T_4 itself.[81,82] In contrast the full diaryl ether structure is required for high affinity for the nuclear receptor (see above and refs. 14, 36–39). Furthermore the 4'-hydroxyl is not necessary for prealbumin binding,[65] but is required for nuclear receptor recognition.[43,65] In addition, there are clear differences in bulk tolerance and enantioselectivity between TBPA and the nuclear receptor for a series of N-acyl, D- and L-T_3 and -T_4 derivatives;[65] these derivatives showed 100–700-fold reductions in receptor binding, but only 2–30-fold reductions in TBPA binding, relative to the nonacylated compounds. These comparative binding data suggest that TBPA is a poor model for the nuclear receptor. TBPA, however, possesses surface grooves which appear to be structurally complementary to double helical DNA;[79] since the nuclear receptor is believed to be bound to DNA in chromatin, it has been suggested that the two proteins, despite the structure–affinity differences, may nevertheless be derived from a common evolutionary precursor.[55]

16.2.5.4.3 *TBPA as a model for the dioxin receptor*

It has been shown that a series of halogenated biphenyls,[82] dioxins and dibenzofurans[87] have high affinity for TBPA. Consequently, TBPA has been used as a model for the dioxin or Ah receptor, and this has been suggested to be useful for the prediction of the toxic potential of halogenated aromatic hydrocarbons.[87] At the present time, there is no convincing evidence to support the main conclusion of these studies, which proposes that dioxin toxicity is the result of persistent thyromimetic activity.[49,80,82,87] Thus there are no reports showing that halogenated aromatic hydrocarbons bind to the T_3 sensitive, physiologically significant nuclear receptor, or that these compounds possess thyromimetic activity in any of the recognized assays. The significance of the high affinity of polychlorinated biphenyls for a T_4 sensitive nuclear extract[49] remains to be established; this binding site has a structure–affinity profile similar to TBPA[49,55] but other evidence suggests that high T_4 nuclear binding is an artefact.[50] In addition, thyroid hormone binding to the Ah receptor has not been demonstrated *in vivo*, and there is no experimental evidence for the proposal that toxin or hormonal binding to a cytosolic protein, followed by complexation with a second nuclear-bound receptor, is necessary for thyromimetic action.[80]

16.2.5.4.4 *TBPA as a model for deiodinase*

Structure–activity relationships for the inhibition of type I rat liver monodeiodinase have been reported.[51] The most active inhibitors reported are rT_3 and tetraiodothyroacetic acid, which have IC_{50} values of 0.3 and 0.2 μM respectively. Substitution at the 3',5'-positions by halogen, nitro or hydroxyl retains inhibitory potency, but isopropyl substitution reduces activity. 2'-Methyl, 2'-hydroxyl and 2',3'-naphthyl substitution is tolerated. 4'-Substitution is optimally hydroxyl, but oxyacetic acid and amino in certain cases retain potency. The side chain tolerance by deiodinase appears substantial, with permissible modifications to *N*-acylalanine, acetic acid and acyloxy. These binding data appear to mimic TBPA structure–affinity relationships closely,[65,81] and, not surprisingly, the most active deiodinase inhibitors were shown[51] by molecular modelling to have structural complementarity with the T_4 recognition site in TBPA.

A number of phenolic plant extracts possess type I monodeiodinase inhibitory activity and of these tri- and tetra-hydroxyaurone flavanoids are the most potent, having inhibitory potencies in the same range as the iodothyronine inhibitors.[52] The kinetics of inhibition by aurones revealed noncompetitive thiol cofactor inhibition. However modelling studies showed that the three-dimensional aurone structure closely resembles iodothyronines and the aurone and T_4 phenolic rings can interact similarly with TBPA. The aurones were also found to have similar affinity to rT_3 in TBPA binding, and on the basis of these structural arguments, the mechanism of action of the aurones was suggested to involve binding to the substrate site of the oxidized form of the enzymes.[52]

16.2.6 BIOLOGICAL PROPERTIES OF SELECTIVE THYROMIMETICS

In Section 16.2.4, it was argued that agents which have thyromimetic activity towards the liver but not the heart could be valuable hypocholesterolaemic drugs. Research at SK & F has identified such selective thyromimetics (Table 4),[44,48] and this section describes in more detail their pharmacological and toxicological properties, and what is known about the mechanism of selectivity.

16.2.6.1 Pharmacological Properties of Selective Thyromimetics

As emphasized in Section 16.2.4, the induction of GPDH in rat tissues is an excellent measure of their responsiveness to the administration of thyromimetics. During our studies, the hepatic and cardiac potencies of novel compounds were compared by measuring tissue GDPH activities 48 h after administration of a single dose to hypothyroid rats. The data in Tables 3 and 4 show that the presence of selected arylmethyl moieties in the 3'-position of various 3,5-dihalothyronines (and their acetic analogues) confers selectivity, in that all are full agonists on the liver (from 1% to 18% as active as T_3) but are either inactive or very much less active (0–1%) than T_3 on the heart. This selectivity is illustrated graphically in Figure 5(a–c). In these experiments euthyroid rats were given seven daily intramuscular injections of 10 different selective thyromimetics, and hepatic, cardiac and renal GPDH were measured 24 h after the final dose. Whole body oxygen consumption was also measured before and after treatment.

In Figure 5a the change in cardiac GPDH activity caused by a single high dose of each of these compounds is plotted as a function of the change in hepatic GPDH. A dose–response curve to T_3 is included for comparison. It is clear that maximal or near maximal effects on the liver can be achieved at doses which had no effect at all on the heart. This is in marked contrast to T_3, where cardiac activity is proportional to hepatic activity. By contrast for each of these compounds, as for T_3, the renal response is proportional to the hepatic response (Figure 5b).

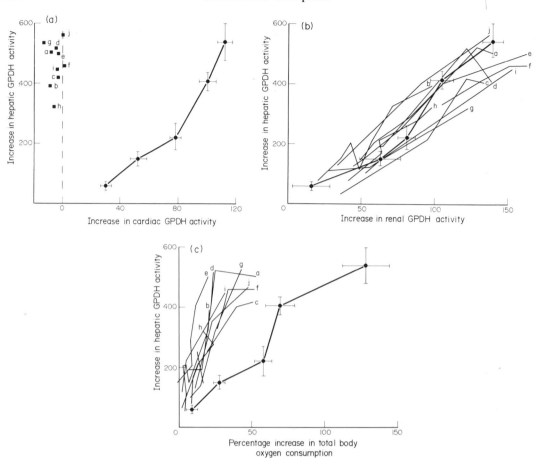

Figure 5   A comparison of the hepatic cardiac, renal and thermogenic effects of selective thyromimetics and T_3. Groups of euthyroid rats were given seven daily intramuscular doses of various selective thyromimetics: 24 h after the final dose, the total body oxygen consumption (L oxygen at STP $kg^{-3/4} h^{-1}$), and hepatic, cardiac and renal GPDH were measured. In each case the absolute increase in hepatic GPDH activity over the vehicle-treated control values is plotted against the absolute increase in cardiac GPDH (a) or renal GPDH (b) or the percentage increase in total body oxygen consumption (c). In (b) and (c) the effects of several doses of selective thyromimetic are shown, but in (a) only the highest dose is illustrated. The selective thyromimetics with the dose range employed in $mg\,kg^{-1}\,d^{-1}$ in parentheses were: (a) compound (**87**) (1.25–20); (b) L-3,5-diiodo-3'-(6-oxo-3(1*H*)-pyridylmethyl)thyroacetic acid (0.16–10); (c) L-3,5-diiodo-3'-(2-oxo-5(1*H*)-thiazolylmethyl) thyronine[57] (1.1–10); (d) compound (**93**) (0.31–20); (e) compound (**99**) (0.25–20); (f) compound (**96**) (0.37–10); (g) compound (**91**) (0.37–10); (h) L-3,5-dibromo-3'-(6-oxo-3(1*H*)-pyridylmethyl)thyronine ethyl ester (0.031–0.5); (i) compound (**95**) (0.1–10); (j) compound (**102**) (0.1–10). A dose–response curve (heavy line) to T_3 ($\bullet$) is shown for comparison. The bars represent 2 SEM

All of these selective thyromimetics have some effect on whole body oxygen consumption, although for any given increase in hepatic GPDH these thermogenic effects are much less than those due to T_3 (Figure 5c). This partial activity might be expected if some organs (*e.g.* liver and kidney) responded to the administration of selective thyromimetics with an increase in oxygen consumption, but others (*e.g.* heart, and perhaps skeletal muscle) did not.

Selective thyromimetics, where tested, have unusual effects on plasma thyroid hormones. The data in Figure 6 are from experiments in which euthyroid rats were given seven daily intramuscular injections of varying doses of three representative selective thyromimetics. It can be seen that the doses chosen increased hepatic GPDH activities, while plasma T_4 concentrations diminished. In contrast, plasma T_3 remained unaffected. In general only doses of selective thyromimetics which are supramaximally active on the liver diminished plasma T_3. The mechanism for this differential action on thyroid hormones is not known. It is difficult to quantify accurately reductions in plasma TSH concentrations in rats to values below those seen in euthyroid animals. However, when hypothyroid rats were given SK & F L-94 901 (**102**), only those doses, which in euthyroid rats reduced circulating T_3, reduced plasma TSH concentrations.[48] Thus, it seems possible that the changes in TSH and T_3 could be causally linked, but this does not explain the greater sensitivity of T_4 to the administration of selective thyromimetics.

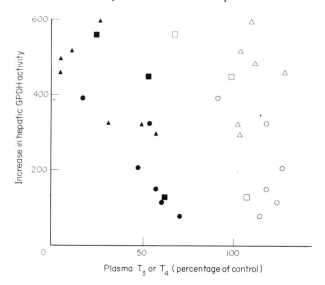

Figure 6 A comparison of the effects of three selective thyromimetics on hepatic GPDH activity and circulating thyroid hormone concentrations. Groups of euthyroid rats were given seven daily intramuscular doses of selective thyromimetics 24 h after the final dose hepatic GPDH, plasma T_3 ($\bigcirc$, $\square$, $\triangle$) and T_4 ($\bullet$, $\blacksquare$, $\blacktriangle$) were measured. In each case the absolute increase in hepatic GPDH activity over the vehicle-treated control value is plotted against thyroid hormone concentration expressed as a percentage of the pretreatment value. The selective thyromimetics, with the dose range employed, in $mg\,kg^{-1}\,d^{-1}$, in parentheses, were: L-3,5-diiodo-3'-(6-oxo-3(1H)-pyridylmethyl)thyroacetic acid, $\bigcirc$, $\bullet$ (0.16–10); compound (**93**), $\triangle$, $\blacktriangle$ (0.07–50); compound (**102**), $\square$, $\blacksquare$ (1.1–10)

As would have been predicted from our hypothesis, these selective thyromimetics also reduce plasma cholesterol concentrations in certain animal models. The data in Figure 7 show that the most potent selective thyromimetic yet identified (**102**) can reduce plasma cholesterol in hypothyroid rats previously made hypercholesterolaemic by feeding them a diet rich in cholesterol. In this experiment (**102**) was as active as T_3, as would have been expected since it is also as potent as T_3 in inducing hepatic GPDH under these conditions. Many other selective thyromimetics have also been shown to reduce plasma cholesterol using this protocol, but are less potent than T_3. (**102**) was also shown to be hypocholesterolaemic in the heterozygous Watanabe rabbit. In the experiment shown in Figure 8 a group of these rabbits was given subcutaneous doses of (**102**) starting at $5\,\mu g\,kg^{-1}\,d^{-1}$ and increasing stepwise to $30\,\mu g\,kg^{-1}\,d^{-1}$ for a total of 63 d. Treatment with $10\,\mu g\,kg^{-1}\,d^{-1}$ caused a significant reduction in plasma cholesterol of about 50% and this was not increased by increasing the dose. On cessation of treatment plasma cholesterol concentrations increased to a level even greater than pretreatment control values. During the course of this experiment, LDL-cholesterol was reduced while HDL-cholesterol remained relatively constant. The choice of animal model for demonstrating this effect is important. Neither (**102**) nor T_3 consistently reduced plasma cholesterol in normocholesterolaemic euthyroid rats. Indeed sometimes the very low concentrations in these animals (about 50 mg %, all in the HDL fraction) were increased by thyromimetics.

Recently Fantappie *et al.*[91] have confirmed that (**102**) can reduce plasma cholesterol in normal and cholesterol-fed rats and have shown that this reduction is associated with an increase in hepatic LDL-receptors. Davidson[92] has also shown that the concentration of the mRNA for Apo B-100 in the livers of rats treated with either T_3 or (**102**) is reduced compared to control animals. It appears therefore that the mechanism of the hypocholesterolaemic effect of (**102**) could involve a reduction in the production of LDL and an enhancement of its removal by the liver.

Thus (**102**) has been shown to be both a potent and selective thyromimetic and also to reduce plasma cholesterol concentrations in suitable models. It was pertinent to ask if it lacked the potential cardiotoxicity of T_3. We approached this question by comparing the effects of T_3 and (**102**) on a number of parameters of cardiac function which are believed to be predictive of deleterious events. In every case hypothyroid rats were given (**102**) at a dose of at least $1\,mg\,kg^{-1}\,d^{-1}$ for 7 or 14 d before measurements were made. No effects of (**102**) were seen on the spontaneous rate of beating of the atria isolated from treated rats, or on the heart rate *in situ* of such rats. No effects on cardiac contractility, as measured by the rate of rise in ventricular pressure were observed, nor was there any change in the duration of the action potential of atrial or papillary muscle cells. Finally there was no

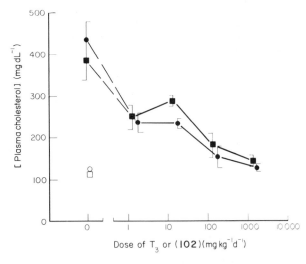

Figure 7 Effects of T_3 and SK & F L-94901 (**102**) on plasma cholesterol in rats. Male hypothyroid rats were fed a diet containing 1.5% cholesterol and 0.5% cholic acid for three weeks to increase their plasma cholesterol concentrations. They were then given seven daily oral doses of either T_3 (■) or (**102**) (●) and plasma cholesterol was determined 24 h after the final dose

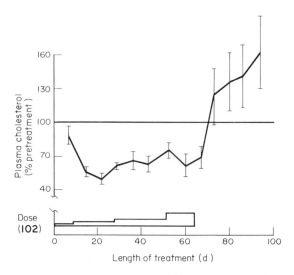

Figure 8 Effect of (**102**) on plasma cholesterol concentrations in Watanabe rabbits. Four heterozygous Watanabe rabbits were given subcutaneous injections of (**102**) daily for 63 d starting with 0.005 mg kg^{-1} d^{-1} rising to 0.01 mg kg^{-1} d^{-1} after 9 d, 0.02 mg kg^{-1} d^{-1} after a further 19 d, and finally to 0.03 mg kg^{-1} d^{-1} after a further 32 d, after which treatment was discontinued. Total plasma cholesterol was determined at various times during the treatment and is expressed as a percentage of the pretreatment control since there was considerable variation in the absolute plasma concentrations between rabbits

potentiation of the ability of coronary artery ligation to produce arrhythmias is perfused hearts from (**102**)-treated rats.[93]

All of these negative results were in direct contrast to those obtained with T_3, which changed all of these parameters at doses of 0.1 mg kg^{-1} d^{-1}, or, in some instances, even 0.01 mg kg^{-1} d^{-1}. We concluded that (**102**) did not share the potential cardiotoxicity of T_3.

16.2.6.2 Mechanisms of Selectivity

Perhaps the commonest reason why some hormonal agonists act on one organ and not on another is that the receptors in the two organs are different from each other, and that the agonist binds to only one receptor. This, however, is not the case for (**102**) since its affinities for both cardiac and hepatic thyroid hormone receptors are about the same, roughly 1–2% of that of T_3. Such results, therefore, not only fail to tell us why (**102**) is selective, they also add a second problem, *viz.*

why is it as active as T_3 *in vivo* on the liver when its affinity for hepatic receptors is only 1% of T_3? This question is partially resolved when *in vivo* binding studies are conducted with selective thyromimetics. As is illustrated in Tables 3 and 4, all selective thyromimetics bind more avidly to hepatic nuclei than cardiac nuclei after *in vivo* administration. Thus an alternative explanation for their selectivity is that liver receptors *in vivo* are exposed to higher concentrations of compounds than are heart receptors. To examine this hypothesis (102) or T_3 was measured in the plasma or hepatic or cardiac cytosol from hypothyroid rats which had been given 0.1 mg kg^{-1} of either (102) or radiolabelled T_3 1 h before they were killed. In addition, the free fractions of both were measured by equilibrium dialysis (Table 5).

Inevitably in such experiments cytosolic samples are contaminated with plasma, and the values in Table 5 are corrected for this contamination. The concentrations of T_3 in liver and heart and of (102) in liver are so high compared with plasma that correction for this plasma contamination makes little difference. However, the measured level of (102) in heart was about 40 ng ml^{-1} and we calculated that most of this was due to plasma contamination. Correction for this resulted in the value of 7 ng ml^{-1} given in the table, though this must necessarily be an approximation. The results show that the total T_3 concentration in liver cytosol was about three times that in heart, and both were greater than plasma total T_3. By contrast there was a massive accumulation of (102) into liver cytosol of about 50-fold and an exclusion of it from the heart. This led to a concentration difference between the two tissues of several hundred fold.[94]

While these results suggest that selectivity is due to the accumulation of (102) in the liver, the situation is complicated by the fact that it is commonly believed that it is the free level of thyroid hormones in plasma and cytosol that determine nuclear levels, and hence receptor occupation. Accordingly free T_3 and (102) concentrations in these fractions were measured (Table 5). Interestingly the free T_3 concentrations in plasma, liver and heart are the same. The apparent concentration of T_3 into the heart and liver therefore is a consequence of enhanced protein binding of T_3 in these organs. Despite the facts that the same doses of T_3 and (102) were used and these produced similar total plasma concentrations, free (102) in plasma is about five times free T_3, showing that (102) is less avidly bound to plasma proteins. Similarly, free (102) in liver is 20 times free T_3 for an equivalent dose.[94] This is presumably partly due to the higher plasma free (102), and may be also due to some active accumulation.

Free (102) in heart cytosol was measured, but because binding was minimal and because most of it was probably derived from plasma, the measured value was not meaningful and has not been included.

At face value then this experiment solved some problems. The unexpectedly high hepatic activity of (102) compared to its receptor affinity is, to some extent, explained by the difference between the free cytosolic (102) and T_3 concentrations after an equivalent dose. It seems likely that selectivity is explained in part by concentration of (102) into the liver, and by exclusion from the heart, although without measurements of free (102) in heart this cannot be proven. If this explanation is true, it suggests that the transport system for (102) into liver cells differs from that in heart cells.

This explanation for selectivity, however, must remain tentative since what was measured as '(102)' was subsequently shown, using HPLC and RIA, to be a mixture of (102) and a metabolite in roughly equal proportions in both heart and liver, though, of course, the absolute levels of both were very different. This observation prompted us to fractionate the radioactivity in hepatic nuclei from rats previously given a dose of (102) labelled to high specific activity with tritium.[94] This experiment

Table 5 The Distribution of Total and Free L-T_3 and (102) between the Plasma and Cytosol Fractions of Hypothyroid Rats Treated with L-T_3[a]

Tissue	Total (ng mL^{-1})		Free (ng mL^{-1})	
	T_3	*(102)*	T_3	*(102)*
Plasma	90 ± 5 (6)	92 ± 1 (4)	0.60	3
Liver cytosol	632 ± 162 (6)	5000 ± 1080 (4)	0.71	17
Heart cytosol	226 (3)	7 ± 0.3 (4)	0.64	

[a] Hypothyroid rats were given an intravenous injection of 0.1 mg kg^{-1} of [^{125}I]-T_3 or (102). Plasma, liver cytosol and heart cytosol fractions were then isolated 1 h later. The concentration of L-T_3 in the plasma and tissue cytosol fractions was determined as acid insoluble ^{125}I and of (102) by RIA. The concentrations of free L-T_3 or (102) in these fractions were determined by equilibrium dialysis of pooled samples, six for T_3 and four for (102). The results are the mean ± SD with the number of observations in parentheses.

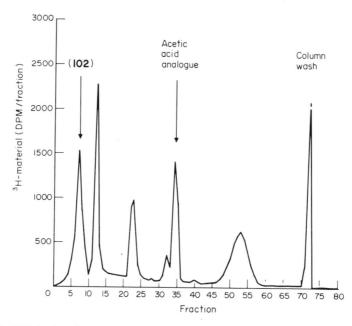

Figure 9 Analysis, by HPLC, of the ^{3}H material extracted from the liver nuclei of rats treated with [^{3}H]-(**102**). [^{3}H]-(**102**)-derived material was extracted from the liver nuclei isolated from a hypothyroid rat treated with [^{3}H]-(**102**) (18.9 nmol kg^{-1} i.v.) previously. This material was analyzed by HPLC. The concentration of ^{3}H material in each fraction has been expressed in DPM ^{3}H label/fraction. The arrows show the running positions of (**102**) and its acetic acid analogue in a separate HPLC run performed on the same day. The column was washed at the 70 min time point and the material which eluted in the following 10 min is shown

revealed that nuclear radioactivity was composed of at least five different fractions (Figure 9). One had the same mobility as parent compound, another the cytoplasmic metabolite [tentatively identified by Pue and Blake at SK & F as the lactic acid analogue of (**102**)] and another had the same mobility as the acetic acid analogue of (**102**). The identity of the remaining components is unknown.

In summary, the reasons for selective thyromimetic activity are still unclear, but it is probably partly due to an enhanced drug accumulation in liver cells, and an exclusion from heart cells. Metabolic activation may also be occurring, but until the metabolites are characterized and their thyromimetic activities are determined, this will remain uncertain.

16.2.6.3 Toxicological Properties of Selective Thyromimetics

Only (**102**) has been subject to extensive toxicity studies. In these, rats were given daily doses ranging from 0.02 to 10 mg kg^{-1} d^{-1} for 30 d. For comparison rats were also given T$_3$ at 1 mg kg^{-1} d^{-1} as a positive control; many of these rats died with their hearts showing signs of myocardial damage. No rats treated with (**102**) died during the in-life phase of the study, and at autopsy no damage to their hearts was observed, nor were there any significant changes in their blood chemistry. However, (**102**) did cause three unusual effects. These consisted of focal fibroplasia on peritoneal surfaces, the appearance of multinucleate cells in the distal tubules of kidneys, and the formation of new trabecular bone in the femur. All of these effects occurred in the rats treated with T$_3$ and it is a reasonable assumption that they are thyromimetic actions.[95] Because of these effects the development of (**102**) has been suspended.

16.2.7 THE USE OF THYROID HORMONES AND THEIR ANALOGUES IN THERAPY

16.2.7.1 Natural Thyroid Hormones

By far the greatest therapeutic use of thyroid hormones is in the treatment of various forms of hypothyroidism, from the complete absence of thyroid function seen in myxoedema to the ill-defined subclinical hypothyroidism, and also including cretinism. Hypothyroidism can be due to a failure of tne thyroid gland itself (primary), to a failure of the pituitary (secondary) or a failure of the hypothalamus (tertiary). Very rarely peripheral resistance to thyroid hormones is seen and this is the only form of hypothyroidism not alleviated by administration of the hormones. Primary hypothyroidism can be due to disease of the gland or for iatrogenic reasons.

The objective of treatment is to restore the patients physiological status and sense of well-being, and not to attain any given plasma concentrations of thyroid hormones or TSH, although measurement of these, especially TSH, can be of value in monitoring the progress of therapy. Formerly desiccated thyroid extract was used orally, the hormones being released by the proteolytic activity of gut enzymes. Potency is based on total iodine content or bioassay, and is somewhat variable. Currently the pure hormones, T_3 and T_4, are used. The former has a relatively rapid onset of action (one to three days), and diminution of its effects on cessation of treatment also occur rapidly (five to seven days). By contrast T_4 acts more slowly (3 to 5 d), but the consequences of discontinuing therapy take longer to manifest (10 to 15 d). Consequently in circumstances where it is desirable to have rapid onset or cessation of activity, such as in patients with heart disease, T_3 is the therapy of choice. Normally, however, T_4 is to be preferred. In general it is preferable to institute therapy cautiously, mainly to avoid stressing the heart. Indeed in some cases full control of hypothyroidism cannot be achieved without precipitating cardiac problems. Such patients may require coronary by-pass surgery.[96]

In the past thyroid hormones have been used to treat obesity in euthyroid patients. However, while pharmacological doses of the hormones undoubtedly result in weight loss, they also promote negative nitrogen balance, resulting in a loss of lean body mass, and may also precipitate cardiac problems.[97] More recently it has been recognized that the diminution in the rate of loss of weight during a calorie-restricted diet coincides with a decrease in circulating plasma T_3. This observation prompted the use of replacement doses of T_3 in conjunction with diet, a manoeuvre which resulted in greater losses of weight than diet alone.[98]

The characteristic behavioural changes associated with altered thyroid status have led to investigations to see if mental disorder in euthyroid patients could be alleviated by treatment with T_3 alone or in combination with other drugs. T_3 alone had an antidepressant activity in patients but also caused 'toxic' (presumably thyromimetic) side effects. Of more value was the observation that lower doses enhanced the speed at which imiprimine exerted its antidepressant effects in female patients.[99] T_3 has also been shown to potentiate the antipsychotic action of chlorpromazine.[100]

16.2.7.2 Synthetic Thyromimetics

Although large numbers of analogues of thyroid hormones have been synthesized, none has yet found a major role in therapy. During the late 1950s and early 1960s, a number of attempts were made to devise hypocholesterolaemic thyromimetics which lacked cardiac and thermogenic activity,[78] and several compounds were administered to man. However, none showed sufficient separation of hypocholesterolaemic from cardiac effects.[101] D-T_4 was used initially in the US Coronary Drug project. However, its use was abandoned when it found that recipients suffered a higher rate of cardiac deaths and nonfatal infarcts.[47] This is perhaps not too surprising since Bantle *et al.* could find no evidence that, in man, D-T_4 showed selective thyromimetic activity.[102] In rats using GPDH induction as a measure of peripheral thyromimetic activity we also found no evidence of selectivity.[103]

Thyroid hormones do not pass the placenta, and, since the foetal thyroid does not begin to function until shortly before birth, most intrauterine development takes place in the absence of thyroid hormones. One action of foetal thyroid hormones in the immediate prepartum phase is to stimulate the lung to synthesize special phospholipids (surfactant) which ensure efficient functioning of the babies' lungs at birth. Premature babies and those delivered of diabetic mothers fail to produce surfactant, and, hence, suffer from respiratory distress syndrome (RDS). Unlike endogenous thyroid hormones 3,5-dimethyl-3'-isopropyl-L-thyronine (DIMIT) does pass through the placenta in animals and exerts thyromimetic effects in the foetus after administration to the mother.[104] It has been suggested that DIMIT could be used to prevent RDS, but its use in women has not been recorded. One disadvantage of this approach is that the mother is exposed to DIMIT and so could become hyperthyroid, albeit for a short time.

So far no other uses of nonnatural thyromimetics in man have been reported. The demonstration that it is possible to synthesize selective thyromimetics, however, leaves open this possibility. It may, for instance, be possible to devise hepatic thyromimetics which do not produce effects on the peritoneum, kidney or bone, and which could be valuable hypocholesterolaemic agents. No convincing evidence has yet been presented that it is possible to produce receptor antagonism of thyroid hormones, but such agents could be valuable especially if selectivity of action could be achieved. For instance, cardio-selective inhibitors of thyroid hormone action could be of value in angina pectoris or cardiac arrythmias.

16.2.8 REFERENCES

1. C. R. Harington, 'The Thyroid Gland, its Chemistry and Physiology', Oxford University Press, London, 1933, chap. 1.
2. R. Pitt-Rivers, in 'Hormonal Proteins and Peptides', ed. C. H. Li, Academic Press, New York, 1978, vol. 6, chap. 7.
3. H. L. Schwartz and J. H. Oppenheimer, *Pharmacol. Ther., Part. B*, 1978, **3**, 349.
4. F. Ismail-Beigi and I. S. Edelman, *Proc. Natl. Acad. Sci. U.S.A.*, 1971, **67**, 1071.
5. M. Folke and L. Sestoft, *J. Physiol. (London)*, 1976, **17**, 12.
6. R. C. Smallridge, in 'Hearts and Heart-like Organs', ed. G. H. Bourne, Academic Press, New York, 1980, chap. 3.
7. I. Busolini, S. B. Flynn, S. G. Parker and A. H. Underwood, unpublished observation.
8. M. Heimberg, J. O. Olubadewo and H. G. Wilcox, *Endocr. Rev.*, 1985, **6**, 590.
9. C. Becker, *Endocr. Rev.*, 1985, **6**, 432.
10. H. Weiner, in 'The Thyroid', 4th edn., ed. S. C. Werner and S. H. Ingbar, Harper and Row, London, 1978, p. 753.
11. H. Weiner, in 'The Thyroid', 4th edn., ed. S. C. Werner and S. H. Ingbar, Harper and Row, London, 1978, p. 911.
12. J. H. Dussault and J. Ruel, *Annu. Rev. Physiol.*, 1987, **49**, 321.
13. J. B. Stanbury, in 'Iodine Deficiency Disorders and Congenital Hypothyroidism', ed. G. Medeiros-Neto, R. M. B. Maciel and A. Halpem, Ache, Sao Paulo, 1986, p. 7.
14. D. Ellis, J. C. Emmett, P. D. Leeson and A. H. Underwood, in 'Handbook of Hormones, Vitamins and Radiopaques', ed. M. Verderame, CRC Press, Boca Raton, FL, 1986, p. 94.
15. O. Spira and A. Gordon, in 'Thyroid Hormone Metabolism', ed. G. Henneman, Dekker, New York, 1986, chap. 17.
16. B. Ahren, *Endocr. Rev.*, 1986, **7**, 149.
17. J. Robbins and L. Bartalena, in 'Thyroid Hormone Metabolism', ed. G. Henneman, Dekker, New York, 1986, chap. 1.
18. R. Ekins, in 'Thyroid Hormone Metabolism', ed. G. Henneman, Dekker, New York, 1986, chap. 3.
19. E. P. Krenning and R. Docteur, in 'Thyroid Hormone Metabolism', ed. G. Henneman, Dekker, New York, 1986, chap. 4.
20. H. L. Schwartz, D. Trence, J. H. Oppenheimer, N. S. Jiang and D. B. Jump, *Endocrinology (Baltimore)*, 1983, **113**, 1236.
21. D. Engler and A. G. Burger, *Endocr. Rev.*, 1984, **5**, 151.
22. J. L. Leonard and T. J. Visser, in 'Thyroid Hormone Metabolism', ed. G. Henneman, Dekker, New York, 1986, chap. 6.
23. T. J. Visser, R. Docteur, E. P. Krenning and G. Henneman, *J. Endocrinol. Invest.*, 1986, **9** (Suppl. 4), 17.
24. J. H. Oppenheimer, *Science (Washington, D.C.)*, 1979, **203**, 971.
25. J. H. Oppenheimer, *Ann. Intern. Med.*, 1985, **102**, 374.
26. C. Weinburger, C. C. Thompson, E. S. Ong, R. Lebo, D. J. Gruol and R. M. Evans, *Nature (London)*, 1986, **324**, 641.
27. J. Sap, A. Munoz, K. Damn, Y. Goldberg, J. Ghysdael, A. Leutz, H. Beug and B. Venstromm, *Nature (London)*, 1986, **324**, 635.
28. C. C. Thompson, C. Weinburger, R. Lebo and R. M. Evans, *Science (Washington, D.C.)*, 1987, **237**, 1610.
29. J. H. Oppenheimer, H. L. Schwartz, C. N. Mariash, W. B. Kinlaw, N. C. W. Wong and H. C. Freake, *Endocr. Rev.*, 1987, **8**, 288.
30. J. W. Barlow, M. L. J. Voz, P. H. Eliard, M. Mathey-Hartert, P. de Nayer, I. V. Economidis, A. Belayew, J. A. Martial and G. G. Rousseau, *Proc. Natl. Acad. Sci. U.S.A.*, 1986, **83**, 9021.
31. P. Narayan and H. C. Towle, *Mol. Cell. Biol.*, 1985, **5**, 2642.
32. J. Segal and S. H. Ingbar, in 'Thyroid Hormone Metabolism', ed. G. Hennemann, Dekker, New York, 1986, chap. 14.
33. J. H. Oppenheimer, H. L. Schwartz, M. I. Surks, D. Koerner and W. H. Dillman, *Recent Prog. Horm. Res.*, 1976, **32**, 529.
34. H. H. Samuels, J. S. Tsai, J. Casanova and F. Stanley, *J. Clin. Invest.*, 1974, **54**, 853.
35. M. G. Benson, D. Ellis, J. C. Emmett, P. D. Leeson, N. J. Pearce, V. P. Shah and A. H. Underwood, *Biochem. Pharmacol.*, 1984, **33**, 3143.
36. H. A. Selenkow and S. P. Asper, *Physiol. Rev.*, 1955, **35**, 426.
37. W. L. Money, S. Kumaoka, R. W. Rawson and R. L. Kroc, *Ann. N.Y. Acad. Sci.*, 1960, **86**, 512.
38. E. C. Jorgensen, in 'Hormonal Proteins and Peptides', ed. C. H. Li, Academic Press, New York, 1978, vol. 6, p. 107.
39. E. C. Jorgensen, in 'Burger's Medicinal Chemistry', 4th edn., ed. M. E. Wolff, Wiley, New York, 1981, part 3, p. 103.
40. S. W. Dietrich, M. B. Bolger, P. A. Kollman and E. C. Jorgensen, *J. Med. Chem.*, 1977, **20**, 863.
41. T. A. Andrea, S. W. Dietrich, W. J. Murray, P. A. Kollman, E. C. Jorgensen and S. Rothenburg, *J. Med. Chem.*, 1979, **22**, 221.
42. M. B. Bolger and E. C. Jorgensen, *J. Biol. Chem.*, 1980, **255**, 10271.
43. P. D. Leeson, D. Ellis, J. C. Emmett, V. P. Shah, G. A. Showell and A. H. Underwood, *J. Med. Chem.*, 1988, **31**, 37.
44. P. D. Leeson, J. C. Emmett, V. P. Shah, G. A. Showell, R. Novelli, H. D. Prain, M. G. Benson, D. Ellis, N. J. Pearce and A. H. Underwood, *J. Med. Chem.*, 1989, **32**, 320.
45. C. R. Harrington and C. Barger, *Biochem. J.*, 1927, **21**, 169.
46. J. H. Oppenheimer, in 'Molecular Basis of Thyroid Hormone Action', ed. J. H. Oppenheimer and H. H. Samuels, Academic Press, New York, 1983, chap. 1.
47. The Coronary Drug Research Group, *J. Am. Med. Assoc.*, 1972, **220**, 996.
48. A. H. Underwood, J. C. Emmett, D. Ellis, S. B. Flynn, P. D. Leeson, G. M. Benson, R. Novelli, N. J. Pearce and V. P. Shah, *Nature (London)*, 1986, **324**, 425.
49. J. McKinney, R. Fannin, S. Jordan, K. Chae, U. Rickenbacker and L. Pedersen, *J. Med. Chem.*, 1987, **30**, 79.
50. J. W. Apriletti, Y. David-Inouye, N. L. Eberhardt and J. D. Baxter, *J. Biol. Chem.*, 1984, **259**, 10941.
51. J. Koehrle, M. Auf'mkolk, H. Rokos, R.-D. Hesch and V. Cody, *J. Biol. Chem.*, 1986, **261**, 11613.
52. M. Auf'mkolk, J. Koehrle, R.-D. Hesch and V. Cody, *J. Biol. Chem.*, 1986, **261**, 11623.
53. I. D. Goldfine, G. J. Smith, C. G. Symons, S. H. Ingbar and E. C. Jorgensen, *J. Biol. Chem.*, 1976, **251**, 4233.

54. F. B. Davis, V. Cody, P. J. Davis, L. J. Borzynski and S. D. Blas, *J. Biol. Chem.*, 1983, **258**, 12373.
55. C. C. F. Blake, *Proc. R. Soc. London, Ser. B*, 1981, **211**, 413.
56. E. C. Jorgensen, in 'Hormonal Proteins and Peptides', ed. C. H. Li, Academic Press, New York, 1978, vol. 6, p. 57.
57. P. D. Leeson and J. C. Emmett, *J. Chem. Soc., Perkin Trans. 1*, 1988, 3085.
58. D. M. B. Hickey, P. D. Leeson, R. Novelli, V. P. Shah, B. E. Burpitt, L. P. Crawford, B. J. Davies, M. B. Mitchell, K. D. Pancholi, D. Tuddenham, N. J. Lewis and C. O'Farrell, *J. Chem. Soc., Perkins Trans. 1*, 1988, 3103.
59. D. M. B. Hickey, P. D. Leeson, S. D. Carter, M. D. Goodyear, S. J. Jones, N. J. Lewis, I. T. Morgan, M. V. Mullane and J. Y. Tricker, *J. Chem. Soc., Perkins Trans. 1*, 1988, 3097.
60. N. Zenker and E. C. Jorgensen, *J. Am. Chem. Soc.*, 1959, **81**, 4643.
61. V. Cody, *Recent Prog. Horm. Res.*, 1978, **34**, 437.
62. V. Cody, *ACS Symp. Ser.*, 1979, **112**, 281.
63. J. C. Emmett and E. S. Pepper, *Nature (London)*, 1975, **257**, 334.
64. P. H. Mazzochi, H. L. Ammon, L. Lin, E. Colicelli, P. Ravi and E. Burrows, *J. Org. Chem.*, 1981, **46**, 4530.
65. R. Somack, T. A. Andrea and E. C. Jorgensen, *Biochemistry*, 1982, **21**, 163.
66. V. Cody, *Acta Crystallogr., Sect. B*, 1981, **37**, 1685.
67. K. Prout, J. Fail, R. M. Jones, R. E. Warner and J. C. Emmett, *J. Chem. Soc., Perkins Trans. 2*, 1988, 265.
68. S. W. Dietrich, E. C. Jorgensen, P. A. Kollman and S. Rothenberg, *J. Am. Chem. Soc.*, 1976, **98**, 8310.
69. D. Koerner, H. L. Schwartz, M. I. Surks, J. H. Oppenheimer and E. C. Jorgensen, *J. Biol. Chem.*, 1975, **250**, 6417.
70. S. B. Barker and M. Shimada, *Proc. Mayo Clinic*, 1964, **39**, 609.
71. J. H. Oppenheimer and H. L. Schwartz, *J. Clin. Invest.*, 1985, **75**, 147.
72. G. S. Rao, *Mol. Cell. Endocrinol.*, 1981, **21**, 97.
73. E. C. Jorgensen, W. J. Murray and P. Block, Jr., *J. Med. Chem.*, 1974, **17**, 434.
74. V. Cody, *J. Med. Chem.*, 1980, **23**, 584.
75. K. Chae and J. McKinney, *J. Med. Chem.*, 1988, **31**, 357.
76. V. Cody, *Endocr. Res. Commun.*, 1982, **9**, 55.
77. B. Goslings, H. L. Schwartz, W. Dillman, M. I. Surks and J. H. Oppenheimer, *Endocrinology (Baltimore)*, 1976, **98**, 666.
78. For example, (a) G. S. Boyd and M. F. Oliver, *J. Endocrinol.*, 1960, **21**, 25; (b) W. F. J. Cuthbertson, P. V. Elcoate, D. M. Ireland, D. C. B. Mills and P. Shearley, *J. Endocrinol.*, 1960, **21**, 45; (c) S. R. Hill, S. B. Barker, J. H. McNeil, J. O. Tingley and L. C. Hibbitt, *J. Clin. Invest.*, 1960, **39**, 523; (d) A. Bander and H. Nahn, *Arzneim.-Forsch.*, 1963, **13**, 1; (e) C. M. Greenberg, B. Blank, F. R. Pfeiffer and J. F. Pauls, *Am. J. Physiol.*, 1963, **205**, 821; (f) B. Blank, F. R. Pfeiffer, C. M. Greenberg and J. F. Kerwin, *J. Med. Chem.*, 1963, **6**, 554, 560; (g) B. Blank, C. M. Greenberg and J. F. Kerwin, *J. Med. Chem.*, 1964, **7**, 53; (h) W. J. Wechter, W. A. Phillips and F. Kagan, *J. Med. Chem.*, 1965, **8**, 474; (i) B. Blank, F. R. Pfeiffer and C. M. Greenberg, *J. Med. Chem.*, 1966, **9**, 932; (j) B. Blank, E. G. Rice, F. R. Pfeiffer and C. M. Greenberg, *J. Med. Chem.*, 1966, **9**, 10; (k) R. Beckman, *Arzneim.-Forsch.*, 1979, **29**, 499.
79. C. C. F. Blake and S. J. Oatley, *Nature (London)*, 1977, **268**, 115.
80. J. D. McKinney, K. Chae, S. J. Oatley and C. C. F. Blake, *J. Med. Chem.*, 1985, **28**, 375.
81. T. A. Andrea, R. R. Cavalieri, I. D. Goldfine and E. C. Jorgensen, *Biochemistry*, 1980, **19**, 55.
82. U. Rickenbacker, J. D. McKinney, S. J. Oatley and C. C. F. Blake, *J. Med. Chem.*, 1986, **29**, 641.
83. J. M. Blaney, E. C. Jorgensen, M. L. Connolly, T. E. Ferrin, R. Langridge, S. J. Oatley, J. M. Burridge and C. C. F. Blake, *J. Med. Chem.*, 1982, **25**, 785.
84. V. Cody and P. Murray-Rust, *J. Mol. Struct.*, 1984, **112**, 189.
85. C. C. F. Blake, J. M. Burridge, S. J. Oatley and P. de la Paz, *Period. Biol.*, 1983, **85** (Suppl. 2), 5.
86. S. J. Oatley, C. C. F. Blake, J. M. Burridge and P. de la Paz, in 'X-Ray Crystallography and Drug Action', ed. A. S. Horn and C. J. De Ranter, Clarendon Press, Oxford, 1984, p. 207.
87. L. G. Pedersen, T. A. Darden, S. J. Oatley and J. D. McKinney, *J. Med. Chem.*, 1986, **24**, 2451.
88. G. M. Crippen, *J. Med. Chem.*, 1981, **24**, 198.
89. Z. Simon, A. Chiriac and V. Chiriac, *Timisoara Med.*, 1981, **26**, 26.
90. J. M. Blaney, P. K. Weiner, A. Dearing, P. A. Kollman, E. C. Jorgensen, S. J. Oatley, J. M. Burridge and C. C. F. Blake, *J. Am. Chem. Soc.*, 1982, **104**, 6424.
91. S. Fantappie, F. M. Maggi and A. L. Catapano, 'Poster Sessions Abstract Book, 8th International Symposium on Atherosclerosis', CIC Edizioni International, Roma, 1988, p. 238.
92. N. Davidson, personal communication.
93. S. B. Flynn, S. Parker, I. Busolini, A. Rothaul, and A. H. Underwood, unpublished experiments.
94. N. J. Pearce, D. Ellis and A. H. Underwood, unpublished experiments.
95. S. J. Kennedy, C. K. Atterwill and A. Poole, *The Toxicologist*, 1988, **8** (1), Abstract no. 348.
96. L. J. DeGroot, P. R. Larsen, S. Refetoff and J. B. Stanbury, in 'The Thyroid and its Diseases', 5th edition, Wiley, New York, 1983, chap. 10.
97. G. A. Bray, in 'International Encyclopedia of Pharmacology and Therapeutics', ed. J. M. Hershman and G. A. Bray, Pergamon, Oxford, 1979, section 101, chap. 28.
98. R. Moore, A. M. Grant, A. H. Howard and I. H. Mills, *Lancet*, 1980, **1**, 223.
99. I. C. Wilson, A. J. Prange, Jr. and P. P. Lara, in 'The Thyroid Axis, Drugs and Behaviour', ed. A. J. Prange, Jr., Raven Press, New York, 1974, p. 49.
100. S. Park, in 'The Thyroid Axis, Drug and Behaviour', ed. A. J. Prange, Jr., Raven Press, New York, 1974, p. 75.
101. G. S. Boyd and M. F. Oliver, *J. Endocrinol.*, 1960, **21**, 33.
102. J. P. Bantle, J. H. Oppenheimer, H. L. Schwartz, D. D. Hunninghake, J. C. Probstfield *et al.*, *Metab. Clin. Exp.*, 1981, **30**, 63.
103. D. Ellis and A. H. Underwood, unpublished experiments.
104. F. Comite, G. N. Burrow and E. C. Jorgensen, *Endocrinology (Baltimore)*, 1978, **102**, 1670.

16.3
Steroid Hormone Receptors

TIIU OJASOO and JEAN-PIERRE RAYNAUD
Roussel-Uclaf, Paris, France

and

JEAN-PAUL MORNON
Université Paris VI, France

16.3.1 INTRODUCTION

The authors of this chapter were faced with the problem that, in a decade where expression cloning has provided complete amino acid sequences for steroid hormone receptors (SHRs) of diverse origins, as yet, no one has produced enough pure SHR to enable structure determination by X-ray crystallography. Even fragments for analysis by NMR are not available. Much effort is being expended to meet these ends but success may not be at the doorstep since SHRs have proven to be particularly labile proteins.

We shall therefore begin this chapter with a description of some of the characteristics of SHRs that may contribute towards the difficulties in their crystallization. We shall present attempts to overcome these difficulties by applying novel structure prediction methods. Then, we shall summarize the wealth of data on the ligands known to bind to SHRs since, until now and even now, they constitute the only means to 3D-mapping of the hormone-binding site on SHRs. Some of these ligands have been particularly useful as probes to detect, assay, photoaffinity label and image SHRs, as tools to unravel molecular mechanisms of action, and as drugs, whether agonists or antagonists.

The following abbreviations are used throughout this chapter: SHR, steroid hormone receptor; ER, estrogen receptor; PR, progestin receptor; AR, androgen receptor; GR, glucocorticoid receptor; MR, mineralocorticoid receptor; kDa, kilodaltons; h, human; DBD, DNA-binding domain; HBD, hormone-binding domain; E_2, estradiol; P, progesterone; T, testosterone; DX, dexamethasone.

16.3.2 CHARACTERIZATION OF THE STEROID HORMONE RECEPTOR

16.3.2.1 Physicochemical Properties and Domain Structure of the Steroid Hormone Receptor (SHR)

16.3.2.1.1 *Difficulties encountered in the study of SHR proteins*

SHRs are not simple proteins to study since, in the course of performing their biological function within the cell, they are found to be associated with diverse elements necessary to their stability and/or activity. Some of these may be isolated together with SHRs; the presence of others may be only fleeting. To name but a few, these are other proteins of similar or smaller molecular weight (*e.g.* 29 kDa,[1] 46 kDa,[2] 59 kDa,[3] 72 kDa,[4] 90 kDa[5,6]) including proteases,[7] kinases[8] and inhibitory factors,[9-11] RNA and, in particular, tRNA,[12-14] ATP,[15,16] cAMP,[17] ions,[18] unsaturated long chain fatty acids and phospholipids,[19,20] sugars,[21,22] steroid ligand, solvent (*i.e.* structured water)[23,24] *etc.*, in fact all the necessary elements to ensure that the right energy, stability, conformation and cofactors are available to transmit the correct message to DNA. Steroid hormone receptors are DNA-binding proteins.[25-27]

Moreover, SHRs can present themselves as hetero-oligomers, an aspect that has further bedevilled their study. The demonstration of the existence of a heterogeneous complex goes back to the time when Sherman proposed an allosteric SHR model and the notion of a mero-receptor (a receptor subunit that binds steroid but lacks nuclear affinity),[28,29] when O'Malley's group identified the A and B subunits of PR,[30,31] and when Notides explained the dissociation kinetics of endogenous estrogens and phenomena of cooperativity by ER dimerization.[32,33] Often the main difficulty resided in distinguishing true subunits or associated proteins from possible degradation products and truncated receptors.

A further complication in the study of SHRs, and one that is fundamental to the comprehension of their mechanism of action, is their *in vivo* localization.[34] The vast majority of experiments have been performed on 'cytosol' which is a high speed supernatant of tissue homogenates prepared in low salt buffers. However, the SHR triggers gene transcription within the nucleus. Sheridan *et al.*[35] have proposed that the distribution of unoccupied SHR molecules between the cytoplasmic and nuclear compartments reflects water structure and distribution and that ligand binding changes the SHR to a more hydrophilic nuclear form. Later, enucleation and immunocytochemical experiments have supported the contention that the unfilled SHR is essentially nuclear.[36,37] Presently, controversy still reigns on the need for hormone in order for SHRs to recognize specific gene regulatory sequences of DNA, the consensus of opinion being that hormone accelerates binding.[38-44] Some experiments would even seem to indicate that the steroid hormone might be able to interact directly with DNA.[45] Whatever the forces that govern the equilibrium between cytoplasm and nucleus,[46] it is important to note that steroid–receptor complexes may not have the same characteristics in these compartments since the cytoplasm is a crowded, semicrystalline (highly structured) environment, whereas the nucleus behaves as a much more aqueous compartment.[35] Water molecules can play an important role in maintaining protein stability and activity.[23,24]

SHRs have long been distinguished from other receptors by their cytosolic and/or nuclear nature and by the fact that they dispense with second messengers such as cAMP. However, a number of teams have detected SHRs in or near rough endoplasmic reticulum and free ribosomes,[47] microsomes[48,49] and membranes.[50-53] It is not yet certain whether some of these observations might not be artefactual as a result of contamination of the test preparations but they are not unexpected if SHRs migrate from their site of synthesis to their site of action. Furthermore, although no second messengers have been detected, the discovery of 'cross-talk' between signalling pathways has opened up fascinating new fields of study. Attempts have been made to explain the well-known antiinflammatory action of glucocorticoids by interference with arachidonic acid metabolism;[54] stimulation of adenylate cyclase by glucocorticoids has been reported in membranes;[55] more recently, negative regulation of gene expression by glucocorticoids has been explained by interference with cAMP responsive enhancers.[56] However, in view of the implication of steroid hormones not only in specific gene expression but in cell differentiation and division, it is during studies of the growth responses of steroid hormones that many new links have been discovered with other signalling pathways, for example estrogens increase uterine weight, progestins result in endometrial proliferation and most androgens are anabolic agents. Present emphasis on devising means to inhibit hormone dependent malignant growth (*e.g.* breast and prostate cancer) have confirmed links with other growth factors,[57-60] protein kinase C (PKC),[61-63] calcium-binding proteins[64-66] *etc.*

In view of the above comments, it is exceedingly difficult to define the precise nature of functional SHRs at any point in space or time and, consequently, the observations in the next section have to be considered with some circumspection since they relate to artificial *in vitro* experimental conditions. It was not until the cDNAs of SHRs were cloned and their sequences determined that a new footing could be established for their study.

16.3.2.1.2 *Physicochemical properties of steroid hormone receptors*

(i) *Solvent interactions*

The SHR is highly water soluble but, in the nucleus, the even moderate affinity of the unoccupied SHR for DNA (*nonspecific* interaction) might result in release of structured water molecules and interaction of hydrophobic surfaces, thus favoring the nuclear localization of unoccupied SHR. The presence of ligand promotes specific salt dependent (electrostatic) interactions with the nucleus at the expense of hydrophobic interactions. This would result in interaction with *specific* DNA sequences for which the SHR has 10 to 50 times greater affinity.[67]

(ii) *Sedimentation properties and Stokes radius*

The untransformed SHR, *i.e.* in the absence of hormone and at low temperature, sediments as an 8–10S moiety in low salt buffer. Exposure to 0.4 M KCl or incubation at $\geq 23\,^{\circ}$C results in 4S moieties for GR and PR also to a 5S species for ER. This disaggregation is prevented by Group VI-A transition element oxyanions, *e.g.* molybdate, an inhibitor of phosphate transfer reactions.[68,69] Hydrodynamic properties have indicated that the 8–10S species is a hetero-oligomer of ≈ 300 kDa, the 4S moiety a monomer of 65–90 kDa and the 5S a dimer. The composition of the larger form is controversial: it would be constituted of the SHR, a low molecular weight activation inhibitor, nonsteroid binding protein(s) and possibly RNA. As an indication, the Stokes radius of untransformed GR is 7–8.3 nm; after activation, it is 5–6 nm.

(iii) *Aqueous two-phase partitioning*

In principle, this technique can detect conformational changes, electrostatic changes, and changes in aggregation of SHRs. In the case of ER, it has shown that the ligand dependent change is due to a conformational change in the ER monomer that has little effect on the net electrostatic properties of the protein. Using hydrophobic affinity partitioning, binding of estradiol was shown to reduce the ability of ER to interact with hydrophobic surfaces.[67]

(iv) Temperature

The temperature dependent transformation of SHRs would seem to be a ligand independent phenomenon: independently of SHR inactivation, heating of the unoccupied SHR results in a large change in structure that occurs at the same rate as transformation of the occupied SHR.[67]

(v) Proteolysis and serine protease binding

Photoaffinity labelling of the SHR with steroid, subsequent proteolysis, and analysis of the fragments by gel electrophoresis or isoelectric focussing has been one of the major approaches to the study of SHRs in combination with the use of specific monoclonal antibodies. SHR complexes can be proteolytically digested into globular fragments, *e.g.* 25–30 kDa (≈ 200 amino acid) fragments that bind steroid have been recovered, whereas partial digestion has led to 45 kDa fragments that retain the capacity to bind DNA.

In contradistinction to the generation of SHR fragments by proteolysis,[70] it is of note that SHRs contain a site which binds both serine protease inhibitors (*e.g.* phenylmethylsulfonyl fluoride; PMSF) and substrates (*e.g.* TosArgOMe, TrpOMe) and which regulates steroid hormone binding.[71] The inhibitor and steroid binding sites would be partially contiguous. This would explain why compounds like PMSF, that are used to prevent proteolysis during SHR assays, can inhibit the binding of estrogen and androgen to their respective SHRs in cytosol.[72]

16.3.2.1.3 *Antibodies to steroid hormone receptors*

The elucidation of the mechanisms of action of steroid hormones received a fantastic boost in the late 1970s and early 1980s when ER and GR when purified and poly- and mono-clonal antibodies against these SHRs were prepared.[73–77] The wide variety of antibodies now available serve many different purposes: for example further purification of SHRs,[78] their assay,[79] their localization in combination with cytochemical techniques,[80,81] the differentiation between different SHR forms (for instance, SHRs bound to estrogen and antiestrogen are not recognized by the same antibodies),[82,83] and the identification of the mRNAs and cDNAs for SHRs of different origins with the concomitant deduction of amino acid composition from genomic nucleotide sequences.[84–91] This last approach established that SHRs, including the receptor for vitamin D and ecdysone, form part of a larger family of proteins comprising the thyroid hormone receptor(s), the product of the retroviral oncogene v-*erb*A, the receptor(s) for the morphogen retinoic acid,[92,93] and transacting proteins such as Knirps [94,95] and COUP.[96] The relationship to v-*erb*A[85] suggested that SHRs were potentially oncogenic.[97]

Sequence analysis combined with functional studies led to the indentification of SHR domains,[98] and further antibodies were raised against synthesized peptides corresponding to the highly conserved DNA-binding domain of the SHRs.[99] Parallelly, nucleotide segments were used as probes to harpoon homologous proteins and revealed the existence of several orphan proteins that have been assimilated to SHRs, but whose natural ligands are not yet known.[100–102] On the other hand, analysis of mRNA or poly(A$^+$)-enriched RNA from human breast tumors by hybridization with hER cDNA helped to detect variant ER species possibly resulting from malignant cellular transformation.[103,104]

16.3.2.1.4 *Functional domains of steroid hormone receptors*[105–111]

The functional significance of SHR domains was determined by the use of deletion mutants or by the construction of chimaeric genes[112,113] which were transfected into cells together with a steroid sensitive marker gene. The regions essential to several functions of the SHR could thus be delimited, *i.e.* to DNA binding, steroid binding, nuclear translocation and enhanced activation. Three main domains were identified (Figure 1). (i) The hydrophobic carboxy domain of approximately 240 amino acids which binds steroid. (ii) The middle domain (≈ 65 amino acids), which is most highly conserved among SHRs of all hormone classes, contains Zn^{2+}-coordinated fingers characteristic of DNA-binding proteins,[114–115] and, moreover, has the ability to regulate gene transcription. The steroid- and DNA-binding domains are connected by a hydrophilic stretch of 50 to 70 amino acids (hinge region) and do not require the presence of the third highly variable N-terminal domain for ligand dependent activation of gene transcription. (iii) The N-terminal domain would appear to be

H_2N ▭--------▭━━━━━━━▭▭▭━━━━━▭ ▭━━━━━━━▭COOH

NTD   **DBD**   **HR**   **HBD**

Figure 1 Domain structure of SHRs showing highly variable N-terminal domain (NTD; ≈ 180 to 600 residues according to SHR), highly conserved Zn^{2+}-coordinated finger structure of DNA-binding domain (DBD; ≈ 70 residues), hinge region (HR; ≈ 40 residues) and moderately conserved C-terminal hormone-binding domain (HBD; ≈ 250 residues)

highly immunogenic and probably modulates hormone responsiveness by facilitating the distinction between unspecific and specific DNA. Although not essential to transcriptional activation, its deletion results in a decrease in induction.

(i) DNA-binding domain (DBD)

The 15 kDa DNA-binding domain (DBD) can be proteolytically removed, indicating that it is accessible to enzyme attack and not buried within the SHR. It is highly conserved among the different SHRs (> 90% sequence identity for PR, GR, MR; > 78% for AR; > 56% for ER)[116] and adopts a two-finger motif in which pairs of Cys are coordinated by Zn^{2+} ions necessary for correct folding and essential for specific DNA recognition.[117-119] The 3D-solution structure of a representative Zn^{2+}-finger (*Xfin*-31) with coordinated Cys and His residues has been determined and described as a 'miniglobular protein, with a close-packed, predominantly hydrophobic core and with polar side chains on the surface'[120] and is in close accord with the model proposed by Berg.[121,122] The N-terminal Zn^{2+}-finger of SHRs has four conserved Cys and determines target gene specificity.[123] The C-terminal finger was initially reported to have five Cys but mutagenesis studies[118,119] suggest that the last Cys is part of the postfinger region. It is implicated in nonsequence-specific interactions with DNA. The two fingers are separated by a α-helix followed by an extended loop.

The Zn^{2+}-fingers would interact with alternate grooves of the double helix of DNA in a helix–turn–helix binding motif. SHRs interact with enhancer like specific DNA sequences termed 'hormone response (or regulatory) elements' (HREs) and thereby stimulate transcription from promoter genes from which they may be separated by some distance, unless looping out of intervening DNA engenders proximity.[126] The HRE for glucocorticoids (GRE) was the first to be identified within the long terminal repeat of mouse mammary tumor virus (MMTV-LTR) which induces breast carcinomas in certain strains of mice. When transfected, the GREs conferred hormone responsiveness upon linked heterologous genes. Later experimentation established that the regulatory region of MMTV-LTR includes HREs that can bind all SHRs other than ER. Nuclear footprint and methylation protection studies indicated that the sites overlap but are not identical.[124,125] GREs have now been identified at variable distances from the promoters of many positively or negatively glucocorticoid-regulated genes including the genes for h-metallothionein IIA, h-growth hormone, chicken lysozyme, rat tyrosine amino transferase, the negatively regulated proopiomelanocortin gene and others. Similar, but less numerous studies, are available on the response elements of receptors belonging to the other hormone classes.

Sequence comparisons of HREs have led to the proposal of a consensus element of 15 nucleotides that fits the description of an imperfect palindrome containing 5–6 base pairs in each half of the palindrome separated by 3 base pairs. This symmetry supports evidence that SHRs bind as dimers[126-128] with enhanced binding affinity. For instance, two ER molecules bind to a HRE with higher affinity than does a single ER molecule.[126] Furthermore, since several HREs may exert functional cooperativity to increase transcription of an adjacent gene, two ER dimers interacting with two cooperating HREs have an affinity 100-fold stronger than a single dimer. These cooperative interactions among SHR molecules would appear to be dependent upon hormone activation.[126]

Mutations of invariant and conserved residues within the DBD of hGR to Gly revealed a good correlation between the conservation of an amino acid and the extent of functional loss (binding and transcription activity).[129] Three amino acids located close to the second pair of Cys of the first Zn^{2+}-finger of ER and GR would be important in determining the specificity of these SHRs.[130] Converting the Lys following the first Zn^{2+}-finger to Gly in hGR gave rise to a mutant that had lost the capacity to efficiently stimulate transcription while maintaining affinity for DNA *in vivo*, suggesting that DNA binding is not sufficient for activation.[129]

The construction of a hybrid gene where the DBD of ER was replaced by that of GR led to the transcription of a glucocorticoid sensitive gene by estradiol[112] showing that the structural SHR domains can display remarkable functional independence. Expression of the DBD in the absence of other receptor sequences results in a high constitutive level of gene expression suggesting that these other sequences normally afford steric hindrance that can be lifted by the steroid hormone. Autonomous transactivation functions have been found to be embodied in the N- and C-terminal segments of the SHR by analysis of the function of hGR-GAL4 hybrids[129] and by other methods.[107,131] Many transcription factors would interact synergistically with SHRs within a complex cluster of binding sites.[132] These interactions of transcription factors and enhancer-activating proteins with DNA may be rate-limiting for promoter activity.[133]

(ii) Nuclear acceptor sites

The differential transcription of the same genes by SHRs activated by different hormones and binding to the same DNA sequences has renewed interest in the nonhistone binding proteins that may explain discrepancies in hormone responsiveness.[134,135] These are a class of nonconjugated, hydrophobic, low molecular weight, slightly acidic specific chromosomal proteins, involved in SHR acceptor sites, and which may be an integral part of the nuclear matrix.[136] 4-Hydroxytamoxifen receptor complexes can be solubilized from Mg^{2+} soluble chromatins by DNAse I digestion, unlike E_2–ER complexes, indicating that there are probably separate DNA and chromatin binding properties of ER.[137]

Experiments with isolated or reconstituted acceptor sites have revealed differences that have not yet been detected with DNA sequences, for instance, the existence in certain tissues (*e.g.* lactating mammary gland) of an inhibitory factor[11] that can impede ER interaction with chromatin acceptor sites. Studies on the binding of ER from different tissues and species to homologous or heterologous acceptor sites have addressed the problem of tissue specificity.[135] Chromatin acceptor sites have detected, on the one hand, nonfunctional SHRs, *e.g.* changes during cytodifferentiation and seasonal variations and, on the other hand, chromatin modification rather than changes in SHRs, as the possible cause of hormone resistance. Future progress on the identification of SHRs from different tissues and species and on the differential regulation of several HREs in cells may help in the interpretation of the results of these studies.

(iii) The N-terminal domain

The highly immunogenic N-terminal domain diverges extensively not only among SHR classes but among a single class from different species. It is, however, in all instances a highly acidic region. It would modulate the magnitude of the transcriptional response from certain target genes[138] by some form of steric hindrance or charge neutralization since its absence in mutants can lead to efficient transcription from genes that are normally not transcribed. It has been suggested that the two PR forms, A and B, recovered in cytosol would correspond respectively to an intact (B) and N-terminal truncated (A) receptor.[139,140]

(iv) The steroid hormone binding domain (HBD)

The highly hydrophobic domain that binds steroid hormone is essential to SHR function. Its truncation from hER or chicken PR generates a constitutive hormone independent mutant that retains only 1–5% of the transcriptional activity of the corresponding wildtype receptor. There are two theories regarding its operation; (i) the unoccupied HBD blocks constitutive activation function localized in or close to the DBD, and (ii) both the HBD and the N-terminal A/B region of the SHR contain autonomous transcription activation functions.

In view of the importance of steroid binding[38–40] in controlling the subsequent 'physiological' function of the SHR, we have focussed our attention on elucidating the 3D-structure of this domain compared to the more universal DBD and the less well-known N-terminal domain. These studies will be described in the next section.

16.3.2.2   Modelling of the Hormone Receptor Binding Site by Hydrophobic Cluster Analysis (HCA)

16.3.2.2.1   Basic principles and methodology

Lim[141] postulated that the nascent polypeptide produced by a ribosome is a fluctuating α-helix which then folds into the native protein.[142] Some preliminary evidence for this has been obtained by electron microscopy studies.[143] Hydrophobic cluster analysis (HCA)[144,145] is based on this premise, *i.e.* a polypeptide chain is an α-helix unless other forces overwhelm this situation. Since hydrophobic interactions are a potentially strong folding force, the distribution of nonpolar sidechains can be examined on a flattened helical presentation to find potential interactions (*i.e.* hydrophobic clusters) that will influence the folding pattern. By extension, one can infer that proteins with similar hydrophobic cores might have similar patterns of hydrophobic clusters.

The stratagem of writing each amino acid sequence on a classical α-helix efficiently condenses information and enables the easy visual detection and analysis of hydrophobic clusters of amino acids on a 2D-plot. The sequence is written on a α-helix of 3.6 amino acids per turn that has been smoothed on a cylinder so that, after 5 turns, residues (i) and (i + 18) are on the same directrix. The cylinder is then cut parallel to the axis, unrolled, and duplicated in order to obtain a better visual impression of the environment of each amino acid (Figure 2). The adjacent and adjacent-but-one amino acids cover a 17 amino acid stretch that is considered necessary for cogent secondary structure predictions by classic methods. Sets of hydrophobic amino acids (V, I, L, F, W, M, Y) are encircled into clusters. Ala and Cys are considered hydrophobic in a hydrophobic environment only.

The 2D-topology (size, shape, orientation) and distribution of the hydrophobic clusters of the DBD and HBD of human SHRs[146–148] have been compared in Figure 2 and confronted with the

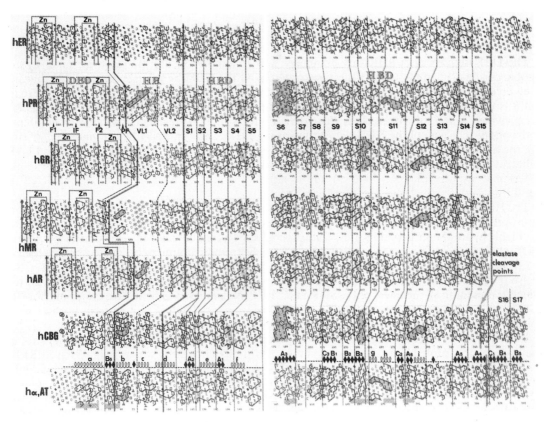

Figure 2 Alignment of the HCA plots of the DNA- and hormone-binding domains (DBD and HBD) of SHRs with the HCA plots of two SERPINs (hα$_1$AT, hCBG). The DNA-binding SHRs are distinguished from the SERPINs by the presence of Cys-coordinated Zn^{2+} fingers (F$_1$ and F$_2$) that are schematically represented in blue (IF and PF: interfinger and postfinger units). The DBD and HBD of SHRs are separated by a hinge region (HR). In the region corresponding to the HBD of the SHRs, alterations in 3D-structure induced by the presence of Pro, Gly, or hydrophilic amino acids are denoted by vertical lines which, when joined, show the correspondence between the major segments (S$_1$ to S$_{15}$) of all the proteins. The SERPINs, hCBG and hα$_1$AT, possess an additional segment (S$_{16}$–S$_{17}$) which is cleaved by neutrophil elastase. The red arrow indicates the cleavage point. hER is distinguished from the other SHRs by a highly hydrophilic C-terminal extension and a longer loop between S$_{10}$ and S$_{11}$ (S456–K472). Examples of characteristic hydrophobic clusters are stippled in black. The HCA plot of hα$_1$AT is capped by a schematic representation of its secondary structure deduced from X-ray crystallography studies (helices a to i, β-strands A to C) (see Figure 4a). Green stippled areas below hα$_1$AT indicate the components of the channel that would be created by elastase cleavage of S$_{16}$ and S$_{17}$ and clearing of the C-terminal peptide. The four amino acids in orange are an example of high conservation of sequence among the proteins (see Figure 3). Abbreviations for the amino acid residues are: A, Ala; C, Cys; D, Asp; E, Glu; F, Phe; ◆, Gly; H, His; I, Ile; K, Lys; L, Leu; M, Met; N, Asn; ∗, Pro; Q, Gln; R, Arg; ⊡, Ser; ☐, Thr; V, Val; W, Trp; and Y, Tyr. The plots are obtained with a Fortran 77 computer program which uses color codes to distinguish basic (blue) and acidic (red) amino acids

HCA plot of another hormone binding protein, human corticosteroid binding globulin (hCBG), that binds endogeneous glucocorticoids and progesterone. hCBG belongs to the family of serine protease inhibitors (SERPINs)[149] and has a 45% sequence identity with human α_1-antitrypsin (hα_1-AT) whose HCA plot is also given in Figure 2. The crystallographic structure of hα_1-AT and of another member of the SERPIN family, antithrombin III, have been determined to a resolution of ≈ 3 Å.[150,151]

Those clusters of greatest similarity, often within identical sequence patterns, were used as anchor points for the manual alignment of the proteins under comparison. Structural segments have been delineated by the positions of Pro or Gly that induce disruptions in structure or by hydrophilic areas that correspond to loops. Insertions or deletions frequently occur in these areas rather than in the hydrophobic core of the protein that maintains stability.[152] The most precise sequence alignment is deduced by proceeding outwards from the hydrophobic centre of each cluster towards the boundary of the structural segment.

A rough HCA homology score can be calculated by noting the topological correspondence of the hydrophobic residues, whatever their precise nature, within clusters from different proteins. Present experience shows that a $\leq 50\%$ score indicates unrelated 3D-structures and a $\geq 75\%$ score very similar 3D-structures.

16.3.2.2.2 Application of HCA to the DBD and HBD of steroid hormone receptors: visual comparison of HCA plots

The DBD sequences of SHRs are extremely well conserved. So are the resulting small hydrophobic clusters (Figure 2). The DBD is separated from the HBD by a hinge region (HR) that has been divided into two segments VL_1 and VL_2. Segment VL_1 or hMR is particularly rich in Pro (*) but it is within segment VL_2 that the greatest variability is observed among SHRs. The HBD has been divided into 15 segments. It is clear that several structural segments (isolated or combined hydrophobic clusters) of the HBD vary little among SHRs and can easily be distinguished *de visu*, *e.g.* the highly conserved segments S_2, S_5, S_6, S_{10}–S_{12}, S_{14} and S_{15} of hPR, hGR, hMR, and hAR. Whereas the sequences of these SHRs end at S_{15}, hER possesses an additional hydrophilic C-terminal segment (S_{16}–S_{17}) and an additional subsegment between S_{10} and S_{11} centered on Ser-451.

The HCA plots of hCBG and hα_1-AT can be aligned with the plots for the HBDs of SHRs without insertion or deletion if due account is taken of proteolysis of SERPINs by elastase with the release of the highly hydrophobic peptide S_{16}–S_{17}. Surprisingly, SHRs end at this cleavage point except for the hydrophilic C-terminal segment of hER. Conserved clusters were found to be located in the segment consecutive to finger F_2 in the DBD, in segment VL_1, and in segments S_1–S_4, S_6, S_8, S_{10}–S_{12}, S_{14} and S_{15} of the HBD. Segment S_6, characterized by a large highly distinctive hydrophobic cluster which is present in all members of the SHR and SERPIN families, was one of the major anchors for the alignment. It is important to note that the marked similarity in HCA plot patterns is observed in spite of the low sequence identity (6–10%) between the HBD of SHRs and hCBG.

HCA homology scores for segments S_1 to S_{15} are a rough estimate of the degree of conservation of the hydrophobic protein core. The scores show that: (i) hCBG belongs structurally to the SERPIN family (HCA score = 83% with regard to hα_1-AT). Apart from human thyroxine binding globulin (hTBG), no other tested hormone binding protein (BP) showed any significant HCA homology with SERPINs nor with SHRs (*i.e.* α-glycoprotein, rat prostatic BP, human sex steroid BP, rabbit uteroglobin, rat androgen BP, human vitamin D BP, cellular retinoic acid BP, β-lactoglobulin, plasma retinol BP, transthyretin, murine α-fetoprotein); (ii) The HBDs of SHRs display structural homology with the SERPINs hCBG, hTBG and hα_1-AT (HCA score = 60–70% when excluding the variable segment S_5); (iii) The HBDs of SHRs that bind 3-keto-Δ^4-steroids (*i.e.* hGR, hPR, hMR, hAR) are structurally interrelated to $> 80\%$ but only related to $\approx 75\%$ with the HBD of hER that binds A-ring phenolic steroids; and (iv) SHRs (e.g. hER and hGR) have an $\approx 70\%$ HCA homology score with vitamin D receptor (hVDR), retinoic acid receptor (hRAR), and thyroid hormone receptor (hTHRβ) which are structurally interrelated to $\geq 80\%$ (HCA plots not shown).

16.3.2.2.3 Application of HCA to the hormone-binding domain (HBD) of steroid hormone receptors: sequence alignment

Matching up of analogous clusters yields an alignment of amino acid sequences that is based on presumed 3D-topology rather than upon maximum sequence identity. This method has enabled the

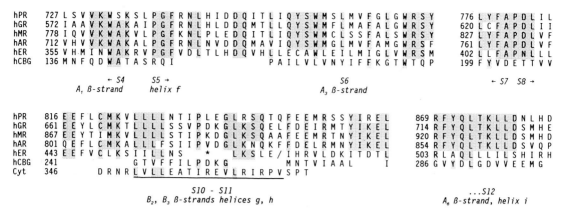

Figure 3 Regions of high contiguous sequence identity within hSHRs and hCBG as deduced from HCA plots. The longer subsegment centered on S463 in hER between segments S_{10} and S_{11} is indicated by an asterisk. The 17 amino acids incorporating the steroid-binding consensus sequence in bovine cytochrome $P450\,c_{17}$ has been aligned with the SHRs by HCA plot analysis and underlined

identification of several regions of high contiguous sequence identity within SHRs (*e.g.* segments S_4, S_6, $S_{7/8}$, S_{10} and S_{12}; Figure 3), some of which, on account of the high degree of conservation, could be implicated in the key functions of SHRs, *i.e.* steroid binding, nuclear translocation. Specific variations within these common zones would define the individual specificity of each SHR. For instance, it may not be incidental that hER, which binds A-ring phenolic steroids, unlike the SHRs that bind 3-keto-Δ_4-steroids and unlike hCBG that binds P and cortisol, has an Ile instead of a Phe residue at 389 (hER numbering).

Only few of the amino acids in these zones are common to SHRs and hCBG. They are, however, highly reactive low polarity amino acids; Trp (W) in segments S_4 and S_6, Tyr (Y) in segments S_7 and S_{12}, Phe (F) in segment S_6 and Leu (L) in segment S_{12}. A variety of chemical studies have suggested the presence of Trp and Tyr residues in the steroid-binding site of hCBG.[153] For instance, excess cortisol can protect hCBG from nitration of Tyr residues by tetranitromethane suggesting the presence of a Tyr residue. Fluorescence quenching studies and analysis of UV difference spectra of hCBG–steroid interaction complexes have led to the conclusion that a Trp (W) residue is present. Trp-modifying agents affected first an accessible then a less accessible Trp, with concomitant inactivation of steroid-binding sites. Two of the three Trp within the first 358 residues of hCBG are found in the SHRs (segments $S_{4/5}$ and S_6). His and Met residues have been covalently labelled in hCBG and also hPR[154] but only a Met in the above segments (S_6 and $S_{7/8}$) is common to both proteins.

According to HCA plot analysis, in 17 identical amino acids of cytochromes $P450\,c_{17}$ and $P450$ c_{21} that have been reported to represent part of the steroid-binding site[155] can be aligned with SHRs and hCBG as shown in Figure 3,[148] *i.e.* with 451–471 rather than 538–554 of hER (the counterpart sequences of mouse ER are 455–474 and 542–558, respectively). This is 80 amino acids upstream from the previously proposed position[155] Our 455–474 location may explain why the mouse ER mutant, MOR 121–538, which is reputed to lack this consensus sequence,[156] is nevertheless able to bind estradiol with significant affinity.

The tail end of the large hydrophobic cluster of segment S_6 of SHRs and SERPINs is characterized by a consensus sequence X111FXXXW where 1 is a hydrophobic residue and X any residue. A data bank search of 21 136 sequences has limited the number of other proteins with this sequence to 28. On these, several such as, for instance, cytochromes, may have further analogies with SHRs. The region of high homology located in S_4–S_5 has been implicated in nuclear translocation (see Section 16.3.2.2.5i).

16.3.2.2.4 Application of HCA to the hormone-binding domain of steroid hormone receptors: structure prediction

Several amino acid sequences can define a single structural motif and the prime objective of HCA is to discern structural analogies rather than sequence identities. Indeed, the shapes of a variety of hydrophobic clusters can be related to identifiable 3D-structural features.[144] Thus, the large highly

distinctive hydrophobic cluster in segment S_6, that is present in all members of the SERPIN and
SHR families and that was used as one of the major anchors for HCA plot alignment, is typical of
a long β-strand. Similarly, the cluster of segment S_{10} is also typical of a β-strand whereas segment
S_{12} is constituted of a β-strand followed by an α-helix. The 2D-structural features of hα₁-AT, as
determined from its X-ray crystallographic structure, cap its HCA plot in Figure 2.

According to current experience, the relatively high HCA score (66–70%) recorded for the
comparison of the HBD sequences of SHRs that bind 3-keto-Δ_4-steroids with the sequence
preceding the elastase cleavage of hα₁-AT justifies the use of the crystal structure of cleaved hα₁-AT
as a first approximation of the 3D-structure of the HBD of a SHR (Figure 4a).

In view of the role of intermolecular disulfide bonds in maintaining the architecture of proteins, we
have examined whether the location of Cys within the HBD of SHRs is compatible with this model,
although, under the reducing conditions prevalent in the cell or *in vitro* in the presence of thiol
reducing agents such as dithiothreitol (DTT), the S—S bridges may be reduced to enable steroid
binding.[157-159] Two Cys residues are relatively well conserved in the HBD of SHRs: C-798/C-820 of
hPR, C-643/C-665 of hGR, C-783/C-805 of hAR, C-417/C-447 of hER (the second Cys is missing in
hMR) and correspond to locations 228 and 240 of a hairpin structure of hα₁-AT. If due allowance is
made for the expected variation between hα₁-AT and SHRs, the distance between these residues is
compatible with the formation of a disulfide bond. GR has an additional Cys tandem (C-622/C-638
of hGR) also compatible with disulfide bond formation since the corresponding hα₁-AT residues are
near positions 203 and 222.

Nevertheless, despite the analogy suggested by HCA plots between the hydrophobic cores of
cleaved hα₁-AT and of the HBD of SHRs, the hα₁-AT model has to be viewed with circumspection

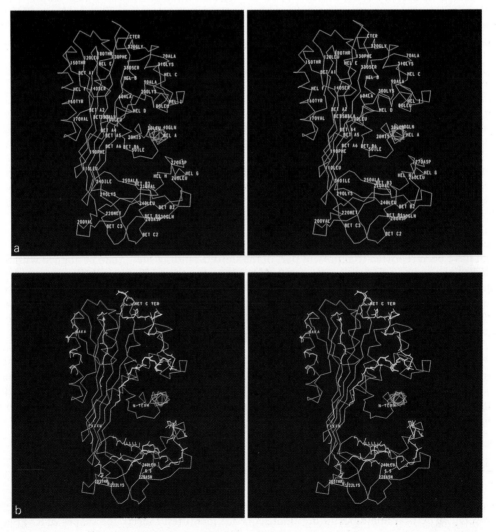

Figure 4   *(Contd.)*

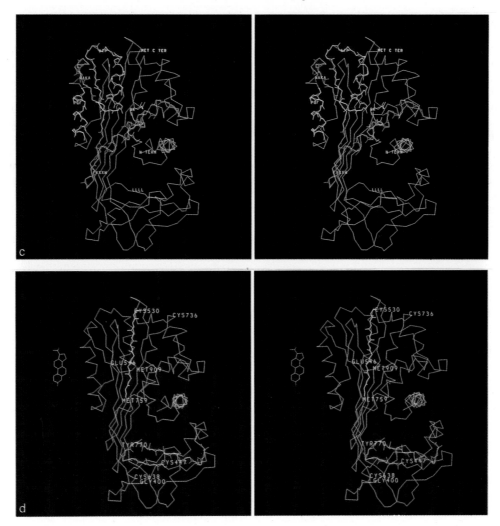

Figure 4 Use of the crystal structure of proteolyzed hα₁AT without cleaved peptide (stereoscopic views) as a first approximation to illustrate the properties of SHRs. (a) Residues 20 to 358 of hα₁AT. β-sheets (BET) and α-helices (HEL) have been labelled as well as every 10th amino acid. (b) Elastase cleavage point of SERPINs (Met 358, C-Terminal); approximate positions of the areas of high contiguous sequence identity in SHRs (pale blue) labelled with consensus sequences (WAKA, FXXXW, LLLL) (see Figures 3 and 5); possible disulfide bridges (– – –) between cysteines (the corresponding amino acids in hα₁AT are Thr 203, Lys 222, Asn 228 and Leu 240); possible contact point of SHR dimers in yellow. (c) Location of sequences that determine nuclear localization (RK in orange), nuclear translocation (WAKA...PGF, mauve...yellow), ATP binding (pale blue loop within α-β-α-β darker blue zone), transcription activation (within ATP-binding zone; see Figure 5). (d) hα₁AT locations corresponding to amino acids near or within steroid-binding site as identified by affinity labelling or mutation. Proposed steroid-binding sites: (i) lower zone of visible cavity that has been formed by removal of the peptide cleaved by elastase, (ii) cavity that would be formed by unfolding of A₄-strand (segment S₁₅ shown in yellow). A progesterone molecule is drawn to scale

in the absence of confirmatory data, whether structural or biochemical. At the present time, molecular graphics and energy minimization programs are being used to develop precise 3D-models of the HBDs of each of the SHRs in order to discern structural variations that may help to explain differences in SHR specificity and in order to be able to confront each model with available biochemical data on the corresponding SHR.

16.3.2.2.5 *Visualization of steroid receptor binding properties using hα₁-AT as a model*

As mentioned in Section 16.3.2.1.1, SHRs do not only bind DNA and steroids, but other proteins, nucleotides, ions, *etc.* The chain of binding events no doubt depends upon the environment which maintains the appropriate SHR conformation and supplies the necessary cofactors. One should not forget the need for many diverse agents (*i.e.* molybdate, sucrose, EGTA (a chelating agent), DTT) to measure steroid binding *in vitro*.

Nascent polypeptide chains emerging from the ribosome would appear to have an α-helical conformation and a similar extended conformation is observed when proteins traverse mitochondrial membranes.[160] It has been proposed that the hydrophobic regions exposed in newly synthesized incompletely folded polypeptides interact with ubiquitous heat shock proteins (HSPs), also designated stress-induced proteins or molecular chaperones,[161] whose role is to stabilize the protein, to prevent improper interactions resulting from transient exposure of hydrophobic or charged surfaces, and to promote proper folding. To fulfil this role, HSPs would use the energy from ATP hydrolysis since they have ATPase activity.[160,162]

In the cytosol, SHRs are associated with a 90 kDa HSP.[5,6,163] Consequently, unfolded hα₁-AT, *i.e.* the linear succession of the secondary structural features of hα₁-AT as deduced by X-ray but also HCA analysis, may prove to be a particularly relevant model to represent schematically the localization of the functions inherent to SHR subdomains. Figure 5 uses this device to represent data obtained from studies on SHRs irrespective of hormone class. Folding this hα₁-AT structure gives a visual impression of the possible locations of these functions in space (Figure 4b) and of the regions of high sequence identity already identified above (Figure 4a).

(i) Nuclear localization sequence

Many nuclear proteins contain sequences that specify nuclear localization. The hinge region starts with a consensus sequence RKXRRXXR for nuclear localization of SHR[164-166] that
                    KK   R
would be an α-helix in a hydrophilic, basic/acidic environment (Figures 4b and 5).

(ii) Transcription activation sequences

Two hormone dependent transactivation sequences, τ_1 and τ_2,[167-170] have been identified, one of which (526–556 for hGR) is situated across S_1 (α-helix) and S_2 (β-strand) (Figures 4b and 5). Their positions need not be unique, their activity is cumulative and their function can be constitutive.

(iii) Phosphorylation and ATP binding

Cellular differentiation and division are controlled by protein phosphorylation which stabilizes differential conformational states of regulated and regulatory molecules. For instance, in the case of

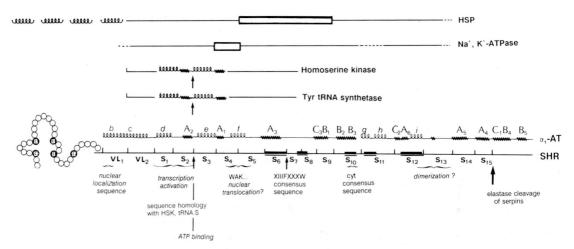

Figure 5 Schematical and hypothetical representation of the C-terminal Zn^{2+} finger of the DBD, the HR (segments VL_1 and VL_2) and the HBD (S_1 to S_{15}) of a SHR. The baseline is capped by the secondary structures deduced from the 3D-crystal structure of hα₁AT. ⁀⁀⁀ , α-helix; ▬▬ , β-strand; —— , loop or other. The underlined bold sections refer to the regions of high sequence identity among SHRs (see Figure 3). The presumed roles of several segments are given below the baseline, whereas three proteins with some sequence identity with a SHR or related receptor (retinoic acid) are shown above the baseline: tyrosine tRNA synthetase (ATP binding), homoserine kinase (ATP binding), Na^+,K^+-ATPase. The fourth protein is HSP, reputedly an unfolding protein with ATPase activity, whose A region, a highly charged α-helix, is complementary with the C-terminal Zn^{2+} finger and which is considered to show strong hydrophobic interaction (▭) with the HBD. This could be over segments S_5 to S_9

glycogen phosphorylase,[171,172] the predominant structural change associated with phosphorylation occurs at the subunit interface as a result of conformational transition at the N-terminus.

SHRs have been reported to be not only substrates for kinases but also to possess kinase activity. However, recent experiments would indicate that a protein with kinase activity can be separated from the SHR protein in purified preparations and therefore that this activity is not inherent to the SHR itself.[8,173] The phosphorylation of SHRs and its implication in SHR activation and transformation, in gene transcription and SHR down regulation are the subject of intensive ongoing study.[174-176]

Although binding of ATP to SHRs was demonstrated long ago,[15] a consensus ATP-binding sequence could only recently be identified in the hinge region of hER.[177] A 42 amino acid homology was later detected between hER and *E. coli* tRNA synthetase.[178] It is located at P-293 to T-334 of hER and corresponds to segments VL_2, S_1, and S_2 shown in Figure 5. A further homology was detected between homoserine kinase and retinoic acid receptor and occurs in the same region.[179] Indeed, the ATP-binding site would appear to be located between segments S_2 and S_3, a region of the HBD of SHRs that is particularly rich in Ser and/or Tyr (Figure 2). This location is in good agreement with reports that ER needs to be phosphorylated on Tyr to bind hormone[175] and with observations of serine phosphorylation of SHRs.[180] It is also compatible with previous observations indicating that the DNA- and ATP-binding sites of SHRs are independent.[181]

(iv) Heat shock protein (HSP) binding

At least two HSPs (72 kDa and 90 kDa) may be associated with the SHR. The 90 kDa phosphoprotein would be released on SHR binding to DNA[182,183] and, for this reason, it has been suggested that part of its structure (the negatively charged α-helical A region) might mimic a DNA configuration.[184] However, since steroid binding is necessary to induce specific DNA binding, the steroid may have a role in dislodging HSP from part of the hormone-binding site. A protein–protein interaction between HSP and an outer highly hydrophobic surface of the HBD could occur across S_5 to S_8.

If, like other HSPs, 90 kDa HSP has ATPase activity, then analogies could be sought with another ATPase that binds steroid hormone. The membrane enzyme Na^+,K^+-ATPase of 1016 amino acids binds cardiac glycosides but also several steroids including progesterone and the antimineralocorticoid canrenone.[185,186] It has regions of homology with hGR and hER in segments S_4 and S_6[177] which are part of the hydrophobic surface defined above.

(v) Nuclear translocation

The region of high homology 'WAK...' located in S_4–S_5 (Figure 5) has been implicated in the nuclear translocation of GR (as the sequence in Section 16.3.2.2.5i).[109] Derepression of DNA binding by the steroid would be transduced by this region which is, moreover, reputed to be involved in SHR binding to a protein such as HSP.

(vi) SHR dimerization

A dimerization function is necessary for high affinity SHR binding to DNA.[187] Experiments where limited trypsin digestion products of ER remained as a dimer after having lost their DBD have suggested that dimerization occurs through hydrophobic interaction of the HBD.[188] Contacts between protein subunits can be formed between residues of symmetry-related helices which interdigitate to form H-bonds and van der Waals contacts. Protein dimerization may occur, for instance, *via* a 'leucine zipper' motif[189] or coiled coil[190] and, for the Fos- and Jun-proteins, this feature is adjacent to a DNA-binding zone.[191] The leucine zipper is a heptameric repeat of Leu or equivalent amino acids (*i.e.* Val, Met, Ile) over 4 to 5 regions and forms an amphipathic α-helix. A linear sequence that seems to meet this criterion has been tentatively identified within the HBD (S_{12} and S_{13}) of SHRs:

e.g. for hAR (858)*L*TKLLDS*V*QPIARE*L*HQFTFD*L*LIKSHM*V*SVDFPE*M*

In SHRs, this region is probably a helix corresponding to helix i of hα-AT followed by another presumably helical structure corresponding to loops in hα$_1$-AT. It is situated close to the ATP-binding (S_2–S_3) and hinge (VL_1, VL_2) regions in the folded hα$_1$-AT 3D-model (Figures 4a and 4b).

(vii) Steroid binding according to affinity labelling and mutation studies

The high chemical reactivity of Cys compared to other residues hinders an objective evaluation of the true importance of the amino acids reported to be in the hormone-binding site by affinity labelling. Whereas chemical modification or mutation studies can indicate whether a particular amino acid is essential for binding affinity, affinity labelling studies only indicate the localization of the amino acid. Several Met and Cys residues are reported to be present within the hormone-binding site of rat GR and hPR: M-622, C-656, C-754 in rGR, M-759 (equivalent to M-622 of rGR) and M-909 in hPR (hPR has no Cys equivalent to C-656 of rGR).[192,193] The $h\alpha_1$-AT residue corresponding to M-622 of rat GR and M-759 of hPR is I-188, and that corresponding to M-909 of hPR is near position 333. Residue I-188 and position 333 are in segments S_6 and S_{14}, respectively. On the other hand, the $h\alpha_1$-AT residues that are the counterparts of C-656 and C-754 (rGR) are situated at the outer surface of the protein.

Recent binding experiments with organometallic estradiol derivatives[194,195] have suggested that vicinal space positioning of a Cys (C) and Lys (K) or Arg (R) are necessary for binding of the estradiol D-ring. These could be amino acids 447–449 of hER, that in our alignment precede the cytochrome consensus sequence in Figure 3, or amino acids 529–531. In 'A-ring binding D-ring acting' model, the steroid A-ring is considered to be involved in tight receptor binding, whereas conformational features and functional groups of the D-ring induce receptor function. Indeed, Cys (C), Lys (K) and Arg (R) residues have already been implicated in ER activation, dimerization, and conversion to a high affinity state for estrogen.[196]

The use of diethyl pyrocarbonate, a reagent which under certain conditions of pH is considered selective for His, has suggested that chick PR and rat and lamb ER contain a His residue in their steroid-binding sites, although this might be an unusually reactive Tyr residue.[197–199]

The substitution of a Val for a Gly at position 400 of hER from MCF_7 cells destabilizes the SHR structure and decreases estradiol affinity at 25 °C but not 4 °C.[200] The mutation Glu to Gly in position 546 of mouse GR results in a poor steroid-binding protein.[201] Asn instead of a Tyr at position 770 of mGR increases the dissociation rate of ligand[201] and deletion of the last 29 amino acids from the carboxy terminus of rat GR reduces steroid binding to 1%.[168]

On the basis of the above evidence, what putative hydrophobic channel(s) could accommodate a steroid? At least two possibilities can be envisaged in the $h\alpha_1$-AT model (Figure 4d). (i) Sequenced SHRs end at, or just before, the cleavage point of $h\alpha_1$-AT by elastase. Whether this observation signifies that sequenced SHRs are all proteolytic cleavage products is disturbing especially as neutrophil elastase can produce 52 kDa and 30 kDa GR fragments in the cytosol of human leukemia cells.[202] Notwithstanding, a highly hydrophobic channel about 20 Å long and 10 Å wide is formed by clearing the cleaved peptide (S-359–Q-393) which fills the core of proteolyzed $h\alpha_1$-AT. Many of the residues protruding into the channel belong to the well-conserved segments S_6, S_{10}–S_{12}, S_{14} and S_{15}. The size of this channel is much larger than that of a steroid, but could vary since the α/β component opposite the β-sheet (strands A_1 to A_6) is part of an apparently flexible structure. The X-ray structures of transthyretin,[203] retinol-binding protein,[204] 3-keto-Δ^5-steroid isomerase[205] complexed with hormone also reveal a binding site sandwiched between a large β-sheet and an α/β structure. (ii) The position of the cleavage point of hCBG suggests that the main part of strand A4 (segment S_{15}) is not buried in native hCBG but can unwind to form an external loop.[150] The mould of this A4 strand within the cleaved 3D-structure forms a hydrophobic channel 17 Å by 6 Å and could feasibly constitute an alternative hormone-binding site. However, since deletion of this segment reduces binding to 1%,[168] this may be a less likely hypothesis. The two proposed sites may hintercommunicate.

In Figures 4a to 4d the folded $h\alpha_1$-AT model has been used as a visual support for the above available information on the HBD and as a means of putting into perspective the long-known 3D-structures of steroid ligands. Further biochemical evidence may help to refine this model whilst awaiting hard crystal data to confirm it.

16.3.2.2.6 Correspondence between the 3D-structures of steroid hormone receptors and steroid ligands

Ligands involved in signalling pathways such as steroids (Figure 6) tend to be small lipophilic molecules that fit specifically into hydrophobic pockets within receptor proteins. Their specificity as substrates is largely determined by hydrogen bonds (H-bonds) whilst other forces stabilize the ligand–macromolecule complex (van der Waals interactions, aromatic–aromatic interactions, elec-

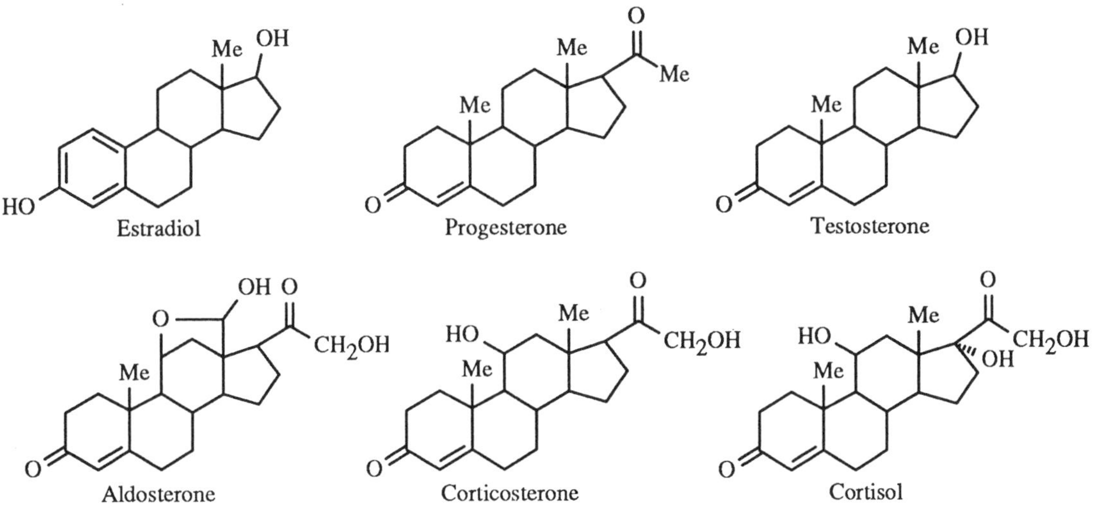

Figure 6 Structural formulae of some natural hormones

trostatic interactions). Van der Waals interactions act over longer distances than H-bonds, are individually of weaker energy, but far more numerous.

Binding of most biologically active steroids to SHRs is associated with an energy of *ca* -12 to -15 kcal mol^{-1} (1 cal $= 4.18$ J), corresponding to a dissociation constant of 10^{-9}–10^{-11} M. One-third to one-half of this energy is supplied by the H-bonds at the C-3 and C-17 ends of the steroid (for all classes of steroid hormones) and at C-11 (for gluco- and mineralo-corticoids), the remainder by van der Waals interactions. For instance, the mean intermolecular van der Waals interaction energy is, respectively, -3 and -3.5 kcal mol^{-1} for appropriately located methyl and ethynyl groups.

Removal of the C-3 and/or C-17 substituents of the natural hormones or replacement by groups unable to form the same directional H-bonds results in a drastic loss in affinity for the SHR unless, for instance, another strong interaction compensates for part of the normal H-bond interaction involving the 3-keto group (≈ 3 kcal mol^{-1}).

To assess the relative contributions of the nature of the substituents of a steroid and of the possibility of deformation of the SHR to binding affinity (and this for several classes of SHR) would require a knowledge of numerous descriptors, in particular the steric hindrance, charge, flexibility, *etc.* of the ligand. A single example will be used to illustrate how many properties might intervene in binding. $7\alpha,17\alpha$-dimethyl-substituted-$\Delta^{4,9,11}$-trienes bind to all SHRs except ER (Figure 7) and form

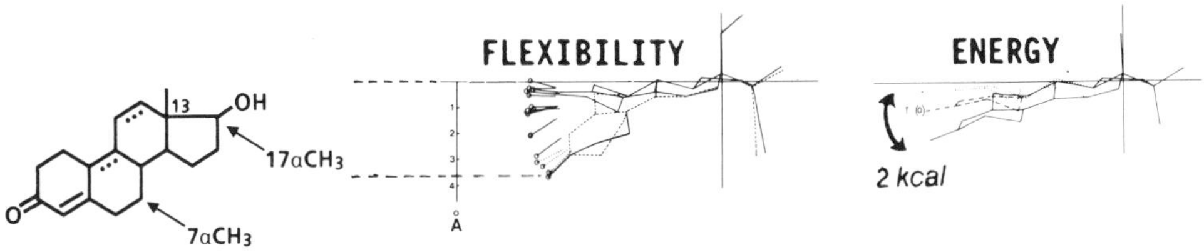

RELATIVE BINDING AFFINITIES

Δ	C-13	ER	PR	AR	MR	GR
Testosterone		0.	\	\\\\\\\	0.	0.
Nortestosterone		0.	\\\\	\\\\\\\\\\\	\	0.
4	CH$_3$	0.	\\\\\\\\\\\\	\\\\\\\	\	\
4, 9	CH$_3$	0.	\\\\\\\\\\\	\\\\\\\	\	\\
4, 9, 11	CH$_3$	0.	\\\\\\\\\\\	\\\\\\\\\\\	\\\\\\	\\\\
4, 9, 11	C$_2$H$_5$	0.	\\\\\\\\\\\	\\\\\\\	\\\\\\\\\	\\\\\\\\\

Figure 7 RBAs of $7\alpha,17\alpha$-dimethyl substituted trienes in a routine screening system[234] according to the gradation scale shown in Figure 15. The RBAs of E$_2$, P, T, aldosterone and DX for their respective receptors were taken to be equal to 100. Flexibility of related $\Delta^{4,9,11}$-trienes as determined by superposition of X-ray crystal structures using a D-ring reference system. The transition energy from a slightly bent to a highly bent conformation is less than 2 kcal mol^{-1}

exceptionally stable complexes with PR. This may be not only because of appropriate directional bonds at the C-3/C-17 extremities and strong van der Waals interactions resulting from the methyl groups, but because their flat pancake nature facilitates entry into a hydrophobic channel and their conformational mobility enhances interaction possibilities. Calculation has shown that extreme conformations, spanning a distance of up to 3 Å, can be covered by an energy increment of ≈ 1 kcal above the minimum energy conformation that can be readily supplied by the binding energy.[206] On the other hand, their C-17α-ethynyl homologs with $\Delta^{4,9,11}$ bonds but lacking a 7α-methyl surprisingly display fast-dissociating kinetics from PR unlike the C-17α-ethynyl-Δ^4 parent compounds which form extremely stable complexes (not shown). This unexpected behavior could be explained by electronic properties but also by a ≈ 1 Å change in the orientation of the 17α-ethynyl resulting from a twist in the skeleton induced by the introduction of the $\Delta^{9,11}$ double bonds.[207,208] Thus small changes (<1 Å) in steroid conformation may be crucial to affinity and specificity and support the hypothesis that the involvement of very few, if not a single, amino acid might condition the subsequent ability of the SHR to bind correctly to DNA and induce gene transcription.

The crystal structures of several hundreds of steroids are known to high resolution.[209-212] This finesse is in sharp contrast to the above rough approximation of the 3D-model of the HBD of SHRs. To illustrate the correspondence between the presumed 3D-structure of the SHR and the possible flexibility of the steroid, SHR and steroid are drawn to the same scale in Figure 4.

16.3.3 STUDY OF STEROID RECEPTOR LIGANDS

16.3.3.1 Aims

In the study of the binding of a ligand to the SHR, at least four different overlapping aims can be distinguished.

Study of the structural requirements for ligand binding and, conversely, mapping of the hormone-binding site of the SHR

The study of the steroid-binding site on SHRs is being tackled on two fronts: (i) by analyzing the amino acid sequences and predicted secondary structures of SHRs, in order to identify putative binding site(s) by computer-assisted modelling techniques as illustrated above; and (ii) by comparing the 3D-structures and relative binding affinities of steroids in order to deduce the structural features compatible with binding to the SHRs and thereby to construct an image of the hydrophobic pocket into which the steroid may fit.[213] The combination of fine deletion mapping and affinity ligand binding should meanwhile help to identify the actual amino acids involved in binding.

Identification of ligands to be used as probes to detect the SHR, assay the number of SHR sites and localize these sites by radio-imaging.

SHR concentrations are considered a useful parameter in assessing hormone sensitivity or dependency. A link has been established between the presence of SHRs and the likelihood of a response to endocrine therapy in several genital and related malignancies.[214,215] SHR assays have thus become routine in breast cancer management, but were only made possible when suitable steroid probes[216-220] or monoclonal antibodies[73,79] had been developed. Initially, steroid probes with high biological potency were selected in order to ensure labelling of a functional SHR, since the objective was to inhibit hormone dependent proliferation by harnessing these SHRs. More recent probes might, however, measure different SHR populations. A probe needs to bind highly selectively to a single class of SHR, to form a stable complex with this SHR, to bind little, if at all, to plasma proteins, to be resistant to degradation during manipulation, amenable to labelling with radioactive, fluorescent or alkylating labels, and to display minimal nonspecific binding. It is because the natural hormones cannot fulfil all these criteria that we first made available to the scientific community the tritiated probes shown in Figure 8. R 2858, R 5020 and R 1881 have since become standard reagents marketed by NEN, and their properties and uses have been amply reviewed.[216-220] Emphasis will be placed in this chapter on the newer compounds i.e. RU 27987, a highly potent progestin; RU 26988 and RU 28362, two glucocorticoids that do not bind to MR;[218-220] and on progress in the development of probes for imaging and covalent labelling.

Ligands used as probes fall broadly into two categories; (i) those whose binding to the SHR is stable but reversible, and (ii) those that bind covalently to the SHR. These two types of probes have so far tended to serve different purposes. Reversible ligands have been used to detect, assay, and image SHRs in hormone sensitive tissues, whether breast tumors, the developing brain etc. They are the compounds that have formed the basis of the classic dextran-coated charcoal (DCC)

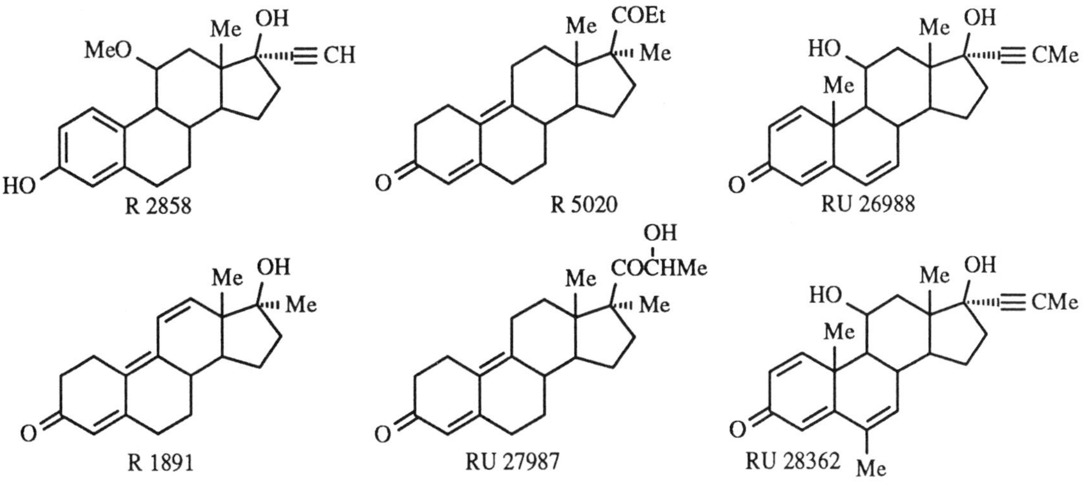

Figure 8 Structures of SHR probes developed by Roussel-Uclaf. For ER, R 2858 (moxestrol); for PR, R 5020 (promegestone) and RU 27987; for AR, RU 1881 (methyltrienolone or metribolone); for GR, RU 26988 and RU 28362.[219,220]

exchange assays on frequently blood-contaminated specimens that contain hormone-binding proteins other than the SHR. Covalent ligands[221,222] are arousing interest in order to identify specific amino acids that form part of the SHR hormone-binding sites although a prime objective has also been the development of site-directed cytotoxic alkylating agents in cancer therapy.[223]

In spite of the array of technology deployed in the development of novel probes, a major problem remains unsolved. What is the functional significance of the SHR that is detected? Temperature dependent differences in the properties of hER with or without a single Val→Gly mutation in the HBD have become apparent.[200] One probe may adequately measure a SHR with a single amino acid mutation, another might not. Ligands that bind PRs from several sources but not PR from chick, hamster nor Tammar Wallaby have been identified.[224-226] Consequently, further work on the functions of SHRs as induced by different ligands (synthesis of different proteins, growth responses) is warranted before the significance of SHR assays by these ligands can be established.

Comparison of ligands of different potency and/or specificity to unravel mechanisms of steroid hormone action

The role of the steroid in eliciting a biological response (or blocking it) is unclear. Changes in SHR that facilitate nuclear retention and DNA binding occur in the presence of ligand, but the exact nature of these changes has yet to be elucidated: the ligand might induce a simple conformational change in the SHR which exposes the previously occluded DNA-binding site, modify the interaction of the SHR with other proteins, lead to the dissociation of an inhibitor of DNA binding, interfere with phosphorylation mechanisms, *etc.* Comparisons between ligands of similar affinity but different activity, between ligands of different specificity, between steroids and nonsteroids with comparable responses can lead to a better understanding of the underlying molecular mechanisms.

Design of ligands for use as potential drugs to either compensate for hormone failure (agonists) or oppose hormone overproduction or action (antagonists)

Research over the last decade has focussed on the design of steroid hormone antagonists[227-230] but the clockwork mechanisms of the endocrine system have so far not proved to be readily amenable to outside control. Antagonists must act on individual molecular mechanisms within highly integrated and complex systems. They may need to: (i) restitute the balance in a system which overproduces or overreacts to hormone, *e.g.* in the treatment of acne, of Cushing's syndrome, of the unopposed estrogen impregnation of the endometrium that leads to luteal deficiency; (ii) interfere with total efficacy at a precise point of a well-regulated system such as the reproductive system for the purposes of fertility control; and (iii) counteract and keep in check, *via* their potential control over hormone responses, changes occurring at other molecular and cellular levels, *e.g.* curbing the progression of hormone dependent cancers. The mechanisms underlying hormone hypersecretion, fertility and cell growth are not well known but two sets of proteins, *i.e.* metabolic enzymes (involved in steroid biosynthesis) and SHRs (involved in steroid action), play important roles. In the past, there has been some success in the design and use of partial agonists/antagonists that rely on subtly modifying the kinetics of formation of SHR complexes, but the design of the more recent SHR antagonists has been based on the general concept of adding reactive substituents onto the skeleton structure of the natural hormone (steroid structure), that may have been modified (A-nor, seco derivatives) or mimicked (*e.g.* triphenylethylene structures). However, the potential toxicity of these reactive substituents may limit the use of the antagonist to severe diseases only; parallel interference with proteins other than SHRs may lead to unexpected side effects. In all cases, the influence of drug kinetics on access to active site(s) and consequently, on the biological responses needs to be considered.[231]

16.3.3.2 Development of a Screening System that Measures Binding to Steroid Hormone Receptors

To meet these aims in a systematic manner, we set up in the mid 1970s a routine screening system in which the binding of each test substance to cytosol SHRs (ER, PR, AR, GR and MR) was measured by a DCC adsorption method.[232,233] Full methodological details have been published[234] and applications of the system have been described in many reviews (*e.g.* refs. 235–238).

Briefly, the relative binding affinity (RBA) of every newly synthesized potential ligand was determined for each SHR in relation to the ability of a reference compound to displace the tritium-labelled natural hormone, or a synthetic probe, from their receptor site(s). Over a thousand steroids were screened in this way for binding to the cytosol SHRs corresponding to the target tissues used as end points in classic animal tests for hormonal activity. Although the relevance of some of these results may, nowadays, be questioned in view of the divergences in the HBDs of SHRs from different tissues and species, it should not be forgotten that many years of empirical experience have validated these animal tests as appropriate models for the testing of drugs destined for humans. Easier access to human tissues and human cell lines would undoubtedly now lead to different options. Furthermore, this criticism does not detract from the inestimable value of a screening system, *i.e.* that all the molecules are tested under perfectly comparable experimental conditions.

The choice of incubation conditions is of paramount importance since these influence the kinetics of formation and dissociation of the ligand–receptor complex. Compounds that dissociate fast from the SHR will have RBAs with respect to a reference substance that decrease as incubation proceeds. On the other hand, if the dissociation rate is slow, the RBAs will tend to increase.[239] It is thus possible, by comparing RBAs at selected incubation times, to infer whether the stability of the complex between ligand and SHR will be greater or less than that formed by the natural hormone. This stability largely determines the dynamics of the biological response.[240] The analysis can be performed for each ligand with respect to all five SHRs to deduce an overall specificity profile.

In the light of these last remarks, a word of caution is called for when reviewing literature on the structure–affinity relationships of steroids. Comparing published data can be misleading since it is unlikely that the experiments have been performed under comparable conditions. The choice of species, organ, radioactive ligand, buffer, cofactors, *etc.* may vary and, most important of all, the choice of incubation time and temperature. In our opinion, it is essential to determine RBA values under two sets of incubation conditions. This is neatly illustrated by the following example: whereas four diversely substituted 17α-derivatives of 11β-methoxyestradiol had highly similar RBAs ranging from 6 to 12 after incubation for 2 h at $0\,^\circ$C, the RBAs after 5 h incubation at $25\,^\circ$C were ranked in a different order from 2.5 to 125 (see Table 1 below). It is thus possible to conclude that whereas recognition between ligand and receptor occurred at comparable rates, the complexes formed had very different kinetic stabilities.

16.3.3.3 The Estrogen *versus* the '3-keto-Δ^4' Receptors

Amino acid sequence and HCA plot comparisons of SHRs have established that ER is the odd-man out; the other SHRs are highly similar. Estradiol has a phenolic A-ring. Progesterone (P), testosterone (T) and endogeneous corticosteroids are all 3-keto-Δ^4-steroids that differ, however, in their C-11 and C-17 substituents (Figure 6): P and T do not possess a β-OH group in C-11; the C-17 substituents are —COMe in P, —OH in T and —CH_2OH in corticosteroids.

There is virtually no overlap between binding to ER and the 3-keto-Δ^4 SHRs[234,235] although, as described below (Section 16.3.3.4.1), certain substituents (*e.g.* in C-11 and C-17α) can introduce minimal binding of A-ring phenolic steroids to these SHRs. On the other hand, presumably because of a high level of regional SHR sequence identity and of similarities in ligand structure (3-keto-Δ^4-), there is a considerable degree of specificity overlap among the binding of the other hormone classes.

This overlap can also be reinforced by certain substituents. Nevertheless, substitution does not necessarily induce new interaction potentials between steroid and SHR but may enhance existing interactions. Substituents in different positions (*e.g.* C-11 and C-17) may even reinforce the interaction in the same zone (*e.g.* C-13).

To define the binding specificity of a SHR, the following interactions need to be analyzed: H-bonding by the functional groups, other possible H-bonds (*e.g.* by permutating a OH group around the steroid skeleton), hydrophobic interactions (*e.g.* by permutating a methyl group), electrostatic or $\pi-\pi$ interactions. Unfortunately, available data is fragmentary. No truly large scale systematic approach has been undertaken, since no single institution has access to all the necessary compounds. Such an experimental comparison may not even be necessary, or desirable, if a suitable artificial intelligence program could be formulated. Already, the application of a multiparametric analysis (*e.g.* correspondence analysis) to available data has shown that it is possible to interpret with confidence RBA measurements subject to influence from uncontrolled factors such as different SHR concentrations, different radioligand specificities, *in vitro* metabolism, etc. Correspondence analysis, by eliminating background interference, highlights those factors that account for most of the variance of the system. It has, furthermore, the advantage of reducing information loss since data on additional molecules and response parameters can be introduced into the existing data matrix used as a model. This fairly sophisticated approach, as applied to RBA data from our screening system, is illustrated in two papers.[241,242] One example of its use is given below.

For the purposes of convenience, we have, in what follows, adopted a more prosaic approach and considered each SHR in turn. The following Sections (16.3.3.4 to 16.3.3.7) will attempt to illustrate for each class of SHR how data obtained from a routine screening can help to meet the aims outlined in Section 16.3.3.1. A review of the entire literature is a monumental task that we have not had the presumption to undertake. Instead, we have tried to illustrate by appropriate examples various strategies than can be adopted to meet these aims. The references given at the beginning of each section refer to articles that review recent knowledge on the particular receptor.

16.3.3.4 Binding to the Estrogen Receptor (ER)[243,244]

16.3.3.4.1 *Structural requirements of the ligand and mapping of the hormone-binding site*

(i) H-bonding and hydroxy groups

The following type of evidence suggests that the hydroxy group in C-3 of the phenol ring of estradiol (E_2) acts as a H-bond donor and that this H-bond is more important than the conformation of the molecule in ER binding (as cited in ref. 245). (i) Although prenortestosterone has a crystal conformation closer to that of E_2 than of 19-nortestosterone, it has no affinity for ER. (ii) 3-Keto-$\Delta^{4,9,11}$-trienes are highly flexible molecules. Some have conformations close to that of ethynylestradiol. Although they bind to PR, AR, MR and GR, they do not bind to ER. (iii) The oxygen at C-3 of 5α-androstan-3β,17β-diol is closer to that of E_2 than of A-nor-2β, 17β-diol-5α-androstan-2α,17α-diethynyl that binds to ER. Nevertheless, it has no affinity for ER. (iv) A hydroxy group in C-2β of a homologous series of A-nor derivatives favored binding to ER and, in C-2α, to AR. A ketone precluded binding to ER and increased affinity for AR. (v) The rank order of binding of 7α-methyl-17α-ethynyl-4-en-17β-ol derivatives for ER is: 3β-OH > 3α-OH ≫ 3-deoxy > 3-keto.

Introduction of hydroxy groups into E_2 leads to a decrease in RBAs for ER,[246] in positions 6α, 7α, 11α and 15α right down to 1% and nearly as far in positions 2 (3%), 11β (7%) and 16α (17%). 16α-hydroxyestradiol (estriol) and 2- and 4-hydroxyestradiol (catechol estrogens) are physiologically important estrogens.[247]

(ii) Alkyl groups

Lengthening the C-13 chain of E_2 (from methyl up to butyl) decreases the RBA, probably because of steric hindrance, and also decreases complex stability.

Methylation of E_2 in the following positions leads to low or moderate RBAs: 1 (15%), 2 (36%), 6α (31%), 15α (racemic 29%), 15β (26%) and 18 (31%),[246] 2 (41%), 4 (27%), 9 (39%) and 18 (31%),[235] but to a relatively high RBA in positions 7 (104%), 11β (65%, 124%), 12β (111%) and 17 (83%).

(iii) 17α substitution

A C-17α-ethynyl substituent enhances binding to ER and would appear to act in synergy, rather than according to a principle of additivity, with certain other substituents. For instance, the combination of an 11β-methoxy or 11β-ethoxy substituent with a 17α-ethynyl substituent is particularly effective in forming a highly stable ER complex, more effective than a combination with a 17α-methyl, 17α-but-2-yn-1-yl or 17α-2-methylallyl substituent (Table 1).

(iv) C-11 and C-7 substitution

The C-11 and C-7 positions were identified in the early 1970s as suitable positions to introduce antigenic chains for the production of high quality antibodies for E_2 radioimmunoassays[248] and, subsequently, as immunoadsorbents to purify ER.[249] The importance of the presence and orientation of a C-11 substituent can be exemplified by two compounds: moxestrol and RU 16117.[239,240,250] Moxestrol is the 11β-methoxy derivative of ethynylestradiol and forms a slowly dissociating complex with ER. It is a highly potent estrogen. Its 11α-methoxy isomer, on the other hand, interacts fleetingly with the ER and is a partial agonist/antagonist similar in activity to estriol on several biological parameters. An 11β-methoxy or 11β-ethoxy group tends to increase the stability of the ER complex whether the substituent in position 17α is methyl, ethynyl, butynyl or methylallyl (Table 1).

C-11 vinyl, allyl, iso- and n-propyl substitution of ethynylestradiol gave RBAs for ER which, although systematically below that of E_2 after 2 h incubation, increased to very high values at 5 h.[251] A series of 11-substituted-phenylestradiols that bind with high affinity to ER has also been synthesized. The compound with a dimethylaminoethoxy side chain in the *para* position of the 11β-phenyl substituent (RU 39411) has potentially interesting antihormonal properties[252] (personnal Communication from M. M. Bouton). This is in line with the general philosophy of introducing bulky reactive substituents in positions where ER affinity can be increased without interfering with the A-ring recognition site.

A 7α-methyl substituent increases affinity for ER. Molecules containing a terminal functional group (acid, alcohol, amine, amide) linked to the steroid at 7α by a decamethylene bridge (*e.g.* the secondary amide ICI 163,964) maintain ER binding affinity (RBA = 13%)[253,254] unlike the 7β-isomer (RBA of ICI 163,964 = 0.18%). ICI 163,964 is a potent but sparingly soluble antiestrogen.

The combined effect of the simultaneous introduction of both 7α-methyl and 11β-methoxy substituents leads to compounds that have lost virtually all affinity for ER (Table 1). The two substituents projecting above and below the plane of the steroid skeleton would seem to bar access to the SHR recognition site probably located at the deep end of a hydrophobic pocket.

Table 1 RBAs for Mouse Uterus Cytosol ER[245]

	Estradiol		11β-methoxyestradiol	
	2 h, 0°C	5 h, 25°C	2 h, 0°C	5 h, 25°C
Substituent at C-17α				
H	100	100	7	28
Me	67	35	6	31
C≡CH	100	220	11	125
C—C≡CMe	—	—	12	19
C—C=CH$_2$ (Me)	—	—	11	2.5
Substituent at C-13				
Me	100	100	11	125
Et	53	33	7	6
Pr^n	30	—	1.5	0.5
Bu^n	14	4	—	—
Substituent at C-7α				
Me	116	330	0.4	3

(v) Binding specificities

The vast majority of steroid estrogen derivatives are highly specific to ER[235] but modifications in C-17, C-11 and C-7 have been shown to induce some, albeit weak, binding to the SHRs of other hormone classes. 17α-ethynylestradiol interacts quite noticeably with PR, much less so with AR and GR. The introduction of an allyl or 2-thienyl substituent in position C-11 does not affect binding to PR, but a vinyl or *p*-methoxymethyl substituent enhances it.[245] In most cases, and in particular in the case of a *p*-methoxymethyl substituent, there is noticeable binding to GR. On the other hand, a 7α-alkyl or 7α-aliphatic substituent would appear to induce some binding to AR.

(vi) Analogies with nonsteroids

A wide variety of nonsteroid derivatives can compete for E_2 binding to ER and the structural analogies between these compounds (*e.g.* secoestradiols, chromans and chromenes, cyclofenil, distilbenes, *etc.*, see Figure 9) and E_2 have been discussed by several teams.[255-259] Estradiol would appear to compete for binding to two types of sites on ER (Type I and Type II). The natural ligand of the Type II sites may be dietary flavonoids.[260]

It is in the case of triphenylethylenes (TPEs) that the closest analogies have been made with steroids substituted at C-7 and/or C-11. X-Ray crystallography studies have established that TPEs adopt a preferential conformation where the orientation of the α-, α′-and β-phenyl rings are fixed but each ring has a certain degree of freedom of rotation. According to our binding data,[261,262] the most likely, but not unique, superposition is one where the α-phenol ring of the TPEs adopts the position of the E_2 A-ring (Figure 10). The reasons for this are apparent from the RBA data for a series of diversely hydroxylated triphenylacrylonitriles in Table 2. The compounds have been classified into three groups: (1) those with RBAs that remain stable or increase when incubation time and temperature are increased; (2) those whose RBAs at 0 °C do not differ substantially from those of group 1 but for which the marked decrease in RBA recorded at 25 °C would seem to indicate that the ligand–receptor complexes are considerably less stable than in group 1; and (3) those with very low RBAs that furthermore decrease with time and temperature. There are only two TPEs in this last category. Close examination of Table 2 reveals that each group is characterized by hydroxylation in a specific position. A *p*-OH on ring α′ (group 3) is least conducive to binding; a *p*-OH on ring

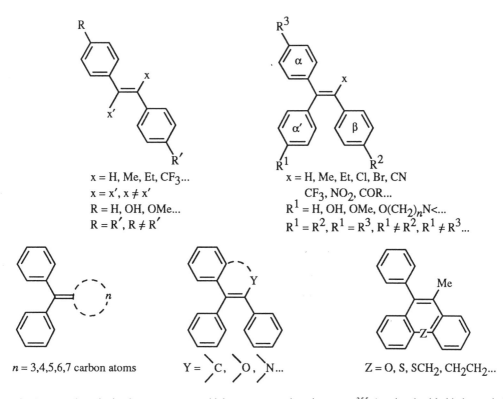

x = H, Me, Et, CF₃...
x = x′, x ≠ x′
R = H, OH, OMe...
R = R′, R ≠ R′

x = H, Me, Et, Cl, Br, CN
CF₃, NO₂, COR...
R¹ = H, OH, OMe, O(CH₂)ₙN<...
R¹ = R², R¹ = R³, R¹ ≠ R², R¹ ≠ R³...

n = 3,4,5,6,7 carbon atoms

Y = $\diagdown$C, $\diagdown$O, $\diagdown$N...

Z = O, S, SCH₂, CH₂CH₂...

Figure 9 Structural analogies between nonsteroidal estrogens and antiestrogens[255] (reprinted with kind permission). According to crystallography studies, angle values for TPEs range from 45–55° for α, 38–47° for α′, and 45–58° for β

Table 2 RBAs[a] of TPEs for E_2-labelled ER Binding in Calf Uterus Cytosol

Compound	R (α)	R_1 (α')	R_2 (β)	RBA 2 h at 0 °C	RBA 5 h at 25 °C
(1)	H	H	H	0.04 ± 0.01	0.09 ± 0.04
(2Z)	OH	H	H	40 ± 8	36 ± 11
(7Z)	OH	Me	H	29 ± 4	28 ± 5
(4)	OH	OH	H	28 ± 4	62 ± 11
(8)	OH	OH	Me	49 ± 9	93 ± 17
(5Z)	OH	H	OH	27 ± 5	74 ± 20
(9Z)	OH	Me	OH	36 ± 9	78 ± 1
(6)	OH	OH	OH	41 ± 6	166 ± 7
(3)	H	H	OH	29 ± 4	3.3 ± 0.7
(5E)	H	OH	OH	19 ± 3	6.1 ± 1.5
(9E)	Me	OH	OH	28 ± 9	9.1 ± 1.6
(2E)	H	OH	H	3.7 ± 0.9	2.2 ± 0.8
(7E)	Me	OH	H	8.1 ± 0.8	2.5 ± 0.6
E_2				100	100

[a] RBAs, determined under two sets of incubation conditions, are the means (± SEM) of at least 4 experimental values. Full methodological details are given in ref. 262.

β (group 2) leads to unstable binding (unless an α-OH group is present). A *p*-OH on ring α (group 1) is essential for stable binding to ER. These results suggest that the OH group in α is the most important, but that the presence of two OH groups is needed to maintain the stability of the complex. The need for a second OH group is confirmed by the negligible RBA recorded for 3-(hydroxyphenyl)-2-phenylacrylonitrile which has an OH group in α, a H in β but no α' phenyl ring. This α' phenyl ring must consequently contribute to the interaction with ER, the interaction being even more effective when this ring is hydroxylated. It is located in the region of the C-11 or C-7,8 atoms of estradiol.[245]

By systematic chemical modification, we have investigated the relative importance of methyl, methoxy, isopropyloxy and even bulkier side chains in a *para* position of the three phenyl rings on binding affinity and kinetics for ER[262] (see Sections 16.3.3.4.3 and 16.3.3.4.4i). These compounds can be compared to the vast number of tested nonsteroid antiestrogens that have recently been the subject of a thorough review.[255]

16.3.3.4.2 Probes for ER

The generation of stable but reversible binding to ER by substitution in position C-11 of the steroid skeleton has been the basis of the development of several probes for ER. Tritiated 11β-methoxyethynylestradiol (R 2858; moxestrol) is a commercial ER radioligand.[263] Most radiohalogenated derivatives, whether halogenated in C-2, C-4, C-16 or C-17, under development for imaging ER retain the C-11 substituent, *e.g.* 11β-methoxy-16α-iodoestradiol and 11β-methoxy-17α-iodovinylestradiol.[264,265] The halogen itself has been introduced into a C-11 substituent. 11β-Chloromethylestradiol exhibits very slow single phase dissociation from ER.[266] Even more recent studies have focussed on labelling C-11-substituted alkenyl or aryl derivatives[267] or compounds with long linear spacer chains at 7α.[268]

In view of the steric analogies between certain nonsteroids and C-11-substituted steroids, it is not surprising that compounds such as hexestrol, the first estrogen to be radiolabelled,[269] and TPEs have also been used as substrates for halogenation to obtain novel radioimaging agents.[270,271] The TPEs, ketononestrol and tamoxifen, have also been affinity-labelled with an aziridine moiety.[272,273] It is hoped that the development of such compounds will help to study ER structure, properties and dynamics under varied biochemical conditions, including in intact cells. An organometallic marker for the detection of ER by FT-IR spectroscopy has been synthesized and is being used to detect amino acids that may be implicated in the ER binding site.[194,195]

The vast number of alkylating groups that have been tested in attempts to develop cytotoxic estrogen derivatives are the subject of an excellent recent review.[223] How systematic comparisons between ER ligands can be used to distinguish between the antiestrogenic and cytotoxic properties of ER ligands will be briefly illustrated in the next section.

16.3.3.4.3   ER ligands as tools to study molecular mechanisms

The growth of benign and neoplastic breast tumor tissue is under the influence of several hormones (*e.g.* insulin, prolactin and steroids) and of different growth factors (GFs, *e.g.* epidermal, transforming and insulin GFs).[57,58] Receptors for these hormones and factors have been identified in a much-investigated cell line, MCF$_7$, derived from a human breast cancer metastasis. Several studies have suggested that the antiproliferative action of TPEs on the growth of estrogen dependent tumors might be mediated by ER. The observations that have led to this hypothesis are (as cited in ref. 262): (i) TPEs can have considerable affinity for ER apart from actions on other molecular targets; (ii) the compounds with the highest affinity for ER are growth inhibitory at the lowest concentrations; (iii) inhibition is abolished in the presence of E$_2$; and (iv) ER negative cells are less sensitive to TPEs.

Little is known about the specific structural features of TPEs that determine ER-binding, growth inhibition and cytotoxicity. In the case of tamoxifen (TAM), it would be the 4-OH metabolite that is particularly active, the OH-group favoring ER binding and the basic side chain being responsible for growth inhibition and/or cytotoxicity.[257]

In order to identify the structural features that might influence these different responses and also in order to establish the relationships between these responses, we undertook a systematic structure–affinity–activity study of a series of over 20 homologous hydroxylated triphenylacrylonitrile derivatives with or without bulky hydrophobic substituents.[262] We measured; (i) their binding to calf uterus ER under two sets of incubation conditions, (ii) their ability to stimulate the proliferation

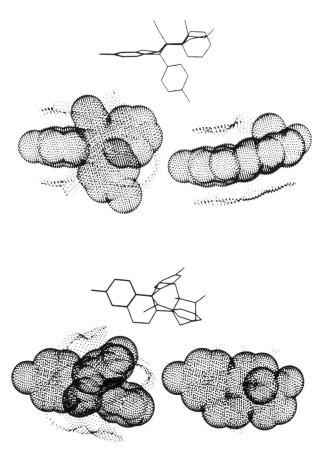

Figure 10 Superpositions of the α-phenol ring of TPE (**7Z**) of Table 2 with the A-ring of estradiol. Beneath the superposition are given the atomic surface (spheres) and van der Waals signature (doted contours) of (**7Z**; left) and E$_2$ (right). The graphic representation of the molecules was performed with the software MANOSK

of ER positive (MCF$_7$) cells or to inhibit the E$_2$-promoted growth of these cells, and (iii) their cytotoxicity in ER positive (MCF$_7$) and ER negative (BT$_{20}$) cells. Results were analyzed by a multiparametric approach (correspondence analysis) in order to detect not only the relationships between structure and response (see Section 16.3.3.4.4ii) but also the relationships between the responses.

The $\Phi_1\Phi_2$ 2-D factorial map in Figure 11, that accounts for 80% of the total variance of the system, illustrates the relative locations of the response parameters and of the TPEs with respect to these parameters. The shading was introduced on the basis of the degree of affiliation revealed by a hierarchical ascending classification. The factorial map highlights the following conclusions; whether RBAs for ER are measured for 2 h at 0 °C or 5 h 25 °C matters little with reference to the possible relevance they may have in the stimulation or inhibition of growth by this population of TPE molecules. RBA values are more relevant to an appreciation of the TPEs' growth-promoting ability than to their inhibition of E$_2$-induced growth ((IC$_{50}$ or % antagonist). The relationship is closer when growth promotion is expressed as an EC$_{50}$ rather than as a maximum response (% agonist). Measurements of cytotoxicity in ER positive (MCF$_7$) and ER negative (BT$_{20}$) cells are germane for this population of TPEs. For each cell line, there is a strong correlation between the two different expressions used to evaluate this cytotoxicity (*i.e* an IC$_{30}$ or a percentage inhibition at

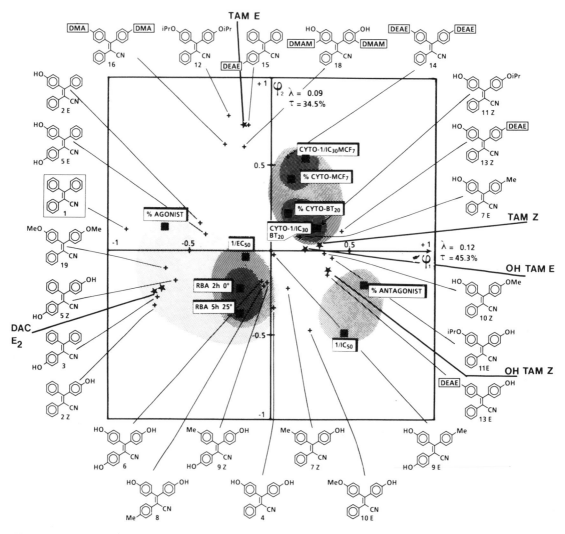

Figure 11 $\Phi_1\Phi_2$ distribution map obtained by correspondence analysis of binding and activity data on 25 TPEs. This distribution map encompasses 80% of the total variance of the system. It shows the relative proximity of the following response parameters (■): RBAs for ER after incubation for 2 h at 0° or 5 h at 25 °C, promotion of MCF$_7$ cell growth expressed either as 1/IC$_{50}$ or as a percent of the maximum E$_2$ response (% agonist), antagonism of E$_2$-promoted growth (similarly expressed), cytotoxicity in MCF$_7$ and BT$_{20}$ cells. The positions of the chemical structures (+) in relation to the parameters (■) show how gradual variations in structure can modify the nature of the response[262]

10^{-5}M TPE, Cyto %). Cytotoxicity is anticorrelated to the RBAs but is not related to any antiestrogen activity on cell growth which is clearly opposed to growth stimulation.

This type of analysis of different estrogen responses *e.g.* ER replenishment, PR induction, enzyme activity (creatine kinase, glucose-6-phosphate dehydrogenase, *etc.*), growth factor induction would be extremely helpful in yielding information on the inherent nature and function of the ligand–ER complex in different cells. How it can be used in the study of structure–activity relationships will be illustrated in Section 16.3.3.4.4ii).

16.3.3.4.4 Drug design: estrogen agonists and antagonists

(i) Estrogens for the menopause and the prevention of osteoporosis

Whereas, over the years, antiestrogens have been the object of increasingly intensive study, particularly as potential treatments of hormone dependent neoplasms, estrogens, although crucial to female physiology, have been sadly neglected because they have rather unjustly earned a bad name. Much emphasis has been laid on their probable carcinogenicity. Nevertheless, despite the periodic scares linking estrogen use with breast and endometrial cancer, only estrogens are able to prevent post menopausal osteoporosis and to successfully palliate the symptoms of the perimenopause (*i.e.* hot flushes, fatigue, insomnia and headache).[274-277]

In view of the pervasive but misled opinion that 'natural' can be equated with 'safe', pharmaceutical firms have had to direct their efforts away from the conception of more active synthetic estrogens to the large scale synthesis of 'natural' estrogens for delivery in novel forms, *e.g.* micronized oral forms, gels, patches, *etc.* Little is publicly known about the potential carcinogenity or mutagenicity of E_2 administered in well above physiological doses by these routes.

Until very recently bone ER had remained elusive[278,279] but its detection will now permit testing of the receptor-mediated activities of synthetic and natural estrogens on bone. It is accepted that, unlike E_2, estriol is inactive in the prevention of osteoporosis but compounds more potent than E_2 may hopefully soon be in the pipeline. Whether these estrogens will also display the favorable central (*e.g.* hot flushes), cardiovascular and peripheral (vaginal trophicity) properties of E_2 will have to be checked. The weak estrogen, RU 16117,[250] can alleviate these symptoms, decrease basal serum LH levels and, somewhat like tranquilizers, modify EEG profiles but, on the other hand, its action on bone remains to be investigated.

(ii) Triphenylethylene antiestrogens

The literature on the design and pharmacological activity of nonsteroid antiestrogens is so vast[257,258,280-282] that it defies summary. Clinical data are, on the other hand, comparatively scarce and concern primarily a single compound, tamoxifen (TAM) which is reputed to have diverse molecular impacts. It would therefore be interesting to know what structural characteristics of the compound are associated with a specific activity (*e.g.* binding to ER, the antiestrogen-binding site, calcium-binding proteins, PKC, estrogenicity, antiestrogenity, cytotoxicity). For the TPEs we have studied, some of this information, which may prove to be useful in the design of tailor made drugs, can be deduced from their position within the factorial map shown in Figure 11. (The present analysis explores the selectivity of the TPEs and does not take into account the absolute activity levels.)

The principal features of the TPEs down the left-hand side of Figure 11 is their essentially agonist character which is, however, more or less pronounced. Except for the unsubstituted TPE (**1**) and the α,α'-dimethoxy compound (**19**), they all bear at least one OH group (**2**E/Z, **3**, **5**E/Z). Those along the bottom are partial agonists/antagonists most often characterized by high ER binding; all are at least α-hydroxylated, though several possess a second (**8**, **9**Z, **4**) if not a third (**6**) OH group. Other substituents are small, *i.e.* either a methyl (**7**Z, **8**, **9**Z) or methoxy (**10**E) group. Compounds up the right-hand side are either estrogen antagonists that retain the α-OH group in the presence, however, of a bulkier α'-substituent (*e.g.* diethylaminoethoxy, **13**E; isopropyl, **11**E) or are α'-hydroxylated molecules with a small to bulky α-substituent (**7**E, **10**Z, **11**Z, **13**Z) that display increased cytotoxic properties and lower binding affinity. Replacing both the α and α'-OH groups by bulky groups (**14** and **12**) or introducing *meta* diethylaminoethoxy substituents into the α,α'-dihydroxylated-TPE (**18**) leads to total breakaway from the antagonist pole and reinforces the element of cytotoxicity (see along top of Figure 11). The coherence of the results lies in the progressive change in biological properties with gradational structural modifications.

That the adopted methodology is particularly well suited to describing structure–activity relationships was confirmed by the introduction of data on six standard reference compounds into the factorial analysis used as a mathematical model (Figure 11). The location of these reference molecules within the $\Phi_1\Phi_2$ map was totally consistent with their known properties. As expected, E_2 and deacetylated cyclofenil (DAC) were located within the sphere of influence of the RBA/agonism poles. On the other hand, 4-OH-TAM-(E) and 4-OH-TAM-(Z) were characterized by their ability to antagonize E_2-induced proliferation and by their cytotoxicity. TAM-(Z) was also both antiestrogenic and cytotoxic whereas TAM-(E) was principally cytotoxic.

A multifactorial approach should be considered in all cases where systematic biological data have been obtained on a substantial number of molecules. Moreover, testing each molecule on each parameter may prove a useful means of building a model for future studies.

16.3.3.5 Binding to the Progestin Receptor (PR)[283–286]

16.3.3.5.1 *Structural requirements of the ligand and mapping of the hormone-binding site[235,287–289]*

(i) H-bonding at O-3 O-20 and O-17

By analyzing the crystal structures of 3-keto compounds with a wide range of RBAs for PR, it has been possible to delineate a narrow zone, located nearer the C-2 than the C-4 side of the ketone and above the β-face of the steroid, within which all the progestins with affinity for PR are able to form H-bonds.[207]

The hydroxy or lactone groups at C-17 or the ketone at C-21 of steroids with high RBAs for PR probably interact with a common polar zone of PR. The OH group can also interact with polar zones in the AR, MR and/or GR binding sites. The reactive zone of PR that forms a H-bond at O-20 or O-17 can be circumscribed as follows, as cited in ref. 146 (Figure 12). (i) Although the O-20 atom of progesterone (P) and the O-17 atom of norethisterone, that also binds with high affinity to PR, differ by about 1.2 Å, less than 2 kcal are needed for a $-10°$ to $-50°$ variation in the C(16)-C(17)-C(20)-O(20) dihedral angle and consequent rotation of the 17β-acetyl side chain. (ii) The position and orientation of the 17β-oxygen atom of the lactone RU 23521 are very close to those of the OH group of norethisterone but the other atoms within this ring restrict H-bond formation to a limited zone as established for spirooxathiolane derivatives. (iii) The 17β side chain of D-norprogesterone (RBA for PR = 3.3 at 2 h) cannot form the appropriate H-bond. (iv) RU 27987, the (21S)-hydroxy derivative of R 5020, binds appreciably to PR, unlike RU 27988 the (21R) derivative, because its 17β side chain is able to adopt a position on the β-face above ring D toward C-16 compatible with strong H-bonding. (v) 21-(Phenylseleno)progesterone (21-PSP) has appreciable binding affinity for PR compared to 17α-(phenylseleno)progesterone (17-PSP). The C(16)-C(17)-C(20)-O(20) dihedral angle of 21-PSP is $-31°$ and enables effective H-bonding between O-20 and PR, whereas that of 17α-PSP is $+13°$ (on the α-side of ring D). The C-21 region is thus large enough to accommodate a bulky phenylselenium group with relative ease whereas the 17α-position can accommodate an acetate with ease but a selenophenyl or a trimethylsilylethynyl (see below) with difficulty.

The literature claims good progestational activities for a variety of 17-hydroxy-17α-substituted compounds, both in the androstene and in the estrene series and for substituted ethynyl and vinyl side chains including propynyl, butynyl, pentynyl, decynyl, chloroethynyl, trifluoropropynyl, trifluorovinyl, trifluoropropenyl and butadinyl. On the other hand, compounds with hydrophilic 17α-substituents (*e.g.* 17α-hydroxyprogesterone) are known to lack progestational activity and have poor affinity for PR, supporting the notion that the 17α-substituent is accommodated by a hydrophobic zone of PR (see HCA plots).

Whereas the reduction of the keto group in position 20 of P drastically reduces PR binding, this effect can be abolished by acylation. 17α-hydroxyprogesterone acetate binds significantly to PR.[235]

The introduction of a hydroxy group in position 17, 16 or 14α or in position 11 or 6α or 6β is highly detrimental to PR binding.

(ii) Methyl groups

The removal of the angular methyl group at C-10 (*i.e.* 19-norsteroids) increases affinity for PR (and also AR) by elimination of steric hindrance, but it also influences the van der Waals energy

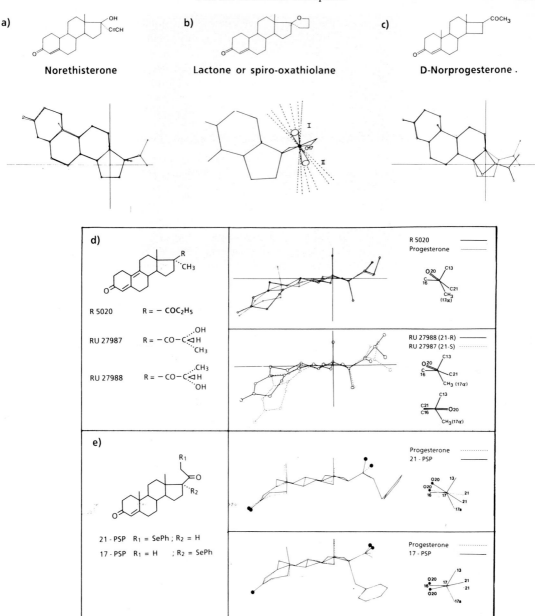

Figure 12 (a) Best-fit superpositions of the crystalline conformations of norethisterone (dark lines) and progesterone (fine lines). (b) Possible H-bond interactions of the O-17 atom of steroids with a C-17 spirooxathiolane or lactone function. (c) Best-fit superposition of the calculated conformation of D-norprogesterone (dark lines) and the observed crystalline conformation of progesterone (fine lines). The crystalline conformation of D-norprogesterone is in good agreement with the calculated conformation (unpublished result). (d) Superposition of R 5020 and progesterone and of the 21-hydroxylated metabolites of R 5020 (RU 27987 = 21-S; RU 27988 = 21-R) using the D-ring as a reference. (e) Best-fit superpositions of progesterone and 21-phenylselenoprogesterone (21-PSP) and of progesterone and 17α-phenylselenoprogesterone (17α-PSP). The Newman projections of the side chain along the C(20)–C(17) bond are shown. The RBAs for rabbit uterus cytosol PR on incubation for 24 h at 0 °C are as follows: Progesterone = 100, R 5020 = 535, RU 27987 = 660, RU 27988 = 10, 21-PSP = 60, 17-PSP = 2[207]

potential of the steroid. $\Delta^{9,11}$-P (R 2061) may have a higher RBA for PR because it is a flatter steroid than P, more suited to a narrow cleft in the receptor and/or because it has a different van der Waals signature (Figure 13).

Several α-methyl-subtituted P derivatives (6α, 7α, 16α) are fair PR ligands but not as effective as P. An 11β-methyl substituent in the 19-nor series is reported to considerably increase progestational activity but lengthening the 11β side chain from methyl to ethyl, propyl or butyl markedly decreases

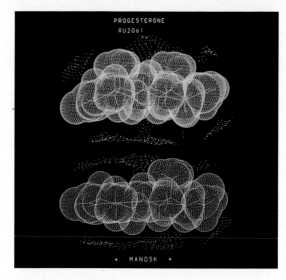

Figure 13 Van der Waals signature (cut-off level = 50%)[290] of P (turquoise) and $\Delta^{9,11}$-P (RU 2061; magenta) shown as dots outside the van der Waals surface.

it. Recent results support these findings: 17α-Propynyldienones with saturated alkyl C-11 substituents competed little for PR binding (Table 3). 16α-ethyl-P was, on the other hand, a fair competitor.

(iii) Steric hindrance and reactivity at C-11 [291-295]

In analogy to the ER probe, 11β-chloromethylestradiol, which dissociates very slowly from ER, 11β-chloronorprogesterone has high affinity for PR suggesting that this zone of the receptor might

Table 3 RBAs[a] of C-11 substituted Steroids for PR (Rabbit Uterus) and GR (Rat Thymus) Binding in a Routine Screening System[146]

R	PR	GR	R	PR	GR	R	PR	GR
H	15	2	H	160	220	OH[b]	5	120
Me	235	60	p-Me	295	295	H	35	50
Et	20	60	m-Me	110	205	C≡CSiMe$_3$	40	105
Pr^n	10	85	Bu^t	50	40	C≡CCH$_2$OH	50	130
Bu^t	1	60	p-OMe	505	300	C≡CCH=CH$_2$[c]	55	80
Cyclopentyl	4	150	m-OMe	15	245	CH$_2$CN	100	ND
2-Furyl	170	280	p-SMe	605	180	Ph	160	180
2-Thienyl	440	300	m-SMe	15	165	CH$_2$C≡CH	165	260
CH=CH$_2$	390	340	p-NMe$_2$	530	300	C≡CPh	250	95
			m-NMe$_2$	5	50	Et	260	95
			p-NHMe	400	295	C≡CCH=CH$_2$	270	165
			p-NH$_2$	40	120	CH=CH$_2$	290	150
			p-F	85	285	CH=C=CH$_2$	305	290
			p-CF$_3$	55	20	C≡CH	350	235
			Ph	280	160	C≡C(CH$_2$)$_2$Me	420	ND
			PhO	180	100	C≡CCl	460	290
			PhC≡C	8	7	C=CMe	530	300
						CH$_2$CH=CH$_2$	840	220

[a] RBAs were determined after incubation for 24 h at 0 °C. PR was labelled with [³H]R 5020, GR with [³H]DX. The RBA of P for PR and DX for GR is set at 100. [b] 17β-ethynyl. [c] 17β-methoxy.

be highly reactive. Thus, although the RBAs of C-11β aliphatic-substituted 17α-propynyl derivatives for PR decreased regularly with the increasing size of the C-11 substituent demonstrating the adverse effect of steric hindrance on binding, unsaturation boosted affinity as demonstrated by changing an ethyl to vinyl, an isopropyl to isopropenyl, or by introducing a phenyl or thienyl (Table 3). The position of this unsaturation is very important since shifting it by one carbon (vinyl→allyl, phenyl→benzyl) practically eliminates affinity. Thus, it would appear that there is either H-bonding between the electron rich unsaturation and PR or a π–π interaction. The increased RBA of *p*-methoxyphenyl and *p*-dimethylamino derivatives and the reduced RBAs of monomethylamino and amino derivatives further support the existence of a direct relation between the electrodonating power of the *para* substituent and the RBA for PR. On the other hand, whereas PR can accommodate unsaturated C-11 substituents up to 12 Å in length (*e.g.* diphenyl (phi–phi) in Figure 14), an *o*-methoxyphenyl group proved to be incompatible with binding, possibly because of a constriction point impeding access to the reactive residue. A *meta* substituent decreased PR binding.

The data in Table 3 confirmed the notion of a hydrophobic pocket within PR located in the close vicinity of the 17α substituent, but achievable hydrophobicity is limited by excessive steric hindrance, as illustrated by the extremely lipophilic but very bulky trimethylsilylethynyl substituent. The propynyl and chloroethynyl groups appear to provide a good compromise between steric hindrance and hydrophobicity.

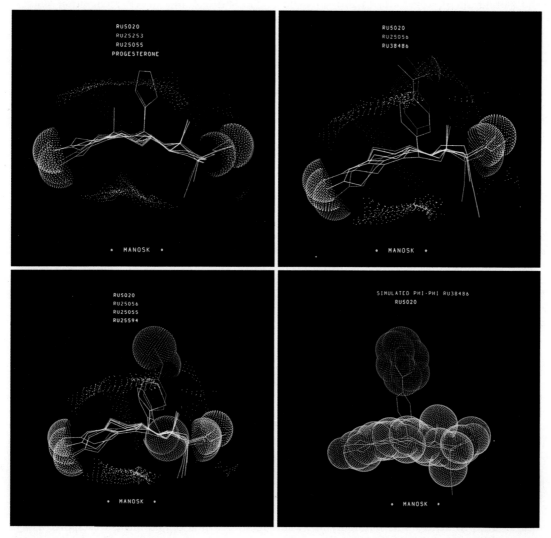

Figure 14 Superpositions by MANOSK of the crystal structures of P, R 5020, RU 24850 (R = vinyl), RU 25055 (R = 2-thienyl), RU 25056 and RU 25594 (R = *p*- and *o*-methoxyphenyl, respectively), RU 38486 (R = dimethylamino-Φ), phi-phi (R = Φ–Φ; constructed)[146]

The 11β and 17α pockets may be continuous. The steroid binding site in PR could be formed by two hydrophobic clefts: a smaller one containing the steroid backbone, about 11 Å in length, limited at either end by a H-bonding zone (with O-3 and O-17 or O-20), and a larger one of at least 20 Å, extending above and below the plane of the steroid. The planes of the two grooves are roughly perpendicular, forming an X-shaped hydrophobic site that might tightly lock the steroid in place.

(iv) Binding specificities

Most of the above C-11-substituted compounds also compete appreciably for binding to GR (Table 3). This is true of many progestins[296] and will be discussed below in Section 16.3.3.7.3 on GR. The most well-known cross specificity is that between binding to PR and AR since 17α-ethynyl-19-nortestosterone derivatives are highly potent progestins and derivatives of 17α-acetoxyproges-terone (17α-AP) are used as antiandrogens.[297] To illustrate this interference, the RBAs of a series of progestins in current clinical use are given in Table 4. Although pregnane derivatives can recognize AR as witnessed by the significant RBAs at very short incubation times, the complexes formed generally dissociate relatively rapidly. This decrease is associated with antiandrogenic activity. On the other hand, the AR complexes formed by androstanes are much more stable and are suspected to be at the origin of their androgenic activity.[236]

17α-AP and T have different functional groups in C-17 but analogous conformations. The 6-chloro-1α,2α-methylene derivative of 17α-AP is cyproterone acetate (CPA), the most frequently used steroid antiandrogen. Its 1α,2α-methylene bridge is deleterious to AR recognition since its removal to give chlormadinone acetate slightly increased AR binding at the short incubation time. Replacement of the chlorine by a methyl (megestrol acetate) slightly decreased AR binding whereas further removal of the Δ^6 double bond (MPA) modified binding kinetics. The RBA of MPA for AR did not decrease but increased with incubation time indicating a stronger association with AR than in the case of the other tested 17α-AP derivatives and explaining the known androgenic activity of this compound. The crystal structure of MPA shows that steric interaction by the 17α-acetate substituent virtually immobilizes the 17β side chain and introduces strain into the backbone that is transmitted to the A-ring. This long range influence together with the strain introduced by the 6α-methyl group results in an inverted A-ring conformation.[298]

16.3.3.5.2 Probes for PR

Since PR is far more labile than ER, its detection remained elusive until the early 1970s, when the addition of stabilizing reagents such as glycerol to the *in vitro* incubation medium or the use of synthetic radioligands such as tritiated R 5020 (promegestone) facilitated its study.[299] Tritiated R 5020 is the PR probe in by far the most widespread use[217–219] followed by tritiated Org 2058[300] marketed several years later. It has become a standard laboratory reagent but should be superseded by its active (21S)-hydroxy metabolite, RU 27987, which does not have the disadvantage of high nonspecific binding is assays on nuclei.[220] If the SHR is primarily nuclear (see Section 16.3.2.1.1), this would be a decisive improvement.

(i) RU 27987, an improved PR probe[220]

RU 27987 has greater affinity for PR than R 5020 and is a biologically more potent progestin. It associates with cytosolic PR at the same rate as R 5020, as would be expected if association rate reflects interaction of the 3-keto-Δ^4 A-ring with a recognition site, but the complex formed has a much slower dissociation rate (*e.g.* $t_{1/2}$ for RU 27987, R 5020 and P respectively: 18 h, 13 h and 1 h in rabbit uterus cytosol) which could be explained by the presence of the 21-OH group and an overall favorable orientation of the 17β side chain (Figure 12). This hydroxylated side chain has virtually no untoward influence on receptor binding specificity. Moreover, binding of RU 27987 to hCBG is $\approx 1\%$ of that of P and similar to that of R 5020, whereas its binding to human serum albumin is weaker.

The stable PR binding, high specificity, and low plasma binding of [³H]R 27987 prompted successful experiments on its suitability as a radioligand for cytosol and nuclear exchange assays. Nuclear PR were assayed in human tissues where the presence of a PR, in the absence of any demonstrable ER (binding to ER induces PR), was long considered enigmatical, *i.e.* in meningioma, a common benign brain tumor whose incidence is seemingly linked to hormonal status,[301,302] and

Table 4 RBAs[a] of Progestins for PR (Rabbit Uterus) and AR (Rat Prostate) Cytosol Binding in a Routine Screening System[314]

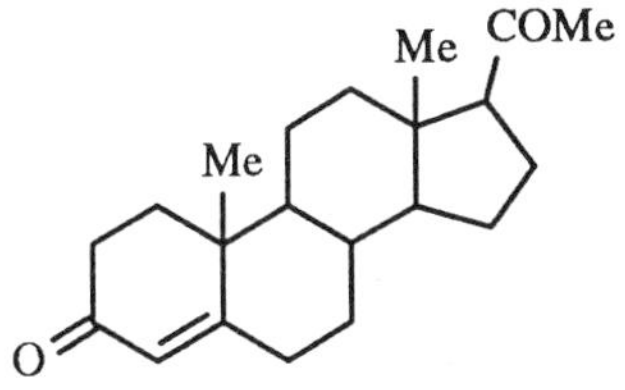

Progesterone

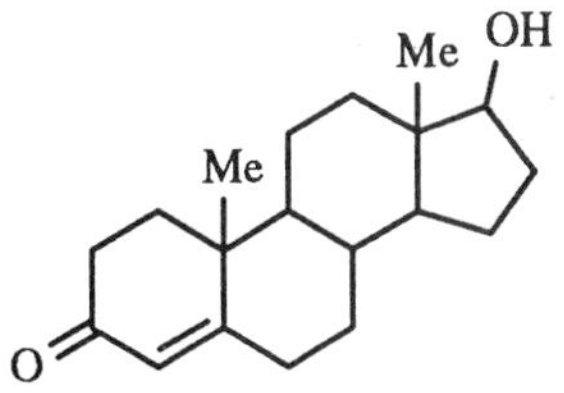

Testosterone

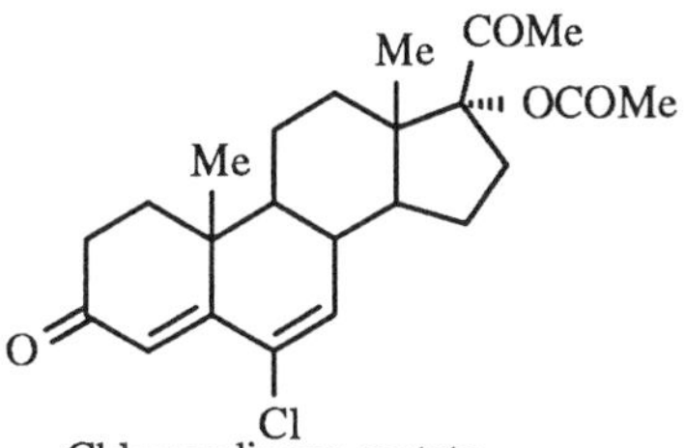

Chlormadinone acetate

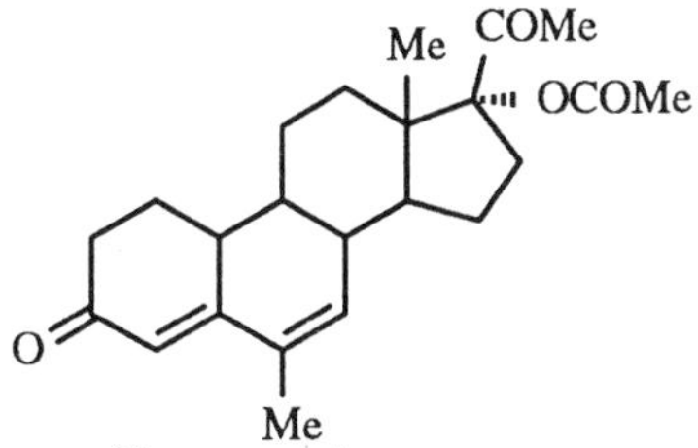

Nomegestrol acetate

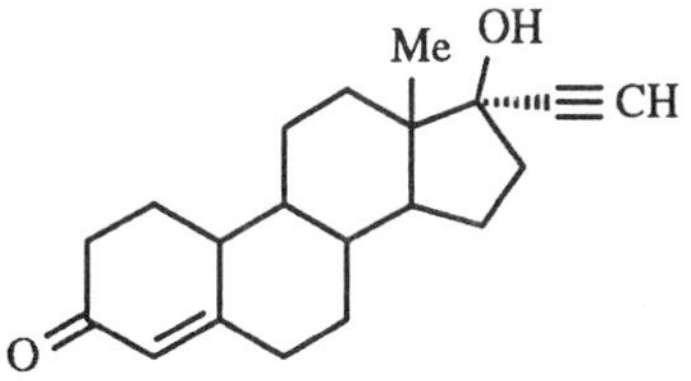

Norethisterone

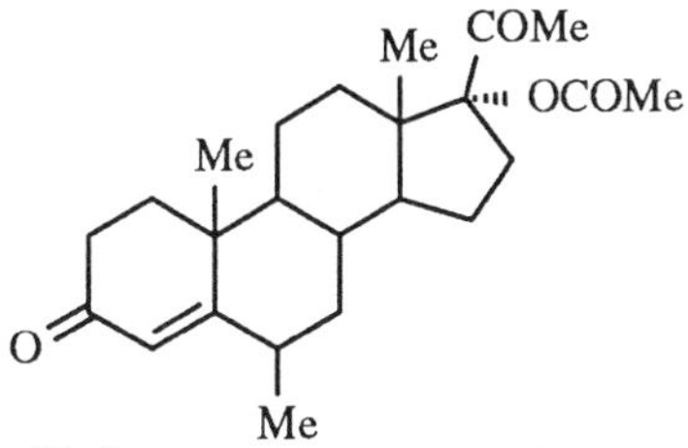

Medroxyprogesterone acetate

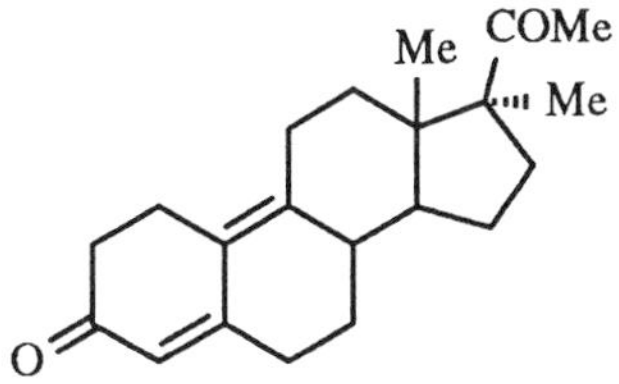

Demegestone

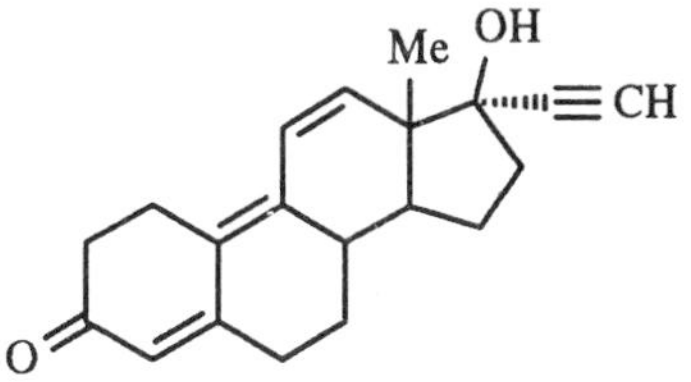

Norgestrienone

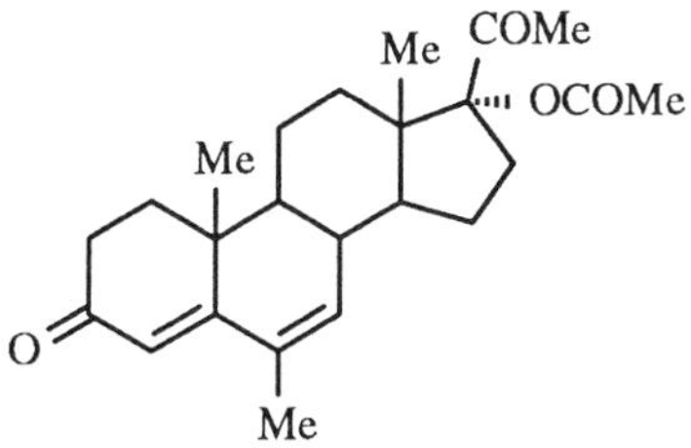

Megestrol acetate

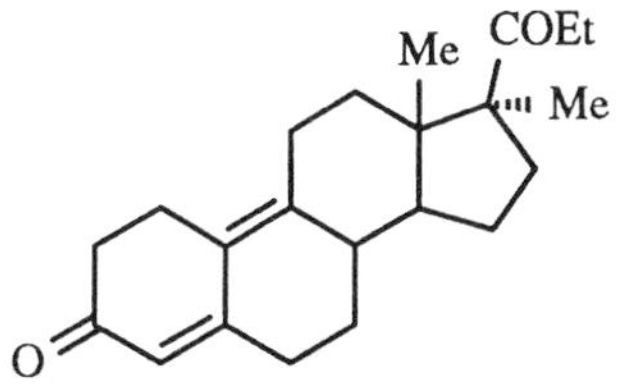

Promegestone

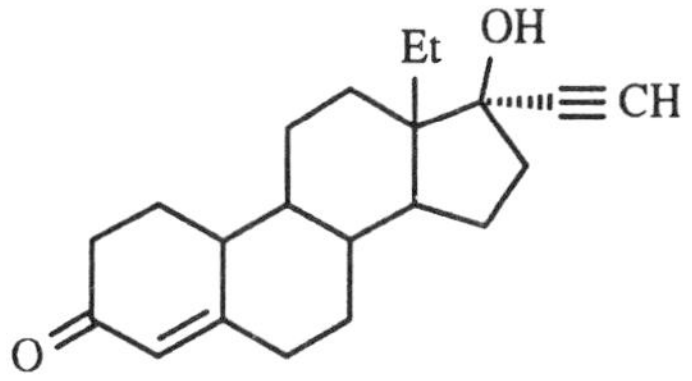

Norgestrel

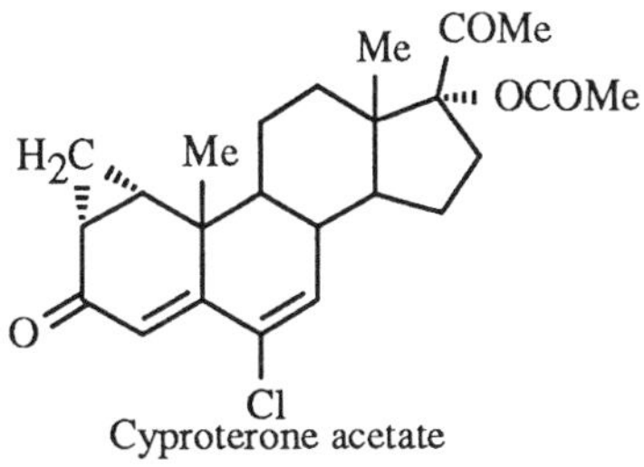

Cyproterone acetate

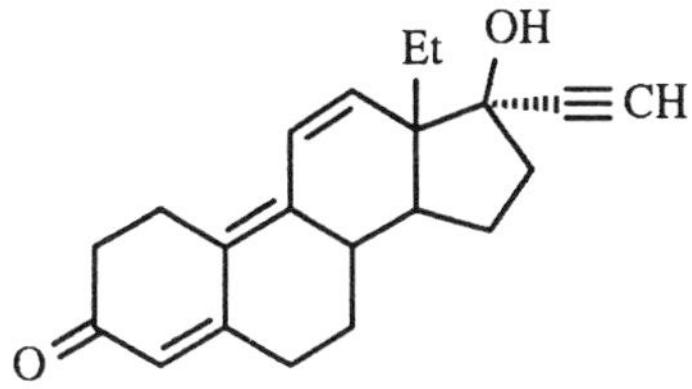

Gestrinone

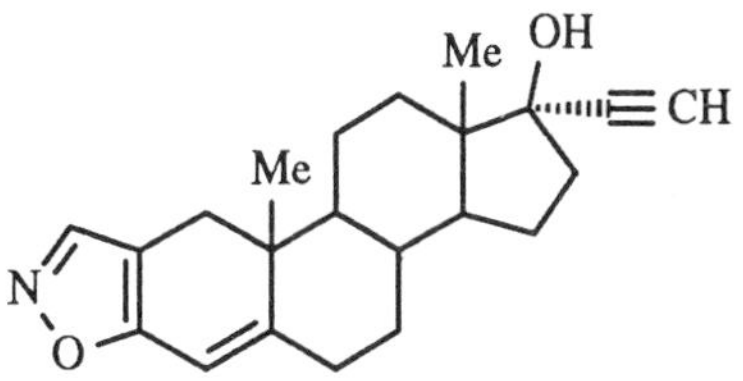

Danazol

	PR		AR	
	2 h, 0 °C	*24 h, 0 °C*	*30 min, 0 °C*	*2 h, 0 °C*
Pregnanes				
Progesterone	100	100	20	5.5
Chlormadinone acetate	175	320	80	20
Medroxyprogesterone acetate	125	305	40	50
Megestrol acetate	150	120	65	20
Cyproterone acetate	80	60	50	15
Nomegestrol acetate	170	450	20	1
Demegestone	230	420	7.5	1
Promegestone (R 5020)	220	535	10	1.5

Table 4 *(Contd.)*

	PR		AR	
	2 h, 0 °C	*24 h, 0 °C*	*30 min, 0 °C*	*2 h, 0 °C*
Androstanes				
Norethisterone	155	265	75	45
Norgestrienone	65	45	95	70
Norgestrel	170	905	110	85
Gestrinone	75	50	95	85
Danazol	9	3	35	8
Testosterone	1	1	100	100

[a] Pr was labelled with [³H]R 5020, AR with [³H]R 1881.

in benign hypertrophic human prostate (BPH), a highly prevalent if not universal disorder in elderly men.[303]

(ii) Covalent labelling of PR

Covalent linkage with the affinity labels 11α- and 16α-(bromoacetoxy)progesterone has been reported to alkylate respectively the 1- and 3-positions of a His residue of PR that would be situated near the steroid C-ring. The 16α-label also alkylates a Met residue near the D-ring.[304]

However, affinity alkylating reagents react only with nucleophilic amino acids and, in certain instances, it is preferable to activate bound ligands *in situ*. Covalent linkage of radioactive ligand to the SHR can be achieved by ultraviolet radiation ($\geq$ 300 nm for 2–5 min), a procedure frequently used for photoaffinity labelling of SHRs in intact cells prior to analysis by gel electrophoresis. Photoaffinity labelling with the high affinity, selective reagent [³H]R 5020 has become a standard procedure for the analysis of PR hormone-binding subunits[305–307] but [³H]RU 27987 is gaining favor.[308] In general, two hormone-binding subunits migrating at $\approx$ 95 kDA and $\approx$ 120 kDA are identified in reducing gels. The method has also earmarked Met 759 and 909 as amino acids located within the hPR steroid-binding site.[193]

The visualization of PR necessitates a fluorescent ligand and the most recent, RU 45196, takes once again advantage of the C-11 substituent.[309] The fluorophore nitrobenzoxadiazole (NBD) was attached to this substituent. RU 45196 has 22% of the affinity of R 5020. Since the receptor steroid-binding site is appreciably hydrophobic, it was hoped that the NBD fluorophore would fluoresce when receptor bound. This did not prove to be the case suggesting that either the fluorophore is exposed to the aqueous environment (it extends outside the binding site) or that it is in a lipophilic environment (up the chimney in Figure 4) where some specific fluorescent quenching mechanism is operative.

16.3.3.5.3 *PR ligands as tools to study molecular mechanisms*

Tritiated R 5020 has proved to be a particularly powerful tool for the detection of steroid-binding units of PR in different species and for the study of subcellular receptor dynamics. Briefly, it would seem that hPR exists as two hormone-binding proteins, A (94 kDa) and B (a triplet of 114, 117 and 120 kDA), that share considerable homology and that may be present in equimolar concentrations[284,305] or not.[307] A would not be a proteolytic fragment of B but rather a truncated form of the receptor with 165 amino acids of the N-terminal missing.[74,284] This difference could be explained by translation from two initiation sites 165 bases apart.[87,310,311] Studies with monoclonal antibodies to A and B have shown that they do not dimerize but each subunit forms homodimers capable of tight nuclear binding. The untransformed human B receptors copurify with nonhormone-binding proteins of 90 kDa and 72 kDa. The 72 kDa protein also copurifies with transformed 4S-B receptors[312] and, like the GR-associated 72 kDa protein[4] and the 90 kDa protein, might be a HSP. However, whereas transformation would result in dissociation of 90 kDa protein, transformed 4S receptors which bind tightly to DNA may be heterodimers composed of one steroid-binding protein and the 72 kDa protein. Both subunits undergo rapid covalent modifications consistent with increased phosphorylation uniquely on Ser residues. The B subunit would be synthesized as a 114 kDa subunit which upon relatively slow post-translational phosphorylation yields the mature

B triplets.[313] Prolongation of progestin treatment results in termination of nuclear receptor action and simultaneous disappearance of both proteins from the cell (they do not reappear in the cytoplasm). This process is termed 'down regulation' or 'nuclear processing'. Progestin treatment thus down regulates PR whereas estrogen treatment induces PR.

16.3.3.5.4 *Drug design: progesterone agonists and antagonists*

(i) *Choosing a progestin*

Progestins have a wide variety of indications and it is essential to choose the most appropriate product for each indication.[314] They are most often selected not only for their progestational activity but also for their antiestrogenic potency and presence or lack of androgenic activity. Antiestrogenic activity is needed to oppose the effects of continuous estrogen impregnation on the endometrium as in women with luteal insufficiency or receiving estrogen therapy. Androgenic activity is associated with pituitary inhibition which is an essential aspect of ovulation suppression (contraception) and of endometrial regression (hyperplasia, endometriosis). On the other hand, antiandrogenic activity is sought in the treatment of acne, hirsutism, benign prostate hyperplasia (BPH), prostate cancer *etc.*

Our receptor screening system is particularly useful in determining the kinetics of the binding of progestins to PR, thereby giving an indication of the likely progestational response, and in establishing the presence of secondary binding activities, *i.e.* binding to AR, MR or GR, thereby helping to better delimit the therapeutical relevance of each progestin[236–238] This has been illustrated for AR binding in Table 4 from which it is not surprising to note that, due account being taken of differences in metabolism,[231] nomegestrol acetate, demegestone and promegestone are favored for luteal insufficiency, norethisterone, norgestrienone and norgestrel for contraception, gestrinone and danazol for endometriosis, and cyproterone acetate for prostate cancer therapy.

The implication of the GR binding of progestins[237,238,296] (not shown) should not be neglected since GR are abundant in brain structures such as the hippocampus and hypothalamus where high PR levels favor progestin uptake. Any antiglucocorticoid activity of progestins due to GR binding is liable to be associated with behavioral effects. P itself has sedative properties and its influence, and that of its metabolites and analogs, on the psychological disorders associated with hormonal disturbances deserves further study.

The antiestrogenic activity of progestins, although grossly correlated to their PR binding,[315] cannot easily be deduced from a routine screening system since progestins do not compete for ER binding. One of the most potent antiestrogenic progestins with no androgenic activity is promegestone (R 5020).[316]

(ii) *Antiprogestins*

The conformationally mobile $\Delta^{4,9,11}$-triene gestrinone (R 2323) was one of the first compounds to be considered an antiprogestin. It has very weak progestin activity and demonstrable antiprogesterone activity in a variety of animal tests. This antihormonal activity would appear to be the result of a variety of actions arising from the compound's overall lack of specificity,[317] *i.e.* equivalently weak and even unstable interactions with PR and AR.[318] Its antiprogesterone activity was first the basis of its development as a contraceptive agent using two novel administration schedules, on the one hand, once weekly oral administration and, on the other, midcycle (days 15, 16, 17) administration based on an arbitrary dating of the ovulatory peak. Despite the relatively low, but nevertheless unacceptable, pregnancy rates (Pearl index $\approx 5\%$), the development of the compound as a contraceptive was forsaken but successfully pursued in other indications such as endometriosis[318,319] and treatment of leiomyomas.[320]

The complexity of endocrine regulation poses the following dilemma: is it wiser to develop drugs with a broad specificity and multiple points of impact, where the resultant dominant activity is successfully exploited and where the secondary actions play a useful role in maintaining homeostasis or is it wiser to seek highly specific drugs with a single molecular impact in the hope of controlling both specificity and intensity of response but with the risk of having to face, in the course of this search, one or more major unwanted side effects? We leave this important but rather philosophical point to your reflection. It is only mentioned here because, whereas gestrinone is derived from the former approach, the other more recent and much publicized antiprogestin RU 38486 is claimed to be a product of the latter. RU 38486 (see Table 3) is a potent antiprogestin that binds to PR, but also highly appreciably to GR. The elimination of this GR-binding component has been the aim of efforts from several industrial quarters but has met with limited success so far.[294,295]

The history of the chemical synthesis, biochemical testing[228,293] and subsequent development of RU 38486 as an abortifacient[321] in association with a prostaglandin[322] has already been retraced and will not be detailed here.

16.3.3.6 Binding to the Androgen Receptor (AR)[323-325]

16.3.3.6.1 *Structural requirements of the AR ligand and mapping of the AR hormone-binding site*

Figure 15 shows the results obtained for the binding of androgens and structurally related analogs to AR, PR and GR.[326] RBAs are indicated by the number of slashes according to the scale given in the bottom left-hand corner of the figure. This representation highlights the specificity of SHR binding.

(i) Functional groups

The natural hormones T and 5α-DHT compete virtually exclusively for binding to AR, 5α-DHT being the more powerful competitor (RBA = 120). The need for a 17β-hydroxy-3-one structure for effective binding to AR is illustrated by the dramatic decreases in RBAs recorded for androstanediols, androstenediols, androstanedione and 5α-androstan-3-one.

The 5α-configuration (5α-DHT) which enhances AR binding of T, decreases PR (100→35) and also AR (5.5→0.4) binding of P. The K_D of A-nor-DHT for AR is increased about 7-fold compared to that of 5α-DHT. Bridging of the 2/3 carbons by a pyrazol or isoxazol group reduces but does not eliminate affinity.

The mean conformation of T is close to that of P but, whereas the —COCH$_3$ group of P can act as a H-bond acceptor only, the 17β-OH of T could act as a donor and/or acceptor. T, however, hardly competes for binding to PR. Nevertheless, binding can be considerably enhanced just by removing the C-10-methyl and introducing $\Delta^{9,11}$ double bonds (RU 2341) to increase flexibility and modify charge distribution. X-Ray crystal data show that ring A of 19-nor-T is subject to 'flip–flap' interconversion from a normal to inverted 1β,2α-half-chair conformation, an interconversion made easier by the loss of the C-10-methyl which reduces the energy difference between these conformations from 11.3 to 4.2 kJ mol^{-1}. The addition of a 9(10) double bond to a 4-en-3-one system also causes A-ring inversion but the further addition of an 11(12) bond tends to promote a restabilization of the normal A-ring conformation.

(ii) Methylation

The introduction of a 17α-methyl substituent into T or 5α-DHT somewhat decreases AR binding (from 120 to 106 for 5α-DHT) and also introduces a slight PR-binding component which is reinforced by eliminating the C-10-methyl (RU 575) and returning to a 4-ene structure (RU 598). The combination of 17α-methyl substitution and unsaturation leads to compounds (RU 598→RU 1881) with high affinity for both AR and PR in the rank order triene > monoene > diene. Like RU 2999 and other analogs with conjugated double bonds extending from rings A and B to C, the highly potent androgen methyltrienolone (RU 1881) is a very flat but also very flexible molecule that can undergo large variations in molecular curvature and torsion resulting from inversion of the A-ring. This behavior could explain its lack of specificity (see also Section 16.3.2.2.6). Removal of the 3-keto group results in a compound (RU 3773) which lacks binding affinity (RBA ≈ 0.5) in confirmation of the hypothesis that the first interaction is between the A-ring of the steroid and a recognition site on the SHR.

Substituting rings A and B of RU 1881 with methyl groups (RU 2922 → RU 2420) showed that a β-methyl at C-2 (RU 2922) decreases binding to AR and PR, a gem-dimethyl even more so (RU 2956). A C-4-methyl (RU 4089) also decreases binding to PR and AR but not to the same extent as a C-2-methyl. A gem-dimethyl at C-6 (RU 4743) decreases PR and GR binding much more markedly than AR binding. 6α-Methyl-P has been reported to bind appreciably to AR. On the other hand, a 7α-methyl (RU 2420) maintains the AR binding and potentiates the PR binding.

Analogous effects are obtained on methylation of 19-nor-T and RU 1881 probably because, even though the A-ring of $\Delta^{4,9,11}$-trienes preferentially adopts a normal half-chair conformation, the

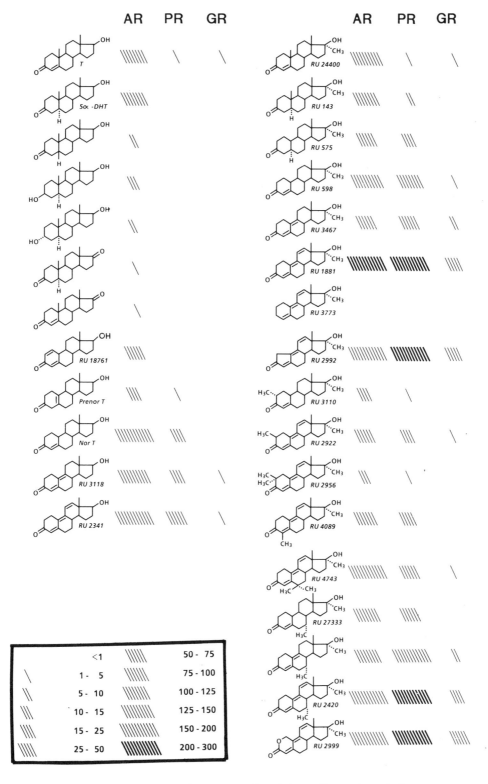

Figure 15 RBAs, measured in a routine screening system and graded according to the scale shown, were measured on cytosol (estrogen-primed immature rabbit uterus for PR, rat prostate for AR, and rat liver for GR) after incubation for 2 h at 0 °C. [³H]R 5020, [³H]R 1881 and [³H]DX were used as radioligands. The RBAs of P, T and DX were set at 100

19-nor-T A-ring can undergo interconversion between the normal and inverted forms. A methyl in C-2α (RU 3110) decreases the binding of 19-nor-T to AR and PR. A 7α-methyl decreases AR binding fractionally and increases PR binding. The specificity of 7α,17α-dimethyl-19-nor-T (mibolerone; not shown) has little to distinguish it from that of RU 1881 as regards binding to AR (RBA = 150 and 175 at 30 min, respectively) and PR (RBA = 80 at 2 h, for both compounds). However, it competes less than RU 1881 for GR. According to the literature, a β-configuration of a C-7-methyl decreases the androgenic potency of 5α-DHT.

1α-Methyl-DHT has been reported to have only about 50% of the affinity of 5α-DHT and 1β-methyl-DHT about 15%, but particularly interesting has been the observation that the introduction of a C-1α- as opposed to a C-1β-methyl into A-nor-(5α)-androstane increases the affinity and also the stability of the AR complex compared to the unsubstituted compound. Equally interesting are the observations that affinity for AR can be maintained, even when the distance between the C-3-keto and the C-17-hydroxy groups is drastically reduced from 10.9 Å (T) to 8.9 Å (des-A-derivatives).[327] The shortening of the skeleton decreases the stability of the interaction as witnessed by the fall in RBAs on increasing incubation time. Here again flexibility and flatness induced by conjugated double bonds through rings B and C enhances binding. In this series, a C-10-methyl group either in the plane of the molecule in the presence of a Δ^9 double bond or equatorial in its absence, that could be considered to mimic the 1-methylene of T, was essential for a significant interaction with AR. However, lengthening the side chain in this position to an ethyl or propyl markedly decreased affinity.

(iii) Heteroatoms

The high affinity of RU 1881 for PR, AR and GR, due to favorable van der Waals forces and unsaturation, can be even further enhanced by the introduction of heteroatom within the A-ring (2-oxa) which possesses the ability to form strong directional bonds (see RU 2999).

(iv) Nonsteroid analogs

A wide variety of nonsteroid compounds[328] have been reported to inhibit AR binding usually weakly and not necessarily in a competitive manner: the antiulcer agent cimetidine which is an imidazole derivative, the antifungal Z-Andron, the pure antiandrogens flutamide[329,330] nilutamide (anandron; RU 23908)[331-333] and ICI 176,334[334,335] the chlorinated hydrocarbon insecticides, dieldrin and o,p′-DDT, the s-triazine herbicides, atrazine and prometryne. More than 80 small polycyclic hydrocarbons have been tested for binding affinity for rat prostate AR.[336] Dihydro- and octahydro-phenanthrene in particular were able to compete for labelled RU 1881 binding and to inhibit the retention of the AR complex by nuclei during incubation of minced prostate with radioactive androgen.

16.3.3.6.2   Probes for AR

Two synthetic tritiated probes for AR are available commercially, methyltrienolone (RU 1881)[337] and mibolerone[338] but neither meets the criteria of an ideal probe because of lack of binding specificity. In current practice, binding to PR and GR is selectively blocked by adding a large excess of triamcinolone acetonide to the incubation medium.[339,340] To our knowledge, no AR specific probe has yet been designed.

Dihydrotestosterone 17β-bromoacetate has been used to covalently label AR[341] but the majority of studies have been performed with RU 1881, in spite of its suspected but unconfirmed photolability.[342] Covalent labelling by photoactivation of [³H]RU 1881 has been used to characterize AR in several partially purified tissue preparations of *in situ*: rat prostate, calf uterus, human prostate adenocarcinomas (PC-82, LNCAP), human cultured genital fibroblasts.[343,344] In general, under denaturing conditions, photolabelling identifies two proteins of molecular mass ≈50 kDa and ≈100 kDa. Apart from enabling comparisons of AR in different tissues and species, these studies are useful in analyzing AR abnormalities in patients with partial or complete androgen insensitivity or with cancer.[345,346]

It should be kept in mind, however, that a synthetic androgen may recognize precursor or degraded forms of receptor that do not bind the natural ligand or even high affinity binding sites that may be different from AR (*e.g.* the methyltrienolone binding site in placenta).[347]

16.3.3.6.3 AR ligands as tools to study molecular mechanisms

We have described a homologous series of diversely substituted ER ligands in order to illustrate how apparently minor modifications in chemical structure can differentially influence binding and biological responses, whether these are presumed to be mediated by ER (growth) or not (cytotoxicity; see Section 16.3.3.4.4ii). The type of multifactorial analysis used has, moreover, emphasized how systematic screening results can provide valuable information on the relationships between the responses (Section 16.3.3.4.3). We have very briefly described how a highly active progestin (R 5020) has furthered our understanding of PR (Section 16.3.3.5.3). We shall now attempt to analyze whether screening results on nonsteroid ligands that apparently compete for steroid binding to SHRs may not sometimes be misleading.

Many of the biological responses of nonsteroids (even inhibitory responses) cannot readily be related to interference with steroid binding sites on SHRs. Simple competition studies do not indicate whether a competitor actually displaces the radioactive label (which often may not even be the endogenous hormone) by usurping its seat or by a phenomenon of allostery. Moreover, binding studies are performed under artificial *in vitro* conditions where the exact relevance of each component in maintaining an 'active' protein conformation is not known (DTT, EDTA, glycerol, sucrose, PMSF, cytosol proteins). Does the ligand interfere with one of these 'cofactors' and/or with other sites on SHRs? Can multiple molecular targets be identified for the nonsteroid ligand and, if so, what are the similarities in the interaction of the ligand with these targets? What do we learn about the analogies in the 'active sites' of these proteins? Needless to say, this type of research, which is still in a very preliminary stage, could help to explain some of the side effects of established drugs.

The example we have chosen is the nonsteroid antiandrogen anandron (5,5-dimethyl-3-[4-nitro-3-(trifluoromethyl)phenyl]-2,4-imidazolidinedione) that interacts fleetingly with AR but with no other SHR in spite of the cross specificity among SHRs that bind 3-keto-Δ^4-steroids.[331] Anandron is a shorter molecule (8.4 Å) than T (10.8 Å), closer in length to the des-A steroids (8.9 Å) mentioned above that also interact with AR. According to its van der Waals surface and signature, it could easily enter and occupy an androgen specific pocket (Figure 16). Superposition with T and a des-A steroid shows how it might substitute for the endogenous hormone within the binding site. It is assumed that one of the oxygens of the NO_2 group of anandron would substitute for the C-3 ketone of the des-A steroid in which case the neighboring CF_3 would occupy the position of the 1α-methylene. This is because among the identified anandron metabolites, only the NO_2 and not the reduced (NH or NH_2) derivatives could compete, even minimally, for binding to AR.[326] However, since anandron has no demonstrable androgenic activity but is a potent antiandrogen, it may not interact with the same residues within this pocket as the endogenous hormone or its influence on the steroid-binding site may be indirect by interference with another site on AR.

The classical receptor concept, which postulates that the receptor sites that bind agonists and those that bind competitive antagonists of these agonists have a topographical identity, excludes those antagonists that act as acceptors or donors of electrons and, thus, disrupt the normal pathway for electron transport and interfere with oxidoreduction processes in biochemical systems. Such compounds may act as uncouples in oxidative phosphorylation. Similarly, it excludes those compounds that may serve as acceptors of phosphate groups. Anandron may fall into one of these categories.

Initially, anandron was selected for further study on the basis not of its ability to compete for AR binding, which was only discovered subsequently, but to inhibit radiolabelled T uptake by rat prostate.[348] In the uptake test, its dichloro analog had analogous inhibitory activity. A Cl atom has approximately the same steric hindrance as a CF_3 and, like a CF_3 or NO_2 group, is an electron attractor. Anandron could be considered a dipolar agent formed by condensation of two reagents, hydantion and trifluoromethylnitrophenol, whose action may lead to loss of ATP- and SHR-binding capacity by analogy with compounds such as 2,4-dinitrophenol.[349]

Anandron competes for hormone binding to AR only. It does not compete for binding to other SHRs, to the hormone carrier SBP nor to tissue protein ABP. The HBD of hAR has only 18% sequence homology with hER but 50–55% homology with the other SHRs. Anandron does, however, have other molecular targets: it modifies 5α-reductase activity in human prostate microsomes (although it is not a competitive inhibitor of this activity; P. M. Martin, personal communication); inhibits 17α-hydroxylase and 17,20-lyase activities in rat testicular microsomes;[350] and competes competitively for hexobarbital hydroxylase and, in a more complex manner, with benzophetamine *N*-demethylase.[351] Preliminary experiments indicate that it might interact with the active site on cytochrome *P*-450. In a limited number of cases, anandron administration to patients

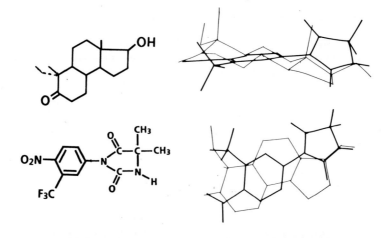

Figure 16 Superposition of anandron, testosterone, and des-A steroids. Top: best-fit superpositions of anandron with 1α-methyl-des-A steroids. Atomic coordinates were calculated by the program SCRIPT. Bottom: van der Waals surfaces and signatures of anandron (yellow) and testosterone (blue)[326]

is associated with specific side effects: visual disturbances, alcohol intolerance, and reversible interstitial pneumonitis. Various proteins, *e.g.* retinol-binding protein and alcohol dehydrogenase, could be implicated in these effects. An expert comparison of the sequences and of the HCA plots of proteins implicated in anandron binding and action is helping to identify the compound's active site(s).

16.3.3.6.4 *Drug design: androgen agonists and antagonists*

(i) *Anabolic agents*[352]

Boosting muscle whether for consumption or 'athletic' performance without engendering sex-related effects[353] has been a challenge that the chemist has found hard to meet since both anabolic and androgenic effects result from interaction with AR, albeit in different tissues. AR is either saturated or down-regulated when plasma androgen levels are in the normal range.[354] Orally or parenterally administered T or 5α-DHT are promptly degraded but the rate of oral catabolism can be decreased by alkylation with a 17α-methyl or 17α-ethyl, a feature that is common to most orally active androgens, whereas esterification of the 17α-hydroxy group and solubilization in lipid facilitate parenteral administration. The longer the ester carbon chain, the slower the release and the more prolonged the action, *e.g.* up to three weeks for testosterone enanthate. Enhance anabolic activity has been achieved by modifying the steroid ring structure: removal of the C-19-methyl, introduction of conjugated double bonds (*e.g.* trenbolone, RU 2341), methylation at C-1 or C-7).

Most anabolic compounds have been developed to treat hypogonadal men and elderly patients, *i.e.* individuals with a recognized deficiency, but the belief that they enhance strength in the healthy man has been at the origin of a long-standing malpractice in many professional and amateur sports, whether in the senior or even junior categories. As evidence of their potential toxic effects became increasingly apparent, they were put on the list of banned substances prior to the 1976 Olympic Games.[355]

In the normal man, AR is saturated with hormone and, to be effective, exogenous substances have to be administered in pharmacological doses. The taking of different compounds simultaneously, the so-called 'stacked pyramid', is a common feature of hormone abuse.[356] However, it is still an open question whether these agents do actually enhance athletic performance. Most published studies are not double-blind and, when they are, the code is too often illusory because of side effects. Moreover, not only is motivation a factor virtually impossible to control, but bettering of performance in a top class league is extremely difficult to assess. In an overview of several trials,[357] Wilson concluded that neither enhancement of weight nor improvement in strength can be demonstrated consistenly when androgens are administered double-blind to athletes.

To achieve an anabolic effect when AR is near saturated requires another mechanism as, for instance, a change in the nitrogen balance. Several androgens can compete for GR binding. Thus, at pharmacological doses, anabolic agents may act as glucocorticoid antagonists decreasing protein degradation rather than increasing protein synthesis. Finally, a part of the weight gain may be due to an increase in blood volume.[358]

(ii) Antiandrogens

Emphasis over the last decade has been placed on the design of nonsteroid antagonists that, unlike CPA and related drugs, are devoid of agonist activity and hormonal side effects and that act solely *via* AR (Table 5). These drugs are intended for the *systemic* treatment of diseases such as BPH and prostate cancer. However, because of the deregulation of the hypothalamo–pituitary–gonad axis they provoke which after a while induces a compensatory increase in LH and T, they are coadministered with a pituitary inhibitor preferably an LHRH analog, in order to sustain and enhance the antiandrogenic action on the prostate.[359] Thus, in the treatment of stage D prostate cancer, anandron is administered to surgically or medically castrated patients to counter the action on the prostate of any residual T, of adrenal androgens, and of the temporary LH and T increase on inception of LHRH analog treatment.[360] The combination therapy, whether with anandron or flutamide, has so far met with a significant degree of success.[361-366] The development of a peripherally active antiandrogen with less central effects (ICI 176,334) is still in its early stages.[335]

For *topical* application in the treatment of acne, hirsutism and male pattern baldness, the emphasis is still on steroid derivatives (for reviews see refs. 367 and 368). Spironolactone and CPA remain the mainstays of the oral treatment of most of these disorders but topical forms of spironolactone, 17α-propylmesteronolone and the des-A steroid RU 38882[369] are under development. Nevertheless, in spite of high activity in animal models, results in the clinic often remain disappointing.

16.3.3.7 Binding to the Glucocorticoid and Mineralocorticoid Receptors (GR and MR)[81,370-373]

16.3.3.7.1 Structural requirements of the ligands and mapping of the hormone-binding sites

We have so far noted the high selectivity of ER ligands and shown that there can be a considerable degree of overlap between PR and AR binding. In this section, we shall emphasize the well-known interference between GR and MR binding, but also the GR binding component of progestins and antiprogestins which, with the synthesis of new analogs, became a focal point of interest in the early 1980s.

For detailed specificity profiles of a large number of well-known glucocorticoids the reader is referred to two previous reviews.[235,242] Here we stress the design of compounds that bind solely to GR (Table 6). Whereas the natural hormones, cortisol and corticosterone, compete appreciably for MR and GR binding in peripheral tissues, as do the well-known synthetic glucocorticoids

Table 5 Some Antiandrogens Reputed to Interact with AR and that have been Investigated or used in the Clinic

Compound	Activity	Proposed indications
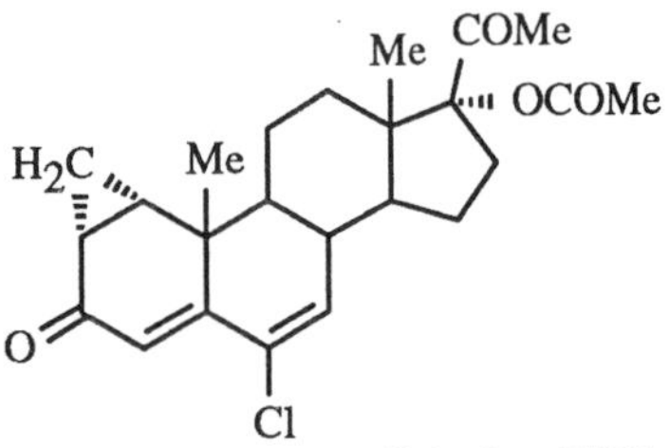 Cyproterone acetate (Schering, FRG)	Progestin Antiandrogen	Acne Hypersexuality Prostate cancer
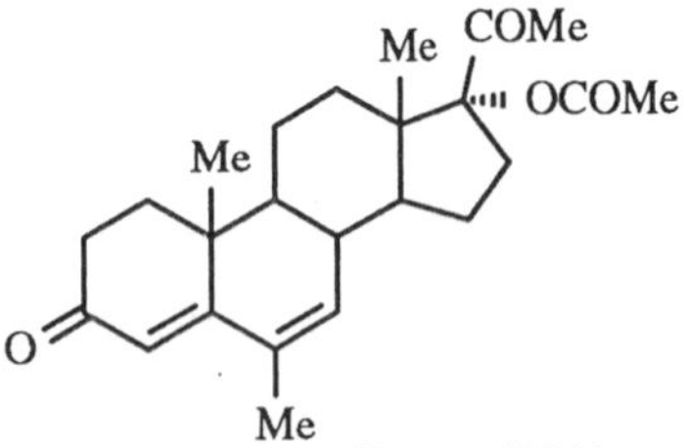 Megestrol acetate (Syntex, USA)	Progestin Antiandrogen	Prostate cancer
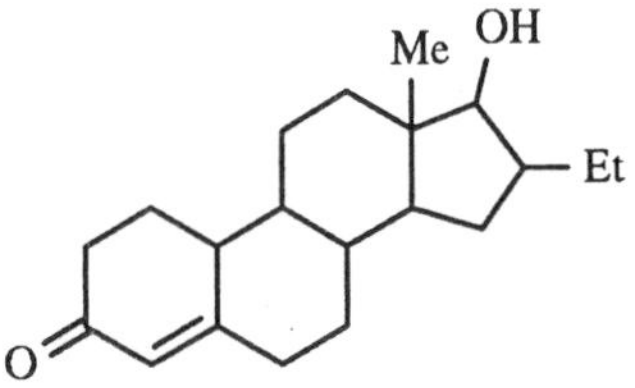 Oxendolone (Takeda, Japan) TSAA-291	Antiandrogen	Benign prostatic hypertrophy
Lipido-steroid complex extracted from the plant *Serenoa repens* Permixon (Pierre Fabre, F)	Antiandrogen	Benign prostatic hypertrophy
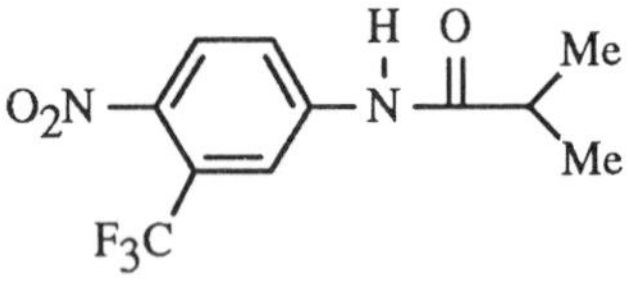 Flutamide (Schering-Plough, USA)	Tested as bactericide Antiandrogen	Prostate cancer
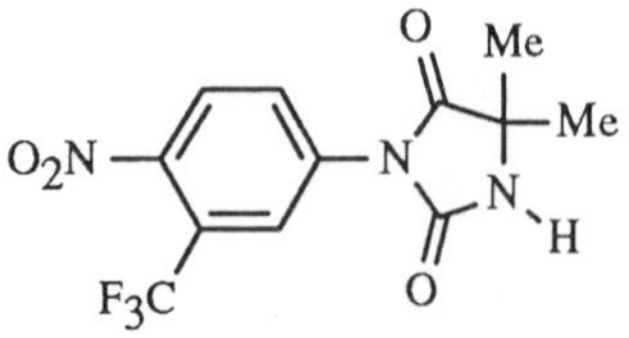 Anandron (Roussel-Uclaf, F)	Selected amongst herbicides Antiandrogen	Prostate cancer in association with castration
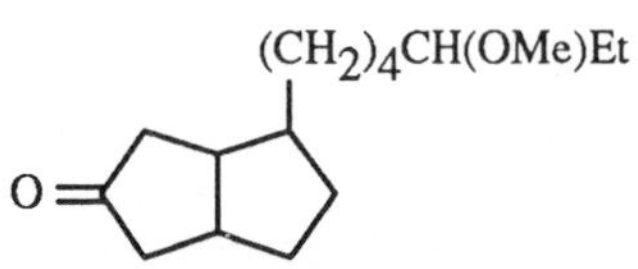 X-Andron (Chantal Labs, USA)	Antifungal Antiandrogen	Prostate cancer Male pattern baldness Keloid scarring

Table 5. *(Contd.)*

Compound	Activity	Proposed indications
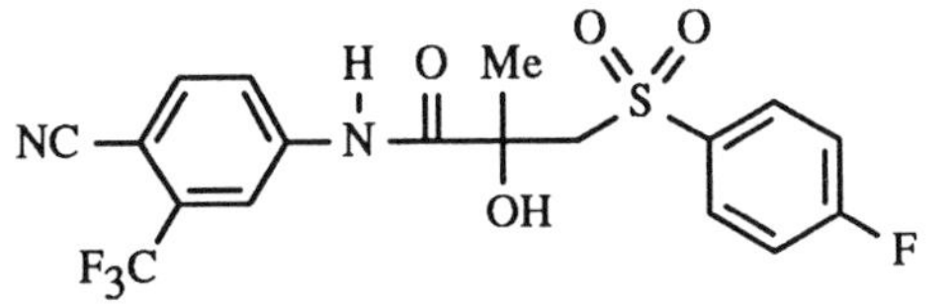 ICI 176,334 (ICI, UK)	Antiandrogen	Androgen-responsive benign and malignant diseases
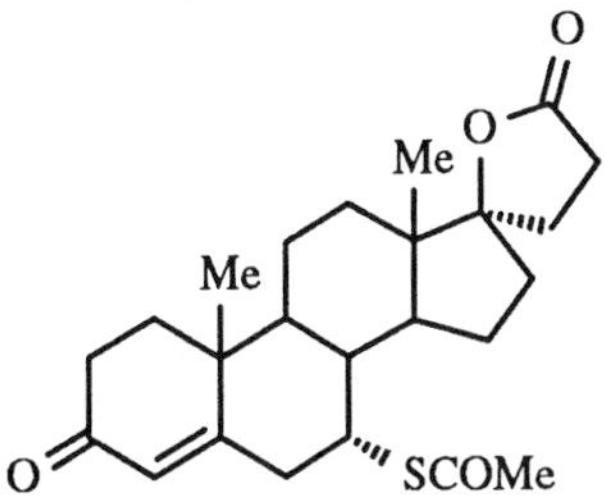 Spironolactone (Searle, USA; Schiapparelli, I)	Aldosterone antagonist Antiandrogen	Acne
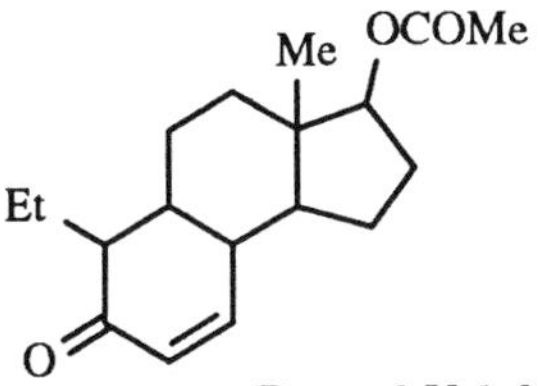 Inocoterone acetate (Roussel-Uclaf, F) RU 38882	Antiandrogen	Acne Hirsutism
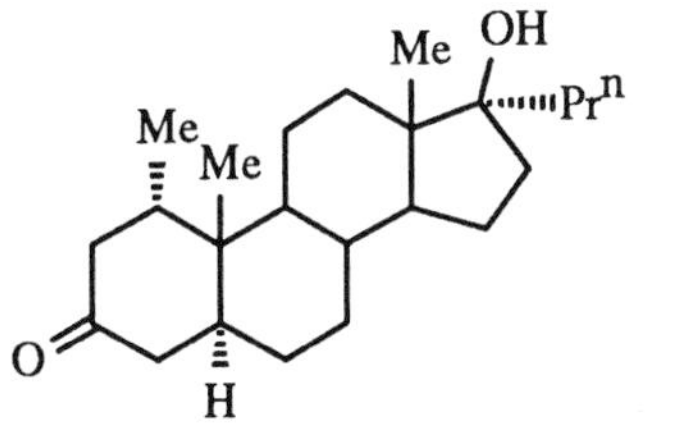 17α-Propylmesterione (Schering, FRG) SH-434	Antiandrogen	Acne

[a] The above list is not exhaustive and in particular does not include all progestins that have been used as antiandrogens. The compounds may also act *via* routes other than AR.

Table 6 RBAs[a] of Glucocorticoids at 0 °C for Cytosol Receptors in a Routine Screening System

Compound	ER 2 h	PR 24 h	AR 2 h	MR 1 h	MR 24 h	GR 2 h	GR 24 h
Cortisol	< 0.1	< 0.1	< 0.1	55	20	30	15
Corticosterone	< 0.1	3	0.5	50	20	65	20
Dexamethasone	< 0.1	< 0.1	< 0.1	135	20	100	100
Triamcinolone acetonide	< 0.1	12	< 0.1	105	8	140	175
RU 26988	< 0.1	0.15	< 0.1	1.5	< 0.1	125	65
RU 28362	< 0.1	1	0.1	0.5	< 0.1	260	240
Aldosterone	< 0.1	0.7	< 0.1	100	100	50	7.5

[a] ER (mouse uterus), PR (rabbit uterus), AR (rat prostate), MR (rate kidney), GR (rat thymus). The receptors were labelled with [³H]E₂, [³H]R 5020, [³H]R 1881, [³H]aldosterone and [³H]DX respectively. The RBAs of E₂, P and T for their respective receptors were set at 100.

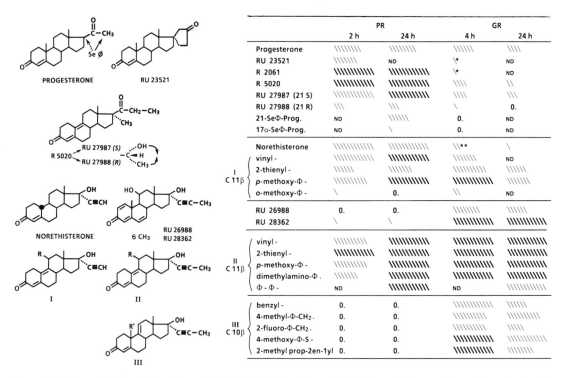

		PR		GR	
		2 h	24 h	4 h	24 h
Progesterone		\\\\\\	\\\\\\	\\\\\	\\\\
RU 23521		\\\\\\	ND	*	ND
R 2061		\\\\\\\\\	\\\\\\\\\	*	ND
R 5020		\\\\\\\\\	\\\\\\\\\	\\\\	\\
RU 27987 (21 S)		\\\\\\\\\	\\\\\\\\\	\\\\	\\\
RU 27988 (21 R)		\\\	\\\	\	0.
21-SeΦ-Prog.		ND	\\\\\\	0.	ND
17α-SeΦ-Prog.		ND	\	0.	ND
Norethisterone		\\\\\\\\\	\\\\\\\\\	**	\
vinyl -		\\\\\\\\\	\\\\\\\\\	\\\\\	ND
2-thienyl -	I C 11β	\\\\\	\\\\\	\\\\\\\\	\\\\\
p-methoxy-Φ -		\\\\\\\\\	\\\\\\\\\	\\\\\\\\\	\\\\\\
o-methoxy-Φ -		\	0.	\\	ND
RU 26988		0.	0.	\\\\\\\	\\\\\\
RU 28362		\	\	\\\\\\\\\	\\\\\\\\\
vinyl -		\\\\\\\	\\\\\\\\\	\\\\\\\\\	\\\\\\\\\
2-thienyl -		\\\\\\\\\	\\\\\\\\\	\\\\\\\\\	\\\\\\\\\
p-methoxy-Φ -	II C 11β	\\\\\\\	\\\\\\\\\	\\\\\\\\\	\\\\\\\\\
dimethylamino-Φ .		\\\\\\	\\\\\\\\\	\\\\\\\\\	\\\\\\\\\
Φ - Φ -		ND	\\\\\\\\\	ND	\\\\\\\\\
benzyl -		0.	0.	\\\\\\\	\\\\\
4-methyl-Φ-CH₂ -		0.	0.	\\\\\\\	\\\\\\
2-fluoro-Φ-CH₂ -	III C 10β	0.	0.	\\\\\\\	\\\\
4-methoxy-Φ-S -		0.	0.	\\\\\\\\	\\\\\\\
2-methyl prop-2en-1yl		0.	0.	\\\\\\\\\	\\\\\\

Figure 17 Rationale of synthesis of certain C-11,17-disubstituted steroids. RBAs, graded according to the scale given in Figure 15, were measured on cytosol from rabbit uterus for PR and rat thymus (*liver) for GR after incubation of test compound at 0 °C (** < 4 h) with either [³H]R 5020 or [³H]DX.[146] The RBAs of progesterone and dexamethasone were set at 100. Increases in RBA over time reflect slow dissociation kinetics, decreases fast dissociation kinetics (ND = not determined)

dexamethasone (DX) and triamcinolone acetonide (TA), both RU 26988 and RU 28362 (the 6β-methyl derivative of RU 26988) compete negligibly for MR. In these compounds, the characteristic C-17 dihydroxyacetone side chain of natural corticosteroids has been replaced by a 17α-alkynyl-17β-hydroxy moiety.[374] The higher and more stable RBA values of RU 28362 for GR indicate that its affinity is greater than that of RU 26988 possibly because of the intermolecular van der Waals interaction energy afforded by the appropriately located 6-methyl group (-3 kcal mol^{-1}). The X-ray crystal structures of RU 26988 and RU 28362, when determined, should provide valuable information on the ligand conformation most suited to stable and biologically pertinent GR binding.

Rather surprisingly, the introduction of C-11 substituents into compounds with a 17α-alkynyl-17β-hydroxy moiety generated marked PR binding without loss of GR binding (Table 3 and Figure 17). An analysis of the data in Table 3 has suggested that the shapes of the hydrophobic pockets close to the steroid are quite different in PR and GR.[291,292] GR has a much wider opening than PR which will not accept a substituent with a diameter larger than the thickness of a phenyl ring (3.4 Å). This wider opening probably explains why C-10-methylsteroids have greater affinity for GR than 19-norsteroids. On the other hand, affinity for PR is increased by elimination of an out-of-pocket methyl.

A strategy was thus successfully developed to synthesize compounds that form highly specific and stable complexes with GR and that do not interact with PR by introducing long C-10 substituents (Figure 17).

16.3.3.7.2 Probes for GR and MR

Of all the SHRs, GR has probably been the subject of the most intensive study and of the most ardent efforts to map the steroid-binding site. This is partly because of the early availability of high affinity, even covalent, ligands such as cortivazol[375,376] and DX-mesylate.[377,378] As described in Section 16.3.2.2.5vii, covalent and photoaffinity labelling of GR have led to the identification of Cys and Met residues within the steroid-binding site.[192,193]

It is often necessary to measure GR in tissues that contain endogenous hormone (corticosterone or cortisol), that are obtained after pretreatment of animals or after glucocorticoid therapy of patients, that may contain high amounts of MR (*e.g.* kidney, hippocampus) and/or that may be contaminated with plasma binding proteins. Under these circumstances, the natural glucocorticoid hormones, corticosterone and cortisol, offer many disadvantages as probes, *i.e.* a high level of binding to CBG, *in vitro* degradation especially in tissues such as the liver, rapid dissociation from GR, binding to SHRs other than GR. To palliate these disadvantages, the use of synthetic radioligands such as [³H]DX and [³H]TA has been widespread, but they lack specificity. For this reason, they are liable to be quickly superseded by more specific GR ligands such as [³H]RU 26988 or [³H]RU 28382 for exchange assays, photoaffinity labelling *etc.*[379,380] Experiments confirming the suitability of [³H]RU 28362 as a GR probe have been described in detail.[220]

Many studies also seek to study MR sites independently of GR. The GR binding component of [³H]aldosterone remained a major handicap until it was proposed to add an excess of a specific glucocorticoid such as RU 26988 or RU 28382 to the medium to neutralize GR binding.[381]

The endogenous hormone aldosterone binds to two types of sites, 'mineralocorticoid-like' Type I sites, for which deoxycorticosterone and corticosterone are high affinity competitors, and Type II sites that are competable by DX.[382] In order to draw a strict distinction between these sites and their associated biological responses,[383] it was necessary to dispose of a probe that was specific to one type of site only. RU 26988 and RU 28362 are specific to Type II sites. Their use has thus enabled discrimination between GR and MR sites in many cell lines and tissues including the pituitary, hypothalamus and hippocampus, glioma cells, thymus, spleen, mononuclear lymphocytes, heart, colon, ileum, kidney, liver, spinal cord, epididymis and mammary glands.[384-391] The biological relevance of these sites remains more difficult to apprehend in view of tissue and species differences, binding to CBG and different circulating concentrations of the natural hormones. Not all these tissues are considered physiological target tissues of mineralocorticoids and it has been suggested that the absence of response, in spite of the high levels of circulating cortisol and corticosterone that can bind to Type I sites, may be due to the presence in certain tissues of 11β-hydroxysteroid dehydrogenase that converts these hormones but not aldosterone to 11-keto analogs that do not bind MR.[392]

16.3.3.7.3 *GR ligands as tools to study molecular mechanisms*

Just as the progestin ligand R 5020 is enabling the study of the steroid binding units of PR and their cellular dynamics (see Section 16.3.3.5.3), RU 28362 is enabling the study of GR functions. The glucocorticoid response of constructs in two different cell lines T47D and XC, has been studied with RU 28362 since DX does not induce MMTV LTR transcription in T47D cells *via* its own receptor. It has thus been possible to distinguish between the contribution of cell specific factors and GR to the hormone response at the MMTV LTR promoter.[393,394] Indirectly, specific GR probes have also facilitated the study of MR. For instance, aldosterone binding to Type I sites in mouse brain has been studied in the presence of the chaotropic anion thiocyanate that is often added to *in vitro* systems to measure SHR binding, whether ER or AR. Thiocyanate induces SHR transformation to a DNA-binding state from which aldosterone dissociates more slowly.[395] This transformed SHR has a higher apparent positive charge and surface hydrophobicity, but a decreased sedimentation coefficient (9.6S→4.7S), Stokes radius (8.0 nm→6.1 nm), and apparent molecular mass (331 kDa→120 kDa). It has been suggested that this transformation is initiated by the dissociation of two molecules of HSP from each steroid/DNA-binding Type I receptor subunit.[395]

However, paradoxically, it is the unspecific C-11-substituted steroids (and in particular the antisteroid RU 38486), described in Section 16.3.3.5.1, which bind with high affinity to both GR and PR, that have been frequently used to pursue the study of GR. RU 38486 stabilizes the hetero-oligomeric form of GR[396,397] but neither promotes GR transformation nor prevents GR inactivation.[398] Research with RU 38486 has been pursued along two main lines: on the one hand, a majority of studies have used RU 38486 to support the notion that the phenomenon observed is glucocorticoid dependent just because it is blocked by RU 38486 and regardless of the mechanism by which such an inhibition is achieved. Most frequently, this has led to the assumption that it is SHR mediated. Although this may be true, such evidence is not sufficient to presume that the interference occurs at the level of the steroid-binding site nor can it discount any interaction of RU 38486 with macromolecules immunologically distinct from SHR. On the other hand, the use of such an unspecific high affinity ligand has furthered the study of the overlap between binding to SHRs. Initially, the measurement of GR binding of several progestins under two sets of incubation conditions in our screening system had established that progestins dissociate rapidly from GR.[296] It was hypothesized that, if their binding to GR is biologically relevant, rapid dissociation kinetics could contribute towards some of the known antiglucocorticoid activities of progestins. These same progestins were also found to accelerate the dissociation of [³H]DX from GR by interacting with a hydrophobic and apparently nonglucocorticoid-binding site with predominantly progestin specificity.[399-401] In contrast, RU 38486 did not increase the dissociation of [³H]DX in spite of its PR binding component.[402] The interdependence between these observations is intriguing. Does progestin bind to two totally different sites on GR or to a partially common site from which it dissociates rapidly and from which it accelerated the dissociation of DX? Does one have to revise the notion of a one-to-one stoichiometry between steroid and SHR? HCA plots have indeed suggested that the SHR could accommodate a steroid at two different yet virtually interconnecting sites (see Section 16.3.2.2.5vii).

16.3.3.7.4 Drug design: glucocorticoid agonists and antagonists

The specificity profiles of powerful marketed glucocorticoids has shown that they all possess a mineralocorticoid component which, in the clinic, leads to undesirable effects on hydric retention. There is therefore a need for highly specific glucocorticoids. Highly powerful glucocorticoids (*e.g.* cortivazol) are also required in the treatment of life-threatening diseases such as leukemia. However, the fashion over the last decade has been to design antihormones to block hormonal responses and antiglucocorticoids are no exception.[403] But, why design an antiglucocorticoid if glucocorticoids are essential to maintain life? The question is not as flippant as it may seem. Apart from the treatment of conditions of flagrant corticoid excess such as Cushing's syndrome[404,405] and associated hypertension[406] with due attention being given to the risk of adrenal insufficiency,[407] other indications can be envisaged in view of the known effects of glucocorticoids on the immune system,[408,409] on stress,[410] on the induction of tissue repair agents, *e.g.* fibronectin, glycosaminoglycans[411-413] on catabolic/antianabolic activity[414,415] *etc.* Particularly interesting is the recent observation that an antiglucocorticoid might reverse the sometimes fatal exacerbation of herpes simplex virus replication in patients undergoing immunosuppressive therapy for organ transplants or cancer treatment.[416]

16.3.4 REFERENCES

1. A. I. Coffer and R. J. B. King, *J. Steroid Biochem.*, 1988, **31**, 745.
2. B. N. Diaz-Chico, Y. Ogasawara, G. C. Chamness, M. Salman and W. L. McGuire, *J. Steroid Biochem.*, 1988, **30**, 315.
3. P. K. K. Tai, Y. Maeda, K. Nakao, N. G. Wakim, J. L. Duhring and L. E. Faber, *Biochemistry*, 1986, **25**, 5269.
4. J. Å. Gustafsson, J. Carlstedt-Duke, Ö. Wrange, S. Okret and A. C. Wikström, *J. Steroid Biochem.*, 1986, **24**, 63.
5. I. Joab, C. Radanyi, M. Renoir, T. Buchou, M. G. Catelli, N. Binart, J. Mester and E. E. Baulieu, *Nature (London)*, 1984, **308**, 850.
6. E. R. Sanchez, D. O. Toft, M. J. Schlesinger and W. B. Pratt, *J. Biol. Chem.*, 1985, **260**, 12 398.
7. B. J. Danzo, *J. Steroid Biochem.*, 1986, **25**, 511.
8. F. Logeat, M. Le Cunff, M. Rauch, S. Brailly and E. Milgrom, *Eur. J. Biochem.*, 1987, **170**, 51.
9. C. C. Lerea, C. M. Klinge, R. A. Bambara, S. Zain and R. Hilf, *Endocrinology*, 1987, **121**, 1146.
10. E. R. Clark, D. Mackay and S. P. Robinson, *J. Steroid Biochem.*, 1988, **29**, 375.
11. G. Shyamala, R. K. Singh, M. F. Ruh and T. S. Ruh, *Endocrinology*, 1986, **119**, 819.
12. R. A. Hiipakka and S. Liao, *Am. J. Clin. Oncol.*, 1988, **11**, (suppl. 2), 18.
13. M. Ali and W. V. Vedeckis, *Science (Washington, D.C.)*, 1987, **235**, 467.
14. A. L. Unger, R. Uppaluri, S. Ahern, J. L. Colby and J. L. Tymoczko, *Mol. Endocrinol.*, 1988, **2**, 952.
15. V. K. Moudgil and D. O. Toft, *Biochim. Biophys. Acta*, 1977, **490**, 477.
16. V. K. Moudgil, in 'Molecular Mechanisms of Steroid Hormone Action', ed. V. K. Moudgil, Gruyter, Berlin, 1985, p. 351.
17. B. Ofenloch-Hähnle and K. Eisele, *Biochemistry*, 1988, **27**, 8592.
18. E. M. Wilson, *J. Biol. Chem.*, 1985, **260**, 8683.
19. C. Benassayag, G. Vallette, J. Hassid, J. P. Raymond and E. A. Nunez, *Endocrinology*, 1986, **118**, 1.
20. P. J. Weatherill and P. A. Bell, *J. Steroid Biochem.*, 1987, **26**, 463.
21. N. Mitsuhashi, M. Mizuno, A. Miyagawa and J. Kato, *J. Endocrinol. Jpn.*, 1988, **35**, 131.
22. A. M. Traish, D. F. Williams and H. H. Wotiz, *Steroids*, 1989, **53**, 169.
23. S. A. Kumar, T. Beach and H. W. Dickerman, *Biochem. Biophys. Res. Commun.*, 1978, **84**, 631.
24. M. Sundaralingam and Y. C. Sekharudu, *Science (Washington, D.C.)*, 1989, **244**, 1333.
25. M. Sluyser (ed.), 'Interaction of Steroid Hormone Receptors with DNA', Horwood, Chichester, 1985.
26. M. Beato, G. Chalepakis, M. Schauer and E. P. Slater, *J. Steroid Biochem.*, 1989, **32**, 737.
27. P. J. Mitchell and R. Tjian, *Science (Washington, D.C.)*, 1989, **245**, 371.
28. M. R. Sherman, F. B. Tuazon, S. C. Diaz and L. K. Miller, *Biochemistry*, 1976, **15**, 980.
29. M. R. Sherman and J. Stevens, *Annu. Rev. Physiol.*, 1984, **46**, 83.

30. W. T. Schrader and B. M. O'Malley, *J. Biol. Chem.*, 1972, **247**, 51.
31. W. T. Schrader, M. Birnbaumer, M. Hughes, N. L. Weigel, W. W. Grody and B. W. O'Malley, *Recent Prog. Horm. Res.*, 1981, **37**, 583.
32. B. M. Weichman and A. C. Notides, *Biochemistry*, 1979, **18**, 220.
33. A. C. Notides, N. Lerner and D. E. Hamilton, *Proc. Natl. Acad. Sci. USA*, 1981, **78**, 4926.
34. C. R. Clark (ed.), 'Steroid Hormone Receptors. Their Intracellular Localisation', Horwood, Chichester, 1987.
35. P. J. Sheridan, K. Blum and P. M. Martin, in 'Steroid Receptors and Disease. Cancer, Autoimmune, Bone and Circulatory Disorders', ed. P. J. Sheridan, K. Blum and M. C. Trachtenberg, Dekker, New York, 1988, p. 49.
36. W. J. King and G. L. Greene, *Nature (London)*, 1984, **307**, 745.
37. W. V. Welshons, W. E. Lieberman and J. Gorski, *Nature (London)*, 1984, **307**, 747.
38. P. B. Becker, B. Gloss, W. Schmid, U. Strähle and G. Schütz, *Nature (London)*, 1986, **324**, 686.
39. T. Willmann and M. Beato, *Nature (London)*, 1986, **324**, 688.
40. M. Schauer, G. Chalepakis, T. Willmann and M. Beato, *Proc. Natl. Acad. Sci. USA*, 1989, **86**, 1123.
41. M. Denis, L. Poellinger, A. C. Wikström and J. Å. Gustafsson, *Nature (London)*, 1988, **333**, 686.
42. M. K. Bagchi, J. F. Elliston, S. Y. Tsai, D. P. Edwards, M. J. Tsai and B. W. O'Malley, *Mol. Endocrinol.*, 1988, **2**, 1221.
43. R. Rodriguez, M. A. Carson, N. L. Weigel, B. W. O'Malley and W. T. Schrader, *Mol. Endocrinol.*, 1989, **3**, 356.
44. D. P. Edwards, B. Kühnel, P. A. Estes and S. K. Nordeen, *Mol. Endocrinol.*, 1989, **3**, 381.
45. L. B. Hendry, *J. Steroid Biochem.*, 1988, **31**, 493.
46. M. R. Walters, in 'Steroid Receptors and Disease. Cancer, Autoimmune, Bone, and Circulatory Disorders', ed. P. J. Sheridan, K. Blum and M. C. Trachtenberg, Dekker, New York, 1988, p. 71.
47. M. Perrot-Applanat, M. T. Groyer-Picart, F. Logeat and E. Milgrom, *J. Cell. Biol.*, 1986, **102**, 1191.
48. T. G. Muldoon, G. H. Watson, A. C. Evans, Jr. and J. Steinsapir, *J. Steroid Biochem.*, 1988, **30**, 23.
49. P. Tuohimaa, A. Niemelä and T. Ylikomi, *J. Steroid Biochem.*, 1988, **30**, 329.
50. C. M. Szego, *Life Sci.*, 1984, **35**, 2381.
51. D. Bression, M. Michard, M. Le Dafniet, M. Pagesy and F. Peillon, *Endocrinology*, 1986, **119**, 1048.
52. Y. Berthois, N. Pourreau-Schneider, P. Gandilhon, H. Mittre, N. Tubiana and P. M. Martin, *J. Steroid Biochem.*, 1986, **25**, 963.
53. J. Kato, A. Takano, N. Mitsuhashi, N. Koike, K. Yoshida and S. Hirata, *J. Steroid Biochem.*, 1987, **27**, 641.
54. A. Náray-Fejes-Tóth, B. Rosenkrantz, J. C. Fröhlich and G. Fejes-Tóth, *J. Steroid Biochem.*, 1988, **30**, 155.
55. C. M. Bergamini, F. Pansini, S. Bettocchi, Jr., V. Segala, F. Dallocchio, B. Bagni and G. Mollica, *J. Steroid Biochem.*, 1985, **22**, 299.
56. P. L. Mellon and I. E. Akerblom, in 'The Steroid/Thyroid Hormone Receptor Family and Gene Regulation', ed. J. Carlstedt-Duke, H. Eriksson and J. Å. Gustafsson, Birkhäuser, Basel, 1989, p. 207.
57. R. B. Dickson and M. E. Lippman, *Endocr. Rev.*, 1987, **8**, 29.
58. G. Wilding, M. E. Lippman and R. B. Dickson, *Prog. Clin. Biol. Res.*, 1988, **262**, 181.
59. A. M. Soto and C. Sonnenschein, *Endocr. Rev.*, 1987, **8**, 44.
60. P. Davies, C. L. Eaton, T. D. France and M. E. A. Philips, *Am. J. Clin. Oncol.*, 1988, **11** (suppl. 2), 1.
61. C. A. O'Brian, R. M. Liskamp, D. H. Solomon and I. B. Weinstein, *Cancer Res.*, 1985, **45**, 2462.
62. E. Bignon, K. Ogita, A. Kishimoto, J. Gilbert, J. Abecassis, J.F. Miquel and Y. Nishizuka, *Biochem. Biophys. Res. Commun.*, 1989, **163**, 1377.
63. D. M. Boyle and A. van der Walt, *J. Steroid Biochem.*, 1988, **30**, 239.
64. C. G. van Bohemen and G. G. Rousseau, *FEBS Lett.*, 1982, **143**, 21.
65. A. Miglaccio, S. Lastoria, B. Moncharmont, A. Rotondi and F. Auricchio, *Biochem. Biophys. Res. Commun.*, 1982, **109**, 1002.
66. H. Y. P. Lam, *Biochem. Biophys. Res. Commun.*, 1984, **118**, 27.
67. J. C. Hansen, W. V. Welshons and J. Gorski, in 'Steroid Receptors and Disease. Cancer, Autoimmune, Bone, and Circulatory Disorders', ed. P. J. Sheridan, K. Blum and M. C. Trachtenberg, Dekker, New York, 1988, p. 3.
68. H. C. Potgieter, T. Klein, F. Magagane, N. Savage and J. L. Wittliff, *J. Steroid Biochem.*, 1986, **25**, 951.
69. J. Meader, T. T. Ilenchuk and M. R. Walters, *J. Steroid Biochem.*, 1988, **30**, 245.
70. M. N. Alexis, M. Baki, C. Elefterrou and C. E. Sekeris, *J. Steroid Biochem.*, 1988, **30**, 225.
71. M. E. Baker and W. R. Kimlinger, *Biochem. Biophys. Res. Commun.*, 1982, **108**, 1067.
72. S. Ganesan, N. Bashirelahi, J. D. Young and S. P. Cohen, *Life Sci.*, 1987, **41**, 2767.
73. G. L. Greene, C. Nolan, J. P. Engler and E. V. Jensen, *Proc. Natl. Acad. Sci. USA*, 1980, **77**, 5115.
74. G. L. Greene, K. Harris, R. Bova, R. Kinders, B. Moore and C. Nolan, *Mol. Endocrinol.*, 1988, **2**, 714.
75. S. Okret, J. Carlstedt-Duke, Ö. Wrange, K. Carlström and J. Å. Gustafsson, *Biochim. Biophys. Acta*, 1981, **677**, 205.
76. E. Milgrom, *Pharmacol. Ther.*, 1985, **28**, 389.
77. M. T. Vu Hai, A. Jolivet, V. Ravet, F. Lorenzo, M. Perrot-Applanat, M. Citerne and E. Milgrom, *Biochem. J.*, 1989, **260**, 371.
78. G. L. Greene, *Mol. Endocrinol.*, 1986, **2**, 714.
79. K. S. McCarty, Jr., B. J. Ferguson, E. Segreti, L. B. Kinsel, J. L. Flowers, J. Konrath, G. S. Leight, G. L. Greene and K. S. McCarty, Sr., in 'Progress in Cancer Research and Therapy, Hormones and Cancer 3', ed. F. Bresciani, R. J. B. King, M. E. Lippman and J. P. Raynaud, Raven Press, New York, 1988, vol. 35, p. 55.
80. M. Misrahi, H. Loosfelt, M. Atger, M. Perrot-Applanat, A. Guiochon-Mantel and E. Milgrom, in 'Progress in Cancer Research and Therapy, Hormones and Cancer 3', ed. F. Bresciani, R. J. B. King, M. E. Lippman and J. P. Raynaud, Raven Press, New York, 1988, vol. 35, p. 27.
81. J. Å. Gustafsson, J. Carlstedt-Duke, L. Poellinger, S. Okret, A. C. Wikström, M. Brönnegård, M. Gillner, Y. Dong, K. Fuxe, A. Cintra, A. Härfstrand and L. Agnati, *Endocr. Rev.*, 1987, **8**, 185.
82. N. Giambiagi and J. R. Pasqualini, *J. Steroid Biochem.*, 1988, **30**, 213.
83. P. M. Martin, Y. Berthois and E. V. Jensen, *Proc. Natl. Acad. Sci. USA*, 1988, **85**, 2533.
84. S. M. Hollenberg, C. Weinberger, E. S. Ong, G. Cerelli, A. Oro, R. Lebo, E. B. Thompson, M. G. Rosenfeld and R. M. Evans, *Nature (London)*, 1985, **318**, 635.
85. S. Green, P. Walter, V. Kumar, A. Krust, J. M. Bornert, P. Argos and P. Chambon, *Nature (London)*, 1986, **320**, 134.
86. G. L. Greene, P. Gilna, M. Waterfield, A. Baker, Y. Hort and J. Shine, *Science (Washington, D.C.)*, 1986, **231**, 1150.

87. M. Misrahi, M. Atger, L. D'Auriol, H. Loosfelt, C. Meriel, F. Fridlansky, A. Guiochon-Mantel, F. Galibert and E. Milgrom, *Biochem. Biophys. Res. Commun.*, 1987, **143**, 740.
88. J. L. Arriza, C. Weinberger, G. Cerelli, T. M. Glaser, B. L. Handelin, D. E. Housman and R. M. Evans, *Science (Washington, D.C.)*, 1987, **237**, 268.
89. J. Trapman, P. Klassen, G. G. J. M. Kuiper, J. A. G. M. van der Korput, P. W. Faber, H. C. J. van Rooij, A. Geurts van Kessel, M. M. Voorhorst, E. Mulder and A. O. Brinkmann, *Biochem. Biophys. Res. Commun.*, 1988, **153**, 241.
90. C. Chang, J. Kokontis and S. Liao, *Proc. Natl. Acad. Sci. USA*, 1988, **85**, 7211.
91. D. B. Lubahn, D. R. Joseph, P. M. Sullivan, H. F. Willard, F. S. French and E. M. Wilson, *Science (Washington, D.C.)*, 1988, **240**, 327.
92. R. M. Evans, *Science (Washington, D.C.)*, 1988, **240**, 889.
93. S. Green and P. Chambon, *Trends Genet.*, 1988, **4**, 309.
94. U. Nauber, M. J. Pankratz, A. Kienlin, E. Seifert, U. Klemm and H. Jäckle, *Nature (London)*, 1988, **336**, 489.
95. A. E. Oro, E. S. Ong, J. S. Margolis, J. W. Posakony, M. McKeown and R. M. Evans, *Nature (London)*, 1988, **336**, 493.
96. L. H. Wang, S. Y. Tsai, R. G. Cook, W. G. Beattle, M. J. Tsai and B. W. O'Malley, *Nature (London)*, 1989, **340**, 163.
97. S. Green and P. Chambon, *Nature (London)*, 1986, **324**, 615.
98. A. Krust, S. Green, P. Argos, V. Kumar, P. Walter, J. M. Bornert and P. Chambon, *EMBO J.*, 1986, **5**, 891.
99. D. F. Smith, D. J. McGormick and D. O. Toft, *J. Steroid Biochem.*, 1988, **30**, 1.
100. V. Giguère, N. Yang, P. Segui and R. M. Evans, *Nature (London)*, 1988, **331**, 91.
101. C. Chang, L. Lan, S. Liao and J. Kokontis, in 'The Steroid/Thyroid Hormone Receptor Family and Gene Regulation', ed. J. Carlstedt-Duke, H. Eriksson and J. Å. Gustafsson, Birkhäuser, Basel, 1989, p. 183.
102. M. G. Parker, *J. Endocrinol.*, 1988, **119**, 175.
103. T. Garcia, S. Lehrer, W. D. Bloomer and B. Schachter, *Mol. Endocrinol.*, 1988, **2**, 785.
104. L. C. Murphy and H. Dotzlaw, *Mol. Endocrinol.*, 1989, **3**, 687.
105. U. Gehring, *Trends Biochem. Sci.*, 1987, **12**, 399.
106. M. G. Parker, in 'Hormones and their Actions. Part 1', ed. B. A. Cooke, R. J. B. King and H. J. van der Molen, Elsevier, Amsterdam, 1988, p. 39.
107. M. Danielsen, J. Northrop, J. Jonklaas and G. M. Ringold, *Mol. Endocrinol.*, 1987, **1**, 816.
108. R. J. B. King, in 'Hormones and their Actions. Part 1', ed. B. A. Cooke, R. J. B. King and H. J. van der Molen, Elsevier, Amsterdam, 1988, p. 29.
109. P. Davies and N. K. Rushmere, *Sci. Prog. (Oxford)*, 1988, **72**, 563.
110. H. Gronemeyer (ed.), 'Affinity Labelling and Cloning of Steroid and Thyroid Hormone Receptors', Horwood, Chichester, 1988.
111. H. Gronemeyer, M. Berry, M. T. Bocquel, J. Eul, S. Green, J. M. Jeltsch, Z. Krozowski, A. Krust, V. Kumar, M. E. Meyer, G. Stack, C. Stricker, B. Turcotte and P. Chambon, in 'Progress in Cancer Research and Therapy, Hormones and Cancer 3', ed. F. Bresciani, R. J. B. King, M. E. Lippman and J. P. Raynaud, Raven Press, New York, 1988, vol. 35, p. 34.
112. S. Green and P. Chambon, *Nature (London)*, 1987, **325**, 75.
113. N. J. G. Webster, S. Green, J. Rui Jin and P. Chambon, *Cell*, 1988, **54**, 199.
114. R. Schleif, *Science (Washington, D.C.)*, 1988, **241**, 1182.
115. A. C. B. Cato, D. Henderson and H. Porta, *EMBO J.*, 1987, **6**, 363.
116. S. M. Hollenberg and R. M. Evans, *Cell*, 1988, **55**, 899.
117. R. M. Evans and S. M. Hollenberg, *Cell*, 1988, **52**, 1.
118. L. P. Freedman, B. F. Luisi, Z. R. Korszun, R. Basavappa, P. B. Sigler and K. R. Yamamoto, *Nature (London)*, 1988, **334**, 543.
119. Y. Severne, S. Wieland, W. Schaffner and S. Rusconi, *EMBO J.*, 1988, **7**, 2503.
120. M. S. Lee, G. P. Gippert, K. V. Soman, D. A. Case and P. E. Wright, *Science (Washington, D.C.)*, 1989, **245**, 635.
121. J. M. Berg, *Proc. Natl. Acad. Sci. USA*, 1988, **85**, 99.
122. J. M. Berg, *Cell*, 1989, **57**, 1065.
123. S. Green, V. Kumar, I. Theulaz, W. Wahli and P. Chambon, *EMBO J.*, 1988, **7**, 3037.
124. A. C. B. Cato, P. Skroch, P. Butkeraitis and H. Ponta, in 'Progress in Cancer Research and Therapy, Hormones and Cancer 3', ed. F. Bresciani, R. J. B. King, M. E. Lippman and J. P. Raynaud, Raven Press, New York, 1988, vol. 35, p. 114.
125. A. D. Otten, M. M. Sanders and G. S. McKnight, *Mol. Endocrinol.*, 1988, **2**, 143.
126. B. W. O'Malley, S. Y. Tsai, M. J. Tsai, O. M. Conneely and W. T. Schrader, in 'The Steroid/Thyroid Hormone Receptor Family and Gene Regulation', ed. J. Carlstedt-Duke, H. Eriksson and J. Å. Gustafsson, Birkhäuser, Basel, 1989, p. 29.
127. L. Klein-Hitpass, S. Y. Tsai, G. L. Greene, J. H. Clark, M. J. Tsai and B. W. O'Malley, *Mol. Cell. Biol.*, 1989, **1**, 9 and 43.
128. B. Théveny, A. Bailly, C. Rauch, M. Rauch, E. Delain and E. Milgrom, *Nature (London)*, 1987, **329**, 79.
129. R. M. Evans, in 'The Steroid/Thyroid Hormone Receptor Family and Gene Regulation', ed. J. Carlstedt-Duke, H. Eriksson and J. Å. Gustafsson, Birkhäuser, Basel, 1989, p. 11.
130. S. Mader, V. Kumar, H. de Verneuil and P. Chambon, *Nature (London)*, 1989, **338**, 271.
131. M. Danielsen, L. Hinck and G. M. Ringold, *Cell*, 1989, **57**, 1131.
132. R. Schüle, M. Muller, C. Kaltschmidt and R. Renkawitz, *Science (Washington, D.C.)*, 1988, **242**, 1418.
133. K. R. Yamamoto, *Am. Rev. Genet.*, 1985, **19**, 209.
134. T. C. Spelsberg, T. Ruh, M. Ruh, A. Goldberger, M. Horton, J. Hora and R. Singh, *J. Steroid Biochem.*, 1988, **31**, 579.
135. M. F. Ruh and T. S. Ruh, in 'Steroid Receptors and Disease. Cancer, Autoimmune, Bone, and Circulatory Disorders', ed. P. J. Sheridan, K. Blum and M. C. Trachtenberg, Dekker, New York, 1988, p. 23.
136. E. R. Barrack, *Endocrinology.*, 1983, **113**, 430.
137. K. Nelson, J. R. van Nagell, H. Gallion, E. S. Donaldson and E. J. Pavlik, *Prog. Clin. Biol. Res.*, 1988, **262**, 85.
138. T. Ojasoo, J. P. Raynaud and J. P. Mornon, unpublished results.
139. K. B. Horwitz, *J. Steroid Biochem.*, 1988, **31**, 573.
140. H. Gronemeyer, B. Turcotte, C. Quirin-Stricker, M. T. Bocquel, M. E. Meyer, Z. Krozowski, J. M. Jeltsch, T. Lerouge, J. M. Garnier and P. Chambon, *EMBO J.*, 1987, **6**, 3985.

141. V. I. Lim, *FEBS Lett.*, 1978, **89**, 10.
142. C. Chothia, *Nature (London)*, 1989, **337**, 204.
143. A. Yonath, K. R. Leonard and H. G. Wittmann, *Science (Washington, D.C.)*, 1987, **236**, 813.
144. C. Gaboriaud, V. Bissery, T. Benchetrit and J. P. Mornon, *FEBS Lett.*, 1987, **224**, 149.
145. B. Henrissat, M. Claessens, P. Tomme, L. Lemesle and J. P. Mornon, *Gene*, 1989, **81**, 83.
146. J. P. Raynaud, V. Bissery, C. Gaboriaud, T. Ojasoo, G. Teutsch and J. P. Mornon, in 'The Steroid/Thyroid Hormone Receptor Family and Gene Regulation, Life Sciences', ed. J. Carlstedt-Duke, H. Eriksson and J. Å. Gustafsson, Birkhauser, Basel, 1989, vol. 4, p. 337.
147. J. P. Raynaud, V. Bissery, C. Gaboriaud, T. Ojasoo, G. Teutsch and J. P. Mornon, in 'Abstracts, 71st Annual Meeting Endocrinological Society', 1989, abstract no. 1372, p. 365.
148. J. P. Mornon, V. Bissery, C. Gaboriaud, A. Thomas, T. Ojasoo and J. P. Raynaud, *J. Steroid Biochem.*, (in press).
149. G. L. Hammond, C. L. Smith, J. S. Goping, D. A. Underhill, M. J. Harley, J. Reventos, N. A. Musto, G. L. Gunsalus and C. W. Bardin, *Proc. Natl. Acad. Sci. USA*, 1987, **84**, 5153.
150. H. Loebermann, R. Tokuoaka, J. Deisenhofer and R. Huber, *J. Mol. Biol.*, 1984, **177**, 531.
151. J. P. Samama, M. Delarue, D. Moras, M. Petitou, J. G. Lormean and J. Choay, *Thromb. Haemostasis*, 1987, **58**, 264.
152. T. E. Creighton and C. Chothia, *Nature (London)*, 1989, **339**, 14.
153. U. Westphal, 'Steroid–Protein Interactions II', Springer-Verlag, Berlin, 1986.
154. S. D. Holmes, N. T. Van, S. Stevens and R. G. Smith, *Endocrinology.*, 1981, **109**, 670.
155. J. Picado-Leonard and L. Miller, *Mol. Endocrinol.*, 1988, **2**, 1145.
156. S. E. Fawell, J. A. Lees and M. G. Parker, *Mol. Endocrinol.*, 1989, **3**, 1002.
157. R. G. MacDonald and W. W. Leavitt, *J. Biol. Chem.*, 1982, **257**, 311.
158. N. R. Miller and S. S. Simons, Jr., *J. Biol. Chem.*, 1988, **263**, 15 217.
159. C. M. Silva and J. A. Cidlowski, *J. Biol. Chem.*, 1989, **254**, 6638.
160. J. Ostermann, A. L. Horwich, W. Neupert and F. U. Hartl, *Nature (London)*, 1989, **341**, 125.
161. J. Ellis, *Nature (London)*, 1987, **328**, 2.
162. E. S. Bochkareva, N. M. Lissin and A. S. Girshovich, *Nature (London)*, 1988, **336**, 254.
163. M. G. Catelli, N. Binart, I. Jung-Testas, J. M. Renoir, E. E. Baulieu, J. R. Feramisco and W. J. Welch, *EMBO J.*, 1985, **4**, 3131.
164. D. Picard and K. R. Yamamoto, *EMBO J.*, 1987, **6**, 3333.
165. B. Wolff, R. B. Dickson and J. A. Hanover, *Trends Pharmacol. Sci.*, 1987, **8**, 119.
166. A. Guiochon-Mantel, H. Loosfelt, P. Lescop, S. Sar, M. Atger, M. Perrot-Applanat and E. Milgrom, *Cell*, 1989, **57**, 1147.
167. V. Giguère, S. M. Hollenberg, M. G. Rosenfeld and R. M. Evans, *Cell*, 1986, **46**, 645.
168. P. J. Godowski, S. Rusconi, R. Miesfeld and K. R. Yamamoto, *Nature (London)*, 1987, **325**, 365.
169. S. M. Hollenberg, V. Giguère, P. Segui and R. M. Evans, *Cell*, 1987, **49**, 39.
170. R. Miesfeld, P. J. Godowski, B. A. Maler and K. R. Yamamoto, *Science (Washington, D.C.)*, 1987, **236**, 423.
171. S. R. Sprang, K. R. Acharya, E. J. Goldsmith, D. I. Stuart, K. Varvill, R. J. Fletterick, N. B. Madsen and L. N. Johnson, *Nature (London)*, 1988, **336**, 215.
172. D. Barford and L. N. Johnson, *Nature (London)*, 1989, **340**, 609.
173. L. A. Denner, W. E. Bingman, III, G. L. Greene and N. L. Weigel, *J. Steroid Biochem.*, 1987, **27**, 235.
174. J. J. Dougherty, R. K. Puri and D. Toft, *Trends Pharmacol. Sci.*, 1985, **6**, 83.
175. F. Auricchio, *J. Steroid Biochem.*, 1989, **32**, 613.
176. P. L. Sheridan, N. L. Krett, J. A. Gordon and K. B. Horwitz, *Mol. Endocrinol.*, 1988, **2**, 1329.
177. M. E. Baker, *Biochem. Biophys. Res. Commun.*, 1986, **139**, 281.
178. M. E. Baker, *FASEB J.*, 1989, **3**, 2086.
179. M. E. Baker, *Biochem. J.*, 1988, **255**, 748.
180. N. Dayani, R. W. McNaught and R. G. Smith, *J. Steroid Biochem.*, 1988, **30**, 219.
181. T. W. Hutchens, C. M. Li and P. K. Besh, *Biochem. Biophys. Res. Commun.*, 1986, **139**, 1250.
182. W. B. Pratt, T. Redmond, E. R. Sanchez, E. H. Bresnick, S. Meshinchi and M. J. Welsh, in 'The Steroid/Thyroid Hormone Receptor Family and Gene Regulation', ed. J. Carlstedt-Duke, H. Eriksson and J. Å. Gustafsson, Birkhäuser, Basel, 1989, p. 109.
183. A. C. Wikström, M. Denis, G. Akner, O. Bakke and J. Å. Gustafsson, in 'The Steroid/Thyroid Hormone Receptor Family and Gene Regulation', ed. J. Carlstedt-Duke, H. Eriksson and J. Å. Gustafsson, Birkhäuser, Basel, 1989, p. 41.
184. N. Binart, B. Chambraud, B. Dumas, D. A. Rowlands, C. Bigogne, J. M. Levin, J. Garnier, E. E. Baulieu and M. G. Catelli, *Biochem. Biophys. Res. Commun.*, 1989, **159**, 140.
185. D. M. Tal and S. J. D. Karlish, *Mol. Pharmacol.*, 1988, **34**, 245.
186. A. V. Kamernitzky, I. G. Reshetova, A. A. Ovchinnikov, I. L. Shamovsky, I. A. Massova and N. M. Mirsalikhova, *J. Steroid Biochem.*, 1989, **32**, 857.
187. S. Y. Tsai, M. J. Tsai and B. O'Malley, *Cell*, 1989, **57**, 443.
188. M. Sabbah, G. Redeuilh and E. E. Baulieu, *J. Biol. Chem.*, 1989, **264**, 2397.
189. W. H. Landschulz, P. F. Johnson and S. L. McKnight, *Science (Washington, D.C.)*, 1988, **240**, 1759.
190. E. K. O'Shea, R. Rutkowski and P. S. Kim, *Science (Washington, D.C.)*, 1989, **243**, 538.
191. T. Kouzaridès and E. Ziff, *Nature (London)*, 1989, **340**, 568.
192. S. S. Simons, Jr., J. G. Pumphrey, S. Rudikoff and H. J. Eisen, *J. Biol. Chem.*, 1987, **262**, 9676.
193. J. Carlstedt-Duke, P. E. Stromstedt, B. Persson, E. Cederlund, J. Å. Gustafsson and H. Jornvall, *J. Biol. Chem.*, 1988, **263**, 6842.
194. I. S. Butler, A. Vessières and G. Jaouen, *Comments Inorg. Chem.*, 1989, **8**, 269.
195. A. Vessières, C. Vaillant, M. Salmain and G. Jaouen, *J. Steroid Biochem.*, (in press).
196. R. E. Muller and A. M. Traish, *Ann. New York Acad. Sci.*, 1986, **464**, 202.
197. M. E. Baker and L. S. Terry, *Steroids*, 1983, **42**, 593.
198. M. E. Baker, D. H. Sklar, L. S. Terry and M. R. Hedges, *Biochem. Int.*, 1985, **11**, 233.
199. J. L. Borgna and J. Scali, *J. Steroid Biochem.*, 1988, **31**, 427.
200. L. Tora, A. Mullick, D. Metzger, M. Ponglikitmongkol, I. Park and P. Chambon, *EMBO J.*, 1989, **8**, 1981.
201. M. Danielson, J. P. Northrop and G. M. Ringold, *EMBO J.*, 1986, **5**, 2513.

202. C. W. Distelhorst, K. E. Janiga, K. J. Howard, S. E. Strandjord and E. J. Campbell, *Blood*, 1987, **70**, 860.
203. C. C. F. Blake, *Proc. Royal Soc. London*, 1981, **B211**, 413.
204. M. E. Newcomer, T. A. Jones, J. Aqvist, J. Sundelin, U. Ericksson, L. Rusk and P. A. Peterson, *EMBO J.*, 1984, **3**, 451.
205. E. M. Westbrook, O. E. Piro and P. B. Sigler, *J. Biol. Chem.*, 1984, **259**, 9096.
206. J. Delettré, J. P. Mornon, G. Lepicard, T. Ojasoo and J. P. Raynaud, *J. Steroid Biochem.*, 1980, **13**, 45.
207. J. Delettré, J. P. Mornon, T. Ojasoo and J. P. Raynaud, in 'Perspectives in Steroid Receptor Research', ed. F. Bresciani, Raven Press, New York, 1980, p. 1.
208. J. P. Raynaud, J. Delettré, T. Ojasoo, G. Lepicard and J. P. Mornon, in 'Physiopathology of Endocrine Diseases and Mechanisms of Hormone Action', ed. R. J. Soto, A. de Nicola and J. Blaquier, Liss, New York, 1981, p. 461.
209. W. L. Duax and D. A. Norton, 'Atlas of Steroid Structure', Plenum Press, New York, 1975, vol. 1.
210. J. F. Griffin, W. L. Duax and C. M. Weeks, 'Atlas of Steroid Structure', Plenum Press, New York, 1984, vol. 2.
211. J. P. Mornon, J. Delettré, G. Lepicard, R. Bailly, E. Surcouf and P. Bondot, *J. Steroid Biochem.*, 1977, **8**, 51.
212. V. J. van Geerestein, Ph.D. Thesis, University of Utrecht, 1988.
213. J. P. Raynaud and T. Ojasoo, in 'Steroid Hormone Receptors: Structure and Function', ed. H. Eriksson and J. Å. Gustafsson, Elsevier, Amsterdam, 1983, p. 141.
214. W. L. McGuire, G. M. Clark, L. G. Dressler and M. A. Owens, *NCI Monograph*, 1986, **1**, 19.
215. P. M. Martin, J. M. Le Goff, T. Ojasoo, J. P. Raynaud and H. Magdelenat, in 'Steroid Receptors and Disease: Cancer, Autoimmune, Bone and Circulatory Disease', ed. P. J. Sheridan, K. Blum and M. C. Trachtenberg, Dekker, New York, 1988, p. 467.
216. J. P. Raynaud, in 'Progesterone Receptors in Normal and Neoplastic Tissues', ed. W. L. McGuire, J. P. Raynaud and E. E. Baulieu, Raven Press, New York, 1977, p. 9.
217. J. P. Raynaud, T. Ojasoo and V. Vaché, in 'Steroid Receptors and the Management of Cancer', ed. E. B. Thompson and M. E. Lippman, CRC Press, Boca Raton, FL, 1979, p. 215.
218. J. P. Raynaud, T. Ojasoo and V. Vaché, in 'Reproductive Processes and Contraception', ed. K. W. McKerns, Plenum Press, New York, 1981, p. 163.
219. J. P. Raynaud, T. Ojasoo, A. Jouquey, M. Moguilewsky and G. Teutsch, in 'Endocrinology', ed. F. Labrie and L. Proulx, Elsevier, Amsterdam, 1984, p. 533.
220. T. Ojasoo, M. Moguilewsky, D. Philibert and J. P. Raynaud, in 'Advances in Steroid Analysis 1987' ed. S. Görög, Akadémiai Kiadó, Budapest, 1988, p. 17.
221. J. A. Katzenellenbogen and B. S. Katzenellenbogen, *Vitam. Horm. (N.Y.)*, 1984, **41**, 213.
222. F. Sweet and G. L. Murdock, *Endocr. Rev.*, 1987, **8**, 154.
223. J. A. Katzenellenbogen and J. A. Zablocki, in 'Pharmacology and Clinical Uses of Inhibitors of Hormone Secretion and Action', ed. B. J. A. Furr and A. E. Wakeling, Tindall, London, p. 41.
224. A. Groyer, Y. Le Bouc, I. Joab, C. Radanyi, J. M. Renoir, P. Robel and E. E. Baulieu, *Eur. J. Biochem.*, 1985, **149**, 445.
225. G. O. Gray and W. W. Leavitt, *J. Steroid Biochem.*, 1987, **28**, 493.
226. T. P. Fletcher and D. R. Blandon, 20th Annual Conference Australian Society Reproductive Biology, 1988, 50.
227. J. P. Raynaud, in 'Receptors. Advances in Pharmacology and Therapeutics', ed. J. Jacob, Pergamon Press, Oxford, 1978, vol. 1, p. 259.
228. J. P. Raynaud and T. Ojasoo, *J. Steroid Biochem.*, 1986, **25**, 811.
229. M. K. Agarwal (ed.), in 'Receptor Mediated Antisteroid Action', Gruyter, Berlin, 1987.
230. J. R. Pasqualini, T. Ojasoo and J. P. Raynaud (eds.), *J. Steroid Biochem.*, 1988, **31**.
231. J. P. Raynaud, T. Ojasoo, J. Pottier and J. Salmon, in 'Biochemical Actions of Hormones', ed. G. Litwack, Academic Press, New York, 1982, vol. 9, p. 305.
232. J. P. Raynaud, C. Bonne, M. M. Bouton, M. Moguilewsky, D. Philibert and G. Azadian-Boulanger, *J. Steroid Biochem.*, 1975, **6**, 615.
233. J. P. Raynaud, in 'Medicinal Chemistry', ed. J. Mathieu, Elsevier, Amsterdam, 1977, vol. 5, p. 451.
234. T. Ojasoo and J. P. Raynaud, *Cancer Res.*, 1978, **38**, 4186.
235. J. P. Raynaud, T. Ojasoo, M. M. Bouton and D. Philibert, in 'Drug Design', ed. E. J. Ariëns, Academic Press, New York, 1979, vol. 8, p. 169.
236. J. P. Raynaud, M. M. Bouton, M. Moguilewsky, T. Ojasoo, D. Philibert, G. Beck, F. Labrie and J. P. Mornon, *J. Steroid Biochem.*, 1980, **12**, 143.
237. J. P. Raynaud, T. Ojasoo and F. Labrie, in 'Mechanisms of Steroid Action', ed. G. P. Lewis and M. Ginsburg, Macmillan, England, 1981, p. 145.
238. T. Ojasoo and J. P. Raynaud, in 'Steroids and Endometrial Cancer', ed. V. M. Jasonni, I. Nenci and C. Flamigni, Raven Press, New York, 1983, p. 11.
239. M. M. Bouton and J. P. Raynaud, *J. Steroid Biochem.*, 1978, **9**, 9.
240. M. M. Bouton and J. P. Raynaud, *Endocrinology*, 1979, **105**, 509.
241. J. C. Doré, J. Gilbert, T. Ojasoo and J. P. Raynaud, *J. Med. Chem.*, 1986, **29**, 54.
242. T. Ojasoo, J. C. Doré, J. Gilbert and J. P. Raynaud, *J. Med. Chem.*, 1988, **31**, 1160.
243. H. Gronemeyer, S. Green, V. Kumar, J. M. Jeltsch and P. Chambon, in 'Steroid Receptors and Disease. Cancer, Autoimmune, Bone, and Circulatory Disorders', ed. P. J. Sheridan, K. Blum and M. C. Trachtenberg, Dekker, New York, 1988, p. 153.
244. S. Green, V. Kumar, P. Walter and P. Chambon, *Cold Spring Harbor Symp. Quant. Biol.*, 1986, **51**, 751.
245. J. P. Raynaud, T. Ojasoo, M. M. Bouton, E. Bignon, M. Pons and A. Crastes de Paulet, in 'Estrogens in the Environment', ed. J. A. McLachlan, Elsevier, Amsterdam, 1985, p. 24.
246. F. J. Zeelen and E. W. Bergink, in 'Cytotoxic Estrogens in Hormone Receptive Tumors', ed. J. Raus, H. Martens and G. Leclercq, Academic Press, New York, 1980, p. 39.
247. G. R. Merriam and M. B. Lipsett (eds.), 'Catechol Estrogens', Raven Press, New York, 1983.
248. J. P. Raynaud, G. Azadian-Boulanger and R. Bucourt, *J. Pharmacol.*, 1974, **5**, 27.
249. R. Bucourt, M. Vignau, V. Torelli, H. Richard-Foy, C. Geynet, C. Secco-Millet, G. Redeuilh and E. E. Baulieu, *J. Biol. Chem.*, 1978, **253**, 8221.
250. J. P. Raynaud, G. Azadian-Boulanger, M. M. Bouton, M. C. Colin, N. Faure, L. Ferland-Proulx, J. P. Gautray, J. M. Husson, A. Jolivet, P. Kelly, F. Labrie, T. Ojasoo and G. Precigoux, *J. Steroid Biochem.*, 1984, **20**, 981.

251. A. Bélanger, D. Philibert and G. Teutsch, *Steroids*, 1981, **37**, 361.
252. V. C. Jordan and R. Koch, *Endocrinology*, 1989, **124**, 1717.
253. A. E. Wakeling and J. Bowler, *J. Steroid Biochem.*, 1988, **30**, 141.
254. P. J. Weatherill, A. P. M. Wilson, R. I. Nicholson, P. Davies and A. E. Wakeling, *J. Steroid Biochem.*, 1988, **30**, 263.
255. J. F. Miquel and J. Gilbert, *J. Steroid Biochem.*, 1988, **31**, 525.
256. J. R. Pasqualini, C. Sumida and N. Giambiagi, *J. Steroid Biochem.*, 1988, **31**, 613.
257. V. C. Jordan, *Pharmacol. Rev.*, 1984, **36**, 245.
258. R. L. Sutherland and V. C. Jordan, 'Nonsteroidal Antiestrogens', Academic Press, Sydney, 1981.
259. W. L. Duax, J. F. Griffin, C. M. Weeks and Z. Wawrzak, *J. Steroid Biochem.*, 1988, **31**, 481.
260. B. M. Markaverich, R. R. Roberts, M. A. Alejandro, G. A. Johnson, B. S. Middleditch and J. H. Clark, *J. Steroid Biochem.*, 1988, **30**, 71.
261. M. Pons, F. Michel, E. Bignon, A. Crastes de Paulet, J. Gilbert, J. F. Miquel, G. Précigoux, M. Hospital, T. Ojasoo and J. P. Raynaud, *Prog. Cancer Res. Ther.*, 1984, **31**, 27.
262. E. Bignon, M. Pons, A. Crastes de Paulet, J. C. Doré, J. Gilbert, J. Abecassis, J. F. Miquel, T. Ojasoo and J. P. Raynaud, *J. Med. Chem.*, 1989, **32**, 2092.
263. J. P. Raynaud, P. M. Martin, M. M. Bouton and T. Ojasoo, *Cancer Res.*, 1978, **38**, 3044.
264. J. E. Zielinski, H. Yabuki, S. L. Pahuja, J. M. Larner and R. B. Hochberg, *Endocrinology*, 1986, **119**, 130.
265. E. M. Jagoda, R. E. Gibson, H. Goodgold, N. Ferreira, B. E. Francis, R. C. Reba, W. J. Rzeszotarski and W. C. Eckelman, *J. Nucl. Med.*, 1984, **25**, 472.
266. R. D. Bindal, K. E. Carlson, G. C. A. Reiner and J. A. Katzenellenbogen, *J. Steroid Biochem.*, 1987, **28**, 361.
267. R. N. Hanson, M. Ghoshal, C. Rosenthal and F. Murphy, *J. Labelled Compounds Radiopharmaceuticals*, 1989, **26**, 393.
268. J. N. Da Silva, C. Crouzel and J. E. van Lier, *J. Labelled Compounds Radiopharmaceuticals*, 1989, **26**, 342.
269. R. F. Glascock and N. G. Hoekstra, *Biochem. J.*, 1959, **72**, 673.
270. T. L. Fevig, J. E. Lloyd, J. A. Zablocki and J. A. Katzenellenbogen, *J. Med. Chem.*, 1987, **30**, 156.
271. E. R. DeSombre, R. C. Mease, J. Sanghavi, T. Singh, R. H. Seavers and A. Hughes, *J. Steroid Biochem.*, 1988, **29**, 583.
272. J. A. Katzenellenbogen, K. E. Carlson, D. F. Heiman, D. W. Robertson and B. S. Katzenellenbogen, *J. Biol. Chem.*, 1983, **258**, 3487.
273. J. A. Katzenellenbogen, in 'Third SCI–RSC Medicinal Chemistry Symposium', ed. R. W. Lambert, Royal Society of Chemistry, London, 1986, p. 312.
274. P. Fioretti, C. Flamigni, V. M. Jasonni and G. B. Melis (eds.), 'Postmenopausal Hormonal Therapy: Benefits and Risks', Raven Press, New York, 1987.
275. R. Lindsay, in 'Osteoporosis: Etiology, Diagnosis, and Management', ed. B. L. Riggs and L. J. Melton, III, Raven Press, New York, 1988, p. 333.
276. C. Christiansen, J. S. Johansen and B. J. Riis (eds.), 'Osteoporosis 1987, Proceedings International Symposium on Osteoporosis', Osteopress, 1987.
277. R. K. Ross, M. C. Pike, B. E. Henderson, T. M. Mack and R. A. Lobo, *Lancet*, 1989, **1**, 505.
278. B. S. Komm, C. T. Terpening, D. J. Benz, K. A. Graeme, A. Gallegos, M. Kore, G. L. Greene, B. O'Malley and M. K. Haussler, *Science (Washington, D.C.)*, 1988, **241**, 81.
279. E. F. Eriksen, D. S. Colvard, N. J. Berg, M. L. Graham, K. G. Mann, T. C. Spelsberg and T. E. Riggs, *Science (Washington, D.C.)*, 1988, **241**, 84.
280. A. E. Wakeling, in 'Pharmacology and Clinical Uses of Inhibitors of Hormone Secretion and Action', ed. B. J. A. Furr and A. E. Wakeling, Tindall, London, 1986, p. 1.
281. B. J. A. Furr and V. C. Jordan, *Pharmacol. Ther.*, 1984, **25**, 127.
282. R. I. Nicholson, in 'Pharmacology and Clinical Uses of Inhibitors of Hormone Secretion and Action', ed. B. J. A. Furr and A. E. Wakeling, Tindall, London, 1986, p. 60.
283. K. B. Horwitz, L. L. Wei and M. D. Francis, *J. Steroid Biochem.*, 1986, **24**, 109.
284. K. B. Horwitz, *J. Steroid Biochem.*, 1988, **31**, 573.
285. D. P. Edwards, P. A. Estes, J. Lawler-Heavner and D. Elashry-Stowers, in 'Steroid Receptors and Disease. Cancer, Autoimmune, Bone, and Circulatory Disorders', ed. P. J. Sheridan, K. Blum and M. C. Trachtenberg, Dekker, New York, 1988, p. 121.
286. A. Bailly, A. Guiochon-Mantel, M. Misrahi, H. Loosfelt, M. Atger, J. F. Savouret, M. Perrot-Applanat, M. T. Vu Hai, M. Rauch, F. Lorenzo, F. Logeat and E. Milgrom, in 'The Steroid/Thyroid Hormone Receptor Family and Gene Regulation', ed. J. Carlstedt-Duke, H. Eriksson and J. Å. Gustafsson, Birkhäuser, Basel, 1989, p. 271.
287. K. Kontula, O. Jänne, R. Vihko, E. de Jager, J. de Visser and F. Zeelen, *Acta Endocrinol. (Copenhagen)*, 1975, **78**, 574.
288. F. Zeelen, *Trends Pharmacol. Sci.*, 1983, **5**, 520.
289. M. Bohl, Z. Simon, A. Vlad, G. Kaufmann and K. Ponsold, *Z. Naturforsch. C, Biosci.*, 1987, **42**, 935.
290. E. Surcouf and J. P. Mornon, *C. R. Hebd. Séances Acad. Sci. Ser. D.*, 1982, **295**, 923.
291. G. Teutsch, in 'Adrenal Steroid Antagonism', ed. M. K. Agarwal, Gruyter, Berlin, 1984, p. 43.
292. G. Teutsch, in 'The Antiprogestin Steroid RU 486 and Human Fertility Control', ed. E. E. Baulieu and S. J. Segal, Plenum Press, New York, 1985, p. 27.
293. G. Teutsch, T. Ojasoo and J. P. Raynaud, *J. Steroid Biochem.*, 1988, **31**, 549.
294. D. Henderson, in 'Pharmacology and Clinical Uses of Inhibitors of Hormone Secretion and Action', ed. B. J. A. Furr and A. E. Wakeling, Tindall, London, 1987, p. 184.
295. H. J. Kloosterboer, G. H. J. Deckers, M. J. van der Heuvel and H. J. J. Loozen, *J. Steroid Biochem.*, 1988, **31**, 567.
296. J. P. Raynaud, M. M. Bouton and T. Ojasoo, *Trends Pharmacol. Sci.*, 1980, **2**, 324.
297. F. Neumann, in 'Pharmacology and Clinical Uses of Inhibitors of Hormone Secretion and Action', ed. B.J.A. Furr and A. E. Wakeling, Tindall, London, 1987, p. 132.
298. W. L. Duax, V. Cody, J. Griffin, J. Hazel and C. M. Weeks, *J. Steroid Biochem.*, 1978, **9**, 901.
299. D. Philibert and J. P. Raynaud, *Steroids*, 1973, **22**, 89.
300. O. Jänne, K. Kontula and R. Vihko, *J. Steroid Biochem.*, 1976, **7**, 1061.
301. M. Poisson and J. P. Raynaud (eds.), *Clin. Neuropharmacol.*, 1984, **7**, 271.
302. M. Poisson and H. Magdelenat, in 'Steroid Receptors and Disease. Cancer, Autoimmune, Bone, and Circulatory Disorders', ed. P. J. Sheridan, K. Blum and M. C. Trachtenberg, Dekker, New York, 1988, p. 525.

303. R. E. Leake and F. Habib, in 'Steroid Hormones: A Practical Approach', ed. B. Green and R. E. Leake, IRL Press, Oxford, 1987, p. 67.
304. S. D. Holmes and R. G. Smith, *Biochemistry*, 1983, **22**, 1729.
305. L. S. Dure, W. T. Schrader and B. W. O'Malley, *Nature (London)*, 1980, **283**, 784.
306. L. L. Wei and K. B. Horwitz, *Steroids*, 1985, **46**, 677.
307. T. T. Ilenchuk and M. R. Walters, *Endocrinology*, 1987, **120**, 1449.
308. D. J. Lamb, P. E. Kima and D. W. Bullock, *Biochemistry*, 1986, **25**, 6319.
309. K. R. Carlson, M. Coppey, H. Magdelenat and J. A. Katzenellenbogen, *J. Steroid Biochem.*, 1989, **32**, 345.
310. O. M. Conneely, B. L. Maxwell, D. O. Toft, W. T. Schrader and B. W. O'Malley, *Biochem. Biophys. Res. Commun.*, 1987, **149**, 493.
311. H. Gronemeyer, B. Turcotte, C. Quirin-Stricker, M. T. Bocquel, M. E. Meyer, Z. Krozowski, J. M. Jeltsch, T. Lerouge, J. M. Garnier and P. Chambon, *EMBO J.*, 1987, **6**, 3985.
312. P. A. Estes, E. J. Suba, J. Lawler-Heavner, D. El-Ashry, L. L. Wei, D. O. Toft, W. P. Sullivan, K. B. Horwitz and D. P. Edwards, *Biochemistry*, 1987, **26**, 6250.
313. P. L. Sheridan, N. L. Krett, J. A. Gordon and K. B. Horwitz, *Mol. Endocrinol.*, 1988, **2**, 1329.
314. J. P. Raynaud, G. Azadian-Boulanger and T. Ojasoo, in 'Pharmacologie Clinique. Bases de la Thérapeutique', ed. J. P. Giroud, G. Mathé and G. Meyniel, Expansion Scientifique Française, 1988, p. 2093.
315. J. P. Raynaud and M. M. Bouton, in 'Cytotoxic Estrogens in Hormone Receptive Tumors', ed. J. Raus, H. Martens and G. Leclercq, Academic Press, New York, 1980, p. 49.
316. J. P. Raynaud and T. Ojasoo, *J. Gynecol. Obstet. Biol. Reprod.*, 1983, **12**, 697.
317. G. Azadian-Boulanger, J. Secchi, F. Laraque, J. P. Raynaud and E. Sakiz, *Am. J. Obstet. Gynecol.*, 1976, **125**, 1049.
318. J. P. Raynaud, T. Ojasoo and L. Martini (eds.), 'Medical Management of Endometriosis', Raven Press, New York, 1984.
319. L. Fedele, L. Arcaini, S. Bianchi, G. B. Candiani and F. Viezzoli, *Fertil. Steril.*, 1989, **51**, 781.
320. E. M. Coutinho and M. T. Gonçalves, *Fertil. Steril.*, 1989, **51**, 939.
321. E. E. Baulieu, *Science (Washington, D.C.)*, 1989, **245**, 1351.
322. M. Bygdeman and M. L. Swahn, *Contraception*, 1985, **32**, 45.
323. M. P. Johnson, D. R. Rowley, C. Y. F. Young, D. J. Tindall and G. R. Cunningham, in 'Steroid Receptors and Disease. Cancer, Autoimmune, Bone, and Circulatory Disorders', ed. P. J. Sheridan, K. Blum and M. C. Trachtenberg, Dekker, New York, 1988, p. 207.
324. P. W. Faber, G. G. J. M. Kuiper, H. C. J. van Rooij, J. A. G. M. van der Korput, A. O. Brinkmann and J. Trapman, in 'The Steroid/Thyroid Hormone Receptor Family and Gene Regulation', ed. J. Carlstedt-Duke, H. Eriksson and J. Å. Gustafsson, Birkhäuser, Basel, 1989, p. 169.
325. M. G. Parker, P. Webb, J. S. Mills, M. Needham and R. White, *J. Steroid Biochem.*, 1988, **30**, 47.
326. T. Ojasoo, J. Delettré, J. P. Mornon, C. Turpin-Vandycke and J. P. Raynaud, *J. Steroid Biochem.*, 1987, **27**, 255.
327. H. Morales-Alanis, M. J. Brienne, J. Jacques, M. M. Bouton, L. Nédélec, V. Torelli and C. Tournemine, *J. Med. Chem.*, 1985, **28**, 1796.
328. T. Ojasoo and J. P. Raynaud, in 'Receptor-mediated Antagonism', ed. M. K. Agarwal, Gruyter, Berlin, 1987, p. 329.
329. H. Koch, *Med. Actual.*, 1984, **20**, 561.
330. R. Neri and N. Kassen, in 'Pharmacology and Clinical Uses of Inhibitors of Hormone Secretion and Action', ed. B. J. A. Furr and A. E. Wakeling, Tindall, London, p. 160.
331. J. P. Raynaud, C. Bonne, M. M. Bouton, L. Lagacé and F. Labrie, *J. Steroid Biochem.*, 1979, **11**, 93.
332. J. P. Raynaud, C. Bonne, M. Moguilewsky, F. A. Lefebvre, A. Bélanger and F. Labrie, *Prostate*, 1984, **5**, 299.
333. J. P. Raynaud, M. Moguilewsky, C. Tournemine, D. Coussediére, J. Salmon, J. M. Husson, C. Bertagna, D. Tremblay, L. Pendyala, J. M. Brisset, G. Vallancien, G. Serment, H. Navratil, A. Dupont and F. Labrie, in 'EORTC Genitourinary Group Monograph 2, Part A. Therapeutic Principles in Metastatic Prostatic Cancer', ed. F. H. Schröder and B. Richards, Liss, New York, 1985, p. 99.
334. A. E. Wakeling, B. J. A. Furr, A. T. Glen and L. R. Hughes, *J. Steroid Biochem.*, 1981, **15**, 355.
335. B. J. A. Furr, in 'Hormonal Therapy of Prostatic Diseases: Basic and Clinical Aspects', ed. M. Motta and M. Serio, Medicom, Netherlands, 1988, p. 148.
336. C. Chang and S. Liao, *J. Steroid Biochem.*, 1987, **27**, 123.
337. C. Bonne and J. P. Raynaud, *Steroids*, 1976, **27**, 497.
338. A. M. Traish, R. E. Müller and H. H. Wotiz, *Endocrinology*, 1986, **118**, 1327.
339. J. Asselin, R. Mélançon, Y. Gourdeau, F. Labrie, C. Bonne and J. P. Raynaud, *J. Steroid Biochem.*, 1979, **10**, 483.
340. D. T. Zava, B. Landrum, K. B. Horwitz and W. L. McGuire, *Endocrinology*, 1979, **104**, 1007.
341. C. H. Chang, T. J. Lobl, D. R. Rowley and D. J. Tindall, *Biochemistry*, 1984, **23**, 2527.
342. W. I. P. Mainwaring and V. A. Randall, *J. Steroid Biochem.*, 1984, **21**, 209.
343. A. O. Brinkmann, G. G. J. M. Kuiper, J. Bolt de Vries and E. Mulder, *J. Steroid Biochem.*, 1988, **30**, 257.
344. A. O. Brinkmann, G. G. J. M. Kuiper, W. de Boer, E. Mulder, J. Bolt, G. J. van Steenbrugge and H. J. van der Molen, *J. Steroid Biochem.*, 1986, **24**, 245.
345. S. Gyorki, G. L. Warne and J. W. Funder, *J. Steroid Biochem.*, 1988, **29**, 611.
346. D. Stamatiadis, M. C. Portois, J. P. Blondeau, I. Mowszowicz and P. Mauvais-Jarvis, *Mol. Cell Endocrinol.*, 1987, **54**, 141.
347. J. O. Macaulay, Z. S. Krozowski and G. L. Warne, *J. Steroid Biochem.*, 1989, **32**, 493.
348. J. P. Raynaud, G. Azadian-Boulanger, C. Bonne, J. Perronnet and E. Sakiz, in 'Androgens and Antiandrogens', ed. L. Martini and M. Motta, Raven Press, New York, 1977, p. 281.
349. D. B. Mendel, J. E. Bodwell and A. Munck, *Nature (London)*, 1986, **324**, 478.
350. M. Ayub and M. J. Levell, *J. Steroid Biochem.*, 1987, **28**, 43.
351. G. Babany, M. Tinel, P. Letteron, E. Freneaux, A. Berson, D. Larrey and D. Pessayre, *Biochem. Pharmacol.*, 1989, **38**, 941.
352. C. D. Kochakian (ed.), 'Anabolic–Androgenic Steroids', Springer-Verlag, Berlin, 1976.
353. M. Tausk, in 'Discoveries in Pharmacology', ed. M. J. Parnham and J. Bruinvels, Elsevier, New York, 1984, vol. 2, p. 307.
354. J. D. Wilson and J. E. Griffin, *Metabolism*, 1980, **9**, 1278.

355. R. Voy, *Am. Pharm.*, 1986, **11**, 39.
356. M. Alen, M. Reinila and R. Vihko, *Med. Sports Exerc.*, 1985, **17**, 354.
357. J. D. Wilson, *Endocr. Rev.*, 1988, **9**, 181.
358. P. Holma, *Am. Clin. Res.*, 1977, **9**, 215.
359. F. Labrie and J. P. Raynaud, *US Pat.*, 4 472 382 (1984).
360. J. P. Raynaud, *Am. J. Clin. Oncol.*, 1988, **11**, (suppl. 2), 132.
361. F. Labrie, A. Dupont, A. Bélanger, C. Labrie, Y. Lacourcière, J. P. Raynaud, J. M. Husson, J. Emond, J. G. Houle, J. G. Girard, G. Monfette, J. P. Paquet, A. Vallières, C. Bosse and R. Delisle, *Prog. Cancer Res. Ther.*, 1984, **31**, 533.
362. M. Namer, J. Amiel and J. Toubol, *Am. J. Clin. Oncol.*, 1988, **11**, (suppl. 2), 191.
363. M. Namer and J. P. Raynaud, in 'Hormones and Cancer 3', ed. F. Bresciani, R. J. B. King, M. E. Lippman and J. P. Raynaud, Raven Press, New York, 1988, p. 501.
364. G. Béland, M. Elhilali, Y. Fradet, B. Laroche, E. W. Ramsey, J. Trachtenberg and P. M. Venner, *Am. J. Clin. Oncol.*, 1988, **11**, (suppl. 2), 187.
365. F. Labrie, A. Dupont, L. Cusan, M. Giguère, N. Bergeron, J. P. Borsanyi, Y. Lacoursière, A. Bélanger, J. Emond, G. Monfette, H. Boucher and R. Lachance, *J. Steroid Biochem.*, 1988, **30**, 107.
366. E. D. Crawford, M. A. Eisenberger, D. G. McLeod, J. T. Spaulding, R. Benson, F. A. Dorr, B. A. Blumenstein, M. A. Davis and P. J. Goodman, *N. Engl. J. Med.*, 1989, **321**, 419.
367. M. Namer, *J. Steroid Biochem.*, 1988, **31**, 719.
368. D. S. Thomson, in 'Pharmacology of the Skin', ed. M. W. Greaves and S. Shuster, Springer-Verlag, Berlin, 1989, p. 483.
369. M. Moguilewsky and M. M. Bouton, *J. Steroid Biochem.*, 1988, **31**, 699.
370. E. B. Thompson, Y. S. Yuh, D. Harbour, J. Ashraf, B. Johnson and J. M. Harmon, in 'The Steroid/Thyroid Hormone Receptor Family and Gene Regulation', ed. J. Carlstedt-Duke, H. Eriksson and J. Å. Gustafsson, Birkhäuser, Basel, 1989, p. 127.
371. J. Carlstedt-Duke and J. Å. Gustafsson, *J. Steroid Biochem.*, 1988, **31**, 593.
372. D. L. Bellingham and J. A. Cidlowski, in 'Steroid Receptors and Disease. Cancer, Autoimmune, Bone, and Circulatory Disorders', ed. P. J. Sheridan, K. Blum and M. C. Trachtenberg, Dekker, New York, 1988, p. 97.
373. J. Carlstedt-Duke, M. Denis, C. Bonifer, P. E. Strömstedt, K. Dahlman, A. C. Wikström, S. Okret, L. Poellinger and J. Å. Gustafsson, in 'Steroid Receptors and Disease. Cancer, Autoimmune, Bone, and Circulatory Disorders', ed. P. J. Sheridan, K. Blum and M. C. Trachtenberg, Dekker, New York, 1988, p. 189.
374. G. Teutsch, G. Costerousse, R. Deraedt, J. Benzoni, M. Fortin and D. Philibert, *Steroids*, 1981, **38**, 651.
375. S. S. Simons, E. B. Thompson and D. F. Johnson, *Biochem. Biophys. Res. Commun.*, 1979, **86**, 793.
376. J. A. Schlechte, S. S. Simons, Jr., D. A. Lewis and E. B. Thompson, *Endocrinology*, 1985, **117**, 1355.
377. S. S. Simons and P. A. Miller, *J. Steroid Biochem.*, 1986, **24**, 25.
378. E. B. Thompson, Y. S. Yuh, J. Ashraf, B. Gametchu, B. Johnson and E. B. Harmon, *J. Steroid Biochem.*, 1988, **30**, 63.
379. C. E. Gomez-Sanchez and E. P. Gomez-Sanchez, *Endocrinology*, 1983, **113**, 1004.
380. T. Hermann, K. Schramm and R. Ghraf, *J. Steroid Biochem.*, 1987, **26**, 417.
381. M. Moguilewsky and J. P. Raynaud, *J. Steroid Biochem.*, 1980, **12**, 309.
382. J. W. Funder and K. Sheppard, *Annu. Rev. Physiol.*, 1987, **49**, 397.
383. J. W. Funder, *Science (Washington, D.C.)*, 1987, **237**, 236.
384. C. P. Bastl, *J. Clin. Invest.*, 1987, **80**, 348.
385. K. Beaumont and K. D. Farestil, *J. Steroid Biochem.*, 1986, **24**, 513.
386. M. Coutard, D. Duval and M. J. Osborne-Pellegrin, *J. Steroid Biochem.*, 1987, **28**, 29.
387. D. Doyle, Z. Krozowski, F. J. Morgan and J. W. Funder, *J. Steroid Biochem.*, 1988, **29**, 415.
388. J. Halevy, E. L. Boulpaep, M. E. Budinger, H. J. Binder and J. P. Hayslett, *Am. J. Physiol.*, 1988, **254**, F153.
389. T. Hermann and R. Ghraf, *J. Steroid Biochem.*, 1988, **30**, 421.
390. A. Sarrieau, W. H. Rostène, M. Moguilewsky, D. Philibert and B. McEwen, in 'Receptor Binding in Drug Research 55. Clinical Pharmacology', ed. R. A. O'Brien, Dekker, New York, 1986, vol. 5, p. 261.
391. W. Sutanto, J. M. H. M. Reul, J. A. M. van Eekelen and G. R. de Kloet, *J. Steroid Biochem.*, 1988, **30**, 417.
392. J. W. Funder, P. T. Pearce, R. Smith and A. I. Smith, *Science (Washington, D.C.)*, 1988, **242**, 583.
393. A. C. B. Cato, P. Skroch, J. Weinmann, P. Butkeraitis and H. Ponta, *EMBO J.*, 1988, **7**, 1403.
394. A. C. B. Cato and J. Weinmann, *J. Cell. Biol.*, 1988, **106**, 2119.
395. W. G. Luttge, M. E. Rupp and S. M. Emadian, *Endocrinology*, 1989, **124**, 1813.
396. P. M. Danze, P. Formstecher, C. Richard and M. Dautrevaux, *Biochim. Biophys. Acta*, 1987, **927**, 129.
397. E. E. Baulieu, *Horm. Res.*, 1987, **28**, 181.
398. P. A. Bell and P. J. Weatherill, *J. Steroid Biochem.*, 1986, **25**, 473.
399. M. B. Suthers, L. A. Pressley and J. W. Funder, *Endocrinology*, 1976, **99**, 260.
400. T. R. Jones and P. A. Bell, *Biochem. J.*, 1980, **188**, 237.
401. M. Moguilewsky and R. Deraedt, *J. Steroid Biochem.*, 1981, **15**, 329.
402. F. Svec, *Endocrinology*, 1988, **123**, 1902.
403. E. Sakiz, in 'Pharmacology and Clinical Uses of Inhibitors of Hormone Secretion and Action', ed. B. J. A. Furr and A. E. Wakeling, Tindall, London, p. 212.
404. X. Bertagna, C. Bertagna, M. H. Laudat, J. M. Husson, F. Girard and J. P. Luton, *J. Clin. Endocrinol. Metab.*, 1986, **63**, 639.
405. G. P. Chrousos, L. Laue, L. K. Nieman, S. Kawai, R. U. Udelsman, D. D. Brandon and D. L. Loriaux, *Kidney Int.*, 1988, **34**, (suppl. 26), 18.
406. J. P. Grünfeld and L. Eloy, *Kidney Int.*, 1988, **34**, (suppl. 25), 49.
407. L. Laue, W. Gallucci, D. L. Loriaux, R. Udelsman and G. P. Chrousos, *J. Clin. Endocrinol. Metab.*, 1988, **67**, 602.
408. P. M. Guyre, M. T. Girard, P. M. Morganelli and P. D. Manganiello, *J. Steroid Biochem.*, 1988, **30**, 89.
409. A. Bateman, A. Singh, T. Kral and S. Solomon, *Endocr. Rev.*, 1989, **10**, 92.
410. R. M. Sapolsky, L. C. Krey and B. S. McEwen, *Endocr. Rev.*, 1986, **7**, 284.
411. S. Durant, D. Duval and F. Homo-Delarche, *Endocr. Rev.*, 1986, **7**, 254.
412. N. A. Oliver, *Arch. Dermatol.*, 1987, **123**, 570.

413. T. J. Smith, *Metabolism*, 1988, **37**, 179.
414. P. A. Danhaive and G. G. Rousseau, *J. Steroid Biochem.*, 1988, **29**, 575.
415. M. Konagaya and S. R. Max, *J. Steroid Biochem.*, 1986, **25**, 305.
416. L. L. Dreyer, R. J. Sydiskis and N. Bashirelahi, in 'Abstracts, 71st Annual Meeting Endocrine Society', Endocrine Society, Bethesda, MD, 1989, no. 1422, p. 378.

Subject Index